TEACHER'S EDITION

HOLT MIDDLE SCHOOL Math

Course 2

Jennie M. Bennett

David J. Chard

Audrey Jackson

Jim Milgram

Janet K. Scheer

Bert K. Waits

HOLT, RINEHART AND WINSTON

A Harcourt Education Company

Orlando • **Austin** • New York • San Diego • Toronto • London

Staff Credits

Editorial

Lila Nissen, *Vice President*
Robin Blakely, *Associate Director*
Joseph Achacoso, *Assistant Managing Editor*
Threasa Boyar, *Editor*

Student Edition
Jennifer Gribble, *Editor*
Kerry Milam, *Associate Editor*
Chris Rankin, *Associate Editor*

Teacher's Edition
Kelli Flanagan, *Senior Editor*

Ancillaries
Mary Fraser, *Executive Editor*
Higinio Dominguez, *Associate Editor*

Technology Resources
John Kerwin, *Executive Editor*
Robyn Setzen, *Senior Editor*
Patricia Platt, *Senior Technology Editor*
Manda Reid, *Technology Editor*

Copyediting
Denise Nowotny, *Copyediting Supervisor*
Patrick Ricci, *Copyeditor*

Support
Jill Lawson, *Senior Administrative Assistant*
Benny Carmona, III, *Editorial Coordinator*

Design

Book Design
Marc Cooper, *Design Director*
Tim Hovde, *Senior Designer*
Lisa Woods, *Designer*
Teresa Carrera-Paprota, *Designer*
Bruce Albrecht, *Design Associate*
Ruth Limon, *Design Associate*
Holly Whittaker, *Senior Traffic Coordinator*

Teacher's Edition
José Garza, *Designer*
Charlie Taliaferro, *Design Associate*

Cover Design
Pronk & Associates

Image Acquisition
Curtis Riker, *Director*
Tim Taylor, *Photo Research Supervisor*
Terry Janecek, *Photo Researcher*
Elaine Tate, *Art Buyer Supervisor*
Joyce Gonzalez, *Art Buyer*
Sam Dudgeon *Senior Staff Photographer*
Victoria Smith, *Staff Photographer*
Lauren Eischen, *Photo Specialist*

New Media Design
Ed Blake, *Design Director*

Media Design
Dick Metzger, *Design Director*
Chris Smith, *Senior Designer*

Graphic Services
Kristen Darby, *Director*
Eric Rupprath, *Ancillary Designer*
Linda Wilbourn, *Image Designer*

Prepress and Manufacturing

Mimi Stockdell, *Senior Production Manager*
Susan Mussey, *Production Supervisor*
Rose Degollado, *Senior Production Coordinator*
Sara Downs, *Production Coordinator*
Jevara Jackson, *Senior Manufacturing Coordinator*
Ivania Lee, *Inventory Analyst*
Wilonda Ieans, *Manufacturing Coordinator*

Printed in the United States of America

ISBN 0-03-065056-9

5 6 7 8 9 048 10 09 08 07 06 05

Holt Middle School Math Course 2

Teacher's Edition Contents

Reviewers

Thomas J. Altonjy
Assistant Principal
Robert R. Lazar Middle School
Montville, NJ

Jane Bash, M.A.
Math Education
Eisenhower Middle School
San Antonio, TX

Charlie Bialowas
District Math Coordinator
Anaheim Union High School District
Anaheim, CA

Lynn Bodet
Math Teacher
Eisenhower Middle School
San Antonio, TX

Louis D' Angelo, Jr.
Math Teacher
Archmere Academy
Claymont, DE

Troy Deckebach
Math Teacher
Tredyffrin-Easttown Middle School
Berwyn, PA

Mary Gorman
Math Teacher
Sarasota, FL

Brian Griffith
Supervisor of Mathematics, K–12
Mechanicsburg Area School District
Mechanicsburg, PA

Ruth Harbin-Miles
District Math Coordinator
Instructional Resource Center
Olathe, KS

Kim Hayden
Math Teacher
Milford Jr. High School
Milford, OH

Susan Howe
Math Teacher
Lime Kiln Middle School
Fulton, MD

Paula Jenniges
Austin, TX

Ronald J. Labrocca
District Mathematics Coordinator
Manhasset Public Schools
Manhasset, NY

Victor R. Lopez
Math Teacher
Washington School
Union City, NJ

George Maguschak
Math Teacher/Building Chairperson
Wilkes-Barre Area
Wilkes-Barre, PA

Dianne McIntire
Math Teacher
Garfield School
Kearny, NJ

Kenneth McIntire
Math Teacher
Lincoln School
Kearny, NJ

Francisco Pacheco
Math Teacher
IS 125
Bronx, NY

Vivian Perry
Edwards, IL

Vicki Perryman Petty
Math Teacher
Central Middle School
Murfreesboro, TN

Jennifer Sawyer
Math Teacher
Shawboro, NC

Russell Sayler
Math Teacher
Longfellow Middle School
Wauwatosa, WI

Raymond Scacalossi
Math Chairperson
Hauppauge Schools
Hauppauge, NY

Richard Seavey
Math Teacher–Retired
Metcalf Jr. High
Eagan, MN

Sherry Shaffer
Math Teacher
Honeoye Central School
Honeoye Falls, NY

Gail M. Sigmund
Math Teacher
Charles A. Mooney Preparatory School
Cleveland, OH

Jonathan Simmons
Math Teacher
Manor Middle School
Killeen, TX

Jeffrey L. Slagel
Math Department Chair
South Eastern Middle School
Fawn Grove, PA

Karen Smith, Ph.D.
Math Teacher
East Middle School
Braintree, MA

Bonnie Thompson
Math Teacher
Tower Heights Middle School
Dayton, OH

Mary Thoreen
Mathematics Subject Area Leader
Wilson Middle School
Tampa, FL

Paul Turney
Math Teacher
Ladue School District
St. Louis, MO

Consulting Authors

Paul A. Kennedy is a Professor in the Mathematics Department at Colorado State University and has recently directed two National Science Foundation projects focusing on inquiry-based learning.

Mary Lynn Raith is the Mathematics Curriculum Specialist for Pittsburgh Public Schools and co-directs the National Science Foundation project PRIME, Pittsburgh Reform in Mathematics Education.

Audrey Jackson
Principal
Claymont Elementary School
Ballwin, MO

Classroom and Learning Environment

"Effective mathematics teaching requires understanding what students know and need to learn and then challenging and supporting them to learn it well."

National Council of Teachers of Mathematics 2000

The fundamental goal of *Holt Middle School Math* is to provide teachers with the necessary tools and understanding of school mathematics to ensure student success at all levels.

Differentiating Instruction

Holt Middle School Math enables teachers to easily differentiate instruction. By implementing the process of scaffolding, the program provides continuous support for challenging work. The section planner in *Holt Middle School Math* assists the teacher in planning and pacing for all students at all levels, while the lesson plans provided with the program help the teacher determine which resources to use to differentiate instruction. The exercises ensure that students have ample opportunities, with guidance, to master the skills taught in the lessons and to then apply these skills with critical thinking. Each lesson includes multiple examples and opportunities to reach all learners through extensions, journal activities, the use of manipulatives, and home connections.

Fostering Successful Instructional Strategies

Holt Middle School Math promotes successful learning by supporting numerous teaching strategies, including direct instruction and cooperative learning. The Hands-On and Technology Labs are ideal for cooperative learning in heterogeneous groups, and the Explorations are designed for discovery learning. The Focus on Problem Solving and Think and Discuss features in each chapter are intended to stimulate student interaction. The exercise sets at the end of each lesson are tied to specific examples to encourage students to direct their own learning and to foster parental help on assignments. Thus, *Holt Middle School Math* can be used to accommodate various styles of the teacher as well as the students.

Creating a Community of Learners

The way we think about our classrooms might be different today, but our goal is the same—mathematics success for all. This program strives to assist teachers in creating the positive environment necessary to build a community of competent and confident learners in a mathematics class. Imagine a classroom where diversity in learning is the norm and the teacher responds to the learners' needs with flexible strategies, open dialogue, and ongoing assessment. Students will learn best when learning opportunities are natural and when connections can be easily made. *Holt Middle School Math* aids teachers in maximizing the capacity of each student every day.

RESEARCH

Glickman, C. 2002.
Leadership for learning.
Alexander, VA: Association for Supervision and Curriculum Development.

National Council of Teachers of Mathematics. 2000.
Principles and standards for school mathematics.
Reston, VA: National Council of Teachers of Mathematics.

Senge, P. 1994.
The fifth discipline fieldbook.
New York, NY: Doubleday.

Tomlinson, C. 1995.
How to differentiate instruction in mixed-ability classrooms.
Alexander, VA: Association for Supervision and Curriculum Development.

Wiggins, G., and J. McTighe. 1998.
Understanding by design.
Alexander, VA: Association for Supervision and Curriculum Development.

Accessibility for All Learners

David J. Chard, Ph.D.
Assistant Professor and Director of Graduate Studies in Special Education
University of Oregon
Eugene, OR

"Students exhibit different talents, abilities, achievements, needs, and interests in mathematics. Nevertheless, all students must have access to the highest-quality mathematics instructional programs."

National Council of Teachers of Mathematics 2000

One of the primary goals of *Holt Middle School Math* is to provide teachers with a resource for teaching students new skills and strategies important for developing their comprehension of mathematics.

Coherent Pedagogical Approach

This program was designed with instructional features that represent a coherent pedagogical approach to mathematics instruction. Each lesson begins with carefully wrought examples of all of the skills, concepts, and strategies addressed. Additionally, the program's examples and counter-examples assist students in understanding the distinct boundaries that exist within each concept and the context in which particular skills and strategies are useful (Bransford, Brown, and Cocking 2000).

Procedural Fluency Development

A second goal is to develop procedural fluency in specific mathematical skills (Mathematics Learning Study Committee 2001). For many students with cognitive disabilities, insufficient practice hampers their ability to develop this fluency. *Holt Middle School Math* provides students with ample opportunities to practice specific computation and problem-solving procedures. Once fluent, students will then have ready access to these tools for use in more sophisticated mathematics.

Sufficient Scaffolding

Key to any instructional program is sufficient scaffolding to support student learning (Vygotsky 1962). In a typical middle school math classroom, some students will require substantial assistance in developing strategies for solving problems. Still others will already have the knowledge necessary to solve problems with little support. In this program, the instructional framework builds the background knowledge essential for ensuring that students are able to solve increasingly complex problems. Scaffolding is utilized in a number of ways throughout the program, from graduated difficulty of new content and applications to frequent opportunities for review, substantive reteaching lessons, and additional examples for extended instruction.

RESEARCH

Bransford, J. D., A. L. Brown, and R. R. Cocking, eds. 2000.
How people learn: Brain, mind, experience, and school.
Washington, DC: National Research Council.

Gersten, R., D. J. Chard, and S. Baker. 2002.
A meta-analysis of research on mathematics instruction for students with learning disabilities.
Eugene, OR: Eugene Research Institute.

Mathematics Learning Study Committee. 2001.
Adding it up: Helping children learn mathematics.
Washington, DC: National Academy Press.

National Council of Teachers of Mathematics. 2000.
Principles and standards for school mathematics.
Reston, VA: National Council of Teachers of Mathematics.

Vygotsky, L. 1962.
Thought and Language.
Cambridge, MA: MIT Press.

Jim Milgram, Ph.D.
Professor of Mathematics
Stanford University
Stanford, CA

Transition to Advanced Mathematics

"...throughout the grades from pre-K through 8 all students can and should ... understand mathematical ideas, compute fluently, solve problems, and engage in logical reasoning."

Mathematics Learning Study Committee 2001

Middle school mathematics instruction occurs at a critical time in students' development and must address the needs specific to this period of learning.

From Foundation Skills to Advanced Topics

When students enter the middle grades, they must prepare for the transition to more advanced mathematical topics such as algebra and geometry while enhancing their basic arithmetic knowledge. It is crucial that they develop abstract reasoning and symbolic manipulation skills. In *Holt Middle School Math* these areas are carefully developed using methods aligned with standard best practices. The program addresses national and state standards while recognizing that some mathematical topics require more sophisticated instruction. All instructional materials, including the vocabulary lists, examples, and reference materials, reflect accurate mathematics. The integrity of the math represented in the program is strictly maintained so that the instructional design contributes positively to students' understanding of the discipline.

Instructional Sequencing

While the introduction of advanced topics requires that students broaden their understanding of mathematical ideas, it also reflects the hierarchical and sequential nature of mathematics as a discipline (Schmidt, Houang, and Cogan 2002). Students need to see the relationships between the math they are learning and real-world scenarios. To foster the development of these connections, the sequence of instruction within each grade and across this program accounts for the elements of mathematics that should be taught first in order to prepare students for later insights. The presentation of mathematical concepts in this program is aligned with that of the most successful international programs.

Enhancing the Role of the Teacher

Middle school mathematics instruction must be supported by materials that assist teachers in helping students successfully learn and do more complex mathematics. Care has been taken to ensure that each instructional lesson develops enough background information so that teachers can demonstrate to their students how the concepts they learn today will tie in to their later mathematical education. Teachers can use this foundation material as a resource when relaying information to their classes. In this way, *Holt Middle School Math* is an asset for teachers as well as for their students.

RESEARCH

Morris, Anne K., and Vladimir M. Stoutsky. 1998.
Understanding of logical necessity: Developmental antecedents and cognitive consequences.
Child Development 69 (3): 721–41.

Mathematics Learning Study Committee. 2001.
Adding it up: Helping children learn mathematics.
Washington, DC: National Academy Press.

Schmidt, William, Richard Houang, and Leland Cogan. 2002.
A coherent curriculum: The case of mathematics.
American Educator 26 (2): 1-17.

Wu, H. H. 2001.
How to prepare students for algebra.
American Educator 25 (2): 10-17.

Jennie M. Bennett, Ed.D.
Instructional Mathematics Supervisor
Houston Independent School District
Houston, TX

RESEARCH

Artzt, Alice F., and Shirel Yaloz-Femia. 1999.
Mathematical reasoning during small-group problem solving. In Developing mathematical reasoning in grades K–12.
Reston, VA: National Council of Teachers of Mathematics.

Jensen, Eric. 1998.
Teaching with the brain in mind.
Alexandria: VA: Association for Supervision and Curriculum Development.

Krulik, Stephen, and Jesse A. Rudnick. 1999.
Innovation tasks to improve critical- and creative-thinking skills. In Developing mathematical reasoning in grades K–12.
Reston, VA: National Council of Teachers of Mathematics.

Levine, Mel. 2002.
A Mind at a Time.
New York, NY: Simon & Schuster.

Schell, Vicki J. 1981.
Learning partners: Reading and mathematics.
Paper presented at 14th annual meeting of the Missouri State Council of the International Reading Association. 13-17 May, at Columbia, MO.

Sullivan, Peter, and David Clarke. 1991.
Catering to all abilities through 'good' questions.
Arithmetic Teacher 39 (2): 14-18.

Strategic Problem Solving

"The single best way to grow a better brain is through challenging problem solving."

Eric Jensen, 1998

Unlike simple numeric computation problems, word problems present unique challenges to some students. One of the goals of this program is to teach students strategies to comprehend and solve word problems.

Development of Critical Thinking Skills

Holt Middle School Math ensures that students have the necessary tools to approach word problems strategically by teaching problem solving as a planned step-by-step process (Levine 2002). Using Polya's method for solving problems (understand the problem, create a plan, carry out the plan, and look back) activates students' critical thinking skills and engages students in making decisions and thinking logically. This program provides students with in-school systemic problem-solving experiences in which these critical skills are developed. Students generate different strategies for solving a problem, select the most feasible one, and arrive at a reasonable solution. These problem-solving skills help students understand how to approach real-world problems strategically both inside and outside the classroom.

Reading Connections

Reading comprehension is necessary to all subjects at all levels, including mathematics (Schell 1981). When students read word problems, they must synthesize or integrate their ideas and determine the operations to use. Reading is therefore a pivotal partner in problem solving; it sets the stage for understanding the problem itself. In this program students are asked to state the details of a problem, identify the necessary information, restate the problem in their own words, and demonstrate knowledge of mathematical vocabulary.

Asking Good Questions

Good questions engage the student in a more active role in learning. When the teacher asks such questions, learning is student-centered rather than teacher-centered. Good questions stimulate and activate communication between the teacher and students and allow students to respond in their own way when solving math problems. These questions can guide students at all levels to experience success with problem solving. Another goal of *Holt Middle School Math* is to assist teachers by suggesting good questions through features such as Focus on Problem Solving and Reaching All Learners.

Janet K. Scheer, Ph.D.
Executive Director
Create A Vision™
Foster City, CA

Concrete Understanding

"When students gain access to mathematical representations and the ideas they represent, they have a set of tools that significantly expand their capacity to think mathematically."

National Council of Teachers of Mathematics 2000

Holt Middle School Math makes use of mathematical modeling and provides many options for the use of manipulatives to enhance student understanding of abstract concepts.

Manipulatives for Concrete Understanding

Educational research demonstrates the effectiveness of hands-on learning in supplementing understanding of mathematical ideas for some students (Threadgill-Sowder and Juilfs 1980). This is especially important in the middle grades, when students are exposed to increasingly abstract concepts. While some middle school students are ready to embrace these abstract topics, others still need the concrete foundation that manipulatives can supply. This program utilizes algebra tiles, pattern blocks, and two-color counters in Hands-On Labs to model topics such as fraction operations and grouping of terms in algebraic expressions. Additionally, the Reaching All Learners features provide teachers with concrete methods for presenting selected topics.

Bridging: Concrete to Symbolic Understanding

Most theories of developmental learning support the use of physical tools to establish a foundation for abstract thought. For this approach to be successful, students must make connections between the manipulatives with which they are working and the abstract mathematical concepts the materials represent; in this way, concrete action is transferred to symbolic understanding (Bohan and Shawaker 1994). It is essential that sufficient context and introduction to a manipulative lesson be provided so that students are able to form connections to symbolic representations in a guided manner (Stein and Bovalino 2001). The modeling activities within this program are intentionally placed after foundation skills have been developed and before symbolic computation is emphasized.

Opportunities to Expand Knowledge

Another advantage of manipulative lessons rooted in foundational skills is that students are given the opportunity to discover new mathematical concepts. The discovery-based knowledge that is developed in this program's Hands-On Labs is solidified by lessons that formalize the mathematical rules and symbolic representations of the concept. In this way, concrete understanding facilitates application of the learned mathematical concepts.

RESEARCH

Bohan, Harry J., and Peggy Bohan Shawaker. 1994.
Using manipulatives effectively: A drive down rounding road.
Arithmetic Teacher 41 (5): 246-48.

National Council of Teachers of Mathematics. 2000.
Principles and standards for school mathematics.
Reston, VA: National Council of Teachers of Mathematics.

Stein, Mary Kay, and Jane W. Bovalino. 2001.
Manipulatives: One piece of the puzzle.
Mathematics Teaching in the Middle School 6 (6): 356-59.

Threadgill-Sowder, Judith, and Patricia Juilfs. 1980.
Manipulative versus symbolic approaches to teaching logical connectives in junior high school: An aptitude x treatment interaction study.
Journal for Research in Mathematics Education 11 (5): 367-74.

Bert K. Waits, Ph.D.
Professor Emeritus of Mathematics
The Ohio State University
Columbus, OH

Technology to Enhance Learning

"Technology is essential in teaching and learning mathematics; it influences the mathematics that is taught and enhances students' learning."

National Council of Teachers of Mathematics 2000

A wide array of technological tools is available for use in mathematics classrooms, including graphing calculators, spreadsheet programs, and geometry software. *Holt Middle School Math* makes use of these tools to reinforce student learning.

Integrated Use of Technology

Research has demonstrated that technology, when used appropriately, can improve students' mathematical understanding and problem-solving skills (Hollar and Norwood 1999). Similarly, technological tools can help teachers challenge students to use and understand mathematics in real-world scenarios. Through the use of integrated technology labs, this program gives students a solid foundation for understanding how to use technology appropriately to learn mathematics. The program puts the NCTM Technology Principle into action in every chapter.

Balanced Curriculum

Holt Middle School Math acknowledges that students must utilize all available tools in the mathematics-learning process. Traditional paper-and-pencil skills are emphasized throughout the program but are supplemented by technology components. Proficiency in mental math computation is stressed as well. Thus, technology is presented not as an end in itself but rather as a means for understanding and application. Current research supports this use of technology. The many technology labs in the program are devoted to the pedagogical use of spreadsheets and dynamic geometry software. Students also use graphing calculators, which are powerful, portable computers with built-in software for graphing, data analysis, and statistics.

Professional Development

This program helps teachers achieve one of the Glenn Commission's major goals in its report to the nation on the crisis in mathematics and science education today. The report states that in order to "inform efforts to promote higher student achievement, teachers should actively work to improve [their] knowledge and skills to incorporate educational technology into [their] learning and teaching" (National Commission on Mathematics and Science Teaching 2000).

RESEARCH

Graham, A. T., and M.O.J. Thomas. 2000.
Building a versatile understanding of algebraic variables with a graphic calculator.
Educational Studies in Mathematics 41 (3): 265-82.

Hollar, Jeannie C., and Karen Norwood. 1999.
The effects of a graphing-approach intermediate algebra curriculum on students' understanding of function.
Journal for Research in Mathematics Education 30 (2): 220-26.

National Commission on Mathematics and Science Teaching for the 21st Century. 2000.
Before it's too late:
The Glenn Commission report.

National Council of Teachers of Mathematics. 2000.
Principles and standards for school mathematics.
Reston, VA: National Council of Teachers of Mathematics.

Problem Solving Handbook

Data Toolbox

Assessment

Student Help

internet connect

Homework Help Online

6, 12, 16, 22, 26, 30, 37, 42, 46

KEYWORD: MS4 HWHelp

Algebra *Indicates algebra included in lesson development*

Number Theory & Algebraic Reasoning

Assessment

go.hrw.com State Test Preparation Online . . . KEYWORD: MS4 TestPrep

Interdisciplinary LINKS

Student Help

internet connect go.hrw.com

Homework Help Online

62, 66, 72, 80, 84, 88, 94, 98, 102, 106, 112, 116

KEYWORD: MS4 HWHelp

Integers and Rational Numbers

Interdisciplinary LINKS

Student Help

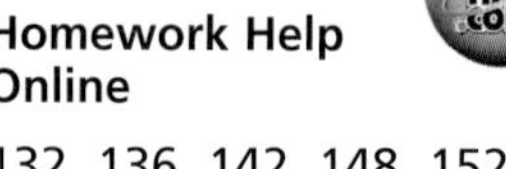

Homework Help Online

132, 136, 142, 148, 152, 158, 164, 168, 172, 176

KEYWORD: MS4 HWHelp

Assessment

State Test Preparation Online .... KEYWORD: MS4 TestPrep

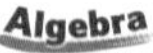

Indicates algebra included in lesson development

Operations with Rational Numbers

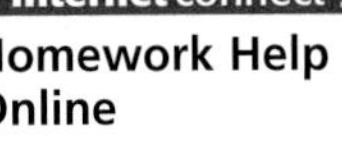

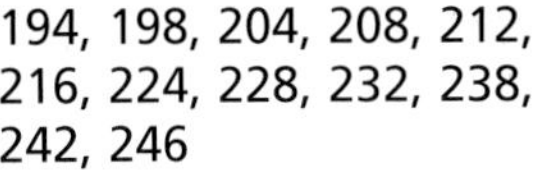

Homework Help Online

194, 198, 204, 208, 212, 216, 224, 228, 232, 238, 242, 246

KEYWORD: MS4 HWHelp

Proportional Reasoning

Assessment

go.hrw.com State Test Preparation Online .... KEYWORD: MS4 TestPrep

Interdisciplinary LINKS

Student Help

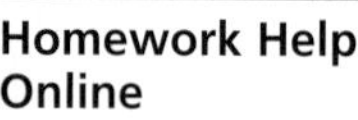

go.hrw.com

Homework Help Online

262, 266, 270, 274, 282, 286, 290

KEYWORD: MS4 HWHelp

Algebra *Indicates algebra included in lesson development*

Percents

Assessment

Interdisciplinary LINKS

Student Help

Homework Help Online

306, 310, 314, 318, 326, 330

KEYWORD: MS4 HWHelp

Plane Figures

Interdisciplinary LINKS

Student Help

internet connect go.hrw.com

Homework Help Online

346, 350, 356, 364, 370, 376, 380, 384, 390, 394, 398

KEYWORD: MS4 HWHelp

Assessment

go.hrw.com State Test Preparation Online .... KEYWORD: MS4 TestPrep

Algebra *Indicates algebra included in lesson development*

Perimeter, Circumference & Area

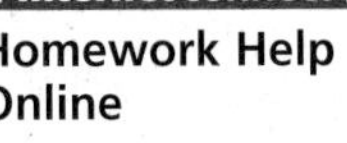

Volume and Surface Area

Student Help

internet connect go.hrw.com

Homework Help Online

474, 478, 482, 489, 494

KEYWORD: MS4 HWHelp

Assessment

go.hrw.com State Test Preparation Online .... KEYWORD: MS4 TestPrep

Algebra *Indicates algebra included in lesson development*

Probability

Assessment

Interdisciplinary LINKS

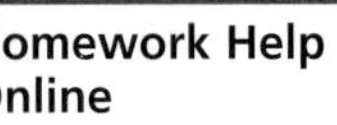

Student Help

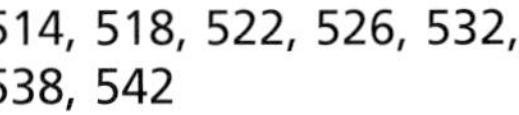

internet connect

Homework Help Online

514, 518, 522, 526, 532, 538, 542

KEYWORD: MS4 HWHelp

Multistep Equations and Inequalities

Assessment

Interdisciplinary LINKS

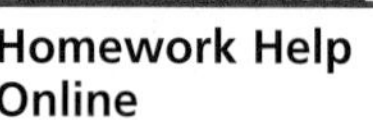

internet connect

Homework Help Online

562, 566, 570, 576, 580, 584, 588

KEYWORD: MS4 HWHelp

Indicates algebra included in lesson development

Graphs and Functions

Assessment

Interdisciplinary LINKS

Student Help

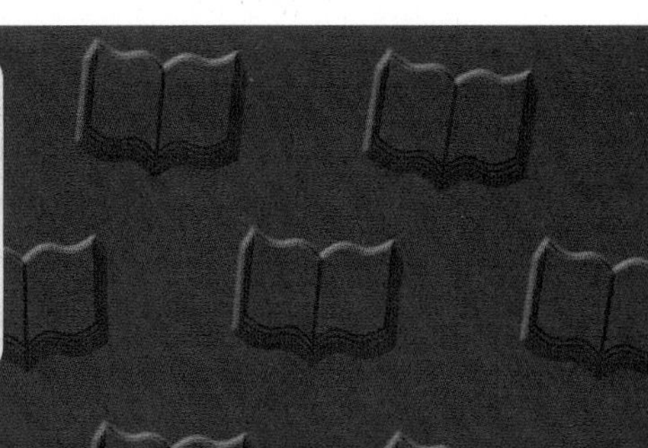

Student Handbook

Math Skills for Life Science

Math Skill	Where Taught
Balance equations (change on one side requires an equivalent change on the other).	Lessons 2-11, 2-12, 3-6, 4-6, 4-12, 6-4, 11-1, 11-2, 11-3; Hands-On Lab 2C
Calculate slope, graph a line with a given slope, and understand slope as a rate of change.	Lessons 12-3, 12-4, 12-5
Combinations	Lesson 10-6
Convert between standard and metric units.	Lesson 5-4
Convert between temperature units.	Lessons 11-2, 12-1; Chapter 11 Extension
Convert between units in one dimension, two dimensions, or three dimensions.	Lessons 8-1, 9-5
Display and read data in bar graphs, line graphs, and circle graphs.	Lessons 1-4, 1-5, 1-7, 1-9; Technology Lab 1B
Find angle measures.	Lessons 7-2, 7-8, 7-9
Find areas.	Lessons 8-4, 8-5, 8-6; Chapter 8 Extension
Find average (mean).	Lesson 1-2
Find perimeter.	Lesson 8-3
Find probability.	Lessons 10-1, 10-2, 10-4, 10-5; Skills Bank p. 694
Find surface area.	Lessons 9-4, 9-5; Chapter 9 Extension
Find surface area to volume ratios.	Skills Bank p. 702
Find volume.	Lessons 9-2, 9-3
Graph on a coordinate plane.	Lessons 1-8, 3-2, 12-1, 12-3, 12-4, 12-5, 12-6, 12-7; Hands-On Labs 1C, 12A
Operate with exponents.	Lessons 2-1, 2-2, 2-4, 8-7; Technology Lab 2A
Operate with fractions.	Lessons 4-7, 4-8, 4-9, 4-10, 4-11, 4-12; Hands-On Labs 4B, 4C
Operate with large whole numbers.	Lessons 2-1, 2-2, 2-3, 2-4, 2-5, 2-6; Technology Lab 2A; Hands-On Lab 2B
Operate with percents.	Lessons 6-1, 6-2, 6-3, 6-4, 6-5, 6-6; Hands-On Lab 6A
Operate with powers of ten.	Lesson 2-2; Technology Lab 2A
Operate with units of rate and convert to compatible units.	Lessons 5-1, 5-3, 5-4
Read metersticks and inch rulers.	Lesson 8-1; Hands-On Lab 8A
Round decimal and whole numbers.	Lessons 4-1, 8-2
Set up and solve proportions.	Lessons 5-2, 5-3, 5-4
Simplify fractions.	Lessons 3-7, 3-8, 3-9, 3-10
Solve equations.	Lessons 2-11, 2-12, 3-6, 4-6, 4-12, 6-4, 11-1, 11-2, 11-3; Hands-On Lab 2C
Solve literal equations (rewrite formulas).	Chapter 11 Extension
Translate words to equations or algebraic expressions.	Lessons 2-7, 2-8
Understand exponential growth behavior.	Lessons 12-6, 12-7; Hands-On Lab 12A
Understand nonlinear relationships, such as half-life.	Lessons 12-6, 12-7; Hands-On Lab 12A; Skills Bank p. 699
Use and operate with scientific notation.	Lesson 2-2; Technology Lab 2A
Use appropriate one-, two-, and three-dimensional measurement units.	Lessons 8-1, 8-2, 8-3, 8-4, 8-5, 8-6, 9-2, 9-3, 9-4, 9-5; Hands-On Lab 8A; Chapter 9 Extension
Use scale models.	Lessons 5-5, 5-6, 5-7; Hands-On Lab 5A
Write equivalent percents, fractions, and decimals.	Lessons 3-7, 3-8, 3-9, 3-10
Write equivalent ratios and ratios in simplest form.	Lessons 5-1, 5-2, 5-3, 5-4

Math Skills for **Earth Science**

Math Skill	Where Taught
Calculate slope, graph a line with a given slope, and understand slope as a rate of change.	Lessons 12-3, 12-4, 12-5
Convert between standard and metric units.	Lesson 5-4
Convert between temperature units.	Lessons 11-2, 12-1; Chapter 11 Extension
Display and read data in bar graphs, line graphs, and circle graphs.	Lessons 1-4, 1-5, 1-7, 1-9; Technology Lab 1B
Find angle measures.	Lessons 7-2, 7-8, 7-9
Find areas.	Lessons 8-4, 8-5, 8-6; Chapter 8 Extension
Find average (mean).	Lesson 1-2
Find surface area.	Lessons 9-4, 9-5; Chapter 9 Extension
Find volume.	Lessons 9-2, 9-3
Graph on a coordinate plane.	Lessons 1-8, 3-2, 12-1, 12-3, 12-4, 12-5, 12-6, 12-7; Hands-On Labs 1C, 12A
Operate with exponents.	Lessons 2-1, 2-2, 2-4, 8-7; Technology Lab 2A
Operate with fractions.	Lessons 4-7, 4-8, 4-9, 4-10, 4-11, 4-12; Hands-On Labs 4B, 4C
Operate with large whole numbers.	Lessons 2-1, 2-2, 2-3, 2-4, 2-5, 2-6; Technology Lab 2A; Hands-On Lab 2B
Operate with percents.	Lessons 6-1, 6-2, 6-3, 6-4, 6-5, 6-6; Hands-On Lab 6A
Operate with powers of ten.	Lesson 2-2; Technology Lab 2A
Operate with units of rate and convert to compatible units.	Lessons 5-1, 5-3, 5-4
Read metersticks and inch rulers.	Lesson 8-1; Hands-On Lab 8A
Round decimal and whole numbers.	Lessons 4-1, 8-2
Set up and solve proportions.	Lessons 5-2, 5-3, 5-4
Simplify fractions.	Lessons 3-7, 3-8, 3-9, 3-10
Solve equations.	Lessons 2-11, 2-12, 3-6, 4-6, 4-12, 6-4, 11-1, 11-2, 11-3; Hands-On Lab 2C
Solve literal equations (rewrite formulas).	Chapter 11 Extension
Translate words to equations or algebraic expressions.	Lessons 2-7, 2-8
Understand nonlinear relationships, such as Richter scale and half-life.	Lessons 12-6, 12-7; Hands-On Lab 12A; Skills Bank pp. 699, 701
Use and operate with scientific notation.	Lesson 2-2; Technology Lab 2A
Use appropriate one-, two-, and three-dimensional measurement units.	Lessons 8-1, 8-2, 8-3, 8-4, 8-5, 8-6, 9-2, 9-3, 9-4, 9-5; Hands-On Lab 8A; Chapter 9 Extension
Use scale models.	Lessons 5-5, 5-6, 5-7; Hands-On Lab 5A
Write equivalent percents, fractions, and decimals.	Lessons 3-7, 3-8, 3-9, 3-10
Write equivalent ratios and ratios in simplest form.	Lessons 5-1, 5-2, 5-3, 5-4

Math Skills for **Physical Science**

Math Skill	**Where Taught**
Balance equations (change on one side requires an equivalent change on the other).	Lessons 2-11, 2-12, 3-6, 4-6, 4-12, 6-4, 11-1, 11-2, 11-3; Hands-On Lab 2C
Calculate slope, graph a line with a given slope, and understand slope as a rate of change.	Lessons 12-3, 12-4, 12-5
Convert between standard and metric units.	Lesson 5-4
Convert between temperature units.	Lessons 11-2, 12-1; Chapter 11 Extension
Convert between units in one dimension, two dimensions, or three dimensions.	Lessons 8-1, 9-5
Display and read data in bar graphs, line graphs, and circle graphs.	Lessons 1-4, 1-5, 1-7, 1-9; Technology Lab 1B
Find angle measures.	Lessons 7-2, 7-8, 7-9
Find areas.	Lessons 8-4, 8-5, 8-6; Chapter 8 Extension
Find average (mean).	Lesson 1-2
Find volume.	Lessons 9-2, 9-3
Graph on a coordinate plane.	Lessons 1-8, 3-2, 12-1, 12-3, 12-4, 12-5, 12-6, 12-7; Hands-On Labs 1C, 12A
Operate with exponents.	Lessons 2-1, 2-2, 2-4, 8-7; Technology Lab 2A
Operate with fractions.	Lessons 4-7, 4-8, 4-9, 4-10, 4-11, 4-12; Hands-On Labs 4B, 4C
Operate with integers.	Lessons 3-3, 3-4, 3-5, 3-6; Hands-On Labs 3A, 3B, 3C
Operate with large whole numbers.	Lessons 2-1, 2-2, 2-3, 2-4, 2-5, 2-6; Technology Lab 2A; Hands-On Lab 2B
Operate with percents.	Lessons 6-1, 6-2, 6-3, 6-4, 6-5, 6-6; Hands-On Lab 6A
Operate with powers of ten.	Lesson 2-2; Technology Lab 2A
Operate with units of rate and convert to compatible units.	Lessons 5-1, 5-3, 5-4
Read metersticks and inch rulers.	Lesson 8-1; Hands-On Lab 8A
Round decimal and whole numbers.	Lessons 4-1, 8-2
Set up and solve proprotions.	Lessons 5-2, 5-3, 5-4
Simplify fractions.	Lessons 3-7, 3-8, 3-9, 3-10
Solve equations.	Lessons 2-11, 2-12, 3-6, 4-6, 4-12, 6-4, 11-1, 11-2, 11-3; Hands-On Lab 2C
Solve literal equations (rewrite formulas).	Chapter 11 Extension
Translate words to equations or algebraic expressions.	Lessons 2-7, 2-8
Understand inverse relationships.	Lessons 12-6, 12-7; Hands-On Lab 12A
Understand linear relationships.	Lessons 12-2, 12-3, 12-4, 12-5
Understand nonlinear relationships, such as acceleration, pH scale, and half-life.	Lessons 12-6, 12-7; Hands-On Lab 12A; Skills Bank pp. 699, 700, 703
Understand parallel and perpendicular line relationships.	Lesson 7-3; Hands-On Lab 7A
Use and operate with scientific notation.	Lesson 2-2; Technology Lab 2A
Use and understand binary numbers.	Skills Bank p. 698
Use appropriate one-, two-, and three-dimensional measurement units.	Lessons 8-1, 8-2, 8-3, 8-4, 8-5, 8-6, 9-2, 9-3, 9-4, 9-5; Hands-On Lab 8A; Chapter 9 Extension
Use scale models.	Lessons 5-5, 5-6, 5-7; Hands-On Lab 5A
Write equivalent percents, fractions, and decimals.	Lessons 3-7, 3-8, 3-9, 3-10
Write equivalent ratios and ratios in simplest form.	Lessons 5-1, 5-2, 5-3, 5-4

NCTM Standards For Grades 6–8

Number and Operations

Understand numbers, ways of representing numbers, relationships among numbers, and number systems

COURSE 1	COURSE 2	COURSE 3
Lessons 1-1, 1-3, 3-1, 3-5, 4-1, 4-2, 4-3, 4-4, 4-5, 4-6, 4-7, 5-5, 8-1, 8-2, 8-7, 8-8, 8-9, 8-10, 9-1, 9-2; Hands-On Labs 3A, 3B, 4A, 4B, 8A; Chapters 1, 4, 8, 9 Extensions	Lessons 2-1, 2-2, 2-4, 2-5, 2-6, 2-7, 2-8, 2-9, 3-1, 3-7, 3-8, 3-9, 3-10, 5-1, 5-2, 6-1, 6-3, 6-5; Hands-On Labs 2B, 8C; Chapter 3 Extension	Lessons 2-6, 2-9, 3-1, 3-10, 7-1, 8-1, 8-2, 8-3, 8-4, 8-5, 8-6, 8-7; Hands-On Lab 7A; Technology Labs 3A, 8B; Chapters 3, 8 Extensions

Understand meanings of operations and how they relate to one another

COURSE 1	COURSE 2	COURSE 3
Lessons 1-4, 1-5, 2-4, 2-5, 2-6, 2-7, 3-9, 3-10, 5-1, 5-2, 5-3, 5-4, 5-7, 5-8, 5-9, 5-10, 9-8; Hands-On Labs 3B, 3D, 5A, 5B, 5C, 5D, 9A, 9B, 9C; Technology Lab 1A	Lessons 2-3, 2-7, 2-8, 2-11, 2-12, 3-3, 3-4, 3-5, 4-2, 4-3, 4-4, 4-5, 4-6, 4-7, 4-8, 4-10, 4-11, 4-12, 6-1, 6-4, 8-2, 8-7, 8-8; Hands-On Labs 2B, 3A, 3B, 4A, 4B, 4C, 6A, 8B; Technology Labs 2A, 2, 4; Chapter 3 Extension	Lessons 1-1, 1-2, 1-3, 1-4, 1-5, 1-6, 2-1, 2-2, 2-3, 2-7, 3-2, 3-4, 3-5, 3-6, 3-7, 3-8, 3-9, 10-1, 10-2, 10-4; Hands-On Labs 2A, 3B, 10A; Technology Lab 12B; Chapter 3 Extension

Compute fluently and make reasonable estimates

COURSE 1	COURSE 2	COURSE 3
Lessons 1-2, 1-3, 1-4, 1-6, 3-2, 3-3, 3-6, 3-7, 3-8, 4-8, 4-9, 5-6, 6-2, 8-4, 8-5, 8-6, 8-7, 8-8, 8-9, 9-4, 9-5, 9-6, 9-7, 11-4; Hands-On Lab 11B	Lessons 3-3, 3-4, 3-5, 4-1, 4-2, 4-3, 4-4, 4-5, 4-7, 4-8, 4-9, 4-10, 4-11, 5-2, 5-3, 5-6, 5-7, 6-2, 6-3, 6-5, 6-6; Hands-On Lab 6A; Chapter 10 Extension	Lessons 1-6, 2-1, 2-2, 2-3, 2-6, 2-7, 2-8, 3-2, 3-3, 3-4, 3-5, 3-9, 4-3, 7-2, 7-3, 8-1, 8-2, 8-3, 8-4, 8-5, 8-6, 8-7, 9-6; Hands-On Lab 3B; Chapter 8 Extension

Algebra

Understand patterns, relations, and functions

COURSE 1	COURSE 2	COURSE 3
Lessons 1-7, 6-6, 12-1, 12-2; Hands-On Lab 12A	Lessons 1-7, 1-8, 12-1, 12-2, 12-3, 12-4, 12-5, 12-6, 12-7; Hands-On Labs 1C, 5A, 7F, 10A, 12A; Technology Lab 12; Chapters 7, 8, 11 Math-Ables	Lessons 1-7, 1-8, 1-9, 2-8, 11-1, 11-2, 11-5, 11-7, 12-1, 12-2, 12-3, 12-4, 12-5, 12-6, 12-7, 12-8; Hands-On Labs 9B, 12A; Technology Lab 1A

Represent and analyze mathematical situations and structures using algebraic symbols

COURSE 1	COURSE 2	COURSE 3
Lessons 2-1, 2-2, 2-3, 2-4, 2-5, 2-6, 2-7, 3-10, 5-4, 5-10, 6-6, 9-3, 9-8; Hands-On Labs 3B, 3D, 5A, 5B, 5C, 5D, 9A, 9B, 9C; Chapter 2 Extension	Lessons 2-7, 2-10, 2-11, 2-12, 3-6, 4-6, 4-12, 6-4, 11-1, 11-2, 11-3, 11-4, 11-5, 11-6, 11-7, 12-5, 12-8; Hands-On Labs 2C, 3C, 11A; Chapters 11, 12 Extensions	Lessons 1-1, 1-2, 1-6, 2-4, 2-5, 3-7, 7-4, 10-4, 10-5, 10-6, 11-3, 11-4; Hands-On Lab 2A; Technology Lab 11A

Use mathematical models to represent and understand quantitative relationships

COURSE 1	COURSE 2	COURSE 3
Lessons 2-4, 2-5, 2-6, 2-7, 3-10, 5-4, 5-10, 9-8, 12-1, 12-2; Hands-On Lab 12A	Lessons 1-9, 12-1, 12-3, 12-4, 12-6; Hands-On Labs 1C, 2C, 3A, 3B, 3C, 4A, 4B, 4C, 5A, 6A, 11A, 12A; Technology Labs 1B, 1C, 1, 3, 5, 9, 12	Lessons 4-2, 4-5, 10-1, 10-2, 10-3, 11-6; Hands-On Labs 6A, 7A, 7B, 7C, 8A, 10A; Chapter 11 Extension

Analyze change in various contexts

COURSE 1	COURSE 2	COURSE 3
Lessons 12-3, 12-4, 12-5, 12-6; Hands-On Lab 12A	Lessons 2-7, 6-5, 6-6, 12-3, 12-5, 12-7; Hands-On Lab 6A	Lessons 5-5, 5-7, 6-6, 6-7, 6-8, 6-9, 7-4, 7-6, 7-9, 8-4, 11-2; Hands-On Labs 5C, 7C

Geometry

Analyze characteristics and properties of two- and three-dimensional geometric shapes and develop mathematical arguments about geometric relationships

COURSE 1	COURSE 2	COURSE 3
Lessons 7-1, 7-2, 7-3, 7-4, 7-5, 7-6, 7-7, 7-8, 7-9, 8-4, 10-1, 10-2, 10-3, 10-4, 10-5, 10-6, 10-7, 10-8, 10-9; Hands-On Labs 7C, 10A, 10B, 10C; Technology Labs 7, 10	Lessons 5-5, 7-1, 7-2, 7-3, 7-4, 7-5, 7-6, 7-7, 7-8, 7-9, 8-8, 9-1, 9-5; Hands-On Labs 5A, 7A, 8B	Lessons 5-1, 5-2, 5-3, 5-4, 5-6, 6-3; Hands-On Labs 5A, 6A, 6B

Specify locations and describe spatial relationships using coordinate geometry and other representational systems

COURSE 1	COURSE 2	COURSE 3
Lessons 6-6, 8-6, 9-3, 12-3, 12-4, 12-5, 12-6; Chapter 9 Math-Ables	Lessons 3-2, 7-10, 12-5; Hands-On Labs 5A, 7A, 7B, 7C, 7D, 7E; Technology Lab 5	Lessons 1-7, 1-8, 5-5, 6-1, 6-2, 6-3, 6-4, 11-2, 11-3; Hands-On Labs 5C, 7C; Chapter 11 Math-Ables

Apply transformations and use symmetry to analyze mathematical situations

COURSE 1	COURSE 2	COURSE 3
Lessons 7-10, 7-11, 7-12; Hands-On Lab 7C	Lessons 7-10, 7-11; Hands-On Lab 7F; Technology Lab 7	Lessons 5-7, 5-8, 5-9, 7-5; Hands-On Labs 5C, 7C; Chapter 6 Extension

Use visualization, spatial reasoning, and geometric modeling to solve problems

COURSE 1	COURSE 2	COURSE 3
Lessons 7-1, 7-5, 7-6, 7-7, 7-8, 7-10, 7-11, 7-12, 8-4, 8-5, 10-1, 10-2, 10-3, 10-4, 10-5, 10-6, 10-7, 10-8, 10-9, 12-3, 12-4, 12-5, 12-6; Hands-On Labs 7A, 7B, 10B, 10C; Chapter 7 Extension	Lessons 3-3, 3-4, 4-5, 9-1, 9-2, 9-3, 9-4, 9-5; Hands-On Labs 2C, 3A, 3B, 3C, 4A, 4B, 4C, 5A, 6A, 7A, 7B, 7C, 7E, 9A, 9B, 11A, 12A; Technology Labs 5, 6, 7, 8, 9; Chapter 9 Extension; Chapters 4, 8, 9 Math-Ables	Lessons 5-1, 5-2, 5-3, 5-4, 5-5, 5-6, 5-7, 5-8, 5-9, 6-1, 6-2, 6-3, 6-4, 6-5, 6-6, 6-7, 6-8, 6-9, 6-10, 7-5, 7-8, 7-9; Hands-On Labs 5A, 5B, 5C, 6A, 6B, 7A, 7B, 7C, 8A; Chapter 7 Extension; Chapter 6 Math-Ables

Measurement

Understand measurable attributes of objects and the units, systems, and processes of measurement

COURSE 1	COURSE 2	COURSE 3
Lessons 3-4, 7-2, 8-3, 10-1, 10-2, 10-7, 10-8, 10-9; Hands-On Labs 3C, 4C	Lessons 5-4, 5-5, 8-1, 8-2, 9-5; Hands-On Labs 5A, 8A	Lessons 6-5, 7-3, 7-7, 7-8, 7-9; Hands-On Lab 7C

Apply appropriate techniques, tools, and formulas to determine measurements

COURSE 1	COURSE 2	COURSE 3
Lessons 8-5, 8-6, 10-1, 10-2, 10-3, 10-4, 10-5, 10-7, 10-9; Hands-On Labs 3C, 10A; Chapter 3 Extension	Lessons 5-4, 5-5, 5-6, 5-7, 8-2, 8-3, 8-4, 8-5, 8-6, 8-8, 9-2, 9-3, 9-4, 9-5; Hands-On Labs 8B, 9B; Technology Labs 8, 9; Chapters 8, 9 Extensions	Lessons 6-1, 6-2, 6-4, 6-6, 6-7, 6-8, 6-9, 6-10, 7-2, 7-6, 7-7, 7-8, 7-9; Hands-On Labs 7B, 7C; Technology Lab 8B

Data Analysis and Probability

Formulate questions that can be addressed with data and collect, organize, and display relevant data to answer them

COURSE 1	COURSE 2	COURSE 3
Lessons 6-1, 6-4, 6-5, 6-7, 6-8, 6-9; Hands-On Lab 8B; Chapter 6 Extension	Lessons 1-1, 1-3, 1-4, 1-5, 1-6, 1-7, 1-8, 1-9; Hands-On Labs 1C, 7D; Technology Labs 1A, 1B	Lessons 4-1, 4-2, 4-3, 4-5, 4-7; Hands-On Labs 4A, 4B

Select and use appropriate statistical methods to analyze data

COURSE 1	COURSE 2	COURSE 3
Lessons 6-2, 6-3, 6-4, 6-5, 6-7, 6-8, 6-9; Hands-On Lab 6A; Chapter 6 Extension	Lessons 1-1, 1-2, 1-3, 1-4, 1-5, 1-6, 1-7, 1-8, 1-9; Technology Lab 1B	Lessons 4-2, 4-3, 4-4, 4-5, 4-6; Hands-On Labs 4A, 4B; Chapter 4 Extension

Develop and evaluate inferences and predictions that are based on data

COURSE 1	COURSE 2	COURSE 3
Lessons 6-7, 6-8, 11-6; Hands-On Labs 8B, 11A	Lessons 1-2, 1-8, 1-9, 10-1, 10-2, 10-4, 12-3; Hands-On Lab 1C	Lessons 4-7, 9-1, 9-2, 9-3, 9-4, 9-5, 9-7, 9-8, 11-7; Technology Lab 9A

Understand and apply basic concepts of probability

COURSE 1	COURSE 2	COURSE 3
Lessons 11-1, 11-2, 11-3, 11-5, 11-6; Hands-On Lab 11B; Chapter 11 Extension	Lessons 10-1, 10-2, 10-3, 10-4, 10-5, 10-6, 10-7; Hands-On Lab 10A; Chapter 10 Extension	Lessons 9-1, 9-2, 9-3, 9-4, 9-5, 9-7, 9-8; Technology Lab 9A

Problem Solving

Build new mathematical knowledge through problem solving

Appears throughout each course in features such as the following:
Problem Solving on Location, Math-Ables, and *Performance Assessment* at the end of each chapter
Problem Solving Applications within each chapter
For example:

COURSE 1
Pages 13, 36–37, 78–79, 86, 128, 140–141, 200, 206, 227, 262, 312, 318

COURSE 2
Pages 48–49, 83, 120, 182, 248–249, 294, 404, 458–459, 502, 592–593, 600, 644

COURSE 3
Pages 48–50, 75, 108, 128, 150–151, 162–164, 218, 338, 351, 434–436, 442, 536, 578–580

Solve problems that arise in mathematics and in other contexts

Appears throughout each course in features such as the following:
Problem Solving on Location and *Math-Ables* at the end of each chapter
Interdisciplinary exercise sets in each chapter and *Problem Solving Applications* within each chapter
For example:

Pages 11, 15, 23, 70, 161, 198–199, 260–261, 285, 310–311, 382, 440, 490

Pages 50, 153, 180–181, 250, 292–293, 399, 402–403, 493, 502, 548, 594, 642–643

Pages 22, 67, 100–102, 134, 226, 264, 268–270, 328, 330–332, 413, 448, 501, 528–530, 575, 620

Apply and adapt a variety of appropriate strategies to solve problems

Appears throughout each course in features such as the following:
Problem Solving Skill lessons, *Focus on Problem Solving,* and *Problem Solving Applications* within each chapter
Problem Solving Handbook at the front of the book
For example:

Pages xviii–xxix, 28–29, 31–32, 52–53, 113, 165, 187, 353, 406, 455

Pages xviii–xxix, 19, 161, 192–195, 219, 230–233, 277, 387, 485, 565, 608–611

Pages xviii–xxix, 8–12, 25, 33, 92–95, 141, 145, 249, 350–354, 361, 415, 421, 456, 498, 513, 607

Monitor and reflect on the process of mathematical problem solving

Appears throughout each course in features such as the following:
Focus on Problem Solving within each chapter and *Problem Solving Applications* at the end of each chapter
Problem Solving Handbook at the front of the book
For example:

Pages xviii–xxix, 36–37, 78–79, 140–141, 198–199, 231, 283, 343, 438–439, 521

Pages xviii–xxix, 48–49, 248–249, 402–403, 443, 500–501, 529, 573, 592–593

Pages xviii–xxix, 48–49, 56, 83, 100–101, 170, 195, 210–211, 276, 299, 388–389, 396, 415, 461, 486–487, 494, 561, 632–633, 640

Reasoning and Proof

Recognize reasoning and proof as fundamental aspects of mathematics

Appears throughout each course in features such as the following:
Think and Discuss in every lesson and lab
Hands-On Labs and *Technology Labs* in every chapter
Math-Ables at the end of each chapter
Additional examples include:

COURSE 1	COURSE 2	COURSE 3
Lessons 1-6, 1-7, 2-2, 3-9, 6-8, 7-6, 7-7, 7-8, 8-2, 8-3, 10-4, 11-4; Chapter 4 Extension	Lessons 2-1, 7-7, 7-9, 10-6, 10-7, 12-2, 12-3, 12-8	Lessons 5-1, 5-2, 5-3, 5-4, 5-5, 12-1, 12-2, 12-3

Make and investigate mathematical conjectures

COURSE 1	COURSE 2	COURSE 3
Lessons 1-7, 7-8; Hands-On Labs 4C, 7B, 8A, 10A, 11B, 12A; Technology Labs 1, 7, 10, 12; Chapters 1, 9 Extensions	Lessons 7-3, 7-5, 10-1, 10-2, 10-4, 10-5; Hands-On Labs 3A, 3B, 4C, 5A, 7D, 12A; Technology Labs 2, 7, 8, 10; Chapters 8, 9, 10 Extensions	Lessons 2-8, 4-7, 6-6, 6-7, 6-8, 6-9, 9-3, 9-7, 9-8, 11-7, 12-1, 12-2, 12-3; Hands-On Labs 3B, 6A, 7B, 12A; Technology Lab 9A

Develop and evaluate mathematical arguments and proofs

Appears throughout each course in features such as the following:
Think and Discuss in every lesson and lab
Hands-On Labs and *Technology Labs* in every chapter
Write About It in the exercise sets
Additional examples include:

COURSE 1	COURSE 2	COURSE 3
Lessons 2-4, 2-5, 2-6, 2-7, 3-10, 4-1, 5-4, 5-10, 7-5, 7-6, 9-8, 11-4; Chapters 4, 9 Extensions	Lessons 2-2, 2-9, 2-10, 3-3, 3-4, 5-5, 7-8, 8-4, 8-5, 8-6, 9-2, 12-6, 12-7	Lessons 4-6, 5-1, 5-2, 5-3,5-6, 6-1, 6-2, 6-3, 6-4, 6-6, 6-7, 6-8, 6-9, 6-10, 7-6, 7-7; Chapter 7 Extension

Select and use various types of reasoning and methods of proof

Appears throughout each course in features such as the following:
Think and Discuss in every lesson and lab
Focus on Problem Solving and *Problem Solving Applications* within each chapter
Performance Assessment at the end of each chapter
Problem Solving Handbook at the front of the book
Choose a Strategy in the exercise sets
Additional examples include:

COURSE 1	COURSE 2	COURSE 3
Lessons 1-7, 2-4, 2-5, 2-6, 2-7, 3-10, 4-8, 4-9, 5-1, 5-4, 5-7, 5-10, 7-6, 7-8, 8-2, 8-3, 9-8, 11-1, 11-2, 11-3; Hands-On Labs 4B, 8A, 10A, 10B, 10C	Lessons 2-10, 7-8, 9-4, 12-6; Hands-On Labs 2C, 7C, 10A, 11A; Technology Labs 5, 7, 8, 9; Chapters 11, 12 Extensions; Chapters 1, 5, 10, 12 Math-Ables	Lessons 2-8, 4-7, 5-1, 5-2, 5-3, 5-4, 6-6, 6-7, 6-8, 6-9, 9-3, 9-7, 9-8, 11-7, 12-1, 12-2, 12-3; Hands-On Labs 3B, 4A, 5C, 6A, 7B, 12A; Technology Lab 9A

Communication

Organize and consolidate mathematical thinking through communication

Appears throughout each course in features such as the following:
Think and Discuss in every lesson and lab
Write About It in the exercise sets
For example:

COURSE 1	COURSE 2	COURSE 3
Pages 5, 7, 9, 13, 21, 63, 67, 70, 72, 93, 97, 99, 103, 133, 197, 225, 300, 329, 401	7, 38, 67, 99, 117, 165, 177, 195, 239, 247, 319, 347, 391, 399, 479, 567, 615, 631	Pages 5, 11, 30, 41, 56, 67, 75, 89, 94, 103, 144, 175, 187, 205, 246, 271, 301, 409, 470, 485, 506, 599, 626

Communicate mathematical thinking coherently and clearly to peers, teachers, and others

Appears throughout each course in features such as the following:
Focus on Problem Solving within each chapter and *Problem Solving Applications* at the end of each chapter
Problem Solving Handbook at the front of the book
For example:

COURSE 1	COURSE 2	COURSE 3
Pages 27, 55, 65, 95, 99, 123, 126, 185, 213, 215, 227, 247, 273, 274, 285, 295	Pages 17, 63, 95, 107, 159, 173, 209, 233, 315, 331, 365, 433, 515, 571, 585, 635	Pages 15, 27, 35, 44, 61, 73, 97, 103, 120, 165, 191, 194, 282, 293, 355, 404, 433, 481, 506, 531, 566, 581, 623

Analyze and evaluate the mathematical thinking and strategies of others

Appears throughout each course in features such as the following:
Think and Discuss in every lesson and lab
What's the Error? and *What's the Question?* in the exercise sets
For example:

COURSE 1	COURSE 2	COURSE 3
Pages 77, 117, 155, 249, 281, 304, 323, 333, 345, 370, 393, 410, 425, 533, 607	Pages 27, 44–47, 85, 99, 113, 133, 177, 205, 247, 315, 385, 399, 543, 619, 639	Pages 20, 42, 51, 63, 77, 97, 116, 125, 143, 213, 233, 284, 349, 403, 450, 457, 475, 505, 592, 612, 616

Use the language of mathematics to express mathematical ideas precisely

Appears throughout each course in features such as the following:
Think and Discuss in every lesson and lab
Write About It and *Write a Problem* in the exercise sets
For example:

COURSE 1	COURSE 2	COURSE 3
Pages 15, 61, 99, 161, 163, 168, 173, 223, 237, 245, 259, 364, 421, 519, 573, 619	Pages 7, 13, 27, 81, 153, 169, 199, 217, 271, 311, 385, 417, 427, 490, 533, 589, 619, 635	Pages 7, 27, 47, 61, 82, 97, 103, 120, 165, 203, 227, 258, 271, 289, 345, 379, 423, 481, 518, 594, 631

Connections

Recognize and use connections among mathematical ideas

COURSE 1	COURSE 2	COURSE 3
Lessons 3-4, 5-9, 8-3, 8-4, 8-5, 8-6, 12-3, 12-4, 12-5, 12-6; Hands-On Labs 3C, 4C; Chapter 4 Extension	Lessons 2-8, 5-1, 5-2, 5-4, 5-5, 5-6, 6-1, 7-3, 7-4, 7-5, 7-6, 7-7, 7-9, 9-5, 12-1, 12-5, 12-6; Hands-On Lab 5A; Technology Lab 5; Chapter 12 Extension	Lessons 5-5, 6-1, 6-2, 6-3, 6-4, 7-6, 7-7, 7-8, 7-9; Hands-On Labs 7A, 7B, 7C, 8A; Chapter 7 Extension

Understand how mathematical ideas interconnect and build on one another to produce a coherent whole

Lessons 3-4, 5-9, 8-3, 8-4, 8-5, 8-6, 12-3, 12-4, 12-5, 12-6; Hands-On Labs 3C, 4C; Chapter 4 Extension

Lessons 3-2, 3-7, 3-8, 3-9, 6-1, 6-5, 7-10, 7-11, 8-3, 8-4, 8-5, 8-6, 8-8, 9-2, 9-3, 9-4, 12-3, 12-4; Technology Lab 7; Chapters 8, 9 Extensions

Lessons 1-6, 5-5, 6-1, 6-2, 6-3, 6-4, 7-6, 7-7, 7-8, 7-9, 10-1, 10-2, 12-4, 12-5, 12-6, 12-7; Hands-On Labs 3B, 7A, 7B, 7C, 8A; Technology Lab 12B; Chapters 6, 7, 11 Extensions

Recognize and apply mathematics in contexts outside of mathematics

Appears throughout each course in features such as the following:
Problem Solving on Location at the end of each chapter
Interdisciplinary exercise sets within each chapter
Chapter openers at the beginning of each chapter
Application problems in the exercise sets
Additional examples include:

Lessons 1-1, 2-7, 3-1, 3-5, 4-6, 4-8, 6-1, 6-4, 6-6, 6-7, 7-8, 7-12, 8-6, 8-9, 9-1, 10-1, 10-2, 10-9, 11-1, 11-6, 12-6; Chapter 8 Extension

Lessons 1-1, 1-2, 1-3, 1-4, 1-5, 1-6, 1-7, 1-8, 1-9, 2-7, 2-10, 5-4, 5-7, 6-2, 6-5, 6-6, 10-1, 10-2, 10-4, 10-5, 12-8; Hands-On Labs 7F, 8A; Chapter 9 Math-Ables

Lessons 1-1, 1-3, 1-4, 2-2, 2-3, 2-4, 2-5, 2-8, 3-2, 3-3, 3-6, 3-7, 6-3, 6-4, 6-6, 6-9, 8-2, 11-1, 11-6; Hands-On Lab 4A

Representation

Create and use representations to organize, record, and communicate mathematical ideas

COURSE 1

Lessons 1-1, 1-3, 2-2, 3-1, 3-5, 4-4, 4-6, 6-1, 6-4, 6-5, 6-7, 6-8, 6-9, 8-5, 12-1, 12-2; Hands-On Lab 4A; Technology Labs 6A, 6; Chapters 1, 6 Extensions

COURSE 2

Lessons 1-3, 1-4, 1-5, 1-6, 1-7, 1-8, 2-3, 2-7, 3-1, 3-2, 3-7, 3-8, 3-10; Hands-On Lab 8B; Technology Labs 1A, 1B, 2, 6, 9; Chapter 9 Math-Ables

COURSE 3

Lessons 1-7, 1-8, 1-9, 4-1, 4-2, 4-5, 4-6, 4-7, 5-5, 6-1, 6-2, 6-3, 6-4, 6-5, 7-6, 7-7, 7-8, 11-1, 11-2, 11-3, 11-4, 12-4, 12-5, 12-6, 12-7; Hands-On Labs 2A, 3B, 4A, 5C, 6A, 6B, 7A, 8A, 7B, 10A, 12A; Technology Labs 1A, 4B, 9A, 12B

Select, apply, and translate among mathematical representations to solve problems

Lessons 4-4, 4-7, 6-1, 6-4, 6-5, 6-7, 6-8, 6-9, 8-7, 8-8, 12-1, 12-2; Hands-On Lab 4A; Chapter 6 Extension

Lessons 1-9, 2-1, 2-2, 2-7, 3-7, 3-8, 3-9, 3-10, 5-4, 6-1, 8-1, 11-4, 12-3; Hands-On Labs 6A, 8A; Technology Labs 1B, 2A, 2; Chapter 1 Math-Ables

Lessons 1-9, 2-9, 7-1, 7-2, 7-3, 8-1, 8-2, 8-3, 8-4, 8-5, 8-6, 8-7; Hands-On Labs 2A, 3B, 4A, 5C, 6A, 6B, 7A, 7B, 8A, 10A, 12A; Technology Labs 1A, 9A, 12B

Use representations to model and interpret physical, social, and mathematical phenomena

Lessons 2-3, 2-4, 2-5, 2-6, 2-7, 3-10, 5-4, 5-10, 6-1, 6-4, 6-5, 6-7, 6-8, 6-9, 8-6, 9-8, 12-2; Hands-On Labs 11A, 8B; Technology Labs 6A, 6, 11; Chapters 2, 6 Extensions

Lessons 3-4, 4-5, 5-7; Hands-On Labs 2C, 3A, 3B, 3C, 4A, 4B, 4C, 5A, 6A, 11A, 12A; Technology Labs 5, 6, 7, 8, 9, 12; Chapters 9, 10, 12 Math-Ables

Lessons 1-8, 1-9, 4-1, 4-2, 4-5, 4-6, 4-7, 7-7, 7-8, 7-9, 9-3, 11-1, 11-2, 11-3, 11-4, 11-5, 11-6, 11-7, 12-4, 12-5, 12-6, 12-7, 12-8; Hands-On Labs 2A, 3B, 4A, 5C, 6A, 6B, 7A, 7B, 7C, 8A, 10A, 12A; Technology Labs 11A, 12B

Stepping into the Future

All the Ways You Teach

Being ready for the future means making sure no student is left behind. Throughout the *Student Edition, Teacher Edition, Premier Online Edition*, and program resources for ***Holt Middle School Math,*** you'll find the help you need to teach, assist, and assess every ability level in your class without spending hours of extra time assigning special assignments and grading extra worksheets.

All the Ways They Learn

The perfect middle school math curriculum for the future ensures that students can master math concepts found in state tests, they are able to learn at their own speed and style, and that they are able to manipulate information to use it in everyday terms with everyday technology.

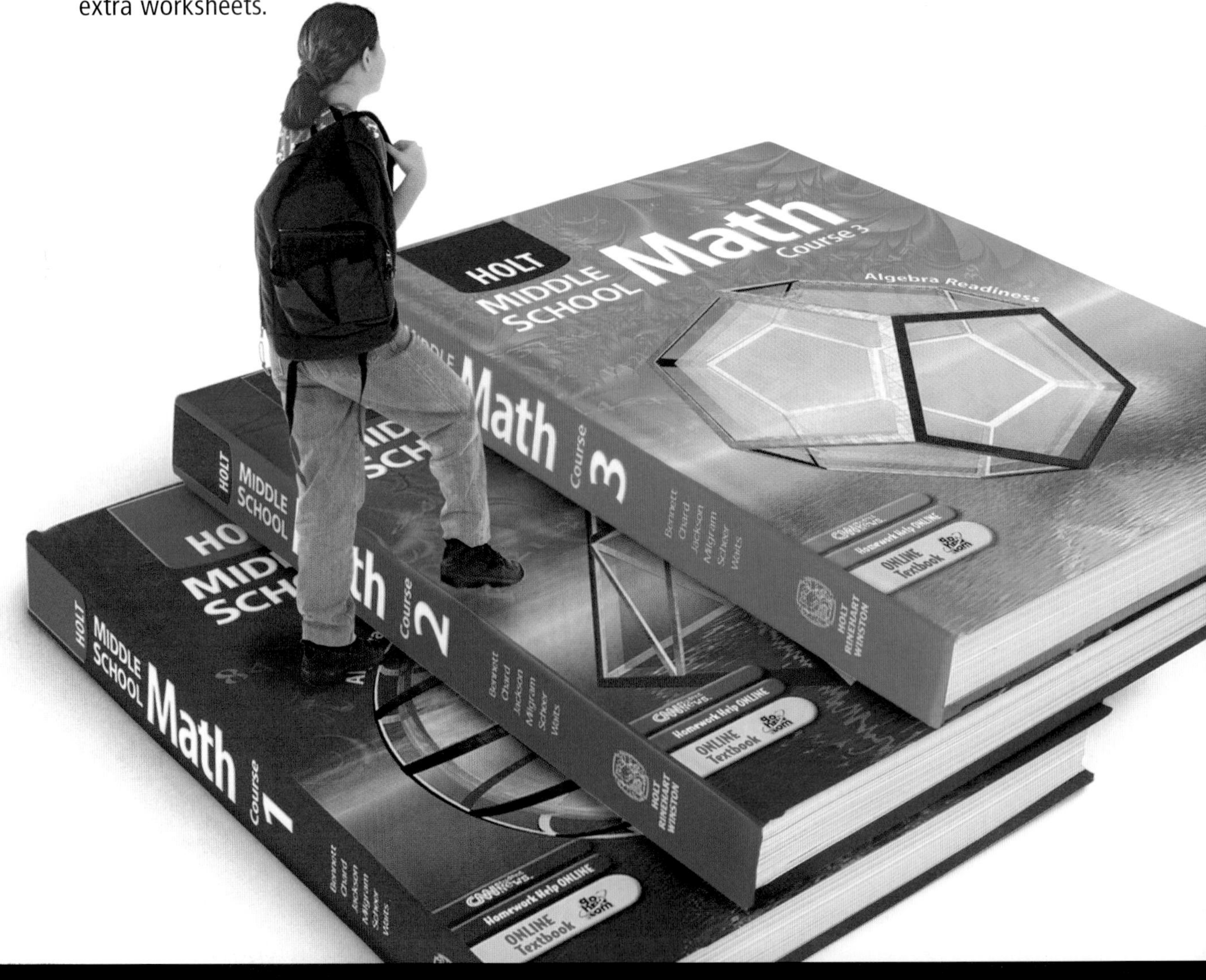

We're With Them Every Step of the Way

Meeting State Standards and Assessment

This program reflects the increased expectation of what students should "know and be able to do" by introducing algebra early and offering test preparation at the lesson and chapter levels and online through **go.hrw.com**.

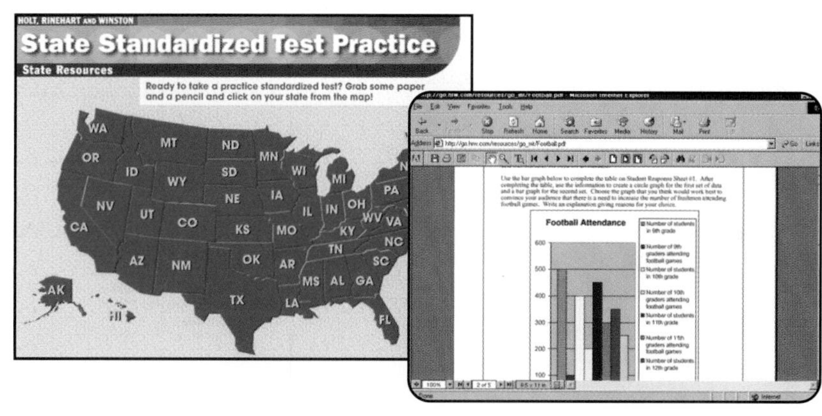

Differentiating Instruction

By offering early intervention and examples that allow students to get help early and practice at their own level of learning, this program helps you reach all learners, including students who need extra help and advanced learners.

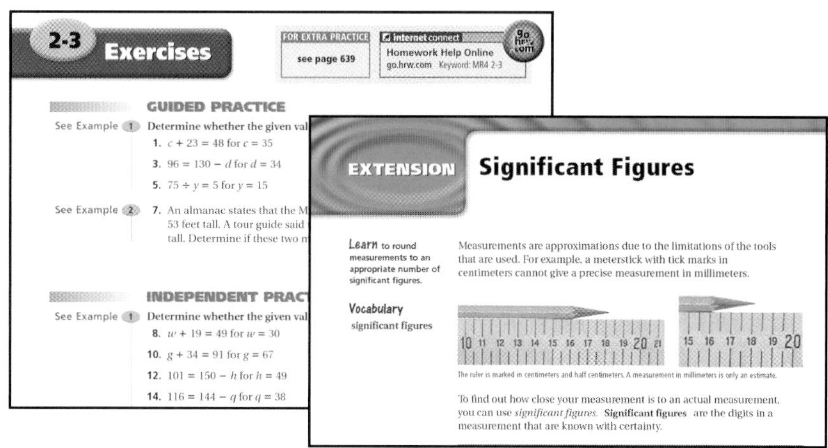

Integrating Technology

This program offers you state-of-the-art technology integrated with your curriculum saving you time and increasing your efficiency with the new test and practice generator on the ***One-Stop Planner® CD-ROM,*** the ***Are You Ready? Intervention CD-ROM,*** and the ***Holt Middle School Math Premier Online Edition.***

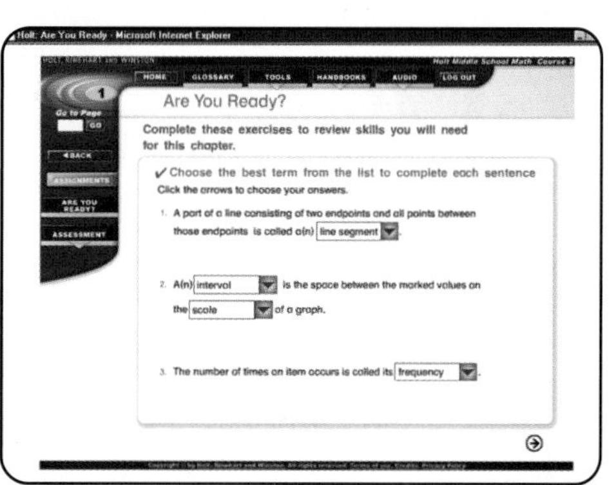

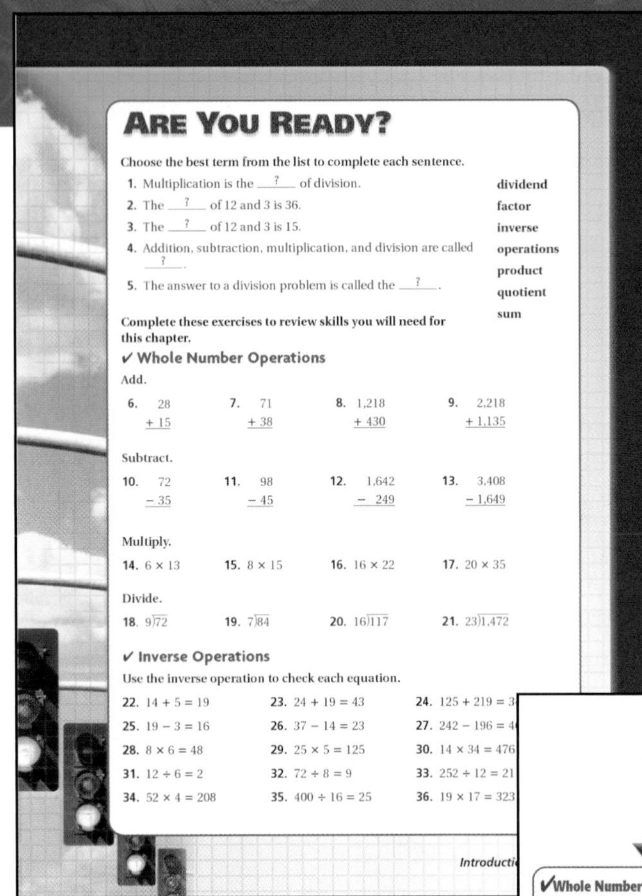

ARE YOU READY?

Choose the best term from the list to complete each sentence.

1. Multiplication is the __?__ of division.
2. The __?__ of 12 and 3 is 36.
3. The __?__ of 12 and 3 is 15.
4. Addition, subtraction, multiplication, and division are called __?__.
5. The answer to a division problem is called the __?__.

dividend
factor
inverse
operations
product
quotient
sum

Complete these exercises to review skills you will need for this chapter.

✓ **Whole Number Operations**

Add.

6. 28 + 15 7. 71 + 38 8. 1,218 + 430 9. 2,218 + 1,135

Subtract.

10. 72 − 35 11. 98 − 45 12. 1,642 − 249 13. 3,408 − 1,649

Multiply.

14. 6 × 13 15. 8 × 15 16. 16 × 22 17. 20 × 35

Divide.

18. 9)72 19. 7)84 20. 16)117 21. 23)1,472

✓ **Inverse Operations**

Use the inverse operation to check each equation.

22. 14 + 5 = 19 23. 24 + 19 = 43 24. 125 + 219 = 3

25. 19 − 3 = 16 26. 37 − 14 = 23 27. 242 − 196 = 4

28. 8 × 6 = 48 29. 25 × 5 = 125 30. 14 × 34 = 476

31. 12 ÷ 6 = 2 32. 72 ÷ 8 = 9 33. 252 ÷ 12 = 21

34. 52 × 4 = 208 35. 400 ÷ 16 = 25 36. 19 × 17 = 323

Introducti

Assessing Prior Knowledge

INTERVENTION

Diagnose and Prescribe

Evaluate your students' performance on this page to determine whether intervention is necessary or whether enrichment is appropriate. Options that provide instruction, practice, and a check are listed below.

Resources for Are You Ready?

- ***Are You Ready? Intervention and Enrichment***
- **Recording Sheet for Are You Ready?**
  Chapter 2 Resource Book . p. 00
- ***Are You Ready? Intervention* CD-ROM**

Diagnose and Prescribe

Holt Middle School Math includes intervention strategies that diagnose students' difficulties with mathematics while providing intervention resources that will bring success to every learner.

ARE YOU READY?

Were students successful with Are You Ready?

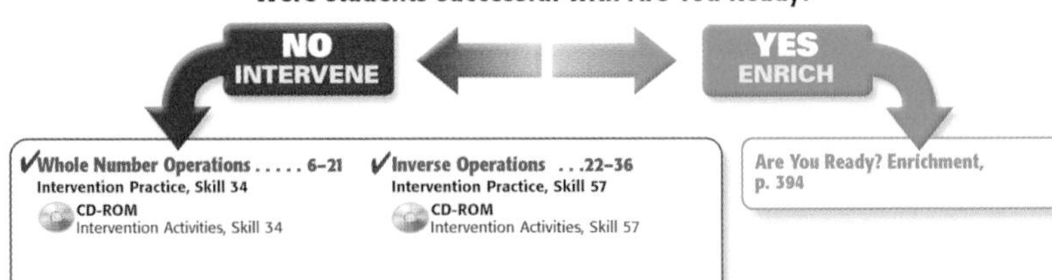

NO INTERVENE
YES ENRICH
✓Whole Number Operations 6–21
Intervention Practice, Skill 34
CD-ROM
Intervention Activities, Skill 34
✓Inverse Operations . . .22–36
Intervention Practice, Skill 57
CD-ROM
Intervention Activities, Skill 57
Are You Ready? Enrichment, p. 394

Intervention Tools

Each chapter begins with **Are You Ready?** assessing students' knowledge of prerequisite skills, and helping you assign either more help or enrichment depending on where students stand.

Intervention Components

Are You Ready? Intervention and Enrichment

This workbook provides additional help for students who have difficulty with a particular math concept through direct instruction, conceptual models, and scaffolded practice. Enrichment masters for every lesson enhance critical-thinking skills, as well as extend lesson objectives. Also available: ***Are You Ready? Intervention CD-ROM***.

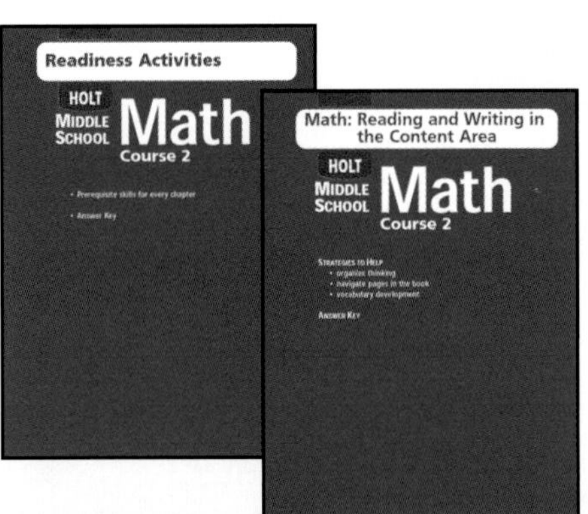

Readiness Activities

This helpful resource contains activities for every chapter and helps students review prerequisite skills needed to complete each lesson.

Math: Reading and Writing in the Content Area

These activities provide strategies for students to help organize their thinking, navigate a page in a math book, and master vocabulary.

Meeting State Standards

Assessment that Gets Results

Throughout each chapter, students have access to a series of assessment resources, including **Chapter Review, Chapter Test, Performance Assessment,** and **Standardized Test Prep.**

Show What You Know

Students are asked to select work from the recently completed chapter—including section reviews, homework assignments, etc.—and create a portfolio from those pieces.

Short Response

Students are asked to execute a series of tasks, including creating their own problems with explanations of how they arrived at their conclusions and collecting magazine or newspaper articles that mention mathematical concepts.

Extended Problem Solving

Students are asked to solve a set of problems using a graph, table, etc. Students are able to use the strategy of their choice to complete the series.

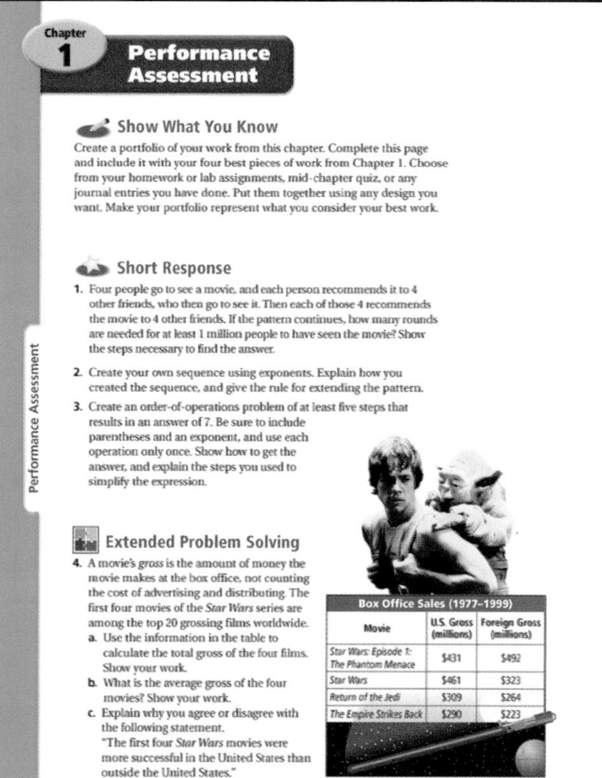

Chapter 1 **Performance Assessment**

Show What You Know

Create a portfolio of your work from this chapter. Complete this page and include it with your four best pieces of work from Chapter 1. Choose from your homework or lab assignments, mid-chapter quiz, or any journal entries you have done. Put them together using any design you want. Make your portfolio represent what you consider your best work.

Short Response

1. Four people go to see a movie, and each person recommends it to 4 other friends, who then go to see it. Then each of those 4 recommends the movie to 4 other friends. If the pattern continues, how many rounds are needed for at least 1 million people to have seen the movie? Show the steps necessary to find the answer.
2. Create your own sequence using exponents. Explain how you created the sequence, and give the rule for extending the pattern.
3. Create an order-of-operations problem of at least five steps that results in an answer of 7. Be sure to include parentheses and an exponent, and use each operation only once. Show how to get the answer, and explain the steps you used to simplify the expression.

Extended Problem Solving

4. A movie's *gross* is the amount of money the movie makes at the box office, not counting the cost of advertising and distributing. The first four movies of the *Star Wars* series are among the top 20 grossing films worldwide.
   a. Use the information in the table to calculate the total gross of the four films. Show your work.
   b. What is the average gross of the four movies? Show your work.
   c. Explain why you agree or disagree with the following statement. "The first four *Star Wars* movies were more successful in the United States than outside the United States."

Box Office Sales (1977–1999)

Movie	U.S. Gross (millions)	Foreign Gross (millions)
Star Wars: Episode 1: The Phantom Menace	$431	$492
Star Wars	$461	$323
Return of the Jedi	$309	$264
The Empire Strikes Back	$290	$223

Performance Assessment

44 *Chapter 1 Number Toolbox*

Assessment Resources

- Inventory Assessment
- Section Quizzes
- Chapter Tests
- Performance Assessment
- Cumulative Tests
- End-of-year Test

Test Prep Toolkit

Countdown to Testing Transparencies

Multiple choice and critical-thinking questions are featured on these transparencies, preparing students for state assessment by building problem-solving skills.

Standardized Test Prep Workbook

This resource includes a two-page test for every chapter as well as two state-specific tests, a diagnostic test and **Test-Taking Tips**.

Standardized Test Prep CD-ROM

This convenient assessment tool provides an easy way to create practice worksheets and tests that correlate to your state assessment.

Standardized Test Prep Video

This video gives visual demonstrations of math problems correlated to the book and to state standards. Hints and suggestions guide students toward solutions, while timed practice gives students experience solving multiple choice and short answer problems.

Assessment

State Test Preparation Online . . . . KEYWORD: MC4 TestPrep

Focus on Problem Solving

To support problem-solving skills needed in state testing, this feature gives students a real-world scenario with the steps, examples, and practice problems needed to fully master the concept.

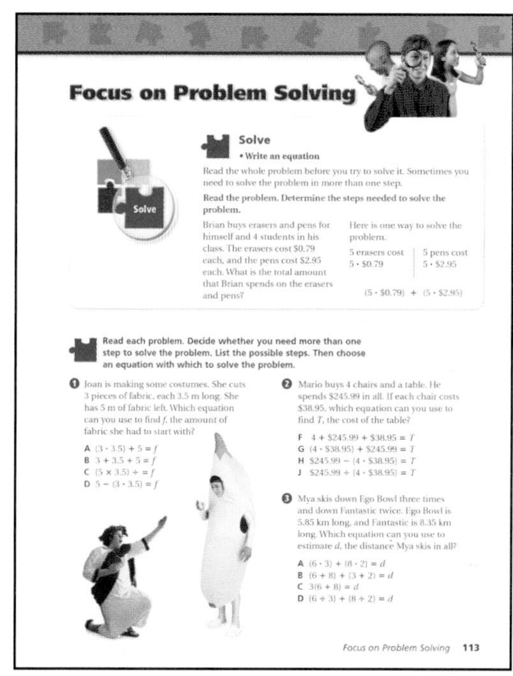

Focus on Problem Solving

Solve

• Write an equation

Read the whole problem before you try to solve it. Sometimes you need to solve the problem in more than one step.

Read the problem. Determine the steps needed to solve the problem.

Brian buys erasers and pens for himself and 4 students in his class. The erasers cost $0.79 each, and the pens cost $2.95 each. What is the total amount that Brian spends on the erasers and pens?

Here is one way to solve the problem.

5 erasers cost 5 · $0.79 | 5 pens cost 5 · $2.95

(5 · $0.79) + (5 · $2.95)

Read each problem. Decide whether you need more than one step to solve the problem. List the possible steps. Then choose an equation with which to solve the problem.

1. Joan is making some costumes. She cuts 3 pieces of fabric, each 3.5 m long. She has 5 m of fabric left. Which equation can you use to find f, the amount of fabric she had to start with?
   - A $(3 \cdot 3.5) + 5 = f$
   - B $3 + 3.5 + 5 = f$
   - C $(5 \times 3.5) \div = f$
   - D $5 - (3 \cdot 3.5) = f$
2. Mario buys 4 chairs and a table. He spends $245.99 in all. If each chair costs $38.95, which equation can you use to find T, the cost of the table?
   - F $4 + \$245.99 + \$38.95 = T$
   - G $(4 \cdot \$38.95) + \$245.99 = T$
   - H $\$245.99 - (4 \cdot \$38.95) = T$
   - J $\$245.99 + (4 \cdot \$38.95) = T$
3. Mya skis down Ego Bowl three times and down Fantastic twice. Ego Bowl is 5.85 km long, and Fantastic is 8.35 km long. Which equation can you use to estimate d, the distance Mya skis in all?
   - A $(6 \cdot 3) + (8 \cdot 2) = d$
   - B $(6 + 8) + (3 + 2) = d$
   - C $3(6 + 8) = d$
   - D $(6 \div 3) + (8 \div 2) = d$

Focus on Problem Solving 113

Assessment

For Students

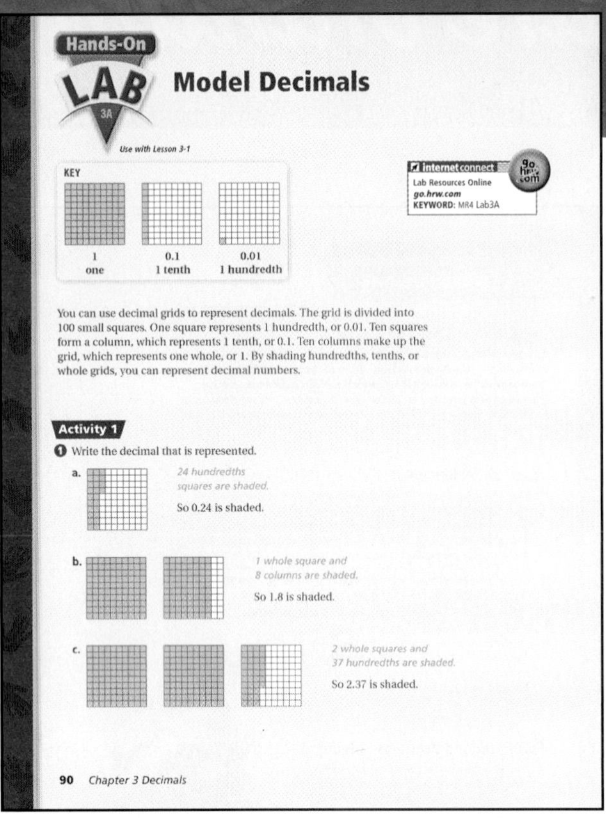
Hands-On LAB 3A

Model Decimals

Use with Lesson 3-1

internet connect
Lab Resources Online
go.hrw.com
KEYWORD: MR4 Lab3A

KEY

1 one	0.1 1 tenth	0.01 1 hundredth

You can use decimal grids to represent decimals. The grid is divided into 100 small squares. One square represents 1 hundredth, or 0.01. Ten squares form a column, which represents 1 tenth, or 0.1. Ten columns make up the grid, which represents one whole, or 1. By shading hundredths, tenths, or whole grids, you can represent decimal numbers.

Activity 1

1. Write the decimal that is represented.

a. *24 hundredths squares are shaded.*
So 0.24 is shaded.

b. *1 whole square and 8 columns are shaded.*
So 1.8 is shaded.

c. *2 whole squares and 37 hundredths are shaded.*
So 2.37 is shaded.

90 *Chapter 3 Decimals*

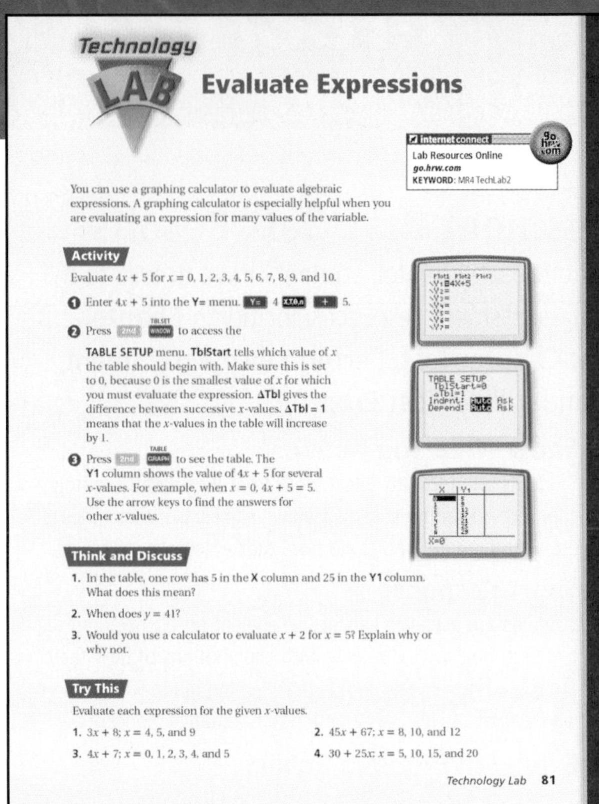
Technology LAB

Evaluate Expressions

internet connect
Lab Resources Online
go.hrw.com
KEYWORD: MR4 TechLab2

You can use a graphing calculator to evaluate algebraic expressions. A graphing calculator is especially helpful when you are evaluating an expression for many values of the variable.

Activity

Evaluate $4x + 5$ for $x = 0, 1, 2, 3, 4, 5, 6, 7, 8, 9$, and 10.

1. Enter $4x + 5$ into the **Y=** menu. Y= 4 X,T,θ,n + 5.
2. Press 2nd WINDOW (TBLSET) to access the **TABLE SETUP** menu. **TblStart** tells which value of x the table should begin with. Make sure this is set to 0, because 0 is the smallest value of x for which you must evaluate the expression. **ΔTbl** gives the difference between successive x-values. **ΔTbl = 1** means that the x-values in the table will increase by 1.
3. Press 2nd GRAPH (TABLE) to see the table. The **Y1** column shows the value of $4x + 5$ for several x-values. For example, when $x = 0$, $4x + 5 = 5$. Use the arrow keys to find the answers for other x-values.

Think and Discuss

1. In the table, one row has 5 in the **X** column and 25 in the **Y1** column. What does this mean?
2. When does $y = 41$?
3. Would you use a calculator to evaluate $x + 2$ for $x = 5$? Explain why or why not.

Try This

Evaluate each expression for the given x-values.

1. $3x + 8$; $x = 4, 5$, and 9
2. $45x + 67$; $x = 8, 10$, and 12
3. $4x + 7$; $x = 0, 1, 2, 3, 4$, and 5
4. $30 + 25x$; $x = 5, 10, 15$, and 20

Technology Lab 81

Kinesthetic Models

Give students an activity to step up learning. Models, algebra tiles, graphs, pictures that represent real-world math, and other visual representations are all incorporated into **Hands-On Lab** giving the reinforcement needed for rigorous content. Lab Resources also available online.

Visual Appeal

A graphing calculator can give learners the support they need to illustrate concepts and help retention of skills. **Technology Lab** walks students through a set of problems using their calculators. Lab Resources also available online.

Reaching All Learners

Alternate Openers: Exploration Transparencies

This notebook of transparencies provides an alternate way to teach each lesson.

Interactive Problem Solving

Blackline masters enable students to work problems for the lesson with step-by-step prompts.

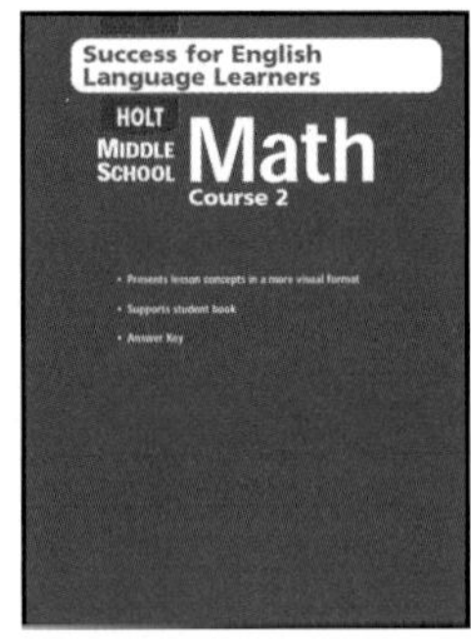

Success for English Language Learners

These masters present the same concepts as the student lesson using fewer words and more visuals. Also includes teacher support with suggested activities and teaching tips.

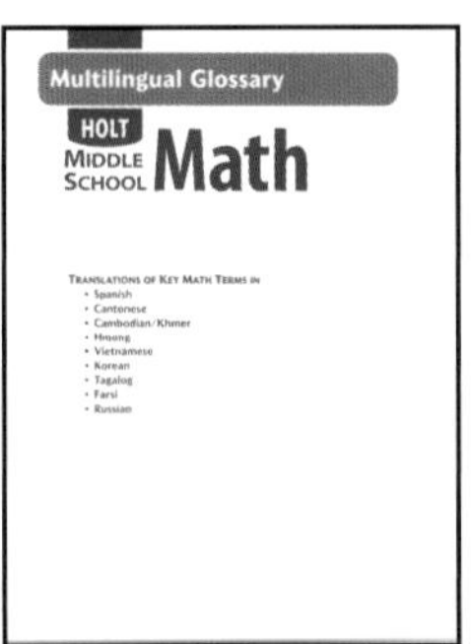

Multilingual Glossary

This glossary contains translations of key mathematical terms in Spanish, Cantonese, Cambodian/Khmer, Hmong, Vietnamese, Korean, Tagalog, Farsi, and Russian.

SPANISH STUDENT EDITIONS AVAILABLE!

Spanish Resources

- Libro de Trabajo: Guía Interactiva de Estudio (Spanish Interactive Study Guide Workbook)
- Libro de Trabajo: Tarea y Práctica (Spanish Homework and Practice Workbook)
- Activades de Apoyo Familia (Family Involvement Activities)

Internet Connect:

Students can link to homework help online directly related to chapter content with this in-text feature.

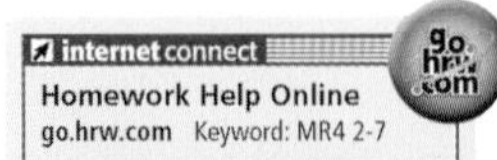

Differentiating Instruction

The risk of death in a house fire can be reduced by up to 50% if the home has a working smoke alarm.

Spark Interest

Show your students that math is needed in the real world.

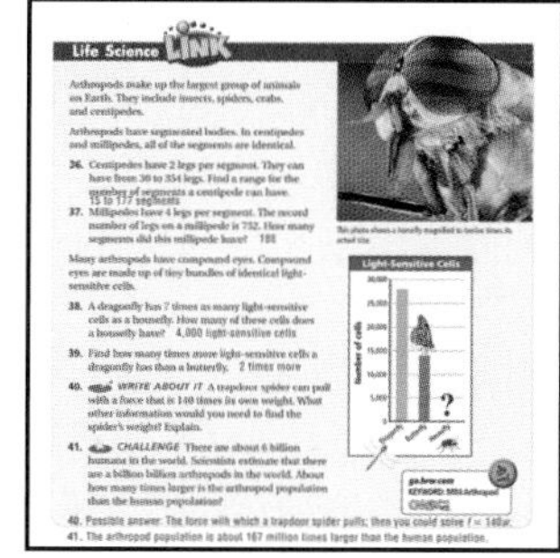

Interdisciplinary Link and Internet Activities

Interdisciplinary Links are featured throughout the program, generating interest and showing students how important math is in our everyday lives. Internet activities online at **go.hrw.com**.

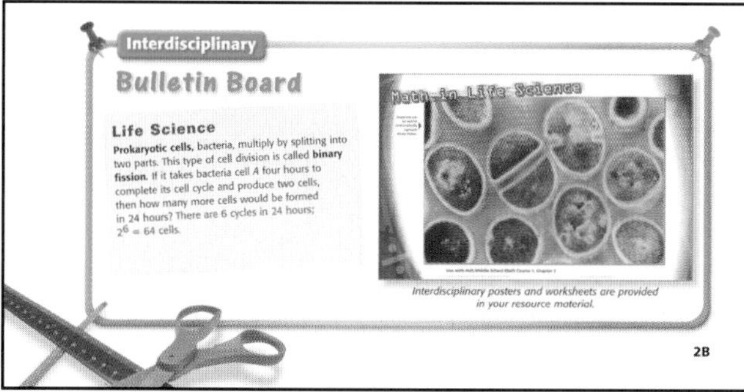

Interdisciplinary Bulletin Board

This feature gives you suggestions about how to update your class visually to complement the section you're about to teach.

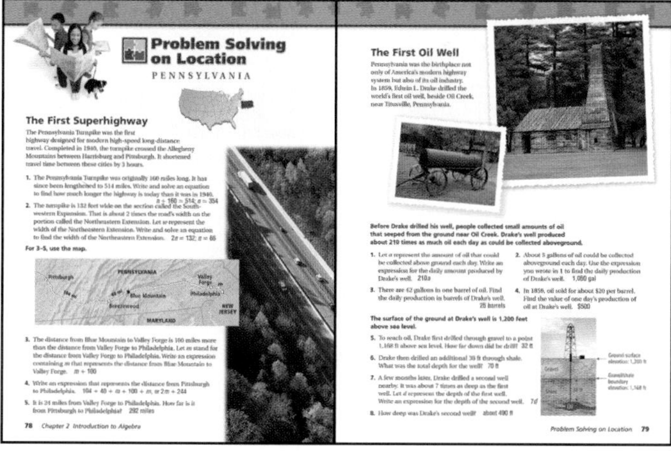

Problem Solving on Location

This feature takes students on a journey to places across the nation. students become familiar with geography and also learn a math lesson specific to that location, helping them sharpen their critical-thinking skills needed for state testing.

Teacher to Teacher

What is Differentiated Instruction?

Differentiated instruction answers the question of how to teach every student in a classroom—regardless of ability level or background—in a way that is equal, effective, and efficient.

Differentiated instruction is more and more becoming the alternative to a "one-size-fits-all classroom." Instead of only offering core information and basic instruction of skills, a curriculum centered around differentiated instruction offers information tailored to a student's readiness, interest, and profile (the way they learn).

How Do I Reach All of My Students?

Holt Middle School Math ensures differentiated instruction by offering content, resources, and technology that speak to all types of learners simultaneously. A visual learner, an auditory learner, a kinesthetic learner, and an English-language learner can all benefit from features and resources such as:

- **Hands-On Lab**
- **Technology Lab**
- **Career Link**
- **Interdisciplinary Links**
- **Internet Activities**
- **Interdisciplinary Bulletin Board**
- **Problem Solving on Location**

What better way to ensure understanding than through a program that helps you do all of this without having to maintain a separate agenda for each student? Differentiated instruction gives each student what he or she needs while they are learning with everyone else in the class. State and national requirements are also taught throughout the program. The differentiated instruction curriculum in ***Holt Middle School Math*** takes care of the teacher as well, making everything streamlined and easy to manage.

Background information on Differentiated Instruction was researched from Carol Ann Tomlinson's book *How to Differentiate Instruction in Mixed-Ability Classrooms* (Alexandria, VA: Association for Supervision and Curriculum Development, 1995). Tomlinson is Professor of Educational Leadership, Foundations, and Policy at the Curry School of Education, UVA. ASCD (Assoc. for Supervision and Curriculum Development) publishes much of her work.

Holt offers a comprehensive and systematic training program to complement ***Holt Middle School Math*** providing high-quality and accessible professional learning opportunities designed to relate to the unique needs of the educator. For more information on professional development services provided by Holt, email us at **holtinfo@hrw.com**.

HOLT Professional Development

For Teachers

Program Resources

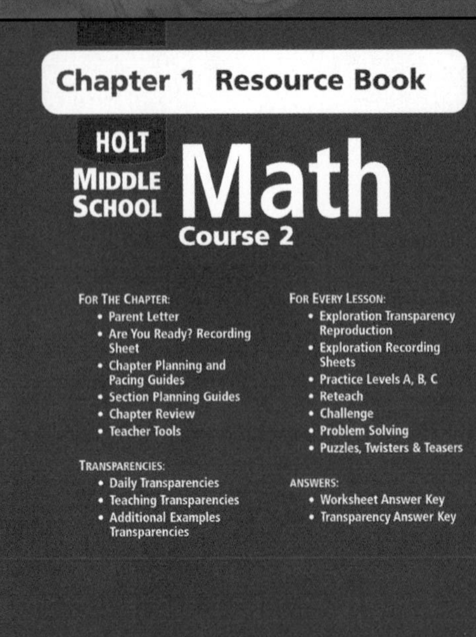

Chapter 1 Resource Book
HOLT
MIDDLE SCHOOL
Math
Course 2
FOR THE CHAPTER:
• Parent Letter
• Are You Ready? Recording Sheet
• Chapter Planning and Pacing Guides
• Section Planning Guides
• Chapter Review
• Teacher Tools
TRANSPARENCIES:
• Daily Transparencies
• Teaching Transparencies
• Additional Examples Transparencies
FOR EVERY LESSON:
• Exploration Transparency Reproduction
• Exploration Recording Sheets
• Practice Levels A, B, C
• Reteach
• Challenge
• Problem Solving
• Puzzles, Twisters & Teasers
ANSWERS:
• Worksheet Answer Key
• Transparency Answer Key

Chapter Resources Booklet

These comprehensive books for each of the twelve chapters include all of the items needed to extend and reinforce the students' and teacher's books. Blackline masters, transparencies, and more are found all in one place making it convenient to plan your lesson.

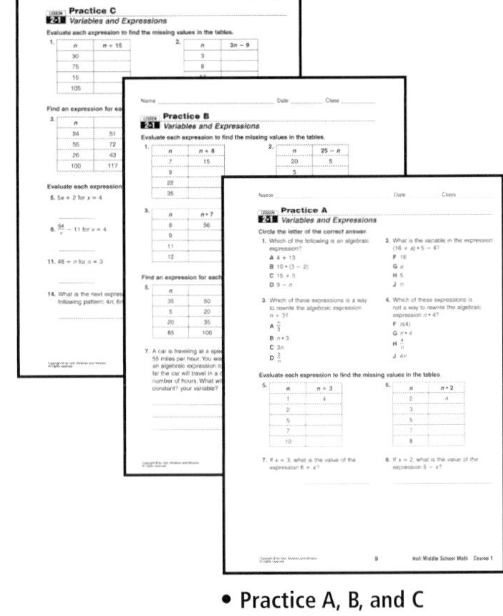

- Practice A, B, and C
- Reteach Masters
- Challenge Masters
- Problem Solving Masters
- Puzzles, Twisters, & Teasers
- and More!

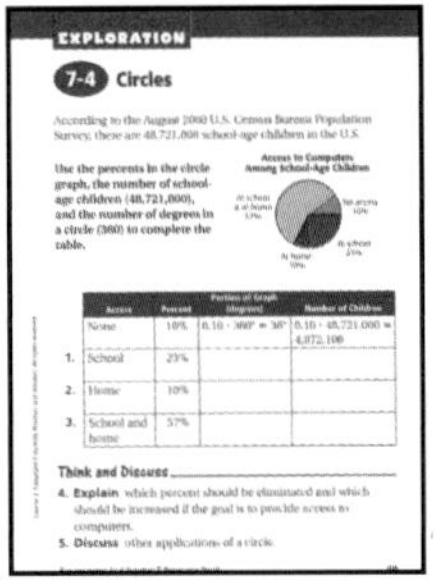

Exploration Transparency

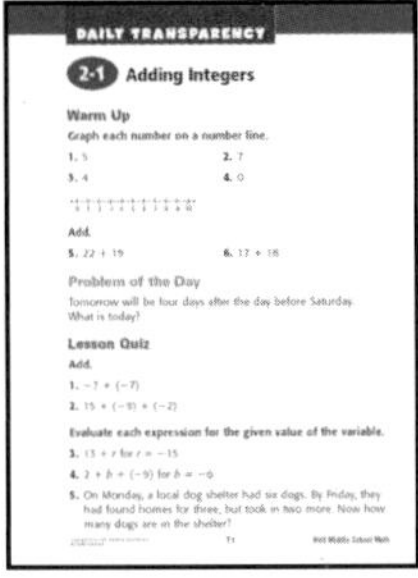

Daily Transparency

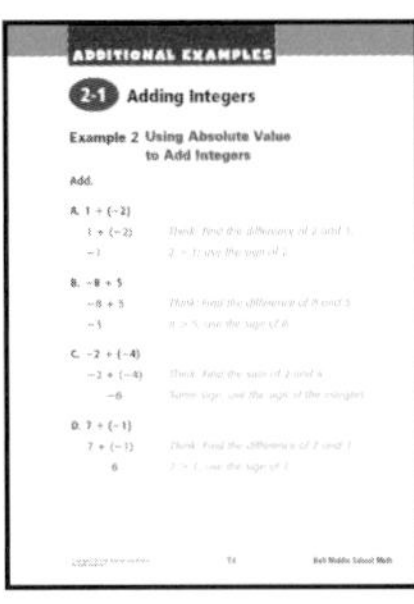

Additional Examples Transparency

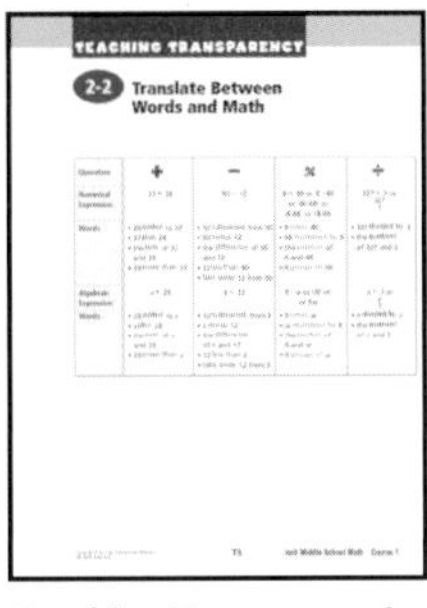

Teaching Transparencies

Assessment and Everyday Teaching Resources

- Assessment Resources
  - Inventory Assessment
  - Section Quizzes
  - Chapter Tests
  - Performance Assessment
  - Cumulative tests
  - End-of-year Test
- Test Prep Tool Kit
- Lesson Plans
- Solution Key
- Answer Transparencies

Homework and Practice Workbook

Interactive Study Guide Workbook

Standardized Test Prep Workbook

Reaching All Learners

- Alternate Openers: Explorations Transparencies
- Are You Ready? Intervention and Enrichment
- Consumer and Career Math
- Family Involvement Activities
- ACTIVIDADES DE APOYO FAMILIAR (Family Involvement Activities)
- Hands-On Lab Activities
- Interdisciplinary Posters and Worksheets
- Interactive Problem Solving
- Math: Reading and Writing in the Content Area
- Multilingual Glossary
- Technology Lab Activities
- Success for English Language Learners
- Readiness Activities
- Interactive Study Guide Workbook
- Standardized Test Prep Workbook
- Homework and Practice Workbook
- Libro de Trabajo: Guía Interactiva de Est (Spanish Interactive Study Guide Workb
- Libro de Trabajo: Tarea y Práctica (Spanish Homework and Practice Workb

Technology that Engages and Expands Learning

Holt Middle School Math **offers an array of technology products that promote mathematics teaching and learning.**

One-Stop Planner® CD-ROM with New! Test and Practice Generator

This convenient tool for planning and managing lessons contains all the print-based teaching resources plus customizable lesson plans. You'll also be able to create tests and quizzes that correlate to your state assessment with the new test generator. All of these resources are accessible with the click of the mouse!

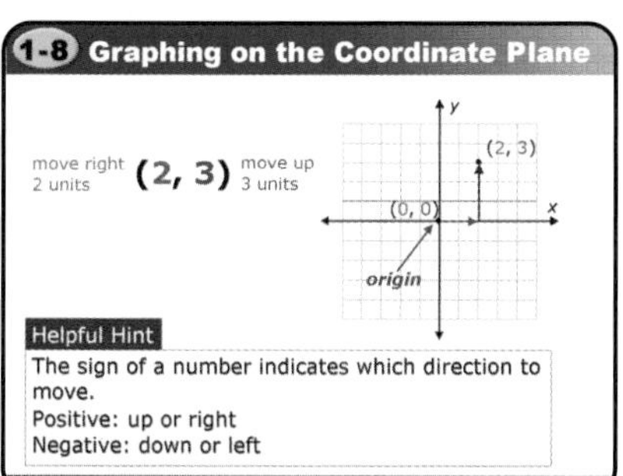

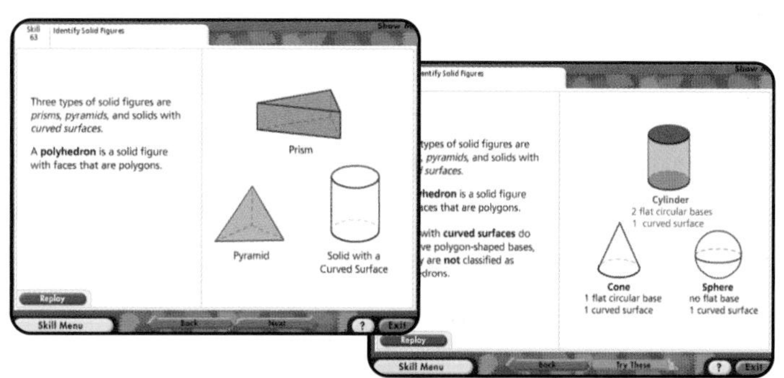

Lesson Presentations CD-ROM

This resource contains colorful, animated electronic lesson presentations—a convenient alternative to the blackboard or overhead projector! This program can also be used by individual students as a tutorial.

Are You Ready? Intervention CD-ROM

This CD-ROM provides an easy method of evaluating students' knowledge and administering additional help with prerequisite skills necessary for success. Students can work independently with computer-guided instruction and practice and can have their skills checked by computer-administered testing.

Electronic Textbooks Lighten the Load

Textbooks from **Holt Online Learning** are portable, expandable, interactive, and yet weigh nothing at all. You'll find interactive exercises and feedback, homework help, presentation materials and much more.

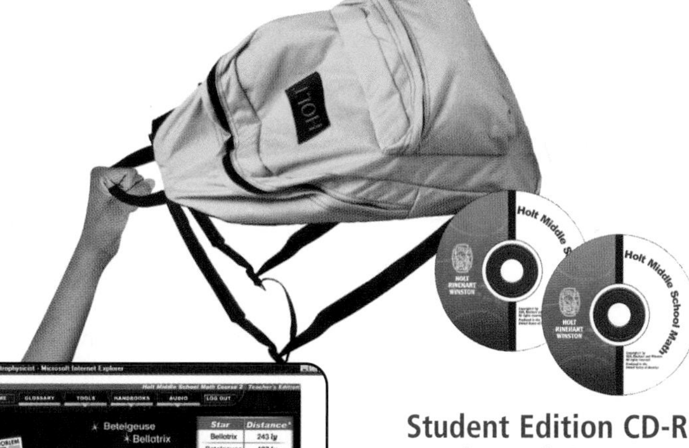

Premier Online Edition

The *Premier Online Edition* features content and assessment correlated to state standards.

Student Edition CD-ROM
Teacher Edition CD-ROM

Internet Connect

Students can link to homework help online directly related to chapter content with this in-text feature.

Technology of the Future

Focus on Problem Solving

The Problem Solving Plan

In order to be a good problem solver, you first need a good problem-solving plan. A plan or strategy will help you to understand the problem, to work through a solution, and to check that your answer makes sense. The plan used in this book is detailed below.

UNDERSTAND the Problem

■ **What are you asked to find?**	Restate the problem in your own words.
■ **What information is given?**	Identify the important facts in the problem.
■ **What information do you need?**	Determine which facts are needed to solve the problem.
■ **Is all the information given?**	Determine whether all the facts are given.

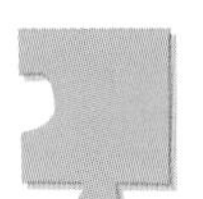

Make a PLAN

■ **Have you ever solved a similar problem?**	Think about other problems like this that you successfully solved.
■ **What strategy or strategies can you use?**	Determine a strategy that you can use and how you will use it.

SOLVE

■ **Follow your plan.**	Show the steps in your solution. Write your answer as a complete sentence.

LOOK BACK

■ **Have you answered the question?**	Be sure that you answered the question that is being asked.
■ **Is your answer reasonable?**	Your answer should make sense in the context of the problem.
■ **Is there another strategy you could use?**	Solving the problem using another strategy is a good way to check your work.
■ **Did you learn anything while solving this problem that could help you solve similar problems in the future?**	Try to remember the problems you have solved and the strategies you used to solve them.

Using the Problem Solving Plan

During summer vacation, Ricardo will go to space camp and then to visit his relatives. He will be gone for 5 weeks and 4 days and will spend 11 more days with his relatives than at space camp. How long will Ricardo stay at each place?

UNDERSTAND the Problem

List the important information.

- Ricardo will be gone for 5 weeks and 4 days.
- He will spend 11 more days with his relatives than at space camp.

The answer will be how long Ricardo stays at each place.

Make a PLAN

You can **draw a diagram** to show how long he will stay at each place. Use boxes for the length of each stay. The length of each box will represent the length of each stay.

SOLVE

Think: There are 7 days in a week, so 5 weeks and 4 days is a total of 39 days. Your diagram might look like this:

Relatives	**? days**	**11 days**	= 39 days
Space camp	**? days**		

$39 - 11 = 28$ *Subtract 11 days from the total number of days.*
$28 \div 2 = 14$ *Divide this number by 2 for the 2 places he visits.*

Relatives	**14 days**	**11 days**	= 25 days
Space camp	**14 days**		= 14 days

So Ricardo will stay with his relatives for 25 days and at space camp for 14 days.

LOOK BACK

Twenty-five days is 11 days longer than 14 days. The total length of the two stays is $25 + 14 = 39$ days, or 5 weeks and 4 days. This solution fits the information given in the problem.

Draw a Diagram

When problems involve objects, distances, or places, you can **draw a diagram** to make the problem easier to understand. You can use the diagram to look for relationships among the given data and to solve the problem.

Problem Solving Strategies

Draw a Diagram	Make a Table
Make a Model	Solve a Simpler Problem
Guess and Test	Use Logical Reasoning
Work Backward	Use a Venn Diagram
Find a Pattern	Make an Organized List

A bald eagle has built a nest 18 feet below the top of a 105-foot-tall oak tree. The eagle sits on a limb 72 feet above the ground. What is the vertical distance between the eagle and its nest?

Understand the Problem Identify the important information.

- The height of the tree is 105 feet.
- The eagle's nest is 18 feet from the top of the tree.
- The eagle is perched 72 feet above the ground.

The answer will be the vertical distance between the eagle and its nest.

Make a Plan Use the information in the problem to **draw a diagram** showing the height of the tree and the locations of the eagle and its nest.

Solve To find the height of the nest's location, subtract the distance of the nest from the top of the tree from the height of the tree.

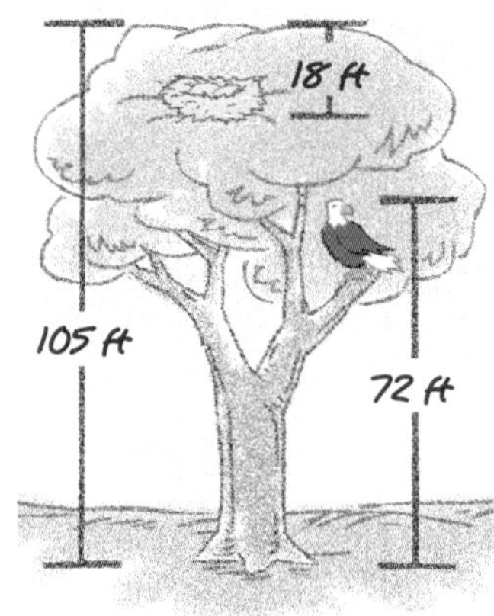

105 feet − 18 feet = 87 feet

To find the vertical distance from the eagle to its nest, subtract the height of the eagle's location from the height of the nest's location.

87 feet − 72 feet = 15 feet

The vertical distance between the eagle and its nest is 15 feet.

Look Back Be sure that you have drawn your diagram correctly. Does it match the information given in the problem?

PRACTICE

1. A truck driver travels 17 miles south to drop off his first delivery. Then he drives 19 miles west to drop off a second delivery, and then he drives 17 miles north to drop off another delivery. Finally, he drives 5 miles east for his last delivery. How far is he from his starting point? **14 miles**

2. A table that is standing lengthwise against a wall is 10 feet long and 4 feet wide. Sarah puts balloons 1 foot apart along the three exposed sides, with one balloon at each corner. How many balloons does she use? **19 balloons**

Make a Model

When problems involve objects, you can **make a model** using those objects or similar objects. This can help you understand the problem and find the solution.

Problem Solving Strategies

Draw a Diagram	Make a Table
Make a Model	Solve a Simpler Problem
Guess and Test	Use Logical Reasoning
Work Backward	Use a Venn Diagram
Find a Pattern	Make an Organized List

A company packages 6 minipuzzles in a decorated 4 in. cube. They are shipped to the toy store in cartons shaped like rectangular prisms. Twenty cubes fit in each carton. If the height of each carton is 8 in., what are possible dimensions of the carton?

Understand the Problem

Identify the important information.

- Each cube is 4 inches on a side.
- Twenty cubes fit in one carton.
- The height of the carton is 8 inches.

The answer is the dimensions of the carton.

Make a Plan

You can use 20 cubes to **make a model** of cubes packed in a carton. Record possible values for length and width, given a height of 8 in.

Solve

Begin with a carton that is 8 in., or 2 cubes, high. Use all 20 cubes to make a rectangular prism.

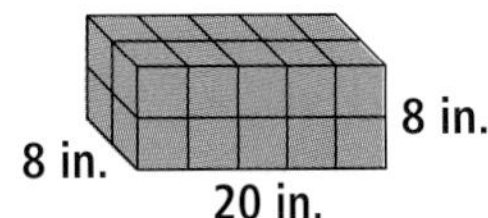

Possible dimensions of the carton are 20 in. × 8 in. × 8 in.

Look Back

The volume of each carton should equal the volume of the 20 cubes.

Volume of cartons: 8 in. × 20 in. × 8 in. = 1,280 in^3

Volume of 1 cube: 4 in. × 4 in. × 4 in. = 64 in^3

Volume of 20 cubes: 20 × 64 = 1,280 in^3

1,280 in^3 = 1,280 in^3 ✔

PRACTICE

1. Give two sets of possible dimensions of a rectangular prism made up of twenty 1-inch cubes. **2 in. × 2 in. × 5 in. and 1 in. × 4 in. × 5 in.**
2. John uses exactly eight 1-inch cubes to form a rectangular prism. Find the length, width, and height of the prism.
   Possible answer: 2 in. × 2 in. × 2 in.

Guess and Test

If you do not know how to solve a problem, you can always make a **guess.** Then **test** your guess using the information in the problem. Use what you find out to make a second guess. Continue to **guess and test** until you find the correct answer.

Problem Solving Strategies

Draw a Diagram	Make a Table
Make a Model	Solve a Simpler Problem
Guess and Test	Use Logical Reasoning
Work Backward	Use a Venn Diagram
Find a Pattern	Make an Organized List

Shannon used equal numbers of quarters and nickels to buy an embossing template that cost \$1.50. How many of each coin did she use?

Understand the Problem

Identify the important information.

- Shannon used equal numbers of quarters and nickels.
- The coins she used total \$1.50.

The answer will be the number of quarters and the number of nickels Shannon used.

Make a Plan

Start with an educated **guess** in which the numbers of quarters and nickels are the same. Then **test** to see whether the coins total \$1.50.

Solve

Make a first guess of 4 quarters and 4 nickels, and find the total value of the coins.

Guess: 4 quarters and 4 nickels
Test: (4 × \$0.25) + (4 × \$0.05) = \$1.00 + \$0.20 = \$1.20

\$1.20 is too low. Increase the number of coins.

Guess: 6 quarters and 6 nickels
Test: (6 × \$0.25) + (6 × \$0.05) = \$1.50 + \$0.30 = \$1.80

\$1.80 is too high. The number of each coin must be between 4 and 6. So Shannon must have used 5 quarters and 5 nickels.

Look Back

Test the answer to see whether the coins add up to \$1.50.
(5 × \$0.25) + (5 × \$0.05) = \$1.25 + \$0.25 = \$1.50 ✓

PRACTICE

1. The sum of Richard's age and his older brother's age is 63. The difference between their ages is 13. How old are Richard and his brother? **25 years and 38 years**

2. In the final game of the basketball season, Trinka scored a total of 25 points on 2-point shots and 3-point shots. She made 5 more 2-point shots than 3-point shots. How many of each did she make?

2. eight 2-point shots and three 3-point shots

Work Backward

Some problems give you a sequence of information and ask you to find something that happened at the beginning. To solve a problem like this, you may want to start at the end of the problem and **work backward.**

Problem Solving Strategies

Draw a Diagram	Make a Table
Make a Model	Solve a Simpler Problem
Guess and Test	Use Logical Reasoning
Work Backward	Use a Venn Diagram
Find a Pattern	Make an Organized List

Tony is selling dried fruit snacks to help raise money for a new school computer. Half of the fruit snacks in the bag are apricots. Of the rest of the fruit snacks, half of them are bananas, and the other 8 are cranberries. How many fruit snacks are in the bag?

Understand the Problem

Identify the important information.

- Half of the fruit snacks are apricots.
- Half of the remaining fruit snacks are bananas.
- The final 8 fruit snacks are cranberries.

The answer will be the total number of fruit snacks in the bag.

Make a Plan

Start with the 8 cranberries, and **work backward** through the information in the problem to the total number of fruit snacks in the bag.

Solve

There are 8 cranberries.	8
The other half of the remaining fruit snacks are bananas, so there must be 8 bananas.	$8 + 8 = 16$
The other half of the fruit snacks are apricots, so there must be 16 apricots.	$16 + 16 = 32$

There are 32 fruit snacks in the bag.

Look Back

Using the starting amount of 32 fruit snacks, work from the beginning of the problem following the steps.

Start: 32
Half of 32: $32 \div 2 = 16$
Half of 16: $16 \div 2 = 8$
Minus 8: $8 - 8 = 0$ ✔

PRACTICE

1. In a trivia competition, each finalist must answer 4 questions correctly. Each question is worth twice as much as the question before it. The fourth question is worth $1,000. How much is the first question worth? **$125**

2. The Ramirez family has 5 children. Sara is 5 years younger than her brother Kenny. Felix is half as old as his sister Sara. Kaitlen, who is 10, is 3 years older than Felix. Kenny and Celia are twins. How old is Celia? **19 years old**

Find a Pattern

In some problems, there is a relationship between different pieces of information. Examine this relationship and try to **find a pattern.** You can then use this pattern to find more information and the solution to the problem.

Problem Solving Strategies

Draw a Diagram	Make a Table
Make a Model	Solve a Simpler Problem
Guess and Test	Use Logical Reasoning
Work Backward	Use a Venn Diagram
Find a Pattern	Make an Organized List

John made a design using hexagons and triangles. The side lengths of each hexagon and triangle are 1 inch. What is the perimeter of the next figure in his design?

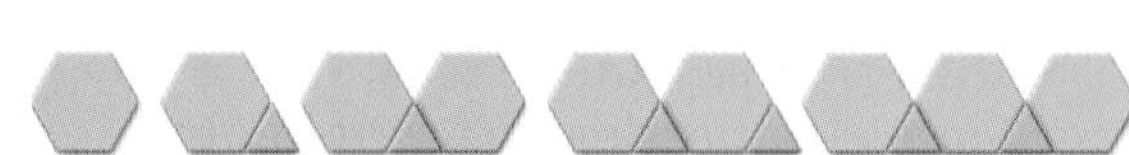

Understand the Problem

Identify the important information.

- The first 5 figures in the design are given.
- The side lengths of each hexagon and triangle are 1 inch.

The answer will be the perimeter of the sixth figure in the design.

Make a Plan

Try to **find a pattern** in the perimeters of the first 5 figures. Use the pattern to find the perimeter of the sixth figure.

Solve

Find the perimeter of the first 5 figures.

Figure	Perimeter (in.)	Pattern
1	6	
2	7	6 + 1 = 7
3	11	7 + 4 = 11
4	12	11 + 1 = 12
5	16	12 + 4 = 16

The pattern appears to be add 1, add 4, add 1, add 4, and so on. So the perimeter of the sixth figure will be 16 + 1, or 17.

Look Back

Use another strategy. **Draw a diagram** of the sixth figure. Then find the perimeter.

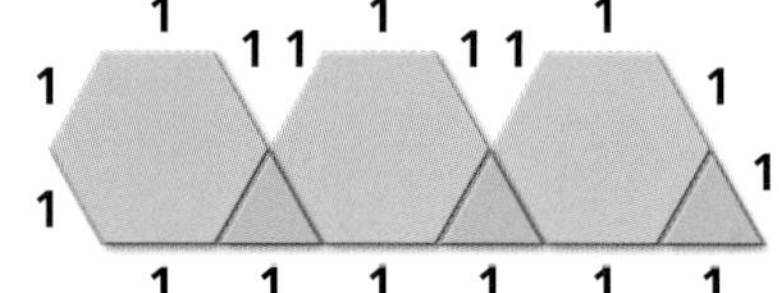

PRACTICE

Describe the pattern, and then find the next number.

1. 1, 5, 9, 13, 17, . . . **Add 4 to the previous number; 21**

2. 1, 4, 16, 64, 256, . . . **Multiply the previous number by 4; 1,024**

Make a Table

When you are given a lot of information in a problem, it may be helpful to organize that information. One way to organize information is to **make a table.**

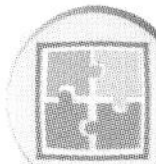

Problem Solving Strategies

Draw a Diagram	**Make a Table**
Make a Model	Solve a Simpler Problem
Guess and Test	Use Logical Reasoning
Work Backward	Use a Venn Diagram
Find a Pattern	Make an Organized List

On November 1, Wendy watered the Gribbles' yard and the Milams' yard. If she waters the Gribbles' yard every 4 days and the Milams' yard every 5 days, when is the next date that Wendy will water both yards?

Understand the Problem

Identify the important information.

- Wendy waters the Gribbles' yard every 4 days and the Milams' yard every 5 days. She watered both yards on November 1.

The answer will be the next date that she waters both yards again.

Make a Plan

Make a table using X's to show the days that Wendy waters each yard. Make one row for the Gribbles and one row for the Milams.

Solve

Start with an X in both rows for November 1. For the Gribbles, add an X on every fourth day after November 1. For the Milams, add an X every fifth day after November 1.

Date	1	2	3	4	5	6	7	8	9	10	11	12	13	14	15	16	17	18	19	20	21
Gribble	X				X				X				X				X				X
Milam	X					X					X					X					X

November 21 is the next date that Wendy will water both yards.

Look Back

The sum of 1 and five 4's should equal the sum of 1 and four 5's.
$1 + 4 + 4 + 4 + 4 + 4 = 21$ $1 + 5 + 5 + 5 + 5 = 21$ ✓

PRACTICE

1. Jess, Kathy, and Linda work on the math club's newspaper. One is the editor, one is the reporter, and one is the writer. Linda does not participate in sports. Jess and the editor play tennis together. Linda and the reporter are cousins. Find each person's job.
Jess–reporter, Kathy–editor, Linda–writer

2. A toll booth accepts any combination of coins that total exactly $0.75, but it does not accept pennies or half dollars. In how many different ways can a driver pay the toll? **18 ways**

Solve a Simpler Problem

Sometimes a problem may contain large numbers or require many steps to solve. It may appear complicated to solve. Try to **solve a simpler problem** that is similar to the original problem.

Problem Solving Strategies

Draw a Diagram	Make a Table
Make a Model	**Solve a Simpler Problem**
Guess and Test	Use Logical Reasoning
Work Backward	Use a Venn Diagram
Find a Pattern	Make an Organized List

Lawrence is making touch pools for a project about sea creatures. The pools are squares that will be arranged side by side. The side of each pool is a 1-meter-long piece of wood. How many meters of wood does Lawrence need to complete 20 square sections of pool?

Understand the Problem Identify the important information.

- Each square side is a 1-meter-long piece of wood.
- There are 20 square sections set side by side.

The answer will be the total meters of wood needed.

Make a Plan You could sketch all 20 pools and then count the number of meters of wood. However, it would be easier to first **solve a simpler problem**. Start with 1 square pool, and then move on to 2 and then 3. Then look for a way to solve the problem for 20 pools.

Solve The first pool requires 4 sides to complete. After that, only 3 sides are needed for each pool.

1 square:

2 squares:

3 squares:

Notice that 1 pool requires 4 meters of wood, and the 19 other pools require 3 meters of wood each. So $4 + (19 \times 3) = 61$. The pools require 61 meters of wood.

Number of Squares	Number of Meters
1	$4(1) = 4$
2	$4 + (1 \times 3) = 7$
3	$4 + (2 \times 3) = 10$
4	$4 + (3 \times 3) = 13$

Look Back If the pattern is correct, Lawrence would need 16 meters of wood for 5 pools. Complete the next row of the table to check this answer.

PRACTICE

1. The numbers 11; 444; and 8,888 all contain repeated single digits. How many numbers between 10 and 1,000,000 contain repeated single digits? **45**
2. How many diagonals are there in a dodecagon (a 12-sided polygon)? **54**

Use Logical Reasoning

Sometimes a problem may provide clues and facts that you must use to find a solution. You can use **logical reasoning** to solve this kind of problem.

Problem Solving Strategies

Draw a Diagram	Make a Table
Make a Model	Solve a Simpler Problem
Guess and Test	**Use Logical Reasoning**
Work Backward	Use a Venn Diagram
Find a Pattern	Make an Organized List

Jennie, Rachel, and Mia play the oboe, the violin, and the drums. Mia does not like the drums, and she is the sister of the oboe player. Rachel has soccer practice with the person who plays the drums. Which instrument does each person play?

Understand the Problem Identify the important information.

- There are three people, and each person plays a different instrument.

Make a Plan Start with clues given in the problem, and **use logical reasoning** to determine which instrument each person plays.

Solve Make a table. Make a column for each instrument and a row for each person. Work with the clues one at a time. Write "Yes" in a box if the clue reveals that a person plays an instrument. Write "No" in a box if the clue reveals that a person does not play an instrument.

a. Mia does not like the drums, so she does not play the drums.

b. Mia is the sister of the person who plays the oboe, so she does not play the oboe.

c. Rachel has soccer practice with the person who plays the drums, so she does not play the drums.

	Oboe	Violin	Drums
Jennie			
Rachel			No
Mia	No		No

Jennie must play the drums, and Mia must play the violin. So Rachel must play the oboe.

Look Back Compare your answer to the clues in the problem. Make sure none of your conclusions conflict with the clues.

PRACTICE

1. Kent, Jason, and Newman have a dog, a fish, and a hamster, though not in that order. Kent's pet does not have fur. The owner of the hamster has class with Jason. Match the owners with their pets. **Kent–fish, Jason–dog, Newman–hamster**

2. Seth, Vess, and Benica are in the sixth, seventh, and eighth grades, though not in that order. Seth is not in seventh grade. The sixth-grader has band with Benica and the same lunchtime as Seth. Match the students with their grades. **Seth–eighth grade, Vess–sixth grade, Benica–seventh grade**

Use a Venn Diagram

You can use a **Venn diagram** to display relationships among sets in a problem. Use ovals, circles, or other shapes to represent individual sets.

Problem Solving Strategies

Draw a Diagram	Make a Table
Make a Model	Solve a Simpler Problem
Guess and Test	Use Logical Reasoning
Work Backward	**Use a Venn Diagram**
Find a Pattern	Make an Organized List

At Landry Middle School, 127 students take French, 145 take Spanish, and 31 take both. How many students take only French? How many students take only Spanish?

Understand the Problem

Identify the important information.

- There are 127 students who take French, 145 who take Spanish, and 31 who take both.

Make a Plan

Use a Venn diagram to show the sets of students who take French and Spanish.

Solve

Draw and label two overlapping circles. Write "31" in the area where the circles overlap. This represents the number of students who take French and Spanish.

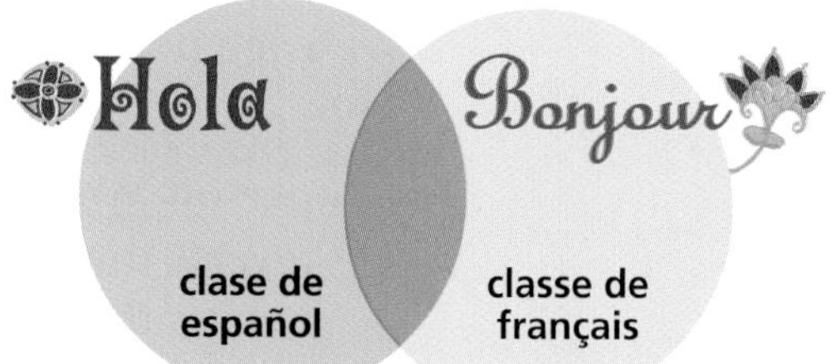

To find the number of students who take only French, subtract the number of students who take both French and Spanish from those who take French. To find the number of students who take only Spanish, subtract the number of students who take both French and Spanish from those who take Spanish.

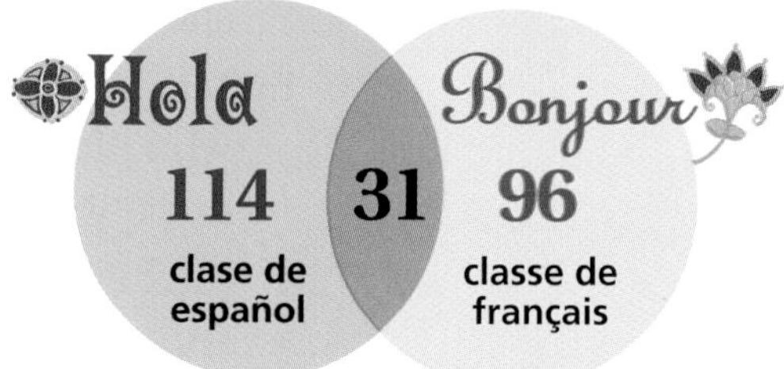

So 96 students take only French, and 114 students take only Spanish.

Look Back

Check your Venn diagram carefully against the information in the problem. Make sure your diagram agrees with the facts given.

PRACTICE

Responding to a survey, there were 60 people who said they like pasta, 45 who like chicken, and 70 who like hot dogs. There were 15 people who said they like both pasta and chicken, 22 who like both hot dogs and chicken, and 17 who like both hot dogs and pasta. Only 8 people said they like all 3.

1. How many people like only pasta? **36 people**

2. How many people like only hot dogs? **39 people**

Make an Organized List

In some problems, you will need to find out exactly how many different ways an event can happen. When solving this kind of problem, it is often helpful to **make an organized list**. This will help you count all the possible outcomes.

Problem Solving Strategies

Draw a Diagram	Make a Table
Make a Model	Solve a Simpler Problem
Guess and Test	Use Logical Reasoning
Work Backward	Use a Venn Diagram
Find a Pattern	**Make an Organized List**

A spinner has 4 different colors: red, blue, yellow, and white. If you spin the spinner 2 times, how many different color combinations could you get?

Identify the important information.

- You spin the spinner 2 times.
- The spinner is divided into 4 different colors.

The answer will be the total number of different color combinations the spinner can land on.

Make an organized list to determine all the possible different color outcomes. List all the different combinations for each color.

First consider the color red. List all the different outcomes for the color red. Then consider blue, adding all the different outcomes, then yellow, and finally white.

Red	Blue	Yellow	White
RR	BB	YY	WW
RB	BY	YW	
RY	BW		
RW			

So there are 10 possible different color combinations.

Make sure that all the possible combinations of color are listed and that each set of colors is different.

PRACTICE

1. The Pizza Planet has 5 different choices of pizza toppings: ham, pineapple, pepperoni, olive, and mushroom. You want to order a pizza with 2 different toppings. How many different combinations of toppings can you order? **10 combinations**
2. How many ways can you make change for a fifty-cent piece by using a combination of dimes, nickels, and pennies? **16 ways**

Chapter 1

Data Toolbox

Section 1A	Section 1B	Section 1C
Organizing Data	**Displaying Data**	**Trends and Relations in Graphs**
Lesson 1-1 Populations and Samples **Technology Lab 1A** Generate Random Numbers **Lesson 1-2** Mean, Median, Mode, and Range **Lesson 1-3** Frequency Tables and Stem-and-Leaf Plots	**Lesson 1-4** Bar Graphs and Histograms **Lesson 1-5** Reading and Interpreting Circle Graphs **Lesson 1-6** Box-and-Whisker Plots **Technology Lab 1B** Use Technology to Create Graphs	**Lesson 1-7** Line Graphs **Hands-On Lab 1C** Explore Scatter Plots **Lesson 1-8** Scatter Plots **Lesson 1-9** Misleading Graphs

Pacing Guide for 45-Minute Classes

Chapter 1

DAY 1	DAY 2	DAY 3	DAY 4	DAY 5
Lesson 1-1	Technology Lab 1A	Lesson 1-2	Lesson 1-3	Mid-Chapter Quiz Lesson 1-4
DAY 6	**DAY 7**	**DAY 8**	**DAY 9**	**DAY 10**
Lesson 1-5	Lesson 1-6	Technology Lab 1B	Mid-Chapter Quiz Lesson 1-7	Hands-On Lab 1C
DAY 11	**DAY 12**	**DAY 13**	**DAY 14**	
Lesson 1-8	Lesson 1-9	Chapter 1 Review	Chapter 1 Assessment	

Pacing Guide for 90-Minute Classes

Chapter 1

DAY 1	DAY 2	DAY 3	DAY 4	DAY 5
Lesson 1-1 Technology Lab 1A	Lesson 1-2 Lesson 1-3	Mid-Chapter Quiz Lesson 1-4 Lesson 1-5	Lesson 1-6 Technology Lab 1B	Mid-Chapter Quiz Lesson 1-7 Hands-On Lab 1C
DAY 6	**DAY 7**	**DAY 8**		
Lesson 1-8 Lesson 1-9	Chapter 1 Review Lesson 2-1	Chapter 1 Assessment Lesson 2-2		

Across the Series

COURSE 1

- Organize data in tables and stem-and-leaf plots, and display data in bar graphs, histograms, box-and-whisker plots, line graphs, and scatter plots.
- Find measures of central tendency.
- Interpret circle graphs.
- Recognize misleading graphs.

COURSE 2

- **Identify populations and choose samples.**
- **Organize data in tables and stem-and-leaf plots, and display data in bar graphs, box-and-whisker plots, line graphs, and scatter plots.**
- **Determine the range and the measures of central tendency.**
- **Read and interpret circle graphs.**
- **Graph relationships, analyze graphs, and recognize misleading graphs.**

COURSE 3

- Identify sampling methods and bias.
- Organize data in tables and stem-and-leaf plots, and display data in bar graphs, histograms, and line graphs.
- Find appropriate measures of central tendency and variability.
- Recognize misleading graphs.
- Create and interpret scatter plots.

Across the Curriculum

LANGUAGE ARTS LINK

Math: Reading and Writing in the Content Area . . . . pp. 1–9
Focus on Problem Solving
Solve . . . . SE p. 19
Journal . . . . TE, last page of each lesson
Write About It . . . . SE pp. 7, 13, 17, 23, 27, 31, 38, 47

SOCIAL STUDIES LINK

Economics . . . . SE p. 13
Social Studies . . . . SE pp. 20, 23, 27, 44
History . . . . SE p. 16

SCIENCE LINK

Life Science . . . . SE pp. 17, 24
Earth Science . . . . SE pp. 25, 38
Health . . . . SE p. 13
Science . . . . SE p. 43

TE = *Teacher's Edition* **SE** = *Student Edition*

Interdisciplinary

Bulletin Board

Social Studies

Demographers measure **population density** by dividing a country's population by its area. Calculate the population density of Latvia and Croatia.

Country	Area (mi^2)	Population
Latvia	25,191	2,385,231
Croatia	22,052	4,334,142

95 people/mi^2 and 197 people/mi^2, respectively

What type of graph might you use to display the population density of all the countries in Eastern Europe? bar graph

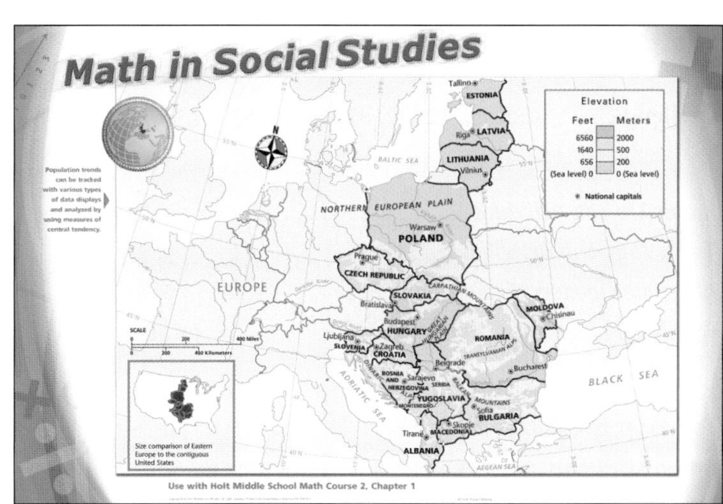

Interdisciplinary posters and worksheets are provided in your resource material.

Resource Options

Chapter 1 Resource Book

Student Resources

Practice (Levels A, B, C) . . . . . pp. 8–10, 17–19, 27–29, 38–40, 48–50, 57–59, 67–69, 76–78, 85–87

Reteach . . . . . pp. 11, 20–21, 30–31, 41–42, 51, 60, 70, 79, 88

Challenge . . . . pp. 12, 22, 32, 43, 52, 61, 71, 80, 89

Problem Solving . . . . pp. 13, 23, 33, 44, 53, 62, 72, 81, 90

Puzzles, Twisters & Teasers . . . . pp. 14, 24, 34, 45, 54, 63, 73, 82, 91

Recording Sheets . . . . pp. 3, 7, 16, 26, 37, 47, 56, 66, 75, 84, 95

Chapter Review . . . . pp. 92–94

Teacher and Parent Resources

Chapter Planning and Pacing Guide . . . . p. 4

Section Planning Guides . . . . pp. 5, 35, 64

Parent Letter . . . . pp. 1–2

Teaching Tools . . . . pp. 98–100

Teacher Support for Chapter Project . . . . p. 96

Transparencies . . . . pp. T1–T35

- Daily Transparencies
- Additional Examples Transparencies
- Teaching Transparencies

Reaching All Learners

English Language Learners

Success for English Language Learners . . . . pp. 1–18

Math: Reading and Writing in the Content Area . . . . pp. 1–9

Spanish Homework and Practice . . . . pp. 1–9

Spanish Interactive Study Guide . . . . pp. 1–9

Spanish Family Involvement Activities . . . . pp. 1–12

Multilingual Glossary

Individual Needs

Are You Ready? Intervention and Enrichment . . pp. 29–32, 145–148, 253–256, 369–372, 405–406

Alternate Openers: Explorations . . . . pp. 1–9

Family Involvement Activities . . . . pp. 1–12

Interactive Problem Solving . . . . pp. 1–9

Interactive Study Guide . . . . pp. 1–9

Readiness Activities . . . . pp. 1–2

Math: Reading and Writing in the Content Area . . . . pp. 1–9

Challenge . . . . . CRB pp. 12, 22, 32, 43, 52, 61, 71, 80, 89

Hands-On

Hands-On Lab Activities . . . . pp. 1–6

Technology Lab Activities . . . . pp. 1–4

Alternate Openers: Explorations . . . . pp. 1–9

Family Involvement Activities . . . . pp. 1–12

Applications and Connections

Consumer and Career Math . . . . pp. 1–4

Interdisciplinary Posters . . . . Poster 1, TE p. 2B

Interdisciplinary Poster Worksheets . . . . pp. 1–3

Transparencies

Alternate Openers: Explorations . . . . pp. 1–9

Exercise Answers Transparencies

Chapter 1 Resource Book . . . . pp. T1–T35

- Daily Transparencies
- Additional Examples Transparencies
- Teaching Transparencies

Technology

Teacher Resources

***Lesson Presentations* CD-ROM** . . . . Chapter 1

***Test and Practice Generator* CD-ROM** . . . . Chapter 1

***One-Stop Planner* CD-ROM** . . . . Chapter 1

Student Resources

***Are You Ready? Intervention* CD-ROM**
Skills 5, 34, 61, 90

internet connect

go.hrw.com

Homework Help Online	**KEYWORD:** MS4 HWHelp1
Math Tools Online	**KEYWORD:** MS4 Tools
Glossary Online	**KEYWORD:** MS4 Glossary
Chapter Project Online	**KEYWORD:** MS4 PSProject1
Chapter Opener Online	**KEYWORD:** MS4 Ch1

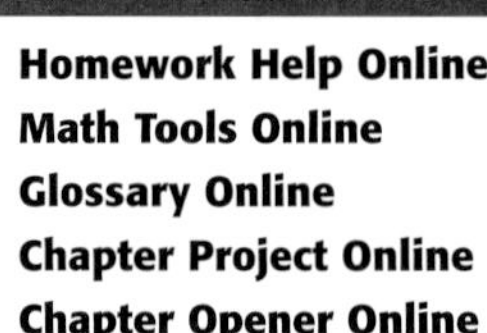

KEYWORD: MS4 CNN1

SE = *Student Edition* **TE** = *Teacher's Edition* **AR** = *Assessment Resources* **CRB** = *Chapter Resource Book* **MK** = *Manipulatives Kit*

Chapter 1

Assessment Options

Assessing Prior Knowledge

Determine whether students have the required prerequisite concepts and skills.

Are You Ready? . . . . SE p. 3
Inventory Test . . . . AR pp. 1–4

Test Preparation

Provide review and practice for chapter and standardized tests.

Standardized Test Prep . . . . SE p. 57
Spiral Review with Test Prep . . . . . SE, last page of each lesson
Study Guide and Review . . . . SE pp. 52–54
Test Prep Tool Kit

Technology

***Test and Practice Generator* CD-ROM**

internet connect

State-Specific Test Practice Online KEYWORD: MS4 TestPrep

Performance Assessment

Assess students' understanding of chapter concepts and combined problem-solving skills.

Performance Assessment . . . . SE p. 56
Includes scoring rubric in TE
Performance Assessment . . . . AR p. 106
Performance Assessment Teacher Support . . . . AR p. 105

Portfolio

Portfolio opportunities appear throughout the Student and Teacher's Editions.

Suggested work samples:

Problem Solving Project . . . . TE p. 2
Performance Assessment . . . . SE p. 56
Portfolio Guide . . . . AR p. xxxv
Journal . . . . TE, last page of each lesson
Write About It . . . . SE, pp. 7, 13, 17, 23, 27, 31, 38, 47

Daily Assessment

Obtain daily feedback on students' understanding of concepts.

Spiral Review and Test Prep . . . . . . SE, last page of each lesson

Also Available on Transparency In Chapter 1 Resource Book

Warm Up . . . . TE, first page of each lesson
Problem of the Day . . . . TE, first page of each lesson
Lesson Quiz . . . . TE, last page of each lesson

Student Self-Assessment

Have students evaluate their own work.

Group Project Evaluation . . . . AR p. xxxii
Individual Group Member Evaluation . . . . AR p. xxxiii
Portfolio Guide . . . . AR p. xxxv
Journal . . . . TE, last page of each lesson

Formal Assessment

Assess students' mastery of concepts and skills.

Section Quizzes . . . . AR pp. 5–7
Mid-Chapter Quizzes . . . . SE pp. 18, 34
Chapter Test . . . . SE p. 55
Chapter Tests (Levels A, B, C) . . . . AR pp. 33–38
Cumulative Tests (Levels A, B, C) . . . . AR pp. 129–140
Standardized Test Prep
Cumulative Assessment . . . . SE p. 57
End-of-Year Test . . . . AR pp. 273–276

Technology

***Test and Practice Generator* CD-ROM**

Make tests electronically. This software includes:

- Dynamic practice for Chapter 1
- Customizable tests
- Multiple-choice items for each objective
- Free-response items for each objective
- Teacher management system

SE = *Student Edition* **TE** = *Teacher's Edition* **AR** = *Assessment Resources* **CRB** = *Chapter Resource Book* **MK** = *Manipulatives Kit*

Chapter 1

Chapter 1 Tests

Three levels (A,B,C) of tests are available for each chapter in the *Assessment Resources*.

LEVEL A

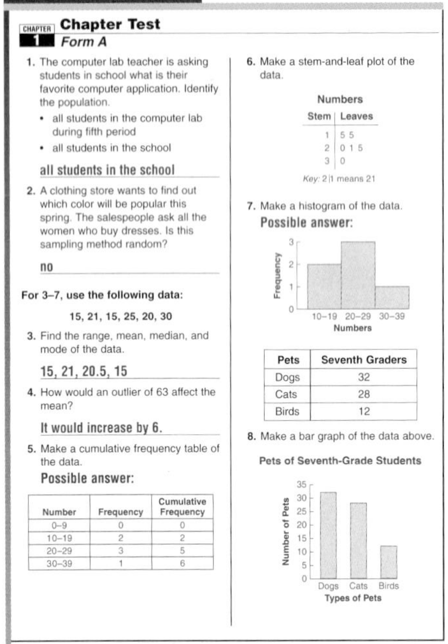

CHAPTER 1 Chapter Test *Form A*

1. The computer lab teacher is asking students in school what is their favorite computer application. Identify the population.
   - all students in the computer lab during fifth period
   - all students in the school

   all students in the school

2. A clothing store wants to find out which color will be popular this spring. The salespeople ask all the women who buy dresses. Is this sampling method random?

   no

For 3–7, use the following data:

15, 21, 15, 25, 20, 30

3. Find the range, mean, median, and mode of the data.

   15, 21, 20.5, 15

4. How would an outlier of 63 affect the mean?

   It would increase by 6.

5. Make a cumulative frequency table of the data.

   Possible answer:

Number	Frequency	Cumulative Frequency
0–9	0	0
10–19	2	2
20–29	3	5
30–39	1	6

6. Make a stem-and-leaf plot of the data.

   Numbers

Stem	Leaves
1	5 5
2	0 1 5
3	0

   Key: 2|1 means 21

7. Make a histogram of the data.

   Possible answer:

Pets	Seventh Graders
Dogs	32
Cats	28
Birds	12

8. Make a bar graph of the data above.

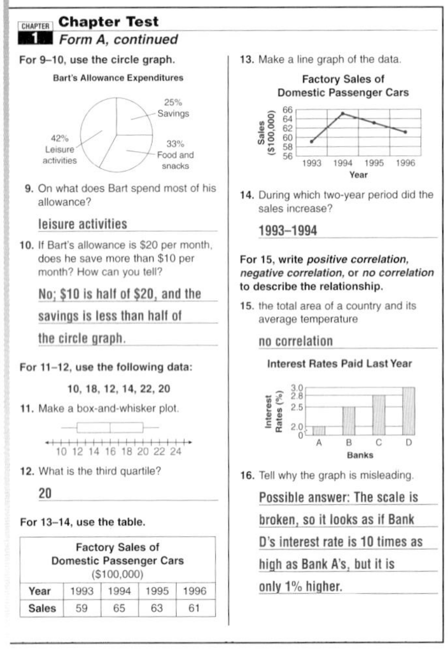

CHAPTER 1 Chapter Test *Form A, continued*

For 9–10, use the circle graph.

9. On what does Bart spend most of his allowance?

   leisure activities

10. If Bart's allowance is $20 per month, does he save more than $10 per month? How can you tell?

    No; $10 is half of $20, and the savings is less than half of the circle graph.

For 11–12, use the following data:

10, 18, 12, 14, 22, 20

11. Make a box-and-whisker plot.

12. What is the third quartile?

    20

For 13–14, use the table.

Factory Sales of Domestic Passenger Cars ($100,000)				
Year	1993	1994	1995	1996
Sales	59	65	63	61

13. Make a line graph of the data.

14. During which two-year period did the sales increase?

    1993–1994

For 15, write *positive correlation, negative correlation,* or *no correlation* to describe the relationship.

15. the total area of a country and its average temperature

    no correlation

16. Tell why the graph is misleading.

    Possible answer: The scale is broken, so it looks as if Bank D's interest rate is 10 times as high as Bank A's, but it is only 1% higher.

LEVEL B

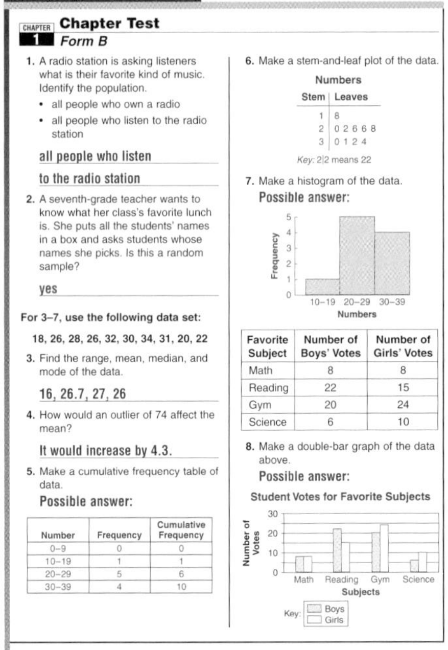

CHAPTER 1 Chapter Test *Form B*

1. A radio station is asking listeners what is their favorite kind of music. Identify the population.
   - all people who own a radio
   - all people who listen to the radio station

   all people who listen to the radio station

2. A seventh-grade teacher wants to know what her class's favorite lunch is. She puts all the students' names in a box and asks students whose names she picks. Is this a random sample?

   yes

For 3–7, use the following data set:

18, 26, 28, 26, 32, 30, 34, 31, 20, 22

3. Find the range, mean, median, and mode of the data.

   16, 26.7, 27, 26

4. How would an outlier of 74 affect the mean?

   It would increase by 4.3.

5. Make a cumulative frequency table of data.

   Possible answer:

Number	Frequency	Cumulative Frequency
0–9	0	0
10–19	1	1
20–29	5	6
30–39	4	10

6. Make a stem-and-leaf plot of the data.

   Numbers

Stem	Leaves
1	8
2	0 2 6 6 8
3	0 1 2 4

   Key: 2|2 means 22

7. Make a histogram of the data.

   Possible answer:

Favorite Subject	Number of Boys' Votes	Number of Girls' Votes
Math	8	8
Reading	22	15
Gym	20	24
Science	6	10

8. Make a double-bar graph of the data above.

   Possible answer:

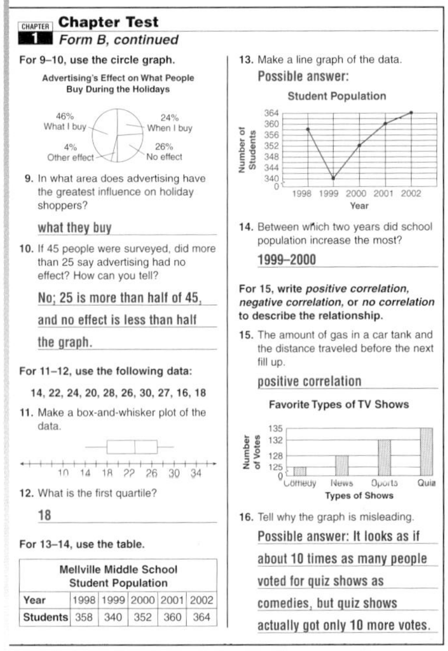

CHAPTER 1 Chapter Test *Form B, continued*

For 9–10, use the circle graph.

9. In what area does advertising have the greatest influence on holiday shoppers?

   what they buy

10. If 45 people were surveyed, did more than 25 say advertising had no effect? How can you tell?

    No; 25 is more than half of 45, and no effect is less than half the graph.

For 11–12, use the following data:

14, 22, 24, 20, 28, 26, 30, 27, 16, 18

11. Make a box-and-whisker plot of the data.

12. What is the first quartile?

    18

For 13–14, use the table.

Melville Middle School Student Population					
Year	1998	1999	2000	2001	2002
Students	358	340	352	360	364

13. Make a line graph of the data.

    Possible answer:

14. Between which two years did school population increase the most?

    1999–2000

For 15, write *positive correlation, negative correlation,* or *no correlation* to describe the relationship.

15. The amount of gas in a car tank and the distance traveled before the next fill up.

    positive correlation

16. Tell why the graph is misleading.

    Possible answer: It looks as if about 10 times as many people voted for quiz shows as comedies, but quiz shows actually got only 10 more votes.

LEVEL C

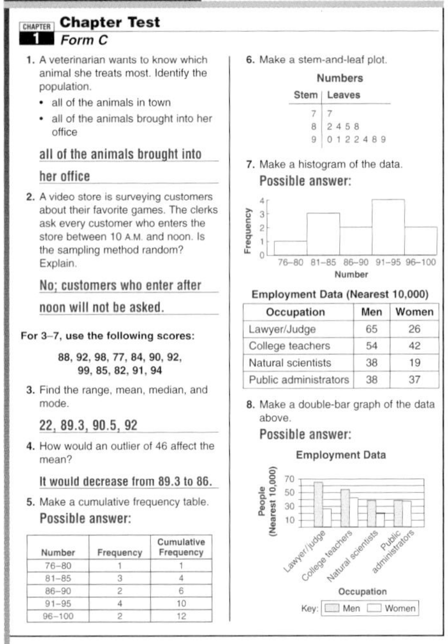

CHAPTER 1 Chapter Test *Form C*

1. A veterinarian wants to know which animal she treats most. Identify the population.
   - all of the animals in town
   - all of the animals brought into her office

   all of the animals brought into her office

2. A video store is surveying customers about their favorite games. The clerks ask every customer who enters the store between 10 A.M. and noon. Is the sampling method random? Explain.

   No; customers who enter after noon will not be asked.

For 3–7, use the following scores:

88, 92, 98, 77, 84, 90, 92, 99, 85, 82, 91, 94

3. Find the range, mean, median, and mode.

   22, 89.3, 90.5, 92

4. How would an outlier of 46 affect the mean?

   It would decrease from 89.3 to 86.

5. Make a cumulative frequency table.

   Possible answer:

Number	Frequency	Cumulative Frequency
76–80	1	1
81–85	3	4
86–90	2	6
91–95	4	10
96–100	2	12

6. Make a stem-and-leaf plot.

   Numbers

Stem	Leaves
7	7
8	2 4 5 8
9	0 1 2 2 4 8 9

7. Make a histogram of the data.

   Possible answer:

Employment Data (Nearest 10,000)		
Occupation	Men	Women
Lawyer/Judge	65	26
College teachers	54	42
Natural scientists	38	19
Public administrators	38	37

8. Make a double-bar graph of the data above.

   Possible answer:

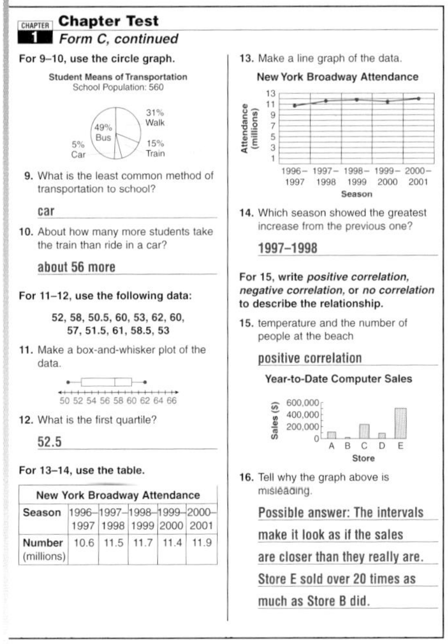

CHAPTER 1 Chapter Test *Form C, continued*

For 9–10, use the circle graph.

9. What is the least common method of transportation to school?

   car

10. About how many more students take the train than ride in a car?

    about 56 more

For 11–12, use the following data:

52, 58, 50.5, 60, 53, 62, 60, 57, 51.5, 61, 58.5, 53

11. Make a box-and-whisker plot of the data.

12. What is the first quartile?

    52.5

For 13–14, use the table.

New York Broadway Attendance					
Season	1996–1997	1997–1998	1998–1999	1999–2000	2000–2001
Number (millions)	10.6	11.5	11.7	11.4	11.9

13. Make a line graph of the data.

14. Which season showed the greatest increase from the previous one?

    1997–1998

For 15, write *positive correlation, negative correlation,* or *no correlation* to describe the relationship.

15. temperature and the number of people at the beach

    positive correlation

16. Tell why the graph above is misleading.

    Possible answer: The intervals make it look as if the sales are closer than they really are. Store E sold over 20 times as much as Store B did.

Test and Practice Generator CD-ROM

Create and customize multiple versions of the same tests with corresponding answers for any chosen chapter objectives.

Chapter 1 State and Standardized Test Preparation

Test Taking Skill Builder and Standardized Test Practice are provided for each chapter in the *Test Prep Tool Kit*.

TEST TAKING SKILL BUILDER

Test Taking Strategy **Context-Based Response Questions**
Chapter 1

Use the information provided in a table, a diagram, or a graph to answer a context-based response question. To receive full credit for this type of question, you need to explain your reasoning and show all of your work in detail. Be sure to check your answer for sense once you complete the question.

Example The swim coach wants his swimmers to stretch nine minutes, on average, before a swim meet. Did the swimmers, on average, stretch for a long enough time? Show your work.

To receive full credit for this question, work through this type of process.

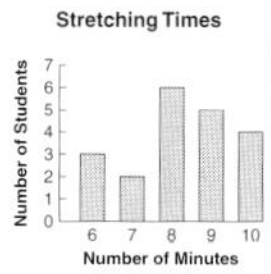

First read over the question again:
What information does the question statement provide? Plan to use this information to solve the problem.

Given: Data from the bar graph can be used to find the average amount of time the swimmers stretched. Then compare this average value to nine minutes to find out if the swimmers, on average, get enough stretching time.

Calculate the average:

$6 \cdot 3 + 7 \cdot 2 + 8 \cdot 6 + 9 \cdot 5 + 10 \cdot 4 = 18 + 14 + 48 + 45 + 40 = 165$

The students stretched for a total of 165 minutes. Since there are 20 swimmers on the swim team, the average amount of stretching is $165 \div 20$, or 8.25 minutes.

Answer in a complete sentence:
The swimmers, on average, did not stretch for a long enough time.

Check that your answer is reasonable:
By looking at the bar graph, the stretching average of 8.25 minutes appears to be reasonable. Since 8.25 is less than 9, it is a reasonable conclusion that the swimmers did not stretch for long enough.

STANDARDIZED TEST PRACTICE

Standardized Test Practice
Chapter 1

Select the best answer for Questions 1–5.

1. In which situation would you survey the population?
   - **A** How much time students your age study across the country?
   - **B** Where students your age hang out on the weekends across the country?
   - **C** the favorite type of movie of all teens in your city
   - **D** the favorite video game of the students in your school

2. The data set shows the number of minutes 7 students could jump rope without stopping. What is the range, mean, median, and mode of the following numbers?

   6, 8, 9, 14, 5, 11, 3

   - **F** range = 8, mean = 12, median = 3, mode = 8
   - **G** range = 11, mean = 8, median = 8, mode = 0
   - **H** range = 8, mean = 8, median = 11, no mode
   - **I** range = 11, mean = 8, median = 8, no mode

3. Use the graph to determine who ran the furthest distance.

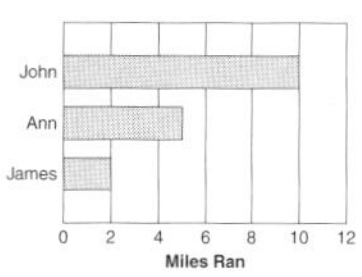

   - **A** Ann
   - **B** Sam
   - **C** James
   - **D** John

4. Use the graph to determine the sum of red and blue planes made in the 3rd quarter.

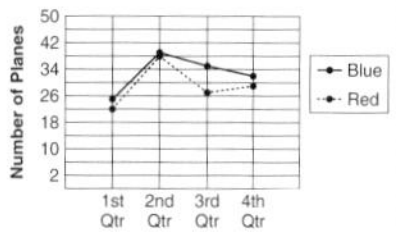

   - **F** 22 planes
   - **G** 55 planes
   - **H** 18 planes
   - **I** 62 planes

internet connect

go.hrw.com

State-Specific Test Practice Online
KEYWORD: MS4 TestPrep

Test Prep Tool Kit

- Standardized Test Prep Workbook
- Countdown to Testing transparencies
- State Test Prep CD-ROM
- Standardized Test Prep Video

Test Taking Strategy
Chapter 1, continued

Exercises
Answer each question. Possible answers are given.

1. Use the data below to create a bar graph for the favorite type of music for teenage boys and girls. Determine how many more girls were surveyed than boys.

	Rock	R & B	Classical	Rap	Country
Boys	8	5	1	7	2
Girls	9	4	9	2	6

   a. What information are you given? What does the question ask? Write a plan for how you will use this information to answer the question.

   a table of data that shows the bed types for teenage boys and girls; find how many more girls were surveyed than boys; Use the data to create a double gar graph and then use the graph to answer the question.

   b. The double bar graph is shown. How can you verify that the graph is correct?

   Compare each bar on the graph to the data in the table.

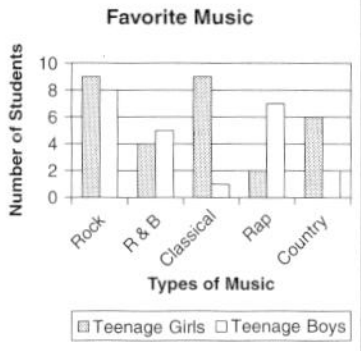

   c. A student wrote the following response. Do you think the student received full credit for the response? Explain.

   The total number of girls surveyed is $9 + 4 + 9 + 2 + 6 = 30$.
   The total number of boys surveyed is $8 + 5 + 1 + 7 + 2 = 23$.
   Subtract: $30 - 23 = 7$
   Seven more teenage girls were surveyed than teenage boys.
   The answer is reasonable because there are more data points corresponding to girls on the graph than to boys.

   Yes; the student correctly calculated the number of girls and boys surveyed, found the difference in the two values, explained his or her reasoning, answered in a complete sentence, and checked his or her work.

Standardized Test Practice
Chapter 1, continued

5. Determine what type of correlation the following graph represents.

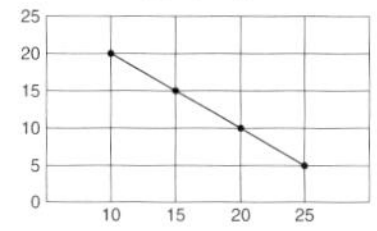

   - **A** no correlation
   - **B** negative
   - **C** positive
   - **D** undefined

Gridded Response
Solve the problems. Use the answer sheet to write and grid-in your answer.

6. The data represents the number of daily phone calls a landscaper received in six days. 15, 20, 18, 16, 19, 20. Which score is the mode?

7. The temperature for the last two weeks has been: 78°, 70°, 69°, 76°, 80°, 82°, 73°, 79°, 70°, 77°, 76°, 80°, 81°, 73°. What is the mean temperature?

8. If a sector is 45% of a circle, what fraction, in simplest form, represents the sector?

Short Response
Solve the problems. Use the answer sheet to write your answers.

9. Explain in words the different ways a graph can be used to show misleading information.

10. What type of graph would you use to show the budget of a local government agency? Explain in words how you determined your answer.

The box-and-whisker plot represents the ages of people who joined a local fitness center in the past month. Use the plot for Questions 11–12.

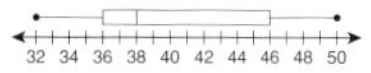

11. What are the first and third quartiles? Explain in words how you determined your answer.

12. What fraction of the data is between 38 and 46? Explain in words how you determined your answer.

Extended Response

13.

Stem	Leaf
2	1 1 2 3 4 4
3	1 2
4	0 0 5 5 6
5	7 8 9
6	1 3 3 4 4 5

Key: 2 | 3 means 2.3

   a. What is the least number? What is the greatest number? What is the range?

   b. Find the mean, median and mode of the data set. Show your work.

   c. Make a cumulative frequency table of the data.

   d. Explain which measure of tendency is easiest to find with a stem-and-leaf plot.

...et

(See Lesson 1-7.)
(See Lesson 1-8.)
20
...sson 1-2.
...ures are used.

10. A circle graph is best because a budget can be represented as a whole and each part of the budget is represented by the pieces of the circle. (See Lesson 1-9.)

11. The first and third quartiles are 36 and 46. You find these values by looking at the two ends of the box. (See Lesson 1-9.)

12. One-fourth of the data is between 38 and 46. This is because in a box-and-whisker plot the data is divided into fourths. The median divides the data in half and then the first and third quartiles divide each half into half. This divides the data into fourths. (See Lesson 1-6.)

Extended Response (See Lesson 1-6.)
Write your answers for Problem 13 on the back of this paper.
See Lesson 1-3.

Customized answer sheets give students realistic practice for actual standardized tests.

Chapter 1

Data Toolbox

Why Learn This?

Tell students that tables are a good way to display data. By using the data in a table, you can analyze information, draw conclusions, and make predictions. Have students look at the data in the table. Point out that data for three types of birds were collected for a period of time from November through April.

Using Data

To begin the study of this chapter, have students:

- Use the table to find the total average number of given bird sightings per month.

  Nov: 11.05; Dec: 12.1; Jan: 13.1; Feb: 12; Mar: 9.8; Apr: 8.9

TABLE OF CONTENTS

Chapter Opener Online
go.hrw.com
KEYWORD: MS4 Ch1

Data Toolbox

Bird	Average Number of Sightings					
	Nov	Dec	Jan	Feb	Mar	Apr
Mourning dove	7.0	8.0	9.0	8.0	6.0	5.0
Red-bellied woodpecker	1.25	1.3	1.3	1.3	1.3	1.5
Carolina chickadee	2.8	2.8	2.8	2.7	2.5	2.4

Career ***Field Biologist***

Field biologists spend time outdoors studying populations of fish, birds, and other living things. The information they collect is often used to determine whether populations are growing or declining.

Sometimes, amateur naturalists help scientists collect information. For example, people with bird feeders can report to Project FeederWatch the number and kinds of birds that they see at their feeders throughout the winter.

Problem Solving Project

Life Science Connection

Purpose: To solve problems using decimals

Materials: Bird Feeder Visitor worksheet

Chapter Project Online: ***go.hrw.com***
KEYWORD: MS4 PSProject1

Understand, Plan, Solve, and Look Back

Have students:

- ✔ Complete the Bird Feeder Visitor worksheet to learn to develop and present information about birds that visit bird feeders.
- ✔ Determine the mean, median, and mode of the three types of birds that visited the feeders.
- ✔ Research the characteristics of the birds in the table. Do students think that the kind of feeder food affects the number and type of bird visitor?
- ✔ Check students' work.

ARE YOU READY?

Choose the best term from the list to complete each sentence.

circle
frequency
interval
line segment
scale

1. A part of a line consisting of two endpoints and all points between those endpoints is called a(n) __?__. **line segment**
2. A(n) __?__ is the space between the marked values on the __?__ of a graph. **interval; scale**
3. The number of times an item occurs is called its __?__. **frequency**

Complete these exercises to review skills you will need for this chapter.

✔ Compare and Order Whole Numbers

Order the numbers from least to greatest.

4. 45, 23, 65, 15, 42, 18 **15, 18, 23, 42, 45, 65**
5. 103, 105, 102, 118, 87, 104 **87, 102, 103, 104, 105, 118**
6. 56, 65, 24, 19, 76, 33, 82 **19, 24, 33, 56, 65, 76, 82**
7. 8, 3, 6, 2, 5, 9, 3, 4, 2 **2, 2, 3, 3, 4, 5, 6, 8, 9**

✔ Add Whole Numbers

Find each sum.

8. 6 + 8 + 10 + 9 + 7 **40**
9. 10 + 23 + 19 + 17 **69**
10. 16 + 32 + 18 + 20 + 15 + 12 **113**
11. 102 + 98 + 64 + 32 + 80 **376**

✔ Subtract Whole Numbers

Find each difference.

12. 133 − 35 **98**
13. 54 − 29 **25**
14. 200 − 88 **112**
15. 1,055 − 899 **156**

✔ Locate Points on a Number Line

Copy the number line. Then graph each number.

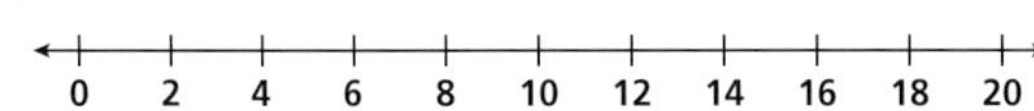

16. 15
17. 2
18. 18
19. 7

✔ Read a Table

Use the data in the table for Exercises 20 and 21.

20. Which animal is the fastest? **lion**
21. Which animal is faster, a rabbit or a zebra? **zebra**

Top Speeds of Some Animals

Animal	Speed (mi/h)
Elephant	25
Lion	50
Rabbit	35
Zebra	40

Assessing Prior Knowledge

INTERVENTION 

Diagnose and Prescribe

Evaluate your students' performance on this page to determine whether intervention is necessary or whether enrichment is appropriate. Options that provide instruction, practice, and a check are listed below.

Resources for Are You Ready?

- ***Are You Ready? Intervention and Enrichment***
- **Recording Sheet for Are You Ready?**
  Chapter 1 Resource Book . . . . . . p. 3

 ***Are You Ready? Intervention* CD-ROM**

internet connect 

Are You Ready? Intervention
go.hrw.com
KEYWORD: MS4 AYR

Answers

16. 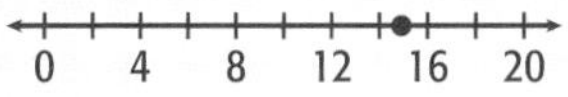 [number line 0–20 with point at 15]
17. 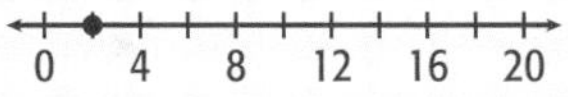 [number line 0–20 with point at 2]
18. [number line 0–20 with point at 18] 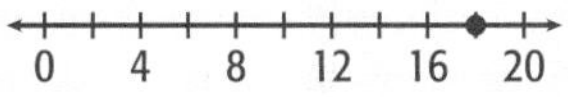
19. 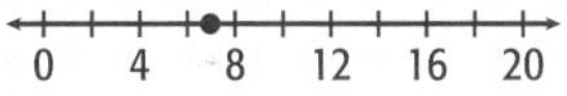 [number line 0–20 with point at 7]

ARE YOU READY?

Were students successful with Are You Ready?

NO INTERVENE  **YES ENRICH**

✔Compare and Order Whole Numbers
Are You Ready? Intervention, Skill 5
Blackline Masters, Online, and
 **CD-ROM** Intervention Activities

✔Add Whole Numbers
Are You Ready? Intervention, Skill 34
Blackline Masters, Online, and
CD-ROM Intervention Activities

✔Subtract Whole Numbers
Are You Ready? Intervention, Skill 34
Blackline Masters, Online, and
 **CD-ROM** Intervention Activities

✔Locate Points on a Number Line
Are You Ready? Intervention, Skill 61
Blackline Masters, Online, and
 **CD-ROM** Intervention Activities

✔Read a Table
Are You Ready? Intervention, Skill 90
Blackline Masters, Online, and
CD-ROM Intervention Activities

Are You Ready? Enrichment, pp. 407–408

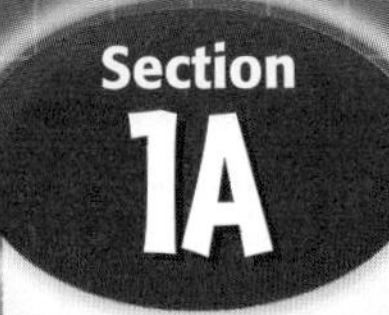

Section 1A Organizing Data

One-Minute Section Planner

Lesson	Materials	Resources
Lesson 1-1 Populations and Samples **NCTM:** Data Analysis and Probability, Communication, Connections **NAEP:** Data Analysis and Probability 3b ☐ SAT-9 ☐ SAT-10 ☐ ITBS ☑ CTBS ☐ MAT ☐ CAT		• *Chapter 1 Resource Book,* pp. 6–14 • Daily Transparency T1, CRB • Additional Examples Transparencies T2–T3, CRB • *Alternate Openers: Explorations,* p. 1
Technology Lab 1A Generate Random Numbers **NCTM:** Data Analysis and Probability, Representation **NAEP:** Data Analysis and Probability 3d ☐ SAT-9 ☐ SAT-10 ☐ ITBS ☐ CTBS ☐ MAT ☐ CAT	**Required** Spreadsheet software	• *Technology Lab Activities,* pp. 1–2
Lesson 1-2 Mean, Median, Mode, and Range **NCTM:** Data Analysis and Probability, Communication, Connections **NAEP:** Data Analysis and Probability 2a ☑ SAT-9 ☑ SAT-10 ☑ ITBS ☑ CTBS ☑ MAT ☑ CAT		• *Chapter 1 Resource Book,* pp. 15–24 • Daily Transparency T4, CRB • Additional Examples Transparencies T5–T6, CRB • *Alternate Openers: Explorations,* p. 2
Lesson 1-3 Frequency Tables and Stem-and-Leaf Plots **NCTM:** Data Analysis and Probability, Communication, Connections, Representation **NAEP:** Data Analysis and Probability 1b ☑ SAT-9 ☑ SAT-10 ☐ ITBS ☑ CTBS ☐ MAT ☑ CAT	**Optional** Teaching Transparency T8 *(CRB)*	• *Chapter 1 Resource Book,* pp. 25–34 • Daily Transparency T7, CRB • Additional Examples Transparencies T9–T10, CRB • *Alternate Openers: Explorations,* p. 3
Section 1A Assessment		• Mid-Chapter Quiz, SE p. 18 • Section 1A Quiz, AR p. 5 • *Test and Practice Generator* CD-ROM

SAT = *Stanford Achievement Tests* **ITBS** = *Iowa Test of Basic Skills* **CTBS** = *Comprehensive Test of Basic Skills/Terra Nova*
MAT = *Metropolitan Achievement Test* **CAT** = *California Achievement Test*

NCTM—Complete standards can be found on pages T27–T33. **NAEP**—Complete standards can be found on pages A35–A39.

SE = *Student Edition* **TE** = *Teacher's Edition* **AR** = *Assessment Resources* **CRB** = *Chapter Resource Book* **MK** = *Manipulatives Kit*

Section Overview

Populations and Samples — *Lesson 1-1*

Why? Usually, it is not possible to collect data from every member of a **population.** Instead, a sample is drawn from the population.

A **sample** needs to be representative of the entire population. This is why a sample should be *random.* If the sample is not random, the information collected could inaccurately represent the population and will reflect a bias.

A magazine conducts a reader survey in which readers mail in responses.

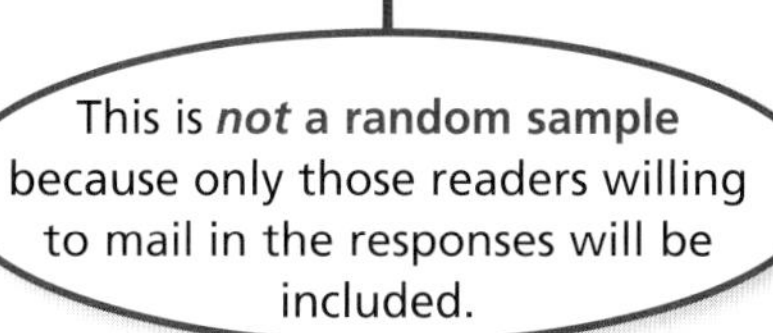

This is *not* a random sample because only those readers willing to mail in the responses will be included.

Measures of Central Tendency — *Lesson 1-2*

Why? In real-world applications of statistics, measures of central tendency—**mean, median,** and **mode**—are often reported. These statistics are convenient to report since they are one-number summaries of a set of data.

Find the measures of central tendency for 23, 25, 24, and 25.

Mean

The sum of data values divided by the number of data items

(23 + 25 + 24 + 25) ÷ 4
= 97 ÷ 4
= 24.25

The mean is 24.25.

Median

- The middle value of an odd number of items arranged in order
- For an even number of items, the average of the two middle values

23, **24**, **25**, 25
(24 + 25) ÷ 2 = 24.5

The median is 24.5.

Mode

The value that occurs most often

The mode is 25.

Notice that **3** is an **outlier** because it is much less than the other values.

The mean is affected by **outliers.**

Mean with outlier (**3** + 23 + 25 + 24 + 25) ÷ 5 = 100 ÷ 5 = 20

Mean without outlier (23 + 25 + 24 + 25) ÷ 4 = 97 ÷ 4 = 24.25

As a measure of central tendency, the median, 24, would be more representative of the data with an outlier than the mean would.

Frequency Tables and Stem-and-Leaf Plots — *Lesson 1-3*

Why? There are many ways to display data. Stem-and-leaf plots retain the original data, and frequency tables usually organize the data into intervals of equal size. A cumulative frequency table keeps a running total of the number of data points from the first to the last interval.

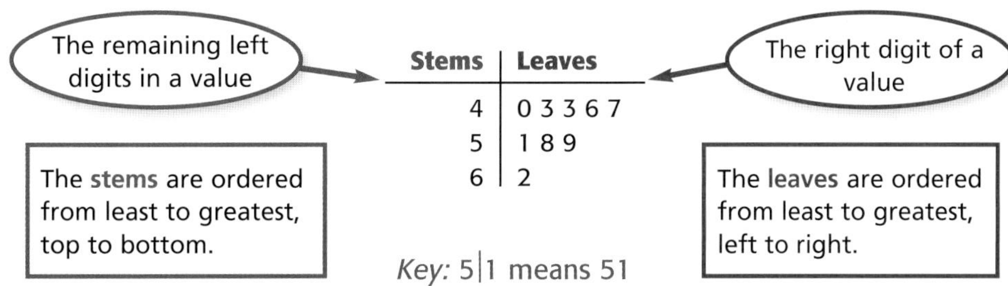

Stems	Leaves
4	0 3 3 6 7
5	1 8 9
6	2

Key: 5|1 means 51

1-1 Organizer

Pacing: Traditional 1 day
Block $\frac{1}{2}$ day

Objective: Students identify populations and random samples.

Warm Up

Simplify.

1. 72 × 10 **720** **2.** 26 + 75 **101**

3. 127 − 34 **93** **4.** 125 ÷ 25 **5**

5. 1,234 + 843 **2,077** **6.** 851 − 653 **198**

7. 43 × 12 **516** **8.** 657 ÷ 3 **219**

Problem of the Day

Why are both products the same?
26 × 51 = 1,326 39 × 34 = 1,326

26 × 51 = (2 × 13) × (3 × 17);
39 × 34 = (3 × 13) × (2 × 17);
the factors are 2, 3, 13, and 17.

Available on Daily Transparency in CRB

Math Humor

The nutty biologist always made things more difficult. To count the number of mice in his sample, he counted legs and divided by four.

1-1 Populations and Samples

Learn to identify populations and random samples.

Vocabulary
population
sample
random sample

When you are gathering information about a group, the whole group is called the **population** . For your information to be absolutely accurate, you must collect data on every member of the population.

However, it is often not practical—or possible—to survey every member of a large group. For this reason, researchers often study a part of the group, called a **sample** .

When scientists track migratory animals, they cannot track each animal. Instead, they tag a sample of the entire population and track the sample. They use the sample to gather statistical data about the population.

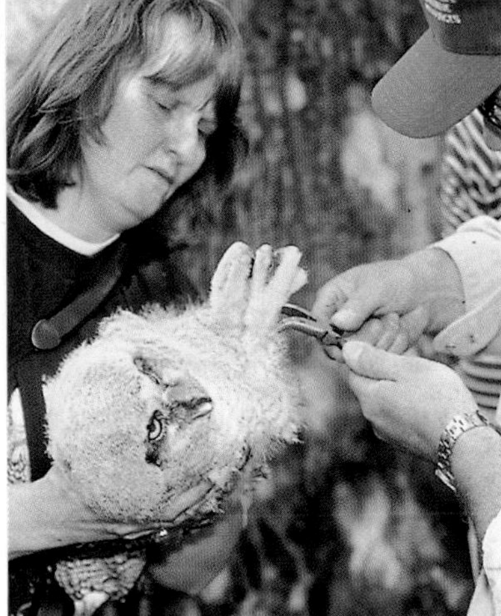
Biologists place a leg band on a young great horned owl.

EXAMPLE 1 Identifying Populations and Samples

Identify the population and sample in each situation.

A A scientist studies lions on a wildlife preserve to learn about the parenting habits of lions.

Population	Sample
All lions	The lions on the preserve

B The school librarian surveys 100 students about the types of books they prefer.

Population	Sample
All students in the school	The 100 students who are surveyed

1 Introduce

Alternate Opener

EXPLORATION

1-1 Populations and Samples

Ms. Johnson has 100 students. She randomly picked 14 students and collected the data shown in the table.

1. In which month do you think the greatest number of Ms. Johnson's 100 students have their birthdays?
2. Do you think there are more boys or more girls in the whole group of 100 students?
3. Do you think that over half of the 100 students are in the band?

Student Number	Height (in.)	Shoe Size	Birth Month	In Band?	Gender
18	65	9	3		M
14	64	9	11		M
19	59	5	9	Y	F
65	55	7	6	Y	M
51	65	9	7		F
92	60	9	7		M
6	55	6	7	Y	F
43	64	7	4		F
25	72	12	6		M
26	60	8	7	Y	F
10	61	8	9	Y	M
11	68	10.5	3		M
28	60	6.5	9		F
47	65	6	1		F

Think and Discuss

4. **Discuss** what it means to have a sample that is *representative* of a population. Do you think the sample of 14 students is representative of the whole class?
5. **Explain** how you might choose a sample of students from your school to determine the average height of students.

Motivate

Invite students to brainstorm ways to discover the person students in the school most admire (e.g., survey the entire student body, survey some of the students, or use a questionnaire). For each suggestion, discuss possible problems students might need to overcome so that their results will accurately reflect the opinion of the students (e.g., how to question every student in the school, who should be on the list, or what the questionnaire should say).

Exploration worksheet and answers on Chapter 1 Resource Book pp. 7 and 101

2 Teach

Lesson Presentation

Guided Instruction

In this lesson, students learn to identify populations and random samples. After reading the examples, emphasize to students that when collecting data using random samples, the sample must give representatives of every member of the population an equal chance of being chosen. Refer back to the discussion in Motivate, and have students identify the population and how they might choose a random sample to identify the person students in the school most admire.

Emphasize that random samples are used to make generalizations about the entire population from which the sample is taken.

Identify the population and sample in each situation.

 A restaurant manager uses comment cards to find out about customer satisfaction.

Population	Sample
All customers	The customers who fill out the comment card

For a sample to be useful, it must be representative of the population. If it is not, then the information gathered from the sample will be inaccurate. One type of representative sample, known as a **random sample**, gives *every* member of the population an equal chance of being chosen.

EXAMPLE 2 Identifying Random Samples

A newspaper reporter is gathering responses from Riverside Middle School band students about the style of their uniforms. Tell whether each sampling method is random. Explain your answer.

A The reporter questions only the students he knows personally.
This sampling method is not random. The students the reporter does not know have no chance of being chosen.

B The reporter questions every tenth student on an alphabetized list of the students, starting with the first student on the list.
While this method is representative of the population, it is not random. The students listed as 2 through 9, 11 through 19, etc., have no chance of being chosen.

C The reporter writes each student's name on a card and puts all of the cards in a hat. He then questions the students whose names he draws.
This sampling method is random. Each student has an equal chance of being chosen.

Think and Discuss

1. **Give an example** of a situation in which you would want to use a sample rather than poll the entire population.
2. **Explain** why it might be difficult to obtain a purely random sample of a large population.

Additional Examples

Example 1

Identify the population and sample in each situation.

A. The mayor surveys 1,000 voters to see if they approve of the job she is doing.
registered voters; 1,000 voters

B. The coach asks the starting five players which uniform the basketball team wants to wear.
basketball team; starting five

C. The local movie theater surveys customers to find which brand of popcorn they prefer.
all customers; those surveyed

Example 2

A teacher questions students about which day to give a math test. Tell whether each sampling method is random. Explain your answer.

A. The teacher writes the name of each student on a piece of paper, draws several pieces of paper from a hat, and questions the students whose names are drawn.
This is random.

B. The teacher questions the students in the first desk in each row.
Students not in the first desk do not have a chance. This is not random.

Close

Reaching All Learners
Through Grouping Strategies

Have students work in groups to plan how to use a random sample to collect data for a questionnaire they create. Students should focus on how they will get a random sample of students from the whole school. Groups can then share and compare plans, vote on the best one, carry it out, and report the results.

Possible answer: As each classroom is visited, assign row numbers to the rows of desks (e.g., 1 through 6). Write each number on a separate slip of paper. Choose a paper from a hat and have the students in that row fill out the questionnaire.

Summarize

Have students describe how to gather accurate information about a population. Then have them describe what makes a random sample truly random. Encourage students to share and compare their descriptions.

Possible answers: To gather accurate information about a population, gather information on every member of the population. In a random sample, everyone in the population must have an equal chance of being chosen for the sample.

Answers to Think and Discuss

Possible answers:

1. A sample is necessary when the population is extremely large (e.g., when predicting the outcome of a national election).
2. Not every member of a population may be available at a particular time or place, and if that were so, every member would not have an equal chance of being chosen.

1-1 PRACTICE & ASSESS

Students may want to refer back to the lesson examples.

Assignment Guide

If you finished Example 1 assign:

Core 1, 2, 5–7, 10–13, 18, 23–31

Enriched 1, 2, 5–7, 10–13, 18, 23–31

If you finished Example 2 assign:

Core 1–9, 11–19 odd, 23–31

Enriched 1, 3, 5, 9, 10–31

Answers

3. Not random; the owner used only customers who shopped at a particular time.

13. Survey the population because the population is not too large to survey.

1-1 Exercises

FOR EXTRA PRACTICE
see page 654

internet connect
Homework Help Online
go.hrw.com Keyword: MS4 1-1

GUIDED PRACTICE

See Example 1 **Identify the population and sample in each situation.**

1. A scientist studies a pod of humpback whales to find out about migration patterns of humpback whales. **population: all humpback whales; sample: the pod of humpback whales being studied**
2. The decoration committee asks 25 students about their ideas for a theme for the seventh-grade party. **population: all seventh-grade students; sample: the 25 students who are asked their ideas**

See Example 2 **The owner of a used car lot is conducting a customer survey. Tell whether each sampling method is random. Explain your answer.**

3. The owner surveys customers on the lot one Saturday morning.
4. The owner questions 100 customers who were randomly selected from a list of all customers. **Random; the owner used a list of all customers.**

INDEPENDENT PRACTICE

See Example 1 **Identify the population and sample in each situation.**

5. Scientists tag the ears of 50 moose to get information on the average life span of a moose in the wild. **population: all wild moose; sample: the 50 moose that are tagged**
6. A disc jockey asks the first ten listeners who call in if they like the last song that was played. **population: all listeners; sample: the 10 listeners who called in**
7. Researchers poll every fifteenth voter after a school board election. **population: all voters; sample: the voters who are polled**

See Example 2 **A librarian is gathering responses from community members. Tell whether each sampling method is random. Explain your answer.**

8. The librarian randomly selects members of the community by drawing their names from a hat. **Random; all members of the community have an equal chance of being chosen.**
9. The librarian sends out questionnaires to families with children. **Not random; families without children have no chances of being chosen.**

PRACTICE AND PROBLEM SOLVING

Tell whether you would survey the population or use a sample. Explain.

10. You want to know the favorite painter of all the employees at the local art museum. **Survey the population because the population is not too large to survey.**
11. You want to know the types of calculators used by middle school students across the country. **Use a sample because the population is too large to survey.**
12. You want to know the favorite magazine of all teens in your state. **Use a sample because the population is too large to survey.**
13. You want to know where the students in your social studies class study for tests.

Math Background

In 1935, George Gallup promised to predict the winner of the 1936 presidential election with more accuracy than the leading poll by the *Literary Digest.* Gallup polled about 3,000 people, as opposed to the nearly 10 million that the *Digest* polled; however, the sample Gallup polled was more representative of the voting public.

The *Digest* predicted that Republican Alf Landon would win with 57% of the vote. Gallup predicted that Franklin D. Roosevelt would win with 54% of the vote. Roosevelt won with 61% of the vote, confirming that Gallup was correct and his sampling methods worked.

RETEACH 1-1

LESSON 1-1 **Reteach**
Populations and Samples

A **population** is the complete collection of the group to be studied.	*Population:* all seventh graders in Richmond
A **sample** is a part of the population.	*Sample:* all seventh graders at Jefferson Middle School
A **random sample** is a sample in which each member of the population has an equal chance of being selected.	*Random sample:* Write the name of each seventh grader in Richmond on a card. Mix up the cards. Draw 100 cards.

Identify the population in each.

1. A teacher is investigating the amount of time students in Adams Middle School spend exercising.
   (A) all students in the school
   B all seventh-grade students in the school
2. A scientist is studying the lifespan of grizzly bears in Katmai National Park.
   A all grizzly bears
   (B) all grizzly bears in Katmai National Park
3. The coach is asking players to choose a captain for their soccer team.
   A all soccer players
   (B) all players on the soccer team

The manager of a book store is conducting a customer survey. Is each sampling method random? Explain your answer.

4. The manager surveys his friends and employees.
   No, customers who are not friends or employees have no chance of being chosen.
5. The manager sends out the survey to 100 customers who were randomly selected from a customer list.
   Yes, all customers have an equal chance of being chosen.
6. The manager surveys the first 10 people who come into his store on Monday, Wednesday, and Friday mornings.
   No, customers who shop in the afternoon or on other days have no chance of being chosen.

PRACTICE 1-1

LESSON 1-1 **Practice B**
Populations and Samples

Identify the population in each situation.

1. A scientist is studying the migration pattern of a flock of snow geese.
   (A) all snow geese
   B all snow geese in the flock
2. The carnival committee asks students about their favorite games for a middle-school carnival.
   (A) all students in the school
   B all seventh-grade students in the school
3. A group of scientists tags the wings of 20 golden eagles to get information on the range of their habitat.
   A all eagles
   (B) all golden eagles

The manager of a supermarket is conducting a customer survey. State whether each sampling method is random. Explain.

4. The manager surveys customers in the store every Monday morning.
   No, customers who do not shop on Monday mornings will not be included in the survey.
5. The manager questions 200 customers who were randomly selected from a list of all customers.
   Yes, each customer has an equal chance of being selected.
6. The manager questions only customers who shop with children.
   No, customers who do not shop with children have no chance of being selected.
7. A student thinks that school bus stops in his community are too far apart. He surveys all the students in his class to see what they think. What is the population? Is the sampling method random? Explain.
   The population is all the students in the community who ride school buses. No, students not in his class have no chance of being selected.

Give a reason why each sampling method may not be random.

14. A reporter calls 100 people from the phone book.

15. A reporter questions all of the customers at one of several entrances to a local supermarket. **Possible answer: customers who use one of the other entrances will not have the chance of being chosen.**

16. A reporter surveys people who are using an Internet site. **Some people do not have access to the Internet.**

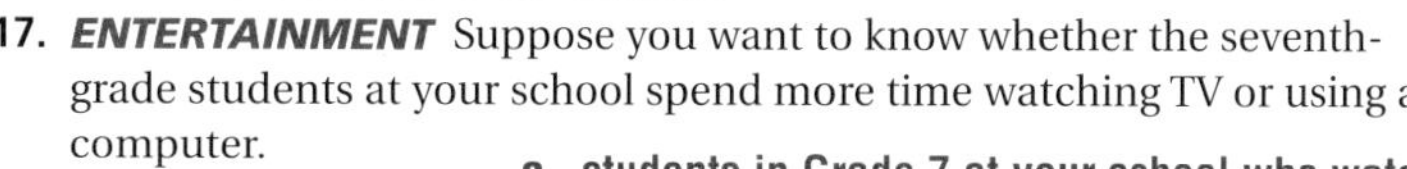

17. ***ENTERTAINMENT*** Suppose you want to know whether the seventh-grade students at your school spend more time watching TV or using a computer.
    a. What is the population for your survey? **a. students in Grade 7 at your school who watch TV or who use a computer**
    b. Describe how you might choose a random sample from the population. **Possible answer: Give a questionnaire to 25 students whose names were randomly chosen from a list of all seventh graders.**

18. ***SCHOOL*** The Mathematics Department at Truman Middle School is conducting a survey to determine in which class students use calculators most often, math or science. What is the population for this survey? Explain your answer. **all students in the school who use calculators and who are in both a math and a science class**

19. ***BUSINESS*** A manufacturer selects every hundredth item to be tested. Tell whether this sampling method is random. Explain your answer.

20. ***WRITE A PROBLEM*** Pick a population and write a survey question directed toward that population. Then describe the sampling method you would use.

21. ***WRITE ABOUT IT*** Explain why using a sample to gather information about a large population is not completely accurate.

22. ***CHALLENGE*** Biased, or unfair, questions can affect the responses given in a survey. Explain why the following question is biased:

    "Do you prefer listening to noisy, ear-splitting rock music or quiet, relaxing classical music?"

Entertainment LINK

The television series *M*A*S*H* ran for 11 years and had 251 episodes.

go.hrw.com KEYWORD: MS4 TV

CNN Student News

Spiral Review

Simplify. (Previous course)

23. 15 + 27 + 5 + 3 + 11 + 16 + 7 + 4 **88**

24. 2 + 6 + 5 + 7 + 100 + 1 + 75 **196**

25. 2 + 9 + 8 + 12 + 6 + 8 + 5 + 6 + 7 **63**

26. 9 + 30 + 4 + 1 + 4 + 1 + 7 + 5 + 18 + 11 **90**

Divide. (Previous course)

27. 88 ÷ 8 **11**

28. 196 ÷ 7 **28**

29. 63 ÷ 9 **7**

30. 90 ÷ 10 **9**

31. **TEST PREP** A baseball stadium has 21,896 seats. To make room for a memorial to past great players, the club wants to remove 530 seats. How many seats will the stadium have after the change? (Previous course) **B**

    A 22,426 **B** 21,366 **C** 17,126 **D** 21,843

Answers

14. Possible answer: Unlisted people cannot be chosen.

19. This sampling method is not random. Items 1–99, 101–199, etc., have no chance of being tested.

20. Possible answers: Ask all students who buy sodas at lunch which brand they prefer. Survey the population.

21. Sample may not be representative of the larger population.

22. The question leads toward classical.

Journal

Have students describe a survey they would use to determine a favorite team, athlete, actor, or musician. Encourage students to tell what population they would survey and how they would choose a random sample.

Test Prep Doctor

For Exercise 31, students can eliminate **A** and **C** by using estimation: 21,900 − 500 = 21,400. Choice **A** is too high; **C** is too low.

Lesson Quiz

1. A TV ratings service is surveying residents of Orlando who bought TVs in the last month about their favorite TV show.

a. Identify the sample.
people who bought TVs in the last month

b. Identify the population.
all residents of Orlando

2. The school newspaper is conducting a survey on the students' favorite subject. Tell whether each sampling method is random. Explain your answers.

a. The newspaper surveys senior students in a math class.
no; students from one level only and one class only

b. The newspaper surveys every twentieth student entering the school. No; not every student entering the school has a chance to be chosen.

Available on Daily Transparency in CRB

CHALLENGE 1-1

LESSON 1-1 **Challenge**
A Sample of Samples

Consider the three sampling methods described below.

Systematic sample: You randomly select an individual and then follow a pattern to select others in the sample. For example, choose a name from the first 50 names in a telephone book. Then choose every fiftieth name after that.

Stratified sample: A population is divided into subgroups, called strata, that contain similar individuals. For example, interview all the boys and girls at a movie. Boys and girls are two strata.

Cluster sample: A population is divided into sections and then a few of the sections are selected. All the members of those sections are chosen. For example, suppose a city has 50 voting districts. Five of those districts are selected, and every person in each district selected is polled.

Identify the type of sampling used as systematic, stratified, or cluster.

1. A teacher selects every third student in the class. **systematic**
2. A teacher surveys all students from each of 5 randomly selected classes. **cluster**
3. A principal selects 3 girls and 3 boys from each of 10 classes. **stratified**
4. A teacher selects 10 students under 12 years old and 10 students over 12 years old. **stratified**
5. A reporter interviews all students in each of 4 randomly selected schools. **cluster**
6. A reporter interviews 20 men and 20 women. **stratified**
7. Workers on an assembly line check every tenth tire in a tire manufacturing plant. **systematic**
8. An advertising consultant surveys all members in each of 3 randomly selected fitness clubs from all the fitness clubs in the city. **cluster**
9. A department store manager selects a customer from the first 20 on a customer list. Then she selects every twentieth customer after that. **systematic**
10. Members of the school board survey 25 elementary school students, 25 middle school students, and 25 high school students. **stratified**

PROBLEM SOLVING 1-1

LESSON 1-1 **Problem Solving**
Populations and Samples

Write the correct answer.

1. A cafeteria chef wants to find out which of his meals the students like best. What is the population in this situation?
   students who use the cafeteria
2. Tony is studying the daytime sleeping habits of housecats. Should he survey the population or use a sample?
   He should use a sample.
3. The owner of Movie Town Video Store wants to know which videos are rented most often by his customers. What is the population?
   customers of the store
4. The president of Mr. Romero's eighth grade class wants to know which issues are most important to her classmates. Should she survey the population or use a sample?
   She should survey the population.

Choose the letter for the best answer.

5. A scientist is studying the eating habits of all the primates at the local zoo. What is the population?
   A all primates
   B the chimpanzees at the zoo
   (C) all primates at the zoo
   D food eaten by primates at the zoo
6. A pollster wants to find out if her candidate will appeal to young voters in Florida. Which population would be the best for her to survey?
   F all voters in Florida
   (G) Florida voters under the age of 25
   H all voters between 18 and 25
   J Florida voters under the age of 50
7. The school board wants to study computer literacy among teachers. Which would represent a random sample of teachers?
   (A) every eighth teacher on an alphabetical list
   B teachers from the middle school whose name begins with N
   C all male teachers
   D all high school math teachers
8. A storeowner at a mall wants to know why more shoppers don't stop in his store. What would be the best random sample for him to survey?
   F every tenth person who enters his store
   G every tenth person eating at the food court
   (H) every tenth person to enter the mall
   J all his employees

1A Generate Random Numbers

Pacing: Traditional 1 day
Block $\frac{1}{2}$ day

Objective: To use a spreadsheet to generate random numbers

Materials: Spreadsheet software

Lab Resources

Technology Lab Activities . . . . . pp. 1–2

Using the Pages

This technology activity shows students how to generate random numbers, which can be done with any spreadsheet software. Specific keystrokes may vary depending on the spreadsheet software used.

The Think and Discuss problems can be used to assess students' understanding of the technology activity. Try This problems 1 and 2 help students become familiar with using spreadsheet software to generate random numbers.

Assessment

1. Generate ten random whole numbers between 0 and 99. What spreadsheet formula did you use?
= INT(100*RAND( ))
2. How would you change the formula to generate ten random whole numbers between 1 and 100?
= INT(100*RAND( )) + 1

Generate Random Numbers

Use with Lesson 1-1

You can use a spreadsheet to generate random numbers. By generating random numbers you can simulate real-world events, such as rolling a number cube.

internet connect
Lab Resources Online
go.hrw.com
KEYWORD: MS4 Lab1A

Activity

1 Use a spreadsheet to generate five random decimal numbers between 0 and 1.

Type **=RAND()** into cell A1 and press **ENTER.** A random number will appear in cell A1.

	A	B	C
1	0.153794		
2			
3			

Click to highlight cell A1. Go to the **EDIT** menu and **COPY** the contents of A1. Then click cell A2 and drag your cursor down to cell A5. Cells A2 through A5 should be highlighted.

	A	B	C
1	0.808811		
2			
3			
4			
5			

Finally, go to the **EDIT** menu and use **PASTE** to fill cells A2 through A5 with the formula in cell A1. Notice that the random number in cell A1 changed when you filled the other cells.

	A	B	C
1	0.224473		
2	0.001325		
3	0.715995		
4	0.506313		
5	0.354271		

2 Use a spreadsheet to generate five random whole numbers between 1 and 10.

RAND() generates numbers greater than or equal to 0 but less than 1. To generate random numbers between 0 and 10, you can multiply by 10.

Enter **=10*RAND()** into cell A1. Copy and paste the contents of A1 into cells A2 through A5.

A2 = =10*RAND()

	A	B	C	D
1	1.97758			
2	2.624973			
3	5.451635			
4	6.931406			
5	5.059039			

Now you have decimal numbers greater than or equal to 0 but less than 10. However, you want whole numbers from 1 to 10.

Click on cell A1. Change the formula to **=INT(10*RAND())** and press **ENTER.** Copy and paste this formula into cells A2 through A5.

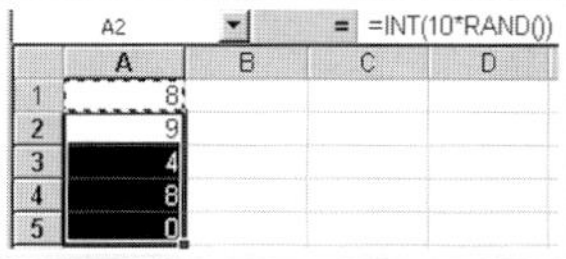

Now you have random whole numbers between 0 and 9, not 1 and 10.

A2	=INT(10*RAND())			
	A	B	C	D
1	8			
2	9			
3	4			
4	6			
5	0			

To shift the range of the numbers up 1, change the formula in A1 to **=INT(10*RAND()) + 1** and press **ENTER.** Copy and paste this formula into cells A2 through A5.

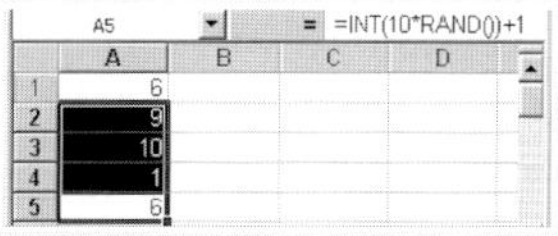

The formula **=INT(10*RAND()) + 1** generates random whole numbers from 1 to 10.

A5	=INT(10*RAND())+1			
	A	B	C	D
1	6			
2	9			
3	10			
4	1			
5	6			

3 Use a spreadsheet to simulate three rolls of a number cube.

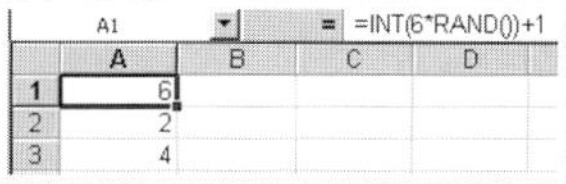

A number cube has whole numbers between 1 and 6. Type **=INT(6*RAND()) + 1** into cell A1 and press **ENTER.** Copy and paste this formula into cells A2 and A3.

In this simulation, the number cube came up 6, 2, and 4.

A1	=INT(6*RAND())+1			
	A	B	C	D
1	6			
2	2			
3	4			

Think and Discuss **Possible answers:**

1. Which part of the formula **=INT(10*RAND())** changes the decimal numbers to whole numbers? **INT**
2. Explain the effect of the number 10 in the formula **=INT(10*RAND()).** **The formula produces integers between 0 and 9.**
3. How could you use a spreadsheet to choose the winner of a door prize fairly? **You can list the names of the people in the first column. Count the number of names and generate that number of random whole numbers in the second column.**

Try This **Possible answers:**

1. Generate five random decimal numbers between 1 and 10. **Check students' random numbers. =(10*RAND()) + 1**
2. Generate ten random whole numbers between 0 and 19. **Check students' random numbers. =INT(20*RAND())**
3. Generate ten random decimal numbers greater than or equal to 0 but less than 25. What spreadsheet formula did you use? **Check students' random numbers. = (25*RAND())**
4. The makers of Berries and Bran cereal randomly insert collectible miniposters in their cereal boxes. The posters are numbered 1 through 8.
   a. Write a spreadsheet formula to generate random whole numbers from 1 to 8. **=INT(8*RAND()) + 1**
   b. Use your formula to simulate buying five boxes of cereal. List the numbers of the posters you simulated getting. Were they all different? **2, 3, 3, 6, 5; no**

1-2 Organizer

Pacing: Traditional 1 day
Block $\frac{1}{2}$ day

Objective: Students find the mean, median, mode, and range of a data set.

Warm Up

Order the numbers from least to greatest.

1. 7, 4, 15, 9, 5, 2
2, 4, 5, 7, 9, 15

2. 70, 21, 36, 54, 22
21, 22, 36, 54, 70

Divide.

3. 820 ÷ 4 **205** **4.** 650 ÷ 10 **65**

5. 1,125 ÷ 25 **45** **6.** 2,275 ÷ 7 **325**

Problem of the Day

Complete the expression using the numbers 3, 4, and 5 so that it equals 19. ▢ + ▢ × ▢

4 + 5 × 3 or 4 + 3 × 5

Available on Daily Transparency in CRB

Math Humor

Why did the statistician cross the road? She was trying to find the median.

1-2 Mean, Median, Mode, and Range

Learn to find the mean, median, mode, and range of a data set.

Vocabulary
mean
median
mode
range
outlier

The most common letter in English is *e*. You can use this information to crack secret messages in code. Begin by listing the number of times each symbol of a code appears in a message. The symbol that appears the most often represents the *mode*, which likely corresponds to *e*.

Navajo Code Talkers used the Navajo language as the basis of a code in World War II.

The mode, along with the *mean* and the *median*, is a measure of *central tendency* used to represent the "middle" of a data set.

- The **mean** is the sum of the data values divided by the number of data items.
- The **median** is the middle value of an odd number of data items arranged in order. For an even number of data items, the median is the average of the two middle values.
- The **mode** is the value or values that occur most often. When all the data values occur the same number of times, there is no mode.

The **range** of a set of data is the difference between the greatest and least values. It is used to show the spread of the data in a data set.

EXAMPLE 1 Finding the Mean, Median, Mode, and Range of Data

Find the mean, median, mode, and range of the data set.

2, 1, 8, 0, 2, 4, 3, 4

mean:
2 + 1 + 8 + 0 + 2 + 4 + 3 + 4 = 24 — *Add the values.*
24 ÷ 8 = 3 — *Divide the sum by the number of items.*
The mean is 3.

median:
0, 1, 2, 2, 3, 4, 4, 8 — *Arrange the values in order.*
2 + 3 = 5   5 ÷ 2 = 2.5 — *Since there are two middle values, find the average of these two values.*
The median is 2.5.

mode:
The modes are 2 and 4. — *The values 2 and 4 occur twice.*

range:
8 − 0 = 8 — *Subtract the least value from the greatest value.*
The range is 8.

1 Introduce

Alternate Opener

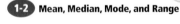

EXPLORATION

1-2 Mean, Median, Mode, and Range

Lucia wrote the minutes she jogged on each of 21 days on index cards.

65	64	59	55	65	60	55
64	72	60	61	68	60	65
47	65	58	56	65	60	63

1. Order the data from least to greatest.
2. The *mode* is the number that appears most often. What is the mode?
3. The *median* is the number in the middle of the data set when the numbers are ordered from least to greatest. What is the median?
4. The *mean* is the average of all the numbers. To find the mean, add the numbers and divide by 21.

Think and Discuss

5. **Describe** the meaning of mean, median, and mode. Which is more appropriate to describe the data above?
6. **Explain** what it means when a sample does not have a mode. Can a sample have more than one mode?

Motivate

Pose the following situation:

Seth is hired for a job that pays $6 per hour at a place where the average wage is $8 per hour. He discovers that most of the employees earn $6 per hour too.

Ask students why they think the average wage is $8 per hour. Explain to students that if the manager and supervisor each earn $16 per hour and eight others earn $6 per hour, the average (mean) is $8 per hour, although it is not very representative.

Exploration worksheet and answers on Chapter 1 Resource Book pp. 16 and 103

2 Teach

Lesson Presentation

Guided Instruction

In this lesson, students learn to find the mean, median, mode, and range of a data set. Focus on the type of information each measure provides and the type of situation in which each is most useful. The mean is a good measure to use to describe data that are close in value. The median more accurately describes data with an outlier. The mode is a good measure to use when you have categorical data; for example, if each student records his or her favorite color, the color (a category) listed most often is the mode of the data.

In the data set below, the value 12 is much less than the other values in the set. An extreme value such as this is called an **outlier**.

35, 38, 27, 12, 30, 41, 31, 35

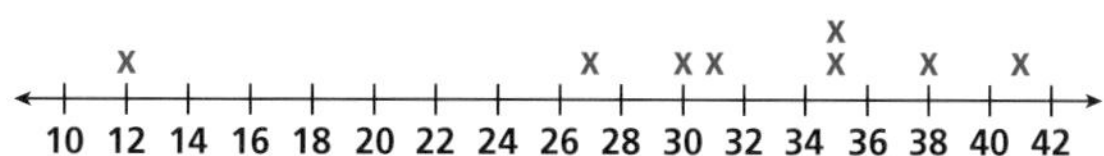

EXAMPLE 2 Exploring the Effects of Outliers on Measures of Central Tendency

The table shows the number of art pieces created by students in a glass-blowing workshop. Identify the outlier in the data set. Then determine how the outlier affects the mean, median, and mode of the data.

Name	Number of Pieces
Suzanne	5
Glen	7
Charissa	4
Eileen	6
Hermann	14
Tom	3

The outlier is 14. To determine its effect on the mean, median, and mode, calculate each value with and without the outlier.

Without the Outlier	With the Outlier
mean:	**mean:**
5 + 7 + 4 + 6 + 3 = 25	5 + 7 + 4 + 6 + 14 + 3 = 39
25 ÷ 5 = 5	39 ÷ 6 = 6.5
The mean is 5.	The mean is 6.5.
median:	**median:**
3, 4, 5, 6, 7	3, 4, 5, 6, 7, 14
	5 + 6 = 11 11 ÷ 2 = 5.5
The median is 5.	The median is 5.5.
mode:	**mode:**
There is no mode.	There is no mode.

Adding the outlier increased the mean by 1.5 and the median by 0.5. The mode did not change.

Think and Discuss

1. **Given** the mean, median, and mode for a set of data, which measure of central tendency must be a data value?
2. **Give an example** of a data set with an outlier. Describe how the outlier affects the mean, median, and mode of the data.

COMMON ERROR ALERT

Students might choose one of the two center numbers in an even number of values as the median. Remind students that if the set has an even number of values, the median is the average of the two middle values.

Additional Examples

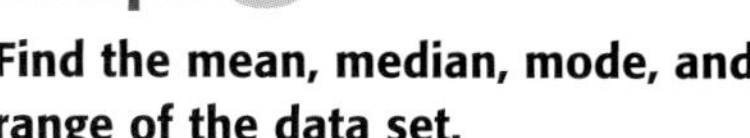

Example 1

Find the mean, median, mode, and range of the data set.

4, 7, 8, 2, 1, 2, 4, 2

mean: 3.75; median: 3; mode: 2; range: 7

Example 2

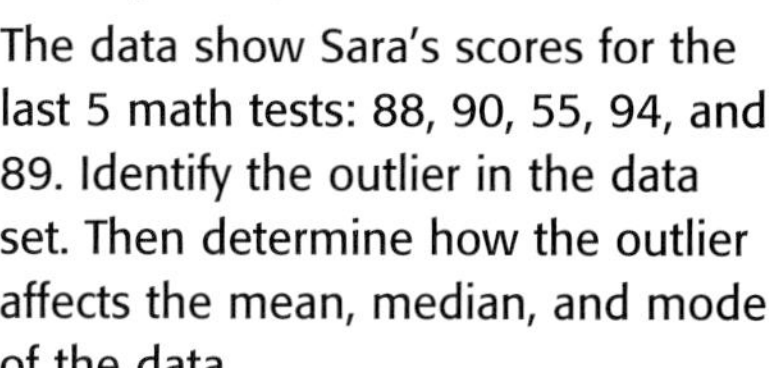

The data show Sara's scores for the last 5 math tests: 88, 90, 55, 94, and 89. Identify the outlier in the data set. Then determine how the outlier affects the mean, median, and mode of the data.

The outlier is 55.
mean with outlier: 83.2
mean without outlier: 90.25
median with outlier: 89
median without outlier: 89.5
Adding the outlier increased the mean by 7.05 and the median by 0.5. There is no mode with or without the outlier.

Example 2 note: Discuss how an outlier can skew the information about a set of data when you are finding the mean. Point out that the description of the data can be misleading, using the mean with the outlier, as in Example 2.

3 Close

Summarize

Display the following data on the chalkboard:
12, 14, 22, 24, 15, 12, 20

Ask volunteers to describe how to find a measure of central tendency without naming it. Have students identify the measure described.

Possible answers: Mean: If I add the numbers and divide by 7, I get 17. Mode: The data value that appears most often is 12. Range: The difference between the highest and lowest value is 12. Median: The middle value is 15.

Reaching All Learners

Through Curriculum Integration

Science Have students research the local daily high and low temperatures for the previous 10 days. Then have students write a paragraph that summarizes the temperature data they collected by incorporating measures of central tendency. Have students share and compare their paragraphs.

Answers to Think and Discuss

Possible answers:

1. Because it is the value that occurs most often in a data set, the mode must be a value in the set.
2. 3, 4, 5, 25; mean with the outlier: 9.25; mean without the outlier: 4; median with outlier: 4.5; median without the outlier: 4; mode: no mode in either case

1-2 PRACTICE & ASSESS

Students may want to refer back to the lesson examples.

Assignment Guide

If you finished Example 1 assign:
Core 1, 2, 4, 5, 9, 12, 16–24
Enriched 1, 4, 8–10, 12, 15–24

If you finished Example 2 assign:
Core 1–11, 16–24
Enriched 1–5 odd, 8–24

Answers

4. 66; 67; 68; 7

5. 14; 11; 11; 14

6. 5; Adding the outlier decreased the mean and the median by 1.5. The mode did not change.

7. 151; Adding the outlier increased the mean by 10 and the median by 7.5. The mode did not change because there was no mode.

1-2 Exercises

FOR EXTRA PRACTICE
see page 654

internet connect
Homework Help Online
go.hrw.com Keyword: MS4 1-2

GUIDED PRACTICE

See Example 1 **Find the mean, median, mode, and range of each data set.**

1. 5, 30, 35, 20, 5, 25, 20
20; 20; 5 and 20; 30

2. 44, 68, 48, 61, 59, 48, 63, 49
55; 54; 48; 24

See Example 2

3. The table shows the number of glasses of water consumed by several students in one day. Identify the outlier in the data set. Then determine how the outlier affects the mean, median, and mode of the data.

Water Consumption								
Name	Randy	Lori	Anita	Jana	Sonya	Victor	Mark	Jorge
Glasses	4	12	3	1	4	7	5	4

12; Adding the outlier increased the mean by 1. The median and the mode did not change.

INDEPENDENT PRACTICE

See Example 1 **Find the mean, median, mode, and range of each data set.**

4.

Daily Low Temperatures							
Day	Sun	Mon	Tue	Wed	Thu	Fri	Sat
Temperature (°F)	68	65	68	61	68	67	65

5.

1995 NFL Touchdown Leaders							
Name	Faulk	Martin	Rhett	Sanders	Smith	Warren	Watters
TD's	11	14	11	11	25	15	11

See Example 2 **Identify the outlier in each data set. Then determine how the outlier affects the mean, median, and mode of the data.**

6. 13, 18, 20, 5, 15, 20, 13, 20

7. 45, 48, 63, 85, 151, 47, 88, 44, 68

PRACTICE AND PROBLEM SOLVING

8. The table shows the amount of snowfall in Colorado Springs during a ten-year period.
   a. Find the mean, median, mode, and range of the data.
   b. Would the mode be a good number to describe the amount of snowfall for these ten years? Explain.

8a. 40.3; 41.5; 57; 39

8b. No; The mode simply indicates that the same amount of snow occurred in two years.

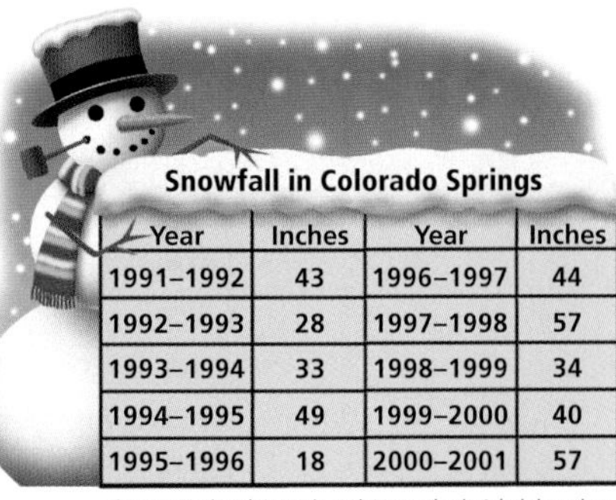

Snowfall in Colorado Springs			
Year	Inches	Year	Inches
1991–1992	43	1996–1997	44
1992–1993	28	1997–1998	57
1993–1994	33	1998–1999	34
1994–1995	49	1999–2000	40
1995–1996	18	2000–2001	57

Source: National Oceanic and Atmospheric Administration

Math Background

Karl Pearson (1857–1936), a British geneticist, coined the term *mode* in 1895 in "Skew Variation in Homogeneous Material." Pearson was known for using statistical methods to analyze and describe biological data. He used the term *mode* to distinguish the information he was describing from the mean and median. He stated, "I have found it convenient to use the term *mode* for the abscissa corresponding to the ordinate of maximum frequency. Thus the 'mean,' the 'mode,' and the 'median' have all distinct characters."

RETEACH 1-2

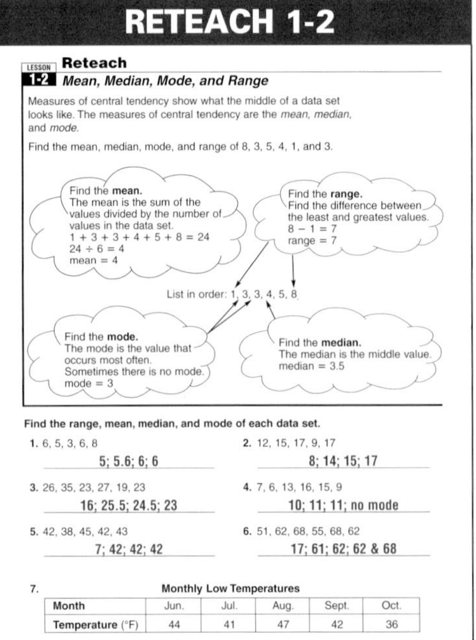

LESSON 1-2 **Reteach**
Mean, Median, Mode, and Range

Measures of central tendency show what the middle of a data set looks like. The measures of central tendency are the *mean, median,* and *mode.*

Find the mean, median, mode, and range of 8, 3, 5, 4, 1, and 3.

Find the **mean.**
The mean is the sum of the values divided by the number of values in the data set.
1 + 3 + 3 + 4 + 5 + 8 = 24
24 ÷ 6 = 4
mean = 4
Find the **range.**
Find the difference between the least and greatest values.
8 − 1 = 7
range = 7
List in order: 1, 3, 3, 4, 5, 8
Find the **mode.**
The mode is the value that occurs most often.
Sometimes there is no mode.
mode = 3
Find the **median.**
The median is the middle value.
median = 3.5

Find the range, mean, median, and mode of each data set.

1. 6, 5, 3, 6, 8
5; 5.6; 6; 6

2. 12, 15, 17, 9, 17
8; 14; 15; 17

3. 26, 35, 23, 27, 19, 23
16; 25.5; 24.5; 23

4. 7, 6, 13, 16, 15, 9
10; 11; 11; no mode

5. 42, 38, 45, 42, 43
7; 42; 42; 42

6. 51, 62, 68, 55, 68, 62
17; 61; 62; 62 & 68

7.

Monthly Low Temperatures					
Month	Jun.	Jul.	Aug.	Sept.	Oct.
Temperature (°F)	44	41	47	42	36

11°F; 42°F; 42°F; no mode

PRACTICE 1-2

LESSON 2-2 **Practice B**
Powers of Ten and Scientific Notation

Multiply.

1. $6 \cdot 10^3$ **6,000**
2. $22 \cdot 10^1$ **220**
3. $8 \cdot 10^2$ **800**
4. $18 \cdot 10^0$ **18**
5. $70 \cdot 10^2$ **7,000**
6. $25 \cdot 10^3$ **25,000**
7. $3 \cdot 10^4$ **30,000**
8. $180 \cdot 10^3$ **180,000**

Find each product.

9. $84 \cdot 10^4$ **840,000**
10. $315 \cdot 10^2$ **31,500**
11. $210 \cdot 10^3$ **210,000**
12. $1{,}004 \cdot 10^3$ **1,004,000**
13. $1{,}764 \cdot 10^1$ **17,640**
14. $856 \cdot 10^0$ **856**
15. $4{,}055 \cdot 10^3$ **4,055,000**
16. $716 \cdot 10^4$ **7,160,000**

Write each number in scientific notation.

17. 34,000 **3.4×10^4**
18. 7,700 **7.7×10^3**
19. 2,100,000 **2.1×10^6**
20. 404,000 **4.04×10^5**
21. 21,000,000 **2.1×10^7**
22. 612.00 **6.12×10^2**
23. 3,001,000 **3.001×10^6**
24. $62.13 \cdot 10^4$ **6.213×10^5**

25. Lake Superior covers an area of about 31,700 square miles. Write this number in scientific notation.
3.17×10^4

26. Mars is about $1.42 \cdot 10^8$ miles from the sun. Write this number in standard form.
142,000,000

27. In 1999, the population of China was about $1.25 \cdot 10^9$. What was the population of China written in standard form?
1,250,000,000

28. A scientist estimates there are 4,800,000 bacteria in a test tube. How does she record the number using scientific notation?
4.8×10^6

9. ***ECONOMICS*** The table shows the monthly salaries for different grades of U.S. government employees. Find the range, mean, and median of the salaries. **$791; $1,822; $1,793**

Grade	Salary
GS-1	$1,461
GS-2	$1,591
GS-3	$1,793
GS-4	$2,013
GS-5	$2,252

Mountain bikes account for over 50% of bicycle sales in the United States.

10. ***SPORTS*** The ages of the participants in a mountain bike race are 14, 23, 20, 24, 26, 17, 21, 31, 27, 25, 14, and 28. **22.5; 23.5; 14**
    a. Find the mean, median, and mode of the ages.
    b. Which measure of central tendency best represents the ages of the participants? Explain. **Possible answer: the mean or the median, since most of the participants were in their twenties**

11. Find the mean, median, and mode of the data displayed in the line plot. Then determine how the outlier affects the mean. **9; 8; 12; Adding the outlier increased the mean by 1.**

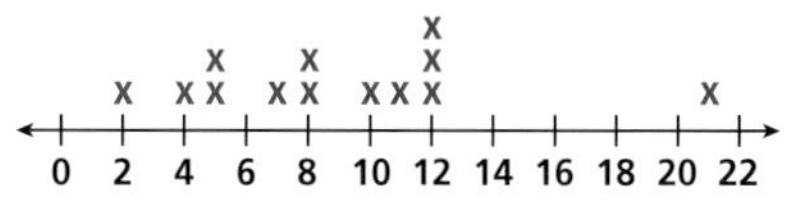

12. ***HEALTH*** Based on the data from three annual checkups, Jon's mean height is 62 in. At the first two checkups Jon's height was 58 in. and 61 in. What was his height at the third checkup? **67 in.**

13. ***WHAT'S THE QUESTION?*** The values in a data set are 10, 7, 9, 5, 13, 10, 7, 14, 8, and 11. What is the question about central tendency that gives the answer 9.5 for the data set? **Possible answer: What is the median of the data set?**

14. ***WRITE ABOUT IT*** Which measure of central tendency is most often affected by including an outlier? Explain.

15. ***CHALLENGE*** Pick a measure of central tendency that describes each situation. Explain your choice.
    a. the number of siblings in a family
    b. the favorite color of students in your math class
    c. the number of days in a month **Mean; use when there are no outliers to distort the data.**

Spiral Review

Round each number to the nearest ten. (Previous course)

16. 52 **50** **17.** 104 **100** **18.** 75 **80** **19.** 817 **820**

Round each number to the nearest hundred. (Previous course)

20. 234 **200** **21.** 961 **1,000** **22.** 1,720 **1,700** **23.** 6,055 **6,100**

24. TEST PREP A VCR is on sale for $79 at Ezra's Electronics. The same VCR costs $113 at Smart Shoppe. Which is the best estimate of the difference in the two prices? (Previous course) **B**

A $20 **B** $30 **C** $50 **D** $70

Some students might make a careless error in solving Exercise 12 by finding the average of the three numbers given rather than finding the missing height. Encourage students to use the problem-solving process of Understand the Problem, Make a Plan, Solve, and Look Back to solve this problem.

Answers

14. Possible answer: The mean is most often affected by including an outlier. Often the median and mode will not change, but the mean will always change.

15. a. Median; use when there are outliers that may distort the data or to describe the middle value.

b. Mode; use when the data are not numerical or when choosing the most popular item.

Journal

Have students describe a situation in their own lives in which one or more of the measures of central tendency could accurately describe the data (e.g., test grades, height over the last 3 years, or which television program they watch most often).

Test Prep Doctor

For Exercise 24, encourage students to use estimation to eliminate incorrect choices. Students should round $79 to $80 and estimate the sum of each choice and $80, looking for the choice that produces the sum close to $113. When $79 is added to either **C** or **D,** the sums are too great, so both choices can be eliminated. When $79 is added to **A,** the sum is too low, so it can be eliminated.

CHALLENGE 1-2

LESSON 1-2 **Challenge**
These Puzzles are Mean

Solve each puzzle.

1. There are 6 whole numbers in a set of numbers. The least number is 8, and the greatest number is 14. The mean, the median, and the mode are 11. What are the numbers?
   Possible answer: 8, 10, 11, 11, 12, 14
2. There are 7 whole numbers in a set of numbers. The least number is 10, and the greatest number is 20. The median is 16, and the mode is 12. The mean is 15. What are the numbers?
   Possible answer: 10, 12, 12, 16, 17, 18, 20
3. There are 8 whole numbers in a set of numbers. The greatest number is 17, and the range is 9. The median and the mean are 12, but 12 is not in the data set. The modes are 9 and 14. What are the numbers?
   Possible answer: 8, 9, 9, 10, 14, 14, 15, 17
4. The mean of a data set of 6 numbers is 8. The mean of a different data set of 6 numbers is 20. What is the mean of the combined data sets? **14**
5. Find the mean of 7 numbers if the mean of the first 4 numbers is 5 and the mean of the last 3 numbers is 12. What is the mean of the combined data sets? **8**
6. The mean of a data set of 3 numbers is 12. The mean of a data set of 9 numbers is 40. What is the mean of the combined data sets? **33**
7. Sasha needs an average of 30 points to move to the next level in her competition. Her scores in the first three events are 28, 35, and 30. What is the lowest score she can score in her last event to move to the next level of competition? **27**
8. Lars has a score of 89 for each of his first 3 science quizzes. The score on his fourth quiz is 92. What score does he need on his fifth quiz to have an average of 90? **91**
9. Jake has a 95 average in math after 4 quizzes. Then he got 0 on the next quiz after being absent. There are 2 more quizzes. What average grade does he need on these last 2 quizzes to keep his average at least 85?
   He can't do it. He would need to score about 108 on each quiz.

PROBLEM SOLVING 1-2

LESSON 1-2 **Problem Solving**
Mean, Median, Mode, and Range

Write the correct answer.

The table to the right shows the leading shot blockers in the WNBA during the 2001 season.

Player	Shots Blocked
Vicky Bullett	58
Margo Drydek	113
Lauren Jackson	64
Lisa Leslie	71
Maria Stepanoya	64

1. What is the range of this set of data? **55**
2. What are the median, mean, and mode of this set of data? **64; 74; 64**
3. What is the outlier in this set of data? **113**
4. How does the outlier affect the mean and median of the data? **It adds 9.75 to the mean and does not affect the median.**

Choose the letter for the best answer.

In a 100-meter dash, the first 5 racers finished with the following times: 11.6 seconds, 12.8 seconds, 10.8 seconds, 11.8 seconds, and 14 seconds.

5. Which measure of central tendency for this set of data is 12.2 seconds?
   (A) mean
   B median
   C mode
   D none of the above
6. Which measure of central tendency for this set of data is 11.8 seconds?
   F mean
   (G) median
   H mode
   J none of the above
7. What is the mode for this set of data?
   A 11.8 seconds
   B 12.8 seconds
   C 12.3 seconds
   (D) none of the above
8. The sixth racer finished with a time of 16.4 seconds. How will that affect the mean for this set of data?
   F decrease it by 0.7 second
   (G) increase it by 0.7 second
   H increase it by 3.28 seconds
   J does not affect the mean

Lesson Quiz

Use the data set 8, 10, 46, 37, 20, 8, 11 to solve each problem.

1. Find the range. **38**

2. Find the mean. **20**

3. Find the median. **11**

4. Find the mode. **8**

Available on Daily Transparency in CRB

1-3 Organizer

Pacing: Traditional 1 day
Block $\frac{1}{2}$ day

Objective: Students organize and interpret data in frequency tables and stem-and-leaf plots.

Warm Up

Use these numbers to answer the following questions.

**136, 151, 104, 168, 140,
124, 162, 121, 118**

1. What is the highest score? **168**
2. What is the lowest score? **104**
3. What is the range of scores? **64**
4. How can you find the median?

Arrange the numbers in order and find the value in the middle.

Problem of the Day

Books A, B, C, and D are on the bookshelf. A is between C and B. B is between A and D. D is not on the right. What is the order of the books from right to left? D, B, A, C

Available on Daily Transparency in CRB

Math Humor

Students watched their stem-and-leaf plots so they wouldn't bubble, because they knew a watched plot never boils.

1-3 Frequency Tables and Stem-and-Leaf Plots

Learn to organize and interpret data in frequency tables and stem-and-leaf plots.

Vocabulary

frequency table

cumulative frequency

stem-and-leaf plot

IMAX® theaters, with their huge screens and powerful sound systems, make viewers feel as if they are in the middle of the action. In 2001, the top IMAX film of all time was *The Dream Is Alive*, with total box office receipts of over $149 million.

To see how common it is for an IMAX movie to attract such a large number of viewers, you could use a *frequency table*. A **frequency table** is a way to organize data into categories or groups. By including a **cumulative frequency** column in your table, you can keep a running total of the frequencies in each category.

EXAMPLE 1 Organizing Data in a Frequency Table

The list shows box office receipts in millions of dollars for 20 IMAX films. Make a cumulative frequency table of the data.

76, 51, 41, 38, 18, 17, 16, 15, 13, 13, 12, 12, 10, 10, 6, 5, 5, 4, 4, 2

Step 1: Look at the range to choose the scale and equal intervals for the data.

Step 2: Find the number of data values in each interval. Write these numbers in the "Frequency" column.

Step 3: Find the cumulative frequency for each row by adding all the frequency values that are above or in that row.

IMAX Films

Receipts ($ million)	Frequency	Cumulative Frequency
0–19	16	16
20–39	1	17
40–59	2	19
60–79	1	20

1 Introduce

Alternate Opener

EXPLORATION

1-3 Frequency Tables and Stem-and-Leaf Plots

The table shows how many cars of each color were parked at a shopping mall at 10 A.M. on a Saturday.

Color of Car	Tally	Frequency
Red	卌 卌 卌 ||	17
Blue	卌 卌 卌 卌 |	
Gray	卌 卌 卌 卌 卌 卌 |	
Gold	卌 卌 |	
Green	卌 ||||	
Black	卌 卌 卌 ||||	

1. Create a frequency table by writing the numbers for each frequency.

You can organize the frequency numbers using a stem-and-leaf plot. For example, the stem for 17 (the number of red cars) will be 1, and the leaf will be 7.

2. Complete the stem-and-leaf plot. For each stem, order the leaves from least to greatest.

Stems	Leaves
0	9
1	
2	
3	

Key: 0|9 means 9

Think and Discuss

3. **Explain** how a stem-and-leaf plot helps to organize data.
4. **Describe** what would happen if you wrote the stems horizontally and stacked the leaves vertically on top of each stem.

Motivate

Initiate a discussion about the common meanings for the following words: *frequency, cumulative, stem,* and *leaf*. Encourage students to share their ideas about what each word means and give example sentences for each. (Example: Frequency means how often something happens. We went to the movies with great frequency.) Help students reach a consensus on a definition and example sentence for each word. Display the definitions and sentences for students to refer to as they read the lesson.

Exploration worksheet and answers on Chapter 1 Resource Book pp. 26 and 105

2 Teach

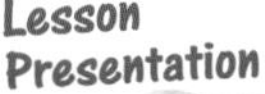

Guided Instruction

In this lesson, students learn to organize and interpret data in frequency tables and stem-and-leaf plots. As you work through the lesson, focus on the similarities and differences between frequency tables and stem-and-leaf plots. Point out that both data displays can be used to show the distribution of data; however, frequency tables show categories of data, not specific values. Stem-and-leaf plots show exactly how many of each value are in a data set.

A **stem-and-leaf plot** can be used to show how often data values occur and how they are distributed. Each *leaf* on the plot represents the right-hand digit in a data value, and each *stem* represents the remaining left-hand digits. The key shows the values of the data on the plot.

Stems	Leaves
2	4 7 9
3	0 6

Key: 2|7 means 27

EXAMPLE 2 Organizing Data in a Stem-and-Leaf Plot

The data shows the number of minutes students spent doing their homework. Make a stem-and-leaf plot of the data.

38, 48, 45, 32, 29, 32, 45, 36, 22, 21, 35, 45, 47, 26, 43, 48, 64

Step 1: Find the least data value and the greatest data value. Since the data values range from 21 to 64, use tens digits for the stems and ones digits for the leaves.

Step 2: List the stems from least to greatest on the plot.

Step 3: List the leaves for each stem from least to greatest.

Step 4: Add a key and a title.

Minutes Doing Homework

Stems	Leaves
2	1 2 6 9
3	2 2 5 6 8
4	3 5 5 5 7 8 8
5	
6	4

Key: 3|2 means 32

The stems are the tens digits.

There are no data values in the 50's.

The leaves are the ones digits.

The entries in the second row represent the data values 32, 32, 35, 36, and 38.

Think and Discuss

1. **Give an example** of when you might use a frequency table to organize data.
2. **Describe** how you would show the numbers 4 and 89 on a stem-and-leaf plot.
3. **Tell** which you would use to determine the number of data values in a set, a cumulative frequency table or a stem-and-leaf plot. Explain.

Additional Examples

Example 1

The list shows the average high temperatures for 20 cities on one February day. Make a cumulative frequency table of the data.

69, 66, 65, 51, 50, 50, 44, 41, 38, 32, 32, 28, 20, 18, 12, 8, 8, 4, 2, 2

Feb. Temperatures in 20 Cities		
Average Highs	Frequency	Cumulative Frequency
0–19	7	7
20–39	5	12
40–59	5	17
60–79	3	20

Example 2

The data shows the number of years coached by the top 15 coaches in all-time NFL coaching victories. Make a stem-and-leaf plot of the data.

33, 40, 29, 33, 23, 22, 20, 21, 18, 23, 17, 15, 15, 12, 17

Number of Years Coached

Stems	Leaves
1	2 5 5 7 7 8
2	0 1 2 3 3 9
3	3 3
4	0

Key: 2|1 means 21

Example 2 note: Discuss how to find the mode of a set of data on a stem-and-leaf plot.

3 Close

Reaching All Learners

Through Critical Thinking

Display a back-to-back stem-and-leaf plot (Teaching Transparency T8, CRB) to show students how to compare information for two data sets.

Math Scores Leaves	Stems	Science Scores Leaves
9, 8, 5	**6**	5, 7, 9, 9
8, 8, 4	**7**	1, 3, 5, 7, 9, 9
9, 9, 7, 2	**8**	2, 2, 4
6, 4, 1, 0	**9**	8

Key: 6|5 means 65

The highest scores for Math and Science are 96 and 98, respectively.

Summarize

Ask students to compare and contrast frequency tables and stem-and-leaf plots. Have students describe the kind of data they would use in each type of display.

Possible answers: Frequency tables group the data into intervals, while stem-and-leaf plots list all the values. Both show frequency of data. Frequency tables can be used to show a data set that has a large range. Stem-and-leaf plots can be used for a data set that has many values close in range. Frequency tables are also good for organizing large data sets (thousands or millions of data points). Stem-and-leaf plots are useless with data sets this large.

Answers to Think and Discuss

Possible answers:

1. A frequency table is good for organizing a data set with a large range into categories or groups (e.g., test scores that range from 35 to 100).
2. The leaf side will show the ones digits and the stem side will show all remaining digits: 0|4, 8|9.
3. Cumulative frequency table; because the number of data values in the set is given in the final entry in the cumulative frequency column; to find the number of data values in a stem-and-leaf plot, it would be necessary to count each value.

1-3 PRACTICE & ASSESS

Assignment Guide

If you finished Example 1 assign:

Core 1, 3, 9, 10, 12, 13, 16–21

Enriched 1, 3, 9–10, 12–14, 16–21

If you finished Example 2 assign:

Core 1–13, 16–21

Enriched 1, 3, 5–21

Answers

1.

Ages of American Presidents

Age	Frequency	Cumulative Frequency
40–49	3	3
50–59	10	13
60–69	5	18

2. **Ages of American Presidents**

Stems	Leaves
4	6 8 9
5	0 1 2 4 6 7 7 7 7 8
6	1 1 4 5 8

Key: 5|2 means 52

3.

States with Drive-ins in 2000

Drive-ins	Frequency	Cumulative Frequency
20–29	6	6
30–39	1	7
40–49	1	8
50–59	3	11

4. **States with Drive-ins in 2000**

Stems	Leaves
2	0 0 1 1 4 9
3	4
4	8
5	2 5 9

Key: 5|2 means 52

8.

	Frequency	Cumulative Frequency
0–9	4	4
10–19	5	9
20–29	2	11
30–39	1	12

1-3 Exercises

FOR EXTRA PRACTICE see page 654

internet connect
Homework Help Online
go.hrw.com Keyword: MS4 1-3

GUIDED PRACTICE

The table shows the ages of the first 18 American presidents when they took office.

President	Age	President	Age	President	Age
Washington	57	Jackson	61	Fillmore	50
Adams	61	Van Buren	54	Pierce	48
Jefferson	57	Harrison	68	Buchanan	65
Madison	57	Tyler	51	Lincoln	52
Monroe	58	Polk	49	Johnson	56
Adams	57	Taylor	64	Grant	46

See Example 1

1. Make a cumulative frequency table of the data.

See Example 2

2. Make a stem-and-leaf plot of the data.

INDEPENDENT PRACTICE

The table shows the states with the most drive-in movie screens in 2000.

State	Drive-ins	State	Drive-ins
Arizona	20	Missouri	21
California	59	New York	48
Florida	29	Ohio	52
Indiana	34	Pennsylvania	55
Kentucky	20	Washington	21
Michigan	24		

Source: USA Today

See Example 1

3. Make a cumulative frequency table of the data.

See Example 2

4. Make a stem-and-leaf plot of the data.

PRACTICE AND PROBLEM SOLVING

Use the stem-and-leaf plot for Exercises 5–8.

Stems	Leaves
0	4 6 6 9
1	2 5 8 8 8
2	0 3
3	1

Key: 1|2 means 12

5. What is the least number? What is the greatest number? What is the range? **4; 31; 27**
6. Find the mean, median, and mode of the data set. **15; 16.5; 18**
7. Which of the following is most likely the source of the data in the stem-and-leaf plot? **b**
   a. shoe sizes of 12 middle-school students
   b. number of hours 12 adults exercised in one month
   c. number of boxes of cereal per household at one time
   d. monthly temperatures in degrees Fahrenheit in Chicago, Illinois
8. Make a cumulative frequency table of the data.

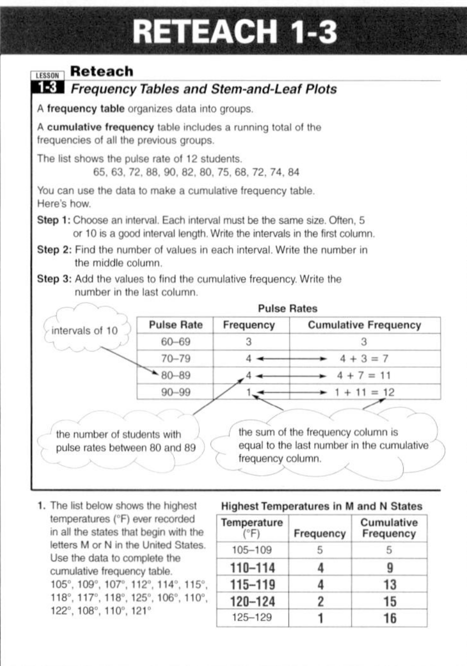

RETEACH 1-3

LESSON 1-3 **Reteach**

Frequency Tables and Stem-and-Leaf Plots

A **frequency table** organizes data into groups.

A **cumulative frequency** table includes a running total of the frequencies of all the previous groups.

The list shows the pulse rate of 12 students.
65, 63, 72, 88, 90, 82, 80, 75, 68, 72, 74, 84

You can use the data to make a cumulative frequency table. Here's how.

Step 1: Choose an interval. Each interval must be the same size. Often, 5 or 10 is a good interval length. Write the intervals in the first column.

Step 2: Find the number of values in each interval. Write the number in the middle column.

Step 3: Add the values to find the cumulative frequency. Write the number in the last column.

Pulse Rates

Pulse Rate	Frequency	Cumulative Frequency
60–69	3	3
70–79	4	4 + 3 = 7
80–89	4	4 + 7 = 11
90–99	1	1 + 11 = 12

1. The list below shows the highest temperatures (°F) ever recorded in all the states that begin with the letters M or N in the United States. Use the data to complete the cumulative frequency table.
105°, 109°, 107°, 112°, 114°, 115°, 118°, 117°, 118°, 125°, 106°, 110°, 122°, 108°, 110°, 121°

Highest Temperatures in M and N States

Temperature (°F)	Frequency	Cumulative Frequency
105–109	5	5
110–114	4	9
115–119	4	13
120–124	2	15
125–129	1	16

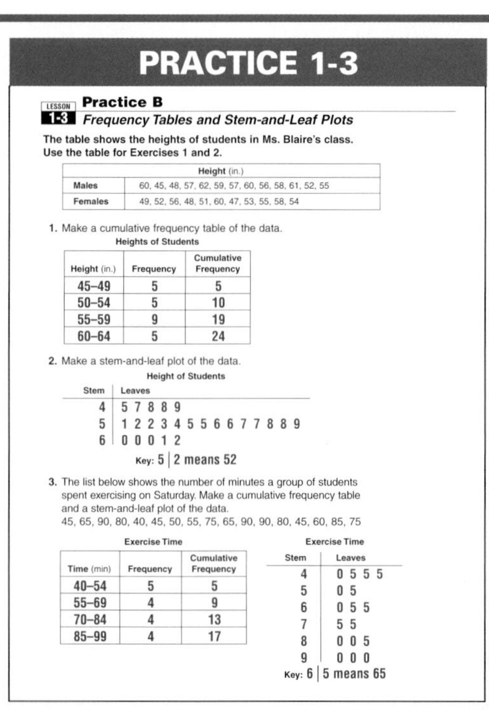

PRACTICE 1-3

LESSON 1-3 **Practice B**

Frequency Tables and Stem-and-Leaf Plots

The table shows the heights of students in Ms. Blaire's class. Use the table for Exercises 1 and 2.

	Height (in.)
Males	60, 45, 48, 57, 62, 59, 57, 60, 56, 58, 61, 52, 55
Females	49, 52, 56, 48, 51, 60, 47, 53, 55, 58, 54

1. Make a cumulative frequency table of the data.

Heights of Students

Height (in.)	Frequency	Cumulative Frequency
45–49	5	5
50–54	5	10
55–59	9	19
60–64	5	24

2. Make a stem-and-leaf plot of the data.

Height of Students

Stem	Leaves
4	5 7 8 8 9
5	1 2 2 3 4 5 5 6 6 7 7 8 8 9
6	0 0 0 1 2

Key: 5|2 means 52

3. The list below shows the number of minutes a group of students spent exercising on Saturday. Make a cumulative frequency table and a stem-and-leaf plot of the data.
45, 65, 90, 80, 40, 45, 50, 55, 75, 65, 90, 90, 80, 45, 60, 85, 75

Exercise Time

Time (min)	Frequency	Cumulative Frequency
40–54	5	5
55–69	4	9
70–84	4	13
85–99	4	17

Exercise Time

Stem	Leaves
4	0 5 5 5
5	0 5
6	0 5 5
7	5 5
8	0 0 5
9	0 0 0

Key: 6|5 means 65

Life Science LINK

The map shows the number of endangered species in each country in South America. A species is classified as endangered when it faces a very high risk of extinction in the wild in the near future.

9. Which country has the fewest endangered species? Which has the most? **Chile and Suriname; Brazil**

10. Make a cumulative frequency table of the data. How many countries have fewer than 20 endangered species? **7**

11. Make a stem-and-leaf plot of the data. What is the mode of the data? **6**

12. Find the mean and the median of the data set. Round to the nearest tenth, if necessary. **18.4; 13**

13. Identify the outlier in the data set. Then determine how the outlier affects the mean of the data.

14. ***WRITE ABOUT IT*** Explain how changing the size of the intervals you used in Exercise 10 affects your cumulative frequency table.

15. ***CHALLENGE*** In a recent year, the number of endangered species in the United States was 150. Show how to represent this number on a stem-and-leaf plot. **15 | 0**

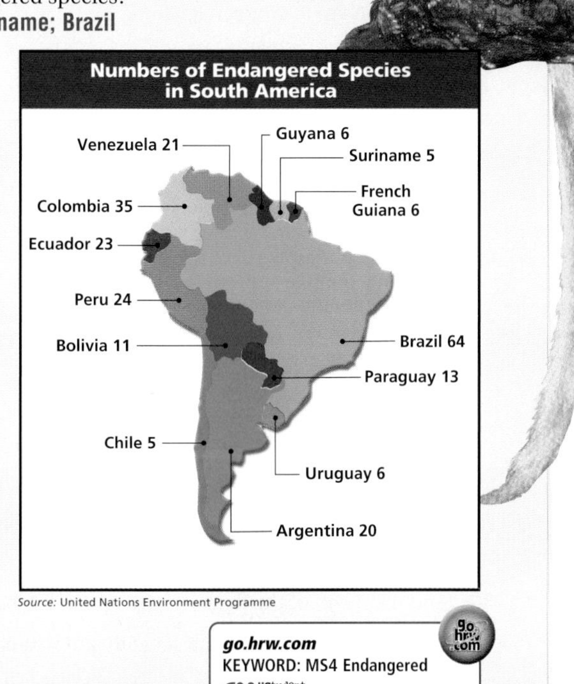

Source: United Nations Environment Programme

go.hrw.com
KEYWORD: MS4 Endangered
CNN Student News

Spiral Review

Tell whether each number is divisible by 6. (Previous course)

16. 24 **yes**

17. 91 **no**

18. 100 **no**

19. 426 **yes**

20. **TEST PREP** Erin started watching a movie at 7:15 P.M. If the movie lasted 1 hour 35 minutes, what time did the movie end? (Previous course) **C**

A 6:40 P.M. C 8:50 P.M.
B 8:45 P.M. D 9:00 P.M.

21. **TEST PREP** Fatima works 17 hr one week and 23 hr the next. If Fatima earns $6 an hr, how much does she earn during the two weeks? (Previous course) **J**

F $50 H $138
G $102 J $240

CHALLENGE 1-3

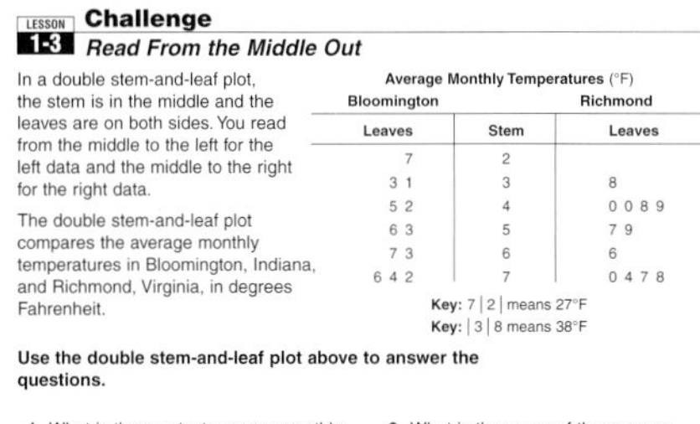

LESSON 1-3 **Challenge**
Read From the Middle Out

In a double stem-and-leaf plot, the stem is in the middle and the leaves are on both sides. You read from the middle to the left for the left data and the middle to the right for the right data.

The double stem-and-leaf plot compares the average monthly temperatures in Bloomington, Indiana, and Richmond, Virginia, in degrees Fahrenheit.

Average Monthly Temperatures (°F)

Bloomington Leaves	Stem	Richmond Leaves
7	2	
3 1	3	8
5 2	4	0 0 8 9
6 3	5	7 9
7 3	6	6
6 4 2	7	0 4 7 8

Key: 7 | 2 | means 27°F
Key: | 3 | 8 means 38°F

Use the double stem-and-leaf plot above to answer the questions.

1. What is the greatest average monthly temperature in Bloomington? in Richmond?
76°F; 78°F

2. What is the range of the average monthly temperatures in Bloomington? in Richmond?
49°F; 40°F

3. Which city has more months with monthly temperatures below 30°F?
Bloomington

4. Which city has more variation in temperatures? Explain.
Bloomington; It has a greater temperature range.

5. What is the median average monthly temperature in Bloomington? in Richmond?
54.5°F; 58°F

6. What is the mean monthly temperature in Richmond?
58°F

7. What is the mean monthly temperature in Bloomington?
53.25°F

8. Compare the mean and the median monthly temperatures in Richmond.
They are the same.

9. Compare the mean and the median monthly temperatures in Bloomington.
The median is 1.25°F, or $1\frac{1}{4}$°F, more than the mean.

PROBLEM SOLVING 1-3

LESSON 1-3 **Problem Solving**
Frequency Tables and Stem-and-Leaf Plots

Write the correct answer.

The table shows the time in minutes that Naima talked on the phone during the last 3 weeks.

Phone Time (min)

	Mon	Tues	Wed	Thurs	Fri	Sat	Sun
Week 1	12	15	25	45	52	30	31
Week 2	22	25	46	51	10	19	33
Week 3	44	21	30	20	10	24	52

1. Naima made a cumulative frequency table of the data using equal intervals. What number would she write in the frequency column for the interval 11–20 minutes?
4

2. What number would Naima write in the cumulative frequency column for the interval 31–40 minutes?
15

3. If Naima makes a stem-and-leaf plot, which stem has the most leaves? What are they?
stem 2; leaves 0, 1, 2, 4, 5, 5

4. In the stem-and-leaf plot, which stems have the same number of leaves?
Stems 4 and 5 each have 3 leaves.

Choose the letter for the best answer.

The list shows the ages of all the presidents inaugurated in the twentieth century. Make a cumulative frequency table and stem-and-leaf plot from the data.
42, 51, 56, 55, 51, 54, 51, 60, 62, 43, 55, 56, 61, 52, 69, 64, 46, 54

5. In a cumulative frequency table of the data, what number belongs in the frequency column for interval 51–55?
A 3 (C) 8
B 7 D 11

6. In a cumulative frequency table of the data, what number belongs in the frequency column for interval 61–65?
(F) 3 H 5
G 4 J 2

7. In a stem-and-leaf plot of the data, how many stems are there?
A 1 (C) 3
B 2 D 4

8. In a stem-and-leaf plot of the data, how many leaves does stem 5 have?
F 3 (H) 10
G 8 J 14

Interdisciplinary LINK

Life Science

Exercises 9–15 involve using data about endangered species. Protection of endangered species is studied in middle school life science programs, such as *Holt Science & Technology.*

Answers

10, 11, 13, 14. Complete answers on p. A1

Journal 

Have students describe the last graph they saw in a newspaper, magazine, or textbook other than their math textbook.

Test Prep Doctor 

For Exercise 21, students can estimate Fatima's earnings for week 2 as $6 \cdot 20 = 120$. Since this means Fatima earns more than $120 just for the second week, they can use this estimate to eliminate **F** and **G.**

Lesson Quiz 

The data shows the ages of some hospital nurses.

33, 35, 23, 39, 23, 24, 34, 21, 57, 45, 57, 60, 45, 24, 31, 42, 61, 45, 35, 38

1. Make a cumulative frequency table of the data.
2. Make a stem-and-leaf plot of the data.

Answers on p. A9

Available on Daily Transparency in CRB

Chapter 1 Mid-Chapter Quiz

Purpose: *To assess students' mastery of concepts and skills in Lessons 1-1 through 1-3*

Assessment Resources

Section 1A Quiz

Assessment Resources .... p. 5

***Test and Practice Generator* CD-ROM**

Additional mid-chapter assessment items in both multiple-choice and free-response format may be generated for any objective in Lessons 1-1 through 1-3.

Answers

1. population: all green iguanas; sample: green iguanas in Costa Rica
2. population: all shoppers; sample: the 15 shoppers asked what kind of vegetable they buy most often

15.

	Frequency	Cumulative Frequency
10–19	1	1
20–29	4	5
30–39	2	7
40	2	9

16.

	Frequency	Cumulative Frequency
6	2	2
7	5	7
8	5	12
9	0	12
10	3	15

17.

Stems	Leaves
0	6 7 8
1	2 8
2	1 3
3	1
4	1

Key: 1|2 means 12

Chapter 1 Mid-Chapter Quiz

Mid-Chapter Quiz

LESSON 1-1 (pp. 4–7)

Identify the population and sample in each situation.

1. A scientist studies a group of green iguanas in Costa Rica to learn about the feeding behavior of green iguanas.
2. A local grocer asks 15 shoppers to name the vegetable they buy most often.

A pollster is gathering responses from students who use the track after school. Tell whether each sampling method is random. Explain your answer.

3. The pollster questions the first five students to run a mile on the track after school. **No; students who run more slowly do not have a chance of being chosen.**
4. The pollster places the names of the students who use the track in a bag and questions the five students whose names he draws. **Yes; drawing names is one way to create a random sample.**

LESSON 1-2 (pp. 10–13)

Find the mean, median, mode, and range of each data set.

5. 64, 38, 29, 47, 52 **46; 47; no mode; 35**
6. 1, 3, 8, 7, 3, 5, 14, 7, 5, 6 **5.9; 5.5; 3, 5, and 7; 13**
7. 56,328; 29,133; 29,133; 48,716 **40,827.5; 38,924.5; 29,133; 27,195**
8. 84, 84, 84, 86, 90, 84, 83 **85; 84; 84; 7**

Use the table for problems 9–13.

Student	Hourly Wage
Michelle	$5
Mary	$3
Sean	$3
Devin	$6
Elliott	$17
Anelise	$8

9. Identify the outlier in the data set. **$17**
10. Find the mean of the data set with and without the outlier. **$7; $5**
11. Find the median of the data set with and without the outlier. **$5.50; $5**
12. Find the mode of the data set with and without the outlier. **$3; $3**
13. Which measure of central tendency is most affected by the outlier? Explain. **mean, because the outlier is added to the sum of the other data**

LESSON 1-3 (pp. 14–17)

Use the stem-and-leaf plot for problems 14 and 15.

Stems	Leaves
1	1
2	0 0 1 6
3	2 7
4	0 8

Key: 3|2 means 32

14. Find the mean, median, mode, and range of the data set. Round to the nearest tenth, if necessary. **28.3; 26; 20; 37**
15. Make a cumulative frequency table of the data.
16. Make a cumulative frequency table of the data 8, 10, 6, 7, 7, 8, 8, 8, 10, 6, 10, 7, 7, 8, 7.
17. Make a stem-and-leaf plot of the data 6, 8, 12, 23, 31, 21, 41, 7, 18.

Focus on Problem Solving

Solve

• Choose an operation: addition or subtraction

In order to decide whether to add or subtract to solve a problem, you need to determine what action is taking place in the problem. If you are combining or putting together numbers, you need to add. If you are taking away or finding how far apart two numbers are, you need to subtract.

Determine the action in each problem. Then determine which operation could be used to solve the problem. Use the table for problems 5 and 6.

1. Betty, Raymond, and Helen ran a three-person relay race. Their individual times were 48 seconds, 55 seconds, and 51 seconds. What was their total time?

2. The Scots pine and the sessile oak are trees native to Northern Ireland. The height of a mature Scots pine is 111 feet, and the height of a mature sessile oak is 90 feet. How much taller is the Scots pine than the sessile oak?

3. Mr. Hutchins has $35.00 to buy supplies for his social studies class. He wants to buy items that cost $19.75, $8.49, and $7.10. Does Mr. Hutchins have enough money to buy all of the supplies?

4. The running time for the 1998 movie *Antz* is 83 minutes. If Jordan has watched 25 minutes of the movie, how many minutes does he have left to watch?

Sizes of Marine Mammals

Mammal	Weight (kg)
Killer whale	3,600
Manatee	400
Sea lion	200
Walrus	750

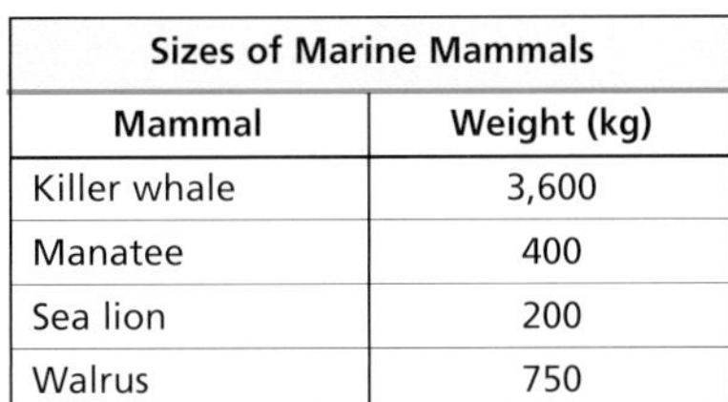

5. The table gives the approximate weights of four marine mammals. How much more does the killer whale weigh than the sea lion?

6. Find the total weight of the manatee, the sea lion, and the walrus. Do these three mammals together weigh more or less than the killer whale?

Answers

1. **48 + 55 + 51 = 154 s**
2. **111 − 90 = 21 ft**
3. $19.75 + $8.49 + $7.10 = $35.34; no, Mr. Hutchins does not have enough money.
4. **83 − 25 = 58 min**
5. **3,600 − 200 = 3,400 kg**
6. 400 + 200 + 750 = 1,350 kg; they weigh less than the killer whale.

Focus on Problem Solving

Purpose: *To focus on choosing an operation (+ or −) to solve a problem*

Problem Solving Resources

Interactive Problem Solving . . . . pp. 1–9
Math: Reading and Writing in the Content Area . . . . pp. 1–9

Problem Solving Process

This page focuses on the third step of the problem-solving process: **Solve**

Discuss

Have students discuss whether they should add or subtract to solve each problem and explain their choices.

Possible answers:

1. Add; the word *total* indicates addition; 48 + 55 + 51.
2. Subtract; the words *how much taller* indicate subtraction; 111 − 90.
3. Add; Mr. Hutchins needs to find the total cost of the items in order to find out if he has enough money; $19.75 + $8.49 + $7.10.
4. Subtract; the words *how many minutes does he have left* indicate subtraction; 83 − 25.
5. Subtract; the words *how much more* indicate subtraction; 3,600 − 200.
6. Add; the words *find the total weight* indicate addition; 400 + 200 + 750.

Section **1B**

Displaying Data

One-Minute Section Planner

Lesson	Materials	Resources
Lesson 1-4 Bar Graphs and Histograms **NCTM:** Data Analysis and Probability, Communication, Connections, Representation **NAEP:** Data Analysis and Probability 1b ☑ SAT-9 ☑ SAT-10 ☐ ITBS ☑ CTBS ☐ MAT ☑ CAT	**Required** Graph paper *(CRB p. 98)* **Optional** Teaching Transparency T12 *(CRB)*	• *Chapter 1 Resource Book,* pp. 36–45 • Daily Transparency T11, CRB • Additional Examples Transparencies T13–T15, CRB • *Alternate Openers: Explorations,* p. 4
Lesson 1-5 Reading and Interpreting Circle Graphs **NCTM:** Data Analysis and Probability, Communication, Connections, Representation **NAEP:** Data Analysis and Probability 1c ☑ SAT-9 ☑ SAT-10 ☐ ITBS ☑ CTBS ☐ MAT ☑ CAT	**Optional** Teaching Transparency T17 *(CRB)* Review Sheet for Reaching All Learners *(CRB, p. 99)*	• *Chapter 1 Resource Book,* pp. 46–54 • Daily Transparency T16, CRB • Additional Examples Transparencies T18–T20, CRB • *Alternate Openers: Explorations,* p. 5
Lesson 1-6 Box-and-Whisker Plots **NCTM:** Data Analysis and Probability, Communication, Connections, Representation **NAEP:** Data Analysis and Probability 1b ☐ SAT-9 ☐ SAT-10 ☐ ITBS ☐ CTBS ☐ MAT ☑ CAT	**Optional** Index cards *(CRB, p. 100)* Teaching Transparency T22 *(CRB)*	• *Chapter 1 Resource Book,* pp. 55–63 • Daily Transparency T21, CRB • Additional Examples Transparencies T23–T24, CRB • *Alternate Openers: Explorations,* p. 6
Technology Lab 1B Use Technology to Create Graphs **NCTM:** Algebra, Data Analysis and Probability, Representation **NAEP:** Data Analysis and Probability 1e ☐ SAT-9 ☐ SAT-10 ☐ ITBS ☐ CTBS ☐ MAT ☐ CAT	**Required** Graphing software	• *Technology Lab Activities,* p. 3
Section 1B Assessment		• Mid-Chapter Quiz, SE p. 34 • Section 1B Quiz, AR p. 6 • *Test and Practice Generator* CD-ROM

SAT = *Stanford Achievement Tests* **ITBS** = *Iowa Test of Basic Skills* **CTBS** = *Comprehensive Test of Basic Skills/Terra Nova*
MAT = *Metropolitan Achievement Test* **CAT** = *California Achievement Test*

NCTM—Complete standards can be found on pages T27–T33. **NAEP**—Complete standards can be found on pages A35–A39.

SE = *Student Edition* **TE** = *Teacher's Edition* **AR** = *Assessment Resources* **CRB** = *Chapter Resource Book* **MK** = *Manipulatives Kit*

Section Overview

Bar Graphs and Histograms — Lesson 1-4

Why? Bar graphs display and compare data. A histogram shows how data fall into different ranges or intervals.

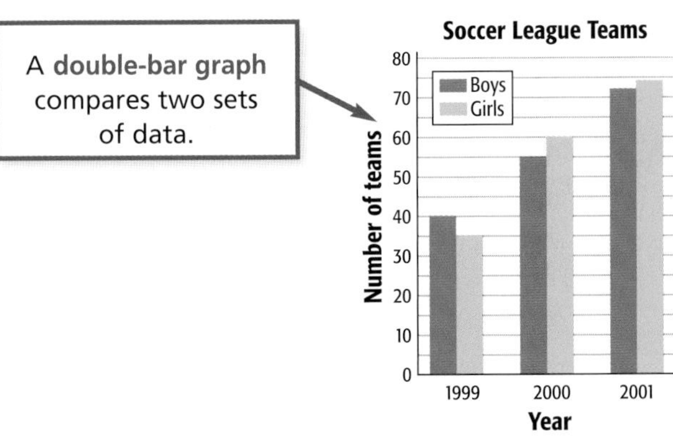

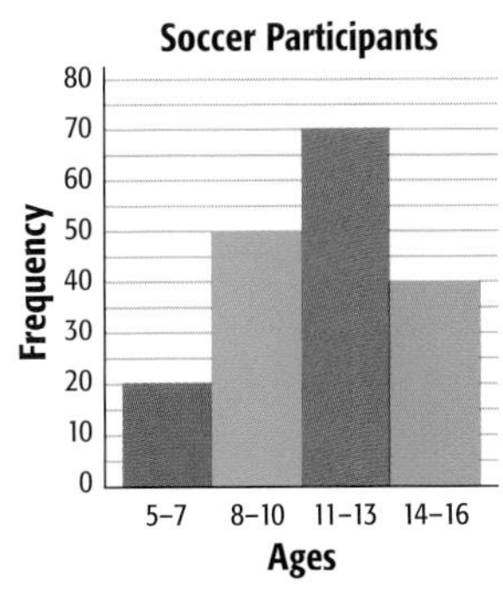

In a **histogram,** the intervals are all the same size, and the bars are all connected.

Circle Graphs — Lesson 1-5

Why? Circle graphs represent data that make up a larger group of data. The whole circle represents 100%, or all, of the data.

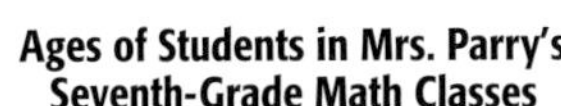

Ages of Students in Mrs. Parry's Seventh-Grade Math Classes

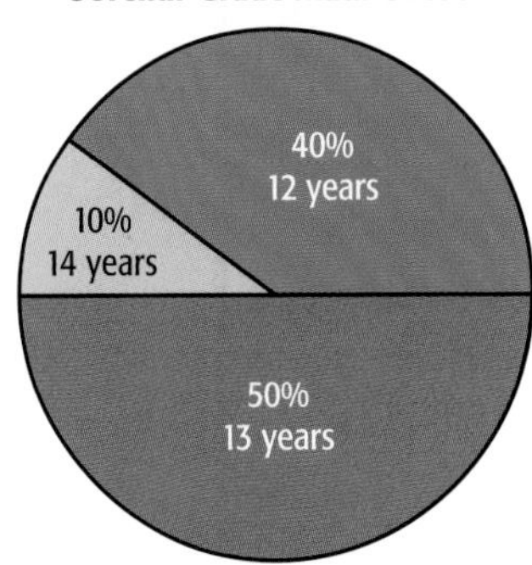

Suppose there are 100 students in Mrs. Parry's classes. Then 50% of 100, or 50 students, are 13 years old.

Box-and-Whisker Plots — Lesson 1-6, Technology Lab 1B

Why? There are different advantages to displaying data in different types of graphs. A box-and-whisker plot is a useful way to summarize a large set of data. It gives a general idea of how the data cluster together.

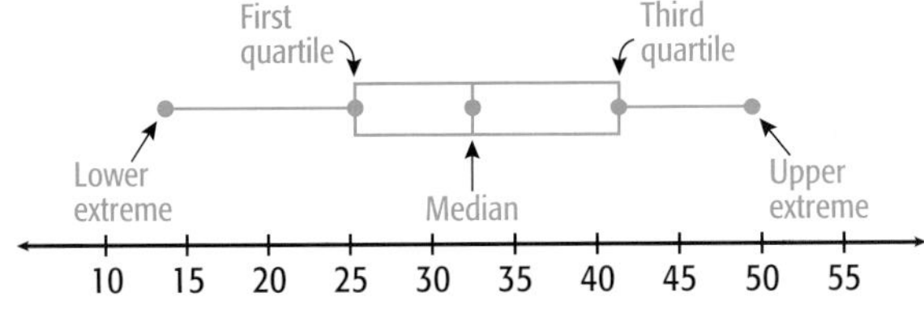

A **box-and-whisker** plot displays only the **median,** the **quartiles,** and the **upper and lower extremes** of the data.

The lower and upper extremes are actual data values. The median and quartiles may or may not be actual data values.

1-4 Organizer

Pacing: Traditional 1 day
Block $\frac{1}{2}$ day

Objective: Students display and analyze data in bar graphs and histograms.

Warm Up

Find the mean, median, mode, and range for the data set.

35, 45, 48, 53, 53, 27, 66, 36, 24

43; 45; 53; 42

Problem of the Day

Which number does not belong with the others? Why?

81, 64, 36, 27, 49

Possible answers: 27; the others are perfect squares.

Available on Daily Transparency in CRB

Additional Examples

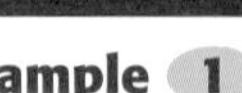

Example 1

Use the bar graph at the top of the lesson to answer each question.

A. Which language has the fewest native speakers? Spanish

B. About how many more people speak Hindi than Spanish? About 50 million more people speak Hindi than speak Spanish.

1-4 Bar Graphs and Histograms

Learn to display and analyze data in bar graphs and histograms.

Vocabulary
bar graph
double-bar graph
histogram

Hundreds of different languages are spoken around the world. The graph shows the numbers of native speakers of four languages.

A **bar graph** can be used to display and compare data. The scale of a bar graph should include all the data values and be easily divided into equal intervals.

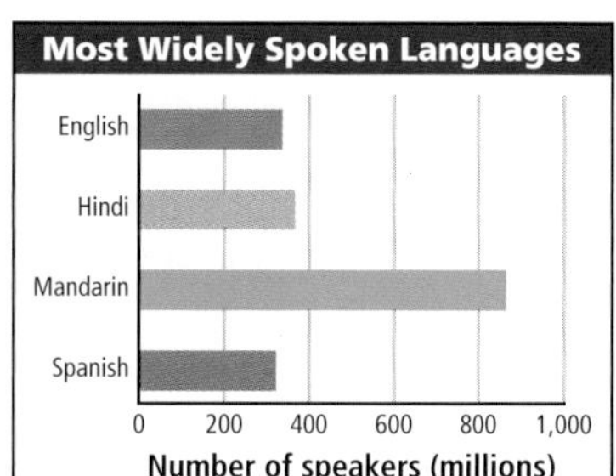

EXAMPLE 1 Interpreting a Bar Graph

Use the bar graph to answer each question.

A **Which language has the most native speakers?**
The bar for Mandarin is the longest, so Mandarin has the most native speakers.

B **About how many more people speak Mandarin than speak Hindi?**
About 500 million more people speak Mandarin than speak Hindi.

You can use a **double-bar graph** to compare two related sets of data.

EXAMPLE 2 Making a Double-Bar Graph

The table shows the life expectancies of people in three Central American countries. Make a double-bar graph of the data.

Country	Male	Female
El Salvador	67	74
Honduras	63	66
Nicaragua	65	70

Honduras
Nicaragua
El Salvador

Step 1: Choose a scale and interval for the vertical axis.

Step 2: Draw a pair of bars for each country's data. Use different colors to show males and females.

Step 3: Label the axes and give the graph a title.

Step 4: Make a key to show what each bar represents.

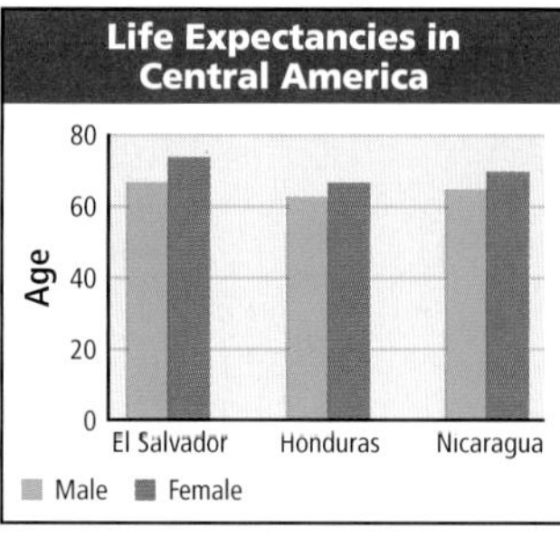

1 Introduce

Alternate Opener

EXPLORATION

1-4 Bar Graphs and Histograms

The bar graph shows Mr. Snowden's students by gender and band membership.

1. How many of Mr. Snowden's students are band members?
2. How many of Mr. Snowden's students are not band members?

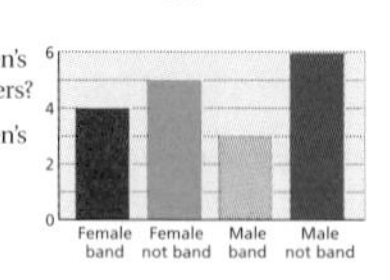

Mr. Snowden ordered the grades his students earned on a test. Using these numbers, he created a *histogram* by grouping the grades into 60's, 70's, 80's, and 90's.

67 75 75 76 78 79 80 80 80 81 83 84 84 85 85 85 85 88 92

3. What does each bar represent?
4. How many students earned a grade between 80 and 100?

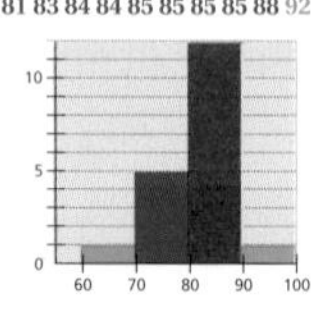

Think and Discuss

5. **Describe** a different way of showing the students' grades.
6. **Explain** how a bar graph and a histogram differ.

Motivate

Encourage students to share what they know and what they want to know about a bar graph, a double-bar graph, and a histogram, including the kind of information each might contain. Display students' ideas in the first two columns of a chart like the one below. Complete the chart at the end of the lesson.

What I Know	What I Want to Know	What I Learned

Exploration worksheet and answers on Chapter 1 Resource Book pp. 37 and 107

2 Teach

Lesson Presentation

Guided Instruction

In this lesson, students learn to display and analyze data in bar graphs (Teaching Transparency T12, CRB) and histograms. Ask students to describe the similarities and differences between a bar graph and a double-bar graph. Discuss the reason for making the bars different colors in a double-bar graph (e.g., to distinguish between related sets of data).

Call students' attention to the relationship between frequency tables and histograms. Students should realize that the frequency data are displayed on the vertical axis of the histogram. Each bar is labeled with the intervals from the frequency table.

A **histogram** is a bar graph that shows the frequency of data within equal intervals. There is no space between the bars in a histogram.

EXAMPLE 3 Making a Histogram

The table below shows survey results about the number of CDs students own. Make a histogram of the data.

Number of CDs									
1	|||	5	𝍸|	9	𝍸|	13	𝍸||||	17	𝍸||||
2	||	6	|||	10	𝍸𝍸	14	𝍸𝍸|	18	𝍸||
3	𝍸	7	𝍸|||	11	𝍸𝍸|	15	𝍸𝍸|	19	||
4	𝍸|	8	𝍸||	12	𝍸𝍸	16	𝍸𝍸|	20	𝍸|

Step 1: Make a frequency table of the data. Be sure to use equal intervals.

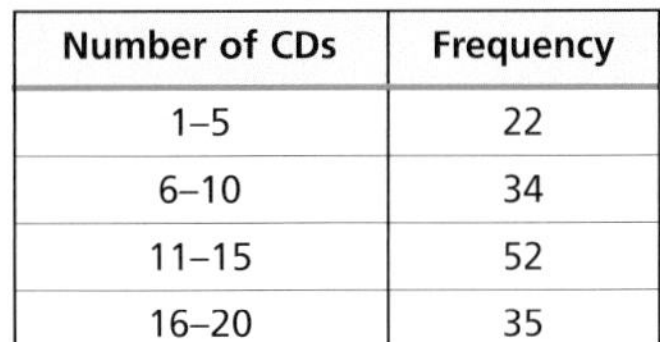

Number of CDs	Frequency
1–5	22
6–10	34
11–15	52
16–20	35

Step 2: Choose an appropriate scale and interval for the vertical axis. The greatest value on the scale should be at least as great as the greatest frequency.

Step 3: Draw a bar for each interval. The height of the bar is the frequency for that interval. Bars must touch but not overlap.

Step 4: Label the axes and give the graph a title.

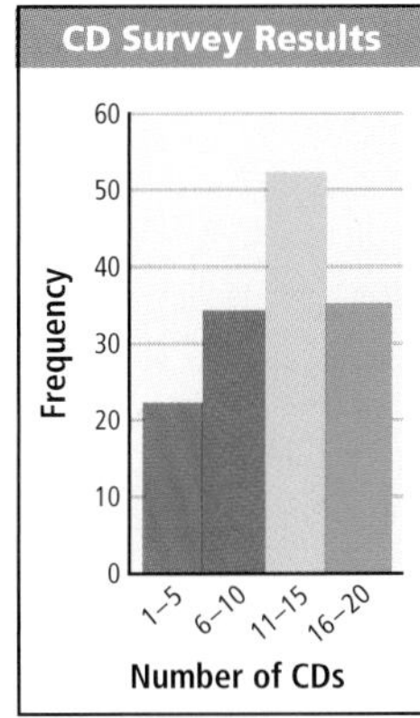

Think and Discuss

1. **Explain** why you might use a horizontal bar graph instead of a vertical bar graph to display data.
2. **Explain** why you might use a double-bar graph instead of two separate bar graphs to display data.
3. **Describe** the similarities and differences between a bar graph and a histogram.

Additional Examples

Example 2

The table shows the highway speed limits on interstate roads within three states. Make a double-bar graph of the data.

State	Urban	Rural
Florida	65 mi/h	70 mi/h
Texas	70 mi/h	70 mi/h
Vermont	55 mi/h	65 mi/h

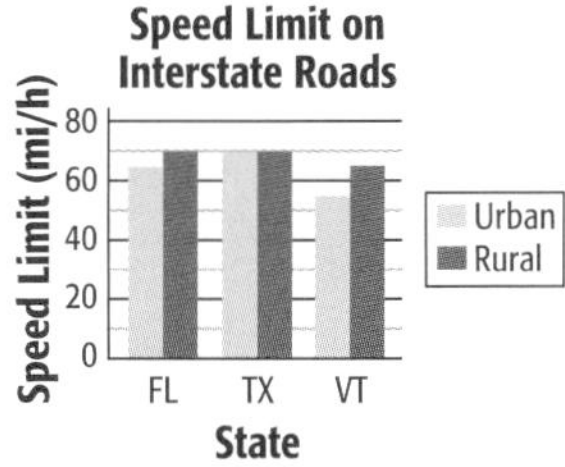

Example 3

The table below shows the number of hours students watch TV in one week. Make a histogram of all the data.

Number of Hours of TV			
1	||	6	|||
2	||||	7	𝍸||||
3	𝍸||||	8	|||
4	𝍸|	9	𝍸
5	𝍸|||		

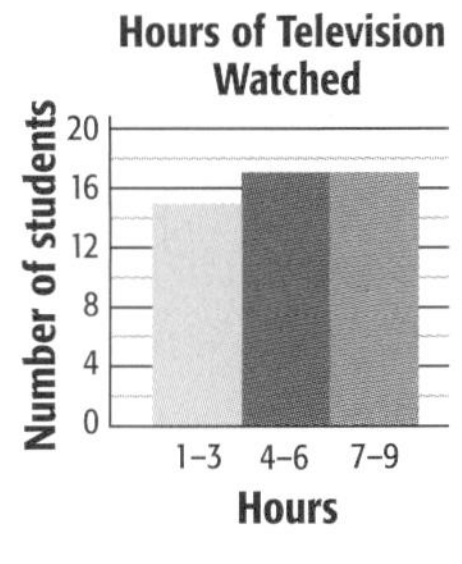

Close

Reaching All Learners

Through Home Connection

With their families, have students record data about the number of lights and windows in any three rooms of their homes. Have the students work with their families to create a double-bar graph to display the data. You may wish to discuss how to label the graphs before students begin their data collection at home. For example, if students choose to make a vertical double-bar graph, they can label the vertical axis with numbers and the horizontal axis with the names of the rooms.

Summarize

Complete the chart from in the Motivate section. Then ask the following questions:

1. What different pets do boys and girls in the class have? How many of each?
2. What is our class's favorite subject?

Have students explain how they would collect the data to answer each question and which data display they would use to present it: a bar graph, a double-bar graph, or a histogram.

Possible answers: 1. Ask each student what pets they have. Tally the totals for each pet, then use a double-bar graph to show the results for boys and girls. 2. List the subjects, take a vote, tally the votes, and show the results in a bar graph.

Answers to Think and Discuss

Possible answers:

1. Graphs are used to visualize data. If the data describe distances cross-country runners ran, you would use a horizontal graph.
2. It is easier to compare two related sets of data in a double bar graph.
3. In a histogram the bars are connected, but they are separate in a bar graph; The width of each bar of a histogram shows a range. This is not true for a bar graph. The height or length of each bar in a histogram shows a frequency, whereas each bar of a bar graph shows a number.

1-4 PRACTICE & ASSESS

Students may want to refer back to the lesson examples.

Assignment Guide

If you finished Example 1 assign:
Core 1, 2, 5, 6, 16–22
Enriched 1, 5, 6, 16–22

If you finished Example 2 assign:
Core 1–3, 5–7, 9–11, 16–22
Enriched 1–7 odd, 9–11, 15–22

If you finished Example 3 assign:
Core 1–13, 16–22
Enriched 1–22

Graph paper is provided on page 98 of the Chapter 1 Resource Book.

Answers

3.
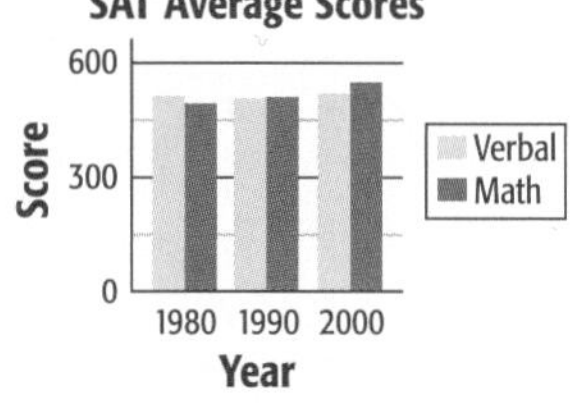

4.
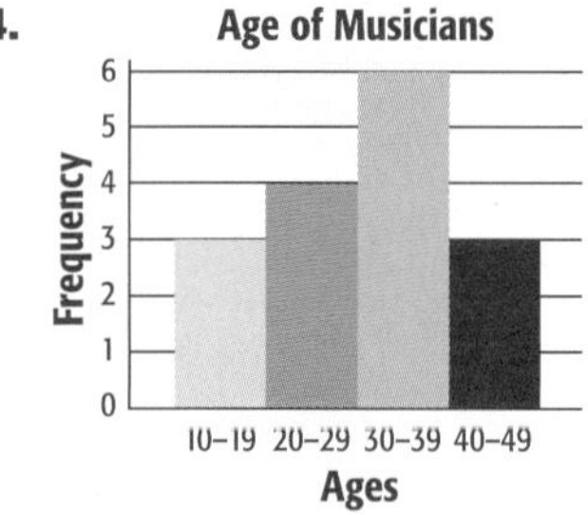

7.
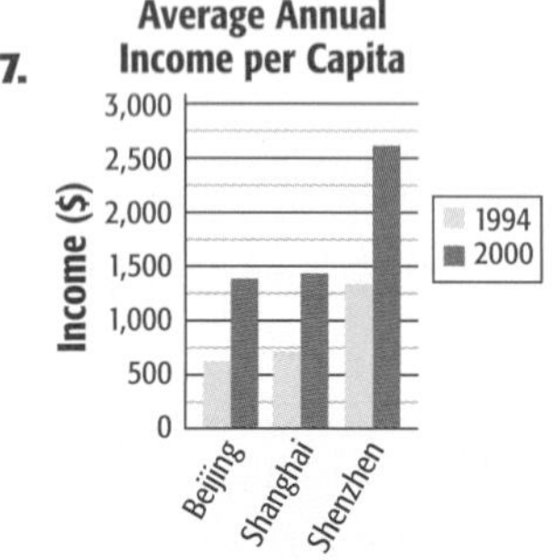

8.
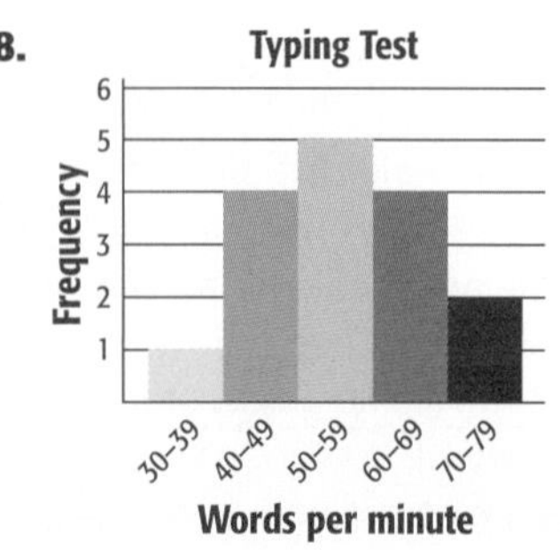

1-4 Exercises

FOR EXTRA PRACTICE
see page 655

internet connect
Homework Help Online
go.hrw.com Keyword: MS4 1-4

GUIDED PRACTICE

See Example 1 **The bar graph shows the average amount of fresh fruit consumed per person in the United States in 1997. Use the graph for Exercises 1 and 2.**

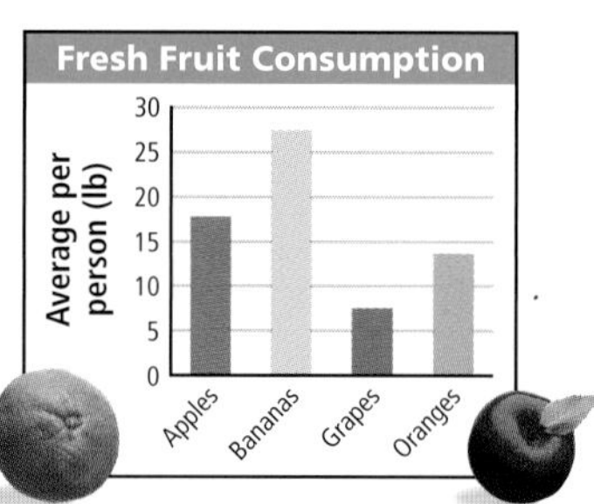

1. Which fruit was eaten the least? **grapes**
2. About how many more pounds of bananas than pounds of oranges were eaten per person? **about 15 pounds**

See Example 2
3. The table shows national average SAT scores for three years. Make a double-bar graph of the data.

Year	Verbal	Math
1980	502	492
1990	500	501
2000	505	514

See Example 3
4. The list below shows the ages of the musicians in a local orchestra. Make a histogram of the data.

14, 35, 22, 18, 49, 38, 30, 27, 45, 19, 35, 46, 27, 21, 32, 30

INDEPENDENT PRACTICE

See Example 1 **The bar graph shows the maximum precipitation in 24 hours for several states. Use the bar graph for Exercises 5 and 6.**

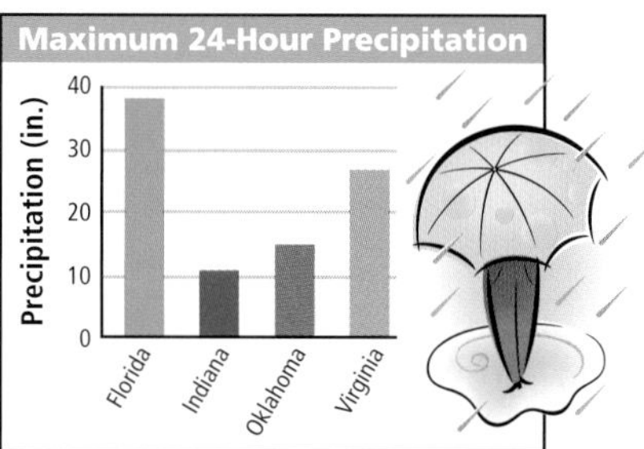

5. Which state received the most precipitation in 24 hours? **Florida**
6. About how many more inches of precipitation did Oklahoma receive than Indiana? **about 4 inches**

See Example 2
7. The table shows the average annual income per capita for three Chinese cities. Make a double-bar graph of the data.

City	1994	2000
Beijing	$614	$1,256
Shanghai	$716	$1,424
Shenzhen	$1,324	$2,626

See Example 3
8. The list below shows the results of a typing test in words per minute. Make a histogram of the data.

62, 55, 68, 47, 50, 41, 62, 39, 54, 70, 56, 47, 71, 55, 60, 42

RETEACH 1-4

LESSON 1-4 **Reteach**
Bar Graphs and Histograms

A **bar graph** uses bars to compare data.
A **double-bar graph** compares two sets of data.

Use the graph for Exercises 1–3. The bar graph shows the approximate amount of passenger traffic through some U. S. airports in 2000.

1. Which airport had more than 60 million arrivals and departures?
Dallas
2. About how many arrivals and departures did Orlando have?
about 31 million
3. About how many more people passed through the Detroit airport than the Philadelphia airport?
about 11 million

Passenger Traffic in 2000 Through Selected U.S. Airports
Passengers (millions)
Dallas, Denver, Detroit, Orlando, Philadelphia
Airport

4. The table shows which sports are played by a seventh-grade class. Use the data in the table to make a double-bar graph.

Sport	Number of Boys	Number of Girls
Soccer	14	8
Tennis	7	10
Basketball	18	6
Swimming	12	20

a. Finish labeling the vertical axis.
What is the vertical axis label?
Number of Students
What is the horizontal axis label?
Sport

b. Draw a bar on the horizontal axis for the number of boys playing each sport. Draw a bar for the number of girls playing each sport. Label the b

Each interval must be the same size.

Sports Participation
Number of Students
Soccer, Tennis, Basketball, Swimming
Sport
Key: Boys Girls

c. Give the graph a title.

PRACTICE 1-4

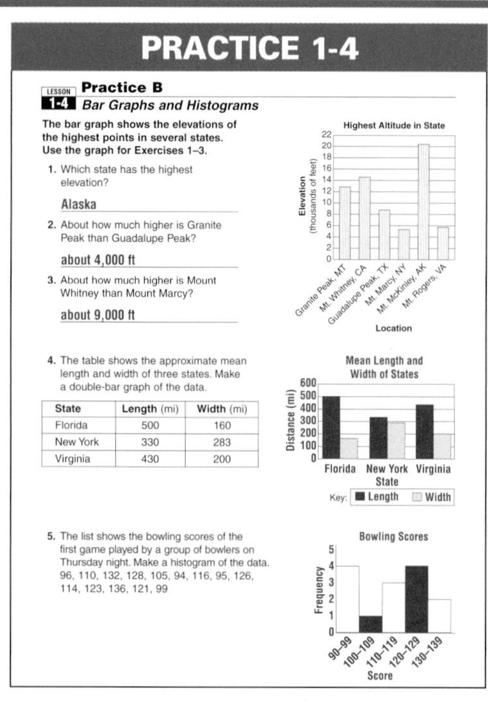
LESSON 1-4 **Practice B**
Bar Graphs and Histograms

The bar graph shows the elevations of the highest points in several states. Use the graph for Exercises 1–3.

1. Which state has the highest elevation?
Alaska
2. About how much higher is Granite Peak than Guadalupe Peak?
about 4,000 ft
3. About how much higher is Mount Whitney than Mount Marcy?
about 9,000 ft

Highest Altitude in State
Elevation (thousands of feet)
Granite Peak, MT; Mt. Whitney, CA; Guadalupe Peak, TX; Mt. Marcy, NY; Mt. McKinley, AK; Mt. Rogers, VA
Location

4. The table shows the approximate mean length and width of three states. Make a double-bar graph of the data.

State	Length (mi)	Width (mi)
Florida	500	160
New York	330	283
Virginia	430	200

Mean Length and Width of States
Distance (mi)
Florida, New York, Virginia
State
Key: Length Width

5. The list shows the bowling scores of the first game played by a group of bowlers on Thursday night. Make a histogram of the data.
96, 110, 132, 128, 105, 94, 116, 95, 126, 114, 123, 136, 121, 99

Bowling Scores
Frequency
90–99, 100–109, 110–119, 120–129, 130–139
Score

In 1896 and 1900, the same candidates ran for president of the United States. The candidates were William McKinley, a Republican, and William Jennings Bryan, a Democrat. The table shows the number of electoral votes each man received in these elections.

William Jennings Bryan

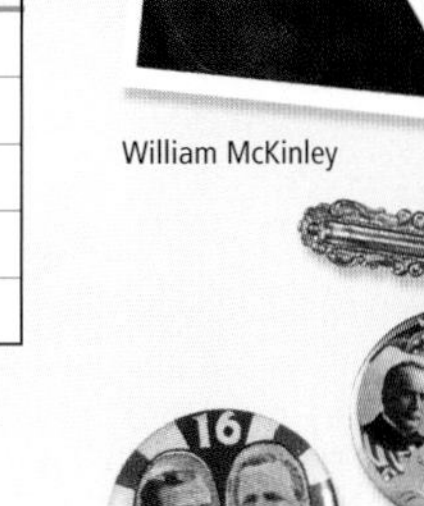

William McKinley

9. Use the data in the table to make a double-bar graph. Label the horizontal axis with the years.

Candidate	1896	1900
McKinley	271	292
Bryan	176	155

10. In which year was the difference between the number of electoral votes each candidate received the greatest? **1900**

11. In 1896, about how many more electoral votes did McKinley get than Bryan? **about 100**

12. The frequency table shows the number of years the first 42 presidents spent in office. How many presidents spent fewer than six years in office? **29**

Years in Office	Frequency
0–2	7
3–5	22
6–8	12
9–11	0
12–14	1

13. Use the frequency table to make a histogram.

14. ***WRITE ABOUT IT*** What does your histogram show you about the number of years the presidents spent in office? **Possible answer: Most presidents spent 3 to 8 years in office.**

15. ***CHALLENGE*** Use the 1896 and 1900 election data to make a second double-bar graph. Label the horizontal axis with the candidates' names. Then write a question about the graph.

Spiral Review

Compare. Write < or >. (Previous course)

16. 37 ▢ 29 > **17.** 165 ▢ 180 < **18.** \$2.13 ▢ \$2.44 <

Order the numbers from least to greatest. (Previous course)

19. 402, 398, 417, 410 **398, 402, 410, 417**

20. \$1.00, \$2.66, \$1.41, \$0.82 **\$0.82, \$1.00, \$1.41, \$2.66**

21. 8°F, 7°F, 14°F, 78°F, 41°F **7°F, 8°F, 14°F, 41°F, 78°F**

22. TEST PREP Which rule best describes the number pattern 3, 6, 9, 12, 15? (Previous course) **B**

A Begin with 3 and multiply by 2 repeatedly.
B Begin with 3 and add 3 repeatedly.
C Write the first five powers of 3.
D Begin with 3 and multiply by 3 repeatedly.

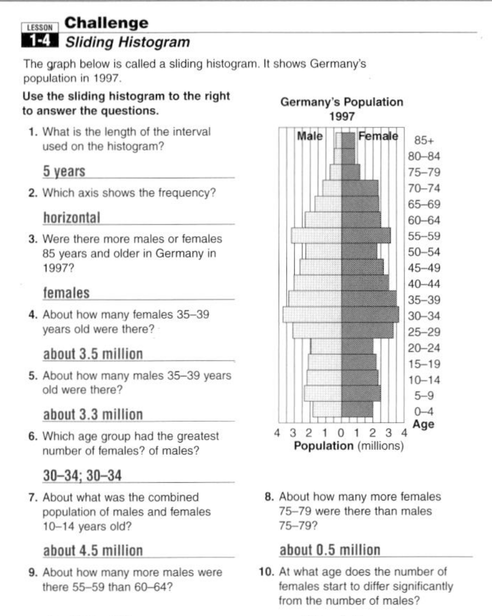

CHALLENGE 1-4

LESSON 1-4 **Challenge**
Sliding Histogram

The graph below is called a sliding histogram. It shows Germany's population in 1997.

Use the sliding histogram to the right to answer the questions.

1. What is the length of the interval used on the histogram? **5 years**
2. Which axis shows the frequency? **horizontal**
3. Were there more males or females 85 years and older in Germany in 1997? **females**
4. About how many females 35–39 years old were there? **about 3.5 million**
5. About how many males 35–39 years old were there? **about 3.3 million**
6. Which age group had the greatest number of females? of males? **30–34; 30–34**
7. About what was the combined population of males and females 10–14 years old? **about 4.5 million**
8. About how many more females 75–79 were there than males 75–79? **about 0.5 million**
9. About how many more males were there 55–59 than 60–64? **about 0.7 million**
10. At what age does the number of females start to differ significantly from the number of males? **age 65 and above**

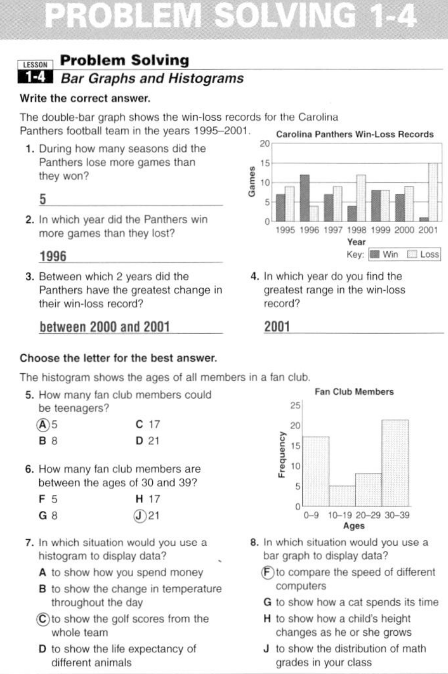

PROBLEM SOLVING 1-4

LESSON 1-4 **Problem Solving**
Bar Graphs and Histograms

Write the correct answer.

The double-bar graph shows the win-loss records for the Carolina Panthers football team in the years 1995–2001.

1. During how many seasons did the Panthers lose more games than they won? **5**
2. In which year did the Panthers win more games than they lost? **1996**
3. Between which 2 years did the Panthers have the greatest change in their win-loss record? **between 2000 and 2001**
4. In which year do you find the greatest range in the win-loss record? **2001**

Choose the letter for the best answer.

The histogram shows the ages of all members in a fan club.

5. How many fan club members could be teenagers?
   (A) 5 C 17
   B 8 D 21
6. How many fan club members are between the ages of 30 and 39?
   F 5 H 17
   G 8 (J) 21
7. In which situation would you use a histogram to display data?
   A to show how you spend money
   B to show the change in temperature throughout the day
   (C) to show the golf scores from the whole team
   D to show the life expectancy of different animals
8. In which situation would you use a bar graph to display data?
   (F) to compare the speed of different computers
   G to show how a cat spends its time
   H to show how a child's height changes as he or she grows
   J to show the distribution of math grades in your class

Answers

9.

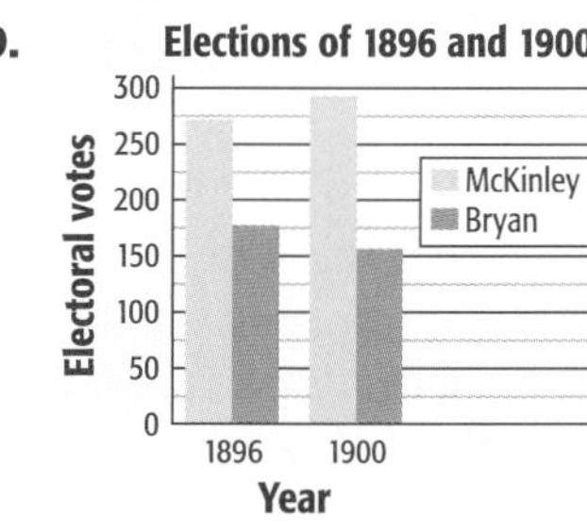

13.

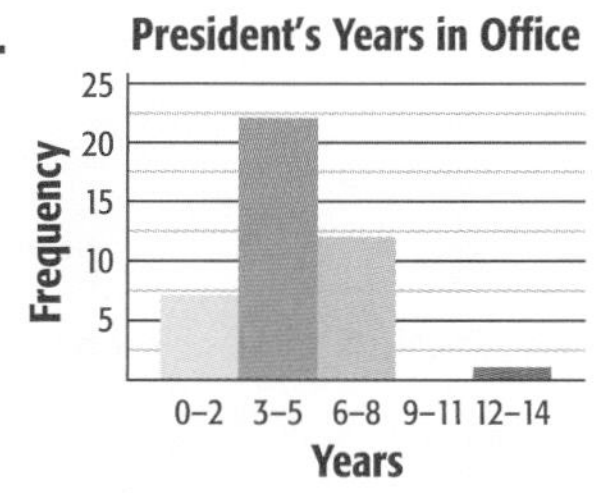

15.

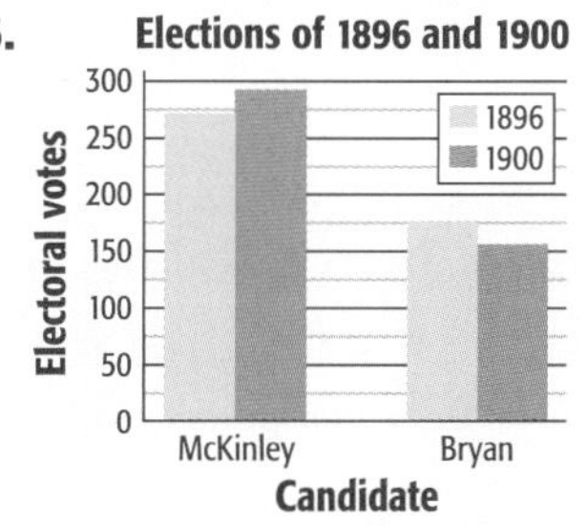

Possible answer: Describe the trend in electoral votes for the two candidates between 1896 and 1900.

Journal

Invite students to write about the advantages of using a double-bar graph instead of a chart for reading and comparing data.

Test Prep Doctor

For Exercise 22, students can eliminate **C** and **D** by recognizing that the second number in the number pattern is not a power of 3.

Lesson Quiz

1. The list shows the number of laps students ran one day. Make a histogram of the data.

   4, 7, 9, 12, 3, 6, 10, 15, 12, 5, 18, 2, 5, 10, 7, 12, 11, 15

2. Make a double-bar graph of the data in the table.

Average Number of Laps Run			
	1990	1995	2000
Boys	12	11	15
Girls	10	8	12

Answers on p. A9

Available on Daily Transparency in CRB

1-5 Organizer

Pacing: Traditional 1 day
Block $\frac{1}{2}$ day

Objective: Students read and interpret data presented in circle graphs.

Warm Up

Write each fraction as a percent.

1. $\frac{3}{4}$ 75% **2.** $\frac{1}{10}$ 10% **3.** $\frac{2}{5}$ 40%

Write each percent as a fraction.

4. 20% $\frac{1}{5}$ **5.** 25% $\frac{1}{4}$ **6.** 60% $\frac{3}{5}$

Problem of the Day

Riddle: When does 1 + 1 + 1 = 1?

1 ft + 1 ft + 1 ft = 1 yd

Available on Daily Transparency in CRB

Additional Examples

Example 1

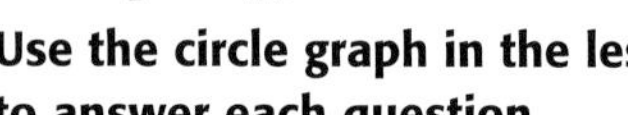

Use the circle graph in the lesson to answer each question.

A. Which group of echinoderms includes the fewest number of species? sea lilies and feather stars

B. Approximately what percent of echinoderm species are brittle stars and basket stars? about 33%

1-5 Reading and Interpreting Circle Graphs

Learn to read and interpret data presented in circle graphs.

Vocabulary

circle graph

sector

A **circle graph**, also called a pie chart, shows how a set of data is divided into parts. The entire circle contains 100% of the data. Each **sector**, or slice, of the circle represents one part of the entire data set.

The circle graph compares the number of species in each group of echinoderms. Echinoderms are marine animals that live on the ocean floor. The name *echinoderm* means "spiny-skinned."

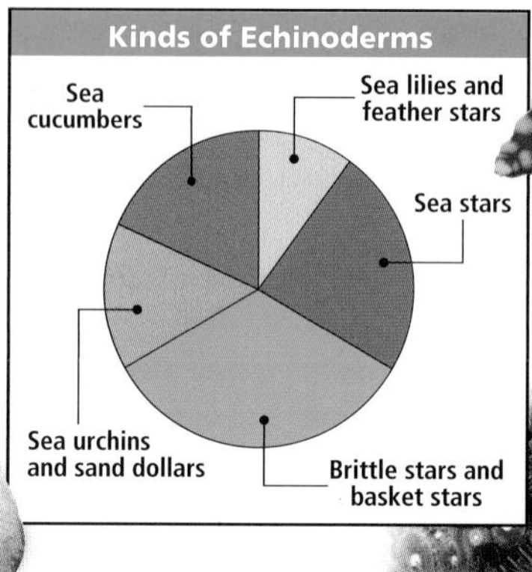

EXAMPLE 1 ***Life Science Application***

Use the circle graph to answer each question.

A **Which group of echinoderms includes the greatest number of species?**

The sector for brittle stars and basket stars is the largest, so this group includes the greatest number of species.

B **Approximately what percent of echinoderm species are sea stars?**

The sector for sea stars makes up about one-fourth of the circle. Since the circle shows 100% of the data, about one-fourth of 100%, or 25%, of echinoderm species are sea stars.

C **Which group is made up of fewer species—sea cucumbers or sea urchins and sand dollars?**

The sector for sea urchins and sand dollars is smaller than the sector for sea cucumbers. This means there are fewer kinds of sea urchins and sand dollars than kinds of sea cucumbers.

1 Introduce

Alternate Opener

EXPLORATION

1-5 Reading and Interpreting Circle Graphs

A circle graph shows a circle divided into sectors, or wedges. The whole circle represents 100%, and each wedge is a percent of the whole circle.

Lucinda interviewed 130 people (men and women) and asked them whether they spoke one language (monolingual) or two languages (bilingual). The graph shows Lucinda's results.

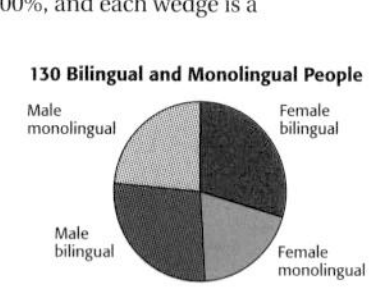

1. Estimate the percent that each sector represents. (*Hint:* The yellow sector is approximately one quarter of the whole circle.)
2. Estimate the number of people that each colored sector represents. (*Hint:* Multiply each estimated percent by 130.)
3. Are there more bilingual women than monolingual men in this group?

Think and Discuss

4. **Describe** a data set that may be represented using a circle graph.
5. **Discuss** what would happen if a circle graph were drawn as a square. Would the whole square still be 100 percent? Would each sector still represent the same percent as in the circle graph?

Motivate

Tell students to suppose that they have $100 to spend on party supplies. Brainstorm a list of items they might buy and an estimated cost for each item. Have students use the list to answer such questions as these:

- Which item costs the most?
- Would more or less than 50% of the money be spent on food?

Explain that in this lesson students will learn how to display data so that they can easily see how to divide the money.

Exploration worksheet and answers on Chapter 1 Resource Book pp. 47 and 110

2 Teach

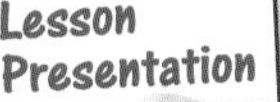

Lesson Presentation

Guided Instruction

In this lesson, students learn to read circle graphs and interpret data presented (Teaching Transparency T17, CRB). Discuss the differences between the circle graphs in Example 1 and Example 2. Ask students why they could use the circle graph in Example 2 to determine the number of people in a specific group but could not use the circle graph in Example 1 to determine the number of echinoderms in a specific group. Students should realize that they need to know the total number represented by the circle graph in order to calculate parts of the whole.

EXAMPLE 2 **Interpreting Circle Graphs**

Leon surveyed 30 people about pet ownership. The circle graph shows his results. Use the graph to answer each question.

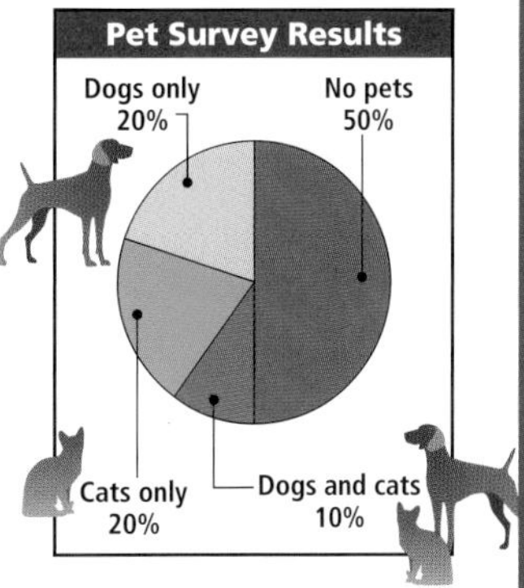

A **How many people do not own pets?**

The circle graph shows that 50%, or one-half, of the people surveyed do not own pets. One-half of 30 is 15, so 15 people do not own pets.

B **Three people responded that they own both dogs and cats. How many people own cats only?**

The circle graph shows that 10% of the people own both dogs and cats and that 20% own cats only. Since 10% is 3 people, 20% (2 · 10%) is 2 · 3, or 6 people. Six people own cats only.

EXAMPLE 3 **Choosing an Appropriate Graph**

Decide whether a bar graph or a circle graph would best display the information. Explain your answer.

Earth Science LINK

Arches National Park, located in southeastern Utah, covers 73,379 acres. The park is famous for its natural sandstone arches.

A **the percent of a nation's electricity supply generated by each of several fuel sources**

A circle graph is the better choice because it makes it easy to see what part of the nation's electricity comes from each fuel source.

B **the number of visitors to Arches National Park in each of the last five years**

A bar graph is the better choice because it makes it easy to see how the number of visitors has changed over the years.

C **the comparison between the time spent in math class and the total time spent in school each day**

A circle graph is the better choice because the sector that represents the time spent in math class could be compared to the entire circle, which represents the total time spent in school.

Think and Discuss

1. **Describe** two ways a circle graph can be used to compare data.
2. **Compare** the use of circle graphs with the use of bar graphs to display data.

Additional Examples

Example 1 *(continued)*

Use the circle graph in the lesson to answer the question.

C. Which group is made up of a greater number of species, sea cucumbers or sea stars? sea stars

Example 2

Use the graph in Example 2 to answer each question.

A. How many people own dogs only? 6

B. If 60 people were surveyed and 12 people said they own dogs only, how many people own both cats and dogs? 6

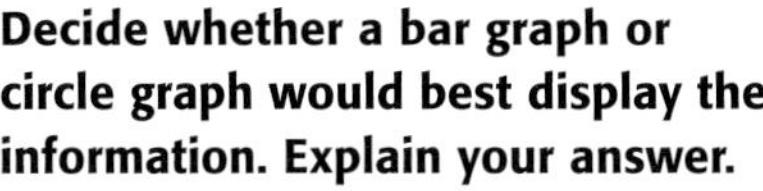

Example 3

Decide whether a bar graph or circle graph would best display the information. Explain your answer.

A. the percent of the U.S. population living in the different regions of the country
Circle graph; it shows how parts of a whole are divided.

B. the number of tickets sold for each performance of a community play
Bar graph; it compares tickets sold for each performance.

C. the comparison between the number of students on the basketball team and the total number of students on all school sports teams
Circle graph; it shows what part of sports students are basketball students.

3 Close

Reaching All Learners

Through Number Sense

Students need to be able to relate sectors of a circle graph to common fractions, decimals, and percents. Use the review sheet provided on page 99 in the Chapter 1 Resource Book to review common equivalent fractions, decimals, and percents with students.

Summarize

Ask students to write an explanation of how to find the number represented by a sector on a circle graph when the percent represented by the sector and the total number that the whole graph represents are given.

Possible answer: Find the percent of the given whole number to get the number for the sector.

Answers to Think and Discuss

Possible answers:

1. You can compare the parts within a data set, or you can compare one part of the data set to the entire set.
2. Both bar graphs and circle graphs are used to display data. Bar graphs are used to compare numbers of different items, such as the number of votes different candidates received. Circle graphs are used to show how the parts of a whole are divided.

1-5 PRACTICE & ASSESS

Students may want to refer back to the lesson examples.

Assignment Guide

If you finished Example 1 assign:
Core 1, 2, 6, 7, 11, 14, 18–24
Enriched 1, 7, 10, 11–14, 18–24

If you finished Example 2 assign:
Core 1–3, 6–8, 12, 13, 18–24
Enriched 2, 3, 6, 7, 11–24

If you finished Example 3 assign:
Core 1–11, 13, 18–24
Enriched 2, 4, 6, 9, 11–24

Answers

10. Bar graph; The length of each bar would represent the amount of rain for 1 month.

1-5 Exercises

FOR EXTRA PRACTICE see page 655

internet connect
Homework Help Online
go.hrw.com Keyword: MS4 1-5

GUIDED PRACTICE

The circle graph shows the estimated spending on advertising in 2000. Use the graph for Exercises 1–3.

See Example 1

1. On which type of advertising was the least amount of money spent? **outdoor**
2. Approximately what percent of spending was on radio and magazine advertising? **25%**

See Example 2

3. Television and magazine advertising made up about 50% of all advertising spending in 2000. If the total amount spent was \$100,000, how much was spent on television and magazine advertising? **\$50,000**

See Example 3

Decide whether a bar graph or a circle graph would best display the information. Explain your answer.

4. the lengths of the five longest rivers in the world **Bar graph; Each bar would show the length of one river.**
5. the percent of citizens who voted for each candidate in an election **Circle graph; Each candidate's share of the votes can be shown in comparison to 100% of the votes.**

INDEPENDENT PRACTICE

The circle graph shows the results of a survey of 100 teens who were asked about their favorite sports. Use the graph for Exercises 6–8.

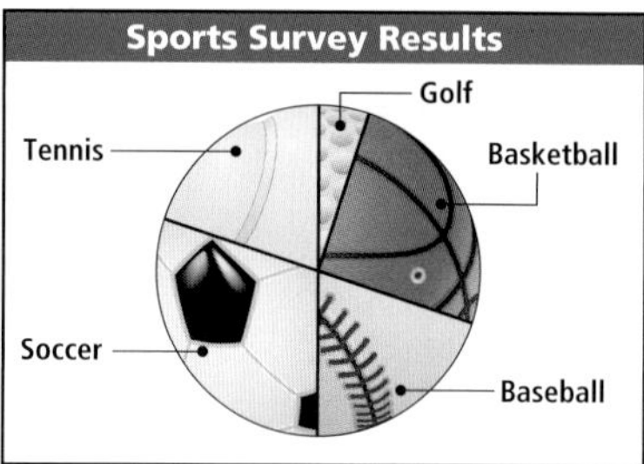

See Example 1

6. Did more teens pick basketball or tennis as their favorite sport? **basketball**
7. Approximately what percent of teens picked soccer as their favorite sport? **30%**

See Example 2

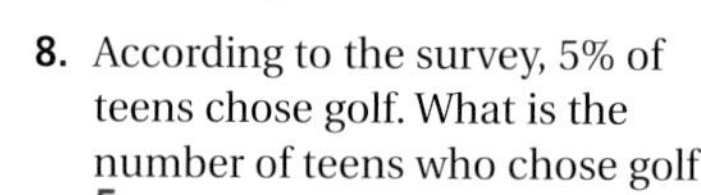

8. According to the survey, 5% of teens chose golf. What is the number of teens who chose golf? **5**

See Example 3

Decide whether a bar graph or a circle graph would best display the information. Explain your answer.

9. the number of calories eaten at breakfast compared with the total number of calories eaten in one day **Circle graph; The total number of calories eaten in one day could be 100%.**
10. the number of inches of rain that fell each month in Honolulu, Hawaii, during one year

Math Background

The use of statistics can be traced back to ancient times. Historical records describe details of census collections. However, it wasn't until the 1920s that statistics began to develop as a branch of science through the efforts of statisticians such as Ronald A. Fisher, Jersey Neymand, and Egon Pearson.

Today statistics and statistical analysis are used in almost every area of life, including insurance, medicine, quality control in manufacturing, and the social sciences.

RETEACH 1-5

LESSON 1-5 **Reteach**
Reading and Interpreting Circle Graphs

A **circle graph** shows how the parts of a complete set of data are related. The circle shows 100% of the data.

Choose a circle graph to show what percent (or part) of the total sales is represented by each type of pizza.

Choose a bar graph to show the number of each type of pizza sold.

Pizza Sales: Cheese, Pepperoni, Mushroom, Sausage; Number of Pizzas Sold 0–120; Type

The circle graph shows that about one-half, or 50%, of the total sales was cheese pizzas. If 200 pizzas were sold, then about half, or 100, were cheese pizzas.

The circle graph shows the results of a survey of 100 teens who were asked about their favorite winter sport. Use the graph to answer each question.

Favorite Winter Sport: Skiing, Ice Skating, Snowmobiling, Snowboarding

1. Did more teens pick skiing or snowboarding? snowboarding
2. About what percent of teens picked skiing? about 25%
3. How many teens chose skiing? 25 teens

Decide whether a bar graph or a circle graph would best display the information. Explain.

4. the number of hurricanes in each state during 1 year
   bar graph; One axis could show the number of hurricanes, and the other could show the states.
5. the number of students who play soccer compared with the total number of students in a school
   circle graph; The sector for those who play soccer could be compared to the entire circle.

PRACTICE 1-5

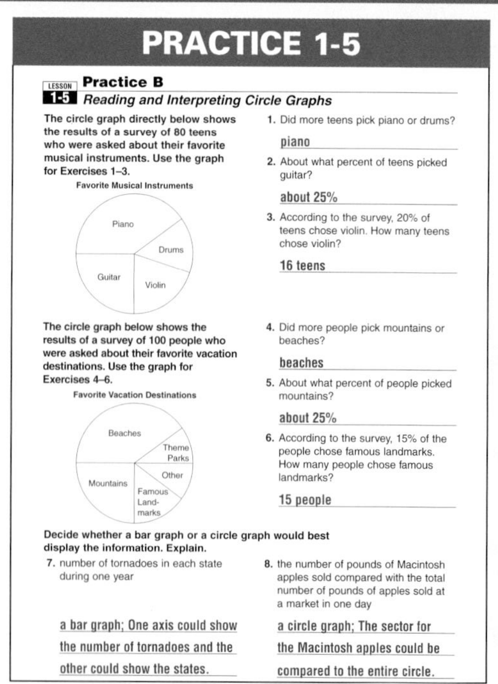

LESSON 1-5 **Practice B**
Reading and Interpreting Circle Graphs

The circle graph directly below shows the results of a survey of 80 teens who were asked about their favorite musical instruments. Use the graph for Exercises 1–3.

Favorite Musical Instruments: Piano, Drums, Guitar, Violin

1. Did more teens pick piano or drums? piano
2. About what percent of teens picked guitar? about 25%
3. According to the survey, 20% of teens chose violin. How many teens chose violin? 16 teens

The circle graph below shows the results of a survey of 100 people who were asked about their favorite vacation destinations. Use the graph for Exercises 4–6.

Favorite Vacation Destinations: Beaches, Theme Parks, Other, Mountains, Famous Land-marks

4. Did more people pick mountains or beaches? beaches
5. About what percent of people picked mountains? about 25%
6. According to the survey, 15% of the people chose famous landmarks. How many people chose famous landmarks? 15 people

Decide whether a bar graph or a circle graph would best display the information. Explain.

7. number of tornadoes in each state during one year
   a bar graph; One axis could show the number of tornadoes and the other could show the states.
8. the number of pounds of Macintosh apples sold compared with the total number of pounds of apples sold at a market in one day
   a circle graph; The sector for the Macintosh apples could be compared to the entire circle.

PRACTICE AND PROBLEM SOLVING

The circle graph shows the percent of Earth's land area covered by each continent. Use the graph for Exercises 11–13.

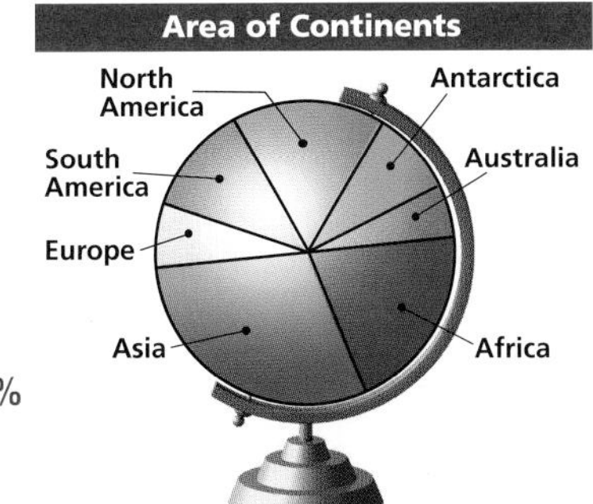

11. List the continents in order of size, from largest to smallest.

11. Asia, Africa, North America, South America, Antarctica, Europe, Australia

12. Approximately what percent of Earth's total land area is Asia? **about 30%**

13. Approximately what percent of Earth's total land area is North America and South America combined? **about 25%**

14. ***SOCIAL STUDIES*** The circle graph shows the diversity of the Hispanic population in Toledo, Ohio. Most of Toledo's Hispanic population are from which country? **Mexico**

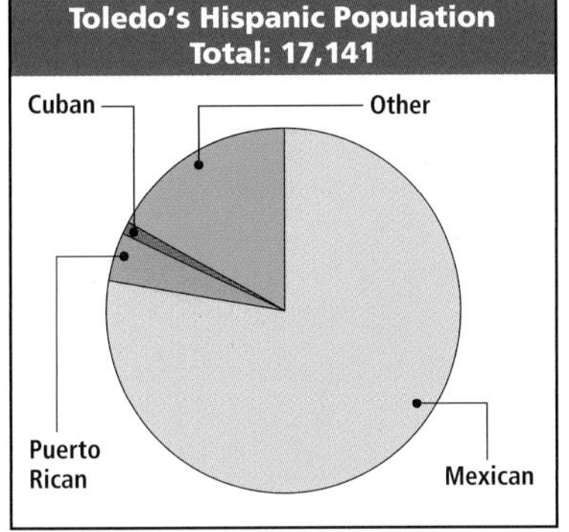

15. ***WHAT'S THE ERROR?*** A student wrote that more of Toledo's Hispanic population are from Cuba than from Puerto Rico. What did the student do wrong?

15. The sector for Puerto Rico is larger than the sector for Cuba, so more of the hispanic population comes from Puerto Rico.

16. ***WRITE ABOUT IT*** What math skills do you use when interpreting information in a circle graph? **16. Possible answer: estimation, percentages, fractions, and ordering numbers**

17. ***CHALLENGE*** Earth's total land area is approximately 57,900,000 square miles. Antarctica is almost 10% of the total area. What is the approximate land area of Antarctica in square miles? **about 5,790,000 mi^2**

Spiral Review

Find the mean of each data set. (Lesson 1-2)

18. 5, 9, 0, 6, 7, 5, 9, 3 **5.5** **19.** 53, 73, 28, 79, 77 **62** **20.** 626, 897, 786, 807 **779**

Find the median of each data set. (Lesson 1-2)

21. 2, 1, 8, 7, 6, 2, 9, 4, 3 **4** **22.** 93, 48, 77, 84, 71, 11 **74** **23.** 423, 298, 801, 944, 190 **423**

24. TEST PREP Which term most completely describes this figure? (Previous course) **B**

A Square **B** Rectangle **C** Triangle **D** Trapezoid

Journal

Ask students to draw and describe a circle graph that shows how they typically spend their time after school.

Test Prep Doctor

For Exercise 24, students should notice that the figure has 4 sides, which eliminates **C,** and that not all sides are equal, which eliminates **A.**

CHALLENGE 1-5

LESSON 1-5 **Challenge**
Circle the Oceans

The table below shows the approximate percent of area that each ocean comprises of the total area of the oceans of the world. These oceans together actually make up one large, connected body of water.

Ocean	Approximate Area
Pacific	49%
Atlantic	25%
Indian	22%
Arctic	4%

1. Complete the circle graph at the right by labeling the ocean and percent of area for each part.

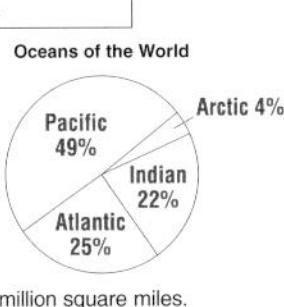

2. The oceans of the world cover almost 130 million square miles. About how many square miles are covered by the Pacific Ocean?
about 64 million mi^2
3. About how many square miles are covered by the Atlantic Ocean?
about 33 million mi^2
4. About how many square miles are covered by the Indian Ocean?
about 29 million mi^2
5. About how many square miles are covered by the Arctic Ocean?
about 5 million mi^2
6. About how many square miles are covered by the Pacific Ocean and the Atlantic Ocean combined?
about 97 million mi^2
7. About how many more total square miles are covered by the Atlantic, Indian, and Arctic oceans than the by Pacific Ocean?
about 3 million mi^2

PROBLEM SOLVING 1-5

LESSON 1-5 **Problem Solving**
Reading and Interpreting Circle Graphs

Write the correct answer.

1. A market research group conducted a survey of 100 sports car owners. The group learned that 50% of the car owners loved their cars. What part of the circle in a circle graph would be represented by that statistic?
$\frac{1}{2}$ of the circle
2. Juanita has 100 CDs. In her collection, 37 of the CDs are rock music, 25 are jazz, and 38 are country music. What part of the circle in a circle graph would represent the jazz CDs?
$\frac{1}{4}$ of the circle
3. Mr. Martin wanted to compare his monthly rent to his total income. Should he use a circle graph or a bar graph?
circle graph
4. Mr. Martin's rent has increased every year for the last 6 years. Should he use a circle graph or bar graph to show the yearly increase?
bar graph

Choose the letter for the best answer. Use the circle graph.

Age of Fitness Club Members

30–39 33%
50–59 17%
18–29 10%
60–69 9%
70+ 7%
Other 2%
40–49 22%

5. To which age group do most of the fitness club members belong?
A 18–20 **(C)** 30–39
B 70+ **D** 40–49
6. There are 100 members in a fitness club. How many members does the graph suggest will be between the ages of 18 and 39?
F 10 **(H)** 43
G 33 **J** 22
7. Which 2 age groups make up more than one-half the members?
A 18–29 and 30–39
(B) 30–39 and 40–49
C 40–49 and 50–59
D 18–29 and 70+
8. Which 2 age groups make up 3 times as many members as those who are between 60 and 69?
F 40–49 and 50–59
G 50–59 and 70+
H 30–39 and 18–29
(J) 18–29 and 50–59

Lesson Quiz

Use the circle graph to answer questions 1–3.

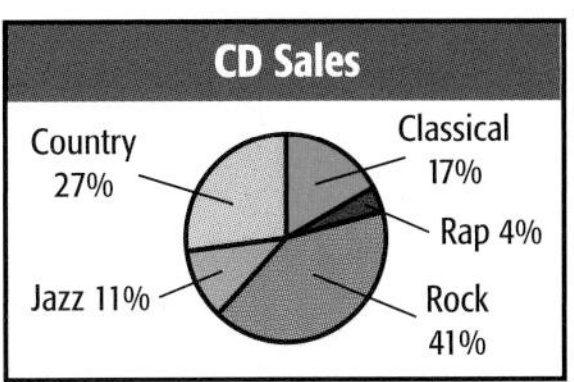

1. Which group of CDs sold the most? rock
2. What percent of the CD sales are country? 27%
3. Which type of CD sells the least? rap
4. Would a bar or circle graph best display the sales of Benny's department store for the last 5 months? bar graph

Available on Daily Transparency in CRB

1-6 Organizer

Pacing: Traditional 1 day
Block $\frac{1}{2}$ day

Objective: Students display and analyze data in box-and-whisker plots.

Warm Up

Use the data below for Questions 1–4.

14, 25, 37, 53, 26, 12, 70, 31

1. What is the mean? **33.5**
2. What is the median? **28.5**
3. What is the mode? none
4. What is the range? **58**

Problem of the Day

If the sixth-graders checked out 160 books, how many does each symbol in this pictograph represent? 32 books

Library Books Checked Out	
6th Grade	● ● ● ● ●
7th Grade	● ● ● ●
8th Grade	● ● ●

Available on Daily Transparency in CRB

Math Fact !!

The name of the box and whisker plot comes from its resemblance to the nose and whiskers of a cat.

1-6 Box-and-Whisker Plots

Learn to display and analyze data in box-and-whisker plots.

Vocabulary
box-and-whisker plot
first quartile
second quartile
third quartile
lower extreme
upper extreme

The table shows the stopping distances of different vehicles from 60 mi/h. To show the distribution of the data, you can use a **box-and-whisker plot** .

To make a box-and-whisker plot for a set of data, you need to divide the data into four parts using *quartiles*. The box-and-whisker plot below shows the distribution of the vehicles' stopping distances.

Vehicle	Stopping Distance (ft)
A	120
B	158
C	142
D	131
E	128
F	167
G	136

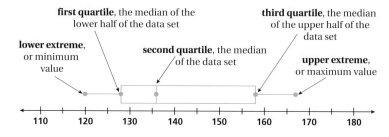

first quartile, the median of the lower half of the data set

third quartile, the median of the upper half of the data set

lower extreme, or minimum value

second quartile, the median of the data set

upper extreme, or maximum value

110 120 130 140 150 160 170 180

EXAMPLE 1 Reading a Box-and-Whisker Plot

Use the box-and-whisker plot of stopping distances to answer each question.

A What is the median stopping distance?
The median stopping distance is represented by the middle point on the box-and-whisker plot. This value is 136 ft.

B What is the range of the stopping distances?
The range is the difference between the lower extreme and the upper extreme: 167 − 120, or 47 ft.

C About what fraction of the stopping distances are less than 158 ft?
Three of the four parts of the box-and-whisker plot fall below 158 ft. This means about three-fourths of the stopping distances are less than 158 ft.

Remember!
The range of a set of data is the difference between the minimum value and the maximum value.

1 Introduce

Alternate Opener

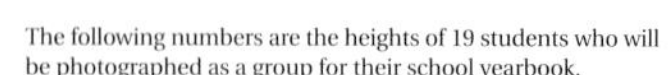

EXPLORATION

1-6 Box-and-Whisker Plots

The following numbers are the heights of 19 students who will be photographed as a group for their school yearbook.

47 55 55 56 58 59 60 60 60 61 63 64 64 65 65 65 65 68 72

Lower half Median Upper half

1. Find the median of the lower half.
2. Find the median of the upper half.
3. The three medians were used to create the following plot. This plot is called a ***box-and-whisker plot*** because the center is a box and the lines extending from each side of the box look like whiskers.

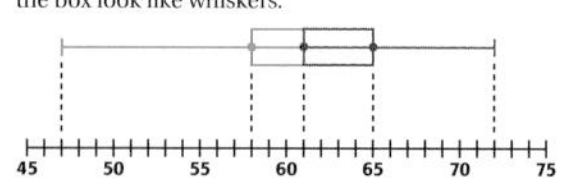

a. Which medians are used for the sides of the box?
b. What numbers are used for the left and right end of the plot?
c. Which median is the line in the middle of the box?

Think and Discuss

4. **Explain** how you would find the median if you had 20 heights instead of 19.
5. **Discuss** why the left whisker is longer than the right whisker.

Motivate

To introduce students to a box-and-whisker plot, ask them to describe situations in which they have heard "the median" used to describe a set of data. Review the meaning of *median* to be sure students understand that it is a middle point of a set of data.

Draw a narrow box on the chalkboard and extend a long line from each end of the box so that it looks like a cat's nose and whiskers. Use the drawing to introduce the name of the box-and-whisker plot.

Exploration worksheet and answers on Chapter 1 Resource Book pp. 56 and 112

2 Teach

Lesson Presentation

Guided Instruction

In this lesson, students learn to display and analyze data in box-and-whisker plots (Teaching Transparency T22, CRB). Illustrate how to divide the data into four parts, first by writing the numbers on cards and dividing them into groups, and then by using the median of the entire set and the medians of the top and bottom halves. Point out that the data values at the end of the whiskers are the least and greatest values in the set. Ask students to describe the significance of the numbers at each end and in the middle of the box.

EXAMPLE 2 **Making a Box-and-Whisker Plot**

Use the data to make a box-and-whisker plot.

26 17 21 23 19 28 17 20 29

Step 1: Find the lower and upper extremes, the median, and the first and third quartiles.

Remember!

The median is the middle number or the average of the two middle numbers in an ordered set of data.

17 17 19 20 21 23 26 28 29 — *Order the data from least to greatest.*

(17) 17 19 20 21 23 26 28 (29) — *Find the lower and upper extremes.*

(17 17 19 20)(21)(23 26 28 29) — *Find the median.*

(17 (17 19) 20) 21 (23 (26 28) 29) — *Find the first and third quartiles.*

$$\text{first quartile} = \frac{17 + 19}{2} = 18$$

$$\text{third quartile} = \frac{26 + 28}{2} = 27$$

Step 2: Draw a number line. Above the number line, plot points representing the lower and upper extremes, the median, and the first and third quartiles.

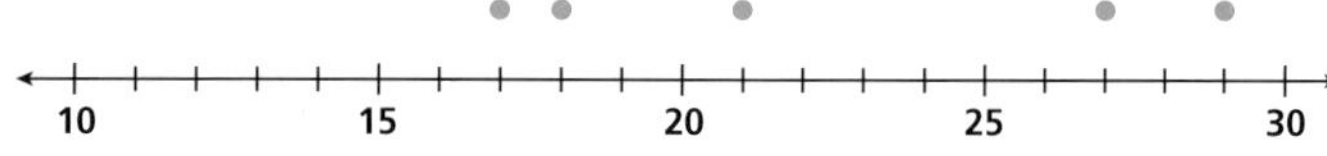

Step 3: Draw a box through the first and third quartiles. Inside the box, draw a vertical line through the median. Then draw lines from the first and third quartiles to the extremes. These lines are called *whiskers*.

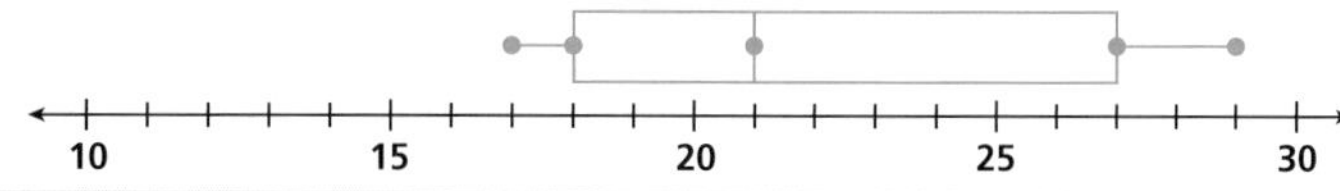

Think and Discuss

1. **Describe** the distribution of the data in Example 2.
2. **Explain** why you cannot find the mean or the mode of a data set by looking at a box-and-whisker plot.
3. **Tell** whether a box-and-whisker plot shows how many data items are included in the data set. Explain.

COMMON ERROR ALERT

Watch for students who have difficulty organizing the data for a box-and-whisker plot. Remind them to write the data values in order before they begin constructing the box-and-whisker plot.

Additional Examples

Example 1

Use the box-and-whisker plot to answer each question.

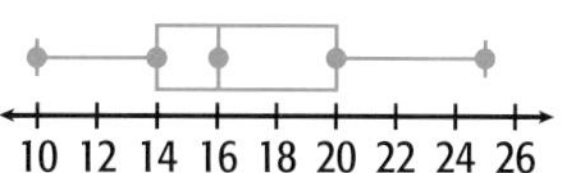

A. What is the largest data value? **25**

B. What is the range of the data values? **15**

C. About what fraction of the values are greater than 20? $\frac{1}{4}$

Example 2

Use the data to make a box-and-whisker plot.

Heights of Basketball Players (in.)

73, 67, 75, 81, 67, 75, 85, 69

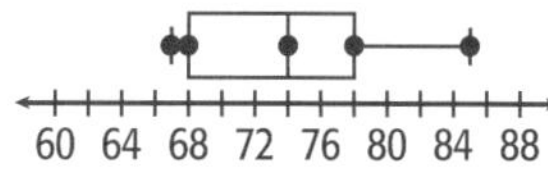

3 Close

Reaching All Learners

Through Concrete Manipulatives

Write data values for Example 2 on index cards (provided on page 100 of the Chapter 1 Resource Book). Have students place the cards in numerical order on a flat surface. Use the cards to determine the extremes, first quartile, median, and third quartile. Then use the cards to illustrate that although the box-and-whisker plot does divide the data into four equal-sized groups, the range of data values in each quartile will probably be different.

Summarize

Ask students to summarize the steps in making a box-and-whisker plot.

Possible answer: Order the data and find the upper and lower extremes, the median, and the first and third quartile values. Draw a number line and plot the points representing these values. Draw a box with edges through the first and third quartiles and a vertical line through the median. Then draw whiskers from the first and third quartiles to the extremes.

Answers to Think and Discuss

Possible answers:

1. The range of the data above the median is greater than the range of the data below the median.
2. The actual data set values must be examined to find the mean and mode. Not all data set values are present on a box-and-whisker plot.
3. No, it shows only the median, quartiles, and extremes.

1-6 PRACTICE & ASSESS

Students may want to refer back to the lesson examples.

Assignment Guide

If you finished Example 1 assign:
Core 1–3, 5–7, 11, 15–20
Enriched 1–7 odd, 11–13, 15–20

If you finished Example 2 assign:
Core 1–11, 15–20
Enriched 1–7 odd, 9–20

Answers

9. a. 5 10 15 20 25 30 35 40

b. 5 10 15 20

c. Possible answer: The whisker between the third quartile and the upper extreme is longer with the outlier.

1-6 Exercises

FOR EXTRA PRACTICE
see page 655

internet connect
Homework Help Online
go.hrw.com Keyword: MS4 1-6

GUIDED PRACTICE

See Example 1 Use the box-and-whisker plot of inches flown by paper airplanes for Exercises 1–3.

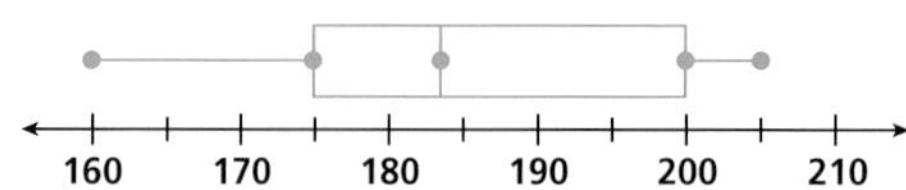

1. What is the first quartile? **175 in.**
2. What is the range of the distances flown? **45 in.**
3. About what fraction of the distances flown are greater than 200 inches? $\frac{1}{4}$

See Example 2
4. Use the data below to make a box-and-whisker plot.

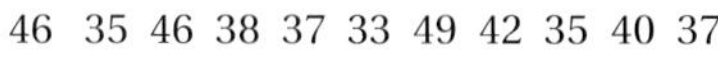

46 35 46 38 37 33 49 42 35 40 37

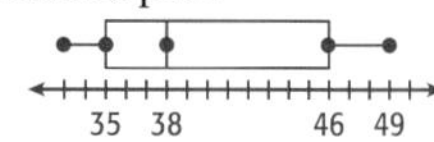

INDEPENDENT PRACTICE

See Example 1 Use the box-and-whisker plot of apartment rental costs for Exercises 5–7.

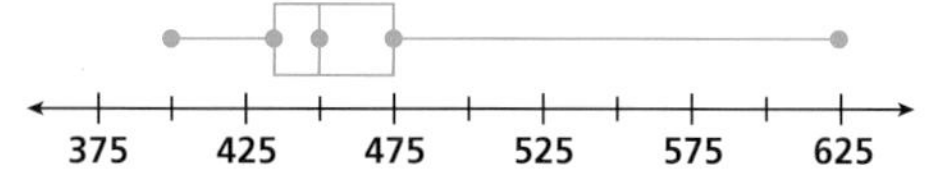

5. What is the third quartile? **$475**
6. What is the range of the rental costs? **$225**
7. About what fraction of the rental costs are between $400 and $450? $\frac{1}{2}$

See Example 2
8. Use the data below to make a box-and-whisker plot.

81 73 88 85 81 72 86 72 79 75 76

72 79 85 88

PRACTICE AND PROBLEM SOLVING

9. The data shows the number of points scored per game by a member of the basketball team.

   12 7 15 23 10 18 39 15 20 8 13

   a. Use the data to make a box-and-whisker plot.

   b. Make a second box-and-whisker plot of the data. This time do not include the outlier.

   c. How does the outlier affect the way the box-and-whisker plot looks?

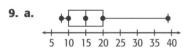

Math Background

The box-and-whisker plot is a popular visual representation of the median. The plot shows the median, the quartiles, and the extremes of a set of data: 50% of the data is in the box, and each whisker represents 25% of the data. Because not all the data values are shown in a box-and-whisker plot, only the median, quartile values, and extremes can be read from the plot.

Box-and-whisker plots provide a clear visual comparison of two or more sets of data. For example, they can be used to compare results for two different classes on the same test or for a class on two or more tests.

RETEACH 1-6

LESSON 1-6 **Reteach**
Box-and-Whisker Plots

A **box-and-whisker plot** presents a summary of a set of data by presenting the data in four equal parts.

Attendance at PTA Meetings

5 6 7 8 9 10 11 12 13 14 15 16 17 18 19 20 21

Use the box-and-whisker plot for Exercises 1–4.

1. What is the range of the data? 14
2. What is the median of the data? 12
3. What is the first quartile? 9
4. What is the third quartile? 16

Use the data to create a box-and-whisker plot:
35, 24, 25, 38, 31, 20, 27

5. Order the data from least to greatest.
   20 24 25 27 31 35 38
6. Find the lower and upper extremes.
   20 and 38
7. Find the median.
   27
8. Find the first quartile and third quartile.
   24, 35
9. Above the number line below, plot points for the lower extreme, first quartile, median, third quartile, and upper extreme.
10. Draw a box around the quartiles and the median. Draw the whiskers connecting the quartiles and the extremes.

18 20 22 24 26 28 30 32 34 36 38 40

Use the data to create a box-and-whisker plot:
63, 69, 61, 74, 78, 72, 68, 70, 65

11. Order the data. 61 63 65 68 69 70 72 74 78
12. Find the lower and upper extremes. 61 and 78
13. Find the median, first quartile, and third quartile. 69, 64, and 73
14. Plot the points, draw the box, and add the whiskers.

60 62 64 66 68 70 72 74 76 78 80

PRACTICE 1-6

LESSON 1-6 **Practice B**
Box-and-Whisker Plots

The table shows the National Baseball League's runs-batted-in leaders from 1995 through 2001. Use the box-and-whisker plot and table for Exercises 1–4.

1. What is the first quartile? 140
2. What is the range of the runs batted in? 32
3. What fraction of the runs batted in was greater than 140? $\frac{3}{4}$ or $\frac{5}{7}$
4. What is the median? 147

Year	Player	Runs Batted In
1995	D. Bichette	128
1996	A. Galarraga	150
1997	A. Galarraga	140
1998	S. Sosa	158
1999	M. McGwire	147
2000	T. Helton	147
2001	S. Sosa	160

120 125 130 135 140 145 150 155 160 165 170

5. Use the data to create a box-and-whisker plot.
   32, 12, 38, 42, 54, 26, 18, 30, 50, 44, 41

   10 15 20 25 30 35 40 45 50 55 60

The table shows the points Jenny scored in her last 9 basketball games. Use the box-and-whisker plot to answer each question.

Date	12/14	12/21	12/28	1/03	1/07	1/11	1/14	1/17	1/22
Points Scored	14	18	22	8	15	21	14	10	21

4 6 8 10 12 14 16 18 20 22 24

6. What is the third quartile?
   21
7. What is the range of the scores?
   14
8. What fraction of the scores is above 12?
   $\frac{3}{4}$ or $\frac{7}{9}$
9. What is Jenny's median score?
   15

10. ***SPORTS*** The table shows the countries that were the top 15 medal winners in the 2000 Olympics.

Country	Medals	Country	Medals	Country	Medals
USA	97	Russia	88	China	59
Australia	58	Germany	57	France	38
Italy	34	Cuba	29	Britain	28
Korea	28	Romania	26	Netherlands	25
Ukraine	23	Japan	18	Belarus	17

a. Make a box-and-whisker plot of the data.

b. Describe the distribution of the number of medals won. **Possible answer: Most countries won between 25 and 58 medals.**

11. ***MEASUREMENT*** The stem-and-leaf plot shows the heights in inches of a class of seventh graders.

Student Heights

Stems	Leaves
5	3 5 6 6 8 8 8 9 9
6	0 0 1 1 1 1 1 2 2 2 4

Key: 5|3 means 53

a. What is the median height? **60 in.**

b. Make a box-and-whisker plot of the data.

c. Are more students taller or shorter than 5 feet? Explain. **Nine students are shorter than 5 feet and nine students are taller than 5 feet.**

12. ***WHAT'S THE ERROR?*** A student made this box-and-whisker plot using the data 2, 9, 5, 14, 8, 13, 7, 5, 8. What did the student do wrong?

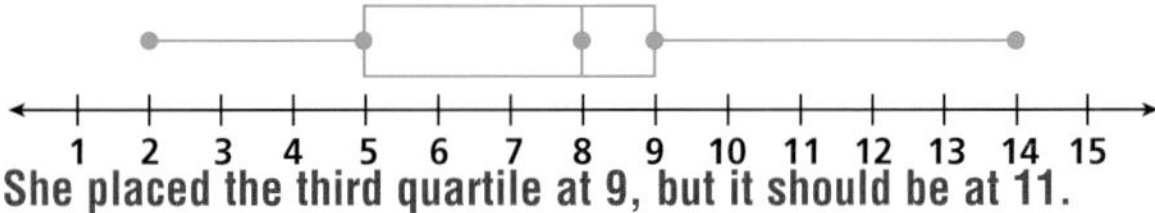

She placed the third quartile at 9, but it should be at 11.

13. ***WRITE ABOUT IT*** Two box-and-whisker plots have the same median and equally long whiskers. If the box of one plot is longer, what can you say about the two data sets? **The plot with the larger box represents a greater range of numbers.**

14. ***CHALLENGE*** The *interquartile range* is the difference between the third and first quartiles. Find the interquartile range for the data set 1, 2, 4, 2, 1, 0, 6, 8, 1, 6, 2. **5**

Spiral Review

Find each sum or difference. (Previous course)

15. 499 + 231 **730**
16. 87 + 1645 **1,732**
17. 503 − 125 **378**
18. 900 − 281 **619**

19. **TEST PREP** Which is not a measure of central tendency for the data set 4, 6, 6, 7, 9, 10, 11, 11? (Previous course) **C**

A 6
B 8
C 9
D 11

20. **TEST PREP** If Lorenzo earns $9 an hour, how many hours must he work to earn $120? (Previous course) **J**

F 10 hours
G 12 hours
H 13 hours
J 14 hours

Answers

10a.

10 20 30 40 50 60 70 80 90 100

11b.

50 55 60 65 70

Journal

Have students describe data that they think would make an interesting box-and-whisker plot, and tell why.

Test Prep Doctor

For Exercise 19, students can easily eliminate **A** and **D** because they are modes of the set. Students will then have to calculate the mean and median to eliminate **C.**

For Exercise 20, students may be able to eliminate **F** and **G** using estimation. Choices **H** and **J** are designed to help them recognize that although 9 goes into $120 thirteen times with a remainder, Lorenzo must work 14 hours to earn the stated amount.

CHALLENGE 1-6

LESSON 1-6 **Challenge**
Plotting Along

You can use box-and-whisker plots to quickly compare distributions of similar data. Draw two box-and-whisker plots of the data sets below. Then use them to answer the questions that follow.

Math grades for top math students on their last ten math tests:

Casey: 100, 96, 100, 98, 97, 92, 99, 90, 96, 94

Nickie: 97, 95, 85, 100, 98, 100, 98, 88, 92, 95

1. Draw a box-and-whisker plot for Casey's math grades.

Casey's Math Grades

84 85 86 87 88 89 90 91 92 93 94 95 96 97 98 99 100

2. Draw a box-and-whisker plot for Nickie's math grades.

Nickie's Math Grades

84 85 86 87 88 89 90 91 92 93 94 95 96 97 98 99 100

3. How do Casey's and Nickie's highest and lowest grades compare?
Casey's lowest score is higher than Nickie's lowest score. They both have the same highest score.

4. Which student had the higher math scores for more than half the tests? How can you tell?
Casey, because Casey's median score is higher than Nickie's. Casey's median score is 96.5, and Nickie's median score is 96.

5. Compare the first quartile for both students. What conclusion can you draw from this data?
Casey's first quartile is 94; Nickie's is 92. Possible answer: This suggests that, overall, Casey got better grades than Nickie.

PROBLEM SOLVING 1-6

LESSON 1-6 **Problem Solving**
Box-and-Whisker Plots

Write the correct answer.

A survey of 10 bicycle shops resulted in 10 different price quotes for a brand-name racing bicycle. The prices are represented in the box-and-whisker plot.

Racing Bicycle Prices

300 400 500 600 700 800

1. What is the range of the price quotes? **$380**

2. What is the third quartile? **$580**

3. About what fraction of the price quotes is greater than $460? **about $\frac{1}{2}$**

4. About what fraction of the price quotes is between $400 and $460? **about $\frac{1}{4}$**

Choose the letter for the best answer.

The box-and-whisker plot shows the distribution of Internet users in 9 countries outside the United States in 2002.

Internet Users Outside the United States (millions)

2 4 6 8 10 12 14 16 18 20 22

5. What is the range of the number of Internet users?
A 6 million
B 10 million
Ⓒ 14 million
D 20 million

6. How many of these 9 countries have at least 10 million Internet users?
F more than 4
G at least 7
H less than 6
Ⓙ at least 5

7. What is the mode of the data?
A 8
B 10
C 13
Ⓓ cannot be determined

8. There were about 115 million Internet users in the United States in 2002. If this data were included in the box-and-whisker plot, which values would change?
Ⓕ the first quartile, median, third quartile, and range
G only the upper extreme
H the median and upper extreme
J the median and range

Lesson Quiz

Use the data for Questions 1–3.

24, 20, 18, 25, 22, 32, 30, 29, 35, 30, 28, 24, 38

1. What is the range? **20**
2. What is the third quartile? **31**
3. Create a box-and-whisker plot of the data.

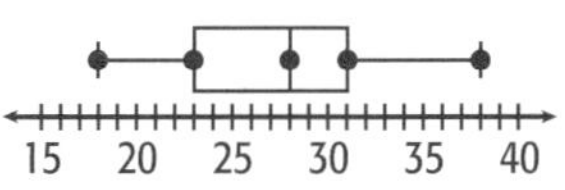

Available on Daily Transparency in CRB

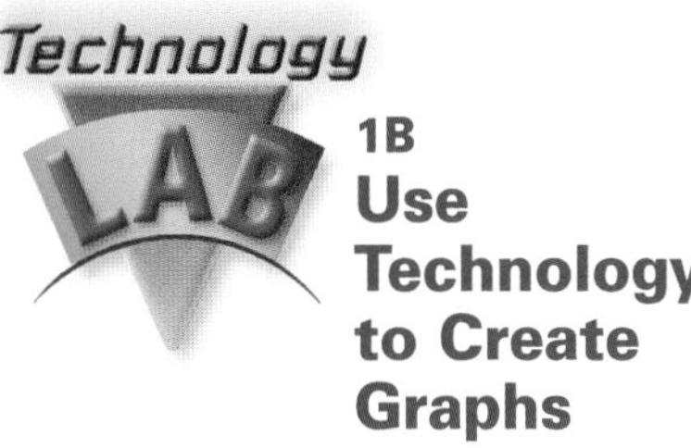

1B Use Technology to Create Graphs

Pacing: Traditional 1 day
Block $\frac{1}{2}$ day

Objective: To use a spreadsheet to create graphs

Materials: Spreadsheet software

Lab Resources

Technology Lab Activities .... p. 3

Using the Pages

This technology activity shows students how to create a graph, which can be done with any spreadsheet software. Specific keystrokes may vary, depending on the spreadsheet software used.

The Think and Discuss problems can be used to assess students' understanding of the technology activity. While bar graphs and line graphs can be drawn without using a spreadsheet, Try This problem 1 helps students become familiar with using spreadsheet software to create bar graphs and line graphs.

Assessment

1. The table shows the number of votes that each person running for class president received. Use a spreadsheet to create a bar graph and a line graph for the data.

Candidate	Number of Votes
Emily	38
Tyler	54
Sean	40
Sarah	63

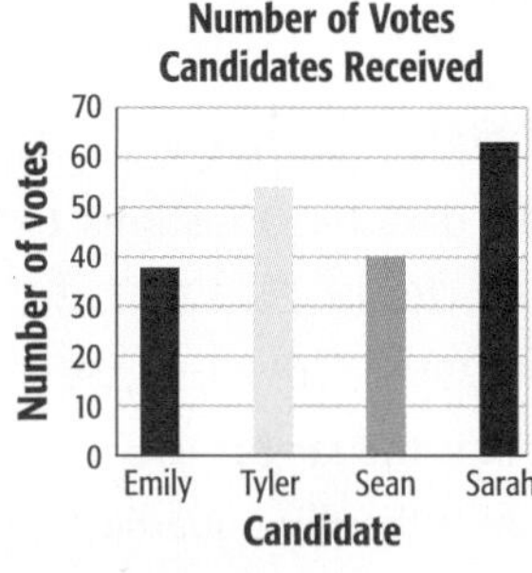

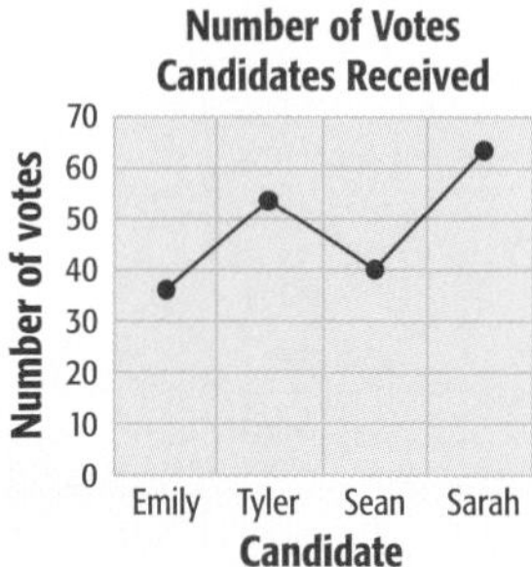

2. Which graph best displays the election results? Why?
Possible answer: The bar graph best displays the election results because it is easier to compare the number of votes that each student received.

Technology LAB 1B: Use Technology to Create Graphs

Use with Lesson 1-7

There are several ways to display data, including bar graphs, line graphs, and circle graphs. A spreadsheet provides a quick way to create these graphs.

internet connect
Lab Resources Online
go.hrw.com
KEYWORD: MS4 Lab1B

Activity

1. Use a spreadsheet to display the Kennedy Middle School Student Council budget shown in the table at right.

Student Council Budget	
Activity	**Amount ($)**
Assemblies	275
Dances	587
Spring Festival	412
Awards Banquet	384
Other	250

Open the spreadsheet program, and enter the data as shown below. Enter the activities in column A and the amount budgeted in column B. Include the column titles in row 1.

	A	B	C
1	Activity	Amount ($)	
2	Assemblies	275	
3	Dances	587	
4	Spring Festival	412	
5	Awards Banquet	384	
6	Other	250	
7			

Highlight the data by clicking on cell A1 and dragging the cursor to cell B6. Click the Chart Wizard icon . Then click **FINISH** to choose the first type of column graph.

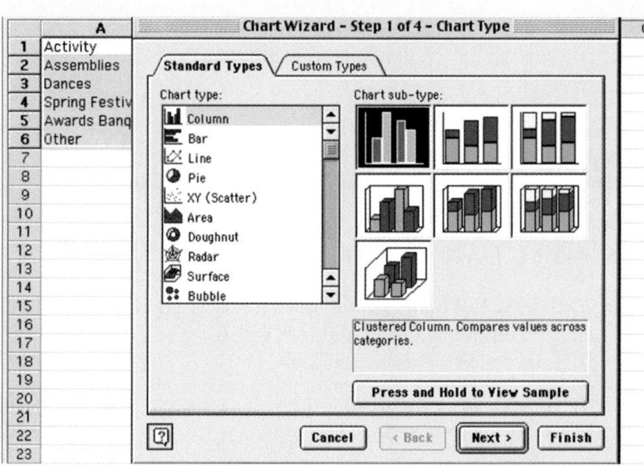

The bar graph of the data appears as shown. Resize or reposition the graph, if necessary.

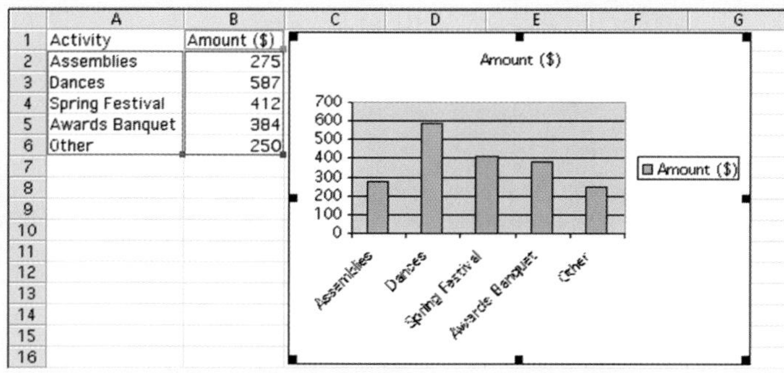

To see a line graph of the data, select the bar graph (as shown above). Click the Chart Wizard icon and choose the line graph. Then click **FINISH** to choose the first type of line graph.

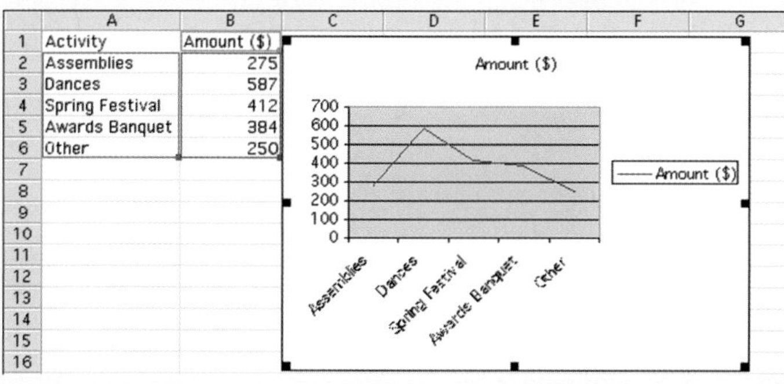

Think and Discuss

1. Which graph best displays the Student Council budget? Why?
2. How would you display the data in a circle graph? **Possible answer: Click the Chart Wizard icon and choose the pie graph. Then click Finish to choose the first type of circle graph.**

Try This

1. The table shows the number of points scored by several members of a girls' basketball team. Use a spreadsheet to create a bar graph and a line graph of the data.

Player	Ana	Angel	Mary	Nia	Tina	Zoe
Points Scored	201	145	89	40	21	8

Answers

Think and Discuss

1. Possible answer: The bar graph best displays the Student Council budget. It is easier to see the amounts in the bar graph than in the line graph.

Try This

1. Possible answer:

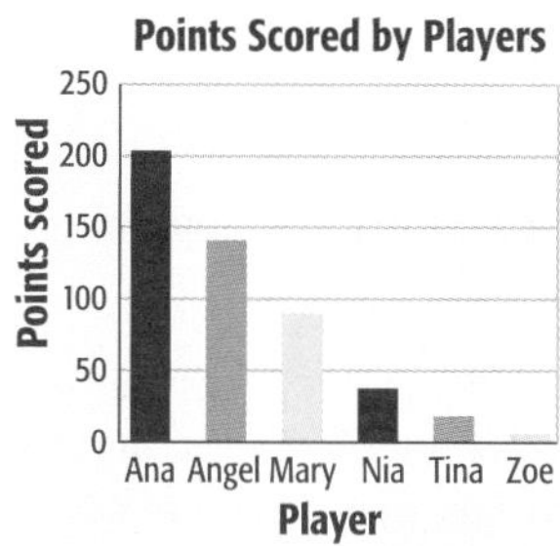

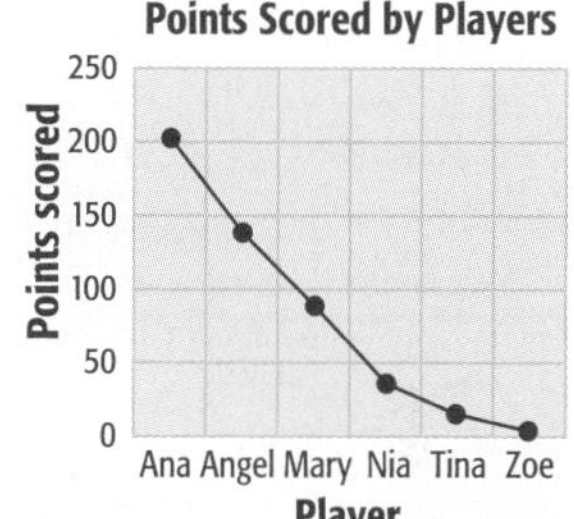

Purpose: *To assess students' mastery of concepts and skills in Lessons 1-1 through 1-6*

Assessment Resources

Section 1B Quiz

Assessment Resources .... p. 6

***Test and Practice Generator* CD-ROM**

Additional mid-chapter assessment items in both multiple-choice and free-response format may be generated for any objective in Lessons 1-1 through 1-6.

Answers

4.

	Frequency	Cumulative Frequency
1–5	5	5
6–10	6	11
11–15	1	12

5.

Stems	Leaves
0	1 3 3 5 5 6 7 7 8 8
1	0 4

Key: 0|3 means 3

6.

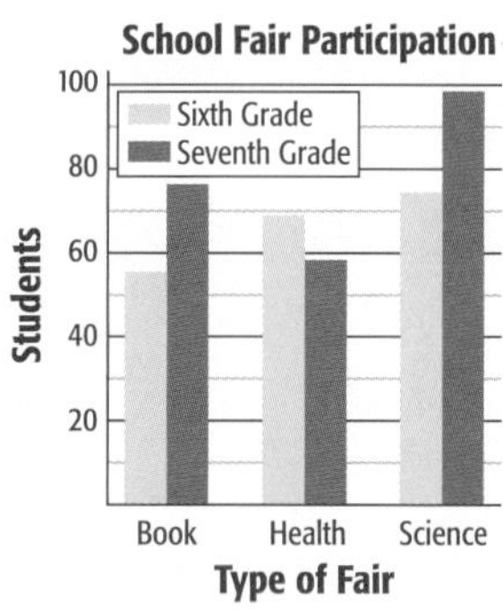

7. Possible answer:

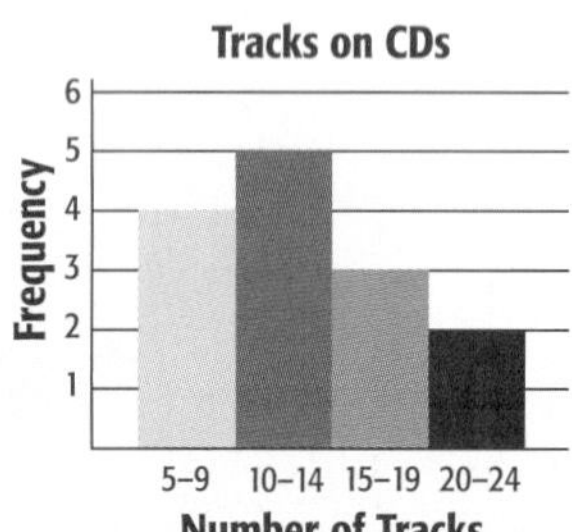

11.

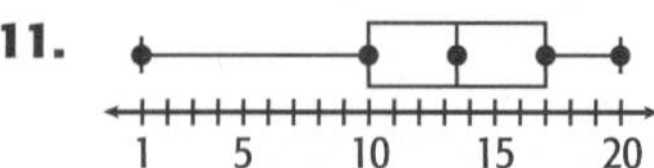

Chapter 1 Mid-Chapter Quiz

LESSON **1-1** (pp. 4–7)

Identify the population and sample.

1. A movie theater manager surveys the first 40 people exiting the theater.
   Possible answer: sample: the 40 people surveyed; population: the people exiting the theater

LESSONS **1-2** AND **1-3** (pp. 10–17)

Use the data set 1, 3, 8, 7, 3, 5, 14, 7, 5, 6, 10, 8 for problems 2–5.

2. Find the mean, median, mode, and range of the data set. Round your answer to the nearest tenth, if necessary. **6.4; 6.5; 3, 5, 7, and 8; 13**
3. Which measure of central tendency best represents the data? **the mean or the median**
4. Make a cumulative frequency table of the data.
5. Make a stem-and-leaf plot of the data.

Mid-Chapter Quiz

LESSON **1-4** (pp. 20–23)

6. The table shows the number of students in sixth and seventh grades who participated in school fairs. Make a double-bar graph of the data.
7. The list below shows the number of tracks on a group of CDs. Make a histogram of the data.

   13, 7, 10, 8, 15, 17, 22, 9, 11, 10, 16, 12, 9, 20

School Fair Participation

Fair	Sixth	Seventh
Book	55	76
Health	69	58
Science	74	98

LESSON **1-5** (pp. 24–27)

Use the circle graph for problems 8–10.

8. Did more students pick sausage or mushrooms as their favorite topping? **mushrooms**
9. Approximately what percent of students picked cheese as their favorite topping? **40%**
10. Out of 200 students, 25% picked pepperoni as their favorite. How many students picked pepperoni?
    50 students

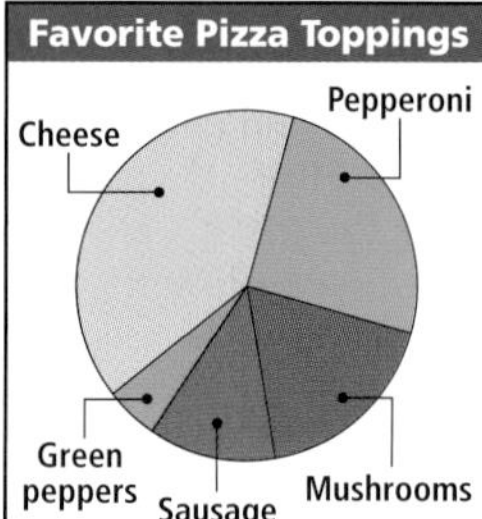

LESSON **1-6** (pp. 28–31)

11. Make a box-and-whisker plot of the data 14, 8, 13, 20, 15, 17, 1, 12, 18, 10.
12. What fraction of the data is greater than 13.5? $\frac{1}{2}$

Section 1C

Trends and Relations in Graphs

One-Minute Section Planner

Lesson	Materials	Resources
Lesson 1-7 Line Graphs **NCTM:** Algebra, Data Analysis and Probability, Communication, Connections, Representation **NAEP:** Data Analysis and Probability 1b ☑ SAT-9 ☐ SAT-10 ☐ ITBS ☑ CTBS ☐ MAT ☑ CAT	**Required** Graph paper *(CRB, p. 98)*	• *Chapter 1 Resource Book,* pp. 65–73 • Daily Transparency T25, CRB • Additional Examples Transparencies T26–T28, CRB • *Alternate Openers: Explorations,* p. 7
Hands-On Lab 1C Explore Scatter Plots **NCTM:** Algebra, Data Analysis and Probability **NAEP:** Data Analysis and Probability 1c ☐ SAT-9 ☐ SAT-10 ☐ ITBS ☐ CTBS ☑ MAT ☑ CAT	**Required** Graph paper *(CRB, p. 98)*	• *Hands-On Lab Activities,* pp. 5–6, 132
Lesson 1-8 Scatter Plots **NCTM:** Algebra, Data Analysis and Probability, Communication, Connections, Representation **NAEP:** Data Analysis and Probability 1a ☐ SAT-9 ☐ SAT-10 ☐ ITBS ☑ CTBS ☑ MAT ☑ CAT	**Required** Graph paper *(CRB, p. 98)* **Optional** Teaching Transparency T30 *(CRB)* Science books	• *Chapter 1 Resource Book,* pp. 74–82 • Daily Transparency T29, CRB • Additional Examples Transparencies T31–T32, CRB • *Alternate Openers: Explorations,* p. 8
Lesson 1-9 Misleading Graphs **NCTM:** Algebra, Data Analysis and Probability, Communication, Connections, Representation **NAEP:** Data Analysis and Probability 1a ☐ SAT-9 ☐ SAT-10 ☐ ITBS ☐ CTBS ☐ MAT ☐ CAT	**Required** Graph paper *(CRB p. 98)* **Optional** Magazines and newspapers	• *Chapter 1 Resource Book,* pp. 83–91 • Daily Transparency T33, CRB • Additional Examples Transparencies T34–T35, CRB • *Alternate Openers: Explorations,* p. 9
Section 1C Assessment		• Section 1C Quiz, AR p. 7 • *Test and Practice Generator* CD-ROM

SAT = *Stanford Achievement Tests* **ITBS** = *Iowa Test of Basic Skills* **CTBS** = *Comprehensive Test of Basic Skills/Terra Nova*
MAT = *Metropolitan Achievement Test* **CAT** = *California Achievement Test*

NCTM—Complete standards can be found on pages T27–T33. **NAEP**—Complete standards can be found on pages A35–A39.

SE = *Student Edition* **TE** = *Teacher's Edition* **AR** = *Assessment Resources* **CRB** = *Chapter Resource Book* **MK** = *Manipulatives Kit*

Section Overview

Line Graphs

Lesson 1-7

Why? Line graphs are the most widely used graphs to show change over time. They can show one set of data changing (single-line graph), or they can compare how two (or more) sets of data change over time (double- or multiple-line graphs).

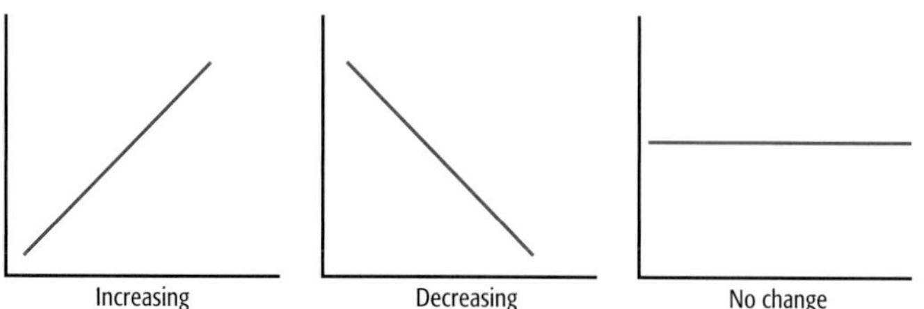

The steeper the line, the greater the increase (or decrease) between the values. A horizontal line indicates no change.

Scatter Plots

Hands-On Lab 1C, Lesson 1-8

Why? Scatter plots are used to analyze how closely two sets of data are related. A relationship may be suggested by the plot; however, no cause and effect are implied.

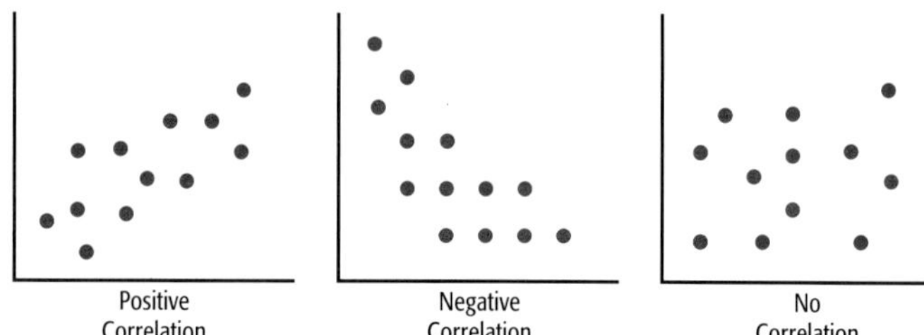

Correlation is used to describe an association between two sets of data.

Misleading Graphs

Lesson 1-9

Why? It is easy to use graphs to cause a misleading impression. Common causes of misleading impressions include a break on one of the axes, an axis that does not start at zero, or irregular intervals.

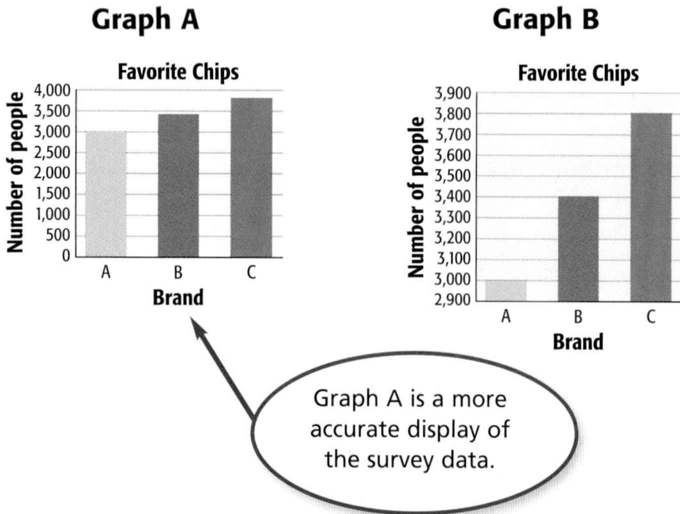

Look for size differences in pictorial graphs or bar graphs that compare two sets of data.

1-7 Line Graphs

Learn to display and analyze data in line graphs.

Vocabulary

line graph

double-line graph

You can use a *line graph* to show how data changes over a period of time. In a **line graph**, line segments are used to connect data points. The result is a visual record of change.

Line graphs can be used for a variety of reasons, including showing the growth of a cat over time.

EXAMPLE 1 **Making a Line Graph**

Make a line graph of the data in the table. Use the graph to determine during which 2-month period the kitten's weight increased the most.

Age (mo)	Weight (lb)
0	0.2
2	1.7
4	3.8
6	5.1
8	6.0
10	6.7
12	7.2

Helpful Hint

To plot each point, start at zero. Move *right* for the time and *up* for the weight.

Step 1: Determine the scale and interval for each axis. Place units of time on the horizontal axis.

Step 2: Plot a point for each pair of values. Connect the points using line segments.

Step 3: Label the axes and give the graph a title.

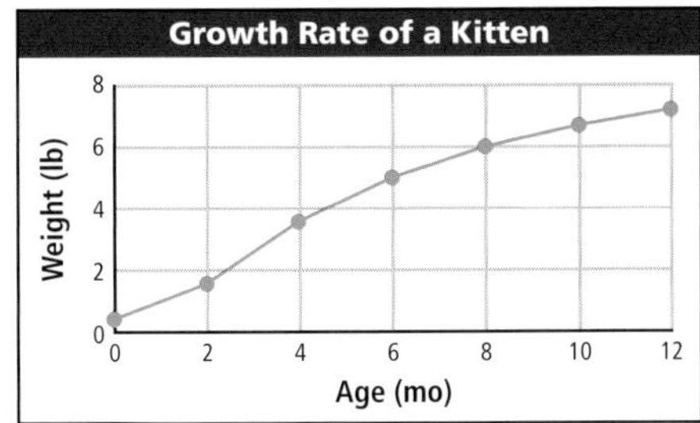

The graph shows the greatest increase between 2 and 4 months. This means the kitten's weight increased most between 2 and 4 months.

1-7 Organizer

Pacing: Traditional 1 day
Block $\frac{1}{2}$ day

Objective: Students display and analyze data in line graphs.

Warm Up

1. What is the x-coordinate of the point (2, 3)? 2
2. To plot the point (3, 7), you would move right ▒ units then up ▒ units. 3, 7
3. To plot the point (4, −5) would you move left or right first? right

Problem of the Day

Find three mistakes on the graph shown.

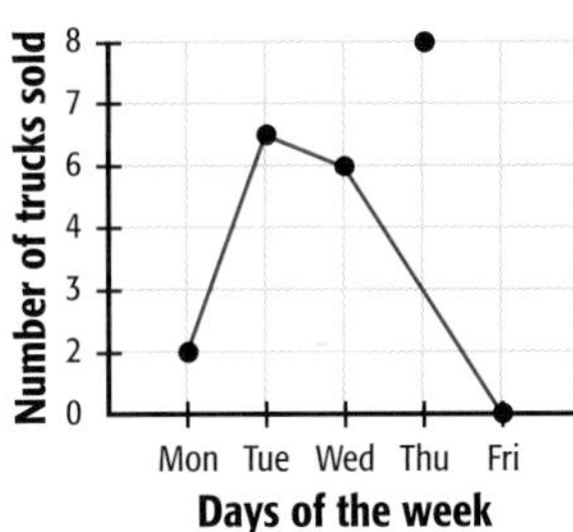

The line does not connect all the sales, the intervals on the vertical scale are not equal, and the data for Tuesday shows sales of 6.5 trucks (which is impossible).

Available on Daily Transparency in CRB

1 Introduce

Alternate Opener

EXPLORATION

1-7 Line Graphs

The line graph shows the number of home sales over a year.

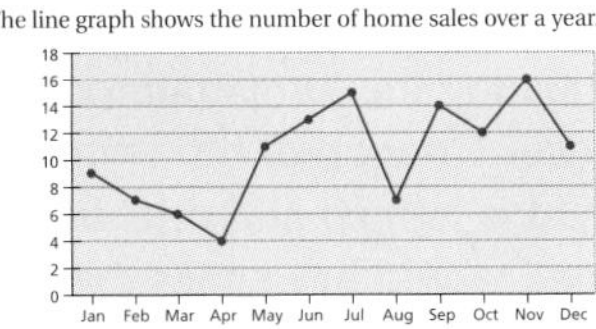

Use the graph to answer each question.

1. Which two months have the most home sales?
2. Which two months have the least home sales?
3. Between which consecutive months does the greatest increase in home sales occur?
4. Between which consecutive months does the greatest decrease in home sales occur?

Think and Discuss

5. **Describe** other types of data that could be represented with a line graph.
6. **Describe** types of data that could not be represented with a line graph.

Motivate

Draw three basic line graphs on the board.

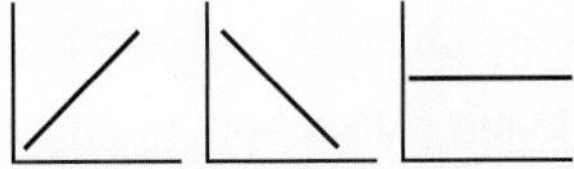

Ask students to describe what kind of data they think each line graph might represent (e.g., from left to right: a person's height from age 1 to age 15, the amount of water left in a reservoir during a drought, and class attendance during a month).

Exploration worksheet and answers on Chapter 1 Resource Book pp. 66 and 114

2 Teach

Lesson Presentation

Guided Instruction

In this lesson, students learn to display and analyze data in line graphs. Discuss the line graph shown at the beginning of the lesson. Ask students to describe what it shows. Line graphs can show trends, so when a line segment connecting two points goes up, the change between the points is positive.

Teaching Tip Point out that a line graph is not necessarily a straight line. Most consist of line segments between points that do not lie on a straight line.

Additional Examples

Example 1

Make a line graph of the data in the table. During which 2-hour period did the temperature change the most?

Time	11 A.M.	1 P.M.	3 P.M.	5 P.M.
Temperature	80°F	88°F	92°F	89°F

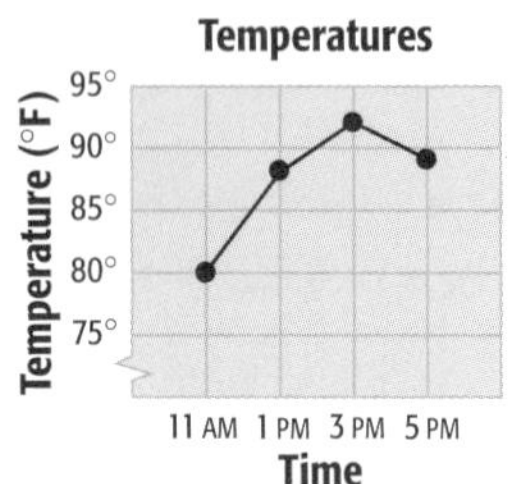

Changes occurred the most between 11 A.M. and 1 P.M.

Example 2

Use the Florida population graph for Example 2 to estimate the population of Florida in 1950.

The population was about 3.5 million.

Example 3

The table shows stock prices for two stocks in one week. Make a double-line graph of the data.

	Mon	Tue	Wed	Thu	Fri
Stock A	$10	$9	$11	$10	$18
Stock B	$6	$12	$8	$14	$14

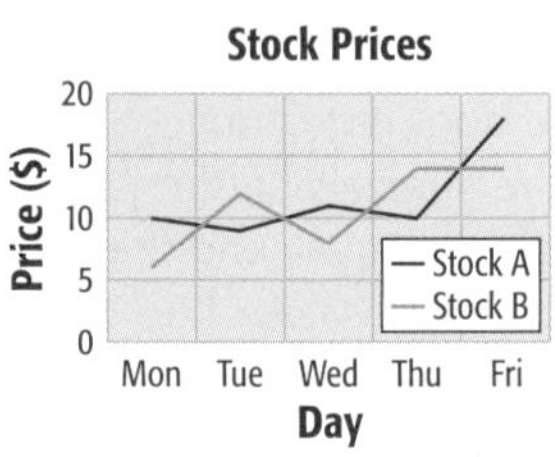

You can use a line graph to estimate values between data points.

EXAMPLE 2 **Using a Line Graph to Estimate Data**

Use the graph to estimate the population of Florida in 1990.

To estimate the population in 1990, find the point on the line between 1980 and 2000 that corresponds to 1990.

The graph shows about 12.5 million. In fact, the population was 12.9 million in 1990.

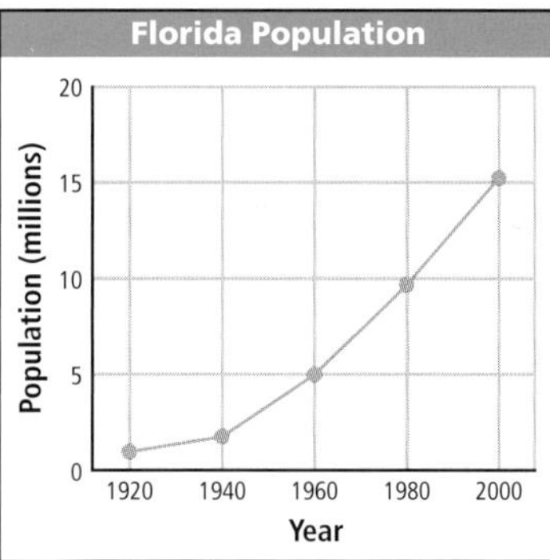

A **double-line graph** shows change over time for two sets of data.

EXAMPLE 3 **Making a Double-Line Graph**

The table shows the normal daily temperatures in degrees Fahrenheit in two Alaskan cities. Make a double-line graph of the data.

Russia
Nome
Alaska
Canada
Anchorage
Gulf of Alaska

Month	Nome	Anchorage
Jan	7	15
Feb	4	19
Mar	9	26
Apr	18	36
May	36	47
Jun	46	54

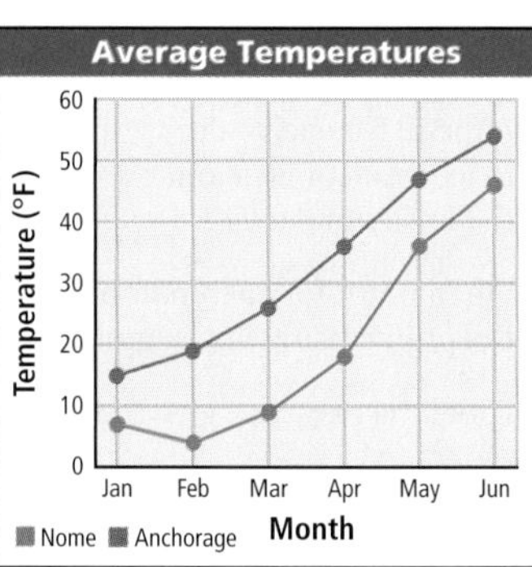

Plot a point for each temperature in Nome and connect the points. Then, using a different color, plot a point for each temperature in Anchorage and connect the points. Make a key to show what each line represents.

Think and Discuss

1. **Describe** how a line graph would look for a set of data that increases and then decreases over time.
2. **Give an example** of a situation that can be described by a double-line graph in which the two sets of data intersect at least once.

Teach

Reaching All Learners

Through World Math

Let students work with partners to research data about another country that can be shown in a line graph (e.g., changes in population, rainfall, or average income over several years). Have each pair construct a graph from the data and then share their research and graph with the class.

3 Close

Summarize

Have students compare a line graph with a double-line graph. Then have them compare the line graph with a bar graph.

Possible answer: A line graph shows how data change over time. A double-line graph shows how two sets of data change over time. A bar graph, on the other hand, compares amounts.

Answers to Think and Discuss

Possible answers:

1. The line would rise and then fall.
2. A graph comparing the temperatures of two liquids over a period of time when one cool liquid is heated and one warm liquid is cooled would have lines that intersect when the temperatures are the same.

1-7 Exercises

FOR EXTRA PRACTICE
see page 656

internet connect
Homework Help Online
go.hrw.com Keyword: MS4 1-7

GUIDED PRACTICE

The table at right shows average movie theater ticket prices in the United States. Use the table for Exercises 1 and 2.

Year	Ticket Price ($)
1965	1.01
1970	1.55
1975	2.05
1980	2.69
1985	3.55
1990	4.23
1995	4.35
2000	5.39

See Example 1
1. Make a line graph of the data in the table. Use the graph to determine during which 5-year period the average ticket price increased the least.

See Example 2
2. Use the graph to estimate the average ticket price in 1997. **about $4.90**

See Example 3
3. The table below shows the amount of two varieties of cheese in pounds consumed per person in the United States. Make a double-line graph of the data.

	1992	1993	1994	1995	1996	1997
American	11.32	11.41	11.55	11.84	11.99	12.03
Italian	9.97	9.82	10.29	10.41	10.79	10.96

INDEPENDENT PRACTICE

The table at right shows the number of teams in the National Basketball Association (NBA). Use the table for Exercises 4–6.

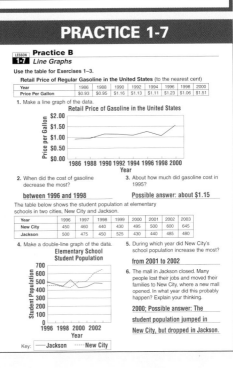

Year	Teams
1965	9
1970	14
1975	18
1980	22
1985	23
1990	27
1995	27
2000	29

See Example 1
4. Make a line graph of the data in the table. Use the graph to determine during which 5-year period the number of NBA teams increased the most.

5. During which 5-year period did the number of teams increase the least? **1990–1995**

See Example 2
6. Use the graph to estimate the number of NBA teams in 1988. **25**

See Example 3
7. The table below shows the normal daily temperatures in degrees Fahrenheit in Peoria, Illinois, and Portland, Oregon. Make a double-line graph of the data.

	Jul	Aug	Sept	Oct	Nov	Dec
Peoria	76	73	66	54	41	27
Portland	68	69	63	55	46	40

RETEACH 1-7

LESSON 1-7 **Reteach**
Line Graphs

A **line graph** shows data changing over time.

A **double-line graph** shows two sets of data changing over time.

1. The table shows the normal daily low temperature in °F in Indianapolis and San Francisco. Use the data to make a double-line graph.

Month	Jan.	Mar.	May	Jul.	Sept.	Nov.
Indianapolis	26°	41°	63°	75°	67°	43°
San Francisco	49°	53°	58°	63°	65°	55°

a. Finish labeling each axis.

What is the vertical axis label?
Temperature (F°)

What is the horizontal axis label?
Month

b. Plot each point for each set of data.

c. Connect the points. Use a dotted line to represent one set of data.

d. Give the graph a title and key.

Daily Normal Low Temperatures
Temperature (°F)
80 70 60 50 40 30 20 10 0
Jan. Mar. May Jul. Sept. Nov.
Month
Key: ---- San Francisco — Indianapolis

2. In which city was the temperature the most constant?
San Francisco

3. During which 2 months in Indianapolis did the temperature increase the most?
March to May

4. Use the graph to estimate the low temperature in October in San Francisco.
about 60°F

5. During which month was the difference in the daily normal low temperatures in Indianapolis and San Francisco most likely the smallest?
September

PRACTICE 1-7

LESSON 1-7 **Practice B**
Line Graphs

Use the table for Exercises 1–3.

Retail Price of Regular Gasoline in the United States (to the nearest cent)

Year	1986	1988	1990	1992	1994	1996	1998	2000
Price Per Gallon	$0.93	$0.95	$1.16	$1.13	$1.11	$1.23	$1.06	$1.51

1. Make a line graph of the data.

Retail Price of Gasoline in the United States
Price per Gallon
$2.00 $1.50 $1.00 $0.50 $0.00
1986 1988 1990 1992 1994 1996 1998 2000
Year

2. When did the cost of gasoline decrease the most?
between 1996 and 1998

3. About how much did gasoline cost in 1995?
Possible answer: about $1.15

The table below shows the student population at elementary schools in two cities, New City and Jackson.

Year	1996	1997	1998	1999	2000	2001	2002	2003
New City	450	460	440	430	495	500	600	645
Jackson	500	475	450	525	430	440	485	480

4. Make a double-line graph of the data.

Elementary School Student Population
Student Population
700 600 500 400 300 200 100 0
1996 1998 2000 2002
Year
Key: — Jackson ---- New City

5. During which year did New City's school population increase the most?
from 2001 to 2002

6. The mall in Jackson closed. Many people lost their jobs and moved their families to New City, where a new mall opened. In what year did this probably happen? Explain your thinking.
2000; Possible answer: The student population jumped in New City, but dropped in Jackson.

1-7 PRACTICE & ASSESS

Assignment Guide

If you finished Example 1 assign:
Core 1, 4, 5, 13–20
Enriched 1, 4, 5, 13–20

If you finished Example 2 assign:
Core 1, 2, 4–6, 13–20
Enriched 1, 2, 4–6, 13–20

If you finished Example 3 assign:
Core 1–9, 13–20
Enriched 1–20

Graph paper is provided on page 98 of the Chapter 1 Resource Book.

Answers

1. **Average Movie Theatre Ticket Prices**

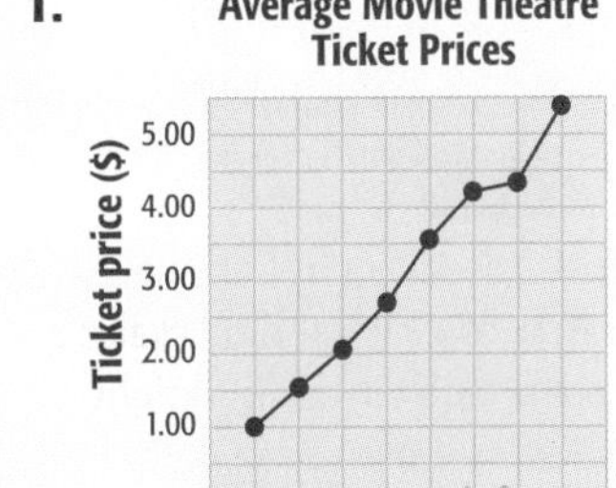

1990–1995

3. **Cheese Consumed per Person in the United States**

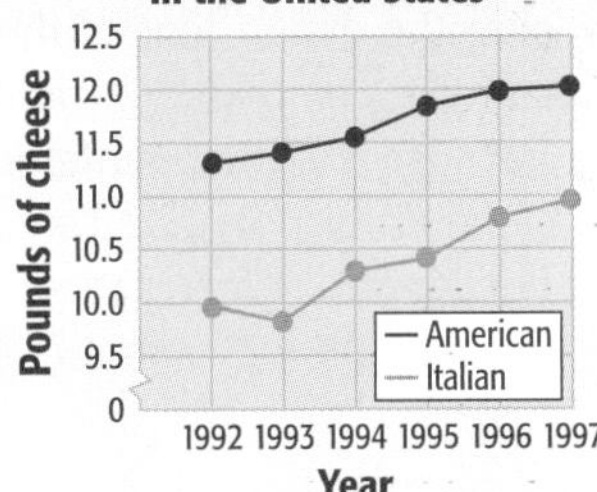

4. **Teams in the NBA**

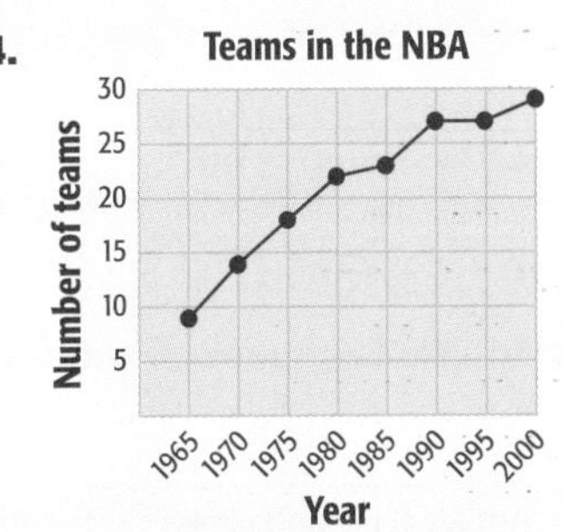

1965–1970

7. **Normal Daily Temperature**

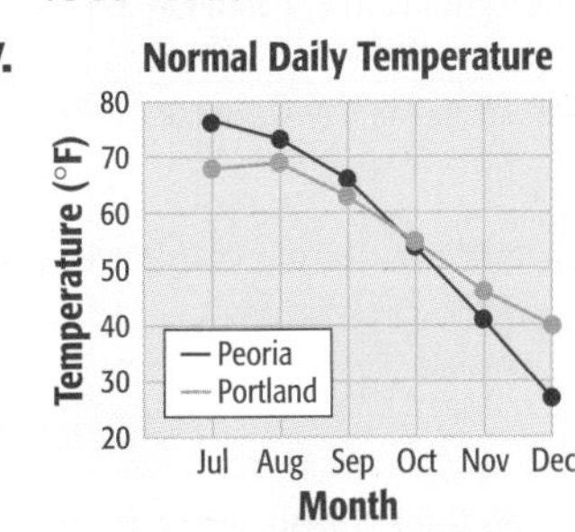

Answers

9. **b.** The number of cars from Japan increased until 1985 and then decreased; the number of cars from Germany was more steady but decreased slightly.

10. Possible answer: In which year were there about the same number of cars imported from Germany and Japan?

12. A double-bar graph shows how the sales for both days compare.

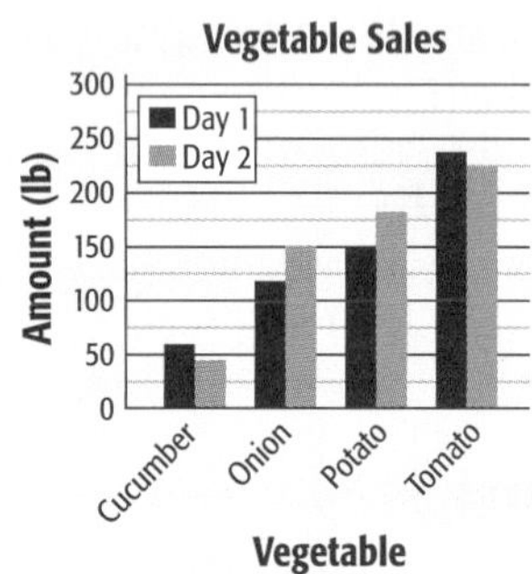

Journal 

Have students describe data about themselves that can be used to make a line graph, such as changes in height, weight, or shoe size over time.

Test Prep Doctor 

In Exercise 20, students may find it helpful to draw a diagram of the problem to visualize the dimensions of the resulting rectangle. Choice **A,** 32, can be eliminated because it is the perimeter of one tile alone. Choice **D,** 128, can be eliminated because it is greater than twice the perimeter of one square.

PRACTICE AND PROBLEM SOLVING

Earth Science LINK

In 1988, forest fires burned millions of acres in Yosemite and Yellowstone National Parks.

8. ***EARTH SCIENCE*** The graph shows the number of acres burned by wildfires in the United States from 1995 to 2000.

   a. During which years did wildfires burn more than 6 million acres? **1996; 2000**

   b. Explain whether the graph would be useful in predicting future data values.
   Possible answer: No, there is no trend.

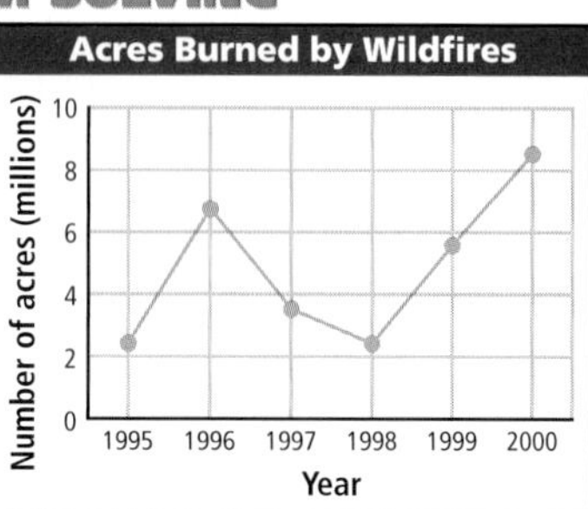

Source: National Interagency Fire Center

9. ***INDUSTRY*** The graph shows the number of new passenger cars imported into the United States from Germany and Japan.

   a. Approximately how many more cars were imported from Japan than from Germany in 1995?

   9a. 0.9 million

   b. Describe how the number of cars imported from both countries changed from 1970 to 1995.

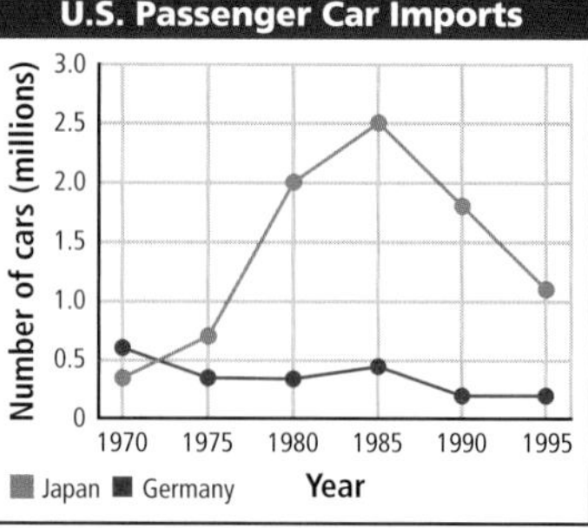

Source: World Almanac

10. ***WRITE A PROBLEM*** Write a question using the double-line graph in Exercise 9.

11. ***WRITE ABOUT IT*** Explain the benefit of drawing a double-line graph rather than two single-line graphs for related sets of data.

11. A double-line graph takes less time to draw and makes it easier to compare data.

12. ***CHALLENGE*** The table shows the amount of vegetables in pounds a family sold at a farmers' market. Make a graph to display the data. Explain your choice of graph.

Vegetable	Day 1	Day 2
Cucumber	60	45
Onion	120	150
Potato	150	180
Tomato	240	225

Spiral Review

Write each number in standard form. (Previous course)

13. 100 + 60 + 8 **168**

14. 7,000 + 300 + 70 + 9 **7,379**

15. 40,000 + 4,000 + 60 + 2 **44,062**

Write each number in expanded form. (Previous course)

16. 306 **300 + 6**

17. 5,047 **5,000 + 40 + 7**

18. 27,684 **18. 20,000 + 7,000 + 600 + 80 + 4**

19. 109,244 **100,000 + 9,000 + 200 + 40 + 4**

20. **TEST PREP** Each side of a square tile is 8 cm. A rectangle is formed by placing two of the tiles next to each other. What is the perimeter of the rectangle in centimeters? (Previous course) **B**

A 32 cm B 48 cm C 64 cm D 128 cm

Lesson Quiz 

Make a double-line graph of the data.

Hot Air Balloon Heights		
Time (A.M.)	**Balloon 1 (feet)**	**Balloon 2 (feet)**
6:00	0	0
6:15	150	175
6:30	250	275
6:45	350	375
7:00	350	400
7:15	250	275

Answers on p. A9

Available on Daily Transparency in CRB

CHALLENGE 1-7

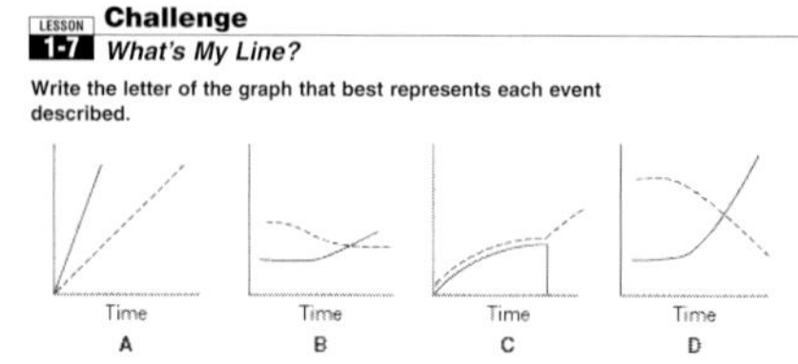

LESSON 1-7 **Challenge**
What's My Line?

Write the letter of the graph that best represents each event described.

Time A Time B Time C Time D

1. Two science students are timing ice melting and water freezing. Which graph shows the temperatures during both experiments?
   B

2. In the music industry, when CDs became popular, sales of cassettes plummeted. Which graph shows this trend?
   D

3. The batter takes a strike on the first pitch but hits a home run on the second pitch. Which graph shows the speed of the ball in each case?
   C

4. Two brothers attend the same school. One walks and the other rides a bike. Which graph compares the time required for them to travel to school?
   A

Draw a double-line graph to solve.
Possible answers are given.

5. The town swimming pool puts aside the last 15 minutes of every hour for an adult swim. Show the change in the number of children and adults in the pool over several hours.

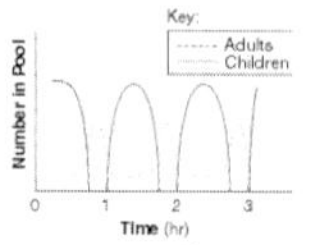

Key: Adults, Children; Number in Pool; Time (hr) 0 1 2 3

6. The Ice Cream Station is open only during the summer months. Cool Guy's Ice Cream is open all year long. Show the change in ice cream sales over the course of a year for each business.

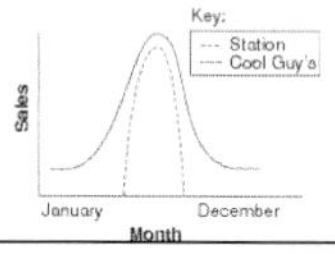

Key: Station, Cool Guy's; Sales; January, December; Month

PROBLEM SOLVING 1-7

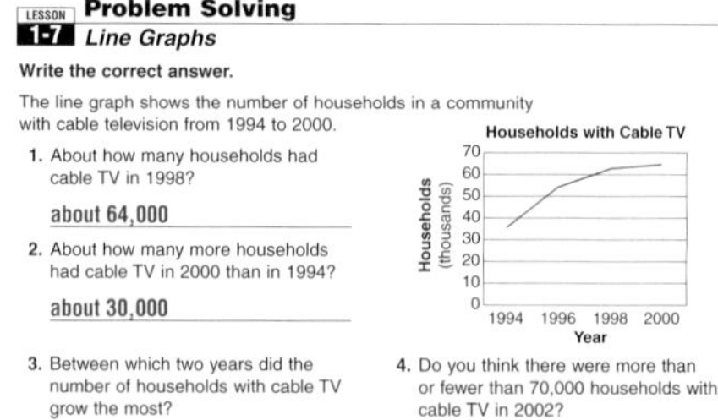

LESSON 1-7 **Problem Solving**
Line Graphs

Write the correct answer.

The line graph shows the number of households in a community with cable television from 1994 to 2000.

Households with Cable TV; Households (thousands) 0–70; 1994 1996 1998 2000; Year

1. About how many households had cable TV in 1998?
   about 64,000

2. About how many more households had cable TV in 2000 than in 1994?
   about 30,000

3. Between which two years did the number of households with cable TV grow the most?
   between 1994 and 1996

4. Do you think there were more than or fewer than 70,000 households with cable TV in 2002?
   fewer than 70,000

Choose the letter for the best answer.

The double-line graph shows the number of tornadoes in the United States during part of 1999 and 2000.

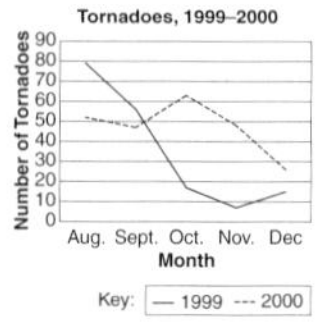

Tornadoes, 1999–2000; Number of Tornadoes 0–90; Aug. Sept. Oct. Nov. Dec; Month; Key: — 1999 --- 2000

5. About how many more tornadoes were there in August 1999 than in August 2000?
   A about 10 Ⓒ about 30
   B about 20 D about 40

6. In which time period did the number of tornadoes increase for both years?
   F Aug. to Sept. H Oct. to Nov.
   G Sept. to Oct. Ⓙ none

7. Which time period showed the greatest decrease in the number of tornadoes?
   A Aug. to Sept. 1999
   B Aug. to Sept. 2000
   Ⓒ Sept. to Oct. 1999
   D Sept. to Oct. 2000

8. During which month were there more than 45 more tornadoes than the same month the previous year?
   Ⓕ Oct. 2000
   G Aug. 2000
   H Dec. 2000
   J Sept. 2000

Explore Scatter Plots

Use with Lesson 1-8

Look at the graph at right. Do you think your shoe size has anything to do with your age? In this activity, you will explore data sets that may or may not have a relationship.

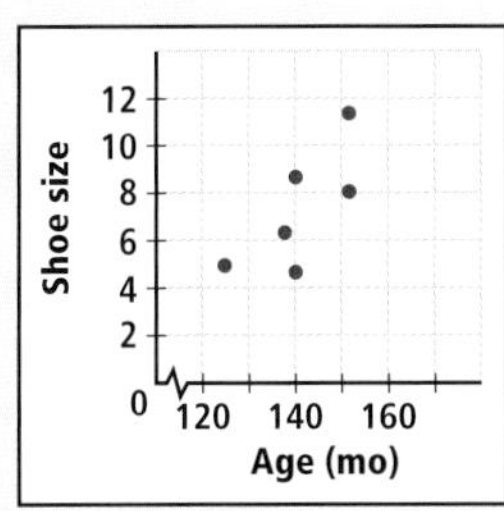

Activity

1 Follow the steps to create a scatter plot.

a. On a piece of graph paper, draw the horizontal and vertical axes for a graph.

b. Select two variables from the list below.

- shoe size
- height
- age in months
- length of forearm
- month of birth
- last two digits of phone number

c. Survey at least six people to find values for these two variables. Write the information you get from each person as an ordered pair. For example, (shoe size, last two digits of phone number) could be (7, 31).

d. Label the axes of your graph with the variables. Then plot the data you gathered as points on the graph.

Think and Discuss

1. Do the points on your graph form a pattern? Explain.
2. Do you have any point that does not fit your pattern? If so, how does this point compare with the other points? **Possible answer: There was no pattern.**
3. Do the points appear to be almost in a straight line? If so, describe the line. **Possible answer: No; the points are not in a line.**

Try This

1. Graph the ordered pairs below. How is the pattern in this graph similar to or different from the pattern in the graph you made in the Activity?

(1, 2), (2, 2), (2, 3), (3, 4), (4, 3), (4, 5), (5, 5), (6, 4), (7, 6), (7, 8), (8, 7)

Paul Turney
St. Louis, Missouri

Teacher to Teacher

To have the scatter plot yield a tactile experience, students could create graphs on oversized graph paper using pieces of candy to plot the points.

This way, students may enjoy a snack as they work or after they complete their graphs. Students can also create scatter plots on poster board and use small three-dimensional objects relevant to the data to plot their points. These scatter plots not only increase student interest but also provide visually appealing displays for school events. Students can also learn kinesthetically by being part of a life-size scatter plot in which the learners *are* the data.

1C Explore Scatter Plots

Pacing: Traditional 1 day
Block $\frac{1}{2}$ day

Objective: Students create and explore scatter plots.

Materials: Graph paper

Lab Resources

Hands-On Lab Activities. . . pp. 5–6, 132

Using the Page

Have students look over the variables on the list. Discuss with students which variables may have a relationship and which variables do not have a relationship.

Graph the following ordered pairs. Describe the pattern.

1. (1, 3), (2, 3), (3, 3), (4, 3)

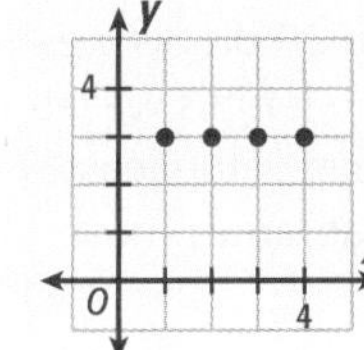

horizontal line

2. (1, 1), (2, 2), (3, 3), (4, 4)

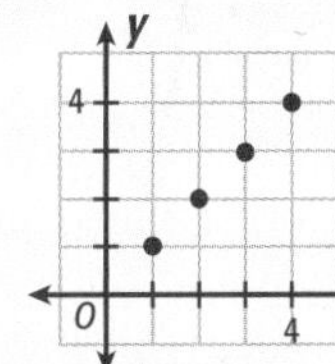

line slanted up from left to right

Answers

Activity

For parts a–d, check students' work.

Think and Discuss

1. Possible answer: The variables shoe size and last two digits of phone number do not appear to form a pattern. There is no relationship between shoe size and the last two digits of phone numbers.

Try This

1. Possible answer:

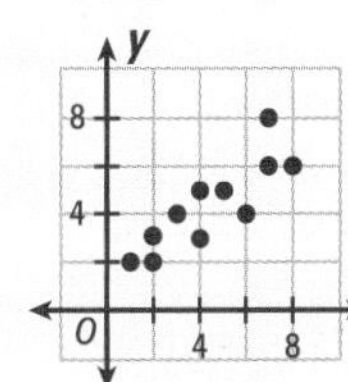

The points in the graph appear to cluster around a straight line slanting up from left to right.

1-8 Organizer

Pacing: Traditional 1 day
Block $\frac{1}{2}$ day

Objective: Students display and analyze data in scatter plots.

Warm Up

Which of the following do you think have a cause-and-effect relationship?

1. height and age yes
2. hand span and address no
3. grade average and shoe size no
4. temperature and date yes

Problem of the Day

From the pizza shop, James bikes 12 blocks south, 22 blocks east, 18 blocks north, then 30 blocks west. James realizes that he left his wallet at the pizza shop. What is the least number of blocks that James must travel to return to the pizza shop? 14

Available on Daily Transparency in CRB

When too many pieces of data are clustered together, I guess you can call it a graphic jam.

1-8 Scatter Plots

Learn to display and analyze data in scatter plots.

Vocabulary
scatter plot
positive correlation
negative correlation
no correlation

The supersaurus, one of the largest known dinosaurs, could weigh as much as 55 tons and grow as long as 100 feet from head to tail. The tyrannosaurus, a large meat-eating dinosaur, was about one-third the length of the supersaurus.

Two sets of data, such as the length and the weight of dinosaurs, may be related. To find out, you can make a *scatter plot* of the data values in each set. A **scatter plot** has two number lines, called *axes*—one for each set of data values. Each point on the scatter plot represents a pair of data values. These points may appear to be scattered or may cluster in the shape of a line or a curve.

EXAMPLE  1 Making a Scatter Plot

Use the data to make a scatter plot. Describe the relationship between the data sets.

Name	Length (ft)	Weight (tons)
Triceratops	30	6
Tyrannosaurus	39	7
Euhelopus	50	25
Brachiosaurus	82	50
Supersaurus	100	55

Step 1: Determine the scale and interval for each axis. Place units of length on the horizontal axis and units of weight on the vertical axis.

Step 2: Plot a point for each pair of values.

Step 3: Label the axes and title the graph.

The scatter plot shows that a dinosaur's weight tends to increase as its length increases.

Dinosaur Sizes
Weight (tons): 0, 20, 40, 60
Length (ft): 0, 40, 80, 120

1 Introduce

Alternate Opener

EXPLORATION

1-8 Scatter Plots

The *scatter plot* relates the variables height and shoe size.

Height (in.)	Shoe Size
65	9
64	9
59	5
55	7
65	9
60	9
55	6
64	7
72	12
60	8
61	8
68	10.5

Shoe size: 4, 5, 6, 7, 8, 9, 10, 11, 12, 13
(65, 9)
Height (in.): 40, 45, 50, 55, 60, 65, 70, 75, 80

1. The first point is plotted. Plot the rest of the points.
2. Use the term ***positive correlation*** (both variables tend to increase) or ***negative correlation*** (one variable tends to increase while the other tends to decrease) to describe the trend shown by the scatter plot.

Think and Discuss

3. **Describe** two variables that may have a negative correlation.
4. **Describe** two variables that may not be correlated at all.

Motivate

To introduce a scatter plot, have every student write his or her birthday month as a number from 1 to 12, and then have each student write the number of pets he or she has. Draw a graph with the vertical axis labeled with the numbers of pets and the horizontal axis labeled with the birthday month numbers. As the students tell their number pairs, plot the points on a graph. Then have students describe the graph.

Exploration worksheet and answers on Chapter 1 Resource Book pp. 75 and 116

2 Teach

Lesson Presentation

Guided Instruction

In this lesson, students learn to display and analyze data in scatter plots. Talk about whether there might be a relationship between length and weight for the dinosaurs and what that relationship could be. Point out that the data can be shown by drawing axes and plotting the individual data points and that each data point (pair of values) represents one dinosaur.

Remind students that to plot the points on a scatter plot, move across to the first number of the data pair and up to the second number of the data pair.

There are three ways to describe data displayed in a scatter plot.

Positive Correlation

The values in both data sets increase at the same time.

Negative Correlation

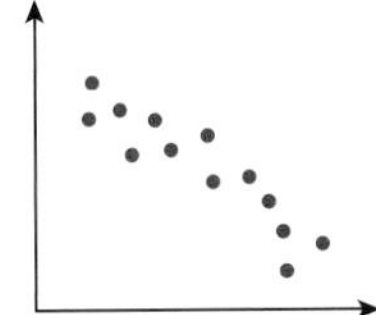

The values in one data set increase as the values in the other set decrease.

No Correlation

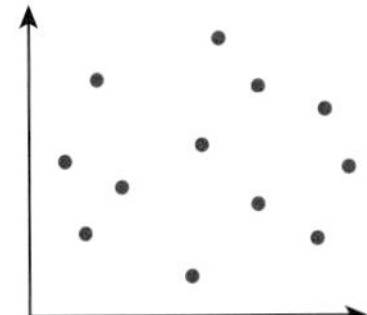

The values in both data sets show no pattern.

EXAMPLE 2 Determining Relationships Between Two Sets of Data

Write *positive correlation, negative correlation,* or *no correlation* to describe each relationship. Explain.

A

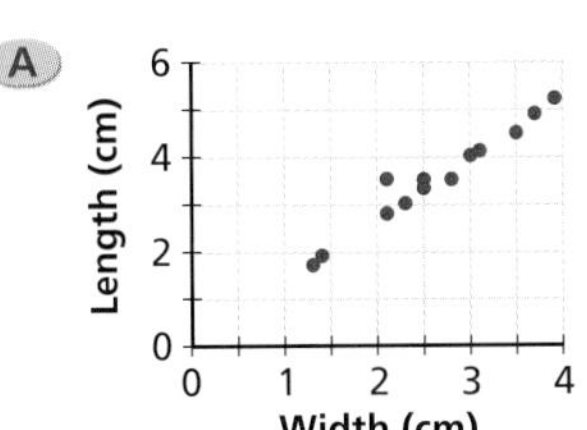

The graph shows that as width increases, length increases. So the graph shows a positive correlation between the data sets.

B

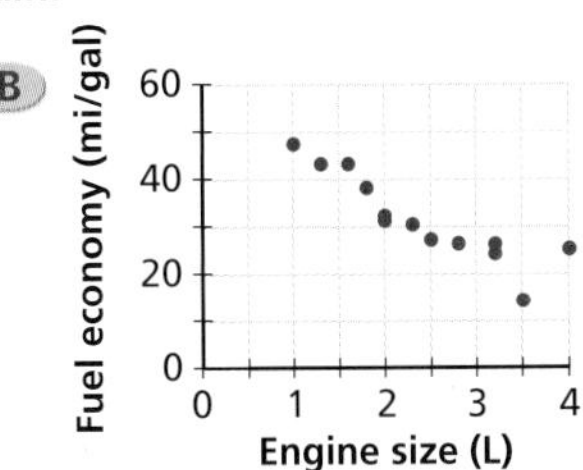

The graph shows that as engine size increases, fuel economy decreases. So the graph shows a negative correlation between the data sets.

C **the ages of people and the number of pets they own**

The number of pets a person owns is not related to the person's age. So there seems to be no correlation between the data sets.

Think and Discuss

1. **Describe** the type of correlation you would expect between the number of absences in a class and the grades in the class.
2. **Give an example** of a relationship between two sets of data that shows a negative correlation. Then give an example of a positive correlation.

Additional Examples

Example 1

Use the data to make a scatter plot. Describe the relationship between the data sets.

Number of Endangered Species

Type	U.S. Only	Rest of World
Mammals	63	251
Birds	78	175
Reptiles	14	64
Amphibians	10	8
Fishes	70	11
Clams	61	2
Miscellaneous	83	5

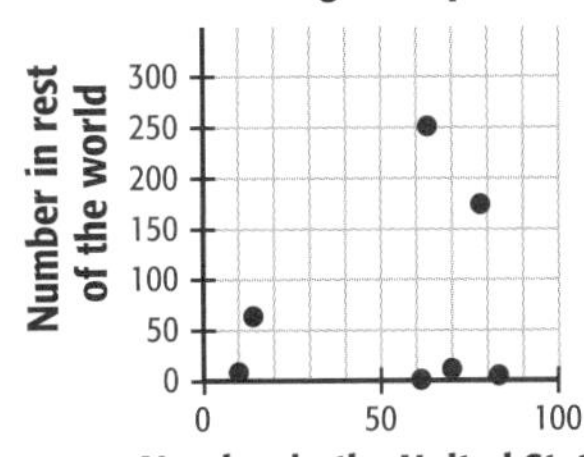

There appears to be no relationship.

Example 2

Write *positive correlation, negative correlation,* or *no correlation* to describe each relationship. Explain.

A.

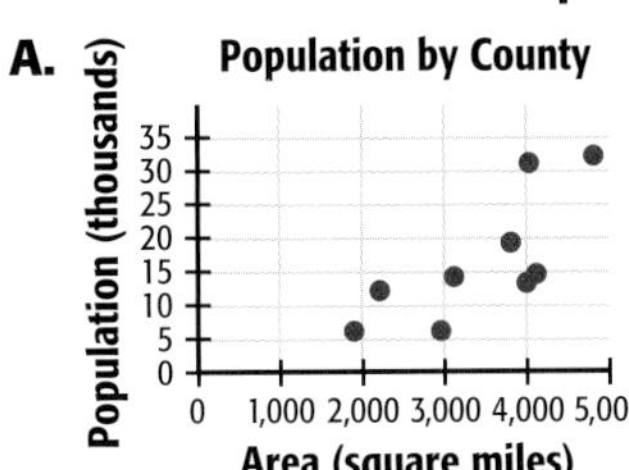

Population increases with area; positive.

B. height and number of vacation days No correlation.

3 Close

Reaching All Learners

Through Curriculum Integration

Science Scientists often display data on a scatter plot because a scatter plot allows them to determine if there is a trend in the data collected. Have students work with partners to find situations in science where they think a scatter plot might be helpful in analyzing the data (e.g., plant height versus hours of sunshine, amount of bacteria versus amount of antibiotics, vitamin content versus cooking time). Ask students to share their findings with the class.

Summarize

Have students describe three situations, one in which data might be correlated positively, one in which it might be correlated negatively, and one in which there would be no correlation.

Possible answer: Positive correlation might occur between age and height. Negative correlation might occur between calories consumed and weight loss. There would probably be no correlation between the number of people in a family and the distance the family lives from the school.

Answers to Think and Discuss

Possible answers:

1. Negative correlation; the more frequently students are absent, the more work they would probably miss, and the poorer their grades would be.
2. negative correlation: number of days spent practicing a jump in skating and the number of times you fall per practice session; positive correlation: time spent studying for a test and the final test grade

1-8 PRACTICE & ASSESS

Students may want to refer back to the lesson examples.

Assignment Guide

If you finished Example 1 assign:
Core 1, 5, 13, 16–21
Enriched 1, 5, 13, 16–21

If you finished Example 2 assign:
Core 1–8, 9–13 odd, 16–21
Enriched 1–7 odd, 9–21

Graph paper is provided on page 98 of the Chapter 1 Resource Book.

Answers

1.
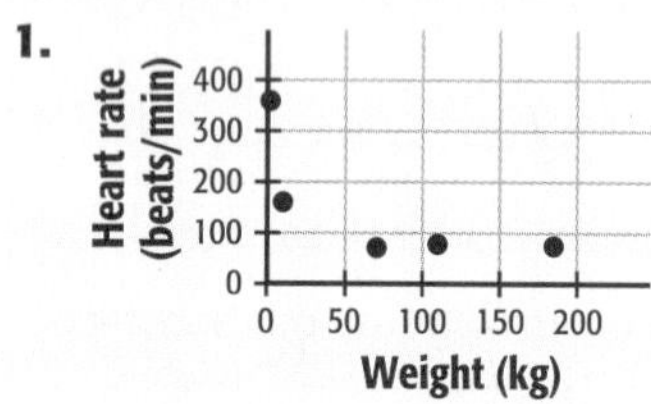

5.
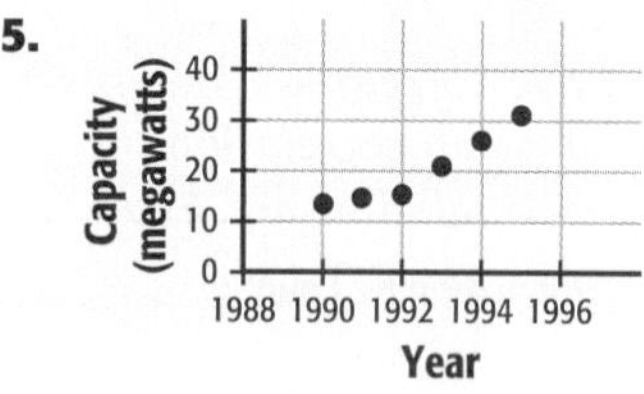

1-8 Exercises

FOR EXTRA PRACTICE
see page 656

GUIDED PRACTICE

See Example 1

1. The table shows the typical weights and heart rates of several mammals. Use the data to make a scatter plot. Describe the relationship between the data sets. **Negative; the heart rate tends to decrease as the size increases.**

Mammal	Weight (kg)	Heart Rate (beats/min)
Ferret	0.6	360
Human	70	70
Llama	185	75
Red deer	110	80
Rhesus monkey	10	160

See Example 2

Write *positive correlation, negative correlation,* or *no correlation* to describe each relationship. Explain.

2.
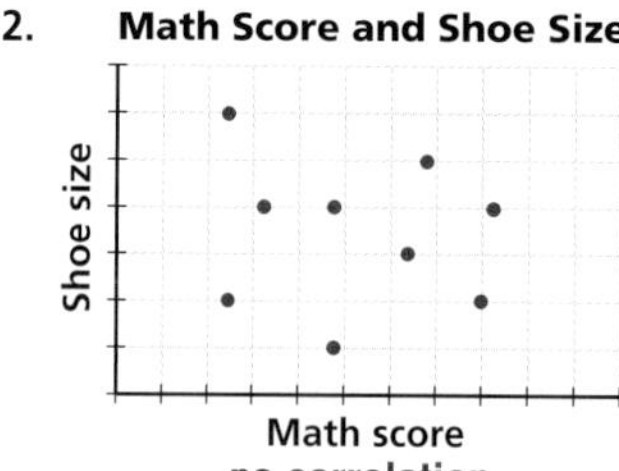

no correlation

3.
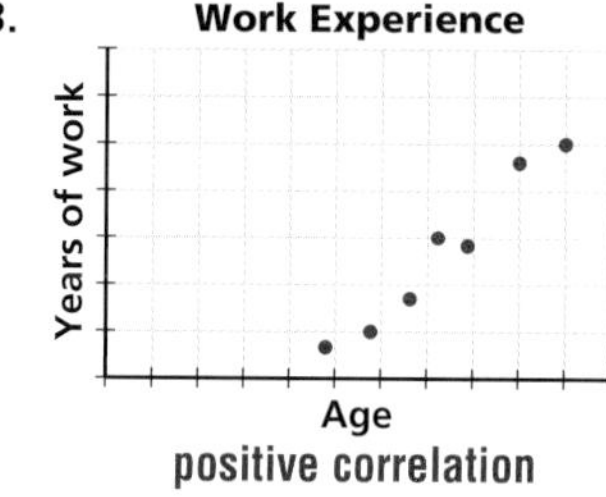

positive correlation

4. the time it takes to drive 100 miles and the driving speed **negative correlation**

INDEPENDENT PRACTICE

See Example 1

5. The table shows solar energy cell capacity (in megawatts) over several years. Use the data to make a scatter plot. Describe the relationship between the data sets. **The scatter plot shows that the capacity increases with time, a positive correlation.**

Year	Capacity	Year	Capacity
1990	13.8	1993	21.0
1991	14.9	1994	26.1
1992	15.6	1995	31.1

See Example 2

Write *positive correlation, negative correlation,* or *no correlation* to describe each relationship. Explain.

6.
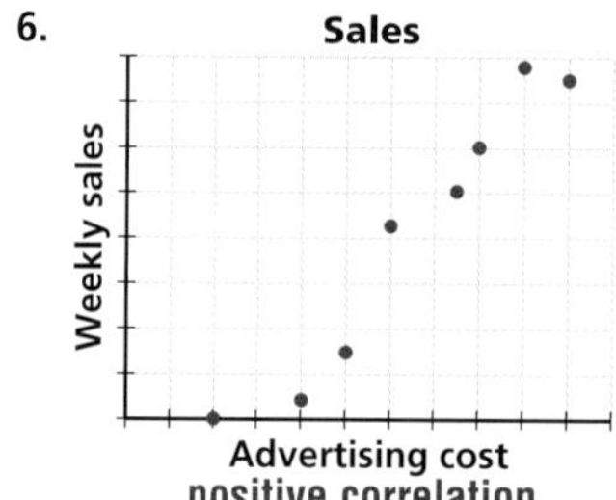

positive correlation

7.
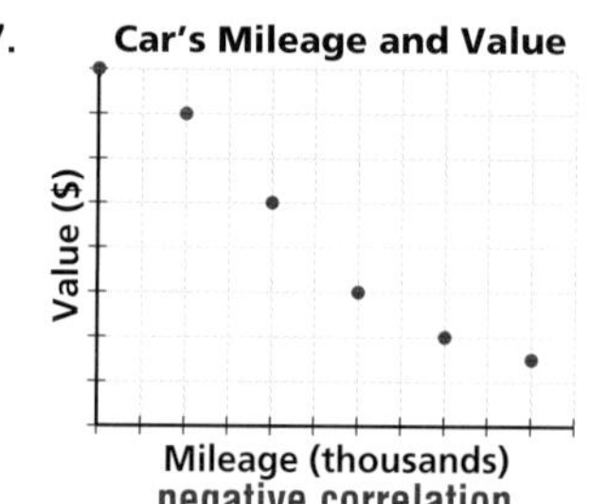

negative correlation

8. the number of students in a school district and the number of buses in the district **positive correlation**

Math Background

The Pearson correlation coefficient is a statistical tool for analyzing data in a scatter plot. It tells whether there is a linear relationship between the variables, x and y. Values range from -1 to $+1$. The correlation between x and y is the same as the correlation between y and x.

For example: The correlation coefficient between calories consumed and weight might be 0.923, indicating a strong positive relationship between the two variables. The correlation coefficient between shoe size and math grade could be 0.01, indicating no relationship. The relationship between the toxicity of a poison and life expectancy could be -0.97, a strong negative relationship.

RETEACH 1-8

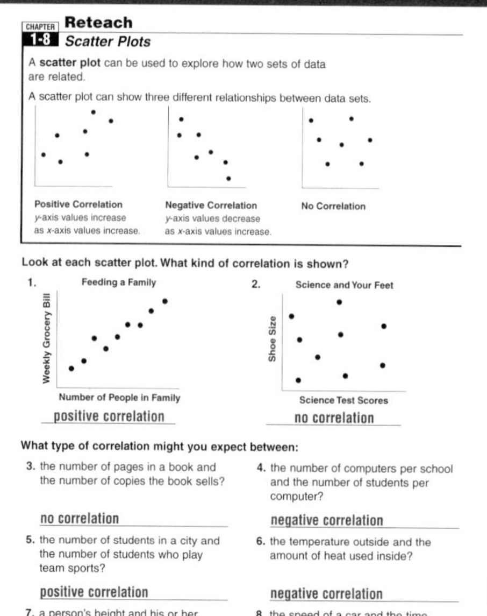

CHAPTER 1-8 **Reteach**
Scatter Plots

A **scatter plot** can be used to explore how two sets of data are related.

A scatter plot can show three different relationships between data sets.

Positive Correlation: *y*-axis values increase as *x*-axis values increase.
Negative Correlation: *y*-axis values decrease as *x*-axis values increase.
No Correlation

Look at each scatter plot. What kind of correlation is shown?

1. Feeding a Family (Weekly Grocery Bill; Number of People in Family) — positive correlation
2. Science and Your Feet (Shoe Size; Science Test Scores) — no correlation

What type of correlation might you expect between:

3. the number of pages in a book and the number of copies the book sells? no correlation
4. the number of computers per school and the number of students per computer? negative correlation
5. the number of students in a city and the number of students who play team sports? positive correlation
6. the temperature outside and the amount of heat used inside? negative correlation
7. a person's height and his or her birthday? no correlation
8. the speed of a car and the time required to travel a certain distance? negative correlation

PRACTICE 1-8

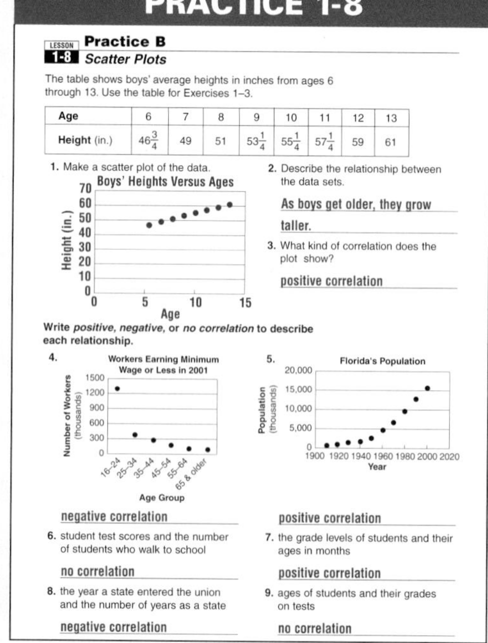

LESSON 1-8 **Practice B**
Scatter Plots

The table shows boys' average heights in inches from ages 6 through 13. Use the table for Exercises 1–3.

Age	6	7	8	9	10	11	12	13
Height (in.)	$46\frac{3}{4}$	49	51	$53\frac{1}{4}$	$55\frac{1}{4}$	$57\frac{1}{4}$	59	61

1. Make a scatter plot of the data. (Boys' Heights Versus Ages; Height (in.); Age)
2. Describe the relationship between the data sets. As boys get older, they grow taller.
3. What kind of correlation does the plot show? positive correlation

Write *positive, negative,* or *no correlation* to describe each relationship.

4. Workers Earning Minimum Wage or Less in 2001 (Number of Workers (thousands); Age Group) — negative correlation
5. Florida's Population (Population (thousands); Year) — positive correlation
6. student test scores and the number of students who walk to school — no correlation
7. the grade levels of students and their ages in months — positive correlation
8. the year a state entered the union and the number of years as a state — negative correlation
9. ages of students and their grades on tests — no correlation

Science LINK

A scientist launching a weather balloon in Antarctica

For Exercises 9–12, tell whether you would expect a positive correlation, a negative correlation, or no correlation. Explain your answers.

9. the elevation of a city and its average daily temperature
10. the average temperature of a location and the amount of rainfall it receives each year **no correlation**
11. the latitude of a location and the amount of snow it receives each year **Positive correlation; the greater the latitude, the more snow expected.**
12. the number of hours of daylight and the amount of rainfall in a day **no correlation**
13. The table at right shows the approximate latitude and average temperature for several locations in the Southern Hemisphere. Construct a scatter plot of the data. What can you conclude from this data? **As latitude increases, temperature decreases.**

Location	Latitude	Temperature
Quito, Ecuador	0° S	55°F
Melbourne, Australia	38° S	43°F
Tucuman, Argentina	27° S	57°F
Tananarive, Madagascar	19° S	60°F
Halley Research Station, Antarctica	76° S	20°F

14. The table below shows altitudes and pressures of Earth's standard atmosphere. Use the data to make a scatter plot. Describe the relationship between the data sets. **As altitude increases, pressure decreases.**

Altitude (km)	Pressure (mb)
0	1013
5	540
10	265
15	121
20	55
25	25

15. ***CHALLENGE*** Suppose that a location's elevation is negatively correlated to its average temperature and positively correlated to the amount of snow it receives. What kind of correlation would you expect between temperature and the amount of snowfall? Explain. **Negative correlation; the lower the temperature, the more snow the location receives.**

Spiral Review

Find each quotient. (Previous course)

16. $45 \div 15$ **3**
17. $24 \div 8$ **3**
18. $63 \div 9$ **7**
19. $36 \div 12$ **3**

20. **TEST PREP** What is the value of 7 in 8.973? (Previous course) **C**
    - A 7 ones
    - B 7 tenths
    - C 7 hundredths
    - D 7 thousandths

21. **TEST PREP** What is 12 ft 8 in. to the nearest foot? (Previous course) **F**
    - F 13 ft
    - G 11 ft
    - H 12 ft
    - J 14 ft

CHALLENGE 1-8

LESSON 1-8 **Challenge**
Time On Task

Use a stopwatch to find out how long it takes to write your first and last names backwards. Do it 10 times, filling in the table with the time of each try. Use the data to make a scatter plot. **Answers will vary.**

Try	Time
1	
2	
3	
4	
5	
6	
7	
8	
9	
10	

Time (s)
0 1 2 3 4 5 6 7 8 9 10
Tries

1. Does your scatter plot show positive, negative, or no correlation?
   Possible answer: negative
2. Summarize the data from the scatter plot.
   Possible answer: The more times I practiced writing my name backwards, the less time it took.
3. Check the tasks that would probably have a scatter plot that is similar to the one you drew above after doing each task 10 times.

Task		Task	
Making tacos in a fast food restaurant	✓	Writing multiplication facts from 1 to 12	✓
Filling boxes on an assembly line	✓	Eating dinner	
Driving from home to school		Talking to a friend on the phone	

4. Based on the data and scatter plot, what conclusion can you make about learning to do a job?
   Possible answer: The more you practice, the better and faster you will do the job.

PROBLEM SOLVING 1-8

LESSON 1-8 **Problem Solving**
Scatter Plots

Write the correct answer.

This scatter plot compares the mean annual income of Americans with the number of years spent in school.

Mean Annual Income vs. Education
Income: $100,000, $80,000, $60,000, $40,000, $20,000, 0
Education Level: Less than 12 years, 12 years, 16 years (B.A.), 18 years (M.A.), 20 years (Ph.D.)

1. Which level of education has a mean annual income between $40,000 and $50,000?
   16 years, B.A.
2. Estimate the range of income data on this scatter plot.
   about $85,000
3. Which level of education has the lowest income?
   less than 12 years
4. Does the scatter plot show a positive correlation, negative correlation, or no correlation between education and income?
   positive correlation

Choose the letter for the best answer.

5. What kind of correlation would you expect to find between a city's annual snowfall amount and the size of its population?
   - A positive correlation
   - B negative correlation
   - (C) no correlation
   - D impossible to say
6. What kind of correlation would you expect to find between a movie's length and the number of times it can be shown in a day?
   - F positive correlation
   - (G) negative correlation
   - H no correlation
   - J impossible to say
7. What kind of correlation would you expect to find between an animal's mass and the number of calories it consumes in a day?
   - (A) positive correlation
   - B negative correlation
   - C no correlation
   - D impossible to say
8. What kind of correlation would you expect to find between a person's height and his or her income?
   - F positive correlation
   - G negative correlations
   - (H) no correlation
   - J impossible to say

Interdisciplinary LINK

Science

Exercises 9–15 involve examining relationships between variables such as location, precipitation, and temperature, which are studied in middle school science courses.

Answers

9, 13, 14. Complete answers on p. A1

Journal 

Ask students to write about a data set that might have a negative correlation, one that might have a positive correlation, and one that would have no correlation.

Test Prep Doctor 

For Exercise 20, suggest that students start at the decimal point to identify the place values. For Exercise 21, it may help students to picture 12 ft 8 in. on a tape measure. The adjacent whole feet are 12 and 13, so choices **G** and **J** can immediately be eliminated.

Lesson Quiz 

1. The table shows the daily attendance at the beach. Use the data to make a scatter plot and describe the relationship. See p. A9.

Temperature(°F)	Attendance
70	100
80	350
75	250
85	400
74	200
82	375
72	260

2. Write positive, negative, or no correlation to describe the relationship shown. negative correlation

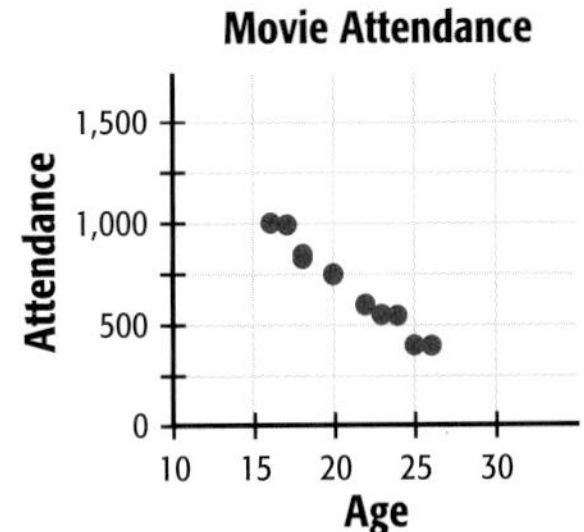

Available on Daily Transparency in CRB

1-9 Organizer

Pacing: Traditional 1 day
Block $\frac{1}{2}$ day

Objective: Students identify and analyze misleading graphs.

Warm Up

Use the graph for questions 1–3.

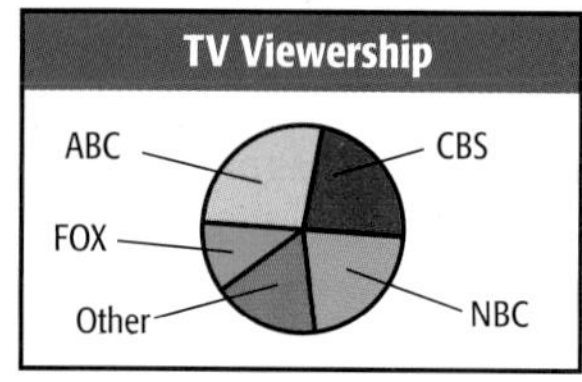

1. What network had the most viewers? ABC
2. What network had the fewest viewers? FOX
3. What network (s) had about the same viewership? ABC, CBS, NBC

Problem of the Day

A bar graph has vertical axis intervals of 6. How would the graph look if the intervals were twice as large?
It would be half as tall.

Available on Daily Transparency in CRB

1-9 Misleading Graphs

Learn to identify and analyze misleading graphs.

Advertisements and news articles often use data to support a point. Sometimes the data is presented in a way that influences how the data is interpreted. A data display that distorts information in order to persuade can be *misleading*.

An axis in a graph can be "broken" to make the graph easier to read. However, a broken axis can also be misleading. In the graph at right, the cost per minute for service with Company B looks like it is twice as much as the cost for service with Company A. In fact, the difference is only $0.10 per minute.

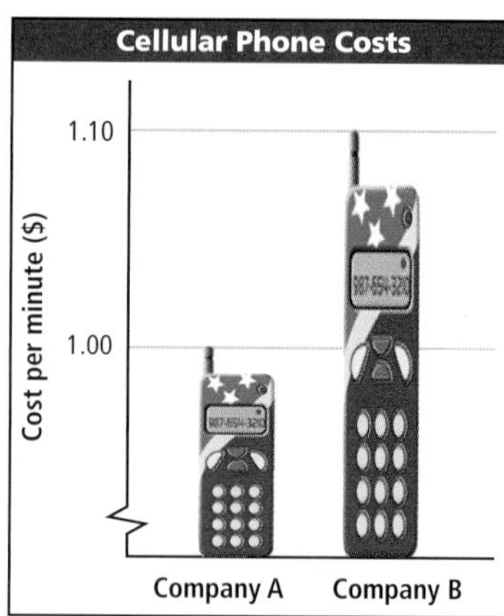

EXAMPLE 1 ***Social Studies Application***

Both bar graphs show the percent of people in California, Maryland, Michigan, and Washington who use seat belts. Which graph could be misleading? Why?

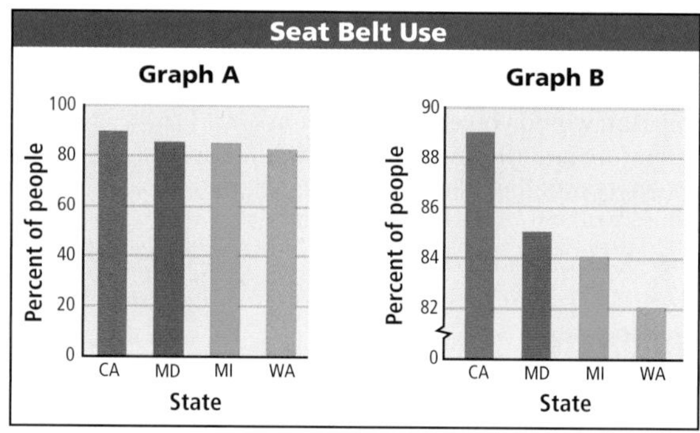

Graph B could be misleading. Because the vertical axis on graph B is broken, it appears that the percent of people in California who wear seat belts is twice as great as the percent in Michigan. In fact, it is only 5% greater. People might conclude from graph B that the percent of people in California who wear seat belts is much greater than the percents in the other states.

1 Introduce

Alternate Opener

EXPLORATION

1-9 Misleading Graphs

Two groups of students created bar graphs to show the number of students in their school by gender and by membership in the Spanish Club.

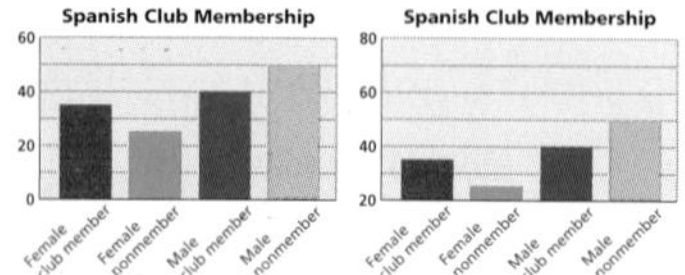

1. What are the differences in the two graphs?
2. Assume that you are the president of the Spanish Club and want to recruit more members. Which graph might you display? Explain.

Think and Discuss

3. **Explain** how the presentation of a graph can be misleading.
4. **Discuss** whether some types of graphs (bar graphs, line graphs, circle graphs, histograms, etc.) are more suitable for showing misleading information.

Motivate

To introduce misleading graphs, present these two possible advertisements:

1) CD players on sale! HUGE savings! Best buy of the year!
2) CD players on sale!

Discuss the fact that neither ad gives any specific information, but the impression made by the first ad is of greater savings. Tie the idea of different impressions to misleading graphs.

Exploration worksheet and answers on Chapter 1 Resource Book pp. 84 and 118

2 Teach

Lesson Presentation

Guided Instruction

In this lesson, students learn to identify and analyze misleading graphs. Discuss why people might construct a graph that is misleading, for example, to make something look better or worse that it is. Point out that people may unintentionally construct a misleading graph by shortening the *y*-axis to save space.

To help students see how misleading a graph with a broken axis can be, redraw the graph with a continuous axis.

EXAMPLE 2 Analyzing Misleading Graphs

Explain why each graph could be misleading.

A

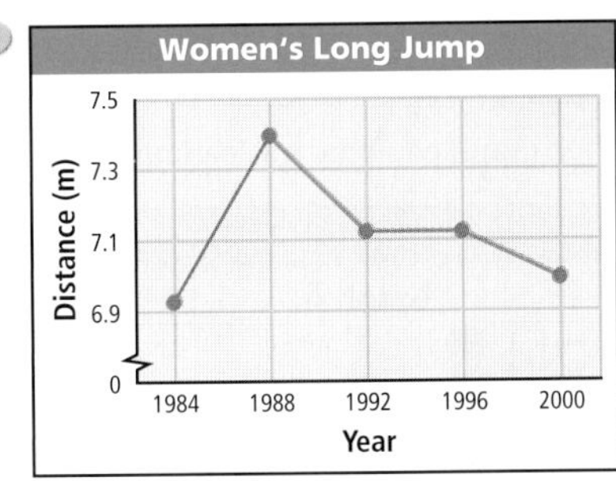

Because the scale on the vertical axis is broken, the distance jumped in 1988 appears to be over two times as far as in 1984. In fact, the distance jumped in 1988 is less than 0.5 meter greater than in the other years.

B

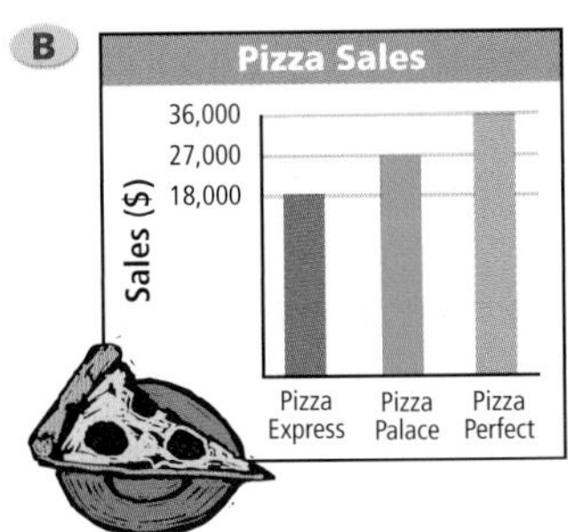

The scale of the graph is wrong. Equal distances on the graph should represent equal intervals of numbers, but in this graph, the first $18,000 in sales is larger than the next $18,000. Because of this, you can't tell from the bars that Pizza Perfect's sales were twice those of Pizza Express.

Think and Discuss

1. **Explain** how to use the scale of a graph to decide if the graph is misleading.
2. **Describe** what might indicate that a graph is misleading.
3. **Give an example** of a situation in which a misleading graph might be used to persuade readers.

Additional Examples

Example 1

Which graph could be misleading? Why?

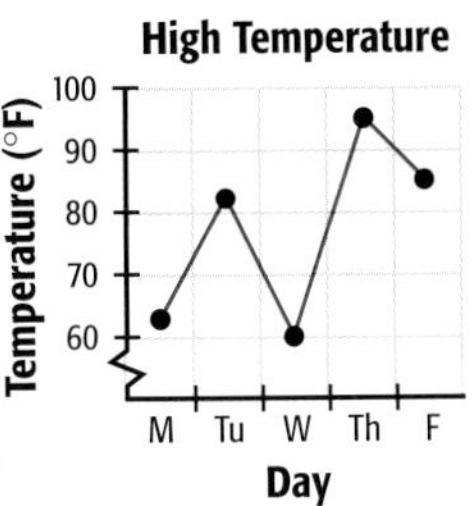

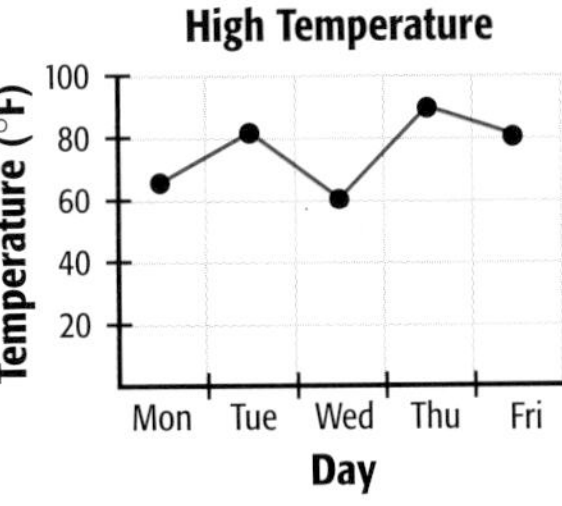

The top graph could be misleading. It gives the impression of greater temperature change because the vertical axis does not begin at zero.

Example 2

Explain how you could redraw each graph in Example 2 so that it would *not* be misleading.

A. Draw the entire vertical scale on the graph.

B. Draw the vertical scale with equal spacing between marks so that the distance between 0 and 18,000 is the same as the distance between 18,000 and 36,000.

3 Close

Reaching All Learners

Through Home Connection

Have students ask someone at home to help them find a graph in a magazine or newspaper that could be misleading. Encourage students to share their graphs with the class and discuss whether or how the graphs might be misleading.

Summarize

Ask students to describe different ways a graph can be misleading.

Possible answers: In a bar graph, the bars might be different widths. The vertical axis might be broken, which would give the impression of greater differences in the heights of the bars. In a line graph, the vertical axis might be broken or distorted, which would make the differences between the data points appear to be greater or less than they are. In a graph using shapes in place of bars, one shape might have a much greater area than another even if it is only twice as tall.

Answers to Think and Discuss

Possible answers:

1. Check that the scale starts at zero, check for a broken axis, and check that the intervals are equal.
2. If a graph has very dramatic differences, it is a good idea to check the data more closely to make sure that the graphs do not distort the actual information.
3. If a reporter has a bias toward a particular point of view, he or she might use a misleading graph to sway the opinion of the reader.

1-9 PRACTICE & ASSESS

Students may want to refer back to the lesson examples.

Assignment Guide

If you finished Example 1 assign:
Core 1, 4, 12–18
Enriched 1, 4, 12–18

If you finished Example 2 assign:
Core 1–8, 12–18
Enriched 1, 3, 4, 5, 7–18

Graph paper is provided on page 98 of the Chapter 1 Resource Book.

Answers

2. The vertical axis is broken, so differences in weight appear greater.
3. The vertical axis does not begin with zero, so differences in scales appear greater.
5. The scale of the graph is not divided into equal intervals, so differences in sales appear less than they actually are.
6. The horizontal axis is broken so differences in number of species appear greater.

1-9 Exercises

FOR EXTRA PRACTICE see page 656

internet connect
Homework Help Online
go.hrw.com Keyword: MS4 1-9

GUIDED PRACTICE

See Example 1

1. Which graph could be misleading? Why?

Graph A; The broken graph exaggerates the differences in lengths.

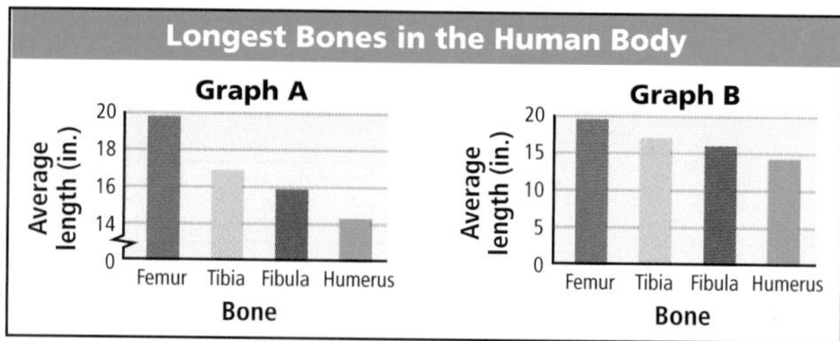

See Example 2

Explain why each graph could be misleading.

2.

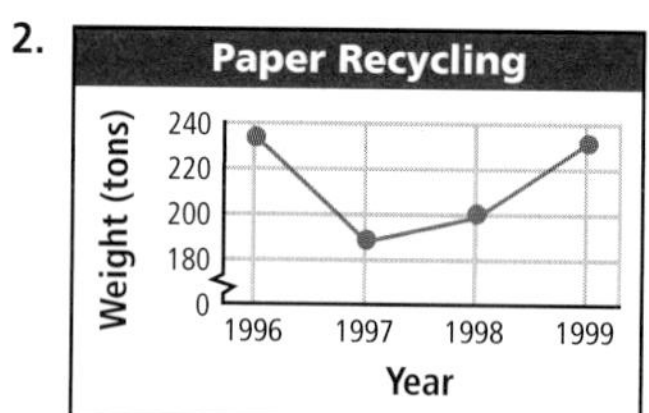

3.

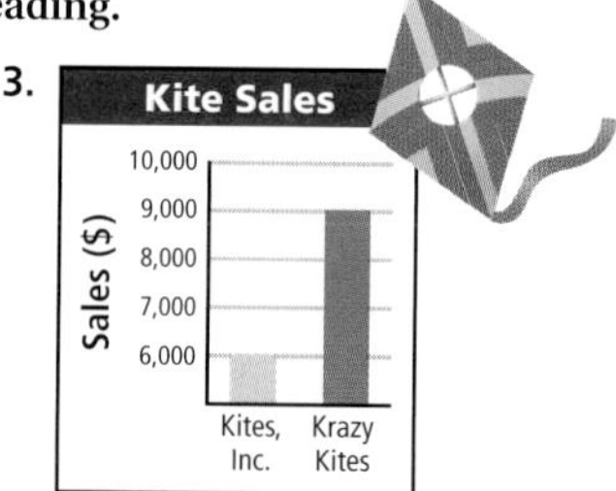

INDEPENDENT PRACTICE

See Example 1

4. Which graph could be misleading? Why?

Graph B; It suggests a greater change between months.

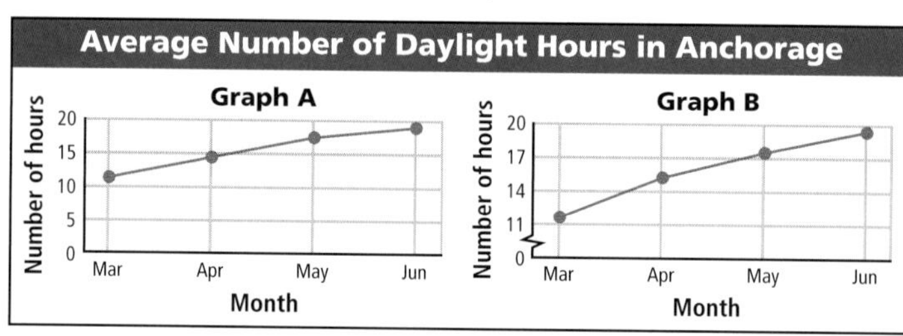

See Example 2

Explain why each graph could be misleading.

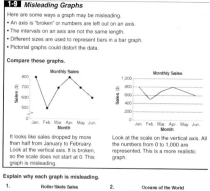

5.

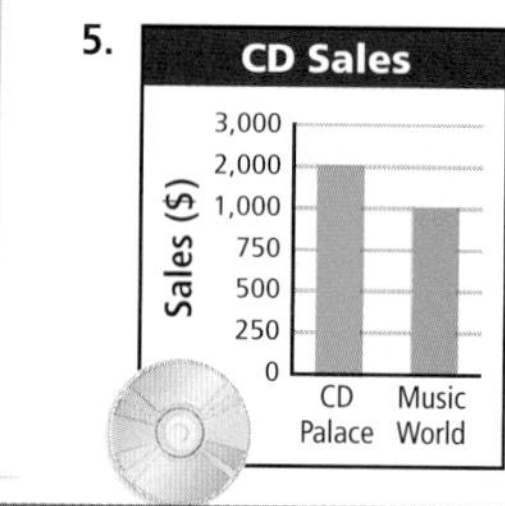

6.

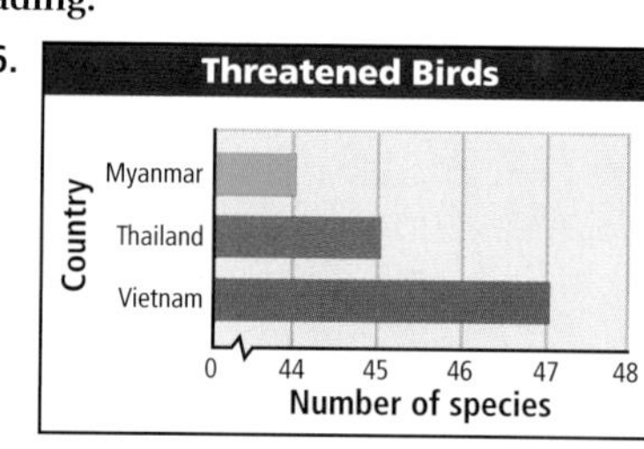

Math Background

The following questions may serve as screening devices to check if graphs and other statistics might be misleading:

1. What is the reputation of the source?
2. Does the presenter have a bias toward a particular point of view?
3. What supportive evidence is presented?
4. Does the information seem reasonable?

RETEACH 1-9

LESSON 1-9 **Reteach**
Misleading Graphs

Here are some ways a graph may be misleading.
• An axis is "broken" or numbers are left out on an axis.
• The intervals on an axis are not the same length.
• Different sizes are used to represent bars in a bar graph.
• Pictorial graphs could distort the data.

Compare these graphs.

It looks like sales dropped by more than half from January to February. Look at the vertical axis. It is broken, so the scale does not start at 0. This graph is misleading.

Look at the scale on the vertical axis. All the numbers from 0 to 1,000 are represented. This is a more realistic graph.

Explain why each graph is misleading.

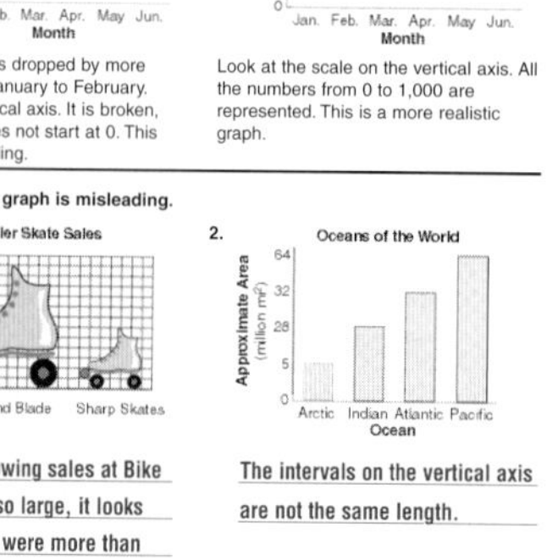

1. The skate showing sales at Bike and Blade is so large, it looks like the sales were more than twice as much.

2. The intervals on the vertical axis are not the same length.

PRACTICE 1-9

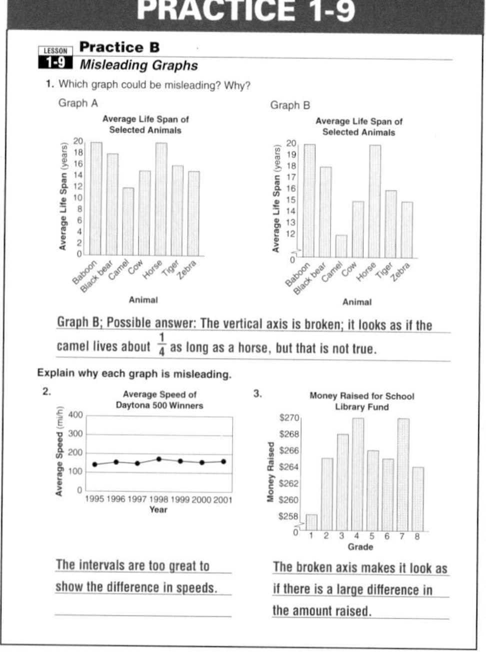

LESSON 1-9 **Practice B**
Misleading Graphs

1. Which graph could be misleading? Why?

Graph B; Possible answer: The vertical axis is broken; it looks as if the camel lives about $\frac{1}{4}$ as long as a horse, but that is not true.

Explain why each graph is misleading.

2. The intervals are too great to show the difference in speeds.

3. The broken axis makes it look as if there is a large difference in the amount raised.

PRACTICE AND PROBLEM SOLVING

7. ***HOBBIES*** The Appalachian Trail is a marked footpath that runs about 2,160 miles from Maine to Georgia. The bar graph shows the number of miles of trail in three states.
   a. Redraw the graph so that it is not misleading.
   b. Compare the two graphs.
   The first graph exaggerates the differences in length of the trail within the three states.

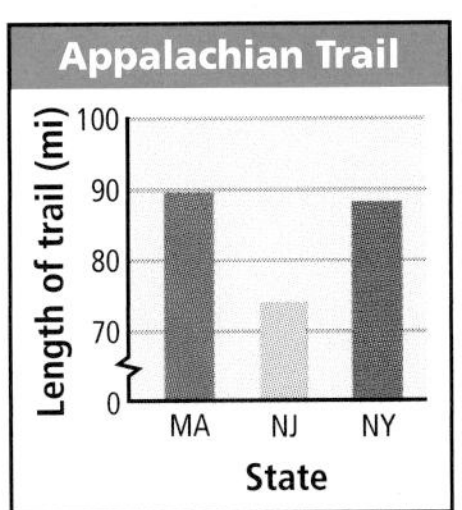

8. The graphs do not use the same scale, so it looks as though September had fewer sales than October, which is not true; redraw the graphs using the same scale.

8. ***BUSINESS*** The weekly sales of a car dealer are shown. Explain why the graphs are misleading. Then tell how you can redraw them so that they are not misleading.

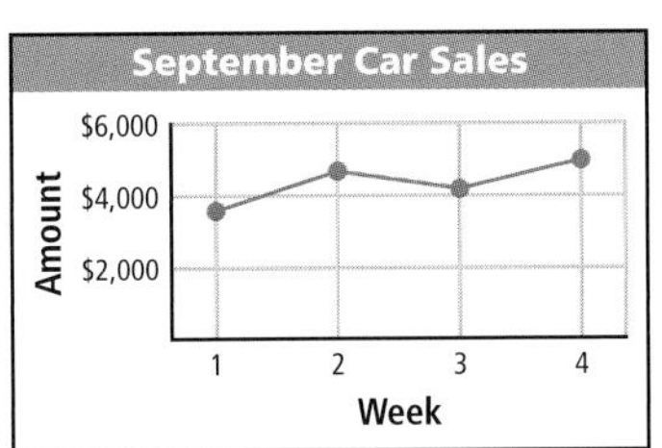

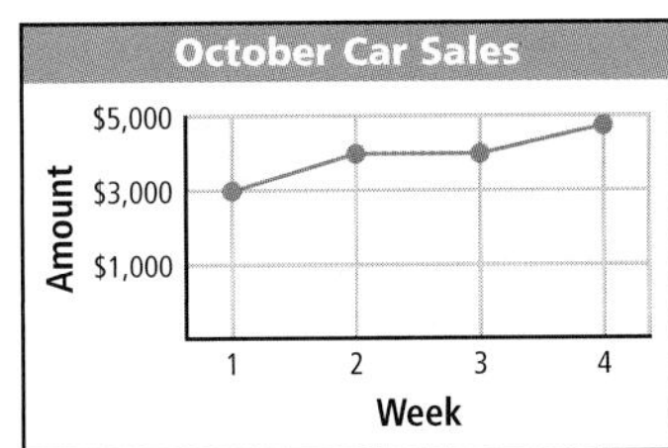

9. ***CHOOSE A STRATEGY*** Tanya had $1.19 in coins. None of the coins were dollars or 50-cent pieces. Josie asked Tanya for change for a dollar, but she did not have the correct change. Which coins did Tanya have? **Possible answer: three quarters, four dimes, and four pennies**

10. ***WRITE ABOUT IT*** Explain why it is important to closely examine graphs in advertisements. **Possible answer: The graph may seem to support a claim that the data really do not support.**

11. ***CHALLENGE*** A company asked 10 people about their favorite brand of toothpaste. Three people chose Sparkle, one person chose Smile, and six people chose Purely White. An advertisement for Sparkle states, "Three times as many people prefer Sparkle over Smile!" Explain why this statement is misleading. **Possible answer: The statement ignores the majority, those who prefer brand Purely White.**

Spiral Review

Simplify. (Previous course)

12. 15 • 7 • 4 **420**
13. 2 • 12 • 5 **120**
14. 3 • 14 • 3 **126**

Find the range of each data set. (Lesson 1-2)

15. 13, 6, 36, 3, 9 **33**
16. 20, 34, 25, 56, 46 **36**
17. 357, 395, 963, 873 **606**

18. **TEST PREP** Sergio has 50 stamps. This is twice as many as Tina has, plus 4. How many stamps does Tina have? (Previous course) **B**

A 21 stamps **B** 23 stamps **C** 29 stamps **D** 104 stamps

CHALLENGE 1-9

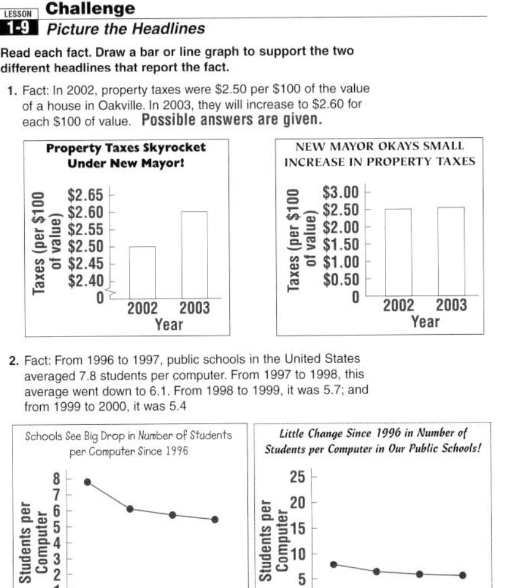

LESSON 1-9 **Challenge**
Picture the Headlines

Read each fact. Draw a bar or line graph to support the two different headlines that report the fact.

1. Fact: In 2002, property taxes were $2.50 per $100 of the value of a house in Oakville. In 2003, they will increase to $2.60 for each $100 of value. **Possible answers are given.**

Property Taxes Skyrocket Under New Mayor!

NEW MAYOR OKAYS SMALL INCREASE IN PROPERTY TAXES

2. Fact: From 1996 to 1997, public schools in the United States averaged 7.8 students per computer. From 1997 to 1998, this average went down to 6.1. From 1998 to 1999, it was 5.7; and from 1999 to 2000, it was 5.4

Schools See Big Drop in Number of Students per Computer Since 1996

Little Change Since 1996 in Number of Students per Computer in Our Public Schools!

PROBLEM SOLVING 1-9

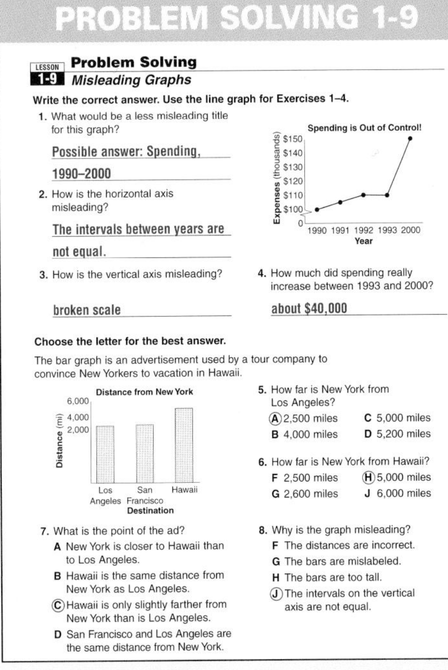

LESSON 1-9 **Problem Solving**
Misleading Graphs

Write the correct answer. Use the line graph for Exercises 1–4.

1. What would be a less misleading title for this graph? Possible answer: Spending, 1990–2000
2. How is the horizontal axis misleading? The intervals between years are not equal.
3. How is the vertical axis misleading? broken scale
4. How much did spending really increase between 1993 and 2000? about $40,000

Choose the letter for the best answer.

The bar graph is an advertisement used by a tour company to convince New Yorkers to vacation in Hawaii.

5. How far is New York from Los Angeles?
   (A) 2,500 miles C 5,000 miles
   B 4,000 miles D 5,200 miles
6. How far is New York from Hawaii?
   F 2,500 miles (H) 5,000 miles
   G 2,600 miles J 6,000 miles
7. What is the point of the ad?
   A New York is closer to Hawaii than to Los Angeles.
   B Hawaii is the same distance from New York as Los Angeles.
   (C) Hawaii is only slightly farther from New York than is Los Angeles.
   D San Francisco and Los Angeles are the same distance from New York.
8. Why is the graph misleading?
   F The distances are incorrect.
   G The bars are mislabeled.
   H The bars are too tall.
   (J) The intervals on the vertical axis are not equal.

Answers

7a.

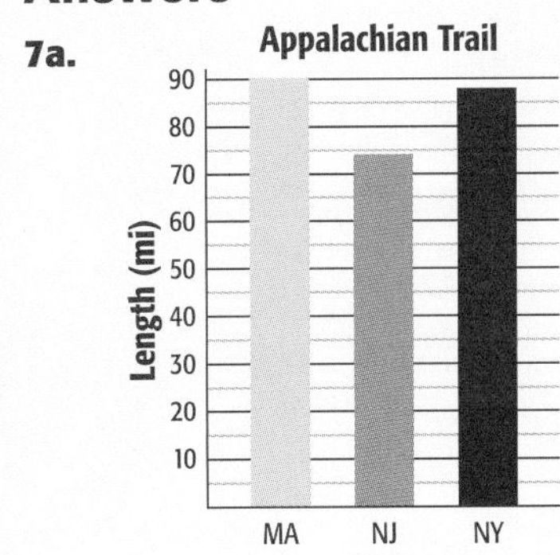

Journal

Have students choose one of the misleading graphs in the lesson and write about why it is misleading and how they would change it so that it would not be as misleading.

Test Prep Doctor

For Exercise 18, suggest that students can eliminate **C** and **D** by observing that Tina must have only about half the number of stamps that Sergio has.

Lesson Quiz

Explain why each graph could be misleading.

1.

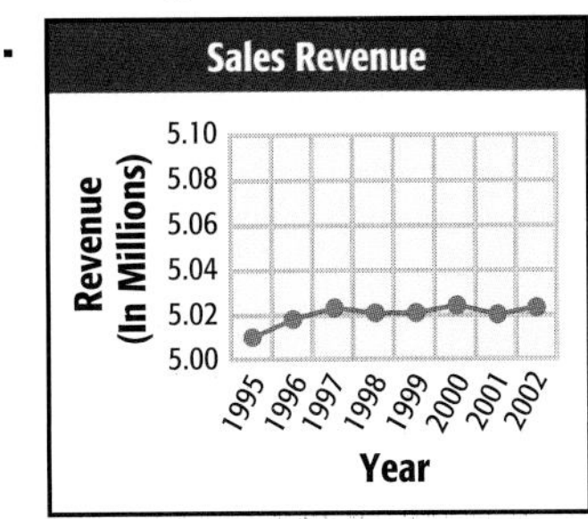

The vertical scale on the graph is not small enough to show the changes, so it appears to be unchanging and flat.

2.

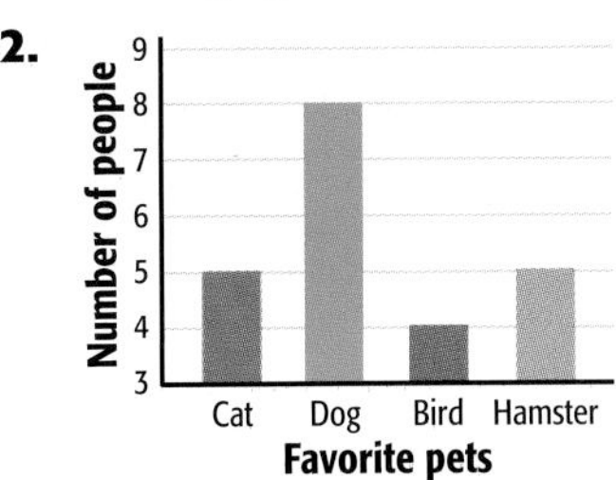

The scale does not start at 0, so it looks like fewer people like each type of animal.

Available on Daily Transparency in CRB

Problem Solving on Location

Ohio

Purpose: *To provide additional practice for problem-solving skills in Chapter 1*

Covered Bridges

- After problem 1, ask students the following questions: Which interval has the greatest frequency? **0–2** Which interval has the smallest frequency? **7–8** What are the cumulative frequencies of these intervals? **11; 16**
- After problem 5, ask the following questions: Which was easiest to find from the stem-and-leaf plot, the mode, the median, or the mean? Possible answer: The mode was easiest to find. How do you find the median of a set of data with an even number of values? Possible answer: Find the average of the two middle values.

Extension Have students look up the average normal temperature for each month in Greater Cincinnati and make a stem-and-leaf plot of the data. Then ask students to find the mode, median, and mean of the data.

Average Monthly Normal Temperatures in Greater Cincinnati (°F)

Stems	Leaves
2	8
3	2 4
4	3 4
5	3 5
6	3 7
7	1 4 5

Key: 3|2 means 32

mode: none; median: 54°F; mean: 53.25°F

Problem Solving on Location

OHIO

Covered Bridges

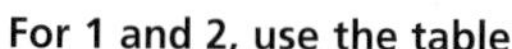

Ohio has many historic covered bridges. They are located in different counties throughout the state. The table shows the number of covered bridges in selected counties in Ohio.

For 1 and 2, use the table.

Covered Bridges in Ohio

County	Number of Bridges	County	Number of Bridges
Hamilton	1	Pickaway	2
Brown	5	Perry	5
Scioto	1	Washington	10
Gallia	0	Ashtabula	16
Vinton	5	Clermont	1
Pike	0	Adams	2
Ross	1	Lawrence	1
Butler	2	Meigs	0
Montgomery	3	Jackson	3

1. Make a cumulative frequency table of the data.
2. Make a histogram of the data.

For 3–5, use the table.

Average Monthly Maximum Temperatures in Greater Cincinnati (°F)

Jan	Feb	Mar	Apr	May	Jun	Jul	Aug	Sep	Oct	Nov	Dec
38	42	52	64	74	82	86	85	78	66	53	42

3. Make a stem-and-leaf plot of the data.
4. Find the mean, median, mode, and range of the data set. **63.5°F; 65°F; 42°F; 48°F**
5. Is the mode a good representation of the average maximum temperatures? Explain.

Answers

1. Possible answer:

Number of Covered Bridges	Number of Counties	Cumulative Frequency
0–2	11	11
3–4	2	13
5–6	3	16
7–8	0	16
9–10	1	17
11 or more	1	18

2. Possible answer:

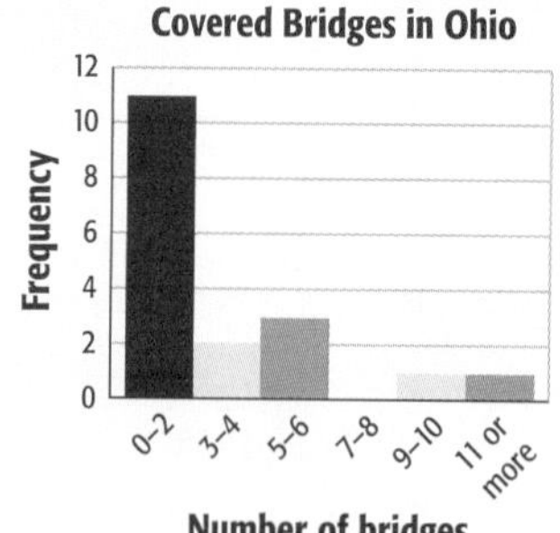

3. Possible answer:

Average Maximum Temperatures in Greater Cincinnati (°F)

Stems	Leaves
3	8
4	2 2
5	2 3
6	4 6
7	4 8
8	2 5 6

Key: 4|2 means 42

5. Possible answer: No, the mode is close to the lowest average monthly maximum temperature. The median or the mean is a better representation of the average monthly maximum temperatures.

Ohio's Agriculture

Among other agricultural commodities, soybeans, corn, and wheat are grown on farms in Ohio. The double-bar graph shows the number of acres of these crops harvested in 1999 and 2000.

For 1–4, use the graph.

1. Which crop had a smaller harvest in 2000 than in 1999? **soybeans**
2. About how many more acres of soybeans were harvested in 1999 than acres of corn? Round to the nearest hundred. **about 1,100 thousand acres**
3. About how many more acres of corn were harvested in 2000 than in 1999? **about 200 thousand acres**
4. About how many more acres of soybeans were harvested in 2000 than acres of wheat? Round to the nearest hundred. **about 3,100 thousand acres**

For 5–8, use the table.

5. Make a double-line graph of the data.
6. Describe how the population of each city changed from 1950 to 1990. **Cleveland's population decreased while Columbus's population increased.**
7. During which ten-year period did the population of Cleveland change the most? **1970 to 1980**
8. During which ten-year period did the population of Columbus change the most? **1950 to 1960**

Populations of Cleveland and Columbus		
Year	Cleveland	Columbus
1950	910,000	380,000
1960	880,000	470,000
1970	750,000	540,000
1980	570,000	570,000
1990	500,000	630,000

Ohio's Agriculture

- After problem 4, have students find the total crop harvest of corn, soybeans, and wheat for 1999 and 2000. Which year had a greater total harvest of these crops? 1999: 8,700,000 acres; 2000: 8,800,000 acres; 2000
- After problem 6, have students find the total decrease in population of Cleveland from 1950 to 1990. 410,000 Then ask students to find the total increase in the population in Columbus from 1950 to 1990. 250,000

Extension Ask students to look up the populations of Cleveland and Columbus in the year 2000 and round the populations to the nearest ten thousand. Cleveland: 478,000; Columbus: 711,000 Then have students extend their double-line graphs to include the population in 2000.

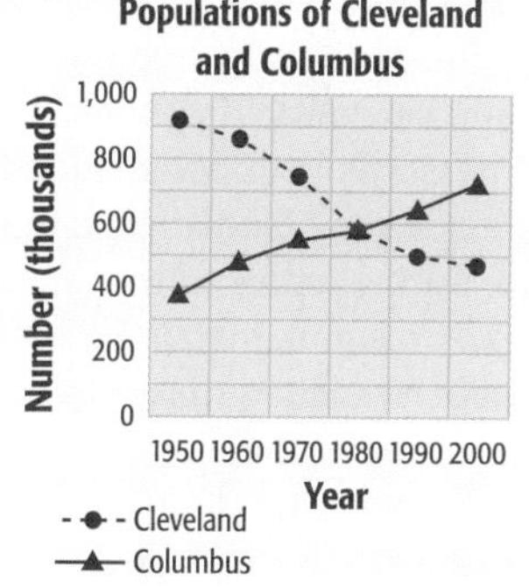

Answer

5. Possible answer:

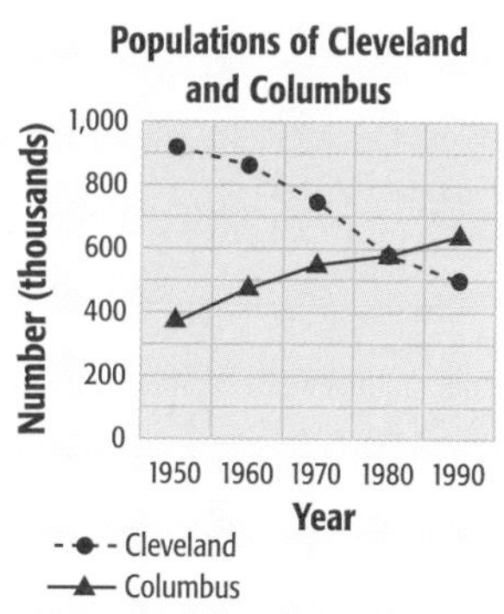

MATH-ABLES

Game Resources

Puzzles, Twisters & Teasers
Chapter 1 Resource Book

Code Breaker

Purpose: *To apply the problem-solving skill of finding a pattern to perform a fun activity*

Discuss: Ask students to use a dictionary to look up the meaning of the word *cryptogram*. Discuss who might use a cryptogram. Which letters should occur most frequently in a cryptogram? Possible answer: A cryptogram is a message written in code. Cryptograms might be used by spies or intelligence agencies. The letters that should occur most frequently are *E, T, A, O, I,* and *N.*

Extend: Have students explain how to make up a code and a secret message. Then invite students to create their own codes and secret messages and trade secret messages with other students. Possible answer: Make a table. In one column, list the letters of the alphabet. In the next column, match each letter with a different letter, making sure to use each letter of the alphabet only once. Then write out the message you want to put into code. Beneath each letter of your message, write the substitute letter from the second column.

MATH-ABLES

Code Breaker

There are two main types of codes, or ciphers: *transposition* and *substitution*. In transposition, you switch the letters to make new words. Can you identify the following words?

REBMUN (Read the word backward.)

RGPAIHGN (Switch every other letter.)

THMA (Switch the first and last part of the word.)

Now try it with the sentence DOGS HAVE FOUR LEGS.

Substitution codes, such as *cryptograms*, are made by substituting different letters, numbers, or symbols for the originals. For example, suppose *RQH* represents *AND*. Each *A* in the puzzle would be written as *R*, each *N* as *Q*, and each *D* as *H*.

You can use math to solve a cryptogram. The following list tells you the probability for the occurrence of each letter of the English alphabet.

A	11	**B**	2	**C**	4	**D**	5	**E**	17	**F**	3
G	2	**H**	7	**I**	10	**J**	0	**K**	1	**L**	5
M	3	**N**	10	**O**	11	**P**	3	**Q**	0	**R**	8
S	9	**T**	13	**U**	4	**V**	1	**W**	3	**X**	0
Y	2	**Z**	0								

By knowing, for example, that *E* appears more often than any other letter, you can decode a message much more easily. Try decoding the following message by counting the number of times each letter appears.

AXMTV KDM VTAGTI YTVVKHTV KGT EJD. LGSIT NXJG XLD AXMT KDM IGN SI XJI XD NXJG EGSTDMV KDM EKYSCN.

Codes and secret messages are fun. Write your own code and try it out on your friends and family.

Technology LAB

Find Mean and Median

internet connect
Lab Resources Online
go.hrw.com
KEYWORD: MS4 TechLab1

The scores on a math test that is worth 25 points were 23, 25, 10, 15, 22, 15, 9, 18, 17, 20, 15, 21, 5, 11, 24, 25, 20, 16, 20, 23, 17, 18, 23, 24, 10, 13, and 20.

Activity

Use your graphing calculator to find the mean and median of the test scores.
To enter the values into list 1 (**L1**), press STAT 1.

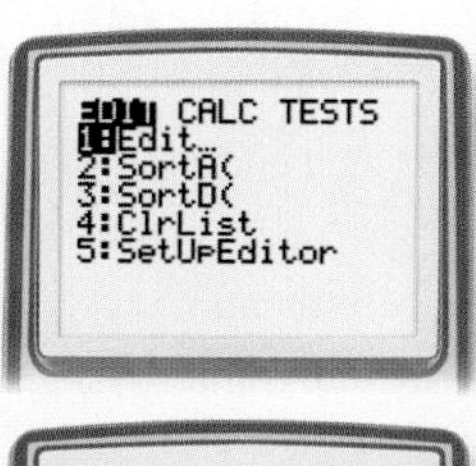

Type the data into **L1**. Press ENTER after each value.

To exit the list, press 2nd MODE (QUIT). Then use the **LIST** menu to find the mean of the data.

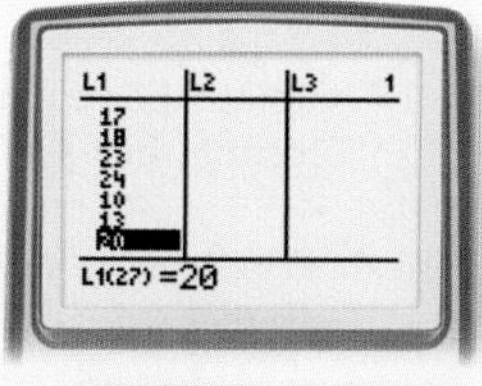

Press 2nd STAT (LIST) ◀ ◀ to highlight **MATH**. Press the down arrow twice to highlight **3: mean(**. Press ENTER.

Then press 2nd 1 ENTER to enter **L1** and see the mean.

The mean of the test scores, to the nearest hundredth, is 17.74.

To find the median, use the **LIST** menu again.

Press 2nd STAT (LIST) ◀ ◀ to highlight **MATH**. Press the down arrow three times to highlight **4: median(**. Press ENTER.

Then press 2nd 1 ENTER. The median of the test scores is 18.

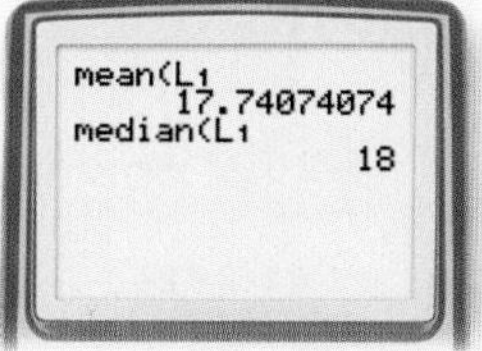

Think and Discuss

1. What do you think the **min** and **max** functions in the **LIST** menu will find?

Try This

Find the mean and median of each data set.

1. 1, 4, 5, 2, 1, 7, 9, 8, 5, 3, 5, 2, 8, 2, 7, 7

2. 55, 40, 70, 75, 60, 80, 70, 75, 70, 80

Answers

Think and Discuss

1. Possible answer: The **min** function will find the minimum, or lowest, value. The **max** function will find the maximum, or highest, value.

Try This

1. mean: 4.75; median: 5

2. mean: 67.5; median: 70

Technology LAB

Find Mean and Median

Objective: To use a graphing calculator to find the mean and median of a data set

Materials: Graphing calculator

Lab Resources

Technology Lab Activities . . . . p. 4

Using the Page

This technology activity shows students how to find the mean and median of a data set on graphing calculator. Specific keystrokes may vary, depending on the kind of graphing calculator used. The keystrokes given are for a TI-83 model. For keystrokes to other models, visit www.go.hrw.com.

The Think and Discuss problem can be used to assess students' understanding of other functions that can be performed on the data in this technology activity. While Try This problems 1 and 2 can be solved without a graphing calculator, they are meant to help students become familiar with using a graphing calculator to find the mean and median.

Assessment

Find the median and mean of each data set to the nearest hundredth.

1. 9, 8, 6, 4, 10, 3, 7, 6, 2, 1, 5
median 6; mean 5.55

2. 95, 83, 72, 89, 68, 75, 98, 87
median 85; mean 83.38

Purpose: *To help students review and practice concepts and skills presented in Chapter 1*

Assessment Resources 

Chapter Review
Chapter 1 Resource Book . . . pp. 92–94

***Test and Practice Generator* CD-ROM**

Additional review assessment items in both multiple-choice and free-response format may be generated for any objective in Chapter 1.

Answers

1. population; sample
2. mean
3. histogram; bar graph
4. negative correlation
5. population: the students in the school; sample: the first 5 students

Chapter 1

Study Guide and Review

Vocabulary

bar graph 20
box-and-whisker plot . . . 28
circle graph 24
cumulative frequency . . . 14
double-bar graph 20
double-line graph 36
first quartile 28
frequency table 14
histogram 21
line graph 35
lower extreme 28
mean 10
median 10
mode 10
negative correlation 41
no correlation 41
outlier 11
population 4
positive correlation 41
random sample 5
range 10
sample 4
scatter plot 40
second quartile 28
sector 24
stem-and-leaf plot 15
third quartile 28
upper extreme 28

Complete the sentences below with vocabulary words from the list above. Words may be used more than once.

1. When gathering information about a(n) __?__, researchers often study part of the group, called a(n) __?__.
2. The sum of the data values divided by the number of data items is called the __?__ of the data.
3. A(n) __?__ is a type of __?__ that shows the frequency of data within equal intervals.
4. If the values in one data set increase as the values in the other set decrease, then the data sets show a(n) __?__.

1-1 Populations and Samples (pp. 4–7)

EXAMPLE

■ **Identify the population and sample.**

A scientist tags 30 Canada geese to learn about the migration pattern of Canada geese.

Population	Sample
All Canada geese	The 30 Canada geese that were tagged

EXERCISES

Identify the population and sample.

5. The band director asks the first 5 students who enter the band hall after school how long they practice each afternoon.

1-2 Mean, Median, Mode, and Range (pp. 10–13)

EXAMPLE

- **Find the mean, median, mode, and range of the data set 3, 7, 10, 2, 3.**

  mean: $3 + 7 + 10 + 2 + 3 = 25 \quad \frac{25}{5} = 5$
  median: 2, 3, 3, 7, 10
  mode: 3 **range:** $10 - 2 = 8$

EXERCISES

Find the mean, median, mode, and range of each data set.

6. 2, 8, 0, 2, 3, 5, 7, 5, 4
7. 324, 233, 324, 399, 233, 299
8. 48, 39, 27, 52, 45, 47, 49, 37

1-3 Frequency Tables and Stem-and-Leaf Plots (pp. 14–17)

EXAMPLE

- **Make a stem-and-leaf plot of the data 27, 19, 35, 28, 25, 16, 39, 32, 29, 31, 16.**

Stems	Leaves
1	6 6 9
2	5 7 8 9
3	1 2 5 9

Key: 2|5 means 25

EXERCISES

Use the data set 35, 29, 14, 19, 32, 25, 27, 16, 8 for Exercises 9 and 10.

9. Make a cumulative frequency table of the data.
10. Make a stem-and-leaf plot of the data.

1-4 Bar Graphs and Histograms (pp. 20–23)

EXAMPLE

- **Make a bar graph of the chess club's results: W, L, W, W, L, W, L, L, W, W, W, L, W.**

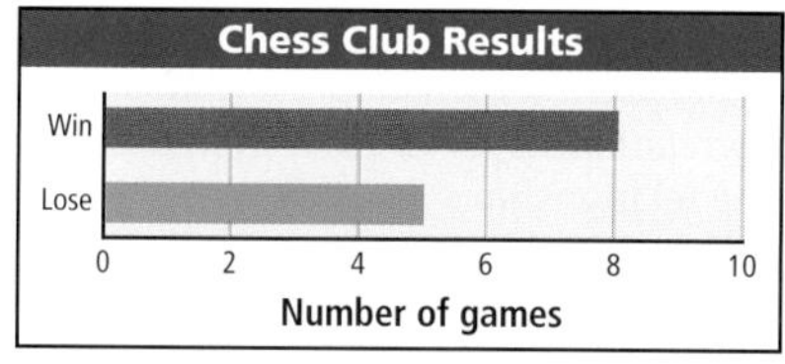

EXERCISES

11. Make a double-bar graph of the data.

Favorite Pet	Girls	Boys
Cat	42	31
Dog	36	52
Fish	3	10
Other	19	7

1-5 Reading and Interpreting Circle Graphs (pp. 24–27)

EXAMPLE

- **About what percent of people said yellow was their favorite color?**
  about 25%

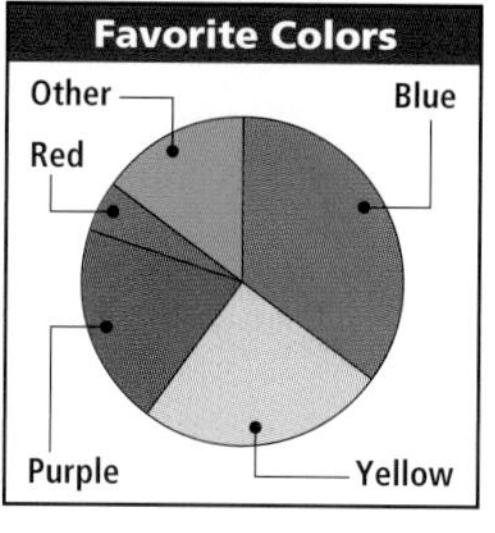

EXERCISES

Use the circle graph for Exercises 12 and 13.

12. Did more people choose purple or yellow as their favorite color?
13. According to the survey results, 35% of people chose blue as their favorite color. Out of the 100 people surveyed, how many people chose blue?

Answers

6. 4; 4; 2 and 5; 8
7. 302; 311.5; 233 and 324; 166
8. 43; 46; none; 25
9.

	Frequency	Cumulative Frequency
0–9	1	1
10–19	3	4
20–29	3	7
30–39	2	9

10.

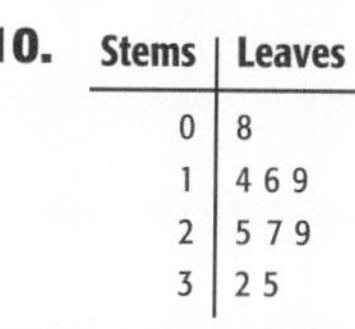

11.

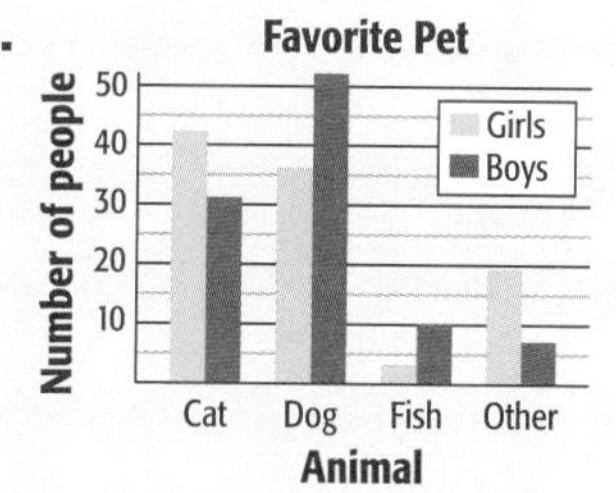

12. yellow
13. 35 people

Answers

14.

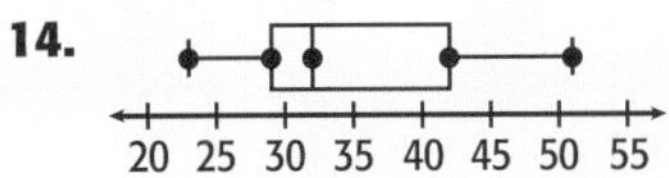

15.

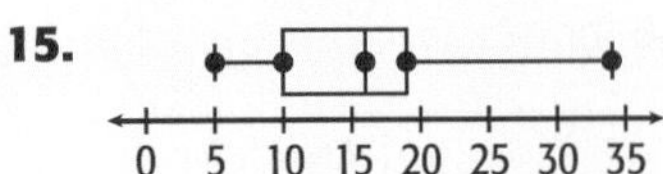

16.

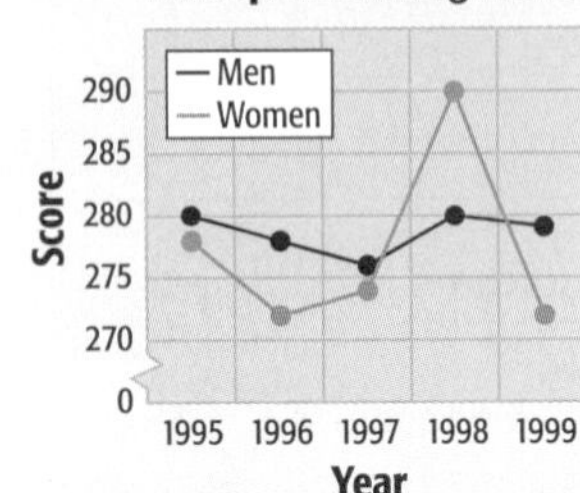

17.

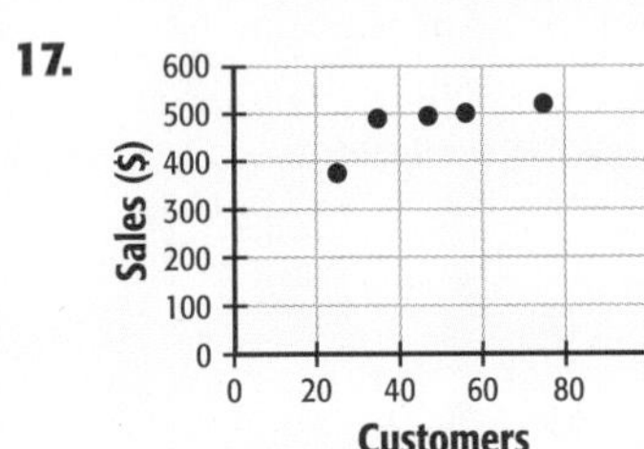

positive correlation

18. The high temperature did not change that much, though the graph makes the changes look significant.

1-6 Box-and-Whisker Plots (pp. 28–31)

EXAMPLE

- **Use the data to make a box-and-whisker plot: 14, 10, 23, 16, 21, 26, 23, 17, 25.**

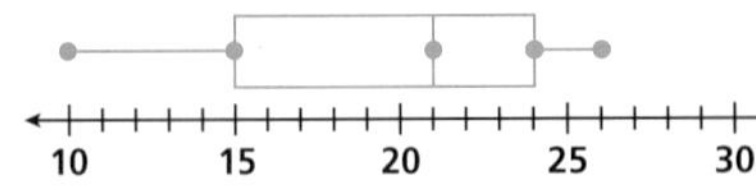

EXERCISES

Use the data to make a box-and-whisker plot.

14. 33, 38, 43, 30, 29, 40, 51, 27, 42, 23, 31

15. 11, 14, 18, 5, 16, 8, 19, 10, 17, 20, 34

1-7 Line Graphs (pp. 35–38)

EXAMPLE

- **Make a line graph of the rainfall data: Apr, 5 in.; May, 3 in.; Jun, 4 in.; Jul, 1 in.**

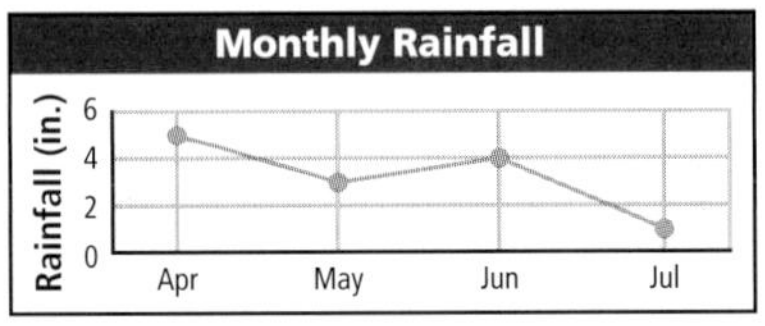

Monthly Rainfall

Rainfall (in.) 0 2 4 6 — Apr May Jun Jul

EXERCISES

16. Make a double-line graph of the data in the table.

U. S. Open Winning Scores					
	1995	**1996**	**1997**	**1998**	**1999**
Men	280	278	276	280	279
Women	278	272	274	290	272

1-8 Scatter Plots (pp. 40–43)

EXAMPLE

- **Write *positive correlation, negative correlation,* or *no correlation* to describe the relationship.**

date of birth and eye color

There seems to be no correlation between the data sets.

EXERCISES

17. Use the data to make a scatter plot. Write *positive correlation, negative correlation,* or *no correlation* to describe the relationship.

Customers	47	56	35	75	25
Sales ($)	495	501	490	520	375

1-9 Misleading Graphs (pp. 44–47)

EXAMPLE

- **Explain why the graph could be misleading.**

Shoe Sales

Sales ($) 0 800 850 900 — A B — Company

Because the vertical axis is broken, it appears that Company A's sales are more than twice Company B's sales.

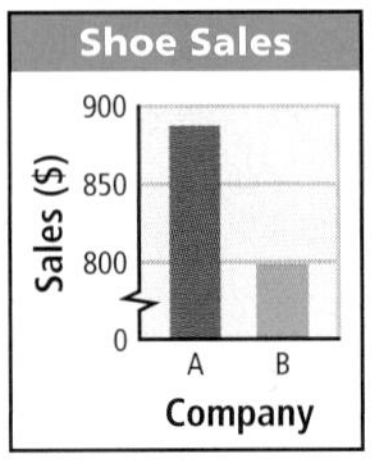

EXERCISES

18. Explain why the graph could be misleading.

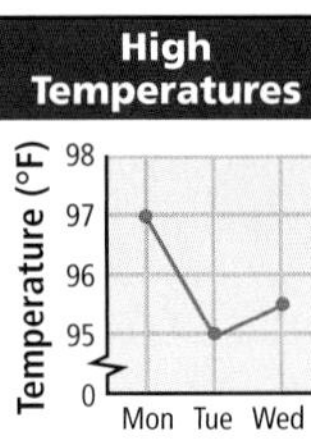

Chapter Test

Chapter 1

1. A swim instructor asks 5 of his students which stroke they prefer. Identify the population and sample. **population: all people taking lessons; sample: the 5 students who are asked their preferences**

Use the data set 12, 18, 12, 22, 28, 23, 32, 10, 29, 36 for problems 2–9.

2. Find the mean, median, mode, and range of the data set. **22.2; 22.5; 12; 26**
3. How would the outlier 57 affect the mean of the data? **It would increase the mean.**
4. Make a cumulative frequency table of the data.
5. Make a stem-and-leaf plot of the data.
6. Make a histogram of the data.
7. Make a box-and-whisker plot of the data.
8. What is the third quartile? **29**
9. What fraction of the data is less than 23? $\frac{1}{2}$

Use the table for problems 10 and 11.

Mammal	Male	Female
Gorilla	450	200
Lion	400	300
Tiger	420	300

10. The table shows the weight in pounds of several mammals. Make a double-bar graph of the data.
11. Which mammal shows the greatest weight difference between the male and the female? **gorilla**

Use the circle graph for problems 12–14.

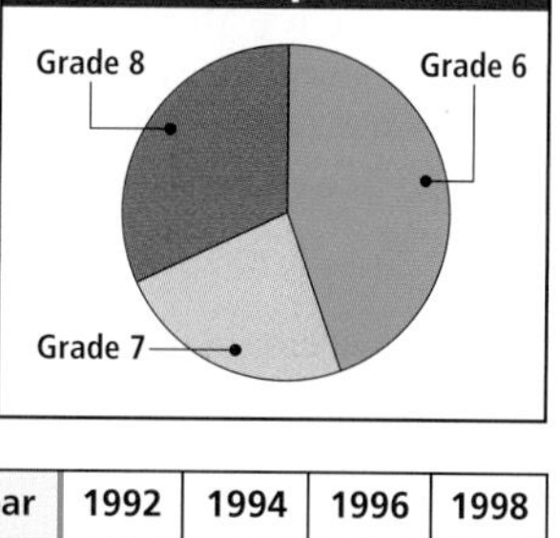

12. Which grade has the most students? **grade 6**
13. Approximately what percent of the students are seventh graders? **25%**
14. If the school population is 1,200 students, are more than 500 students in eighth grade? Explain. **No; about $\frac{1}{3}$ of school is grade 8, and $\frac{1}{3}$ of 1,200 is 400.**

Use the table for problems 15–17.

Year	1992	1994	1996	1998
Rate	21.0	20.7	21.2	21.6

15. The table shows passenger car fuel rates in miles per gallon for several years. Make a line graph of the data.
16. During which 2-year period did the fuel rate decrease? **1992–1994**
17. Estimate the fuel rate in 1997. **21.4 miles per gallon**

For problems 18 and 19, write *positive correlation, negative correlation,* or *no correlation* to describe each relationship.

18. size of hand and typing speed **no correlation**
19. height from which an object is dropped and time it takes to hit the ground **positive correlation**

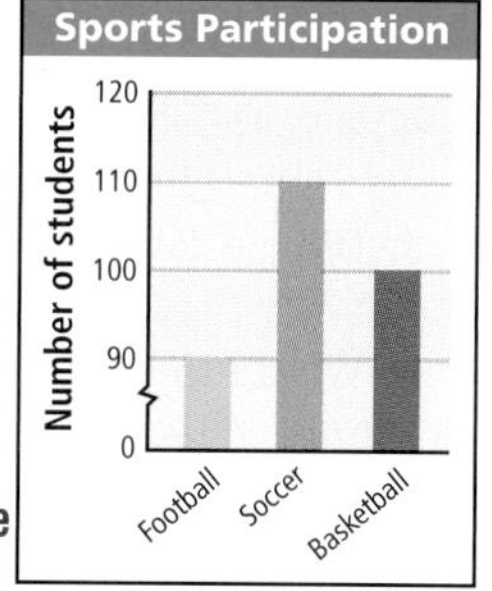

20. Explain why the graph at right could be misleading. **Part of the vertical scale is missing, making the values appear to differ greatly.**

Answers

4.

	Frequency	Cumulative Frequency
10–19	4	4
20–29	4	8
30–39	2	10

5.

Stem	Leaves
1	0 2 2 8
2	2 3 8 9
3	2 6

Key: 3|2 means 32

6.

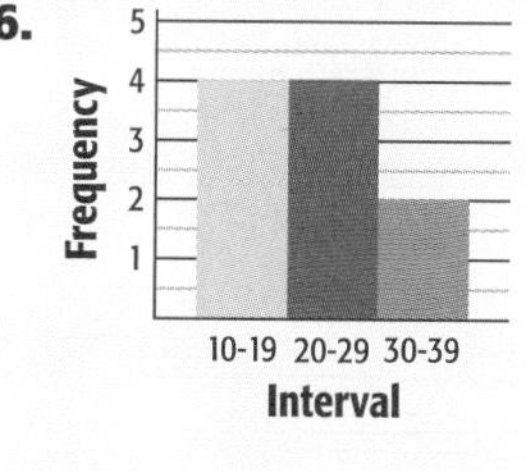

7.

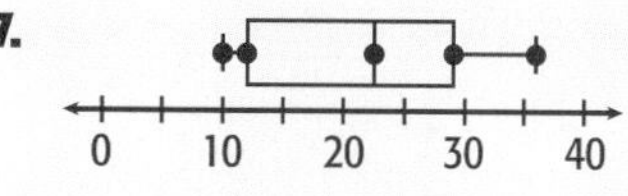

10.

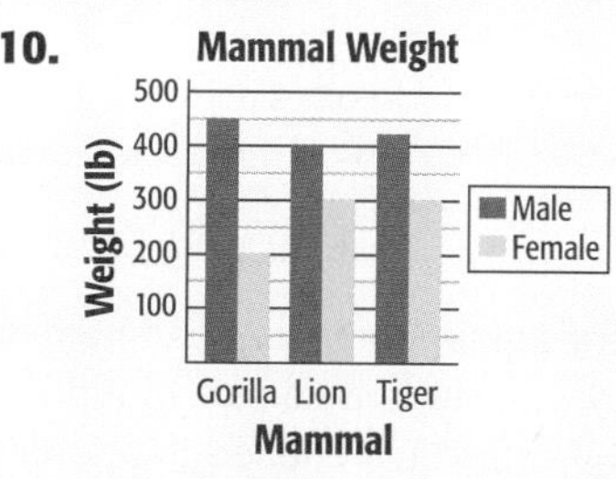

15.

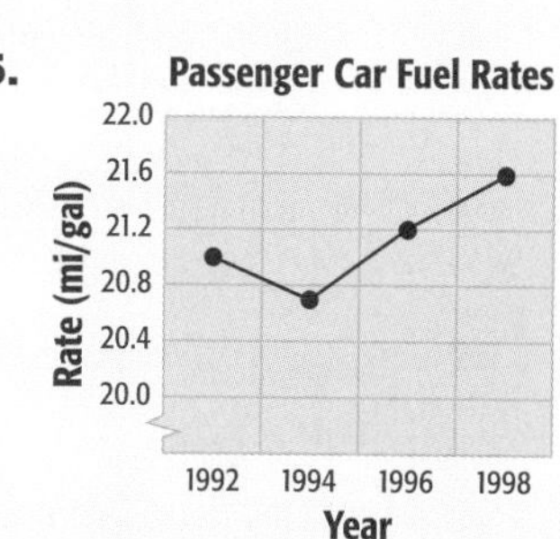

Chapter Test

Purpose: *To assess students' mastery of concepts and skills in Chapter 1*

Assessment Resources

Chapter 1 Tests (Levels A, B, C)
Assessment Resources ..... pp. 33–38

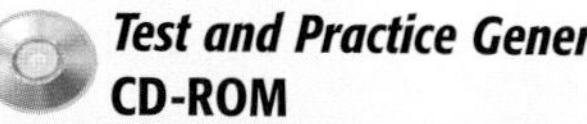

***Test and Practice Generator* CD-ROM**

Additional assessment items in both multiple-choice and free-response format may be generated for any objective in Chapter 1.

Chapter Test

Chapter 1 Performance Assessment

Purpose: *To assess students' understanding of concepts in Chapter 1 and combined problem-solving skills*

Assessment Resources

Answers

4. See Level 3 work sample below.

Scoring Rubric for Problem Solving Item 4

Level 3
Accomplishes the purposes of the task.
Student gives clear explanations, shows understanding of mathematical ideas and processes, and computes accurately.

Level 2
Purposes of the task not fully achieved.
Student demonstrates satisfactory but limited understanding of the mathematical ideas and processes.

Level 1
Purposes of the task not accomplished.
Student shows little evidence of understanding the mathematical ideas and processes and makes computational and/or procedural errors.

Chapter 1 Performance Assessment

Show What You Know

Create a portfolio of your work from this chapter. Complete this page and include it with your four best pieces of work from Chapter 1. Choose from your homework or lab assignments, mid-chapter quizzes, or any journal entries you have done. Put them together using any design you want. Make your portfolio represent what you consider your best work.

Short Response

1. Find the mean, median, mode, and range of the data set 48, 53, 46, 61, 63, 58, 52, 44, 51, and 63. Which measure of central tendency best represents the data? Explain your answer.

1. 53.9; 52.5; 63; 19; mean or median; because most of the data items are closest to these measures

2. The circle graph shows the results of a survey about favorite kinds of pie. Do more people prefer apple pie than pecan and pumpkin pie combined? Explain your answer.

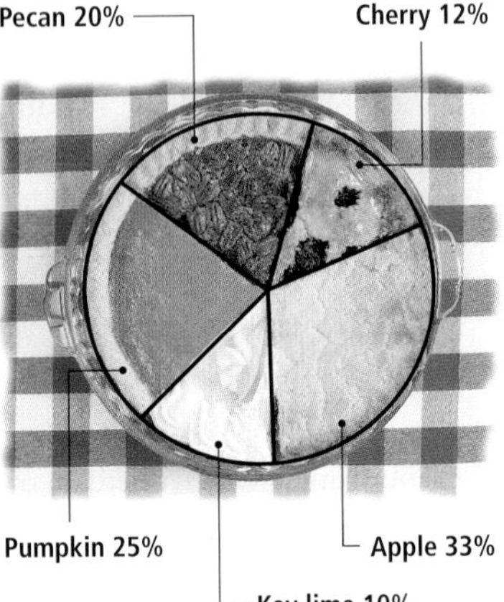

2. No; together the sectors for pecan and pumpkin pie are larger than the sector for apple pie.

3. For ten days, Marcia went to the park and interviewed joggers for a report on physical fitness. The list shows the number of joggers she interviewed each day.

   12, 20, 5, 7, 8, 17, 13, 11, 3, 17

   Create a cumulative frequency table of the data. On how many days did Marcia interview fewer than 11 joggers?

3. Possible answer:

Number of Joggers	Frequency	Cumulative Frequency
1–5	2	2
6–10	2	4
11–15	3	7
16–20	3	10

; 4

Extended Problem Solving

4. Mr. Parker wants to identify the types of activities in which high school students participate after school, so he surveys the twelfth-graders in his science classes. The table shows the results of the survey.

Activity	Boys	Girls
Play sports	36	24
Talk to friends	6	30
Do homework	15	18
Work	5	4

   a. Use the data in the table to construct a double-bar graph.

   b. What is the mean number of girls per activity? Show your work.

   c. Identify the population and the sample in the survey. Explain why Mr. Parker's sampling method may not be random.

Student Work Samples for Item 4

Level 3

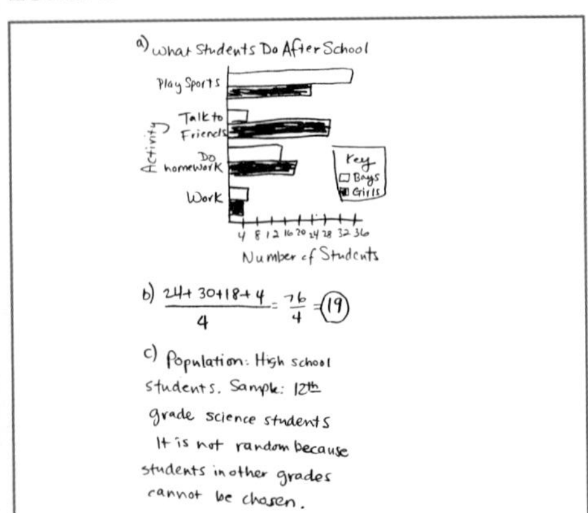

The student created an accurate graph with labels and a key, correctly calculated the mean, and explained a possible bias in the experiment.

Level 2

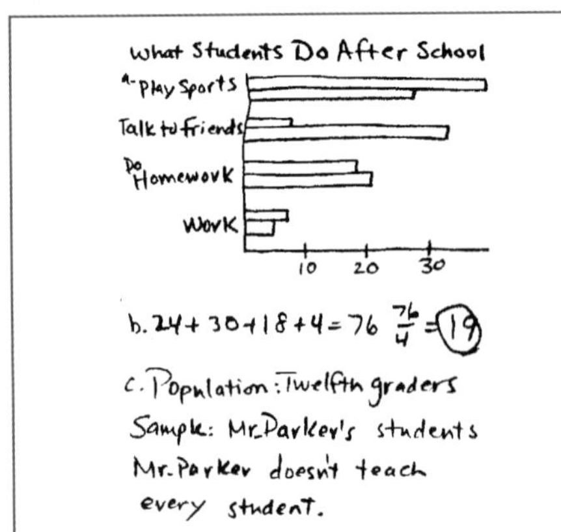

The student's graph appears accurate but lacks a key. The student correctly found the mean but incorrectly identified the population in part **c**.

Level 1

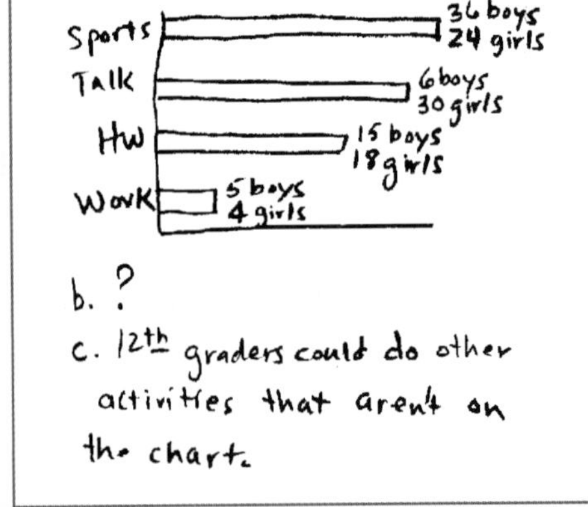

The student failed to make a double-bar graph and did not scale the axis. The student also did not give complete answers for parts **b** and **c**.

internet connect

State-Specific Test Practice Online
go.hrw.com Keyword: MS4 TestPrep

Standardized Test Prep

Chapter 1

Cumulative Assessment, Chapter 1

Use the numbers 8, 6, 7, 9, 8, 17, 8, 9 for items 1–3.

1. What is the mean of the numbers? **B**

Ⓐ 8 Ⓑ 9 Ⓒ 8 and 9 Ⓓ 10

2. What is the mode of the numbers? **F**

Ⓕ 8 Ⓖ 9 Ⓗ 8 and 9 Ⓙ 10

3. What is the median of the numbers? **A**

Ⓐ 8 Ⓑ 9 Ⓒ 8 and 9 Ⓓ 10

Use the circle graph for items 4 and 5.

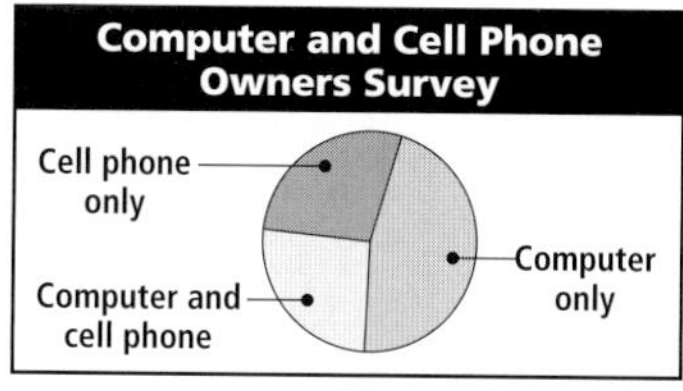

4. What percent of the people interviewed own a computer? **H**

Ⓕ 46% Ⓖ 52% Ⓗ 72% Ⓙ 100%

5. The circle graph shows the results of a survey of 200 people. How many of the people surveyed own a cell phone only? **C**

Ⓐ 28 Ⓑ 45 Ⓒ 56 Ⓓ 108

6. What are the stems in a stem-and-leaf plot of the following data? **F**
18, 23, 15, 27, 16, 35, 38, 48, 19

Ⓕ 1, 2, 3, 4 Ⓖ 3, 5, 7, 8, 9 Ⓗ 1–9 Ⓙ 0–9

Use the line graph for items 7 and 8.

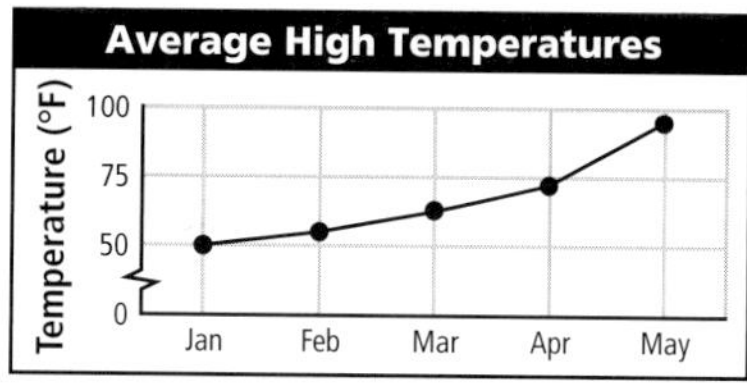

7. The line graph shows average high temperatures over a 5-month period. These temperatures increased the most between which two months? **D**

Ⓐ Jan and Feb Ⓑ Feb and Mar Ⓒ Mar and Apr Ⓓ Apr and May

TEST TAKING TIP!
Eliminate choices by using the definitions you have learned.

8. What is the range of the average high temperatures in the graph? **F**

Ⓕ 45°F Ⓖ 62°F Ⓗ 68°F Ⓙ 95°F

9. ***SHORT RESPONSE*** At the movie theater, Aimee and her brother bought 2 drinks for $2 each and a bucket of popcorn for $3. She gave the clerk a $10 bill. How much change should Aimee receive? Show your work.

10. ***SHORT RESPONSE*** A survey was conducted to determine which age group (0–19, 20–39, or 40–59) the most visitors at a local museum belonged to. The ages of the ten people surveyed were 12, 25, 17, 33, 31, 4, 15, 47, 51, and 7. Make a cumulative frequency table of the data. Then tell which age group the most visitors belonged to.

Standardized Test Prep

Answers

9. $3
$\$10 - (2 \cdot \$2 + \$3) =$
$\$10 - (\$4 + \$3) = \$10 - \$7 = \$3$

10.

Age Group	Frequency	Cumulative Frequency
0–19	5	5
20–39	3	8
40–59	2	10

0–19

Standardized Test Prep

Chapter 1

Purpose: *To provide review and practice for Chapter 1 and standardized tests*

Assessment Resources

Cumulative Tests (Levels A, B, C)
Assessment Resources . . . pp. 129–140

State-Specific Test Practice Online
KEYWORD: MS4 TestPrep

Test Prep Doctor

Expand on the test-taking tip given for item 8 by suggesting that students read the temperature at the highest point of the line graph and at the lowest point and then subtract the two values. Point out to students that by estimating the difference between the values, **J** can be eliminated as too great.

Chapter 2

Number Theory and Algebraic Reasoning

Section 2A	Section 2B	Section 2C
Exponents	**Factors and Multiples**	**Beginning Algebra**
Lesson 2-1 Exponents	**Hands-On Lab 2B** Divisibility	**Lesson 2-7** Variables and Algebraic Expressions
Lesson 2-2 Powers of Ten and Scientific Notation	**Lesson 2-4** Prime Factorization	**Lesson 2-8** Translate Words into Math
Technology Lab 2A Scientific Notation with a Calculator	**Lesson 2-5** Greatest Common Factor	**Lesson 2-9** Combining Like Terms
Lesson 2-3 Order of Operations	**Lesson 2-6** Least Common Multiple	**Lesson 2-10** Equations and Their Solutions
		Hands-On Lab 2C Model Equations
		Lesson 2-11 Solving Equations by Adding or Subtracting
		Lesson 2-12 Solving Equations by Multiplying or Dividing

Pacing Guide for 45-Minute Classes

Chapter 2

DAY 15 Lesson 2-1	DAY 16 Lesson 2-2	DAY 17 Technology Lab 2A	DAY 18 Lesson 2-3	DAY 19 Mid-Chapter Quiz Hands-On Lab 2B
DAY 20 Lesson 2-4	DAY 21 Lesson 2-5	DAY 22 Lesson 2-6	DAY 23 Mid-Chapter Quiz Lesson 2-7	DAY 24 Lesson 2-8
DAY 25 Lesson 2-9	DAY 26 Lesson 2-10	DAY 27 Hands-On Lab 2C	DAY 28 Lesson 2-11	DAY 29 Lesson 2-12
DAY 30 Chapter 2 Review	DAY 31 Chapter 2 Assessment			

Pacing Guide for 90-Minute Classes

Chapter 2

DAY 7 Chapter 1 Review Lesson 2-1	DAY 8 Chapter 1 Assessment Lesson 2-2	DAY 9 Technology Lab 2A Lesson 2-3	DAY 10 Mid-Chapter Quiz Hands-On Lab 2B Lesson 2-4	DAY 11 Lesson 2-5 Lesson 2-6
DAY 12 Mid-Chapter Quiz Lesson 2-7 Lesson 2-8	DAY 13 Lesson 2-9 Lesson 2-10	DAY 14 Hands-On Lab 2C Lesson 2-11	DAY 15 Lesson 2-12 Chapter 2 Review	DAY 16 Chapter 2 Assessment Lesson 3-1

Across the Series

COURSE 1

- Use the order of operations, including exponents.
- Translate between words and math.
- Solve one-step equations and inequalities.
- Find the GCF and LCM of numbers.

COURSE 2

- **Use exponents and evaluate powers.**
- **Express numbers in scientific notation.**
- **Use the order of operations, including exponents.**
- **Review divisibility rules and prime factorization, and find the GCF and LCM of numbers.**
- **Evaluate algebraic expressions.**
- **Translate between words and math.**
- **Combine like terms.**
- **Solve one-step equations.**

COURSE 3

- Write and evaluate algebraic expressions including exponents and combining like terms.
- Solve and graph one-step and multi-step equations and inequalities.
- Write solutions of equations as ordered pairs.
- Operate with rational numbers.

Across the Curriculum

LANGUAGE ARTS LINK

Math: Reading and Writing in the Content Area . . . . pp. 10–21

Focus on Problem Solving

Solve . . . . SE p. 75

Look Back. . . . . SE p. 91

Journal . . . . TE, last page of each lesson

Write About It . . . . . . SE pp. 63, 67, 73, 81, 85, 89, 95, 99, 103, 113, 117

SOCIAL STUDIES LINK

Social Studies . . . . SE pp. 63, 89

SCIENCE LINK

Life Science. . . . . SE pp. 63, 99

Earth Science. . . . . SE pp. 58, 61, 67, 73, 107

Physical Science. . . . . SE pp. 95, 113

Health. . . . . SE p. 115

Nutrition. . . . . SE p. 99

TE = *Teacher's Edition* **SE** = *Student Edition*

Interdisciplinary Bulletin Board

Life Science

The food pyramid is used to portray the recommended daily allowance of each food group. Have students write an inequality that represents the recommended number of servings of rice or cereal that would satisfy the bottom part of the pyramid.

$6 \leq \frac{1}{2}x \leq 11$

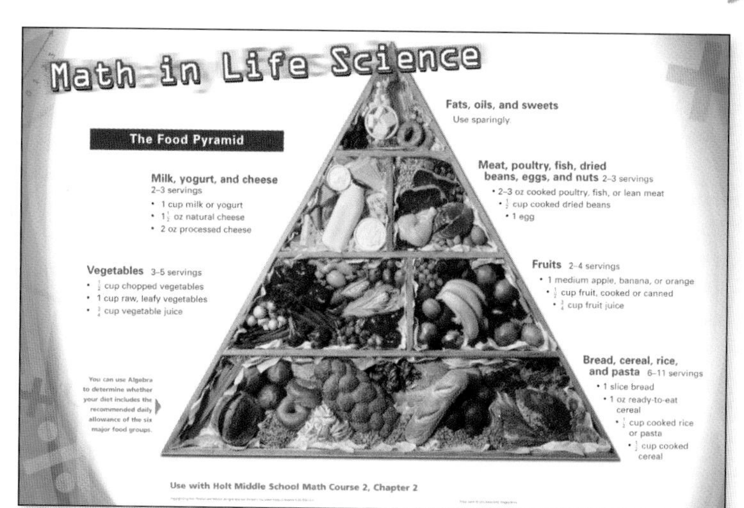

Interdisciplinary posters and worksheets are provided in your resource material.

Chapter 2

Resource Options

Chapter 2 Resource Book

Student Resources

Practice (Levels A, B, C) . . . . pp. 9–11, 18–20, 27–29, 37–39, 46–48, 55–57, 65–67, 74–76, 84–86, 93–95, 102–104, 111–113

Reteach . . . pp. 12, 21, 30, 40, 49, 58, 68, 77, 87, 96, 105, 114

Challenge . pp. 13, 22, 31, 41, 50, 59, 69, 78, 88, 97, 106, 115

Problem Solving . . . . pp. 14, 23, 32, 42, 51, 60, 70, 79, 89, 98, 107, 116

Puzzles, Twisters & Teasers . . . . pp. 15, 24, 33, 43, 52, 61, 71, 80, 90, 99, 108, 117

Recording Sheets . . . . . . pp. 3–4, 8, 17, 26, 36, 45, 54, 64, 73, 83, 92, 101, 110, 121, 125, 128

Chapter Review . . . . pp. 118–120

Teacher and Parent Resources

Chapter Planning and Pacing Guide . . . . p. 5

Section Planning Guides . . . . pp. 6, 34, 62

Parent Letter . . . . pp. 1–2

Teaching Tools . . . . pp. 124–129

Teacher Support for Chapter Project . . . . p. 122

Transparencies . . . . pp. T1–T46

- Daily Transparencies
- Additional Examples Transparencies
- Teaching Transparencies

Reaching All Learners

English Language Learners

Success for English Language Learners . . . . pp. 19–42

Math: Reading and Writing in the Content Area . pp. 10–21

Spanish Homework and Practice . . . . pp. 10–21

Spanish Interactive Study Guide . . . . pp. 10–21

Spanish Family Involvement Activities . . . . pp. 13–24

Multilingual Glossary

Individual Needs

Are You Ready? Intervention and Enrichment . . . pp. 13–16, 37–44, 149–152, 407–408

Alternate Openers: Explorations . . . . pp. 10–21

Family Involvement Activities . . . . pp. 13–24

Interactive Problem Solving . . . . pp. 10–21

Interactive Study Guide . . . . pp. 10–21

Readiness Activities . . . . pp. 3–4

Math: Reading and Writing in the Content Area . pp. 10–21

Challenge . . . . pp. 13, 22, 31, 41, 50, 59, 69, 78, 88, 97, 106, 115

Hands-On

Hands-On Lab Activities . . . . pp. 7–11

Technology Lab Activities . . . . pp. 5–8

Alternate Openers: Explorations . . . . pp. 10–21

Family Involvement Activities . . . . pp. 13–24

Applications and Connections

Consumer and Career Math . . . . pp. 5–8

Interdisciplinary Posters . . . . Poster 2, TE p. 58B

Interdisciplinary Poster Worksheets . . . . pp. 4–6

Transparencies

Alternate Openers: Explorations . . . . pp. 10–21

Exercise Answers Transparencies

Chapter 2 Resource Book . . . . pp. T1–T46

- Daily Transparencies
- Additional Examples Transparencies
- Teaching Transparencies

Technology

Teacher Resources

***Lesson Presentations* CD-ROM** . . . . Chapter 2

***Test and Practice Generator* CD-ROM** . . . . Chapter 2

***One-Stop Planner* CD-ROM** . . . . Chapter 2

Student Resources

***Are You Ready? Intervention* CD-ROM**
Skills 1, 7, 8, 35

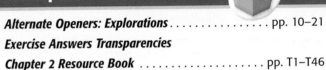

internet connect — go.hrw.com

Homework Help Online	**KEYWORD:** MS4 HWHelp2
Math Tools Online	**KEYWORD:** MS4 Tools
Glossary Online	**KEYWORD:** MS4 Glossary
Chapter Project Online	**KEYWORD:** MS4 PSProject2
Chapter Opener Online	**KEYWORD:** MS4 Ch2

CNN Student News™ **KEYWORD:** MS4 CNN2

SE = *Student Edition* **TE** = *Teacher's Edition* **AR** = *Assessment Resources* **CRB** = *Chapter Resource Book* **MK** = *Manipulatives Kit*

Assessment Options

Assessing Prior Knowledge

Determine whether students have the required prerequisite concepts and skills.

Are You Ready? . . . . SE p. 59
Inventory Test . . . . AR pp. 1–4

Test Preparation

Provide review and practice for chapter and standardized tests.

Standardized Test Prep . . . . SE p. 127
Spiral Review with Test Prep . . . . . SE, last page of each lesson
Study Guide and Review . . . . SE pp. 122–124
Test Prep Tool Kit

Technology 

 ***Test and Practice Generator* CD-ROM**

internet connect  

State-Specific Test Practice Online KEYWORD: MS4 TestPrep

Performance Assessment

Assess students' understanding of chapter concepts and combined problem-solving skills.

Performance Assessment . . . . SE p. 126
Includes scoring rubric in TE
Performance Assessment . . . . AR p. 108
Performance Assessment Teacher Support . . . . AR p. 107

Portfolio

Portfolio opportunities appear throughout the Student and Teacher's Editions.

Suggested work samples:

Problem Solving Project . . . . TE p. 58
Performance Assessment . . . . SE p. 126
Portfolio Guide . . . . AR p. xxxv
Journal . . . . TE, last page of each lesson
Write About It . . . . . SE, pp. 63, 67, 73, 81, 85, 89, 95, 99, 103, 113, 117

Daily Assessment

Obtain daily feedback on students' understanding of concepts.

Spiral Review and Test Prep . . . . . . SE, last page of each lesson

Also Available on Transparency In Chapter 2 Resource Book

Warm Up . . . . TE, first page of each lesson
Problem of the Day . . . . TE, first page of each lesson
Lesson Quiz . . . . TE, last page of each lesson

Student Self-Assessment

Have students evaluate their own work.

Group Project Evaluation . . . . AR p. xxxii
Individual Group Member Evaluation . . . . AR p. xxxiii
Portfolio Guide . . . . AR p. xxxv
Journal . . . . TE, last page of each lesson

Formal Assessment

Assess students' mastery of concepts and skills.

Section Quizzes . . . . AR pp. 8–10
Mid-Chapter Quizzes . . . . SE pp. 74, 90
Chapter Test . . . . SE p. 125
Chapter Tests (Levels A, B, C) . . . . AR pp. 39–44
Cumulative Tests (Levels A, B, C) . . . . AR pp. 141–152
Standardized Test Prep
Cumulative Assessment . . . . SE p. 127
End-of-Year Test . . . . AR pp. 273–276

Technology 

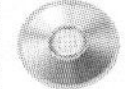 ***Test and Practice Generator* CD-ROM**

Make tests electronically. This software includes:

- Dynamic practice for Chapter 2
- Customizable tests
- Multiple-choice items for each objective
- Free-response items for each objective
- Teacher management system

SE = *Student Edition* **TE** = *Teacher's Edition* **AR** = *Assessment Resources* **CRB** = *Chapter Resource Book* **MK** = *Manipulatives Kit*

Chapter 2

Chapter 2 Tests

Three levels (A,B,C) of tests are available for each chapter in the *Assessment Resources.*

LEVEL A

CHAPTER 2 Chapter Test
Form A

Find each value.

1. 3^2 — 9
2. 2^3 — 8

Multiply.

3. $28 \cdot 10^3$ — 28,000
4. $7.3 \cdot 10^5$ — 730,000

Write each number in scientific notation.

5. 1,250 — 1.25×10^3
6. 15,400 — 1.54×10^4
7. Find the product of $23 \cdot 10^3$. — 23,000

Evaluate.

8. $4 \cdot 6 - 6$ — 18
9. $32 + 4^3 \div 8$ — 40
10. $5 \cdot (9 - 6)$ — 15

Use a factor tree to find the prime factorization.

11. 28 — $2^2 \cdot 7$
12. 80 — $2^4 \cdot 5$
13. 200 — $2^3 \cdot 5^2$

Find the greatest common factor (GCF).

14. 30, 45 — 15
15. 36, 54 — 18
16. 14, 28, 70 — 14

Find the least common multiple (LCM).

17. 8, 12 — 24
18. 2, 8 — 8
19. 6, 12, 15 — 60

CHAPTER 2 Chapter Test
Form A, continued

Evaluate each algebraic expression for the given variable values.

20. $n + 12 + n$ for $n = 8$ — 28
21. $3x^2 - 2x$ for $x = 6$ — 96
22. $4m - 3n + 5$ for $m = 12$ and $n = 4$ — 41

Write as an algebraic expression.

23. the product of a number and 4 — $4n$
24. 5 less than a number — $n - 5$
25. 12 divided by a number — $\frac{12}{n}$

Combine like terms.

26. $y + 4 + 3y$ — $4y + 4$
27. $6a + 3b + 4a^2 + a$ — $4a^2 + 7a + 3b$
28. $9c + 2 + 2c^2 - 5c$ — $2c^2 + 4c + 2$
29. $7s^2 + 15 - 2s^2 - 12$ — $5s^2 + 3$
30. Is 10 a solution of $p + 23 = 32$? — no
31. Is 5 a solution of $52 = 10n + 2$? — yes
32. Is 12 a solution of $3n - 3 = 39$? — no

Solve the equation.

33. $m + 32 = 56$ — $m = 24$
34. $b - 35 = 3$ — $b = 38$
35. $5 + d = 19$ — $d = 14$
36. $w \cdot 24 = 24$ — $w = 1$
37. $\frac{r}{3} = 24$ — $r = 72$
38. $a \div 6 = 18$ — $a = 108$
39. Ed is 12 years old. Write an expression to determine his age in y years. — $12 + y$
40. Jeremy is 58 inches tall. Write an expression to show Jeremy's height in y years if he grows an average of 1.5 inches each year. — $58 + 1.5y$

LEVEL B

CHAPTER 2 Chapter Test
Form B

Find each value.

1. 2^5 — 32
2. 15^2 — 225

Multiply.

3. $3.85 \cdot 10^5$ — 385,000
4. $8.304 \cdot 10^6$ — 8,304,000

Write the number in scientific notation.

5. 4,375,000 — 4.375×10^6
6. 12,400,000 — 1.24×10^7
7. Find the product of $2.3 \cdot 10^3$. — 2,300

Evaluate.

8. $8 \cdot (36 - 24)$ — 96
9. $(48 \div 2) - 2^3 \cdot 3$ — 0
10. $3 \cdot (12 - 2^3) + 5$ — 17

Use a factor tree to find the prime factorization.

11. 105 — $3 \cdot 5 \cdot 7$
12. 256 — 2^8
13. 600 — $2^3 \cdot 3 \cdot 5^2$

Find the greatest common factor (GCF).

14. 48, 112 — 16
15. 36, 60, 96 — 12
16. 27, 48, 60 — 3

Find the least common multiple (LCM).

17. 3, 7 — 21
18. 6, 8,12 — 24
19. 2, 8, 9 — 72

CHAPTER 2 Chapter Test
Form B, continued

Evaluate each algebraic expression for the given variable values.

20. $7n - 34 + n$ for $n = 9$ — 38
21. $2y^3 - y^2 + y$ for $y = 3$ — 48
22. $12a - 3b^2 + b$ for $a = 25$ and $b = 4$ — 256

Write as an algebraic expression.

23. a number times the sum of 12 and 32 — $n(12 + 32)$
24. 12 less than the quotient of a number and 20 — $\frac{n}{20} - 12$
25. the sum of 59 times a number and 3 — $59n + 3$

Combine like terms.

26. $8w + 7 + 12w - 2$ — $20w + 5$
27. $4d^2 + 12w - d^2 + 18$ — $3d^2 + 12w + 18$
28. $32 + 32a - 16 - 32a$ — 16
29. $8m^3 - 5m^2 - m^3 - 12 + 5m^3$ — $12m^3 - 5m^2 - 12$
30. Is 27 a solution of $50 = \frac{n}{9} + 47$? — yes
31. Is 8 a solution of $84 - 6n = 36$? — yes
32. Is 7 a solution of $5p + 23 = 35$? — no

Solve the equation.

33. $552 = y + 4$ — $y = 548$
34. $k - 127 = 178$ — $k = 305$
35. $15 + z = 32$ — $z = 17$
36. $p \cdot 18 = 162$ — $p = 9$
37. $\frac{a}{8} = 80$ — $a = 640$
38. $j \div 12 = 6$ — $j = 72$
39. Faxing letters from a store costs \$3.25 plus \$0.50 per page. Write an expression to show how much it costs to fax a letter with p pages from the store. — $3.25 + 0.50p$
40. Sam bought a season pass to the zoo for \$75. If Sam donates \$2.50 each time he visits the zoo, what expression shows how much Sam will contribute for the season? — $75 + 2.5v$

LEVEL C

CHAPTER 2 Chapter Test
Form C

Find each value.

1. $3^4 + 3^2$ — 90
2. $22^3 - 11^2$ — 10,527

Multiply.

3. $3.4 \cdot 10^{10}$ — 34,000,000,000
4. $2.346 \cdot 10^6$ — 2,346,000

Write each number in scientific notation.

5. 14,300,000,000 — 1.43×10^{10}
6. 390,468,000 — 3.90468×10^8
7. Find the product of $2{,}003 \cdot 10^5$. — 200,300,000

Evaluate.

8. $(12 - 8) \cdot (6 \cdot 3^2)$ — 216
9. $145 - 5^3 \div [5 \cdot (44 - 39)]$ — 140
10. $(200 + 4^3) \times [8 \div (4^2 - 12)]$ — 528

Use a factor tree to find the prime factorization.

11. 378 — $2 \cdot 3^3 \cdot 7$
12. 2,000 — $2^4 \cdot 5^3$
13. 8,500 — $2^2 \cdot 5^3 \cdot 17$

Find the greatest common factor (GCF).

14. 48, 80, 96, 112 — 16
15. 63, 84, 105,126 — 21
16. 26, 52, 65, 104 — 13

Find the least common multiple (LCM).

17. 6, 8, 9, 12 — 72
18. 12, 15, 20, 30 — 60
19. 4, 6, 9, 18 — 36

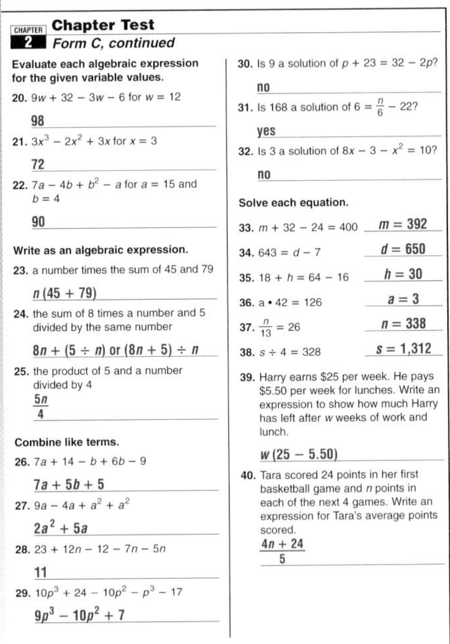

CHAPTER 2 Chapter Test
Form C, continued

Evaluate each algebraic expression for the given variable values.

20. $9w + 32 - 3w - 6$ for $w = 12$ — 98
21. $3x^3 - 2x^2 + 3x$ for $x = 3$ — 72
22. $7a - 4b + b^2 - a$ for $a = 15$ and $b = 4$ — 90

Write as an algebraic expression.

23. a number times the sum of 45 and 79 — $n(45 + 79)$
24. the sum of 8 times a number and 5 divided by the same number — $8n + (5 \div n)$ or $(8n + 5) \div n$
25. the product of 5 and a number divided by 4 — $\frac{5n}{4}$

Combine like terms.

26. $7a + 14 - b + 6b - 9$ — $7a + 5b + 5$
27. $9a - 4a + a^2 + a^2$ — $2a^2 + 5a$
28. $23 + 12n - 12 - 7n - 5n$ — 11
29. $10p^3 + 24 - 10p^2 - p^3 - 17$ — $9p^3 - 10p^2 + 7$
30. Is 9 a solution of $p + 23 = 32 - 2p$? — no
31. Is 168 a solution of $6 = \frac{n}{6} - 22$? — yes
32. Is 3 a solution of $8x - 3 - x^2 = 10$? — no

Solve each equation.

33. $m + 32 - 24 = 400$ — $m = 392$
34. $643 = d - 7$ — $d = 650$
35. $18 + h = 64 - 16$ — $h = 30$
36. $a \cdot 42 = 126$ — $a = 3$
37. $\frac{n}{13} = 26$ — $n = 338$
38. $s \div 4 = 328$ — $s = 1{,}312$
39. Harry earns \$25 per week. He pays \$5.50 per week for lunches. Write an expression to show how much Harry has left after w weeks of work and lunch. — $w(25 - 5.50)$
40. Tara scored 24 points in her first basketball game and n points in each of the next 4 games. Write an expression for Tara's average points scored. — $\frac{4n + 24}{5}$

Test and Practice Generator CD-ROM

Create and customize multiple versions of the same tests with corresponding answers for any chosen chapter objectives.

Chapter 2 State and Standardized Test Preparation

Test Taking Skill Builder and Standardized Test Practice are provided for each chapter in the *Test Prep Tool Kit.*

TEST TAKING SKILL BUILDER

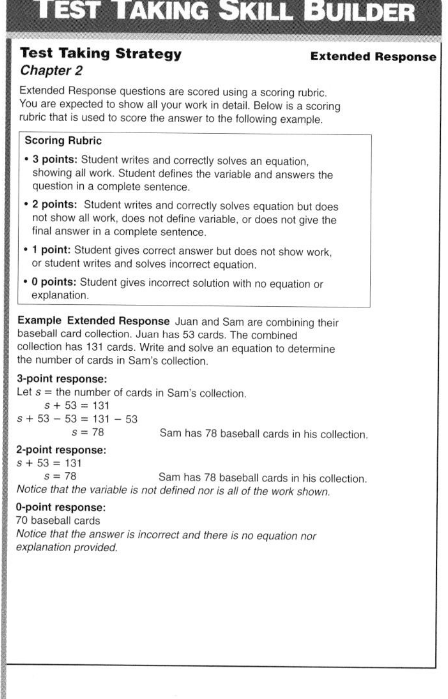

Test Taking Strategy **Extended Response**
Chapter 2

Extended Response questions are scored using a scoring rubric. You are expected to show all your work in detail. Below is a scoring rubric that is used to score the answer to the following example.

Scoring Rubric

- **3 points:** Student writes and correctly solves an equation, showing all work. Student defines the variable and answers the question in a complete sentence.
- **2 points:** Student writes and correctly solves equation but does not show all work, does not define variable, or does not give the final answer in a complete sentence.
- **1 point:** Student gives correct answer but does not show work, or student writes and solves incorrect equation.
- **0 points:** Student gives incorrect solution with no equation or explanation.

Example Extended Response Juan and Sam are combining their baseball card collection. Juan has 53 cards. The combined collection has 131 cards. Write and solve an equation to determine the number of cards in Sam's collection.

3-point response:
Let s = the number of cards in Sam's collection.
$s + 53 = 131$
$s + 53 - 53 = 131 - 53$
$s = 78$ Sam has 78 baseball cards in his collection.

2-point response:
$s + 53 = 131$
$s = 78$ Sam has 78 baseball cards in his collection.
Notice that the variable is not defined nor is all of the work shown.

0-point response:
70 baseball cards
Notice that the answer is incorrect and there is no equation nor explanation provided.

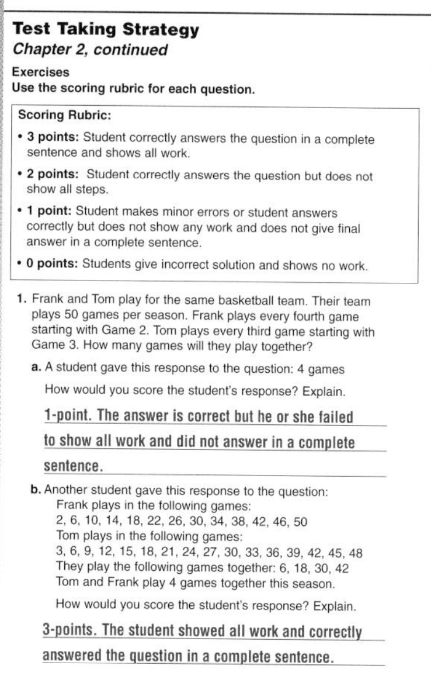

Test Taking Strategy
Chapter 2, continued

Exercises
Use the scoring rubric for each question.

Scoring Rubric:

- **3 points:** Student correctly answers the question in a complete sentence and shows all work.
- **2 points:** Student correctly answers the question but does not show all steps.
- **1 point:** Student makes minor errors or student answers correctly but does not show any work and does not give final answer in a complete sentence.
- **0 points:** Students give incorrect solution and shows no work.

1. Frank and Tom play for the same basketball team. Their team plays 50 games per season. Frank plays every fourth game starting with Game 2. Tom plays every third game starting with Game 3. How many games will they play together?
   a. A student gave this response to the question: 4 games
   How would you score the student's response? Explain.
   1-point. The answer is correct but he or she failed to show all work and did not answer in a complete sentence.
   b. Another student gave this response to the question:
   Frank plays in the following games:
   2, 6, 10, 14, 18, 22, 26, 30, 34, 38, 42, 46, 50
   Tom plays in the following games:
   3, 6, 9, 12, 15, 18, 21, 24, 27, 30, 33, 36, 39, 42, 45, 48
   They play the following games together: 6, 18, 30, 42
   Tom and Frank play 4 games together this season.
   How would you score the student's response? Explain.
   3-points. The student showed all work and correctly answered the question in a complete sentence.

STANDARDIZED TEST PRACTICE

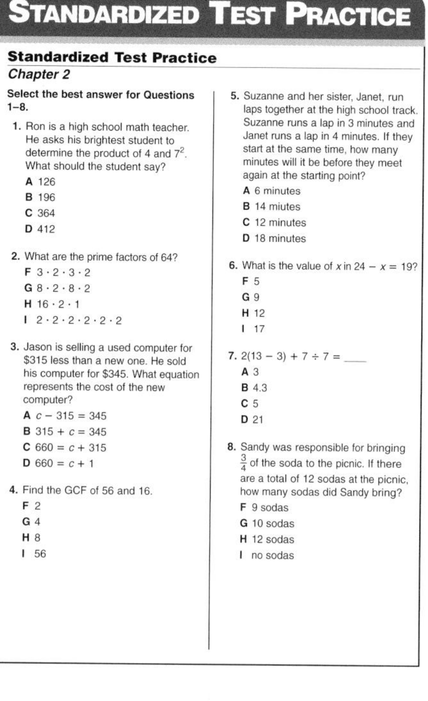

Standardized Test Practice
Chapter 2

Select the best answer for Questions 1–8.

1. Ron is a high school math teacher. He asks his brightest student to determine the product of 4 and 7^2. What should the student say?
   A 126
   B 196
   C 364
   D 412
2. What are the prime factors of 64?
   F $3 \cdot 2 \cdot 3 \cdot 2$
   G $8 \cdot 2 \cdot 8 \cdot 2$
   H $16 \cdot 2 \cdot 1$
   I $2 \cdot 2 \cdot 2 \cdot 2 \cdot 2 \cdot 2$
3. Jason is selling a used computer for $315 less than a new one. He sold his computer for $345. What equation represents the cost of the new computer?
   A $c - 315 = 345$
   B $315 + c = 345$
   C $660 = c + 315$
   D $660 = c + 1$
4. Find the GCF of 56 and 16.
   F 2
   G 4
   H 8
   I 56
5. Suzanne and her sister, Janet, run laps together at the high school track. Suzanne runs a lap in 3 minutes and Janet runs a lap in 4 minutes. If they start at the same time, how many minutes will it be before they meet again at the starting point?
   A 6 minutes
   B 14 minutes
   C 12 minutes
   D 18 minutes
6. What is the value of x in $24 - x = 19$?
   F 5
   G 9
   H 12
   I 17
7. $2(13 - 3) + 7 \div 7 =$ ____
   A 3
   B 4.3
   C 5
   D 21
8. Sandy was responsible for bringing $\frac{3}{4}$ of the soda to the picnic. If there are a total of 12 sodas at the picnic, how many sodas did Sandy bring?
   F 9 sodas
   G 10 sodas
   H 12 sodas
   I no sodas

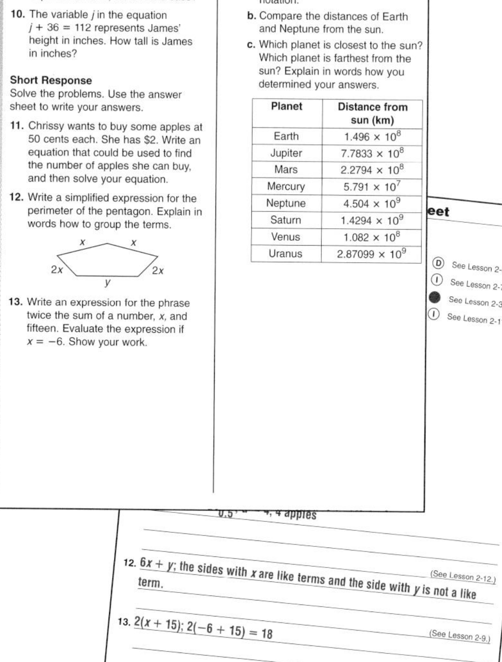

Standardized Test Practice
Chapter 2, continued

Gridded Response
Solve the problems. Use the answer sheet to write and grid-in your answer.

9. If the number 225 is written in exponential form, what is the base?
10. The variable j in the equation $j + 36 = 112$ represents James' height in inches. How tall is James in inches?

Short Response
Solve the problems. Use the answer sheet to write your answers.

11. Chrissy wants to buy some apples at 50 cents each. She has $2. Write an equation that could be used to find the number of apples she can buy, and then solve your equation.
12. Write a simplified expression for the perimeter of the pentagon. Explain in words how to group the terms.

13. Write an expression for the phrase twice the sum of a number, x, and fifteen. Evaluate the expression if $x = -6$. Show your work.

Extended Response

14. Use the table to answer the following questions.
   a. Rewrite the distances in standard notation.
   b. Compare the distances of Earth and Neptune from the sun.
   c. Which planet is closest to the sun? Which planet is farthest from the sun? Explain in words how you determined your answers.

Planet	Distance from sun (km)
Earth	1.496×10^8
Jupiter	7.7833×10^8
Mars	2.2794×10^8
Mercury	5.791×10^7
Neptune	4.504×10^9
Saturn	1.4294×10^9
Venus	1.082×10^8
Uranus	2.87099×10^9

eet

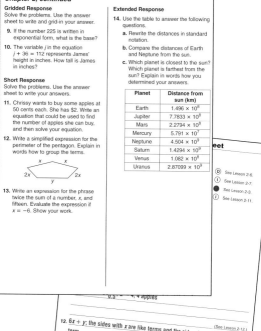

D See Lesson 2-6.
I See Lesson 2-7.
● See Lesson 2-3.
I See Lesson 2-11.

0.5 ... 4; 4 apples

12. $6x + y$; the sides with x are like terms and the side with y is not a like term. (See Lesson 2-12.)

13. $2(x + 15)$; $2(-6 + 15) = 18$ (See Lesson 2-9.)

Extended Response (See Lesson 2-8.)
Write your answers for Problem 14 on the back of this paper.
See Lesson 2-2.

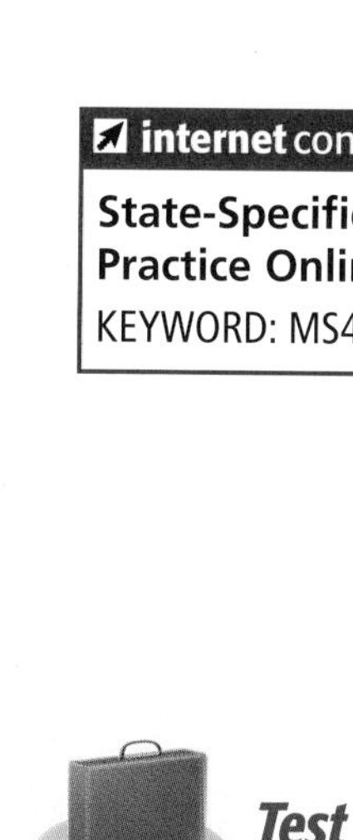

internet connect
State-Specific Test Practice Online
KEYWORD: MS4 TestPrep

Test Prep Tool Kit

- Standardized Test Prep Workbook
- Countdown to Testing transparencies
- State Test Prep CD-ROM
- Standardized Test Prep Video

Customized answer sheets give students realistic practice for actual standardized tests.

Chapter 2

Number Theory and Algebraic Reasoning

Why Learn This?

Tell students that sometimes large numbers may be written in a different form. Have students look at the table. The distances between the Sun and each planet, and the nearest star are given in kilometers. Since these distances are very large, they are expressed in scientific notation. Scientific notation is used to write large numbers in a shorter way by expressing the number with a power of ten.

Using Data

To begin the study of this chapter, have students:

- Write each distance in the table in standard form.
  Mercury: 58,000,000 km; Venus: 108,200,000 km; Earth: 149,500,000 km; Mars: 227,900,000 km; Jupiter: 778,000,000 km; Saturn: 1,430,000,000 km; Uranus: 2,900,000,000 km; Neptune: 4,400,000,000 km; Pluto: 5,800,000,000 km; nearest star: 39,730,000,000,000 km
- Tell which planet is farthest from the Sun. Pluto
- Tell which planet is closest to the Sun. Mercury

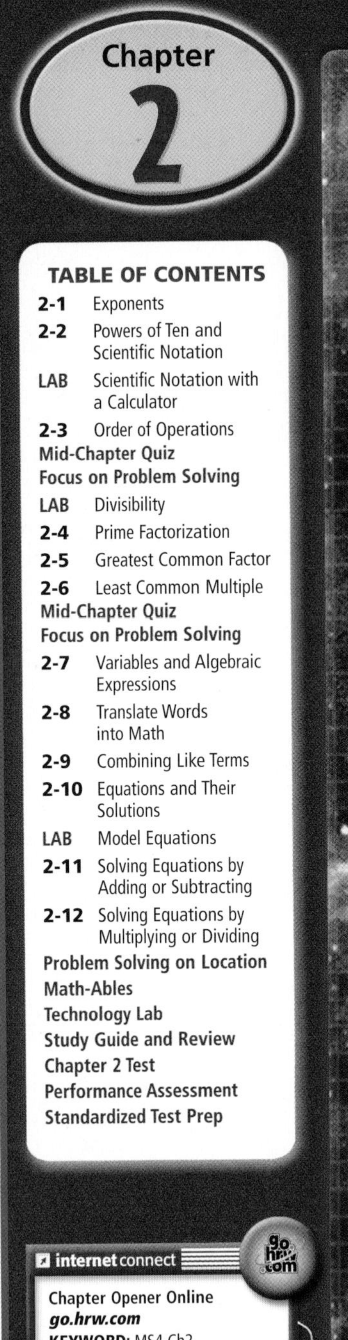

Chapter 2

TABLE OF CONTENTS

internet connect
Chapter Opener Online
go.hrw.com
KEYWORD: MS4 Ch2

Number Theory and Algebraic Reasoning

Astronomical Distances

Object	Distance from the Sun (km)*
Mercury	5.80×10^7
Venus	1.082×10^8
Earth	1.495×10^8
Mars	2.279×10^8
Jupiter	7.780×10^8
Saturn	1.43×10^9
Uranus	2.90×10^9
Neptune	4.40×10^9
Pluto	5.80×10^9
Nearest star	3.973×10^{13}

*Distances of planets from the Sun are average distances.

Career ***Cosmologist***

Dr. Stephen Hawking is a cosmologist. Cosmologists study the universe as a whole. They are interested in the origins, the structure, and the interaction of space and time.

The invention of the telescope has extended the vision of scientists far beyond nearby stars and planets. It has enabled them to view distant galaxies and structures that at one time were only theorized by astrophysicists such as Dr. Hawking. Astronomical distances are so great that we must use special mathematical notation to represent them conveniently.

Problem Solving Project

Earth Science Connection

Purpose: To use exponents to help model the solar system

Materials: Space Spaces worksheet, modeling materials

internet connect
Chapter Project Online: ***go.hrw.com***
KEYWORD: MS4 PSProject2

Understand, Plan, Solve, and Look Back

Have students:

- ✓ Complete the Space Spaces worksheet to develop a model for the relative distances of planets, and the nearest star.
- ✓ Make a chart showing the distance of the other planets from Earth.
- ✓ Discover what a light-year is and how it makes measuring the universe easier to understand.
- ✓ Check students' work.

ARE YOU READY?

Choose the best term from the list to complete each sentence.

1. The operation that gives the quotient of two numbers is ___?___. **division**	**division**
2. The ___?___ of the digit 3 in 4,903,672 is thousands. **place value**	**factor**
3. A number that is multiplied by another number is called a ___?___. **factor**	**multiplication**
4. The operation that gives the product of two numbers is ___?___. **multiplication**	**place value**
5. In the equation $15 \div 3 = 5$, the ___?___ is 5. **quotient**	**product**
	quotient

Complete these exercises to review skills you will need for this chapter.

✔ Find Place Value

Give the place value of the digit 4 in each number.

6. 4,092 **thousands**
7. 608,241 **tens**
8. 7,040,000 **ten thousands**
9. 4,556,890,100 **billions**
10. 3,408,289 **hundred thousands**
11. 34,506,123 **millions**
12. 500,986,402 **hundreds**
13. 3,540,277,009 **ten millions**

✔ Use Repeated Multiplication

Find each product.

14. $2 \cdot 2 \cdot 2$ **8**
15. $9 \cdot 9 \cdot 9 \cdot 9$ **6,561**
16. $14 \cdot 14 \cdot 14$ **2,744**
17. $10 \cdot 10 \cdot 10 \cdot 10$ **10,000**
18. $3 \cdot 3 \cdot 5 \cdot 5$ **225**
19. $2 \cdot 2 \cdot 5 \cdot 7$ **140**
20. $3 \cdot 3 \cdot 11 \cdot 11$ **1,089**
21. $5 \cdot 10 \cdot 10 \cdot 10$ **5,000**

✔ Find Multiples

Find the first five multiples of each number.

22. 2 **2, 4, 6, 8, 10**
23. 9 **9, 18, 27, 36, 45**
24. 15 **15, 30, 45, 60, 75**
25. 1 **1, 2, 3, 4, 5**
26. 101 **101, 202, 303, 404, 505**
27. 54 **54, 108, 162, 216, 270**
28. 326 **326, 652, 978, 1,304, 1,630**
29. 1,024 **1,024, 2,048, 3,072, 4,096, 5,120**

✔ Find Factors

List all the factors of each number.

30. 8 **1, 2, 4, 8**
31. 22 **1, 2, 11, 22**
32. 36 **1, 2, 3, 4, 6, 9, 12, 18, 36**
33. 50 **1, 2, 5, 10, 25, 50**
34. 108 **1, 2, 3, 4, 6, 9, 12, 18, 27, 36, 54, 108**
35. 84 **1, 2, 3, 4, 6, 7, 12, 14, 21, 28, 42, 84**
36. 256 **1, 2, 4, 8, 16, 32, 64, 128, 256**
37. 630 **1, 2, 3, 5, 6, 7, 9, 10, 14, 15, 18, 21, 30, 35, 42, 45, 63,70, 90, 105, 126, 210, 315, 630**

Assessing Prior Knowledge

INTERVENTION 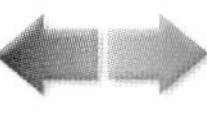

Diagnose and Prescribe

Evaluate your students' performance on this page to determine whether intervention is necessary or whether enrichment is appropriate. Options that provide instruction, practice, and a check are listed below.

Resources for Are You Ready?

- ***Are You Ready? Intervention and Enrichment***
- **Recording Sheet for Are You Ready?** *Chapter 2 Resource Book*. . . pp. 3–4

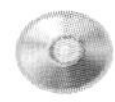 ***Are You Ready? Intervention* CD-ROM**

internet connect

Are You Ready? Intervention
go.hrw.com
KEYWORD: MS4 AYR

ARE YOU READY?

Were students successful with Are You Ready?

NO INTERVENE  **YES ENRICH**

✔ Find Place Value
Are You Ready? Intervention, Skill 1
Blackline Masters, Online, and
 **CD-ROM** Intervention Activities

✔ Use Repeated Multiplication
Are You Ready? Intervention, Skill 35
Blackline Masters, Online, and
CD-ROM Intervention Activities

✔ Find Multiples
Are You Ready? Intervention, Skill 7
Blackline Masters, Online, and
 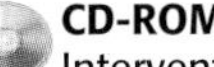 **CD-ROM** Intervention Activities

✔ Find Factors
Are You Ready? Intervention, Skill 8
Blackline Masters, Online, and
 **CD-ROM** Intervention Activities

Are You Ready? Enrichment, pp. 409–410

Exponents

One-Minute Section Planner

Lesson	Materials	Resources
Lesson 2-1 Exponents **NCTM:** Number and Operations, Reasoning and Proof, Communication, Representation **NAEP:** Algebra 3b ☑ SAT-9 ☑ SAT-10 ☑ ITBS ☑ CTBS ☑ MAT ☑ CAT	**Optional** 10-by-10 grids *(MK, CRB, p. 124)* Calculators	• *Chapter 2 Resource Book,* pp. 7–15 • Daily Transparency T1, CRB • Additional Examples Transparencies T2–T3, CRB • *Alternate Openers: Explorations,* p. 10
Lesson 2-2 Powers of Ten and Scientific Notation **NCTM:** Number and Operations, Reasoning and Proof, Communication, Representation **NAEP:** Number Properties 1f ☑ SAT-9 ☑ SAT-10 ☑ ITBS ☑ CTBS ☐ MAT ☐ CAT	**Optional** Calculators	• *Chapter 2 Resource Book,* pp. 16–24 • Daily Transparency T4, CRB • Additional Examples Transparencies T5–T7, CRB • *Alternate Openers: Explorations,* p. 11
Technology Lab 2A Scientific Notation with a Calculator **NCTM:** Number and Operations, Representation **NAEP:** Number Properties 1f ☐ SAT-9 ☐ SAT-10 ☐ ITBS ☐ CTBS ☐ MAT ☐ CAT	**Required** Calculators	• *Technology Lab Activities,* p. 5
Lesson 2-3 Order of Operations **NCTM:** Number and Operations, Communication, Representation **NAEP:** Algebra 3b ☐ SAT-9 ☐ SAT-10 ☐ ITBS ☑ CTBS ☑ MAT ☑ CAT	**Optional** Calculators Recording Sheet for Reaching All Learners *(CRB, p. 125)* Teaching Transparency T9 *(CRB)*	• *Chapter 2 Resource Book,* pp. 25–33 • Daily Transparency T8, CRB • Additional Examples Transparencies T10–T12, CRB • *Alternate Openers: Explorations,* p. 12
Section 2A Assessment		• Mid-Chapter Quiz, SE p. 74 • Section 2A Quiz, AR p. 8 • *Test and Practice Generator* CD-ROM

SAT = *Stanford Achievement Tests* **ITBS** = *Iowa Test of Basic Skills* **CTBS** = *Comprehensive Test of Basic Skills/Terra Nova*
MAT = *Metropolitan Achievement Test* **CAT** = *California Achievement Test*

NCTM—Complete standards can be found on pages T27–T33. **NAEP**—Complete standards can be found on pages A35–A39.

SE = *Student Edition* **TE** = *Teacher's Edition* **AR** = *Assessment Resources* **CRB** = *Chapter Resource Book* **MK** = *Manipulatives Kit*

Section Overview

Using Exponents — *Lesson 2-1*

Why? Powers provide a shorthand notation for products in which the factor is repeated many times. Understanding powers is essential to an understanding of roots, a concept explored in later chapters.

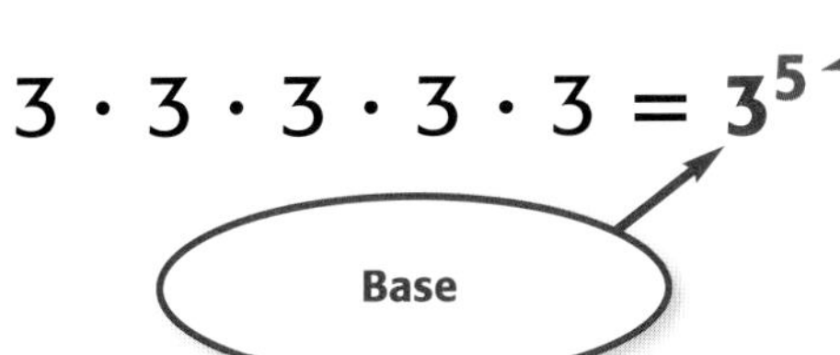

$3 \cdot 3 \cdot 3 \cdot 3 \cdot 3 = 3^5$
The exponent tells how many times the base is used as a factor.
Base

Expressing Numbers in Scientific Notation — *Lesson 2-2, Technology Lab 2A*

Why? In real-world applications, numbers can be very large or very small. Scientific notation makes it easier to work with those numbers.

Scientific Notation	Not Scientific Notation
2×10^3	250
3.6×10^2	36×10^2
5.45×10^5	0.5×10^5

A number written in scientific notation is the product of two factors.

a decimal greater than or equal to 1 but less than 10 × a power of 10

Using the Order of Operations — *Lesson 2-3*

Why? The order of operations is a set of rules used to make sure everyone gets the same answer when evaluating a numerical or an algebraic expression. These rules tell you the order in which operations are performed in an expression.

Order of Operations

1. Perform operations within grouping symbols.
2. Evaluate powers.
3. Multiply and divide in order from left to right.
4. Add and subtract in order from left to right.

Evaluate.

$5 + 40 \div 5 \cdot (4 - 2)^2$

$5 + 40 \div 5 \cdot (4 - 2)^2$ ← 1. grouping symbols

$5 + 40 \div 5 \cdot 2^2$ ← 2. powers

$5 + 40 \div 5 \cdot 4$

$5 + 8 \cdot 4$ ← 3. left to right multiplication and division

$5 + 32$ ← 4. addition

37

2-1 Organizer

Pacing: Traditional 1 day
Block $\frac{1}{2}$ day

Objective: Students represent numbers by using exponents.

Warm Up

Simplify.

1. $2 \cdot 2 \cdot 2$	8
2. $3 \cdot 3 \cdot 3 \cdot 3$	81
3. $5 \cdot 5 \cdot 5$	125
4. $4 \cdot 4 \cdot 4$	64
5. $6 \cdot 6 \cdot 6 \cdot 6 \cdot 6$	7,776

Problem of the Day

You have just installed a water pond in your backyard. You intend to place water lilies in the pond. According to the package a water lily doubles in size every day. From the time you install the first lily until the entire surface of the pond is covered will take 20 days. How long will it take for the pond to be half covered? 19 days

Available on Daily Transparency in CRB

Math Humor

Before he learned about exponents, the Little League player kept making outs because he couldn't find the bases.

2-1 Exponents

Learn to represent numbers by using exponents.

Vocabulary

power
exponent
base

A DNA molecule makes a copy of itself by splitting in half. Each half becomes a molecule that is identical to the original. The molecules continue to split so that the two become four, the four become eight, and so on.

Each time DNA copies itself, the number of molecules doubles. After four copies, the number of molecules is $2 \cdot 2 \cdot 2 \cdot 2 = 16$.

This multiplication can also be written as a **power** , using a *base* and an *exponent*. The **exponent** tells how many times to use the **base** as a factor.

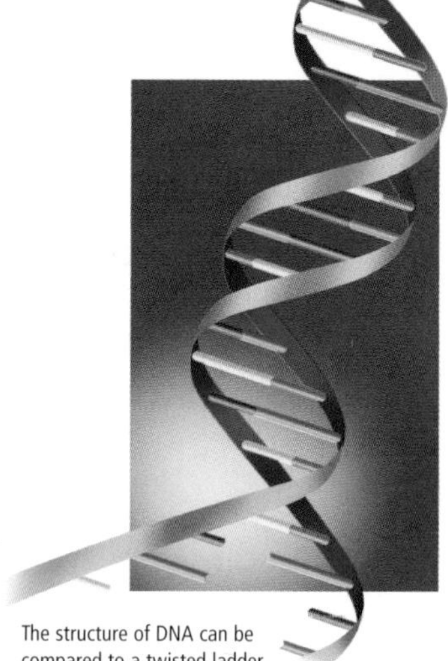

The structure of DNA can be compared to a twisted ladder.

Reading Math

Read 2^4 as "the fourth power of 2" or "2 to the fourth power."

Base ⟶ 2^4 ⟵ Exponent

EXAMPLE 1 Evaluating Powers

Find each value.

A 5^2

$5^2 = 5 \cdot 5$ *Use 5 as a factor 2 times.*
$= 25$

B 2^6

$2^6 = 2 \cdot 2 \cdot 2 \cdot 2 \cdot 2 \cdot 2$ *Use 2 as a factor 6 times.*
$= 64$

Recall that any number to the first power is equal to that number.

$6^1 = 6$ $13^1 = 13$ $25^1 = 25$

Any number to the zero power, except zero, is equal to 1.

$6^0 = 1$ $10^0 = 1$ $19^0 = 1$

Zero to the zero power is *undefined,* meaning that it does not exist.

1 Introduce

Alternate Opener

EXPLORATION

2-1 Exponents

You can multiply $5 \cdot 5 \cdot 5 \cdot 5 \cdot 5 \cdot 5$ using exponents and a calculator.

The number 5 is a factor 6 times, so you can write $5 \cdot 5 \cdot 5 \cdot 5 \cdot 5 \cdot 5$ as 5^6.

The expressions are equivalent because they have the same value.

$5 \cdot 5 \cdot 5 \cdot 5 \cdot 5 \cdot 5 = 15{,}625$ and $5^6 = 15{,}625$

Guess the missing exponent in each statement. Use a calculator after each guess to check your answer.

1. $3^{\square} = 729$ **2.** $2^{\square} = 4{,}096$
3. $9^{\square} = 4{,}782{,}969$ **4.** $4^{\square} = 1{,}024$

Think and Discuss

5. Describe the strategies you used to find the missing exponents.
6. Explain how you can find the value of 2^{11} if you know that $2^{10} = 1{,}024$.

Motivate

To help students visualize an exponential increase, have them color squares on 10 × 10 grids (Chapter 2 Resource Book p. 124) to show the value for each of the following:

2	$2 \cdot 2$	$2 \cdot 2 \cdot 2$
3	$3 \cdot 3$	$3 \cdot 3 \cdot 3$

Point out that the size of each colored area doubles progressively for the 2's and triples for the 3's. Have students predict how areas would change for 4, $4 \cdot 4$, and $4 \cdot 4 \cdot 4$. Students should predict that the area would quadruple each time.

Exploration worksheet and answers on Chapter 2 Resource Book pp. 8 and 130

2 Teach

Guided Instruction

In this lesson, students learn to represent numbers by using exponents. Discuss with students the relationship between multiplication and a number written as a power. The exponent tells you how many times the base is used as a factor.

Show students how to use the ENTER key on a calculator to find the value of a number written as a power. Demonstrate how to find the value of 3^6 by pressing the following keys: 3 × 3 ENTER  ENTER  ENTER  ENTER  ENTER.

To express a whole number as a power, write the number as the product of equal factors. Then write the product using the base and an exponent. For example, $10{,}000 = 10 \cdot 10 \cdot 10 \cdot 10 = 10^4$.

EXAMPLE 2 Expressing Whole Numbers as Powers

Write each number using an exponent and the given base.

A 49, base 7

$49 = 7 \cdot 7$ *7 is used as a factor 2 times.*

$= 7^2$

B 81, base 3

$81 = 3 \cdot 3 \cdot 3 \cdot 3$ *3 is used as a factor 4 times.*

$= 3^4$

EXAMPLE 3 *Earth Science Application*

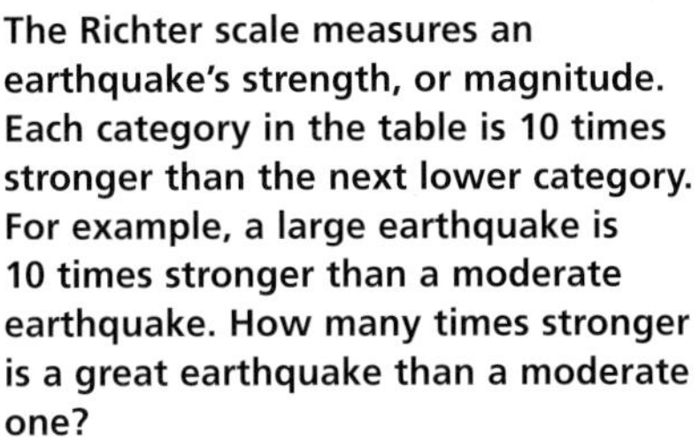

An earthquake measuring 7.2 on the Richter scale struck Duzce, Turkey, on November 12, 1999.

The Richter scale measures an earthquake's strength, or magnitude. Each category in the table is 10 times stronger than the next lower category. For example, a large earthquake is 10 times stronger than a moderate earthquake. How many times stronger is a great earthquake than a moderate one?

Earthquake Strength	
Category	Magnitude
Moderate	5
Large	6
Major	7
Great	8

An earthquake with a magnitude of 6 is 10 times stronger than one with a magnitude of 5.

An earthquake with a magnitude of 7 is 10 times stronger than one with a magnitude of 6.

An earthquake with a magnitude of 8 is 10 times stronger than one with a magnitude of 7.

$$10 \cdot 10 \cdot 10 = 10^3 = 1{,}000$$

A great earthquake is 1,000 times stronger than a moderate one.

Think and Discuss

1. **Describe** the relationship between 3^5 and 3^6.
2. **Tell** which power of 8 is equal to 2^6. Explain.
3. **Explain** why any number to the first power is equal to that number.

COMMON ERROR ALERT

Some students may make the mistake of multiplying the base times the exponent to find the value of a power. Encourage students who make this mistake to write out the power as factors before evaluating it.

Additional Examples

Example 1

Find each value.

A. 4^4 **256**

B. 7^3 **343**

Example 2

Write each number using an exponent and the given base.

A. 625, base 5 5^4

B. 64, base 2 2^6

Example 3

On Monday, Erik tells 3 people a secret. The next day each of them tells 3 more people. If this pattern continues, how many people besides Erik will know the secret on Friday?

On Friday 243 people besides Erik will know the secret.

3 Close

Reaching All Learners
Through Critical Thinking

Have students explore multiplication of numbers written as powers. Partners can work together to find the values of pairs of expressions such as: $3^2 \cdot 3^3$ and $3^1 \cdot 3^4$

$2^2 \cdot 2^4$ and $2^3 \cdot 2^3$

$4^3 \cdot 4^3$ and $4^1 \cdot 4^5$

243 and 243; 64 and 64; 4,096 and 4,096; The values of both expressions in each pair are the same. The exponents in each pair have equal sums. You can add the exponents to multiply powers with the same base, for example, $2^2 \cdot 2^4 = 2^6$.

Summarize

Have students name the base and exponent for 15^7. Then have them read the expression. Ask students to explain how they would write 1,728 as a product of equal factors of 12 and as a power with a base of 12.

The base is 15. The exponent is 7. The expression reads, "15 to the seventh power." $1{,}728 = 12 \cdot 12 \cdot 12 = 12^3$.

Answers to Think and Discuss

1. The value of 3^6 is 3 times the value of 3^5. $3^6 = 729$, $3^5 = 243$
2. $8^2 = 2^6$; $2 \cdot 2 \cdot 2 = 8$, so $8^2 = 2 \cdot 2 \cdot 2 \cdot 2 \cdot 2 \cdot 2 = 2^6$.
3. Possible answer: The exponent tells how many times the base is used as a factor. If the exponent is 1, then the base is used only once as a factor; therefore, it is equal to itself.

2-1 PRACTICE & ASSESS

Students may want to refer back to the lesson examples.

Assignment Guide

If you finished Example **1** assign:
Core 1–4, 10–21, 37–43 odd, 53–57
Enriched 1, 3, 11–21 odd, 36–44, 53–57

If you finished Example **2** assign:
Core 1–8, 10–30, 33–43 odd, 53–57
Enriched 1–7 odd, 10–30, 32–44, 53–57

If you finished Example **3** assign:
Core 1–31, 33–49 odd, 53–57
Enriched 1–31 odd, 32–57

Notes

2-1 Exercises

FOR EXTRA PRACTICE
see page 657

internet connect
Homework Help Online
go.hrw.com Keyword: MS4 2-1

GUIDED PRACTICE

See Example 1 Find each value.

1. 2^5 **32** **2.** 3^3 **27** **3.** 6^2 **36** **4.** 9^0 **1**

See Example 2 Write each number using an exponent and the given base.

5. 25, base 5 5^2 **6.** 16, base 4 4^2 **7.** 27, base 3 3^3 **8.** 100, base 10 10^2

See Example 3 **9.** On the Richter scale, a great earthquake is 10 times stronger than a major one, and a major one is 10 times stronger than a large one. How many times stronger is a great earthquake than a large one?
100 times stronger

INDEPENDENT PRACTICE

See Example 1 Find each value.

10. 11^2 **121** **11.** 3^5 **243** **12.** 8^3 **512** **13.** 1^0 **1**

14. 4^3 **64** **15.** 3^4 **81** **16.** 2^5 **32** **17.** 5^1 **5**

18. 2^3 **8** **19.** 5^3 **125** **20.** 30^1 **30** **21.** 10^4 **10,000**

See Example 2 Write each number using an exponent and the given base.

22. 81, base 9 9^2 **23.** 4, base 4 4^1 **24.** 64, base 4 4^3

25. 1, base 7 7^0 **26.** 32, base 2 2^5 **27.** 128, base 2 2^7

28. 1,600, base 40 40^2 **29.** 2,500, base 50 50^2 **30.** 100,000, base 10 10^5

See Example 3 **31.** In a game, a contestant had a starting score of one point. He tripled his score every turn for four turns. Write his score after four turns as a power. Then find his score. $3^4 = 81$ **points**

PRACTICE AND PROBLEM SOLVING

Give two ways to represent each number using powers.

32. 81 3^4 or 9^2 **33.** 16 2^4 or 4^2 **34.** 64 8^2, 4^3 or 2^6 **35.** 729 9^3 or 3^6

Find each value.

36. $2^2 + 2^5$ **36** **37.** $3^2 + 4^2$ **25** **38.** $8^2 + 9^2$ **145**

39. $3^4 + 3^3$ **108** **40.** $6^2 + 6^0$ **37** **41.** $125^1 + 125^0$ **126**

42. $1{,}254^0 \cdot 82$ **82** **43.** $19^0 + 17^0 + 10^0$ **3** **44.** $3^3 + 4^2 - 5^1$ **38**

45. To find the volume of a cube, find the third power of the length of an edge of the cube. What is the volume of a cube that is 6 inches long on an edge? **216 cubic inches**

Math Background

Another term for *exponent* is *logarithm.* In the equation $3^4 = 81$, 4 is the logarithm of the number 81 to the base 3. As a logarithm it is written as $\log_3 81 = 4$. It would read, "4 is the logarithm of the number 81 to the base 3." The general rule to express the value of any exponent in terms of a logarithm is this: if $b^x = p$, then $x = \log_b p$.

Logarithms can be used to find an unknown exponent for any equation in the form $b^x = p$, where b and p are known.

RETEACH 2-1

LESSON 2-1 **Reteach**
Exponents

The exponent tells you how many times to multiply the base by itself.

base → 3^4 ← exponent

• To find 3^4, multiply the base (3) times itself 4 times.
$3^4 = 3 \cdot 3 \cdot 3 \cdot 3 = 81$

To multiply, say to yourself:
3 times 3 is 9
9 times 3 is 27
27 times 3 is 81

Find each value.

1. $4^3 =$ 4 • 4 • 4 $= 64$
2. $1^5 =$ 1 • 1 • 1 • 1 • 1 = 1

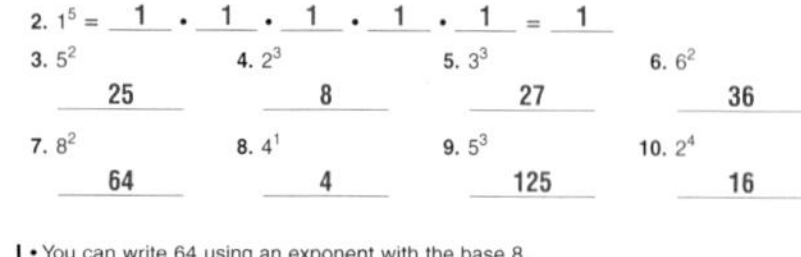

3. 5^2 25 4. 2^3 8 5. 3^3 27 6. 6^2 36
7. 8^2 64 8. 4^1 4 9. 5^3 125 10. 2^4 16

• You can write 64 using an exponent with the base 8.

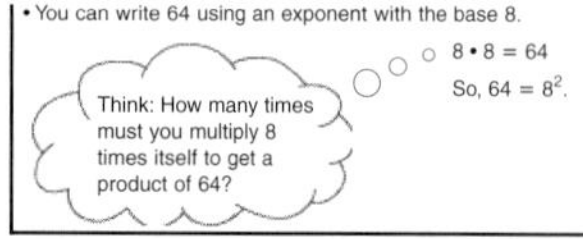

Think: How many times must you multiply 8 times itself to get a product of 64?

$8 \cdot 8 = 64$
So, $64 = 8^2$.

Write each number using an exponent and the given base.

11. 216, base 6: = 36 • 6 and 36 • 6 = 6 • 6 • 6 so, 216 = 6^3.
12. 16, base 4 4^2 13. 8, base 2 2^3 14. 9, base 3 3^2
15. 81, base 9 9^2 16. 27, base 3 3^3 17. 49, base 7 7^2

PRACTICE 2-1

LESSON 2-1 **Practice B**
Exponents

Find each value.

1. 5^2 25 2. 2^4 16 3. 3^3 27 4. 7^2 49
5. 4^4 256 6. 12^2 144 7. 10^3 1,000 8. 11^1 11
9. 1^6 1 10. 20^2 400 11. 6^3 216 12. 7^3 343

Write each number using an exponent and the given base.

13. 16, base 4 4^2 14. 25, base 25 25^1 15. 100, base 10 10^2 16. 125, base 5 5^3
17. 32, base 2 2^5 18. 243, base 3 3^5 19. 900, base 30 30^2 20. 121, base 11 11^2
21. 3,600, base 60 60^2 22. 256, base 4 4^4 23. 512, base 8 8^3 24. 196, base 14 14^2

25. Damon has 4 times as many stamps as Julia. Julia has 4 times as many stamps as Claire. Claire has 4 stamps. Write the number of stamps Damon has in both exponential form and standard form.
4^3 stamps; 64 stamps

26. Holly starts a jump rope exercise program. She jumps rope for 3 minutes the first week. In the second week, she triples the time she jumps. In the third week, she triples the time of the second week, and in the fourth week, she triples the time of the third week. How many minutes does she jump rope during the fourth week?
81 minutes

46. $3^7 = 2187¢$ or $21.87

46. Domingo decided to save $0.03 the first day and to triple the amount he saves each day. How much will he save on the seventh day?

47. ***SOCIAL STUDIES*** If the populations of the cities in the table double every 10 years, what will their populations be in 2029? **Yuma: 484,152; Phoenix: 9,272,112**

City	Population (1999)
Yuma, AZ	60,519
Phoenix, AZ	1,159,014

48. ***HOBBIES*** Malia is making a quilt with a pattern of rings. In the center ring, she uses four stars. In each of the next three rings, she uses three times as many stars as in the one before. How many stars does she use in the fourth ring? Write the answer as a power and find its value. **$4 \cdot 3^3 = 108$ stars**

49. ***LIFE SCIENCE*** The cells of some kinds of bacteria divide every 30 minutes. If you begin with a single cell, how many cells will there be after 1 hour? 2 hours? 3 hours? **4, 16, and 64**

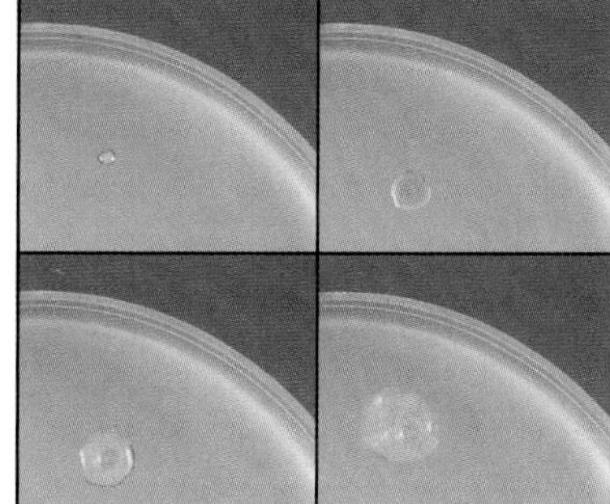

Bacteria divide by pinching in two. This process is called binary fission.

50. ***WHAT'S THE ERROR?*** A student wrote 64 as $8 \cdot 2$. What did the student do wrong? **64 is $8 \cdot 8$, or 8^2**

51. ***WRITE ABOUT IT*** Is 2^5 greater than or less than 3^3? Explain your answer.

52. ***CHALLENGE*** What is the length of the edge of a cube if its volume is 1,000 cubic meters? **10 m**

Spiral Review

53. Trent assigned each student in his class a number. Which of the following gives a random sample? (Lesson 1-1) **a**

a. Trent puts the numbers on slips of paper in a bag and draws 10 numbers.

b. Trent puts the numbers on slips of paper and picks 10 even numbers.

Find the mean of each data set. (Lesson 1-2)

54. 54, 68, 29, 73 **56**

55. 2, 5, 3, 6, 8, 1, 7, 4, 2, 5 **4.3**

56. TEST PREP Given the range, mean, median, and mode of a set of data, which measure must be one of the values in the set? (Lesson 1-2) **D**

A range **C** median

B mean **D** mode

57. TEST PREP The median of the lower half of a data set is called the ___?___ . (Lesson 1-6) **F**

F first quartile **H** third quartile

G second quartile **J** lower extreme

CHALLENGE 2-1

LESSON 2-1 **Challenge**
Money Grows

If an investment of $50 doubles in value, your investment will be worth $\$50 \cdot 2 = \$100$.

If it doubles again, your investment will be worth $\$50 \cdot 2 \cdot 2 = \$200$. You can also write this as $\$50 \cdot 2^2 = \$200$.

If your money doubles a third time, it will be worth $\$50 \cdot 2^3 = \$400$.

Write the correct answer.

1. If you invest $400, how much will it be worth if it doubles in value twice? **$1,600**
2. If an investment of $550 doubles in value twice, how much will it be worth? **$2,200**
3. If you invest $75, how much will it be worth if it doubles in value 4 times? **$1,200**
4. If you invest $125, how much will it be worth if it doubles in value 4 times? **$2,000**
5. If an investment of $75 triples in value 3 times, how much will it be worth? **$2,025**
6. If an investment of $125 triples in value 4 times, how much will it be worth? **$10,125**

When Jasmine turned 13, she started saving $5 per month until she turned 18. She then invested her total savings so that it doubled in value every 7 years.

7. How much money did Jasmine save by the time she turned 18? **$300**
8. How many times will her investment double from age 18 to age 60? **6 times**
9. How much will Jasmine's investment be worth when she turns 60? **$19,200**

When Jake turned 13, he started saving $1.50 per week until he turned 19. He then invested his total savings so that it tripled in value every 12 years.

10. How much money did Jake save by the time he turned 19? **$468**
11. How many times will his investment triple from age 19 to age 55? **3 times**
12. How much will Jake's investment be worth when he turns 55? **$12,636**

PROBLEM SOLVING 2-1

LESSON 2-1 **Problem Solving**
Exponents

Write the correct answer.

1. The cells of the bacteria *E. coli* can double every 20 minutes. If you begin with a single cell, how many cells can there be after 4 hours? **4,096 cells**
2. The population of metropolitan Orlando, Florida, has doubled about every 16 years since 1960. In 2000, the population was 1,644,561. At this doubling rate, what could the population be in 2048? **13,156,488**
3. A prizewinner can choose Prize A, $2,000 per year for 15 years, or Prize B, 3 cents the first year, with the amount tripling each year through the fifteenth year. Which prize is more valuable? How much is it worth? **Prize B: $143,489.07**
4. Maria had triplets. Each of her 3 children had triplets. If the pattern continued for 2 more generations, how many great-great-grandchildren would Maria have? **81 great-great-grandchildren**

Choose the letter for the best answer.

5. A theory states that the CPU clock speed in a computer doubles every 18 months. If the clock speed was 33 MHz in 1991, how can you use exponents to find out how fast the clock speed is after doubling 3 times?
   A 33^3 **(C)** $2^3 \cdot 33$
   B $3^2 \cdot 33$ **D** 33^2
6. The classroom is a square with a side length of 13 feet and an area of 169 square feet. How can you write the area in exponential form?
   F 2^{13} **H** 3^{13}
   (G) 13^2 **J** 13^3
7. In 2000, Wake County, North Carolina, had a population of 610,284. This is about twice the population in 1980. If the county grows at the same rate every 20 years, what will its population be in 2040?
   A 915,426 **C** 1,830,852
   B 1,220,568 **(D)** 2,441,136
8. The number of cells of a certain type of bacteria doubles every 45 minutes. If you begin with a single cell, how many cells could there be after 6 hours?
   F 64 **H** 360
   (G) 256 **J** 540

COMMON ERROR ALERT

Students often evaluate a number to the 0 power as 0. Before students begin Exercises 36–44, remind them that any nonzero number to the 0 power is always 1.

Answers

51. Possible answer: 2^5 is greater than 3^3 because $2^5 = 2 \cdot 2 \cdot 2 \cdot 2 \cdot 2 = 32$ and $3^3 = 3 \cdot 3 \cdot 3 = 27$.

Journal

Ask students to think about how exponents can be used to write large numbers more efficiently. Have students write an explanation about why this is useful and give examples to demonstrate the efficiency of this method.

Test Prep Doctor

For Exercise 56, encourage students to think about how to find each measure. Choices **A, B,** and **C** may or may not be in a data set. Since the mode is the value that appears most often and therefore must be a member of the data set, **D** is the answer.

Lesson Quiz

Find each value.

1. 7^3 343 **2.** 6^3 216

3. 3^4 81 **4.** 8^5 32,768

Write each number using an exponent and the given base.

5. 125, base 5 5^3

6. 16, base 2 2^4

7. Find the volume of a cube if each side is 12 inches long. $1{,}728 \text{ in}^3$

Available on Daily Transparency in CRB

2-2 Organizer

Pacing: Traditional 1 day
Block $\frac{1}{2}$ day

Objective: Students express large numbers in scientific notation.

Warm Up

Find each value.

1. 9^2 **81** **2.** 12^2 **144**
3. 15^2 **225** **4.** 10^2 **100**
5. 10^3 **1,000** **6.** 10^4 **10,000**

Problem of the Day

Each day, Lowell runs one more lap than he did the day before. After seven days he has run 77 laps. How many laps did he run on the first day? **8**

Available on Daily Transparency in CRB

Math Fact !

A googol is a very large number that is written as 10^{100} in exponential form.

2-2 Powers of Ten and Scientific Notation

Learn to express large numbers in scientific notation.

Vocabulary
standard form
scientific notation

The distance from Venus to the Sun is over 100,000,000 kilometers. You can write this number as a power of ten by using a base of ten and an exponent.

$$10 \cdot 10 \cdot 10 \cdot 10 \cdot 10 \cdot 10 \cdot 10 \cdot 10 = 10^8$$

Power of ten (points to 10^8)

The table shows several powers of ten.

Power of 10	Meaning	Value
10^1	10	10
10^2	$10 \cdot 10$	100
10^3	$10 \cdot 10 \cdot 10$	1,000
10^4	$10 \cdot 10 \cdot 10 \cdot 10$	10,000

Astronomers estimate that there are 100 billion billion, or 10^{20}, stars in the universe.

EXAMPLE 1 Multiplying by Powers of Ten

Multiply $21 \cdot 10^4$.

$21 \cdot 10^4 = 21 \cdot (10 \cdot 10 \cdot 10 \cdot 10)$ *Use 10 as a factor 4 times.*
$= 21 \cdot 10{,}000$ *Multiply.*
$= 210{,}000$

You can also find the product of a number and a power of ten simply by moving the decimal point of the number. For powers of ten with positive exponents, move the decimal point to the right.

EXAMPLE 2 Multiplying by Powers of Ten Mentally

Find each product.

A $137 \cdot 10^3$

$137 \cdot 10^3 = 137.000$ (3 places) *Move the decimal point 3 places. (You will need to add 3 zeros.)*
$= 137{,}000$

B $46.2 \cdot 10^5$

$46.2 \cdot 10^5 = 46.20000$ (5 places) *Move the decimal point 5 places. (You will need to add 4 zeros.)*
$= 4{,}620{,}000$

1 Introduce

Alternate Opener

EXPLORATION

2-2 Powers of Ten and Scientific Notation

1. Complete the table and look for a pattern.

Power of 10	Factors	Product
10^1	10	10
10^2	$10 \cdot 10$	100
10^3	$10 \cdot 10 \cdot 10$	1,000
10^4		
10^5		
10^6		
10^8		

2. Use the pattern you observed in the table to write 10,000,000 as a power of 10.

Think and Discuss

3. **Describe** the pattern you observed in the table.
4. **Explain** how you know that $100{,}000 = 10^5$ is a true statement.

Motivate

Have students brainstorm about types of data that usually contain very large numbers (e.g., the distances between planets, populations of large countries, age of Earth, and so on). Have students think about why scientists would want to use a more efficient system to express very large numbers (e.g., it is inconvenient to write and compute with such large numbers).

Exploration worksheet and answers on Chapter 2 Resource Book pp. 17 and 132

2 Teach

Lesson Presentation

Guided Instruction

In this lesson, students learn to express large numbers in scientific notation. Emphasize the relationship between the number of places the decimal point is moved and the number in the exponent. If the decimal moves one place to the right, the exponent becomes one number larger. Demonstrate this relationship by multiplying the number by the appropriate number of tens. When writing a number in scientific notation, guide students to notice that the first factor is always greater than or equal to 1 and less than 10. So it has exactly one digit to the left of the decimal point.

Numbers are usually written in **standard form**. For example, 17,900,000 is in standard form. **Scientific notation** is a kind of shorthand that can be used to write large numbers. Numbers expressed in scientific notation are written as the product of two factors. In scientific notation, 17,900,000 is written as

Writing Math

In scientific notation, it is customary to use a multiplication cross (×) instead of a dot.

$$1.79 \times 10^7$$

A number greater than or equal to 1 but less than 10 → 1.79; *A power of 10* → 10^7

EXAMPLE 3 Writing Numbers in Scientific Notation

Write each number in scientific notation.

A 9,580,000

6 places

9,580,000 = 9,580,000. *Move the decimal point to get a number that is greater than or equal to 1 and less than 10.*

= 9.58×10^6 *The exponent is equal to the number of places the decimal point is moved.*

B 813,000,000

8 places

813,000,000 = 813,000,000. *Move the decimal point to get a number that is greater than or equal to 1 and less than 10.*

= 8.13×10^8 *The exponent is equal to the number of places the decimal point is moved.*

EXAMPLE 4 Writing Numbers in Standard Form

Pluto is about 3.7×10^9 miles from the Sun. Write this distance in standard form.

3.7×10^9 = 3.700000000 *Since the exponent is 9, move the decimal point 9 places to the right.*

= 3,700,000,000

Pluto is about 3,700,000,000 miles from the Sun.

Think and Discuss

1. **Tell** whether 15×10^9 is in scientific notation. Explain.
2. **Compare** $4 \cdot 10^3$ and $3 \cdot 10^4$. Explain how you know which is greater.

COMMON ERROR ALERT

Some students add the same number of zeros as the number in the exponent, rather than counting decimal places when multiplying by powers of ten. For example, they might write 3.43×10^2 as 34,300, since there is a 2 in the exponent. Have students circle the decimal point in the first factor before moving it and placing zeros to the right.

Additional Examples

Example 1

Multiply $14 \cdot 10^3$. 14,000

Example 2

Find each product.

A. $212 \cdot 10^4$ 2,120,000

B. $31.6 \cdot 10^3$ 31,600

Example 3

Write each number in scientific notation.

A. 4,340,000 4.34×10^6

B. 327,000,000 3.27×10^8

Example 4

The population of China in the year 2000 was estimated to be about 1.262×10^9. Write this number in standard form.

The population of China was about 1,262,000,000 people.

3 Close

Reaching All Learners
Through Curriculum Integration

Science Ask students to research the mass of each of the nine planets of the solar system and use scientific notation to report each planet's mass in tons. Have students make up questions about the planets for their classmates to answer.

Possible answer: Mercury: 3.64×10^{20} tons; Venus: 5.37×10^{21} tons; Earth: 6.58×10^{21} tons; Mars: 7.08×10^{20} tons; Jupiter: 2.09×10^{24} tons; Saturn: 6.27×10^{23} tons; Uranus: 9.57×10^{22} tons; Neptune: 1.13×10^{23} tons; Pluto: 1.38×10^{19} tons; Which planet's mass is closest to the mass of Venus? Earth's mass is closest to that of Venus.

Summarize

Have students share what they previously knew about scientific notation and what they learned about it in this lesson. Encourage students to share at least three different facts they now know about scientific notation.

Possible answers: Scientific notation is used to write large numbers as the product of two factors, one of which is a power of 10. Scientific notation makes it easier to read and write large numbers. The first factor in scientific notation is a number greater than or equal to 1 and less than 10.

Answers to Think and Discuss

1. For an expression to be in scientific notation, one of the factors must be greater than or equal to 1 and less than 10. Since neither factor meets that requirement, the number is not in scientific notation. In scientific notation, this number is written 1.5×10^{10}.
2. Possible answer: $3 \cdot 10^4$ is greater; the power of 10 is greater in the expression $3 \cdot 10^4$ than it is in the expression $4 \cdot 10^3$.

2-2 PRACTICE & ASSESS

Students may want to refer back to the lesson examples.

Assignment Guide

If you finished Example 1 assign:
Core 1–4, 14–21, 53–56
Enriched 1–4, 14–21, 53–56

If you finished Example 2 assign:
Core 1–8, 14–29, 53–56
Enriched 1–8, 14–29, 53–56

If you finished Example 3 assign:
Core 1–12, 14–37, 41–47 odd, 53–56
Enriched 1–11 odd, 14–37, 40–48, 53–56

If you finished Example 4 assign:
Core 1–39, 41–49 odd, 53–56
Enriched 1–13 odd, 14–56

Notes

2-2 Exercises

FOR EXTRA PRACTICE see page 657

internet connect
Homework Help Online
go.hrw.com Keyword: MS4 2-2

GUIDED PRACTICE

See Example 1 — Multiply.

1. $15 \cdot 10^2$ **1,500**
2. $18 \cdot 10^3$ **18,000**
3. $11 \cdot 10^0$ **11**
4. $12 \cdot 10^4$ **120,000**

See Example 2 — Find each product.

5. $208 \cdot 10^3$ **208,000**
6. $113 \cdot 10^7$ **1,130,000,000**
7. $47.2 \cdot 10^4$ **472,000**
8. $3.622 \cdot 10^2$ **362.2**

See Example 3 — Write each number in scientific notation.

9. 3,600,000 **3.6×10^6**
10. 214,000 **2.14×10^5**
11. 8,000,000,000 **8.0×10^9**
12. 42,000 **4.2×10^4**

See Example 4

13. A drop of water contains about 2.0×10^{21} molecules. Write this number in standard form. **2,000,000,000,000,000,000,000**

INDEPENDENT PRACTICE

See Example 1 — Multiply.

14. $21 \cdot 10^2$ **2,100**
15. $8 \cdot 10^4$ **80,000**
16. $25 \cdot 10^5$ **2,500,000**
17. $40 \cdot 10^4$ **400,000**
18. $11 \cdot 10^2$ **1,100**
19. $19 \cdot 10^3$ **19,000**
20. $20 \cdot 10^0$ **20**
21. $14 \cdot 10^1$ **140**

See Example 2 — Find each product.

22. $268 \cdot 10^3$ **268,000**
23. $105 \cdot 10^0$ **105**
24. $4.16 \cdot 10^4$ **41,600**
25. $2.164 \cdot 10^2$ **216.4**
26. $550 \cdot 10^7$ **5,500,000,000**
27. $1.020 \cdot 10^3$ **1,020**
28. $2,115 \cdot 10^5$ **211,500,000**
29. $70,030 \cdot 10^1$ **700,300**

See Example 3 — Write each number in scientific notation.

30. 428,000 **4.28×10^5**
31. 1,610,000 **1.61×10^6**
32. 3,000,000,000 **3.0×10^9**
33. 60,100 **6.01×10^4**
34. 52.000 **5.2×10^1**
35. $29.8 \cdot 10^7$ **2.98×10^8**
36. 8,900,000 **8.9×10^6**
37. $500 \cdot 10^3$ **5×10^5**

See Example 4

38. Ancient Egyptians hammered gold into sheets so thin that it took 3.67×10^5 sheets to make a pile 2.5 centimeters high. Write this quantity in standard form. **367,000**

39. In a vacuum, light travels at a speed of about nine hundred and eighty million feet per second. Write this speed in scientific notation. **9.8×10^8 feet per second**

PRACTICE AND PROBLEM SOLVING

Find the missing number or numbers.

40. $24,500 = 2.45 \times 10^{\square}$ **4**
41. $16,800 = \square \times 10^4$ **1.68**
42. $\square = 3.40 \times 10^2$ **340**
43. $280,000 = 2.8 \times 10^{\square}$ **5**
44. $5.4 \times 10^8 = \square$ **540,000,000**
45. $60,000,000 = \square \times 10^{\square}$ **6.0; 7**
46. $\square = 5.92 \times 10^5$ **592,000**
47. $244,000,000 = \square \times 10^{\square}$ **2.44; 8**

Math Background

Here are some interesting estimates that show the magnitude of different powers of 10:

10^{10} is about the number of stars in our galaxy.

10^{20} is the total number of stars in the universe.

10^{30} kilograms is about the mass of the Sun.

10^{67} is about the total number of ways of arranging 52 cards.

$10^{40,000}$ is about the chance of a monkey's correctly typing *Hamlet* by hitting random keys on a computer keyboard.

RETEACH 2-2

LESSON 2-2 **Reteach**
Powers of Ten and Scientific Notation

To multiply by a power of 10, use the exponent to find the number of zeros in the product.

• Multiply $42 \cdot 10^4$.

$42 \cdot 10^4 = 420,000$

The exponent **4** tells you to write **4** zeros after 42 in the product.

Find each product.

1. $84 \cdot 10^3$
   The product should have **3** zeros.
   $84 \cdot 10^3 =$ **84,000**
2. $61 \cdot 10^5$
   The product should have **5** zeros.
   $61 \cdot 10^5 =$ **6,100,000**
3. $22 \cdot 10^6$ **22,000,000**
4. $753 \cdot 10^3$ **753,000**
5. $825 \cdot 10^2$ **82,500**
6. $123 \cdot 10^1$ **1,230**

• Write 926,000 in scientific notation.

First, write the digits before the zeros as a number greater than or equal to 1 and less than 10. The number must have only 1 digit to the left of the decimal point. That digit cannot be zero.

0 1 2 3 4 5 6 7 8 9 10

Think: 9.26 is greater than 1 and less than 10.

Then multiply 9.26 by the power of 10 that gives 926,000 as the product.

$926000 = 9.26 \times 10^5$

The decimal point moves **5** places so the exponent is **5.**

Write each number in scientific notation.

7. 5,100
   The decimal point moves **3** places.
   $5,100 =$ **5** . **1** $\times 10^{\mathbf{3}}$
8. 1,840,000
   The decimal point moves **6** places.
   $1,840,000 =$ **1** . **84** $\times 10^{\mathbf{6}}$
9. 641,000 **6.41×10^5**
10. 47,300 **4.73×10^4**
11. 8,250,000 **8.25×10^6**
12. 703,000 **7.03×10^5**

PRACTICE 2-2

LESSON 2-2 **Practice B**
Powers of Ten and Scientific Notation

Multiply.

1. $6 \cdot 10^3$ **6,000**
2. $22 \cdot 10^1$ **220**
3. $8 \cdot 10^2$ **800**
4. $18 \cdot 10^0$ **18**
5. $70 \cdot 10^2$ **7,000**
6. $25 \cdot 10^3$ **25,000**
7. $3 \cdot 10^4$ **30,000**
8. $180 \cdot 10^3$ **180,000**

Find each product.

9. $84 \cdot 10^4$ **840,000**
10. $315 \cdot 10^2$ **31,500**
11. $210 \cdot 10^3$ **210,000**
12. $1,004 \cdot 10^3$ **1,004,000**
13. $1,764 \cdot 10^1$ **17,640**
14. $856 \cdot 10^0$ **856**
15. $4,055 \cdot 10^3$ **4,055,000**
16. $716 \cdot 10^4$ **7,160,000**

Write each number in scientific notation.

17. 34,000 **3.4×10^4**
18. 7,700 **7.7×10^3**
19. 2,100,000 **2.1×10^6**
20. 404,000 **4.04×10^5**
21. 21,000,000 **2.1×10^7**
22. 612.00 **6.12×10^2**
23. 3,001,000 **3.001×10^6**
24. $62.13 \cdot 10^4$ **6.213×10^5**
25. Lake Superior covers an area of about 31,700 square miles. Write this number in scientific notation.
   3.17×10^4
26. Mars is about $1.42 \cdot 10^8$ miles from the sun. Write this number in standard form.
   142,000,000
27. In 1999, the population of China was about $1.25 \cdot 10^9$. What was the population of China written in standard form?
   1,250,000,000
28. A scientist estimates there are 4,800,000 bacteria in a test tube. How does she record the number using scientific notation?
   4.8×10^6

Earth Science LINK

48. The earliest rocks native to Earth formed during the Archean eon. Calculate the length of this eon. Write your answer in scientific notation. **1.3×10^9 years**

49. Dinosaurs lived during the Mesozoic era. After this era they were extinct. Calculate the length of the Mesozoic era. Write your answer in scientific notation. **1.83×10^8 years**

50. Tropites were prehistoric marine animals. Because they lived for a relatively short time on Earth, their fossil remains can be used to date the rock formations in which they are found. Such fossils are known as *index fossils.* Tropites lived between 2.08×10^8 and 2.30×10^8 years ago. During what geologic time period did they live? **Triassic**

Geologic Time Scale

Eon	Era	Period
Phanerozoic (540 mya*–present)	**Cenozoic** (65 mya–present)	**Quaternary** (1.8 mya–present) **Holocene epoch** (11,000 yrs ago–present) **Pleistocene epoch** (1.8 mya–11,000 yrs ago) **Tertiary** (65 mya–1.8 mya) **Pliocene epoch** (5.3 mya–1.8 mya) **Miocene epoch** (23.8 mya–5.3 mya) **Oligocene epoch** (33.7 mya–23.8 mya) **Eocene epoch** (54.8 mya–33.7 mya) **Paleocene epoch** (65 mya–54.8 mya)
	Mesozoic (248 mya–65 mya)	**Cretaceous** (144 mya–65 mya) **Jurassic** (206 mya–144 mya) **Triassic** (248 mya–206 mya)
	Paleozoic (540 mya–248 mya)	**Permian** (290 mya–248 mya) **Pennsylvanian** (323 mya–290 mya) **Mississippian** (354 mya–323 mya) **Devonian** (417 mya–354 mya) **Silurian** (443 mya–417 mya) **Ordovician** (490 mya–443 mya) **Cambrian** (540 mya–490 mya)
Proterozoic (2,500 mya–540 mya)		
Archean (3,800 mya–2,500 mya)		
Hadean (4,600 mya–3,800 mya)		

*mya = million years ago

51. ***WRITE ABOUT IT*** Explain why scientific notation is especially useful in earth science. **The Earth, its formations, and its inhabitants date back so long that the measures of these time frames are extremely large numbers.**

52. ***CHALLENGE*** We live in the Holocene epoch. Write the age of this epoch in scientific notation. **1.1×10^4 years old**

Spiral Review

53. Make a stem-and-leaf plot of the data 48, 60, 57, 62, 43, 62, 45, 51. (Lesson 1-3)

54. The following data gives the number of students who attended the homecoming football game each year: 1995, 418 students; 1996, 330 students; 1997, 377 students; 1998, 403 students. Make a bar graph of the data. (Lesson 1-4)

55. TEST PREP What is the value of 4^6? (Lesson 2-1) **C**

A 24 C 4,096
B 1,024 D 16,384

56. TEST PREP Evaluate $2^3 + 3^2$. (Lesson 2-1) **G**

F 12 H 43
G 17 J 55

Interdisciplinary LINK

Earth Science

Exercises 48–52 involve using a geologic time scale to find the ages of objects from various eras. Geologic times scales are used in middle school Earth science programs, such as *Holt Science & Technology.*

Answers

53.

Stems	Leaves
4	3 5 8
5	1 7
6	0 2 2

Key: 4|5 means 45

54.

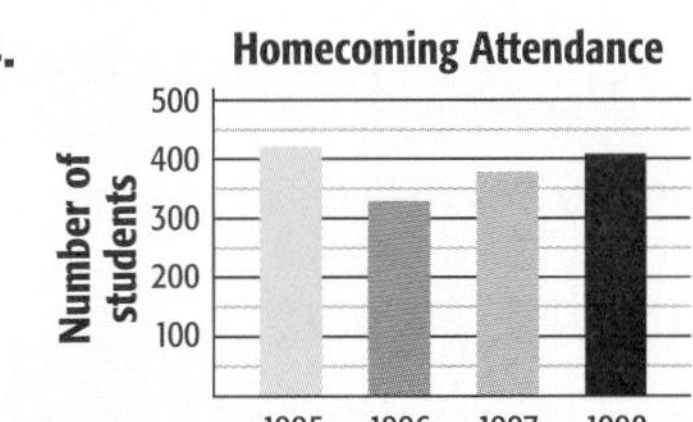

Journal

Have students think about how they might use scientific notation in their own lives. Ask them to describe a science or social studies project in which they would use scientific notation to describe the data being researched.

Test Prep Doctor

For Exercise 55, students who chose **A** multiplied the base and the exponent. Choice **B** is the answer for 4^5, and choice **D** is the answer for 4^7. Choice **C** is the correct answer for 4^6.

CHALLENGE 2-2

LESSON 2-2 **Challenge**
Computer Bytes

Each byte in a computer's memory represents about one character. The major units of computer memory are kilobytes (KB), megabytes (MB), and gigabytes (GB).

1 kilobyte	= 1,000 bytes	1 KB = 1,000 bytes
1 megabyte	= 1,000 kilobytes	1 MG = 1,000 KB
1 gigabyte	= 1,000 megabytes	1 GB = 1,000 MB

Write your answers using scientific notation.

1. In 1984, many personal computers had 64 KB of active (RAM) memory. How many bytes does this represent? **6.4×10^4 bytes**
2. In 1992, many personal computers had 40 MB of hard drive memory. How many bytes does this represent? **4×10^7 bytes**
3. In 1997, many personal computers had 1 GB of hard drive memory. How many bytes does this represent? **1×10^9 bytes**
4. By 2001, many personal computers had 20 GB of hard drive memory. How many bytes does this represent? **2×10^{10} bytes**

Ming saved his computer files on floppy disks. Each disk holds up to 1.44 MB of memory. He used these disks to transfer his files to another computer.

5. How many bytes could each floppy disk hold? **1.44×10^6 bytes**
6. Ming's new computer has 12 GB of memory. How many disks could he transfer if each disk held 1.2 MB? **10,000 disks**

Rachel decided to back up her hard drive's computer files by copying them onto compact disks (CDs). Each CD can hold up to 650 MB of memory, but Rachel saves only 600 MB on each.

7. How many bytes could each CD potentially hold? **6.5×10^8 bytes**
8. If Rachel backs up 6 GB of memory, how many bytes of memory will she need? **6×10^9 bytes**

PROBLEM SOLVING 2-2

LESSON 2-2 **Problem Solving**
Powers of Ten and Scientific Notation

Write the correct answer.

1. Earth is about 150,000,000 kilometers from the sun. Write this distance in scientific notation. **1.5×10^8 km**
2. The planet Neptune is about 4.5×10^9 kilometers from the sun. Write this distance in standard form. **4,500,000,000 km**
3. In 1999, the U.S. federal debt was about $5 trillion, 600 billion. Write the amount of the debt in standard form and in scientific notation. **$5,600,000,000,000; 5.6×10^{12}**
4. Canada is about 1.0×10^7 square kilometers in size. Brazil is about 8,500,000 square kilometers in size. Which country has a greater area? **Canada**

Choose the letter for the best answer.

5. China's population in 2001 was approximately 1,273,000,000. Mexico's population for the same year was about 1.02×10^8. How much greater was China's population than Mexico's?
   A 1,375,000,000
   B 1,274,020,000
   (C) 1,171,000,000
   D 102,000,000
6. In mid-2001, the world population was approximately 6.137×10^9. By 2050, the population is projected to be 9.036×10^9. By how much will world population increase?
   F 151,730,000
   G 289,900,000
   H 1,517,300,000
   (J) 2,899,000,000
7. The Alpha Centauri star system is about 4.3 light-years from Earth. One light-year, the distance light travels in 1 year, is about 6 trillion miles. About how many miles away from Earth is Alpha Centauri?
   (A) 2.58×10^{13} miles
   B 6×10^{13} miles
   C 1.03×10^{12} miles
   D 2.58×10^9 miles
8. In the fall of 2001, students in Columbia, South Carolina, raised $440,000 to buy a new fire truck for New York City. If the money had been collected in pennies, how many pennies would that have been?
   F 4.4×10^6
   G 4.4×10^5
   (H) 4.4×10^7
   J 4.4 3 10^8

Lesson Quiz

Multiply.

1. 25×10^2 **2,500**

2. 18×10^4 **180,000**

Find each product.

3. 110×10^2 **11,000**

4. 3.742×10^3 **3,742**

Write each number in scientific notation.

5. 7,400,000 **7.4×10^6**

6. 45,000 **4.5×10^4**

7. Earth is about 9.292×10^7 miles from the Sun. Write this number in standard form. **92,920,000**

Available on Daily Transparency in CRB

2A Scientific Notation with a Calculator

Pacing: Traditional 1 day
Block $\frac{1}{2}$ day

Objective: To use a graphing calculator to express large numbers in scientific notation and to evaluate expressions using scientific notation

Materials: Graphing calculator

Lab Resources

Technology Lab Activities . . . . p. 5

Using the Pages

This technology activity shows students how to express large numbers in scientific notation and evaluate expressions using scientific notation, which can be done on any graphing calculator. Specific keystrokes may vary, depending on the make and model of the graphing calculator used. The keystrokes given are for a TI-83 model. For keystrokes to other models, visit www.go.hrw.com.

The Think and Discuss problems can be used to assess students' understanding that a number with more than ten digits is expressed in scientific notation on a graphing calculator. While Try This problems 1–5 can be done without a graphing calculator, they are meant to help students become familiar with using numbers expressed in scientific notation on a graphing calculator.

Assessment

1. Show 5,093,000,000,000 in scientific notation on the graphing calculator. **5.093 E 12**
2. Write the expression 61,000,000 · 752,300 using scientific notation. Then evaluate the expression using a graphing calculator. **$(6.1 \times 10^7) \cdot (7.523 \times 10^5)$; 4.58903×10^{13}**

Scientific Notation with a Calculator

Use with Lesson 2-2

Scientists often have to work with very large numbers. For example, the Andromeda Galaxy contains over 200,000,000,000 stars. Scientific notation is a compact way of expressing large numbers such as this.

internet connect
Lab Resources Online
go.hrw.com
KEYWORD: MS4 Lab2A

Activity

1. Show 200,000,000,000 in scientific notation.

Enter 200,000,000,000 on your graphing calculator. Then press ENTER.

200000000000
2E11

2 E 11 on the calculator display means 2×10^{11}, which is 200,000,000,000 in scientific notation. Your calculator automatically puts very large numbers into scientific notation.

You can use the **EE** function (the second function for the *comma* key) to enter 2×10^{11} directly into the calculator.

Enter 2×10^{11} by pressing 2 2nd EE , 11 ENTER.

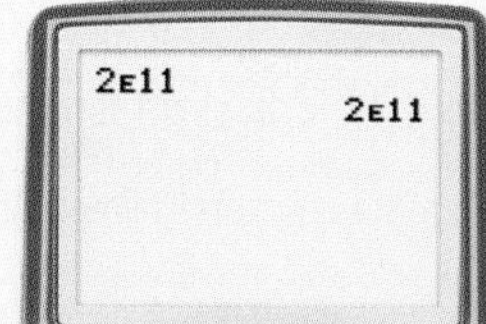

2. Evaluate 230,000,000 × 650,000.

Write 230,000,000 and 650,000 in scientific notation.

$230{,}000{,}000 = 2.3 \times 10^8$

$650{,}000 = 6.5 \times 10^5$

Press 2.3 2nd EE , 8 × 6.5 2nd EE , 5 ENTER.

In scientific notation, 230,000,000 × 650,000 is equal to 1.495×10^{14}.

3 Evaluate (340,000,000,000 ÷ 1,235) × 4,568.

Write each number in scientific notation.

$340,000,000,000 = 3.4 \times 10^{11}$

$1,235 = 1.235 \times 10^3$

$4,568 = 4.568 \times 10^3$

Press (3.4 2nd EE , 11 ÷ 1.235 2nd EE , 3) ×

4.568 2nd EE , 3 ENTER.

(340,000,000,000 ÷ 1,235) × 4,568 is equal to $1.257587045 \times 10^{12}$.

Because this calculator displays results to only ten decimal places, this answer is not exact. The exact answer is $1.2575870445344110 \times 10^{12}$.

Think and Discuss

1. What happens when you add 9,999,999,999 + 1 on a graphing calculator? Explain why this happens.

Try This

In space, light travels about 9,460,000,000,000 kilometers per year. This distance is known as a **light-year.** Use a calculator to find the distance in kilometers from Earth to each astronomical object. Write the results in scientific notation.

1. the star Altair, 16.3 light-years away **1.54198×10^{14} kilometers**
2. the Large Magellanic Cloud Galaxy, 180,000 light-years away **1.7028×10^{18} kilometers**
3. the Andromeda Galaxy, 2,900,000 light-years away **2.7434×10^{19} kilometers**

In 1999, astronomers at the Space Telescope Science Institute estimated that there are 125 billion galaxies in the observable universe.

4. The number 125 billion is equal to 125,000,000,000. Write this number in scientific notation. **1.25×10^{11}**
5. Suppose the universe is made up of 125,000,000,000 galaxies, each containing 200,000,000,000 stars. Use this data to find the number of stars in the universe. Express your answer in scientific notation and in standard form. **2.5×10^{22} = 25,000,000,000,000,000,000,000 stars**

Answers

Think and Discuss

1. Possible answer: The calculator expresses a number with more than ten digits in scientific notation. The maximum number of digits that can be displayed is ten digits. 9,999,999,999 + 1 = 10,000,000,000, which is 11 digits.

2-3 Organizer

Pacing: Traditional 1 day
Block $\frac{1}{2}$ day

Objective: Students use the order of operations to simplify numerical expressions.

Warm Up

Evaluate in order from left to right.

1. $18 \div 3 + 7$ 13

2. $10^2 \div 4 - 8$ 17

3. $10 + 23 - 8 + 7$ 32

4. $8 \times 2 - 3 + 24$ 37

5. $81 \div 9 \times 3 + 15$ 42

Problem of the Day

Classify each statement as true or false. If the statement is false, insert parentheses to make it true.

1. $4 \times (5 + 6) = 44$ false

2. $(24 - 4) \times 2 = 40$ false

3. $25 \div 5 + 6 \times 3 = 23$ true

4. $14 - 2^2 \div 2 = 12$ true

Available on Daily Transparency in CRB

Math Humor

What's a seventh grader's favorite excuse for not doing homework?
I have a solar-powered calculator, and yesterday it was cloudy all day.

2-3 Order of Operations

Learn to use the order of operations to simplify numerical expressions.

Vocabulary

numerical expression

order of operations

When you get ready for school, you put on your socks *before* you put on your shoes. In mathematics, as in life, some tasks must be done in a certain order.

A **numerical expression** is made up of numbers and operations. When simplifying a numerical expression, rules must be followed so that everyone gets the same answer. That is why mathematicians have agreed upon the **order of operations**.

ORDER OF OPERATIONS

1. Perform operations within grouping symbols.
2. Evaluate powers.
3. Multiply and divide in order from left to right.
4. Add and subtract in order from left to right.

EXAMPLE 1 Using the Order of Operations

Evaluate.

A $27 - 18 \div 6$

$27 - 18 \div 6$ *Divide.*

$27 - 3$ *Subtract.*

24

B $36 - 18 \div 2 \cdot 3 + 8$

$36 - 18 \div 2 \cdot 3 + 8$ *Divide and multiply from left to right.*

$36 - 9 \cdot 3 + 8$

$36 - 27 + 8$ *Subtract and add from left to right.*

$9 + 8$

17

C $5 + 6^2 \cdot 10$

$5 + 6^2 \cdot 10$ *Evaluate the power.*

$5 + 36 \cdot 10$ *Multiply.*

$5 + 360$ *Add.*

365

1 Introduce

Alternate Opener

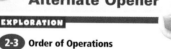

EXPLORATION

2-3 Order of Operations

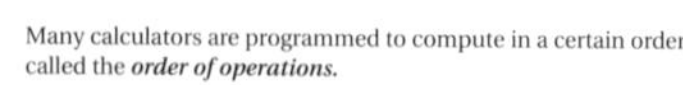

Many calculators are programmed to compute in a certain order, called the ***order of operations.***

1. Determine the order the calculator follows for each expression in the window.

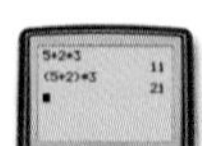

Use the necessary operation symbols +, −, ×, and ÷ and the grouping symbols) and (to make each statement true. Verify with your calculator.

2. 4 3 6 = 7 **3.** 4 3 6 = 6

4. 4 3 6 = 22 **5.** 4 3 6 = 42

6. 4 3 6 = 2 **7.** 6 3 4 = 8

Think and Discuss

8. Explain how the grouping symbols) and (are used in the order of operations.

9. Describe the order of operations in your own words.

Motivate

Initiate a discussion about the importance of order in various activities. Ask students to describe activities or situations in which the order of the steps is important (e.g., cooking, getting dressed, or building a house). Then have students evaluate the expression $2 + 7 \cdot 5$. Students may give either 37 or 49 as the answer. Have students share their methods and discuss why a standard order of operations is important.

Exploration worksheet and answers on Chapter 2 Resource Book pp. 26 and 134

2 Teach

Lesson Presentation

Guided Instruction

In this lesson, students learn to use the order of operations (Teaching Transparency T9, CRB) to simplify numerical expressions. Point out that the order of operations not only sets the rules for the order of operations but also indicates the direction (from left to right). Discuss how the value for the expression in Example 1B changes if students multiply before they divide.

$36 - 18 \div 2 \cdot 3 + 8$
$36 - 18 \div 6 + 8$
$36 - 3 + 8 = 41$

Teaching Tip Be sure students realize that grouping symbols include brackets as well as parentheses.

EXAMPLE 2 **Using the Order of Operations with Grouping Symbols**

Evaluate.

A $36 - (2 \cdot 6) \div 3$

$36 - (2 \cdot 6) \div 3$ — *Perform the operation inside the parentheses.*

$36 - 12 \div 3$

$36 - 4$

32

Helpful Hint

When an expression has a set of grouping symbols within a second set of grouping symbols, begin with the innermost set.

B $[(4 + 12 \div 4) - 2]^3$

$[(4 + 12 \div 4) - 2]^3$ — *The parentheses are inside the brackets, so perform the operations inside the parentheses first.*

$[(4 + 3) - 2]^3$

$[7 - 2]^3$

5^3

125

EXAMPLE 3 ***Career Application***

Maria works part-time in a law office, where she earns $20 per hour. The table shows the number of hours she worked last week. Evaluate the expression (6 + 5 · 3) · 20 to find out how much money Maria earned last week.

Day	Hours
Monday	6
Tuesday	5
Wednesday	5
Thursday	5

$(6 + 5 \cdot 3) \cdot 20$ — *Perform the operations inside the parentheses.*

$(6 + 15) \cdot 20$

$21 \cdot 20$

420

Maria earned $420 last week.

Think and Discuss

1. **Apply** the order of operations to determine if the expressions $3 + 4^2$ and $(3 + 4)^2$ have the same value.
2. **Give** the correct order of operations for evaluating $(5 + 3 \cdot 20) \div 13 + 3^2$.
3. **Determine** where grouping symbols should be inserted in the expression $3 + 9 - 4 \cdot 2$ so that its value is 13.

COMMON ERROR ALERT

Some students may perform the operations in an expression in the order in which the operations appear from left to right. In the expression $9 - 4 \cdot 2$, students might subtract before multiplying. Encourage students to number the operations in the order they should work them before they begin to compute the value of the expression.

Additional Examples

Example 1

Evaluate.

A. $3 + 15 \div 5$ — **6**

B. $44 - 14 \div 2 \cdot 4 + 6$ — **22**

C. $3 + 2^3 \cdot 5$ — **43**

Example 2

Evaluate.

A. $42 - (3 \cdot 4) \div 6$ — **40**

B. $[(26 - 4 \cdot 5) + 6]^2$ — **144**

Example 3

Sandy runs 4 miles per day. She ran 5 days during the first week of the month. She ran only 3 days each week for the next 3 weeks. Evaluate the expression $(5 + 3 \cdot 3) \cdot 4$ to find how many miles she ran last month.

Sandy ran 56 miles last month.

Example 3 note: Students should realize that the numbers within the grouping symbols, $6 + 5 \cdot 3$, are the number of hours worked in one week.

3 Close

Reaching All Learners

Through Grouping Strategies

Have students work in groups to decide which operation sign belongs in each box to make the number sentences true. (Recording Sheet for Reaching All Learners, CRB p. 125) Students may need to use operations more than once in each number sentence.

1. Operation signs: +, –, ·
   Number sentence:
   12 ▢ 4 ▢ 6 ▢ 3 ▢ 7 = 37
   12 · 4 – 6 · 3 + 7 = 37
2. Operation signs: ÷, +, –
   Number sentence:
   18 ▢ 2 ▢ 24 ▢ 12 ▢ 4 = 22
   18 + 2 – 24 ÷ 12 + 4 = 22

Summarize

Have volunteers restate the order of operations without referring to the textbook. Then ask students to describe or write an example of a numerical expression in which they will have to add or subtract first before multiplying.

Possible answers: (1) Perform operations within grouping symbols. (2) Evaluate powers. (3) Multiply and divide in order from left to right. (4) Add and subtract in order from left to right. You would have to add before multiplying in an expression that has addition within parentheses and uses multiplication outside of the parentheses, for example, $8 \cdot (6 + 4)$.

Answers to Think and Discuss

1. The expressions do not have the same value. $3 + 4^2 = 3 + 16 = 19$; $(3 + 4)^2 = 49$.
2. The order of operations for the expression is as follows:
   1) Multiply $3 \cdot 20$.
   2) Add 5 to the product.
   3) Square 3.
   4) Divide the result from step 2 by 13.
   5) Add the result from step 3 to the quotient.
   The result of the expression is 14.
3. $3 + (9 - 4) \cdot 2 = 13$

2-3 PRACTICE & ASSESS

Students may want to refer back to the lesson examples.

Assignment Guide

If you finished Example 1 assign:
Core 1–3, 8–10, 37–39
Enriched 1–3, 8–10, 37–39

If you finished Example 2 assign:
Core 1–6, 8–16, 19–29 odd, 37–39
Enriched 1–5 odd, 9–15 odd, 19–30, 37–39

If you finished Example 3 assign:
Core 1–18, 19–33 odd, 37–39
Enriched 1–17 odd, 19–39

Notes

2-3 Exercises

FOR EXTRA PRACTICE see page 657

internet connect
Homework Help Online
go.hrw.com Keyword: MS4 2-3

GUIDED PRACTICE

See Example 1 Evaluate.

1. $43 + 16 \div 4$ **47**
2. $28 - 4 \cdot 3 \div 6 + 4$ **30**
3. $25 - 4^2 \div 8$ **23**

See Example 2
4. $26 - (7 \cdot 3) + 2$ **7**
5. $(3^2 + 11) \div 5$ **4**
6. $32 + 6(4 - 2^2) + 8$ **40**

See Example 3
7. Caleb earns $10 per hour. He worked 4 hours on Monday, Wednesday, and Friday. He worked 8 hours on Tuesday and Thursday. Evaluate the expression $(3 \cdot 4 + 2 \cdot 8) \cdot 10$ to find out how much Caleb earned in all. **$280**

INDEPENDENT PRACTICE

See Example 1 Evaluate.

8. $3 + 7 \cdot 5 - 1$ **37**
9. $5 \cdot 9 - 3$ **42**
10. $3 - 2 + 6 \cdot 2^2$ **25**

See Example 2
11. $(3 \cdot 3 - 3)^2 \div 3 + 3$ **15**
12. $2^5 - (4 \cdot 5 + 3)$ **9**
13. $(3 \div 3) + 3 \cdot (3^3 - 3)$ **73**
14. $4^3 \div 8 - 2$ **6**
15. $(8 - 2)^2 \cdot (8 - 1)^2 \div 3$ **588**
16. $9{,}234 \div [3 \cdot 3(1 + 8^3)]$ **2**

See Example 3
17. Maki paid a $14 basic fee plus $25 a day to rent a car. Evaluate the expression $14 + 5 \cdot 25$ to find out how much it cost her to rent the car for 5 days. **$139**
18. Enrico spent $20 per square yard for carpet and $35 for a carpet pad. Evaluate the expression $35 + 20(12^2 \div 9)$ to find out how much Enrico spent to carpet a 12 ft by 12 ft room. **$355**

PRACTICE AND PROBLEM SOLVING

Compare. Write <, >, or =.

19. $8 \cdot 3 - 2$ ▒ $8 \cdot (3 - 2)$ **>**
20. $(6 + 10) \div 2$ ▒ $6 + 10 \div 2$ **<**
21. $12 \div 3 \cdot 4$ ▒ $12 \div (3 \cdot 4)$ **>**
22. $18 + 6 - 2$ ▒ $18 + (6 - 2)$ **=**
23. $[6(8 - 3) + 2]$ ▒ $6(8 - 3) + 2$ **=**
24. $(18 - 14) \div (2 + 2)$ ▒ $18 - 14 \div 2 + 2$ **<**

Insert grouping symbols to make each statement true.

25. $4 \cdot (8 - 3) = 20$
26. $5 + (9 - 3) \div 2 = 8$
27. $(12 - 2)^2 \div 5 = 20$
28. $4 \cdot (2 + 6) = 32$
29. $(4 + 6 - 3) \div 7 = 1$
30. $9 \cdot (8 - 6) \div 3 = 6$

31. Bertha earned $8.00 per hour for 4 hours babysitting and $10.00 per hour for 5 hours painting a room. Evaluate the expression $8 \cdot 4 + 10 \cdot 5$ to find out how much Bertha earned in all. **$82**

Math Background

A History of Mathematical Notations, by Florian Cajori, describes the history of various mathematical symbols. According to Cajori, parentheses and brackets have been used as grouping symbols since the sixteenth century. A work published in 1556, *General trattao di numeri e misure,* by Nicolo Tartaglia, is one of the first works in which parentheses are used. Brackets have been found as early as 1550 in a manuscript edition of *Algebra,* by Rafael Bombelli.

RETEACH 2-3

LESSON 2-3 **Reteach**
Order of Operations

To help you remember the order of operations use the phrase "**P**lease **E**xcuse **M**y **D**ear **A**unt **S**ally."

P: first, **p**arentheses (if any)
E: second, **e**xponents (if any)
M and **D**: then, **m**ultiplication and **d**ivision, in order from left to right
A and **S**: finally, **a**ddition and **s**ubtraction, in order from left to right

Evaluate. $39 \div (9 + 4) + 5 - 2^2$
Parentheses → $39 \div 13 + 5 - 2^2$
Exponents → $39 \div 13 + 5 - 4$
Multiply and divide from left to right → $3 + 5 - 4$
Add and subtract from left to right → $8 - 4 = 4$

Evaluate.

1. $12 \cdot 4 - 2$ — **48** $- 2$ — **46**
2. $15 \div 3 \cdot 5$ — **5** $\cdot 5$ — **25**
3. $15 \cdot 3 \div 5$ — **45** $\div 5$ — **9**
4. $8 + 20 \div 4$ **13**
5. $5 - 2 \cdot 6 \div 4 + 1$ **3**
6. $3^2 + 6 \cdot 4 - 5^2$ **8**
7. $1 + 4 \cdot 9 \div 6 - 7$ **0**
8. $18 \div (6 \div 3)$ **9**
9. $(18 \div 6) \div 3$ **1**
10. $4 \cdot 5 + 8 \div 2 - 7$ **17**
11. $2 \cdot 3 - 8 \div 2^2$ **4**
12. $8(7 - 6) \div 2^3$ **1**

PRACTICE 2-3

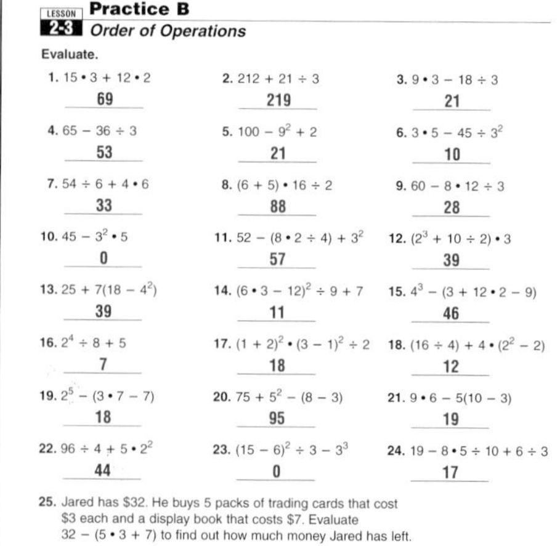

LESSON 2-3 **Practice B**
Order of Operations

Evaluate.

1. $15 \cdot 3 + 12 \cdot 2$ **69**
2. $212 + 21 \div 3$ **219**
3. $9 \cdot 3 - 18 \div 3$ **21**
4. $65 - 36 \div 3$ **53**
5. $100 - 9^2 + 2$ **21**
6. $3 \cdot 5 - 45 \div 3^2$ **10**
7. $54 \div 6 + 4 \cdot 6$ **33**
8. $(6 + 5) \cdot 16 \div 2$ **88**
9. $60 - 8 \cdot 12 \div 3$ **28**
10. $45 - 3^2 \cdot 5$ **0**
11. $52 - (8 \cdot 2 \div 4) + 3^2$ **57**
12. $(2^3 + 10 \div 2) \cdot 3$ **39**
13. $25 + 7(18 - 4^2)$ **39**
14. $(6 \cdot 3 - 12)^2 \div 9 + 7$ **11**
15. $4^3 - (3 + 12 \cdot 2 - 9)$ **46**
16. $2^4 \div 8 + 5$ **7**
17. $(1 + 2)^2 \cdot (3 - 1)^2 \div 2$ **18**
18. $(16 \div 4) + 4 \cdot (2^2 - 2)$ **12**
19. $2^5 - (3 \cdot 7 - 7)$ **18**
20. $75 + 5^2 - (8 - 3)$ **95**
21. $9 \cdot 6 - 5(10 - 3)$ **19**
22. $96 \div 4 + 5 \cdot 2^2$ **44**
23. $(15 - 6)^2 \div 3 - 3^3$ **0**
24. $19 - 8 \cdot 5 \div 10 + 6 \div 3$ **17**
25. Jared has $32. He buys 5 packs of trading cards that cost $3 each and a display book that costs $7. Evaluate $32 - (5 \cdot 3 + 7)$ to find out how much money Jared has left.
$10
26. David buys 3 movie tickets for $6 each and 2 bags of popcorn for $2 each. Evaluate $3 \cdot 6 + 2 \cdot 2$ to find out how much money David spent in all.
$22

32a. (27 + 24 + 28 + 33)/4; 28°F

32b. (33 − 24) − (28 − 27)

33a. 4 · 15

33b. 2 · 30

35. First add 2 and 4, and then square the result. Multiply 2 times 3, and subtract from 36. Then divide that answer by 6.

32. ***EARTH SCIENCE*** The graph shows the average temperatures for each of four months in Juneau, Alaska.
   a. Write and evaluate an expression to find the average temperature over the 4-month period.
   b. Write an expression that shows the difference between the range of average temperatures from December to February and the range of average temperatures from January to March.

Average Monthly Temperatures in Juneau, AK

Temperature (°F): 0, 5, 10, 15, 20, 25, 30, 35, 40

Months: Dec, Jan, Feb, Mar

33. ***CONSUMER MATH*** Anelise bought four shirts and two pairs of jeans. She paid $6 in sales tax.
   a. Write an expression that shows how much she spent on shirts.
   b. Write an expression that shows how much she spent on jeans.
   c. Write and evaluate an expression to show how much she spent on clothes, including sales tax. **4 · 15 + 2 · 30 + 6; $126**

34. ***CHOOSE A STRATEGY*** There are four children in a family. The sum of the squares of the ages of the three youngest children equals the square of the age of the oldest child. How old are the children? **A**

   A 1, 4, 8, 9 **B** 1, 3, 6, 12 **C** 4, 5, 8, 10 **D** 2, 3, 8, 16

35. ***WRITE ABOUT IT*** Describe in what order you would perform the operations to find the value of $[(2 + 4)^2 - 2 \cdot 3] \div 6$.

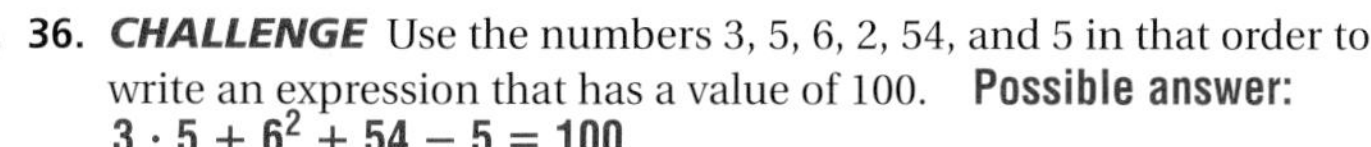

36. ***CHALLENGE*** Use the numbers 3, 5, 6, 2, 54, and 5 in that order to write an expression that has a value of 100. **Possible answer: $3 \cdot 5 + 6^2 + 54 - 5 = 100$**

Spiral Review

37. Hal recorded the following gas prices per gallon over a six-week period: $1.79, $1.88, $2.25, $1.90, $1.70, and $1.85. Construct a line graph to show the prices. (Lesson 1-7)

38. **TEST PREP** Which of the following is **not** equal to 64? (Lesson 2-1) **A**

   A 64^0 **C** 2^6
   B 4^3 **D** 8^2

39. **TEST PREP** Which number is equivalent to 5.3×10^7? (Lesson 2-2) **H**

   F 5,000,003 **H** 53,000,000
   G 5,300,000 **J** 530,000,000

CHALLENGE 2-3

LESSON 2-3 **Challenge**
Fixed and Variable Costs

A *fixed cost* is a one-time cost. A *variable cost* changes depending on your use of a product or a service.

The annual enrollment fee per year at a fitness club (fixed cost) is $30. You also pay $2 per visit (variable cost), and you visit the club 8 times per month. What is your total annual cost?

2 • (8 • 12)	variable cost times total visits
30 + 2 • (8 • 12)	total annual cost
222	Your total annual cost is $222.

Use the information above to solve problems 1–4.

1. Suppose the annual fee is $25, but the cost per visit is $3. What is your annual cost? **$313**
2. Suppose you visit the club 3 times per week instead of 8 times per month. What is your annual cost? **$342**
3. Suppose the cost per visit is $3 after the first 50 visits per year. What is your annual cost? **$268**
4. Suppose you pay for up to 75 visits per year. Any additional visits are free. What is your annual cost? **$180**

The school band is raising money for a trip. The members ordered 5 dozen jerseys for $7 each and sold them for $12 each. They also ordered 4 dozen sweatshirts for $11 each and sold them for $18 each. The band paid $35 to create the design.

5. Write and evaluate an expression to calculate the band's variable costs for the clothing.
   7(5 • 12) + 11(4 • 12); $948
6. Write and evaluate an expression to calculate the band's total cost, including fixed costs.
   7(5 • 12) + 11(4 • 12) + 35; $983
7. Write and evaluate an expression to calculate the band's profit.
   12(5 • 12) + 18(4 • 12) − [7(5 • 12) + 11(4 • 12) + 35]; $601
8. What would the profit be if jerseys sold for $10 and sweatshirts for $20?
   $577

PROBLEM SOLVING 2-3

LESSON 2-3 **Problem Solving**
Order of Operations

Write the correct answer.

1. In 1975, the minimum wage was $2.10 per hour. Write and evaluate an expression to show wages earned in a 35-hour week after a $12 tax deduction.
   35 • 2.10 − 12; $61.50
2. George bought 3 boxes of Girl Scout cookies at $3.50 per box and 4 boxes at $3.00 per box. Write and evaluate an expression to show his total cost.
   3 • 3.50 + 4 • 3; $22.50
3. In 1 week Ed works 4 days, 3 hours a day, for $12 per hour, and 2 days, 6 hours a day, for $15 per hour. Evaluate 12(4 • 3) + 15(2 • 6) to find Ed's weekly earnings.
   $324 per week
4. Keisha had $150. She bought jeans for $27, a sweater for $32, 3 blouses for $16 each, and 2 pairs of socks for $6 each. Evaluate 150 − [27 + 32 + (3 • 16) + (2 • 6)] to find out how much money she has left.
   She has $31 left.

Choose the letter for the best answer.

5. As of September 1, 1997, the minimum wage was $5.15 per hour. How much more would someone earn now than in 1997 if she earns $5 more per hour for a 40-hour week?
   A $206 more
   Ⓑ $200 more
   C $406 more
   D $400 more
6. Gary received $200 in birthday gifts. He bought 5 CDs for $15 each, 2 posters for $12 each, and a $70 jacket. How much money does he have left?
   Ⓕ $31
   G $10
   H $132
   J $169
7. Yvonne took her younger brother and his friends to the movies. She bought 5 tickets for $8 each, 4 drinks for $2 each, and two $3 containers of popcorn. How much did she spend?
   A $22
   B $51
   Ⓒ $54
   D $38
8. On a business trip, Mr. Chang stayed in a hotel for 7 nights. He paid $149 per night. While he was there, he made 8 phone calls at $2 each and charged $81 to room service. How much did he spend?
   F $246
   G $946
   H $1,043
   Ⓙ $1,140

COMMON ERROR ALERT

For Exercise 32a, students might forget to divide by the number of months. Remind students that to find the average, they must first find the sum of the data values and then divide by the total number of values.

Answers

37.

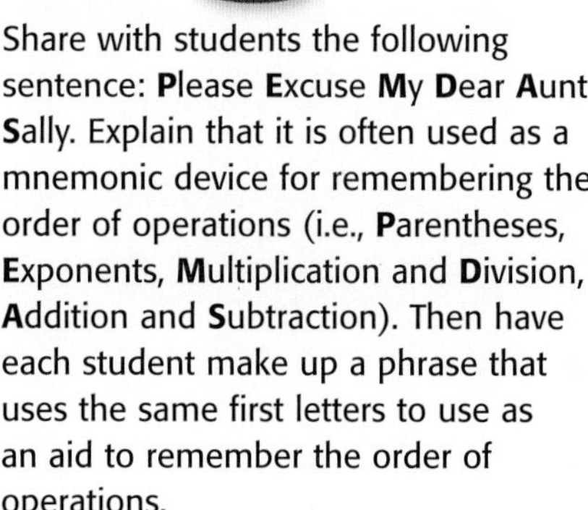

Journal

Share with students the following sentence: **P**lease **E**xcuse **M**y **D**ear **A**unt **S**ally. Explain that it is often used as a mnemonic device for remembering the order of operations (i.e., **P**arentheses, **E**xponents, **M**ultiplication and **D**ivision, **A**ddition and **S**ubtraction). Then have each student make up a phrase that uses the same first letters to use as an aid to remember the order of operations.

Test Prep Doctor

For Exercise 38, be sure students realize they are looking for the choice that does **not** equal 64. Any choice that does equal 64 can be eliminated. Students can use mental math to quickly eliminate **B** and **D.**

Lesson Quiz

Evaluate.

1. 27 + 56 ÷ 7 **35**
2. 9 · 7 − 5 **58**
3. (28 − 8) ÷ 4 **5**
4. $136 - 10^2 \div 5$ **116**
5. $(9 - 5)^3 \cdot (7 + 1)^2 \div 4$ **1,024**
6. Denzel paid a basic fee of $35 per month plus $2 for each phone call beyond his basic plan. Evaluate 35 + 8(2) to find out how much Denzel paid for a month with 8 calls outside of the basic plan. **$51**

Available on Daily Transparency in CRB

Chapter 2 Mid-Chapter Quiz

Purpose: *To assess students' mastery of concepts and skills in Lessons 2-1 through 2-3*

Assessment Resources

Section 2A Quiz
Assessment Resources .... p. 8

***Test and Practice Generator* CD-ROM**

Additional mid-chapter assessment items in both multiple-choice and free-response format may be generated for any objective in Lessons 2-1 through 2-3.

Chapter 2 Mid-Chapter Quiz

Mid-Chapter Quiz

LESSON 2-1 (pp. 60–63)

Find each value.

1. 6^3 **216** **2.** 12^2 **144** **3.** 11^0 **1** **4.** 3^4 **81**

5. 2^7 **128** **6.** 10^6 **1,000,000** **7.** 5^3 **125** **8.** 7^2 **49**

9. 17^1 **17** **10.** 9^2 **81** **11.** 8^4 **4,096** **12.** 4^5 **1,024**

13. The number of a certain bacteria doubles every hour. How many bacteria cells will there be after 8 hours if there is one cell to start? Write your answer as a power. $\mathbf{2^8 = 256}$ **cells**

LESSON 2-2 (pp. 64–67)

Find each product.

14. $32 \cdot 10^3$ **32,000** **15.** $147 \cdot 10^4$ **1,470,000** **16.** $44.2 \cdot 10^2$ **4,420**

17. $23 \cdot 10^6$ **23,000,000** **18.** $80.4 \cdot 10^3$ **80,400** **19.** $140.02 \cdot 10^5$ **14,002,000**

Write each number in scientific notation.

20. 39,500,000 $\mathbf{3.95 \times 10^7}$ **21.** 5,400 $\mathbf{5.4 \times 10^3}$ **22.** $800 \cdot 10^4$ $\mathbf{8 \times 10^6}$

23. $21.6 \cdot 10^5$ $\mathbf{2.16 \times 10^6}$ **24.** 107,000 $\mathbf{1.07 \times 10^5}$ **25.** $5{,}010 \cdot 10^3$ $\mathbf{5.01 \times 10^6}$

LESSON 2-3 (pp. 70–73)

Evaluate.

26. $20 - 4 \cdot 3 + 2$ **10** **27.** $16 + 34 - 2 \cdot 8$ **34**

28. $12 \div 4 \cdot 6 + 16 - 4$ **30** **29.** $12 \cdot 2 + 2 \div 2 - 5$ **20**

30. $3 + 9 - 6 \cdot 4 \div 8$ **9** **31.** $4 \cdot 7 - 14 \div 2$ **21**

32. $2 + (12 \div 4)^2 \div 3$ **5** **33.** $[6 \cdot (5 + 7) \div 9]^2$ **64**

34. There are normally 365 days in a year. Every fourth year, called a *leap year,* has 366 days. Evaluate the expression $2(365 \cdot 3 + 366)$ to find out how many days there are in 8 consecutive years. **2,922 days**

35. Audry spent \$8 per square foot for floor tile and \$20 for tile glue. Evaluate the expression $8(48 \cdot 30 \div 12^2) + 20$ to find out how much she spent to tile a 48-inch by 30-inch entryway. **\$100**

36. Siras earns \$9 per hour plus a commission of \$12 for every sale he makes. Evaluate the expression $8 \cdot 9 + 14 \cdot 12$ to find out how much Siras earned during an 8-hour shift in which he made 14 sales. **Siras earned \$240.**

Focus on Problem Solving

Solve

• **Choose an operation: multiplication or division**

To solve a word problem, you must determine which mathematical operation you can use to find the answer. One way of doing this is to determine the action the problem is asking you to take. If you are putting equal parts together, then you need to multiply. If you are separating something into equal parts, then you need to divide.

Decide what action each problem is asking you to take, and tell whether you must multiply or divide. Then explain your decision.

1. Judy plays the flute in the band. She practices for 3 hours every week. Judy practices only half as long as Angie, who plays the clarinet. How long does Angie practice playing the clarinet each week?

2. Each year, members of the band and choir are invited to join the bell ensemble for the winter performance. There are 18 bells in the bell ensemble. This year, each student has 3 bells to play. How many students are in the bell ensemble this year?

3. For every percussion instrument in the band, there are 4 wind instruments. If there are 48 wind instruments in the band, how many percussion instruments are there?

4. A group of 4 people singing together in harmony is called a quartet. At a state competition for high school choir students, 7 quartets from different schools competed. How many students competed in the quartet competition?

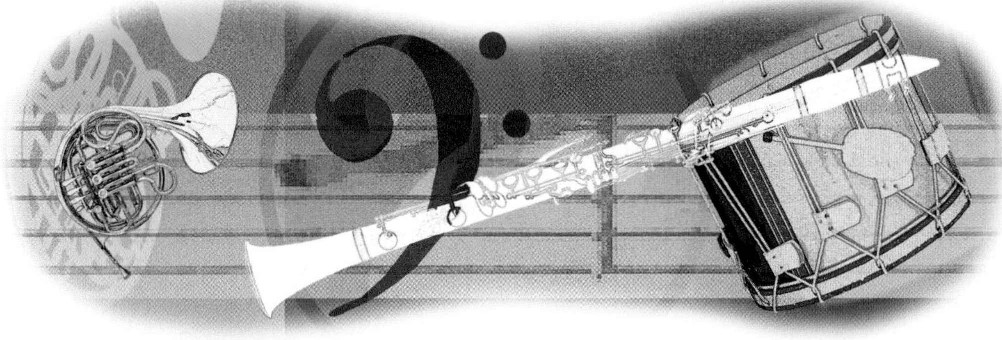

Answers

1. $3 \cdot 2 = 6$ hr
2. $18 \div 3 = 6$ students
3. $48 \div 4 = 12$ percussion instruments
4. $7 \cdot 4 = 28$ students

Focus on Problem Solving

Purpose: *To focus on choosing an operation (× or ÷) to solve a problem*

Problem Solving Resources

Interactive Problem Solving . . pp. 10–21

Math: Reading and Writing in the Content Area . . . . pp. 10–21

Problem Solving Process

This page focuses on the third step of the problem-solving process: **Solve**

Discuss

Have students discuss whether they should multiply or divide to solve each problem. Have them explain their choices.

Possible answers:

1. Multiply; since Judy practices half as much as Angie, multiply the number of hours Judy practices by 2; $3 \cdot 2$.
2. Divide the number of bells by the number each student will play; $18 \div 3$.
3. Divide; since there are 4 times as many wind instruments as percussion instruments, divide to find the number of percussion instruments; $48 \div 4$.
4. Multiply; there are 4 people in a quartet and 7 quartets; $7 \cdot 4$.

Section 2B

Factors and Multiples

One-Minute Section Planner

Lesson	Materials	Resources
Hands-On Lab 2B Divisibility **NCTM:** Number and Operations, Communication **NAEP:** Number Properties 5d ☑ SAT-9 ☑ SAT-10 ☑ ITBS ☑ CTBS ☑ MAT ☑ CAT	**Required** 100 Chart *(Hands-On Lab Activities)*	• *Hands-On Lab Activities,* pp. 7–8
Lesson 2-4 Prime Factorization **NCTM:** Number and Operations, Communication **NAEP:** Number Properties 5b ☑ SAT-9 ☑ SAT-10 ☐ ITBS ☑ CTBS ☑ MAT ☐ CAT	**Optional** Graph paper (*CRB, p. 126)*	• *Chapter 2 Resource Book,* pp. 35–43 • Daily Transparency T13, CRB • Additional Examples Transparencies T14–T15, CRB • *Alternate Openers: Explorations,* p. 13
Lesson 2-5 Greatest Common Factor **NCTM:** Number and Operations, Problem Solving, Communication **NAEP:** Number Properties 5b ☑ SAT-9 ☑ SAT-10 ☐ ITBS ☐ CTBS ☑ MAT ☐ CAT	**Optional** Two-color counters (*MK*)	• *Chapter 2 Resource Book,* pp. 44–52 • Daily Transparency T16, CRB • Additional Examples Transparencies T17–T18, CRB • *Alternate Openers: Explorations,* p. 14
Lesson 2-6 Least Common Multiple **NCTM:** Number and Operations, Communication **NAEP:** Number Properties 5b ☑ SAT-9 ☑ SAT-10 ☐ ITBS ☐ CTBS ☑ MAT ☑ CAT	**Optional** Calendar for September *(CRB, p. 127)* Calculators	• *Chapter 2 Resource Book,* pp. 53–61 • Daily Transparency T19, CRB • Additional Examples Transparencies T20–T22, CRB • *Alternate Openers: Explorations,* p. 15
Section 2B Assessment		• Mid-Chapter Quiz, SE p. 90 • Section 2B Quiz, AR p. 9 • *Test and Practice Generator* CD-ROM

SAT = *Stanford Achievement Tests* **ITBS** = *Iowa Test of Basic Skills* **CTBS** = *Comprehensive Test of Basic Skills/Terra Nova*
MAT = *Metropolitan Achievement Test* **CAT** = *California Achievement Test*

NCTM—Complete standards can be found on pages T27–T33. **NAEP**—Complete standards can be found on pages A35–A39.

SE = *Student Edition* **TE** = *Teacher's Edition* **AR** = *Assessment Resources* **CRB** = *Chapter Resource Book* **MK** = *Manipulatives Kit*

Section Overview

Writing Prime Factorizations *Hands-On Lab 2B, Lesson 2-4*

Why? Being able to find the prime factorization of numbers makes it much easier to find both the greatest common factor and the least common multiple of two or more numbers. This concept is important for work with fractions.

Two Ways to Find the Prime Factorization of 180

Factor Tree

180

$2 \cdot 90$

$2 \cdot 3 \cdot 30$

$2 \cdot 3 \cdot 5 \cdot 6$

$2 \cdot 3 \cdot 5 \cdot 2 \cdot 3$

Step Diagram

2|180

2|90

3|45

3|15

5

$$180 = 2^2 \cdot 3^2 \cdot 5$$

Finding the Greatest Common Factor *Lesson 2-5*

Why? Knowing how to find the greatest common factor is an important skill for computing with and simplifying fractions.

Find the greatest common factor (GCF) of 60 and 72.

$60 = 2^2 \cdot 3 \cdot 5$

$72 = 2^3 \cdot 3^2$

$GCF = 2^2 \cdot 3 = 12$

The **GCF** is the product of the common prime factors: 2^2 and 3.

Finding the Least Common Multiple *Lesson 2-6*

Why? The least common multiple will be used in later chapters to find the least common denominator of two or more fractions. Common denominators are necessary to add and subtract fractions and mixed numbers.

Find the least common multiple (LCM) of 45 and 12.

$45 = 3^2 \cdot 5$

$12 = 2^2 \cdot 3$

$LCM = 2^2 \cdot 3^2 \cdot 5 = 180$

The **LCM** is the product of the greater powers of each prime factor: 2^2, 3^2, and 5.

2B Divisibility

Pacing: Traditional 1 day
Block $\frac{1}{2}$ day

Objective: To use divisibility rules for 2, 3, 5, 8, and 9 and to use the sieve of Eratosthenes to find prime numbers less than 100.

Lab Resources

Hands-On Lab Activities .... pp. 6–7

Using the Pages

Make sure students understand what it means to find the sum of the digits of a number. If students are having difficulty writing the rules while doing the activity, let them refer to the rules in the table in the Try This problems.

Use number tiles for each description to find a number in which no digit is repeated.

1. a 3-digit number divisible by 5 and 10
   Possible answer: 530
2. a 3-digit number divisible by 3 and 9
   Possible answer: 963
3. a 3-digit number divisible by 8
   Possible answer: 128
4. a 3-digit number divisible by 6
   Possible answer: 258

Answers

Activity

1. Possible answer: A number is divisible by 2 if it ends in 0, 2, 4, 6, or 8. 84 and 50 are divisible by 2.
2. Possible answer: A number is divisible by 3 if the sum of its digits is divisible by 3. 75 and 240 are divisible by 3.
3. Possible answer: A number is divisible by 5 if it ends in 0 or 5. 95 and 120 are divisible by 5.
4. Possible answer: A number is divisible by 8 if the last three digits form a number divisible by 8. 136 and 2,400 are divisible by 8.
5. Possible answer: A number is divisible by 9 if the sum of its digits is divisible by 9. 333 and 909 are divisible by 9.

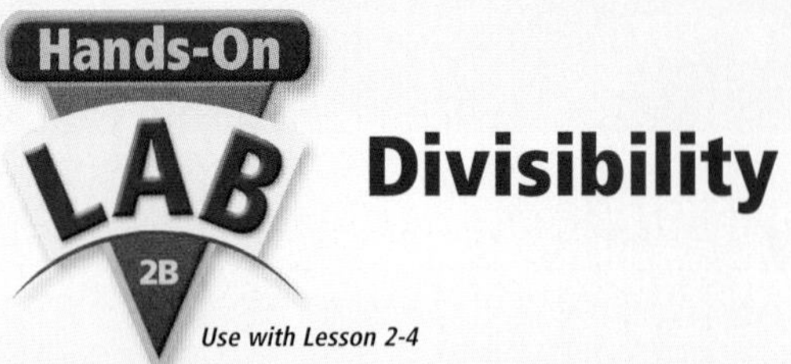

Divisibility

Use with Lesson 2-4

REMEMBER
- A number is divisible by another number if there is no remainder when you divide the numbers.
- Even numbers end in 0, 2, 4, 6, or 8.
- Odd numbers end in 1, 3, 5, 7, or 9.

Activity

The following numbers are divisible by 2: **12; 248; 3,006;** and **420.**
The following numbers are **not** divisible by 2: **81; 633; 5,977;** and **629.**

1. Write a rule for numbers that are divisible by 2. Write two different numbers that are divisible by 2.

The following numbers are divisible by 3: **387; 426; 8,004;** and **420.**
The following numbers are **not** divisible by 3: **782; 425; 1,451;** and **332.**

2. Write a rule for numbers that are divisible by 3. Write two different numbers that are divisible by 3.

The following numbers are divisible by 5: **2,000; 425; 860;** and **9,015.**
The following numbers are **not** divisible by 5: **3,046; 249; 551;** and **68.**

3. Write a rule for numbers that are divisible by 5. Write two different numbers that are divisible by 5.

The following numbers are divisible by 8: **5,248; 16,320;** and **14,864.**
The following numbers are **not** divisible by 8: **6,110; 14,596;** and **2,005.**

4. Write a rule for numbers that are divisible by 8. Write two different numbers that are divisible by 8.

The following numbers are divisible by 9: **18; 378;** and **6,057.**
The following numbers are **not** divisible by 9: **644; 5,817;** and **6,524.**

5. Write a rule for numbers that are divisible by 9. Write two different numbers that are divisible by 9.

The sieve of Eratosthenes is a method you can use to find prime numbers. Start by crossing out the number 1 in a table like the one at right. Next, circle the number 2, and then cross out all of the numbers that are divisible by 2. Next, circle the number 3, and then cross out all of the numbers that are divisible by 3. Continue in this pattern until all of the composite numbers are crossed out and all of the prime numbers are circled.

~~1~~	(2)	3	~~4~~	5	~~6~~	7	~~8~~	9	~~10~~
11	~~12~~	13	~~14~~	15	~~16~~	17	~~18~~	19	~~20~~
21	~~22~~	23	~~24~~	25	~~26~~	27	~~28~~	29	~~30~~
31	~~32~~	33	~~34~~	35	~~36~~	37	~~38~~	39	~~40~~
41	~~42~~	43	~~44~~	45	~~46~~	47	~~48~~	49	~~50~~
51	~~52~~	53	~~54~~	55	~~56~~	57	~~58~~	59	~~60~~
61	~~62~~	63	~~64~~	65	~~66~~	67	~~68~~	69	~~70~~
71	~~72~~	73	~~74~~	75	~~76~~	77	~~78~~	79	~~80~~
81	~~82~~	83	~~84~~	85	~~86~~	87	~~88~~	89	~~90~~
91	~~92~~	93	~~94~~	95	~~96~~	97	~~98~~	99	~~100~~

Use this method to find all of the prime numbers in the table.

Think and Discuss

1. Are all even numbers divisible by 2? Why or why not?
2. Are all odd numbers divisible by 3? Why or why not?

Try This

For each divisibility rule, name one number that would satisfy the rule and one that would not.

	A number is divisible by . . .	Divisible	Not Divisible
1.	**2** if the last digit is even (0, 2, 4, 6, or 8).	☐	☐
2.	**3** if the sum of the digits is divisible by 3.	☐	☐
3.	**4** if the last two digits form a number divisible by 4.	☐	☐
4.	**5** if the last digit is 0 or 5.	☐	☐
5.	**6** if the number is divisible by 2 and 3.	☐	☐
6.	**8** if the last three digits form a number divisible by 8.	☐	☐
7.	**9** if the sum of the digits is divisible by 9.	☐	☐
8.	**10** if the last digit is 0.	☐	☐

Use number tiles to find a number in which no digit is repeated for each description.

Possible answers:

9. 4-digit number divisible by 5 and 10 **1,230**
10. 4-digit number divisible by 3 and 5 **1,245**
11. 4-digit number divisible by 3, 5, and 9 **4,905**
12. 4-digit number divisible by 4 and 9 **2,916**
13. 4-digit number divisible by 3 and 4 **1,056**
14. 3-digit number divisible by 2, 3, and 6 **396**

Answers

Think and Discuss

1. Possible answer: Yes, since all even numbers end in 0, 2, 4, 6, or 8, all even numbers are divisible by 2.
2. No, the sum of the digits must be divisible by 3 for the number to be divisible by 3. The number 13 is not divisible by 3.

Try This

Possible answers:

1. **64; 65**
2. **96; 97**
3. **124; 125**
4. **105; 106**
5. **144; 146**
6. **408; 412**
7. **765; 762**
8. **110; 115**

2-4 Organizer

Pacing: Traditional 1 day
Block $\frac{1}{2}$ day

Objective: Students find the prime factorizations of composite numbers.

Warm Up

Write each number as a product of two whole numbers in as many ways as possible.

1. 6 $1 \cdot 6, 2 \cdot 3$

2. 16 $1 \cdot 16, 2 \cdot 8, 4 \cdot 4$

3. 17 $1 \cdot 17$

4. 36 $1 \cdot 36, 2 \cdot 18, 3 \cdot 12, 4 \cdot 9, 6 \cdot 6$

5. 23 $1 \cdot 23$

Problem of the Day

Nicholas bikes every third day and skates every other day. Today is April 5, and Nicholas biked and skated. On what date will he both bike and skate? April 11

Available on Daily Transparency in CRB

Math Humor

What time is it when the big hand is on the 3 and the little hand is on the 5?
Prime time

2-4 Prime Factorization

Learn to find the prime factorizations of composite numbers.

Vocabulary
prime number
composite number
prime factorization

In June 1999, Nayan Hajratwala discovered the first known *prime number* with more than one million digits. The new prime number, $2^{6,972,593} - 1$, has 2,098,960 digits.

Nayan Hajratwala received a $50,000 award for discovering a new prime number.

A **prime number** is a whole number greater than 1 that has exactly two factors, 1 and itself. Three is a prime number because its only factors are 1 and 3.

A **composite number** is a whole number that has more than two factors. Six is a composite number because it has more than two factors—1, 2, 3, and 6. The number 1 has exactly one factor and is neither prime nor composite.

A composite number can be written as the product of its prime factors. This is called the **prime factorization** of the number.

You can use a factor tree to find the prime factors of a composite number.

EXAMPLE 1 Using a Factor Tree to Find Prime Factorization

Write the prime factorization of each number.

A 36

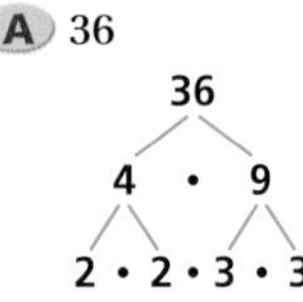

Write 36 as the product of two factors.

Continue factoring until all factors are prime.

The prime factorization of 36 is $2 \cdot 2 \cdot 3 \cdot 3$. Using exponents, you can write this as $2^2 \cdot 3^2$.

B 280

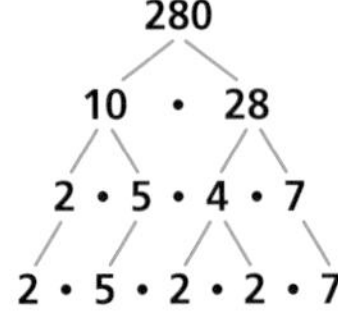

Write 280 as the product of two factors.

Continue factoring until all factors are prime.

The prime factorization of 280 is $2 \cdot 2 \cdot 2 \cdot 5 \cdot 7$, or $2^3 \cdot 5 \cdot 7$.

1 Introduce

Alternate Opener

EXPLORATION

2-4 Prime Factorization

0	1	(2)	3	4	5
6	7	8	9	10	11
12	13	14	15	16	17
18	19	20	21	22	23
24	25	26	27	28	29
30	31	32	33	34	35
36	37	38	39	40	41
42	43	44	45	46	47
48	49	50	51	52	53

54	55	56	57	58	59
60	61	62	63	64	65
66	67	68	69	70	71
72	73	74	75	76	77
78	79	80	81	82	83
84	85	86	87	88	89
90	91	92	93	94	95
96	97	98	99	100	101
102	103	104	105	106	107

Use the number chart to complete the steps.

1. Circle the number 2. Then cross out all of the multiples of 2.
2. Circle the number 3. Then cross out all of the multiples of 3.
3. Circle the number 5. Then cross out all of the multiples of 5.
4. Circle any number remaining if its only factors are itself and 1, and cross out the others.

Think and Discuss

5. **Compare** your chart with others. Do your charts agree? Why or why not?
6. **Describe** some patterns you discovered in the number chart.

Motivate

Tell students that 7 is a prime number and 8 is a composite number. Distribute graph paper (provided on p. 126 of the Chapter 2 Resource Book). Challenge students to use the factors of each number to draw as many rectangular areas as they can for each number. Students can draw 1 rectangular area for 7: 7 by 1 or they can draw two arrays for 8: 4 by 2 and 8 by 1. Encourage students to draw conclusions such as: Prime numbers have only two factors, and composite numbers have more than two factors.

Exploration worksheet and answers on Chapter 2 Resource Book pp. 36 and 136

2 Teach

Lesson Presentation

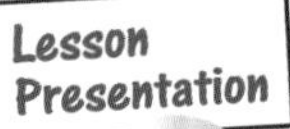

Guided Instruction

In this lesson, students learn to find the prime factorizations of composite numbers. As you read the lesson with students, point out that while the order of factors in a factor tree may differ, the prime factors of a number are always the same. To demonstrate this, show an alternate factor tree for Example 1B.

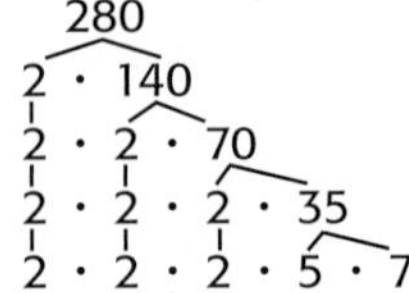

You can also use a step diagram to find the prime factorization of a number. At each step, divide by the smallest possible prime number. Continue dividing until the quotient is 1. The prime factors of the number are the prime numbers you divided by.

EXAMPLE 2 Using a Step Diagram to Find Prime Factorization

Write the prime factorization of each number.

A 252

Divisor	Quotient	
2	252	*Divide 252 by 2. Write the quotient below 252.*
2	126	*Keep dividing by a prime number.*
3	63	
3	21	
7	7	
	1	*Stop when the quotient is 1.*

The prime factorization of 252 is $2 \cdot 2 \cdot 3 \cdot 3 \cdot 7$, or $2^2 \cdot 3^2 \cdot 7$.

B 495

Divisor	Quotient	
3	495	*Divide 495 by 3.*
3	165	*Keep dividing by a prime number.*
5	55	
11	11	
	1	*Stop when the quotient is 1.*

The prime factorization of 495 is $3 \cdot 3 \cdot 5 \cdot 11$, or $3^2 \cdot 5 \cdot 11$.

There is only one prime factorization for any given composite number. Example 2B began by dividing 495 by 3, the smallest prime factor of 495. Beginning with any prime factor of 495 gives the same result.

Divisor	Quotient
5	495
3	99
3	33
11	11
	1

Divisor	Quotient
11	495
3	45
5	15
3	3
	1

The prime factorizations are $5 \cdot 3 \cdot 3 \cdot 11$ and $11 \cdot 3 \cdot 5 \cdot 3$, which are the same as $3 \cdot 3 \cdot 5 \cdot 11$.

Think and Discuss

1. **Explain** how to decide whether 47 is prime.
2. **Compare** prime numbers and composite numbers.
3. **Tell** how you know when you have found the prime factorization of a number.

COMMON ERROR ALERT

Some students do not continue to factor until all of the factors are prime. For example, they might write $2 \cdot 5^2 \cdot 9$ as the prime factorization of 450. Suggest that students keep a list of the prime numbers less than 20 against which to check their prime factorizations.

Additional Examples

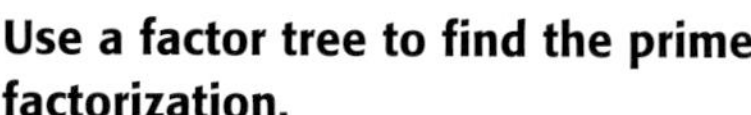

Example 1

Use a factor tree to find the prime factorization.

A. 24

The prime factorization of 24 is $2 \cdot 2 \cdot 2 \cdot 3 = 2^3 \cdot 3$.

B. 150

The prime factorization of 150 is $2 \cdot 3 \cdot 5^2$.

Example 2

Use a step diagram to find the prime factorization.

A. 476

The prime factorization of 476 is $2^2 \cdot 7 \cdot 17$.

B. 275

The prime factorization of 275 is $5^2 \cdot 11$.

Example 2 note: Students should recognize in Example 2B that they could not start with 2 because 495 is odd.

Reaching All Learners
Through Curriculum Integration

Language Arts Give students a number, such as 315, and ask them to write a paragraph describing how they would find the prime factors of the number.

Point out that making a factor tree or showing the division steps will help make their process clear and logical. Possible answer: Because 315 is divisible by 5, begin by writing $5 \cdot 63$. Then since 63 is divisible by 3, write $5 \cdot 3 \cdot 21$. Factor 21 as $3 \cdot 7$, so $315 = 3 \cdot 3 \cdot 5 \cdot 7$, or $3^2 \cdot 5 \cdot 7$.

3 Close

Summarize

Have volunteers tell whether each of the following statements is true or false and give an explanation for their answers. (1) A number can have more than one factor tree. (2) A number can have more than one prime factorization. (3) Two different numbers can have the same prime factorization.

Possible answers: (1) True; a number such as 90 can have different factor trees. For example, one tree can begin with $2 \cdot 45$ and another can begin with $3 \cdot 30$. (2) False; there is only one prime factorization for any given composite number. (3) False; the same factors will always have the same product.

Answers to Think and Discuss

1. Divide 47 by the prime numbers 2, 3, 5, and 7. Since 47 divided by 7 is less than 7, any other factors of 47 except 47 itself would be less than 7. Since 1 and 47 are the only factors of 47, it is prime.
2. A prime number has only two factors, 1 and itself. A composite number has factors in addition to 1 and itself.
3. Possible answer: When all of the factors are prime numbers, you have found the prime factorization of the number.

2-4 PRACTICE & ASSESS

Students may want to refer back to the lesson examples.

Assignment Guide

If you finished Example 1 assign:
Core 1–8, 17–28, 41–57 odd, 62–69
Enriched 1–7 odd, 17–27 odd, 41–58, 62–69

If you finished Example 2 assign:
Core 1–40, 41–57 odd, 62–69
Enriched 1–39 odd, 41–69

Answers

41–44. Complete answers on p. A1.

2-4 Exercises

FOR EXTRA PRACTICE
see page 658

internet connect
Homework Help Online
go.hrw.com Keyword: MS4 2-4

GUIDED PRACTICE

See Example 1

Write the prime factorization of each number.

1. 16 2^4 **2.** 54 $2 \cdot 3^3$ **3.** 81 3^4 **4.** 105 $3 \cdot 5 \cdot 7$

16: 4 • 4; ? • ? • ? • ?
54: 6 • 9; ? • ? • ? • ?
81: 9 • ?; ? • ? • ? • ?
105: 5 • ?; ? • ? • ?

5. 18 $2 \cdot 3^2$ **6.** 26 $2 \cdot 13$ **7.** 45 $3^2 \cdot 5$ **8.** 80 $2^4 \cdot 5$

See Example 2

9. 50 $2 \cdot 5^2$ **10.** 90 $2 \cdot 3^2 \cdot 5$ **11.** 100 $2^2 \cdot 5^2$ **12.** 60 $2^2 \cdot 3 \cdot 5$

13. 63 $3^2 \cdot 7$ **14.** 14 $2 \cdot 7$ **15.** 1,000 $2^3 \cdot 5^3$ **16.** 140 $2^2 \cdot 5 \cdot 7$

INDEPENDENT PRACTICE

See Example 1

Write the prime factorization of each number.

17. 68 $2^2 \cdot 17$ **18.** 75 $3 \cdot 5^2$ **19.** 120 $2^3 \cdot 3 \cdot 5$ **20.** 150 $2 \cdot 3 \cdot 5^2$

21. 135 $3^3 \cdot 5$ **22.** 48 $2^4 \cdot 3$ **23.** 154 $2 \cdot 7 \cdot 11$ **24.** 210 $2 \cdot 3 \cdot 5 \cdot 7$

25. 800 $2^5 \cdot 5^2$ **26.** 310 $2 \cdot 5 \cdot 31$ **27.** 625 5^4 **28.** 2,000 $2^4 \cdot 5^3$

See Example 2

29. 315 $3^2 \cdot 5 \cdot 7$ **30.** 728 $2^3 \cdot 7 \cdot 13$ **31.** 189 $3^3 \cdot 7$ **32.** 396 $2^2 \cdot 3^2 \cdot 11$

33. 242 $2 \cdot 11^2$ **34.** 700 $2^2 \cdot 5^2 \cdot 7$ **35.** 187 $11 \cdot 17$ **36.** 884 $2^2 \cdot 13 \cdot 17$

37. 1,225 $5^2 \cdot 7^2$ **38.** 288 $2^5 \cdot 3^2$ **39.** 360 $2^3 \cdot 3^2 \cdot 5$ **40.** 1,152 $2^7 \cdot 3^2$

PRACTICE AND PROBLEM SOLVING

Complete each factor tree to find the prime factorization.

41. 144: 9 • 16 $2^4 \cdot 3^2$ **42.** 144: 12 • 12 $2^4 \cdot 3^2$ **43.** 200: 20 • 10 $2^3 \cdot 5^2$ **44.** 200: 25 • 8 $2^3 \cdot 5^2$

45. One way to factor 64 is $1 \cdot 64$. What other ways can 64 be written as the product of two factors? $2 \cdot 32$, $4 \cdot 16$, $8 \cdot 8$

46. How many prime factorizations of 64 are there? **one**

Write the composite number for each prime factorization.

47. $2^2 \cdot 3^2 \cdot 5$ **180** **48.** $2^6 \cdot 5$ **320** **49.** $4^3 \cdot 7$ **448** **50.** $3^2 \cdot 5^2 \cdot 7$ **1,575**

51. $2 \cdot 3 \cdot 7 \cdot 11$ **52.** $23 \cdot 29$ **667** **53.** $3^2 \cdot 13$ **117** **54.** $2^3 \cdot 5^3 \cdot 13$

51. 462
54. 13,000

Math Background

Ancient Greeks started to study prime numbers about 300 B.C. They observed that there were an infinite number of prime numbers and that there were irregular gaps between successive prime numbers.

In 1984, Samuel Yates coined the term *titanic prime.* He used this term to refer to any prime number with 1,000 digits or more. When he first defined a titanic prime, there were only 110 of them known. Today more than 110,000 titanic prime numbers have been identified.

RETEACH 2-4

LESSON 2-4 **Reteach**
Prime Factorization

To write the **prime factorization** of a number, write the number as the product of only prime numbers. A prime number has only two factors, itself and 1.

Use a *factor tree* to find the prime factorization of 18.

18 → 6, 3; 6 → 2, 3

Keep factoring until all the factors are prime.

Use a *factor tree* to find the prime factorization of 36.

36 → 4, 9; 4 → 2, 2; 9 → 3, 3

The prime factorization of 18 is $2 \cdot 3 \cdot 3$, or $2 \cdot 3^2$.

The prime factorization of 36 is $2 \cdot 2 \cdot 3 \cdot 3$, or $2^2 \cdot 3^2$.

Use a factor tree to find the prime factorization.

1. 20 $2^2 \cdot 5$ 2. 28 $2^2 \cdot 7$ 3. 54 $2 \cdot 3^3$ 4. 63 $3^2 \cdot 7$

Use a *step diagram* to find the prime factorization of 60.

2|60
2|30
3|15
5|5
1

1) The divisors must be prime numbers.
2) Keep dividing until the quotient is 1.
3) The divisors are the factors in the prime factorization.

Use a *step diagram* to find the prime factorization of 75.

3|75
5|25
5|5
1

The prime factorization of 60 is $2 \cdot 2 \cdot 3 \cdot 5$, or $2^2 \cdot 3 \cdot 5$.

The prime factorization of 75 is $3 \cdot 5 \cdot 5$, or $3 \cdot 5^2$.

Use a step diagram to find the prime factorization.

5. 48 $2^4 \cdot 3$ 6. 24 $2^3 \cdot 3$ 7. 40 $2^3 \cdot 5$ 8. 98 $2 \cdot 7^2$

PRACTICE 2-4

LESSON 2-4 **Practice B**
Prime Factorization

Use a factor tree to find the prime factorization.

1. 57 $3 \cdot 19$ 2. 49 7^2 3. 88 $2^3 \cdot 11$ 4. 95 $5 \cdot 19$

5. 105 $3 \cdot 5 \cdot 7$ 6. 98 $2 \cdot 7^2$ 7. 52 $2^2 \cdot 13$ 8. 42 $2 \cdot 3 \cdot 7$

9. 68 $2^2 \cdot 17$ 10. 91 $7 \cdot 13$ 11. 60 $2^2 \cdot 3 \cdot 5$ 12. 72 $2^3 \cdot 3^2$

13. 189 $3^3 \cdot 7$ 14. 270 $2 \cdot 3^3 \cdot 5$ 15. 140 $2^2 \cdot 5 \cdot 7$ 16. 1,323 $3^3 \cdot 7^2$

Use a step diagram to find the prime factorization.

17. 56 $2^3 \cdot 7$ 18. 144 $2^4 \cdot 3^2$ 19. 370 $2 \cdot 5 \cdot 37$ 20. 168 $2^3 \cdot 3 \cdot 7$

21. 124 $2^2 \cdot 31$ 22. 515 $5 \cdot 103$ 23. 725 $5^2 \cdot 29$ 24. 220 $2^2 \cdot 5 \cdot 11$

25. 126 $2 \cdot 3^2 \cdot 7$ 26. 104 $2^3 \cdot 13$ 27. 66 $2 \cdot 3 \cdot 11$ 28. 175 $5^2 \cdot 7$

29. 450 $2 \cdot 3^2 \cdot 5^2$ 30. 1,000 $2^3 \cdot 5^3$ 31. 1,040 $2^4 \cdot 5 \cdot 13$ 32. 2,500 $2^2 \cdot 5^4$

33. The prime factorization of a number is $3^2 \cdot 5 \cdot 11$. What is the number?

495

55. If the prime factors of a number are all the prime numbers less than 10 and no factor is repeated, what is the number? **210**

56. A number n is a prime factor of 28 and 63. What is the number? **7**

57. A rectangular area on a farm has side lengths that are factors of 308. One of the side lengths is a prime number. Which of the areas in the diagram have the correct dimensions? **the chicken coop and the sheep pen**

58. ***BUSINESS*** Eric is catering a party for 152 people. He wants to seat the same number of people at each table. He also wants more than 2 people but fewer than 10 people at a table. How many people can he seat at each table? **4 or 8 people**

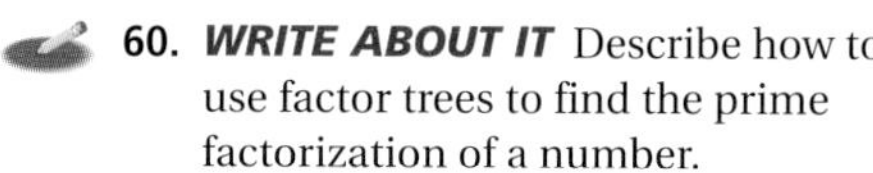

59. ***WRITE A PROBLEM*** Using the information in the table, write a problem using prime factorization that includes the number of calories per serving of the melons.

60. ***WRITE ABOUT IT*** Describe how to use factor trees to find the prime factorization of a number.

Fruit	Calories per Serving
Cantaloupe	66
Watermelon	15
Honeydew	42

61. ***CHALLENGE*** Find the smallest number that is divisible by 2, 3, 4, 5, 6, 7, 8, 9, and 10. **2,520**

Spiral Review

Find the median of each data set. (Lesson 1-2)

62. 17, 25, 16, 94, 24 **24**

63. 7, 9, 6, 3, 5, 2, 7, 3 **5.5**

Find each value. (Lesson 2-1)

64. 8^2 **64**

65. 23^1 **23**

66. 18^0 **1**

67. 7^3 **343**

68. **TEST PREP** What is 2,430,000 in scientific notation? (Lesson 2-2) **D**

A 243×10^4
B 24.3×10^5
C 2.43×10^5
D 2.43×10^6

69. **TEST PREP** Which of the following equals 16? (Lesson 2-3) **H**

F $6 \cdot (2 + 4)$
G $6^2 + 4$
H $6 \cdot 2 + 4$
J $(6 \div 2) \cdot 4$

Answers

59. Possible answer: A serving of watermelon has $3 \cdot 5$ calories. Write the number of calories as a composite number.

60. Possible answers: Begin by factoring the number into two factors. Continue to factor any number that is not prime until all the factors are prime. The answer will always be the same.

Journal

Have students tell which method they prefer for finding the prime factorization of a composite number—a factor tree or a step diagram. Ask students to explain why they prefer the chosen method and to describe how they use it.

Test Prep Doctor

For Exercise 68, students can immediately eliminate **A** and **B** because the first factor in each is not between 1 and 10.

CHALLENGE 2-4

LESSON 2-4 **Challenge**
A Different Point of View

Create two more factor trees with different factors for each number. **Possible answers are given.**

1.
225 → 25, 9 → 5, 5, 3, 3
225 → 15, 15 → 3, 5, 3, 5
225 → 45, 5; 45 → 5, 9; 9 → 3, 3

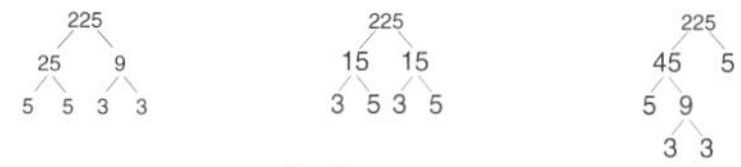

Prime factorization of 225: $3^2 \bullet 5^2$

2.
504 → 3, 168; 168 → 8, 21; 8 → 4, 2; 21 → 7, 3; 4 → 2, 2
504 → 2, 252; 252 → 3, 84; 84 → 12, 7; 12 → 4, 3; 4 → 2, 2
504 → 8, 63; 8 → 2, 4; 63 → 7, 9; 4 → 2, 2; 9 → 3, 3

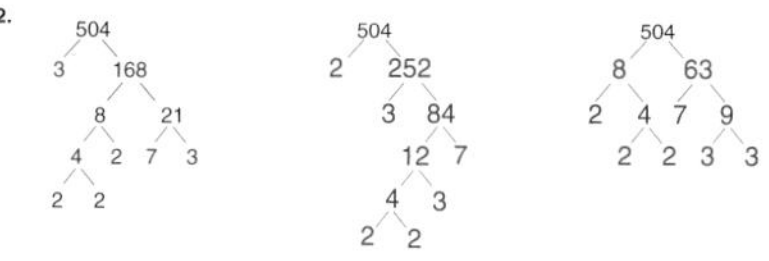

Prime factorization of 504: $2^3 \bullet 3^2 \bullet 7$

3. In 1742, Christian Goldbach wrote his now famous Goldbach's Conjecture, which states that every even number greater than 2 can be represented as the sum of 2 primes. Although this conjecture is still an open question, it can be supported. Choose 3 even numbers greater than 2 to help support Goldbach's Conjecture.

Possible answer: 12 = 7 + 5; 32 = 19 + 13; 44 = 13 + 31

4. Goldbach also made a conjecture that every odd number is the sum of 3 primes. Choose 3 odd numbers to support this conjecture.

Possible answer: 13 = 3 + 5 + 5; 15 = 5 + 5 + 5; 33 = 23 + 5 + 5

PROBLEM SOLVING 2-4

LESSON 2-4 **Problem Solving**
Prime Factorization

Write the correct answer.

1. The width of a swimming pool (in feet) is a prime number greater than 10. The width and length of the pool are factors of 408. What are the dimensions of the pool?

17 ft by 24 ft

2. The area of the dining room at Thomas Jefferson's home in Monticello is about 342 square feet. If the approximate length of one side is a prime number less than 25, what are the approximate dimensions of the room?

19 ft by 18 ft

3. A university has a lounge that can be converted into a meeting hall for 250 people. If the hall is filled and everyone is in equal groups, what are the different ways the people can be grouped so that there are no more than 10 groups?

5 groups of 50; 2 groups of 125; 10 groups of 25

4. You want to read a mystery that has 435 pages. If you read the same number of pages per day and the number is a prime number greater than 20, how many pages per day will you read?

29 pages per day for 15 days

Choose the letter of the best answer.

5. There are 228 seventh graders. Each seventh-grade homeroom starts the year with the same number of students and has at least 15 students. What is the least number of rooms that are needed?

A 17
B 19
(C) 12
D 21

6. Solve this riddle: I am a number whose prime factors are all the prime numbers between 6 and 15. No factor is repeated. What number am I?

F 9,009
G 91
(H) 1,001
J 6,006

7. What is the prime factorization of 1,485?

(A) $3 \bullet 3 \bullet 3 \bullet 5 \bullet 11$
B $3 \bullet 3 \bullet 5 \bullet 5 \bullet 11$
C $3 \bullet 5 \bullet 9 \bullet 11$
D $5 \bullet 11 \bullet 27$

8. Solve this riddle: I am a prime factor of 39 and 65. What number am I?

F 3
G 5
H 11
(J) 13

Lesson Quiz

Use a factor tree to find the prime factorization.

1. 27 3^3
2. 36 $2^2 \cdot 3^2$
3. 28 $2^2 \cdot 7$

Use a step diagram to find the prime factorization.

4. 132 $2^2 \cdot 3 \cdot 11$
5. 52 $2^2 \cdot 13$
6. 108 $2^2 \cdot 3^3$

Available on Daily Transparency in CRB

2-5 Organizer

Pacing: Traditional 1 day
Block $\frac{1}{2}$ day

Objective: Students find the greatest common factor of two or more whole numbers.

Warm Up

Write the prime factorization of each number.

1. 20 $2^2 \cdot 5$ **2.** 100 $2^2 \cdot 5^2$
3. 30 $2 \cdot 3 \cdot 5$ **4.** 128 2^7
5. 70 $2 \cdot 5 \cdot 7$

Problem of the Day

Use the clues to find the numbers being described.

1. a. The greatest common factor (GCF) of two numbers is 5.
b. The sum of the numbers is 75.
c. The difference between the numbers is 5. **35 and 40**

2. a. The GCF of three different numbers is 4.
b. The sum of the numbers is 64.
Possible answer: 12, 16, 36

Available on Daily Transparency in CRB

2-5 Greatest Common Factor

Learn to find the greatest common factor of two or more whole numbers.

Vocabulary
greatest common factor (GCF)

When getting ready for the Fall Festival, Sasha and David used the greatest common factor to make matching party favors.

The **greatest common factor (GCF)** of two or more whole numbers is the greatest whole number that divides evenly into each number.

One way to find the GCF of two or more numbers is to list all the factors of each number. The GCF is the greatest factor that appears in all the lists.

EXAMPLE 1 Using a List to Find the GCF

Find the greatest common factor (GCF).

24, 36, 48

24: 1, 2, 3, 4, 6, 8, (12), 24 — *List all the factors of each number.*
36: 1, 2, 3, 4, 6, 9, (12), 18, 36
48: 1, 2, 3, 4, 6, 8, (12), 16, 24, 48 — *Circle the greatest factor that is in all the lists.*

The GCF is 12.

EXAMPLE 2 Using Prime Factorization to Find the GCF

Find the greatest common factor (GCF).

A **60, 45**

$60 = 2 \cdot 2 \cdot (3) \cdot (5)$ — *Write the prime factorization of each number and circle the common prime factors.*
$45 = (3) \cdot 3 \cdot (5)$
$3 \cdot 5 = 15$ — *Multiply the common prime factors.*

The GCF is 15.

B **504, 132, 96, 60**

$504 = 2 \cdot 2 \cdot 2 \cdot (3) \cdot 3 \cdot 7$ — *Write the prime factorization of each number and circle the common prime factors.*
$132 = 2 \cdot 2 \cdot (3) \cdot 11$
$96 = 2 \cdot 2 \cdot 2 \cdot 2 \cdot 2 \cdot (3)$
$60 = 2 \cdot 2 \cdot (3) \cdot 5$
$2 \cdot 2 \cdot 3 = 12$ — *Multiply the common prime factors.*

The GCF is 12.

1 Introduce

Alternate Opener

EXPLORATION

Greatest Common Factor

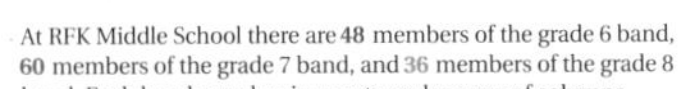

At RFK Middle School there are 48 members of the grade 6 band, 60 members of the grade 7 band, and 36 members of the grade 8 band. Each band marches in a rectangular array of columns.

1. One possible formation for the 48 members of the grade 6 band is shown. Draw all possible formations of the grade 6 band.

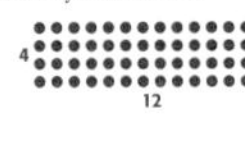

2. One possible formation for the 60 members of the grade 7 band is shown. Draw all possible formations of the grade 7 band.

3. One possible formation for the 36 members of the grade 8 band is shown. Draw all possible formations of the grade 8 band.

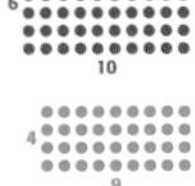

4. How can the band director put all three bands together in separate rectangular blocks that have the same number of columns and the greatest number of columns possible? Sketch a diagram of this formation.

Think and Discuss

5. **Compare** your solutions with the solutions of others.
6. **Discuss** how you decided what the final formation of all three grades should look like.

Motivate

Distribute 12 red counters and 16 yellow counters (provided in the Manipulatives Kit) to small groups. Challenge students to make the tallest stacks possible while making sure that every stack has the same number of counters and that the counters in each stack are all the same color. Have students compare their methods and solutions. Students should find that the greatest number of counters in each stack is 4. Guide students to notice that 4 is a factor of 12 and of 16.

Exploration worksheet and answers on Chapter 2 Resource Book pp. 45 and 138

2 Teach

Guided Instruction

In this lesson, students learn to find the greatest common factor of two or more whole numbers. Use Example 2B to show students how to use exponents when using the prime factorization to find the GCF.

$504 = 2^3 \cdot 3^2 \cdot 7$ $132 = 2^2 \cdot 3 \cdot 11$
$96 = 2^5 \cdot 3$ $60 = 2^2 \cdot 3 \cdot 5$

Explain that the GCF is the product of the least power of each common prime factor that appears as a divisor for each term. The common prime factors are 2 and 3. Their least powers are 2^2 and 3. Therefore, the GCF is $2^2 \cdot 3$, or 12.

EXAMPLE 3 **PROBLEM SOLVING APPLICATION**

Sasha and David are making centerpieces for the Fall Festival. They have 50 small pumpkins and 30 ears of corn. What is the greatest number of matching centerpieces they can make using all of the pumpkins and corn?

 **Understand the Problem**

Rewrite the question as a statement.

- Find the greatest number of centerpieces they can make.

List the **important information:**

- There are 50 pumpkins.
- There are 30 ears of corn.
- Each centerpiece must have the same number of pumpkins and the same number of ears of corn.

The **answer** will be the GCF of 50 and 30.

 **Make a Plan**

You can write the prime factorizations of 50 and 30 to find the GCF.

 **Solve**

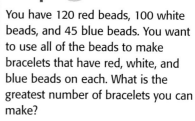

50 = ②·⑤· 5
30 = ②· 3 ·⑤ *Multiply the prime factors that are common to both 50 and 30.*
$2 \cdot 5 = 10$
Sasha and David can make 10 centerpieces.

4 Look Back

If Sasha and David make 10 centerpieces, each one will have 5 pumpkins and 3 ears of corn, with nothing left over.

Think and Discuss

1. **Tell** what the letters GCF stand for and explain what the GCF of two numbers is.
2. **Discuss** whether the GCF of two numbers could be a prime number.
3. **Explain** whether every factor of the GCF of two numbers is also a factor of each number. Give an example.

COMMON ERROR ALERT

Some students may try to find the GCF for only the first two numbers. When students are finding the GCF for more than two numbers, caution them to include only factors that are common to all of the numbers.

Example 1

Find the greatest common factor (GCF).

12, 36, 54

The GCF is 6.

Example 2

Find the greatest common factor (GCF).

A. 40, 56

The GCF is 8.

B. 252, 180, 96, 60

The GCF is 12.

Example 3

You have 120 red beads, 100 white beads, and 45 blue beads. You want to use all of the beads to make bracelets that have red, white, and blue beads on each. What is the greatest number of bracelets you can make?

You can make 5 bracelets.

3 Close

Reaching All Learners
Through Curriculum Integration

Language Explore nonmathematical meanings for the words *greatest* and *common*. Ask students to brainstorm a list of synonyms for each term. Synonyms for *greatest* might include *highest, biggest,* and *largest.* Synonyms for *common* might include *same, shared,* and *mutual.* Finally, have students define *greatest common factor* using some of the synonyms they listed.

Possible answers: largest shared factor; biggest same factor; highest mutual factor

Summarize

Have volunteers choose one method of finding the GCF but not identify it. Have them describe the method as classmates guess which method they are describing.

Answers to Think and Discuss

Possible answers:

1. The letters stand for *greatest common factor.* The GCF of two or more numbers is the largest value that is a factor of each of the numbers.
2. Yes, all numbers have factors that are prime numbers. Three is a prime number.
3. Yes, every factor of the GCF is also a factor of each number.
 20: 1, 2, 4, 5, 10, 20
 30: 1, 2, 3, 5, 6, 10, 15, 30
 The GCF of 20 and 30 is 10. Ten has factors 1, 2, 5, and 10, all of which are factors of both 20 and 30.

2-5 PRACTICE & ASSESS

Students may want to refer back to the lesson examples.

Assignment Guide

If you finished Example 1 assign:
Core 1–3, 8–13, 21–35 odd, 44–50
Enriched 1, 3, 9–13 odd, 21–36, 44–50,

If you finished Example 2 assign:
Core 1–6, 8–19, 21–37 odd, 44–50
Enriched 1–5 odd, 9–19 odd, 21–37, 44–50

If you finished Example 3 assign:
Core 1–20, 21–39 odd, 44–50
Enriched 1–19 odd, 21–50

Notes

2-5 Exercises

FOR EXTRA PRACTICE see page 658

internet connect
Homework Help Online
go.hrw.com Keyword: MS4 2-5

GUIDED PRACTICE

See Example 1 Find the greatest common factor (GCF).

1. 30, 42 **6**
2. 36, 45 **9**
3. 24, 36, 60, 84 **12**

See Example 2

4. 60, 231 **3**
5. 12, 28 **4**
6. 20, 40, 50, 120 **10**

See Example 3

7. The Math Club members are preparing identical welcome kits for the sixth-graders. They have 60 pencils and 48 memo pads. What is the greatest number of welcome kits they can prepare using all of the pencils and memo pads? **12 kits**

INDEPENDENT PRACTICE

See Example 1 Find the greatest common factor (GCF).

8. 60, 126 **6**
9. 12, 36 **12**
10. 75, 90 **15**
11. 22, 121 **11**
12. 28, 42 **14**
13. 38, 76 **38**

See Example 2

14. 28, 60 **4**
15. 54, 80 **2**
16. 30, 45, 60, 105 **15**
17. 26, 52 **26**
18. 11, 44, 77 **11**
19. 18, 27, 36, 48 **3**

See Example 3

20. Hetty is making identical gift baskets for the Senior Citizens Center. She has 39 small soap bars and 26 small bottles of lotion. What is the greatest number of baskets she can make using all of the soap bars and bottles of lotion? **13 baskets**

PRACTICE AND PROBLEM SOLVING

Find the greatest common factor (GCF).

21. 5, 7 **1**
22. 12, 15 **3**
23. 4, 6 **2**
24. 9, 11 **1**
25. 22, 44, 66 **22**
26. 77, 121 **11**
27. 80, 120 **40**
28. 20, 28 **4**
29. 2, 3, 4, 5, 7 **1**
30. 4, 6, 10, 22 **2**
31. 14, 21, 35, 70 **7**
32. 6, 10, 11, 14 **1**
33. 6, 15, 33, 48 **3**
34. 18, 45, 63, 81 **9**
35. 13, 39, 52, 78 **13**

36. Which pair of numbers has a GCF that is a prime number, 48 and 90 or 105 and 56? **105 and 56 have a GCF of 7.**

37. Find the prime factorization of 132. $2^2 \cdot 3 \cdot 11$

38. Museum employees are preparing an exhibit of ancient coins. They have 49 copper coins and 35 silver coins to arrange on shelves. Each shelf will have the same number of copper coins and the same number of silver coins. How many shelves will the employees need for this exhibit? **7 shelves**

Math Background

Euclid's Algorithm can be used to find the GCF of two numbers. Divide the lesser number into the greater number. If the remainder is 0, the lesser number is the GCF. If the remainder is not 0, continue dividing the remainder into the previous divisor until the remainder is 0. The last divisor is the GCF of the two numbers.

Example: Find the GCF of 128 and 176.

Step 1: 176 ÷ 128 = 1 R48

Step 2: 128 ÷ 48 = 2 R32

Step 3: 48 ÷ 32 = 1 R16

Step 4: 32 ÷ 16 = 2 R0

16 is the last divisor; therefore, the GCF of 128 and 176.

RETEACH 2-5

LESSON 2-5 **Reteach**
Greatest Common Factor

The **greatest common factor** (GCF) of a group of numbers is the greatest number that can divide each of the numbers without having a remainder.

Use a list to find the GCF of 45, 60, and 75.
List all the factors of each number.

45: 1, 3, 5, 9, 15, 45
60: 1, 2, 3, 4, 5, 6, 10, 12, 15, 20, 30, 60
75: 1, 3, 5, 15, 25, 75

The common factors are 1, 3, 5, and 15.
The GCF is 15.

List the factors of each number. Find the greatest common factor (GCF).

1. 9: 1, 3, 9
   24: 1, 2, 3, 4, 6, 8, 12, 24
   GCF = 3
2. 18: 1, 2, 3, 6, 9, 18
   54: 1, 2, 3, 6, 9, 18, 27, 54
   GCF = 18
3. 45: 1, 3, 5, 9, 15, 45
   55: 1, 5, 11, 55
   GCF = 5
4. 12: 1, 2, 3, 4, 6, 12
   20: 1, 2, 4, 5, 10, 20
   GCF = 4
5. 6: 1, 2, 3, 6
   12: 1, 2, 3, 4, 6, 12
   24: 1, 2, 3, 4, 6, 8, 12, 24
   GCF = 6
6. 6: 1, 2, 3, 6
   18: 1, 2, 3, 6, 9, 18
   27: 1, 3, 9, 27
   GCF = 3

Find the greatest common factor (GCF).

7. 27, 45 — 9
8. 14, 18 — 2
9. 12, 30 — 6
10. 10, 45, 70 — 5

PRACTICE 2-5

LESSON 2-5 **Practice B**
Greatest Common Factor

Find the greatest common factor (GCF).

1. 12, 15 — 3
2. 22, 33 — 11
3. 63, 45 — 9
4. 15, 50 — 5
5. 18, 81 — 9
6. 18, 48 — 6
7. 20, 24 — 4
8. 14, 42, 49 — 7
9. 3, 6, 9 — 3
10. 16, 24, 30 — 2
11. 16, 40, 88 — 8
12. 42, 70 — 14
13. 25, 125, 200 — 25
14. 26, 39, 52 — 13
15. 36, 100 — 4
16. 35, 77 — 7
17. 56, 84 — 28
18. 14, 49, 56, 84 — 7
19. 30, 75, 60, 90 — 15
20. 12, 38, 40, 94 — 2
21. 48, 66, 96, 102 — 6

22. Volunteers are preparing identical backpacks for refugees. There are 32 maps and 24 dictionaries to use for the backpacks. What is the greatest number of backpacks they can prepare using all of the maps and dictionaries?
    8 backpacks

23. Alyssa is preparing identical fruit baskets. There are 36 oranges and 60 apples to use for the baskets. What is the greatest number of fruit baskets she can prepare using all of the oranges and apples?
    12 baskets

The sculpture *Spoonbridge and Cherry* by Claes Oldenburg and Coosje van Bruggen is 30 ft high and over 50 ft long.

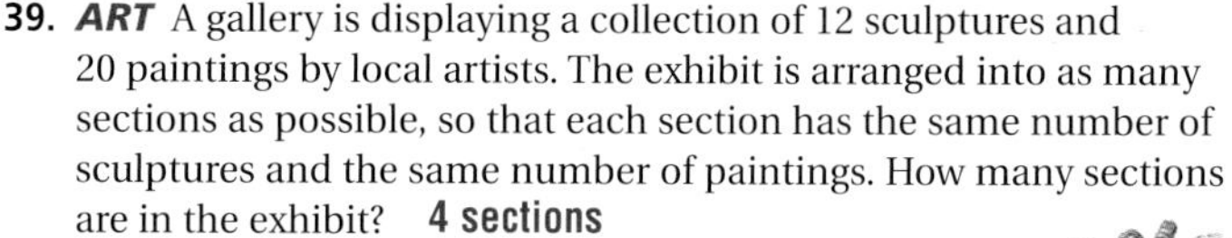

39. ***ART*** A gallery is displaying a collection of 12 sculptures and 20 paintings by local artists. The exhibit is arranged into as many sections as possible, so that each section has the same number of sculptures and the same number of paintings. How many sections are in the exhibit? **4 sections**

40. ***SCHOOL*** Some of the students in the Math Club signed up to bring food and drinks to a party.

Food and Drink Sign-up Sheet
Student
Item
Amount
Erica
Apples
14
Alejandro
Pizza
21 slices
Michael
Juice
7 cans
Jennifer
Gingerbread cookies
35

   a. If each club member gets the same amount of each item at the party, how many students are in the Math Club? **7 students**

   b. How many cookies, pizza slices, cans of juice, and apples can each club member have at the party?

40b. 5 cookies, 3 pizza slices, 1 can of juice, and 2 apples

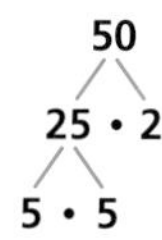

41. ***WHAT'S THE ERROR?*** A student used these factor trees to find the GCF of 50 and 70. The student decided that the GCF is 5. Explain the student's error and give the correct GCF.

50	70
25 • 2	7 • 10
5 • 5	7 • 2 • 5

42. ***WRITE ABOUT IT*** The GCF of 1,274 and 1,365 is 91, or 7 • 13. Are 7, 13, and 91 factors of both 1,274 and 1,365? Explain.

43. ***CHALLENGE*** Find three *composite* numbers that have a GCF of 1. **Possible answer: 12, 35, and 143.**

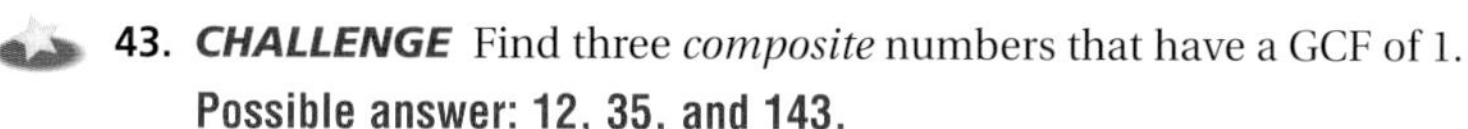

Spiral Review

44. Find the range of the data set 19, 12, 8, 25, 33, 6, 8, and 8. (Lesson 1-2) **27**

45. Make a stem-and-leaf plot of the data set 17, 19, 23, 39, 22, 27, 10, 25, 29, and 31. (Lesson 1-3)

Evaluate each expression. (Lesson 2-3)

46. $8 - 2^3 \div 4$ **6**

47. $12 + (9 - 4 \cdot 2)$ **13**

48. $24 \div (8 - 6)^2$ **6**

49. **TEST PREP** Which of the following is the prime factorization of 92? (Lesson 2-4) **C**

   A $2^3 \cdot 3$ **C** $2^2 \cdot 23$
   B $2^2 \cdot 3^2$ **D** 2^5

50. **TEST PREP** Which of the following is the prime factorization of 6,600? (Lesson 2-4) **F**

   F $2^3 \cdot 3 \cdot 5^2 \cdot 11$ **H** $2 \cdot 3 \cdot 10^2 \cdot 11$
   G $2^2 \cdot 3^2 \cdot 5^2$ **J** $6^{1,100}$

Answers

41. Possible answer: The first tree does not show the factor of 2 being brought to the last line. The factors of 50 should be 5 · 5 · 2, so the GCF is 10.

42. Yes; every factor of the GCF of two numbers is also a factor of each number.

45.

Stems	Leaves
1	0 7 9
2	2 3 5 7 9
3	1 9

Key: 2|5 means 25

Journal

Review the two methods used for finding the GCF—using a list and using prime factorization. Have students explain which method they think is better for finding the GCF of larger numbers and why.

Test Prep Doctor

For Exercise 49, students can use the divisibility test for 3 to eliminate **A** and **B.** The number 92 is not divisible by 3, so 3 is not a prime factor of 92.

CHALLENGE 2-5

LESSON 2-5 Challenge
The School Trip Factor

There are 24 students in the seventh grade and 36 students in the eighth grade. Solve each problem below about their school trip. Then use your solutions to complete the permission slip each student must have signed in order to go on the trip.

1. The students will visit the zoo, the museum, or the planetarium. Each class will buy its own tickets. Both classes must agree upon the trip that will cost the least. Use the table at right to decide which trip the students will choose.

Trip	Single Tickets	Group Rate	Number of Tickets per Group
Zoo	\$8	\$24	6
Museum	\$5	\$12	4
Planetarium	\$4	\$30	12

2. The principal will provide transportation for both classes. The school PTA will pay the cost but wants the most cost-efficient method of transportation. Use the table at right to decide which method of transportation the PTA will choose.

Type of Transportation	Number of Passengers	Cost
Mini-bus	12	\$35
School Bus	70	\$185
Mini-van	10	\$30

3. The class student council will provide lunch for each class. Each class must agree on the lowest price and then buy at least one lunch pack per student. Use the table at right to decide which lunch deal the students will choose.

Lunch	Number of Lunches per Pack	Cost per Pack
Sandwich and Juice Packs	6	\$15
Yogurt and Drink Packs	8	\$20
Soup and Sandwich Packs	4	\$12

To the Seventh and Eighth-grade Parents:
On Friday, your child will be taking a school trip to the **planetarium**. The school will pay \$**60** for the seventh-graders' tickets and \$**90** for the eigth-graders' tickets. The PTA has graciously offered to pay \$**175** for **5** [number] **mini-buses** [vehicles] to transport the students. Each class's student council will pay for its class's lunches. Both classes will buy **10** [number] **sandwich and juice** [type] packs at a total cost of \$**60** for the seventh graders and \$**90** for the eighth graders.

_______________ Parent's signature for student's permission

PROBLEM SOLVING 2-5

LESSON 2-5 Problem Solving
Greatest Common Factor

Write the correct answer.

1. Fabric is sold in stores from bolts that are 45 or 60 inches wide. What is the width of the widest strips of fabric you can cut from either bolt without wasting any of the fabric if each strip has the same width?
   15 inches

2. The parents are making sandwiches for the class picnic. They have 72 turkey slices, 48 cheese slices, and 96 tomato slices. What is the greatest number of sandwiches they can make if each sandwich has the same filling?
   24 sandwiches

3. Two bicycle enthusiasts are leaving Cincinnati at the same time. One is biking 840 miles to Boston. The other is biking 440 miles to Atlanta. What is the greatest number of miles a day each can bike if they want to cover equal distances each day?
   40 miles per day

4. A fruit salad made on a TV cooking program requires chunks of cantaloupe and honeydew. What is the greatest number of servings you can make using all of the fruit if you have 30 chunks of cantaloupe and 42 chunks of honeydew?
   6 servings

Choose the letter for the best answer.

5. Ari is making patriotic pins. He has 105 red ribbons, 147 white ribbons, and 189 blue ribbons. What is the greatest number of identical pins he can make if he uses all his ribbons?
   A 52 pins **C** 93 pins
   B 19 pins **(D)** 21 pins

6. Cheryce is making fruit baskets. She has 60 bananas, 72 pears, 96 apples, and 108 oranges. What is the greatest number of equal baskets she can make with the fruit?
   F 3 baskets **(H)** 12 baskets
   G 6 baskets **J** 24 baskets

7. There are 100 senators and 435 representatives in the United States Congress. How many identical groups could be formed from all the senators and representatives?
   A 1 group
   (B) 5 groups
   C 10 groups
   D 15 groups

8. There are 14 baseball teams in the American League and 16 teams in the National League. There are 30 National Hockey League teams. If equal groups of teams are formed, how many hockey teams will be in each group?
   F 3 hockey teams
   G 8 hockey teams
   H 7 hockey teams
   (J) 15 hockey teams

Lesson Quiz

Find the greatest common factor (GCF).

1. 28, 40 **4**
2. 24, 56 **8**
3. 54, 99 **9**
4. 20, 35, 70 **5**
5. The math clubs from 3 schools agreed to a competition. Members from each club must be divided into teams, and teams from all clubs must be equally sized. What is the greatest number of members that can be on a team if Georgia has 16 members, Williams has 24 members, and Fulton has 72 members? **8**

Available on Daily Transparency in CRB

2-6 Organizer

Pacing: Traditional 1 day
Block $\frac{1}{2}$ day

Objective: Students find the least common multiple of two or more whole numbers.

Warm Up

Write the prime factorization of each number.

1. 68 $2^2 \cdot 17$ **2.** 225 $3^2 \cdot 5^2$

3. 940 $2^2 \cdot 5 \cdot 47$

Find the greatest common factor.

4. 27 and 45 **9** **5.** 32 and 80 **16**

6. 50 and 71 **1**

Problem of the Day

Franklin had some counters. When he counted them by twos, threes, fours, and fives, he had one left over. If Franklin had more than 100 and fewer than 150 counters, how many did he have? **121**

Available on Daily Transparency in CRB

Math Fact !!

It takes about 1.88 years for Mars to orbit the Sun. If Mars is in line with Earth and the Sun, it won't be in line with Earth and the Sun again for 47 years.

2-6 Least Common Multiple

Learn to find the least common multiple of two or more whole numbers.

Vocabulary
multiple
least common multiple (LCM)

The maintenance schedule on Ken's pickup truck shows that the tires should be rotated every 7,500 miles and that the oil filter should be replaced every 5,000 miles. What is the lowest mileage at which both services are due at the same time? To find the answer, you can use *least common multiples.*

A **multiple** of a number is the product of that number and a whole number. Some multiples of 7,500 and 5,000 are as follows:

7,500: 7,500, **15,000**, 22,500, **30,000**, 37,500, 45,000, . . .
5,000: 5,000, 10,000, **15,000**, 20,000, 25,000, **30,000**, . . .

A common multiple of two or more numbers is a number that is a multiple of each of the given numbers. So **15,000** and **30,000** are common multiples of 7,500 and 5,000.

The **least common multiple (LCM)** of two or more numbers is the common multiple with the least value. The LCM of 7,500 and 5,000 is 15,000. This is the lowest mileage at which both services are due at the same time.

EXAMPLE 1 Using a List to Find the LCM

Find the least common multiple (LCM).

A 3, 5

3: 3, 6, 9, 12, (15), 18 — *List some multiples of each number.*
5: 5, 10, (15), 20, 25 — *Find the least value that is in both lists.*

The LCM is 15.

B 4, 6, 12

4: 4, 8, (12), 16, 20, 24, 28 — *List some multiples of each number.*
6: 6, (12), 18, 24, 30 — *Find the least value that is in all the lists.*
12: (12), 24, 36, 48

The LCM is 12.

1 Introduce

Alternate Opener

EXPLORATION

2-6 Least Common Multiple

Earl, Mindy, and Sarah run laps around a park.

- Mindy can complete one lap in 24 minutes. → 24 min
- Earl can complete one lap in 36 minutes. → 36 min
- Sarah can complete one lap in 18 minutes. → 18 min

1. After how many minutes will Mindy and Earl end a lap together? → 24, 36
2. After how many minutes will Earl and Sarah end a lap together? → 36, 18
3. After how many minutes will Mindy and Sarah end a lap together? → 24, 18
4. What are three different times at which they can all end a lap together?

Think and Discuss

5. **Compare** your solutions with the solutions of others.
6. **Discuss** how you found your answers to number 4.

Motivate

Pose the following situation to students:

On August 31, Jesse and Jorge start jogging. Jesse jogs every third day. Jorge jogs every fifth day. On what date will they go jogging together again?

Display a calendar for the month of September (provided on p. 127 of the Chapter 2 Resource Book). Discuss how to use the calendar to solve the problem. Students should find that the next date on which Jesse and Jorge will jog together is on September 15.

Exploration worksheet and answers on Chapter 2 Resource Book pp. 54 and 140

2 Teach

Lesson Presentation

Guided Instruction

In this lesson, students learn to find the least common multiple of two or more whole numbers. Show students how to use exponents when using prime factorization to find the LCM. Use Example 2B to demonstrate. Write the prime factorizations in terms of exponents.

$9 = 3^2$ $27 = 3^3$ $45 = 3^2 \cdot 5$

Explain that the LCM is the product of the greatest power of each factor in all the prime factorizations. The factors in the factorizations are 3 and 5. The greatest power of 3 is 3^3, and the greatest power of 5 is 5. Therefore, the LCM is $3^3 \cdot 5 = 135$.

Sometimes, listing the multiples of numbers is not the easiest way to find the LCM. For example, the LCM of 78 and 110 is 4,290. You would have to list 55 multiples of 78 and 39 multiples of 110 to reach 4,290!

EXAMPLE 2 Using Prime Factorization to Find the LCM

Find the least common multiple (LCM).

A 78, 110

78 = (2) · 3 · 13	*Write the prime factorization of each number.*
110 = (2) · 5 · 11	*Circle the common prime factors.*
(2), 3, 13, 5, 11	*List the prime factors of the numbers, using the circled factors only once.*
2 · 3 · 13 · 5 · 11	*Multiply the factors in the list.*

The LCM is 4,290.

B 9, 27, 45

9 = (3) · (3)	*Write the prime factorization of each number.*
27 = (3) · (3) · 3	*Circle the common prime factors.*
45 = (3) · (3) · 5	
(3), (3), 3, 5	*List the prime factors of the numbers, using the circled factors only once.*
3 · 3 · 3 · 5	*Multiply the factors in the list.*

The LCM is 135.

EXAMPLE 3 *Recreation Application*

Charla and her little brother are running laps on a track. Charla runs one lap every 4 minutes, and her brother runs one lap every 6 minutes. They start together. In how many minutes will they be together at the starting line again?

Find the LCM of 4 and 6.

4 = (2) · 2

6 = (2) · 3

The LCM is (2) · 2 · 3 = 12.

They will be together at the starting line in 12 minutes.

Think and Discuss

1. **Tell** what the letters LCM stand for and explain what the LCM of two numbers is.
2. **Describe** a way to remember the difference between GCF and LCM.
3. **List** four common multiples of 6 and 9 that are not the LCM.

COMMON ERROR ALERT

Some students make careless errors when listing all factors to find the LCM using prime factorization. Suggest that students check off each factor they use to be sure they haven't used matching factors more than once and that they haven't left any out.

Additional Examples

Example 1

Find the least common multiple (LCM).

A. 2, 7

The LCM is 14.

B. 3, 6, 9

The LCM is 18.

Example 2

Find the least common multiple (LCM).

A. 60, 130

The LCM is 780.

B. 14, 35, 49

The LCM is 490.

Example 3

Mr. Washington will set up the band chairs all in rows of 6 or all in rows of 8. What is the least number of chairs he will set up?

He will set up at least 24 chairs.

Example 3 note: You may wish to have students check the solution by using a list of multiples for 4 and 6.

3 Close

Reaching All Learners

Through Number Sense

Have students work in pairs to find three numbers with an LCM of $3^3 \cdot 5 \cdot 7$. Encourage student to discuss different possible methods. Provide calculators to help. When they are finished, have students share and compare their answers and their methods.

Possible answer: 315, 189, 135; Remove different factors one at a time from the prime factorization of the LCM to generate the numbers: $3^2 \cdot 5 \cdot 7 = 315$, $3^3 \cdot 7 = 189$, $3^3 \cdot 5 = 135$.

Summarize

Ask students to write the steps they would follow to find the LCM of 15, 30, and 45. Encourage students to number the steps as they list them in the correct order. Have students share and compare their steps and solutions. Initiate a discussion about which methods students chose and why.

Possible answer: Step 1: List the multiples of 15: 15, 30, 45, 60, 75, 90, 105. Step 2: List the multiples of 30: 30, 60, 90, 120. Step 3: List the multiples of 45: 45, 90, 135. Step 4: Find the least number that is in all of the lists: 90.

Answers to Think and Discuss

1. LCM stands for "least common multiple". It is the smallest value that is a multiple of two or more numbers.
2. Possible answer: The GCF is a factor and will be equal to or smaller than each number. The LCM is a multiple of each number and must be equal to or greater than each number.
3. The LCM for 6 and 9 is 18. Possible answers: 36, 54, 72, 108.

2-6 PRACTICE & ASSESS

Students may want to refer back to the lesson examples.

Assignment Guide

If you finished Example 1 assign:
Core 1–3, 8–13, 21–29 odd, 43–51
Enriched 1, 3, 7–13 odd, 22–29, 43–51

If you finished Example 2 assign:
Core 1–6, 8–19, 23–35 odd, 43–51
Enriched 1–5 odd, 9–19 odd, 22–36, 44–52

If you finished Example 3 assign:
Core 1–21, 23–39 odd, 44–52
Enriched 1–21 odd, 22–51

Notes

2-6 Exercises

FOR EXTRA PRACTICE
see page 658

internet connect
Homework Help Online
go.hrw.com Keyword: MS4 2-6

GUIDED PRACTICE

See Example 1 Find the least common multiple (LCM).

1. 4, 7 **28**
2. 14, 21, 28 **84**
3. 4, 8, 12, 16 **48**

See Example 2

4. 30, 48 **240**
5. 3, 9, 15 **45**
6. 10, 40, 50 **200**

See Example 3

7. Jerry and his dad are running around the same track. Jerry completes one lap every 8 minutes. His dad completes one full lap every 6 minutes. They start together. In how many minutes will they be together at the starting line again? **24 minutes**

INDEPENDENT PRACTICE

See Example 1 Find the least common multiple (LCM).

8. 6, 9 **18**
9. 8, 12 **24**
10. 15, 20 **60**
11. 6, 14 **42**
12. 18, 27 **54**
13. 8, 10, 12 **120**

See Example 2

14. 6, 27 **54**
15. 16, 20 **80**
16. 12, 15, 22 **660**
17. 10, 15, 18, 20 **180**
18. 11, 22, 44 **44**
19. 8, 12, 18, 20 **360**

See Example 3

20. On her bicycle, Anna circles the block every 4 minutes. Her brother, on his scooter, circles the block every 10 minutes. They start out together. How many minutes will it be before they meet again at the starting point? **20 minutes**
21. Rod helped his mom plant a vegetable garden. Rod planted a row every 30 minutes, and his mom planted a row every 20 minutes. If they started together, how long will it be before they both finish a row at the same time? **60 minutes**

PRACTICE AND PROBLEM SOLVING

Find the least common multiple (LCM).

22. 3, 7 **21**
23. 2, 5 **10**
24. 4, 6 **12**
25. 9, 12 **36**
26. 22, 44, 66 **132**
27. 9, 27, 36 **108**
28. 80, 120 **240**
29. 10, 18 **90**
30. 3, 5, 7 **105**
31. 3, 6, 12 **12**
32. 5, 7, 9 **315**
33. 24, 36, 48 **144**
34. 2, 3, 4, 5 **60**
35. 4, 6, 10, 12 **60**
36. 14, 21, 35, 70 **210**
37. Jack mows the lawn every three weeks and washes the car every two weeks. If he does both today, how many days will pass before he does them both on the same day again? **42 days**
38. Can two numbers have the same LCM as their GCF? Explain.

38. only if the two numbers are the same

Math Background

One of the earliest known uses of the term *least common multiple* can be found in J. Mitchell's *Dictionary of Mathematics & Physical Science,* published in 1823. The term appears in the phrase: "To find the least common Multiple of several Numbers…." The term *lowest common multiple* (abbreviated as "L. C. M.") appears in *Elements of Algebra,* by G. A. Wentworth, published in 1881.

RETEACH 2-6

LESSON 2-6 **Reteach**
Least Common Multiple

The **least common multiple** (LCM) of two numbers is the least multiple that the two numbers have in common.

- To list the multiples of a number, multiply the number by 1, 2, 3, and so on.

	8 • 1	8 • 2	8 • 3	8 • 4	8 • 5
Multiples of 8	8	16	24	32	40

	6 • 1	6 • 2	6 • 3	6 • 4	6 • 5
Multiples of 6	6	12	18	24	30

- To find the least common multiple of 6 and 8, list several multiples of each number.

Step 1: List multiples of the greater number. Multiples of 8: 8 16 **24** 32 40

Step 2: List the multiples of the lesser number until you find a multiple that is common to each list. Multiples of 6: 6 12 18 **24**

Since 24 is the first number common to both lists, it is the least common multiple. So the LCM of 6 and 8 is 24.

Find the least common multiple (LCM).

1. 4, 9
   Multiples of 9: 9, 18, 27, 36, 45, 54
   Multiples of 4: 4, 8, 12, 16, 20, 24, 28, 32, 36
   LCM of 4 and 9: **36**
2. 6, 7
   Multiples of 7: 7, 14, **21**, **28**, **35**, **42**, **49**, **56**
   Multiples of 6: 6, 12, **18**, **24**, **30**, **36**, **42**
   LCM of 6 and 7: **42**
3. 15, 20
   Multiples of 20: **20**, **40**, **60**, **80**, **100**
   Multiples of 15: **15**, **30**, **45**, **60**
   LCM of 15 and 20: **60**
4. 12, 18 **36**
5. 16, 20 **80**
6. 4, 6, 9 **36**

PRACTICE 2-6

LESSON 2-6 **Practice B**
Least Common Multiple

Find the least common multiple (LCM).

1. 8, 10 **40**
2. 10, 15 **30**
3. 6, 9 **18**
4. 12, 16 **48**
5. 18, 30 **90**
6. 5, 11 **55**
7. 15, 45 **45**
8. 7, 28 **28**
9. 4, 14 **28**
10. 3, 10, 12 **60**
11. 9, 36, 60 **180**
12. 5, 15 **15**
13. 7, 14, 49 **98**
14. 8, 12, 24, 96 **96**
15. 5, 25, 30 **150**
16. 5, 9, 18 **90**
17. 4, 10, 12, 15 **60**
18. 4, 9, 12, 18 **36**
19. 4, 12, 24, 36 **72**
20. 24, 30, 48, 60 **240**
21. 5, 9, 15, 18 **90**
22. Jasmine is helping her father plant trees to create a border around the back yard. Jasmine plants a tree every 25 minutes, and her father plants a tree every 15 minutes. If they started together, how long before they would finish planting a tree at the same time?
    75 minutes
23. Two dancers are rehearsing in a studio. One dancer's routine lasts 12 minutes. The other dancer's routine lasts 15 minutes. If they start together and take no breaks between their routines, how long before they start together again?
    60 minutes
24. Evan and Renzo are swimming laps in the pool. It takes Evan 8 minutes to complete 1 lap and Renzo 6 minutes to complete 1 lap. They start together at the tops of their lanes. In how many minutes will they be together again at the tops of their lanes?
    24 minutes

Social Studies 

Most calendars are based on cycles. Such calendars include the Mayan, the Chinese, and the standard western calendar.

39. The Mayan ceremonial calendar, or *tzolkin*, was 260 days long. It was composed of two independent cycles, a 13-day cycle and a 20-day cycle. At the beginning of the calendar, both cycles are at day 1. Will both cycles be at day 1 at the same time again before the 260 days are over? If so, when? Explain your answer. **No. The LCM of 13 and 20 is 260.**

40. The Chinese calendar has 12 months of 30 days each and 6-day weeks. The Chinese new year begins on the first day of a month and the first day of a week. Will the first day of a month and the first day of a week occur again at the same time before the 360-day year is over? If so, when? Explain your answer. **Yes. The first day of every month is the first day of a week. The LCM of 6 and 30 is 30.**

41. ***WRITE ABOUT IT*** The Julian Date calendar assigns each day a unique number. It begins on day 0 and adds 1 for each new day. So JD 2266296, or October 12, 1492, is 2,266,296 days from the beginning of the calendar. What are some advantages of using the Julian Date calendar? What are some advantages of using calendars that are based on cycles?

42. ***CHALLENGE*** The Mayan Long Count calendar used the naming system at right. Assuming the calendar began on JD 584285, express JD 2266296 in terms of the Mayan Long Count calendar. Start by finding the number of pictun that had passed up to that date.

Mayan Long Count Calendar

1 Pictun = 20 Baktun = 2,880,000 days
1 Baktun = 20 Katun = 144,000 days
1 Katun = 20 Tun = 7,200 days
1 Tun = 18 Winal = 360 days
1 Winal = 20 Kin = 20 days
1 Kin = 1 day

October 12, 1492 is 11 Baktun, 13 Katun, 12 Tun, 4 Winal, 11 Kin

Spiral Review

Evaluate. (Lesson 2-1)

43. 6^0 **1** **44.** 15^2 **225** **45.** 10^3 **1,000** **46.** 5^4 **625**

Write each number in scientific notation or in standard form. (Lesson 2-2)

47. 102.45 **1.0245×10^2** **48.** 62,100,000 **6.21×10^7** **49.** 7.69×10^2 **769** **50.** 8.00×10^5 **800,000**

51. TEST PREP What is the greatest common factor (GCF) of 30 and 105? (Lesson 2-5) **D**

A 5 **B** 3 **C** 25 **D** 15

Interdisciplinary LINK

Social Studies

Exercises 39–42 focus on information about the cycles of different calendars, such as the Mayan calendar. The Mayan calendar is studied in middle school social studies programs such as Holt, Rinehart & Winston's *People, Places, and Change.*

Answers

41. Possible answer: Dates on cyclical calendars are easier to keep track of. Cyclical calendars based on a solar year are particularly useful for keeping track of the seasons and the timing of holidays. On the other hand, Julian dates are useful for finding the elapsed time in days between dates.

Journal 

Have students describe a situation in their own lives in which finding the LCM would be useful. Remind students about problems that can be solved by finding the LCM, such as finding when two events will coincide that begin at the same time but have different time spans.

Test Prep Doctor 

For Exercise 51, students can eliminate choice **C** by noticing that 25 is not a factor of 30. By examining choices **A** and **B,** they can eliminate Choice **B** since it is less than Choice **A.**

CHALLENGE 2-6

LESSON 2-6 **Challenge**
Multiple Solutions

Write the two numbers from each box that have the lowest least common multiple. Then write the LCM.

1. [5 12 / 6 8] → Numbers: **6; 12** LCM: **12**
2. [2 7 / 9 10] → Numbers: **2; 10** LCM: **10**
3. [2 10 / 5 3] → Numbers: **2; 3** LCM: **6**
4. [7 2 / 10 12] → Numbers: **2; 10** LCM: **10**
5. [6 4 / 7 5] → Numbers: **4; 6** LCM: **12**
6. [9 10 / 15 45] → Numbers: **10; 15** LCM: **30**
7. [8 10 / 6 5] → Numbers: **5; 10** LCM: **10**
8. [24 35 / 32 14] → Numbers: **14; 35** LCM: **70**
9. [15 10 / 7 8] → Numbers: **10; 15** LCM: **30**
10. [3 10 / 12 7] → Numbers: **3; 12** LCM: **12**

Use the table at the bottom of the page to solve the riddle. In the middle row, write the LCM of each exercise above the exercise number. Then choose the letter from the Answer Key that matches the LCM and write it in the appropriate box.

Answer Key

C	A	T	E	H
70	6	30	12	10

11. What animal copies from the others on a math test?

T	H	E		C	H	E	E	T	A	H
30	10	12		70	10	12	12	30	6	10
9	4	5		8	2	1	5	6	3	7

PROBLEM SOLVING 2-6

LESSON 2-6 **Problem Solving**
Least Common Multiple

Write the correct answer.

1. Earth revolves around the sun every year. Jupiter revolves around the sun every 12 years. If Earth and Jupiter passed the same point of the sun sometime in 2002, when will they pass that point together again?

2014

2. House representatives are elected every 2 years. The President of the United States is elected every 4 years. Both will be elected in 2004. When is the next year after 2004 both will be elected?

2008

3. A cat runs a mile every 2 minutes. A squirrel runs a mile every 5 minutes. A cat and a squirrel start together running around a 1-mile track. How long will it be before they meet at the starting point?

10 minutes

4. A car manual recommends changing the oil every 5,000 miles and inspecting the engine coolant system every 15,000 miles. At how many miles will both be done together for the first time? for the second time?

15,000 mi; 30,000 mi

Choose the letter for the best answer.

5. Mr. Walters receives a dividend every 5 months and a royalty payment every 6 months. He received both in January 2002. When is the next time he would receive both payments in the same month?
A January 2003
B April 2004
C July 2002
(D) July 2004

6. Rag Rite Cloth Store always rounds amounts less than whole yards up to the next yard for ribbon purchases. The ribbon that you want to buy comes in rolls of 8 feet. How many rolls should you buy to get the best buy?
F 1 roll
G 2 rolls
(H) 3 rolls
J 4 rolls

7. The sanitation department picks up recyclable plastics every 3 days. The paper recycling center picks up papers every 4 days. They both picked up on May 4. When will they next pick up on the same day?
A May 7
B May 12
C May 11
(D) May 16

8. Hal and Jess both volunteer at the local nursing home. Hal volunteers every 6 days, and Jess volunteers every 8 days. They were both there on Monday. In how many days will they both volunteer together again?
F in 14 days
(G) in 24 days
H in 48 days
J in 2 days

Lesson Quiz 

Find the least common multiple (LCM).

1. 18, 21 **126** **2.** 24, 27 **216**

3. 4, 6, 15 **60** **4.** 4, 8, 16 **16**

5. You are planning a picnic. You can purchase paper plates in packages of 30, paper napkins in packages of 50, and paper cups in packages of 20. What is the least number of each type of package that you can buy and have an equal number of each?
10 packages of plates
6 packages of napkins
15 packages of cups

Available on Daily Transparency in CRB

Chapter 2

Mid-Chapter Quiz

Purpose: *To assess students' mastery of concepts and skills in Lessons 2-1 through 2-6*

Assessment Resources

Section 2B Quiz

Assessment Resources .... p. 9

***Test and Practice Generator* CD-ROM**

Additional mid-chapter assessment items in both multiple-choice and free-response format may be generated for any objective in Lessons 2-1 through 2-6.

Chapter 2

Mid-Chapter Quiz

LESSONS 2-1 AND 2-3 (pp. 60–63 and 70–73)

Evaluate.

1. 12^2 **144**
2. $10^4 + 3 \cdot 9$ **10,027**
3. $81 \div 9^2$ **1**
4. $4 \div 2 + 7 \cdot 3$ **23**
5. $2^5 \div 8 + 6$ **10**
6. $6 \div 3 \cdot 15 + 8 - 1$ **37**
7. $(1 + 4^3) \div 5 \cdot 3^2$ **117**
8. $(1 + 4) \cdot (35 - 23)^2$ **720**

LESSON 2-2 (pp. 64–67)

Write each number in scientific notation.

9. 52,000 **5.2×10^4**
10. 109 **1.09×10^2**
11. 634,000,000 **6.34×10^8**
12. 82,000,000,000 **8.2×10^{10}**
13. $30.0 \cdot 10^2$ **3×10^3**
14. $5{,}210 \cdot 10^3$ **5.21×10^6**
15. $45.1 \cdot 10^5$ **4.51×10^6**
16. $70{,}800 \cdot 10^7$ **7.08×10^{11}**

LESSON 2-4 (pp. 78–81)

Complete each factor tree to find the prime factorization.

17. 24 → 6 · 4 → ? · ? · ? · ? **2 · 2 · 2 · 3**
18. 140 → 14 · 10 → ? · ? · ? · ? **2 · 2 · 5 · 7**
19. 45 → 3 · ? → 3 · ? · ? **3 · 3 · 5**
20. 42 → ? · ? → 3 · 7 · ? **2 · 3 · 7**

Write the prime factorization of each number.

21. 96 **$2^5 \cdot 3$**
22. 125 **5^3**
23. 99 **$3^2 \cdot 11$**
24. 105 **$3 \cdot 5 \cdot 7$**

LESSON 2-5 (pp. 82–85)

Find the greatest common factor (GCF).

25. 66, 96 **6**
26. 18, 27, 45 **9**
27. 16, 28, 44 **4**
28. 14, 28, 56 **14**
29. 85, 102 **17**
30. 76, 95 **19**
31. 52, 91, 104 **13**
32. 30, 75, 90 **15**

LESSON 2-6 (pp. 86–89)

Find the least common multiple (LCM).

33. 35, 40 **280**
34. 8, 25 **200**
35. 64, 72 **576**
36. 12, 20 **60**
37. 21, 33 **231**
38. 6, 30 **30**
39. 20, 42 **420**
40. 9, 13 **117**
41. Eddie goes jogging every other day, lifts weights every third day, and swims every fourth day. If Eddie begins all three activities on Monday, how many days will it be before he does all three activities on the same day again? **12 days**

Mid-Chapter Quiz

Focus on Problem Solving

Look Back

• Check that your answer is reasonable

In some situations, such as when you are looking for an estimate or completing a multiple-choice question, check to see whether a solution or answer is reasonably accurate. One way to do this is by rounding the numbers to the nearest multiple of 10 or 100, depending on how large the numbers are. Sometimes it is useful to round one number up and another down.

Read each problem, and determine whether the given solution is too high, is too low, or appears to be correct. Explain your answer.

1. The cheerleading team is preparing to host a spaghetti dinner as a fund-raising project. They have set up and decorated 54 tables in the gymnasium. Each table can seat 8 people. How many people can be seated at the spaghetti dinner?

   Solution: 432 people

2. The cheerleaders need to raise $4,260 to attend a cheerleader camp. How much money must they charge each person if they are expecting 400 people at the spaghetti dinner?

   Solution: $4

3. To help out the fund-raising project, local restaurants have offered $25 gift certificates to give as door prizes. One gift certificate will be given for each door prize, and there will be six door prizes in all. What is the total value of all of the gift certificates given by the restaurants?

   Solution: $250

4. The total cost of hosting the spaghetti dinner will be about $270. If the cheerleaders make $3,280 in ticket sales, how much money will they have after paying for the spaghetti dinner?

   Solution: $3,000

5. Eighteen cheerleaders and two coaches plan to attend the camp. If each person will have an equal share of the $4,260 expense money, how much money will each person have?

   Solution: $562

Answers

1. $54 \cdot 8 = 432$
2. $\$4,260 \div 400 = \$10.65$
3. $\$25 \cdot 6 = \$150$
4. $\$3,280 - 270 = \$3,010$
5. $\$4,260 \div 20 = \$213$

Focus on Problem Solving

Purpose: *To focus on checking for a reasonable answer*

Problem Solving Resources

Interactive Problem Solving . . pp. 10–21

Math: Reading and Writing in the Content Area . . . . pp. 10–21

Problem Solving Process

This page focuses on the last step of the problem-solving process: **Look Back**

Discuss

Have students discuss why they think the possible answer given for each exercise is too high, is too low, or appears to be right. Suggest that students tell how they estimated the answer.

Possible answers:

1. The answer appears to be right. Since 54 is a little more than 50 and $50 \cdot 8$ is 400, the answer should be a little more than 400.
2. The answer is too low. If you round, $4,260 is about $4,000, and $4,000 divided by 400 is $10 per person.
3. The answer is too high. If you round $25 to $30, $\$30 \cdot 6 = \$180$.
4. The answer appears to be right. If you round, $3,280 is about $3,300, and $270 is about $300. When you subtract one from the other, you have $\$3,300 - 300 = \$3,000$.
5. The answer appears to be too high. If you round, $4,260 is about $4,000. Since there are 20 people going, $4,000 divided by 20 is $200 per person.

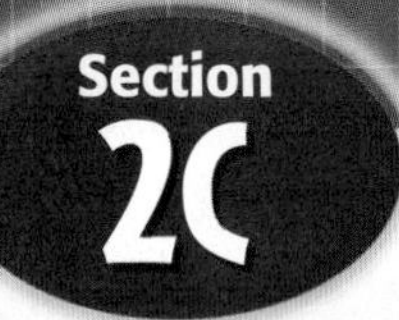

Beginning Algebra

One-Minute Section Planner

Lesson	Materials	Resources
Lesson 2-7 Variables and Algebraic Expressions **NCTM:** Number and Operations, Algebra, Communication, Connections, Representation **NAEP:** Algebra 3b ☑ SAT-9 ☑ SAT-10 ☑ ITBS ☑ CTBS ☑ MAT ☑ CAT	**Optional** Recording Sheet for Reaching All Learners *(CRB, p. 128)*	• *Chapter 2 Resource Book,* pp. 62–71 • Daily Transparency T23, CRB • Additional Examples Transparencies T24–T25, CRB • *Alternate Openers: Explorations,* p. 16
Lesson 2-8 Translate Words into Math **NCTM:** Number and Operations, Communication, Connections **NAEP:** Algebra 3a ☑ SAT-9 ☑ SAT-10 ☑ ITBS ☑ CTBS ☑ MAT ☑ CAT	**Optional** Teaching Transparency T27 *(CRB)*	• *Chapter 2 Resource Book,* pp. 72–80 • Daily Transparency T26, CRB • Additional Examples Transparencies T28–T29, CRB • *Alternate Openers: Explorations,* p. 17
Lesson 2-9 Combining Like Terms **NCTM:** Number and Operations, Reasoning and Proof, Communication **NAEP:** Algebra 3b ☑ SAT-9 ☑ SAT-10 ☐ ITBS ☑ CTBS ☐ MAT ☑ CAT	**Optional** Algebra tiles *(MK, CRB, p. 129)* Teaching Transparency T31 *(CRB)*	• *Chapter 2 Resource Book,* pp. 81–90 • Daily Transparency T30, CRB • Additional Examples Transparencies T32–T33, CRB • *Alternate Openers: Explorations,* p. 18
Lesson 2-10 Equations and Their Solutions **NCTM:** Algebra, Reasoning and Proof, Communication, Connections **NAEP:** Algebra 4a ☑ SAT-9 ☑ SAT-10 ☑ ITBS ☑ CTBS ☑ MAT ☑ CAT	**Optional** Teaching Transparency T35 *(CRB)*	• *Chapter 2 Resource Book,* pp. 91–99 • Daily Transparency T34, CRB • Additional Examples Transparencies T36–T38, CRB • *Alternate Openers: Explorations,* p. 19
Hands-On Lab 2C Model Equations **NCTM:** Algebra, Geometry, Reasoning and Proof, Representation **NAEP:** Algebra 2a ☐ SAT-9 ☑ SAT-10 ☐ ITBS ☐ CTBS ☑ MAT ☑ CAT	**Required** Algebra tiles (*MK, CRB, p. 129*)	• *Hands-On Lab Activities,* pp. 9–11, 126
Lesson 2-11 Solving Equations by Adding or Subtracting **NCTM:** Number and Operations, Communication, Connections **NAEP:** Algebra 4a ☑ SAT-9 ☑ SAT-10 ☐ ITBS ☐ CTBS ☑ MAT ☑ CAT	**Optional** Teaching Transparency T40 *(CRB)*	• *Chapter 2 Resource Book,* pp. 100–108 • Daily Transparency T39, CRB • Additional Examples Transparencies T41–T42, CRB • *Alternate Openers: Explorations,* p. 20
Lesson 2-12 Solving Equations by Multiplying or Dividing **NCTM:** Number and Operations, Algebra, Communication **NAEP:** Algebra 4a ☑ SAT-9 ☑ SAT-10 ☐ ITBS ☐ CTBS ☑ MAT ☑ CAT	**Optional** Teaching Transparency T44 *(CRB)*	• *Chapter 2 Resource Book,* pp. 109–117 • Daily Transparency T43, CRB • Additional Examples Transparencies T45–T46, CRB • *Alternate Openers: Explorations,* p. 21
Section 2C Assessment		• Section 2C Quiz, AR p. 10 • *Test and Practice Generator* CD-ROM

SAT = *Stanford Achievement Tests* **ITBS** = *Iowa Test of Basic Skills* **CTBS** = *Comprehensive Test of Basic Skills/Terra Nova*
MAT = *Metropolitan Achievement Test* **CAT** = *California Achievement Test*

NCTM—Complete standards can be found on pages T27–T33. **NAEP**—Complete standards can be found on pages A35–A39.

SE = *Student Edition* **TE** = *Teacher's Edition* **AR** = *Assessment Resources* **CRB** = *Chapter Resource Book* **MK** = *Manipulatives Kit*

Section Overview

Evaluating Algebraic Expressions — Lesson 2-7

Why? In order to use formulas and algebraic expressions to solve problems, we must be able to substitute number values for the variables and find the resulting numerical value of the entire expression.

The **order of operations** is the same for evaluating both numerical and algebraic expressions.

Evaluate $5 + 4y$ for $y = 3$.

$5 + 4y$
$5 + 4(3)$
$5 + 12$
17

Evaluate $5 + 4y^2$ for $y = 3$.

$5 + 4y^2$
$5 + 4(3)^2$
$5 + 4(9)$
$5 + 36$
41

Translating Words into Math — Lesson 2-8

Why? The first step in solving real-world problems using algebra is learning to represent quantities and situations with variables and expressions.

Algebraic expressions can represent an infinite number of possibilities in a situation.

In the situation at the right, the expression $8h$ represents many different possibilities as the variable number of hours changes.

Situation: **$8 per hour**
Variable: h
Expression: $8h$

The **variable** h represents the number of hours.

The **expression** $8h$ represents the amount of money earned by working h hours.

Combining Like Terms — Lesson 2-9

Why? Evaluating an expression for a given value of a variable is usually easier if the expression is first simplified by combining like terms.

Expression	Like Terms	Like Terms Combined
$3a - 3b + 3c$	none	$3a - 3b + 3c$
$8n + 2 - 7n$	$8n$ and $7n$	$n + 2$
$2x^2 - y + 6 + x^2 + 2$	$2x^2$ and x^2; 6 and 2	$3x^2 - y + 8$

Solving Equations — Hands-On Lab 2C, Lessons 2-10, 2-11, 2-12

Why? Students often solve one-step equations by observation. However, they will need the concepts learned at this level to solve multistep equations.

Equation	Operation in Equation	Identify the Inverse Operation	Isolating the Variable
$x + 7 = 15$	Addition	Subtraction	$x = 8$
$y - 5 = 9$	Subtraction	Addition	$y = 14$
$6 \cdot n = 24$	Multiplication	Division	$n = 4$
$\frac{a}{9} = 3$	Division	Multiplication	$a = 27$

2-7 Organizer

Pacing: Traditional 1 day
Block $\frac{1}{2}$ day

Objective: Students evaluate algebraic expressions.

Warm Up

Evaluate.

1. $5(7) - 1$ **34**
2. $7(18 - 11)$ **49**
3. $22 + 17 \times 8 + 3$ **161**
4. $36 + 15(40 - 35)$ **111**
5. $3^3 + 7(12 - 4)$ **83**

Problem of the Day

How much will it cost to cut a log into eight pieces if cutting it into four pieces costs $12? **$28**

Available on Daily Transparency in CRB

Math Humor

After a sloppy meal, the equation-munching cube was told, "Wipe that expression off your face."

2-7 Variables and Algebraic Expressions

Learn to evaluate algebraic expressions.

Vocabulary
variable
constant
algebraic expression
evaluate

Ron Howard was born in 1954. You can find out what year Ron turned 16 by adding the year he was born to his age.

$$1954 + 16$$

In algebra, letters are often used to represent numbers. You can use a letter such as a to represent Ron Howard's age. When he turns a years old, the year will be

$$1954 + a.$$

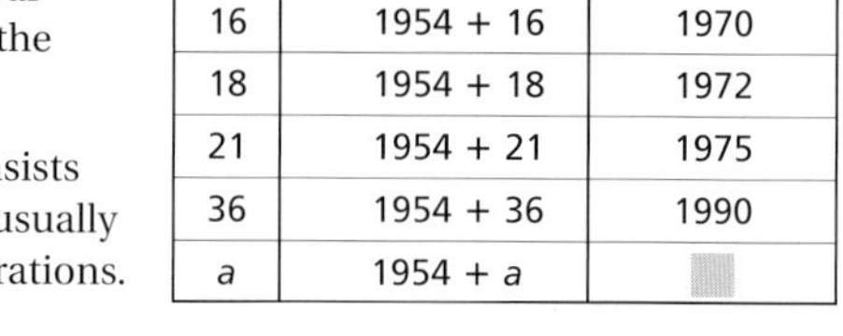

The letter a has a value that can change, or *vary.* When a letter represents a number that can vary, it is called a **variable**. The year 1954 is a **constant** because the number cannot change.

Age	Year born + age = year at age	
16	1954 + 16	1970
18	1954 + 18	1972
21	1954 + 21	1975
36	1954 + 36	1990
a	1954 + a	■

An **algebraic expression** consists of one or more variables. It usually contains constants and operations. For example, $1954 + a$ is an algebraic expression for the year Ron Howard turns a certain age.

To **evaluate** an algebraic expression, substitute a number for the variable.

EXAMPLE 1 Evaluating Algebraic Expressions

Evaluate $n + 7$ for each value of n.

A $n = 3$

$n + 7$
$3 + 7$ *Substitute 3 for n.*
10 *Add.*

B $n = 5$

$n + 7$
$5 + 7$ *Substitute 5 for n.*
12 *Add.*

1 Introduce

Alternate Opener

EXPLORATION

2-7 Variables and Algebraic Expressions

Suzanne entered a walk-a-thon for a local charity. Her sponsor provided the $20 entry fee and will provide $4 for each mile she walks.

1. Complete the table.

Miles Walked	Expression	Amount ($)
1	20 + 4(1)	24
2	20 + 4(2)	
3		
4		
5		
6		

2. If Suzanne walks 12 miles, how much money will she collect for the charity?
3. Suppose Suzanne wants to give $100 to the charity. How many miles must she walk?

Think and Discuss

4. **Explain** how the number of miles walked is used to determine the amount of money collected.
5. **Describe** how to write an expression for the amount of money collected if the number of miles walked is replaced by the variable m.

Motivate

To introduce students to constants and variables, ask volunteers to give examples of quantities that vary (e.g., temperatures, prices) and quantities that stay the same (e.g., the year someone was born, length of a day). Use students' input to write definitions of *constant* and *variable.*

Exploration worksheet and answers on Chapter 2 Resource Book pp. 64 and 142

2 Teach

Lesson Presentation

Guided Instruction

In this lesson, students learn to evaluate algebraic expressions. A given value is substituted for the variable, and the expression is simplified just like a numerical expression. Remind students to use order of operations: 1) parentheses, 2) exponents, 3) multiplication and division, 4) addition and subtraction.

Teaching Tip Discuss how to choose a letter to represent a variable quantity. After students have come up with ideas, point out that using the first letter of the word being represented can help them remember what the variable stands for. For example, if the variable is the amount of dollars, you should use the letter *d.*

Multiplication and division of variables can be written in several ways, as shown in the table.

When evaluating expressions, use the order of operations.

Multiplication		Division	
$7t$	$7 \cdot t$	$\frac{q}{2}$	$q/2$
$7(t)$	$7 \times t$	$q \div 2$	
ab	$a \cdot b$	$\frac{s}{r}$	s/r
$a(b)$	$a \times b$	$s \div r$	

EXAMPLE 2 Evaluating Algebraic Expressions Involving Order of Operations

Evaluate each expression for the given value of the variable.

A $3x - 2$ for $x = 5$

$3(5) - 2$ *Substitute 5 for x.*

$15 - 2$ *Multiply.*

13 *Subtract.*

B $n \div 2 + n$ for $n = 4$

$4 \div 2 + 4$ *Substitute 4 for n.*

$2 + 4$ *Divide.*

6 *Add.*

C $6y^2 + 2y$ for $y = 2$

$6(2)^2 + 2(2)$ *Substitute 2 for y.*

$6(4) + 2(2)$ *Evaluate the power.*

$24 + 4$ *Multiply.*

28 *Add.*

EXAMPLE 3 Evaluating Algebraic Expressions with Two Variables

Evaluate $\frac{3}{n} + 2m$ for $n = 3$ and $m = 4$.

$\frac{3}{n} + 2m$

$\frac{3}{3} + 2(4)$ *Substitute 3 for n and 4 for m.*

$1 + 8$ *Divide and multiply from left to right.*

9 *Add.*

Think and Discuss

1. Write each expression another way. **a.** $12x$ **b.** $\frac{4}{y}$ **c.** $\frac{3xy}{2}$

2. Explain the difference between a variable and a constant.

COMMON ERROR ALERT

Watch for students who substitute the wrong value for the variable. Caution students to be sure that they are substituting the correct value for each variable in expressions with more than one variable.

Additional Examples

Example 1

Evaluate $k + 9$ for each value of k.

A. $k = 5$ 14

B. $k = 2$ 11

Example 2

Evaluate each expression for the given value of the variable.

A. $4x - 3$, for $x = 2$ 5

B. $s \div 5 + s$, for $s = 15$ 18

C. $5x^2 + 3x$, for $x = 2$ 26

Example 3

Evaluate $\frac{6}{a} + 4b$, for $a = 3$ and $b = 2$. 10

3 Close

Reaching All Learners

Through Grouping Strategies

Have students work in groups to solve a magic square. A recording sheet is provided on p. 128 of the Chapter 2 Resource Book. A magic square is an array of numbers in which each row, column, and diagonal has the same sum. Ask students, Is this array a magic square if $x = 4$? if $x = 6$? if $x = 0$?

$x + 7$	x	$2x + 1$
$x + 2$	$0.5x + 6$	$x + 6$
$3x - 5$	$3x$	$x + 1$

The array is a magic square if $x = 4$, but not if $x = 6$ or 0.

Summarize

You may wish to have students write definitions of the new vocabulary terms in the lesson: *variable, constant, algebraic expression,* and *evaluate.* Discuss how the terms relate to each other.

Possible answers: A variable is a quantity that changes. A constant is a quantity that stays the same. Constants and variables combined with operations make algebraic expressions. If you have a value for the variable, you can evaluate the expression.

Answers to Think and Discuss

Possible answers:

1. **a.** $12 \cdot x$ or $12(x)$
   b. $4 \div y$ or $4 \cdot \frac{1}{y}$
   c. $3xy \div 2$ or $3xy \cdot \frac{1}{2}$
2. The value of a variable can change, and the value of a constant remains the same. Variables are represented by letters.

2-7 PRACTICE & ASSESS

Students may want to refer back to the lesson examples.

Assignment Guide

If you finished Example **1** assign:
Core 1–3, 9–11, 38–44
Enriched 1–3, 9–11, 38–44

If you finished Example **2** assign:
Core 1–6, 9–17, 21–25 odd, 38–44
Enriched 1–5 odd, 9–17, 20–23, 25, 26, 38–44

If you finished Example **3** assign:
Core 1–19, 21–33 odd, 38–44
Enriched 1–19 odd, 20–44

Notes

2-7 Exercises

FOR EXTRA PRACTICE see page 659

internet connect
Homework Help Online
go.hrw.com Keyword: MS4 2-7

GUIDED PRACTICE

See Example 1 Evaluate $n + 9$ for each value of n.

1. $n = 3$ **12** 2. $n = 2$ **11** 3. $n = 11$ **20**

See Example 2 Evaluate each expression for the given value of the variable.

4. $2x - 3$ for $x = 4$ **5** 5. $n \div 3 + n$ for $n = 6$ **8** 6. $5y^2 + 3y$ for $y = 2$ **26**

See Example 3 Evaluate each expression for the given values of the variables.

7. $\frac{8}{n} + 3m$ for $n = 2$ and $m = 5$ **19** 8. $5a - 3b + 5$ for $a = 4$ and $b = 3$ **16**

INDEPENDENT PRACTICE

See Example 1 Evaluate $n + 5$ for each value of n.

9. $n = 17$ **22** 10. $n = 9$ **14** 11. $n = 0$ **5**

See Example 2 Evaluate each expression for the given value of the variable.

12. $5y - 1$ for $y = 3$ **14** 13. $10b - 9$ for $b = 2$ **11** 14. $p \div 7 + p$ for $p = 14$ **16**

15. $n \div 5 + n$ for $n = 20$ **24** 16. $3x^2 + 2x$ for $x = 10$ **320** 17. $3c^2 - 5c$ for $c = 3$ **12**

See Example 3 Evaluate each expression for the given values of the variables.

18. $\frac{12}{n} + 7m$ for $n = 6$ and $m = 4$ **30** 19. $7p - 2t + 3$ for $p = 6$ and $t = 2$ **41**

PRACTICE AND PROBLEM SOLVING

Evaluate each expression for the given values of the variables.

20. $20x - 10$ for $x = 4$ **70**
21. $4d^2 - 3d$ for $d = 2$ **10**
22. $22p \div 11 + p$ for $p = 3$ **9**
23. $q + q^2 + q \div 2$ for $q = 4$ **22**
24. $\frac{16}{k} + 7h$ for $k = 8$ and $h = 2$ **16**
25. $f \div 3 + f$ for $f = 18$ **24**
26. $3t \div 3 + t$ for $t = 13$ **26**
27. $9 + 3p - 5t + 3$ for $p = 2$ and $t = 1$ **13**
28. Write $\frac{4ab}{3}$ another way. **Possible answer: $4ab \div 3$**
29. You can factor $6a^2$ as $2 \cdot 3 \cdot a \cdot a$. Factor $10c^3d^2$ in the same manner. **$2 \cdot 5 \cdot c \cdot c \cdot c \cdot d \cdot d$**
30. The expression $60m$ gives the number of seconds in m minutes. Evaluate $60m$ for $m = 7$. How many seconds are there in 7 minutes? **420; 420 seconds**
31. ***MONEY*** Betsy has n quarters. You can use the expression $0.25n$ to find the total value of her coins. What is the value of 18 quarters? **$4.50**

Math Background

In early forms of algebra, algebraic expressions were written with words. Indian mathematicians of the seventh century used *ya*, short for *yavat havat*, meaning "unknown quantity." The convention in the Middle Ages was to use *cosa*, which means "thing," for the unknown. Today, mathematicians often choose the last letters of the alphabet (e.g., *x*, *y*, *z*) to represent variables, and the first letters (e.g., *a*, *b*, *c*) to represent constants.

RETEACH 2-7

LESSON 2-7 **Reteach**
Variables and Algebraic Expressions

A **variable** is a letter that represents a number than can change in an expression. When you **evaluate** an algebraic expression, you substitute the value given for the variable in the expression.

- Algebraic expression: $x - 3$

The value of the expression depends on the value of the variable x.
If $x = 7 \rightarrow 7 - 3 = 4$
If $x = 11 \rightarrow 11 - 3 = 8$
If $x = 15 \rightarrow 15 - 3 = 12$

- Evaluate $4n + 1$ for $n = 5$.

Replace the variable n with 5. $\rightarrow 4(5) + 1 = 20 + 1 = 21$

Evaluate each expression for the given value.

1. $a + 7$ for $a = 3$
$a + 7 = 3 + 7 =$ **10**
2. $k - 5$ for $k = 13$
$k - 5 =$ **13** $- 5 =$ **8**
3. $y \div 3$ for $y = 6$
$y \div 3 =$ **6** $\div 3 =$ **2**
4. $12 + m$ for $m = 9$
$12 + m =$ **12** $+$ **9** $=$ **21**
5. $3n - 2$ for $n = 5$
$3n - 2 = 3($**5**$) - 2 =$ **15** $- 2 =$ **13**
6. $5x + 4$ for $x = 4$
$5x + 4 = 5($**4**$) +$ **4** $=$ **20** $+$ **4** $=$ **24**
7. $c - 9$ for $c = 11$ **2**
8. $b + 16$ for $b = 4$ **20**
9. $a - 4$ for $a = 9$ **5**
10. $25 - g$ for $g = 12$ **13**
11. $w + 5$ for $w = 2$ **7**
12. $3 + s$ for $s = 8$ **11**
13. $7q$ for $q = 10$ **70**
14. $2y + 9$ for $y = 8$ **25**
15. $6x - 3$ for $x = 1$ **3**

PRACTICE 2-7

LESSON 2-7 **Practice B**
Variables and Algebraic Expressions

Evaluate $n - 5$ for each value of n.

1. $n = 8$ **3**
2. $n = 121$ **116**
3. $n = 32$ **27**
4. $n = 59$ **54**

Evaluate each algebraic expression for the given variable values.

5. $3n + 15$ for $n = 4$ **27**
6. $h \div 12$ for $h = 60$ **5**
7. $32x - 32$ for $x = 2$ **32**
8. $\frac{c}{2}$ for $c = 24$ **12**
9. $(n \div 2)5$ for $n = 14$ **35**
10. $8p + 148$ for $p = 15$ **268**
11. $e^2 - 7$ for $e = 8$ **57**
12. $3d^2 + d$ for $d = 5$ **80**
13. $40 - 4k^3$ for $k = 2$ **8**
14. $2y - z$ for $y = 21$ and $z = 19$ **23**
15. $3h^2 + 8m$ for $h = 3$ and $m = 2$ **43**
16. $18 \div a + b \div 9$ for $a = 6$ and $b = 45$ **8**
17. $10x - 4y$ for $x = 14$ and $y = 5$ **120**
18. You can find the area of a rectangle with the expression lw where l represents the length and w represents the width. What is the area of the rectangle at right in square feet?

5 ft
2 ft

10 square feet

19. Rita drove an average of 55 mi/h on her trip to the mountains. You can use the expression $55h$ to find out how many miles she drove in h hours. If she drove for 5 hours, how many miles did she drive?

275 miles

32. ***PHYSICAL SCIENCE*** A color TV has a power rating of 200 watts. The expression $200t$ gives the power used by t color TV sets. Evaluate $200t$ for $t = 13$. How much power is used by 13 TV sets? **2,600; 2,600 watts**

33. ***PHYSICAL SCIENCE*** The expression $1.8c + 32$ can be used to convert a temperature in degrees Celsius c to degrees Fahrenheit. What is the temperature in degrees Fahrenheit if the temperature is 30°C? **86°F**

34. ***PHYSICAL SCIENCE*** The graph shows the changes of state for water.
   a. What is the boiling point of water in degrees Celsius? **100°C**
   b. Use the expression $1.8c + 32$ to find the boiling point of water in degrees Fahrenheit. **212°F**

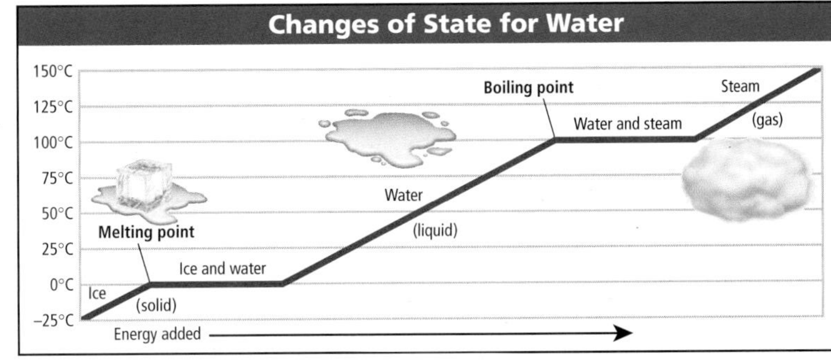

36. Possible answer: Using different values in place of a variable will cause the value of the expression to vary. If $x = 4$, $3x + 5 = 17$. If $x = 8$, $3x + 5 = 29$.

35. ***WHAT'S THE ERROR?*** A student was asked to identify the variable in the expression $72x + 8$. The student's answer was $72x$. What was the student's error? **A variable is a letter that represents a number, so x is the variable. $72x$ is an expression that contains a variable.**

36. ***WRITE ABOUT IT*** Explain why letters such as x, p, and n used in algebraic expressions are called variables. Use examples to illustrate your response.

37. ***CHALLENGE*** Evaluate the expression $\frac{x + y}{y - x}$ for $x = 6$ and $y = 8$. **7**

Spiral Review

38. A box-and-whisker plot is made using the numbers 24, 9, 17, 35, 16, and 27. Which number is the upper extreme? (Lesson 1-6) **35**

Write the prime factorization of each number. (Lesson 2-4)

39. 99 **$3^2 \cdot 11$**
40. 24 **$2^3 \cdot 3$**
41. 56 **$2^3 \cdot 7$**
42. 80 **$2^4 \cdot 5$**

43. **TEST PREP** Which expression does **not** simplify to 81? (Lesson 2-3) **C**

A $9 \cdot (4 + 5)$ B $7 + 16 \cdot 4 + 10$ C $3 \cdot 25 + 2$ D $10^2 - 4 \cdot 5 + 1$

44. **TEST PREP** What is the least common multiple (LCM) of 9 and 12? (Lesson 2-6) **G**

F 24 G 36 H 54 J 108

Journal

Have students think of and write a description of real-world situations in which algebraic expressions could be used.

Test Prep Doctor

In Exercise 44, encourage students to eliminate incorrect choices by using the definition of least common multiple. Choice **F,** 24, is not a multiple of 9, and **H,** 54, is not a multiple of 12. Eliminating those leaves **G,** 36, and **J,** 108. Both are common multiples of 9 and 12, and 36 is clearly smaller.

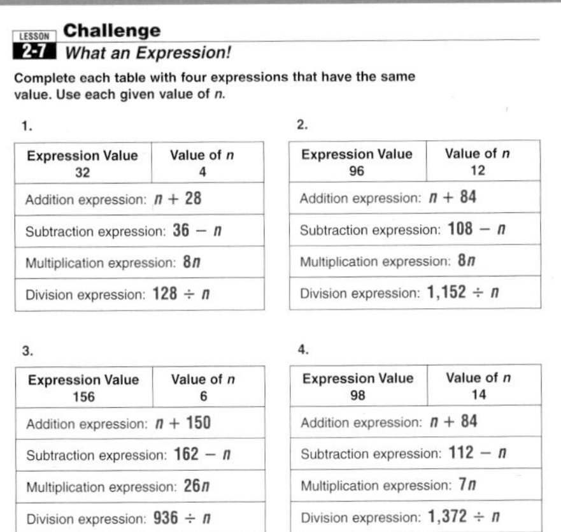

CHALLENGE 2-7

LESSON 2-7 **Challenge**
What an Expression!

Complete each table with four expressions that have the same value. Use each given value of *n*.

1.

Expression Value 32	Value of *n* 4
Addition expression: $n + 28$	
Subtraction expression: $36 - n$	
Multiplication expression: $8n$	
Division expression: $128 \div n$	

2.

Expression Value 96	Value of *n* 12
Addition expression: $n + 84$	
Subtraction expression: $108 - n$	
Multiplication expression: $8n$	
Division expression: $1{,}152 \div n$	

3.

Expression Value 156	Value of *n* 6
Addition expression: $n + 150$	
Subtraction expression: $162 - n$	
Multiplication expression: $26n$	
Division expression: $936 \div n$	

4.

Expression Value 98	Value of *n* 14
Addition expression: $n + 84$	
Subtraction expression: $112 - n$	
Multiplication expression: $7n$	
Division expression: $1{,}372 \div n$	

5.

Expression Value 57	Value of *n* 12
Addition expression: $n + 45$	
Subtraction expression: $69 - n$	
Multiplication expression: $4.75n$	
Division expression: $684 \div n$	

6.

Expression Value 248	Value of *n* 124
Addition expression: $n + 124$	
Subtraction expression: $372 - n$	
Multiplication expression: $2n$	
Division expression: $30{,}752 \div n$	

PROBLEM SOLVING 2-7

LESSON 2-7 **Problem Solving**
Variables and Expressions

Write the correct answer.

1. In 2000, people in the United States watched television an average of 29 hours per week. Use the expression $29w$ for $w = 4$ to find out about how many hours per month this is.

about 116 hours

2. Find the value of the variable w in the expression $29w$ to find the average number of hours people watched television in a year. Find the value of the expression.

52; 1,508 hours

3. The expression $y + 45$ gives the year when a person will be 45 years old, where y is the year of birth. When will a person born in 1992 be 45 years old?

2037

4. The expression $24g$ gives the number of miles Guy's car can travel on g gallons of gas. If the car has 6 gallons of gas left, how much farther can he drive?

144 miles

Choose the letter for the best answer.

5. Sam is 5 feet tall. The expression $0.5m + 60$ can be used to calculate his height in inches if he grows an average of 0.5 inch each month. How tall will Sam be in 6 months?
A 56 inches
B 5 feet 6 inches
(C) 63 inches
D 53 inches

6. The winner of the 1911 Indianapolis 500 auto race drove at a speed of about $s - 56$ mi/h, where s is the 2001 winning speed of about 131 mi/h. What was the approximate winning speed in 1911?
(F) 75 mi/h
G 186 mi/h
H 85 mi/h
J 187 mi/h

7. The expression $1{,}587v$ gives the number of pounds of waste produced per person in the United States in v years. How many pounds of waste per person is produced in the United States in 6 years?
A 1,581 pounds
B 1,593 pounds
C 9,348 pounds
(D) 9,522 pounds

8. The expression \$1.25*p* + \$3.50 can be used to calculate the total charge for faxing *p* pages at a business services store. How much would it cost to fax 8 pages?
F \$12.50
G \$4.75
(H) \$13.50
J \$10.00

Lesson Quiz

Evaluate $n + 7$ for each value of n.

1. $n = 25$ 32 2. $n = 31$ 38

Evaluate each algebraic expression for the given values of the variables.

3. $6y - 5$ for $y = 7$ 37

4. $4x^2 + 3x$ for $x = 6$ 162

5. $\frac{56}{x} + 3y$ for $x = 4$ and $y = 3$ 23

6. The expression $7d$ gives the number of days in d weeks. Evaluate $7d$ for $d = 12$. How many days are in 12 weeks? 84

Available on Daily Transparency in CRB

2-8 Organizer

Pacing: Traditional 1 day
Block $\frac{1}{2}$ day

Objective: Students translate words into numbers, variables, and operations.

Warm Up

Evaluate each algebraic expression for the given values of the variables.

1. $7x + 4$ for $x = 6$ **46**
2. $8y - 22$ for $y = 9$ **50**
3. $12x + \frac{8}{y}$ for $x = 7$ and $y = 4$ **86**
4. $y + 3z$ for $y = 5$ and $z = 6$ **23**

Problem of the Day

A farmer had some ducks and cows in the field. He sent his two children out to count the number of animals. Jean counted 50 heads. Charles counted 154 legs. How many of each kind were counted?
23 ducks and 27 cows

Available on Daily Transparency in CRB

Math Fact !

The word *algebra* comes from the title of a book, *Hisab al-jabr w'al-muqabala,* by al-Khwârizmî (A.D. 780–850, Baghdad). All of al-Khwârizmî's mathematics was written in words; he did not use symbols. *Al-jabr* means "completion."

2-8 Translate Words into Math

Problem Solving Skill

Learn to translate words into numbers, variables, and operations.

Vocabulary
verbal expressions

Although they are closely related, a Great Dane weighs about 40 times as much as a Chihuahua. An expression for the weight of the Great Dane could be $40c$, where c is the weight of the Chihuahua.

When solving real-world problems, you will need to translate words, or **verbal expressions**, into algebraic expressions.

Operation	Verbal Expressions	Algebraic Expression
+	• add 3 to a number • a number plus 3 • the sum of a number and 3 • 3 more than a number • a number increased by 3	$n + 3$
−	• subtract 12 from a number • a number minus 12 • the difference of a number and 12 • 12 less than a number • a number decreased by 12 • take away 12 from a number • a number less 12	$x - 12$
×	• 2 times a number • 2 multiplied by a number • the product of 2 and a number	$2m$ or $2 \cdot m$
÷	• 6 divided into a number • a number divided by 6 • the quotient of a number and 6	$a \div 6$ or $\frac{a}{6}$

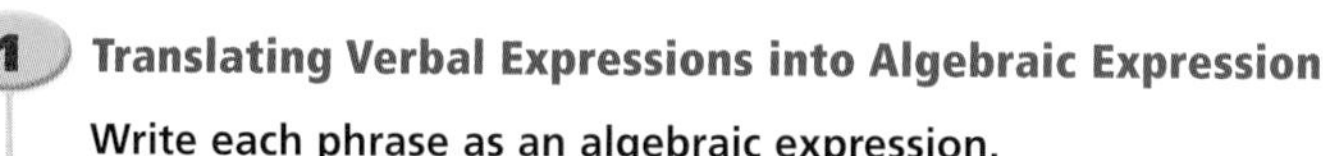

EXAMPLE 1 Translating Verbal Expressions into Algebraic Expressions

Write each phrase as an algebraic expression.

A the product of 20 and t
product means "multiply"
$20t$

B 24 less than a number
less than means "subtract from"
$n - 24$

1 Introduce

Alternate Opener

EXPLORATION

2-8 Translate Words into Math

Follow the steps below, showing your work for each step.

Step 1: Choose any whole number between 1 and 10.
Step 2: Add to it the next two whole numbers that come after it.
Step 3: Divide the result by 3.
Step 4: Subtract the number that you began with.
Step 5: Tell what number you end with.

1. Compare your results with any other students who began with the same whole number for Step 1. Do your results agree?
2. Compare your results with any other students who did not begin with the same whole number for Step 1. Do your results agree?

Think and Discuss

3. **Describe** the operation in step 2. What numbers are involved?
4. **Look for a pattern** in all the results. Describe what you find.

Motivate

To introduce students to translating words into *algebraic expressions,* discuss translating a sentence from one language into another. Students who are bilingual or who study a language can be asked to give examples. Responses should mention the need to understand the vocabulary, the grammar, and special expressions.

Exploration worksheet and answers on Chapter 2 Resource Book pp. 73 and 144

2 Teach

Lesson Presentation

Guided Instruction

In this lesson, students learn to translate words into numbers, variables, and operations. The chart in this lesson (Teaching Transparency T27 in the Chapter 2 Resource Book) organizes the important vocabulary for translating word phrases into algebraic expressions. Many word phrases translate word for word into algebraic expressions (e.g., a number minus 12), while others are not so direct (e.g., the quotient of a number and 6).

Teaching Tip For differences and quotients, order is important. Remind students to use numbers and variables in the order presented.

Write each phrase as an algebraic expression.

C **4 times the sum of a number and 2**

4 times the sum of a number and 2

$4 \cdot \quad n + 2$

$4(n + 2)$

D **the sum of 4 times a number and 2**

the sum of 4 times a number and 2

$4 \cdot n \quad + 2$

$4n + 2$

When solving real-world problems, you may need to determine the action to know which operation to use.

Action	Operation
Put parts together	Add
Put equal parts together	Multiply
Find how much more	Subtract
Separate into equal parts	Divide

EXAMPLE 2 Translating Real-World Problems into Algebraic Expressions

A **Jed reads p pages each day of a 200-page book. Write an algebraic expression for how many days it will take Jed to read the book.**

You need to *separate* the total number of pages *into equal parts*. This involves division.

$$\frac{\text{total number of pages}}{\text{pages read each day}} = \frac{200}{p}$$

B **To rent a certain car for a day costs \$84 plus \$0.29 for every mile the car is driven. Write an algebraic expression to show how much it costs to rent the car for a day.**

The cost includes \$0.29 per mile. Use m for the number of miles.

Multiply to *put equal parts together:* $0.29m$

In addition to the fee per mile, the cost includes a flat fee of \$84.

Add to *put parts together:* $84 + 0.29m$

Think and Discuss

1. **Write** three different verbal expressions that can be represented by $2 - y$. Then rewrite them so they can be represented by $y - 2$.
2. **Explain** how you would determine which operation to use to find the number of chairs in 6 rows of 100 chairs each.

COMMON ERROR ALERT

Students might translate "6 less than a number" as "$6 < n$." Explain that $=$, $<$, and $>$ are symbols for verbs and should be used when you see the words *is*, *is less than*, or *is greater than*.

Additional Examples

Example 1

Write each phrase as an algebraic expression.

A. the quotient of a number and 4
$\frac{n}{4}$

B. w increased by 5
$w + 5$

C. the difference of 3 times a number and 7 $3x - 7$

D. the quotient of 4 and a number, increased by 10 $\frac{4}{n} + 10$

Example 2

A. Mr. Campbell drives at 55 mi/h. Write an expression for how far he can drive in h hours. $55h$

B. On a history test Maritza scored 50 points on the essay. Besides the essay, each short-answer question was worth 2 points. Write an expression for her total points if she answered q short-answer questions correctly.
$50 + 2q$

Example 2 note: Point out that the quotient in this division problem is the *size* of the equal parts. The divisor is the *number* of equal parts.

3 Close

Summarize

Have students restate important vocabulary for translating words into algebraic expressions: *sum*, *difference*, *product*, *quotient*, *increased*, and *decreased*.

Possible answers: *Sum* is the result of addition. *Difference* is the result of subtraction. *Product* is the result of multiplication. *Quotient* is the result of division. *Increased* tells us something was added, and *decreased* tells us something was subtracted.

Reaching All Learners

Through Home Connection

Have students work with family members at home to come up with situations in which they could translate words into mathematical expressions (e.g., oranges cost \$0.40 more per pound this week than last week). Family members can suggest the situations, and students can translate the words into mathematical expressions. Encourage students to share the situations and mathematical expressions with the class.

Answers to Think and Discuss

Possible answers:

1. for $2 - y$: y less than 2, y subtracted from 2, or 2 decreased by y; for $y - 2$: 2 less than y, 2 subtracted from y, or y decreased by 2
2. Since equal parts are being put together, you would multiply.

2-8 PRACTICE & ASSESS

Students may want to refer back to the lesson examples.

Assignment Guide

If you finished Example 1 assign:
Core 1–3, 6–10, 13–23 odd, 32–39
Enriched 1, 6, 9, 13–24, 32–39

If you finished Example 2 assign:
Core 1–12, 13–27 odd, 32–39
Enriched 1–11 odd, 13–39

Answers

Possible answers:

22. 5 times the quantity a minus 8

23. the difference between 4 times p and 10

24. the sum of r and 1 divided by 14

2-8 Exercises

FOR EXTRA PRACTICE
see page 659

internet connect
Homework Help Online
go.hrw.com Keyword: MS4 2-8

GUIDED PRACTICE

See Example 1 — **Write each phrase as an algebraic expression.**

1. the product of 7 and p **$7p$**
2. 3 less than a number **$n - 3$**
3. 3 times the sum of a number and 5 **$3(n + 5)$**

See Example 2

4. Carly spends \$5 for n notebooks. Write an algebraic expression to represent the cost of one notebook. **$\$5 \div n$ or $\frac{5}{n}$**
5. A company charges \$46 for cable TV installation and \$21 per month for basic cable service. Write an algebraic expression to represent the total cost of m months of basic cable service, including installation. **$46 + 21m$**

INDEPENDENT PRACTICE

See Example 1 — **Write each phrase as an algebraic expression.**

6. the sum of 5 and a number **$5 + x$**
7. 2 less than a number **$y - 2$**
8. the quotient of a number and 8 **$n \div 8$**
9. 9 times a number **$9n$**
10. 10 less than the product of a number and 3 **$3y - 10$**

See Example 2

11. Video Express sells used tapes. Marta bought v tapes for \$45. Write an algebraic expression for the cost of each tape. **$45 \div v$**
12. A 5-foot pine tree was planted and grew 2 feet each year. Write an algebraic expression for the height of the tree after t years. **$5 + 2t$**

PRACTICE AND PROBLEM SOLVING

Write each phrase as an algebraic expression.

13. m plus 6 times n **$m + 6n$**
14. t less than 23 divided by u **$\frac{23}{u} - t$**
15. 14 less than k times 6 **$6k - 14$**
16. 2 times the sum of y and 5 **$2(y + 5)$**
17. the quotient of 100 and the quantity 6 plus w **$100 \div (6 + w)$**
18. 35 multiplied by the quantity r less 45 **$35(r - 45)$**

Write a verbal expression for each algebraic expression. **Possible answers:**

19. $h + 3$ **h plus 3**
20. $90 \div y$ **90 divided by y**
21. $s - 405$ **s minus 405**
22. $5(a - 8)$
23. $4p - 10$
24. $(r + 1) \div 14$

25. An ice machine can produce 17 pounds of ice in one hour. Write an algebraic expression to describe the following:
    a. the number of pounds of ice produced in n hours **$17n$**
    b. the number of pounds of ice produced in d days **$17 \cdot 24d$**

Math Background

The translation of words into symbols is an essential problem solving skill. Students who are intimidated by "word problems" often try to do too much at once. Building a verbal model or stripping the language of the problem down to its key words often helps to make the structure of the algebraic expression clearer.

RETEACH 2-8

LESSON 2-8 **Reteach**
Translate Words Into Math

Use the operation clues in a word phrase to translate word phrases into algebraic expressions.

Addition	
add	plus
sum	more than
increased by	

Subtraction	
subtract	minus
difference	less than
decreased by	take away

Multiplication
times
multiplied by
product

Division
divided by
divided into
quotient

Write an algebraic expression for the difference of a number and 8.

1. What operation would you choose? **subtraction**
2. Write an algebraic expression. **$n - 8$**

Write an algebraic expression for 3 more than a number.

3. What operation would you choose? **addition**
4. Write an algebraic expression. **$n + 3$**

Write an algebraic expression for the quotient of a number and 15.

5. What operation would you choose? **division**
6. Write an algebraic expression. **$n \div 15$**

Write an algebraic expression.

7. the product of 12 and a number k **$12k$**
8. a number d increased by 9 **$d + 9$**
9. a number h divided by 4 **$h \div 4$**

PRACTICE 2-8

LESSON 2-8 **Practice B**
Translate Words Into Math

Write as an algebraic expression.

1. 125 decreased by a number **$125 - n$**
2. 359 more than z **$z + 359$**
3. the product of a number and 35 **$35f$**
4. the quotient of 100 and w **$100 \div w$**
5. twice a number, plus 27 **$2r + 27$**
6. 12 less than 15 times x **$15x - 12$**
7. the product of e and 4, divided by 12 **$4e \div 12$**
8. y less than 18 times 6 **$18 \bullet 6 - y$**
9. 48 more than the quotient of a number and 64 **$m \div 64 + 48$**
10. 500 less than the product of 4 and a number **$4t - 500$**
11. the quotient of p and 4, decreased by 320 **$p \div 4 - 320$**
12. 13 multiplied by the amount 60 minus w **$13(60 - w)$**
13. the quotient of 45 and the sum of c and 17 **$45 \div (c + 17)$**
14. twice the sum of a number and 600 **$2(d + 600)$**
15. There are twice as many flute players as there are trumpet players in the band. If there are n flute players, write an expression to find out how many trumpet players there are. **$n \div 2$**
16. The Nile River is the longest river in the world at 4,160 miles. A group of explorers traveled along the entire Nile in x days. They traveled the same distance each day. Write an expression to find each day's distance. **$4{,}160 \div x$**
17. A slice of pizza has 290 calories, and a stalk of celery has 5 calories. Write an expression to find out how many calories there are in a slices of pizza and b stalks of celery. **$290a + 5b$**
18. Grant pays 10¢ per minute plus \$5 per month for telephone long distance. Write an expression for m minutes of long-distance calls in one month. **$0.10m + 5$**

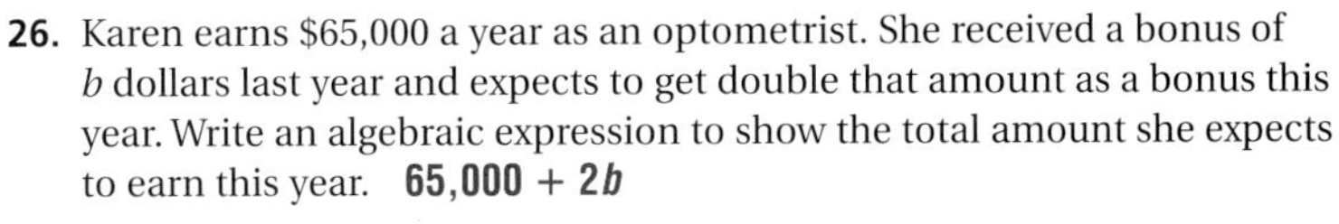

26. Karen earns \$65,000 a year as an optometrist. She received a bonus of b dollars last year and expects to get double that amount as a bonus this year. Write an algebraic expression to show the total amount she expects to earn this year. **65,000 + 2*b***

Life Science LINK

Up to 25 follicle mite nymphs can hatch in a single hair follicle.

27. ***LIFE SCIENCE*** Follicle mites are tiny and harmless, and they live in our eyebrows and eyelashes. They are relatives of spiders and like spiders, they have eight legs. Write an algebraic expression for the number of legs in m mites. **8*m***

28. ***NUTRITION*** The table shows the estimated number of grams of carbohydrates commonly found in various types of foods.

Food	Carbohydrates
1 c skim milk	12 g
1/2 c vegetable	5 g
1 piece of fruit	15 g
1 slice of bread	15 g
1 oz lean meat	0 g

   a. Write an algebraic expression for the number of grams of carbohydrates in y pieces of fruit and 1 cup of skim milk. **15*y* + 12**

   b. How many grams of carbohydrates are in a sandwich made from t ounces of lean meat and 2 slices of bread? **30 g**

29. ***WHAT'S THE QUESTION?*** Jimmy has twice as many baseball cards as Frank and four times as many football cards as Joe. The expression $2x + 4y$ can be used to show the total number of baseball and football cards Jimmy has. If the answer is y, then what is the question? **Possible answer: Which variable represents how many football cards Joe has?**

30. ***WRITE ABOUT IT*** If you are asked to compare two numbers, what two operations might you use? Why?

31. ***CHALLENGE*** In 1996, one U.S. dollar was equivalent, on average, to \$1.363 in Canadian money. Write an algebraic expression for the number of U.S. dollars you could get for n Canadian dollars. **$n \div 1.363$**

Answer

30. Possible answers: You could use subtraction to find the difference between two numbers, or division to find how many times a number can fit into another number. Another explanation could be that by using subtraction, you are finding the difference in values, while with division you are finding the relative value of one in terms of the other.

Journal

Have students describe a situation that could be represented by the algebraic expression $8x + 2$.

Spiral Review

Find the mean of each data set. (Lesson 1-2)

32. 25, 18, 27, 30 **25**
33. 108, 77, 90, 97 **93**
34. 239, 247, 233, 263, 268 **250**

35. What is another way to write $8 \cdot 8 \cdot 8 \cdot 8$? (Lesson 2-1) **Possible answer: 8^4**

Find each product. (Lesson 2-2)

36. $612 \cdot 10^3$ **612,000**
37. $43.8 \cdot 10^6$ **43,800,000**
38. $590 \cdot 10^5$ **59,000,000**

39. **TEST PREP** What is the value of the expression $18 - 1 \cdot 9 \div 3$? (Lesson 2-3) **B**

   A 2　　B 15　　C 51　　D 153

Test Prep Doctor

For Exercise 39, remind students of the order of operations. If a student selects **C** or **D,** it indicates that he or she worked left to right without regard to the order of operations.

CHALLENGE 2-8

LESSON 2-8 **Challenge**
What's My Equation?

Match each equation with the word problem it represents. Write the equation and corresponding letter. Then write the letter of the equation in the circle that has the problem number. Discover the message formed by the letters.

P $2k = 14$	D $\frac{p}{3} = 2.50$	A $\frac{m}{5} = 8$	U $3t = 21$
M $a - 18 = 33$	S $w + 7 = 25$	T $x + 7 = 22$	H $n - 12 = 37$

1. Tom has 7 more CDs than Rick does. If Tom has 22 CDs, how many does Rick have? **$x + 7 = 22$; T**
2. Maria is 18 years younger than Kim. If Maria is 33, how old is Kim? **$a - 18 = 33$; M**
3. Five friends went out for dinner. They shared the cost of the meal equally. If each person paid \$8, what was the total cost of the meal? **$\frac{m}{5} = 8$; A**
4. Max paid 3 times as much for a tape as his friend did. If Max paid \$21, how much did his friend pay? **$3t = 21$; U**
5. Marisa and her two friends share a pizza. The cost of the pizza is shared equally among them. If each person pays \$2.50, how much does the pizza cost? **$\frac{p}{3} = 2.50$; D**
6. Lee has scored twice as many goals as Jiang has. If Lee's goal total is 14, how many goals has Jiang scored? **$2k = 14$; P**
7. Jamal sold 7 more magazine subscriptions than Wayne did. If Jamal sold 25 subscriptions, how many did Wayne sell? **$w + 7 = 25$; S**
8. Shelly delivered 12 fewer newspapers this week than last week. If she delivered 37 papers this week, how many did she deliver last week? **$n - 12 = 37$; H**

M	A	T	H	A	D	D	S	U	P
2	3	1	8	3	5	5	7	4	6

PROBLEM SOLVING 2-8

LESSON 2-8 **Problem Solving**
Translate Words into Math

Write the correct answer.

1. Employers in the United States allocate n fewer vacation days than the 25 days given by the average Japanese employer. Write an expression to show the number of vacation days given U.S. workers. **$25 - n$**
2. There are 112 members in the Somerset Marching Band. They will march in r equal rows. Write an expression for the number of band members in each row. **$112 \div r$**
3. A cup of cottage cheese has 26 grams of protein. Write an expression for the amount of protein in s cups of cottage cheese. **$26s$**
4. Every morning Sasha exercises for 20 minutes. She exercises k minutes every evening. Next week she will double her exercise time at night. Write an expression to show how long Sasha will exercise each day next week. **$20 + 2k$**

Choose the letter for the best answer.

5. One centimeter equals 0.3937 inches. Which expression shows how many inches are in c centimeters?
   A $0.3937 + c$
   B $0.3937 \div c$
   C $c \div 0.3937$
   (D) $0.3937c$
6. In 1957, the Soviet Union launched *Sputnik 1*, the first satellite to orbit Earth. It circled Earth's orbit every 1.6 hours for 92 days, then burned up. If the satellite traveled m miles per hour, which expression shows the length of the orbit?
   F $92m$
   (G) $1.6m$
   H $m \div 1.6$
   J $92 \div m$
7. Gina's heart rate is 70 beats per minute. Which expression shows the number of beats in h hours?
   A $70h$
   B $60h$
   (C) $4{,}200h$
   D $3{,}600h$
8. The Harris family went on vacation for w weeks and 3 days. Which expression shows the total number of days of their vacation?
   F $7w$
   G $3w$
   (H) $7w + 3$
   J $3w + 7$

Lesson Quiz

Write each phrase as an algebraic expression.

1. 18 less than a number　**$x - 18$**
2. the quotient of a number and 21　**$\frac{x}{21}$**
3. 8 times the sum of x and 15　**$8(x + 15)$**
4. 7 less than the product of a number and 5　**$5n - 7$**
5. The county fair charges an admission of \$6 and then charges \$2 for each ride. Write an algebraic expression to represent the total cost after r rides at the fair. **$6 + 2r$**

Available on Daily Transparency in CRB

2-9 Organizer

Pacing: Traditional 1 day
Block $\frac{1}{2}$ day

Objective: Students combine like terms.

Warm Up

Evaluate each expression for $y = 3$.

1.	$3y + y$	12
2.	$7y$	21
3.	$10y - 4y$	18
4.	$9y$	27
5.	$y + 5y + 6y$	36
6.	$10y$	30

Problem of the Day

Emilia saved nickels, dimes, and quarters in a jar. When the jar was full, she counted the money. She had as many quarters as dimes, but twice as many nickels as dimes. If the jar had 844 coins, how much money had she saved? **\$94.95**

Available on Daily Transparency in CRB

The student's second semester seemed so much like her first that she hoped she could graduate sooner by combining like terms.

2-9 Combining Like Terms

Learn to combine like terms.

Vocabulary
term
coefficient
like terms

In the expression $7x + 5$, $7x$ and 5 are called *terms*. A **term** can be a number, a variable, or a product of numbers and variables. Terms in an expression are separated by + and −.

$$\underbrace{7x}_{\text{term}} + \underbrace{5}_{\text{term}} - \underbrace{3y^2}_{\text{term}} + \underbrace{y}_{\text{term}} - \underbrace{\tfrac{x}{3}}_{\text{term}}$$

In the term $7x$, 7 is called the *coefficient*. A **coefficient** is a number that is multiplied by a variable in an algebraic expression. A variable by itself, like y, has a coefficient of 1. So $y = 1y$.

Coefficient → **7x** ← Variable

Term	$4a$	$\frac{2}{3}y$	$3k^5$	x^2	$\frac{x}{9}$	$4.7t$
Coefficient	4	$\frac{2}{3}$	3	1	$\frac{1}{9}$	4.7

Like terms are terms with the same variable raised to the same power. The coefficients do not have to be the same. Constants, like 5, $\frac{1}{2}$, and 3.2, are also like terms.

Like Terms	$3x$ and $2x$	w and $\frac{w}{7}$	5 and 1.8
Unlike Terms	$5x^2$ and $2x$ *The exponents are different.*	$6a$ and $6b$ *The variables are different.*	3.2 and n *Only one term contains a variable.*

EXAMPLE 1 Identifying Like Terms

Identify like terms in the list.

$5a \quad \frac{t}{2} \quad 3y^2 \quad 7t \quad x^2 \quad 4z \quad k \quad 4.5y^2 \quad 2t \quad \frac{2}{3}a$

Look for like variables with like powers.

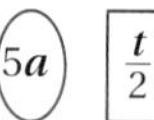

$5a \quad \frac{t}{2} \quad 3y^2 \quad 7t \quad x^2 \quad 4z \quad k \quad 4.5y^2 \quad 2t \quad \frac{2}{3}a$

Like terms: $5a$ and $\frac{2}{3}a$ $\quad \frac{t}{2}$, $7t$, and $2t$ $\quad 3y^2$ and $4.5y^2$

Helpful Hint

Use different shapes or colors to indicate sets of like terms.

1 Introduce

Alternate Opener

EXPLORATION

2-9 Combining Like Terms

Philipe is organizing the storerooms at an athletic club. He finds **3 cases** and **2 cans** of tennis balls in one room and **5 cases** and **6 cans** of tennis balls in another room. He combines them and has **8 cases** and **8 cans**.

You can represent this situation with algebra tiles and with symbols.

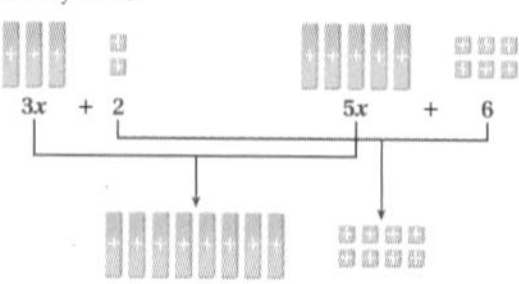

Draw algebra tiles to represent each expression, and combine like terms.

1. $4x + 6x$
2. $5x + 2 + 7x$
3. $x + 1 + 2x + 7$
4. $3x + 4 + 3x + 5$

Think and Discuss

5. **Discuss** your method for combining like terms.
6. **Explain** what you could combine when adding $3x + 2 + 5x$.

Motivate

To introduce students to combining like terms, discuss real-world situations that involve objects of different types (e.g., buying adult and student tickets for a movie). Discuss the fact that objects of the same type can be combined but different types cannot.

Exploration worksheet and answers on Chapter 2 Resource Book pp. 82–83 and 146

2 Teach

Lesson Presentation

Guided Instruction

In this lesson, students learn to combine like terms. You may use Teaching Transparency T31, provided in the Chapter 2 Resource Book. Be certain that students can name the coefficient and the variable parts of a term. Students locate like terms by searching for identical variables—the variables and their exponents must match. Students combine like terms by adding or subtracting coefficients.

Teaching Tip Remind students what x^2 and x^3 mean to help them see that these terms are not like terms and cannot be combined: $x^2 = x \cdot x$ and $x^3 = x \cdot x \cdot x$.

Combining like terms is like grouping similar objects.

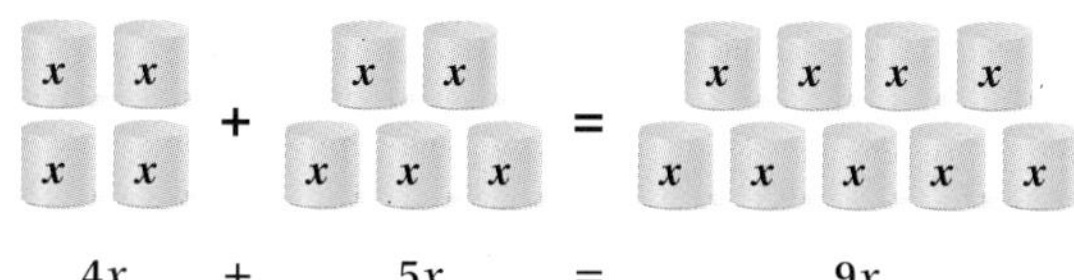

To combine like terms that have variables, add or subtract the coefficients.

EXAMPLE 2 Combining Like Terms

Combine like terms.

A $7x + 2x$

$7x + 2x$ — *7x and 2x are like terms.*

$9x$ — *Add the coefficients.*

B $5x^3 + 3y + 7x^3 - 2y - 4x^2$

$5x^3 + 3y + 7x^3 - 2y - 4x^2$ — *Identify like terms.*

$(5x^3 + 7x^3) + (3y - 2y) - 4x^2$ — *Group like terms.*

$12x^3 + y - 4x^2$ — *Add or subtract the coefficients.*

C $3a + 4a^2 + 2b$

In this expression, there are no like terms to combine.

EXAMPLE 3 *Geometry Application*

Remember!

To find the perimeter of a figure, add the lengths of the sides.

Write an expression for the perimeter of the rectangle shown. Combine like terms in the expression.

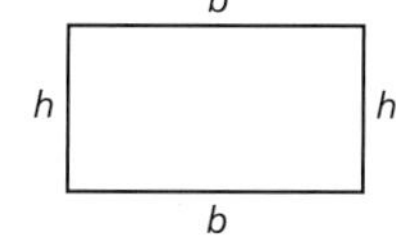

$b + h + b + h$ — *Write an expression using the side lengths.*

$(b + b) + (h + h)$ — *Identify and group like terms.*

$2b + 2h$ — *Add the coefficients.*

Think and Discuss

1. **Identify** the variable and the coefficient in each term.
   a. $11t$ b. $-3a$ c. $\frac{x}{2}$ d. $\frac{4}{5}n$
2. **Explain** whether $5x$, $5x^2$, and $5x^3$ are like terms.
3. **Explain** how you know which terms to combine in an expression.

COMMON ERROR ALERT

In combining like terms, students might neglect to add single variables. Remind students that x is $1x$, so adding x to another x term increases the coefficient by 1.

Additional Examples

Example 1

Identify like terms.

$3t \quad 5w^2 \quad 7t \quad 9v \quad 4w^2 \quad 8v$

Like terms: $3t$ and $7t$, $5w^2$ and $4w^2$, $9v$ and $8v$

Example 2

Combine like terms.

A. $6t - 4t$ — $2t$

B. $45x - 37y + 87$ — no like terms

C. $3a^2 + 5b + 11b^2 - 4b + 2a^2 - 6$ — $5a^2 + b + 11b^2 - 6$

Example 3

Write an expression for the perimeter of the triangle shown. Combine like terms in the expression.

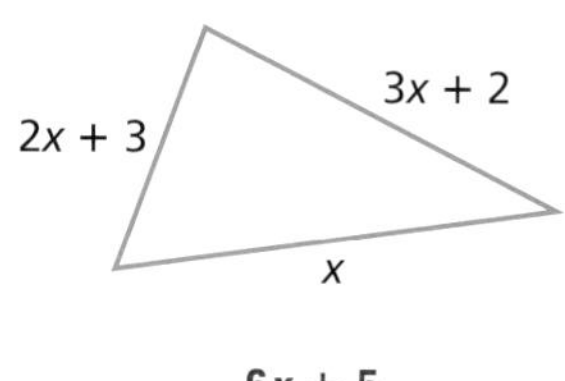

$6x + 5$

3 Close

Reaching All Learners
Through Concrete Manipulatives

Provide students with algebra tiles (provided in the Manipulatives Kit and on Chapter Resource Book p. 129). Distinguish the x from the y, and then let students model the following expressions.

$3x + 2x + 5$	$5x + 5$
$2y^2 + 4y^2 + 8 + 3$	$6y^2 + 11$
$2y + 3y + 2y^2 + 4x$	$2y^2 + 5y + 4x$

Students should combine tiles of the same type to create simplified models of the expressions. Then have the students write the simplifed expressions.

Summarize

You may wish to have the students explain *like terms* and *combining like terms* in their own words.

Possible answers: *Like terms* are terms that have the same variables raised to the same powers. To *combine like terms,* add or subtract the coefficients but keep the variables and exponents the same.

Answers to Think and Discuss

1. a. The variable is t; the coefficient is 11.
   b. The variable is a; the coefficient is -3.
   c. The variable is x; the coefficient is $\frac{1}{2}$.
   d. The variable is n; the coefficient is $\frac{4}{5}$.
2. Possible answer: $5x$, $5x^2$, and $5x^3$ are not like terms because the exponent is different in each term.
3. Possible answer: You can combine terms that have the same variable raised to the same power.

2-9 PRACTICE & ASSESS

Students may want to refer back to the lesson examples.

Assignment Guide

If you finished Example 1 assign:
Core 1, 2, 7–10, 36–44
Enriched 1, 2, 7–10, 36–44

If you finished Example 2 assign:
Core 1–5, 7–16, 19–25 odd, 36–44
Enriched 1–15 odd, 18–26, 36–44

If you finished Example 3 assign:
Core 1–17, 19–31 odd, 36–44
Enriched 1–17 odd, 18–44

Notes

2-9 Exercises

FOR EXTRA PRACTICE
see page 659

internet connect
Homework Help Online
go.hrw.com Keyword: MS4 2-9

GUIDED PRACTICE

See Example 1 — Identify like terms in each list.

1. $6b \quad 5x^2 \quad 4x^3 \quad \frac{b}{2} \quad x^2 \quad 2e$ **$6b$ and $\frac{b}{2}$, $5x^2$ and x^2**
2. $12a^2 \quad 4x^3 \quad b \quad 4a^2 \quad 3.5x^3 \quad \frac{5}{6}b$ **$12a^2$ and $4a^2$, $4x^3$ and $3.5x^3$, b and $\frac{5}{6}b$**

See Example 2 — Combine like terms.

3. $5x + 3x$ **$8x$**
4. $6a^2 - a^2 + 16$ **$5a^2 + 16$**
5. $4a^2 + 5a + 14b$ **There are no like terms.**

See Example 3

6. Write an expression for the perimeter of the rectangle. Combine like terms in the expression. **$10n + 12b$**

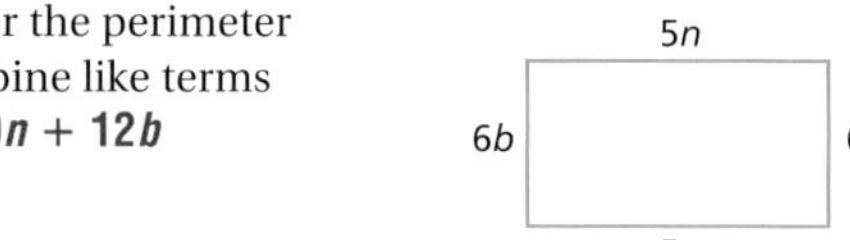

INDEPENDENT PRACTICE

See Example 1 — Identify like terms in each list.

7. $2b \quad b^6 \quad b \quad x^4 \quad 3b^6 \quad 2x^2$ **b^6 and $3b^6$, $2b$ and b**
8. $6 \quad 2n \quad 3n^2 \quad 6m^2 \quad \frac{n}{4} \quad 7$ **$2n$ and $\frac{n}{4}$, 6 and 7**
9. $10k^2 \quad m \quad 3^3 \quad \frac{p}{6} \quad 2m \quad 2$ **m and $2m$, 3^3 and 2**
10. $6^3 \quad y^3 \quad 3y^2 \quad 6^2 \quad y \quad 5y^3$ **6^3 and 6^2, y^3 and $5y^3$**

See Example 2 — Combine like terms.

11. $3a + 2b + 5a$ **$8a + 2b$**
12. $a + 2b + 2a + b + 2c$ **$3a + 3b + 2c$**
13. $5b + 7b + 10$ **$12b + 10$**
14. $y + 4 + 2x + 3y$ **$2x + 4y + 4$**
15. $18 + 2d^3 + d + 3d$ **$18 + 2d^3 + 4d$**
16. $q^2 + 2q + 2q^2$ **$3q^2 + 2q$**

See Example 3

17. Write an expression for the perimeter of the given figure. Combine like terms in the expression. **$11a + 4n$**

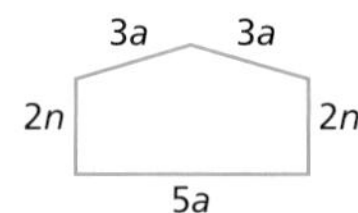

PRACTICE AND PROBLEM SOLVING

Combine like terms.

18. $4x + 5x$ **$9x$**
19. $32y - 5y$ **$27y$**
20. $4c^2 + 5c + 2c$ **$4c^2 + 7c$**
21. $5d^2 - 3d^2 + d$ **$2d^2 + d$**
22. $5f^2 + 2f + f^2$ **$6f^2 + 2f$**
23. $7x + 8x^2 - 3y$ **no like terms**
24. $p + 9q + 9 + 14p$ **$15p + 9q + 9$**
25. $6b + 6b^2 + 4b^3$ **no like terms**
26. $a^2 + 2b + 2a^2 + b + 2c$ **$3a^2 + 3b + 2c$**
27. Write an expression that has four terms and simplifies to $16x + 5$ when you combine like terms. **Possible answer: $8x + 2 + 8x + 3$**
28. At a bake sale, Emily sold 4 pies, and Mark sold 3 pies and 2 cakes. Write an algebraic expression describing how many items they sold.

28. Possible answer: $4p + 3p + 2c$

Math Background

Combining like terms is actually an application of the Associative, Commutative, and Distributive Properties.

$x + (3x + 2) + (2x + 3)$	
$x + 3x + (2 + 2x) + 3$	Associative
$x + 3x + (2x + 2) + 3$	Commutative
$(x + 3x + 2x) + (2 + 3)$	Associative
$x(1 + 3 + 2) + (2 + 3)$	Distributive
$x(6) + (5)$	Addition
$6x + 5$	Commutative

Students who are bothered by the rearrangement of terms should be reminded that these properties allow us to rearrange problems for easier calculation.

RETEACH 2-9

LESSON 2-9 **Reteach**
Combining Like Terms

Look at the following expressions: $x = 1x$
$x + x = 2x$
$x + x + x = 3x$

The numbers 1, 2, and 3 are called **coefficients** of x.

Identify each coefficient.

1. $3n$ **3**
2. $7y$ **7**
3. m **1**
4. 9 **0**

An algebraic expression has terms that are separated by + and −.
In the expression $2x + 5y$, the **terms** are $2x$ and $5y$.

Expression	Terms
$8x + 4y$	$8x$ and $4y$
$m - 3n$	m and $3n$
$4a^2 - 2b + a$	$4a^2$, $2b$, and a
$6d + 2p$	$6d$ and $2p$

Sometimes the terms of an expression can be combined.
Only **like terms** can be combined.

$7w + w$	like terms
$2x - 2y + 2$	unlike terms because x and y are different variables
$8e - 3e + 2e$	like terms
$5d + 25g$	unlike terms because d and g are different variables

To simplify an expression:
Step 1: Combine like terms.
Step 2: Add or subtract the coefficients of the variable.

$7w + w = 8w$
$6y + 1 - 3y = 3y + 1$

Combine like terms.

5. $y + 5y$ **$6y$**
6. $9x - 4x$ **$5x$**
7. $5s - 2s$ **$3s$**
8. $3d + 7d$ **$10d$**
9. $3b + b + 6$ **$4b + 6$**
10. $8a - a - 3$ **$7a - 3$**
11. $2p + 4p + r$ **$6p + r$**
12. $9b - 8b + c$ **$b + c$**

PRACTICE 2-9

LESSON 2-9 **Practice B**
Combining Like Terms

Identify like terms.

1. $3a \quad b^2 \quad b^3 \quad 4b^2 \quad 4 \quad 5a$
$3a$ and $5a$; b^2 and $4b^2$
2. $x \quad x^4 \quad 4x \quad 4x^2 \quad 4x^4 \quad 3x^2$
x and $4x$; x^4 and $4x^4$; $4x^2$ and $3x^2$
3. $6m \quad 6m^2 \quad n^2 \quad 2n \quad 2 \quad 4m \quad 5n$
$6m$ and $4m$; $2n$ and $5n$
4. $12s \quad 7s^4 \quad 9s \quad s^2 \quad 5 \quad 5s^4 \quad 2$
$12s$ and $9s$; $7s^4$ and $5s^4$; 5 and 2

Combine like terms.

5. $2p + 22q^2 - p$ **$p + 22q^2$**
6. $x^2 + 3x^2 - 4^2$ **$4x^2 - 16$**
7. $n^4 + n^3 + 3n - n - n^3$ **$n^4 + 2n$**
8. $4a + 4b + 2 - 2a + 5b - 1$ **$2a + 9b + 1$**
9. $32m^2 + 14n^2 - 12m^2 + 5n - 3$ **$20m^2 + 14n^2 + 5n - 3$**
10. $2h^2 + 3g - 2h^2 + 2^2 - 3 + 4g$ **$7g + 1$**
11. Write an expression for the perimeter of the figure at right. Combine like terms in the expression. **$2v + 8s + 5$**

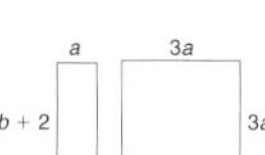

12. Write an expression for the combined perimeters of the figures at right. Combine like terms in the expression. **$14a + 2b + 4$**

a
3a
b + 2
3a

29. Write an expression for the perimeter of the given triangle. Then evaluate the perimeter when n is 1, 2, 3, 4, and 5.

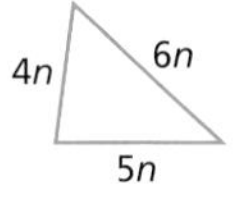

n	1	2	3	4	5
Perimeter					

expression $4n + 5n + 6n = 15n$; 15, 30, 45, 60, 75

Twenty-three grocery baggers competed in the 2002 National Best Bagger Competition.

30. ***BUSINESS*** Ashley earns \$8 per hour working at a grocery store. Last week she worked h hours bagging groceries and twice as many hours stocking shelves. Write an expression for the amount of money Ashley earned last week and combine like terms. **$8h + 8(2h)$; $24h$**

31. ***BUSINESS*** Brad makes d dollars per hour as a cook at a deli. The table shows the number of hours he worked each week in June.

Hours Brad Worked in June	
Week	Hours
1	21.5
2	23
3	15.5
4	19

a. Write an expression for the amount of money Brad earned in June. Combine like terms in the expression.

b. Evaluate your expression from part **a** for d = \$9.50. **\$750.50**

c. What does your answer to part **b** represent? **the amount Brad earned in June**

31. a. $21.5d + 23d + 15.5d + 19d$; $79d$

32. The terms $23x$, $23x^2$, $6y^2$, $18x$, y^2 and one other term can be written in an expression which, when simplified, equals $5x + 7y^2$. Identify the missing term from the list and write the expression. **$23x^2$; $23x + 23x^2 + 6y^2 - 18x + y^2 - 23x^2$**

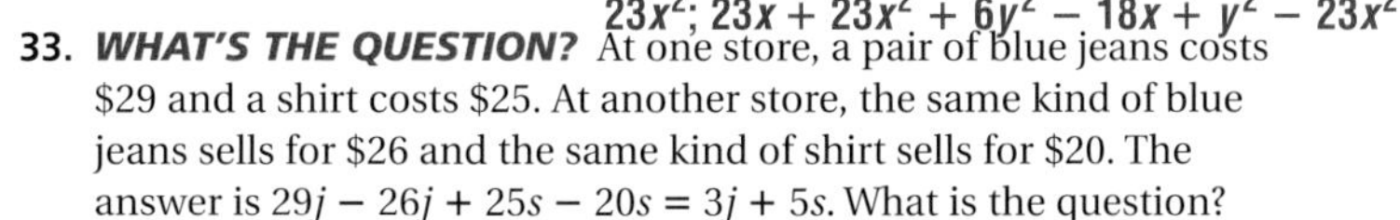

33. ***WHAT'S THE QUESTION?*** At one store, a pair of blue jeans costs \$29 and a shirt costs \$25. At another store, the same kind of blue jeans sells for \$26 and the same kind of shirt sells for \$20. The answer is $29j - 26j + 25s - 20s = 3j + 5s$. What is the question?

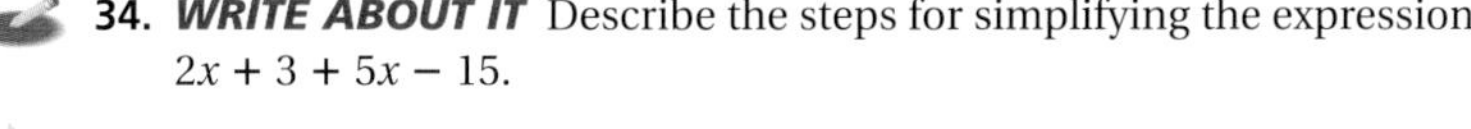

34. ***WRITE ABOUT IT*** Describe the steps for simplifying the expression $2x + 3 + 5x - 15$.

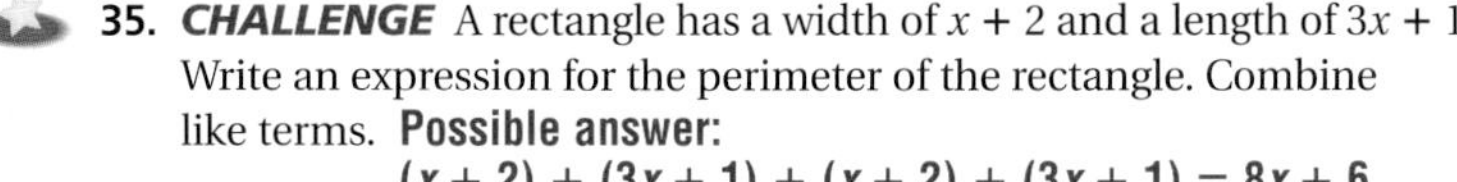

35. ***CHALLENGE*** A rectangle has a width of $x + 2$ and a length of $3x + 1$. Write an expression for the perimeter of the rectangle. Combine like terms. **Possible answer: $(x + 2) + (3x + 1) + (x + 2) + (3x + 1) = 8x + 6$**

Spiral Review

Write each number using an exponent and the given base. (Lesson 2-1)

36. 343, base 7 **7^3**
37. 243, base 3 **3^5**
38. 36, base 6 **6^2**
39. 125, base 5 **5^3**

Find the greatest common factor (GCF). (Lesson 2-5)

40. 45, 54 **9**
41. 81, 36 **9**
42. 84, 48 **12**
43. 132, 44 **44**

44. **TEST PREP** What is the value of $7t$ for $t = 9$? (Lesson 2-7) **D**

A 16 B 54 C 61 D 63

Answers

33. Possible answer: What is the difference between the cost of buying both shirts and jeans from one store and the cost of buying them from the other store?

34. Add the coefficients of the x terms. Then combine the numbers: $7x - 12$.

Journal 

Have students describe a situation in which they might have to count different types of objects. Ask them to distinguish between the like and the unlike terms.

Test Prep Doctor 

Exercise 44 asks students to evaluate a simple algebraic expression. Remind students of the importance of being able to recall basic math facts quickly to save time on tests. If students choose **A,** remind them that a coefficient with a variable is a product and not a sum.

CHALLENGE 2-9

LESSON 2-9 **Challenge**
Matching Terms

Draw a line from each set of terms in Column A to its equivalent combination in Column B. Then circle each letter in Column B that does not have a matching term. Unscramble those letters to answer the riddle.

Column A	Column B
1. $2x + 7 + 5x - 4 - x$	A. $5y + 9x + 12$
2. $5 + 7x + 2x - 3 + 6$	B. $12y + 6x + 24$
3. $x + y + 4x - 3x + 2y + 3y$	C. 15
4. $3x^2 + 5x - 17 + 6x + 20$	D. $9x + 8$
5. $4x + x^2 + 12 - 4 + 2x$	E. 4
6. $12y + 12x + 12 - 6x + 12$	F. $6x + 3$
7. $12y + 4 + x - 7y + 8 + 8x$	G. $11x + y + 7$
8. $5x + x^2 + 2x + 5 - 4 - x^2$	H. $x^2 + 6x + 8$
9. $5x^2 + 8x + 7x^2 + 6x$	I. $4x$
10. $12x + 6 - 8x - 4x - 3 + 12$	J. $3x^2 + 11x + 3$
11. $5x + 4 - 3x + 5 + 2x - 9$	K. $3x + 2$
12. $4x + 2y + 8 - 3 - y - x$	L. $3x^2$
13. $4x + 5 + 7x + 2y + 2 - y$	M. $6x$
14. $2y + 2x + 8 - 6 + x - 2y$	N. $x^2 + 3x$
15. $4x + 6y + 6 + 7x + y$	O. $6x^2 + 6y + 1$
16. $3x^2 + 4x - 2x^2 - 3x + 2x$	P. $12x^2 + 14x$
17. $8x + 4 - 4 - 4x + x$	Q. $7x + 1$
18. $y + 5x + 6y + 9 - 6$	R. x^2
19. $x^2 + 3 + 2x^2 + 4 - 7$	S. $5x + 7y + 3$
20. $5y + 3 + 7x^2 - 2 - x^2 + y$	T. 0
	U. $2x + 6y$
	V. $3x + y + 5$
	W. $11x + 7y + 6$
	X. $5x$

Riddle: What can be a word, a number, a period of time, or a variable?

A **T** **E** **R** **M**

PROBLEM SOLVING 2-9

LESSON 2-9 **Problem Solving**
Combining Like Terms

Write the correct answer. Use the figures for Problems 1–3.

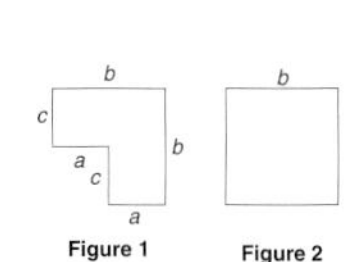

Figure 1 Figure 2

1. Figure 1 shows the length of each side of a garden. Write an expression for the perimeter of the garden.

$2a + 2b + 2c$

2. Figure 2 is a square swimming pool. Write an expression to show the perimeter of the pool.

$4b$

3. Write an expression for the combined perimeter of the garden and the pool.

$2a + 6b + 2c$

4. The Pantheon in Rome has n granite columns in each of 3 rows. Write an addition expression to show the number of columns, then combine like terms and evaluate the expression for $n = 8$.

$n + n + n$; $3n = 24$; 24 columns

Choose the letter for the best answer.

5. Which is an expression that shows the earnings of a telemarketer who worked for 23 hours at a salary of d dollars per hour?

A $d + 23$ (B) $23d$ C $d \div 23$ D $23 \div d$

6. The minimum wage in 1997 was \$5.15 per hour. Evaluate the expression $40h$ where h = \$5.15 to find a worker's weekly salary.

F \$20.60 G \$200 H \$515.00 (J) \$206.00

7. What is the perimeter of a triangle with sides the following lengths: $2a + 4c$, $3c + 7$, and $6a - 4$. Combine like terms in the expression.

A $8a + 11c$
B $6a + 7c + 3$
(C) $8a + 7c + 3$
D $8a + 7c + 11$

8. A hexagon is a 6-sided figure. Find the perimeter of a hexagon where all of the sides are the same length. The expression $x + y$ represents the length of a side. Combine like terms in the expression.

(F) $6x + 6y$
G $6 + x + y$
H $6x + y$
J $6xy$

Lesson Quiz 

Identify like terms.

1. $3n^2$ $5n$ $2n^3$ $8n$ **$5n$, $8n$**

2. a^5 $2a^2$ a^3 $3a$ $4a^2$ **$2a^2$, $4a^2$**

Combine like terms.

3. $4a + 3b + 2a$ **$6a + 3b$**

4. $x^2 + 2y + 8x^2$ **$9x^2 + 2y$**

5. Write an expression for the perimeter of the given figure. **$6x + 8y$**

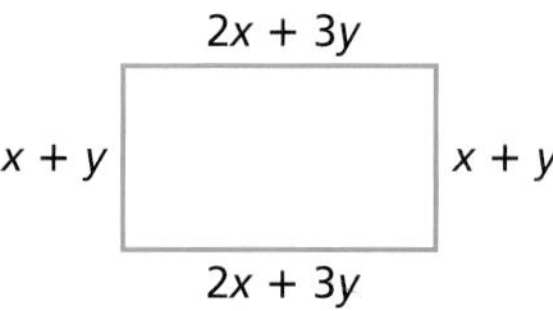

Available on Daily Transparency in CRB

2-10 Organizer

Pacing: Traditional 1 day
Block $\frac{1}{2}$ day

Objective: Students determine whether a number is a solution of an equation.

Warm Up

Evaluate each expression for $x = 12$.

1. $x + 2$	14	**2.** $\frac{x}{4}$	3		
3. $x - 8$	4	**4.** $10x - 4$	116		
5. $2x + 12$	36	**6.** $5x + 7$	67		

Problem of the Day

Alicia buys buttons at a cost of 8 for $20. She in turn resells them in her shop for $5 each. How many buttons does Alicia need to sell in order to make a profit of $120? 48 buttons

Available on Daily Transparency in CRB

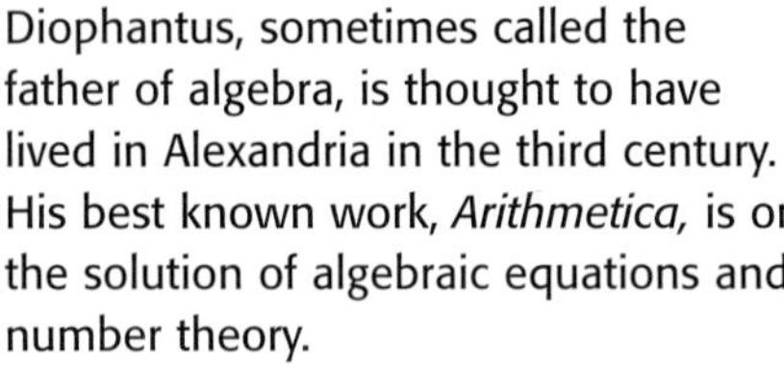

Math Fact !!

Diophantus, sometimes called the father of algebra, is thought to have lived in Alexandria in the third century. His best known work, *Arithmetica,* is on the solution of algebraic equations and number theory.

2-10 Equations and Their Solutions

Learn to determine whether a number is a solution of an equation.

Vocabulary
equation
solution

Nicole has 82 CDs. This is 9 more than her friend Jessica has.

This situation can be written as an *equation.* An **equation** is a mathematical statement that two expressions are equal in value.

An equation is like a balanced scale.

Number of CDs Nicole has	is equal to	9 more than Jessica has.
82	=	$j + 9$

Left expression — Right expression

Just as the weights on both sides of a balanced scale are exactly the same, the expressions on both sides of an equation represent exactly the same value.

When an equation contains a variable, a value of the variable that makes the statement true is called a **solution** of the equation.

Reading Math
The symbol ≠ means "is not equal to."

$x + 3 = 10$ $x = 7$ is a solution because $7 + 3 = 10$.

$12 = t + 9$ $t = 4$ is not a solution because $12 \neq 4 + 9$.

EXAMPLE 1 Determining Whether a Number Is a Solution of an Equation

Determine whether each number is a solution of $18 = s - 7$.

A 11

$18 = s - 7$

$18 \stackrel{?}{=} 11 - 7$ *Substitute 11 for s.*

$18 \stackrel{?}{=} 4$ ✗

11 **is not** a solution of $18 = s - 7$.

B 25

$18 = s - 7$

$18 \stackrel{?}{=} 25 - 7$ *Substitute 25 for s.*

$18 \stackrel{?}{=} 18$ ✓

25 **is** a solution of $18 = s - 7$.

1 Introduce

Alternate Opener

EXPLORATION

2-10 Equations and Their Solutions

Marie spent $2. She has $5 left. How much did she have before she spent the $2?

The equation $x - 2 = 5$ represents the problem.

Because $7 - 2 = 5$ is a true statement, $x = 7$.

The solution to the equation $x - 2 = 5$ is 7, and the answer to the question is $7.

1. Make up three real-world problems that have 7 for an answer.
2. Write three equations that represent your problems in number 1.

Think and Discuss

3. **Explain** what a solution to an equation is.
4. **Describe** how to determine whether 75 is a solution to the equation $25 = 100 - x$.

Motivate

Display a balance scale (Teaching Transparency T35 provided in the Chapter 2 Resource Book) to introduce students to equations and their solutions. Ask students how they would find the weight of an object placed on one pan of the balance. Then have them explain how they will know when they have found the correct weight. Lead students to conclude that the scale will balance when the correct, or matching, weight is placed in the second balance pan.

Exploration worksheet and answers on Chapter 2 Resource Book pp. 92 and 148

2 Teach

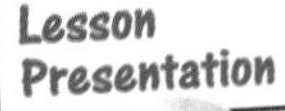

Lesson Presentation

Guided Instruction

In this lesson, students learn to determine whether a given number is a solution of an equation. Teach students to evaluate the side of the equation containing the variable by substituting a given value of the variable, and to determine whether the value of that expression matches the number on the other side of the equal sign. If so, the given value of the variable is a solution.

Teaching Tip After several examples, students might ask if there is only one solution for each equation. While most equations will have only one solution, there are equations that have more than one solution and equations that have no solution.

EXAMPLE 2 ***Consumer Application***

Nicole has 82 CDs. This is 9 more than her friend Jessica has. The equation 82 = j + 9 can be used to represent the number of CDs Jessica has. Does Jessica have 91 CDs, 85 CDs, or 73 CDs?

91 CDs

$82 = j + 9$

$82 \stackrel{?}{=} 91 + 9$ *Substitute 91 for j.*

$82 \stackrel{?}{=} 100$ ✗

85 CDs

$82 = j + 9$

$82 \stackrel{?}{=} 85 + 9$ *Substitute 85 for j.*

$82 \stackrel{?}{=} 94$ ✗

73 CDs

$82 = j + 9$

$82 \stackrel{?}{=} 73 + 9$ *Substitute 73 for j.*

$82 \stackrel{?}{=} 82$ ✓

Jessica has 73 CDs.

EXAMPLE 3 **Writing an Equation to Determine Whether a Number Is a Solution**

Tyler wants to buy a new skateboard. He has $57, which is $38 less than he needs. Does the skateboard cost $90 or $95?

If s represents the price of the skateboard, then $s - 38 = 57$.

$90

$s - 38 = 57$

$90 - 38 \stackrel{?}{=} 57$ *Substitute 90 for s.*

$52 \stackrel{?}{=} 57$ ✗

$95

$s - 38 = 57$

$95 - 38 \stackrel{?}{=} 57$ *Substitute 95 for s.*

$57 \stackrel{?}{=} 57$ ✓

The skateboard costs $95.

Think and Discuss

1. **Compare** equations with expressions.
2. **Give an example** of an equation whose solution is 5.

COMMON ERROR ALERT

Watch for students who do not recognize equivalent expressions. Remind students to use the order of operations and to simplify fractions completely. While a value may not appear to be a solution, simplifying the expression may prove that both sides are identical.

Additional Examples

Example 1

Determine whether each number is a solution of $t + 9 = 17$.

A. 26

26 is not a solution of $t + 9 = 17$.

B. 8

8 is a solution of $t + 9 = 17$.

Example 2

The Bulldogs scored 84 points in a game, 12 points more than the Hawks scored. The equation $84 = h + 12$ can be used to represent the number of points the Hawks scored. Did the Hawks score 96 points or 72 points?

The Hawks scored 72 points.

Example 3

Mrs. Jenkins had $32 when she returned home from grocery shopping. If she spent $17 at the supermarket, did she have $52 or $49 before she went shopping?

Mrs. Jenkins had $49 before she went shopping.

3 Close

Reaching All Learners
Through Critical Thinking

Present the equation $x = x$. Ask students to determine whether $x = 7$ or $x = 45$ is a solution. Encourage students to think of other solutions. Then present this equation: $y = y + 1$. Have students try these values as solutions: $y = 4$ and $y = 23$. Ask students if they can think of any solution for the equation.

Both $x = 7$ and $x = 45$ are solutions of $x = x$. All numbers are solutions of this equation, which is called an identity. Neither $y = 4$ nor $y = 23$ is a solution of $y = y + 1$. The equation has no solution.

Summarize

You may wish to have students explain in their own words how they would determine if a given value is a solution of an equation. Extend the discussion by asking students how they might use the fact that a certain value is not a solution to help them find the solution.

Possible answer: Substitute the value for the variable and simplify. If the answer is larger than the number on the other side, try a smaller value for the variable. If the answer is too small, try a larger number.

Answers to Think and Discuss

Possible answers:

1. An equation compares two values and says that they are equal. An expression is used to find a single value and does not compare it to any other value.
2. $x + 3 = 8$

2-10 PRACTICE & ASSESS

Students may want to refer back to the lesson examples.

Assignment Guide

If you finished Example 1 assign:
Core 1–4, 7–14, 17–25 odd, 33–41
Enriched 1, 3, 7–13 odd, 17–26, 33–41

If you finished Example 2 assign:
Core 1–5, 7–15, 17–29 odd, 33–41
Enriched 1–15 odd, 17–30, 33–41

If you finished Example 3 assign:
Core 1–16, 17–29 odd, 33–41
Enriched 1–5 odd, 6, 7–15 odd, 16–41

Notes

Math Background

The essence of most methods of solving equations is intelligent application of "guess and check." Methods used in practice usually combine applications of general principles with checking explicit values.

2-10 Exercises

FOR EXTRA PRACTICE
see page 659

internet connect
Homework Help Online
go.hrw.com Keyword: MS4 2-10

GUIDED PRACTICE

See Example 1 — **Determine whether each number is a solution of $19 = x + 4$.**

1. 5 **no** **2.** 14 **no** **3.** 15 **yes** **4.** 23 **no**

See Example 2 — **5.** Nancy has 94 baseball cards. This is 6 more than Claire has. The equation $94 = c + 6$ can be used to represent the number of baseball cards Claire has. Does Claire have 88 or 93 baseball cards? **88 cards**

See Example 3 — **6.** Mavis wants to buy a book. She has \$25, which is \$9 less than she needs. Does the book cost \$34 or \$38? **\$34**

INDEPENDENT PRACTICE

See Example 1 — **Determine whether each number is a solution of $24 = 34 - n$.**

7. 58 **no** **8.** 20 **no** **9.** 14 **no** **10.** 10 **yes**

Determine whether each number is a solution of $p + 18 = 29$.

11. 18 **no** **12.** 11 **yes** **13.** 9 **no** **14.** 47 **no**

See Example 2 — **15.** Nadia has 47 video games. This is 6 less than Benjamin has. The equation $47 = v - 6$ can be used to represent the number of video games Benjamin has. Does Benjamin have 39, 41, or 53 video games? **53 video games**

See Example 3 — **16.** Curtis wants to buy a new snowboard. He has \$119, which is \$56 less than he needs. Does the snowboard cost \$165 or \$175? **\$175**

PRACTICE AND PROBLEM SOLVING

Determine whether each given number is a solution of the given equation.

17. $j = 6$ for $15 - j = 21$ **no**
18. $x = 36$ for $48 = x + 12$ **yes**
19. $m = 18$ for $16 = 34 - m$ **yes**
20. $k = 23$ for $17 + k = 40$ **yes**
21. $y = 8$ for $9y + 2 = 74$ **yes**
22. $c = 12$ for $100 - 2c = 86$ **no**
23. $q = 13$ for $5q + 7 - q = 51$ **no**
24. $w = 15$ for $13w - 2 - 6w = 103$ **yes**
25. $t = 12$ for $3(50 - t) - 10t = 104$ **no**
26. $r = 21$ for $4r - 8 + 9r - 1 = 264$ **yes**

27. Monique has a collection of stamps from 6 different countries. She compared her collection with Jeremy's and found that Jeremy has stamps from 3 fewer countries than she does. Write an equation showing this, using j as the number of countries from which Jeremy has stamps. **Possible answer: $6 - j = 3$**

RETEACH 2-10

LESSON 2-10 **Reteach**
Equations and Their Solutions

Number sentences that contain an equal sign (=) are called **equations.**

Equations may be true, or they may be false.

True	False
$3 + 4 = 7$	$3 + 1 = 7$
$8 - 6 = 2$	$8 - 2 = 5$

An equation may contain a variable.

variable → $x + 4 = 6$

Whether this equation is true or false depends on the value of x.

You can decide if a number is a *solution* of an equation. Substitute the number for the variable in the equation. If the equation is a true equation, then the number is the **solution.**

Equation: $x + 4 = 6$

Is 2 a solution?	Is 3 a solution?
$x + 4 = 6$	$x + 4 = 6$
Substitute 2 for x	Substitute 3 for x
$2 + 4 \stackrel{?}{=} 6$	$3 + 4 \stackrel{?}{=} 6$
$6 \stackrel{?}{=} 6$ True	$7 \stackrel{?}{=} 6$ False
2 is a solution of $x + 4 = 6$.	3 is not a solution of $x + 4 = 6$.

Determine if the number is a solution of the equation.

1. Is 3 a solution of $y + 3 = 9$? **no**
2. Is 4 a solution of $n + 6 = 10$? **yes**
3. Is 2 a solution of $w - 1 = 1$? **yes**
4. Is 1 a solution of $x + 50 = 49$? **no**
5. Is 6 a solution of $c + 23 = 30$? **no**
6. Is 9 a solution of $v - 9 = 0$? **yes**
7. Is 20 a solution of $t - 17 = 3$? **yes**
8. Is 16 a solution of $12 + a = 24$? **no**
9. Is 25 a solution of $38 - m = 13$? **yes**
10. Is 8 a solution of $15 = e + 5$? **no**

PRACTICE 2-10

LESSON 2-10 **Practice B**
Equations and Their Solutions

Determine if each number is a solution of $21 = x - 3$.

1. 18 **no**
2. 26 **no**
3. 17 **no**
4. 24 **yes**

Determine if each number is a solution of $b + 19 = 52$.

5. 71 **no**
6. 3 **no**
7. 33 **yes**
8. 13 **no**

Determine if the given numbers are solutions of the given equations.

9. $k = 24$ for $3k = 6$ **no**
10. $m = 3$ for $42 = m + 39$ **yes**
11. $y = 8$ for $8y + 6 = 70$ **yes**
12. $s = 5$ for $18 = 3s - 3$ **no**
13. $k = 7$ for $23 - k = 30$ **no**
14. $v = 12$ for $84 = 7v$ **yes**
15. $c = 15$ for $45 - 2c = 15$ **yes**
16. $x = 10$ for $x + 25 - 2x + 4 = 19$ **yes**
17. $e = 6$ for $42 = 51 - e$ **no**
18. $p = 15$ for $19 = p - 4$ **no**
19. $h = 9$ for $120 - 3h = 97$ **no**
20. $a = 25$ for $300 = 500 - 8a$ **yes**
21. Earth's diameter is about 7,926 miles. This is about 407 miles greater than the diameter of Venus. The equation $7{,}926 = v + 407$ can be used to represent the length of Venus' diameter. Is the diameter of Venus 8,333 miles or 7,519 miles? **7,519 miles**
22. Jason and Maya have their own Web sites on the Internet. As of last week, Jason's Web site had 2,426 visitors. This is twice as many visitors as Maya had. Did Maya have 1,213 visitors or 4,852 visitors to her Web site? **1,213 visitors**

Earth Science LINK

28. The diagram shows approximate elevations for different climate zones in the Colorado Rockies. Use the diagram to write an equation that shows the vertical distance d from the summit of Mount Evans (14,264 ft) to the tree line, which marks the beginning of the alpine tundra zone. **$10{,}500 + d = 14{,}264$**

Source: Colorado Mall

Maroon Bells in the Colorado Rockies

29. The top wind speed of an F5 tornado, the strongest known kind of tornado, is 246 mi/h faster than the top wind speed of an F1 tornado, the weakest kind of tornado. The top wind speed of an F1 tornado is 72 mi/h. Is the top wind speed of an F5 tornado 174 mi/h, 218 mi/h, or 318 mi/h? **318 mi/h**

30. In 2001, Tropical Storm Allison dropped an estimated 37 inches of rain on Houston in five days. This was only 9 inches less than Houston's average yearly rainfall. Is Houston's average yearly rainfall 28 inches, 46 inches or 49 inches? **46 inches**

31. ***WRITE A PROBLEM*** There has been an increase of about 1°F in the mean surface temperature of Earth from 1861 to 1998. In 1998, the mean surface temperature was about 60°F. Use this information to write a problem involving an equation with a variable. **Possible answer: Solve $t + 1 = 60$ to find the mean temperature of the Earth in 1861.**

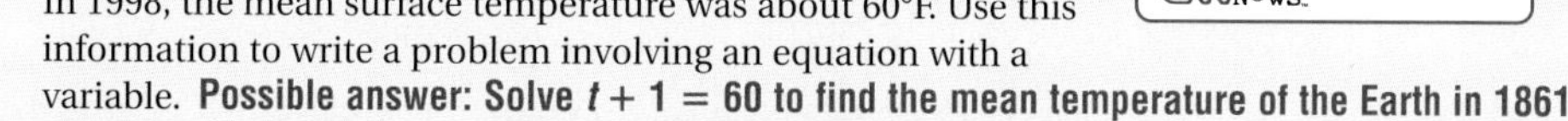

go.hrw.com
KEYWORD: MS4 Storms
CNN Student News

32. ***CHALLENGE*** In the 1980s, about 9.3×10^4 acres of tropical forests were destroyed each year due to deforestation. About how many acres of tropical forests were destroyed during the 1980s? **about 9.3×10^5**

Spiral Review

Evaluate. (Lesson 2-3)

33. $2(4 + 6) \div 5$ **4**
34. $8^2 - 9 \div (6 - 3)$ **61**
35. $14 \cdot 10 + 4 \div 2$ **142**
36. $36 \div 2 - 3 \cdot 6 + 5$ **5**

Write the prime factorization of each number. (Lesson 2-4)

37. 56 **$2^3 \cdot 7$**
38. 72 **$2^3 \cdot 3^2$**
39. 108 **$2^2 \cdot 3^3$**
40. 522 **$2 \cdot 3^2 \cdot 29$**

41. **TEST PREP** Which of the following is **not** a common factor of 24 and 60? (Lesson 2-5) **C**

A 3 B 4 C 5 D 6

Interdisciplinary LINK

Earth Science

Exercises 28–32 involve topics, including climate and global warming, elevation, and minerals, from middle school Earth science programs such as *Holt Science & Technology.*

Journal

Ask students to describe a situation in which they might test possible answers to find a solution to a problem. How would they determine which answer was best?

Test Prep Doctor

In Exercise 41, remind students to use divisibility tests. If the digits of a number add to a multiple of 3, then the number is divisible by 3. Numbers divisible by 5 will end in 5 or 0. By applying the divisibility tests, students can eliminate **A, B,** and **D** as both 24 and 60 are divisible by 3, 4, and 6.

CHALLENGE 2-10

LESSON 2-10 **Challenge**
The Solution Is BINGO!

Find the solution to each problem or equation. Cross it out on the board below to get BINGO!

1. Is 37, 47, or 67 a solution for $52 = n + 15$? **37**
2. Is 14, 17, or 21 a solution for $8y - 7 = 129$? **17**
3. Is 14, 22, or 24 a solution for $132 - (4x - 5) = 81$? **14**
4. Is 12, 15, or 18 a solution for $3(60 - s) - 2s = 105$? **15**
5. Garret scored 18 points in his last basketball game, which is 6 fewer points than Vince scored. The equation $18 = p - 6$ can be used to represent Vince's points. Did Vince score 12, 24, or 28 points? **24**
6. In 3 years, Sarah's sister will be twice as old as Sarah. If Sarah is now 3 years old, will her sister be 6, 9, or 12 years old in 3 years? **12**
7. The highest recorded temperature in Alaska was 100°F in 1915. This was 56 years before the lowest recorded temperature of −80°F. Was the lowest recorded temperature in 1856, 1956, or 1971? **1971**
8. In 1999, Florida had 2,145 elementary schools. This was 288 fewer elementary schools than 3 times the number of elementary schools in South Carolina during the same year. Did South Carolina have 427, 811, or 1,857 elementary schools in 1999? **811**

B	I	N	G	O
~~17~~	67	24	~~37~~	~~1971~~
6	~~24~~	47	1,857	22
427	1956	FREE	18	~~14~~
~~12~~	9	16	~~811~~	1856
28	23	21	19	~~15~~

PROBLEM SOLVING 2-10

LESSON 2-10 **Problem Solving**
Equations and Their Solutions

Write the correct answer.

1. The jet airplane was invented in 1939. This is 12 years after the first television was invented. Was television invented in 1927 or 1951? **1927**
2. There are three times as many students in the high school as in the junior high school, which has 330 students. Does the high school have 990 students or 110 students? **990 students**
3. The frigate bird has been recorded at speeds up to 95 mi/h. The only faster bird ever recorded was the spine-tailed swift at 11 mi/h faster. Was the speed of the spine-tailed swift 84 mi/h or 106 mi/h? **106 mi/h**
4. As of February 2000, 14.6 million households in Canada were online. This is 10.1 million more households online than in Australia. Were 24.7 million or 4.5 million households online in Australia? **4.5 million**

Choose the letter for the best answer.

5. In the United States, the average school year is 180 days. This is 71 days less than the average school year in China. What is the average school year in China?
   (A) 251 days
   B 109 days
   C 151 days
   D 271 days
6. The longest bridge in the world is the Akashi Kaikyo Bridge in Japan. Its main span is 1,290 feet longer than a mile. A mile is 5,280 feet. How long is the Akashi Kaikyo bridge?
   F 3,990 feet
   G 6,400 feet
   H 4,049 feet
   (J) 6,570 feet
7. *Ornithomimus* stood about 6 feet tall and was the fastest dinosaur at a speed of about 50 mi/h. The largest dinosaur, *Seismosaurus,* was 20 times as tall. How tall was *Seismosaurus?*
   A 12 feet
   B 70 feet
   (C) 120 feet
   D 26 feet
8. Milton collects sports trading cards. He has 80 baseball cards. He has half as many basketball cards as football cards. He has 20 more hockey cards than basketball cards and half as many football cards as baseball cards. How many hockey cards does he have?
   F 20 hockey cards
   (G) 40 hockey cards
   H 60 hockey cards
   J 80 hockey cards

Lesson Quiz

Determine if each number is a solution of $5 + x = 47$.

1. $x = 42$ yes **2.** $x = 52$ no

Determine if each number is a solution of $57 - y = 18$.

3. $y = 75$ no **4.** $y = 39$ yes

5. Kwan has 14 marbles. This is 7 more than Drue has. Does Drue have 21 or 7 marbles? 7

Available on Daily Transparency in CRB

2C Model Equations

Pacing: Traditional 1 day
Block $\frac{1}{2}$ day

Objective: To use algebra tiles to model equations

Materials: Algebra tiles

Lab Resources

Hands-On Lab Activities. . pp. 9–11, 126

Using the Pages

Discuss with students what each algebra tile represents and how to model equations with algebra tiles. Make sure students understand that the variable is represented by the long, narrow tile.

Use algebra tiles to model each equation.

1. $x + 4 = 5$

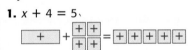

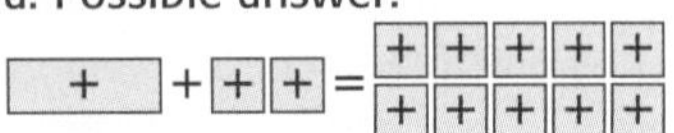

2. $x + 3 = 2$

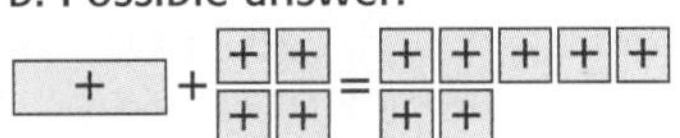

Answers

Activity

1. a. Possible answer:

b. Possible answer:

c. Possible answer:

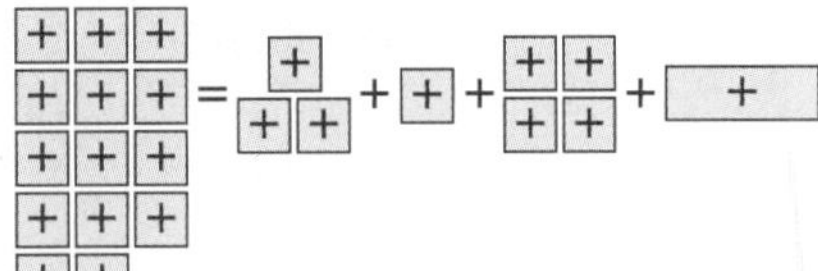

Model Equations

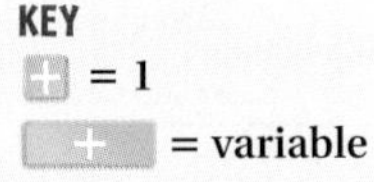

Use with Lesson 2-11

KEY

= 1

= variable

REMEMBER

- In an equation, the expressions on both sides of the equal sign are equivalent.
- A variable can have any value that makes the equation true.
- To solve for a variable, you must get the variable alone on one side of the equal sign.

internet connect
Lab Resources Online
go.hrw.com
KEYWORD: MS4 Lab2C

You can use algebra tiles to model and solve equations involving addition and subtraction.

Activity

Marcus has 16 CDs. If Jill gets 3 more CDs, she will have the same number of CDs as Marcus.

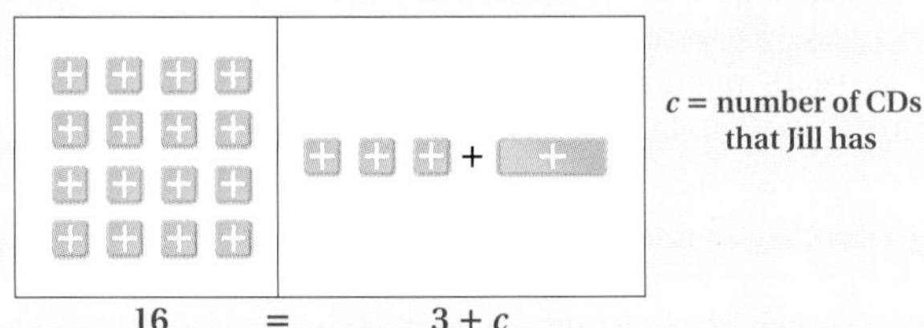

1 Use algebra tiles to model each situation involving addition.

a. Jordan needs 2 more goals to tie the record of 10 goals in a single game.

b. Amy lives 7 miles from school. She lives 4 miles farther from school than Jack does.

c. There are 14 students in the school orchestra. Three students play the trombone, 1 plays the piano, 4 play the violin, and the rest play the drums.

At the county fair, five rides closed down when it started to rain. Only three rides continued to run in the rain.

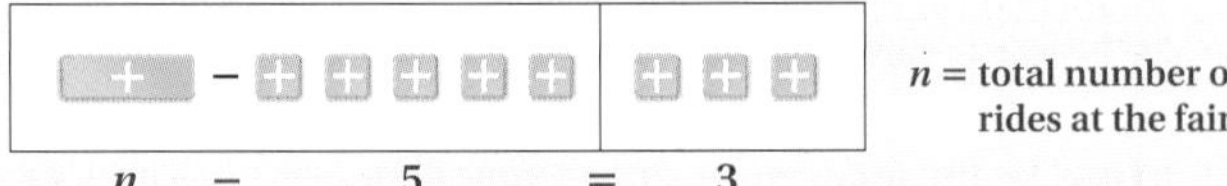

Teacher to Teacher

Susan Nolan
Coshocton, Ohio

A balance scale can provide a good visual introduction to solving equations. I keep a real one on my desk to remind students how to keep it balanced. The balance scale I use to model solving equations is on an overhead transparency. I use plus and minus signs, large *x*'s, and tiles, all made from transparency film.

To model solving the equation $x + 4 = 7$, I place an *x*, a plus sign, and four tiles on one side of the balance scale, and I place seven tiles on the other side. I remind students that what I do to one side of the scale, I must do to the other side to keep it balanced. I then remove four tiles from both sides, and we see that *x* equals 3. The equation balances.

2 Use algebra tiles to model each situation involving subtraction.

a. The French Club sold 15 handmade friendship bracelets on Tuesday for a fund-raiser and had 7 bracelets left over at the end of the day.

b. David caught 6 fish during a fishing trip, but he had to throw 2 of them back because they were too small.

c. Simone made 14 cornbread muffins. Her sister ate 2 of them, her brother ate 3 of them, and Simone ate some also. Then there were only 8 muffins left.

Think and Discuss **Possible answers:**

1. What would you need to do to solve the equation $16 = 3 + c$ with pencil and paper? Remember that to keep an equation equal, you must perform the same operations on both sides. **Subtract 3 from both sides of the equation.**
2. What would you need to do to solve the equation $n - 5 = 3$ with pencil and paper? **Add 5 to both sides of the equation.**
3. How could you check to see whether your solutions were correct? **Substitute the answer into the problem.**

Try This

Use algebra tiles to model each equation.

1. $4 + x = 6$
2. $3 + 5 = n$
3. $5 - r = 9$
4. $n - 9 = 12$
5. $p + 8 = 14$
6. $3 + y = 10$
7. $t - 8 = 3$
8. $11 - 5 = f$
9. $2 + h = 15$
10. $y + 7 = 9$
11. $13 - 7 = g$
12. $12 - c = 6$

Write an algebraic equation for each. **Possible answers:**

13. **$1 + n = 2$**

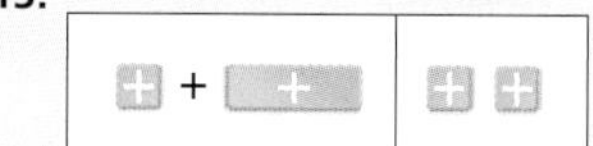

14. **$4 - n = 2$**

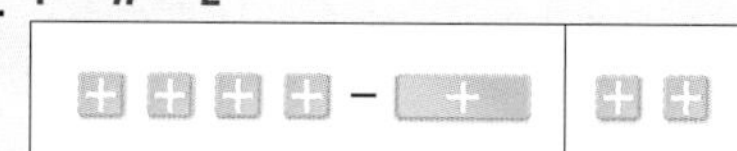

15. **$n - 4 = 2$**

16. **$n + 3 = 5$**

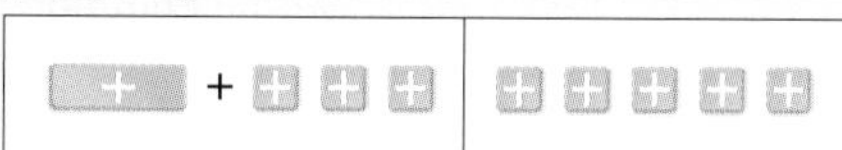

17. **$n = 6 + 2$**

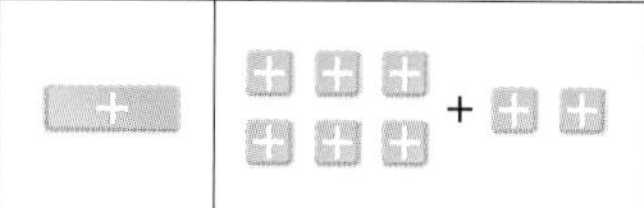

18. **$9 = n + 3$**

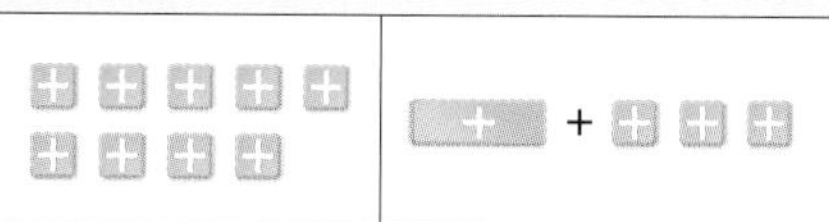

Answers

Activity

2. a. Possible answer:

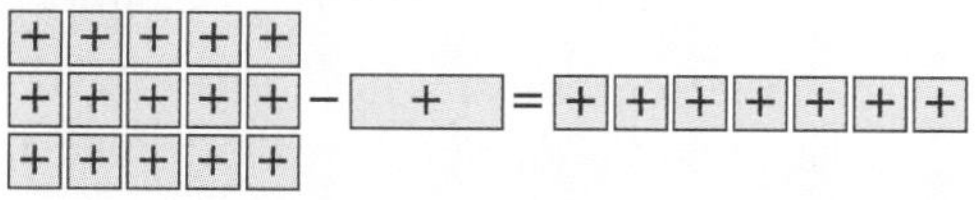

b. Possible answer:

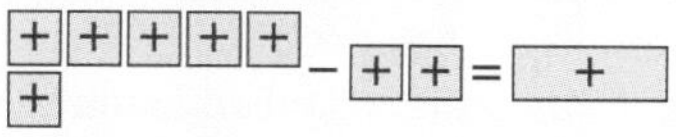

c. Possible answer:

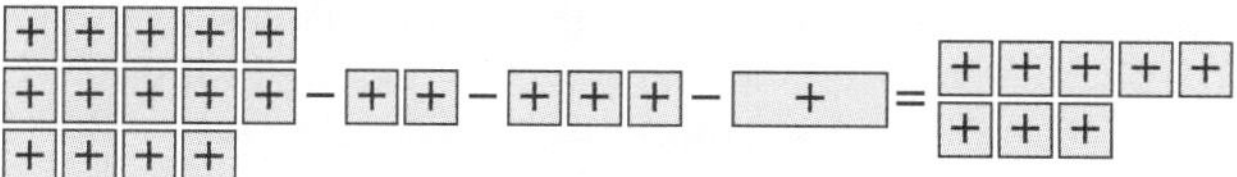

Answers

Try This

Possible answers:

1.

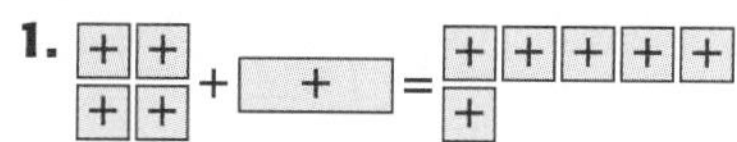

2.

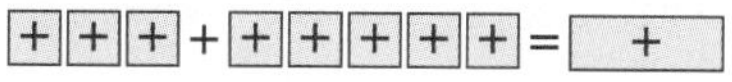

3.

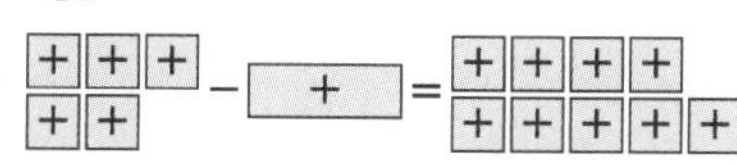

4.

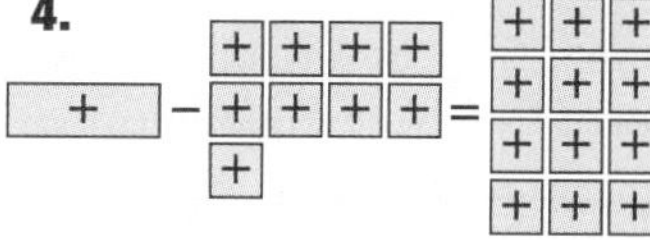

5.

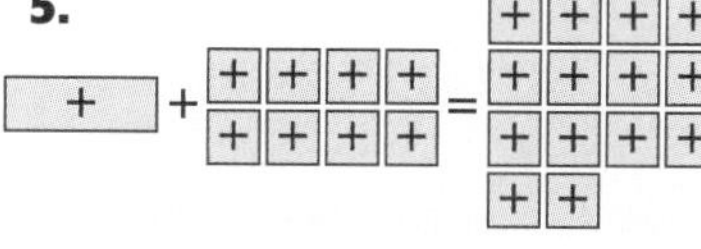

6.

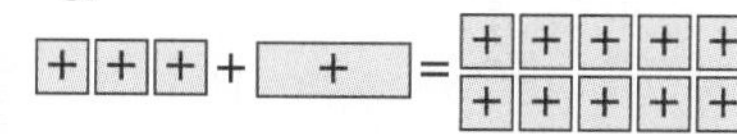

7.

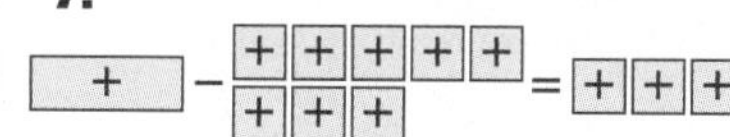

8.

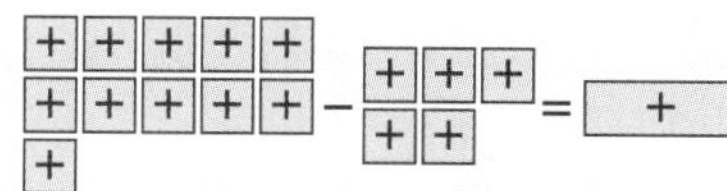

9.

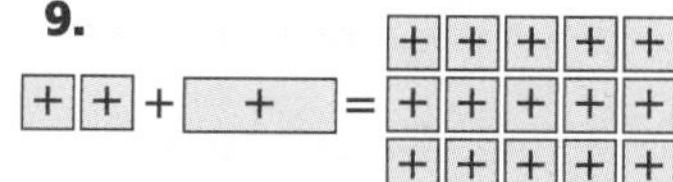

10.

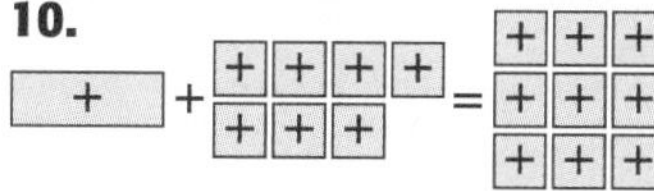

11.

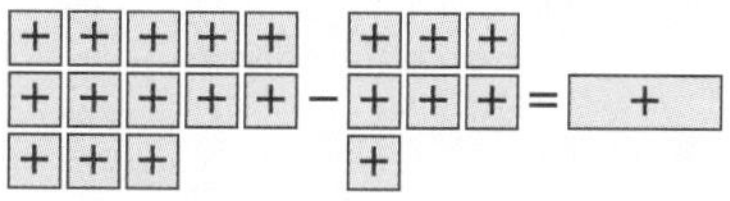

12.

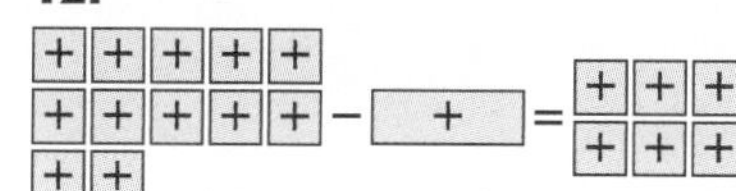

2-11 Organizer

Pacing: Traditional 1 day
Block $\frac{1}{2}$ day

Objective: Students solve one-step equations by using addition or subtraction.

Warm Up

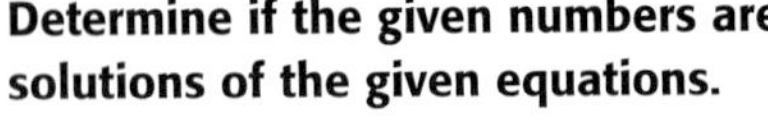

Determine if the given numbers are solutions of the given equations.

1. $y = 9$ for $y - 8 = 1$ yes
2. $x = 2$ for $4x = 9$ no
3. $x = 5$ for $8x + 2 = 42$ yes
4. $x = 15$ for $7(x - 5) = 70$ yes
5. $x = 4$ for $3(x - 2) = 10$ no

Problem of the Day

Four couples have dinner together each month. The wives are Ginny, Helen, Sarah, and Bridget. The husbands are Mark, Alex, Stephen, and Henry. Who is married to whom?

- Sarah is Mark's sister.
- Sarah introduced Henry to his wife.
- Bridget has 2 brothers, but her husband is an only child.
- Ginny is married to Stephen.

Ginny and Stephen, Helen and Mark, Sarah and Alex, Bridget and Henry

Available on Daily Transparency in CRB

2-11 Solving Equations by Adding or Subtracting

Learn to solve one-step equations by using addition or subtraction.

Vocabulary
solve
isolate the variable
Addition Property of Equality
inverse operations
Subtraction Property of Equality

To **solve** an equation means to find a solution to the equation. To do this, **isolate the variable** —that is, get the variable alone on one side of the equal sign.

$x = 8 - 5$ $7 - 3 = y$	$x + 5 = 8$ $7 = 3 + y$
The variables are isolated.	The variables are *not* isolated.

Recall that an equation is like a balanced scale. If you increase or decrease the weights by the same amount on both sides, the scale will remain balanced.

ADDITION PROPERTY OF EQUALITY

Words	Numbers	Algebra
You can add the same amount to both sides of an equation, and the statement will still be true.	$2 + 3 = 5$ $\underline{+4} \quad \underline{+4}$ $2 + 7 = 9$	$x = y$ $\underline{+z} \quad \underline{+z}$ $x + z = y + z$

Use *inverse operations* when isolating a variable. Addition and subtraction are **inverse operations** , which means that they "undo" each other.

EXAMPLE  **Solving an Equation by Addition**

Solve the equation $x - 8 = 17$. Check your answer.

$x - 8 = 17$ *Think: 8 is **subtracted** from x, so*
$\underline{+8} \quad \underline{+8}$ ***add** 8 to both sides to isolate x.*
$x = 25$

Check

$x - 8 = 17$
$25 - 8 \stackrel{?}{=} 17$ *Substitute 25 for x.*
$17 \stackrel{?}{=} 17$ ✔ *25 is a solution.*

1 Introduce

Alternate Opener

EXPLORATION

2-11 Solving Equations by Adding or Subtracting

Find a solution to each equation.

Equations with Addition	Equations with Subtraction
1. $n + 100 = 135$ $n =$ ____	5. $91 - n = 10$ $n =$ ____
2. $10 + n = 91$ $n =$ ____	6. $n - 10 = 43$ $n =$ ____
3. $n + 25 = 75$ $n =$ ____	7. $75 - n = 25$ $n =$ ____
4. $13 + n = 23$ $n =$ ____	8. $n - 15 = 23$ $n =$ ____

Think and Discuss

9. **Discuss** your strategies for solving the equations.
10. **Describe** how the operations of addition and subtraction "undo" each other.

Motivate

Pose simple puzzles that can be represented by equations (e.g., "I'm thinking of a number. Four more than my number is 7. What's my number?"). When students provide the correct solution, ask them to explain how they found the answer.

Exploration worksheet and answers on Chapter 2 Resource Book pp. 101 and 150

2 Teach

Lesson Presentation

Guided Instruction

In this lesson, students learn to solve one-step equations by using addition and subtraction. Use intuitive solutions as a starting point, and remind students that equations are like a balanced scale. Remind them to keep the scale balanced by always doing the same thing to both sides. Help students understand that inverse operations undo each other (e.g., adding 5 then subtracting 5 results in no change).

Teaching Tip Some students might have difficulty determining which operation to use. Encourage them to use the operation that is the opposite of what they see in the equation.

SUBTRACTION PROPERTY OF EQUALITY

Words	Numbers	Algebra
You can subtract the same amount from both sides of an equation, and the statement will still be true.	$4 + 7 = 11$ $\underline{-3} \quad \underline{-3}$ $4 + 4 = 8$	$x = y$ $\underline{-z} \quad \underline{-z}$ $x - z = y - z$

EXAMPLE 2 **Solving an Equation by Subtraction**

Solve the equation $a + 5 = 11$. Check your answer.

$$\begin{aligned} a + 5 &= 11 \\ \underline{-5} \quad &\underline{-5} \\ a \quad &= 6 \end{aligned}$$

*Think: 5 is **added** to a, so **subtract** 5 from both sides to isolate a.*

Check

$a + 5 = 11$

$6 + 5 \stackrel{?}{=} 11$ — *Substitute 6 for a.*

$11 \stackrel{?}{=} 11$ ✔ — *6 is a solution.*

EXAMPLE 3 ***Sports Application***

Michael Jordan's highest point total for a single game was 69. The entire team scored 117 points in that game. How many points did his teammates score?

Let p represent the points scored by the rest of the team.

Michael Jordan's points	+	*Rest of the team's points*	=	*Final team score*
69	+	p	=	117

$$\begin{aligned} 69 + p &= 117 \\ \underline{-69} \quad &\underline{-69} \\ p &= 48 \end{aligned}$$

Subtract 69 from both sides to isolate p.

The rest of the team scored 48 points.

Think and Discuss

1. **Explain** how to decide which operation to use in order to isolate the variable in an equation.
2. **Describe** what would happen if a number were added or subtracted on one side of an equation but not on the other side.

COMMON ERROR ALERT

Watch for students who might be tempted to use the operation in the equation rather than its inverse to solve the equation. Have students estimate before solving and check their answers afterward.

Additional Examples

Example 1

Solve the equation $b - 7 = 24$. Check your answer.

$b = 31$

Example 2

Solve the equation $t + 14 = 29$. Check your answer.

$t = 15$

Example 3

The Giants scored 13 points in a game against Dallas. They scored 7 points for a touchdown and the rest of their points for field goals. How many points did they score on field goals?

They scored 6 points on field goals.

Reaching All Learners

Through Grouping Strategies

Have students work with a partner to create "mind reading" puzzles that depend upon inverse operations to return to the original number. An example might be a puzzle like this one: "Pick a number. Add 4. Subtract 1. Add 7. Subtract 5. Subtract 4. Add 5. Subtract 7. Add 1. Your answer is the number you started with."

3 Close

Summarize

You may wish to have the students state the addition and subtraction properties of equality in their own words. Discuss the meaning of inverse operations. Ask students to explain how they would solve an equation.

Possible answers: If you add or subtract the same amount on both sides of an equation, the equation is still balanced. Inverse operations cancel out each other. If a number is subtracted from the variable, add that number to both sides. If a number is added to the variable, subtract it from both sides.

Answers to Think and Discuss

Possible answers:

1. Use the operation that undoes the operation used on the variable.
2. Adding or subtracting on one side of an equation but not the other would throw the equation out of balance.

2-11 PRACTICE & ASSESS

Students may want to refer back to the lesson examples.

Assignment Guide

If you finished Example 1 assign:
Core 1–3, 8–11, 25, 29, 37–44
Enriched 1, 3, 7–11 odd, 20, 22, 25, 26, 29, 37–44

If you finished Example 2 assign:
Core 1–6, 8–17, 21–29 odd, 37–44
Enriched 1–5 odd, 8–17, 20–29, 37–44

If you finished Example 3 assign:
Core 1–19, 21–33 odd, 37–44
Enriched 1–19 odd, 20–44

Notes

2-11 Exercises

FOR EXTRA PRACTICE see page 659

internet connect
Homework Help Online
go.hrw.com Keyword: MS4 2-11

GUIDED PRACTICE

See Example 1
Solve each equation. Check your answer.

1. $r - 77 = 99$ $r = 176$
2. $102 = v - 66$ $v = 168$
3. $x - 22 = 66$ $x = 88$

See Example 2

4. $d + 83 = 92$ $d = 9$
5. $45 = 36 + f$ $f = 9$
6. $987 = 16 + m$ $m = 971$

See Example 3

7. After a gain of 9 yards, your team has gained a total of 23 yards. How many yards had your team gained before the 9-yard gain? **14 yd**

INDEPENDENT PRACTICE

See Example 1
Solve each equation. Check your answer.

8. $n - 36 = 17$ $n = 53$
9. $t - 28 = 54$ $t = 82$
10. $b - 41 = 26$ $b = 67$
11. $m - 51 = 23$ $m = 74$

See Example 2

12. $x + 15 = 43$ $x = 28$
13. $w + 19 = 62$ $w = 43$
14. $110 = s + 65$ $s = 45$
15. $x + 47 = 82$ $x = 35$
16. $97 = t + 45$ $t = 52$
17. $q + 13 = 112$ $q = 99$

See Example 3

18. Hank is on a field trip. He has to travel 56 miles to reach his destination. He has traveled 18 miles so far. How much farther does he have to travel? **38 mi**
19. Sandy read 8 books in one month. If her book club requires her to read 6 books each month, how many more books did she read than what was required? **2 books**

PRACTICE AND PROBLEM SOLVING

Solve each equation. Check your answer.

20. $p - 7 = 3$ $p = 10$
21. $n + 17 = 98$ $n = 81$
22. $356 = y - 219$ $y = 575$
23. $105 = a + 60$ $a = 45$
24. $651 + c = 800$ $c = 149$
25. $f - 63 = 937$ $f = 1{,}000$
26. $16 = h - 125$ $h = 141$
27. $s + 841 = 1{,}000$ $s = 159$
28. $63 + x = 902$ $x = 839$
29. $z - 712 = 54$ $z = 766$
30. After Renee deposited a check for \$65, her new account balance was \$315. Write and solve an equation to find the amount that was in her account before the deposit. **\$65 + a = \$315; a = \$250**
31. Adam collected 48 types of insects for his biology project. This was 34 more than he had collected in the first week. Write and solve an equation to find how many insects he found in the first week.

31. $34 + f = 48$; $f = 14$

Math Background

A single linear equation is solved using the properties of equality to isolate the variable on one side of the equation and the constants on the other side. This is accomplished by adding the inverse of the constant term to both sides of the equation. For the student unacquainted with rational numbers this appears to be two different processes: addition and subtraction. If the constant term is negative, we add a positive, which is seen as addition. If the constant is positive, we add a negative, which is seen as subtraction. When students are comfortable solving a linear equation, they are ready for the study of systems of linear equations in more advanced classes.

RETEACH 2-11

LESSON 2-11 **Reteach**
Solving Equations by Adding or Subtracting

Solving an equation is like balancing a scale. If you add the same weight to both sides of a balanced scale, the scale will remain balanced. You can use this same idea to solve an equation.

Think of the equation $x - 7 = 12$ as a balanced scale. The equal sign keeps the balance.

x−7 | 12

$-7 + 7 = 0$

$x - 7 = 12$
$x - 7 + 7 = 12 + 7$ Add 7 to both sides.
$x + 0 = 19$ Combine like terms.
$x = 19$

When you solve an equation, the idea is to get the variable by itself. What you do to one side of the equation, you must do to the other side.

- To solve a subtraction equation, use addition.
- To solve an addition equation, use subtraction.

Solve and check: $y + 8 = 14$.

$+8 - 8 = 0$

$y + 8 = 14$
$y + 8 - 8 = 14 - 8$ Subtract 8 from both sides.
$y + 0 = 6$ Combine like terms.
$y = 6$

Check: $y + 8 = 14$ To check, substitute 6 for y.
$6 + 8 \stackrel{?}{=} 14$
$14 \stackrel{?}{=} 14$ ✓

A true sentence, $14 = 14$, means the solution is correct.

Solve and check.

1. $x - 2 = 8$
$x - 2 + \underline{2} = 8 + \underline{2}$
$x - 0 = \underline{10}$

2. $b + 5 = 11$
$b + 5 - \underline{5} = 11 - \underline{5}$
$b + 0 = \underline{6}$

3. $n + 8 = 11$ $n = 3$
4. $y - 6 = 2$ $y = 8$
5. $a - 9 = 4$ $a = 13$
6. $m + 2 = 18$ $m = 16$

PRACTICE 2-11

LESSON 2-11 **Practice B**
Solving Equations by Adding or Subtracting

Solve the equation. Check your answer.

1. $33 = y - 44$ $y = 77$
2. $r - 32 = 77$ $r = 109$
3. $125 = x - 29$ $x = 154$
4. $k + 18 = 25$ $k = 7$
5. $589 + x = 700$ $x = 111$
6. $96 = 56 + t$ $t = 40$
7. $a - 9 = 57$ $a = 66$
8. $b - 49 = 254$ $b = 303$
9. $987 = f - 11$ $f = 998$
10. $32 + d = 1{,}400$ $d = 1{,}368$
11. $w - 24 = 90$ $w = 114$
12. $95 = g - 340$ $g = 435$
13. $e - 35 = 59$ $e = 94$
14. $84 = v + 30$ $v = 54$
15. $h + 15 = 81$ $h = 66$
16. $110 = a + 25$ $a = 85$
17. $45 + c = 91$ $c = 46$
18. $p - 29 = 78$ $p = 107$
19. $56 - r = 8$ $r = 48$
20. $39 = z + 8$ $z = 31$
21. $93 + g = 117$ $g = 24$
22. The Morales family is driving from Philadelphia to Boston. So far, they have driven 167 miles. This is 129 miles less than the total distance they must travel. How many miles is Philadelphia from Boston?
The total distance is 296 miles.
23. Ron has \$1,230 in his savings account. This is \$400 more than he needs to buy a new big screen TV. Write and solve an equation to find out how much the TV costs.
1,230 = t + 400; The TV costs \$830.

32. ***PHYSICAL SCIENCE*** An object weighs less when it is in water. This is because water exerts a *buoyant force* on the object. The weight of an object out of water is equal to the object's weight in water plus the buoyant force of the water. Suppose an object weighs 103 pounds out of water and 55 pounds in water. Write and solve an equation to find the buoyant force of the water.
Possible answer: $55 + b = 103$, $b = 48$ lb

33. ***MUSIC*** Jason wants to buy the trumpet advertised in the classified ads. He has saved \$156. Using the information from the ad, write and solve an equation to find how much more money he needs to buy the trumpet.
$\$195 = \$156 + m$; $m = \$39$

TICKETS, Friday10/5, Ampitheatre, 7:30 p.m. Good seats. \$100/both. Will deliver tickets to you! Jason.123-456-7852.

TICKETS, Rafael Mendoza in concert, Escamillo's on Haney Island, 10/4, two great seats, row 17. \$75 123-567-1234.

TRUMPET, Coronado, mint condition with immaculate finish, asking only \$195, Dave, 987-654-3210.

TURNTABLES, 2, Traject 6700 Vestax 85, professional mixer, 2 Rush M-888 needles, great condition. Must sell fast, \$1000/best. First buyer takes all. Chad, 321-321-3211.

TURNTABLES and mixer, 2 Traject 6700MZ2 turntables and HS-JD6700 mixer, boxed. \$950. Matt, 123-123-5000.

TURNTABLES, Trio 504, 522, Atwood, KCV, Ultrasonic 16-33-45-78 rpm, \$100. Shure V-15, Mesto, Lanquid

34. ***WHAT'S THE ERROR?*** Describe and correct the error. $x = 50$ for $(8 + 4)2 + x = 26$

35. ***WRITE ABOUT IT*** Explain how you know whether to add or subtract to solve an equation.

36. ***CHALLENGE*** Kwan keeps a record of his football team's gains and losses on each play of the game. The record is shown in the table below. Find the missing information by writing and solving an equation. **$4 + x = -7$; $x = -11$ yd**

Play	Play Gain/Loss	Overall Gain/Loss
1st down	Gain of 2 yards	Gain of 2 yards
2nd down	Loss of 5 yards	Loss of 3 yards
3rd down	Gain of 7 yards	Gain of 4 yards
4th down		Loss of 7 yards

Loss of 11 yd

34. 24 was added to 26 instead of subtracted from 26; $x = 2$

35. Possible answer: If the equation involves addition, you subtract to solve it; if the equation involves subtraction, you add to solve it.

Spiral Review

Find each value. (Lesson 2-1)

37. 8^6 **262,144**
38. 9^3 **729**
39. 4^5 **1,024**
40. 3^3 **27**

Find each product. (Lesson 2-2)

41. $147 \cdot 10^2$ **14,700**
42. $36.5 \cdot 10^4$ **365,000**

43. **TEST PREP** Evaluate the expression $60 - 30 \div 5 \cdot 3$. (Lesson 2-3) **C**

A 2
B 18
C 42
D 58

44. **TEST PREP** Evaluate the expression $12 \cdot 3 - 6 \cdot 3$. (Lesson 2-3) **H**

F 4
G 16
H 18
J 21

Journal

Have students describe real-world situations that use inverse operations (e.g., putting on a shoe and taking it off).

Test Prep Doctor

Exercise 43 tests students' understanding of the order of operations. If students answer **D,** remind them to perform multiplication and division as they meet them and not to jump over the division to do the multiplication first. Exercise 44 can be evaluated more quickly if students recognize it as an example of the Distributive Property $(12 \cdot 3 - 6 \cdot 3 = (12 - 6)3 = 18)$ and choose **H.**

CHALLENGE 2-11

LESSON **2-11** **Challenge**
Equation Maker

Use each term once to make up one addition and one subtraction equation, then solve the equations. Possible answers given.

1. m, n, 12, 6, 54, 9
$n - 12 = 54$; $n = 66$
$m + 6 = 9$; $m = 3$

2. x, y, 7, 15, 32, 45
$x - 15 = 32$; $x = 47$
$y + 7 = 45$; $y = 38$

3. p, q, 19, 44, 72, 8
$p + 19 = 72$; $p = 53$
$q - 8 = 44$; $q = 52$

4. a, b, 67, 102, 6, 8
$a - 102 = 6$; $a = 108$
$b + 8 = 67$; $b = 59$

5. c, d, 11, 12, 18, 35
$c - 18 = 35$; $c = 53$
$d + 11 = 12$; $d = 1$

6. s, t, 115, 123, 32, 0
$s + 115 = 123$; $s = 8$
$t - 32 = 0$; $t = 32$

7. w, y, 1, 2, 3, 4
$w - 2 = 1$; $w = 3$
$y + 3 = 4$; $y = 1$

8. n, p, 6, 22, 99, 400
$n - 6 = 400$; $n = 406$
$p + 22 = 99$; $p = 77$

9. e, f, 52, 4, 75, 18
$e + 4 = 75$; $e = 71$
$f - 18 = 52$; $f = 70$

10. g, h, 61, 88, 94, 117
$g - 117 = 61$; $g = 178$
$h + 88 = 94$; $h = 6$

11. k, l, 302, 54, 115, 79
$k - 54 = 115$; $k = 169$
$l + 79 = 302$; $l = 223$

12. r, s, 90, 14, 71, 15
$r + 15 = 90$; $r = 75$
$s - 14 = 71$; $s = 85$

13. u, v, 8, 12, 37, 44
$u - 37 = 44$; $u = 81$
$v + 8 = 12$; $v = 4$

14. x, y, 198, 0, 231, 4
$x - 198 = 4$; $x = 202$
$y + 0 = 231$; $y = 231$

PROBLEM SOLVING 2-11

LESSON **2-11** **Problem Solving**
Solving Equations by Adding or Subtracting

Write the correct answer.

1. In an online poll, 1,927 people voted for Coach as the best job at the Super Bowl. The job of Announcer received 8,055 more votes. Write and solve an equation to find how many votes the job of Announcer received.
$1{,}927 = v - 8{,}055$; $v = 9{,}982$; 9,982 votes

2. In 2001, the largest bank in the world was Mizuho Holdings, Japan, with \$1,295 billion in assets. This was \$351 billion more than the largest bank in the United States, Citigroup. Write and solve an equation to find Citigroup's assets.
$1{,}295 = a + 351$; $a = 944$; \$944 billion

3. The two smallest countries in the world are Vatican City and Monaco. Vatican City is 1.37 square kilometers smaller than Monaco, which is 1.81 square kilometers in area. What is the area of Vatican City?
0.44 square km

4. The Library of Congress is the largest library in the world. It has 24 million books, which is 8 million more than the National Library of Canada has. How many books does the National Library of Canada have?
16 million books

Choose the letter for the best answer.

5. The first track on Sean's new CD has been playing for 55 seconds. This is 42 seconds less than the time of the entire first track. How long is the first track on this CD?
A 37 seconds
B 63 seconds
(C) 97 seconds
D 93 seconds

6. There are 45 students on the school football team. This is 13 more than the number of students on the basketball team. How many students are on the basketball team?
F 58 students
G 48 students
(H) 32 students
J 42 students

7. A used mountain bike costs \$79.95. This is \$120 less than the cost of a new one. If c is the cost of the new bike, which equation can you use to find the cost of a new bike?
A $79.95 = c + 120$
B $120 = 79.95 - c$
(C) $79.95 = c - 120$
D $120 = 79.95 + c$

8. The goal of the School Bake Sale is to raise \$125 more than last year's sale. Last year the Bake Sale raised \$320. If it reaches its goal, how much will the Bake Sale raise this year?
(F) \$445
G \$195
H \$525
J \$425

Lesson Quiz

Solve each equation. Check your answer.

1. $x - 9 = 4$ **$x = 13$**
2. $y + 6 = 72$ **$y = 66$**
3. $21 = n - 41$ **$n = 62$**
4. $127 = w + 31$ **$w = 96$**
5. $81 = x - 102$ **$x = 183$**
6. Tamika has sold 16 dozen cookies this week. This was 7 dozen more than she sold last week. Write and solve an equation to find how many dozen cookies she sold last week. **$x + 7 = 16$; 9 dozen**

Available on Daily Transparency in CRB

2-12 Organizer

Pacing: Traditional 1 day
Block $\frac{1}{2}$ day

Objective: Students solve one-step equations by using multiplication or division.

Warm Up

Solve.

1. $x + 5 = 9$ — $x = 4$

2. $x - 34 = 72$ — $x = 106$

3. $124 = x - 39$ — $x = 163$

Problem of the Day

What 4-digit number am I? **4,039**

- I am greater than 4,000 and less than 5,000.
- The sum of my hundreds digit and my ones digit is 9.
- Twice my tens digit is 2 more than my thousands digit.
- The product of my hundreds digit and my ones digit is 0.
- I am not an even number.

Available on Daily Transparency in CRB

Which animals are the best mathematicians? The snakes are adders, but the rabbits multiply.

2-12 Solving Equations by Multiplying or Dividing

Learn to solve one-step equations by using multiplication or division.

Vocabulary

Multiplication Property of Equality

Division Property of Equality

Like addition and subtraction, multiplication and division are inverse operations. They "undo" each other.

$2 \cdot 5 = 10$

$10 \div 5 = 2$

MULTIPLICATION PROPERTY OF EQUALITY

Words	Numbers	Algebra
You can multiply both sides of an equation by the same number, and the statement will still be true.	$3 \cdot 4 = 12$ $2 \cdot 3 \cdot 4 = 2 \cdot 12$ $6 \cdot 4 = 24$	$x = y$ $zx = zy$

If a variable is divided by a number, you can often use multiplication to isolate the variable. Multiply both sides of the equation by the number.

EXAMPLE 1  **Solving an Equation by Multiplication**

Solve the equation $\frac{x}{7} = 20$. Check your answer.

$\frac{x}{7} = 20$

$(7)\frac{x}{7} = 20(7)$ — *Think: x is* ***divided*** *by 7, so* ***multiply*** *both sides by 7 to isolate x.*

$x = 140$

Check

$\frac{x}{7} = 20$

$\frac{140}{7} \stackrel{?}{=} 20$ — *Substitute 140 for x.*

$20 \stackrel{?}{=} 20$ ✔ — *140 is a solution.*

Remember!
You cannot divide by 0.

DIVISION PROPERTY OF EQUALITY

Words	Numbers	Algebra
You can divide both sides of an equation by the same nonzero number, and the statement will still be true.	$5 \cdot 6 = 30$ $\frac{5 \cdot 6}{3} = \frac{30}{3}$ $5 \cdot \frac{6}{3} = 10$ $5 \cdot 2 = 10$	$x = y$ $\frac{x}{z} = \frac{y}{z}$ $z \neq 0$

1 Introduce

Alternate Opener

EXPLORATION

2-12 Solving Equations by Multiplying or Dividing

Find a solution to each equation.

Equations with Multiplication	Equations with Division
1. $n \cdot 4 = 56$ $n =$ ____	**5.** $n \div 5 = 100$ $n =$ ____
2. $13 \cdot n = 65$ $n =$ ____	**6.** $75 \div n = 15$ $n =$ ____
3. $n \cdot 15 = 75$ $n =$ ____	**7.** $n \div 2 = 75$ $n =$ ____
4. $25 \cdot n = 525$ $n =$ ____	**8.** $125 \div n = 25$ $n =$ ____

Think and Discuss

9. Discuss your strategies for solving the equations.

10. Describe how the operations of multiplication and division "undo" each other.

Motivate

To prepare to solve equations by multiplying or dividing, pose questions about factor pairs (e. g., "One factor of 42 is 3. What's the other factor of 42 that goes with 3?") Ask students to explain how they determined the other factor. Guide the discussion to review the concept of inverse operations by explaining that if you multiply by a factor and then divide by it, you get the original number. This is why multiplication and division are inverse operations.

Exploration worksheet and answers on Chapter 2 Resource Book pp. 110 and 152

2 Teach

Lesson Presentation

Guided Instruction

In this lesson, students learn to solve one-step equations by using multiplication or division. Remind students that the goal is to isolate the variable by performing the inverse operation. Students can multiply both sides of the equation by the same number to undo division or divide both sides by the same number to undo multiplication (Teaching Transparency T43 in the Chapter 2 Resource Book).

Before they solve an equation, suggest that students estimate the value of the variable. This will help them choose the correct operation.

If a variable is multiplied by a number, you can often use division to isolate the variable. You divide both sides of the equation by the number.

EXAMPLE 2 **Solving an Equation by Division**

Solve the equation 240 = 4z. Check your answer.

$240 = 4z$ — *Think: z is **multiplied** by 4, so **divide** both sides by 4 to isolate z.*

$\frac{240}{4} = \frac{4z}{4}$

$60 = z$

Check

$240 = 4z$

$240 \stackrel{?}{=} 4(60)$ — *Substitute 60 for z.*

$240 \stackrel{?}{=} 240$ ✔ — *60 is a solution.*

EXAMPLE 3 ***Health Application***

In 2002, Lance Armstrong completed the 2,051-mile Tour de France in 82 hours, 5 minutes, and 12 seconds.

go.hrw.com KEYWORD: MS4 Lance

If you count your heartbeats for 10 seconds and multiply that number by 6, you can find your heart rate in beats per minute. Lance Armstrong, who won the Tour de France four years in a row, from 1999 to 2002, has a resting heart rate of 30 beats per minute. How many times does his heart beat in 10 seconds?

Use the given information to write an equation, where b is the number of heartbeats in 10 seconds.

Beats in 10 s	*times 6*	*= beats per minute*
b	$\cdot$ 6	= 30

$6b = 30$ — *Think: b is **multiplied** by 6, so **divide** both sides by 6 to isolate b.*

$\frac{6b}{6} = \frac{30}{6}$

$b = 5$

Lance Armstrong's heart beats 5 times in 10 seconds.

Think and Discuss

1. **Explain** how to check your solution to an equation.
2. **Describe** how to solve $13x = 91$.
3. When you solve $5p = 35$, will p be greater than 35 or less than 35? **Explain** your answer.
4. When you solve $\frac{p}{5} = 35$, will p be greater than 35 or less than 35? **Explain** your answer.

COMMON ERROR ALERT

Some students might use division rather than multiplication to solve equations of the form $\frac{x}{a} = c$, particularly when the divisor, a, is a factor of the constant, c. Remind students to be certain they are using the inverse operation and to check their answers.

Additional Examples

Example 1

Solve the equation $\frac{h}{2} = 13$. Check your answer.

$h = 26$

Example 2

Solve the equation $51 = 17x$. Check your answer.

$3 = x$

Example 3

Trevor's heart rate is 78 beats per minute. How many times does his heart beat in 10 seconds?

Trevor's heart beats 13 times in 10 seconds.

3 Close

Reaching All Learners

Through Critical Thinking

Present this situation: "To solve an equation, Jenny multiplied both sides by 5. To solve the same equation, George divided both sides by 5. They knew that only one of them could be right, yet they got the same answer! How could this happen?"

Possible answer: This could happen with equations of the form $5x = 0$ or $\frac{x}{5} = 0$. Although only one student would have used the correct process, both would get an answer of 0 because $0 \div 5 = 0$ and $0 \cdot 5 = 0$.

Summarize

Have students explain how they would use multiplication or division to solve an equation. Ask them how they would choose which operation to use.

Possible answers: To undo division, multiply both sides by the same number. To undo multiplication, divide both sides by the same number. Use the operation that is the opposite, or inverse, of the operation in the equation.

Answers to Think and Discuss

Possible answers:

1. Substitute the solution for the variable and evaluate the equation.
2. Divide both sides of the equation by 13 to undo the multiplication and isolate the variable.
3. p will be less than 35 because the product of two numbers, if both are greater than 1, is greater than either of the factors.
4. p will be greater than 35 because 5 goes into p 35 times.

2-12 PRACTICE & ASSESS

Students may want to refer back to the lesson examples.

Assignment Guide

If you finished Example 1 assign:
Core 1–3, 8–13, 21, 26, 29, 30, 41–46
Enriched 1, 3, 9–13 odd, 21, 25, 26, 27, 29, 30, 41–46

If you finished Example 2 assign:
Core 1–6, 8–19, 21–29 odd, 41–46
Enriched 1, 4, 8–19, 21–30, 41–46

If you finished Example 3 assign:
Core 1–20, 27–37 odd, 41–46
Enriched 1–19 odd, 20–46

Notes

Math Background

Division is defined as multiplication by the reciprocal. To solve $3x = 15$, for example, we could multiply both sides by $\frac{1}{3}$, which would be equivalent to dividing by 3. While most students would rather divide by 3 than multiply by $\frac{1}{3}$, this alternate interpretation may be useful when trying to solve equations such as $\frac{2}{3}x = 4$. Dividing by $\frac{2}{3}$ is equivalent to multiplying by $\frac{3}{2}$.

2-12 Exercises

FOR EXTRA PRACTICE see page 659

GUIDED PRACTICE

See Example 1 Solve the equation. Check your answer.

1. $\frac{s}{77} = 11$ **$s = 847$**
2. $b \div 25 = 4$ **$b = 100$**
3. $y \div 8 = 5$ **$y = 40$**

See Example 2

4. $72 = 8x$ **$x = 9$**
5. $3c = 96$ **$c = 32$**
6. $x \cdot 18 = 18$ **$x = 1$**

See Example 3

7. On Friday nights, a local bowling alley charges $5 per person to bowl all night. If Carol and her friends paid a total of $45 to bowl, how many people were in their group? **9 people**

INDEPENDENT PRACTICE

See Example 1 Solve the equation. Check your answer.

8. $12 = s \div 4$ **$s = 48$**
9. $\frac{k}{18} = 72$ **$k = 1{,}296$**
10. $13 = \frac{z}{5}$ **$z = 65$**
11. $\frac{c}{5} = 35$ **$c = 175$**
12. $\frac{w}{11} = 22$ **$w = 242$**
13. $17 = n \div 18$ **$n = 306$**

See Example 2

14. $17x = 85$ **$x = 5$**
15. $63 = 3p$ **$p = 21$**
16. $6u = 222$ **$u = 37$**
17. $97a = 194$ **$a = 2$**
18. $9q = 108$ **$q = 12$**
19. $495 = 11d$ **$d = 45$**

See Example 3

20. It costs $6 per ticket for groups of ten or more people to see a minor league baseball game. If Albert's group paid a total of $162 for game tickets, how many people were in the group? **27 people**

PRACTICE AND PROBLEM SOLVING

Solve the equation. Check your answer.

21. $9 = g \div 3$ **$g = 27$**
22. $150 = 3j$ **$j = 50$**
23. $7r = 84$ **$r = 12$**
24. $5x = 35$ **$x = 7$**
25. $b + 33 = 95$ **$b = 62$**
26. $\frac{p}{15} = 6$ **$p = 90$**
27. $504 = c - 212$ **$c = 716$**
28. $8a = 288$ **$a = 36$**
29. $21 = d \div 2$ **$d = 42$**
30. $\frac{h}{20} = 83$ **$h = 1{,}660$**

Translate each sentence into an equation. Then solve the equation.

31. A number d divided by 4 equals 3. **$d \div 4 = 3$; $d = 12$**
32. The product of a number b and 5 is 250. **$5b = 250$; $b = 50$**
33. Nine weeks from now Susan hopes to buy a bicycle that costs $180. How much money must she save per week? **$9x = \$180$; $x = \$20$**

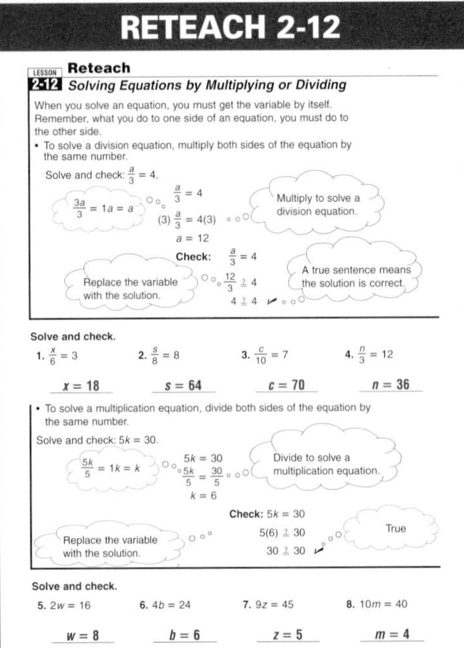

RETEACH 2-12

LESSON 2-12 **Reteach**
Solving Equations by Multiplying or Dividing

When you solve an equation, you must get the variable by itself. Remember, what you do to one side of an equation, you must do to the other side.

- To solve a division equation, multiply both sides of the equation by the same number.

Solve and check: $\frac{a}{3} = 4$.

$\frac{a}{3} = 4$

$(3)\frac{a}{3} = 4(3)$

$a = 12$

Check: $\frac{a}{3} = 4$

$\frac{12}{3} \stackrel{?}{=} 4$

$4 \stackrel{?}{=} 4$ ✓

$\frac{3a}{3} = 1a = a$
Multiply to solve a division equation.
Replace the variable with the solution.
A true sentence means the solution is correct.

Solve and check.

1. $\frac{x}{6} = 3$ **$x = 18$**
2. $\frac{s}{8} = 8$ **$s = 64$**
3. $\frac{c}{10} = 7$ **$c = 70$**
4. $\frac{n}{3} = 12$ **$n = 36$**

- To solve a multiplication equation, divide both sides of the equation by the same number.

Solve and check: $5k = 30$.

$5k = 30$

$\frac{5k}{5} = \frac{30}{5}$

$k = 6$

Check: $5k = 30$

$5(6) \stackrel{?}{=} 30$

$30 \stackrel{?}{=} 30$ ✓

$\frac{5k}{5} = 1k = k$
Divide to solve a multiplication equation.
Replace the variable with the solution.
True

Solve and check.

5. $2w = 16$ **$w = 8$**
6. $4b = 24$ **$b = 6$**
7. $9z = 45$ **$z = 5$**
8. $10m = 40$ **$m = 4$**

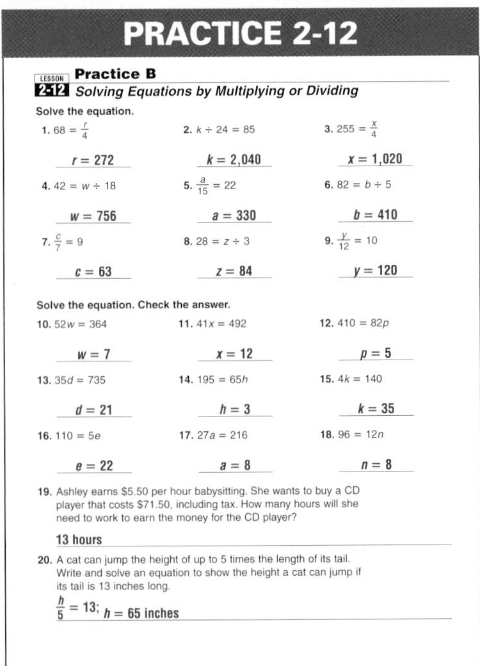

PRACTICE 2-12

LESSON 2-12 **Practice B**
Solving Equations by Multiplying or Dividing

Solve the equation.

1. $68 = \frac{r}{4}$ **$r = 272$**
2. $k \div 24 = 85$ **$k = 2{,}040$**
3. $255 = \frac{x}{4}$ **$x = 1{,}020$**
4. $42 = w \div 18$ **$w = 756$**
5. $\frac{a}{15} = 22$ **$a = 330$**
6. $82 = b \div 5$ **$b = 410$**
7. $\frac{c}{7} = 9$ **$c = 63$**
8. $28 = z \div 3$ **$z = 84$**
9. $\frac{y}{12} = 10$ **$y = 120$**

Solve the equation. Check the answer.

10. $52w = 364$ **$w = 7$**
11. $41x = 492$ **$x = 12$**
12. $410 = 82p$ **$p = 5$**
13. $35d = 735$ **$d = 21$**
14. $195 = 65h$ **$h = 3$**
15. $4k = 140$ **$k = 35$**
16. $110 = 5e$ **$e = 22$**
17. $27a = 216$ **$a = 8$**
18. $96 = 12n$ **$n = 8$**
19. Ashley earns $5.50 per hour babysitting. She wants to buy a CD player that costs $71.50, including tax. How many hours will she need to work to earn the money for the CD player?
13 hours
20. A cat can jump the height of up to 5 times the length of its tail. Write and solve an equation to show the height a cat can jump if its tail is 13 inches long.
$\frac{h}{5} = 13$; $h = 65$ inches

34. At a bake sale, the pies were cut into eight equally sized pieces before being sold. If there were 40 pieces in all, how many whole pies were there? **5 pies**

35. ***SCHOOL*** A school club is collecting toys for a children's charity. There are 18 students in the club. The goal is to collect 216 toys. Each member will collect the same number of toys. How many toys should each member collect? **12 toys**

36. ***TRAVEL*** Lissa drove from Los Angeles to New York City and averaged 45 miles per hour. Her driving time totaled 62 hours. Write and solve an equation to find the distance Lissa traveled. **$45 = x \div 62$; $x = 2{,}790$ mi**

37. ***BUSINESS*** A store rents space in a building at a cost of $19 per square foot. If the store is 700 square feet, how much is the rent? **$13,300**

38. ***WHAT'S THE ERROR?*** For the equation $16x = 102$, a student found the value of x to be 7. What was the student's error?

39. ***WRITE ABOUT IT*** How do you know whether to use multiplication or division to solve an equation?

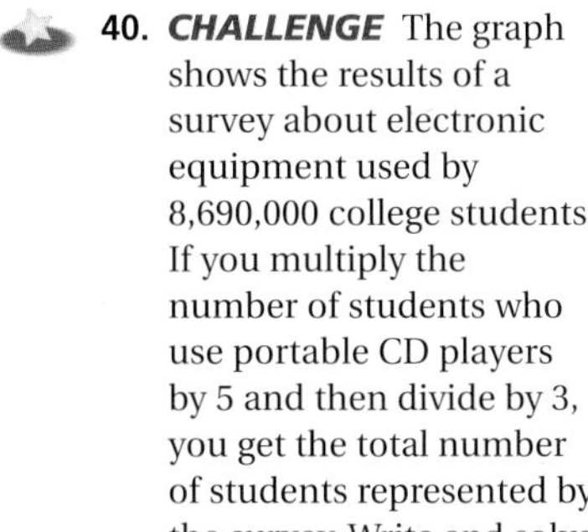

40. ***CHALLENGE*** The graph shows the results of a survey about electronic equipment used by 8,690,000 college students. If you multiply the number of students who use portable CD players by 5 and then divide by 3, you get the total number of students represented by the survey. Write and solve an equation to find the number of students who use portable CD players.
$5s \div 3 = 8{,}690{,}000$; $s = 5{,}214{,}000$

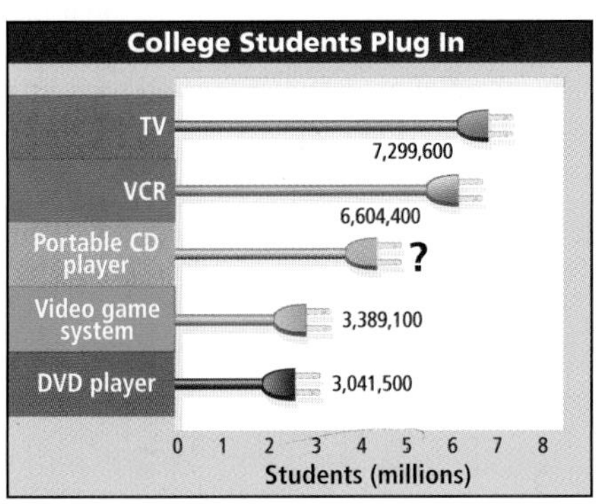

Spiral Review

Evaluate each expression for the given value of the variable. (Lesson 2-7)

41. $r^2 + 6$ for $r = 2$ **10**

42. $(11 - n)5$ for $n = 4$ **35**

Combine the like terms in each expression. (Lesson 2-9)

43. $8x^2 + 9 - x^2 - 3$ **$7x^2 + 6$**

44. $n + 82m - n^4 + 5n - 20m$ **$6n + 62m - n^4$**

45. **TEST PREP** Translate into an algebraic expression: 7 times the sum of a number and 5. (Lesson 2-8) **D**

A $7 \cdot 5$ C $7 + n + 5$
B $7n + 5$ D $7(n + 5)$

46. **TEST PREP** Solve $x - 28 = 7$. (Lesson 2-11) **H**

F 21 H 35
G 27 J 43

Answers

38. Possible answer: The student made an error when dividing 102 by 16. The correct answer should be $x = 6.375$

39. Possible answer: In a multiplication equation, identify the number being multiplied by the variable. Then divide both sides of the equation by this number and simplify. In a division equation, identify the number by which the variable is being divided. Then multiply both sides of the equation by this number and simplify.

Journal

Have students describe a real-world problem that could be represented by a multiplication equation. What method could be used to solve it? Remind them that multiplication of whole numbers can also be thought of as repeated addition.

Test Prep Doctor

Exercise 46 involves solving a one-step equation by using addition. Students can eliminate **F** and **G** by inspection, since both answers are less than 28, which needs to be added to 7 to find the solution.

CHALLENGE 2-12

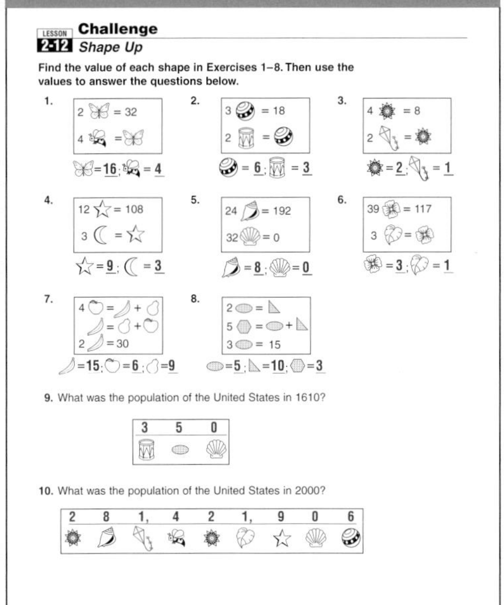

LESSON 2-12 **Challenge**
Shape Up

Find the value of each shape in Exercises 1–8. Then use the values to answer the questions below.

1. 2 [butterfly] = 32; 4 [bee] = [butterfly]; [butterfly] = **16**; [bee] = **4**
2. 3 [ball] = 18; 2 [drum] = [ball]; [ball] = **6**; [drum] = **3**
3. 4 [sun] = 8; 2 [kite] = [sun]; [sun] = **2**; [kite] = **1**
4. 12 [star] = 108; 3 [moon] = [star]; [star] = **9**; [moon] = **3**
5. 24 [conch] = 192; 32 [shell] = 0; [conch] = **8**; [shell] = **0**
6. 39 [flower] = 117; 3 [leaf] = [flower]; [flower] = **3**; [leaf] = **1**
7. 4 [apple] = [banana] + [pear]; [banana] = [pear] + [apple]; 2 [banana] = 30; [banana] = **15**; [apple] = **6**; [pear] = **9**
8. 2 [oval] = [triangle]; 5 [hexagon] = [oval] + [triangle]; 3 [oval] = 15; [oval] = **5**; [triangle] = **10**; [hexagon] = **3**

9. What was the population of the United States in 1610?

3 5 0

10. What was the population of the United States in 2000?

2 8 1, 4 2 1, 9 0 6

PROBLEM SOLVING 2-12

LESSON 2-12 **Problem Solving**
Solving Equations by Multiplying or Dividing

Write the correct answer.

1. The Panama Canal cost $387,000,000 to build. Each ship pays $34,000 to pass through the canal. How many ships had to pass through the canal to pay for the cost to build it?
11,383 ships

2. The rate of exchange for currency changes daily. One day you could get $25 for 3,302.75 Japanese yen. Write and solve a multiplication equation to find the number of yen per dollar on that day.
$25y = 3{,}302.75$; $y = 132.11$; 132.11 yen per dollar

3. Franklin D. Roosevelt was in office as president for 12 years. This is three times as long as Jimmy Carter was president. Write and solve an equation to show how long Jimmy Carter was president.
$12 = 3y$; $y = 4$; 4 years

4. The mileage from Dallas to Miami is 1,332 miles. To the nearest hour, how many hours would it take to drive from Dallas to Miami at an average speed of 55 mi/h?
24 hours

Choose the letter for the best answer.

5. The total bill for a bike rental for 8 hours was $38. How much per hour was the rental cost?
A $8 per hour
(B) $4.75 per hour
C $30 per hour
D $5.25 per hour

6. If a salesclerk earns $5.75 per hour, how many hours per week does she work to earn her weekly salary of $207?
F 30 hours
G 32 hours
(H) 36 hours
J 4 hours

7. At a cost of $0.07 per minute, which equation could you use to find out how many minutes you can talk for $3.15?
A $\$0.07 \div m = \$3.15$
B $\$3.15 \cdot m = \$0.07$
(C) $\$0.07m = \$3.15$
D $\$0.07 \div \$3.15 = m$

8. Which equation shows how to find a runner's distance if he ran a total of m miles in 36 minutes at an average of a mile every 7.2 minutes?
(F) $36 \div m = 7.2$
G $7.2 \div m = 36$
H $36m = 7.2$
J $7.2 \div 36 = m$

Lesson Quiz

Solve the equation. Check your answer.

1. $12 = 4x$ $x = 3$
2. $18z = 90$ $z = 5$
3. $12 = \frac{x}{4}$ $x = 48$
4. $840 = 12y$ $y = 70$
5. $\frac{h}{22} = 9$ $h = 198$
6. The cost of each ticket at the carnival was $0.25. Li bought $7.50 worth of tickets. How many tickets did she buy? **30**

Available on Daily Transparency in CRB

Problem Solving on Location

New York City

Purpose: *To provide additional practice for problem-solving skills in Chapters 1–2*

The Rose Center for Earth and Space

- After problem 1, have students consider the following question: What is the approximate total area of the glass panes? about 38,640 ft^2
- After problem 4, have students write in scientific notation the number of people who would visit the Empire State Building in ten years. **3.6×10^7**

Extension Encourage students to use the data in the table to write a problem about a visit to the Empire State Building. Then have students exchange problems and solve. Possible answer: About how many visitors are there to the Empire State Building each month?

Problem Solving on Location

NEW YORK

The Rose Center for Earth and Space

New York City's new planetarium, the Rose Center for Earth and Space, is housed in an 87-foot sphere. The sphere is enclosed in a glass cube 95 feet tall. The walls of the cube are made up of 736 glass panes.

1. The panes of glass that make up the walls of the Rose Center have an average area of about 52.5 square feet, with an average height of about 5 feet. Write and solve an equation to find the average width of each pane of glass. (*Hint:* The area of a rectangle is found by multiplying its length ℓ by its width w.) **$5w = 52.5$; $w = 10.5$ ft**
2. There are 2,000 pounds in every ton. Using p for the weight in pounds of the planetarium's sphere, write an expression that can be used to find the sphere's weight in tons. **$\frac{p}{2,000}$**

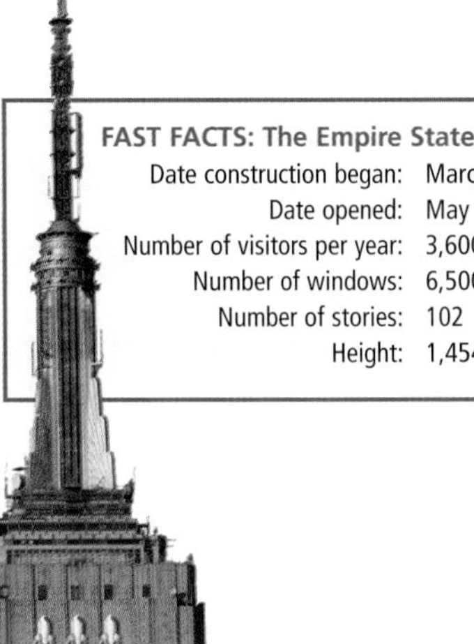

FAST FACTS: The Empire State Building	
Date construction began:	March 17, 1930
Date opened:	May 1, 1931
Number of visitors per year:	3,600,000
Number of windows:	6,500
Number of stories:	102
Height:	1,454 ft

Another famous New York City landmark is the Empire State Building. For 3–5, use the information at left.

3. Write the number of people who visit the Empire State Building each year in scientific notation. **3.6×10^6**
4. Write an expression for the number of visitors in n years. **$3,600,000n$**
5. Before the Empire State Building was built, the Chrysler Building, also in New York City, was the world's tallest building. The Empire State Building is 408 feet taller than the Chrysler Building. Write and solve an equation to find the height of the Chrysler Building. **$408 + n = 1,454$; $n = 1,046$ ft**

New York City Subway System

New York's first subway line, the IRT, opened on October 28, 1904. The line ran from City Hall Station to 145th Street.

1. Write and solve an equation to find out how old the New York City subway system is.
Possible answer: $1904 + n = 2002$; $n = 98$ years
2. As of 1999, about 1,300,000,000 people per year used the New York City subway system. Write this number in scientific notation.
1.3×10^9
3. The average number of weekday subway riders is 4.3×10^6. Write this number in standard notation and in word form.
4,300,000; four million three hundred thousand

There are 25 different subway routes in the New York City subway system. The map shows part of the B and D line, which runs through the Bronx.

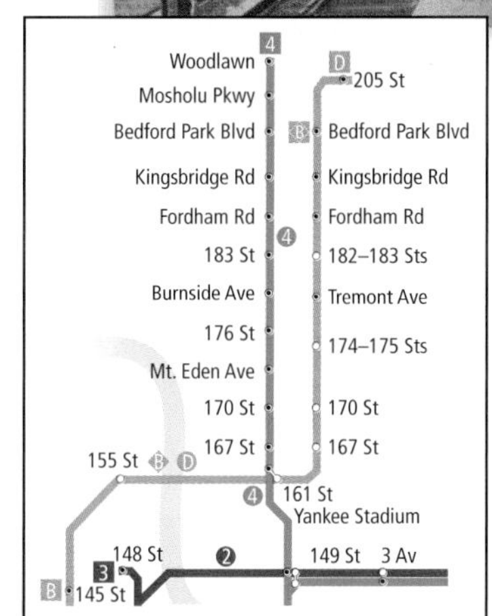

4. Suppose southbound B trains arrive at Fordham Road every 5 minutes, and northbound B trains arrive every 9 minutes, starting at 6:00 A.M. At what times between 6:00 A.M. and 9:00 A.M. will there be both a southbound train and a northbound train at the Fordham Road station? **6:00 A.M., 6:45 A.M., 7:30 A.M., 8:15 A.M., and 9:00 A.M.**
5. Of the total length of track, 443 miles are underground and 156 miles are elevated. There is also track at *grade*, or *open cut*, level. Write an expression that describes the total length in miles of track. **$443 + 156 + n$**
6. There are 1,871 miles of bus routes in the Metropolitan Transit Authority of New York. This is 1,215 more miles than the total length of tracks in the subway. Write and solve an equation to find the length in miles of track in the subway system.
$1{,}871 = 1{,}215 + n$; $n = 656$ miles
7. There are about 4,370 buses, which is about three-fourths the number of subway cars. This means that four times the number of buses is equal to three times the number of subway cars. Write and solve an equation to find out how many subway cars there are. Round your answer to the nearest ten.
$\frac{3}{4}n = 4{,}370$; $n = 5{,}830$

The New York Subway System

- After problem 4, have students consider the following question: Suppose northbound B trains arrive every 5 minutes and southbound B trains arrive every 8 minutes at Fordham Road starting at 4:00 P.M. At what times between 4:00 P.M. and 8:00 P.M. will there be both a northbound train and southbound train at the station? 4:00 P.M., 4:40 P.M., 5:20 P.M., 6:00 P.M., 6:40 P.M., 7:20 P.M., 8:00 P.M.
- After problems 5 and 6, have students use the equation from problem 5 and the solution from problem 6 to find the length in miles of track at grade level. 57 mi

Extension Ask students to find the total number of weekday riders over a period of 5 weekdays and to write the answer in standard form and in scientific notation. 21,500,000; 2.15×10^7 Then have students find the average number of weekday subway riders per hour to the nearest whole number. 179,167 weekday riders per hour

MATH-ABLES

Game Resources

Puzzles, Twisters & Teasers
Chapter 2 Resource Book

Jumping Beans

Purpose: *To apply logical reasoning to play a fun game using beans and a grid*

Discuss: Ask how many grids it is possible to mark off after students have placed the nine beans in the spaces as shown.
Possible answer: There are only 2 possible 3-by-3 grids.

Extend: Have students place the beans in the indicated squares, numbered 10 to 18, and to move them onto the 3-by-3 grid, numbered 1 to 9, in 10 or fewer moves.

		13	14	15	16
	17	12	1	2	3
	18	11	4	5	6
		10	7	8	9

Possible answer:

1. Move the bean on 17 to 1.
2. Move the bean on 13 to 5.
3. Move the bean on 12 to 2 and then to 8.
4. Move the bean on 14 to 4 and then to 6.
5. Move the bean on 18 to 4.
6. Move the bean on 10 to 2.
7. Move the bean on 16 to 3.
8. Move the bean on 1 to 7 and then to 9.
9. Move the bean on 15 to 1.
10. Move the bean on 11 to 7.

Trading Spaces

Purpose: *To apply logical reasoning to play a fun game using counters and a game board*

Discuss: Have students count the number of moves necessary until the positions of the red counters and yellow counters are switched. Discuss why some students might choose a number of moves different from that of other students.

MATH-ABLES

Jumping Beans

You will need a grid that is 4 squares by 6 squares. Each square must be large enough to contain a bean. Mark off a 3-square by 3-square section of the grid. Place nine beans in the nine spaces, as shown below.

You must move all nine beans to the nine marked-off squares in the fewest number of moves.

Follow the rules below to move the beans.

1. You may move to any empty square in any direction.
2. You may jump over another bean in any direction to an empty square.
3. You may jump over other beans as many times as you like.

19	20	21	22	23	24
13	14	15	16	17	18
7	8	9	10	11	12
1	2	3	4	5	6

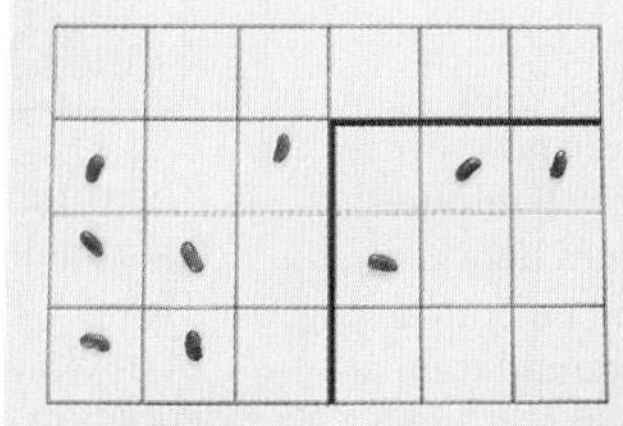

Moving all the beans in ten moves is not too difficult, but can you do it in nine moves?

Possible answer:

1. Move the bean on 3 to 4.
2. Move the bean on 9 to 10.
3. Move the bean on 1 to 3 and then 5. (2 jumps)
4. Move the bean on 7 to 9 and then 11. (2 jumps)
5. Move the bean on 13 to 3 and then 17. (2 jumps)
6. Move the bean on 14 to 16 and then 18. (2 jumps)
7. Move the bean on 2 to 14, then to 16, and then to 6. (3 jumps)
8. Move the bean on 8 to 22 and then 12. (2 jumps)
9. Move the bean on 15 to 16.

Trading Spaces

The purpose of the game is to replace the red counters with the yellow counters, and the yellow counters with the red counters, in the fewest moves possible. The counters must be moved one at a time in an L-shape. No two counters may occupy the same square.

internet connect
For a complete copy of the rules and to print out a game board, go to ***go.hrw.com***
KEYWORD: MS4 Game2

1 (A)	2	3 (B)
4	5	6
7 (C)	8	9 (D)

Possible answer: The solution below is for when the game pieces start out in positions A1, B3, C7, and D9, where A and B represent red pieces and C and D represent yellow pieces. These are the steps to switching positions.

1. A6
2. C2
3. A7
4. B8
5. B1
6. D4
7. D3
8. C9
9. B6
10. A2
11. B7
12. D8
13. D1
14. C4
15. C3
16. A9

Piece A ends up switching places with piece D, and piece B ends up switching places with piece C. Help students notice that there is a pattern in the solution. The first eight steps and the last eight steps are basically the same. The pieces are rotated around the board. After the first eight steps, the board looks as if it has been turned 90°, and after the last eight steps, the board looks as if it has been turned 180°.

Extend: Have students determine the fewest number of moves possible to reverse the positions of the red counters and yellow counters. **16**

Explore Order of Operations

REMEMBER
The order of operations
1. Perform operations within grouping symbols.
2. Evaluate powers.
3. Multiply and divide in order from left to right.
4. Add and subtract in order from left to right.

Many calculators have an x^2 key that allows you to find the square of a number. On calculators that do not have this key, or to use exponents other than 2, you can use the caret key, ^.

For example, to evaluate 3^5, press 3 ^ 5, and then press ENTER.

Activity

1. Evaluate $4 \cdot 2^3$ using paper and pencil. Check your answer with a calculator.

   First evaluate the expression using paper and pencil: $4 \cdot 2^3 = 4 \cdot 8 = 32$.

   Then evaluate $4 \cdot 2^3$ using your calculator.

   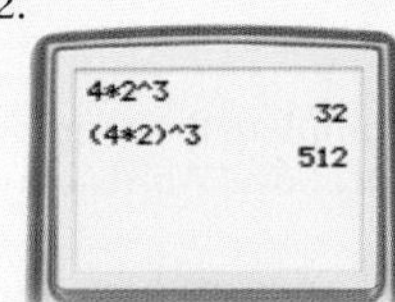

   Notice that the calculator automatically evaluates the power first. If you want to multiply first, you must put that operation inside parentheses.

2. Use a calculator to evaluate $\frac{(2 + 5 \cdot 4)^3}{4^2}$.

Think and Discuss

1. Is $2 + 5 \cdot 4^3 + 4^2$ equivalent to $(2 + 5 \cdot 4^3) + 4^2$? Explain.

Try This

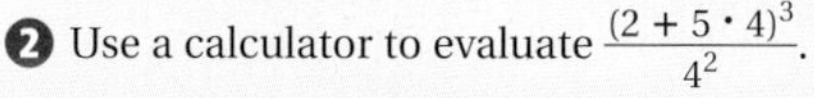

Evaluate each expression with pencil and paper. Check your answers with a calculator.

1. $3 \cdot 2^3 + 5$ **29**
2. $3 \cdot (2^3 + 5)$ **39**
3. $(3 \cdot 2)^2$ **36**
4. $3 \cdot 2^2$ **12**
5. $2^{(3 \cdot 2)}$ **64**

Use a calculator to evaluate each expression. Round your answers to the nearest hundredth.

6. $(2.1 + 5.6 \cdot 4^3) \div 6^4$ **0.28**
7. $[(2.1 + 5.6) \cdot 4^3] \div 6^4$ **0.38**

Answers

Think and Discuss

1. Possible answer: Yes, the expressions are equivalent.
   $2 + 5 \cdot 4^3 + 4^2$
   $= 2 + 5 \cdot 64 + 16$
   $= 2 + 320 + 16 = 338$
   $(2 + 5 \cdot 4^3) + 4^2$
   $=(2 + 5 \cdot 64) + 4^2 = (2 + 320) + 4^2 =$
   $322 + 16 = 338$

Explore Order of Operations

Objective: To use a graphing calculator to evaluate expressions with exponents

Materials: Graphing calculator

Lab Resources

Technology Lab Activities . . . . p. 8

Using the Page

This technology activity shows students how to evaluate expressions with exponents on a graphing calculator. Specific keystrokes may vary depending on the make and model of the graphing calculator used. The keystrokes given are for a TI-83 model.

The Think and Discuss problem can be used to assess students' understanding of order of operations and exponents. Students should first do the Try This problems 1–5 without a graphing calculator. Then students should work the problems again with a graphing calculator to check their results. Try This problems 6 and 7 help students become familiar with using a graphing calculator to evaluate expressions with parentheses and exponents.

Assessment

Use a calculator to evaluate each expression. Round the answer to the nearest hundredth, if necessary.

1. $5 \cdot 2^4 - 15$ **65**
2. $(8.2 + 2.5 \cdot 3^3) \div 5^2$ **3.03**

Chapter 2

Study Guide and Review

Purpose: *To help students review and practice concepts and skills presented in Chapter 2*

Assessment Resources

Chapter 2 Resource Book . pp. 118–120

***Test and Practice Generator* CD-ROM**

Additional review assessment items in both multiple-choice and free-response format may be generated for any objective in Chapter 2.

Answers

1. exponent; base

2. numerical expression

3. composite number

4. algebraic expression

5. 81

6. 10

7. 128

8. 1

9. 121

Chapter 2

Study Guide and Review

Study Guide and Review

Vocabulary

Addition Property of Equality 110
algebraic expression 92
base 60
coefficient 100
composite number 78
constant 92
Division Property of Equality 114
equation 104
evaluate 92
exponent 60
greatest common factor (GCF) 82
inverse operations 110
isolate the variable 110
least common multiple (LCM) 86
like terms 100
multiple 86
Multiplication Property of Equality 114
numerical expression 70
order of operations 70
power 60
prime factorization 78
prime number 78
scientific notation 65
solution 104
solve 110
standard form 65
Subtraction Property of Equality ... 111
term 100
variable 92
verbal expression 96

Complete the sentences below with vocabulary words from the list above. Words may be used more than once.

1. The __?__ tells how many times to use the __?__ as a factor.

2. A(n) __?__ is a mathematical phrase made up of numbers and operations.

3. A(n) __?__ is a whole number with more than two factors.

4. A(n) __?__ consists of constants, variables, and operations.

2-1 Exponents (pp. 60–63)

EXAMPLE

■ **Find the value of 4^3.**

$4^3 = 4 \cdot 4 \cdot 4$
$= 64$

EXERCISES

Find each value.

5. 9^2 **6.** 10^1 **7.** 2^7 **8.** 1^7 **9.** 11^2

2-2 Powers of Ten and Scientific Notation (pp. 64–67)

EXAMPLE

- Find the product of $157 \cdot 10^4$.

$157 \cdot 10^4 = 1570000$
$= 1,570,000$

EXERCISES

Find each product.

10. $144 \cdot 10^2$ **11.** $1.32 \cdot 10^3$ **12.** $22 \cdot 10^7$
13. $34 \cdot 10^1$ **14.** $56 \cdot 10^4$ **15.** $7.8 \cdot 10^2$

2-3 Order of Operations (pp. 70–73)

EXAMPLE

- Evaluate $(18 + 6) \cdot 5$.

$(18 + 6) \cdot 5 = 24 \cdot 5 = 120$

EXERCISES

Evaluate.

16. $2 + (9 - 6) \div 3$ **17.** $12 \cdot 3^2 - 5$

2-4 Prime Factorization (pp. 78–81)

EXAMPLE

- Write the prime factorization of 56.

$56 = 8 \cdot 7 = 2 \cdot 2 \cdot 2 \cdot 7$

EXERCISES

Write the prime factorization.

18. 88 **19.** 27 **20.** 162 **21.** 96

2-5 Greatest Common Factor (pp. 82–85)

EXAMPLE

- Find the GCF of 32 and 12.

32: 1, 2, (4), 8, 16, 32
12: 1, 2, 3, (4), 6, 12 The GCF is 4.

EXERCISES

Find the greatest common factor.

22. 120, 210 **23.** 81, 132
24. 36, 60, 96 **25.** 220, 440, 880

2-6 Least Common Multiple (pp. 86–89)

EXAMPLE

- Find the LCM of 8 and 10.

8: 8, 16, 24, 32, (40)
10: 10, 20, 30, (40) The LCM is 40.

EXERCISES

Find the least common multiple.

26. 5, 12 **27.** 4, 32 **28.** 3, 27
29. 15, 18 **30.** 6, 12 **31.** 5, 7, 9

2-7 Variables and Algebraic Expressions (pp. 92–95)

EXAMPLE

- Evaluate $5a - 6b + 7$ for $a = 4$ and $b = 3$.

$5a - 6b + 7$
$5(4) - 6(3) + 7 = 20 - 18 + 7 = 9$

EXERCISES

Evaluate for the given values.

32. $4x - 5$ for $x = 6$
33. $8y^3 + 3y$ for $y = 4$

Study Guide and Review

Answers

10. 14,400
11. 1,320
12. 220,000,000
13. 340
14. 560,000
15. 780
16. 3
17. 103
18. $2^3 \cdot 11$
19. 3^3
20. $2 \cdot 3^4$
21. $2^5 \cdot 3$
22. 30
23. 3
24. 12
25. 220
26. 60
27. 32
28. 27
29. 90
30. 12
31. 315
32. 19
33. 524

Answers

34. $4 \div (n + 12)$
35. $2(t - 11)$
36. $10b^2 + 8$
37. $15a^2 + 2$
38. $x^4 + x^3 + 6x^2$
39. yes
40. no
41. no
42. $b = 8$
43. $n = 32$
44. $c = 18$
45. $t = 112$
46. $n = 72$
47. $p = 9$
48. $d = 98$
49. $x = 13$

Study Guide and Review

2-8 Translate Words into Math (pp. 96–99)

EXAMPLE

- Write as an algebraic expression.

5 times the sum of a number and 6
$5(n + 6)$

EXERCISES

Write as an algebraic expression.

34. 4 divided by the sum of a number and 12

35. 2 times the difference of a number and 11

2-9 Combining Like Terms (pp. 100–103)

EXAMPLE

- Combine like terms.

$4x^3 + 5y + 8x^3 - 4y - 5x^2$
$4x^3 + 5y + 8x^3 - 4y - 5x^2$
$12x^3 + y - 5x^2$

EXERCISES

Combine like terms.

36. $7b^2 + 8 + 3b^2$

37. $12a^2 + 4 + 3a^2 - 2$

38. $x^2 + x^3 + x^4 + 5x^2$

2-10 Equations and Their Solutions (pp. 104–107)

EXAMPLE

- Determine whether 22 is a solution.

$24 = s - 13$
$24 \stackrel{?}{=} 22 - 13$
$24 \stackrel{?}{=} 9$ ✗ *22 is not a solution.*

EXERCISES

Determine whether each number is a solution of $36 = n - 12$.

39. 48 **40.** 54 **41.** 3

2-11 Solving Equations by Adding or Subtracting (pp. 110–113)

EXAMPLE

- Solve the equation. Then check.

$b + 12 = 16$
$\underline{-12 \quad -12}$
$b = 4$

$b + 12 \stackrel{?}{=} 16$
$4 + 12 \stackrel{?}{=} 16$
$16 \stackrel{?}{=} 16$ ✓

EXERCISES

Solve each equation. Then check.

42. $8 + b = 16$ **43.** $20 = n - 12$

44. $27 + c = 45$ **45.** $t - 68 = 44$

2-12 Solving Equations by Multiplying or Dividing (pp. 114–117)

EXAMPLE

- Solve the equation. Then check.

$2r = 12$
$\frac{2r}{2} = \frac{12}{2}$
$r = 6$

$2r = 12$
$2(6) \stackrel{?}{=} 12$
$12 \stackrel{?}{=} 12$ ✓

EXERCISES

Solve each equation. Then check.

46. $n \div 12 = 6$ **47.** $3p = 27$

48. $\frac{d}{14} = 7$ **49.** $6x = 78$

Notes

Chapter Test

Chapter 2

Find each value.

1. 6^2 **36** **2.** 7^5 **16,807** **3.** 8^6 **262,144** **4.** 3^5 **243**

Find each product.

5. $148 \cdot 10^2$ **14,800** **6.** $56.3 \cdot 10^3$ **56,300** **7.** $6.89 \cdot 10^4$ **68,900** **8.** $7.5 \cdot 10^4$ **75,000**

Evaluate.

9. $18 \cdot 3 \div 3^3$ **2** **10.** $36 + 16 - 50$ **2** **11.** $149 - (2^8 - 200)$ **93** **12.** $(4 \div 2) \cdot 9 + 11$ **29**

Write the prime factorization of each number.

13. 30 **$2 \cdot 3 \cdot 5$** **14.** 66 **$2 \cdot 3 \cdot 11$** **15.** 78 **$2 \cdot 3 \cdot 13$** **16.** 110 **$2 \cdot 5 \cdot 11$**

Find the greatest common factor (GCF).

17. 18, 27, 45 **9** **18.** 16, 28, 44 **4** **19.** 14, 28, 56 **14** **20.** 24, 36, 64 **4**

Find the least common multiple (LCM).

21. 24, 36, 64 **576** **22.** 24, 72, 144 **144** **23.** 12, 15, 36 **180** **24.** 9, 16, 25 **3,600**

Evaluate each algebraic expression for the given values of the variables.

25. $4a + 6b + 7$ for $a = 2$ and $b = 3$ **33** **26.** $7y^2 + 7y$ for $y = 3$ **84**

Write each phrase as an algebraic expression.

27. a number increased by 12 **$r + 12$** **28.** the quotient of a number and 7 **$d \div 7$**

29. 5 less than the product of 7 and a number **$7z - 5$**

30. the difference between three times a number and 4 **$3k - 4$**

Combine like terms.

31. $b + 2 + 5b$ **$6b + 2$** **32.** $16 + 5b + 3b + 9$ **$8b + 25$** **33.** $5a + 6t + 9 + 2a$ **$7a + 6t + 9$**

Determine whether each number is a solution of $30 = s + 6$.

34. 15 **no** **35.** 24 **yes** **36.** 18 **no**

Solve each equation.

37. $x + 9 = 19$ **$x = 10$** **38.** $21 = y - 20$ **$y = 41$** **39.** $m - 54 = 72$ **$m = 126$** **40.** $136 = y + 114$ **$y = 22$**

41. $16 = \frac{y}{3}$ **$y = 48$** **42.** $102 = 17y$ **$y = 6$** **43.** $\frac{r}{7} = 1{,}400$ **$r = 9{,}800$** **44.** $6x = 42$ **$x = 7$**

45. A caterer charged $15 per person to prepare a meal for a banquet. If the total catering charge for the banquet was $1,530, how many people attended? **102 people**

Chapter Test

Chapter Test

Chapter 2

Purpose: *To assess students' mastery of concepts and skills in Chapter 2*

Assessment Resources

Chapter 2 Tests (Levels A, B, C)

Assessment Resources ..... pp. 39–44

***Test and Practice Generator* CD-ROM**

Additional assessment items in both multiple-choice and free-response format may be generated for any objective in Chapter 2.

Chapter 2 **Performance Assessment**

Purpose: To assess students' understanding of concepts in Chapter 2 and combined problem-solving skills

Assessment Resources 

Performance Assessment
Assessment Resources . . . . p. 108

Performance Assessment Teacher Support
Assessment Resources . . . . p. 107

Answers

4. See Level 3 work sample below.

Scoring Rubric for Problem Solving Item 4

Level 3
Accomplishes the purpose of the task.
Student gives clear explanations, shows understanding of mathematical ideas and processes, and computes accurately.

Level 2
Purposes of the task not fully achieved.
Student demonstrates satisfactory but limited understanding of the mathematical ideas and processes.

Level 1
Purposes of the task not accomplished.
Student shows little evidence of understanding the mathematical ideas and processes and makes computional and/or procedural errors.

Chapter 2 Performance Assessment

Performance Assessment

 Show What You Know

Create a portfolio of your work from this chapter. Complete this page and include it with your four best pieces of work from Chapter 2. Choose from your homework or lab assignments, mid-chapter quizzes, or any journal entries you have done. Put them together using any design you want. Make your portfolio represent what you consider your best work.

2. $2w = 2 + w$; $2w - w = 2$; $w = 2$; $d - 2 = \frac{d}{2}$; $2(d - 2) = d$; $2d - 4 = d$; $2d - d = 4$; $d = 4$

 Short Response

1. You have enough pens to divide them into 12 equal groups or 10 equal groups. What is the least number of pens you could have? Explain how you found your answer. **60 pens; find the LCM of 10 and 12.**

2. What value of w makes the expressions $2w$ and $2 + w$ equal? What value of d makes the expressions $d - 2$ and $\frac{d}{2}$ equal? Show the steps that you used to find each answer.

3. Describe and correct the error: $2 + 3 \cdot 4 + 5 = 5 \cdot 9 = 45$.
The error was adding first and then multiplying. You should use the correct order of operations and multiply first; $2 + 3 \cdot 4 + 5 = 2 + 12 + 5 = 19$.

Extended Problem Solving

4. The Lakemont Lions and the Hillcrest Hurricanes are buying new uniforms this year. Each team member receives a cap, a jersey, and a pair of pants.

   a. Let l represent the number of Lakemont team members, and let h represent the number of Hillcrest team members. Write an expression that gives the total cost of the Lions' uniforms. Write a second expression for the total cost of the Hurricanes' uniforms.

   b. Using the expressions from part **a**, write a new expression that represents the difference between the cost of the Hurricanes' uniforms and the cost of the Lions' uniforms.

   c. Using $l = 15$ and $h = 18$, evaluate the expressions from part **a** and find the difference between the cost of the Hurricanes' uniforms and the cost of the Lions' uniforms. Then evaluate the expression from part **b**. Explain why the results are the same.

Student Work Samples for Item 4

Level 3

a) Lions cost = 75l + 60l + 15l
= 150l
Hurricanes cost: 75h + 60h + 15h
= 150h
b) 150h − 150l
c) Lions: 150(15) = $2,250
Hurricanes: 150 (18) = $2,700
Difference: 2,700 − 2,250
= $450
150 (18) − 150 (15) = $450
You can subtract or evaluate first and still get the answer.

The student correctly wrote the expressions in parts **a** and **b**, calculated the differences, and offered an adequate explanation.

Level 2

A. cost = 150l and 150h
B. 150l − 150h
C. 150(15) = 2,250
150(18) = 2,700
2,700
− 2,250
$450
The Hurricane's Uniforms cost $450 more.

The student answered the first part correctly but reversed the expressions in part **b.** The explanation in part **c** is also inadequate.

Level 1

a. l = Lakemont
h = Hillcrest
b. h − l
c. 18 − 15 = 3
15 − 18 = 3
They both equal 3 because

The student used the variables but failed to write expressions for total cost. The explanation in part **c** shows little understanding of the concepts involved.

internet connect
State-Specific Test Practice Online
go.hrw.com Keyword: MS4 TestPrep

Standardized Test Prep

Chapter 2

Cumulative Assessment, Chapters 1–2

1. What is the value of $9t$ for $t = 7$? **C**

Ⓐ 16 Ⓒ 63
Ⓑ 54 Ⓓ 71

2. What is another way to write $5 \cdot 5 \cdot 5 \cdot 5 \cdot 5$? **G**

Ⓕ $5 \cdot 5$ Ⓗ 55,555
Ⓖ 5^5 Ⓙ 5 cubed

3. What is the value of the expression $8 - 1 \cdot 4 \div 2$? **B**

Ⓐ 2 Ⓒ 14
Ⓑ 6 Ⓓ 18

4. Which expression does **not** have a value of 38? **H**

Ⓕ $(8 + 2) \cdot 3 + 8$ Ⓗ $45 - (15 + 8)$
Ⓖ $8 + 2 \cdot 15$ Ⓙ $(40 - 20) + 2 \cdot 9$

TEST TAKING TIP!
Eliminate choices by using the definition of *product*.

5. Which expression represents the product of 6 and a number n? **A**

Ⓐ $6n$ Ⓒ $6 - n$
Ⓑ $6 + n$ Ⓓ $\frac{6}{n}$

6. Which expression is the prime factorization of 36? **G**

Ⓕ $4 \cdot 9$ Ⓗ $2^3 \cdot 3$
Ⓖ $2^2 \cdot 3^2$ Ⓙ $2^3 \cdot 9$

Use the stem-and-leaf plot for Items 7–9.

Attendance at Weekly Baseball Game

Stems	Leaves
5	5 8 8 9
6	0 3 4 7
7	1 5 5 7 8
8	0 2 7 7 7 9

Key: 5 | 9 means 59

7. What is the range of the attendance at the baseball games? **B**

Ⓐ 30 Ⓒ 75
Ⓑ 34 Ⓓ 87

8. What is the mode of the attendance at the baseball games? **J**

Ⓕ 34 Ⓗ 75
Ⓖ 58 Ⓙ 87

9. What is the median of the attendance at the baseball games? **C**

Ⓐ 55 Ⓒ 75
Ⓑ 72 Ⓓ 87

10. ***SHORT RESPONSE*** Paul is on the twentieth floor of a building. He climbs the stairs to the thirty-fifth floor. Represent this situation by writing an equation that includes a variable. Explain what the variable represents.

11. ***SHORT RESPONSE*** Use the following temperatures to make a box-and-whisker plot: 54°F, 70°F, 62°F, 55°F, 56°F, 66°F, and 62°F. Then give the median temperature.

Standardized Test Prep

Answers

10. $20 + x = 35$; the variable represents the number of floors Paul went up while climbing the stairs.

11. 

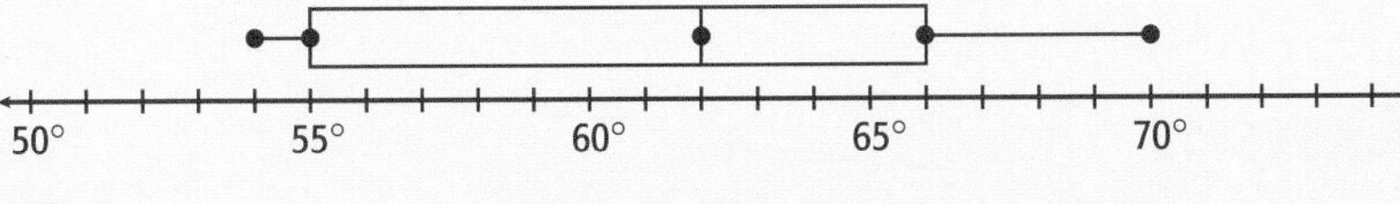

62°F

Standardized Test Prep

Purpose: *To provide review and practice for Chapters 1–2 and standardized tests*

Assessment Resources

Cumulative Tests (Levels A, B, C)
Assessment Resources . . . . pp. 141–152

State-Specific Test Practice Online
KEYWORD: MS4 TestPrep

Test Prep Doctor

Point out to students that **A** and **D** in item 1 can be eliminated because they are not multiples of 9.

Expand on the test-taking tip given for item 5 by reminding students to read all of the choices before choosing one. Point out that sometimes a choice may seem correct, but after reading all choices, it may become clear that it is not.

Chapter 3

Integers and Rational Numbers

Section 3A

Integers

Lesson 3-1
Integers

Lesson 3-2
The Coordinate Plane

Hands-On Lab 3A
Model Integer Addition

Lesson 3-3
Adding Integers

Hands-On Lab 3B
Model Integer Subtraction

Lesson 3-4
Subtracting Integers

Lesson 3-5
Multiplying and Dividing Integers

Hands-On Lab 3C
Model Integer Equations

Lesson 3-6
Solving Equations Containing Integers

Section 3B

Rational Numbers

Lesson 3-7
Fractions and Decimals

Lesson 3-8
Equivalent Fractions and Mixed Numbers

Lesson 3-9
Equivalent Fractions and Decimals

Lesson 3-10
Comparing and Ordering Rational Numbers

Extension
Irrational Numbers

Pacing Guide for 45-Minute Classes

Chapter 3

DAY 32	DAY 33	DAY 34	DAY 35	DAY 36
Lesson 3-1	Lesson 3-2	Hands-On Lab 3A	Lesson 3-3	Hands-On Lab 3B
DAY 37	**DAY 38**	**DAY 39**	**DAY 40**	**DAY 41**
Lesson 3-4	Lesson 3-4	Lesson 3-5	Hands-On Lab 3C	Lesson 3-6
DAY 42	**DAY 43**	**DAY 44**	**DAY 45**	**DAY 46**
Mid-Chapter Quiz Lesson 3-7	Lesson 3-8	Lesson 3-9	Lesson 3-10	Extension
DAY 47	**DAY 48**			
Chapter 3 Review	Chapter 3 Assessment			

Pacing Guide for 90-Minute Classes

Chapter 3

DAY 16	DAY 17	DAY 18	DAY 19	DAY 20
Chapter 2 Assessment Lesson 3-1	Lesson 3-2 Hands-On Lab 3A	Lesson 3-3 Hands-On Lab 3B	Lesson 3-4	Lesson 3-5 Hands-On Lab 3C
DAY 21	**DAY 22**	**DAY 23**	**DAY 24**	**DAY 25**
Lesson 3-6 Lesson 3-7	Mid-Chapter Quiz Lesson 3-8 Lesson 3-9	Lesson 3-10 Extension	Chapter 3 Review Lesson 4-1	Chapter 3 Assessment Lesson 4-2

Across the Series

COURSE 1

- Compare, order, add, subtract, multiply, and divide rational numbers.
- Graph and identify ordered pairs.
- Solve one-step equations with integers.
- Write equivalent fractions, decimals, and mixed numbers.

COURSE 2

- **Compare, order, add, subtract, multiply, and divide integers.**
- **Graph and identify ordered pairs.**
- **Solve one-step equations with integers.**
- **Write decimals in expanded form.**
- **Write equivalent fractions, decimals, and mixed numbers.**
- **Recognize irrational numbers.**

COURSE 3

- Compare, order, add, subtract, multiply, and divide integers and rational numbers.
- Graph and identify ordered pairs.
- Solve one-step equations and inequalities.
- Apply properties of exponents.
- Write equivalent rational numbers, and determine whether a number is rational or irrational.

Across the Curriculum

LANGUAGE ARTS LINK

Math: Reading and Writing in the Content Area .... pp. 22–31

Focus on Problem Solving

Make a Plan .... SE p. 161

Journal .... TE, last page of each lesson

Write About It ...... SE pp. 133, 137, 143, 153, 159, 165, 169, 173, 177

SOCIAL STUDIES LINK

Social Studies .... SE pp. 132, 133, 169

Economics .... SE p. 173

SCIENCE LINK

Life Science .... SE p. 177

Earth Science .... SE pp. 153, 163, 177

Physical Science .... SE pp. 159, 176

Astronomy .... SE p. 149

Ecology .... SE p. 177

TE = *Teacher's Edition* **SE** = *Student Edition*

Interdisciplinary Bulletin Board

Mechanics

Fire trucks are designed to operate in various types of emergency situations. If a ladder engine has to be able to reach a height of 87 feet and a fire truck supplier makes ladders in 10-ft runs, how many runs of ladder should be on the engine? 9 runs of ladder

Interdisciplinary posters and worksheets are provided in your resource material.

Chapter 3

Resource Options

Chapter 3 Resource Book

Student Resources

Practice (Levels A, B, C) . . . . . pp. 8–10, 17–19, 26–28, 35–37, 44–46, 53–55, 64–66, 73–75, 83–85, 92–94

Reteach . . . . . pp. 11, 20, 29, 38, 47, 56–57, 67, 76–77, 86, 95

Challenge . . . . pp. 12, 21, 30, 39, 48, 58, 68, 78, 87, 96

Problem Solving . . . . . pp. 13, 22, 31, 40, 49, 59, 69, 79, 88, 97

Puzzles, Twisters & Teasers . . . . pp. 14, 23, 32, 41, 50, 60, 70, 80, 89, 98

Recording Sheets . . . . pp. 3, 7, 16, 25, 34, 43, 52, 63, 72, 82, 91, 102

Chapter Review . . . . pp. 99–101

Teacher and Parent Resources

Chapter Planning and Pacing Guide . . . . p. 4

Section Planning Guides . . . . pp. 5, 61

Parent Letter . . . . pp. 1–2

Teaching Tools . . . . pp. 105–107

Teacher Support for Chapter Project . . . . p. 103

Transparencies . . . . pp. T1–T45

- Daily Transparencies
- Additional Examples Transparencies
- Teaching Transparencies

Reaching All Learners

English Language Learners

Success for English Language Learners . . . . pp. 43–62

Math: Reading and Writing in the Content Area . . . . pp. 22–31

Spanish Homework and Practice . . . . pp. 22–31

Spanish Interactive Study Guide . . . . pp. 22–31

Spanish Family Involvement Activities . . . . pp. 25–32

Multilingual Glossary

Individual Needs

Are You Ready? Intervention and Enrichment . . pp. 213–216, 221–228, 237–240, 409–410

Alternate Openers: Explorations . . . . pp. 22–31

Family Involvement Activities . . . . pp. 25–32

Interactive Problem Solving . . . . pp. 22–31

Interactive Study Guide . . . . pp. 22–31

Readiness Activities . . . . pp. 5–6

Math: Reading and Writing in the Content Area . . . . pp. 22–31

Challenge . . . . CRB pp. 12, 21, 30, 39, 48, 58, 68, 78, 87, 96

Hands-On

Hands-On Lab Activities . . . . pp. 12–19

Technology Lab Activities . . . . pp. 5–8

Alternate Openers: Explorations . . . . pp. 22–31

Family Involvement Activities . . . . pp. 25–32

Applications and Connections

Consumer and Career Math . . . . pp. 9–12

Interdisciplinary Posters . . . . Poster 3, TE p. 128B

Interdisciplinary Poster Worksheets . . . . pp. 7–9

Transparencies

Alternate Openers: Explorations . . . . pp. 22–31

Exercise Answers Transparencies

Chapter 3 Resource Book . . . . pp. T1–T45

- Daily Transparencies
- Additional Examples Transparencies
- Teaching Transparencies

Technology

Teacher Resources

***Lesson Presentations* CD-ROM** . . . . Chapter 3

***Test and Practice Generator* CD-ROM** . . . . Chapter 3

***One-Stop Planner* CD-ROM** . . . . Chapter 3

Student Resources

***Are You Ready? Intervention* CD-ROM**
Skills 51, 53, 54, 57

internet connect

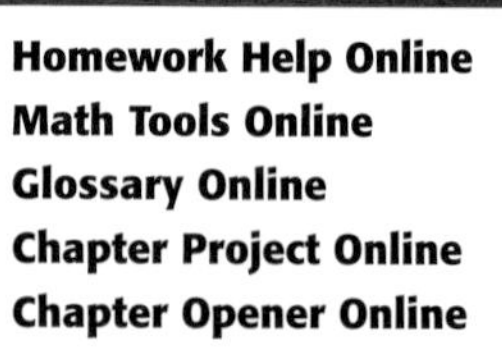

Homework Help Online	**KEYWORD:** MS4 HWHelp3
Math Tools Online	**KEYWORD:** MS4 Tools
Glossary Online	**KEYWORD:** MS4 Glossary
Chapter Project Online	**KEYWORD:** MS4 PSProject3
Chapter Opener Online	**KEYWORD:** MS4 Ch3
CNN Student News	**KEYWORD:** MS4 CNN3

SE = *Student Edition* **TE** = *Teacher's Edition* **AR** = *Assessment Resources* **CRB** = *Chapter Resource Book* **MK** = *Manipulatives Kit*

Chapter 3

Assessment Options

Assessing Prior Knowledge

Determine whether students have the required prerequisite concepts and skills.

Are You Ready? . . . . SE p. 129
Inventory Test . . . . AR pp. 1–4

Test Preparation

Provide review and practice for chapter and standardized tests.

Standardized Test Prep . . . . SE p. 189
Spiral Review with Test Prep . . . . . SE, last page of each lesson
Study Guide and Review . . . . SE pp. 184–186
Test Prep Tool Kit

Technology

Test and Practice Generator **CD-ROM**

internet connect

State-Specific Test Practice Online KEYWORD: MS4 TestPrep

Performance Assessment

Assess students' understanding of chapter concepts and combined problem-solving skills.

Performance Assessment . . . . SE p. 188
Includes scoring rubric in TE
Performance Assessment . . . . AR p. 110
Performance Assessment Teacher Support . . . . AR p. 109

Portfolio

Portfolio opportunities appear throughout the Student and Teacher's Editions.

Suggested work samples:

Problem Solving Project . . . . TE p. 128
Performance Assessment . . . . SE p. 188
Portfolio Guide . . . . AR p. xxxv
Journal . . . . TE, last page of each lesson
Write About It . . . . . . SE pp. 133, 137, 143, 153, 159, 165, 169, 173, 177

Daily Assessment

Obtain daily feedback on students' understanding of concepts.

Spiral Review and Test Prep . . . . . . SE, last page of each lesson

Also Available on Transparency In Chapter 3 Resource Book

Warm Up . . . . TE, first page of each lesson
Problem of the Day . . . . TE, first page of each lesson
Lesson Quiz . . . . TE, last page of each lesson

Student Self-Assessment

Have students evaluate their own work.

Group Project Evaluation . . . . AR p. xxxii
Individual Group Member Evaluation . . . . AR p. xxxiii
Portfolio Guide . . . . AR p. xxxv
Journal . . . . TE, last page of each lesson

Formal Assessment

Assess students' mastery of concepts and skills.

Section Quizzes . . . . AR pp. 11–12
Mid-Chapter Quiz . . . . SE p. 160
Chapter Test . . . . SE p. 187
Chapter Tests (Levels A, B, C) . . . . AR pp. 45–50
Cumulative Tests (Levels A, B, C) . . . . AR pp. 153–164
Standardized Test Prep
Cumulative Assessment . . . . SE p. 189
End-of-Year Test . . . . AR pp. 273–276

Technology

Test and Practice Generator **CD-ROM**

Make tests electronically. This software includes:

- Dynamic practice for Chapter 3
- Customizable tests
- Multiple-choice items for each objective
- Free-response items for each objective
- Teacher management system

SE = *Student Edition* **TE** = *Teacher's Edition* **AR** = *Assessment Resources* **CRB** = *Chapter Resource Book* **MK** = *Manipulatives Kit*

Chapter 3

Chapter 3 Tests

Three levels (A,B,C) of tests are available for each chapter in the *Assessment Resources.*

LEVEL A

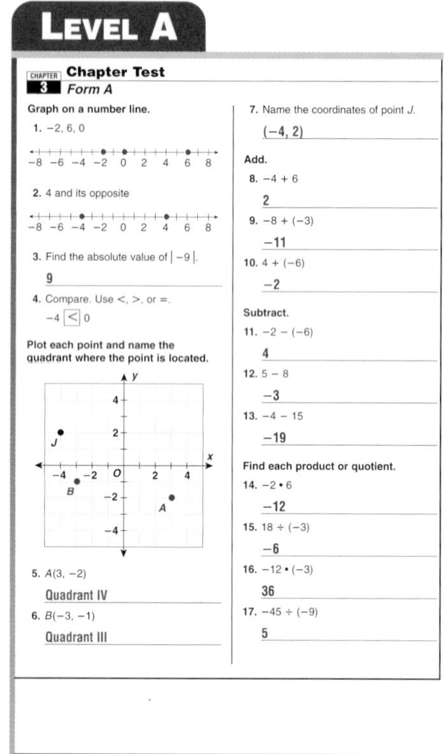

CHAPTER 3 Chapter Test
Form A

Graph on a number line.

1. $-2, 6, 0$
2. 4 and its opposite
3. Find the absolute value of $|-9|$.
   9
4. Compare. Use <, >, or =.
   -4 [<] 0

Plot each point and name the quadrant where the point is located.

5. $A(3, -2)$
   Quadrant IV
6. $B(-3, -1)$
   Quadrant III
7. Name the coordinates of point J.
   (−4, 2)

Add.

8. $-4 + 6$
   2
9. $-8 + (-3)$
   −11
10. $4 + (-6)$
    −2

Subtract.

11. $-2 - (-6)$
    4
12. $5 - 8$
    −3
13. $-4 - 15$
    −19

Find each product or quotient.

14. $-2 \cdot 6$
    −12
15. $18 \div (-3)$
    −6
16. $-12 \cdot (-3)$
    36
17. $-45 \div (-9)$
    5

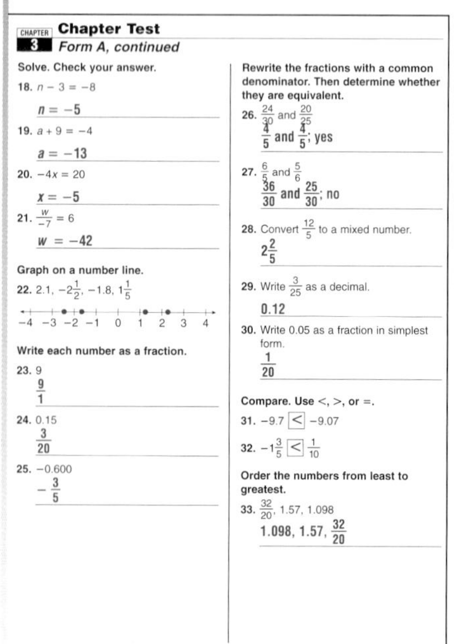

CHAPTER 3 Chapter Test
Form A, continued

Solve. Check your answer.

18. $n - 3 = -8$
    $n = -5$
19. $a + 9 = -4$
    $a = -13$
20. $-4x = 20$
    $x = -5$
21. $\frac{w}{-7} = 6$
    $w = -42$

Graph on a number line.

22. $2.1, -2\frac{1}{2}, -1.8, 1\frac{1}{5}$

Write each number as a fraction.

23. 9
    $\frac{9}{1}$
24. 0.15
    $\frac{3}{20}$
25. −0.600
    $-\frac{3}{5}$

Rewrite the fractions with a common denominator. Then determine whether they are equivalent.

26. $\frac{24}{30}$ and $\frac{20}{25}$
    $\frac{4}{5}$ and $\frac{4}{5}$; yes
27. $\frac{6}{5}$ and $\frac{5}{6}$
    $\frac{36}{30}$ and $\frac{25}{30}$; no
28. Convert $\frac{12}{5}$ to a mixed number.
    $2\frac{2}{5}$
29. Write $\frac{3}{25}$ as a decimal.
    0.12
30. Write 0.05 as a fraction in simplest form.
    $\frac{1}{20}$

Compare. Use <, >, or =.

31. -9.7 [<] -9.07
32. $-1\frac{3}{5}$ [<] $\frac{1}{10}$

Order the numbers from least to greatest.

33. $\frac{32}{20}$, 1.57, 1.098
    1.098, 1.57, $\frac{32}{20}$

LEVEL B

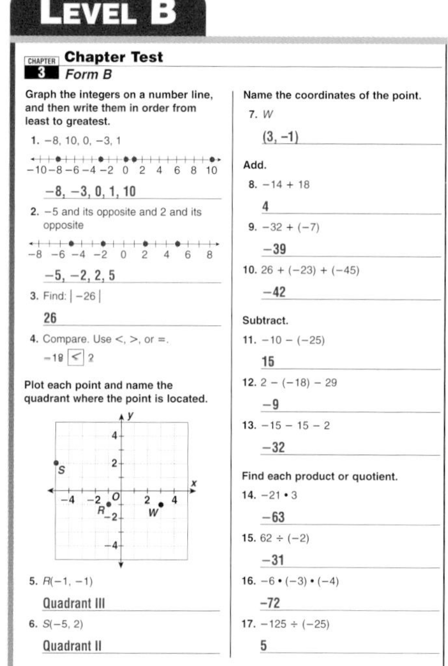

CHAPTER 3 Chapter Test
Form B

Graph the integers on a number line, and then write them in order from least to greatest.

1. $-8, 10, 0, -3, 1$
   −8, −3, 0, 1, 10
2. −5 and its opposite and 2 and its opposite
   −5, −2, 2, 5
3. Find: $|-26|$
   26
4. Compare. Use <, >, or =.
   -18 [<] 2

Plot each point and name the quadrant where the point is located.

5. $R(-1, -1)$
   Quadrant III
6. $S(-5, 2)$
   Quadrant II

Name the coordinates of the point.

7. W
   (3, −1)

Add.

8. $-14 + 18$
   4
9. $-32 + (-7)$
   −39
10. $26 + (-23) + (-45)$
    −42

Subtract.

11. $-10 - (-25)$
    15
12. $2 - (-18) - 29$
    −9
13. $-15 - 15 - 2$
    −32

Find each product or quotient.

14. $-21 \cdot 3$
    −63
15. $62 \div (-2)$
    −31
16. $-6 \cdot (-3) \cdot (-4)$
    −72
17. $-125 \div (-25)$
    5

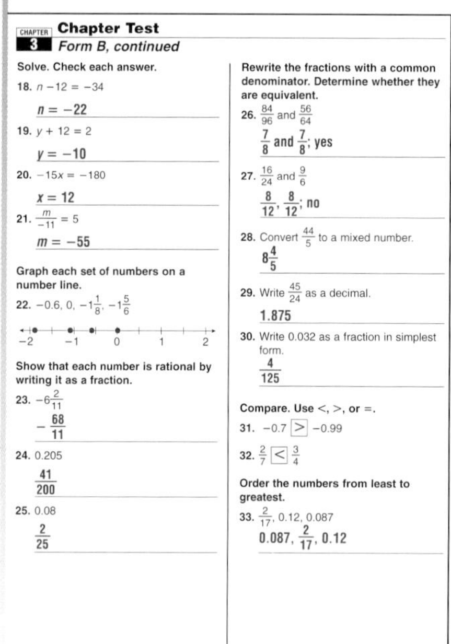

CHAPTER 3 Chapter Test
Form B, continued

Solve. Check each answer.

18. $n - 12 = -34$
    $n = -22$
19. $y + 12 = 2$
    $y = -10$
20. $-15x = -180$
    $x = 12$
21. $\frac{m}{-11} = 5$
    $m = -55$

Graph each set of numbers on a number line.

22. $-0.6, 0, -1\frac{1}{8}, -1\frac{5}{6}$

Show that each number is rational by writing it as a fraction.

23. $-6\frac{2}{11}$
    $-\frac{68}{11}$
24. 0.205
    $\frac{41}{200}$
25. 0.08
    $\frac{2}{25}$

Rewrite the fractions with a common denominator. Determine whether they are equivalent.

26. $\frac{84}{96}$ and $\frac{56}{64}$
    $\frac{7}{8}$ and $\frac{7}{8}$; yes
27. $\frac{16}{24}$ and $\frac{9}{6}$
    $\frac{8}{12}, \frac{8}{12}$; no
28. Convert $\frac{44}{5}$ to a mixed number.
    $8\frac{4}{5}$
29. Write $\frac{45}{24}$ as a decimal.
    1.875
30. Write 0.032 as a fraction in simplest form.
    $\frac{4}{125}$

Compare. Use <, >, or =.

31. -0.7 [>] -0.99
32. $\frac{2}{7}$ [<] $\frac{3}{4}$

Order the numbers from least to greatest.

33. $\frac{2}{17}$, 0.12, 0.087
    0.087, $\frac{2}{17}$, 0.12

LEVEL C

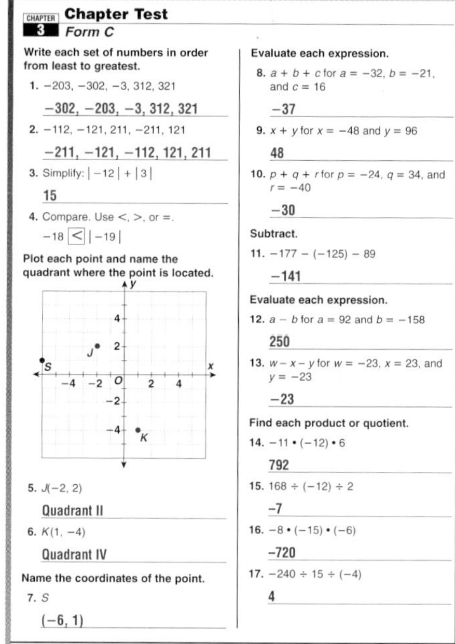

CHAPTER 3 Chapter Test
Form C

Write each set of numbers in order from least to greatest.

1. $-203, -302, -3, 312, 321$
   −302, −203, −3, 312, 321
2. $-112, -121, 211, -211, 121$
   −211, −121, −112, 121, 211
3. Simplify: $|-12| + |3|$
   15
4. Compare. Use <, >, or =.
   -18 [<] $|-19|$

Plot each point and name the quadrant where the point is located.

5. $J(-2, 2)$
   Quadrant II
6. $K(1, -4)$
   Quadrant IV

Name the coordinates of the point.

7. S
   (−6, 1)

Evaluate each expression.

8. $a + b + c$ for $a = -32$, $b = -21$, and $c = 16$
   −37
9. $x + y$ for $x = -48$ and $y = 96$
   48
10. $p + q + r$ for $p = -24$, $q = 34$, and $r = -40$
    −30

Subtract.

11. $-177 - (-125) - 89$
    −141

Evaluate each expression.

12. $a - b$ for $a = 92$ and $b = -158$
    250
13. $w - x - y$ for $w = -23$, $x = 23$, and $y = -23$
    −23

Find each product or quotient.

14. $-11 \cdot (-12) \cdot 6$
    792
15. $168 \div (-12) \div 2$
    −7
16. $-8 \cdot (-15) \cdot (-6)$
    −720
17. $-240 \div 15 \div (-4)$
    4

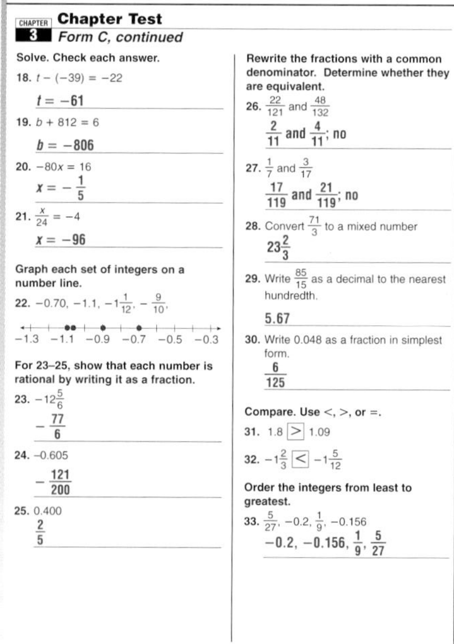

CHAPTER 3 Chapter Test
Form C, continued

Solve. Check each answer.

18. $t - (-39) = -22$
    $t = -61$
19. $b + 812 = 6$
    $b = -806$
20. $-80x = 16$
    $x = -\frac{1}{5}$
21. $\frac{x}{24} = -4$
    $x = -96$

Graph each set of integers on a number line.

22. $-0.70, -1.1, -1\frac{1}{12}, -\frac{9}{10}$

For 23–25, show that each number is rational by writing it as a fraction.

23. $-12\frac{5}{6}$
    $-\frac{77}{6}$
24. −0.605
    $-\frac{121}{200}$
25. 0.400
    $\frac{2}{5}$

Rewrite the fractions with a common denominator. Determine whether they are equivalent.

26. $\frac{22}{121}$ and $\frac{48}{132}$
    $\frac{2}{11}$ and $\frac{4}{11}$; no
27. $\frac{1}{7}$ and $\frac{3}{17}$
    $\frac{17}{119}$ and $\frac{21}{119}$; no
28. Convert $\frac{71}{3}$ to a mixed number
    $23\frac{2}{3}$
29. Write $\frac{85}{15}$ as a decimal to the nearest hundredth.
    5.67
30. Write 0.048 as a fraction in simplest form.
    $\frac{6}{125}$

Compare. Use <, >, or =.

31. 1.8 [>] 1.09
32. $-1\frac{2}{3}$ [<] $-1\frac{5}{12}$

Order the integers from least to greatest.

33. $\frac{5}{27}$, −0.2, $\frac{1}{9}$, −0.156
    −0.2, −0.156, $\frac{1}{9}$, $\frac{5}{27}$

***Test and Practice Generator* CD-ROM**

Create and customize multiple versions of the same tests with corresponding answers for any chosen chapter objectives.

Chapter 3 State and Standardized Test Preparation

Test Taking Skill Builder and Standardized Test Practice are provided for each chapter in the *Test Prep Tool Kit.*

TEST TAKING SKILL BUILDER

Test Taking Strategies **Multiple Choice—Working Backwards**
Chapter 3

There will be times that you may not know how to solve a multiple choice test question. If the test does not penalize you for guessing, then you need to provide an answer to every question. One method to help you to make an educated guess is to use the answer choices provided and work backwards to solve the question.

Example 1 Find the value of x that makes the equation true.
$x + -4 = -9$

A $x = 13$ B $x = 5$ C $x = -5$ D $x = -13$

Work backwards to find the correct solution.

Try Choice A: $x = 13$
$x + -4 = -9$
$13 + -4 \stackrel{?}{=} -9$ Substitute 13 into the equation.
$9 \neq -9$ $x = 13$ is not the correct solution.

Try Choice B: $x = 5$
$x + -4 = -9$
$5 + -4 \stackrel{?}{=} -9$ Substitute 5 into the equation.
$1 \neq -9$ $x = 5$ is not the correct solution.

Try Choice C: $x = -5$
$x + -4 = -9$
$-5 + -4 \stackrel{?}{=} -9$ Substitute -5 into the equation.
$-9 = -9$ $x = -5$ is the correct solution.

The correct answer is Choice C. You do not have to try Choice D since you found the answer.

Example 2 Solve for x. $4x = -16$

F 4 G 2 H -4 I -8

Try Choice F: $x = 4$
$4x = -16$
$4 \cdot 4 \stackrel{?}{=} -16$ Substitute 4 into the equation.
$16 \neq -16$ $x = 4$ is not the correct solution.

Try Choice H next since the only thing wrong with Choice F was the negative sign: $x = -4$
$4x = -16$
$4(-4) \stackrel{?}{=} -16$ Substitute -4 into the equation.
$-16 = -16$ $x = -4$ is the correct solution.

The correct answer is Choice H.

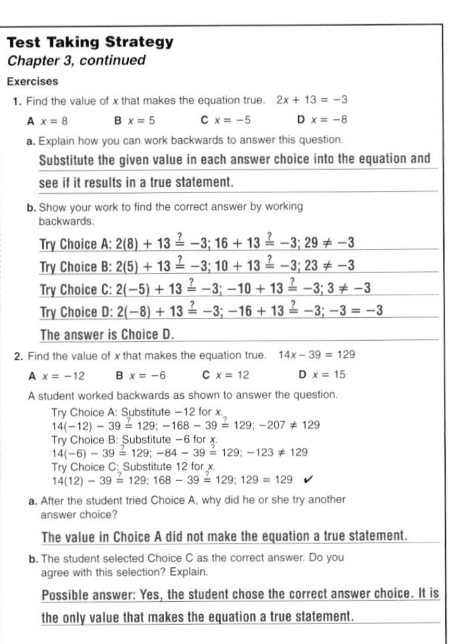

Test Taking Strategy
Chapter 3, continued

Exercises

1. Find the value of x that makes the equation true. $2x + 13 = -3$
   A $x = 8$ B $x = 5$ C $x = -5$ D $x = -8$
   a. Explain how you can work backwards to answer this question.
   Substitute the given value in each answer choice into the equation and see if it results in a true statement.
   b. Show your work to find the correct answer by working backwards.
   Try Choice A: $2(8) + 13 \stackrel{?}{=} -3$; $16 + 13 \stackrel{?}{=} -3$; $29 \neq -3$
   Try Choice B: $2(5) + 13 \stackrel{?}{=} -3$; $10 + 13 \stackrel{?}{=} -3$; $23 \neq -3$
   Try Choice C: $2(-5) + 13 \stackrel{?}{=} -3$; $-10 + 13 \stackrel{?}{=} -3$; $3 \neq -3$
   Try Choice D: $2(-8) + 13 \stackrel{?}{=} -3$; $-16 + 13 \stackrel{?}{=} -3$; $-3 = -3$
   The answer is Choice D.
2. Find the value of x that makes the equation true. $14x - 39 = 129$
   A $x = -12$ B $x = -6$ C $x = 12$ D $x = 15$
   A student worked backwards as shown to answer the question.
   Try Choice A: Substitute -12 for x.
   $14(-12) - 39 \stackrel{?}{=} 129$; $-168 - 39 \stackrel{?}{=} 129$; $-207 \neq 129$
   Try Choice B: Substitute -6 for x.
   $14(-6) - 39 \stackrel{?}{=} 129$; $-84 - 39 \stackrel{?}{=} 129$; $-123 \neq 129$
   Try Choice C: Substitute 12 for x.
   $14(12) - 39 \stackrel{?}{=} 129$; $168 - 39 \stackrel{?}{=} 129$; $129 = 129$ ✔
   a. After the student tried Choice A, why did he or she try another answer choice?
   The value in Choice A did not make the equation a true statement.
   b. The student selected Choice C as the correct answer. Do you agree with this selection? Explain.
   Possible answer: Yes, the student chose the correct answer choice. It is the only value that makes the equation a true statement.

STANDARDIZED TEST PRACTICE

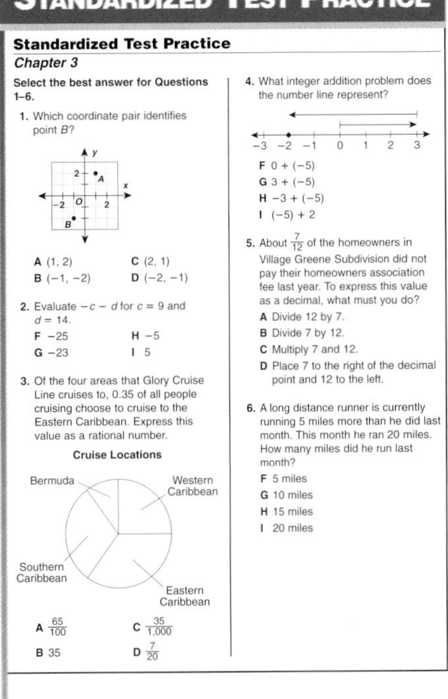

Standardized Test Practice
Chapter 3

Select the best answer for Questions 1–6.

1. Which coordinate pair identifies point B?
   A (1, 2) C (2, 1)
   B (−1, −2) D (−2, −1)
2. Evaluate $-c - d$ for $c = 9$ and $d = 14$.
   F −25 H −5
   G −23 I 5
3. Of the four areas that Glory Cruise Line cruises to, 0.35 of all people cruising choose to cruise to the Eastern Caribbean. Express this value as a rational number.
   Cruise Locations

   A $\frac{65}{100}$ C $\frac{35}{1,000}$
   B 35 D $\frac{7}{20}$
4. What integer addition problem does the number line represent?
   F $0 + (-5)$
   G $3 + (-5)$
   H $-3 + (-5)$
   I $(-5) + 2$
5. About $\frac{7}{12}$ of the homeowners in Village Greene Subdivision did not pay their homeowners association fee last year. To express this value as a decimal, what must you do?
   A Divide 12 by 7.
   B Divide 7 by 12.
   C Multiply 7 and 12.
   D Place 7 to the right of the decimal point and 12 to the left.
6. A long distance runner is currently running 5 miles more than he did last month. This month he ran 20 miles. How many miles did he run last month?
   F 5 miles
   G 10 miles
   H 15 miles
   I 20 miles

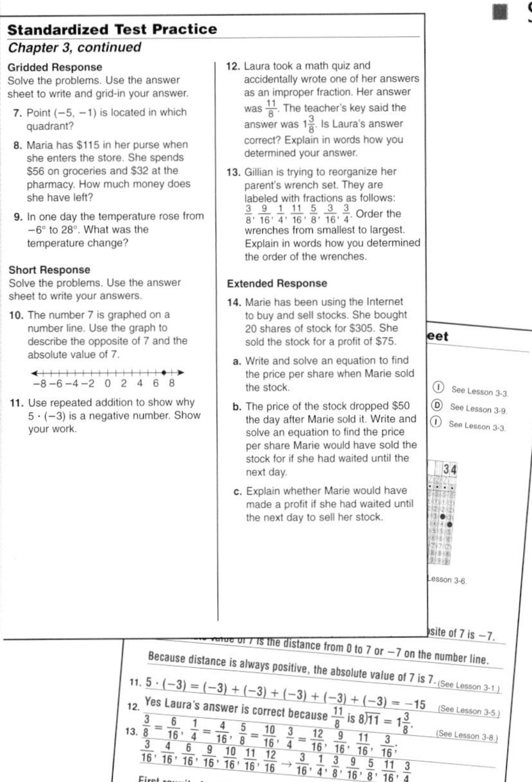

Standardized Test Practice
Chapter 3, continued

Gridded Response
Solve the problems. Use the answer sheet to write and grid-in your answer.

7. Point (−5, −1) is located in which quadrant?
8. Maria has $115 in her purse when she enters the store. She spends $56 on groceries and $32 at the pharmacy. How much money does she have left?
9. In one day the temperature rose from −6° to 28°. What was the temperature change?

Short Response
Solve the problems. Use the answer sheet to write your answers.

10. The number 7 is graphed on a number line. Use the graph to describe the opposite of 7 and the absolute value of 7.
11. Use repeated addition to show why $5 \cdot (-3)$ is a negative number. Show your work.
12. Laura took a math quiz and accidentally wrote one of her answers as an improper fraction. Her answer was $\frac{11}{8}$. The teacher's key said the answer was $1\frac{3}{8}$. Is Laura's answer correct? Explain in words how you determined your answer.
13. Gillian is trying to reorganize her parent's wrench set. They are labeled with fractions as follows: $\frac{3}{8}, \frac{9}{16}, \frac{1}{4}, \frac{11}{16}, \frac{5}{8}, \frac{3}{16}, \frac{3}{4}$. Order the wrenches from smallest to largest. Explain in words how you determined the order of the wrenches.

Extended Response

14. Marie has been using the Internet to buy and sell stocks. She bought 20 shares of stock for $305. She sold the stock for a profit of $75.
    a. Write and solve an equation to find the price per share when Marie sold the stock.
    b. The price of the stock dropped $50 the day after Marie sold it. Write and solve an equation to find the price per share Marie would have sold the stock for if she had waited until the next day.
    c. Explain whether Marie would have made a profit if she had waited until the next day to sell her stock.

...eet
(I) See Lesson 3-3
(D) See Lesson 3-9
(I) See Lesson 3-3
...esson 3-6
...value of 7 is the distance from 0 to 7 or −7 on the number line. ...site of 7 is −7.
Because distance is always positive, the absolute value of 7 is 7. (See Lesson 3-1)
11. $5 \cdot (-3) = (-3) + (-3) + (-3) + (-3) + (-3) = -15$ (See Lesson 3-5)
12. Yes Laura's answer is correct because $\frac{11}{8}$ is $8\overline{)11} = 1\frac{3}{8}$. (See Lesson 3-8)
13. $\frac{3}{8} = \frac{6}{16}$, $\frac{1}{4} = \frac{4}{16}$, $\frac{5}{8} = \frac{10}{16}$, $\frac{3}{4} = \frac{12}{16}$, $\frac{9}{16}, \frac{11}{16}, \frac{3}{16}$;
$\frac{3}{16}, \frac{4}{16}, \frac{6}{16}, \frac{9}{16}, \frac{10}{16}, \frac{11}{16}, \frac{12}{16} \rightarrow \frac{3}{16}, \frac{1}{4}, \frac{3}{8}, \frac{9}{16}, \frac{5}{8}, \frac{11}{16}, \frac{3}{4}$
First rewrite fractions with common denominators.
Then order them by their numerators. (See Lesson 3-10)
Extended Response
Write your answers for Problem 14 on the back of this paper. See Lesson 3-6

internet connect
State-Specific Test Practice Online
KEYWORD: MS4 TestPrep

Test Prep Tool Kit

- Standardized Test Prep Workbook
- Countdown to Testing transparencies
- State Test Prep CD-ROM
- Standardized Test Prep Video

Customized answer sheets give students realistic practice for actual standardized tests.

Chapter 3

Integers and Rational Numbers

Why Learn This?

Tell students that the speed of sound is different under different conditions. Have students look at the table. The table shows the speed of sound through different materials at various temperatures.

Using Data

To begin the study of this chapter, have students read the page and find the speed of sound through air at 0°C, 20°C, and 100°C.

0°C: 332 m/s

20°C: 344 m/s

100°C: 392 m/s

Chapter 3

Integers and Rational Numbers

TABLE OF CONTENTS

internet connect
Chapter Opener Online
go.hrw.com
KEYWORD: MS4 Ch3

Speed of Sound Through Different Materials

Material	Speed (m/s)
Air at 20°C	344
Water at 20°C	1,500
Wood (oak) at 20°C	3,850
Glass at 20°C	4,540
Steel at 20°C	5,200

Career ***Oceanographer***

Is Earth warming? Or is it cooling? The temperature of the oceans is a very important factor in answering these questions. Oceanographers have been studying the temperature of the Pacific Ocean by measuring the speed of sound waves in the water.

How does this work? The speed of sound is affected by the temperature of the material through which the sound travels. In air, for example, the speed of sound increases about 0.6 meter per second for every degree Celsius that the temperature rises. By measuring the speed of sound in water, scientists can tell the water's temperature.

Problem Solving Project

Earth Science Connection

Purpose: To solve problems using integers

Materials: Sound Speed worksheet, sound insulating materials

internet connect
Chapter Project Online: ***go.hrw.com***
KEYWORD: MS4 PSProject3

Understand, Plan, Solve, and Look Back

Have students:

- ✔ Complete the Sound Speed worksheet to learn, develop, and present information about the speed of sound as it passes through various materials.
- ✔ Create an equation to show that the speed of sound in air increases by about 0.6 meter per second for every degree Celsius that the temperature rises.
- ✔ Research the concept of the sound barrier. What does it mean when an airplane goes through the sound barrier?
- ✔ Check students' work.

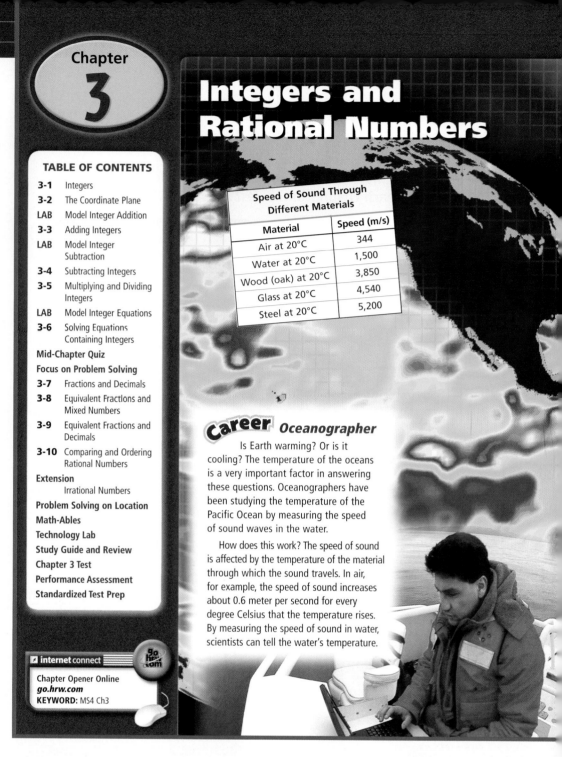

ARE YOU READY?

Choose the best term from the list to complete each sentence.

1. To __?__ a number on a number line, mark and label the point that corresponds to that number. **graph**	whole number
2. The expression $5 > 3 > 1$ tells the __?__ of these three numbers on a number line. **order**	expression
3. A(n) __?__ is a mathematical statement showing two things are equal. **equation**	graph
4. Each number in the set 0, 1, 2, 3, 4, 5, 6, 7, ... is a(n) __?__. **whole number**	solve
5. To __?__ an equation, find a value that makes it true. **solve**	equation
	order

Complete these exercises to review skills you will need for this chapter.

✔ Order of Operations

Simplify.

6. $7 + 9 - 5 \cdot 2$ **6**
7. $12 \cdot 3 - 4 \cdot 5$ **16**
8. $115 - 15 \cdot 3 + 9(8 - 2)$ **124**
9. $20 \cdot 5 \cdot 2(7 + 1) \div 4$ **400**

✔ Evaluate Expressions with Variables

Evaluate each expression for the given value of n.

10. $n + 3$ for $n = 2$ **5**
11. $3n - 9$ for $n = 10$ **21**
12. $\frac{6n}{5} + 2^2$ for $n = 5$ **10**
13. $501 + 9 - n^2$ for $n = 20$ **110**

✔ Use Inverse Operations to Solve Equations

Solve.

14. $n + 3 = 10$ **$n = 7$**
15. $x - 4 = 16$ **$x = 20$**
16. $9p = 63$ **$p = 7$**
17. $\frac{t}{5} = 80$ **$t = 400$**
18. $x - 3 = 14$ **$x = 17$**
19. $\frac{q}{3} = 21$ **$q = 63$**
20. $9 + r = 91$ **$r = 82$**
21. $15p = 45$ **$p = 3$**

✔ Words for Operations

Write an algebraic expression for each.

22. the sum of 3 and a number **$3 + n$**
23. the difference of 4 and a number **$4 - n$**
24. 6 minus the product of a number and 10 **$6 - (n \cdot 10)$**

Assessing Prior Knowledge

INTERVENTION

Diagnose and Prescribe

Evaluate your students' performance on this page to determine whether intervention is necessary or whether enrichment is appropriate. Options that provide instruction, practice, and a check are listed below.

Resources for Are You Ready?

- ***Are You Ready? Intervention and Enrichment***
- **Recording Sheet for Are You Ready?** *Chapter 3 Resource Book* p. 3

***Are You Ready? Intervention* CD-ROM**

Are You Ready? Intervention
go.hrw.com
KEYWORD: MS4 AYR

ARE YOU READY?

Were students successful with Are You Ready?

NO INTERVENE

YES ENRICH

✔Order of Operations
Are You Ready? Intervention, Skill 51
Blackline Masters, Online, and

CD-ROM
Intervention Activities

✔Evaluate Expressions with Variables
Are You Ready? Intervention, Skill 54
Blackline Masters, Online, and

CD-ROM
Intervention Activities

✔Use Inverse Operations to Solve Equations
Are You Ready? Intervention, Skill 57
Blackline Masters, Online, and

CD-ROM
Intervention Activities

✔Words for Operations
Are You Ready? Intervention, Skill 53
Blackline Masters, Online, and

CD-ROM
Intervention Activities

Are You Ready? Enrichment, pp. 411–412

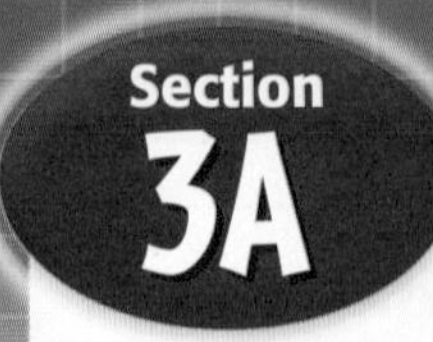

Section 3A Integers

One-Minute Section Planner

Lesson	Materials	Resources
Lesson 3-1 Integers **NCTM:** Number and Operations, Communication, Representation **NAEP:** Number Properties 1b ☑ SAT-9 ☑ SAT-10 ☑ ITBS ☑ CTBS ☑ MAT ☑ CAT	Optional Teaching Transparency T2 *(CRB)*	• *Chapter 3 Resource Book,* pp. 6–14 • Daily Transparency T1, CRB • Additional Examples Transparencies T3–T4, CRB • *Alternate Openers: Explorations,* p. 22
Lesson 3-2 The Coordinate Plane **NCTM:** Geometry, Communication, Connections, Representation **NAEP:** Algebra 2c ☐ SAT-9 ☐ SAT-10 ☐ ITBS ☐ CTBS ☐ MAT ☐ CAT	**Required** Graph paper *(CRB, p. 105)* Optional Teaching Transparency T6 *(CRB)* Coordinate Grid for Reaching all Learners *(CRB, p. 106)*	• *Chapter 3 Resource Book,* pp. 15–23 • Daily Transparency T5, CRB • Additional Examples Transparencies T7–T8, CRB • *Alternate Openers: Explorations,* p. 23
Hands-On Lab 3A Model Integer Addition **NCTM:** Number and Operations, Algebra, Geometry, Reasoning and Proof, Representation **NAEP:** Number Properties 3a ☐ SAT-9 ☐ SAT-10 ☐ ITBS ☐ CTBS ☐ MAT ☑ CAT	**Required** Algebra Tiles *(MK)*	• *Hands-On Lab Activities,* pp. 12–13, 126
Lesson 3-3 Adding Integers **NCTM:** Number and Operations, Algebra, Geometry, Reasoning and Proof, Communication **NAEP:** Number Properties 3a ☑ SAT-9 ☑ SAT-10 ☑ ITBS ☑ CTBS ☑ MAT ☑ CAT	Optional Two-color counters *(MK)* Teaching Transparency T10 *(CRB)*	• *Chapter 3 Resource Book,* pp. 24–32 • Daily Transparency T9, CRB • Additional Examples Transparencies T11–T13, CRB • *Alternate Openers: Explorations,* p. 24
Hands-On Lab 3B Model Integer Subtraction **NCTM:** Number and Operations, Algebra, Geometry, Reasoning and Proof, Representation **NAEP:** Number Properties 3a ☐ SAT-9 ☐ SAT-10 ☐ ITBS ☐ CTBS ☐ MAT ☐ CAT	**Required** Algebra Tiles *(MK)*	• *Hands-On Lab Activities,* pp. 14–16, 126
Lesson 3-4 Subtracting Integers **NCTM:** Number and Operations, Geometry, Reasoning and Proof, Communication **NAEP:** Number Properties 3a ☑ SAT-9 ☑ SAT-10 ☐ ITBS ☑ CTBS ☑ MAT ☑ CAT	Optional Two-color counters *(MK)*	• *Chapter 3 Resource Book,* pp. 33–41 • Daily Transparency T14, CRB • Additional Examples Transparencies T15–T17, CRB • *Alternate Openers: Explorations,* p. 25
Lesson 3-5 Multiplying and Dividing Integers **NCTM:** Number and Operations, Communication **NAEP:** Number Properties 3a ☑ SAT-9 ☑ SAT-10 ☐ ITBS ☑ CTBS ☑ MAT ☑ CAT	Optional Teaching Transparency T19 *(CRB)*	• *Chapter 3 Resource Book,* pp. 42–50 • Daily Transparency T18, CRB • Additional Examples Transparencies T20–T21, CRB • *Alternate Openers: Explorations,* p. 26
Hands-On Lab 3C Model Integer Equations **NCTM:** Algebra, Geometry, Representation **NAEP:** Algebra 4a ☐ SAT-9 ☐ SAT-10 ☐ ITBS ☐ CTBS ☐ MAT ☐ CAT	**Required** Algebra Tiles *(MK)*	• *Hands-On Lab Activities,* pp. 17–19, 126
Lesson 3-6 Solving Equations Containing Integers **NCTM:** Algebra, Communication **NAEP:** Algebra 4a ☐ SAT-9 ☐ SAT-10 ☐ ITBS ☐ CTBS ☐ MAT ☐ CAT	Optional Algebra Tiles *(MK)* Colored pencils	• *Chapter 3 Resource Book,* pp. 51–60 • Daily Transparency T22, CRB • Additional Examples Transparencies T23–T26, CRB • *Alternate Openers: Explorations,* p. 27
Section 3A Assessment		• Mid-Chapter Quiz, SE p. 160 • Section 3A Quiz, AR p. 11 • *Test and Practice Generator* CD-ROM

NCTM—Complete standards can be found on pages T27–T33. **NAEP**—Complete standards can be found on pages A35–A39.

Section Overview

Understanding Integers — Lesson 3-1

Why? Integers are used to represent real-world quantities, such as temperatures below zero.

The **integers** are the set of whole numbers and their **opposites.**

Opposites are the same distance from 0, but on opposite sides of 0.

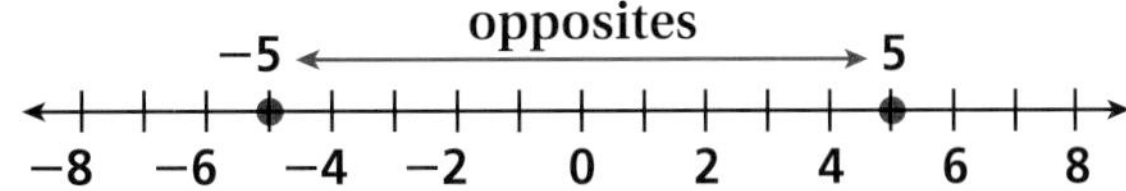

Graphing on a Coordinate Plane — Lesson 3-2

Why? When a coordinate plane includes integers, the horizontal and vertical axes divide the plane into four quadrants.

Each point on a coordinate plane is identified by an **ordered pair** of numbers: an *x*-coordinate and a *y*-coordinate.

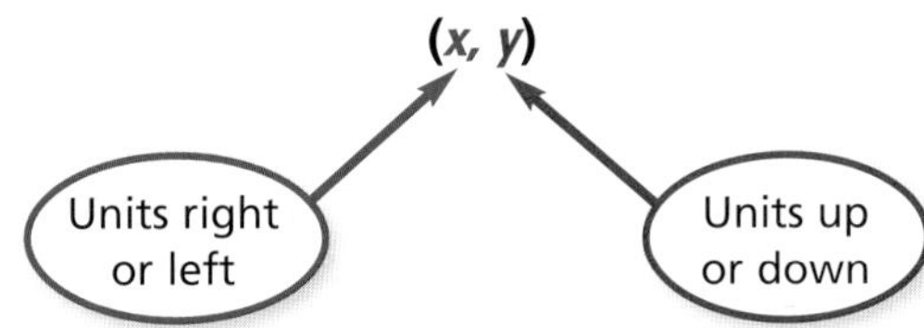

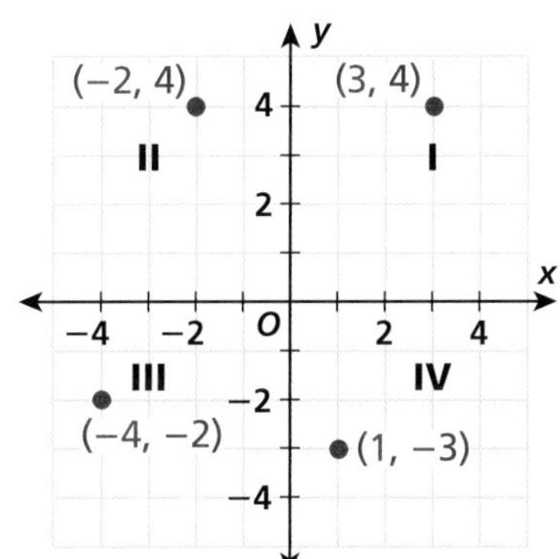

Integer Operations and Equations — Hands-On Labs 3A, 3B, 3C; Lessons 3-3 through 3-6

Why? When you know how to operate with integers, you can solve equations and problems involving integers.

Operation	Rule	Examples
Add integers with the same sign.	Find the sum of their absolute values. Then use the sign of the integers.	$5 + (+4) = 9$ $(-6) + (-2) = -8$
Add integers with different signs.	Find the difference of their absolute values. Then use the sign of the integer with the greater absolute value.	$9 + (-3) = 6$ $-8 + 7 = -1$
Subtract integers.	To subtract an integer, add its opposite.	$2 - (-3) = 2 + 3 = 5$ $-7 - 1 = -7 + (-1) = -8$
Multiply or divide integers.	If the signs are the same, the answer will be positive. If the signs are different, the answer will be negative.	$4 \cdot 5 = 20$; $-24 \div -6 = 4$ $-8 \cdot 3 = -24$; $36 \div -4 = -9$

When solving equations with integers, the goal is the same as with whole numbers—isolate the variable on one side of the equation.

$$-8z = -72$$
$$\frac{-8z}{-8} = \frac{-72}{-8} \quad \text{Divide both sides by } -8.$$
$$z = 9$$

3-1 Organizer

Pacing: Traditional 1 day
Block $\frac{1}{2}$ day

Objective: Students compare and order integers and determine absolute value.

Warm Up

Compare. Use <, >, or =.

1. 7 ▢ 5 > **2.** 32 ▢ 65 <
3. 82 ▢ 28 > **4.** 64 ▢ 48 >

Problem of the Day

Place 4, 5, 6, 7, 8, and 9 in the empty circles so that each side has the same sum.

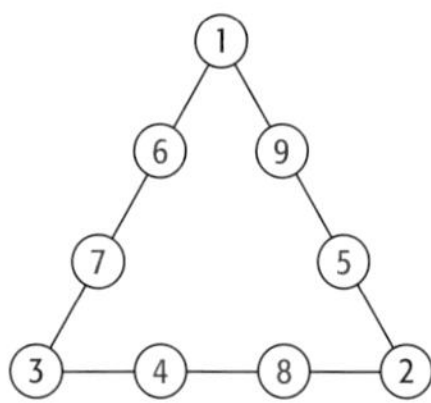

Available on Daily Transparency in CRB

Math Fact !!!

The coldest temperature on record in the U.S. is −80°F, recorded in 1971 in Alaska.

3-1 Integers

Learn to compare and order integers and to determine absolute value.

Vocabulary
opposite
integer
absolute value

The **opposite** of a number is the same distance from 0 on a number line as the original number, but on the other side of 0. Zero is its own opposite.

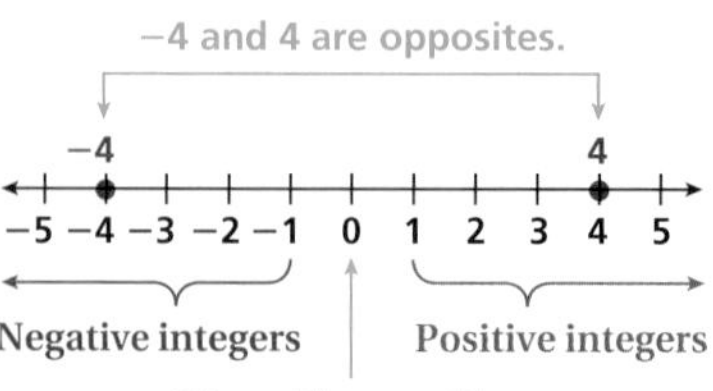

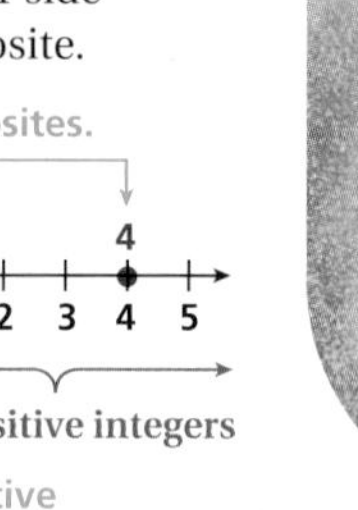

Dr. Sylvia Earle holds the world record for the deepest solo dive.

Remember!
The whole numbers are the counting numbers and zero: 0, 1, 2, 3, ...

The **integers** are the set of whole numbers and their opposites. By using integers, you can express elevations above, below, and at sea level. Sea level has an elevation of 0 feet. Sylvia Earle's record dive was to an elevation of −1,250 feet.

EXAMPLE 1 Graphing Integers and Their Opposites on a Number Line

Graph each integer and its opposite on a number line.

A 5

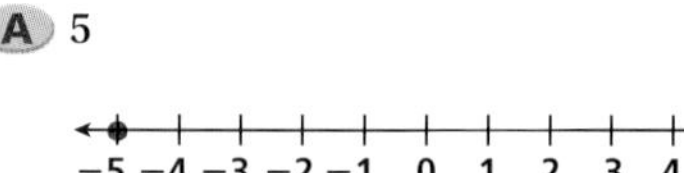

The opposite of 5 is −5.

B −3

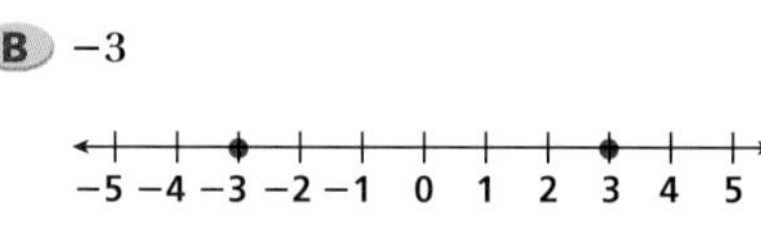

The opposite of −3 is 3.

Remember!
The symbol < means "is less than," and the symbol > means "is greater than."

Integers increase in value as you move to the right along a number line. They decrease in value as you move to the left.

−6 < −2 and 1 > −3

1 Introduce

Alternate Opener

EXPLORATION

3-1 Integers

You can use a thermometer to determine whether to use the symbol < or > when comparing integers.

Because 70° **is lower than** 80°, you can write:

70 < 80

Because 80° **is higher than** 70°, you can write:

80 > 70

1. Find −40° and −20° on the thermometer. Write two statements with −40 and −20 using the symbols < and >.

°F 90 80 70 60 50 40 30 20 10 0 −10 −20 −30 −40 −50

Compare. Write < or >.

2. 60 ☐ 20 **3.** 0 ☐ 30
4. 0 ☐ −30 **5.** −40 ☐ −10
6. −10 ☐ 15 **7.** 10 ☐ −15
8. −20 ☐ −30 **9.** 20 ☐ 30
10. 20 ☐ −30

Think and Discuss

11. Explain why −20 < −10 is a correct statement.
12. Describe how to order the integers 0, −3, 5, 1, −2, −7, and 2 from least to greatest.

Motivate

To introduce students to integers, ask them to give examples of opposites. Focus on pairs that can be represented by numbers (e.g., up and down, hot and cold, winning and losing). Give examples of real-world uses of integers (e.g., temperatures, football yardage, and altitude). Use students' input to write a definition of the opposite of a number. Point out that with opposites, the direction is different, but the distance between two points is always the same.

Exploration worksheet and answers on Chapter 3 Resource Book pp. 7 and 108

2 Teach

Lesson Presentation

Guided Instruction

In this lesson, students learn to compare and order integers and to determine absolute value. As students begin to work with ordering integers, encourage them to place the integers on the number line before ordering them. Ask students to state each number's distance from zero. Use responses to define *absolute value.*

Teaching Tip Suggest that students think of the zero on a number line as a mirror. Each integer has a reflection, its opposite, an equal distance from zero but on the other side. (You may want to use Teaching Transparency T2 in the Chapter 3 Resource Book.)

EXAMPLE 2 Writing Integers in Order

Graph the integers on a number line, and then write them in order from least to greatest.

$-2, 5, -4, 1, -1, 0$

$-4, -2, -1, 0, 1, 5$

A number's **absolute value** is its distance from 0 on a number line. Since distance can never be negative, absolute values are never negative. They are always positive or zero. The symbol || represents the absolute value of a number. This symbol is read as "the absolute value of." For example, $|-3|$ is the absolute value of -3.

EXAMPLE 3 Finding Absolute Value

Use a number line to find each absolute value.

A $|7|$

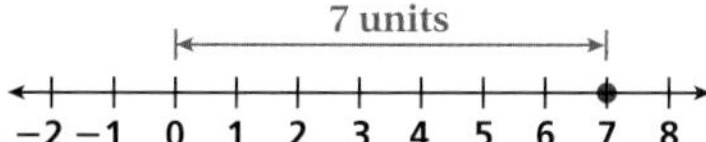

7 is 7 units from 0, so $|7| = 7$.

B $|-4|$

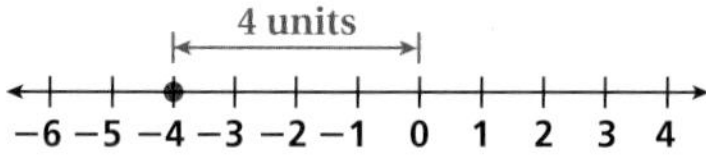

-4 is 4 units from 0, so $|-4| = 4$.

Think and Discuss

1. **Tell** whether two different integers can have the same absolute value. If yes, give an example. If no, explain why not.
2. **Name** the greatest negative integer and the least nonnegative integer. Then compare the absolute values of these integers.
3. **Give an example** in which a negative number has a greater absolute value than a positive number.

COMMON ERROR ALERT

When ordering negative numbers, some students might look at the absolute value of the number and say that the number with the greater absolute value is greater; for example, they might say that -10 is greater than -3, but it is not. Encourage students to think about the position of each integer on the number line.

Additional Examples

Example 1

Graph each integer and its opposite on a number line.

A. 4 (−4, 0, 4 5)

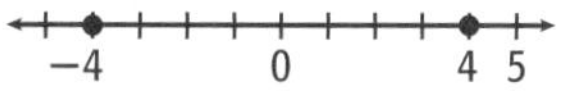

B. −7 (−7 −4 −2 0 2 4 6 7 8)

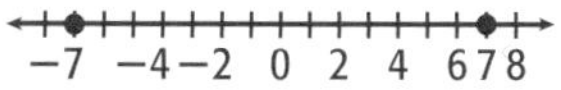

Example 2

Graph the integers on a number line, and then write them in order from least to greatest.

$-3, 6, -5, 2, 0, -8$

−8 −6 −4 −2 0 2 4 6 8

$-8, -5, -3, 0, 2, 6$

Example 3

Use a number line to find each absolute value.

A. $|8|$ $\quad |8| = 8$

B. $|-12|$ $\quad |-12| = 12$

3 Close

Reaching All Learners
Through Critical Thinking

Pose this question: What is the opposite of the opposite of a number? Encourage students to test several examples to show the opposite of the opposite of a number and then state a rule.

Possible answer:
The opposite of 4 is -4. The opposite of -4 is 4. So the opposite of the opposite of 4 is 4. The opposite of -7 is 7. The opposite of 7 is -7. So the opposite of the opposite of 7 is 7. Rule: The opposite of the opposite of a number is the original number.

Summarize

You may wish to have students explain absolute value in their own words. Discuss the difference between whole numbers and integers.

Possible answer: A number's absolute value tells how far from zero the number is but does not tell which direction. Whole numbers include positive numbers and zero, while integers contain negatives as well.

Answers to Think and Discuss

1. Yes. Possible answer: $|-1| = 1$, and $|1| = 1$.
2. The greatest negative integer is -1. The least nonnegative integer is 0. The absolute value of -1 is 1. The absolute value of 0 is 0. The absolute value of -1 is greater than the absolute value of 0.
3. Possible answer: The absolute value of -5 is 5. The absolute value of 3 is 3.

3-1 PRACTICE & ASSESS

Students may want to refer back to the lesson examples.

Assignment Guide

If you finished Example 1 assign:
Core 1–4, 12–15, 41–43, 49–65
Enriched 1–4, 12–15, 41–43, 49–65

If you finished Example 2 assign:
Core 1–7, 12–18, 41–45 odd, 49–65
Enriched 1–7 odd, 12–18, 41–45, 49–65

If you finished Example 3 assign:
Core 1–22, 23–45 odd, 49–65
Enriched 1–21 odd, 23–65

Answers

1–22. Complete answers on p. A1

3-1 Exercises

FOR EXTRA PRACTICE
see page 660

internet connect
Homework Help Online
go.hrw.com Keyword: MS4 3-1

GUIDED PRACTICE

See Example 1 Graph each integer and its opposite on a number line.

1. 2 **2.** −9 **3.** −1 **4.** 6

See Example 2 Graph the integers on a number line, and then write them in order from least to greatest.

5. 6, −3, −1, −5, 4 **−5, −3, −1, 4, 6**
6. 8, −2, 7, 1, −8 **−8, −2, 1, 7, 8**
7. −6, −4, 3, 0, 1 **−6, −4, 0, 1, 3**

See Example 3 Use a number line to find each absolute value.

8. $|-2|$ **2** **9.** $|8|$ **8** **10.** $|-7|$ **7** **11.** $|-10|$ **10**

INDEPENDENT PRACTICE

See Example 1 Graph each integer and its opposite on a number line.

12. −4 **13.** 10 **14.** −12 **15.** 7

See Example 2 Graph the integers on a number line, and then write them in order from least to greatest.

16. −3, 2, −5, −6, 5 **−6, −5, −3, 2, 5**
17. −7, −9, −2, 0, −5 **−9, −7, −5, −2, 0**
18. 3, −6, 9, −1, −2 **−6, −2, −1, 3, 9**

See Example 3 Use a number line to find each absolute value.

19. $|-16|$ **16** **20.** $|12|$ **12** **21.** $|-20|$ **20** **22.** $|15|$ **15**

PRACTICE AND PROBLEM SOLVING

Compare. Write <, >, or =.

23. −25 ▢ 25 **<** **24.** 18 ▢ −55 **>** **25.** $|-21|$ ▢ 21 **=** **26.** −9 ▢ −27 **>**

27. 34 ▢ $|34|$ **=** **28.** 64 ▢ $|-75|$ **<** **29.** 7 ▢ −8 **>** **30.** $|-3|$ ▢ $|3|$ **=**

31. $|-2|$ ▢ −10 **>** **32.** 2 ▢ −25 **>** **33.** −100 ▢ −82 **<** **34.** $|-6|$ ▢ $|-15|$ **<**

Find each absolute value.

35. $|-294|$ **294** **36.** $|61|$ **61** **37.** $|-45|$ **45** **38.** $|-380|$ **380**

39. What is the opposite of $|32|$? **−32**

40. What is the opposite of $|-29|$? **−29**

41. ***SOCIAL STUDIES*** Death Valley, California, is 282 feet below sea level. Write the elevation of Death Valley as an integer. **−282**

42. ***BUSINESS*** A company reported a net loss of $2,000,000 during its first year. In its second year it reported a profit of $5,000,000. Write each amount as an integer. **−2,000,000; 5,000,000**

Math Background

Some early mathematicians resisted the idea of negative numbers, but others developed symbols to work with the concept. The ancient Chinese used red tiles to represent positive numbers and black tiles to represent negative numbers. Today, accountants use a reverse color assignment.

The mathematical concept of absolute value parallels the notion of magnitude in science. Forces act on bodies with a magnitude, or size, and a direction. The sign of an integer tells its direction, and the absolute value tells its magnitude.

RETEACH 3-1

LESSON 3-1 **Reteach**
Integers

This number line shows integers.

0 is neither positive nor negative
negative integers | positive integers
−5 −4 −3 −2 −1 0 1 2 3 4 5

Every integer has an **opposite** integer. A number and its opposite are the same distance from 0.

opposites
4 | 4
−5 −4 −3 −2 −1 0 1 2 3 4 5

1. How many units is 4 from 0? **4**
2. How many units is −4 from 0? **4**
3. 4 and −4 are called **opposite integers**.

Graph each integer and its opposite on a number line.

4. 2
−5 −4 −3 −2 −1 0 1 2 3 4 5

5. −3
−5 −4 −3 −2 −1 0 1 2 3 4 5

You can use a number line to compare and order numbers. The numbers get greater as you move to the right on the number line.

−5 −4 −3 −2 −1 0 1 2 3 4 5

6. What is the order from least to greatest of −1, 2, and −3? **−3; −1; 2**

Write the integers in order from least to greatest.

7. −2; −6; 4 **−6; −2; 4**
8. −3; 7; 1 **−3; 1; 7**

The absolute value of an integer is its distance from 0 on a number line. −5 is 5 units from 0. The absolute value of −5 is 5. You write $|-5| = 5$.

5 units | 5 units
−5 −4 −3 −2 −1 0 1 2 3 4 5

9. How many units from 0 is −3? **3**

PRACTICE 3-1

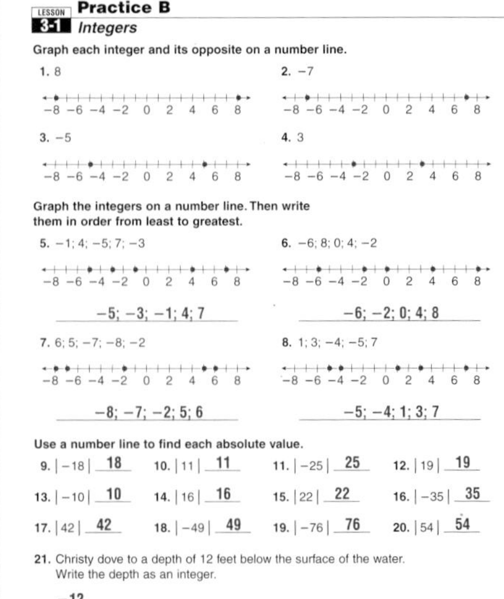

LESSON 3-1 **Practice B**
Integers

Graph each integer and its opposite on a number line.

1. 8
−8 −6 −4 −2 0 2 4 6 8

2. −7
−8 −6 −4 −2 0 2 4 6 8

3. −5
−8 −6 −4 −2 0 2 4 6 8

4. 3
−8 −6 −4 −2 0 2 4 6 8

Graph the integers on a number line. Then write them in order from least to greatest.

5. −1; 4; −5; 7; −3
−8 −6 −4 −2 0 2 4 6 8
−5; −3; −1; 4; 7

6. −6; 8; 0; 4; −2
−8 −6 −4 −2 0 2 4 6 8
−6; −2; 0; 4; 8

7. 6; 5; −7; −8; −2
−8 −6 −4 −2 0 2 4 6 8
−8; −7; −2; 5; 6

8. 1; 3; −4; −5; 7
−8 −6 −4 −2 0 2 4 6 8
−5; −4; 1; 3; 7

Use a number line to find each absolute value.

9. $|-18|$ **18** 10. $|11|$ **11** 11. $|-25|$ **25** 12. $|19|$ **19**

13. $|-10|$ **10** 14. $|16|$ **16** 15. $|22|$ **22** 16. $|-35|$ **35**

17. $|42|$ **42** 18. $|-49|$ **49** 19. $|-76|$ **76** 20. $|54|$ **54**

21. Christy dove to a depth of 12 feet below the surface of the water. Write the depth as an integer.
−12

22. The highest point in North Carolina is Mt. Mitchell, with a height of 6,684 feet. Write the height of Mt. Mitchell as an integer.
6,684

Wakeboarding is a combination of surfing and waterskiing. Tony Finn started the sport with his invention of the Skurfer. Herb O'Brien made improvements to the Skurfer, and the wakeboard was born.

43. ***SPORTS*** The graph shows how participation in several sports changed between 1999 and 2000 in the United States.

a. Which sport showed the greatest decrease in participation?

b. By about what percent did participation in racquetball increase or decrease?

c. By about what percent did participation in wall climbing increase or decrease?

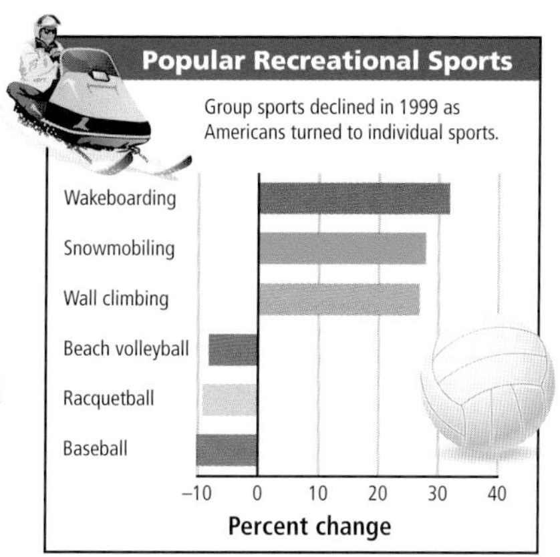

Source: *USA Today,* July 6, 2001

44. ***SOCIAL STUDIES*** Lines of latitude are imaginary lines that circle the globe in an east-west direction. They measure distances north and south of the equator. The equator represents 0° latitude.

a. What latitude is opposite of 30° north latitude? **30° south**

b. How do these latitudes' distances from the equator compare? **They are the same.**

45. ***BUSINESS*** In one year, a company reported a loss of $1,200,000 during its second quarter and a loss of $750,000 during its fourth quarter. During which quarter did the company report a greater loss? **second quarter**

46. ***WHAT'S THE ERROR?*** At 9 A.M. the outside temperature was −3°F. By noon, the temperature was −12°F. A newscaster said that it was getting warmer outside. Why is this incorrect? **−12°F < −3°F, so it was getting colder outside.**

47. ***WRITE ABOUT IT*** Explain how to compare two integers.

48. ***CHALLENGE*** What values can x have if $|x| = 11$? **11 or −11**

Spiral Review

Find each value. (Lesson 2-1)

49. 8^2 **64** 50. 3^4 **81** 51. 15^0 **1** 52. 6^3 **216**

53. 2^6 **64** 54. 5^3 **125** 55. 4^4 **256** 56. 12^2 **144**

Evaluate each expression for $a = 2$ and $b = 9$. (Lesson 2-7)

57. $6a + 7b$ **75** 58. $b - a^2$ **5** 59. $44 \div (a + b)$ **4** 60. $10b + 9a \cdot b$ **252**

61. $b^3 - (6a)^2$ **585** 62. $b(a^2 - a) + 2b$ **36** 63. $a^3 \div 2a - a$ **0** 64. $7b + b^2 \div 3 - a^4$ **74**

65. **TEST PREP** Which is a solution of $b - 25 = 75$? (Lesson 2-11) **C**

A $b = 3$ B $b = 50$ C $b = 100$ D $b = 150$

CHALLENGE 3-1

LESSON 3-1 **Challenge**
Order That Integer!

Use two < signs to correctly order each set of integers.

1. −12; 12; −11 **−12 < −11 < 12**
2. −12; −210; −201 **−210 < −201 < −12**
3. |−3|; |−6|; |1| **|1| < |−3| < |−6|**
4. |−38|; |3|; −15 **−15 < |3| < |−38|**

Use two > signs to correctly order each set of integers.

5. −4; −40; 4 **4 > −4 > −40**
6. 0; −8; |−18| **|−18| > 0 > −8**
7. |−75|; |12|; 15 **|−75| > 15 > |12|**
8. −16; −12; 1 **1 > −12 > −16**

Find each missing integer. Write its corresponding letter in each blank to answer the riddle.

A	B	C	E	V	T	L	S	U	O	N
−4	−6	7	6	−3	0	−7	−1	1	2	−2

WHAT DID THE CAR DEALER SAY TO THE CUSTOMER?
THIS DEAL IS

A	N
−5; **−4**; −3	−3; **−2**; −1

A	B	S	O	L	U	T	E
−4; −3; −2	−7; **−6**; −5	**−1**; 0; 1	0; 1; **2**	−9; −8; **−7**	−1; 0; **1**	−1; **0**; 1	5; **6**; 7

V	A	L	U	E
−3; −2; −1	−6; −5; **−4**	**−7**; −6; −5	0; **1**; 2	**6**; 7; 8

PROBLEM SOLVING 3-1

LESSON 3-1 **Problem Solving**
Integers

Write the correct answer.

1. The coldest place on record in the United States was in Alaska in 1971. It was 80°F below zero. Write this temperature as an integer. **−80**

2. The temperature outside was −4°F at Jared's house and −8°F at Mario's house. Where was the temperature warmer? **outside Jared's house**

3. A small business reported a net loss of $62,500 during its first year. In its second year, it reported a profit of $34,100. Write each amount as an integer. **−62,500; 34,100**

4. For one day, Lacy recorded the low temperatures in five U.S. cities. The temperatures were 5°C, −1°C, −3°C, 2°C, and 0°C. Write the temperatures in order from least to greatest. **−3°C; −1°C; 0°C; 2°C; 5°C**

Choose the letter for the best answer.

5. Which number is not an integer?
$-3; 5; \frac{1}{5}; 0$
A −3 (C) $\frac{1}{5}$
B 5 D 0

6. Basha says |5| and |−5| are the same number. Danny says |5| and |−5| are different numbers. Kim says |5| and |−5| both equal 0. Who is correct?
(F) Basha
G Danny
H Kim
J They are all wrong.

7. Use the table at right. Which continent has the highest point?
(A) Asia C Africa
B South America D Australia

8. Use the table at right. Which continent has the lowest point?
F Europe H North America
G Australia (J) Asia

Continent	Highest Point (ft)	Lowest Point (ft)
North America	20,320	−282
South America	22,834	−131
Africa	19,340	−512
Asia	29,028	−1,339
Australia	7,310	−52
Europe	18,510	−92

Answers

43. **a.** baseball
b. decreased by about 9%
c. increased by about 27%

47. Possible answer: Think about their placement on a number line. The integer to the right is the greater integer.

Journal 

Have students describe real-world situations that could be represented using integers. For each situation, ask students what zero would represent. Ask students to discuss what the absolute value of a number would signify in each situation.

Test Prep Doctor 

Exercise 65 tests students' understanding of inverse operations. Two incorrect answer choices, **A** and **B,** are answers students might choose if they use the incorrect operation. Plugging in answer choices can be a successful strategy here, since a quick substitution will let students identify and eliminate incorrect choices.

Lesson Quiz 

Compare. Use <, >, or =.

1. −32 ▒ 32 <

2. 26 ▒ |−26| =

3. −8 ▒ −12 >

4. Graph the numbers −2, 3, −4, 5, and −1 on a number line. Then list the numbers in order from least to greatest.

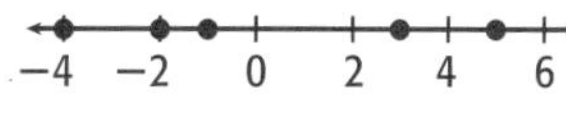

−4, −2, −1, 3, 5

5. The coldest temperature ever recorded east of the Mississippi is fifty-four degrees below zero in Danbury, Wisconsin, on January 24, 1922. Write the temperature as an integer. **−54**

Available on Daily Transparency in CRB

3-2 Organizer

Pacing: Traditional 1 day
Block $\frac{1}{2}$ day

Objective: Students plot and identify ordered pairs on a coordinate plane.

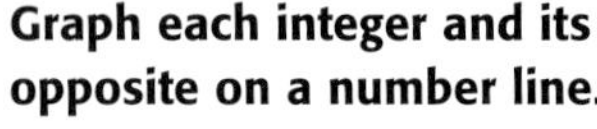

Warm Up

Graph each integer and its opposite on a number line.

1. 4 **2.** −7 **3.** −2

−7 −4 −2 2 4 7
−8 −6 −4 −2 0 2 4 6 8

Graph the integers on a number line.

4. 7, −2, 0, 3, −5

−5 −2 0 3 7
−8 −6 −4 −2 0 2 4 6 8

Problem of the Day

What number am I? I am less than 50. When divided by 5, my remainder is 4. The sum of my digits is 11.
29

Available on Daily Transparency in CRB

Math Fact

Archaeologists use a coordinate system at dig sites to record the original location of each artifact found.

3-2 The Coordinate Plane

Learn to plot and identify ordered pairs on a coordinate plane.

Vocabulary
coordinate plane
x-axis
y-axis
origin
quadrant
ordered pair

A **coordinate plane** is a plane containing a horizontal number line, the **x-axis**, and a vertical number line, the **y-axis**. The intersection of these axes is called the **origin**.

The axes divide the coordinate plane into four regions called **quadrants**, which are numbered I, II, III, and IV.

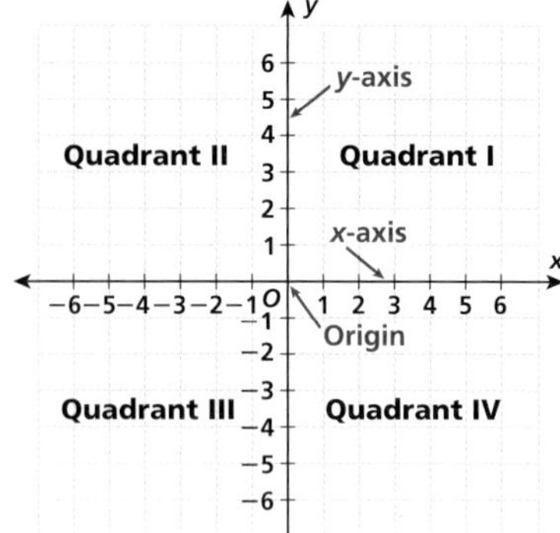

EXAMPLE 1 Identifying Quadrants on a Coordinate Plane

Identify the quadrant that contains each point.

A *P*
P lies in Quadrant II.

B *Q*
Q lies in Quadrant IV.

C *R*
R lies on the *x*-axis, between Quadrants II and III.

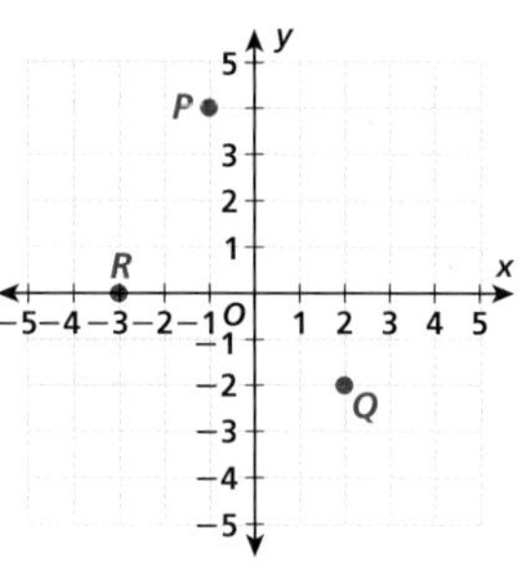

Remember!
A plane is a flat surface that extends indefinitely in all directions.

Points on a coordinate plane are identified by *ordered pairs.* An **ordered pair** consists of two numbers in a certain order. The origin is the point (0, 0).

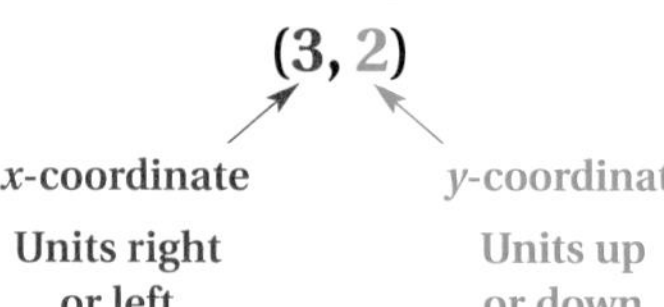

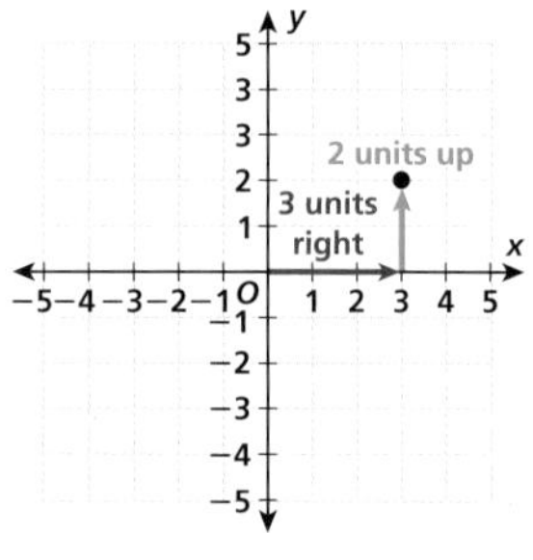

1 Introduce

Alternate Opener

EXPLORATION

3-2 The Coordinate Plane

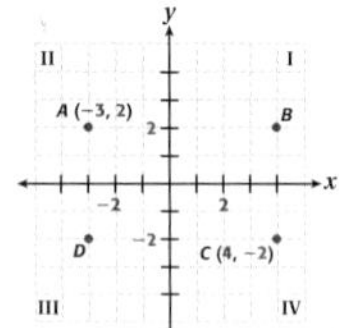

The grid shown has a horizontal number line and a vertical number line that meet in the middle, called the *origin.*

Point *A* is located 3 units to the left of the vertical number line and 2 units above the horizontal number line. Point *A* can be represented with the coordinates (−3, 2).

Point *C* is located 4 units to the right of the vertical number line and 2 units below the horizontal number line. Point *C* is represented with the coordinates (4, −2).

1. Name the coordinates that represent point *B*.
2. Name the coordinates that represent point *D*.

Think and Discuss

3. **Describe** how points *A*, *B*, *C*, and *D* are represented with coordinates.

Motivate

To introduce students to a coordinate plane, have them discuss their experiences with locating a place by using the intersection of two lines (e.g., the streets and avenues in a city or the letters and numbers of a map grid). Students may have played a popular game in which players located "battleships" by using a letter-number grid.

Exploration worksheet and answers on Chapter 3 Resource Book pp. 16 and 110

2 Teach

Lesson Presentation

Guided Instruction

In this lesson, students learn to plot points on a coordinate plane and to name the coordinates of a point. Have students identify the components of a coordinate plane: the two number lines, one placed horizontally (the *x*-axis) and the other placed vertically (the *y*-axis), dividing the plane into four quadrants. Point out that the quadrants are numbered counterclockwise, beginning at the upper right, with the Roman numerals I, II, III, and IV (Teaching Transparency T6 in CRB).

Teaching Tip Remind students that the familiar horizontal number line they studied in Lesson 3-1 corresponds to the *x*-axis.

EXAMPLE 2 Plotting Points on a Coordinate Plane

Plot each point on a coordinate plane.

A $G(2, 5)$

Start at the origin. Move 2 units right and 5 units up.

B $N(-3, -4)$

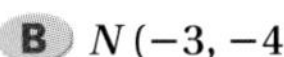

Start at the origin. Move 3 units left and 4 units down.

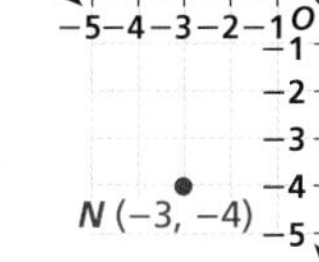

C $P(0, 0)$

Point P is on the origin.

EXAMPLE 3 Identifying Points on a Coordinate Plane

Give the coordinates of each point.

A J

Start at the origin. Point J is 3 units right and 2 units down.

$(3, -2)$

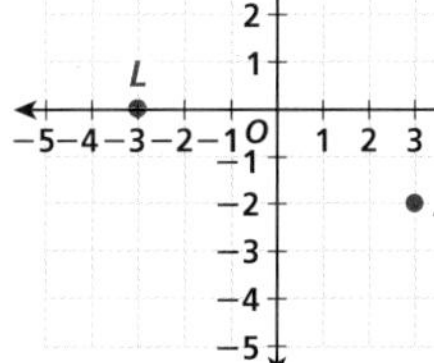

B K

Start at the origin. Point K is 2 units left and 4 units up.

$(-2, 4)$

C L

Start at the origin. Point L is 3 units left on the x-axis.

$(-3, 0)$

Think and Discuss

1. **Explain** whether point (4, 5) is the same as point (5, 4).
2. **Name** the x-coordinate of a point on the y-axis. Name the y-coordinate of a point on the x-axis.
3. **Suppose** the equator is the x-axis on a map of Earth and a line called the *prime meridian,* which passes through England, is the y-axis. Which of these directions—east, west, north, and south—are positive? Which are negative?

Additional Examples

Use the coordinate plane below for Additional Examples 1–3.

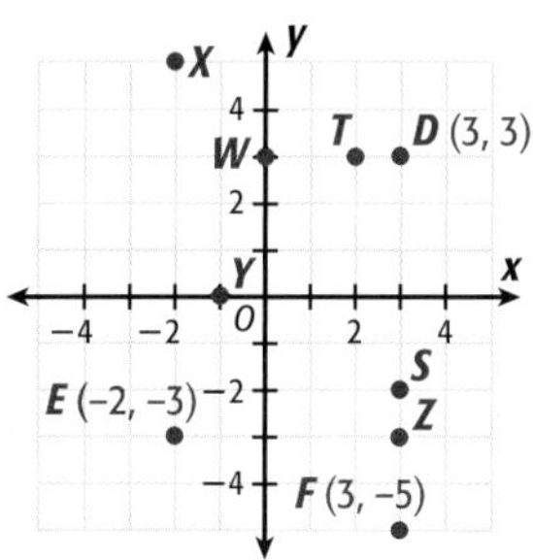

Example 1

Identify the quadrant that contains each point.

A. *S* *S* lies in Quadrant IV.

B. *T* *T* lies in Quadrant I.

C. *W* *W* lies on the *y*-axis between Quadrants I and II.

Example 2

Plot each point on a coordinate plane.

A. *D* (3, 3) **B.** *E* (−2, −3)

C. *F* (3, −5)

See points *D, E,* and *F* above.

Example 3

Give the coordinates of each point.

A. *X* (−2, 5)

B. *Y* (−1, 0)

C. *Z* (3, −3)

3 Close

Reaching All Learners

Through Grouping Strategies

Have students work in three teams to play coordinate tic-tac-toe. Use a coordinate plane that is 5 units from the origin in all directions (provided in the Chapter 3 Resources Book on p. 106). Players on each team alternate calling out the coordinates of a point. Another player on the team locates the point. The mark is placed at the coordinates called, even if it is not the intended point. The first team to place three marks in an uninterrupted row horizontally, vertically, or diagonally wins the round.

Summarize

You may wish to have students write brief definitions of new vocabulary terms in the lesson: *coordinate plane, x-axis, y-axis, origin, quadrant,* and *ordered pair.*

Possible answers: A coordinate plane has a horizontal number line and a vertical number line. The *x*-axis is the horizontal number line. The *y*-axis is the vertical number line. The origin is where the *x*-axis and the *y*-axis cross. The *x*-axis and *y*-axis divide the plane into four sections called quadrants. An ordered pair is made up of two numbers. The first number shows how far to the right or left to move from the origin, and the second shows how far up or down.

Answers to Think and Discuss

1. No, they are not the same point. Possible answer: Point (4, 5) lies 4 units to the right of the origin and 5 units up, while point (5, 4) lies 5 units to the right and 4 units up.
2. The *x*-coordinate of a point on the *y*-axis is 0 because there is no need to move left or right of the *y*-axis. The *y*-coordinate of a point on the *x*-axis is 0 because there is no need to move above or below the *x*-axis.
3. East of the prime meridian is positive, and west is negative. North of the equator is positive, and south is negative.

3-2 PRACTICE & ASSESS

Students may want to refer back to the lesson examples.

Assignment Guide

If you finished Example 1 assign:
Core 1–4, 13–16, 31, 33, 39–44
Enriched 1, 3, 13, 15, 31–34, 39–44

If you finished Example 2 assign:
Core 1–8, 13–20, 27–33 odd, 39–44
Enriched 1–7 odd, 13–20, 27–34, 39–44

If you finished Example 3 assign:
Core 1–26, 27–35 odd, 39–44
Enriched 1–11 odd, 13–44

Answers

5–8.

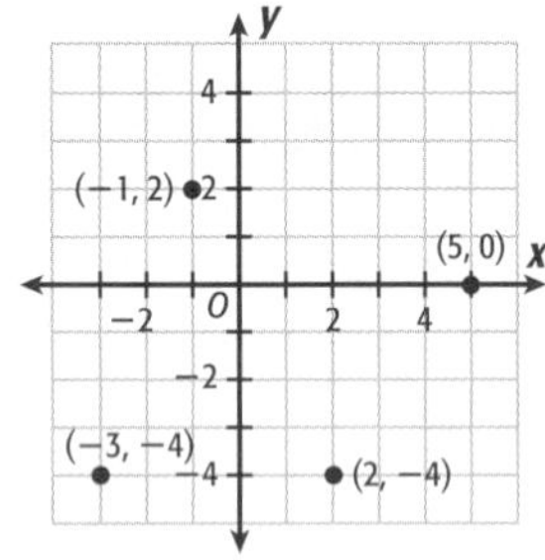

17–20, 27, 28. See p. A1

3-2 Exercises

FOR EXTRA PRACTICE
see page 660

internet connect
Homework Help Online
go.hrw.com Keyword: MS4 3-2

GUIDED PRACTICE

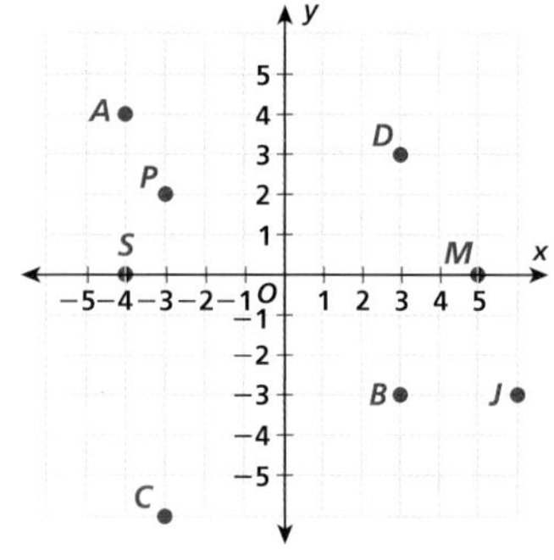

See Example 1 Identify the quadrant that contains each point.

1. A **II**
2. B **IV**
3. C **III**
4. D **I**

See Example 2 Plot each point on a coordinate plane.

5. $(-1, 2)$
6. $(2, -4)$
7. $(-3, -4)$
8. $(5, 0)$

See Example 3 Give the coordinates of each point.

9. J **(6, −3)**
10. P **(−3, 2)**
11. S **(−4, 0)**
12. M **(5, 0)**

INDEPENDENT PRACTICE

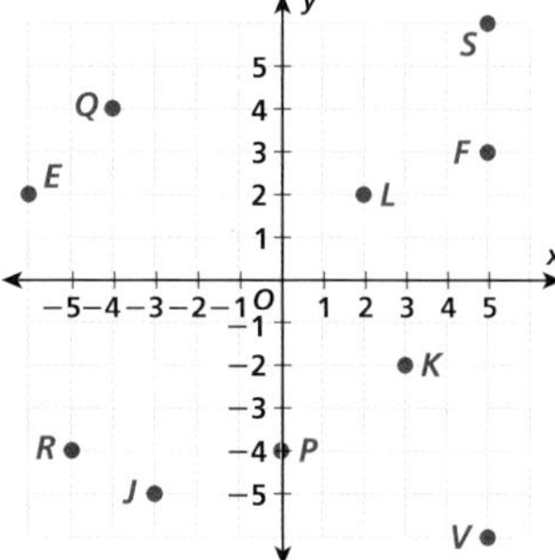

See Example 1 Identify the quadrant that contains each point.

13. F **I**
14. J **III**
15. K **IV**
16. E **II**

See Example 2 Plot each point on a coordinate plane.

17. $(-1, 1)$
18. $(2, -2)$
19. $(-5, -5)$
20. $(0, -3)$

See Example 3 Give the coordinates of each point.

21. Q **(−4, 4)**
22. V **(5, −6)**
23. R **(−5, −4)**
24. P **(0, −4)**
25. S **(5, 6)**
26. L **(2, 2)**

PRACTICE AND PROBLEM SOLVING

For Exercises 27and 28, use graph paper to graph the ordered pairs. Use a different coordinate plane for each exercise.

27. $(-8, 1)$; $(4, 3)$; $(-3, 6)$
28. $(-8, -2)$; $(-1, -2)$; $(-1, 3)$; $(-8, 3)$
29. Draw line segments to connect the points in Exercise 27 in the order listed. Name the figure and the quadrants in which it is located. **triangle; Quadrants I and II**
30. Draw line segments to connect the points in Exercise 28 in the order listed. Name the figure and the quadrants in which it is located. **rectangle; Quadrants II and III**

Math Background

The concept of the rectangular coordinate system is generally credited to French mathematician and philosopher René Descartes (dā • kärt′) and, therefore, is sometimes referred to as the Cartesian plane. Because all real numbers, not just integers, are used, every point on a plane can be located. The points represented by integer coordinates are sometimes called lattice points.

RETEACH 3-2

LESSON 3-2 **Reteach**
The Coordinate Plane

Numbers are graphed on a number line. **Ordered pairs** of numbers are graphed on a **coordinate plane.** A coordinate plane has two perpendicular number lines that divide it into **4 quadrants.** The following chart will help you identify the quadrants and the **coordinates** of points on a coordinate plane.

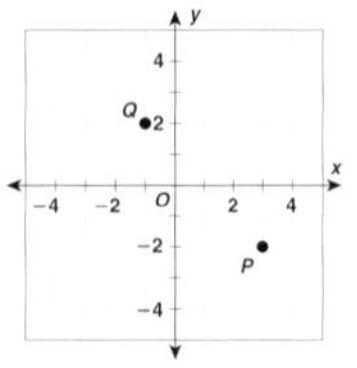

Quadrant II	Quadrant I
(−,+) (←, ↑)	(+, +) (→, ↑)
Quadrant III	**Quadrant IV**
(−, −) (←, ↓)	(+, −) (→, ↓)

To find the coordinates of P, start at (0, 0). Move 3 units →, then 2 units ↓. So the coordinates of P are (3, −2), and P is in quadrant IV.

To plot point Q with coordinates (−1, 2), start at (0, 0). Move 1 unit ←, then 2 units ↑. Q is in quadrant II.

Identify the quadrant and the coordinates of each point on the coordinate plane at the right.

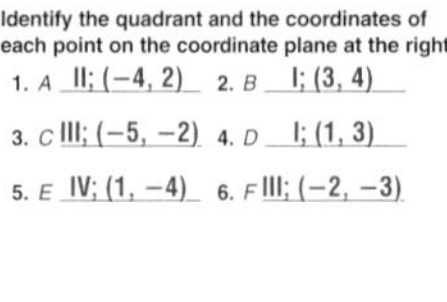

1. A II; (−4, 2)
2. B I; (3, 4)
3. C III; (−5, −2)
4. D I; (1, 3)
5. E IV; (1, −4)
6. F III; (−2, −3)

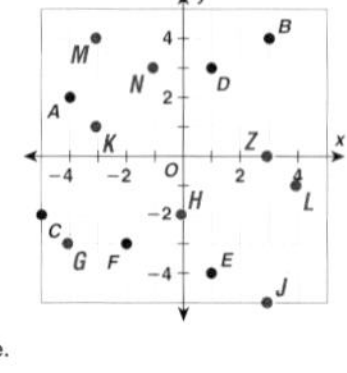

Plot each point on the coordinate plane above.

7. $G\,(-4, -3)$
8. $H\,(0, -2)$
9. $J\,(3, -5)$
10. $K\,(-3, 1)$
11. $L\,(4, -1)$
12. $M\,(-3, 4)$
13. $N\,(-1, 3)$
14. $Z\,(3, 0)$

PRACTICE 3-2

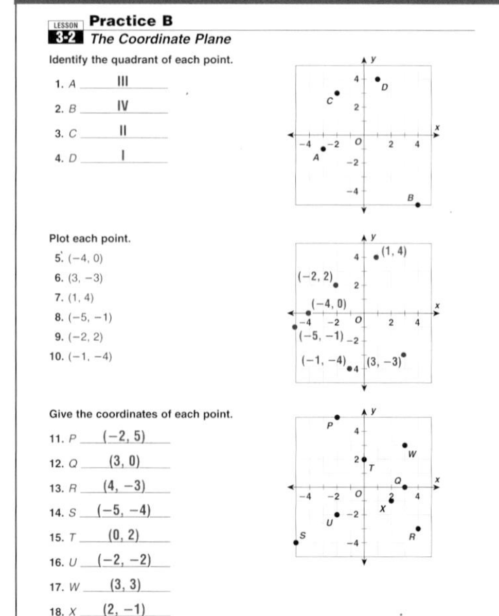

LESSON 3-2 **Practice B**
The Coordinate Plane

Identify the quadrant of each point.

1. A III
2. B IV
3. C II
4. D I

Plot each point.

5. (−4, 0)
6. (3, −3)
7. (1, 4)
8. (−5, −1)
9. (−2, 2)
10. (−1, −4)

Give the coordinates of each point.

11. P (−2, 5)
12. Q (3, 0)
13. R (4, −3)
14. S (−5, −4)
15. T (0, 2)
16. U (−2, −2)
17. W (3, 3)
18. X (2, −1)

Identify the quadrant of each point described below.

31. The x-coordinate and the y-coordinate are both negative. **III**

32. The x-coordinate and the y-coordinate are both positive. **I**

33. The x-coordinate is negative and the y-coordinate is positive. **II**

34. The y-coordinate is negative and the x-coordinate is positive. **IV**

Weather LINK

When the wind speed of a tropical storm reaches 74 mi/h, it is called a hurricane or typhoon, depending on where in the world the storm is located.

go.hrw.com
KEYWORD: MS4 Hurricane

CNN Student News

35. ***WEATHER*** The chart shows the coordinates of Hurricane Andrew in 1992. Use positive for north latitude and negative for west longitude.

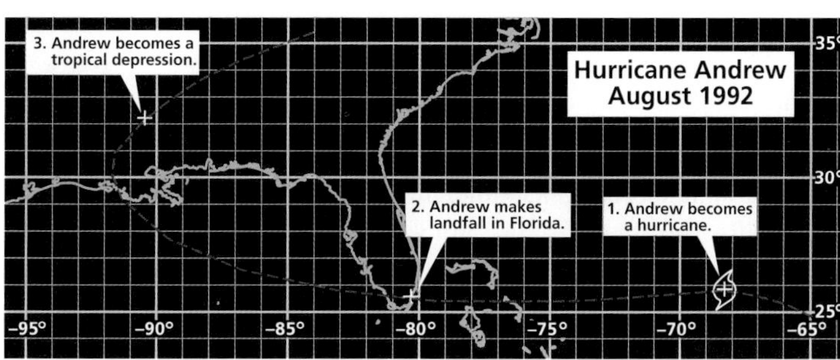

Source: National Hurricane Center

a. Estimate to the nearest integer the coordinates of the storm when it first became a hurricane. **(−68°, 26°)**

b. Estimate to the nearest integer the coordinates of the storm when it made landfall in Florida. **(−80°, 26°)**

c. Estimate to the nearest integer the coordinates of the storm when it weakened to a tropical depression. **(−91°, 32°)**

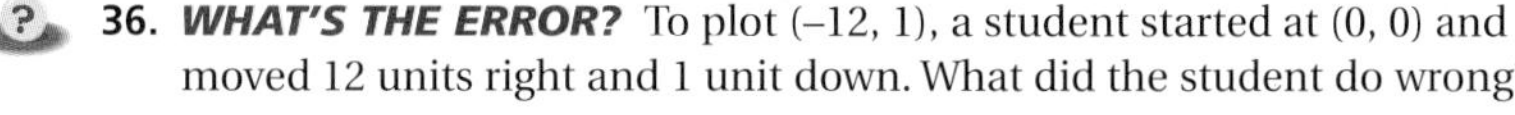

36. ***WHAT'S THE ERROR?*** To plot (–12, 1), a student started at (0, 0) and moved 12 units right and 1 unit down. What did the student do wrong?

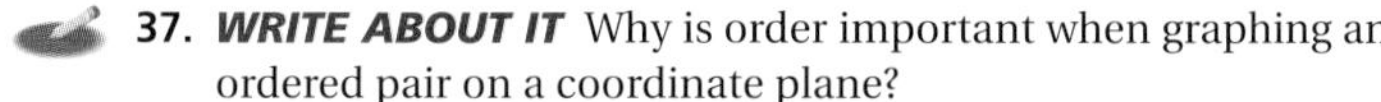

37. ***WRITE ABOUT IT*** Why is order important when graphing an ordered pair on a coordinate plane?

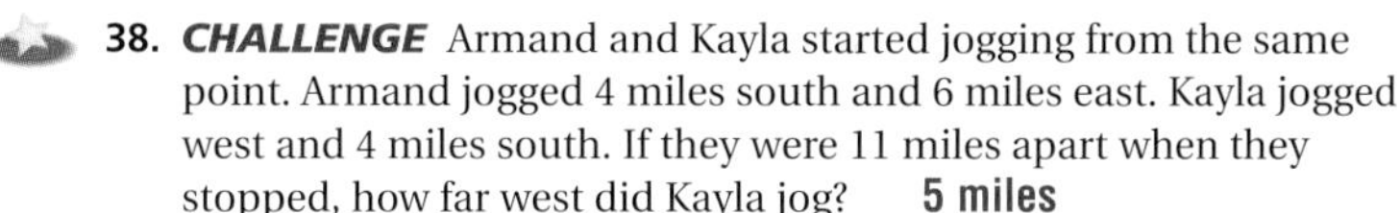

38. ***CHALLENGE*** Armand and Kayla started jogging from the same point. Armand jogged 4 miles south and 6 miles east. Kayla jogged west and 4 miles south. If they were 11 miles apart when they stopped, how far west did Kayla jog? **5 miles**

Spiral Review

Evaluate the expression $9y - 3$ for each given value of the variable. (Lesson 2-7)

39. $y = 2$ **15**
40. $y = 8$ **69**
41. $y = 10$ **87**
42. $y = 18$ **159**

43. **TEST PREP** Simplify $8(2 + 5) - 12$. (Lesson 2-3) **C**

A 3 B 9 C 44 D 49

44. **TEST PREP** Which is the least common multiple of 12 and 20? (Lesson 2-6) **G**

F 4 G 60 H 120 J 240

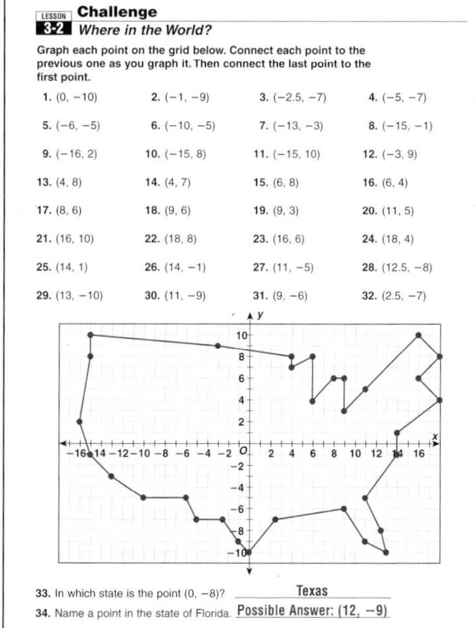

CHALLENGE 3-2

LESSON 3-2 **Challenge**
Where in the World?

Graph each point on the grid below. Connect each point to the previous one as you graph it. Then connect the last point to the first point.

1. (0, −10)	2. (−1, −9)	3. (−2.5, −7)	4. (−5, −7)
5. (−6, −5)	6. (−10, −5)	7. (−13, −3)	8. (−15, −1)
9. (−16, 2)	10. (−15, 8)	11. (−15, 10)	12. (−3, 9)
13. (4, 8)	14. (4, 7)	15. (6, 8)	16. (6, 4)
17. (8, 6)	18. (9, 6)	19. (9, 3)	20. (11, 5)
21. (16, 10)	22. (18, 8)	23. (16, 6)	24. (18, 4)
25. (14, 1)	26. (14, −1)	27. (11, −5)	28. (12.5, −8)
29. (13, −10)	30. (11, −9)	31. (9, −6)	32. (2.5, −7)

33. In which state is the point (0, −8)? **Texas**

34. Name a point in the state of Florida. **Possible Answer: (12, −9)**

PROBLEM SOLVING 3-2

LESSON 3-2 **Problem Solving**
The Coordinate Plane

Write the correct answer.

1. Use the coordinate plane at right. In which quadrant(s) would the figure drawn by connecting points *J*, *K*, and *N* be?

Quadrant IV

2. Use the coordinate plane at right. In which quadrant(s) would the figure drawn by connecting points *C*, *F*, and *M* be?

Quadrants II and III

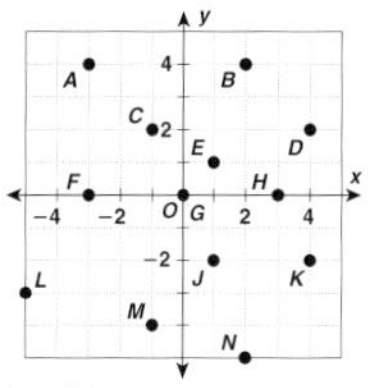

3. Maxine left home and walked 5 blocks north, 5 blocks west, 5 blocks south, and 5 blocks east. Where did she end up?

back at home

4. Mr. Chin drove 2 miles north, then 3 miles east, then 2 miles south. How far is Mr. Chin from where he started?

3 miles

Choose the letter for the best answer.

5. Which one of these points lies in Quadrant II of the coordinate plane above?

A (5, 1) Ⓒ (−5, 1)
B (5, −1) D (−5, −1)

6. In which quadrant of the coordinate plane above is the figure formed by joining (−4, −5), (−2, −3) and (−1, −1)?

F Quadrant I Ⓗ Quadrant III
G Quadrant II J Quadrant IV

7. Abe and Carlos left the library at the same time. Abe walked 4 blocks north and 5 blocks west. Carlos walked 4 blocks east and 4 blocks north. How far apart were they?

A 10 blocks C 8 blocks
Ⓑ 9 blocks D 5 blocks

8. When a point lies on the x-axis, which of these must be true?

F The x-coordinate is 0.
Ⓖ The y-coordinate is 0.
H The x-coordinate is greater than the y-coordinate.
J The y-coordinate is greater than the x-coordinate.

Answers

36. The student should have moved 12 units left from the origin and then 1 unit up.

37. If order is disregarded, a pair of coordinates could refer to either of two points in the same plane.

Journal

Have students render the features of a familiar neighborhood on a coordinate plane. Tell them to designate a landmark such as a library or school as the origin. Ask students to supply the coordinates of the other landmarks as well as written directions for traveling from the origin to the other sites.

Test Prep Doctor

For Exercise 44, choice **F**, 4, is the *greatest common factor* of 12 and 20, which students might confuse with the *least common multiple*. Choices **H** and **J** are designed to tempt students who have not fully examined which factors 12 and 20 have in common. Encourage students to find the prime factorization of each number before choosing an answer.

Lesson Quiz

Give the coordinates of each point and identify the quadrant that contains each point.

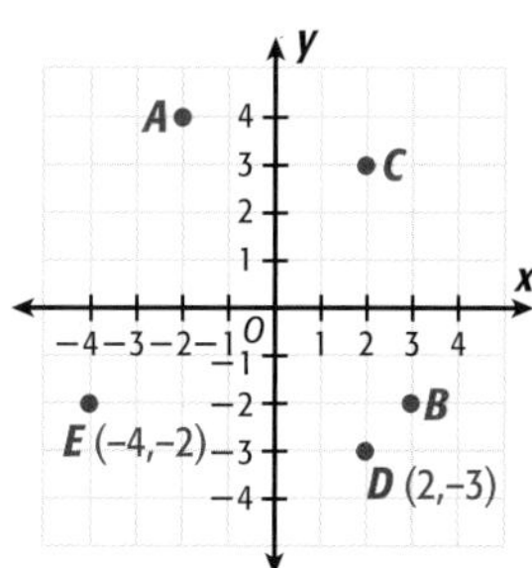

1. A (−2, 4); II
2. B (3, −2); IV
3. C (2, 3); I

Plot each point on a coordinate plane.

4. D (2, −3)
5. E (−4, −2)

See points D and E above.

6. To plot (7, −2) a student started at (0, 0) and moved 7 units left and 2 units down. What did the student do wrong? He should have moved 7 units right.

Available on Daily Transparency in CRB

3A Model Integer Addition

Pacing: Traditional 1 day
Block $\frac{1}{2}$ day

Objective: To use integer chips to model adding integers

Materials: Yellow integer chips and red integer chips

Lab Resources

Hands-On Lab Activities .... pp. 12–13, 126

Using the Pages

Discuss with students what each color integer chip represents and how to represent positive and negative integers with integer chips. Ask students to tell how to represent the number 0 using integer chips.

Be sure students understand that 1 red chip and 1 yellow chip together represent the number zero.

Use integer chips to model and solve the following addition problems.

1. $2 + 3$ 5
2. $-4 + (-2)$ -6
3. $5 + (-1)$ 4
4. $-6 + 3$ -3

Answers

Activity

1. a. 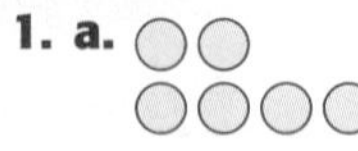

b. 

2. a. 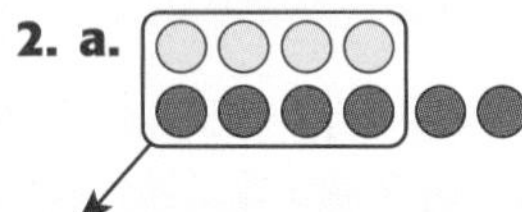

b. 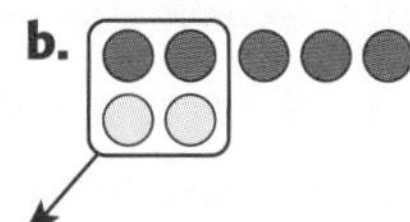

Model Integer Addition

Use with Lesson 3-3

KEY
(yellow chip) = 1
(red chip) = −1
(yellow chip) + (red chip) = 0

REMEMBER
Removing a zero from an expression does not change the expression's value.

internet connect
Lab Resources Online
go.hrw.com
KEYWORD: MS4 Lab3A

You can model integer addition by using integer chips.

Activity

When you model adding numbers with the same sign, you can count the total number of chips to find the sum.

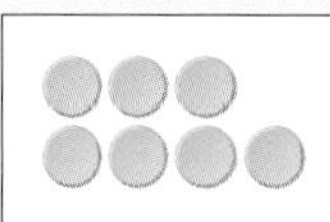

The total number of positive chips is 7.

$3 + 4 = 7$

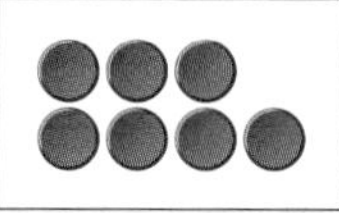

The total number of negative chips is 7.

$-3 + (-4) = -7$

1 Model each expression.

a. $2 + 4$ **b.** $-2 + (-4)$

When you model adding numbers with different signs, you cannot count the chips to find their sum.

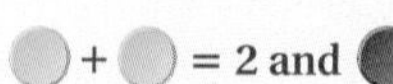

(yellow) + (yellow) = 2 and (red) + (red) = −2

but (yellow) + (red) = 0   *A red chip and a yellow chip make a neutral pair.*

When you model adding a positive and a negative number, you need to remove all of the neutral pairs that you can find—that is, all pairs of 1 red chip and 1 yellow chip. These pairs have a value of zero, so they do not affect the sum.

Vivian Perry
Edwards, Illinois

Teacher to Teacher

Students often get confused with this concept unless they understand that the farther a negative number is from zero on the number line, the smaller its actual value. Give 8–10 students cards with questions on them such as "You just bought a $3 slice of pizza. How much money do you have now?" and "You just received $10 for babysitting last week. How much money do you have?" Have students write equations on the board using a specified beginning dollar amount from a number line ranging from −10 to 10, and check their work on the number line.

After several equations are listed, ask students if they see a way to solve these equations without using tiles or counting on the number line.

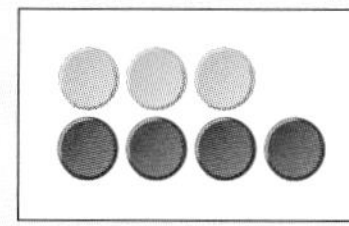

You cannot just count the colored chips to find their sum.

$3 + (-4) = \square$

Before you count the chips, you need to remove all of the neutral pairs.

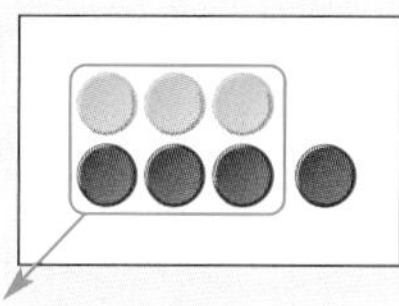

When you remove the neutral pairs, there is one red chip left. So the sum of the chips is −1.

$3 + (-4) = -1$

2 Model each expression.

a. $4 + (-6)$

b. $-5 + 2$

Think and Discuss

1. Will $8 + (-3)$ and $-3 + 8$ give the same answer? Why or why not? **Yes, 8 + (−3) and −3 + 8 will give the same answer. Addition is a commutative operation.**
2. If you have more red chips than yellow chips in a group, is the sum of the chips positive or negative? **negative**
3. If you have more yellow chips than red chips in a group, is the sum of the chips positive or negative? **positive**
4. Make a rule for the sign of the answer when negative and positive integers are added. Give examples. **The sign of the answer is the same as the sign of the number that is farther from zero. 7 + (−3) = 4, −7 + 3 = −4**

Try This

Use integer chips to model and solve each addition problem.

1. $4 + (-7)$ **−3**
2. $-5 + (-4)$ **−9**
3. $-5 + 1$ **−4**

Write the addition problems modeled below.

4. 

4 + (−5)

5. 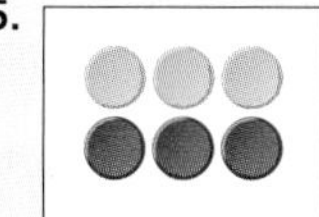

3 + (−3)

6. 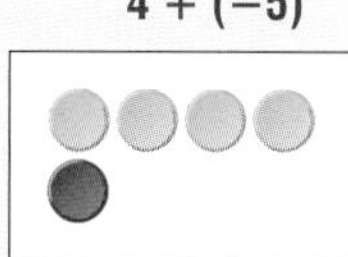

4 + (−1)

7. 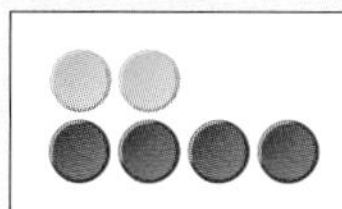

2 + (−4)

3-3 Organizer

Pacing: Traditional 1 day
Block $\frac{1}{2}$ day

Objective: Students add integers.

Warm Up

Find each absolute value.

1. $|8|$ 8 **2.** $|-6|$ 6
3. $|-9|$ 9 **4.** $|-7|$ 7
5. $|-12|$ 12 **6.** $|53|$ 53

Problem of the Day

Jan's yearly salary is $30,000, and it will be increased by $3,000 each year. Phil's salary is $20,000, and it will be increased by $5,000 each year. In how many years will Jan and Phil both have the same yearly salary? 5 years

Available on Daily Transparency in CRB

It's easy to understand why the sum of -4 and 3 complains more than the sum of -3 and 4. It's the negative one.

3-3 Adding Integers

Learn to add integers.

The Debate Club wanted to raise money for a trip to Washington, D.C. They began by estimating their income and expenses.

Income items are positive, and expenses are negative. By adding all your income and expenses, you can find your total earnings or losses.

Welcome to Washington
Club Ledger
Estimated Income and Expenses
Description | Amount
Car wash supplies | −$25.00
Car wash earnings | $300.00
Bake sale supplies | −$50.00
Bake sale earnings | $250.00
T-shirt decorating supplies | −$65.00
T-shirt sale earnings | $400.00

EXAMPLE  **1 Modeling Integer Addition**

Add.

A $-3 + (-6)$

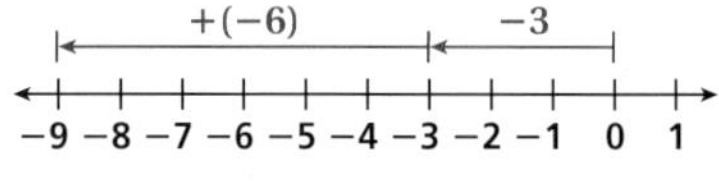

Start at 0. Move left 3 spaces. Then move left 6 more spaces.

$-3 + (-6) = -9$

B $4 + (-7)$

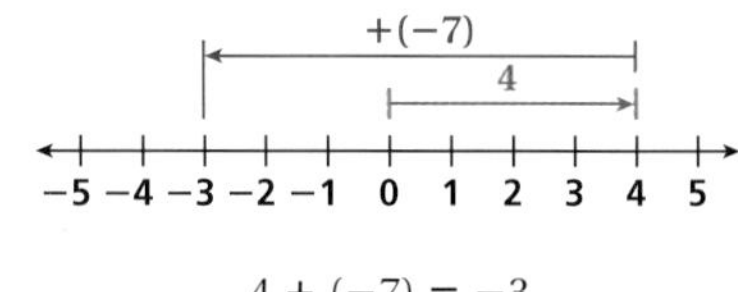

Start at 0. Move right 4 spaces. Then move left 7 spaces.

$4 + (-7) = -3$

Adding Integers

To add two integers with the same sign, find the sum of their absolute values. Use the sign of the two integers.

To add two integers with different signs, find the difference of their absolute values. Use the sign of the integer with the greater absolute value.

1 Introduce

Alternate Opener

EXPLORATION

3-3 Adding Integers

You can use the idea of *net worth* to model integer addition.

Suppose you start with $3 and then add a **debt of $5**. You can show your net worth as an addition statement.

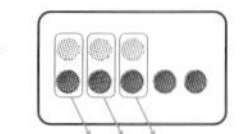

$3 + (-5) = -2$

1. Write two other addition statements with a sum of -2.

a. ___ + ___ = -2

b. ___ + ___ = -2

2. Suppose you start with a **debt of $3** and then add another **debt of $1**. Complete the addition statement.

$-3 + (-1) =$ ___

3. Write two other addition statements with a sum of -4.

a. ___ + ___ = -4

b. ___ + ___ = -4

Think and Discuss

4. Explain how to find net worth when you have positives and negatives.

5. Describe a net worth situation for the expression $-20 + 10$.

Motivate

To introduce students to adding integers, discuss examples of saving and spending. Be sure to use only whole dollar amounts. Ask students to explain how they would know whether a particular combination of saving and spending results in a total saving or in a total spending. Encourage students to explain their methods for finding the total.

Exploration worksheet and answers on Chapter 3 Resource Book pp. 25 and 112

2 Teach

Lesson Presentation

Guided Instruction

In this lesson, students learn to add integers. Start by showing students the addition of two positive numbers. Then show that addition of two negative numbers follows a similar pattern. Focus your presentation on integers with different signs. Use the number line to model addition of a positive integer and a negative integer. Incorporate students' examples when discussing the rules for adding integers using absolute values. Students evaluate addition expressions with integer values for variables.

EXAMPLE 2 Adding Integers Using Absolute Values

Add.

A $8 + 6$

$8 + 6$ — *The signs are the **same**.* *Find the **sum** of the absolute values.* *Think: $8 + 6 = 14$.*

14 — *Use the sign of the two integers **(positive)**.*

B $-12 + (-4)$

$-12 + (-4)$ — *The signs are the **same**.* *Find the **sum** of the absolute values.* *Think: $12 + 4 = 16$.*

-16 — *Use the sign of the two integers **(negative)**.*

Helpful Hint

To help you remember the rules for adding integers, think: If the signs are the *same*, find the *sum*. If the signs are *different*, find the *difference*.

EXAMPLE 3 Evaluating Expressions with Integers

Evaluate $a + b$ for the given values.

$a = 6, b = -10$

$a + b$

$6 + (-10)$ — *Substitute for **a** and **b**.* *The signs are **different**.* *Find the **difference** of the absolute values.* *Think: $10 - 6 = 4$.*

-4 — *Use the sign of the integer with the greater absolute value **(negative)**.*

EXAMPLE 4 *Banking Application*

The Debate Club's income from a car wash was $300, including tips. Supply expenses were $25. Use integer addition to find the club's total profit or loss.

$300 + (-25)$ — *Use negative for the expenses.*

$300 - 25$ — *Find the difference of the absolute values.*

275 — *The answer is positive.*

The club earned $275.

Think and Discuss

1. **Explain** whether $-7 + 2$ is the same as $7 + (-2)$.
2. **Explain** whether $3 + (-5)$ is the same as $-5 + 3$.

COMMON ERROR ALERT

Some students may forget to record the negative sign in the answer when adding integers using absolute values. Encourage these students to check the sign on every sum.

Additional Examples

Example 1

Add.

A. $-7 + (-4)$ $-7 + (-4) = -11$

B. $-12 + 19$ $-12 + 19 = 7$

Example 2

Add.

A. $-4 + 8$ $-4 + 8 = 4$

B. $23 + (-35)$ $23 + (-35) = -12$

Example 3

Evaluate $x + y$ for the given values.

$x = -42, y = 71$

29

Example 4

The jazz band's income from a bake sale was $286. Expenses were $21. Use integer addition to find the band's total profit or loss.

The band's profit was $265.

Example 4 note: Discuss with students the concepts of profit and loss. Encourage students to describe under what conditions the Debate Club would have a loss.

3 Close

Reaching All Learners

Through Concrete Manipulatives

Students may find it helpful to model integer addition with two-color counters (provided in the Manipulatives Kit). Designate the yellow counter as positive and the red counter as negative. Opposites add to zero and can be removed. The remaining counters show the sum.

Example: $(+4) + (-6) = -2$

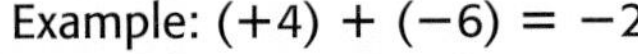

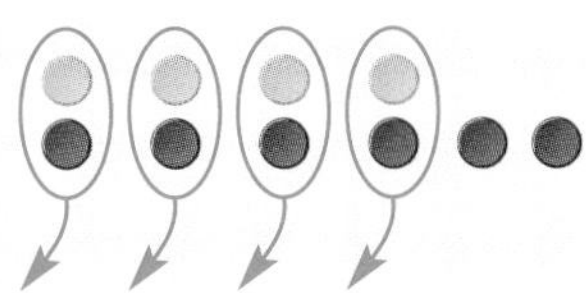

Summarize

Ask students to write rules for adding integers in their own words. Have students share their rules with the class. Discuss the common points.

Possible answer: If the signs are the same, add and keep the sign. If the signs are different, subtract and use the sign of the number with the greater absolute value.

Answers to Think and Discuss

1. $-7 + 2$ has a negative sum, -5, while $7 + (-2)$ has a positive sum, 5; therefore, the two expressions are not the same.
2. Possible answer: $3 + (-5)$ and $-5 + 3$ give the same sum, -2.

3-3 PRACTICE & ASSESS

Students may want to refer back to the lesson examples.

Assignment Guide

If you finished Example 1 assign:
Core 1–4, 13–20, 33–47 odd, 61–65
Enriched 1, 3, 13–19 odd, 33–47, 61–65

If you finished Example 2 assign:
Core 1–8, 13–28, 33–47 odd, 61–65
Enriched 1–7 odd, 13–28, 33–47, 61–65

If you finished Example 3 assign:
Core 1–11, 13–31, 33–53 odd, 61–65
Enriched 1–3 odd, 33–53, 61–65

If you finished Example 4 assign:
Core 1–32, 33–57 odd, 61–65
Enriched 1–11 odd, 12, 13–31 odd, 32–65

3-3 Exercises

FOR EXTRA PRACTICE see page 660

internet connect
Homework Help Online
go.hrw.com Keyword: MS4 3-3

GUIDED PRACTICE

See Example 1 Add.

1. $9 + 3$ **12**
2. $-4 + (-2)$ **−6**
3. $7 + (-9)$ **−2**
4. $-3 + 6$ **3**

See Example 2

5. $7 + 8$ **15**
6. $-1 + (-12)$ **−13**
7. $-25 + 10$ **−15**
8. $31 + (-20)$ **11**

See Example 3 Evaluate $a + b$ for the given values.

9. $a = 5, b = -17$ **−12**
10. $a = 8, b = -8$ **0**
11. $a = -4, b = -16$ **−20**

See Example 4

12. A football team gains 8 yards on one play and then loses 13 yards on the next. What is the team's total yardage? **−5 yards**

INDEPENDENT PRACTICE

See Example 1 Add.

13. $-16 + 7$ **−9**
14. $-5 + (-1)$ **−6**
15. $4 + 9$ **13**
16. $-7 + 8$ **1**
17. $10 + (-3)$ **7**
18. $-20 + 2$ **−18**
19. $-12 + (-5)$ **−17**
20. $-95 + 6$ **−89**

See Example 2

21. $-13 + (-6)$ **−19**
22. $14 + 25$ **39**
23. $-22 + 6$ **−16**
24. $35 + (-50)$ **−15**
25. $-81 + (-7)$ **−88**
26. $28 + (-3)$ **25**
27. $-70 + (15)$ **−55**
28. $-18 + (-62)$ **−80**

See Example 3 Evaluate $c + d$ for the given values.

29. $c = 6, d = -20$ **−14**
30. $c = -8, d = -21$ **−29**
31. $c = -45, d = 32$ **−13**

See Example 4

32. The temperature dropped 17°F in 6 hours. If the final temperature was −3°F, what was the starting temperature? **14°F**

PRACTICE AND PROBLEM SOLVING

Find each sum.

33. $-8 + (-5)$ **−13**
34. $-12 + 16$ **4**
35. $-6 + (-9)$ **−15**
36. $14 + (-7)$ **7**
37. $18 + 9$ **27**
38. $-41 + 15$ **−26**
39. $-22 + (-18) + 22$ **−18**
40. $27 + (-29) + 16$ **14**
41. $-30 + 71 + (-70)$ **−29**

Compare. Write $<$, $>$, or $=$.

42. $-23 + 18$ ▒ -41 **$>$**
43. $59 + (-59)$ ▒ 0 **$=$**
44. $31 + (-20)$ ▒ 9 **$>$**
45. $-24 + (-24)$ ▒ 48 **$<$**
46. $25 + (-70)$ ▒ -95 **$>$**
47. $16 + (-40)$ ▒ -24 **$=$**

Evaluate each expression for $w = -12, x = 10$, and $y = -7$.

48. $w + 6$ **−6**
49. $x + (-3)$ **7**
50. $w + y$ **−19**
51. $x + y$ **3**
52. $w + x$ **−2**
53. $w + x + y$ **−9**

Math Background

The same properties students learned for whole number addition are used for adding integers. The Commutative and Associative Properties allow addition of three or more addends to be rewritten in the most convenient order. Generally, this involves first grouping the positives and then grouping the negatives. Be certain students keep the sign with its number when they change the order.

By using integers we can talk about the additive inverse (opposite) of a number. Students will quickly see that the sum of a number and its inverse is always zero.

RETEACH 3-3

LESSON 3-3 **Reteach**
Adding Integers

This balance scale "weighs" positive and negative numbers. Negative numbers go on the left of the balance, and positive numbers go on the right.

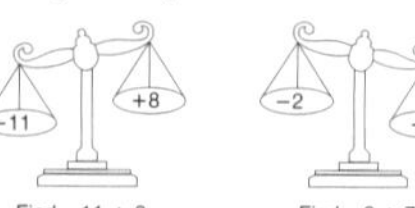

Find −11 + 8.

The scale will tip to the left side because the sum of −11 and +8 is negative.

−11 + 8 = −3

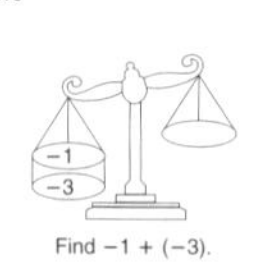

Find −2 + 7.

The scale will tip to the right side because the sum of −2 and +7 is positive.

−2 + 7 = 5

−1
−3

Find −1 + (−3).

Both −1 and −3 go on the left side. The scale will tip to the left side because the sum of −1 and −3 is negative.

−1 + (−3) = −4

Find 3 + (−9).

1. Should you add or subtract? **subtract**
2. Will the sum be positive or negative? **negative**

3 + (−9) = −6

the sign of the integer with the greatest absolute value

|9| − |3|

Find −5 + (−8).

3. Should you add or subtract? **add**
4. Will the sum be positive or negative? **negative**
5. −5 + (−8) = **−13**

Add.

6. 7 + −3 = **4**
7. −2 + −3 = **−5**
8. −5 + 4 = **−1**
9. −3 + −1 = **−4**
10. −7 + 9 = **2**
11. 4 + −9 = **−5**

PRACTICE 3-3

LESSON 3-3 **Practice B**
Adding Integers

Add.

1. −19 + (−6) **−25**
2. 9 + 6 **15**
3. −10 + 3 **−7**
4. −5 + 7 **2**
5. 14 + (−7) **7**
6. −20 + 5 **−15**
7. −18 + (−12) **−30**
8. −25 + 6 **−19**
9. −51 + (−9) **−60**
10. 27 + (−6) **21**
11. 1 + (−30) **−29**
12. 15 + (−25) **−10**
13. 50 + (−7) **43**
14. −19 + (−15) **−34**
15. (−23) + 9 **−14**
16. −19 + (−21) **−40**
17. −17 + 11 **−6**
18. 20 + (−8) **12**
19. (−15) + (−7) **−22**
20. 12 + (−14) **−2**

Evaluate $e + f$ for the given values.

21. $e = 9, f = -24$ **−15**
22. $e = -17, f = -7$ **−24**
23. $e = 32, f = -19$ **13**
24. $e = -15, f = -15$ **−30**
25. $e = -20, f = 20$ **0**
26. $e = -30, f = 12$ **−18**

27. The temperature rose 9°F in 3 hours. If the starting temperature was −5°F, what was the final temperature?
4°F

28. Matt is playing a game. He gains 7 points, loses 10 points, gains 2 points, and then loses 8 points. What is his final score?
−9 points

The Appalachian Trail extends about 2,160 miles from Maine to Georgia. It takes about 5 to 7 months to hike the entire trail.

54. ***PERSONAL FINANCE*** Last week, Cody made deposits of \$45, \$18, and \$27 into his checking account. He then wrote checks for \$21 and \$93. What is the overall change in Cody's account balance? **Cody's balance is reduced by \$24.**

55. ***RECREATION*** Hikers along the Appalachian Trail camped overnight at Horns Pond, at an of elevation 3,100 ft. Then they hiked along the ridge of the Bigelow Mountains to West Peak, which is one of Maine's highest peaks. Use the chart to determine the elevation of West Peak. **4,150 ft**

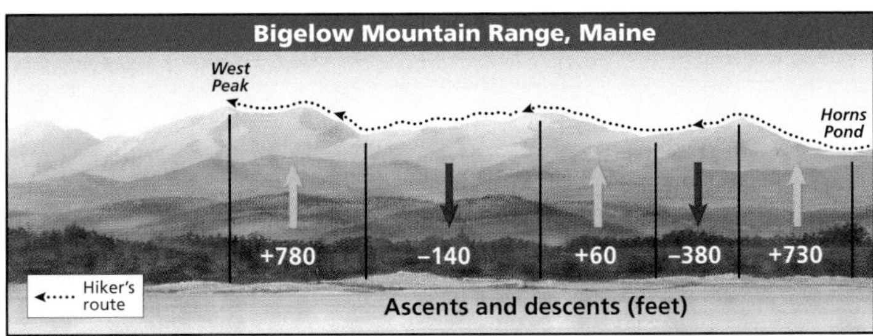

56. Hector and Luis play a game in which points can be gained or lost. In the game, each player starts with 0 points, and the player with the most points at the end wins. Hector gains 5 points, loses 3, loses 2, and then gains 3. Luis loses 5 points, gains 1, gains 5, and then loses 3. Who wins the game and by how much?

57. ***PERSONAL FINANCE*** Amanda borrowed \$62 from her parents to buy a camera. She paid back \$37 last week and \$21 this week. How much does Amanda still owe? **\$4**

58. ***WHAT'S THE QUESTION?*** The temperature was −8°F at 6 A.M. and rose 15°F by 9 A.M. The answer is 7°F. What is the question? **What was the temperature at 9 A.M.?**

59. ***WRITE ABOUT IT*** Compare the method used to add integers with the same sign and the method used to add integers with different signs.

60. ***CHALLENGE*** A business had a loss of \$225 million, a profit of \$15 million, a profit of \$125 million, a loss of \$75 million, and a loss of \$375 million. How much was its overall profit or loss? **loss of \$535 million**

Spiral Review

Write each number in scientific notation. (Lesson 2-2)

61. 839,000 **8.39×10^5**
62. 2,100,000 **2.1×10^6**
63. 4,023,000,000 **4.023×10^9**

64. **TEST PREP** Which is the greatest common factor of 40 and 24? (Lesson 2-5) **C**

A 2
B 4
C 8
D 12

65. **TEST PREP** Which is a solution of the equation $6y = 96$? (Lesson 2-12) **F**

F $y = 16$
G $y = 90$
H $y = 102$
J $y = 576$

Answers

56. Hector; Hector has 3 points, while Luis has −2 points, so Hector wins by 5 points.

59. Possible answer: First add integers with like signs. The sign of the sum is the sign of the integers. Then add unlike integers by finding the difference of their absolute values. Use the sign of the integer with the greater absolute value.

Journal

Have students describe real-world situations in which integer addition is used (e.g., changes in temperature, altitude, or stock prices). Ask students to explain how to find the sum.

Test Prep Doctor

For Exercise 64, remind students to eliminate wrong answers. Choice **D** can be eliminated because 12 is not a factor of 40. The remaining answers are all common factors of 40 and 24, but **C** is the greatest common factor.

CHALLENGE 3-3

LESSON 3-3 **Challenge**
Alphabet Addition

Find the value of each word. Each vowel has a value as shown in the table. All consonants have a value of 2.

A	E	I	O	U
−5	−11	−8	−3	−6

1. ALGEBRA **−13**
2. INTEGER **−22**
3. POSITIVE **−22**
4. NEGATIVE **−27**
5. SIGN **−2**
6. ADDITION **−16**
7. GREATER **−19**
8. LESS **−5**
9. EQUAL **−18**

Write <, >, or = to compare the values of each word pair.

10. MANY **>** FEW
11. ALL **=** NOTHING
12. SCHOOL **>** HOME
13. DOG **>** CAT
14. ADD **<** SUBTRACT
15. STOP **>** GO
16. EVALUATE **<** SOLVE
17. MORE **<** LESS
18. EMPTY **<** FULL

19. Write your name and the first names of 3 other friends or family members. Find the value of each name. Write the names in order from least to greatest value.
Answers will vary.

20. Write a word with a value of 3.
Possible answer: chalk

21. Write a word with a value of −3.
Possible answer: bench

22. What is the highest value word you can think of? Compare it with your classmates' words.
Answers will vary.

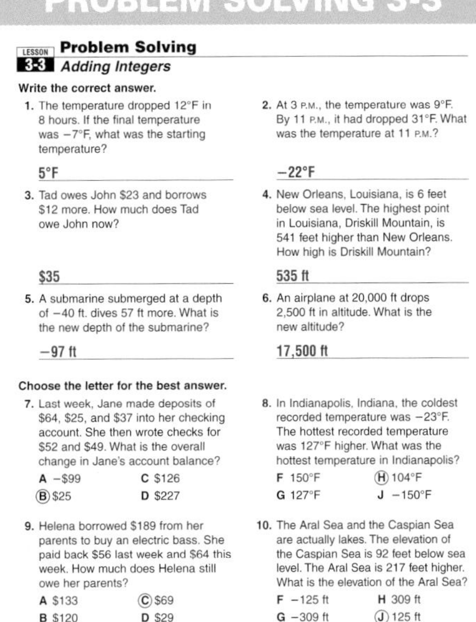

PROBLEM SOLVING 3-3

LESSON 3-3 **Problem Solving**
Adding Integers

Write the correct answer.

1. The temperature dropped 12°F in 8 hours. If the final temperature was −7°F, what was the starting temperature?
5°F

2. At 3 P.M., the temperature was 9°F. By 11 P.M., it had dropped 31°F. What was the temperature at 11 P.M.?
−22°F

3. Tad owes John \$23 and borrows \$12 more. How much does Tad owe John now?
\$35

4. New Orleans, Louisiana, is 6 feet below sea level. The highest point in Louisiana, Driskill Mountain, is 541 feet higher than New Orleans. How high is Driskill Mountain?
535 ft

5. A submarine submerged at a depth of −40 ft. dives 57 ft more. What is the new depth of the submarine?
−97 ft

6. An airplane at 20,000 ft drops 2,500 ft in altitude. What is the new altitude?
17,500 ft

Choose the letter for the best answer.

7. Last week, Jane made deposits of \$64, \$25, and \$37 into her checking account. She then wrote checks for \$52 and \$49. What is the overall change in Jane's account balance?
A −\$99
(B) \$25
C \$126
D \$227

8. In Indianapolis, Indiana, the coldest recorded temperature was −23°F. The hottest recorded temperature was 127°F higher. What was the hottest temperature in Indianapolis?
F 150°F
G 127°F
(H) 104°F
J −150°F

9. Helena borrowed \$189 from her parents to buy an electric bass. She paid back \$56 last week and \$64 this week. How much does Helena still owe her parents?
A \$133
B \$120
(C) \$69
D \$29

10. The Aral Sea and the Caspian Sea are actually lakes. The elevation of the Caspian Sea is 92 feet below sea level. The Aral Sea is 217 feet higher. What is the elevation of the Aral Sea?
F −125 ft
G −309 ft
H 309 ft
(J) 125 ft

Lesson Quiz

Add.

1. $-7 + (-6)$ **−13**
2. $-15 + 24 + (-9)$ **0**
3. $-24 + 7 + (-3)$ **−20**
4. Evaluate $x + y$ for $x = -2$ and $y = -15$. **−17**
5. The math club's income from a bake sale was \$217. Advertising expenses were \$32. What is the club's total profit or loss? \$185 profit

Available on Daily Transparency in CRB

3B Model Integer Subtraction

Pacing: Traditional 1 day
Block $\frac{1}{2}$ day

Objective: To use integer chips to model subtracting integers

Materials: Yellow integer chips and red integer chips

Lab Resources

Hands-On Lab Activities. pp. 14–16, 126

Using the Pages

Review what each integer chip represents and how to represent positive and negative integers with integer chips. Review with students how to represent the number zero using integer chips. Discuss why it is sometimes necessary to add chips in order to subtract.

Use integer chips to model and solve the following subtraction problems.

1. 6 − 5 **1**
2. −4 − (−2) **−2**
3. −3 + 3 **0**
4. −1 − 3 **−4**
5. 2 − 7 **−5**
6. 1 − (−2) **3**

Answers

Activity

1. Possible answer:

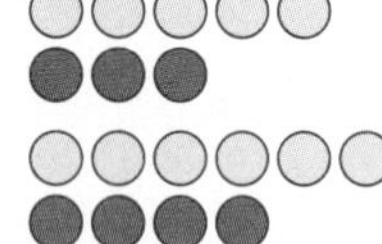

2. Possible answer:

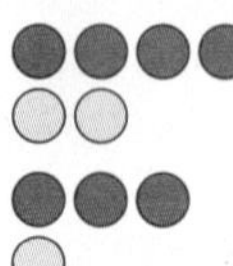

3. a. 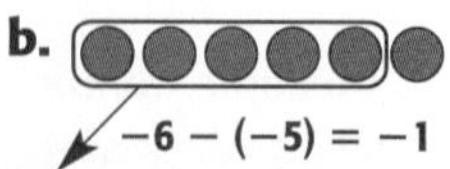

6 − 5 = 1

b. −6 − (−5) = −1

Model Integer Subtraction

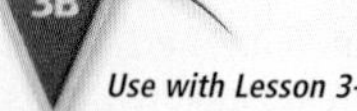

Use with Lesson 3-4

KEY

 = 1

 = −1

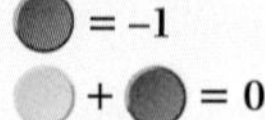 = 0

REMEMBER

Adding or removing a zero from an expression does not change the expression's value.

internet connect
Lab Resources Online
go.hrw.com
KEYWORD: MS4 Lab3B

You can model integer subtraction by using integer chips.

Activity

These groups of chips show three different ways of modeling 2.

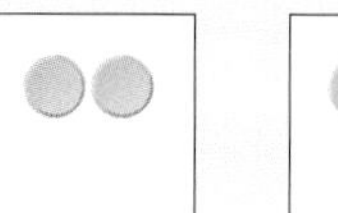
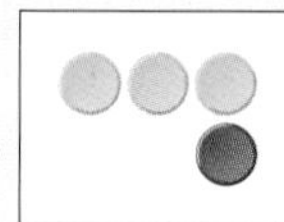
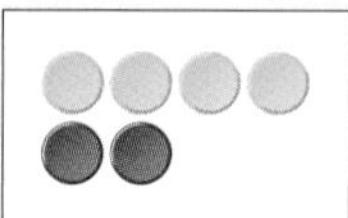

1 Show two other ways of modeling 2.

These groups of chips show two different ways of modeling −2.

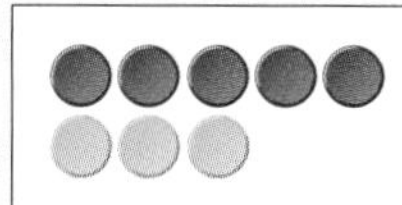

2 Show two other ways of modeling −2.

You can model some subtraction problems by taking away chips.

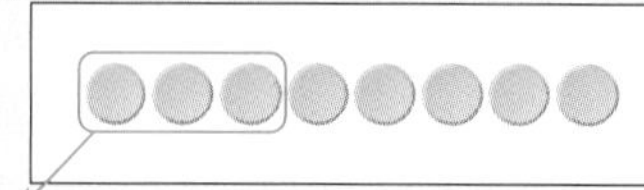

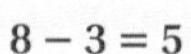

8 − 3 = 5

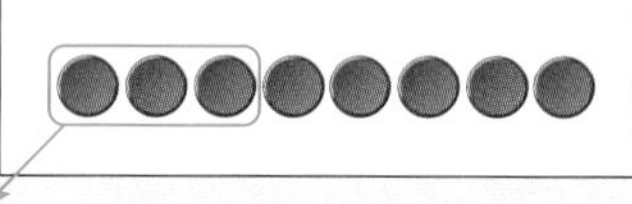

−8 − (−3) = −5

3 Model each expression.

a. 6 − 5

b. −6 − (−5)

To model some subtraction problems, such as $-6 - 3$, you will need to add neutral pairs before you can take chips away.

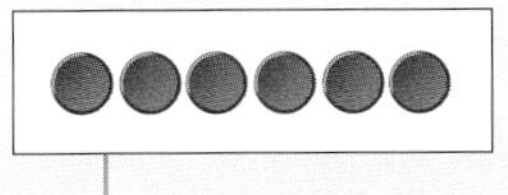

First place 6 red chips to represent -6.

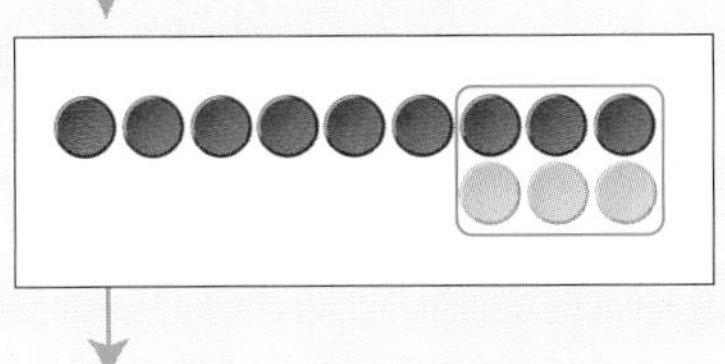

Since you cannot take away 3 yellow chips, add 3 yellow chips paired with 3 red chips.

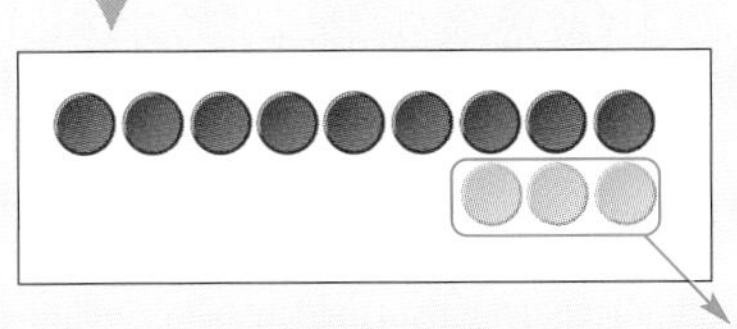

Now you can take away 3 yellow chips.

$-6 - 3 = -9$

4 Model each expression.

a. $-6 - 5$

b. $5 - (-6)$

c. $4 - 7$

d. $-2 - (-3)$

Think and Discuss

1. How could you model the expression $0 - 5$?
2. When you add neutral pairs to model subtraction using chips, does it matter how many neutral pairs you add?
3. Would $2 - 3$ have the same answer as $3 - 2$? Why or why not?
4. Make a rule for the sign of the answer when negative and positive integers are subtracted. Give examples.

Try This

Use integer chips to model and solve each subtraction problem.

1. $4 - 2$ **2**
2. $-4 - (-2)$ **−2**
3. $-2 - (-3)$ **1**
4. $3 - 4$ **−1**
5. $2 - 3$ **−1**
6. $0 - 3$ **−3**
7. $5 - 3$ **2**
8. $-3 - (-5)$ **2**
9. $6 - (-4)$ **10**

Answers

Activity

4. a.

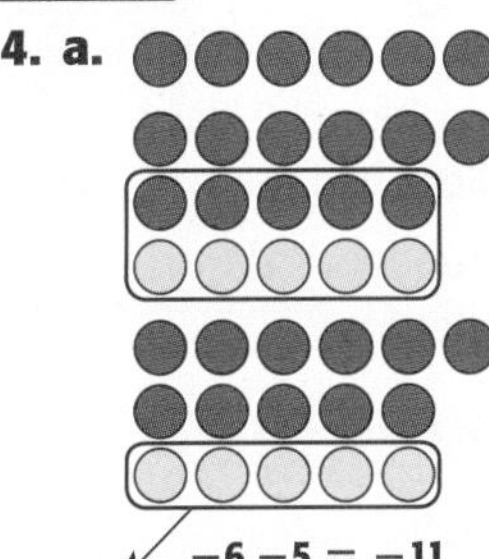

$-6 - 5 = -11$

b.

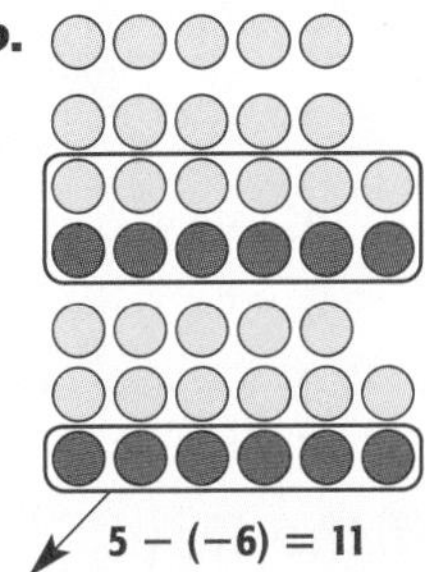

$5 - (-6) = 11$

c.

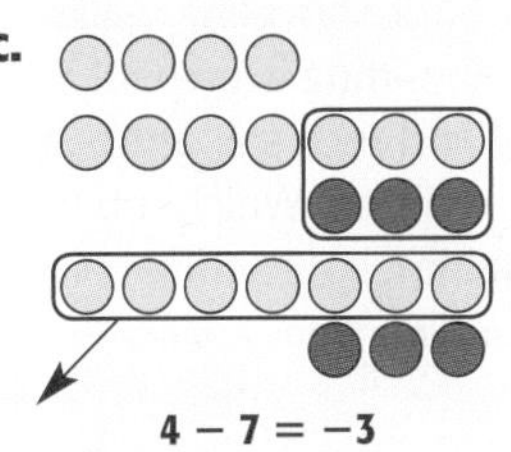

$4 - 7 = -3$

d.

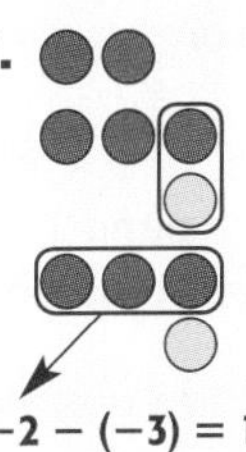

$-2 - (-3) = 1$

Think and Discuss

1. Represent 0 with 5 red chips and 5 yellow chips. Remove 5 yellow chips. There will be 5 red chips left. $0 - 5 = -5$.
2. No; if you add extra neutral pairs, they each represent zero.
3. No; $2 - 3$ and $3 - 2$ do not have the same answer. $2 - 3 = -1$ and $3 - 2 = 1$.
4. negative integer − positive integer = − sum of integers without signs; $-5 - 2 = -(5 + 2) = -7$; $-3 - 6 = -(3 + 6) = -9$

3-4 Organizer

Pacing: Traditional 2 days
Block 1 day

Objective: Students subtract integers.

Warm Up

Add.

1. $-2 + 6$ 4 **2.** $-3 + (-4)$ -7

3. $7 + (-5)$ 2 **4.** $3 + (-4)$ -1

5. $-6 + (-1)$ -7 **6.** $-6 + 1$ -5

Problem of the Day

Ray earned $172 shoveling walks and $188 babysitting. He spent $21 for a shovel and rock salt and $26 for toys for children. Which job was more profitable? babysitting

Available on Daily Transparency in CRB

Math Fact !

Chinese mathematicians around 100 B.C. were the first to use negative numbers.

3-4 Subtracting Integers

Learn **to subtract integers.**

During its flight to and from Earth, the space shuttle may be exposed to temperatures as cold as $-250°F$ and as hot as 3,000°F.

To find the difference in these temperatures, you need to know how to subtract integers with different signs.

You can model the difference between two integers using a number line. When you subtract a positive number, the difference is *less* than the original number, so you move to the *left*. To subtract a negative number, move to the *right*.

Helpful Hint

If the number being subtracted is less than the number it is subtracted from, the answer will be positive. If the number being subtracted is greater, the answer will be negative.

EXAMPLE 1 Modeling Integer Subtraction

Use a number line to find each difference.

A $3 - 8$

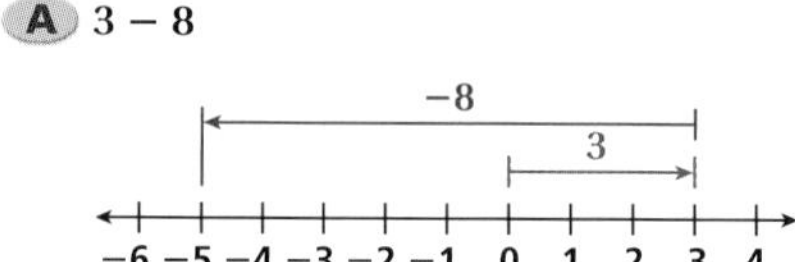

Start at 0.
Move right 3 spaces.
To subtract 8,
move to the left.

$3 - 8 = -5$

B $-4 - 2$

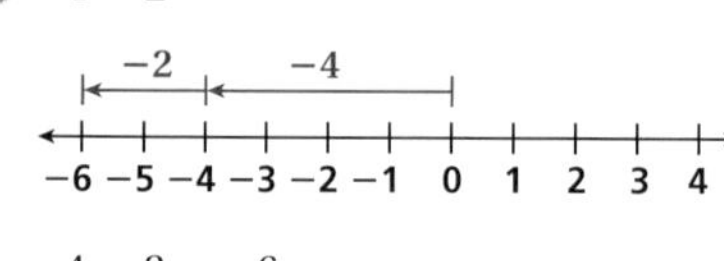

Start at 0.
Move left 4 spaces.
To subtract 2,
move to the left.

$-4 - 2 = -6$

C $2 - (-3)$

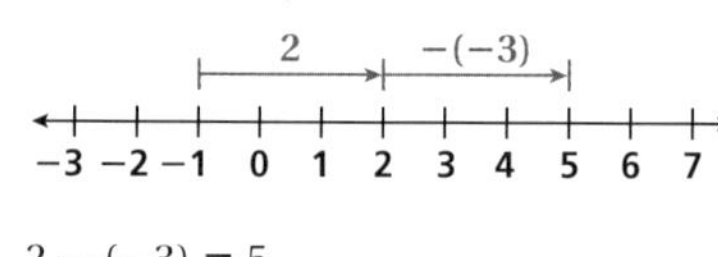

Start at 0.
Move right 2 spaces.
To subtract −3,
move to the right.

$2 - (-3) = 5$

Addition and subtraction are inverse operations—they "undo" each other. Instead of subtracting a number, you can *add its opposite.*

1 Introduce

Alternate Opener

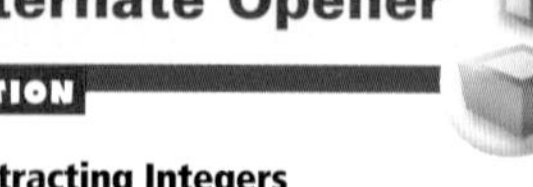

EXPLORATION

3-4 Subtracting Integers

Suppose you have a debt of $5 and then subtract a debt of $3. This subtraction statement can be written as an equivalent addition statement.

$-5 - (-3) = -2$ is equivalent to $-5 + 3 = -2$

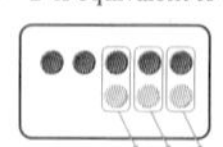

Write each subtraction statement as an equivalent addition statement.

Subtraction Statements	Addition Statements
1. $-8 - (-2) = -6$	$-8 + \_\_ = -6$
2. $-4 - (-1) = -3$	$-4 + \_\_ = -3$
3. $-12 - (-8) = -4$	$-12 + \_\_ = -4$
4. $-15 - (-8) = -7$	$-15 + \_\_ = -7$

*Think and Discuss*________

5. Explain why subtracting a negative number is equivalent to adding a positive number.

Motivate

To introduce students to subtracting integers, ask them to explain how they would subtract a greater number from a lesser number. Some might say it is not possible, while others might suggest a negative result. Relate negative integers to borrowing money to buy something you do not have enough money for. For example, if you have $5 but want to buy something that costs $8, you would borrow $3 and have a $3 debt.
$5 - 8 = -3$

Exploration worksheet and answers on Chapter 3 Resource Book pp. 34 and 114

2 Teach

Lesson Presentation

Guided Instruction

In this lesson, students learn to subtract integers. Subtraction is modeled as the directed distance between two integers. Encourage students to locate the integers on the number line, count the distance, and then use the Helpful Hint to determine the sign. Present subtraction as adding the opposite. Subtracting a positive integer is the same as adding a negative integer. Subtracting a negative integer is the same as adding a positive integer.

Teaching Tip Subtracting integers by adding the opposite requires students to learn only one set of rules—the rules for adding integers.

EXAMPLE 2 Subtracting Integers by Adding the Opposite

Subtract.

A $5 - 9$

$5 + (-9)$ *Add the opposite of 9.*

-4

B $-9 - (-2)$

$-9 + 2$ *Add the opposite of −2.*

-7

C $-4 - 3$

$-4 + (-3)$ *Add the opposite of 3.*

-7

EXAMPLE 3 Evaluating Expressions with Integers

Evaluate $a - b$ for each set of values.

A $a = -6, b = 7$

$a - b$

$-6 - 7 = -6 + (-7)$ *Substitute for a and b.*

$= -13$ *Add the opposite of 7.*

B $a = 14, b = -9$

$a - b$

$14 - (-9) = 14 + 9$ *Substitute for a and b.*

$= 23$ *Add the opposite of −9.*

EXAMPLE 4 *Temperature Application*

Find the difference between 3,000°F and −250°F, the temperatures the Space Shuttle must endure.

$3{,}000 - (-250)$

$3{,}000 + 250 = 3{,}250$ *Add the opposite of −250.*

The difference in temperatures the shuttle must endure is 3,250°F.

Think and Discuss

1. **Suppose** you subtract one negative integer from another. Will your answer be greater than or less than the number you started with?
2. **Tell** whether you can reverse the order of integers when subtracting and still get the same answer. Why or why not?

Additional Examples

Example 1

Use a number line to find each difference.

A. 4 − 1 3

B. −3 − 1 −4

C. −2 − (−4) 2

Example 2

Subtract.

A. 5 − (−2) 7

B. −3 − 7 −10

C. −1 − (−8) 7

Example 3

Evaluate $x - y$ for each set of values.

A. $x = -3$ and $y = 2$ −5

B. $x = 4$ and $y = -6$ 10

Example 4

Find the difference between 32°F and −10°F.

The difference is 42°F.

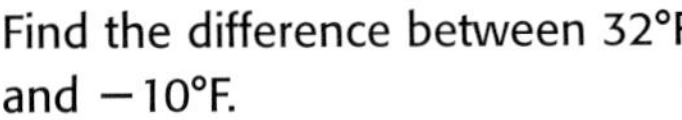

3 Close

Reaching All Learners

Through Concrete Manipulatives

Have students model integer subtraction with two-color counters (in the manipulatives kit). Direct students to start the activity with an equal number of positive (yellow) and negative (red) counters. Establish that their total value is zero. Have students take away a number of the positive counters. Then discuss the result. Repeat, but this time have students remove a number of the negative counters.

Students should conclude that a positive number subtracted from zero has a negative difference and a negative number subtracted from zero has a positive difference.

Summarize

You may wish to have students explain in their own words how to subtract integers and, in particular, how to determine the sign of the difference.

Possible answer: To subtract an integer, add the opposite of that integer. For example, to subtract −3 from 4, find the opposite of −3, which is 3, and then add it to 4. So $4 - (-3) = 4 + 3 = 7$.

Answers to Think and Discuss

Possible answers:

1. The result will be greater because subtracting a negative integer is equivalent to adding a positive integer.
2. Subtraction is not commutative. You cannot reverse the order of integers when subtracting. However, when subtraction is rewritten as adding the opposite integer, the order of the addends can be reversed.

3-4 PRACTICE & ASSESS

Students may want to refer back to the lesson examples.

Assignment Guide

If you finished Example 1 assign:
Core 1–4, 13–20, 37–47 odd, 59–66
Enriched 1, 3, 13–19 odd, 36–48, 59–66

If you finished Example 2 assign:
Core 1–8, 13–28, 37–47 odd, 59–66
Enriched 1–7 odd, 13–27 odd, 36–48, 59–66

If you finished Example 3 assign:
Core 1–11, 13–34, 37–51odd, 59–66
Enriched 1–11 odd, 13–34, 36–52, 59–66

If you finished Example 4 assign:
Core 1–35, 37–47 odd, 49–57, 59–66
Enriched 1–11 odd, 13–35, 36–66

Answers

1–4, 13–20. Complete answers on pp. A1–A2

3-4 Exercises

FOR EXTRA PRACTICE see page 660

internet connect
Homework Help Online
go.hrw.com Keyword: MS4 3-4

GUIDED PRACTICE

See Example 1 — Use a number line to find each difference.

1. $4 - 7$ **−3** 2. $-6 - 5$ **−11** 3. $2 - (-4)$ **6** 4. $-8 - (-2)$ **−6**

See Example 2 — Subtract.

5. $6 - 10$ **−4** 6. $-3 - (-8)$ **5** 7. $-1 - 9$ **−10** 8. $-12 - (-2)$ **−10**

See Example 3 — Evaluate $a - b$ for each set of values.

9. $a = 5, b = -2$ **7** 10. $a = -8, b = 6$ **−14** 11. $a = 4, b = 18$ **−14**

See Example 4 — 12. In 1980, in Great Falls, Montana, the temperature rose from −32°F to 15°F in seven minutes. How much did the temperature increase? **47°F**
(Source: http://www.wrh.noaa.gov/greatfalls/topweather.html)

INDEPENDENT PRACTICE

See Example 1 — Use a number line to find each difference.

13. $7 - 12$ **−5** 14. $-5 - (-9)$ **4** 15. $2 - (-6)$ **8** 16. $7 - (-8)$ **15**

17. $9 - (-3)$ **12** 18. $-4 - 10$ **−14** 19. $8 - (-8)$ **16** 20. $-3 - (-3)$ **0**

See Example 2 — Subtract.

21. $-22 - (-5)$ **−17** 22. $-4 - 21$ **−25** 23. $27 - 19$ **8** 24. $-10 - (-7)$ **−3**

25. $30 - (-20)$ **50** 26. $-15 - 15$ **−30** 27. $12 - (-6)$ **18** 28. $-31 - 15$ **−46**

See Example 3 — Evaluate $a - b$ for each set of values.

29. $a = 9, b = -7$ **16** 30. $a = -11, b = 2$ **−13** 31. $a = -2, b = 3$ **−5**

32. $a = 8, b = 19$ **−11** 33. $a = -10, b = 10$ **−20** 34. $a = -4, b = -15$ **11**

See Example 4 — 35. In 1918, in Granville, North Dakota, the temperature rose from −33°F to 50°F in 12 hours. How much did the temperature increase? **83°F**
(Source: http://www.infoplease.com/ipa/A0005317.html)

PRACTICE AND PROBLEM SOLVING

Simplify.

36. $2 - 8$ **−6** 37. $-5 - 9$ **−14** 38. $15 - 12 - 8$ **−5**

39. $6 + (-5) - 3$ **−2** 40. $1 - 8 + (-6)$ **−13** 41. $4 - (-7) - 9$ **2**

42. $-11 - (-5) - (-6)$ **0** 43. $5 - (-8) - (-3)$ **16** 44. $10 - 12 + 2$ **0**

45. $(2 - 3) - (5 - 6)$ **0** 46. $(3 - 8) - (-2 + 9)$ **−12**

47. $15 - 6 + 4 - 7 + 10$ **16** 48. $12 - (-5) - [3 - (-1)]$ **13**

Evaluate each expression for $m = -5$, $n = 8$, and $p = -14$.

49. $m - n + p$ **−27** 50. $n - m - p$ **27** 51. $p - m - n$ **−17** 52. $m + n - p$ **17**

Math Background

Although elementary-school students traditionally learn the "take-away" model first, subtraction is more formally defined as addition of the opposite—or additive inverse. The integers are closed under the operations of addition and subtraction, which means that adding or subtracting any two integers will produce another integer.

RETEACH 3-4

LESSON 3-4 **Reteach**
Subtracting Integers

The total value of the three cards shown is −6.

3 −4 −5

What if you **take away** the 3 card?
Cards −4 and −5 are left.
The new value is −9.
−6 − 3 = −9

What if you **take away** the −4 card?
Cards 3 and −5 are left.
The new value is −2.
−6 − (−4) = −2

Answer each question.

1. Suppose you have the cards shown. The total value of the cards is 12.

a. What if you take away the 7 card? 12 − 7 = **5**
b. What if you take away the 13 card? 12 − 13 = **−1**
c. What if you take away the −8 card? 12 − (−8) = **20**

2. Subtract −4 − (−2).
a. −4 < −2. Will the answer be positive or negative? **negative**
b. |4| − |2| = **2**
c. −4 − (−2) = **−2**

3. Subtract 21 − 13.
a. 21 > 13. Will the answer be positive or negative? **positive**
b. |21| − |13| = **8**
c. 21 − 13 = **8**

Subtract.

4. 31 − (− 9) = **40** 5. 15 − 18 = **−3** 6. −9 − 17 = **−26**
7. −8 − (−8) = **0** 8. 29 − (−2) = **31** 9. 13 − 18 = **−5**

PRACTICE 3-4

LESSON 3-4 **Practice B**
Subtracting Integers

Model the subtraction with a number line, and then give the answer.

1. −2 − 3
3 units 2 units
−6 −5 −4 −3 −2 −1 0 1 2
−5

2. 5 − (−1)
5 units 1 unit
−1 0 1 2 3 4 5 6 7
6

Subtract.

3. −6 − 4 **−10** 4. −7 − (−12) **5** 5. 12 − 16 **−4** 6. 5 − (−19) **24**
7. −18 − (−18) **0** 8. 23 − (−23) **46** 9. −10 − (−9) **−1** 10. 29 − (−13) **42**
11. 9 − 15 **−6** 12. −12 − 14 **−26** 13. 22 − (−8) **30** 14. −16 − (−11) **−5**

Evaluate the expression $x - y$ for each set of values.

15. $x = 14, y = -2$ **16** 16. $x = -11, y = 11$ **−22** 17. $x = -8, y = -15$ **7**
18. $x = -9, y = -9$ **0** 19. $x = 19, y = -20$ **39** 20. $x = 20, y = 25$ **−5**

21. The high temperature one day was −1°F. The low temperature was −5°F.What was the difference between the high and low temperatures for the day?
4°F

22. The temperature changed from 5°F at 6 P.M. to −2°F at midnight. How much did the temperature decrease?
7°F

Astronomy 

Maat Mons volcano on Venus
Source: NASA (computer-generated from the *Magellan* probe)

53. The temperature of Mercury, the planet closest to the Sun, can be as high as 873°F. The temperature of Pluto, the planet farthest from the Sun, is −393°F. What is the difference between these temperatures? **1,266°F**

54. One side of Mercury always faces the Sun. The temperature on this side of Mercury can reach 873°F. The temperature on the other side can be as low as −361°F. What is the difference between the two temperatures? **1,234°F**

55. Earth's moon rotates relative to the Sun about once a month. The side facing the Sun at a given time can be as hot as 224°F. The side away from the Sun can be as cold as −307°F. What is the difference between these temperatures? **531°F**

56. The highest recorded temperature on Earth is 136°F. The lowest is −129°F. What is the difference between these temperatures? **265°F**

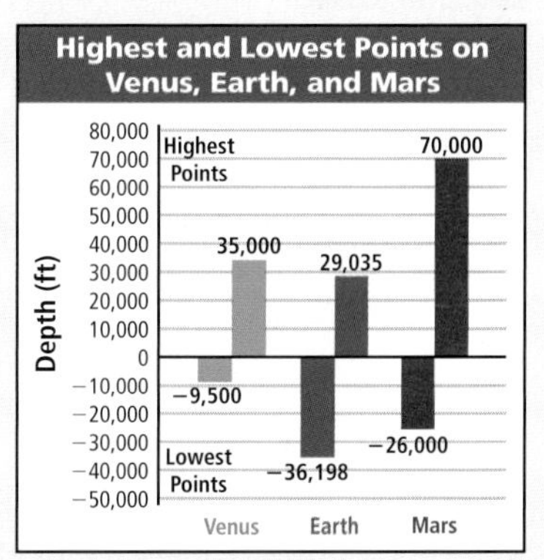

Use the graph for Exercises 57 and 58.

57. How much deeper is the deepest canyon on Mars than the deepest canyon on Venus? **16,500 ft**

58. ***CHALLENGE*** What is the difference between Earth's highest mountain and its deepest ocean canyon? What is the difference between Mars' highest mountain and its deepest canyon? Which difference is greater? How much greater is it?
65,233 ft; 96,000 ft; 96,000 ft (Mars); 30,767 ft

Spiral Review

Simplify. (Lesson 2-3)

59. $6 + 4 \div 2$ **8**

60. $9 \cdot 1 - 4$ **5**

61. $5^2 - 3$ **22**

62. $8(10 + 2)$ **96**

63. $\left(\frac{14}{7} - 2\right)4$ **0**

64. $8 \div 1 + 3^3$ **35**

65. **TEST PREP** Which is the prime factorization of 36? (Lesson 2-4) **B**

A $4 \cdot 9$
B $2^2 \cdot 3^2$
C $2^3 \cdot 3$
D $2 \cdot 3^2$

66. **TEST PREP** Which ordered pair is in Quadrant III? (Lesson 3-2) **J**

F (3, 3)
G (1, −3)
H (−3, 1)
J (−1, −1)

Interdisciplinary 

Astronomy

Exercises 53–58 involve temperature and elevation data from various planets. These topics are studied in middle school Earth science courses such as *Holt Science & Technology.*

Sources for Exercises 53–58

Go to: **go.hrw.com**
KEYWORD: **MS4 Astronomy**

Journal 

Have students explain how to subtract a negative integer as if they were explaining it to another student who missed this lesson.

Test Prep Doctor 

For Exercise 65, remind students to examine all choices carefully. Choice **A** can be eliminated because neither factor is prime, but the remaining choices are similar. Choice **D** shows a prime factorization with only one power of 2. It can be eliminated since 36 is divisible by 4, which is the second power of 2.

CHALLENGE 3-4

LESSON 3-4 **Challenge**
Subtract-a-Fact

Complete each temperature and elevation fact. Write the answer in the tables below.

Temperature Facts

1. Louisiana's lowest recorded temperature is (−15 − 1)°F.
2. The highest recorded temperature for Texas is [−18 − (−138)]°F.
3. The normal January temperature for Fairbanks, Alaska, is (−5 − 5)°F.
4. The normal July temperature for Tampa, Florida, is [45 − (−37)]°F.
5. The lowest temperature of 2000 in Detroit, Michigan, was (87 − 90)°F.
6. The highest temperature of 2000 in Norfolk, Virginia, was [−42 − (−138)]°F.
7. North Carolina's lowest recorded temperature is (57 − 91)°F.
8. South Carolina's lowest recorded temperature is (−4 − 15)°F.

Elevation Facts

9. Death Valley's elevation is (−25 − 257) ft.
10. The Caspian Sea's elevation is (125 − 217) ft.
11. Mount Everest's elevation is [−26 − (−29,061)] ft.
12. Mount McKinley's elevation is Mount Everest's elevation − 8,715 ft.
13. Lake Eyre's elevation is (68 − 120) ft.
14. The Dead Sea's elevation is (−761 − 587) ft.
15. Mount Elbrus's elevation is [11,500 − (−7,010)] ft.
16. Lake Assal's elevation is (−254 − 258) ft.

Temperature Facts	°F
Louisiana's lowest	**−16°**
Texas's highest	**120°**
Fairbanks normal January	**−10°**
Tampa normal July	**82°**
Lowest in Detroit in 2000	**−3°**
Highest in Norfolk in 2000	**96°**
North Carolina's lowest	**−34°**
South Carolina's lowest	**−19°**

Highest and Lowest Points on Continents	Elevation
Death Valley, North America	**−282 ft**
Caspian Sea, Europe	**−92 ft**
Mount Everest, Asia	**29,035 ft**
Mount McKinley, North America	**20,320 ft**
Lake Eyre, Australia	**−52 ft**
Dead Sea, Asia	**−1,348 ft**
Mount Elbrus, Europe	**18,510 ft**
Lake Assal, Africa	**−512 ft**

PROBLEM SOLVING 3-4

LESSON 3-4 **Problem Solving**
Subtracting Integers

Write the correct answer.

1. The daytime temperature on Mercury can reach 430°C. The nighttime temperature can drop to −180°C. How much can the temperature drop during one day?
610°C

2. An ice cream company reported a net profit of $24,000 in 2002 and a net loss of $11,000 in 2003. How much did the company's profits change from 2002 to 2003?
$35,000

3. A small business reported a net loss of $86,000 in 1998 and a net profit of $32,000 in 1999. How much did the company's profits change from 1998 to 1999?
$118,000

4. The daytime high temperature on the Moon can reach 130°C. At night, the temperature can drop to −110°C. What is the difference between the high and low temperatures?
240°C

Choose the letter for the best answer.

5. The low point of the Tonga Trench, in the Pacific Ocean, is −10,630 meters. The low point of the Mariana Trench, also in the Pacific Ocean, is 890 meters lower. What is the depth of the Mariana Trench?
A 10,630 meters
(B) −11,520 meters
C −9,740 meters
D 9,740 meters

6. On Wednesday night in St. Petersburg, Russia, the temperature is −11°C. On the same night in Bombay, India, the temperature is 17°C. What is the difference in temperature?
F −6°C
G 50°C
H −187°C
(J) 28°C

7. Climax, Colorado, is the highest town in the United States at 11,560 feet. The lowest town is Calipatria, California, which is 185 feet below sea level. What is the difference in elevation?
A −185 feet
B 11,375 feet
C 11,560 feet
(D) 11,745 feet

8. The low point of the Japanese Trench, in the Pacific Ocean, is −10,372 meters. The low point of the Puerto Rico Trench, in the Atlantic Ocean, is 1,172 meters higher. What is the depth of the Puerto Rico Trench?
(F) −9,200 meters
G 8,200 meters
H −1,172 meters
J −11,544 meters

Lesson Quiz 

Subtract.

1. 3 − 9 **−6**

2. −7 − 4 **−11**

3. −3 − (−5) **2**

4. Evaluate $x - y + z$ for $x = -4$, $y = 5$, and $z = -10$. **−19**

5. On January 1, 2002, the high temperature was 81°F in Kona, Hawaii. The low temperature was −29°F in Barrow, Alaska. What was the difference between the two temperatures? **110°F**

Available on Daily Transparency in CRB

3-5 Organizer

Pacing: Traditional 1 day
Block $\frac{1}{2}$ day

Objective: Students multiply and divide integers.

Warm Up

Evaluate each expression.

1. 17 · 5 **85** **2.** 8 · 34 **272**
3. 4 · 86 **344** **4.** 20 · 850 **17,000**
5. 275 ÷ 5 **55** **6.** 112 ÷ 4 **28**

Problem of the Day

To discourage random guessing on a multiple-choice test, a teacher assigns 5 points for a correct answer, −2 points for an incorrect answer, and 0 points for leaving the question unanswered. What is the score for a student who had 22 correct answers, 15 incorrect answers, and 7 unanswered questions? **80**

Available on Daily Transparency in CRB

Why is an indecisive third-base coach like multiplying or dividing by a negative integer? In both cases, the sign changes.

3-5 Multiplying and Dividing Integers

Learn to multiply and divide integers.

You can think of multiplication as repeated addition.

$$3 \cdot 2 = 2 + 2 + 2 = 6 \text{ and } 3 \cdot (-2) = (-2) + (-2) + (-2) = -6$$

EXAMPLE 1 Multiplying Integers Using Repeated Addition

Find each product.

A $3 \cdot (-3)$

$3 \cdot (-3) = (-3) + (-3) + (-3)$ *Think: 3 · (−3) means 3 groups of −3*
$= -9$

B $-4 \cdot 2$

$-4 \cdot 2 = (-4) + (-4)$ *Think: −4 · 2 = 2 · (−4), or 2 groups of −4*
$= -8$

Remember!
The Commutative Property of Multiplication states that order does not matter when you multiply.

Example 1 suggests that when the signs of two numbers are different, the product is *negative.*

To decide what happens when both numbers are negative, look at the pattern at right. Notice that each product is 3 more than the preceding one. This pattern suggests that the product of two negative integers is *positive.*

$$-3 \cdot (2) = -6$$
$$-3 \cdot (1) = -3$$
$$-3 \cdot (0) = 0$$
$$-3 \cdot (-1) = 3$$
$$-3 \cdot (-2) = 6$$

EXAMPLE 2 Multiplying Integers

Multiply.

$-4 \cdot (-2)$
$-4 \cdot (-2) = 8$ *Both signs are negative, so the product is positive.*

Multiplication and division are inverse operations. They "undo" each other. You can use this fact to discover the rules for division of integers.

$4 \cdot (-2) = -8$ $\quad -8 \div (-2) = 4$ — Same signs → Positive

$-4 \cdot (-2) = 8$ $\quad 8 \div (-2) = -4$ — Different signs → Negative

The rule for division is like the rule for multiplication.

1 Introduce

Alternate Opener

3-5 Multiplying and Dividing Integers

Suppose you start at \$0 and add \$10 to your net worth each day for 3 days. You can write a multiplication statement to show how much money you have after 3 days.

$$3 \cdot 10 = 30$$

1. Suppose you start at \$0 and add a debt of \$10 to your net worth each day for 3 days.
   a. What is your net worth after 3 days?
   b. Write a multiplication statement for this situation.

Suppose 3 people share \$12 equally. You can write a division statement to show how much each person receives.

$$12 \div 3 = 4$$

2. Suppose 3 people share a debt of \$12 equally.
   a. What do they each add to their net worth?
   b. Write a division statement for this situation.

Evaluate each expression.

3. $3 \cdot -9$ **4.** $5 \cdot -6$ **5.** $-20 \div 5$ **6.** $-56 \div 8$

Think and Discuss

7. Describe a possible net worth situation for each expression in numbers 3–6.

Motivate

To introduce students to multiplying integers, ask them to complete repeated addition problems with integers. Discuss multiplication as a shortcut for repeated addition. Demonstrate taking \$2 from a savings account 3 days in a row, for example: $3 \cdot (-2) = -2 + (-2) + (-2) = -6$. Then ask students to consider the expression $-3 \cdot (-2)$ and offer suggestions for the product.

Exploration worksheet and answers on Chapter 3 Resource Book pp. 43 and 116

2 Teach

Lesson Presentation

Guided Instruction

In this lesson, students learn to multiply and divide integers. As you discuss the sign of the product of two negative integers, encourage students to think of the product of two negatives as the opposite of the product of a negative and a positive. Give students the opportunity to state rules for multiplying integers from their own experiences, and assure students that the same rules apply to division, since division undoes multiplication.

Encourage students to multiply or divide the absolute values and then apply the rules for multiplying and dividing integers.

MULTIPLYING AND DIVIDING INTEGERS

If the signs are:		Your answer will be:
the same	→	positive
different	→	negative

EXAMPLE 3 Dividing Integers

Find each quotient.

A 72 ÷ (−9)

72 ÷ (−9) *Think: 72 ÷ 9 = 8.*

−8 *The signs are different, so the quotient is negative.*

B −144 ÷ 12

−144 ÷ 12 *Think: 144 ÷ 12 = 12.*

−12 *The signs are different, so the quotient is negative.*

C −100 ÷ (−5)

−100 ÷ (−5) *Think: 100 ÷ 5 = 20.*

20 *The signs are the same, so the quotient is positive.*

EXAMPLE 4 Averaging Integers

Weather LINK

Each year there are about 16 million thunderstorms around the globe. Thunderstorms develop when moist air rises and encounters cooler air.

Jonie recorded the temperature change every hour for five hours as a cold front approached. The table below shows her data. What was the average temperature change per hour?

Hour	1	2	3	4	5
Temperature Change (°F)	2	−2	−8	−10	−2

2 + (−2) + (−8) + (−10) + (−2) = −20 *Find the sum of the changes in temperature.*

$\frac{-20}{5} = -4$ *Divide to find the average.*

The average temperature change per hour was −4°F.

Think and Discuss

1. **List** at least four different multiplication examples that have 24 as their product. Use both positive and negative integers.
2. **Suppose** −3 is the answer to a division problem and −12 is the number being divided. What is the divisor? Explain your answer.

COMMON ERROR ALERT

Students may try to apply the rules for integer addition to multiplication. For integer addition, if the signs of the addends are the same, the sum has that same sign. In multiplication and division, if signs are the same, the product or quotient is always positive.

Additional Examples

Example 1

Find each product.

A. −7 · 2 **−14**

B. −8 · 3 **−24**

Example 2

Multiply.

−6 · (−5) **30**

Example 3

Find each quotient.

A. −27 ÷ 9 **−3**

B. 35 ÷ (−5) **−7**

C. −32 ÷ (−8) **4**

Example 4

Mrs. Johnson kept track of a stock she was considering buying. She recorded the price change each day. What was the average change per day?

Mon	Tue	Wed	Thu	Fri
−$1	$3	$2	−$5	$6

The average change was $1 per day.

3 Close

Reaching All Learners
Through Curriculum Integration

Language Arts Present the following statement to the students:

I am not unable to swim.

Discuss with students the meaning of the double-negative language of *not unable.* Encourage students to draw connections with integers. Have students restate the sentence in positive terms: I am able to swim. Point out that just as a double negative makes the statement positive, the product of two negative integers is positive.

Summarize

Ask students to restate the rules for multiplying and dividing integers. Discuss how integer multiplication or division can be checked using the opposite operation.

Possible answer: To multiply or divide integers, multiply or divide the absolute values. If the signs of the numbers are the same, the result is positive. If signs are different, the result is negative.

To check the product of integer multiplication, divide the product by one of the factors. The quotient should match the other factor. To check integer division, multiply the quotient by the divisor. The product should match the dividend.

Answers to Think and Discuss

Possible answers:

1. −4 · (−6), 2 · 12, −3 · (−8), and 24 · 1. In each factor pair, the factors should have the same sign.
2. Possible answer: −12 ÷ 4 = −3. The divisor must have an absolute value of 4, since 4 · 3 = 12. Also, the divisor must be positive because −12 must be divided by a positive integer to have an answer of −3.

3-5 PRACTICE & ASSESS

Students may want to refer back to the lesson examples.

Assignment Guide

If you finished Example 1 assign:
Core 1–3, 12–14, 23, 36, 37, 41, 51–58
Enriched 1, 3, 13, 23, 30, 36–38, 41, 42, 51–58

If you finished Example 2 assign:
Core 1–6, 12–17, 24–28 even, 33–37 odd, 41, 51–58
Enriched 1–5 odd, 13–17 odd, 23, 24, 26, 28–38, 40–42, 51–58

If you finished Example 3 assign:
Core 1–10, 12–21, 23–43 odd, 51–58
Enriched 1–9 odd, 13–21 odd, 23–43, 51–58

If you finished Example 4 assign:
Core 1–22, 23–47 odd, 51–58
Enriched 1–21 odd, 23–58

Notes

3-5 Exercises

FOR EXTRA PRACTICE
see page 660

internet connect
Homework Help Online
go.hrw.com Keyword: MS4 3-5

GUIDED PRACTICE

See Example 1 Find each product.

1. $5 \cdot (-3)$ **−15**
2. $5 \cdot (-2)$ **−10**
3. $-3 \cdot 5$ **−15**

See Example 2 Multiply.

4. $-5 \cdot (-3)$ **15**
5. $-2 \cdot (-5)$ **10**
6. $-3 \cdot (-5)$ **15**

See Example 3 Find each quotient.

7. $32 \div (-4)$ **−8**
8. $-18 \div 3$ **−6**
9. $-20 \div (-5)$ **4**
10. $49 \div (-7)$ **−7**

See Example 4

11. The table shows how the elevation changed as Denise walked along a path. What was the average change in elevation per minute? **3 ft**

Minute	1	2	3	4
Change in Elevation (ft)	−6	8	12	−2

INDEPENDENT PRACTICE

See Example 1 Find each product.

12. $2 \cdot (-1)$ **−2**
13. $-5 \cdot 2$ **−10**
14. $-4 \cdot 2$ **−8**

See Example 2 Multiply.

15. $-4 \cdot (-6)$ **24**
16. $-6 \cdot (-8)$ **48**
17. $-8 \cdot (-4)$ **32**

See Example 3 Find each quotient.

18. $48 \div (-6)$ **−8**
19. $-35 \div (-5)$ **7**
20. $-16 \div 4$ **−4**
21. $-64 \div 8$ **−8**

See Example 4

22. The table shows temperature change over time. What was the average temperature change per hour? **−6°F**

Hour	1	2	3	4	5	6
Change in Temperature (°F)	−11	−18	−20	−15	12	16

PRACTICE AND PROBLEM SOLVING

Find each product or quotient.

23. $-4 \cdot 10$ **−40**
24. $-3 \cdot (-9)$ **27**
25. $-45 \div 15$ **−3**
26. $-3 \cdot 4 \cdot (-1)$ **12**
27. $-500 \div (-10)$ **50**
28. $5 \cdot (-4) \cdot (-2)$ **40**
29. $-4 \cdot (-6) \cdot (-5)$ **−120**
30. $225 \div (-75)$ **−3**
31. $-2 \cdot (-5) \cdot 9$ **90**

Simplify.

32. $(-3)^2$ **9**
33. $(-2)^4$ **16**
34. $(-5)^3$ **−125**
35. $(-1)^5$ **−1**
36. $8 \cdot (-7) + 9$
37. $-3 \cdot (4) - 12$
38. $25 - (-2) \cdot 4^2$
39. $8 + 6 \div (-2)$

36. −47
37. −24
38. 57
39. 5

Math Background

The Distributive Property can be used to algebraically demonstrate that a positive integer times a negative integer is a negative integer. Begin with the sum of any integer and its opposite. For example, $5 + (-5) = 0$. Use the Distributive Property to multiply by a positive integer.

$$3[5 + (-5)] = 3 \cdot 5 + 3 \cdot (-5) = 0$$
$$15 + \square = 0$$
$$15 + (-15) = 0$$

So $3 \cdot (-5)$ must equal −15.

To demonstrate that a negative integer times a negative integer is a positive integer, begin with the same sum but multiply by a negative integer.

RETEACH 3-5

LESSON 3-5 **Reteach**
Multiplying and Dividing Integers

Look for the patterns in these products and quotients.

$1 \cdot 3 = 3$	$-1 \cdot 3 = -3$	$3 \div 1 = 3$	$3 \div (-1) = -3$
$2 \cdot 3 = 6$	$-2 \cdot 3 = -6$	$6 \div 2 = 3$	$6 \div (-2) = -3$
$-3 \cdot (-3) = 9$	$3 \cdot (-3) = -9$	$-9 \div (-3) = 3$	$-9 \div 3 = -3$
$-4 \cdot (-3) = 12$	$4 \cdot (-3) = -12$	$-12 \div (-4) = 3$	$-12 \div 4 = -3$

Look at how to find the signs of the products.

- The product of two integers with the **same sign** is **positive.**
  $(+) \cdot (+) = (+)$ $(-) \cdot (-) = (+)$
- The product of two integers with **different signs** is **negative.**
  $(+) \cdot (-) = (-)$ $(-) \cdot (+) = (-)$

Look at how to find the signs of the quotients.

- The quotient of two integers with the **same sign** is **positive.**
  $(+) \div (+) = (+)$ $(-) \div (-) = (+)$
- The quotient of two integers with **different signs** is **negative.**
  $(+) \div (-) = (-)$ $(-) \div (+) = (-)$

Find each product or quotient.

1. $-5 \cdot 4$ **−20**
2. $2 \cdot (-8)$ **−16**
3. $-1 \cdot (-1)$ **1**
4. $-6 \cdot 3$ **−18**
5. $7 \cdot (-3)$ **−21**
6. $-8 \cdot (-4)$ **32**
7. $-6 \cdot 5$ **−30**
8. $-9 \cdot (-9)$ **81**
9. $36 \div (-4)$ **−9**
10. $-27 \div 9$ **−3**
11. $-24 \div (-6)$ **4**
12. $-30 \div 5$ **−6**
13. $18 \div 6$ **3**
14. $32 \div (-8)$ **−4**
15. $-45 \div 9$ **−5**
16. $-40 \div (-10)$ **4**

PRACTICE 3-5

LESSON 3-5 **Practice B**
Multiplying and Dividing Integers

Find each product.

1. $8 \cdot (-5)$ **−40**
2. $-4 \cdot 7$ **−28**
3. $-6 \cdot (-3)$ **18**
4. $-2 \cdot 4$ **−8**
5. $-6 \cdot (-6)$ **36**
6. $9 \cdot (-3)$ **−27**
7. $-2 \cdot (-8)$ **16**
8. $5 \cdot (-7)$ **−35**
9. $10 \cdot 8$ **80**
10. $-5 \cdot 9$ **−45**
11. $9 \cdot (-6)$ **−54**
12. $(-4) \cdot (-11)$ **44**

Find each quotient.

13. $25 \div (-5)$ **−5**
14. $-54 \div (-6)$ **9**
15. $-10 \div 5$ **−2**
16. $-28 \div (-4)$ **7**
17. $-42 \div (-7)$ **6**
18. $-21 \div 3$ **−7**
19. $36 \div (-6)$ **−6**
20. $-81 \div (-9)$ **9**
21. $-32 \div 8$ **−4**
22. $45 \div (-9)$ **−5**
23. $-72 \div (-8)$ **9**
24. $50 \div 10$ **5**

25. The table below shows how the elevation changed each minute for 4 minutes as Kim walked along a path. What was the average change in elevation per minute for the 4 minutes?
−1 ft

Minute	1	2	3	4
Change in Elevation (ft)	9	−5	−7	−1

26. The table below shows how the temperature changed each hour for 6 hours. What was the average temperature change per hour for the 6 hours?
−2°F

Hour	1	2	3	4	5	6
Change in Temperature (°F)	−3	−4	−2	−2	2	−3

Evaluate each expression for $a = -5$, $b = 6$, and $c = -12$.

40. $-2c + b$ **30** 41. $4a - b$ **−26** 42. $ab + c$ **−42** 43. $ac \div b$ **10**

44. ***EARTH SCIENCE*** The table shows the depths of major caves in the United States. Subtract the depth of the deepest cave from the depth of the shallowest cave to find their difference. **885 ft**

Depths of Major U.S. Caves

Cave	Depth (ft)
Carlsbad Caverns	−1,022
Caverns of Sonora	−150
Ellison's Cave	−1,000
Jewel Cave	−696
Kartchner Caverns	−137
Mammoth Cave	−379

Source: NSS U.S.A. Long Cave List, Caves over one mile long as of 10/18/2001

45. ***EARTH SCIENCE*** A scuba diver is swimming at a depth of −12 feet. Then she dives down to a coral reef that is at five times this depth. What is the depth of the coral reef? **−60 ft**

46. ***PERSONAL FINANCE*** Does each person end up with more or less money than they started with? By how much?
 a. Kevin spends $24 a day for 3 days. **less; −$72**
 b. Devin earns $15 a day for 5 days. **more; $75**
 c. Evan spends $20 a day for 3 days. Then he earns $18 a day for 4 days. **more; $12**

47. The average change was $55 per day.

47. ***BUSINESS*** The table shows the deposits and withdrawals made by the Purple Tomato Cafe to and from their bank account in one week. What was the average daily change in the account?

Day	1	2	3	4	5	6	7
Amount ($)	−150	−280	160	190	250	−140	355

48. If the integers have opposite signs, the quotient will be negative.

48. ***WHAT'S THE ERROR?*** A student writes, "The quotient of an integer divided by an integer of the opposite sign has the sign of the integer with the greater absolute value." What is the student's error?

49. ***WRITE ABOUT IT*** Explain how to find the product and the quotient of two integers.

50. ***CHALLENGE*** Use > or < to compare $-2 \cdot (-1) \cdot 4 \cdot 2 \cdot (-3)$ and $-1 + (-2) + 4 + (-25) + (-10)$. **<**

Spiral Review

Combine like terms. (Lesson 2-9)

51. $6x + 2y - 4x$ **$2x + 2y$** 52. $3x^2 + 5x + 3x - x^2$ **$2x^2 + 8x$** 53. $6a^2 + 2 + 2a^2 - 2$ **$8a^2$**

54. $y - 3y^2 + y^2\ y - 2y^2$ **$y - 2y^2$** 55. $x^2 + 2y + 6 - x^2$ **$2y + 6$** 56. $4a^2 - 6a^2 + 9a + 2a^2$ **$9a$**

57. **TEST PREP** In the equation $4 + b = 20$, what is the value of b? (Lesson 2-10) **D**
 A 5 B 80 C 24 D 16

58. **TEST PREP** In the equation $q \cdot 7 = 21$, what is the value of q? (Lesson 2-12) **H**
 F 14 G 147 H 3 J 28

Answers

49. Multiply or divide as with whole numbers. If both integers have the same sign, the product or quotient is positive. If integers have unlike signs, the product or quotient is negative.

Journal

Have students describe how they would decide which sign to use for the product of more than two integers. Encourage them to come up with examples to support their methods.

Test Prep Doctor

In Exercise 57, encourage students to use substitution to quickly eliminate incorrect choices. Choice **A** can be easily eliminated with mental math, since 4 + 5 equals 9, not 20. Choice **B** can be similarly eliminated, as 4 + 80 equals 84, not 20.

CHALLENGE 3-5

LESSON 3-5 **Challenge**
Football Follies

Phil the Fumbler and Sack'im Sam play for two different football teams. Last year, they both had their worst season ever. Read their interview with a local sports announcer. Find out which player had the worse year by completing the table below.

Announcer: Well Phil, you didn't have a very good season, did you?

Phil: No, I guess losing 42 yards in each of the first 6 games was not what I had hoped to do.

Sam: Gee, that wasn't a very good opening, Phil. At least I gained 53 yards in each of my first 2 games, although, I did lose 88 yards in each of the next 4 games.

Announcer: Yes, Sam, that's true. Now can you tell us how you did in games 7 through 12 last season?

Sam: I can, but I don't really want to.

Announcer: I heard you were sacked and lost 125 yards in each of those games. Is this accurate.

Sam: Yup.

Announcer: Phil, how did you do in games 7 through 12?

Phil: Not that bad. I fumbled quite a bit in games 7 through 11, so I lost 130 yards in each of those games. But I came back in game 12 and gained 85 yards during that one.

Announcer: And what was your yardage for games 13 through 16?

Phil: I lost 95 yards in each game.

Sam: Me, too.

Announcer: Well, I sure hope next season is better for both of you.

Phil and Sam: ME, TOO!

Complete the table.

	Phil	Sam
Total Yards Gained	**85 yd**	**106 yd**
Total Yards Lost	**−1,282 yd**	**−1,482 yd**
Total Yards	**−1,197 yd**	**−1,376 yd**
Average per Game for 16 Games (to the nearest tenth)	**−74.8 yd**	**−86 yd**
Which player had the worse year?		✓

PROBLEM SOLVING 3-5

LESSON 3-5 **Problem Solving**
Multiplying and Dividing Integers

Gerald recorded the temperature change every hour for 6 hours each day from Monday through Thursday. The chart shows his data.

	Hour	1	2	3	4	5	6
Change in Temperature (°F)	Monday	−8	−5	3	5	−1	−6
	Tuesday	−4	−2	3	8	2	−1
	Wednesday	−9	−9	−7	−2	1	8
	Thursday	2	−1	−1	4	5	9

Write the correct answer.

1. What was the average temperature change per hour on Tuesday?
 1°

2. What was the average temperature change on Wednesday?
 −3°

3. What was the average temperature change on Thursday?
 3°

4. What was the average temperature change on Monday?
 −2°

Choose the letter for the best answer.

5. A small company had a profit of −$528 in January. If it continues to have the same profit each month for 4 months, what will be the company's total profit for 4 months?
 A −$132 (C) −$2,112
 B $132 D $2,112

6. Evi's watch is water resistant up to −15 feet. Mateo's watch is water resistant up to 8 times the depth of Evi's watch. Mateo's watch is water resistant to what maximum depth?
 F −7 feet (H) −120 feet
 G 120 feet J 7 feet

7. A submarine at −235 meters dives to a depth 8 times its initial depth. To what depth does the submarine dive?
 A −227 meters
 B −243 meters
 (C) −1,880 meters
 D −8,235 meters

8. A 1-kilogram rock dropped into the ocean would take 37 minutes to reach −6,660 meters. Which integer represents the average rate of fall?
 F 167 meters per minute
 G −167 meters per minute
 (H) −180 meters per minute
 J 188 meters per minute

Lesson Quiz

Find each product or quotient.

1. $-8 \cdot 12$ **−96**
2. $-3 \cdot 5 \cdot (-2)$ **30**
3. $-75 \div 5$ **−15**
4. $-110 \div (-2)$ **55**
5. The temperature in Bar Harbor, Maine, was −3°F. It then dropped during the night to be four times as cold. What was the temperature then? **−12°F**

Available on Daily Transparency in CRB

3C Model Integer Equations

Pacing: Traditional 1 day
Block $\frac{1}{2}$ day

Objective: To use algebra tiles to model solving equations containing integers

Materials: Algebra tiles

Lab Resources

Hands-On Lab Activities . . . . pp. 17–19, 126

Using the Pages

Discuss with students what each algebra tile represents and how to represent equations with algebra tiles. Explain that algebra tiles can be added or removed as long as the same amount is added or removed on each side of the equation.

Use algebra tiles to model and solve each equation.

1. $x + 4 = 6$ $x = 2$

2. $x + (-3) = -7$ $x = -4$

3. $x - 5 = 2$ $x = 7$

4. $x - (-1) = -4$ $x = -5$

Model Integer Equations

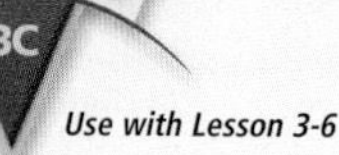

Use with Lesson 3-6

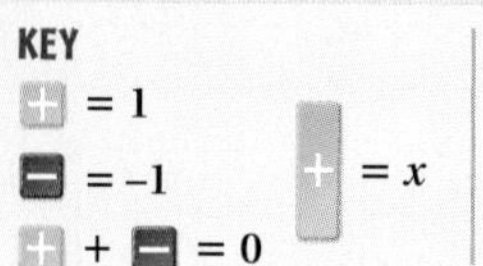

KEY

+ tile = 1
− tile = −1
+ tile + − tile = 0
long + tile = x

REMEMBER

Adding or removing a zero from an expression does not change the expression's value.

internet connect
Lab Resources Online
go.hrw.com
KEYWORD: MS4 Lab3C

You can use algebra tiles to solve equations.

Activity

To solve the equation $x + 2 = 3$, you need to get x alone on one side of the equal sign. You can add or remove tiles as long as you add the same amount or remove the same amount on both sides.

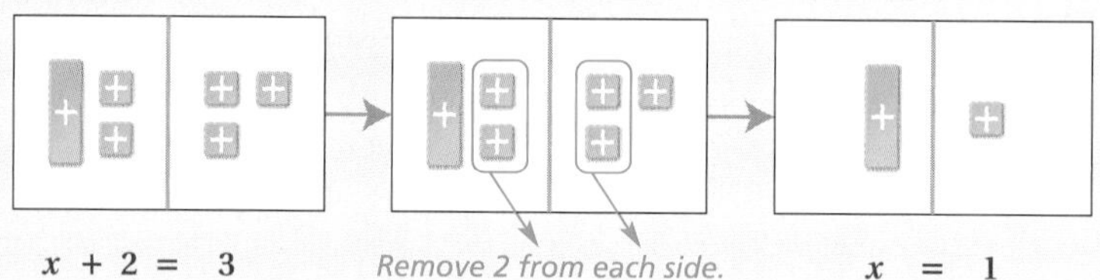

x + 2 = 3
Remove 2 from each side.
x = 1

1 Use algebra tiles to model and solve each equation.

a. $x + 3 = 5$ $x = 2$ **b.** $x + 4 = 9$ $x = 5$ **c.** $x + 5 = 8$ $x = 3$ **d.** $x + 6 = 6$ $x = 0$

The equation $x + 6 = 4$ is more difficult to model because there are not enough tiles on the right side. You can use the fact that $1 + (-1) = 0$ to help solve the equation.

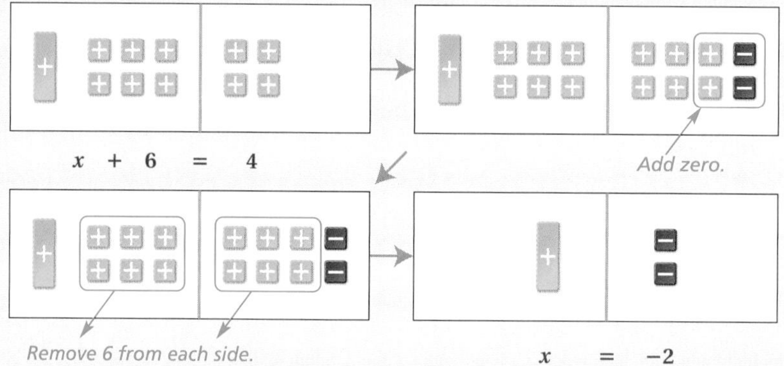

x + 6 = 4
Add zero.
Remove 6 from each side.
x = −2

2 Use algebra tiles to model and solve each equation.

a. $x + 5 = 3$ **$x = -2$** **b.** $x + 4 = 2$ **$x = -2$** **c.** $x + 7 = -3$ **$x = -10$** **d.** $x + 6 = -2$ **$x = -8$**

When modeling an equation that involves subtraction, such as $x - 6 = 2$, you must first rewrite the equation as an addition equation. For example, the equation $x - 6 = 2$ can be rewritten as $x + (-6) = 2$.

Modeling equations that involve addition of negative numbers is similar to modeling equations that involve addition of positive numbers.

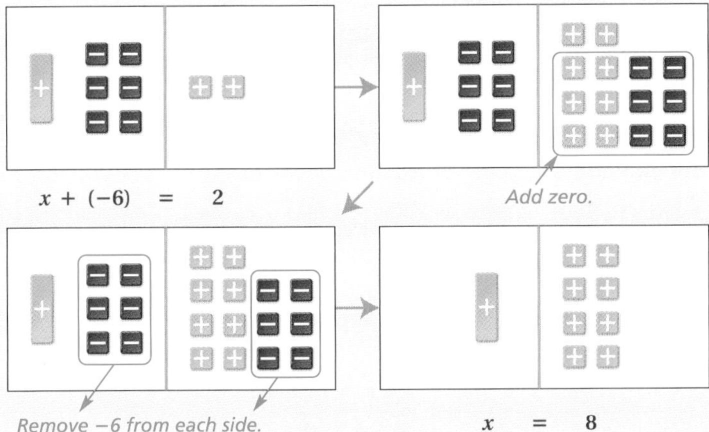

x + (−6) = 2
Add zero.
Remove −6 from each side.
x = 8

3 Use algebra tiles to model and solve each equation.

a. $x - 4 = 3$ **$x = 7$** **b.** $x - 2 = 8$ **$x = 10$** **c.** $x - 5 = -5$ **$x = 0$** **d.** $x - 7 = 0$ **$x = 7$**

Think and Discuss

1. When you use neutral pairs to add zero to an equation, how do you know the number of yellow tiles and red tiles that you need?
   The number of red tiles and yellow tiles must be the same.
2. When you remove tiles, what operation are you representing? When you add tiles, what operation are you representing?
   Removing tiles is subtraction; adding tiles is addition.
3. How can you use the original model to check your solution?
   Replace the variable tile with red or yellow tiles and find the sum or difference.
4. To model $x - 6 = 2$, you must rewrite the equation as $x + (-6) = 2$. Why are you allowed to do this? **Subtracting is the same as adding the opposite.**

Try This

Use algebra tiles to model and solve each equation.

1. $x + 7 = 10$ **$x = 3$** **2.** $x - 5 = -8$ **$x = -3$** **3.** $x + (-5) = -4$ **$x = 1$** **4.** $x - 2 = 1$ **$x = 3$**

5. $x + 4 = 8$ **$x = 4$** **6.** $x + 3 = -2$ **$x = -5$** **7.** $x + (-1) = 9$ **$x = 10$** **8.** $x - 7 = -6$ **$x = 1$**

3-6 Organizer

Pacing: Traditional 1 day
Block $\frac{1}{2}$ day

Objective: Students solve one-step equations with integers.

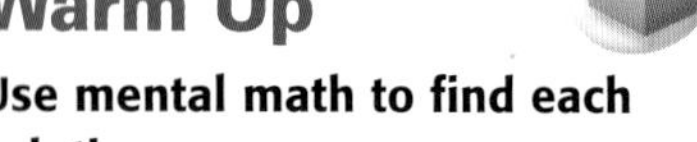

Warm Up

Use mental math to find each solution.

1. $7 + y = 15$ — $y = 8$
2. $x \div 9 = 9$ — $x = 81$
3. $6x = 24$ — $x = 4$
4. $x - 12 = 30$ — $x = 42$

Problem of the Day

Zelda sold her wet suit to a friend for \$156. She sold her tank, mask, and snorkel for \$85 less than she sold her wet suit. She bought a used wet suit for \$80 and a used tank, mask, and snorkel for \$36. If she started with \$0, how much money does she have left? **\$111**

Available on Daily Transparency in CRB

Math Humor

There are three kinds of people in the world: those who can count and those who can't.

3-6 Solving Equations Containing Integers

Learn to solve one-step equations with integers.

When you are solving equations with integers, the goal is the same as with whole numbers—isolate the variable on one side of the equation. One way to isolate the variable is to add opposites. Recall that the sum of a number and its opposite is 0.

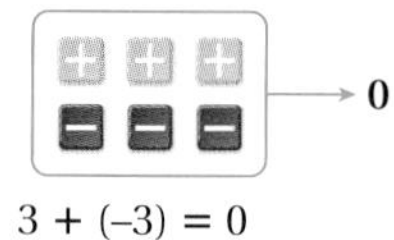

$3 + (-3) = 0$

$a + (-a) = 0$

Helpful Hint

$3 + (-3) = 0$
3 is the opposite of -3.

EXAMPLE 1 Solving Addition and Subtraction Equations

Solve. Check each answer.

A $-3 + y = -5$

$$\begin{aligned} -3 + y &= -5 \\ \underline{+3} \quad & \quad \underline{+3} \\ y &= -2 \end{aligned}$$

Add 3 to both sides to isolate the variable.

Check

$-3 + y = -5$
$-3 + (-2) \stackrel{?}{=} -5$ — *Substitute –2 for y in the original equation.*
$-5 \stackrel{?}{=} -5$ ✔ — *True. –2 is the solution to –3 + y = –5.*

B $n + 3 = -10$

$$\begin{aligned} n + 3 &= -10 \\ \underline{+(-3)} \quad & \quad \underline{+(-3)} \\ n &= -13 \end{aligned}$$

Add –3 to both sides to isolate the variable.

Check

$n + 3 = -10$
$-13 + 3 \stackrel{?}{=} -10$ — *Substitute –13 for n in the original equation.*
$-10 \stackrel{?}{=} -10$ ✔ — *True. –13 is the solution to n + 3 = –10.*

C $x - 8 = -32$

$$\begin{aligned} x - 8 &= -32 \\ \underline{+8} \quad & \quad \underline{+8} \\ x &= -24 \end{aligned}$$

Add 8 to both sides to isolate the variable.

Check

$x - 8 = -32$
$-24 - 8 \stackrel{?}{=} -32$ — *Substitute –24 for x in the original equation.*
$-32 \stackrel{?}{=} -32$ ✔ — *True. –24 is the solution to x – 8 = –32.*

1 Introduce

Alternate Opener

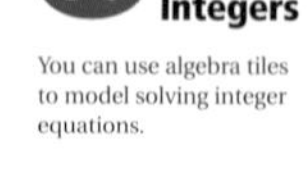

EXPLORATION

3-6 Solving Equations Containing Integers

You can use algebra tiles to model solving integer equations.

represents an unknown amount x. represents –1. represents 1.

The equation $x - 4 = -7$ is modeled as shown. Notice that 4 is being subtracted from x.

$x - 4 = -7$

To get x alone on one side, perform the inverse operation on both sides.

$x - 4 + 4 = -7 + 4$

$x = -3$

Use algebra tiles to solve each equation.

1. $x + 5 = 9$ **2.** $x - 6 = 2$ **3.** $x + 4 = -1$
4. $6 = x - 7$ **5.** $8 = x + 2$ **6.** $3 = x - 9$

Think and Discuss

7. Explain how you know what operation to perform on both sides of an equation.

Motivate

Ask students to suggest a story or problem that might fit the equation in Example 1: $-3 + y = -5$. You might suggest real-world contexts, such as owing money, degrees below zero, or feet below sea level. For example, it's 3 degrees below zero and the forecaster predicts a low of 5 degrees below zero. How many more degrees does the temperature need to drop in order to reach the predicted low temperature?

Exploration worksheet and answers on Chapter 3 Resource Book pp. 52 and 118

2 Teach

Lesson Presentation

Guided Instruction

In this lesson, students learn to solve one-step equations with integers. Show students that the inverse operation with the same integer is applied to each side to isolate the variable, using the properties of equality. As students look at an equation, you may want to suggest that they begin solving by asking themselves, "What has been done to the variable?" and "What is the opposite of doing that?"

Teaching Tip Have students work in pairs, with one student identifying the integer and the other student identifying the inverse operation needed to isolate the variable and solve the equation.

EXAMPLE 2 Solving Multiplication and Division Equations

Solve. Check each answer.

A $\frac{a}{-3} = 9$

$\frac{a}{-3} = 9$

$(-3)\left(\frac{a}{-3}\right) = (-3)9$ *Multiply both sides by −3 to isolate the variable.*

$a = -27$

Check

$\frac{a}{-3} = 9$

$\frac{-27}{-3} \stackrel{?}{=} 9$ *Substitute −27 for a in the original equation.*

$9 \stackrel{?}{=} 9$ ✔ *True. −27 is the solution to $\frac{a}{-3} = 9$.*

B $-120 = 6x$

$-120 = 6x$

$\frac{-120}{6} = \frac{6x}{6}$ *Divide both sides by 6 to isolate the variable.*

$-20 = x$

Check

$-120 = 6x$

$-120 \stackrel{?}{=} 6(-20)$ *Substitute −20 for x in the original equation.*

$-120 \stackrel{?}{=} -120$ ✔ *True. −20 is the solution to −120 = 6x.*

EXAMPLE 3 *Business Application*

A shoe manufacturer made a profit of $800 million. This amount is $200 million more than last year's profit. What was last year's profit?

Let p represent last year's profit (in millions of dollars).

Profit this year = $p + 200$

Profit this year = $800 million

$p + 200 = 800$

$\underline{-200 \quad -200}$

$p = 600$

Last year's profit was $600 million.

Think and Discuss

1. **Tell** what value of n makes $-n + 32$ equal to zero.
2. **Explain** why you would or would not multiply both sides of an equation by 0 to solve it.

COMMON ERROR ALERT

Some students might apply the inverse operation to only the variable side of the equation. Encourage students to show the inverse operation step on a separate line so that they can easily notice if they neglect to apply the inverse operation to both sides.

Additional Examples

Example 1

Solve. Check each answer.

A. $-6 + x = -7$ $x = -1$

B. $p + 5 = -3$ $p = -8$

C. $y - 9 = -40$ $y = -31$

Example 2

Solve. Check each answer.

A. $\frac{b}{-5} = 6$ $b = -30$

B. $-400 = 8y$ $-50 = y$

Example 3

In 2003, a manufacturer made a profit of $300 million. This amount was $100 million more than the profit in 2002. What was the profit in 2002?

The profit was $200 million in 2002.

Example 2 note: Students might incorrectly divide 9 by −3 instead of multiplying. Encourage students to write the step that shows multiplying each side by the same integer.

Reaching All Learners
Through Graphic Cues

Suggest that students use colored pencils to circle the integer that must be moved (or operated on) in order to isolate the variable. Then students can use a different color to write the step of performing the inverse operation on each side of the equation.

3 Close

Summarize

Ask students which operations undo, or are inverses of, each other. Discuss why it is necessary to perform the same operation on both sides of the equation when isolating the variable.

Possible answer: Addition and subtraction are inverse operations that undo each other. Multiplication and division are inverse operations that undo each other. In order for the rewritten equation to have the same solution as the original, you must keep the equation in balance by doing exactly the same operation on both sides.

Answers to Think and Discuss

Possible answers:

1. The expression $-n + 32$ is equal to 0 when $n = 32$.
2. Both sides would equal zero, and you would lose all the information of the equation.

3-6 PRACTICE & ASSESS

Students may want to refer back to the lesson examples.

Assignment Guide

If you finished Example 1 assign:
Core 1–3, 8–13, 23, 29, 31, 35, 48–55
Enriched 1, 3, 9–13 odd, 22, 23, 26, 29, 31, 35, 37, 38, 48–55

If you finished Example 2 assign:
Core 1–6, 8–19, 21–37 odd, 48–55
Enriched 1–5 odd, 9–19 odd, 21–38, 48–55

If you finished Example 3 assign:
Core 1–20, 21–43 odd, 48–55
Enriched 1–19 odd, 21–55

Notes

Math Background

The Properties of Equality are used to transform an equation into an equivalent equation whose solution can be easily seen.

The Addition Property of Equality: If a, b, and c are real numbers and $a = b$, then $a + c = b + c$ and $c + a = c + b$.

The Subtraction Property of Equality: If a, b, and c are real numbers and $a = b$, then $a - c = b - c$.

The Multiplication Property of Equality: If a, b, and c are real numbers and $a = b$, then $ac = bc$ and $ca = cb$.

The Division Property of Equality: If a and b are real numbers, c is any nonzero real number, and $a = b$, then $\frac{a}{c} = \frac{b}{c}$.

3-6 Exercises

FOR EXTRA PRACTICE
see page 660

internet connect
Homework Help Online
go.hrw.com Keyword: MS4 3-6

GUIDED PRACTICE

See Example 1 Solve. Check each answer.

1. $w - 6 = -2$ **$w = 4$**
2. $x + 5 = -7$ **$x = -12$**
3. $k = -18 + 11$ **$k = -7$**

See Example 2

4. $\frac{n}{-4} = 2$ **$n = -8$**
5. $-240 = 8y$ **$y = -30$**
6. $-5a = 300$ **$a = -60$**

See Example 3

7. Last year, a chain of electronics stores had a loss of \$45 million. This year the loss is \$12 million more than last year's loss. What is this year's loss? **This year's loss is \$57 million.**

INDEPENDENT PRACTICE

See Example 1 Solve. Check each answer.

8. $b - 7 = -16$ **$b = -9$**
9. $k + 6 = 3$ **$k = -3$**
10. $s + 2 = -4$ **$s = -6$**
11. $v + 14 = 10$ **$v = -4$**
12. $c + 8 = -20$ **$c = -28$**
13. $a - 25 = -5$ **$a = 20$**

See Example 2

14. $9c = -99$ **$c = -11$**
15. $\frac{t}{8} = -4$ **$t = -32$**
16. $-16 = 2z$ **$z = -8$**
17. $\frac{n}{-5} = -30$ **$n = 150$**
18. $200 = -25p$ **$p = -8$**
19. $\frac{l}{-12} = 12$ **$l = -144$**

See Example 3

20. The temperature in Nome, Alaska, was −50°F. This was 18°F less than the temperature in Anchorage, Alaska, on the same day. What was the temperature in Anchorage? **−32°F**

PRACTICE AND PROBLEM SOLVING

Solve. Check each answer.

21. $9y = 900$ **$y = 100$**
22. $d - 15 = 45$ **$d = 60$**
23. $j + 56 = -7$ **$j = -63$**
24. $\frac{s}{-20} = 7$ **$s = -140$**
25. $-85 = -5c$ **$c = 17$**
26. $v - 39 = -16$ **$v = 23$**
27. $11y = -121$ **$y = -11$**
28. $\frac{n}{36} = 9$ **$n = 324$**
29. $w + 41 = 0$ **$w = -41$**
30. $\frac{r}{238} = 8$ **$r = 1{,}904$**
31. $-23 = x + 35$ **$x = -58$**
32. $0 = -15m$ **$m = 0$**
33. $4x = 2 + 14$ **$x = 4$**
34. $c + c + c = 6$ **$c = 2$**
35. $t - 3 = 4 + 2$ **$t = 9$**
36. $4y + y = 10$ **$y = 2$**
37. $23 + h - 4 = 39$ **$h = 20$**
38. $k - 32 = 16 - 2 + 4$ **$k = 50$**
39. The three angles of a triangle have equal measures. The sum of their measures is 180°. What is the measure of each angle? **60°**
40. ***SPORTS*** Herb has 42 days to prepare for a cross-country race. During his training, he will run a total of 126 miles. If Herb runs the same distance every day, how many miles will he run each day? **3 mi**

RETEACH 3-6

LESSON 3-6 **Reteach**
Solving Equations Containing Integers

- You can use addition to solve an equation involving subtraction. Addition undoes subtraction. Adding the same number to both sides of the equation keeps the equation balanced.

	Check
$x - 5 = -6$	$x - 5 = -6$
$x - 5 + 5 = -6 + 5$	$-1 - 5 \stackrel{?}{=} -6$
$x = -1$	$-6 \stackrel{?}{=} -6$ ✓

- You can use subtraction to solve an equation involving addition. Subtraction undoes addition. Subtracting the same number from both sides of the equation keeps the equation balanced.

	Check
$n + 4 = -15$	$n + 4 = -15$
$n + 4 - 4 = -15 - 4$	$-19 + 4 \stackrel{?}{=} -15$
$n = -19$	$-15 \stackrel{?}{=} -15$ ✓

Solve. Check your answer.

1. $p - 9 = -3$
   $p - 9 + \underline{9} = -3 + \underline{9}$
   $\underline{p = 6}$
2. $w - 2 = -14$
   $w - 2 + \underline{2} = -14 + \underline{2}$
   $\underline{w = -12}$
3. $x - 12 = -5$
   $x - 12 + \underline{12} = -5 + \underline{12}$
   $\underline{x = 7}$
4. $f - 8 = 6$
   $f - 8 + \underline{8} = 6 + \underline{8}$
   $\underline{f = 14}$
5. $6 = m - 7$ $\underline{m = 13}$
6. $-4 = s - 10$ $\underline{s = 6}$
7. $-8 = y - 2$ $\underline{y = -6}$
8. $a + 19 = 7$ $\underline{a = -12}$
9. $b + 15 = -9$ $\underline{b = -24}$
10. $39 + t = 45$ $\underline{t = 6}$
11. $-5 = x + 7$ $\underline{x = -12}$
12. $-2 = k + 11$ $\underline{k = -13}$
13. $10 = -3 + j$ $\underline{j = 13}$

PRACTICE 3-6

LESSON 3-6 **Practice B**
Solving Equations Containing Integers

Solve. Check your answers.

1. $y - 5 = -4$ $\underline{y = 1}$
2. $n - 9 = -14$ $\underline{n = -5}$
3. $13 = x - 15$ $\underline{x = 28}$
4. $p + 18 = 14$ $\underline{p = -4}$
5. $q + 6 = -2$ $\underline{q = -8}$
6. $0 = w + 4$ $\underline{w = -4}$
7. $9h = -36$ $\underline{h = -4}$
8. $-3b = 36$ $\underline{b = -12}$
9. $-100 = -4u$ $\underline{u = 25}$
10. $\frac{d}{5} = -7$ $\underline{d = -35}$
11. $\frac{c}{4} = -20$ $\underline{c = -80}$
12. $\frac{s}{-9} = 9$ $\underline{s = -81}$
13. $f + 15 = -16$ $\underline{f = -31}$
14. $-75 = 3v$ $\underline{v = -25}$
15. $g - 19 = -21$ $\underline{g = -2}$
16. $-63 = -9s$ $\underline{s = 7}$
17. $14 + m = -10$ $\underline{m = -24}$
18. $12 = \frac{w}{4}$ $\underline{w = 48}$
19. $x = 15 - 31$ $\underline{x = -16}$
20. $\frac{e}{-7} = 8$ $\underline{e = -56}$
21. $-6 = 21 - n$ $\underline{n = 27}$
22. The temperature in Buffalo, New York, was −2°F one day. This was 42 degrees warmer than the temperature in Nome, Alaska, on the same day. What was the temperature in Nome?
    −44°F
23. LaSanda bought 20 shares of stock for \$175. She sold the stock for a total profit of \$25. What was the selling price of each share of stock?
    \$10

41. ***PERSONAL FINANCE*** Jared bought one share of stock for \$225.
   a. He sold the stock for a profit of \$55. What was the selling price of the stock? **\$280**
   b. The price of the stock dropped \$40 the day after Jared sold it. At what price would Jared have sold it if he had waited until then? **\$240**
   c. What would Jared's profit have been if he had waited until the next day to sell his stock? **\$15**

42. ***PHYSICAL SCIENCE*** On the Kelvin temperature scale, pure water boils at 373 K. The difference between the boiling point and the freezing point of water on this scale is 100 K. What is the freezing point of water? **273 K**

The graph shows the most popular destinations for people who traveled over the 2001 Labor Day weekend. Use the graph shown for Exercises 43 and 44.

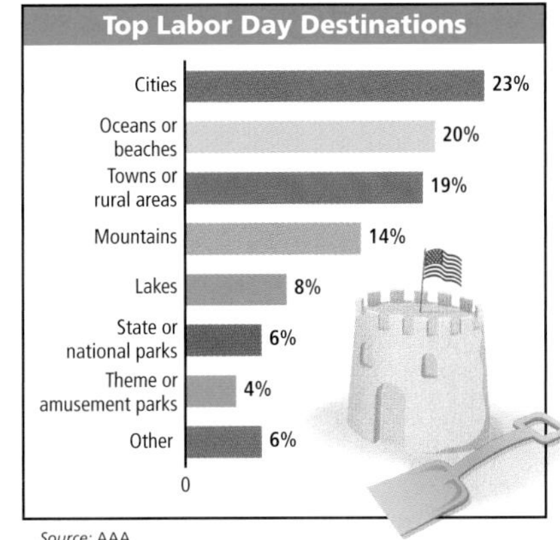

43. ***RECREATION*** Which destination was 5 times more popular than theme or amusement parks? **oceans or beaches**

44. ***RECREATION*** According to the graph, the mountains were as popular as state or national parks and what other destination combined? **lakes**

46. Use addition to solve equations with subtraction, subtraction with addition, multiplication with division, and division with multiplication. Follow all rules for computing with integers.

45. ***CHOOSE A STRATEGY*** Matthew (*M*) earns \$23 less a week than his sister Allie (*A*). Their combined salaries are \$93. How much does each of them earn per week? **C**

   A *A:* \$35; *M:* \$12 B *A:* \$35; *M:* \$58 C *A:* \$58; *M:* \$35

46. ***WRITE ABOUT IT*** Explain how to use inverse operations to isolate a variable in an equation.

47. ***CHALLENGE*** Write an equation that includes the variable *p* and the numbers 5, 3, and 31 so that the solution is $p = 16$.
   Possible answer: $5 \cdot 3 + p = 31$

Spiral Review

Order each set of integers from least to greatest. (Lesson 3-1)

48. −9, 12, −15, −1, 6
   −15, −9, −1, 6, 12
49. −3, −10, 7, 0, −8
   −10, −8, −3, 0, 7
50. 2, −3, −2, 1, −6
   −6, −3, −2, 1, 2
51. 4, −3, −1, 2, 0
   −3, −1, 0, 2, 4
52. −15, −21, 6, 9, −8
   −21, −15, −8, 6, 9
53. −2, 7, 10, −9, −1
   −9, −2, −1, 7, 10

54. **TEST PREP** Which ordered pair lies on the *y*-axis? (Lesson 3-2) **A**

   A (0, −6) B (4, 0) C (1, 8) D (−2, −9)

55. **TEST PREP** Simplify 3 + (−4). (Lesson 3-3) **G**

   F 7 G −1 H 1 J −7

Journal

Ask students to write an explanation of the differences and similarities among the equations $-3 + y = -5$, $y - 3 = -5$, and $y + 5 = 3$. This comparison will help students think about the concepts involved and not just about how to do the steps.

Test Prep Doctor

For Exercise 54, encourage students to think about coordinates of points on the *y*-axis. Once students realize that all points on the *y*-axis have an *x*-coordinate of 0, they can eliminate **B, C,** and **D.**

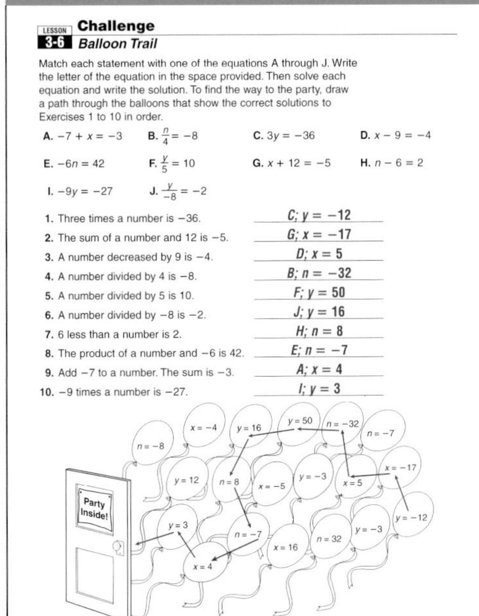

CHALLENGE 3-6

LESSON 3-6 **Challenge**
Balloon Trail

Match each statement with one of the equations A through J. Write the letter of the equation in the space provided. Then solve each equation and write the solution. To find the way to the party, draw a path through the balloons that show the correct solutions to Exercises 1 to 10 in order.

A. $-7 + x = -3$ B. $\frac{n}{4} = -8$ C. $3y = -36$ D. $x - 9 = -4$

E. $-6n = 42$ F. $\frac{y}{5} = 10$ G. $x + 12 = -5$ H. $n - 6 = 2$

I. $-9y = -27$ J. $\frac{y}{-8} = -2$

1. Three times a number is −36. **C; $y = -12$**
2. The sum of a number and 12 is −5. **G; $x = -17$**
3. A number decreased by 9 is −4. **D; $x = 5$**
4. A number divided by 4 is −8. **B; $n = -32$**
5. A number divided by 5 is 10. **F; $y = 50$**
6. A number divided by −8 is −2. **J; $y = 16$**
7. 6 less than a number is 2. **H; $n = 8$**
8. The product of a number and −6 is 42. **E; $n = -7$**
9. Add −7 to a number. The sum is −3. **A; $x = 4$**
10. −9 times a number is −27. **I; $y = 3$**

PROBLEM SOLVING 3-6

LESSON 3-6 **Problem Solving**
Solving Equations Containing Integers

Write the correct answer.

1. Jolene has 30 days to prepare for a bicycle race. She will bicycle 15 miles each day. How many miles will Jolene have bicycled during her training?
   450 mi

2. When the amount of money spent is greater than the amount of income, it is called a deficit. In 1990, the U.S. budget deficit was −\$220 billion. By 1992, it was −\$290 billion. How much did the deficit go up during those two years?
   \$70 billion

3. Two angles of a triangle have a sum of 110°. The sum of all three angles is 180°. What is the measure of the third angle?
   70°

4. The Statue of Liberty was erected in New York City in 1886. How old is the statue?
   Possible answer: 118 years old (in 2004)

Choose the letter for the best answer.

5. Lonnie swam 3 miles each day for 45 days. How many miles did Lonnie swim?
   (A) 135 miles
   B 48 miles
   C 125 miles
   D 45 miles

6. On the hottest day in Richmond, Virginia, the temperature was 105°F. On the coldest day, the temperature was 117°F lower. What was the coldest temperature in Richmond?
   F −117°F
   (G) −12°F
   H 12°F
   J 117°F

7. Mr. Marco sold 50 shares of Gizmo stock for \$1,250. What was the selling price of the stock per share?
   A \$1,200
   B \$250
   C \$50
   (D) \$25

8. The U.S. Bullion Depository at Fort Knox contains about 315 million troy ounces of gold. At a market price of \$300 per troy ounce, what is the approximate value of the gold stored at Fort Knox?
   F \$9 billion
   (G) \$95 billion
   H \$950 million
   J \$950 billion

Lesson Quiz

Solve. Check your answer.

1. $-8y = -800$ 100
2. $x - 22 = -18$ 4
3. $-\frac{y}{7} = 7$ −49
4. $w + 72 = -21$ −93
5. Last year a phone company had a loss of \$25 million. This year the loss is \$14 million more than last year. What is this year's loss? \$39 million

Available on Daily Transparency in CRB

Purpose: *To assess students' mastery of concepts and skills in Lessons 3-1 through 3-6*

Assessment Resources

Section 3A Quiz

Assessment Resources .... p. 11

***Test and Practice Generator* CD-ROM**

Additional mid-chapter assessment items in both multiple-choice and free-response format may be generated for any objective in Lessons 3-1 through 3-6.

Chapter 3 Mid-Chapter Quiz

LESSON **3-1** (pp. 130–133)

Use a number line to find each absolute value.

1. $|-23|$ **23**
   23 units; −25 −20 −10 0
2. $|17|$ **17**
   17 units; 0 5 10 15 20
3. $|-20|$ **20**
   20 units; −20 −10 0
4. $|14|$ **14**
   14 units; 0 5 10 15

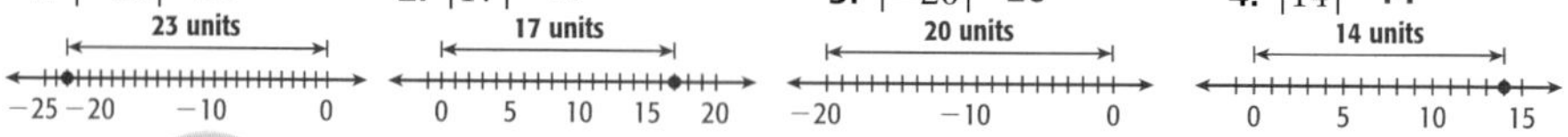

LESSON **3-2** (pp. 134–137)

Plot each point and identify the quadrant in which it is contained.

5. $A(-4, 2)$ **II**
6. $B(1, 3)$ **I**
7. $C(3, 3)$ **I**
8. $D(-2, 4)$ **II**

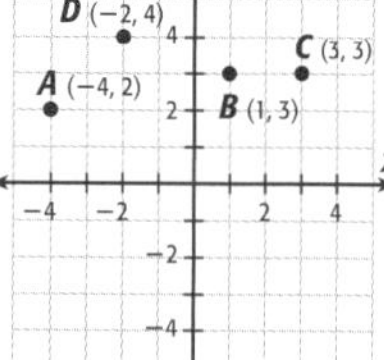

LESSON **3-3** (pp. 140–143)

Evaluate $p + t$ for the given values.

9. $p = 5, t = -18$ **−13**
10. $p = -4, t = -13$ **−17**
11. $p = -37, t = 39$ **2**
12. $p = -25, t = 15$ **−10**

LESSON **3-4** (pp. 146–149)

Subtract.

13. $-21 - (-7)$ **−14**
14. $9 - (-11)$ **20**
15. $6 - 17$ **−11**
16. $18 - 10 - 8$ **0**
17. $(5 - 9) - (-3 + 8)$ **−9**
18. $14 - (-11) - (-5)$ **30**

LESSON **3-5** (pp. 150–153)

Find each product or quotient.

19. $-7 \cdot 3$ **−21**
20. $48 \div 6$ **8**
21. $-5 \cdot (-9)$ **45**
22. $30 \div (-15)$ **−2**

LESSON **3-6** (pp. 156–159)

Solve.

23. $3x = 30$ **x = 10**
24. $k - 25 = 50$ **k = 75**
25. $y + 16 = -8$ **y = −24**
26. $\frac{90}{m} = -15$ **m = −6**
27. This year, 72 students did projects for the science fair. This was 23 more students than last year. How many students did projects for the science fair last year? **49 students**

Mid-Chapter Quiz

Focus on Problem Solving

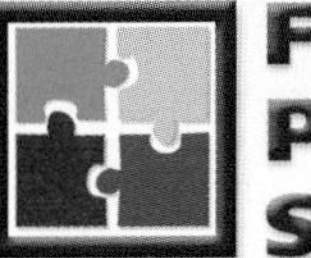

Make a Plan

• Choose a method of computation

When you know the operation you must use and you know exactly which numbers to use, a calculator might be the easiest way to solve a problem. Sometimes, such as when the numbers are small or are multiples of 10, it may be quicker to use mental math.

Sometimes, you have to write the numbers to see how they relate in an equation. When you are working an equation, using a pencil and paper is the simplest method to use because you can see each step as you go.

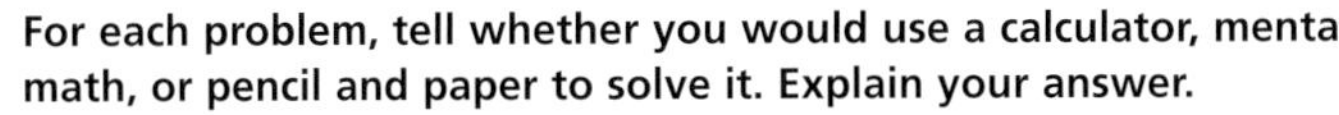

For each problem, tell whether you would use a calculator, mental math, or pencil and paper to solve it. Explain your answer.

1. A scouting troop is collecting aluminum cans to raise money for charity. Their goal is to collect 3,000 cans in 6 months. If they set a goal to collect an equal number of cans each month, how many cans can they expect to collect each month?

2. The Grand Canyon is 29,000 meters wide at its widest point. The Empire State Building, located in New York City, is 381 meters tall. Laid end to end, how many Empire State Buildings would fit in the Grand Canyon at its widest point?

3. On a piano keyboard, all but one of the black keys are arranged in groups so that there are 7 groups with 2 black keys each and 7 groups with 3 black keys each. How many black keys are there on a piano?

4. Some wind chimes are made of rods. The rods are usually of different lengths, producing different sounds. The frequency (which determines the pitch) of the sound is measured in hertz (Hz). If one rod on a chime has a frequency of 55 Hz and another rod has a frequency that is twice that of the first rod's, what is the frequency of the second rod?

Focus on Problem Solving

Purpose: *To focus on choosing a method of computation*

Problem Solving Resources

Interactive Problem Solving. . pp. 22–31

Math: Reading and Writing in the Content Area. . . . . pp. 22–31

Problem Solving Process

This page focuses on the second step of the problem-solving process: **Make a Plan.**

Discuss

Have students discuss how they decided to use a calculator, mental math, or paper and pencil to solve each problem.

Possible answers:

1. Mental math; dividing 3,000 by 6 is similar to dividing 30 by 6.

2. Calculator; divide 29,000 by 381.

3. pencil and paper; 7 groups of 2 black keys plus 7 groups of 3 black keys plus 1 black key not in a group

4. Mental math; multiplying 2 and 55 is the same as $2(50 + 5) = 2(50) + 2(5) = 100 + 10 = 110$.

Answers

1. 500 cans

2. 76 Empire State Buildings

3. 36 black keys

4. 110 Hz

Section **3B**

Rational Numbers

One-Minute Section Planner

Lesson	Materials	Resources
Lesson 3-7 Fractions and Decimals **NCTM:** Number and Operations, Communication, Connections, Representation **NAEP:** Number Properties 1b ☑ SAT-9 ☑ SAT-10 ☑ ITBS ☑ CTBS ☑ MAT ☑ CAT	**Optional** Teaching Transparency T28 *(CRB)*	• *Chapter 3 Resource Book,* pp. 62–70 • Daily Transparency T27, CRB • Additional Examples Transparencies T29–T31, CRB • *Alternate Openers: Explorations,* p. 28
Lesson 3-8 Equivalent Fractions and Mixed Numbers **NCTM:** Number and Operations, Communication, Connections, Representation **NAEP:** Number Properties 1d ☑ SAT-9 ☑ SAT-10 ☑ ITBS ☑ CTBS ☑ MAT ☑ CAT	**Optional** Measuring cups	• *Chapter 3 Resource Book,* pp. 71–80 • Daily Transparency T32, CRB • Additional Examples Transparencies T33–T35, CRB • *Alternate Openers: Explorations,* p. 29
Lesson 3-9 Equivalent Fractions and Decimals **NCTM:** Number and Operations, Communication, Connections, Representation **NAEP:** Number Properties 1a ☑ SAT-9 ☑ SAT-10 ☑ ITBS ☑ CTBS ☑ MAT ☑ CAT	**Required** Calculators **Optional** Teaching Transparency T37 *(CRB)*	• *Chapter 3 Resource Book,* pp. 81–89 • Daily Transparency T36, CRB • Additional Examples Transparencies T38–T40, CRB • *Alternate Openers: Explorations,* p. 30
Lesson 3-10 Comparing and Ordering Rational Numbers **NCTM:** Number and Operations, Communication, Representation **NAEP:** Number Properties 1i ☑ SAT-9 ☑ SAT-10 ☐ ITBS ☑ CTBS ☑ MAT ☑ CAT	**Optional** Calculators	• *Chapter 3 Resource Book,* pp. 90–98 • Daily Transparency T41, CRB • Additional Examples Transparencies T42–T43, CRB • *Alternate Openers: Explorations,* p. 31
Extension Irrational Numbers **NCTM:** Number and Operations **NAEP:** Number Properties 2a ☐ SAT-9 ☐ SAT-10 ☐ ITBS ☐ CTBS ☐ MAT ☐ CAT	**Required** Calculators	• Additional Examples Transparencies T44–T45, CRB
Section 3B Assessment		• Section 3B Quiz, AR p. 12 • *Test and Practice Generator* CD-ROM

SAT = *Stanford Achievement Tests* **ITBS** = *Iowa Test of Basic Skills* **CTBS** = *Comprehensive Test of Basic Skills/Terra Nova*
MAT = *Metropolitan Achievement Test* **CAT** = *California Achievement Test*

NCTM—Complete standards can be found on pages T27–T33. **NAEP**—Complete standards can be found on pages A35–A39.

SE = *Student Edition* **TE** = *Teacher's Edition* **AR** = *Assessment Resources* **CRB** = *Chapter Resource Book* **MK** = *Manipulatives Kit*

Section Overview

Identifying Rational Numbers — Lesson 3-7

Why? Rational numbers name quantities that are used every day.

A **rational number** is any number that can be written as a quotient of two integers.

$\frac{3}{-8}$ ← Quotient of two integers

Integers, mixed numbers, and **some decimals** are rational numbers because they can be written as a quotient of two integers.

The **integer** -7 can be written as $\frac{-7}{1}$.

The **mixed number** $3\frac{1}{2}$ can be written as $\frac{7}{2}$.

The **decimal** 0.9 can be written as $\frac{9}{10}$.

Finding Equivalent Fractions and Decimals — Lessons 3-8, 3-9

Why? Recognizing equivalent expressions for a value is an important problem-solving skill.

To write **equivalent fractions,** multiply or divide both the numerator and the denominator of a fraction by the same number.

$$\frac{3}{12} = \frac{3 \cdot \mathbf{2}}{12 \cdot \mathbf{2}} = \frac{6}{24}$$

$$\frac{3}{12} = \frac{3 \div \mathbf{3}}{12 \div \mathbf{3}} = \frac{1}{4}$$

$$\frac{1}{4} \rightarrow 4\overline{)1.00} = 0.25 \qquad \begin{array}{r} 1.00 \\ -8 \\ \hline 20 \\ -20 \\ \hline 0 \end{array}$$

To write a fraction as a decimal, divide the **numerator** by the **denominator.**

$\frac{3}{12}, \frac{6}{24}, \frac{1}{4},$ and 0.25 are equivalent expressions because they name the same value.

Comparing and Ordering Rational Numbers — Lesson 3-10

Why? Comparing and ordering rational numbers is an important part of understanding numbers.

Comparing Two Fractions with Different Denominators

Compare $\frac{5}{8}$ and $\frac{2}{3}$.

$$\frac{5}{8} = \frac{5 \cdot 3}{8 \cdot 3} = \frac{15}{\mathbf{24}} \qquad \frac{2}{3} = \frac{2 \cdot 8}{3 \cdot 8} = \frac{16}{\mathbf{24}}$$

Write the fractions as **fractions with the same denominators.** Then compare the numerators.

$$\frac{15}{24} < \frac{16}{24}, \text{ so } \frac{5}{8} < \frac{2}{3}$$

Comparing Decimals

Compare 0.387 and 0.39.

0.387

0.390

So, 0.387 < 0.390

Write the **decimals with the same number of decimal places.** Compare each place from left to right.

3-7 Organizer

Pacing: Traditional 1 day
Block $\frac{1}{2}$ day

Objective: Students identify rational numbers and place them on a number line.

Warm Up

Divide.

1. 63 ÷ 9   7   **2.** 27 ÷ 3   9

3. 102 ÷ 3   34   **4.** 225 ÷ 25   9

Problem of the Day

What three numbers between 0 and 10 can be multiplied together to make a product that matches their sum? 1, 2, and 3

Available on Daily Transparency in CRB

Jonah told Sherry a joke about decimals, but she didn't get the point!

3-7 Fractions and Decimals

Learn to identify rational numbers and to place them on a number line.

Vocabulary
rational number

You can show −5 and 15 on a number line marked off by 5's.

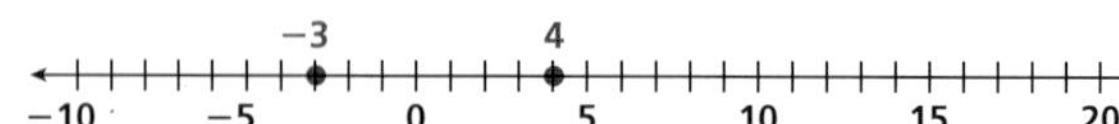

You can show –3 and 4 on a number line marked off by 1's.

−3   4

−10   −5   0   5   10   15   20

A number line can have as much detail as you want. The number line below shows that you can write numbers in many different ways.

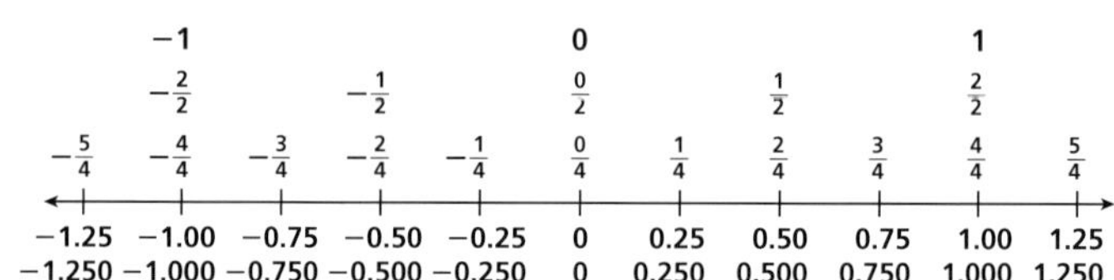

EXAMPLE 1 Graphing Numbers on a Number Line

Graph each number on a number line.

A $3\frac{1}{2}$

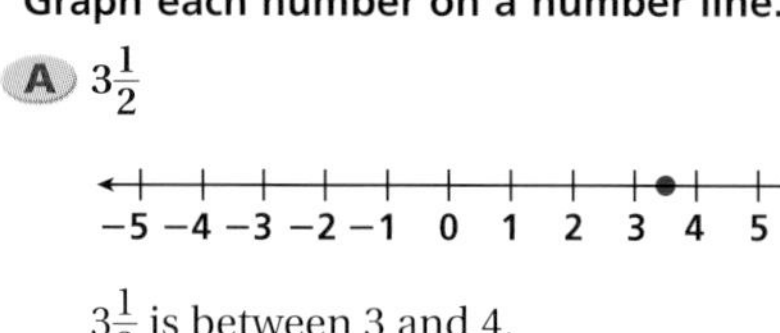

$3\frac{1}{2}$ is between 3 and 4.

B −1.9

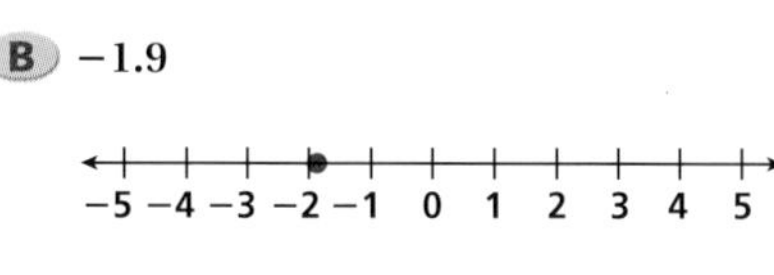

−1.9 is between −1 and −2.

Remember!
The top number in a fraction is called the *numerator.* The bottom number is called the *denominator.* So in the fraction $\frac{1}{2}$, the numerator is 1 and the denominator is 2.

The numbers shown on the number lines in Example 1 are called *rational numbers.* **Rational numbers** are numbers that can be written as fractions, with integers for numerators and denominators. Integers and certain decimals are rational numbers because they can be written as fractions.

$15 = \frac{15}{1}$ $-5 = -\frac{5}{1}$ $0.75 = \frac{3}{4}$ $-1.25 = -\frac{5}{4}$

1 Introduce

Alternate Opener

EXPLORATION

3-7 Fractions and Decimals

Just as you can locate integers on a number line, you can also locate fractions and decimals on a number line.

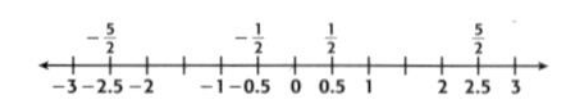

1. The number line below shows each unit divided into ten equal pieces, or tenths. Label the tenths.

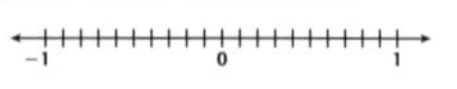

2. The number line below shows each unit divided into four equal pieces, or fourths. Label the fourths.

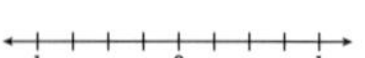

Think and Discuss

3. **Explain** how you could label eighths on a number line.
4. **Describe** how the number lines show that 0.5, $\frac{2}{4}$, and $\frac{1}{2}$ are equal.

Motivate

Begin by asking students to suggest different ways of representing the number 2 (e.g., 2.0, $\frac{10}{5}$, and $\frac{2}{1}$). Compare this with a person who wears several different outfits. The person is the same whether dressed in casual clothes or in a suit. Lead students to see that the word *fraction* usually refers to a particular way of representing a number.

Exploration worksheet and answers on Chapter 3 Resource Book pp. 63 and 120

2 Teach

Lesson Presentation

Guided Instruction

In this lesson, students learn how to identify rational numbers and place them on a number line. Emphasize that a rational number can be written as the ratio of two integers. (You may use Teaching Transparency T28 in the Chapter 3 Resource Book.) This means that 7 is a rational number, whether or not it is written as a fraction, because it is the ratio of 7 to 1.

One way to contrast integers and rational numbers is to point out that between 1 and 3, there is only one *integer,* 2, but there are infinitely many *rational numbers* (e.g., 1.1, 1.01, 1.0001, $1\frac{1}{2}$, $1\frac{1}{3}$, $1\frac{1}{4}$, $1\frac{1}{5}$, and so on).

EXAMPLE 2 Writing Rational Numbers as Fractions

Show that each number is a rational number by writing it as a fraction.

A -0.500

$-0.500 = -\frac{1}{2}$

B 0.25

$0.25 = \frac{1}{4}$

C -0.75

$-0.75 = -\frac{3}{4}$

EXAMPLE 3 *Earth Science Application*

High tide in Astoria, Oregon, on July 1 was at 11:31 A.M. The graph shows how much earlier or later in minutes that high tide occurred in nearby towns.

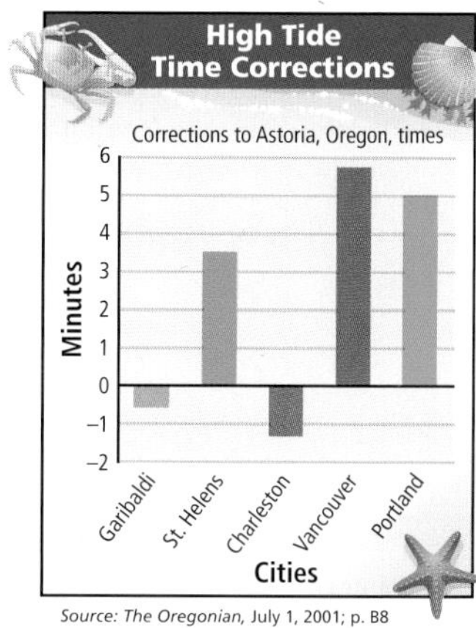

Source: *The Oregonian*, July 1, 2001; p. B8

A Use a fraction to estimate how much later in minutes high tide occurred in St. Helens.

The bar is about midway between 3 and 4.

$3\frac{1}{2}$ minutes later

B Use a decimal to estimate how much earlier in minutes high tide occurred in Garibaldi.

0.5 minutes earlier *The bar is about midway between 0 and −1.*

C Use a fraction and a decimal to estimate the greatest value and the least value represented on the graph.

The greatest value is about $5\frac{3}{4}$, or 5.75.

The least value is about $-1\frac{1}{4}$, or -1.25.

Think and Discuss

1. **Give** examples of three rational numbers that come between 1 and 2 on the number line.
2. **Tell** whether zero is a rational number. Explain your answer.
3. **Write** −1 and 1 as fractions with different denominators, and tell what these fractions have in common.

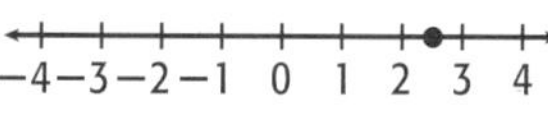

Additional Examples

Example 1

Graph each number on a number line.

A. $2\frac{1}{2}$ (number line −4 to 4, point at $2\frac{1}{2}$)

B. -1.4 (number line −4 to 4, point at −1.4)

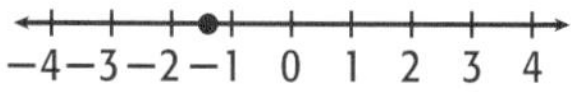

Example 2

Show that each number is a rational number by writing it as a fraction.

A. -1.25 $-\frac{5}{4}$

B. 0.75 $\frac{3}{4}$

C. -1.00 $-\frac{1}{1}$

Example 3

A. Use a decimal to estimate how much later in minutes high tide occurred in Vancouver.

5.75 minutes later

B. Use a fraction to estimate how much earlier in minutes high tide occurred in Charleston.

$1\frac{1}{4}$ minute earlier

C. Use a fraction and a decimal to estimate the difference between the value for St. Helens and the value for Charleston represented on the graph.

about $4\frac{3}{4}$, or 4.75 minutes

Example 2 note: Students should use the number line on page 162 that relates decimals and fractions for Example 2.

3 Close

Reaching All Learners

Through Number Sense

To review changing a mixed number, such as $2\frac{1}{4}$, to a fraction and to show that it is a rational number, discuss with students the number of quarters in \$2. After students recognize that there are 8 quarters in \$2, have them rewrite $2\frac{1}{4}$ as $\frac{8}{4} + \frac{1}{4}$, or $\frac{9}{4}$.

Summarize

Ask students to explain in their own words how to tell whether a given number is a rational number. Then have them show that $2\frac{1}{2}$ is a rational number.

Possible answer: A number is rational if you can write it as a fraction that has an integer as the numerator and the denominator. The mixed number $2\frac{1}{2}$ is a rational number because it can be rewritten as $\frac{5}{2}$.

Answers to Think and Discuss

Possible answers:

1. 1.2, 1.5, and $1\frac{3}{4}$
2. Zero is a rational number because it can be written as a fraction. For example, it can be written as $\frac{0}{5}$.
3. $\frac{-3}{3}$, $\frac{2}{2}$; in both fractions the absolute value of the numerator is the same as the denominator.

3-7 PRACTICE & ASSESS

Students may want to refer back to the lesson examples.

Assignment Guide

If you finished Example 1 assign:
Core 1–4, 9–16, 25, 36–41
Enriched 1, 3, 9–16, 24, 25, 36–41

If you finished Example 2 assign:
Core 1–7, 9–22, 25–31 odd, 36–41
Enriched 1–7, 9–22, 24–31, 36–41

If you finished Example 3 assign:
Core 1–23, 25–31 odd, 36–41
Enriched 1–23 odd, 24–41

Notes

Answers

1–4, 9–16, 24, 25. Complete answers on p. A2

Math Background

There are many numbers on a real number line that are *not* rational. The number π is not rational, and it can be located on a real number line by using geometry. The number π is not *equal* to $\frac{22}{7}$, which is only an approximation of the value of π. Another approximation of π is $\frac{355}{113}$, which is accurate to 6 places, but no fraction is exactly equal to π. The number π is exactly equal to the ratio of the circumference of a circle to its diameter, so $\pi = \frac{C}{d}$. Other irrational numbers, which also can be located on a real number line, are $\sqrt{2}$, $\sqrt{5}$, and $\sqrt{21}$.

3-7 Exercises

FOR EXTRA PRACTICE
see page 661

internet connect
Homework Help Online
go.hrw.com Keyword: MS4 3-7

GUIDED PRACTICE

See Example 1 — Graph each number on a number line.

1. $-2\frac{1}{4}$ 2. 3.25 3. -1.5 4. $\frac{1}{2}$

See Example 2 — Show that each number is a rational number by writing it as a fraction.

5. -0.25 **$-\frac{1}{4}$** 6. 0.750 **$\frac{3}{4}$** 7. -0.5 **$-\frac{1}{2}$**

See Example 3

8. The graph shows the amount of rainfall above and below the average rainfall for 4 months.
   a. Use a fraction to estimate the amount of rainfall below the average for January. **$-\frac{1}{2}$ in.**
   b. Use a decimal to estimate the amount of rainfall above the average for March. **1.75 in.**

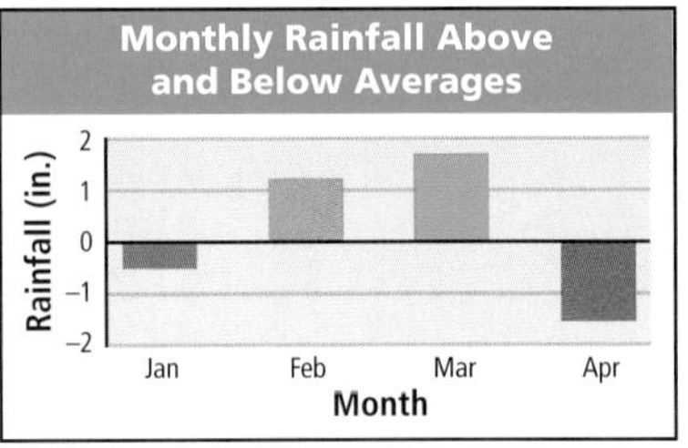

INDEPENDENT PRACTICE

See Example 1 — Graph each number on a number line.

9. $\frac{2}{3}$ 10. 0.5 11. -1.1 12. $-4\frac{1}{2}$
13. $\frac{1}{5}$ 14. -2.25 15. $-\frac{3}{4}$ 16. 3.6

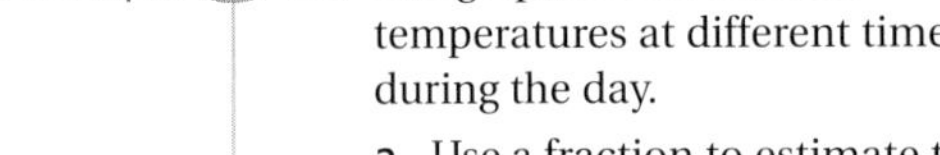

See Example 2 — Show that each number is a rational number by writing it as a fraction.

17. 1.25 **$\frac{5}{4}$** 18. 0.250 **$\frac{1}{4}$** 19. -1 **$-\frac{1}{1}$**
20. -0.750 **$-\frac{3}{4}$** 21. 0 **$\frac{0}{1}$** 22. -1.250 **$-\frac{5}{4}$**

See Example 3

23. The graph shows outdoor temperatures at different times during the day.
   a. Use a fraction to estimate the temperature at noon. **about $\frac{3}{2}$°C**
   b. Use a decimal to estimate the temperature at 11 A.M. **about −3.5°C**

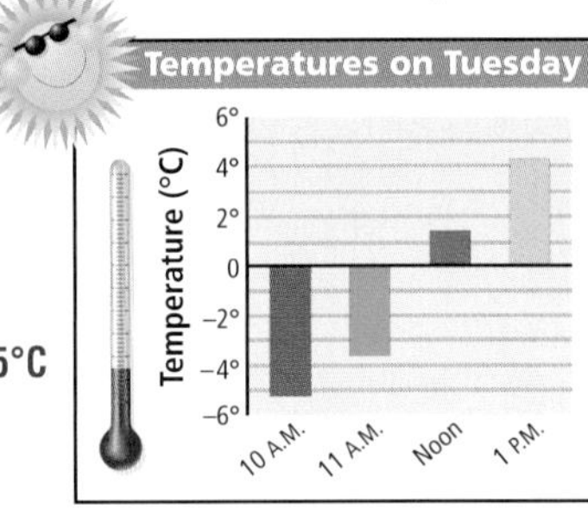

PRACTICE AND PROBLEM SOLVING

Graph each set of numbers on a number line.

24. 2.5, −3.75, $4\frac{1}{2}$, −1, 2
25. −4, 0, 3.25, $2\frac{3}{4}$, $-2\frac{1}{2}$

RETEACH 3-7

LESSON 3-7 **Reteach**
Fractions and Decimals

Fractions, integers, and decimals are all rational numbers because they can be written as fractions.

$-\frac{11}{12}$ $-6 = \frac{-6}{1}$ $1.25 = 1\frac{25}{100} = 1\frac{1}{4} = \frac{5}{4}$

You can describe the position of a rational number on a number line.

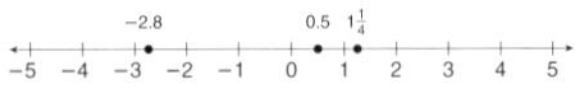

−2.8 0.5 $1\frac{1}{4}$
−5 −4 −3 −2 −1 0 1 2 3 4 5

- −2.8 is between −2 and −3 and closer to −3 than to −2.
- 0.5 is between 0 and 1 and exactly halfway between 0 and 1.
- $1\frac{1}{4}$ is between 1 and 2 and closer to 1 than to 2.

Use the number line.

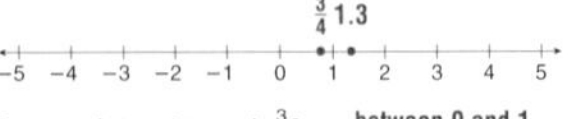

1. Between what two integers is $\frac{3}{4}$? **between 0 and 1**
2. To which integer is $\frac{3}{4}$ closer? **1**
3. Between what two integers is 1.3? **between 1 and 2**
4. To which integer is 1.3 closer? **1**

Show that each number is a rational number by writing it as a fraction.

5. $-2 = -\frac{2}{1}$ 6. $4.5 = 4\frac{5}{10} = 4\frac{1}{2} = \frac{9}{2}$
7. $-0.25 = \frac{-25}{100} = -\frac{1}{4}$ 8. $1\frac{3}{4} = 1\frac{3}{4} = \frac{7}{4}$
9. 6.3 **$\frac{63}{10}$** 10. $-5\frac{1}{6}$ **$-\frac{31}{6}$** 11. 0.05 **$\frac{1}{20}$** 12. −1.6 **$-\frac{8}{5}$**

PRACTICE 3-7

LESSON 3-7 **Practice B**
Fractions and Decimals

Place each number on a number line.

1. −1.2 2. $\frac{1}{4}$

−1.2 $\frac{1}{4}$
−5 −4 −3 −2 −1 0 1 2 3 4 5

3. −3.75 4. $2\frac{2}{3}$

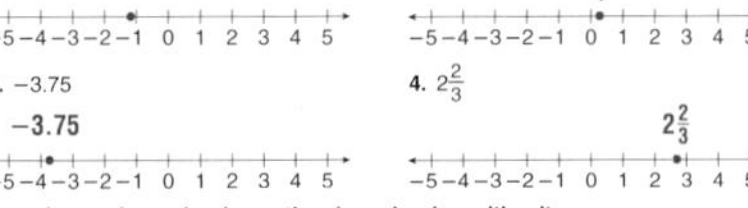

Show that each number is a rational number by writing it as a fraction.

5. $1\frac{1}{2}$ **$\frac{3}{2}$** 6. −2 **$-\frac{2}{1}$** 7. $3\frac{1}{5}$ **$\frac{16}{5}$** 8. −1.9 **$-\frac{19}{10}$**
9. $-7\frac{1}{3}$ **$-\frac{22}{3}$** 10. 2.5 **$\frac{5}{2}$** 11. $-4\frac{3}{4}$ **$-\frac{19}{4}$** 12. −0.25 **$-\frac{1}{4}$**
13. −3.75 **$-\frac{15}{4}$** 14. $2\frac{2}{5}$ **$\frac{12}{5}$** 15. 3.1 **$\frac{31}{10}$** 16. $5\frac{2}{7}$ **$\frac{37}{7}$**

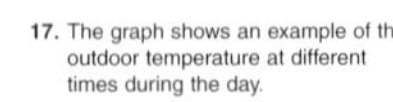

17. The graph shows an example of the outdoor temperature at different times during the day.
   a. Use a fraction to estimate the temperature at 1 P.M. **$-4\frac{1}{2}$°F**
   b. Use a decimal to estimate the temperature at 3 P.M. **3.5°F**

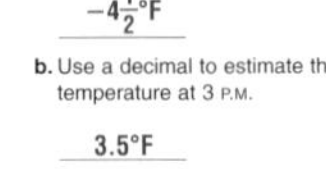

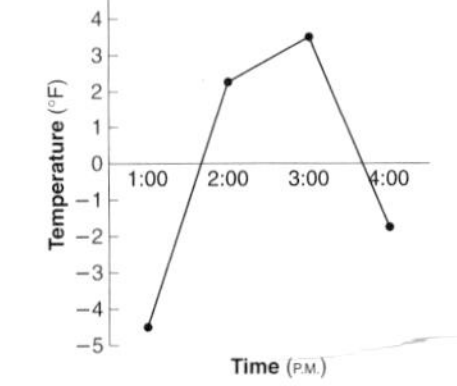

Show that each number is a rational number. **Possible answers:**

26. -1.00 **$-\frac{1}{1}$** 27. -0.250 **$-\frac{1}{4}$** 28. 6 **$\frac{6}{1}$**

29. 0.75 **$\frac{3}{4}$** 30. 1.250 **$\frac{5}{4}$** 31. 0.50 **$\frac{1}{2}$**

32. ***ENTERTAINMENT*** The circle graph shows the number of words in the titles of 20 Oscar-winning movies.

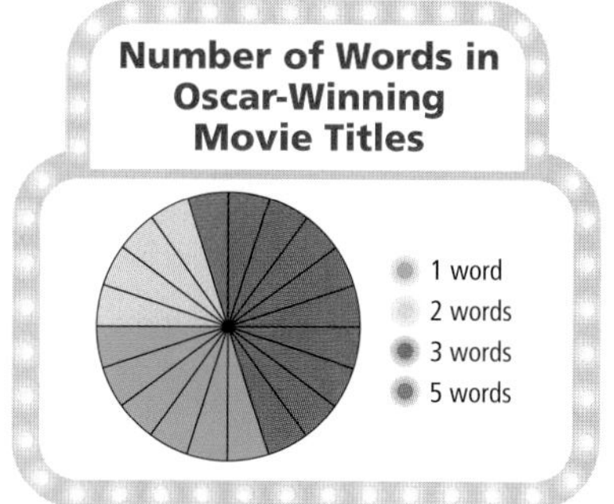
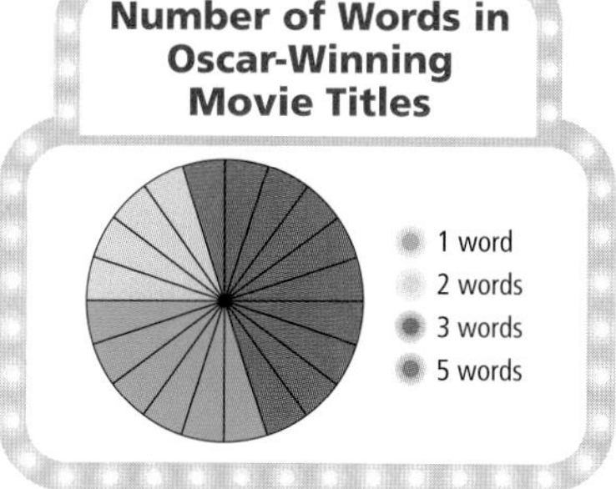

a. What fraction of the 20 movie titles are made up of three words? **$\frac{9}{20}$**

b. Which two colors represent the movie titles that together make up $\frac{3}{4}$ of the graph? **blue and purple**

33. ***WHAT'S THE QUESTION?*** The numbers 4 and -0.75 are rational numbers. The answer is $\frac{4}{1}$ and $-\frac{3}{4}$. What is the question?

34. ***WRITE ABOUT IT*** The Venn diagram at right shows how different sets of numbers are related. Some sets of numbers are parts of other sets of numbers, just as boxes are inside of other boxes in the diagram. Use the diagram to explain how integers, fractions, and rational numbers are related.

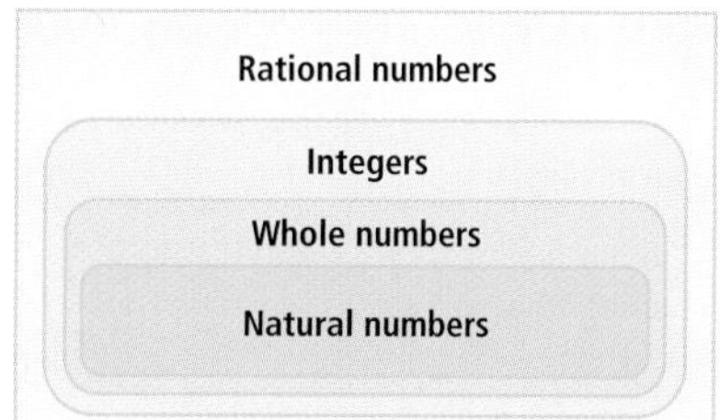

35. ***CHALLENGE*** If $0.25 = \frac{1}{4}$, $0.75 = \frac{3}{4}$, and $1.25 = \frac{5}{4}$, what is the fraction equivalent of 3.25? **$\frac{13}{4}$**

Spiral Review

Find the mean of each set of numbers. (Lesson 1-2)

36. 5, 12, 16, 21, 21 **15**

37. 2.4, 3.6, 3.6, 4.1, 5.2, 8.1 **4.5**

Evaluate. (Lesson 2-3)

38. $5(3^2 - 1) + 6$ **46**

39. $12(18 \div 3 + 2) - 5^2$ **71**

40. **TEST PREP** The GCF of 18 and 45 is __?__. (Lesson 2-5) **B**

A 1 C 18
B 9 D 4

41. **TEST PREP** In simplest form, $3x + 5x - 2x^2$ is __?__. (Lesson 2-9) **J**

F $3x + 5x - 2x^2$ H $6x$
G $6x^2$ J $8x - 2x^2$

Answers

33. What fractions can be written to show that each number is rational?

34. The rational numbers include both fractions and integers.

Journal

Ask students to explain in writing how to decide whether 3.6 is a rational number and where to place it on a number line.

Test Prep Doctor

For Exercise 41, encourage students to first notice the like terms. Then ask them to think about how many terms must be in the simplified answer. Students should realize that there should be two terms in the simplified answer, which eliminates **F, H,** and **G.**

CHALLENGE 3-7

LESSON 3-7 **Challenge**
Ancient Egyptian Fractions

Ancient Egyptians used pictures, called hieroglyphs, to represent numbers.

1 10 100 1,000 245

They also represented fractions using these symbols. Most of the fractions they wrote were unit fractions, which are fractions with a numerator of 1. The pictures were placed under the oval hieroglyph to represent the denominators of the fraction. Notice that the pictures for digits of lesser values are to the left of the oval hieroglyph.

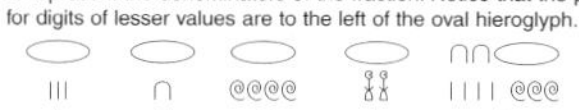

$\frac{1}{3}$ $\frac{1}{10}$ $\frac{1}{400}$ $\frac{1}{2,000}$ $\frac{1}{324}$

Write the rational number for the Egyptian number.

1. **$\frac{1}{4}$** 2.  **$\frac{1}{25}$** 3.  **3,062**

4. **136** 5.  **$\frac{1}{208}$** 6.  **$\frac{1}{42}$**

Draw the rational number using Egyptian hieroglyphs.

7. $\frac{1}{2}$ 8. 612 9. $\frac{1}{30}$

10. $\frac{1}{110}$ 11. $\frac{1}{222}$  12. $\frac{1}{1,000}$

PROBLEM SOLVING 3-7

LESSON 3-7 **Problem Solving**
Fractions and Decimals

Use the graph to answer exercises 1–3.

A student pilot is practicing hovering a helicopter at a constant height above ground. The helicopter rises and falls from the specified height.

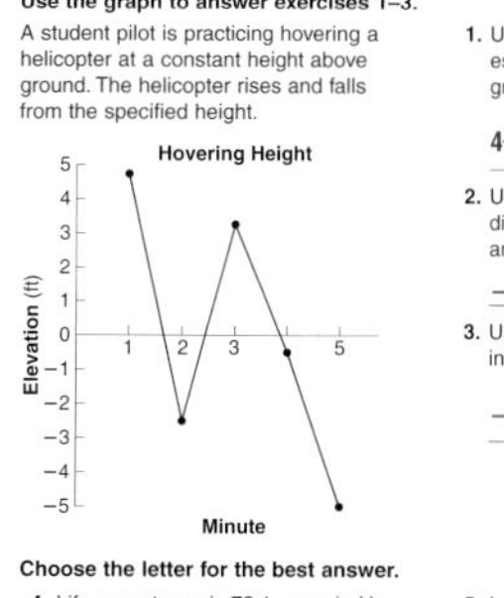

1. Use a fraction and decimal to estimate the greatest value on the graph.
$4\frac{3}{4}$ ft, 4.75 ft

2. Use a decimal to estimate the difference between the actual height and the specified height at minute 2.
-2.5 ft

3. Use a fraction to estimate the change in height from minute 4 to minute 5.
$-4\frac{1}{2}$ ft

Choose the letter for the best answer.

4. Life expectancy is 79.1 years in Hong Kong and 76.8 years in the United States. Life expectancy in Sweden lies between that of Hong Kong and the United States. What is the possible life expectancy in Sweden?
A 79.5 years **(C)** 79.0 years
B 79.2 years D 75.5 years

5. In 1990, about 5.5 million Americans owned second homes. By 2000, about 6.4 million Americans owned second homes. The number of second homes in 1995 was somewhere in between. About how many second homes were owned in 1995?
F 5.0 million H 6.5 million
(G) 5.9 million J 6.6 million

6. In September, Chicago receives an average of 3.5 inches of rain. Which shows 3.5 as a rational number?
(A) $\frac{35}{10}$ C $\frac{3}{5}$
B $\frac{3}{50}$ D $\frac{35}{50}$

7. During December, the average wind speed in Chicago is 11.0 miles per hour. Which shows 11.0 as a rational number?
F $\frac{11}{0}$ H $\frac{11}{10}$
G $\frac{11}{11}$ **(J)** $\frac{11}{1}$

Lesson Quiz

Graph each number on a number line.

1. -2, $1\frac{1}{2}$, $-3\frac{3}{4}$, $\frac{1}{2}$

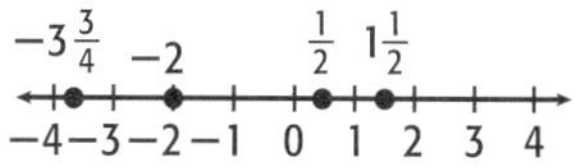

$-3\frac{3}{4}$ -2 $\frac{1}{2}$ $1\frac{1}{2}$
$-4\ -3\ -2\ -1\ \ 0\ \ 1\ \ 2\ \ 3\ \ 4$

Show that each number is a rational number by writing it as a fraction.

2 0.5 $\frac{1}{2}$

3. $1\frac{1}{4}$ $\frac{5}{4}$

4. 0.25 $\frac{1}{4}$

Available on Daily Transparency in CRB

3-8 Organizer

Pacing: Traditional 1 day
Block $\frac{1}{2}$ day

Objective: Students identify, write, and convert between equivalent fractions and mixed numbers.

Warm Up

Name a common factor for each pair. Possible answers:

1. 5 and 10 5 **2.** 9 and 12 3
3. 20 and 24 4 **4.** 10 and 14 2
5. 6 and 8 2 **6.** 8 and 15 1

Problem of the Day

Find a number less than 100 for which all three statements are true:

- Divided by 3. Remainder of 2.
- Divided by 4. Remainder of 3.
- Divided by 5. Remainder of 4.

59

Available on Daily Transparency in CRB

Math Humor

A man orders a cheese pizza. The pizza maker asks, "Do you want that cut into six slices or eight slices?" "Six slices," the man answers, "I'm not hungry enough to eat eight."

3-8 Equivalent Fractions and Mixed Numbers

Learn to identify, write, and convert between equivalent fractions and mixed numbers.

Vocabulary
equivalent fractions
improper fraction
mixed number

In some recipes the amounts of ingredients are given as fractions, and sometimes those amounts don't equal the fractions on a measuring cup. Knowing how fractions relate to each other can be very helpful.

Different fractions can name the same number.

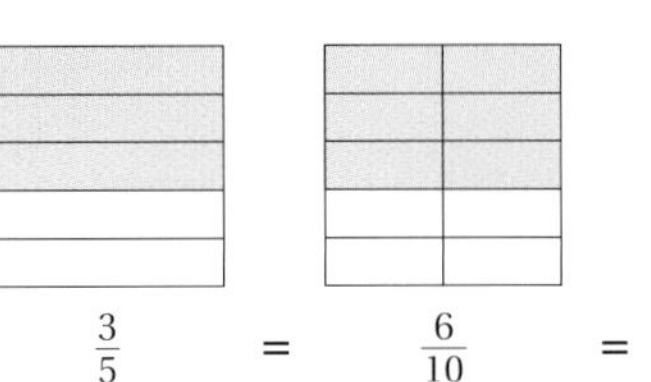
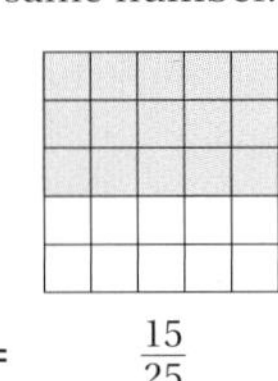

$$\frac{3}{5} = \frac{6}{10} = \frac{15}{25}$$

In the diagram, $\frac{3}{5} = \frac{6}{10} = \frac{15}{25}$. These are called **equivalent fractions** because they are different expressions for the same nonzero number.

> **Remember!**
> $\frac{3}{5}$ is in *simplest form* because the greatest common factor of 3 and 5 is 1.

To create fractions equivalent to a given fraction, multiply or divide the numerator and denominator by the same number.

$$\frac{3}{5} = \frac{3 \cdot 2}{5 \cdot 2} = \frac{6}{10} \qquad \frac{15}{25} = \frac{15 \div 5}{25 \div 5} = \frac{3}{5}$$

EXAMPLE 1 Finding Equivalent Fractions

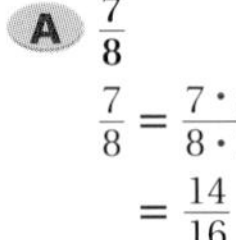

Find a fraction equivalent to the given fraction.

A $\frac{7}{8}$

$\frac{7}{8} = \frac{7 \cdot 2}{8 \cdot 2}$ *Multiply numerator and denominator by 2.*

$= \frac{14}{16}$

B $\frac{24}{36}$

$\frac{24}{36} = \frac{24 \div 12}{36 \div 12}$ *Divide numerator and denominator by 12.*

$= \frac{2}{3}$

To determine if two fractions are equivalent, find a common denominator and compare the numerators.

1 Introduce

Alternate Opener

EXPLORATION

3-8 Equivalent Fractions and Mixed Numbers

Use the fraction model to list the fractions that have the same value as the given fraction.

1. $\frac{1}{2}$
2. $\frac{5}{6}$
3. $\frac{3}{4}$
4. $\frac{2}{5}$

The model shows that the fraction $\frac{6}{4}$ is the same as $1\frac{1}{2}$.

5. Write a fraction and mixed number represented by the model below.

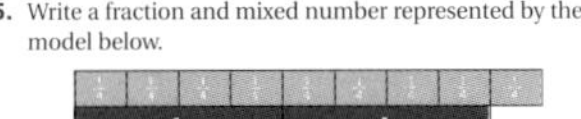

Think and Discuss

6. **Explain** how $\frac{3}{4}$ is related to eighths.
7. **Describe** a relationship between two other fractions.

Motivate

Begin by asking students to suppose that they have a box of red marbles and green marbles and that there are twice as many red marbles as green ones. Have students offer possibilities for the numbers of green and red marbles. Record the answers as fractions in the form $\frac{\text{green marbles}}{\text{red marbles}}$; for example, $\frac{2}{4}$, $\frac{5}{10}$, $\frac{50}{100}$, and $\frac{7}{14}$. Point out that all the fractions represent the same value, $\frac{1}{2}$.

Exploration worksheet and answers on Chapter 3 Resource Book pp. 72 and 122

2 Teach

Lesson Presentation

Guided Instruction

In this lesson, students learn to identify, write, and convert between equivalent fractions and mixed numbers. In Example 1, be sure students understand that the value of the original fraction does not change in the second step. The second step is the same as multiplying $\frac{7}{8}$ by 1, in the equivalent form of $\frac{2}{2}$.

Teaching Tip You may want to write the following steps as another way to show that $\frac{6}{8}$ can be written as $\frac{3}{4}$:

$$\frac{6}{8} = \frac{2 \cdot 3}{2 \cdot 4} = \frac{2}{2} \cdot \frac{3}{4} = 1 \cdot \frac{3}{4} = \frac{3}{4}.$$

EXAMPLE 2 Determining Whether Fractions Are Equivalent

Write the fractions with a common denominator. Then determine if they are equivalent.

A $\frac{6}{8}$ and $\frac{9}{12}$

Both fractions can be written with a denominator of 4.

$\frac{6}{8} = \frac{6 \div 2}{8 \div 2} = \frac{3}{4}$

$\frac{9}{12} = \frac{9 \div 3}{12 \div 3} = \frac{3}{4}$

The numerators are equal, so the fractions are equivalent.

B $\frac{18}{15}$ and $\frac{25}{20}$

Both fractions can be written with a denominator of 60.

$\frac{18}{15} = \frac{18 \cdot 4}{15 \cdot 4} = \frac{72}{60}$

$\frac{25}{20} = \frac{25 \cdot 3}{20 \cdot 3} = \frac{75}{60}$

The numerators are *not* equal, so the fractions are *not* equivalent.

$\frac{8}{5}$ is an **improper fraction**. Its numerator is greater than its denominator.

$\frac{8}{5} = 1\frac{3}{5}$

$1\frac{3}{5}$ is a **mixed number**. It contains both a whole number and a fraction.

EXAMPLE 3 Converting Between Improper Fractions and Mixed Numbers

Remember!

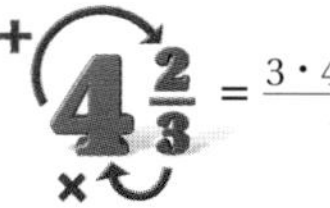

A **Write $\frac{21}{4}$ as a mixed number.**

First divide the numerator by the denominator.

$\frac{21}{4} = 5\frac{1}{4}$ *Use the quotient and remainder to write the mixed number.*

B **Write $4\frac{2}{3}$ as an improper fraction.**

First multiply the denominator and whole number, and then add the numerator.

$4\frac{2}{3} = \frac{3 \cdot 4 + 2}{3} = \frac{14}{3}$ *Use the result to write the improper fraction.*

Think and Discuss

1. **Explain** a process for finding common denominators.
2. **Describe** how to convert between improper fractions and mixed numbers.

Additional Examples

Example 1

Find a fraction equivalent to the given fraction.

A. $\frac{5}{7}$ $\quad \frac{15}{21}$

B. $\frac{18}{24}$ $\quad \frac{9}{12}$

Example 2

Write the fractions with a common denominator. Then determine if they are equivalent.

A. $\frac{4}{6}$ and $\frac{28}{42}$ $\quad \frac{4}{6} = \frac{2}{3}$, $\frac{28}{42} = \frac{2}{3}$

The fractions are equivalent.

B. $\frac{6}{10}$ and $\frac{20}{25}$ $\quad \frac{6}{10} = \frac{30}{50}$, $\frac{20}{25} = \frac{40}{50}$

The fractions are *not* equivalent.

Example 3

A. Write $\frac{13}{5}$ as a mixed number.

$2\frac{3}{5}$

B. Write $7\frac{2}{3}$ as an improper fraction.

$\frac{23}{3}$

Example 2 note: In Example 2A, one way to determine quickly whether the fractions are equivalent is to find the cross products, which in this case are $6 \cdot 12$ and $8 \cdot 9$. If the cross products are equal, the fractions are equivalent.

3 Close

Reaching All Learners

Through Home Connection

Suggest that students look at measuring cups at home and write each fraction marked on the cups as three other equivalent fractions.

Summarize

Ask students to explain in their own words (a) how to decide whether two fractions are equivalent, (b) how to write a mixed number as a fraction, and (c) how to write an improper fraction as a mixed number.

Possible answer: (a) Write both fractions with the same denominator; if the numerators are the same, the fractions are equivalent. (b) Multiply the denominator of the fraction by the whole number, add the numerator of the fraction, and put the total over the same denominator. (c) Divide the denominator into the numerator to get the whole number; then write the fraction by putting the remainder over the denominator.

Answers to Think and Discuss

Possible answers:

1. Multiply the denominators.
2. To convert to a mixed number, divide the numerator by the denominator. The quotient is the whole number of the mixed number, and the remainder is the numerator of the mixed number. The denominator stays the same. To convert to an improper fraction, multiply the denominator of the fraction by the whole number, and then add the numerator. This result is the numerator of the improper fraction, and the denominator is the denominator of the improper fraction.

3-8 PRACTICE & ASSESS

Students may want to refer back to the lesson examples.

Assignment Guide

If you finished Example **1** assign:
Core 1–4, 17–24, 41–51 odd, 68–77
Enriched 1, 3, 17–23 odd, 41–52, 68–77

If you finished Example **2** assign:
Core 1–8, 17–32, 41–55 odd, 68–77
Enriched 1–7 odd, 17–31 odd, 41–55, 68–77

If you finished Example **3** assign:
Core 1–40, 41–63 odd, 68–77
Enriched 1–39 odd, 41–77

Answers

Possible answers:

8. $\frac{45}{24}, \frac{38}{24}$; no
25. $\frac{1}{2}, \frac{1}{2}$; yes
26. $\frac{90}{120}, \frac{100}{120}$; no
27. $\frac{5}{4}, \frac{5}{4}$; yes
28. $\frac{80}{40}, \frac{90}{40}$; no
29. $\frac{2}{3}, \frac{2}{3}$; yes
30. $\frac{24}{36}, \frac{24}{36}$; yes
31. $\frac{6}{11}, \frac{7}{11}$; no
32. $-\frac{125}{75}, \frac{175}{75}$; no

3-8 Exercises

FOR EXTRA PRACTICE see page 661

internet connect
Homework Help Online
go.hrw.com Keyword: MS4 3-8

GUIDED PRACTICE

See Example 1 Find a fraction equivalent to the given fraction. **Possible answers:**

1. $\frac{1}{2}$ **$\frac{2}{4}$** 2. $\frac{3}{5}$ **$\frac{12}{20}$** 3. $\frac{10}{12}$ **$\frac{30}{36}$** 4. $\frac{15}{40}$ **$\frac{45}{120}$**

See Example 2 Write the fractions with a common denominator. Then determine if they are equivalent. **Possible answers:**

5. $\frac{3}{9}$ and $\frac{6}{8}$ **$\frac{24}{72}, \frac{54}{72}$; no** 6. $\frac{10}{12}$ and $\frac{20}{24}$ **$\frac{5}{6}, \frac{5}{6}$; yes** 7. $\frac{8}{6}$ and $\frac{20}{15}$ **$\frac{4}{3}, \frac{4}{3}$; yes** 8. $\frac{15}{8}$ and $\frac{19}{12}$

See Example 3 Write each as a mixed number.

9. $\frac{15}{4}$ **$3\frac{3}{4}$** 10. $\frac{22}{5}$ **$4\frac{2}{5}$** 11. $\frac{17}{13}$ **$1\frac{4}{13}$** 12. $\frac{14}{3}$ **$4\frac{2}{3}$**

Write each as an improper fraction.

13. $6\frac{1}{5}$ **$\frac{31}{5}$** 14. $1\frac{11}{12}$ **$\frac{23}{12}$** 15. $7\frac{3}{5}$ **$\frac{38}{5}$** 16. $2\frac{7}{16}$ **$\frac{39}{16}$**

INDEPENDENT PRACTICE

See Example 1 Find a fraction equivalent to the given fraction. **Possible answers:**

17. $\frac{1}{3}$ **$\frac{3}{9}$** 18. $\frac{5}{6}$ **$\frac{20}{24}$** 19. $\frac{18}{20}$ **$\frac{9}{10}$** 20. $\frac{25}{50}$ **$\frac{5}{10}$**
21. $\frac{3}{4}$ **$\frac{9}{12}$** 22. $\frac{2}{7}$ **$\frac{8}{28}$** 23. $\frac{9}{15}$ **$\frac{18}{30}$** 24. $\frac{42}{70}$ **$\frac{21}{35}$**

See Example 2 Write the fractions with a common denominator. Then determine if they are equivalent.

25. $\frac{5}{10}$ and $\frac{14}{28}$ 26. $\frac{15}{20}$ and $\frac{20}{24}$ 27. $\frac{125}{100}$ and $\frac{40}{32}$ 28. $\frac{10}{5}$ and $\frac{18}{8}$
29. $\frac{2}{3}$ and $\frac{12}{18}$ 30. $\frac{8}{12}$ and $\frac{24}{36}$ 31. $\frac{54}{99}$ and $\frac{84}{132}$ 32. $-\frac{25}{15}$ and $\frac{175}{75}$

See Example 3 Write each as a mixed number.

33. $\frac{19}{3}$ **$6\frac{1}{3}$** 34. $\frac{13}{9}$ **$1\frac{4}{9}$** 35. $\frac{81}{11}$ **$7\frac{4}{11}$** 36. $\frac{71}{8}$ **$8\frac{7}{8}$**

Write each as an improper fraction.

37. $25\frac{3}{5}$ **$\frac{128}{5}$** 38. $4\frac{7}{16}$ **$\frac{71}{16}$** 39. $9\frac{2}{3}$ **$\frac{29}{3}$** 40. $4\frac{16}{31}$ **$\frac{140}{31}$**

PRACTICE AND PROBLEM SOLVING

Write a fraction equivalent to the given number. **Possible answers:**

41. 5 **$\frac{10}{2}$** 42. 8 **$\frac{8}{1}$** 43. $6\frac{1}{2}$ **$\frac{52}{8}$** 44. $2\frac{2}{3}$ **$\frac{16}{6}$**
45. $\frac{8}{21}$ **$\frac{32}{84}$** 46. $9\frac{8}{11}$ **$\frac{107}{11}$** 47. $\frac{55}{10}$ **$\frac{11}{2}$** 48. $4\frac{26}{13}$ **$\frac{78}{13}$**
49. 101 **$\frac{202}{2}$** 50. $6\frac{15}{21}$ **$\frac{141}{21}$** 51. $\frac{475}{75}$ **$\frac{19}{3}$** 52. $11\frac{23}{50}$ **$\frac{573}{50}$**

Math Background

The process for finding and writing equivalent fractions is based on two properties. The first is that a nonzero number divided by itself is 1, or $\frac{a}{a} = 1$, $a \neq 0$. The second is that 1 is the multiplicative identity, or $1 \cdot x = x$.

The process of writing an equivalent fraction by dividing the numerator and denominator by the same number is also based on the property that $\frac{ac}{bd} = \frac{a}{b} \cdot \frac{c}{d}$ $(b, d \neq 0)$.

RETEACH 3-8

LESSON 3-8 **Reteach**
Equivalent Fractions and Mixed Numbers

Equivalent fractions name the same number.
- You can use fraction strips to find equivalent fractions.

Find two fractions equivalent to $\frac{6}{8}$.

$\frac{1}{8}$	$\frac{1}{8}$	$\frac{1}{8}$	$\frac{1}{8}$	$\frac{1}{8}$	$\frac{1}{8}$

First, use fraction strips to model $\frac{6}{8}$.

$\frac{1}{8}$	$\frac{1}{8}$	$\frac{1}{8}$	$\frac{1}{8}$	$\frac{1}{8}$	$\frac{1}{8}$	$\frac{6}{8}$

Then find equivalent fractions by placing other fraction strips with the same length below the model.

$\frac{1}{4}$	$\frac{1}{4}$	$\frac{1}{4}$	$\frac{3}{4}$

$\frac{3}{4}$ and $\frac{12}{16}$ are equivalent to $\frac{6}{8}$.

$\frac{1}{16}$	$\frac{1}{16}$	$\frac{1}{16}$	$\frac{1}{16}$	$\frac{1}{16}$	$\frac{1}{16}$	$\frac{1}{16}$	$\frac{1}{16}$	$\frac{1}{16}$	$\frac{1}{16}$	$\frac{1}{16}$	$\frac{1}{16}$	$\frac{12}{16}$

Use fractions strips to find a fraction equivalent to each fraction. Possible answers given.

1. $\frac{1}{2}$ **$\frac{2}{4}$** 2. $\frac{1}{4}$ **$\frac{2}{8}$** 3. $\frac{2}{5}$ **$\frac{4}{10}$** 4. $\frac{2}{3}$ **$\frac{4}{6}$**

- You can use cross products to determine if two fractions are equivalent.

$\frac{8}{10} \bowtie \frac{12}{15}$ $8 \cdot 5 \stackrel{?}{=} 10 \cdot 12$
$120 = 120$

$\frac{8}{10}$ and $\frac{12}{15}$ are equivalent. Their cross products are equal.

$\frac{9}{15} \bowtie \frac{2}{3}$ $9 \cdot 3 \stackrel{?}{=} 15 \cdot 2$
$27 \neq 30$

$\frac{9}{15}$ and $\frac{2}{3}$ are not equivalent. Their cross products are not equal.

Find two fractions equivalent to each fraction. Possible answers given.

5. $\frac{12}{20}$ **$\frac{3}{5}$ and $\frac{6}{10}$** 6. $\frac{30}{40}$ **$\frac{3}{4}$ and $\frac{6}{8}$** 7. $\frac{5}{8}$ **$\frac{10}{16}$ and $\frac{15}{24}$** 8. $\frac{14}{21}$ **$\frac{2}{3}$ and $\frac{28}{42}$**

PRACTICE 3-8

LESSON 3-8 **Practice B**
Equivalent Fractions and Mixed Numbers

Find two fractions equivalent to each fraction. Possible answers given.

1. $\frac{2}{9}$ **$\frac{4}{18}, \frac{6}{27}$** 2. $\frac{8}{15}$ **$\frac{16}{30}, \frac{24}{45}$** 3. $\frac{7}{8}$ **$\frac{14}{16}, \frac{21}{24}$**
4. $\frac{16}{24}$ **$\frac{2}{3}, \frac{32}{48}$** 5. $\frac{12}{20}$ **$\frac{3}{5}, \frac{24}{40}$** 6. $\frac{9}{12}$ **$\frac{3}{4}, \frac{18}{24}$**

Rewrite the fractions with a common denominator. Then determine if they are equivalent. Possible answers given.

7. $\frac{8}{10}$ and $\frac{12}{15}$ **$\frac{24}{30}, \frac{24}{30}$; yes** 8. $\frac{6}{8}$ and $\frac{8}{12}$ **$\frac{18}{24}, \frac{16}{24}$; no** 9. $\frac{3}{9}$ and $\frac{4}{8}$ **$\frac{24}{72}, \frac{36}{72}$; no**
10. $\frac{7}{4}$ and $\frac{9}{5}$ **$\frac{35}{20}, \frac{36}{20}$; no** 11. $\frac{15}{12}$ and $\frac{20}{16}$ **$\frac{60}{48}, \frac{60}{48}$; yes** 12. $\frac{15}{9}$ and $\frac{30}{18}$ **$\frac{30}{18}, \frac{30}{18}$; yes**

Write each improper fraction as a mixed number.
Write each mixed number as an improper fraction.

13. $\frac{21}{8}$ **$2\frac{5}{8}$** 14. $\frac{37}{4}$ **$9\frac{1}{4}$** 15. $\frac{16}{5}$ **$3\frac{1}{5}$** 16. $\frac{49}{9}$ **$5\frac{4}{9}$**
17. $8\frac{2}{3}$ **$\frac{26}{3}$** 18. $1\frac{7}{12}$ **$\frac{19}{12}$** 19. $25\frac{3}{4}$ **$\frac{103}{4}$** 20. $7\frac{5}{6}$ **$\frac{47}{6}$**

21. Maria's desk is $33\frac{3}{4}$ inches long. Write this number as an improper fraction.
$\frac{135}{4}$

22. Leon walked $\frac{5}{8}$ mile. Liz walked $\frac{10}{16}$ mile. Did they walk the same distance?
yes

Food LINK

A single bread company can make as many as 1,217 loaves of bread each minute, and the average American eats about 53 pounds of bread each year.

Find the equivalent pair of fractions in each set.

53. $\frac{6}{15}, \frac{21}{35}, \frac{3}{5}$ **$\frac{21}{35}, \frac{3}{5}$**
54. $\frac{7}{12}, \frac{12}{20}, \frac{6}{10}$ **$\frac{12}{20}, \frac{6}{10}$**
55. $\frac{2}{3}, \frac{12}{15}, \frac{20}{30}, \frac{15}{24}$ **$\frac{2}{3}, \frac{20}{30}$**

There are 12 inches in 1 foot. Write a mixed number to represent each measurement in feet. (Example: 14 inches = $1\frac{2}{12}$ feet or $1\frac{1}{6}$ feet)

56. 18 inches **$1\frac{6}{12}$ or $1\frac{1}{2}$ ft**
57. 25 inches **$2\frac{1}{12}$ ft**
58. 100 inches **$8\frac{4}{12}$ or $8\frac{1}{3}$ ft**
59. 362 inches **$30\frac{2}{12}$ or $30\frac{1}{6}$ ft**
60. 42 inches **$3\frac{6}{12}$ or $3\frac{1}{2}$ ft**
61. 965 inches **$80\frac{5}{12}$ ft**
62. ***SOCIAL STUDIES*** A dollar bill is $15\frac{7}{10}$ centimeters long and $6\frac{13}{20}$ centimeters wide. Write each number as an improper fraction. **$\frac{157}{10}, \frac{133}{20}$**
63. ***FOOD*** A bakery uses $37\frac{1}{2}$ cups of flour to make 25 loaves of bread each day. Write a fraction that shows how many $\frac{1}{4}$ cups of flour are used to make bread each day at the bakery. **$\frac{150}{4}$**
64. ***PERSONAL FINANCE*** Every month, Adrian pays for his own long-distance calls made on the family phone. Last month, 15 of the 60 minutes of long-distance charges were Adrian's, and he paid $2.50 of the $12 long-distance bill. Did Adrian pay his fair share? **No, Adrian should have paid $3.**

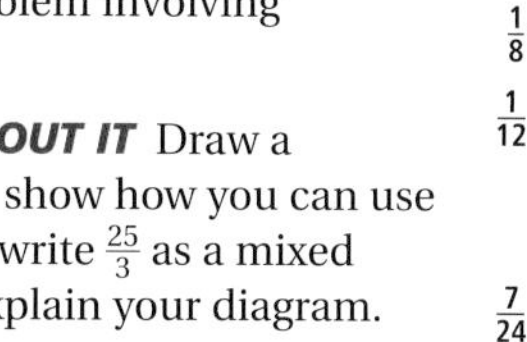

65. ***WRITE A PROBLEM*** Cal made a graph to show how he spends his time each day. Use the graph to write a problem involving fractions.

How Cal Spends His Day

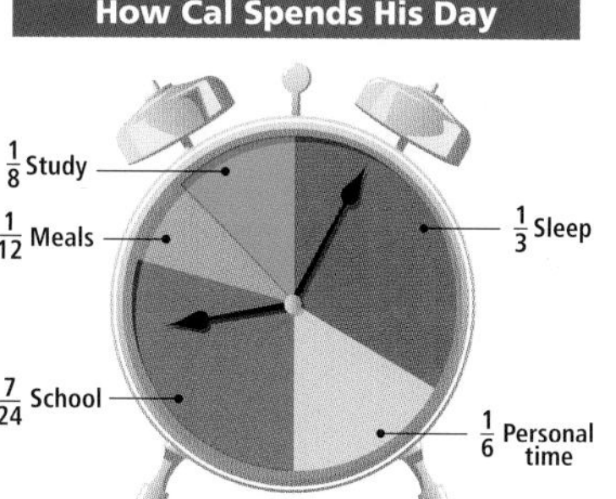

66. ***WRITE ABOUT IT*** Draw a diagram to show how you can use division to write $\frac{25}{3}$ as a mixed number. Explain your diagram.

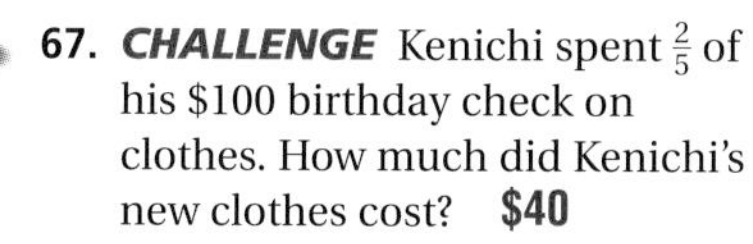

67. ***CHALLENGE*** Kenichi spent $\frac{2}{5}$ of his $100 birthday check on clothes. How much did Kenichi's new clothes cost? **$40**

Spiral Review

Evaluate each number. (Lesson 2-1)

68. 5^3 **125**
69. 6^2 **36**
70. 2^8 **256**
71. 10^5 **100,000**

Write each number in scientific notation. (Lesson 2-2)

72. 1,230,000 **1.23×10^6**
73. 475,000 **4.75×10^5**
74. 968 **9.68×10^2**
75. 88 **8.8×10^1**

76. **TEST PREP** The prime factorization of 1,000 is __?__. (Lesson 2-4) **C**

A $10 \cdot 10 \cdot 10$
B $2^2 \cdot 5^2$
C $2^3 \cdot 5^3$
D $8 \cdot 125$

77. **TEST PREP** The solution of $x - 4 = 12$ is __?__. (Lesson 2-10) **J**

F 7
G 8
H 12
J 16

CHALLENGE 3-8

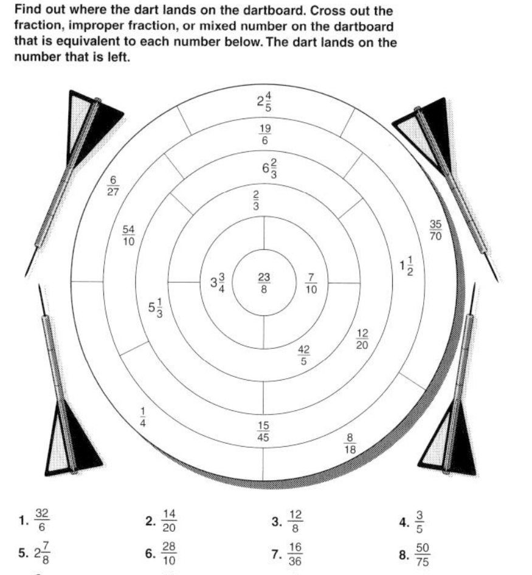

LESSON 3-8 **Challenge**
Target Practice

Find out where the dart lands on the dartboard. Cross out the fraction, improper fraction, or mixed number on the dartboard that is equivalent to each number below. The dart lands on the number that is left.

1. $\frac{32}{6}$
2. $\frac{14}{20}$
3. $\frac{12}{8}$
4. $\frac{3}{5}$
5. $2\frac{7}{8}$
6. $\frac{28}{10}$
7. $\frac{16}{36}$
8. $\frac{50}{75}$
9. $\frac{2}{9}$
10. $\frac{20}{3}$
11. $\frac{5}{15}$
12. $3\frac{1}{6}$
13. $\frac{3}{12}$
14. $5\frac{2}{5}$
15. $\frac{45}{12}$
16. $\frac{1}{2}$

17. The dart lands on **$\frac{42}{5}$**

PROBLEM SOLVING 3-8

LESSON 3-8 **Problem Solving**
Equivalent Fractions and Mixed Numbers

Write the correct answer.

1. Bert bicycles 136 miles each week. If he bikes the same distance daily and bikes each day of the week, how many miles does he bike each day? Write your answer as a mixed number.
$19\frac{3}{7}$ miles

2. The Eiffel Tower in Paris, France, was designed so well that even in the highest winds the tower never sways more than $4\frac{1}{2}$ inches. Write two fractions that are equivalent to $4\frac{1}{2}$.
Possible answer: $\frac{9}{2}, \frac{18}{4}$

3. In October 2000, almost 13 inches of rain fell in Miami, Florida, in a 24-hour period. Write a fraction that shows about how many $\frac{1}{4}$ inches of rain fell on that one day.
$\frac{52}{4}$ inches

4. Elena is 58 inches tall. Write a mixed number to represent her height in feet.
$4\frac{5}{6}$ feet

Choose the letter for the best answer.

5. Randi runs 48 miles each week. She runs the same distance daily and runs each day of the week. How many miles does she run each day? Write your answer as a mixed number.
(A) $6\frac{6}{7}$ miles
B $6\frac{5}{6}$ miles
C $6\frac{7}{48}$ miles
D $7\frac{1}{7}$ miles

6. A bakery used $4\frac{3}{4}$ cups of salt to make 120 loaves of sourdough bread. Write a fraction that shows how many $\frac{1}{4}$ cups of salt were used to make the bread.
F $\frac{30}{4}$ cups
G $\frac{24}{4}$ cups
H $\frac{12}{4}$ cups
(J) $\frac{19}{4}$ cups

7. One of the driest summers in the Northeast was in 1909, with $\frac{896}{100}$ inches of precipitation. Which mixed number is equivalent to $\frac{896}{100}$?
A $89\frac{6}{10}$
B $8\frac{96}{10}$
(C) $8\frac{24}{25}$
D $8\frac{4}{5}$

8. The Central Ohio Transit Authority has $957\frac{3}{5}$ miles of routes. Which fraction is equivalent to $957\frac{3}{5}$?
F $\frac{4,781}{5}$
(G) $\frac{4,788}{5}$
H $\frac{4,783}{5}$
J $\frac{9,573}{5}$

COMMON ERROR ALERT

To prevent errors in problems that involve converting units, ask students to estimate an answer before they calculate. For example, students can ask themselves, "Will the number of feet in 18 inches be greater than or less than 18?" This will often prevent errors caused by using the reciprocal of the correct conversion factor.

Answers

65. Possible answer: Find common denominators to determine if the amount of time Cal spends sleeping is equivalent to the amount of time Cal spends at school.
66. Possible answer: Nine circles divided into thirds; 8 wholes and 1 third should be shaded. The diagram shows 25 thirds, divided into groups of 3; 8 wholes and remainder of 1 third.

Journal 

Give students two equivalent fractions. Have students draw pictures of the equivalent fractions and then explain in writing how to show two fractions are equivalent.

Test Prep Doctor 

For Exercise 76, ask students to notice that **A, C,** and **D** all equal 1,000. Point out that only one of the choices meets the condition required.

Lesson Quiz 

1. Write a fraction equivalent to $\frac{12}{24}$.
Possible answer: $\frac{1}{2}$
2. Write $\frac{17}{8}$ as a mixed number. $2\frac{1}{8}$
3. Write $4\frac{3}{7}$ as an improper fraction. $\frac{31}{7}$
4. A carpenter is building a stairway. Each stair has to be $12\frac{7}{8}$ in. wide. The carpenter's ruler is marked in sixteenths. What length should he measure? $12\frac{14}{16}$ in.

Available on Daily Transparency in CRB

3-9 Organizer

Pacing: Traditional 1 day
Block $\frac{1}{2}$ day

Objective: Students write fractions as decimals, and vice versa, and determine whether a decimal is terminating or repeating.

Warm Up

Write each fraction in simplest form.

1. $\frac{4}{12}$ $\frac{1}{3}$
2. $\frac{18}{46}$ $\frac{9}{23}$
3. $\frac{21}{63}$ $\frac{1}{3}$
4. $\frac{100}{72}$ $\frac{25}{18}$, or $1\frac{7}{18}$

Problem of the Day

For Martin's 4-H project he recorded how much a bean plant grew each week. The first week the plant grew $\frac{4}{7}$ of an inch. It grew $\frac{7}{8}$ of an inch the second week and $\frac{7}{9}$ of an inch the third week. During which week did the plant grow the least? week 1

Available on Daily Transparency in CRB

Why can't you fire $\frac{1}{3}$? Because you can't terminate a repeating decimal.

3-9 Equivalent Fractions and Decimals

Learn to write fractions as decimals, and vice versa, and to determine whether a decimal is terminating or repeating.

Vocabulary

terminating decimal

repeating decimal

In baseball, a player's batting average compares the number of hits with the number of times the player has been at bat. The statistics below are for the 2001 Major League Baseball season.

Sammy Sosa had 189 hits in the 2001 season.

Player	Hits	At Bats	$\frac{\text{Hits}}{\text{at Bats}}$	Batting Average (thousandths)
Mark Grace	142	476	$\frac{142}{476}$	$142 \div 476 \approx 0.298$
Cal Ripken, Jr.	114	477	$\frac{114}{477}$	$114 \div 477 \approx 0.239$
Ivan Rodriguez	136	442	$\frac{136}{442}$	$136 \div 442 \approx 0.308$
Sammy Sosa	189	577	$\frac{189}{577}$	$189 \div 577 \approx 0.328$

To convert a fraction to a decimal, divide the numerator by the denominator.

EXAMPLE 1 Writing Fractions as Decimals

Write each fraction as a decimal. Round to the nearest hundredth, if necessary.

A $\frac{3}{4}$

$$4\overline{)3.00} = 0.75$$

-28, 20, -20, 0

$\frac{3}{4} = 0.75$

B $\frac{6}{5}$

$$5\overline{)6.0} = 1.2$$

-5, 10, -10, 0

$\frac{6}{5} = 1.2$

C $\frac{1}{3}$

$$3\overline{)1.000} = 0.333$$

-9, 10, -9, 10, -9, 1

$\frac{1}{3} \approx 0.33$

Helpful Hint

You can use a calculator to check your division:
3 ÷ 4 = 0.75
6 ÷ 5 = 1.2
1 ÷ 3 = 0.333...

1 Introduce

Alternate Opener

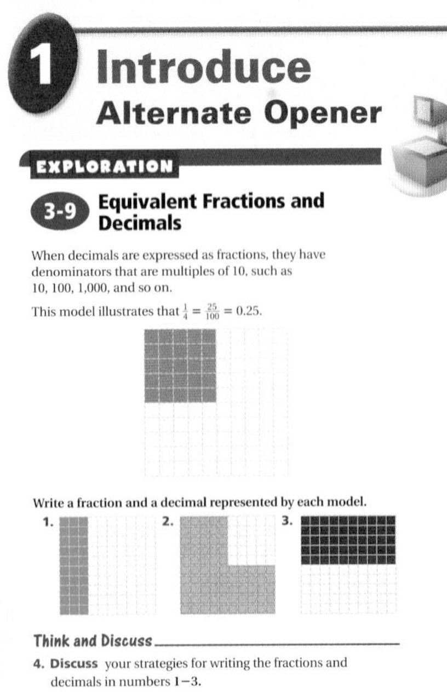

EXPLORATION

3-9 Equivalent Fractions and Decimals

When decimals are expressed as fractions, they have denominators that are multiples of 10, such as 10, 100, 1,000, and so on.

This model illustrates that $\frac{1}{4} = \frac{25}{100} = 0.25$.

Write a fraction and a decimal represented by each model.

1. 2. 3.

Think and Discuss

4. Discuss your strategies for writing the fractions and decimals in numbers 1–3.

Motivate

Discuss the fraction used for finding batting averages for baseball, $\frac{\text{hits}}{\text{at bats}}$. Ask students to explain the meaning of the numerator and the denominator in the fraction $\frac{4}{12}$ in terms of hits and at bats. Students should realize that it means 4 hits in 12 times at bat. Have students find equivalent fractions for 8, 20, and 25 hits. The fractions would be $\frac{8}{24}$, $\frac{20}{60}$, and $\frac{25}{75}$.

Exploration worksheet and answers on Chapter 3 Resource Book pp. 82 and 124

2 Teach

Lesson Presentation

Guided Instruction

In this lesson, students learn to write fractions as decimals, and vice versa, and to determine whether a decimal is terminating or repeating. You might ask students what decimal represents one-fourth of a dollar, then one-half of a dollar, and finally, three-fourths of a dollar. Students can often answer a question about money without realizing that it means they know the decimal equivalent of a fraction.

Teaching Tip Encourage students to memorize some of the most common fraction and decimal equivalents, such as $\frac{1}{3} = 0.333\ldots$, $\frac{1}{4} = 0.25$, and $\frac{1}{8} = 0.125$.

The decimals 0.75 and 1.2 in Example 1 are **terminating decimals** because the decimals come to an end. The decimal 0.333… is a **repeating decimal** because the decimal repeats a pattern forever. You can also write a repeating decimal with a bar over the repeating part.

$0.333\ldots = 0.\overline{3}$ $\quad 0.8333\ldots = 0.8\overline{3}$ $\quad 0.727272\ldots = 0.\overline{72}$

You can use place value to convert a terminating decimal to a fraction.

Place	Thousands	Hundreds	Tens	Ones	·	Tenths	Hundredths	Thousandths
Place Value	1,000	100	10	1		$0.1 = \frac{1}{10}$	$0.01 = \frac{1}{100}$	$0.001 = \frac{1}{1,000}$

EXAMPLE 2 Writing Decimals as Fractions

Write each decimal as a fraction in simplest form.

A 0.036

$$0.036 = \frac{36}{1,000} = \frac{36 \div 4}{1,000 \div 4} = \frac{9}{250}$$

B −0.8

$$-0.8 = -\frac{8}{10} = -\frac{8 \div 2}{10 \div 2} = -\frac{4}{5}$$

C 1.88

$$1.88 = \frac{188}{100} = \frac{188 \div 4}{100 \div 4} = \frac{47}{25}, \text{ or } 1\frac{22}{25}$$

EXAMPLE 3 *Sports Application*

Steve Young holds the record for the best career completion rate as a quarterback in the NFL. During his career, he completed 2,667 of the 4,149 passes he attempted. Find his completion rate. Write your answer as a decimal rounded to the nearest thousandth.

Fraction	What the Calculator Shows	Completion Rate
$\frac{2,667}{4,149}$	2667  4,149 ENTER 0.642805495	0.643

His completion rate is 0.643.

Think and Discuss

1. **Tell** how to write a fraction as a decimal.
2. **Describe** the difference between a terminating decimal and a repeating decimal.
3. **Explain** how to use place value to convert a terminating decimal to a fraction.

COMMON ERROR ALERT

When writing a decimal such as 5.09 as a mixed number, some students might work with the 0.09 and forget to put the whole-number part in the answer. Remind students to include the 5.

Additional Examples

Example 1

Write each fraction as a decimal. Round to the nearest hundredth, if necessary.

A. $\frac{1}{4}$ **0.25**

B. $\frac{9}{5}$ **1.8**

C. $\frac{5}{3}$ **1.67**

Example 2

Write each decimal as a fraction in simplest form.

A. 0.018 $\frac{9}{500}$

B. −0.6 $-\frac{3}{5}$

C. 1.55 $\frac{31}{20}$ or $1\frac{11}{20}$

Example 3

A football player completed 1,546 of the 3,875 passes he attempted. Find his completion rate. Write your answer as a decimal rounded to the nearest thousandth. **0.399**

Reaching All Learners
Through World Math

Invite students to tell what they know about popular team sports in other countries (e.g., rugby and cricket in Britain, jai alai in Mexico, and polo in India). Choose one sport and have students research statistics that are connected with that sport.

3 Close

Summarize

Review the fact that any fraction can be written as a decimal using division. Decimals that terminate can be written as fractions by using the appropriate power of ten as the denominator. Decimals that repeat a group of digits forever are called repeating decimals. Have students explain how to indicate in a decimal that a group of digits repeats.

Possible answer: Drawing a bar over the group of digits shows that the complete group of digits repeats forever.

Answers to Think and Discuss

Possible answers:

1. To write a fraction as a decimal, divide the numerator by the denominator.
2. A terminating decimal comes to an end, while a repeating decimal has a pattern of digits that repeats forever.
3. The place value of the last decimal place tells what power of ten to use for the denominator. The numbers to the right of the decimal point, starting with the first nonzero number, become the numerator.

3-9 PRACTICE & ASSESS

Students may want to refer back to the lesson examples.

Assignment Guide

If you finished Example 1 assign:
Core 1–4, 10–17, 47–55
Enriched 1–4, 10–17, 47–55

If you finished Example 2 assign:
Core 1–8, 10–25, 27–41 odd, 47–55
Enriched 1–7 odd, 11–25 odd, 27–42, 47–55

If you finished Example 3 assign:
Core 1–26, 27–43 odd, 47–55
Enriched 1–25 odd, 26–55

Notes

3-9 Exercises

FOR EXTRA PRACTICE see page 661

internet connect
Homework Help Online
go.hrw.com Keyword: MS4 3-9

GUIDED PRACTICE

See Example 1 Write each fraction as a decimal. Round to the nearest hundredth, if necessary.

1. $\frac{3}{5}$ **0.6** 2. $\frac{21}{8}$ **2.63** 3. $\frac{11}{6}$ **1.83** 4. $\frac{7}{9}$ **0.78**

See Example 2 Write each decimal as a fraction in simplest form.

5. 0.008 $\mathbf{\frac{1}{125}}$ 6. −0.6 $\mathbf{-\frac{3}{5}}$ 7. −2.05 $\mathbf{-\frac{41}{20}}$ **or** $\mathbf{-2\frac{1}{20}}$ 8. 3.75 $\mathbf{\frac{15}{4}}$ **or** $\mathbf{3\frac{3}{4}}$

See Example 3

9. After sweeping the Baltimore Orioles at home in 2001, the Seattle Mariners had a record of 103 wins out of 143 games played. Find the Mariners' winning rate. Write your answer as a decimal rounded to the nearest thousandth. **0.720**

INDEPENDENT PRACTICE

See Example 1 Write each fraction as a decimal. Round to the nearest hundredth, if necessary.

10. $\frac{9}{10}$ **0.9** 11. $\frac{32}{5}$ **6.4** 12. $\frac{18}{25}$ **0.72** 13. $\frac{7}{8}$ **0.88**

14. $\frac{16}{11}$ **1.45** 15. $\frac{500}{500}$ **1** 16. $\frac{17}{3}$ **5.67** 17. $\frac{23}{12}$ **1.92**

See Example 2 Write each decimal as a fraction in simplest form.

18. 0.45 $\mathbf{\frac{9}{20}}$ 19. 0.01 $\mathbf{\frac{1}{100}}$ 20. −0.25 $\mathbf{-\frac{1}{4}}$ 21. −0.08 $\mathbf{-\frac{2}{25}}$

22. 1.8 $\mathbf{\frac{9}{5}}$ **or** $\mathbf{1\frac{4}{5}}$ 23. 15.25 $\mathbf{\frac{61}{4}}$ **or** $\mathbf{15\frac{1}{4}}$ 24. 5.09 $\mathbf{\frac{509}{100}}$ **or** $\mathbf{5\frac{9}{100}}$ 25. 8.375 $\mathbf{\frac{67}{8}}$ **or** $\mathbf{8\frac{3}{8}}$

See Example 3

26. On a test, Caleb answered 73 out of 86 questions correctly. What portion of his answers was correct? Write your answer as a decimal rounded to the nearest thousandth. **0.849**

PRACTICE AND PROBLEM SOLVING

Possible answers:

Give two numbers equivalent to each fraction or decimal.

27. $8\frac{3}{4}$ **8.75,** $\mathbf{8\frac{6}{8}}$ 28. 0.66 $\mathbf{\frac{66}{100}, \frac{33}{50}}$ 29. 5.05 $\mathbf{5\frac{1}{20}, 5\frac{5}{100}}$ 30. $\frac{8}{25}$ $\mathbf{0.32, \frac{16}{50}}$

31. 15.35 $\mathbf{15\frac{7}{20}, \frac{307}{20}}$ 32. $8\frac{3}{8}$ **8.375,** $\mathbf{\frac{67}{8}}$ 33. $4\frac{3}{1{,}000}$ **4.003,** $\mathbf{\frac{4{,}003}{1{,}000}}$ 34. $3\frac{1}{3}$ $\mathbf{\frac{10}{3}, 3.\overline{3}}$

Determine if the numbers in each pair are equivalent.

35. $\frac{3}{4}$ and 0.75 **yes** 36. $\frac{7}{20}$ and 0.45 **no** 37. $\frac{11}{21}$ and 0.55 **no** 38. 0.8 and $\frac{4}{5}$ **yes**

39. 0.275 and $\frac{11}{40}$ **yes** 40. $1\frac{21}{25}$ and 1.72 **no** 41. 0.74 and $\frac{16}{25}$ **no** 42. 0.35 and $\frac{7}{20}$ **yes**

Math Background

You can use the following steps to find the fraction that is equal to a repeating decimal.

$$x = 3.5\overline{721}$$

Multiply each side by 10 to bring the repeating term just to the right of the decimal point.

$$10x = 35.\overline{721}$$

Multiply each side by 1,000 to shift the repeating part to the other side of the decimal.

$$10{,}000x = 35{,}721.\overline{721}$$

Subtract the first equation from the second.

$$9{,}990x = 35{,}686$$

so $x = \frac{35{,}686}{9{,}990}$, or $\frac{17{,}843}{4{,}995}$.

RETEACH 3-9

LESSON 3-9 **Reteach**
Equivalent Fractions and Decimals

To write a fraction as a decimal, divide the numerator of the fraction by the denominator of the fraction.

Write $\frac{3}{7}$ as a decimal.
- Divide 3 by 7.
- To round your answer to the nearest thousandth, add 4 zeros

$7\overline{)3.0000} = 0.4285$; −28, 20, −14, 60, −56, 40, −35

0.4285 rounded to the nearest thousandth is 0.429.

1. Write $\frac{2}{5}$ as a decimal. $5\overline{)2.0} = \mathbf{0.4}$; **− 2 0**, **0** $\frac{2}{5}$ = **0.4**

Write each fraction as a decimal. Round to the nearest thousandth, if necessary.

2. $\frac{3}{4}$ **0.75** 3. $\frac{7}{8}$ **0.875** 4. $\frac{3}{2}$ **1.5** 5. $\frac{5}{3}$ **1.667**

To write a decimal as a fraction:
Step 1: Ignore the decimal point.
Step 2: Write the number after the decimal point as if it were an integer as the numerator.
Step 3: Write the denominator as a power of ten. The number of zeros will be the same as the number of places in the decimal.
Step 4: Simplify.

Write 1.6 as a fraction.
$1.6 = \frac{16}{10} = \frac{8}{5}$

Write 0.005 as a fraction.
$0.005 = \frac{5}{1{,}000} \div \frac{5}{5} = \frac{1}{200}$

Write each decimal as a fraction or mixed number in simplest form.

6. 0.8 $\mathbf{\frac{4}{5}}$ 7. 2.25 $\mathbf{\frac{9}{4}}$ **or** $\mathbf{2\frac{1}{4}}$ 8. −0.02 $\mathbf{-\frac{1}{50}}$

PRACTICE 3-9

LESSON 3-9 **Practice B**
Equivalent Fractions and Decimals

Write each fraction as a decimal. Round to the nearest thousandth, if necessary.

1. $\frac{2}{10}$ **0.2** 2. $\frac{19}{20}$ **0.95** 3. $\frac{5}{8}$ **0.625** 4. $\frac{11}{5}$ **2.2**

5. $\frac{19}{6}$ **3.167** 6. $\frac{17}{4}$ **4.25** 7. $\frac{13}{12}$ **1.083** 8. $\frac{30}{7}$ **4.286**

9. $\frac{13}{13}$ **1.0** 10. $\frac{19}{3}$ **6.333** 11. $\frac{3}{40}$ **0.075** 12. $\frac{9}{11}$ **0.818**

Write each decimal as a fraction or mixed number in simplest form.

13. 0.85 $\mathbf{\frac{17}{20}}$ 14. 0.11 $\mathbf{\frac{11}{100}}$ 15. −0.25 $\mathbf{-\frac{1}{4}}$

16. 4.3 $\mathbf{4\frac{3}{10}}$ **or** $\mathbf{\frac{43}{10}}$ 17. 7.75 $\mathbf{7\frac{3}{4}}$ **or** $\mathbf{\frac{31}{4}}$ 18. 5.03 $\mathbf{5\frac{3}{100}}$ **or** $\mathbf{\frac{503}{100}}$

19. −1.06 $\mathbf{-1\frac{3}{50}}$ **or** $\mathbf{-\frac{53}{50}}$ 20. 0.375 $\mathbf{\frac{3}{8}}$ 21. −2.65 $\mathbf{-2\frac{13}{20}}$ **or** $\mathbf{-\frac{53}{20}}$

22. −5.6 $\mathbf{-5\frac{3}{5}}$ **or** $\mathbf{-\frac{28}{5}}$ 23. 1.12 $\mathbf{1\frac{3}{25}}$ **or** $\mathbf{\frac{28}{25}}$ 24. 0.005 $\mathbf{\frac{1}{200}}$

Write each answer as a decimal rounded to the nearest thousandth.

25. In the 1998 Winter Olympics, a total of 205 medals were awarded. The United States won 13 medals. What portion of the medals did the United States win?
0.063

26. On a test, Hailey answered 64 out of 75 questions correctly. What portion of her answers was correct?
0.853

Economics LINK

Use the table for Exercises 43 and 44.

XYZ Stock Values (October 2001)				
Date	Open	High	Low	Close
Oct 15	16.9	17.9	16.4	17.89
Oct 16	17.89	18.05	17.5	17.8
Oct 17	18.01	18.04	17.15	17.95
Oct 18	17.84	18.55	17.81	18.20

43. Write the highest value of stock XYZ for each day as a mixed number in simplest form.

44. On which of the four dates shown did the price of stock XYZ rise by $\frac{9}{25}$ of a dollar between the open and close of the day? **October 18**

Traders watch the stock prices change from the floor of a stock exchange and decide what stocks to buy or sell and when.

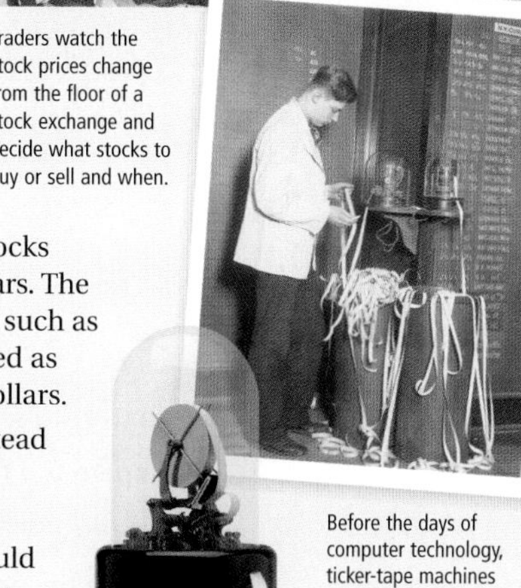

45. ***WRITE ABOUT IT*** Until recently, prices of stocks were expressed as mixed numbers, such as $24\frac{15}{32}$ dollars. The denominators of such fractions were multiples of 2, such as 2, 4, 6, 8, and so forth. Today, the prices are expressed as decimals to the nearest hundredth, such as 32.35 dollars.

a. What are some advantages of using decimals instead of fractions?

b. The old ticker tape machine punched stock prices onto a tape. Perhaps because fractions could not be shown using the machine, the stock values were punched as decimal equivalents of fractions. Write some decimal equivalents of fractions that the machine might print.

Before the days of computer technology, ticker-tape machines were used to punch the stock prices onto paper strands.

46. ***CHALLENGE*** Write $\frac{1}{9}$ and $\frac{2}{9}$ as decimals. Use the results to predict the decimal equivalent of $\frac{8}{9}$. **$0.\overline{1}$, $0.\overline{2}$, $0.\overline{8}$**

go.hrw.com
KEYWORD: MS4 Stock
CNN Student News

Spiral Review

Find the LCM of the numbers. (Lesson 2-6)

47. 16, 32 **32** **48.** 8, 20 **40** **49.** 9, 12 **36** **50.** 3, 7, 10 **210**

Find the GCF of the numbers. (Lesson 2-5)

51. 18, 45 **9** **52.** 25, 50 **25** **53.** 16, 72 **8** **54.** 15, 32 **1**

55. **TEST PREP** The value of $(-3) \cdot (-8) \div (-2)$ is __?__. (Lesson 3-5) **B**

A −48 B −12 C 12 D 48

Interdisciplinary LINK

Economics

Exercises 43–45 involve comparing stock prices. The information includes some history about the fractions used in stock values and their decimal equivalents on the ticker tape.

Answers

43. $17\frac{9}{10}$, $18\frac{1}{20}$, $18\frac{1}{25}$, $18\frac{11}{20}$

45. Possible answers:

a. Decimals are easier to add and subtract. Decimals written to the nearest hundredth represent the dollar amount written to the nearest cent. Also, there are more possible divisions using decimals than 32nds.

b. **0.15625; 0.125; 0.1875**

Journal

Ask students to write a paragraph comparing and contrasting terminating and repeating decimals. Have them include specific examples.

Test Prep Doctor

For Exercise 55, suggest that students first determine the sign of the answer. Once they realize that the answer must be negative, they can immediately eliminate **C** and **D**.

CHALLENGE 3-9

LESSON 3-9 **Challenge**
Decimal Patterns

Repeating decimals continue without end with a repeating pattern. Some decimals continue without end, but do not have a repeating pattern. These decimals are called *nonrepeating, nonterminating* decimals. Although they continue without end, these decimals may have a pattern.

Examples of nonrepeating, nonterminating decimals with patterns:

5.121121112...
0.881882883...

Write *r* if the decimal is a repeating decimal and *n* if the decimal is a nonrepeating, nonterminating decimal.

1. 4.562222... **r**
2. 6.1323323332... **n**
3. 8.355355... **r**
4. 0.230230023... **n**
5. 10.7727227... **n**
6. 4.121314... **n**
7. 0.42818181... **r**
8. 29.7053053... **r**
9. 1.221221222... **n**
10. 5.67167672... **n**
11. 75.320333... **r**
12. 4.121231234... **n**

Identify the pattern in each nonrepeating, nonterminating decimal. Use the pattern to extend the decimal several places.

13. 0.010203... **0.01020304...**
14. 8.636336333... **8.63633633363333...**
15. 25.121231234... **25.12123123412345...**
16. 9.989796... **9.98979695...**
17. Write an example of a repeating decimal. **Possible answer: 1.2222...**
18. Write an example of a nonrepeating, nonterminating decimal with a pattern. **Possible answer: 1.191991999...**

PROBLEM SOLVING 3-9

LESSON 3-9 **Problem Solving**
Equivalent Fractions and Decimals

Write the correct answer.

1. On a test, Shane answered 37 out of 40 questions correctly. What portion of his answers was correct? Write your answer as a decimal rounded to the nearest thousandth. **0.925**
2. Sammy Sosa hit 66 home runs in 1998. He had 643 at bats. Write his home run average as a decimal rounded to the nearest thousandth. **0.103**
3. In February, Chicago receives an average of $1\frac{2}{5}$ inches of rain. Write a decimal to show the number of inches of rain. **1.4 in.**
4. On a test, Ellen answered 51 out of 64 questions correctly. What portion of her answers was correct? Write your answer as a decimal rounded to the nearest thousandth. **0.797**

Choose the letter for the best answer.

Use the graph for 5–6.

World Energy Consumption 1999
(in quadrillions of British Thermal Units, BTU)

North America	115.7
Far East/Oceania	98.2
Western Europe	70.5
Eastern Europe	48.9
Central/South America	20.4
Middle East	16.4
Africa	11.8

Axis: 0 20 40 60 80 100 120

5. Which mixed number shows the energy, in quadrillions of BTU, consumed in Western Europe in 1999?
   (A) $70\frac{1}{2}$ C $70\frac{1}{10}$ B $70\frac{1}{5}$ D $70\frac{2}{5}$
6. Which mixed number shows the energy, in quadrillions of BTU, consumed in Africa in 1999?
   F 11 **(H)** $11\frac{4}{5}$ G $11\frac{1}{4}$ J $11\frac{4}{8}$
7. Jill sold 478 out of 520 tickets to the opening night of her theater performance. What portion of the tickets did she sell?
   A 0.998 **(C)** 0.919 B 1.088 D 0.081
8. The high school sold 369 out of 460 tickets to the opening night of a concert series. What portion of the tickets was sold?
   F 0.198 H 1.247 G 0.829 **(J)** 0.802

Lesson Quiz

Write each fraction as a decimal.

1. $\frac{16}{5}$ 3.2 **2.** $\frac{21}{8}$ 2.625

Write each decimal as a fraction in simplest form.

3. 0.42 $\frac{21}{50}$ **4.** 8.625 $\frac{69}{8}$ or $8\frac{5}{8}$

5. If your soccer team wins 21 out of 30 games, what is your team's winning rate? **0.70**

Available on Daily Transparency in CRB

3-10 Organizer

Pacing: Traditional 1 day
Block $\frac{1}{2}$ day

Objective: Students compare and order rational numbers.

Warm Up

Write each mixed number as an improper fraction.

1. $1\frac{3}{4}$ $\frac{7}{4}$ **2.** $2\frac{7}{8}$ $\frac{23}{8}$

3. $1\frac{5}{6}$ $\frac{11}{6}$ **4.** $8\frac{1}{12}$ $\frac{97}{12}$

Problem of the Day

Hot dogs are sold in packs of 6. Buns are sold in bags of 8. What is the least number of hot dog packages and the least number of bun packages you would need to buy in order to have the same number of hot dogs and buns? 4 packages of hot dogs and 3 packages of buns

Available on Daily Transparency in CRB

Math Humor

The two fractions were able to settle their differences peacefully because, fortunately, they were both rational.

3-10 Comparing and Ordering Rational Numbers

Learn to compare and order fractions and decimals.

Which is greater, $\frac{7}{9}$ or $\frac{2}{9}$?

When two fractions have the same denominator, just compare the numerators.

$\frac{7}{9} > \frac{2}{9}$ because $7 > 2$.

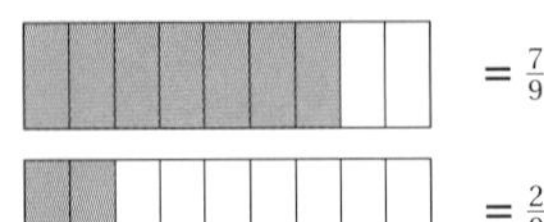

I would like an extra-large pizza with $\frac{1}{2}$ pepperoni, $\frac{4}{5}$ sausage, $\frac{1}{3}$ anchovies on the pepperoni side, $\frac{3}{8}$ peanut butter fudge, $\frac{5}{11}$ pineapple, $\frac{2}{13}$ doggy treats…and extra cheese.

EXAMPLE 1 Comparing Fractions

Compare the fractions. Write < or >.

A $\frac{5}{11} \;\square\; \frac{3}{8}$

Both fractions can be written with a denominator of 88.

$\frac{5}{11} = \frac{5 \cdot 8}{11 \cdot 8} = \frac{40}{88}$

$\frac{3}{8} = \frac{3 \cdot 11}{8 \cdot 11} = \frac{33}{88}$

Write as fractions with common denominators.

$\frac{40}{88} > \frac{33}{88}$, and so $\frac{5}{11} > \frac{3}{8}$.

B $-\frac{3}{5} \;\square\; -\frac{5}{9}$

Both fractions can be written with a denominator of 45.

$-\frac{3}{5} = \frac{-3 \cdot 9}{5 \cdot 9} = \frac{-27}{45}$

$-\frac{5}{9} = \frac{-5 \cdot 5}{9 \cdot 5} = \frac{-25}{45}$

Write as fractions with common denominators. Put the negative signs in the numerators.

$\frac{-27}{45} < \frac{-25}{45}$, and so $-\frac{3}{5} < -\frac{5}{9}$.

1 Introduce

Alternate Opener

EXPLORATION

3-10 Comparing and Ordering Rational Numbers

The fraction model can be used to compare fractions. For example, $\frac{1}{2}$ is greater than $\frac{1}{4}$, but $\frac{1}{2}$ is equal to $\frac{2}{4}$.

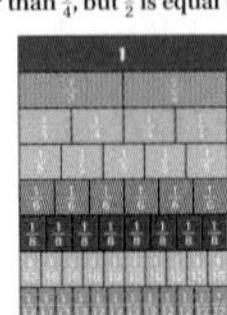

Use the fraction model to compare each pair of fractions. Write <, >, or =.

1. $\frac{1}{2} \square \frac{5}{6}$ 2. $\frac{1}{2} \square \frac{3}{8}$ 3. $\frac{7}{12} \square \frac{8}{12}$ 4. $\frac{1}{2} \square \frac{9}{12}$
5. $\frac{7}{12} \square \frac{5}{8}$ 6. $\frac{2}{5} \square \frac{3}{8}$ 7. $\frac{7}{8} \square \frac{5}{6}$ 8. $\frac{1}{12} \square \frac{1}{8}$
9. Use the fraction model to compare the fractions $\frac{1}{2}$, $\frac{3}{4}$, and $\frac{4}{5}$. Notice that all of the fractions have a numerator that is one less than the denominator.

Think and Discuss

10. **Describe** your strategies for comparing and ordering fractions using the fraction model.

Motivate

Begin a discussion by asking, "Which is more, 7 oranges or 9 oranges?" Explain that when students compare like things, they can simply compare how many there are. This means that they can compare 7 ninths and 2 ninths by comparing 7 and 2. However, when fractions have different denominators, such as $\frac{5}{9}$ and $\frac{4}{7}$, finding the greater fraction is not so obvious. Using a calculator quickly shows that these fractions are only 0.02 apart in value and that $\frac{4}{7}$ is the greater fraction.

Exploration worksheet and answers on Chapter 3 Resource Book pp. 91 and 126

2 Teach

Lesson Presentation

Guided Instruction

In this lesson, students learn to compare and order fractions and decimals. Remind students of the process of multiplying a fraction by 1 to rewrite the fractions being compared so that they have the same denominator. Students can compare decimals by comparing the digits in the matching places.

Teaching Tip Remind students that a positive number is always greater than a negative number and that if the signs of the two numbers being compared are different, there is no need to do further calculations.

To compare decimals, line up the decimal points and compare digits from left to right until you find the place where the digits are different.

EXAMPLE 2 Comparing Decimals

Compare the decimals. Write $<$ or $>$.

$0.841 \ \square \ 0.848$

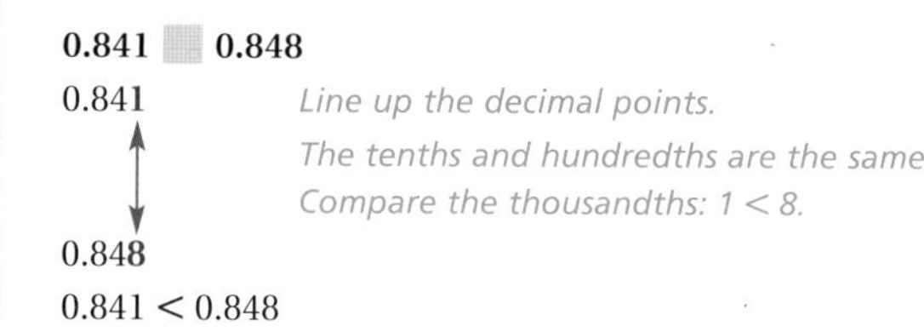

0.841 — *Line up the decimal points.*

The tenths and hundredths are the same.

Compare the thousandths: $1 < 8$.

0.848

$0.841 < 0.848$

EXAMPLE 3 Ordering Fractions and Decimals

Order the numbers from least to greatest.

$\frac{3}{5}$, 0.78, and 0.7

$\frac{3}{5} = 0.60 \qquad 0.78 = 0.78 \qquad 0.7 = 0.70$ — *Write as decimals with the same number of places.*

> **Remember!**
> You can place zeros at the end of a decimal without changing its value. 2.045 = 2.045000

Graph the numbers on a number line.

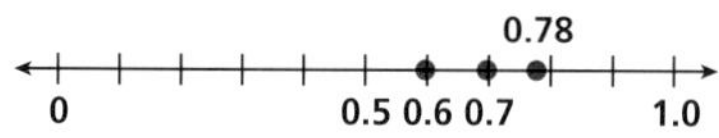

The values on a number line increase as we move from left to right.

$0.60 < 0.70 < 0.78$ — *Place the decimals in order.*

$\frac{3}{5}$, 0.7, 0.78

Think and Discuss

1. **Describe** how to compare two fractions with different denominators.
2. **Explain** why -0.61 is greater than -0.625 even though $2 > 1$.

COMMON ERROR ALERT

Some students may be confused about the meaning of the $<$ and $>$ signs. One way to help students remember that $<$ means "is less than" is to point out that the smaller end of the sign should be next to the smaller number.

Additional Examples

Example 1

Compare the fractions. Write $<$ or $>$.

A. $\frac{7}{9} \ \square \ \frac{5}{8}$

$>$

B. $-\frac{2}{5} \ \square \ -\frac{3}{7}$

$>$

Example 2

Compare the decimals. Write $<$ or $>$.

$0.427 \ \square \ 0.425 \quad >$

Example 3

Order the numbers from least to greatest.

$\frac{4}{5}$, 0.93, and 0.9

$\frac{4}{5}$, **0.9, 0.93**

3 Close

Reaching All Learners
Through Grouping Strategies

Have students work with partners: one student writes two different fractions or two different decimals, and the other writes the correct inequality symbol to compare them. Then ask students to exchange roles.

Summarize

A positive number is always greater than a negative number. When two fractions have the same denominator, the fraction with the greater numerator is the greater fraction. If necessary, write the two fractions with a common denominator. Decimals can be compared place by place.

Answers to Think and Discuss

Possible answers:

1. When comparing two fractions with different denominators, write the fractions with a common denominator and then compare numerators.
2. As you move left on the number line, the numbers decrease in value. Even though the absolute value of -0.625 is greater than the absolute value of -0.61, the number with the larger absolute value (-0.625) is actually smaller.

3-10 PRACTICE & ASSESS

Students may want to refer back to the lesson examples.

Assignment Guide

If you finished Example 1 assign:
Core 1–4, 12–19, 37, 41, 50–58
Enriched 1–4, 12–19, 37, 41, 50–58

If you finished Example 2 assign:
Core 1–8, 12–25, 37–41 odd, 50–58
Enriched 1–7 odd, 12–25, 36–39, 41, 42, 50–58

If you finished Example 3 assign:
Core 1–34, 35–45 odd, 50–58
Enriched 1–11 odd, 12–58

Answers

26. $\frac{5}{8}$, 0.7, 0.755

27. 1.6, $1\frac{4}{5}$, 1.82

30. -2.98, $-2\frac{9}{10}$, 2.88

Math Background

An alternative way to compare two fractions, $\frac{a}{b}$ and $\frac{c}{d}$, is to find the cross products ad and bc. If $ad > bc$, then $\frac{a}{b} > \frac{c}{d}$. This shortcut works because when you find the common denominator, bd, the numerator of the first fraction is ad and the numerator of the second fraction is bc. Essentially, you are comparing $\frac{a \cdot d}{b \cdot d}$ with $\frac{c \cdot b}{d \cdot b}$. This means that comparing ad with bc is the same as finding the common denominator and comparing the rewritten fractions.

3-10 Exercises

FOR EXTRA PRACTICE
see page 661

internet connect
Homework Help Online
go.hrw.com Keyword: MS4 3-10

GUIDED PRACTICE

See Example 1 Compare the fractions. Write $<$ or $>$.

1. $\frac{3}{5}$ ■ $\frac{4}{5}$ $<$ **2.** $-\frac{5}{8}$ ■ $-\frac{7}{8}$ $>$ **3.** $-\frac{2}{3}$ ■ $-\frac{4}{7}$ $<$ **4.** $3\frac{4}{5}$ ■ $3\frac{2}{3}$ $>$

See Example 2 Compare the decimals. Write $<$ or $>$.

5. 0.622 ■ 0.625 $<$ **6.** -0.405 ■ -0.45 $>$

7. -0.89 ■ -0.089 $<$ **8.** 3.822 ■ 3.819 $>$

See Example 3 Order the numbers from least to greatest.

9. 0.55, $\frac{3}{4}$, 0.505 **0.505, 0.55, $\frac{3}{4}$**
10. 2.5, 2.05, $\frac{13}{5}$ **2.05, 2.5, $\frac{13}{5}$**
11. $\frac{5}{8}$, -0.875, 0.877 **-0.875, $\frac{5}{8}$, 0.877**

INDEPENDENT PRACTICE

See Example 1 Compare the fractions. Write $<$ or $>$.

12. $\frac{6}{11}$ ■ $\frac{7}{11}$ $<$ **13.** $-\frac{5}{9}$ ■ $-\frac{6}{9}$ $>$ **14.** $-\frac{5}{6}$ ■ $-\frac{8}{9}$ $>$ **15.** $10\frac{3}{4}$ ■ $10\frac{3}{5}$ $>$

16. $\frac{5}{7}$ ■ $\frac{2}{7}$ $>$ **17.** $-\frac{3}{4}$ ■ $\frac{1}{4}$ $<$ **18.** $\frac{7}{4}$ ■ $-\frac{1}{4}$ $>$ **19.** $-\frac{2}{3}$ ■ $\frac{4}{3}$ $<$

See Example 2 Compare the decimals. Write $<$ or $>$.

20. 3.8 ■ 3.6 $>$ **21.** 0.088 ■ 0.109 $<$ **22.** -4.26 ■ 4.266 $<$

23. -1.902 ■ 0.920 $<$ **24.** -0.7 ■ -0.07 $<$ **25.** 3.08 ■ 3.808 $<$

See Example 3 Order the numbers from least to greatest.

26. 0.7, 0.755, $\frac{5}{8}$
27. 1.82, 1.6, $1\frac{4}{5}$
28. 2.25, 2.05, $\frac{21}{10}$ **2.05, $\frac{21}{10}$, 2.25**

29. -3, -3.02, $1\frac{1}{2}$ **-3.02, -3, $1\frac{1}{2}$**
30. 2.88, -2.98, $-2\frac{9}{10}$
31. $\frac{5}{6}$, $\frac{4}{5}$, 0.82 **$\frac{4}{5}$, 0.82, $\frac{5}{6}$**

32. 2, $2\frac{2}{10}$, 2.02 **2, 2.02, $2\frac{2}{10}$**
33. -1.02, -1.20, $-1\frac{2}{5}$ **$-1\frac{2}{5}$, -1.20, -1.02**
34. $2\frac{5}{10}$, $2\frac{3}{5}$, 2.7 **$2\frac{5}{10}$, $2\frac{3}{5}$, 2.7**

PRACTICE AND PROBLEM SOLVING

Choose the greater number.

35. $\frac{3}{4}$ or 0.7 **$\frac{3}{4}$** **36.** 0.999 or 1.0 **1.0** **37.** $\frac{7}{8}$ or $\frac{13}{20}$ **$\frac{7}{8}$** **38.** -0.93 or 0.2 **0.2**

39. 0.32 or 0.088 **0.32** **40.** $-\frac{1}{2}$ or -0.05 **-0.05** **41.** $-\frac{9}{10}$ or $-\frac{7}{8}$ **$-\frac{7}{8}$** **42.** 23.44 or 23 **23.44**

43. ***PHYSICAL SCIENCE*** Twenty-four karat gold is considered pure. If a gold coin is 22 karat, what is its purity as a fraction and as a decimal rounded to the nearest thousandth? **$\frac{22}{24}$, 0.917**

RETEACH 3-10

LESSON 3-10 **Reteach**
Comparing and Ordering Rational Numbers

You can use fraction strips to compare two fractions that have different denominators.

Compare $\frac{2}{3}$ and $\frac{1}{2}$.
$\frac{2}{3}$ is greater than $\frac{1}{2}$.
$\frac{2}{3} > \frac{1}{2}$

$\frac{1}{3}$	$\frac{1}{3}$

$\frac{1}{2}$

Compare $\frac{2}{5}$ and $\frac{3}{4}$.
$\frac{2}{5}$ is less than $\frac{3}{4}$.
$\frac{2}{5} < \frac{3}{4}$

$\frac{1}{5}$	$\frac{1}{5}$

$\frac{1}{4}$	$\frac{1}{4}$	$\frac{1}{4}$

Use fraction strips to compare. Write $<$ or $>$.

1. $\frac{1}{3}$ $<$ $\frac{1}{2}$

$\frac{1}{3}$

$\frac{1}{2}$

2. $\frac{3}{4}$ $>$ $\frac{5}{8}$

$\frac{1}{4}$	$\frac{1}{4}$	$\frac{1}{4}$

$\frac{1}{8}$	$\frac{1}{8}$	$\frac{1}{8}$	$\frac{1}{8}$	$\frac{1}{8}$

3. $\frac{1}{2}$ $<$ $\frac{3}{5}$ **4.** $\frac{1}{5}$ $>$ $\frac{1}{8}$ **5.** $\frac{3}{8}$ $>$ $\frac{1}{3}$

To compare decimals:

1) Add zeros so that each decimal has the same number of decimal places.

2) Ignore the decimal points and compare the numbers as if they were integers.

Compare 4.3 and 4.27.

4.3 4.27 — add a zero — 4.30 4.27

1 decimal place

2 decimal places

$430 > 427$, so $4.3 > 4.27$.

Compare the decimals using $<$ or $>$.

6. 7.2 $<$ 7.8 **7.** 0.64 $>$ 0.604 **8.** 2.09 $<$ 2.817

PRACTICE 3-10

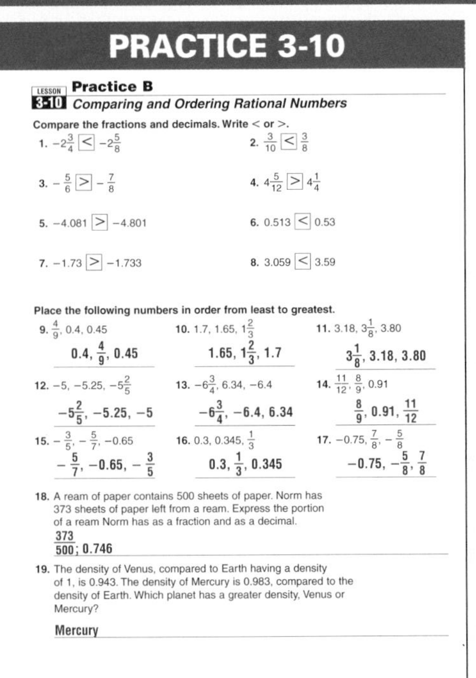
LESSON 3-10 **Practice B**
Comparing and Ordering Rational Numbers

Compare the fractions and decimals. Write $<$ or $>$.

1. $-2\frac{3}{4}$ $<$ $-2\frac{5}{8}$ **2.** $\frac{3}{10}$ $<$ $\frac{3}{8}$

3. $-\frac{5}{6}$ $>$ $-\frac{7}{8}$ **4.** $4\frac{5}{12}$ $>$ $4\frac{1}{4}$

5. -4.081 $>$ -4.801 **6.** 0.513 $<$ 0.53

7. -1.73 $>$ -1.733 **8.** 3.059 $<$ 3.59

Place the following numbers in order from least to greatest.

9. $\frac{4}{9}$, 0.4, 0.45 **0.4, $\frac{4}{9}$, 0.45**
10. 1.7, 1.65, $1\frac{2}{3}$ **1.65, $1\frac{2}{3}$, 1.7**
11. 3.18, $3\frac{1}{8}$, 3.80 **$3\frac{1}{8}$, 3.18, 3.80**

12. -5, -5.25, $-5\frac{2}{5}$ **$-5\frac{2}{5}$, -5.25, -5**
13. $-6\frac{3}{4}$, 6.34, -6.4 **$-6\frac{3}{4}$, -6.4, 6.34**
14. $\frac{11}{12}$, $\frac{8}{9}$, 0.91 **$\frac{8}{9}$, 0.91, $\frac{11}{12}$**

15. $-\frac{3}{5}$, $-\frac{5}{7}$, -0.65 **$-\frac{5}{7}$, -0.65, $-\frac{3}{5}$**
16. 0.3, 0.345, $\frac{1}{3}$ **0.3, $\frac{1}{3}$, 0.345**
17. -0.75, $\frac{7}{8}$, $-\frac{5}{8}$ **-0.75, $-\frac{5}{8}$, $\frac{7}{8}$**

18. A ream of paper contains 500 sheets of paper. Norm has 373 sheets of paper left from a ream. Express the portion of a ream Norm has as a fraction and as a decimal.
$\frac{373}{500}$; 0.746

19. The density of Venus, compared to Earth having a density of 1, is 0.943. The density of Mercury is 0.983, compared to the density of Earth. Which planet has a greater density, Venus or Mercury?
Mercury

Sloths live in the trees of South and Central America. An algae that grows in their fur makes them look slightly green. This helps the sloths blend into the trees and stay out of sight from predators.

44. ***LIFE SCIENCE*** Sloths are tree-dwelling mammals that live in South and Central America. They sleep for up to 18 hours a day. Write the portion of the day a sloth spends sleeping as a fraction in simplest form and as a decimal. $\mathbf{\frac{3}{4}}$, **0.75**

45. ***EARTH SCIENCE*** Density is a measure of the amount of matter in a specific unit of space. The mean densities (measured in grams per cubic centimeter) of the planets of our solar system are given in order of the planets' distance from the Sun. Rearrange the planets from least to most dense.

Planet	Density	Planet	Density	Planet	Density
Mercury	5.43	Mars	3.93	Uranus	1.32
Venus	5.20	Jupiter	1.32	Neptune	1.64
Earth	5.52	Saturn	0.69	Pluto	2.05

46. ***ECOLOGY*** Of Beatrice's total household water use, $\frac{5}{9}$ is for bathing, toilet flushing, and laundry. How does her water use for these purposes compare with that shown in the graph?

47. ***WHAT'S THE ERROR?*** A recipe for a large cake called for $4\frac{1}{2}$ cups of flour. The chef added 10 one-half cupfuls of flour to the mixture. What was the chef's error?

48. ***WRITE ABOUT IT*** Explain how to compare a mixed number with a decimal.

49. ***CHALLENGE*** Scientists estimate that Earth is approximately 4.6 billion years old. We are currently in what is called the Phanerozoic eon, which has made up about $\frac{7}{60}$ of the time that Earth has existed. The first eon, called the Hadean, made up approximately 0.175 of the time Earth has existed. Which eon represents the most time? $\mathbf{0.175 > \frac{7}{60}}$**, so the Hadean eon was longer.**

Spiral Review

Write each number in scientific notation. (Lesson 2-2)

50. 32,000 $\mathbf{3.2 \times 10^4}$ **51.** 108 $\mathbf{1.08 \times 10^2}$ **52.** 188,000 $\mathbf{1.88 \times 10^5}$ **53.** 10,000,000 $\mathbf{1 \times 10^7}$

Solve each equation. (Lesson 2-12)

54. $5x = 30$ $\mathbf{x = 6}$ **55.** $\frac{a}{2} = 14.2$ $\mathbf{a = 28.4}$ **56.** $1.1y = 44$ $\mathbf{y = 40}$ **57.** $\frac{c}{3.2} = 100$ $\mathbf{c = 320}$

58. TEST PREP The integers −2, −8, 4, and 2 written from least to greatest are __?__. (Lesson 3-1) **B**

A −2, −8, 2, 4 **B** −8, −2, 2, 4 **C** 4, 2, −2, −8 **D** 4, 2, −8, −2

Answers

45. Saturn (0.69), Jupiter and Uranus (1.32), Neptune (1.64), Pluto (2.05), Mars (3.93), Venus (5.20), Mercury (5.43), Earth (5.52)

46. Because $\frac{5}{9} < \frac{3}{5}$, her usage is less than average.

47. The chef added one half-cupful too many.

48. Possible answer: Write the mixed number as an improper fraction, and then divide the numerator by the denominator to get the number in decimal form. The two decimal numbers can then be compared.

Journal

Ask students to write a paragraph explaining which process they find easier: ordering fractions or ordering decimals. Have students list any unanswered questions they may have about either process.

Test Prep Doctor

For Exercise 58, point out that two of the choices can be eliminated simply because the question asks for an order from least to greatest. Because the negative numbers must come before the positive ones, **C** and **D** can be eliminated.

CHALLENGE 3-10

LESSON 3-10 **Challenge**
Another Rational Number

Between any two rational numbers, there are other rational numbers.

Examples: $\frac{2}{3}$ lies between $\frac{1}{2}$ and $\frac{5}{6}$.
−6 lies between −5.9 and −6.1.
$1\frac{1}{4}$ lies between 1 and $1\frac{1}{2}$.

Write a rational number that lies between each pair of rational numbers below. **Possible answers given.**

1. 0 and $\frac{1}{5}$ $\mathbf{\frac{1}{10}}$
2. 3.4 and 3.5 **3.41**
3. 1.08 and 1.8 **1.1**
4. −7 and −7.5 **−7.2**
5. −12.1 and −12.2 **−12.15**
6. 0 and $-\frac{1}{2}$ $\mathbf{-\frac{1}{4}}$
7. $1\frac{1}{8}$ and $1\frac{1}{2}$ $\mathbf{1\frac{1}{4}}$
8. $-2\frac{1}{10}$ and $-2\frac{1}{2}$ $\mathbf{-2\frac{1}{5}}$
9. 3.01 and 3.02 **3.015**
10. 4.2 and $4\frac{1}{2}$ **4.3**
11. −1 and −1.1 **−1.01**
12. 3.5 and $3\frac{7}{8}$ **3.6**
13. $-2\frac{3}{8}$ and −2.8 **−2.5**
14. 0 and −0.3 **−0.1**
15. $7\frac{1}{10}$ and 7.5 $\mathbf{7\frac{1}{4}}$
16. $5\frac{7}{8}$ and $5\frac{11}{12}$ $\mathbf{5\frac{9}{10}}$
17. $-\frac{2}{3}$ and $-\frac{3}{4}$ $\mathbf{-\frac{7}{10}}$
18. $3\frac{1}{5}$ and 3.19 **3.195**

PROBLEM SOLVING 3-10

LESSON 3-10 **Problem Solving**
Comparing and Ordering Rational Numbers

Write the correct answer.

1. Some of the wettest summers in the Northeast had the following amounts of precipitation, in inches: $14\frac{7}{10}$, $14\frac{1}{4}$, $14\frac{4}{5}$, and 14.69. Order the amounts of precipitation from least to greatest.
$\mathbf{14\frac{1}{4}, 14.69, 14\frac{7}{10}, 14\frac{4}{5}}$

2. The U.S. soybean crop increased steadily from 1995 to 1998. Production for each year was approximately $2\frac{3}{5}$, 2.25, $2\frac{3}{4}$, and 2.4 billion bushels. Match the soybean crop, in billions of bushels, with its year.
1995: 2.25; 1996: 2.4; 1997: $\mathbf{2\frac{3}{5}}$**; 1998:** $\mathbf{2\frac{3}{4}}$

3. Mark's batting average last year was 0.334. Ken's was 0.304, and Ty's was 0.343. Write the batting averages in order from lowest to highest.
0.304, 0.334, 0.343

4. Kiki lives 0.097 miles from the school, and George lives 0.131 miles from the school. Who lives farthest from the school?
George

Choose the letter for the best answer. Use the graph for problems 5–6.

NFL Field Goal Success Rate

Year	Rate
1992	0.726
1993	0.766
1994	0.789
1995	0.774
1996	0.800
1997	0.781
1998	0.796
1999	0.777
2000	0.797

5. In which year did NFL teams have the greatest success rate?
A 1992 **(C)** 1996
B 1994 D 2000

6. In which year was the success rate of NFL teams greater than 0.775 and less than 0.78?
F 1994 H 1997
G 1995 **(J)** 1999

Lesson Quiz

Choose the greater number.

1. $\frac{3}{7}$ or $\frac{4}{10}$ $\mathbf{\frac{3}{7}}$

2. $\frac{5}{8}$ or $\frac{2}{3}$ $\mathbf{\frac{2}{3}}$

Place the numbers in order from least to greatest.

3. 0.3, 0.32, 0.312 **0.3, 0.312, 0.32**

4. $\frac{5}{6}$, 0.8, 0.826 **0.8, 0.826,** $\mathbf{\frac{5}{6}}$

5. Dana's cross-country team is getting ready for a big meet. On Monday they ran 3.7 miles, on Tuesday they ran $3\frac{3}{8}$ miles, and on Wednesday they ran $\frac{11}{4}$ miles. On which day did they run the greatest distance? Monday

Available on Daily Transparency in CRB

CHAPTER 3 Extension

Pacing: Traditional 1 day
Block $\frac{1}{2}$ day

Objective: Students define and recognize irrational numbers.

Using the Pages

In Lesson 3-7, students learned to recognize and identify rational numbers. In this extension, students will define and recognize irrational numbers and compare and contrast them with rational numbers.

EXTENSION Irrational Numbers

Learn to define and recognize irrational numbers.

Vocabulary
nonterminating decimal
irrational number

All rational numbers have decimal forms that either terminate or repeat. A terminating decimal, such as 0.5, is one that comes to an end. A **nonterminating decimal**, such as 0.33333. . ., goes on forever.

Repeating decimals are nonterminating decimals that have a digit or a sequence of digits that repeats without ever stopping. Examples are 0.333333. . . and 0.181818. . . . If a pattern is not too long, you can see it on your calculator screen.

Rational Numbers		
Rational Number	Decimal Form	Decimal Type
$\frac{1}{2}$	0.5	Terminating
$\frac{1}{3}$	0.33333. . . (written $0.\overline{3}$)	Nonterminating, repeating
$\frac{2}{11}$	0.181818. . . (written $0.\overline{18}$)	Nonterminating, repeating

Irrational Numbers		
Irrational Number	Decimal Form	Decimal Type
$\sqrt{2}$	1.4142135. . .	Nonterminating, nonrepeating
π	3.1415926. . .	Nonterminating, nonrepeating

Irrational numbers are numbers whose decimal forms are nonterminating, with *no* repeating pattern.

EXAMPLE 1 **Investigating Rational Numbers with a Calculator**

Use a calculator to determine if the decimal form of each rational number terminates or repeats. If it repeats, show the pattern by writing a bar over the digit or sequence of digits that repeats.

A $\frac{3}{16}$

3 ÷ 16 ENTER 0.1875

$\frac{3}{16}$ is a terminating decimal.

B $\frac{1}{27}$

1 ÷ 27 ENTER 0.037037037

$0.\overline{037}$

$\frac{1}{27}$ is a repeating decimal.

1 Introduce

Motivate

Ask students if they think they can use mental math to estimate the square root of 41.

Point out that they can use what they know about perfect squares to estimate the square roots of numbers that are not perfect squares. Discuss students' ideas, and lead them to see that the square root of 41 will be between the square root of the perfect squares of 36 and 49, or between 6 and 7.

Have students use a calculator to support this reasoning. $\sqrt{41} = 6.403124$

Repeat for other numbers between familiar perfect squares, for example, 62 and 93. $\sqrt{62} = 7.8740079$ and $\sqrt{93} = 9.6436508$

2 Teach

Lesson Presentation

Guided Instruction

In this extension, students learn how to define and recognize irrational numbers. Have students study the two charts showing rational and irrational numbers. Discuss how these numbers are alike and how they are different. Guide students to see that both can be shown in decimal form but that only rational numbers terminate or repeat.

Calculators can reveal a repeating pattern only if the pattern occurs within the number of places the calculator shows. Some repeating decimals have very long patterns. For example, the decimal form of $\frac{1}{97}$ has a pattern that is 96 digits long!

Because you can write only an approximate value of irrational numbers in decimal form, symbols are sometimes used to represent the exact values.

Irrational Number Symbol (Exact)	Approximate Value
π	3.14159
$\sqrt{5}$	2.23607

EXAMPLE 2 **Investigating Irrational Numbers with a Calculator**

Use a calculator to evaluate each square root. Does there seem to be a repeating pattern?

A $\sqrt{6}$

There is no apparent pattern.

B $\sqrt{8}$

2nd x^2 8 ENTER 2.828427125

There is no apparent pattern.

Example 2 suggests, but does not prove, the following important fact: **If a whole number is not a perfect square, its square root is irrational.**

EXTENSION Exercises

Use a calculator to determine if the decimal form of each rational number terminates or repeats. If it repeats, show the pattern by writing a bar over the digit or sequence of digits that repeats.

1. $\frac{3}{16}$ **terminates**
2. $\frac{5}{16}$ **terminates**
3. $\frac{7}{16}$ **terminates**
4. $\frac{1}{54}$ **repeats, $0.0\overline{185}$**
5. $\frac{1}{9}$ **repeats, $0.\overline{1}$**
6. $\frac{2}{9}$ **repeats, $0.\overline{2}$**
7. $\frac{1}{99}$ **repeats, $0.\overline{01}$**
8. $\frac{1}{82}$ **repeats, $0.0\overline{12195}$**
9. $\frac{1}{7}$ **repeats, $0.\overline{142857}$**
10. $\frac{1}{37}$ **repeats, $0.\overline{027}$**
11. $\frac{1}{22}$ **repeats, $0.0\overline{45}$**
12. $\frac{1}{39}$ **repeats, $0.\overline{025641}$**

Use a calculator to find the square root of each number. Tell whether each square root is rational or irrational.

13. $\sqrt{196}$ **rational**
14. $\sqrt{169}$ **rational**
15. $\sqrt{14}$ **irrational**
16. $\sqrt{144}$ **rational**
17. $\sqrt{1{,}600}$ **rational**
18. $\sqrt{18}$ **irrational**
19. $\sqrt{400}$ **rational**
20. $\sqrt{444}$ **irrational**
21. $\sqrt{10}$ **irrational**
22. $\sqrt{100}$ **rational**
23. $\sqrt{1{,}000}$
24. $\sqrt{10{,}000}$

23. **irrational**
24. **rational**

COMMON ERROR ALERT

Students may assume that all multiples of 10 are perfect squares since 100 is a perfect square. For example, they may decide that $\sqrt{1{,}000}$ is rational although it is not. ($\sqrt{1{,}000} \approx 31.622777$) Encourage students to always use their calculators and check by squaring when determining whether the square root of a multiple of 10 is rational or irrational.

Additional Examples

Example 1

Use a calculator to determine if the decimal form of each rational number terminates or repeats. If it repeats, show the pattern by writing a bar over the digit or sequence of digits that repeats.

A. $\frac{5}{8}$

$\frac{5}{8}$ is a terminating decimal.

B. $\frac{4}{11}$

$\frac{4}{11} = 0.\overline{36}$

$\frac{4}{11}$ is a repeating decimal.

Example 2

Use a calculator to evaluate each square root. Does there seem to be a repeating pattern?

A. $\sqrt{17}$

$\sqrt{17} \approx 4.123105626$

There is no apparent pattern.

B. $\sqrt{23}$

$\sqrt{23} \approx 4.795831523$

There is no apparent pattern.

3 Close

Summarize

You may want to have the students review the important lesson concepts by having them explain how rational and irrational numbers are alike and different. Encourage students to include examples to illustrate their statements.

Possible answer: Both rational numbers and irrational numbers have decimal forms. Both rational numbers and irrational numbers can be square roots. $\sqrt{4}$ is rational. $\sqrt{2}$ is irrational.

All rational numbers can be written as a ratio of integers. Rational numbers may be repeating decimals or terminating decimals. Irrational numbers are nonterminating and have no repeating pattern.

Students can use pencil and paper to show repeating decimal patterns that calculators cannot display. For example, students can show the decimal form for $\frac{1}{13}$ by carrying out the decimal to twelve places: $\frac{1}{13}$ in decimal form is 0.076923076923, or $0.\overline{076923}$.

Problem Solving on Location

Virginia

Purpose: *To provide additional practice for problem-solving skills in Chapters 1–3*

Virginia's Historical Triangle

- After problem 3, have students consider the following problem: About how many days did it take the ships to travel from England to Virginia? about 135 days
- After problem 5, have students write the distance from Charles City to Piney Grove as a mixed number. $6\frac{1}{10}$ Then ask students to write the distances from Charles City to Berkeley Plantation and to Shirley Plantation as mixed numbers and improper fractions. Berkeley Plantation: $7\frac{1}{2}, \frac{15}{2}$; Shirley Plantation: $9\frac{1}{2}, \frac{19}{2}$

Extension Have students research information about the the *Discovery*, the *Godspeed*, and the *Susan Constant*. Ask them to find out which ship was the largest and which ship was the smallest. largest: the *Susan Constant;* smallest: the *Discovery*

Problem Solving on Location

VIRGINIA

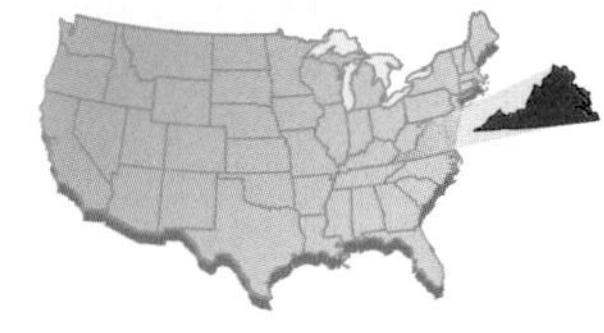

Virginia's Historical Triangle

The colonial district of Williamsburg, which is one mile long and about $\frac{1}{2}$ mile wide, has been restored so that it looks as it did in the late 1700s. Nearby are the original sites of Jamestown, settled in 1607, and Charles City.

1. The capitol in Williamsburg was built by Henry Cary. It is made up of two buildings connected by an arcade. The buildings are each 25 yards long by $8\frac{1}{3}$ yards wide. Write the width of each building as an improper fraction. $\frac{25}{3}$
2. The distance from the capitol to the governor's palace in Colonial Williamsburg is about $\frac{9}{10}$ mile. Write the distance as a decimal. **0.9**
3. The *Discovery, Godspeed,* and *Susan Constant* are the ships that carried the original Williamsburg settlers to the New World. Their replicas are moored near James Fort. The voyage that the original ships made to Virginia from England took 4.5 months. Write this decimal as a mixed number and as an improper fraction. $4\frac{1}{2}, \frac{9}{2}$

In 1930, the governor's palace was restored to look as it did in colonial times.

Charles City was established in 1616. Several plantations near Charles City are now open to the public. The table shows the distances of these plantations from Charles City. For 4 and 5, use the table.

Plantations Near Charles City	Distance (mi)
Berkeley	7.5
Edgewood	2
North Bend	2
Piney Grove	6.1
Shirley	9.5

4. Write the distances of the plantations from Charles City in order from least to greatest. **2, 2, 6.1, 7.5, 9.5**
5. Write the distance from Charles City to Piney Grove as an improper fraction. $\frac{61}{10}$

Chesapeake Bay Bridge-Tunnel

The bridges and tunnels that make up the Chesapeake Bay Bridge-Tunnel cross Chesapeake Bay between Virginia's Eastern Shore and South Hampton Roads. Four islands, one at each end of the two tunnels, were built to help hold up the structure. To construct the islands, 1,183,295 tons of rock armor were used. The total cost of the structure was $450,000,000.

1. The bridge-tunnel consists of a series of low-level trestles, two 1-mile-long tunnels, two bridges, 2 miles of causeway, four constructed islands, and $5\frac{1}{2}$ miles of approach roads. Write the number of miles of approach roads as a decimal. **5.5**
2. Two of the trestles that support the bridge are 12.2 miles long. Write the length as an improper fraction. $\mathbf{\frac{61}{5}}$
3. The shore-to-shore distance of the Chesapeake Bay Bridge-Tunnel is 17.6 miles. Write the distance as a mixed number. $\mathbf{17\frac{6}{10}}$ **or** $\mathbf{17\frac{3}{5}}$

The depth of the water along the route ranges from 25 feet below sea level to 100 feet below sea level.

4. Write these numbers as integers. **−25, −100**
5. How much deeper is the deepest water level then the shallowest water level? **75 feet deeper**
6. Each of the four constructed islands rises 30 feet above sea level. The islands were built up from the sea floor, with the deepest point being 100 feet below sea level. How far from the deepest point do the islands rise? **130 ft**

After it opened, the Chesapeake Bay Bridge-Tunnel was named as one of the seven engineering wonders of the modern world.

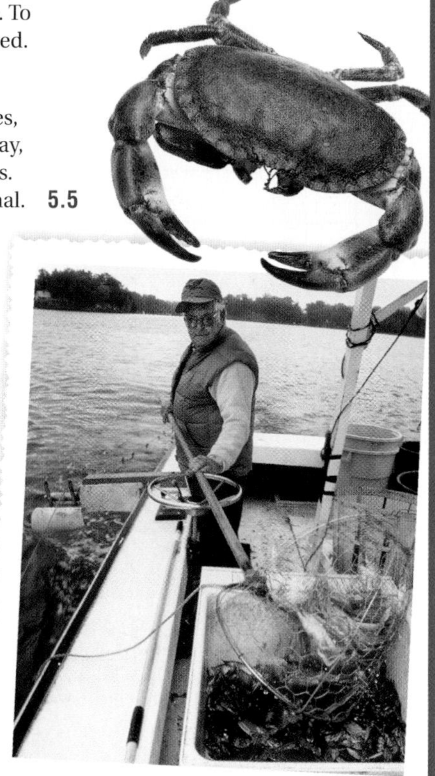

Chesapeake Bay Bridge-Tunnel

- After problem 3, have students solve the following problem:

  The total length from shore to shore is 17.6 miles. However, the total length including the approach roads is 23 miles. What length of the Chesapeake Bay Bridge-Tunnel is not over water? 5.4 miles
- After problem 5, ask the following: Did you add or subtract the integers to find the difference between the deepest water level and the shallowest water level? subtract

Extension It took 3.5 years to build the northbound crossing and $3\frac{5}{6}$ years to build the southbound crossing. Have students write each of these numbers as improper fractions. Ask students to determine which crossing took longer to build. $3.5 = \frac{7}{2}$, $3\frac{5}{6} = \frac{23}{6}$; it took longer to build the southbound crossing.

MATH-ABLES

Game Resources

Puzzles, Twisters & Teasers
Chapter 3 Resource Book

Magic Squares

Purpose: *To apply the problem-solving skill of guess and check to solve a fun puzzle*

Discuss: Ask students to cover any block of 4 squares. Have students repeat the procedure by covering a different block of 4 squares. How many squares are 2 squares away from a corner of each block and fall on a diagonal of the block? Possible answer: There is only 1 square that is 2 squares away from a corner of each block and falls on a diagonal of the block.

Extend: Challenge students to create their own 4 × 4 magic squares using the numbers 1–16. What is the magic sum? Possible answer:

16	2	3	13
5	11	10	8
9	7	6	12
4	14	15	1

The magic sum is 34.

Modified Tic-Tac-Toe

Purpose: *To practice finding a given sum*

Discuss: When a student gets "tic-tac-toe," have him or her demonstrate for the class how the winning solution was obtained.

Extend: Have students make a 5 × 5 tic-tac-toe board numbered 1–25. The goal of the game is for a player to select squares such that any five of a player's squares add up to 65. Possible answer: The board should be numbered as follows: row 1, 1–5; row 2, 6–10; row 3, 11–15; row 4, 16–20; row 5, 21–25. If a student selects the squares on the diagonal from the upper left to the lower right numbered 1, 7, 13, 19, and 25, the sum is 65.

MATH-ABLES

Magic Squares

A magic square is a grid with numbers, such that the numbers in each row, column, and diagonal have the same "magic" sum. Test the square at right to see an example of this.

You can use a magic square to do some amazing calculations. Cover a block of four squares (2 × 2) with a piece of paper. There is a way you can find the sum of these squares without looking at them. Try to find it. (*Hint:* What number in the magic square can you subtract from the magic sum to give you the sum of the numbers in the block? Where is that number located?)

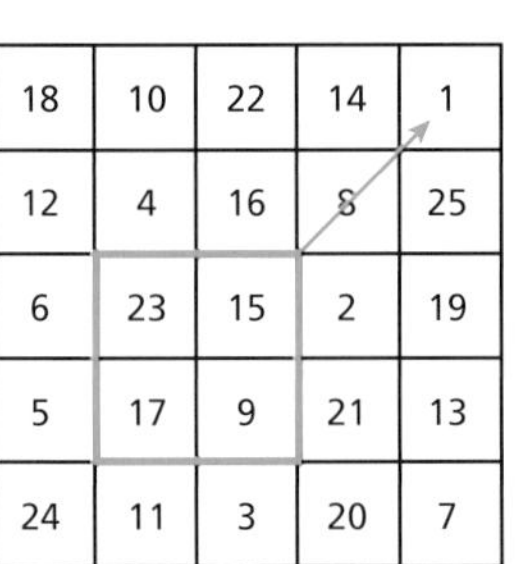

Here's the answer: To find the sum of any block of four numbers, take 65 (the magic sum) and subtract from it the number that is diagonally two squares away from a corner of the block.

18	10	22	14	1
12	4	16	8	25
6	23	15	2	19
5	17	9	21	13
24	11	3	20	7

$65 - 21 = 44$

18	10	22	14	1
12	4	16	8	25
6	23	15	2	19
5	17	9	21	13
24	11	3	20	7

$65 - 1 = 64$

The number you subtract must fall on an extension of a diagonal of the block. For each block that you choose, there will be only one direction you can go.

Try to create a 3 × 3 magic square with the numbers 1–9.

Modified Tic-Tac-Toe

The board has a row of nine squares numbered 1 through 9. Players take turns selecting squares. The goal of the game is for a player to select squares such that any three of a player's squares add up to 15. The game can also be played with a board numbered 1 through 16 and a sum goal of 34.

internet connect
For a complete copy of the rules and to print out a set of cards, go to ***go.hrw.com***
KEYWORD: MS4 Game3

Graph Points Using a Calculator

To graph on a calculator, you may need to use the **WINDOW** menu. This is where you choose the viewing boundaries and scale settings. If you do not choose these yourself, the calculator will use the standard viewing window, such as the one shown.

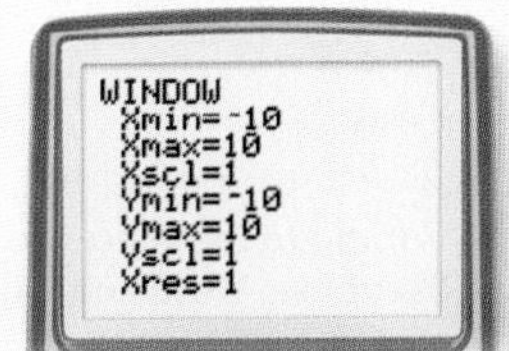

In the standard window, the x- and y-values go from -10 to 10. These are the boundary values. They are set by **Xmin, Xmax, Ymin,** and **Ymax**.

The scale values, **Xscl** and **Yscl**, give the distance between tick marks. In the standard window, tick marks are 1 unit apart.

Activity

1. Graph the points (1.5, 5), $\left(\frac{10}{3}, 3\right)$, $\left(-\frac{3}{2}, 6\right)$, and (5.75, −3.5) using the standard window.

   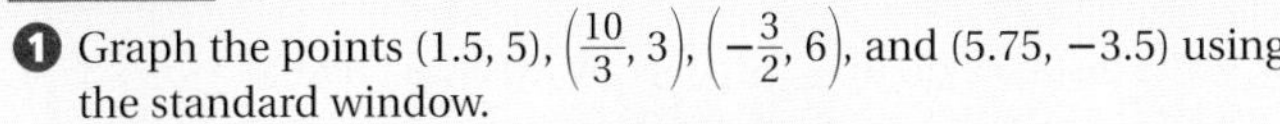

   To graph (1.5, 5), press 2nd PRGM (DRAW) ▶.
   You will get the screen shown at right.

   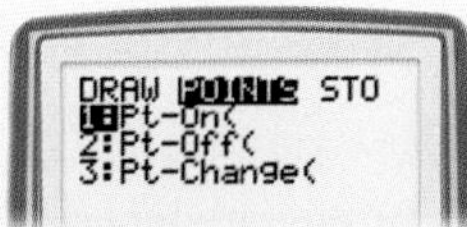

   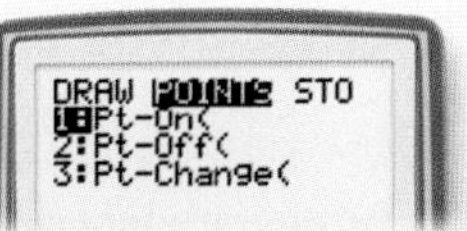

   Then press ENTER 1.5 , 5 ENTER.

   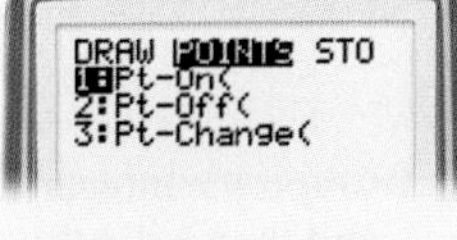

   After you see the grid with a point at (1.5, 5), press 2nd MODE (QUIT).

   Repeat the steps above to graph $\left(\frac{10}{3}, 3\right)$, $\left(-\frac{3}{2}, 6\right)$, and (5.75, −3.5).
   Your graph should then look like the one shown at right.

   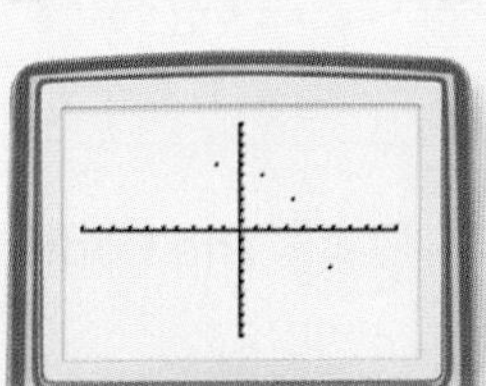

   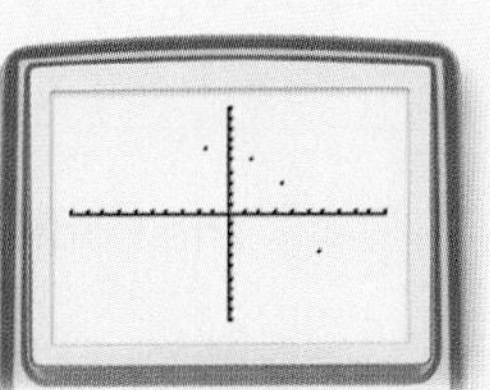

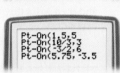

Think and Discuss

1. Explain when you might want to change the **WINDOW** dimensions. **Possible answer: If the points you want to plot have coordinates greater than 10 or less than −10, you will need to change the window to see all the points.**

Try This

1. Graph (−3, 9), (−2, 4), (13, 1), (2, 4), (3, 9), and (4, 16) using the standard window. How many points do you see? Why? **Four points are visible. Two of the points have coordinates greater than 10.**

Answers

Try This

1. 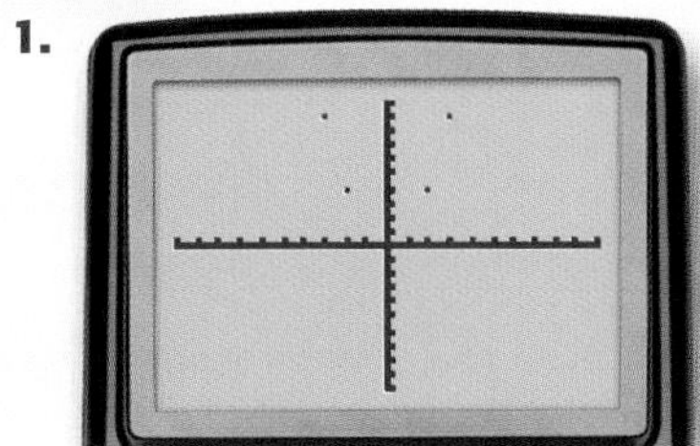

Graph Points Using a Calculator

Pacing: Traditional 1 day
Block $\frac{1}{2}$ day

Objective: To use a graphing calculator to graph points

Materials: Graphing calculator

Lab Resources

Technology Lab Activities . . . . p. 15

Using the Page

This technology activity shows students how to graph points, which can be done on any graphing calculator. Specific keystrokes may vary, depending on the make and model of the graphing calculator used. The keystrokes given are for a TI-83 model. For keystrokes to other models, visit www.go.hrw.com.

The Think and Discuss problem can be used to assess students' understanding that the standard window will not always be an appropriate window to use. Sometimes boundary values should be changed, and sometimes the distance between tick marks should be changed. Try This problem 1 is meant to provide students with practice graphing points and an understanding that if students change the **WINDOW** dimensions, they will see all of the points.

Assessment

1. Graph the points (5, 2), (−3, 4), (−8, −7), (1, 12), (−4, −11), and (6, −6) using the standard window.

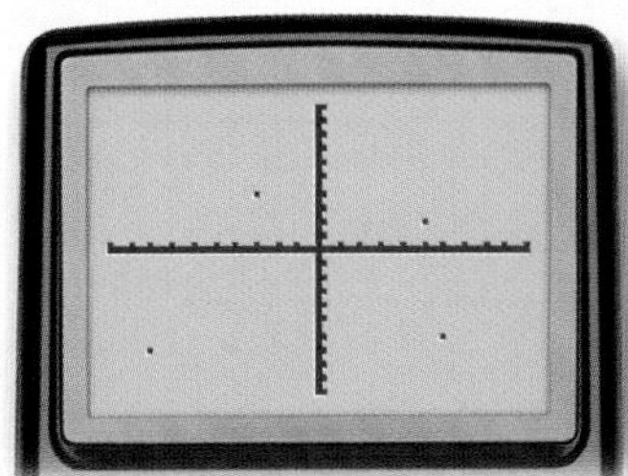

2. How many points do you see? **4**

Chapter 3 Study Guide and Review

Purpose: *To help students review and practice concepts and skills presented in Chapter 3*

Assessment Resources 

Chapter Review

Chapter 3 Resource Book . . pp. 99–101

***Test and Practice Generator* CD-ROM**

Additional review assessment items in both multiple-choice and free-response format may be generated for any objective in Chapter 3.

Answers

1. rational number; integer; terminating decimal
2. ordered pair; x-axis
3. 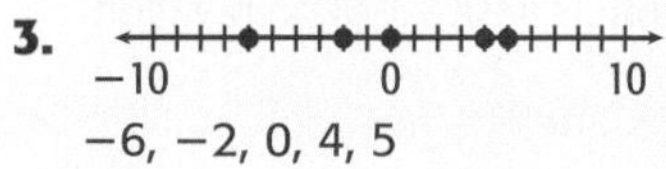

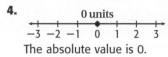

−6, −2, 0, 4, 5
4. 0 units
−3 −2 −1 0 1 2 3
The absolute value is 0.
5. 17 units
−4 0 4 8 12 16
The absolute value is 17.
6. 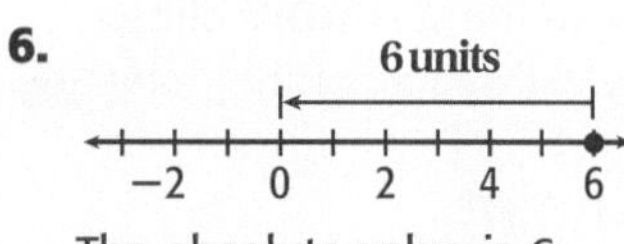

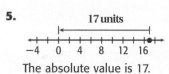

The absolute value is 6.

7–10.

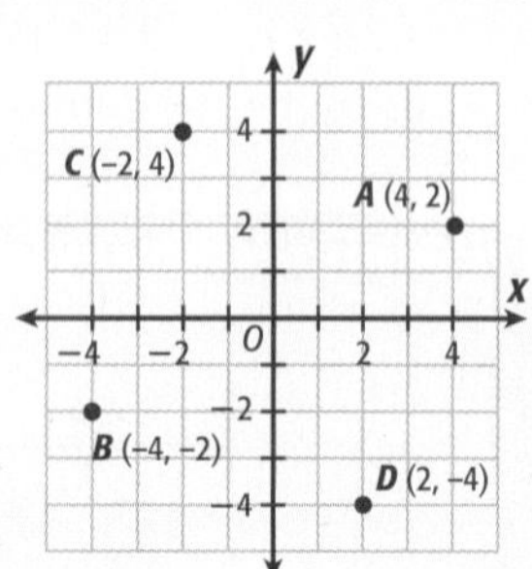

7. I
8. III
9. II
10. IV

Chapter 3 Study Guide and Review

Study Guide and Review

Vocabulary

absolute value 131	mixed number 167	rational number 162
coordinate plane 134	opposite 130	repeating decimal 171
equivalent fractions 166	ordered pair 134	terminating decimal . . . 171
improper fraction 167	origin 134	x-axis 134
integer 130	quadrant 134	y-axis 134

Complete the sentences below with vocabulary words from the list above. Words may be used more than once.

1. A(n) __?__ can be written as the ratio of one __?__ to another and can be represented by a repeating or __?__.
2. When you graph a(n) __?__, the distance on the __?__ is always listed first.

3-1 Integers (pp. 130–133)

EXAMPLE

- Graph the integers on a number line, and then write them in order from least to greatest.

3, 4, −2, 1, −3

−6 −4 −2 0 2 4 6

−3, −2, 1, 3, 4

EXERCISES

Graph the integers on a number line, and then write them in order from least to greatest.

3. −6, 4, 0, −2, 5

Use a number line to find each absolute value.

4. $|0|$
5. $|-17|$
6. $|6|$

3-2 The Coordinate Plane (pp. 134–137)

EXAMPLE

- Give the coordinates of each point and tell in which quadrant it lies.

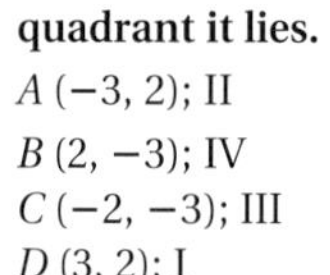

A (−3, 2); II
B (2, −3); IV
C (−2, −3); III
D (3, 2); I

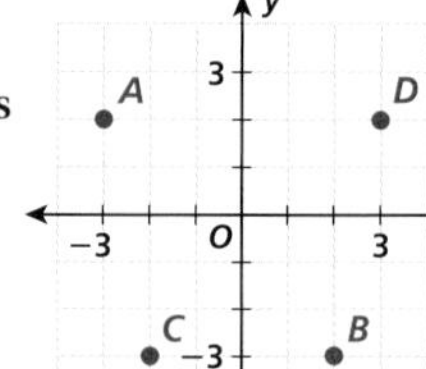

EXERCISES

Plot each point and tell in which quadrant it lies.

7. *A* (4, 2)
8. *B* (−4, −2)
9. *C* (−2, 4)
10. *D* (2, −4)

3-3 Adding Integers (pp. 140–143)

EXAMPLE

- Add.

$-7 + (-11)$

$-7 + (-11)$ *The signs are the same.*

-18

EXERCISES

Add.

11. $-8 + 5$ **12.** $7 + (-6)$

13. $-16 + (-40)$ **14.** $-9 + 18$

15. $-2 + 16$ **16.** $12 + (-18)$

3-4 Subtracting Integers (pp. 146–149)

EXAMPLE

- Subtract.

$-5 - (-3)$

$-5 + 3$ *Add the opposite of −3.*

-2

EXERCISES

Subtract.

17. $8 - 2$ **18.** $10 - 19$

19. $-6 - (-5)$ **20.** $-5 - 4$

3-5 Multiplying and Dividing Integers (pp. 150–153)

EXAMPLE

Find each product or quotient.

- $12 \cdot (-3)$ *The signs are different, so the product is negative.*
  -36
- $-16 \div (-4)$ *The signs are the same, so the quotient is positive.*
  4

EXERCISES

Find each product or quotient.

21. $5 \cdot (-10)$ **22.** $-27 \div (-9)$

23. $-2 \cdot (-8)$ **24.** $-40 \div 20$

25. $-3 \cdot 4$ **26.** $45 \div (-15)$

3-6 Solving Equations Containing Integers (pp. 156–159)

EXAMPLE

Solve.

- $x - 12 = 4$
  $\underline{+12} \quad \underline{+12}$ *Add 12 to each side.*
  $x = 16$
- $-10 = -2f$
  $\frac{-10}{-2} = \frac{-2f}{-2}$ *Divide each side by −2.*
  $5 = f$

EXERCISES

Solve.

27. $7y = 70$ **28.** $d - 8 = 6$

29. $j + 23 = -3$ **30.** $\frac{n}{36} = 2$

31. $-26 = -2c$ **32.** $28 = -7m$

Study Guide and Review

Answers

11. −3
12. 1
13. −56
14. 9
15. 14
16. −6
17. 6
18. −9
19. −1
20. −9
21. −50
22. 3
23. 16
24. −2
25. −12
26. −3
27. $y = 10$
28. $d = 14$
29. $j = -26$
30. $n = 72$
31. $c = 13$
32. $m = -4$

Answers

33–35.

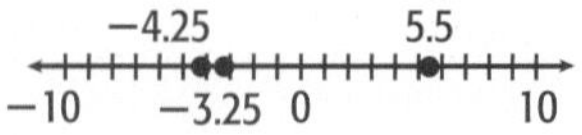

36. $\frac{12}{1}$

37. $\frac{1}{4}$

38. $-\frac{37}{10}$

39. $\frac{21}{5}$

40. $\frac{19}{6}$

41. $\frac{43}{4}$

42. $3\frac{1}{3}$

43. $2\frac{1}{2}$

44. $2\frac{3}{7}$

45. $\frac{1}{4}$

46. $-\frac{1}{250}$

47. $\frac{1}{20}$

48. 3.5

49. −0.6

50. 0.667

51. $<$

52. $>$

53. $>$

Study Guide and Review

3-7 Rational Numbers: Fractions and Decimals (pp. 162–165)

EXAMPLE

Show that each number is a rational number by writing it as a fraction.

- 0.75

  $0.75 = \frac{3}{4}$

- −2.2

  $-2.2 = -\frac{22}{10}$ or $-\frac{11}{5}$

EXERCISES

Graph each number on a number line.

33. 5.5 **34.** −4.25 **35.** $-3\frac{1}{4}$

Show that each number is a rational number by writing it as a fraction.

36. 12

37. 0.25

38. −3.7

3-8 Equivalent Fractions and Mixed Numbers (pp. 166–169)

EXAMPLE

- Write $5\frac{2}{3}$ as an improper fraction.

  $5\frac{2}{3} = \frac{3 \cdot 5 + 2}{3} = \frac{17}{3}$

- Write $\frac{17}{4}$ as a mixed number.

  $\frac{17}{4} = 4\frac{1}{4}$ *Divide the numerator by the denominator.*

EXERCISES

Write each as an improper fraction.

39. $4\frac{1}{5}$ **40.** $3\frac{1}{6}$ **41.** $10\frac{3}{4}$

Write each as a mixed number.

42. $\frac{10}{3}$ **43.** $\frac{5}{2}$ **44.** $\frac{17}{7}$

3-9 Equivalent Fractions and Decimals (pp. 170–173)

EXAMPLE

- Write 0.75 as a fraction in simplest form.

  $0.75 = \frac{75}{100} = \frac{75 \div 25}{100 \div 25} = \frac{3}{4}$

- Write $\frac{-5}{4}$ as a decimal.

  $\frac{-5}{4} = -5 \div 4 = -1.25$

EXERCISES

Write each decimal as a fraction in simplest form.

45. 0.25 **46.** −0.004 **47.** 0.05

Write each fraction as a decimal.

48. $\frac{7}{2}$ **49.** $-\frac{3}{5}$ **50.** $\frac{2}{3}$

3-10 Comparing and Ordering Rational Numbers (pp. 174–177)

EXAMPLE

- Compare. Write $<$ or $>$.

  $-\frac{3}{4}$ ▒ $-\frac{2}{3}$

  $-\frac{3}{4} \cdot \frac{3}{3}$ ▒ $-\frac{2}{3} \cdot \frac{4}{4}$ *Write as fractions with common denominators.*

  $-\frac{9}{12} < -\frac{8}{12}$

EXERCISES

Compare. Write $<$ or $>$.

51. $\frac{4}{5}$ ▒ 0.81

52. 0.22 ▒ $\frac{3}{20}$

53. $-\frac{3}{5}$ ▒ −1.5

Chapter Test

Graph the integers on a number line, and then write them in order from least to greatest.

1. −4, 3, −2, 0, 1 **−4, −2, 0, 1, 3**

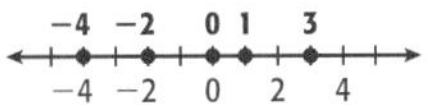

2. 7, −6, 5, −8, −3 **−8, −6, −3, 5, 7**

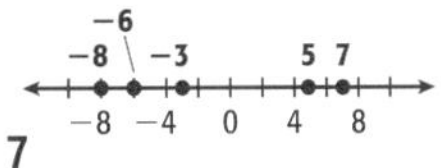

Compare. Write <, >, or =.

3. −5 ▒ 5 **<**
4. |−5| ▒ 5 **=**
5. 8 ▒ −7 **>**
6. −10 ▒ −9 **<**

Plot each point and identify the quadrant in which it is contained.

7. *A* (4, −3) **IV**
8. *B* (−5, 2) **II**
9. *C* (7, 1) **I**
10. *D* (−7, −2) **III**

Add or subtract.

11. −7 + (−3) **−10**
12. −11 + 15 **4**
13. 17 + (−27) + (−2) **−12**
14. 102 + (−97) + 3 **8**
15. −6 − 3 **−9**
16. 10 − 15 **−5**
17. 12 − (−7) **19**
18. 17 − (−9) −8 **18**

Find each product or quotient.

19. −3 · 20 **−60**
20. −36 ÷ 12 **−3**
21. −400 ÷ (−10) **40**
22. −5 · (−2) · 9 **90**

Solve.

23. $w - 4 = -6$ **$w = -2$**
24. $x + 5 = -5$ **$x = -10$**
25. $-6a = 60$ **$a = -10$**
26. $\frac{n}{-4} = 12$ **$n = -48$**

Graph each number on a number line.

27. 4.1
28. $-3\frac{1}{3}$
29. −1.6
30. $1\frac{3}{8}$

27–30.

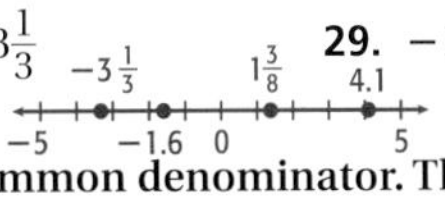

Write the fractions with a common denominator. Then determine if they are equivalent.

31. $\frac{6}{12}$ and $\frac{13}{26}$ **$\frac{1}{2}, \frac{1}{2}$, yes**
32. $\frac{17}{20}$ and $\frac{20}{24}$ **$\frac{102}{120}, \frac{100}{120}$, no**
33. $\frac{30}{24}$ and $\frac{35}{28}$ **$\frac{5}{4}, \frac{5}{4}$, yes**
34. $\frac{5}{3}$ and $\frac{8}{5}$ **$\frac{25}{15}, \frac{24}{15}$, no**

Write each fraction as a decimal. Write each decimal as a fraction in simplest form.

35. $\frac{3}{50}$ **0.06**
36. $\frac{25}{10}$ **2.5**
37. 3.15 **$3\frac{3}{20}$**
38. 0.004 **$\frac{1}{250}$**

Compare. Write < or >.

39. $\frac{2}{3}$ ▒ 0.62 **>**
40. 1.5 ▒ $1\frac{6}{20}$ **>**
41. $-\frac{9}{7}$ ▒ −1 **<**
42. $\frac{11}{5}$ ▒ $1\frac{2}{3}$ **>**

43. Three brothers stood in order of height from shortest to tallest for a family photo. Brad is $5\frac{1}{2}$ ft tall, Brandon is 5.29 ft tall, and Lee is 5.6 ft tall. Tell in what order the brothers stood in the photo. **Brandon, Brad, Lee**

Chapter Test

Chapter 3 Chapter Test

Purpose: *To assess students' mastery of concepts and skills in Chapter 3*

Assessment Resources

Chapter 3 Tests (Levels A, B, C)
Assessment Resources . . . . pp. 45–50

***Test and Practice Generator* CD-ROM**

Additional assessment items in both multiple-choice and free-response format may be generated for any objective in Chapter 3.

Answers

7–10.

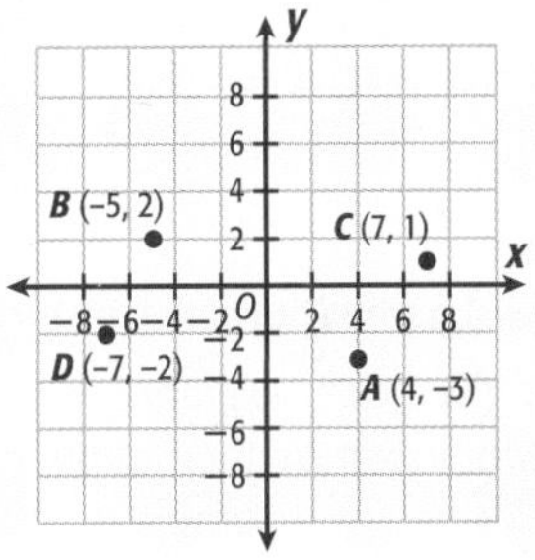

Chapter 3 **Performance Assessment**

Purpose: *To assess students' understanding of concepts in Chapter 3 and combined problem-solving skills*

Assessment Resources

Performance Assessment
Assessment Resources . . . . p. 110

Performance Assessment Teacher Support
Assessment Resources . . . . p. 109

Answers

4. See Level 3 work sample below.

Scoring Rubric for Problem Solving Item 4

Level 3
Accomplishes the purposes of the task.
Student gives clear explanations, shows understanding of mathematical ideas and processes, and computes accurately.

Level 2
Purposes of the task not fully achieved.
Student demonstrates satisfactory but limited understanding of the mathematical ideas and processes.

Level 1
Purposes of the task not accomplished.
Student shows little evidence of understanding the mathematical ideas and processes, and makes computational and/or procedural errors.

Chapter 3 **Performance Assessment**

Performance Assessment

Show What You Know

Create a portfolio of your work from this chapter. Complete this page and include it with your four best pieces of work from Chapter 3. Choose from your homework or lab assignments, mid-chapter quiz, or any journal entries you have done. Put them together using any design you want. Make your portfolio represent what you consider your best work.

Short Response

1. Jana began the month with \$102 in her checking account. During the month, she added \$8 that she earned from babysitting, spent \$10 for a CD, added \$5 her aunt gave her, and spent \$7 at the movies. Write an expression using integers to show the month's activity. Simplify your expression to find how much Jana had in her checking account at the end of the month.
$102 + 8 + (-10) + 5 + (-7)$; she had \$98 at the end of the month.
2. After dark, the temperature dropped 5 degrees for every hour for 4 hours. Write an integer that represents the total drop in temperature 4 hours after dark. Show the steps that you used to find your answer. **$-5° \cdot 4 = -20°$**
3. Kyle needs a piece of 1 in. by 4 in. lumber that measures $2\frac{3}{4}$ feet in length and another piece of 1 in. by 2 in. lumber that measures $2\frac{5}{8}$ feet in length. Which piece of lumber is longer? Support your answer. **1 in. by 4 in.; $2\frac{3}{4} = 2\frac{6}{8}$ and $2\frac{6}{8} > 2\frac{5}{8}$, so $2\frac{3}{4} > 2\frac{5}{8}$**

Extended Problem Solving

4. Gina and Alex are comparing recipes for smoothies. Gina prefers strawberry smoothies, and Alex prefers orange.
   a. Which recipe calls for more yogurt? Write an expression that justifies your answer.
   b. Write the amount of fruit called for by the strawberry-smoothie recipe as an improper fraction and as a decimal.
   c. Gina and Alex each make their favorite smoothie. Who makes more? Tell how you know.

Strawberry Smoothie
$2\frac{1}{2}$ cups strawberries
$1\frac{1}{2}$ cups frozen yogurt

Orange Smoothie
$\frac{1}{2}$ cup orange juice
1 cup mashed bananas
1 cup frozen yogurt

Student Work Samples for Item 4

Level 3

a. Strawberry smoothie calls for more yogurt.
$1\frac{1}{2} > 1$
b. $2\frac{1}{2} = \frac{5}{2} = 2.5$
improper fraction, decimal
c. Gina makes more. The strawberry smoothie makes 4 cups. The orange smoothie only makes $2\frac{1}{2}$ cups.

The student correctly answered each part, used proper notation, and showed the total volumes in part **c.**

Level 2

a. Strawberry is more because $1\frac{1}{2}$ is more than 1.
b. $2\frac{1}{2} = \frac{5}{2}$ or 5.2
c. Gina makes more because she uses more fruit and more yogurt.

The student answered part **a** correctly but did not write an algebraic expression. The decimal in part **b** is incorrect, and the explanation in part **c** could be improved.

Level 1

a. orange is more because a whole cup is more than a half.
b. 2.5
c. Gina makes more

The student shows little understanding of fractions in parts **a** and **c.** The answer to part **b** is incomplete.

internet connect
State-Specific Test Practice Online
go.hrw.com Keyword: MS4 TestPrep

Standardized Test Prep

Chapter 3

Cumulative Assessment, Chapters 1–3

1. Which is a list of equivalent numbers? **C**

   Ⓐ 0.8, $\frac{2}{50}$, $\frac{8}{100}$ Ⓒ 0.02, $\frac{1}{50}$, $\frac{2}{100}$

   Ⓑ 40, 0.4, $\frac{1}{2}$ Ⓓ 10, 0.01, $\frac{1}{11}$

2. What is the sum of −6, 3, and −9? **G**

   Ⓕ 162 Ⓗ −18

   Ⓖ −12 Ⓙ −162

3. What is the mean of 8, −12, and 4? **A**

   Ⓐ 0 Ⓒ 6.67

   Ⓑ 4 Ⓓ 8

TEST TAKING TIP!

Eliminate choices: When finding the value of a power, you can eliminate any choices that are not divisible by the base of the power.

4. What is the value of 3^5? **H**

   Ⓕ 15 Ⓗ 243

   Ⓖ 125 Ⓙ 320

5. What is 753,000 written in scientific notation? **D**

   Ⓐ 75.3×10^4 Ⓒ 753×10^3

   Ⓑ 7.53×10^3 Ⓓ 7.53×10^5

6. What is the greatest common factor of 45 and 15? **H**

   Ⓕ 3 Ⓗ 15

   Ⓖ 5 Ⓙ 45

7. What is the least common multiple of 12 and 20? **B**

   Ⓐ 240 Ⓒ 20

   Ⓑ 60 Ⓓ 12

8. Which number is between 0 and −1? **G**

   Ⓕ −5.0 Ⓗ 0.5

   Ⓖ −0.3 Ⓙ 3.0

9. ***SHORT RESPONSE*** The Spanish Club provided 48 sandwiches for a picnic. After the picnic, *s* sandwiches were left.

   a. Write an expression that shows how many sandwiches were eaten.

   b. Evaluate your expression for $s = 9$. What does your answer represent?

10. ***SHORT RESPONSE*** The circle graph shows how Amy spends her earnings each month. If Amy earned $100 in June, how much did she spend on entertainment and clothing combined? Show or explain how you got your answer.

How Amy Spends Her Earnings

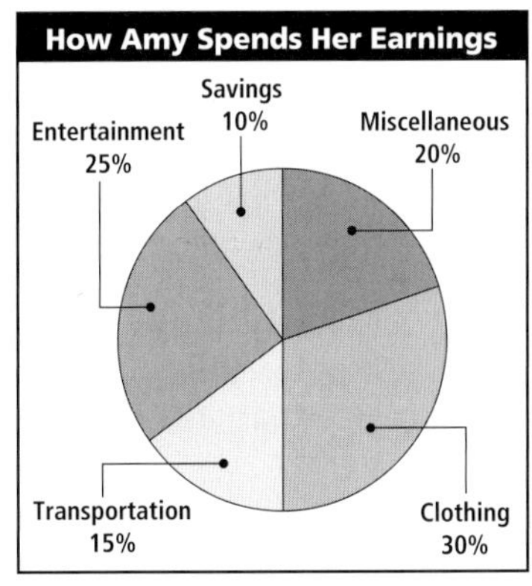

Standardized Test Prep

Answers

9. a. $48 - s$

b. $48 - 9 = 39$; the number of sandwiches that were eaten

10. $55; since a circle graph represents 100% and Amy earned $100, each percent represents $1. 25% + 30% = 55%, so Amy spent $55.

Standardized Test Prep

Chapter 3

Purpose: *To provide review and practice for Chapters 1–3 and standardized tests*

Assessment Resources

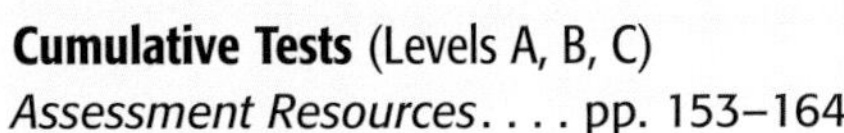

Cumulative Tests (Levels A, B, C)
Assessment Resources. . . . pp. 153–164

State-Specific Test Practice Online
KEYWORD: MS4 TestPrep

Test Prep Doctor

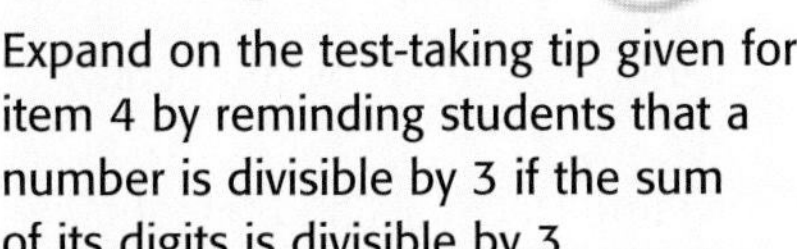

Expand on the test-taking tip given for item 4 by reminding students that a number is divisible by 3 if the sum of its digits is divisible by 3.

Point out to students that all incorrect choices in item 1 may be eliminated by comparing only two of the three numbers listed in each choice. For example, noting that $0.8 \neq \frac{8}{100}$ eliminates **A.**

Operations with Rational Numbers

Section 4A

Decimal Operations

Lesson 4-1
Estimate with Decimals

Lesson 4-2
Adding and Subtracting Decimals

Hands-On Lab 4A
Model Decimal Multiplication

Lesson 4-3
Multiplying Decimals

Lesson 4-4
Dividing Decimals by Integers

Lesson 4-5
Dividing Decimals and Integers by Decimals

Lesson 4-6
Solving Equations Containing Decimals

Section 4B

Fraction Operations

Hands-On Lab 4B
Model Fraction Multiplication and Division

Lesson 4-7
Multiplying Fractions and Mixed Numbers

Lesson 4-8
Dividing Fractions and Mixed Numbers

Lesson 4-9
Estimate with Fractions

Hands-On Lab 4C
Model Fraction Addition and Subtraction

Lesson 4-10
Adding and Subtracting Fractions

Lesson 4-11
Adding and Subtracting Mixed Numbers

Lesson 4-12
Solving Equations Containing Fractions

Pacing Guide for 45-Minute Classes

Chapter 4

DAY 49	DAY 50	DAY 51	DAY 52	DAY 53
Lesson 4-1	Lesson 4-2	Hands-On Lab 4A	Lesson 4-3	Lesson 4-4
DAY 54	**DAY 55**	**DAY 56**	**DAY 57**	**DAY 58**
Lesson 4-5	Lesson 4-6	Mid-Chapter Quiz Hands-On Lab 4B	Lesson 4-7	Lesson 4-8
DAY 59	**DAY 60**	**DAY 61**	**DAY 62**	**DAY 63**
Lesson 4-9	Hands-On Lab 4C	Lesson 4-10	Lesson 4-11	Lesson 4-12
DAY 64	**DAY 65**			
Chapter 4 Review	Chapter 4 Assessment			

Pacing Guide for 90-Minute Classes

Chapter 4

DAY 24	DAY 25	DAY 26	DAY 27	DAY 28
Chapter 3 Review Lesson 4-1	Chapter 3 Assessment Lesson 4-2	Hands-On Lab 4A Lesson 4-3	Lesson 4-4 Lesson 4-5	Lesson 4-6 Hands-On Lab 4B
DAY 29	**DAY 30**	**DAY 31**	**DAY 32**	**DAY 33**
Mid-Chapter Quiz Lesson 4-7 Lesson 4-8	Lesson 4-9 Hands-On Lab 4C	Lesson 4-10 Lesson 4-11	Lesson 4-12 Chapter 4 Review	Chapter 4 Assessment Lesson 5-1

Across the Series

COURSE 1

- Compare and order decimals and fractions.
- Estimate and operate with fractions and decimals, including mixed numbers and improper fractions.
- Solve equations containing fractions or decimals.

COURSE 2

- **Estimate decimal sums, differences, products, and quotients.**
- **Add, subtract, multiply, and divide decimals.**
- **Solve one-step equations with decimals.**
- **Estimate sums and differences of fractions.**
- **Add and subtract fractions and mixed numbers.**
- **Solve one-step equations with fractions.**

COURSE 3

- Operate with rational numbers.
- Solve equations and inequalities containing rational numbers.
- Identify irrational numbers.

Across the Curriculum

LANGUAGE ARTS LINK

Math: Reading and Writing in the Content Area . . . . pp. 32-43

Focus on Problem Solving

Look Back. . . . . SE p. 219

Journal . . . . TE, last page of each lesson

Write About It . . . . . . SE pp. 195, 199, 205, 209, 225, 233, 239, 243, 247

SOCIAL STUDIES LINK

Social Studies . . . . SE pp. 195, 217, 227

History . . . . SE p. 247

SCIENCE LINK

Life Science. . . . . SE pp. 233, 239, 247

Earth Science. . . . . SE pp. 203, 213

Physical Science . . . . SE pp. 199, 225, 245

Astronomy . . . . SE pp. 195, 237

Nutrition. . . . . SE p. 209

TE = *Teacher's Edition* **SE** = *Student Edition*

Interdisciplinary Bulletin Board

Earth Science

Deep-water waves become shallow-water waves when they reach depths of less than half of their wavelength. At what depth do deep-water waves with a wavelength of 9 ft become shallow-water waves? 4.5 ft

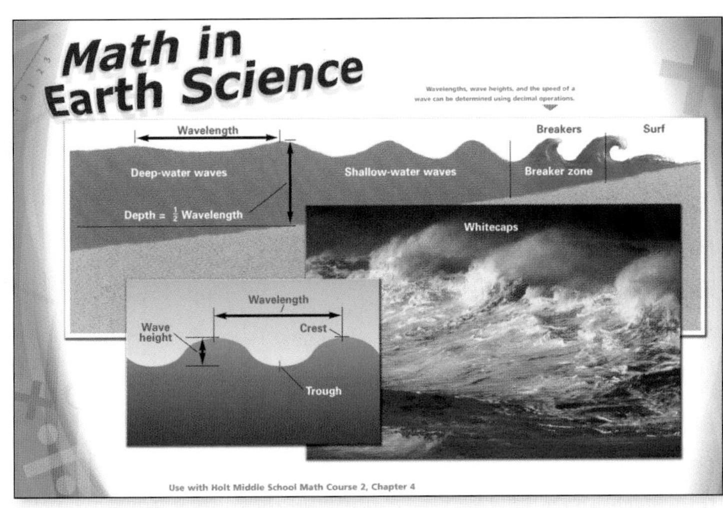

Interdisciplinary posters and worksheets are provided in your resource material.

Resource Options

Chapter 4 Resource Book

Student Resources

Practice (Levels A, B, C). . . . . pp. 8–10, 17–19, 26–28, 35–37, 44–46, 54–56, 65–67, 74–76, 83–85, 92–94, 101–103, 111–113

Reteach . . . . pp. 11, 20, 29, 38, 47–48, 57–58, 68, 77, 86, 95, 104–105, 114–115

Challenge. . pp. 12, 21, 30, 39, 49, 59, 69, 78, 87, 96, 106, 116

Problem Solving. . . . . pp. 13, 22, 31, 40, 50, 60, 70, 79, 88, 97, 107, 117

Puzzles, Twisters & Teasers . . . . pp. 14, 23, 32, 41, 51, 61, 71, 80, 89, 98, 108, 118

Recording Sheets . . . . pp. 3, 7, 16, 25, 34, 43, 53, 64, 73, 82, 91, 100, 110, 122, 125, 127

Chapter Review . . . . pp. 119–121

Teacher and Parent Resources

Chapter Planning and Pacing Guide. . . . . p. 4

Section Planning Guides . . . . pp. 5, 62

Parent Letter . . . . pp. 1–2

Teaching Tools . . . . pp. 125–127

Teacher Support for Chapter Project . . . . p. 123

Transparencies . . . . pp. T1–T51

- Daily Transparencies
- Additional Examples Transparencies
- Teaching Transparencies

Reaching All Learners

English Language Learners

Success for English Language Learners . . . . pp. 63–86

Math: Reading and Writing in the Content Area . . pp. 32–43

Spanish Homework and Practice . . . . pp. 32–43

Spanish Interactive Study Guide . . . . pp. 32–43

Spanish Family Involvement Activities . . . . pp. 33–40

Multilingual Glossary

Individual Needs

Are You Ready? Intervention and Enrichment . . pp. 85–88, 93–100, 197–200, 411–412

Alternate Openers: Explorations . . . . pp. 32–43

Family Involvement Activities . . . . pp. 33–40

Interactive Problem Solving . . . . pp. 32–43

Interactive Study Guide . . . . pp. 32–43

Readiness Activities . . . . pp. 7–8

Math: Reading and Writing in the Content Area . . pp. 32–43

Challenge. . . . . CRB pp. 12, 21, 30, 39, 49, 59, 69, 78, 87, 96, 106, 116

Hands-On

Hands-On Lab Activities . . . . pp. 20–30

Technology Lab Activities . . . . pp. 16–21

Alternate Openers: Explorations . . . . pp. 32–43

Family Involvement Activities . . . . pp. 33–40

Applications and Connections

Consumer and Career Math . . . . pp. 13–16

Interdisciplinary Posters . . . . Poster 4, TE p. 190B

Interdisciplinary Poster Worksheets . . . . pp. 10–12

Transparencies

Alternate Openers: Explorations . . . . pp. 32–43

Exercise Answers Transparencies

Chapter 4 Resource Book . . . . pp. T1–T51

- Daily Transparencies
- Additional Examples Transparencies
- Teaching Transparencies

Technology

Teacher Resources

***Lesson Presentations* CD-ROM** . . . . Chapter 4

***Test and Practice Generator* CD-ROM** . . . . Chapter 4

***One-Stop Planner* CD-ROM** . . . . Chapter 4

Student Resources

***Are You Ready? Intervention* CD-ROM**
Skills 19, 21, 22, 47

internet connect

Homework Help Online	**KEYWORD:** MS4 HWHelp4
Math Tools Online	**KEYWORD:** MS4 Tools
Glossary Online	**KEYWORD:** MS4 Glossary
Chapter Project Online	**KEYWORD:** MS4 PSProject4
Chapter Opener Online	**KEYWORD:** MS4 Ch4
CNN Student News™	**KEYWORD:** MS4 CNN4

SE = *Student Edition* **TE** = *Teacher's Edition* **AR** = *Assessment Resources* **CRB** = *Chapter Resource Book* **MK** = *Manipulatives Kit*

Chapter 4

Assessment Options

Assessing Prior Knowledge

Determine whether students have the required prerequisite concepts and skills.

Are You Ready? . . . . SE p. 191
Inventory Test . . . . AR pp. 1–4

Test Preparation

Provide review and practice for chapter and standardized tests.

Standardized Test Prep . . . . SE p. 257
Spiral Review with Test Prep . . . . . SE, last page of each lesson
Study Guide and Review . . . . SE pp. 252–254
Test Prep Tool Kit

Technology

***Test and Practice Generator* CD-ROM**

internet connect

State-Specific Test Practice Online KEYWORD: MS4 TestPrep

Performance Assessment

Assess students' understanding of chapter concepts and combined problem-solving skills.

Performance Assessment . . . . SE p. 256
Includes scoring rubric in TE
Performance Assessment . . . . AR p. 112
Performance Assessment Teacher Support . . . . AR p. 111

Portfolio

Portfolio opportunities appear throughout the Student and Teacher's Editions.

Suggested work samples:

Problem Solving Project . . . . TE p. 190
Performance Assessment . . . . SE p. 256
Portfolio Guide . . . . AR p. xxxv
Journal . . . . TE, last page of each lesson
Write About It . . . . SE pp. 195, 199, 205 209, 225, 233, 239, 243, 247

Daily Assessment

Obtain daily feedback on students' understanding of concepts.

Spiral Review and Test Prep . . . . . . SE, last page of each lesson

Also Available on Transparency In Chapter 4 Resource Book

Warm Up . . . . TE, first page of each lesson
Problem of the Day . . . . TE, first page of each lesson
Lesson Quiz . . . . TE, last page of each lesson

Student Self-Assessment

Have students evaluate their own work.

Group Project Evaluation . . . . AR p. xxxii
Individual Group Member Evaluation . . . . AR p. xxxiii
Portfolio Guide . . . . AR p. xxxv
Journal . . . . TE, last page of each lesson

Formal Assessment

Assess students' mastery of concepts and skills.

Section Quizzes . . . . AR pp. 13, 14
Mid-Chapter Quiz . . . . SE p. 218
Chapter Test . . . . SE p. 255
Chapter Tests (Levels A, B, C) . . . . AR pp. 51–56
Cumulative Tests (Levels A, B, C) . . . . AR pp. 165–176
Standardized Test Prep
Cumulative Assessment . . . . SE p. 257
End-of-Year Test . . . . AR pp. 273–276

Technology

***Test and Practice Generator* CD-ROM**

Make tests electronically. This software includes:

- Dynamic practice for Chapter 4
- Customizable tests
- Multiple-choice items for each objective
- Free-response items for each objective
- Teacher management system

SE = *Student Edition* **TE** = *Teacher's Edition* **AR** = *Assessment Resources* **CRB** = *Chapter Resource Book* **MK** = *Manipulatives Kit*

Chapter 4

Chapter 4 Tests

Three levels (A,B,C) of tests are available for each chapter in the *Assessment Resources.*

LEVEL A

Chapter 4 Chapter Test *Form A*

Estimate. Estimates will vary. Possible answers given.

1. $61.16 + 39.87$ — **100**
2. $8.19 \cdot 19.97$ — **160**
3. $41.8 \div 5.91$ — **7**

Add or subtract. Estimate to check whether your answer is reasonable.

4. $2.975 + 8.82$ — **11.795**
5. $5.1 - 2.8$ — **2.3**
6. $8 + 2.78$ — **10.78**

Multiply.

7. $6.3 \cdot 5.6$ — **35.28**
8. $2.8 \cdot 3.6$ — **10.08**
9. $5.65 \cdot 6.6$ — **37.29**

Divide. Estimate to check whether your answer is reasonable.

10. $45.75 \div 5$ — **9.15**
11. $8.75 \div 5$ — **1.75**
12. $0.45 \div 9$ — **0.05**
13. $5.12 \div 0.8$ — **6.4**
14. $12.5 \div 2.5$ — **5**
15. $0.675 \div 0.15$ — **4.5**

Solve.

16. $6.2n = 93$ — $n = 15$
17. $a - 8.5 = 3.9$ — $a = 12.4$
18. $\frac{x}{5.4} = 3.6$ — $x = 19.44$

Multiply. Write each answer in simplest form.

19. $\frac{3}{4} \cdot \frac{2}{3}$ — $\frac{1}{2}$
20. $7 \cdot \frac{3}{4}$ — $5\frac{1}{4}$
21. $\frac{2}{3} \cdot \frac{5}{6}$ — $\frac{5}{9}$

Divide. Write each answer in simplest form.

22. $\frac{7}{8} \div \frac{3}{4}$ — $1\frac{1}{6}$
23. $6 \div \frac{3}{5}$ — 10
24. $\frac{5}{6} \div \frac{1}{2}$ — $1\frac{2}{3}$

Chapter 4 Chapter Test *Form A, continued*

Estimate each sum or difference. Estimates may vary. Possible answers given.

25. $\frac{7}{9} + \frac{1}{10}$ — 1
26. $9\frac{9}{17} - 4\frac{7}{8}$ — $4\frac{1}{2}$

Add or subtract. Write each answer in simplest form.

27. $\frac{7}{12} + \frac{11}{12}$ — $1\frac{1}{2}$
28. $\frac{2}{3} - \frac{5}{9}$ — $\frac{1}{9}$
29. $\frac{3}{4} + \frac{5}{6}$ — $1\frac{7}{12}$
30. $5\frac{1}{2} + 3\frac{7}{8}$ — $9\frac{3}{8}$
31. $8\frac{3}{4} - 1\frac{2}{3}$ — $7\frac{1}{12}$
32. $2\frac{5}{8} + 6\frac{1}{2}$ — $9\frac{1}{8}$

Solve. Write each answer in simplest form.

33. $x - \frac{2}{5} = \frac{3}{5}$ — $x = 1$
34. $\frac{7}{10} + b = \frac{4}{5}$ — $b = \frac{1}{10}$
35. $\frac{5}{6}a = \frac{2}{9}$ — $a = \frac{4}{15}$

Decide if you need an exact answer or if an estimate is enough.

36. There are 2,400 tickets for a concert, and $\frac{3}{4}$ have been sold. How many tickets have been sold? — **exact answer**

LEVEL B

Chapter 4 Chapter Test *Form B*

Estimate. Estimates will vary. Possible answers given.

1. $-21.09 + 59.9$ — **39**
2. $6.86 \cdot -24.88$ — **−175**
3. $73.09 \div 8.261$ — **9**

Add or subtract. Estimate to check whether your answer is reasonable.

4. $-9.175 + (-4.92)$ — **−14.095**
5. $9.35 - 4.8$ — **4.55**
6. $6.9 + 2.78$ — **9.68**

Multiply.

7. $-8.04 \cdot 0.6$ — **−4.824**
8. $2.008 \cdot 11.5$ — **23.092**
9. $54.65 \cdot 12.37$ — **676.0205**

Divide. Estimate to check whether your answer is reasonable.

10. $3.84 \div -12$ — **−0.32**
11. $41.04 \div 12$ — **3.42**
12. $123.28 \div 23$ — **5.36**
13. $-4.55 \div (-0.7)$ — **6.5**
14. $13.75 \div 2.5$ — **5.5**
15. $3.6 \div 0.06$ — **60**

Solve.

16. $9.7x = -79.54$ — $x = -8.2$
17. $a + 6.84 = -21.9$ — $a = -28.74$
18. $\frac{t}{-6.24} = -6$ — $t = 37.44$

Multiply. Write each answer in simplest form.

19. $12 \cdot \left(-\frac{2}{3}\right)$ — -8
20. $2\frac{1}{4} \cdot \frac{4}{5} \cdot 4$ — $7\frac{1}{5}$
21. $1\frac{1}{2} \cdot \frac{5}{6}$ — $\frac{5}{4}$ or $1\frac{1}{4}$

Divide. Write each answer in simplest form.

22. $\frac{1}{8} \div \frac{4}{5}$ — $\frac{5}{32}$
23. $-\frac{5}{8} \div \left(-1\frac{5}{6}\right)$ — $\frac{15}{44}$
24. $\frac{3}{5} \div \frac{5}{12}$ — $\frac{36}{25}$ or $1\frac{11}{25}$

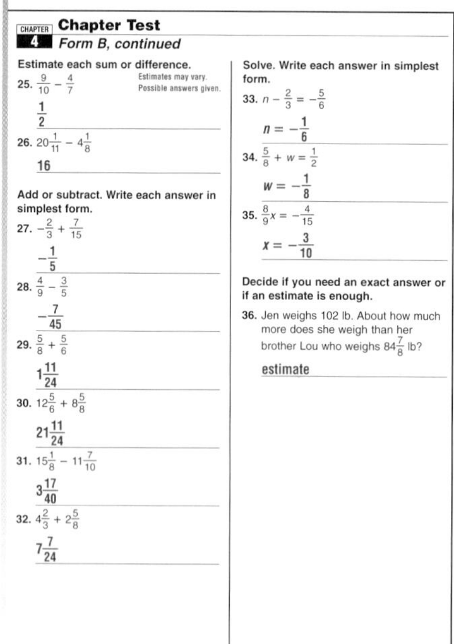

Chapter 4 Chapter Test *Form B, continued*

Estimate each sum or difference. Estimates may vary. Possible answers given.

25. $\frac{9}{10} - \frac{4}{7}$ — $\frac{1}{2}$
26. $20\frac{1}{11} - 4\frac{1}{8}$ — 16

Add or subtract. Write each answer in simplest form.

27. $-\frac{2}{3} + \frac{7}{15}$ — $-\frac{1}{5}$
28. $\frac{4}{9} - \frac{3}{5}$ — $-\frac{7}{45}$
29. $\frac{5}{8} + \frac{5}{6}$ — $1\frac{11}{24}$
30. $12\frac{5}{6} + 8\frac{5}{8}$ — $21\frac{11}{24}$
31. $15\frac{1}{8} - 11\frac{7}{10}$ — $3\frac{17}{40}$
32. $4\frac{2}{3} + 2\frac{5}{8}$ — $7\frac{7}{24}$

Solve. Write each answer in simplest form.

33. $n - \frac{2}{3} = -\frac{5}{6}$ — $n = -\frac{1}{6}$
34. $\frac{5}{8} + w = \frac{1}{2}$ — $w = -\frac{1}{8}$
35. $\frac{8}{9}x = -\frac{4}{15}$ — $x = -\frac{3}{10}$

Decide if you need an exact answer or if an estimate is enough.

36. Jen weighs 102 lb. About how much more does she weigh than her brother Lou who weighs $84\frac{7}{8}$ lb? — **estimate**

LEVEL C

Chapter 4 Chapter Test *Form C*

Estimate. Estimates will vary. Possible answers given.

1. $-11.2 + 27.814 - 2.98$ — **14**
2. $7.16 \cdot (-4.81) \cdot 2.107$ — **−70**
3. $-55.904 \div 7.165$ — **−8**

Add or subtract. Estimate to check whether your answer is reasonable.

4. $-1.823 - 6.17 + 21.9$ — **13.907**
5. $32.4 - 4.6 + 3.8$ — **31.6**
6. $6.9 - 8 + 2.78$ — **1.68**

Multiply.

7. $1.5 \cdot (-2.82) \cdot 0.56$ — **−2.3688**
8. $2.008 \cdot (-3.6) \cdot (-11.5)$ — **83.1312**
9. $-54.65 \cdot 12.37 \cdot 6.6$ — **−4,461.7353**

Divide. Estimate to check whether your answer is reasonable.

10. $-51.72 \div 120$ — **−0.431**
11. $48.75 \div (-25)$ — **−1.95**
12. $-0.055 \div 11$ — **−0.005**
13. $-1.529 \div (-0.22)$ — **6.95**
14. Evaluate $12.5 \div 2.5 - 6.8$ — **−1.8**
15. Evaluate $(3.6 + 2.9) \div 0.05$ — **130**

Solve.

16. $6.04x = -20.838$ — $x = -3.45$
17. $6.5 + m = 2.39$ — $m = -4.11$
18. $\frac{w}{-0.084} = -0.25$ — $w = 0.021$

Multiply. Write each answer in simplest form.

19. $-\frac{4}{9} \cdot \frac{3}{14} \cdot \left(-\frac{7}{8}\right) \cdot \frac{1}{2}$ — $\frac{1}{24}$
20. $3\frac{1}{2} \cdot \left(-1\frac{6}{7}\right) \cdot 21 \cdot \frac{2}{3}$ — -91
21. $-\frac{2}{3} \cdot 1\frac{1}{2} \cdot \frac{5}{6}$ — $-\frac{5}{6}$

Divide. Write each answer in simplest form.

22. $\left(2\frac{1}{2} + 3\frac{3}{8}\right) \div \frac{5}{8}$ — $9\frac{2}{5}$
23. $-16\frac{2}{3} \div 4\frac{1}{6}$ — -4
24. $\frac{3}{5} \div \frac{5}{6} \div \frac{1}{2}$ — $1\frac{11}{25}$

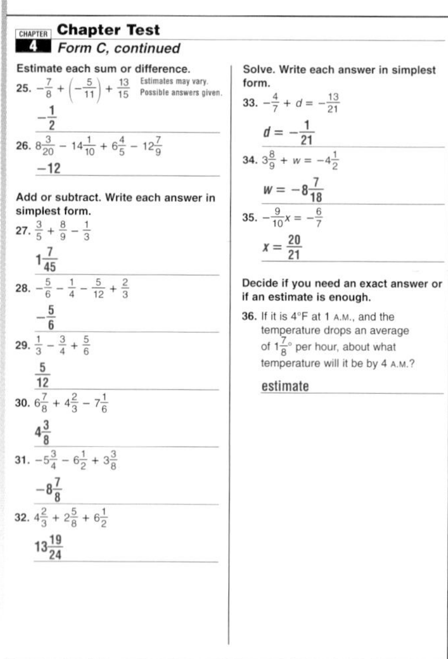

Chapter 4 Chapter Test *Form C, continued*

Estimate each sum or difference. Estimates may vary. Possible answers given.

25. $-\frac{7}{8} + \left(-\frac{5}{11}\right) + \frac{13}{15}$ — $-\frac{1}{2}$
26. $8\frac{3}{20} - 14\frac{1}{10} + 6\frac{4}{5} - 12\frac{7}{9}$ — -12

Add or subtract. Write each answer in simplest form.

27. $\frac{3}{5} + \frac{8}{9} - \frac{1}{3}$ — $1\frac{7}{45}$
28. $-\frac{5}{6} - \frac{1}{4} - \frac{5}{12} + \frac{2}{3}$ — $-\frac{5}{6}$
29. $\frac{1}{3} - \frac{3}{4} + \frac{5}{6}$ — $\frac{5}{12}$
30. $6\frac{7}{8} + 4\frac{2}{3} - 7\frac{1}{6}$ — $4\frac{3}{8}$
31. $-5\frac{3}{4} - 6\frac{1}{2} + 3\frac{3}{8}$ — $-8\frac{7}{8}$
32. $4\frac{2}{3} + 2\frac{5}{8} + 6\frac{1}{2}$ — $13\frac{19}{24}$

Solve. Write each answer in simplest form.

33. $-\frac{4}{7} + d = -\frac{13}{21}$ — $d = -\frac{1}{21}$
34. $3\frac{8}{9} + w = -4\frac{1}{2}$ — $w = -8\frac{7}{18}$
35. $-\frac{9}{10}x = -\frac{6}{7}$ — $x = \frac{20}{21}$

Decide if you need an exact answer or if an estimate is enough.

36. If it is 4°F at 1 A.M., and the temperature drops an average of $1\frac{7}{8}$° per hour, about what temperature will it be by 4 A.M.? — **estimate**

Test and Practice Generator CD-ROM

Create and customize multiple versions of the same tests with corresponding answers for any chosen chapter objectives.

Chapter 4 State and Standardized Test Preparation

Test Taking Skill Builder and Standardized Test Practice are provided for each chapter in the *Test Prep Tool Kit.*

TEST TAKING SKILL BUILDER

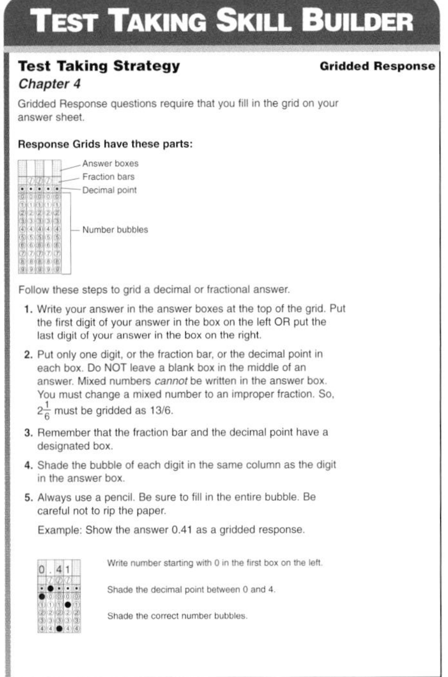

Test Taking Strategy **Gridded Response**
Chapter 4

Gridded Response questions require that you fill in the grid on your answer sheet.

Response Grids have these parts:

Follow these steps to grid a decimal or fractional answer.

1. Write your answer in the answer boxes at the top of the grid. Put the first digit of your answer in the box on the left OR put the last digit of your answer in the box on the right.
2. Put only one digit, or the fraction bar, or the decimal point in each box. Do NOT leave a blank box in the middle of an answer. Mixed numbers *cannot* be written in the answer box. You must change a mixed number to an improper fraction. So, $2\frac{1}{6}$ must be gridded as 13/6.
3. Remember that the fraction bar and the decimal point have a designated box.
4. Shade the bubble of each digit in the same column as the digit in the answer box.
5. Always use a pencil. Be sure to fill in the entire bubble. Be careful not to rip the paper.

Example: Show the answer 0.41 as a gridded response.

Write number starting with 0 in the first box on the left.
Shade the decimal point between 0 and 4.
Shade the correct number bubbles.

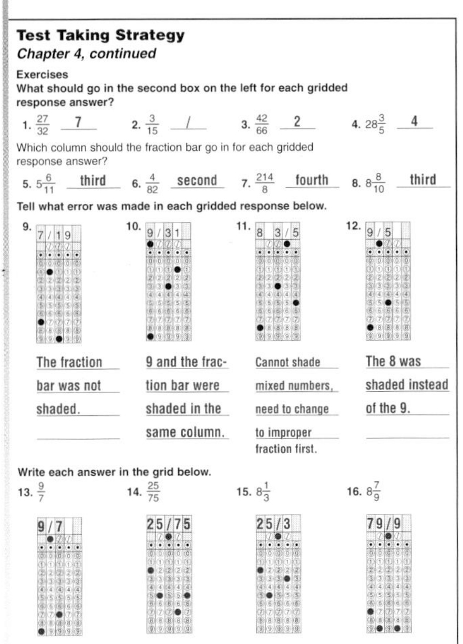

Test Taking Strategy
Chapter 4, continued

Exercises
What should go in the second box on the left for each gridded response answer?

1. $\frac{27}{32}$ 7
2. $\frac{3}{15}$ /
3. $\frac{42}{66}$ 2
4. $28\frac{3}{5}$ 4

Which column should the fraction bar go in for each gridded response answer?

5. $5\frac{6}{11}$ third
6. $\frac{4}{82}$ second
7. $\frac{214}{8}$ fourth
8. $8\frac{8}{10}$ third

Tell what error was made in each gridded response below.

9. The fraction bar was not shaded.
10. 9 and the fraction bar were shaded in the same column.
11. Cannot shade mixed numbers, need to change to improper fraction first.
12. The 8 was shaded instead of the 9.

Write each answer in the grid below.

13. $\frac{9}{7}$
14. $\frac{25}{75}$
15. $8\frac{1}{3}$
16. $8\frac{7}{9}$

STANDARDIZED TEST PRACTICE

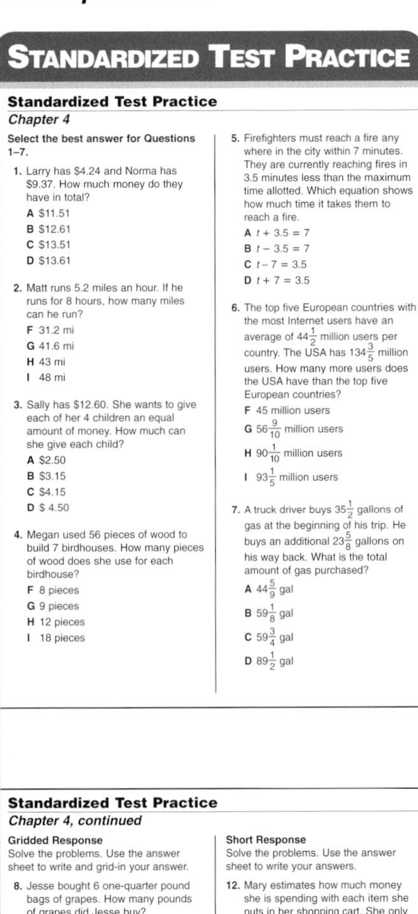

Standardized Test Practice
Chapter 4

Select the best answer for Questions 1–7.

1. Larry has \$4.24 and Norma has \$9.37. How much money do they have in total?
   A \$11.51
   B \$12.61
   C \$13.51
   D \$13.61
2. Matt runs 5.2 miles an hour. If he runs for 8 hours, how many miles can he run?
   F 31.2 mi
   G 41.6 mi
   H 43 mi
   I 48 mi
3. Sally has \$12.60. She wants to give each of her 4 children an equal amount of money. How much can she give each child?
   A \$2.50
   B \$3.15
   C \$4.15
   D \$ 4.50
4. Megan used 56 pieces of wood to build 7 birdhouses. How many pieces of wood does she use for each birdhouse?
   F 8 pieces
   G 9 pieces
   H 12 pieces
   I 18 pieces
5. Firefighters must reach a fire any where in the city within 7 minutes. They are currently reaching fires in 3.5 minutes less than the maximum time allotted. Which equation shows how much time it takes them to reach a fire.
   A $t + 3.5 = 7$
   B $t - 3.5 = 7$
   C $t - 7 = 3.5$
   D $t + 7 = 3.5$
6. The top five European countries with the most Internet users have an average of $44\frac{1}{2}$ million users per country. The USA has $134\frac{3}{5}$ million users. How many more users does the USA have than the top five European countries?
   F 45 million users
   G $56\frac{9}{10}$ million users
   H $90\frac{1}{10}$ million users
   I $93\frac{1}{5}$ million users
7. A truck driver buys $35\frac{1}{2}$ gallons of gas at the beginning of his trip. He buys an additional $23\frac{5}{8}$ gallons on his way back. What is the total amount of gas purchased?
   A $44\frac{5}{9}$ gal
   B $59\frac{1}{8}$ gal
   C $59\frac{3}{4}$ gal
   D $89\frac{1}{2}$ gal

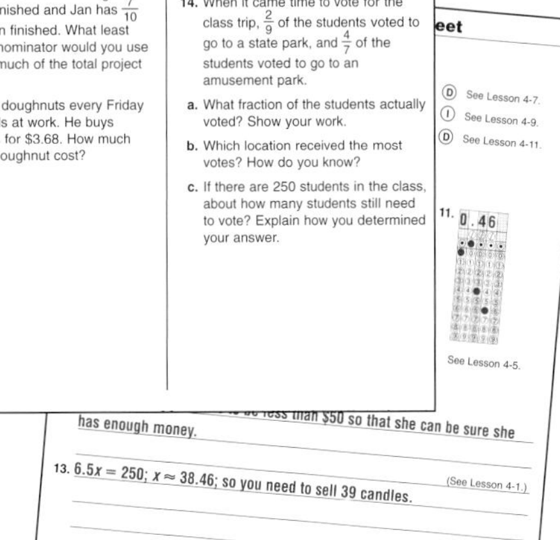

Standardized Test Practice
Chapter 4, continued

Gridded Response
Solve the problems. Use the answer sheet to write and grid-in your answer.

8. Jesse bought 6 one-quarter pound bags of grapes. How many pounds of grapes did Jesse buy?
9. Dividing a number by one-third is the same as multiplying the number by what number?
10. In a partner project, Leo has $\frac{3}{5}$ of his portion finished and Jan has $\frac{7}{10}$ of her portion finished. What least common denominator would you use to find how much of the total project is finished?
11. Carlos buys doughnuts every Friday for his friends at work. He buys 8 doughnuts for \$3.68. How much does each doughnut cost?

Short Response
Solve the problems. Use the answer sheet to write your answers.

12. Mary estimates how much money she is spending with each item she puts in her shopping cart. She only has \$50 to spend. Does she want her estimate to be greater or less than \$50? Explain in words how you determined your answer.
13. You need to earn \$250 to go to camp. You earn \$6.50 for each candle that you sell. Write an equation that could be used to determine the number of candles you need to sell, and then solve your equation.

Extended Response

14. When it came time to vote for the class trip, $\frac{2}{9}$ of the students voted to go to a state park, and $\frac{4}{7}$ of the students voted to go to an amusement park.
    a. What fraction of the students actually voted? Show your work.
    b. Which location received the most votes? How do you know?
    c. If there are 250 students in the class, about how many students still need to vote? Explain how you determined your answer.

eet

(D) See Lesson 4-7.
(I) See Lesson 4-9.
(D) See Lesson 4-11.

11. 0.46

See Lesson 4-5.

... less than \$50 so that she can be sure she has enough money.

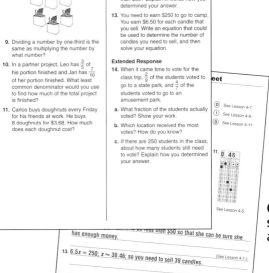

13. $6.5x = 250$; $x \approx 38.46$; so you need to sell 39 candles. (See Lesson 4-1.)

(See Lesson 4-6.)

Extended Response
Write your answers for Problem 14 on the back of this paper.
See Lesson 4-10.

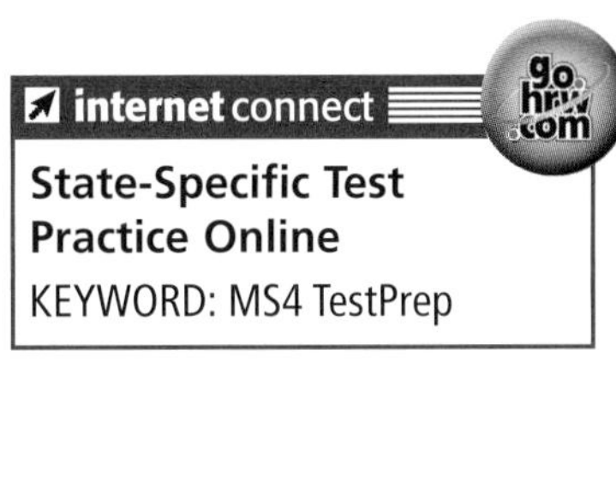

internet connect

State-Specific Test Practice Online
KEYWORD: MS4 TestPrep

Test Prep Tool Kit

- Standardized Test Prep Workbook
- Countdown to Testing transparencies
- State Test Prep CD-ROM
- Standardized Test Prep Video

Customized answer sheets give students realistic practice for actual standardized tests.

Operations with Rational Numbers

Why Learn This?

Explain that fractions are used in many daily activities, including cooking. Ask students to think of examples of fractions that they regularly use (e.g., half hour, $\frac{1}{2}$ gallon, $\frac{1}{4}$ mile, $85\frac{1}{2}$ lb).

Using Data

To begin the study of this chapter, have students:

- Explain how to determine the amount of each ingredient needed to make 1 waffle. Divide the amount of each ingredient in the recipe for 10 waffles by 10.
- Find the amount of each ingredient needed to make 1 waffle. 1 c flour, $\frac{1}{2}$ tsp salt, $\frac{1}{4}$ tsp baking soda, $\frac{1}{4}$ c buttermilk, 2 tsp butter
- Explain how to determine the amount of each ingredient needed to make 100 waffles. Possible answer: Multiply the amount of each ingredient in the recipe for 50 waffles by 2.
- Find the amount of each ingredient needed to make 100 waffles. 100 c flour, 50 tsp salt, 25 tsp baking soda, 25 c buttermilk, 200 tsp butter

TABLE OF CONTENTS

internet connect

Chapter Opener Online
go.hrw.com
KEYWORD: MS4 Ch4

Operations with Rational Numbers

Ingredients	10 Waffles	25 Waffles	50 Waffles
Flour	10 c	25 c	50 c
Salt	5 tsp	$12\frac{1}{2}$ tsp	25 tsp
Baking soda	$2\frac{1}{2}$ tsp	$6\frac{1}{4}$ tsp	$12\frac{1}{2}$ tsp
Buttermilk	$2\frac{1}{2}$ c	$6\frac{1}{4}$ c	$12\frac{1}{2}$ c
Butter (melted)	20 tsp	50 tsp	100 tsp

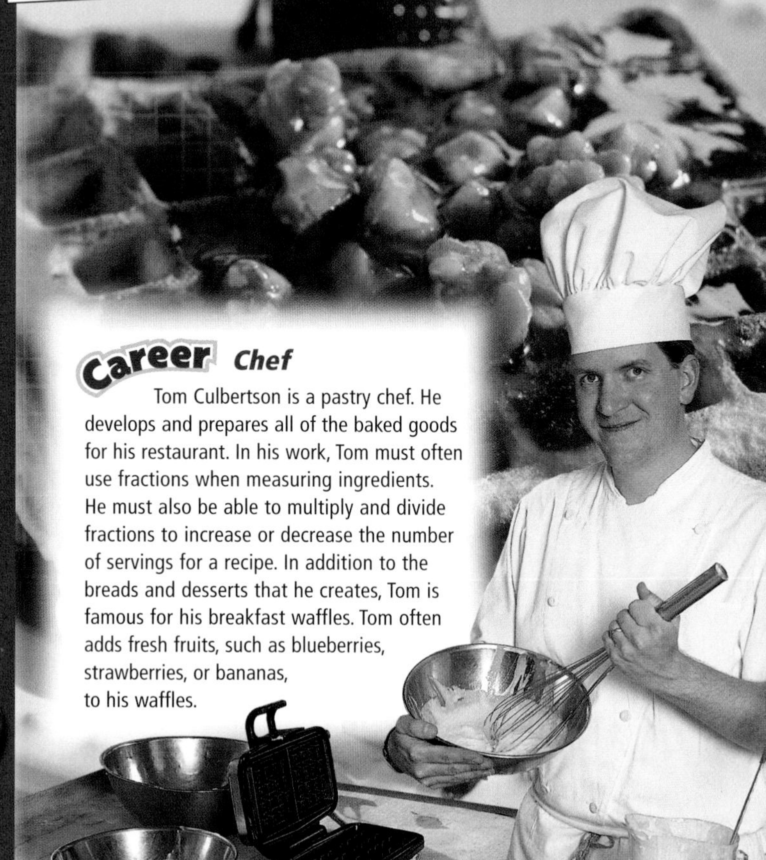

Career ***Chef***

Tom Culbertson is a pastry chef. He develops and prepares all of the baked goods for his restaurant. In his work, Tom must often use fractions when measuring ingredients. He must also be able to multiply and divide fractions to increase or decrease the number of servings for a recipe. In addition to the breads and desserts that he creates, Tom is famous for his breakfast waffles. Tom often adds fresh fruits, such as blueberries, strawberries, or bananas, to his waffles.

Problem Solving Project

Cooking Connection

Purpose: To solve problems by using operations with decimals and fractions

Materials: Wafflefest worksheet, waffle materials (optional)

internet connect

Internet Activity: ***go.hrw.com***
KEYWORD: MS4 PSProject4

Understand, Plan, Solve, and Look Back

Have students:

- ✔ Complete the Wafflefest worksheet to learn how to adjust a recipe using fractions and decimals.
- ✔ Make a table that describes the measurement units used in the recipe. What other units are used in recipes? How are the units related?
- ✔ Take a poll to discover who prefers pancakes and who prefers waffles. Compare the results using decimals, fractions, and a circle graph.
- ✔ Research the history of waffles. How did waffles get their name? When was the first waffle iron created? Who was the creator?
- ✔ Check students' work.

ARE YOU READY?

Choose the best term from the list to complete each sentence.

1. A(n) __?__ is a number that is written using the base-ten place value system. **decimal**
2. An example of a(n) __?__ is $\frac{14}{5}$. **improper fraction**
3. A(n) __?__ is a number that represents a part of a whole. **fraction**

decimal
fraction
improper fraction
mixed number
simplest form

Complete these exercises to review the skills you will need for this chapter.

✓ Simplify Fractions

Write each fraction in simplest form.

4. $\frac{24}{40}$ $\frac{3}{5}$
5. $\frac{64}{84}$ $\frac{16}{21}$
6. $\frac{66}{78}$ $\frac{11}{13}$
7. $\frac{64}{192}$ $\frac{1}{3}$
8. $\frac{21}{35}$ $\frac{3}{5}$
9. $\frac{11}{99}$ $\frac{1}{9}$
10. $\frac{16}{36}$ $\frac{4}{9}$
11. $\frac{20}{30}$ $\frac{2}{3}$

✓ Write Mixed Numbers as Fractions

Write each mixed number as an improper fraction.

12. $7\frac{1}{2}$ $\frac{15}{2}$
13. $2\frac{5}{6}$ $\frac{17}{6}$
14. $1\frac{14}{15}$ $\frac{29}{15}$
15. $3\frac{2}{11}$ $\frac{35}{11}$
16. $3\frac{7}{8}$ $\frac{31}{8}$
17. $8\frac{4}{9}$ $\frac{76}{9}$
18. $4\frac{1}{7}$ $\frac{29}{7}$
19. $5\frac{9}{10}$ $\frac{59}{10}$

✓ Write Fractions as Mixed Numbers

Write each improper fraction as a mixed number.

20. $\frac{23}{6}$ $3\frac{5}{6}$
21. $\frac{17}{3}$ $5\frac{2}{3}$
22. $\frac{29}{7}$ $4\frac{1}{7}$
23. $\frac{39}{4}$ $9\frac{3}{4}$
24. $\frac{48}{5}$ $9\frac{3}{5}$
25. $\frac{82}{9}$ $9\frac{1}{9}$
26. $\frac{69}{4}$ $17\frac{1}{4}$
27. $\frac{35}{8}$ $4\frac{3}{8}$

✓ Add, Subtract, Multiply, or Divide Integers

Find each sum, difference, product, or quotient.

28. $-11 + (-24)$ **−35**
29. $-11 - 7$ **−18**
30. $-4 \cdot (-10)$ **40**
31. $-22 \div (-11)$ **2**
32. $23 + (-30)$ **−7**
33. $-33 - 74$ **−107**
34. $-62 \cdot (-34)$ **2,108**
35. $84 \div (-12)$ **−7**

Assessing Prior Knowledge

INTERVENTION 

Diagnose and Prescribe

Evaluate your students' performance on this page to determine whether intervention is necessary or whether enrichment is appropriate. Options that provide instruction, practice, and a check are listed below.

Resources for Are You Ready?

- Are You Ready? Intervention and Enrichment
- **Recording Sheet for Are You Ready?**
  Chapter 4 Resource Book...... p. 3

 ***Are You Ready? Intervention* CD-ROM**

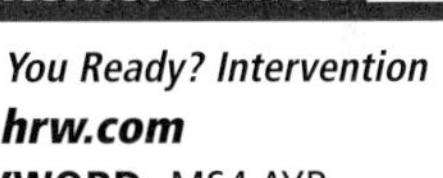

Are You Ready? Intervention
go.hrw.com
KEYWORD: MS4 AYR

ARE YOU READY?

Were students successful with Are You Ready?

YES
ENRICH

✓Simplify Fractions
Are You Ready? Intervention, Skill 19
Blackline Masters, Online, and
 **CD-ROM** Intervention Activities

✓Write Mixed Numbers as Fractions
Are You Ready? Intervention, Skill 22
Blackline Masters, Online, and
CD-ROM Intervention Activities

✓Write Fractions as Mixed Numbers
Are You Ready? Intervention, Skill 21
Blackline Masters, Online, and
 **CD-ROM** Intervention Activities

✓Add, Subtract, Multiply, or Divide Integers
Are You Ready? Intervention, Skill 47
Blackline Masters, Online, and
 **CD-ROM** Intervention Activities

Are You Ready? Enrichment, pp. 413–414

Section 4A Decimal Operations

One-Minute Section Planner

Lesson	Materials	Resources
Lesson 4-1 Estimate with Decimals **NCTM:** Number and Operations, Problem Solving, Communication **NAEP:** Number Properties 2b ☑ SAT-9 ☑ SAT-10 ☑ ITBS ☑ CTBS ☑ MAT ☑ CAT	**Optional** Advertisements showing prices Calculators	• *Chapter 4 Resource Book,* pp. 6–14 • Daily Transparency T1, CRB • Additional Examples Transparencies T2–T3, CRB • *Alternate Openers: Explorations,* p. 32
Lesson 4-2 Adding and Subtracting Decimals **NCTM:** Number and Operations, Communication **NAEP:** Number Properties 3a ☑ SAT-9 ☑ SAT-10 ☑ ITBS ☑ CTBS ☑ MAT ☑ CAT	**Optional** Recording Sheet for Reaching All Learners *(CRB, p. 125)*	• *Chapter 4 Resource Book,* pp. 15–23 • Daily Transparency T4, CRB • Additional Examples Transparencies T5–T6, CRB • *Alternate Openers: Explorations,* p. 33
Hands-On Lab 4A Model Decimal Multiplication **NCTM:** Number and Operations, Algebra, Geometry, Representation **NAEP:** Number Properties 3a ☐ SAT-9 ☐ SAT-10 ☐ ITBS ☐ CTBS ☐ MAT ☐ CAT	**Required** Base-ten blocks *(MK)* Decimal grids *(CRB)*	• *Hands-On Lab Activities* pp. 20–23, 129–130
Lesson 4-3 Multiplying Decimals **NCTM:** Number and Operations, Communication **NAEP:** Number Properties 3a ☑ SAT-9 ☑ SAT-10 ☑ ITBS ☑ CTBS ☑ MAT ☑ CAT	**Optional** Calculators Teaching Transparency T8 *(CRB)*	• *Chapter 4 Resource Book,* pp. 24–32 • Daily Transparency T7, CRB • Additional Examples Transparencies T9–T11, CRB • *Alternate Openers: Explorations,* p. 34
Lesson 4-4 Dividing Decimals by Integers **NCTM:** Number and Operations, Communication **NAEP:** Number Properties 3a ☑ SAT-9 ☑ SAT-10 ☑ ITBS ☑ CTBS ☑ MAT ☑ CAT	**Optional** Graph paper *(CRB, p. 126)* Calculators Measuring tape Teaching Transparency T13 *(CRB)*	• *Chapter 4 Resource Book,* pp. 33–41 • Daily Transparency T12, CRB • Additional Examples Transparencies T14–T16, CRB • *Alternate Openers: Explorations,* p. 35
Lesson 4-5 Dividing Decimals and Integers by Decimals **NCTM:** Number and Operations, Geometry, Communication, Representation **NAEP:** Number Properties 3a ☑ SAT-9 ☑ SAT-10 ☑ ITBS ☑ CTBS ☑ MAT ☑ CAT	**Optional** Calculators Teaching Transparency T18 *(CRB)*	• *Chapter 4 Resource Book,* pp. 42–51 • Daily Transparency T17, CRB • Additional Examples Transparencies T19–T21, CRB • *Alternate Openers: Explorations,* p. 36
Lesson 4-6 Solving Equations Containing Decimals **NCTM:** Number and Operations, Algebra, Communication **NAEP:** Algebra 4a ☐ SAT-9 ☐ SAT-10 ☑ ITBS ☑ CTBS ☑ MAT ☑ CAT	**Optional** Graph paper *(CRB, p. 126)*	• *Chapter 4 Resource Book,* pp. 52–61 • Daily Transparency T22, CRB • Additional Examples Transparencies T23–T25, CRB • *Alternate Openers: Explorations,* p. 37
Section 4A Assessment		• Mid-Chapter Quiz, SE p. 218 • Section 4A Quiz, AR p. 13 • *Test and Practice Generator* CD-ROM

SAT = *Stanford Achievement Tests* **ITBS** = *Iowa Test of Basic Skills* **CTBS** = *Comprehensive Test of Basic Skills/Terra Nova*
MAT = *Metropolitan Achievement Test* **CAT** = *California Achievement Test*

NCTM—Complete standards can be found on pages T27–T33. **NAEP**—Complete standards can be found on pages A35–A39.

SE = *Student Edition* **TE** = *Teacher's Edition* **AR** = *Assessment Resources* **CRB** = *Chapter Resource Book* **MK** = *Manipulatives Kit*

Section Overview

Estimating with Decimals *Lesson 4-1*

Why? Estimation can be used to determine whether answers are reasonable. Estimation is also a useful strategy for eliminating incorrect answers on multiple-choice tests.

Estimate:
8.649 + 14.07
9 + 14 = 23

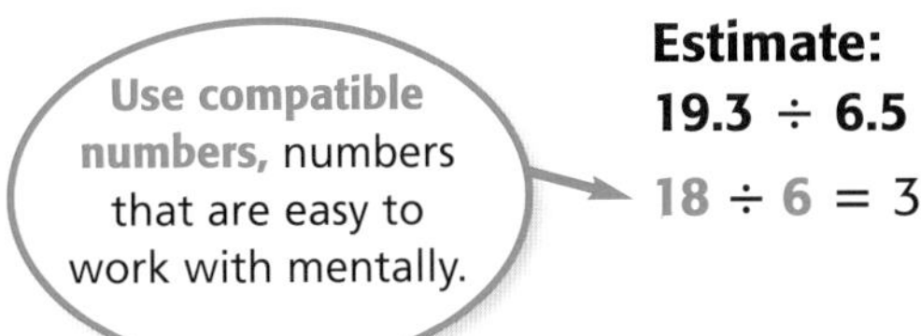

Use compatible numbers, numbers that are easy to work with mentally.

Estimate:
19.3 ÷ 6.5
18 ÷ 6 = 3

Operations with Decimals *Hands-On Lab 4A, Lessons 4-2, 4-3, 4-4, 4-5*

Why? The most common application of decimal operations is using money. Align the decimal point when adding or subtracting decimals. The sign rules for adding and subtracting decimals are the same as for integers.

Add 5.63 + 11.8.

$$\begin{array}{r} 11.80 \\ +\ 5.63 \\ \hline 17.43 \end{array}$$

Use zeros at the end when necessary to write an **equivalent decimal** so that all addends have the same number of digits to the right of the decimal point.

Subtract 12 − 4.31.

$$\begin{array}{r} 12.00 \\ -\ 4.31 \\ \hline 7.69 \end{array}$$

Multiply 0.004 · (−2.6).

0.004 · (−2.6) = −0.0104

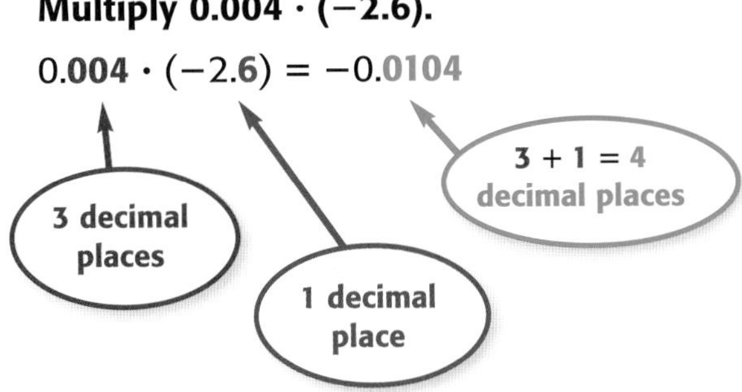

Divide 9.06 ÷ 0.3.

9.06 ÷ **0.3**
= (10 · 9.06) ÷ (10 · 0.3)
= 90.6 ÷ **3**
= 30.2

Make the **divisor** a whole number by multiplying the dividend and the divisor by the same **power of ten.**

Solving Equations Containing Decimals *Lesson 4-6*

Why? To solve one-step equations with decimals, apply the rules for computing with decimals when you are isolating the variable.

Equation	Operation	Inverse Operation	Isolate the Variable
$x + 9.7 = 15$	**Addition**	**Subtraction**	$x = 5.3$
$y - 0.5 = -3.9$	**Subtraction**	**Addition**	$y = -3.4$
$-6 \cdot n = 2.4$	**Multiplication**	**Division**	$n = -0.4$
$\frac{a}{1.7} = 3$	**Division**	**Multiplication**	$a = 5.1$

4-1 Organizer

Pacing: Traditional 1 day
Block $\frac{1}{2}$ day

Objective: Students estimate decimal sums, differences, products, and quotients.

Warm Up

Estimate.

1. 27 · 30 **900** **2.** 85 · 92 **8,100**
3. 12 · 28 **300** **4.** 185 · 201 **40,000**

Problem of the Day

I am a two-digit decimal greater than 0.25 and less than $\frac{2}{5}$. My hundredths digit is 3 times my tenths digit. What number am I? **0.26 or 0.39**

Available on Daily Transparency in CRB

Math Fact !!

Since five digits round up (5, 6, 7, 8, 9) and only four (1, 2, 3, 4) round down, scientists sometimes use an additional rule for rounding to avoid that bias. Numbers with 5 in the place to the right of the number being rounded are rounded to an even number. For example, 27.5 rounds to 28, and 16.5 rounds to 16.

4-1 Estimate with Decimals

Problem Solving Skill

Learn to estimate decimal sums, differences, products, and quotients.

Vocabulary
compatible numbers

Jessie earned \$27.00 for baby-sitting. She wants to use the money to buy a ticket to a waterpark for \$14.75 and a souvenir T-shirt for \$13.20.

To find out if Jessie has enough money to buy both items, you can use estimation. To estimate the total cost of the ticket and the T-shirt, round each price to the nearest dollar, or integer. Then add the rounded values.

\$14.75	*7 > 5, so round to \$15.*	\$15
\$13.20	*2 < 5, so round to \$13.*	+ \$13
		\$28

The estimated cost is \$28, so Jessie does not have enough money to buy both items.

To estimate decimal sums and differences, round each decimal to the nearest integer and then add or subtract.

EXAMPLE 1 Estimating Sums and Differences of Decimals

Estimate by rounding to the nearest integer.

Remember!
To round to the nearest integer, look at the digit in the tenths place. If it is greater than or equal to 5, round to the next integer. If it is less than 5, keep the same integer.

A 86.9 + 58.4

86.9	→	87	*9 > 5, so round to 87.*
+ 58.4	→	+ 58	*4 < 5, so round to 58.*
		145	← *Estimate*

B 10.38 − 6.721

10.38	→	10	*3 < 5, so round to 10.*
− 6.721	→	− 7	*7 > 5, so round to 7.*
		3	← *Estimate*

C −26.3 + 15.195

−26.3	→	−26	*3 < 5, so round to −26.*
+ 15.195	→	+ 15	*1 < 5, so round to 15.*
		−11	← *Estimate*

You can use *compatible numbers* when estimating. **Compatible numbers** are numbers that replace the numbers in the problem and are easy to use.

1 Introduce

Alternate Opener

EXPLORATION

4-1 Estimate with Decimals

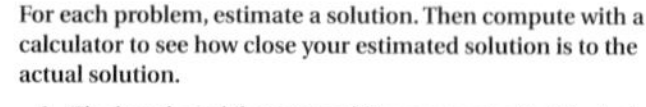

For each problem, estimate a solution. Then compute with a calculator to see how close your estimated solution is to the actual solution.

1. The lengths in kilometers of five segments of a bike trail are as follows:

4.75 6.36 4.29 5.09 8.2

		Estimate	Actual
a.	How long is the entire bike trail?		
b.	How long in miles is the bike trail? (*Hint:* 1 mile = 1.609 km. Use 6.2 mi = 10 km for your estimate.)		
c.	Sally traveled 7.7 kilometers in 32 minutes. At this rate, how long will it take her to complete the whole bike trail?		

Think and Discuss

2. **Discuss** the estimation strategies you used.
3. **Describe** a situation in which all you need is an estimated solution and a situation in which you must calculate an exact solution.

Motivate

To introduce estimating with decimals, present several advertisements showing prices for clothing or other items that students might want to purchase. Tell students to suppose that they have \$100 to spend and to choose two or three items to purchase. Then brainstorm ways students can decide whether they have enough money to purchase the items they have chosen, without adding the actual prices.

Exploration worksheet and answers on Chapter 4 Resource Book pp. 7 and 128

2 Teach

Lesson Presentation

Guided Instruction

In this lesson, students learn to estimate decimal sums, differences, products, and quotients. The examples show how to use both rounding and compatible numbers in estimation. Point out that the goal is to use numbers that are easy to compute so that students can estimate mentally.

Teaching Tip Discuss when to use compatible numbers versus rounding. Point out that rounding usually gives an estimate closer to the actual value than using compatible numbers does. However, for multiplication and division problems, using compatible numbers is often more convenient for mental computation.

Guidelines for Using Compatible Numbers	
When multiplying . . .	**When dividing . . .**
round numbers to the nearest nonzero integer or to numbers that are easy to multiply.	round numbers so that they divide without leaving a remainder.

EXAMPLE 2 Estimating Products and Quotients of Decimals

Helpful Hint

By rounding to multiples of 10, you can solve problems mentally.

Use compatible numbers to estimate.

A $32.66 \cdot 7.69$

32.66	→	30	*Round to the nearest multiple of 10.*
× 7.69	→	× 8	*6 > 5, so round to 8.*
		240 ←	*Estimate*

B $36.5 \div (-8.241)$

36.5	→	36	*37 is prime, so round to 36.*
−8.241	→	−9	*−9 divides into 36 without a remainder.*

$36 \div (-9) = -4$ ← *Estimate*

When you solve problems, using an estimate can help you decide whether your answer is reasonable.

EXAMPLE 3 *School Application*

On a math test, a student worked the problem 6.2)55.9 and got the answer 0.9. Use estimation to check whether the answer is reasonable.

55.9	→	56	*9 > 5, so round to 56.*
6.2	→	7	*7 divides into 56 without a remainder.*

$56 \div 7 = 8$ ← *Estimate*

The estimate is almost ten times the student's answer, so 0.9 is not a reasonable answer.

Think and Discuss

1. **Explain** whether your estimate will be greater than or less than the actual answer when you round both numbers down in an addition or multiplication problem.
2. **Describe** a situation in which you would want your estimate to be greater than the actual amount.

COMMON ERROR ALERT

Students might round incorrectly if they begin rounding with the place farthest to the right rather than identifying the place they need to round to. For example, to round 48.49 to the nearest whole number, they might first round to 48.5 and then round to 49. Suggest that students circle the place to which they are rounding, then underline the digit to the right of it, and disregard the other digits.

Additional Examples

Example 1

Estimate by rounding to the nearest integer.

A. 4.5 + 8.9 — 14

B. 28.3 − 11.7 — 16

C. 57.2 + (−23.72) — 33

Example 2

Use compatible numbers to estimate.

A. 45.99 · 2.31 — 100

B. 51.33 ÷ −7.98 — −7

Example 3

Cara spent $58.80 on 4.8 pounds of lobster. Is it reasonable to say that Cara spent about $12 per pound on lobster?

yes

3 Close

Reaching All Learners

Through Home Connection

Encourage each student to accompany a family member on a shopping trip to the grocery store. Ask students to estimate the total cost of the purchases before going through the check-out line and then compare the estimate to the actual total.

Summarize

Have students describe how they decide whether to round or use compatible numbers to solve a problem.

Possible answer: Round to the nearest integer to estimate sums and differences of numbers less than 100. Use compatible numbers to estimate products or quotients.

Answers to Think and Discuss

Possible answers:

1. Since both numbers are rounded down, the estimate will be less than the actual answer because smaller numbers are being added or multiplied.
2. If you are trying to see whether you have enough money to buy something, you probably would want to round up.

4-1 PRACTICE & ASSESS

Students may want to refer back to the lesson examples.

Assignment Guide

If you finished Example 1 assign:
Core 1–3, 8–13, 21–25 odd, 45–53
Enriched 1, 3, 9–13 odd, 21–26, 45–53

If you finished Example 2 assign:
Core 1–6, 8–19, 21–35 odd, 45–53
Enriched 1–5 odd, 9–19 odd, 21–35, 45–53

If you finished Example 3 assign:
Core 1–20, 21–41 odd, 45–53
Enriched 1–19 odd, 20–53

Answers

37. about 8 weeks

4-1 Exercises

FOR EXTRA PRACTICE see page 662

internet connect
Homework Help Online
go.hrw.com Keyword: MS4 4-1

GUIDED PRACTICE

See Example 1
Estimate by rounding to the nearest integer.

1. $37.2 + 25.83$ **63**
2. $18.256 - 5.71$ **12**
3. $-9.916 + 12.4$ **2**

See Example 2
Use compatible numbers to estimate. **Possible answers:**

4. $8.09 \cdot 28.32$ **240**
5. $-3.45 \cdot 73.6$ **−225**
6. $41.9 \div 6.391$ **7**

See Example 3

7. A student worked the following homework problem: $35.8 \cdot 9.3$. The student's answer was 3,329.4. Use estimation to check whether this answer is reasonable. **no, $36 \cdot 10 = 360$**

INDEPENDENT PRACTICE

See Example 1
Estimate by rounding to the nearest integer.

8. $5.982 + 37.1$ **43**
9. $68.2 + 23.67$ **92**
10. $-36.8 + 14.217$ **−23**
11. $15.23 - 6.835$ **8**
12. $6.88 + (-8.1)$ **−1**
13. $80.38 - 24.592$ **55**

See Example 2
Use compatible numbers to estimate. **Possible answers:**

14. $51.38 \cdot 4.33$ **200**
15. $46.72 \div 9.24$ **5**
16. $32.91 \cdot 6.28$ **180**
17. $-3.45 \cdot 43.91$ **−120**
18. $2.81 \cdot (-79.2)$ **−240**
19. $28.22 \div 3.156$ **9**

See Example 3

20. Amanda has a piece of ribbon that is 12.35 meters long. She wants to cut it into smaller pieces that are each 3.6 meters long. She thinks she will get about 3 smaller pieces of ribbon. Use estimation to check whether her assumption is reasonable. **yes; $12 \div 4 = 3$**

PRACTICE AND PROBLEM SOLVING

Estimate. **Possible answers:**

21. $5.921 - 13.2$ **−7**
22. $-7.98 - 8.1$ **−16**
23. $-42.25 + (-17.091)$ **−59**
24. $98.6 + 43.921$ **143**
25. $4.69 \cdot (-18.33)$ **−90**
26. $62.84 - 35.169$ **28**
27. $-48.28 + 11.901$ **−36**
28. $31.53 \div (-4.12)$ **−8**
29. $35.9 - 24.71$ **11**
30. $69.7 - 7.81$ **62**
31. $-6.56 \cdot 14.2$ **−98**
32. $4.513 + 72.45$ **77**
33. $-8.9 \cdot (-24.1)$ **225**
34. $6.92 \cdot (-3.714)$ **−28**
35. $-78.3 \div (-6.25)$ **13**

36. Jo needs 10 lb of ground beef for a party. She has packages that weigh 4.23 lb and 5.09 lb. Does she have enough? **no; $4 + 5 = 9$**

37. ***CONSUMER MATH*** Ramón saves $8.35 each week. He wants to buy a video game that costs $61.95. For about how many weeks will Ramón have to save his money before he can buy the video game?

Math Background

Clustering is another effective method of estimating with decimals. Clustering is useful if several values are close. Choose one value around which all the values cluster, and multiply it by the number of values. To use clustering to estimate the sum of $34.27, $29.75, and $28.79:

choose a cluster value: $30
multiply: $3 \cdot 30 = 90$

The estimate from clustering is $90.

RETEACH 4-1

LESSON 4-1 **Reteach**
Estimate with Decimals

You can estimate with decimals by rounding each number to its greatest **place**.

Estimate: 52.38 + 9.006
The greatest place of 52.38 is **tens.**
The greatest place of 9.006 is **ones.**
52.38 → 50   9.006 → 9
50 + 9 = 59
So, 52.38 + 9.006 is about 59.

Estimate: 97.45 − 14.9
The greatest place of 97.45 is **tens.**
The greatest place of 14.9 is **tens.**
97.45 → 1 00   14.9 → 10
100 − 10 = 90
So, 97.45 − 14.9 is about 90.

Estimate: 16.35 • 1.8
The greatest place of 16.35 is **tens.**
The greatest place of 1.8 is **ones.**
16.35 → 20   1.8 → 2
20 • 2 = 40
So, 16.35 • 1.8 is about 40.

Estimate: 29.7 ÷ 3.65
The greatest place of 29.7 is **tens.**
The greatest place of 3.65 is **ones.**
29.7 → 30   3.65 → 4
30 ÷ 4 is about 32 ÷ 4 = 8
So, 29.7 ÷ 3.65 is about 8.

Estimate.

1. 7.843 + 54.1
Greatest place of 7.843 **ones**
7.843 rounds to **8**
Greatest place of 54.1 **tens**
54.1 rounds to **50**
Estimate: **8 + 50 = 58**

2. 28.45 − 14.602
Greatest place of 28.45 **tens**
28.45 rounds to **30**
Greatest place of 14.602 **tens**
14.602 rounds to **10**
Estimate: **30 − 10 = 20**

3. 6.41 • (−19.725)
Greatest place of 6.41 **ones**
6.41 rounds to **6**
Greatest place of −19.75 **tens**
−19.725 rounds to **−20**
Estimate: **6 • (−20) = −120**

4. 44.67 ÷ 8.6
Greatest place of 44.67 **tens**
44.67 rounds to **40**
Greatest place of 8.6 **ones**
8.6 rounds to **9**
40 ÷ 9 is about **45 ÷ 9**
Estimate: **45 ÷ 9 = 5**

5. 36.5 + 78.09 **120**
6. 9.45 + (−2.75) **6**
7. 98.56 − 53.381 **50**
8. 33.52 • 5.29 **150**
9. −68.3 • 4.344 **−280**
10. 24.65 ÷ 4.92 **5**

PRACTICE 4-1

LESSON 4-1 **Practice B**
Estimate with Decimals

Estimate by rounding. **Estimates may vary.**

1. 7.45 + 35.84 **43**
2. 64.08 − 23.47 **41**
3. 6.842 + 14.05 **21**
4. 7.156 + 8.34 **15**
5. 84.23 + (−78.24) **6**
6. 3.78 − 2.078 **2**
7. 46.47 − 98.75 **−53**
8. 357.24 − 56.38 **301**
9. 6.324 + 60.324 **66**
10. −28.318 + 18.955 **−9**
11. 35.082 + 8.37 **43**
12. −62.49 − 12.84 **−75**

Estimate using compatible numbers. **Sample answers given.**

13. 59.69 ÷ 19.904 **3**
14. 86.234 • 9.876 **860**
15. 54.87 • 19.47 **1,100**
16. −16.04 • 10.45 **−160**
17. 31.25 • 6.57 **210**
18. 92.67 ÷ 32.89 **3**
19. 5.548 • 12.38 **72**
20. 88.42 ÷ 7.589 **11**
21. 90.05 ÷ 6.21 **15**

22. Lisha works 20 hours per week at the bowling alley and makes $8.55 an hour. She gets a raise of $1.30 an hour. Approximately how much more will she make each week with her raise?
$20

23. Miguel is able to save $87.34 each month. He wants to buy a guitar that costs $542.45. For about how many months will Miguel have to save before he can buy the guitar?
about 6 months

38. ***TRANSPORTATION*** Kayla stopped for gasoline at a station that was charging $1.119 per gallon. If Kayla had $5.25 in cash, approximately how many gallons of gas could she buy? **approximately 5 gallons**

Social Studies LINK

Inuktitut, the language of the Inuit people, is spoken by more than 60,000 people in Canada, Alaska, and Greenland. The Inuktitut word for "school" is *ilinniarvic.*

39. ***SOCIAL STUDIES*** The circle graph shows the languages spoken in Canada.

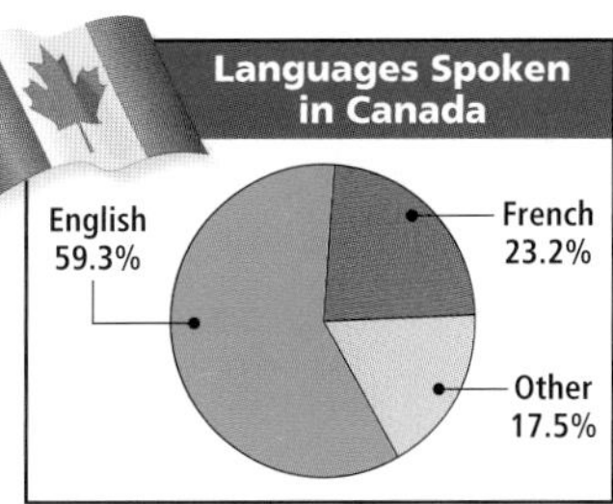

a. Which is the most common language spoken in Canada? **English**

b. What is the approximate difference between the percent of people who speak English and the percent who speak French? **36%**

40. ***ASTRONOMY*** Jupiter is 5.20 astronomical units (AU) from the Sun. Neptune is almost 6 times as far from the Sun as Jupiter is. Estimate Neptune's distance from the Sun in astronomical units. **about 30 AU**

41. ***SPORTS*** Scott must earn a total of 27 points to advance to the final round in an ice-skating competition. He earns scores of 5.9, 5.8, 6.0, 5.8, and 6.0. Scott estimates that his total score will allow him to advance. Is his estimate reasonable? Explain.

42. ***WRITE A PROBLEM*** Write a problem that can be solved by estimating with decimals.

43. ***WRITE ABOUT IT*** Explain how an estimate helps you decide whether an answer is reasonable.

44. ***CHALLENGE*** Estimate.
$6.35 - 15.512 + 8.744 - 4.19 - 72.7 + 25.008$ **−53**

Spiral Review

Order the integers from least to greatest. (Lesson 3-1)

45. −17, 9, −3, 6, −12 **−17, −12, −3, 6, 9**

46. 14, 23, −18, −32, 0 **−32, −18, 0, 14, 23**

47. 4, −5, 2, −1, −3 **−5, −3, −1, 2, 4**

Simplify. (Lesson 3-3)

48. $-14 + 7$ **−7**

49. $28 + (-18)$ **10**

50. $31 + (-50)$ **−19**

51. $-102 + 67$ **−35**

52. **TEST PREP** The low temperatures over a 6-day period in Fairbanks, Alaska, were −3°F, −10°F, −7°F, −9°F, −8°F, and −8°F. What are the mean, median, and mode of these temperatures? (Lesson 1-2) **B**

A −7.5°F, −9°F, −8°F

B −7.5°F, −8°F, −8°F

C 7.5°F, −8°F, −8°F

D −7.5°F, −8°F, 8°F

53. **TEST PREP** Solve $\frac{n}{-3} = 12$. (Lesson 3-6) **F**

F −36

G −4

H 4

J 36

Answers

41. Yes; Possible answer: Round down each score and multiply by the total number of scores: $5 \cdot 5 = 25$. Add 2 for the pair of 6's, so his score is at least 27. In fact, it is more since each other score is greater than 5.

42. Possible answer: A track is 3.7 miles long. A runner went around it 2.5 times. How many miles did the runner cover?

43. Possible answer: You can compare an estimate to the exact answer to see if the exact answer makes sense. If the answers are close, then the answer is reasonable.

Journal

Have students describe three examples of how they can use estimation in their daily lives.

Test Prep Doctor

In Exercise 52, students can eliminate **C** and **D** because all the measures will be negative. Because both **A** and **B** have the same values for the mean and mode, students only need to calculate the median. In Exercise 53, students can eliminate **H** and **J** because the answer must be negative.

CHALLENGE 4-1

LESSON 4-1 **Challenge**
Just Estimate

Use estimates to compare: 8.62 − 15.91 [?] − 2.4(3.8)

8.62 − 15.91 [?] − 2.4(3.8)

Think: 9 − 16 = −7   **Think:** −2 • 4 = −8

−7 > −8, so 8.62 − 15.91 > −2.4(3.8)

Estimate to compare. Use > or <.

1. 3.45 + 11.65 [>] 16.8 − 4.1
2. −0.54(14.22) [>] −23.65 + 9.44
3. −2.59 − 5.18 [<] 6.12 − 13.3
4. −9.6(−7.25) [<] 82.45 − 10.3
5. 24.7 ÷ 4.5 [<] 12.8 − 5.3
6. −20.8 + 12.3 [>] −20.2 ÷ 1.8
7. 125.95 − 25.4 [>] 1.5(50.38)
8. −14.57 − 7.34 [<] −39.62 ÷ 2.3
9. 4.9(−11.6) [<] 40.29 + 20.51
10. 47.6 − 17.7 [<] −7.7(−4.1)
11. 23.6 ÷ 5.5 [<] 13.08 − 8.4
12. 9.83 − 23.41 [<] −6.42 − 5.19
13. 18.45 ÷ 1.82 [<] 49.5 ÷ 5.46
14. 0.35(−3.55) [<] 4.68 − 5.54
15. 32.7 ÷ (−2.6) [<] −5.28(1.52)
16. −5.49(−4.06) [>] 24.62 − 6.4
17. −3.24 − 16.4 [>] −6.6(2.8)
18. 0.78(56.5) [<] −9.1 + 66.65
19. −45.3 ÷ 4.55 [>] 79.9 ÷ (−8.48)
20. −6.7(−5.08) [<] 18.5(1.54)
21. 65.36 ÷ (−10.7) [>] −9.3 + 1.48
22. −3.53(−2.45) [<] −119.5 ÷ (−11.7)
23. 65.5 − 67.09 [<] 34.4 ÷ 33.55
24. −40.06(−3.1) [>] 97.8 + 19.7

PROBLEM SOLVING 4-1

LESSON 4-1 **Problem Solving**
Estimate with Decimals

Write the correct answer. **Estimates may vary. Sample answers given.**

1. The Spanish Club makes a profit of $1.85 on every pie sold at a bake sale. The goal is to earn $40.00 selling pies. Will the club have to sell more than or fewer than 20 pies to meet the goal?
more than 20 pies

2. Murray and 4 friends split the cost of a pizza, with each paying the same amount. Murray has $3.36. The pizza costs $14.20. Does Murray have enough to pay for his share? About what is his share?
yes; about $3.00

3. Luis has 22 MB of free space on his MP3 player. He wants to download 5 songs. They will take up 5.1, 4.1, 4.3, 8.2, and 3.6 MB of space. Does Luis have enough free space? About how much space is needed?
no; about 25 MB

4. Debi has a gift certificate worth $50 for a local book-and-music store. She decides to buy a book that costs $18.95 and some CDs. Each CD costs $13.99. How many CDs can she buy?
2 CDs

Choose the letter for the best answer.

This table shows the number of dollars foreign tourists spent while visiting different countries in 2000.

Spending By Tourists in 2000

Country	Amount Spent by Foreign Tourists ($ billions)
United States	85.2
Spain	31.0
France	29.9
Italy	27.4
United Kingdom	19.5
China	16.2
Canada	10.8
Mexico	8.3
Hong Kong	7.9
Turkey	7.6

5. The amount spent in which two countries was about equal to the amount spent in China?
A Canada and Turkey
B Hong Kong and Canada
C Italy and Canada
(D) Hong Kong and Turkey

6. About how much did tourists spend in Spain, France, and Italy altogether?
(F) $88 billion
G $90 billion
H $61 billion
J $58 billion

7. If the amount spent by foreign tourists remains the same, about how much will foreign tourists spend in the United States over 5 years?
F $125 billion
G $225 billion
H $325 billion
(J) $450 billion

Lesson Quiz

Estimate by rounding to the nearest integer.

1. $68.4 + 29.5$ **98**

2. $7.24 + (-10.5)$ **−4**

Use compatible numbers to estimate. Possible answers:

3. $48.27 \cdot 4.67$ **250**

4. $54.37 \div 5.67$ **9**

5. Ray is catering a party for 60 people. He needs to have 30 pounds of potato salad. He has made 6.21 pounds and 22.68 pounds. Does he have enough for the party? no

Available on Daily Transparency in CRB

4-2 Organizer

Pacing: Traditional 1 day
Block $\frac{1}{2}$ day

Objective: Students add and subtract decimals.

Warm Up

Estimate by rounding to the nearest integer.

1. 3.62 + 4.1 **8**
2. 7.47 + (−8.23) **−1**
3. 8.52 − 3.16 **6**
4. 5.826 + 11.729 **18**
5. 15.39 − 6.24 **9**

Problem of the Day

Complete the magic square. The sum of each row, column, and diagonal must be the same number.

6.375	0.5	7
5.25	4.625	4
2.25	8.75	**2.875**

Available on Daily Transparency in CRB

Math Humor

How is the sum of 15 hundredths and 5 hundredths like a pair of teepees? It's two tents.

4-2 Adding and Subtracting Decimals

Learn to add and subtract decimals.

One of the coolest summers on record in the Midwest was in 1992. The average summertime temperature that year was 66.8°F. Normally, the average temperature is 4°F higher than it was in 1992.

To find the normal average summertime temperature in the Midwest, you can add 66.8°F and 4°F.

$$\begin{array}{r} 66.8 \\ +\ 4.0 \\ \hline 70.8 \end{array}$$

Use zero as a placeholder so that both numbers have the same number of digits after their decimal points.

Add each column just as you would add integers.

Line up the decimal points.

The normal average summertime temperature in the Midwest is 70.8°F.

EXAMPLE 1 Adding Decimals

Add. Estimate to check whether each answer is reasonable.

A 3.62 + 18.57

$$\begin{array}{r} 3.62 \\ +\ 18.57 \\ \hline 22.19 \end{array}$$

Line up the decimal points.
Add.

Estimate

4 + 19 = 23 *22.19 is a reasonable answer.*

B 9 + 3.245

$$\begin{array}{r} 9.000 \\ +\ 3.245 \\ \hline 12.245 \end{array}$$

Use zeros as placeholders.
Line up the decimal points.
Add.

Estimate

9 + 3 = 12 *12.245 is a reasonable answer.*

1 Introduce

Alternate Opener

EXPLORATION

4-2

Adding and Subtracting Decimals

Sue roller-skated 4.25 miles. She wants to roller-skate 10 miles. How many more miles does she need to roller skate?

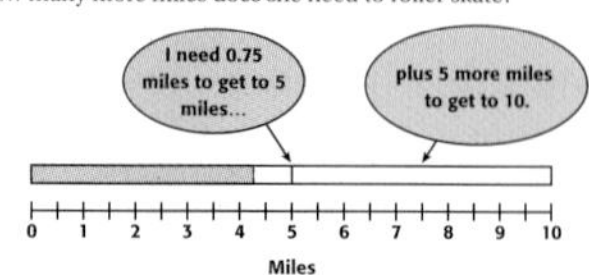
I need 0.75 miles to get to 5 miles...
plus 5 more miles to get to 10.
0
1
2
3
4
5
6
7
8
9
10
Miles

So Sue needs to roller-skate 5.75 more miles.

Sue used mental math and the strategy of adding up to the next whole number.

Use Sue's method to subtract the following decimals.

1. 12 − 9.8 **2.** 45 − 17.8
3. 10 − 3.37 **4.** 15 − 6.75

Think and Discuss

5. Write the steps for the strategy of adding up that you used in numbers 1–4. Then ask someone in class to follow your written steps to solve 67 − 24.3.
6. Describe how you can use mental math and adding up to find 200 − 176.25.

Motivate

To introduce adding and subtracting decimals, ask students to describe situations in which they might need to add or subtract decimals (e.g., to find the total cost of a number of purchases, calculating the number of miles a car has traveled over several days).

Exploration worksheet and answers on Chapter 4 Resource Book pp. 16 and 130

2 Teach

Lesson Presentation

Guided Instruction

In this lesson, students learn to add and subtract decimals. Direct students' attention to the data in the graph, and discuss what it shows. Ask students how using zero as a placeholder helps them to find the correct sum. Encourage students to use an estimate to check the reasonableness of the answer.

Teaching Tip You may wish to remind students that zeros can be written to the right of the last decimal place without changing the value of the decimal. For example, the decimals 4.2, 4.20, and 4.200 all name the same number.

Remember!

When adding numbers with the same sign, find the sum of their absolute values. Then use the sign of the numbers.

Add. Estimate to check whether each answer is reasonable.

C $-5.78 + (-18.3)$

$-5.78 + (-18.3)$	*Think: 5.78 + 18.3.*
5.78	*Line up the decimal points.*
+18.30	*Use zero as a placeholder.*
24.08	*Add.*
$-5.78 + (-18.3) = -24.08$	*Use the sign of the two numbers.*

Estimate

$-6 + (-18) = -24$ *−24.08 is a reasonable answer.*

EXAMPLE 2 Subtracting Decimals

Subtract.

A 12.49 − 7.25

12.49	*Line up the decimal points.*
− 7.25	
5.24	*Subtract.*

B 14 − 7.32

$\overset{13\ \ 9\ 10}{\cancel{14}.\cancel{00}}$	*Use zeros as placeholders.*
− 7.32	*Line up the decimal points.*
6.68	*Subtract.*

EXAMPLE 3 *Transportation Application*

During one month in the United States, 492.23 million commuter trips were taken on buses, and 26.331 million commuter trips were taken on light rail. How many more trips were taken on buses than on light rail? Estimate to check whether your answer is reasonable.

492.230	*Use zero as a placeholder.*
− 26.331	*Line up the decimal points.*
465.899	*Subtract.*

Estimate

490 − 30 = 460 *465.899 is a reasonable answer.*

465,899,000 more trips were taken on buses than on light rail.

Think and Discuss

1. **Tell** whether the addition is correct. If it is not, explain why not.

$$\begin{array}{r} 12.3 \\ +\ 4.68 \\ \hline 5.91 \end{array}$$

2. **Describe** how you can check an answer when adding and subtracting decimals.

COMMON ERROR ALERT

If students have difficulty aligning the decimal points, have them use graph paper to align the problem to be subtracted before they complete the computation.

Additional Examples

Example 1

Add. Estimate to check whether each answer is reasonable.

A. 4.55 + 11.3 **15.85**

Estimate: 5 + 11 = 16

B. 6.44 + 16 **22.44**

Estimate: 6 + 16 = 22

C. −8.33 + (−10.972) **−19.302**

Estimate: −8 + (−11) = −19

Example 2

Subtract.

A. 5.34 − 2.08 **3.26**

B. 28 − 15.911 **12.089**

Example 3

In Example 3 on page 197, what was the total number of trips taken on buses and light rail? Estimate to check whether your answer is reasonable.

518.561 million trips

Estimate: 492 + 26 = 518; reasonable

Example 3 note: Discuss the words in the problem that help students decide whether to add or subtract (e.g., total, difference).

3 Close

Summarize

Ask students to describe the steps necessary to add or subtract decimals.

Possible answer: Write the decimals in a column with the decimal points aligned. Write zeros as needed so that all the decimals have the same number of places. Then add or subtract as with whole numbers, placing the decimal in the answer directly below the decimal points in the numbers being added or subtracted.

Reaching All Learners

Through Number Sense

Have students solve a magic square with decimals. You may use the recording sheet provided on Chapter 4 Resource Book p. 125. A magic square is a square array of numbers in which each row, column, and diagonal have the same sum. Have students find the missing numbers in the following magic square. The sum is 10.2.

0.3	7.1	**0.5**	2.3
5.3	1.1	**3.7**	0.1
1.7	**1.3**	4.1	**3.1**
2.9	0.7	1.9	4.7

Answers to Think and Discuss

Possible answers:

1. The answer is not correct because the decimal points are not lined up. The solution should be as follows:

$$\begin{array}{r} 12.30 \\ +\ 4.68 \\ \hline 16.98 \end{array}$$

2. Check the reasonableness by estimating. Add to check subtraction. Add again to check addition, or subtract to check addition.

4-2 PRACTICE & ASSESS

Students may want to refer back to the lesson examples.

Assignment Guide

If you finished Example 1 assign:
Core 1–3, 8–13, 38–47
Enriched 1, 3, 9–13, odd, 22, 27–29, 38–47

If you finished Example 2 assign:
Core 1–6, 8–19, 23–31 odd, 38–47
Enriched 1–5 odd, 9–19 odd, 22–31, 37–47

If you finished Example 3 assign:
Core 1–21, 23–31 odd, 32–34, 38–47
Enriched 1–21 odd, 22–47

Notes

4-2 Exercises

FOR EXTRA PRACTICE
see page 662

internet connect
Homework Help Online
go.hrw.com Keyword: MS4 4-2

GUIDED PRACTICE

See Example 1 **Add. Estimate to check whether each answer is reasonable.**

1. 5.37 + 16.45 **21.82**
2. −5.62 + (−12.9) **−18.52**
3. 7 + 5.826 **12.826**

See Example 2 **Subtract.**

4. 7.89 − 5.91 **1.98**
5. 18.31 − 8.66 **9.65**
6. 4.97 − 3.2 **1.77**

See Example 3

7. In 1990, international visitors to the United States spent $58.3 billion. In 1999, international visitors spent $95.5 billion. By how much did spending by international visitors increase from 1990 to 1999? **$37.2 billion**

INDEPENDENT PRACTICE

See Example 1 **Add. Estimate to check whether each answer is reasonable.**

8. 7.82 + 31.23 **39.05**
9. 5.98 + 12.99 **18.97**
10. 4.917 + 12 **16.917**
11. 6 + 9.33 **15.33**
12. −3.29 + (−12.6) **−15.89**
13. −9.82 + (−15.7) **−25.52**

See Example 2 **Subtract.**

14. 5.45 − 3.21 **2.24**
15. 12.87 − 3.86 **9.01**
16. 15.39 − 2.6 **12.79**
17. 5 − 0.53 **4.47**
18. 14 − 8.9 **5.1**
19. 41 − 9.85 **31.15**

See Example 3

20. Angela runs her first lap around the track in 4.35 minutes and her second lap in 3.9 minutes. What is her total time for the two laps? **8.25 min**
21. A jeweler has 122.83 grams of silver. He uses 45.7 grams of the silver to make a necklace and earrings. How much silver does he have left? **77.13 g**

PRACTICE AND PROBLEM SOLVING

Add or subtract. Estimate to check whether each answer is reasonable.

22. −7.238 + 6.9 **−0.338**
23. 4.16 − 9.043 **−4.883**
24. 5.23 − (−9.1) **14.33**
25. −123 − 2.55 **−125.55**
26. 32.6 − (−15.86) **48.46**
27. −32.7 + 62.82 **30.12**
28. 1.99 + 4.8 + 12.9 + 8.532 **28.222**
29. 219.7 + 43.92 + 7.482 + 390.8 **661.902**
30. 5.9 − 10 + 2.84 **−1.26**
31. −8.3 + 5.38 − 0.537 **−3.457**

32. 1,642.5 mi

32. ***PHYSICAL EDUCATION*** The students at Union Middle School are trying to run a total of 2,462 mi, which is the distance from Los Angeles to New York City. So far, the sixth grade has run 273.5 mi, the seventh grade has run 275.8 mi, and the eighth grade has run 270.2 mi. How many more miles do the students need to run to reach their goal?

Math Background

Consider the fractional form of a problem such as 4.8 + 3.76 to help students understand why it is possible to align decimal points and add zeros to the right of decimals without changing their values.

$$4.8 + 3.76 = 4\tfrac{8}{10} + 3\tfrac{76}{100}$$

To add, rewrite with a common denominator of 100.

$$4\tfrac{8}{10} + 3\tfrac{76}{100} = 4\tfrac{80}{100} + 3\tfrac{76}{100}.$$

Showing the sum in this format relates directly to the addition of the decimals 4.80 and 3.76 and shows why the zero can be written to the right of the 8 without changing the value of the decimal.

RETEACH 4-2

LESSON 4-2 **Reteach**
Adding and Subtracting Decimals

You can use a place-value chart to add decimals.

Add: 3.48 + 2.7

Step 1: Line up the decimal points. Use 0 as a placeholder for hundredths in 2.7.

	Ones	.	Tenths	Hundredths
	3	.	4	8
+	2	.	7	0

Step 2: Add. Place the decimal point in the answer.

	Ones	.	Tenths	Hundredths
	1			
	3	.	4	8
+	2	.	7	0
	6		1	8

Step 3: Estimate: 3 + 3 = 3.
So, 6.18 is a reasonable answer.

Subtract: 68 − 5.9

Step 1: Line up the decimal points. Use 0 as a placeholder for tenths in 68.

	Tens	Ones	.	Tenths
	6	8	.	0
−		5	.	9

Step 2: Subtract. Place the decimal point in the answer.

	Tens	Ones	.	Tenths
		7		10
	6	~~8~~	.	~~0~~
−		5	.	9
	6	2	.	1

Step 3: Estimate to check: 68 − 6 = 62
So, 62.1 is a reasonable answer.

Add or subtract. Estimate to check your answer.

1. 19.67 + 8.45

	Tens	Ones	.	Tenths	Hundredths
	1	9	.	6	7
+		8	.	4	5
	2	**8**	.	**1**	**2**

2. 9.36 − 7.29

	Tens	Ones	.	Tenths	Hundredths
		9	.	3	6
−		7	.	2	9
		2	.	**0**	**7**

3. 25.36 − 9.7

	Tens	Ones	.	Tenths	Hundredths
	2	5	.	3	6
−		9	.	7	**0**
	1	**5**	.	**6**	**6**

4. 12.89 + 37.07

	Tens	Ones	.	Tenths	Hundredths
	1	2	.	8	9
+	3	7	.	0	7
	4	**9**	.	**9**	**6**

5. 34.71 + 9.19 **43.9**
6. 57.06 − 27.38 **29.68**
7. 48.3 + (−10.73) **37.57**

PRACTICE 4-2

LESSON 4-2 **Practice B**
Adding and Subtracting Decimals

Add. Estimate to check whether your answer is reasonable.

1. 6.14 + 8.91 **15.05**
2. 4.51 + 13.08 **17.59**
3. 12.54 + 21.08 **33.62**
4. 34.22 + (−18.5) **15.72**
5. −10.10 + (−5.9) **−16**
6. 6.87 + (−31.6) **−24.73**
7. 9 + 5.68 **14.68**
8. −15.51 + 8.55 **−6.96**
9. 36.36 + 54.54 **90.9**

Subtract. Estimate to check whether your answer is reasonable.

10. 6.23 − 3.62 **2.61**
11. 8.67 − 6.87 **1.8**
12. 28.94 − 9.48 **19.46**
13. 23.57 − 6.84 **16.73**
14. 16.61 − 7.56 **9.05**
15. 32.08 − 12.37 **19.71**
16. 19 − 6.92 **12.08**
17. 42 − 31.89 **10.11**
18. 23 − 21.45 **1.55**
19. 46.2 − 0.27 **45.93**
20. 22 − 18.63 **3.37**
21. 58.9 − 29.582 **29.318**
22. Anna swims the length of the pool in 38.45 seconds and then swims the length of the pool again in 42.38 seconds. What is her total time for 2 lengths of the pool? **80.83 seconds**
23. Po has 2 gerbils named Yip and Yap. Yip weighs 3.62 ounces, and Yap weighs 2.79 ounces. How much heavier is Yip than Yap? **0.83 ounces**

Egg-drop competitions challenge students to build devices that will protect eggs when they are dropped from as high as 100 ft.

33. ***PHYSICAL SCIENCE*** To float in water, an object must have a density of less than 1 gram per milliliter. The density of a fresh egg is about 1.2 grams per milliliter. If the density of a spoiled egg is about 0.3 grams per milliliter less than that of a fresh egg, what is the density of a spoiled egg? How can you use water to tell if an egg is spoiled? **0.9 g/mL; if the egg floats in water, it is spoiled.**

34. ***WEATHER*** The graph shows the five coolest summers recorded in the Midwest. The average summertime temperature in the Midwest is 70.8°F.

    a. How much warmer was the average summertime temperature in 1950 than in 1915? **1.6°F**

    b. In what year was the temperature 4.4°F cooler than the average summertime temperature in the Midwest? **1915**

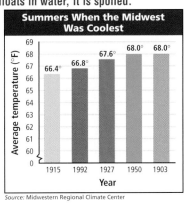

Summers When the Midwest Was Coolest

Year	Average temperature (°F)
1915	66.4°
1992	66.8°
1927	67.6°
1950	68.0°
1903	68.0°

Source: Midwestern Regional Climate Center

35. ***CHOOSE A STRATEGY*** How much larger in area is Agua Fria than Pompeys Pillar? **B**

    A 6.6 thousand acres

    B 71.049 thousand acres

    C 70.59 thousand acres

    D 20.1 thousand acres

National Monument	Area (thousand acres)
Agua Fria	71.1
Pompeys Pillar	0.051

36. ***WRITE ABOUT IT*** Explain how to find the sum or difference of two decimals. **Possible answer: Line up the decimal points. If needed, use zeros as placeholders. Add or subtract.**

37. ***CHALLENGE*** Find the missing number.

$5.11 + 6.9 - 15.3 + \square = 20$ **23.29**

Spiral Review

Evaluate. (Lesson 3-5)

38. $-5 \cdot 12$ **−60** 39. $-63 \div (-9)$ **7** 40. $20 \cdot (-7)$ **−140** 41. $18 \div (-3)$ **−6**

Solve. (Lesson 3-6)

42. $x - 12 = -26$ **$x = -14$** 43. $-7 + w = 12$ **$w = 19$** 44. $-3y = 21$ **$y = -7$** 45. $\frac{p}{6} = -11$ **$p = -66$**

46. **TEST PREP** Which fraction shows $\frac{24}{36}$ in simplest form? (Lesson 3-8) **D**

A $\frac{12}{18}$ B $\frac{4}{9}$ C $\frac{4}{6}$ D $\frac{2}{3}$

47. **TEST PREP** Which decimal is equivalent to $\frac{1}{8}$? (Lesson 3-9) **F**

F 0.125 G 0.8 H 0.18 J 0.0125

Journal

Have students describe real-world situations in which addition or subtraction of decimals is used.

Test Prep Doctor

For Exercise 46, students can eliminate **A** and **C** because they are not in simplest form. If students notice that $4 \cdot 6 = 24$ but $9 \cdot 6 = 54$, they can eliminate **B** as well.

CHALLENGE 4-2

LESSON 4-2 **Challenge**
Answer Match

Add or subtract. Draw lines to match equivalent answers in each column. Every answer in the middle column matches an answer in each outside column.

1. −61.244 + 59.014 **−2.23**	2. 21.65 + 14.2 + 10.03 **45.88**	3. 41.729 + 14.92 **59.649**
4. 4.018 + 7.052 **11.07**	5. 212.8 − 136.2 **76.6**	6. 42.25 − 13.174 **29.076**
7. −104.02 + 149.9 **45.88**	8. 0.015 − 6.72 **−6.705**	9. −0.673 + (−5.707) **−6.38**
10. −5.23 − 0.804 + 35.11 **29.076**	11. −70.6 + 48.05 + 33.62 **11.07**	12. 22.015 + 23.865 **45.88**
13. 60.25 − 0.601 **59.649**	14. 65.109 − 5.46 **59.649**	15. 7.17 − 9.4 **−2.23**
16. −1.08 + 3.797 − 9.422 **−6.705**	17. 10.25 − 12.03 − 0.45 **−2.23**	18. 16.02 + 44.48 + 16.1 **76.6**
19. 15.25 + 4.03 + 17.706 **36.986**	20. 130.82 − 101.744 **29.076**	21. −5.61 − 1.095 **−6.705**
22. 11.691 − 21.1 + 3.029 **−6.38**	23. 45.006 + (−8.02) **36.986**	24. 52.73 − 53.71 + 12.05 **11.07**
25. −33.42 − (−110.02) **76.6**	26. 46.01 + 9.9 − 62.29 **−6.38**	27. 6.007 + 74.2 − 43.221 **36.986**

PROBLEM SOLVING 4-2

LESSON 4-2 **Problem Solving**
Adding and Subtracting Decimals

Write the correct answer.

1. In the Pacific Ocean, the Philippine Trench is 10.047 kilometers deep. In the Atlantic Ocean, the Brazil Basin is 6.119 kilometers deep. How much deeper is the Philippine Trench than the Brazil Basin?
3.928 kilometers

2. Hawaii's Mauna Kea measures 9.754 kilometers from its base to its peak. Part of Mauna Kea lies 5.549 kilometers below the ocean. What is the height of the part of Mauna Kea that is above sea level?
4.205 kilometers

3. A team of mountain climbers makes camp 1.48 kilometers above sea level. They climb another 2.91 kilometers to the mountain's peak. How tall is the mountain?
4.39 kilometers

4. At dawn, the temperature at the summit of a mountain was −8.5°C. By noon, the temperature had increased 3.6°C. What was the temperature at noon?
−4.9°C

Choose the letter for the best answer.

This table gives the heights of the tallest mountains on each of the 7 continents.

The Seven Summits

Mountain	Country	Height (km)
Mt. Everest	Nepal-Tibet	8.848
Mt. Aconcagua	Argentina	6.960
Mt. McKinley	United States	6.194
Mt. Kilimanjaro	Tanzania	5.896
Mt. Elbrus	Russia	5.642
Vinson Massif	Antartica	4.897
Puncak Jaya	New Guinea	4.884

5. In 2000, Joby Ogwyn became the youngest person to climb each of the Seven Summits. How much farther did he climb on Vinson Massif than on Puncak Jaya?

   (A) 0.013 km C 0.181 km
   B 0.097 km D 4.888 km

6. Mt. Kilimanjaro, Mt. Elbrus, and Mt. Aconcagua were the first 3 of the Seven Summits Joby climbed. What was the total height he climbed?

   (A) 18.498 km C 21.45 km
   B 25.458 km D 19.164 km

7. Mt. Aconcagua is about 1.3 kilometers taller than which mountain?

   F Mt. Everest H Mt. McKinley
   (G) Mt. Elbrus J Vinson Massif

Lesson Quiz

Add. Estimate to check whether each answer is reasonable.

1. $6.98 + 14.27$ **21.25**
2. $-8.46 + (-19.2)$ **−27.66**

Subtract.

3. $6.72 - 4.16$ **2.56**
4. $24 - 3.8$ **20.2**
5. Renee finished her first lap in the 200 m freestyle event in 28.76 seconds. She completed the second lap in 29.17 seconds. What was her total time for the two laps? 57.93 seconds

Available on Daily Transparency in CRB

4A Model Decimal Multiplication

Pacing: Traditional 1 day
Block $\frac{1}{2}$ day

Objective: To use base-ten blocks and decimal grids to model multiplication

Materials: Base-ten blocks, decimal grids

Lab Resources

Hands-On Lab Activities . . . . pp. 20–23, 129–130

Using the Pages

Discuss with students what each base-ten block represents and how to represent decimals using base-ten blocks. Then discuss how to represent decimals on decimal grids.

Use base-ten blocks to model and evaluate each expression.

1. 6 · 0.02

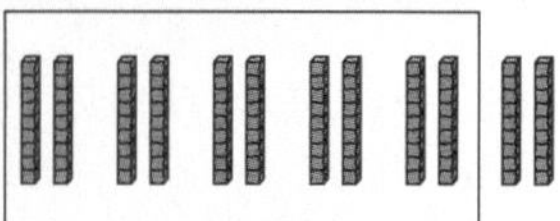

0.12

2. 3 · 0.007

0.021

Use a decimal grid to model and evaluate each expression.

3. 0.2 · 0.7

0.14

4. 0.3 · 0.5

0.15

Model Decimal Multiplication

Use with Lesson 4-3

KEY

= 1 = 0.1 = 0.01 = 0.001

REMEMBER

When using base-ten blocks, always use the largest value block possible.

internet connect
Lab Resources Online
go.hrw.com
KEYWORD: MS4 Lab4A

You can use base-ten blocks to model multiplying decimals by whole numbers.

Activity 1

Use base-ten blocks to find 3 · 0.1.

Multiplication is repeated addition, so 3 · 0.1 = 0.1 + 0.1 + 0.1.

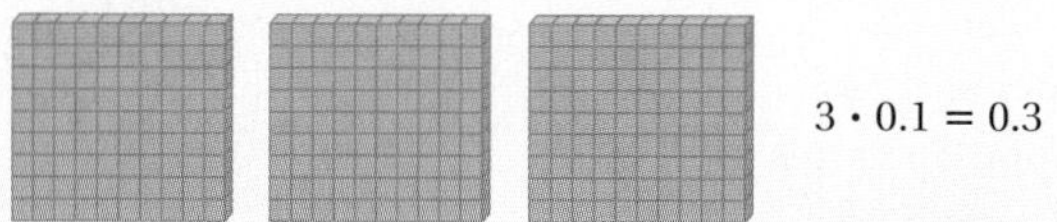

1 Use base-ten blocks to model and evaluate each expression.

a. 2 · 0.001 **0.002** **b.** 0.11 · 3 **0.33** **c.** 5 · 0.1 **0.5** **d.** 1.1 · 4 **4.4**

Use base-ten blocks to find 5 · 0.03.

5 · 0.03 = 0.03 + 0.03 + 0.03 + 0.03 + 0.03

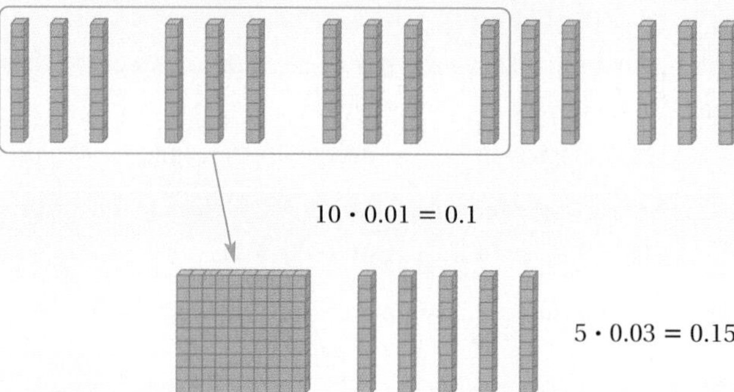

2 Use base-ten blocks to model and evaluate each expression.

a. 5 · 0.2 **1** **b.** 8 · 0.11 **0.88** **c.** 7 · 0.15 **1.05** **d.** 6 · 0.12 **0.72**

Think and Discuss

1. Why can't you use base-ten blocks to model multiplying a decimal by a decimal? **You can use only whole blocks, not partial blocks.**

Try This

Use base-ten blocks to model and evaluate each expression.

1. $4 \cdot 0.5$ **2** **2.** $2 \cdot 0.04$ **0.08** **3.** $3 \cdot 0.16$ **0.48** **4.** $5 \cdot 0.123$ **0.615**

5. $6 \cdot 0.2$ **1.2** **6.** $3 \cdot 0.33$ **0.99** **7.** $0.25 \cdot 5$ **1.25** **8.** $0.42 \cdot 3$ **1.26**

You can use decimal grids to model multiplying decimals by decimals.

Activity 2

Use a decimal grid to find $0.4 \cdot 0.7$.

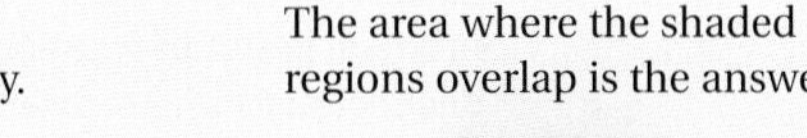

Shade 0.4 horizontally. | Shade 0.7 vertically. | The area where the shaded regions overlap is the answer.

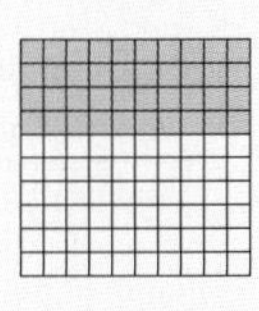

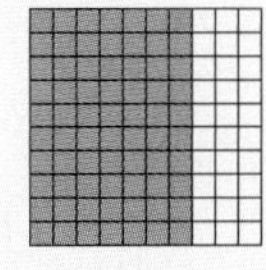

=

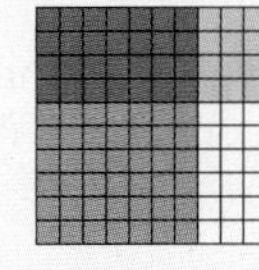

0.4 × 0.7 = 0.28

1 Use decimal grids to model and evaluate each expression.

a. $0.3 \cdot 0.4$ **0.12** **b.** $0.1 \cdot 0.1$ **0.01** **c.** $0.2 \cdot 0.2$ **0.04** **d.** $0.1 \cdot 0.2$ **0.02**

Think and Discuss

1. First shade 5 rows one color, and then shade 5 columns a second color. The answer is the region that was shaded twice.

1. Explain the steps you would take to model $0.5 \cdot 0.5$ with a decimal grid.
2. How could you use decimal grids to model multiplying a decimal by a whole number?
Shade the number of squares for the decimal as many times as the whole number.

Try This

Use a decimal grid to model and evaluate each expression.

1. $0.6 \cdot 0.6$ **0.36** **2.** $0.5 \cdot 0.4$ **0.2** **3.** $0.3 \cdot 0.8$ **0.24** **4.** $0.2 \cdot 0.8$ **0.16**

5. $3 \cdot 0.3$ **0.9** **6.** $0.8 \cdot 0.8$ **0.64** **7.** $2 \cdot 0.5$ **1** **8.** $0.1 \cdot 0.9$ **0.09**

4-3 Organizer

Pacing: Traditional 1 day
Block $\frac{1}{2}$ day

Objective: Students multiply decimals.

Warm Up

Multiply.

1. 842 × 76 **63,992**
2. 1,240 × 83 **102,920**
3. 821 × 712 **584,552**
4. 302 × 15 **4,530**
5. 1,823 × 12 **21,876**

Problem of the Day

Tickets to the district swim meet cost \$7.50 for adults, \$3.50 for children, \$5.00 for senior citizens, and \$4.00 for students. The total revenue for the meet was \$8,570. What missing information do you need in order to find out how many senior citizens were at the game?
number of adults, children, and students who attended the meet

Available on Daily Transparency in CRB

Decimals in a multiplication problem are like a pin factory. They make a product with a point.

4-3 Multiplying Decimals

Learn to multiply decimals.

You can use decimal grids to model multiplication of decimals. Each large square represents 1. Each row and column represents 0.1. Each small square represents 0.01. The area where the shading overlaps shows the product of the two decimals.

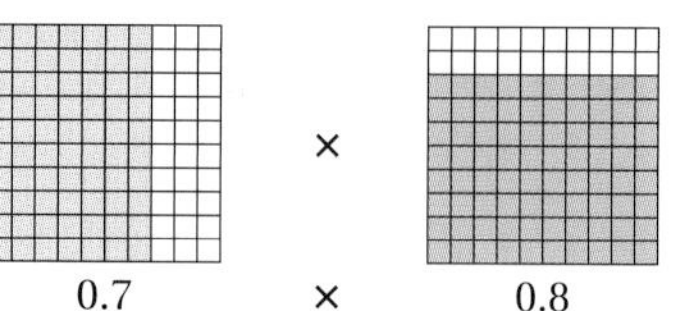

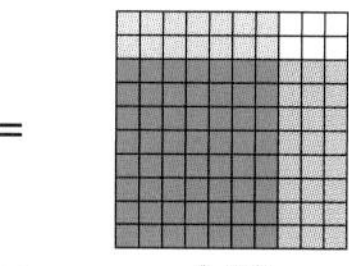

0.7 × 0.8 = 0.56

To multiply decimals, multiply as you would with integers. To place the decimal point in the product, count the number of decimal places in each factor. The product should have the same number of decimal places as the sum of the decimal places in the factors.

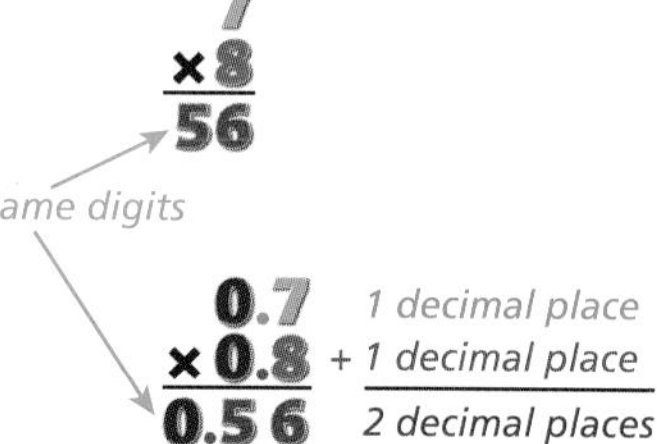

EXAMPLE 1 Multiplying Integers by Decimals

Multiply.

A $6 \cdot 0.1$

6	*0 decimal places*
× 0.1	*1 decimal place*
0.6	*0 + 1 = 1 decimal place*

B $-2 \cdot 0.04$

−2	*0 decimal places*
× 0.04	*2 decimal places*
−0.08	*0 + 2 = 2 decimal places. Use zero as a placeholder.*

C $1.25 \cdot 23$

1.25	*2 decimal places*
× 23	*0 decimal places*
3 75	
+ 25 00	
28.75	*2 + 0 = 2 decimal places*

1 Introduce

Alternate Opener

EXPLORATION

 **Multiplying Decimals**

Estimate each product. Then use a calculator to calculate the actual answer.

1. Ricardo averages 15.5 miles each hour he cycles.

		Estimate	Actual
a.	How far can he go in 3.75 hours?		
b.	How far can he go in 5.5 hours?		

Each of the following answers needs a decimal point. Use estimation to complete each product and to decide where to put the decimal point. Check your work with a calculator.

2. 10.5 · 2.4 = 2 5 2
3. 0.75 · 54 = 4 0 5
4. 64 · 3.125 = 2 0 0
5. 25.2 · 2.35 = 5 9 2 2

Think and Discuss

6. **Discuss** the estimation strategies you used.
7. **Explain** how you know where to place the decimal point in a product when you estimate and when you calculate the answer.

Motivate

Present the following situation:

> Potato salad costs \$0.99 per pound at the deli counter. About how much do you think 6.5 pounds of potato salad will cost?

Have volunteers share their answers and explain their reasoning. Students should realize that 99 cents is almost a dollar, so 6.5 lb of potato salad will cost about \$6.50. Point out that estimating products with decimals is similar to estimating products with whole numbers.

Exploration worksheet and answers on Chapter 4 Resource Book pp. 25 and 132

2 Teach

Lesson Presentation

Guided Instruction

In this lesson, students learn to multiply decimals. After reading through the examples, have students predict the number of decimal places in the product of 3.45 · 1.22. Write their predictions on the chalkboard. Then have students use a calculator to multiply the decimals. Challenge students to explain why there are four decimal places total in the factors, but only three decimal places in the product as shown by the calculator, 4.209. Have students do the multiplication using pencil and paper to see that the fourth decimal place is a zero, which is dropped by the calculator. Discuss how the value of the number does not change with or without the zero.

EXAMPLE 2 Multiplying Decimals by Decimals

Multiply. Estimate to check whether each answer is reasonable.

A $1.2 \cdot 1.6$

1.2	*1 decimal place*
× 1.6	*1 decimal place*
72	
120	
1.92	*1 + 1 = 2 decimal places*

Estimate

$1 \cdot 2 = 2$ *1.92 is a reasonable answer.*

B $-2.78 \cdot 0.8$

−2.78	*2 decimal places*
× 0.8	*1 decimal place*
−2.224	*2 + 1 = 3 decimal places*

Estimate

$-3 \cdot 1 = -3$ *−2.224 is a reasonable answer.*

EXAMPLE 3 *Earth Science Application*

On average, 0.36 kg of carbon dioxide is added to the atmosphere for each mile a single car is driven. How many kilograms of carbon dioxide are added for each mile the 132 million cars in the United States are driven?

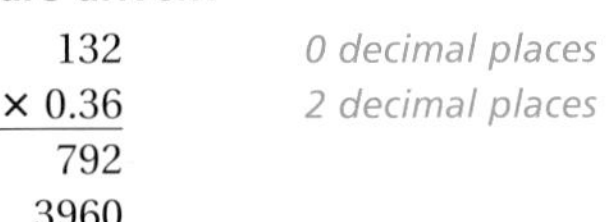

132	*0 decimal places*
× 0.36	*2 decimal places*
792	
3960	
47.52	*0 + 2 = 2 decimal places*

Estimate

$130 \cdot 0.5 = 65$ *47.52 is a reasonable answer.*

Approximately 47.52 million (47,520,000) kilograms of carbon dioxide are added to the atmosphere for each mile driven.

Think and Discuss

1. **Explain** whether the multiplication $2.1 \cdot 3.3 = 69.3$ is correct.
2. **Compare** multiplying integers with multiplying decimals.

COMMON ERROR ALERT

Some students write zeros as placeholders at the wrong side of the number in exercises such as Example 1B. Remind students to always count from right to left when placing the decimal point.

Additional Examples

Example 1

Multiply.

A. $7 \cdot 0.1$ **0.7**

B. $-3 \cdot 0.03$ **−0.09**

C. $2.45 \cdot 35$ **85.75**

Example 2

Multiply. Estimate to check whether each answer is reasonable.

A. $2.4 \cdot 1.8$ **4.32**

Estimate: $2 \cdot 2 = 4$

B. $-3.84 \cdot 0.9$ **−3.456**

Estimate: $-4 \cdot 1 = -4$

Example 3

To find your weight on another planet, multiply the relative gravitational pull of the planet and your weight. The relative gravitational pull on Mars is 0.38. What would a person who weighs 85 pounds on Earth weigh on Mars?

32.3 pounds

3 Close

Reaching All Learners

Through Curriculum Integration

Science Have students find the record temperatures for Alaska and Florida (given below in degrees Celsius) to the nearest degree Fahrenheit.

Record Temperatures Through 1999

State	High	Low
Alaska	37.8°C	−62.2°C
Florida	42.8°C	−18.9°C

Explain that to convert from Celsius to Fahrenheit, students must multiply by 1.8 and then add 32: $F = 1.8C + 32$.

Alaska: 100°F, −80°F; Florida: 109°F, −2°F

Summarize

Have students explain how to decide if the product of two decimal factors is correct.

Possible answer: First estimate the product, and then check that the number of decimal places in the product equals the total number of decimal places in the factors.

Answers to Think and Discuss

Possible answers:

1. It cannot be correct because there is only one decimal place in the product and there are two decimal places in the factors. Also, an estimate of $2.1 \cdot 3.3$ is $2 \cdot 3 = 6$. 69.3 is too great.
2. Multiplying integers and multiplying decimals are the same in the way the numbers are multiplied. When multiplying decimals, there is the additional step of placing the decimal point in the product.

4-3 PRACTICE & ASSESS

Students may want to refer back to the lesson examples.

Assignment Guide

If you finished Example 1 assign:
Core 1–3, 8–13, 42–49
Enriched 1–3, 8–13, 42–49

If you finished Example 2 assign:
Core 1–6, 8–19, 23–35 odd, 42–49
Enriched 1–5, odd, 9–19, odd, 22–35, 40–49

If you finished Example 3 assign:
Core 1–21, 23–37 odd, 42–49
Enriched 1–21 odd, 22–49

Notes

4-3 Exercises

FOR EXTRA PRACTICE see page 662

internet connect — Homework Help Online go.hrw.com Keyword: MS4 4-3

GUIDED PRACTICE

See Example 1 **Multiply.**

1. $-9 \cdot 0.4$ **−3.6**
2. $3 \cdot 0.2$ **0.6**
3. $0.06 \cdot 3$ **0.18**

See Example 2 **Multiply. Estimate to check whether each answer is reasonable.**

4. $1.7 \cdot 1.2$ **2.04**
5. $2.6 \cdot 0.4$ **1.04**
6. $1.5 \cdot (-0.21)$ **−0.315**

See Example 3

7. If Carla is able to drive her car 24.03 miles on one gallon of gas, how far could she drive on 13.93 gallons of gas? **334.7379 miles**

INDEPENDENT PRACTICE

See Example 1 **Multiply.**

8. $8 \cdot 0.6$ **4.8**
9. $5 \cdot 0.07$ **0.35**
10. $-3 \cdot 2.7$ **−8.1**
11. $6 \cdot 4.9$ **29.4**
12. $1.7 \cdot (-12)$ **−20.4**
13. $43 \cdot 2.11$ **90.73**

See Example 2 **Multiply. Estimate to check whether each answer is reasonable.**

14. $2.4 \cdot 3.2$ **7.68**
15. $2.8 \cdot 1.6$ **4.48**
16. $5.3 \cdot 4.6$ **24.38**
17. $-5.14 \cdot 0.03$ **−0.1542**
18. $1.04 \cdot (-8.9)$ **−9.256**
19. $4.31 \cdot (-9.5)$ **−40.945**

See Example 3

20. Nicholas bicycled 15.8 kilometers each day for 18 days last month. How many kilometers did he bicycle last month? **284.4 km**
21. While walking, Lara averaged 3.63 miles per hour. How far did she walk in 1.5 hours? **5.445 mi**

PRACTICE AND PROBLEM SOLVING

Multiply. Estimate to check whether each answer is reasonable.

22. $-9.6 \cdot 2.05$ **−19.68**
23. $0.07 \cdot 0.03$ **0.0021**
24. $-1.08 \cdot (-0.4)$ **0.432**
25. $1.46 \cdot (-0.06)$ **−0.0876**
26. $-325.9 \cdot (1.5)$ **−488.85**
27. $14.7 \cdot 0.13$ **1.911**
28. $-7.02 \cdot (-0.05)$ **0.351**
29. $1.104 \cdot (-0.7)$ **−0.7728**
30. $0.3 \cdot 2.8 \cdot (-10.6)$ **−8.904**
31. $1.3 \cdot (-4.2) \cdot (-3.94)$ **21.5124**
32. $0.6 \cdot (-0.9) \cdot 0.05$ **−0.027**
33. $-6.5 \cdot (-1.02) \cdot (-12.6)$ **−83.538**
34. $-22.08 \cdot (-5.6) \cdot 9.9$ **1,224.1152**
35. $-63.75 \cdot 13.46 \cdot 7.8$ **−6,692.985**

36. ***FINANCE*** Wanda earns $8.95 per hour plus commission. Last week, she worked 32.5 hours and earned $28.75 in commission. How much did Wanda earn last week? **$319.63**

Math Background

Evidence of tallying, or counting, was found on a bone fossil from 8500 B.C. The fossil had groups of notches in three columns. Making notches or scratches to tally is consistent with the origin of the word *tally*. It comes from the French word *tailler*, "to cut." The root Latin word is *talea*, which means "twig" or "cutting."

Tally sticks were used not only in ancient times. The British Exchequer accepted tally sticks as promissory notes up until the year 1846.

RETEACH 4-3

LESSON 4-3 **Reteach**
Multiplying Decimals

To multiply two decimals:
Step 1: Round each number to the nearest integer.
Step 2: Multiply the integers to estimate the product.
Step 3: Multiply the decimals.
Step 4: Place the decimal point in the product to make it closest to the estimate.

Multiply: 2.7 • 4.3

```
  4.3
  2.7
  301
  860
11.61
```

Think:
2.7 rounds to 3
4.3 rounds to 4
3 • 4 = 12
Place the decimal point in the product to make it closest to 12.

11.61 is close to 12.

Multiply.

1. 6.7 • 9.1
   6.7 rounds to **7**
   9.1 rounds to **9**
   The product is close to **63**.
   Product: **60.97**
2. −3.21 • 8.8
   −3.21 rounds to **−3**
   8.8 rounds to **9**
   The product is close to **−27**.
   Product: **−28.248**
3. 4.1 • 0.8
   4.1 rounds to **4**
   0.8 rounds to **1**
   The product is close to **4**.
   Product: **3.28**
4. 12.3 • (−2.7)
   12.3 rounds to **12**
   −2.7 rounds to **−3**
   The product is close to **−36**.
   Product: **−33.21**

Multiply. Estimate to place the decimal point.

5. 2.06 • 7.9 **16.274**
6. −4.89 • 0.6 **−2.934**
7. 8.23 • (−4.2) **−34.566**

PRACTICE 4-3

LESSON 4-3 **Practice B**
Multiplying Decimals

Multiply.

1. 6 • 0.3 **1.8**
2. 3 • 0.05 **0.15**
3. 0.7 • 4 **2.8**
4. 8 • 6.1 **48.8**
5. 7.4 • 6 **44.4**
6. 1.4 • 9 **12.6**
7. 4.8 • 7 **33.6**
8. 3 • 8.2 **24.6**
9. 5.5 • 8 **44**
10. 1.5 • 6 **9**
11. 7.9 • 2 **15.8**
12. 5 • 6.9 **34.5**

Multiply. Estimate to check whether your answer is reasonable.

13. 6.3 • 7.8 **49.14**
14. 9.7 • (−4.7) **−45.59**
15. 6.8 • 0.9 **6.12**
16. 2.8 • 8.2 **22.96**
17. −7 • 6.42 **−44.94**
18. 1.9 • 7.22 **13.718**
19. −5.3 • (−8.4) **44.52**
20. 7.16 • 0.03 **0.2148**
21. 1.56 • (−7.8) **−12.168**
22. 4.6 • 3.1 **14.26**
23. 0.62 • 1.45 **0.899**
24. −5.74 • 1.9 **−10.906**
25. Jordan jogged 4.8 miles each day for 21 days last month. How many miles did she jog last month? **100.8 miles**

37a. about 47 million people

37. ***RECREATION*** The graph shows the results of a survey about river recreation activities.

a. About how many people participated in these river recreation activities in 1999–2000?

b. In 1999–2000, almost 3 times as many people reported that they enjoyed canoeing than was reported in 1994–1995. If this trend continues, about how many people will report that they enjoy canoeing in 2004–2005? **about 60 million people**

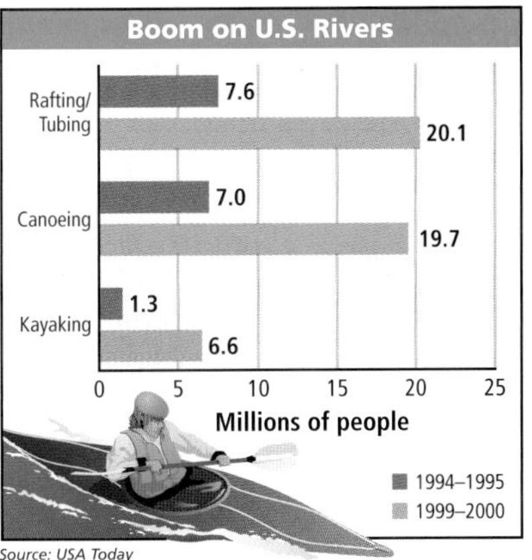

Source: USA Today

38. ***WEATHER*** As a hurricane increases in intensity, the air pressure within its eye decreases. In a Category 5 hurricane, which is the most intense, the air pressure measures approximately 27.16 inches of mercury. In a Category 1 hurricane, which is the least intense, the air pressure is about 1.066 times that of a Category 5 hurricane. What is the air pressure within the eye of a Category 1 hurricane? Round your answer to the nearest hundredth. **28.95 in. of mercury**

39. Possible answer: What is the total mass of the rocks in the collection?

39. ***WHAT'S THE QUESTION?*** In a collection, each rock sample has a mass of 4.35 kilograms. There are a dozen rocks in the collection. If the answer is 52.2 kilograms, what is the question?

40. ***WRITE ABOUT IT*** How do the products $4.3 \cdot 0.56$ and $0.43 \cdot 5.6$ compare? Explain.

41. ***CHALLENGE*** Evaluate $(0.2)^5$. **0.00032**

Spiral Review

Evaluate each expression for the given values of the variables. (Lesson 2-7)

42. $a^2 - 6a + 2$ for $a = 7$ **9**

43. $6m - 3p - 1$ for $m = 8$ and $p = 4$ **35**

Find each quotient. (Lesson 3-5)

44. $-49 \div (-7)$ **7**

45. $-75 \div 3$ **−25**

46. $64 \div (-4)$ **−16**

47. $-120 \div 5$ **−24**

48. **TEST PREP** Which number is less than −1.8? (Lesson 3-10) **A**

A $-1\frac{24}{25}$ B $-1\frac{8}{15}$ C 0 D 1.6

49. **TEST PREP** Amos has a gift certificate for $10.00. He wants to buy a book for $8.95 and a magazine for $3.50. How much more money does he need? (Lesson 4-2) **H**

F $12.45 G $6.50 H $2.45 J $1.05

COMMON ERROR ALERT

Some students may give a positive sign to the product of three negative numbers since all of the signs are alike, as in Exercise 33. Have students first find the product of two factors and then multiply that product times the third factor to show that the final product has a negative sign. It may be useful for students to just identify the sign of the solution for several problems without actually solving the problem. This gives them added practice efficiently.

Answers

40. They are the same: 2.408. Possible answer: The factors differ only in the placement of the decimal points. However, the product has the same number of digits after the decimal point.

Journal

Ask students to write the most helpful concept or rule they learned in this lesson. Encourage them to share and compare their responses.

Test Prep Doctor

For Exercise 49, students can estimate $8 + $3 = $11 and $9 + $4 = $13. Therefore, Amos will need between $1 and $3. Students can eliminate **F** and **G.**

CHALLENGE 4-3

LESSON 4-3 **Challenge**
Decimal Round

Think about numbers that could have resulted in this estimate.

$$0.8 \cdot 3 = 2.4$$

The *least possible factors* that could have been rounded up are 0.75 and 2.5. So, the *least product* is 0.75 • 2.5 = 1.875.

The *greatest possible factors* that could have been rounded down are 0.84 and 3.4. So, the *greatest product* is 0.84 • 3.4 = 2.856.

Find the products of the rounded numbers below. Write the least and greatest factors for each product before rounding. Then find the least and greatest products.

	Rounded Product	Least Product	Greatest Product
1.	18 • 12 = **216**	**17.5 • 11.5 = 201.25**	**18.4 • 12.4 = 228.16**
2.	3.3 • 4 = **13.2**	**3.25 • 3.5 = 11.375**	**3.34 • 4.4 = 14.696**
3.	0.9 • 0.7 = **0.63**	**0.85 • 0.65 = 0.5525**	**0.94 • 0.74 = 0.6956**
4.	1.8 • 2.2 = **3.96**	**1.75 • 2.15 = 3.7625**	**1.84 • 2.24 = 4.1216**
5.	6 • 0.1 = **0.6**	**5.5 • 0.05 = 0.275**	**6.4 • 0.14 = 0.896**
6.	4.5 • 0.6 = **2.7**	**4.45 • 0.55 = 2.4475**	**4.54 • 0.64 = 2.9056**
7.	10 • 1.1 = **11**	**9.5 • 1.05 = 9.975**	**10.4 • 1.14 = 11.856**
8.	0.3 • 15 = **4.5**	**0.25 • 14.5 = 3.625**	**0.34 • 15.4 = 5.236**
9.	8.7 • 5.1 = **44.37**	**8.65 • 5.05 = 43.6825**	**8.74 • 5.14 = 44.9236**
10.	1.4 • 1.9 = **2.66**	**1.35 • 1.85 = 2.4975**	**1.44 • 1.94 = 2.7936**

PROBLEM SOLVING 4-3

LESSON 4-3 **Problem Solving**
Multiplying Decimals

Write the correct answer.

1. A group of 6 adults bought tickets to a play at the community center. The tickets cost $17.50 each. How much did the tickets cost in all?

$105

2. Student tickets for the basketball playoffs cost $9.25 each. How much do 9 student tickets cost?

$83.25

3. Movie tickets for senior citizens cost 0.8 times as much as regular adult tickets. Adult tickets cost $7.50. How much do senior citizen tickets cost?

$6.00

4. About 30.5 million Americans attend classical music concerts. The average concertgoer attends 2.9 concerts per year. About how many tickets to classical concerts are sold each year?

about 88.45 million tickets

Choose the letter for the best answer.

5. IBM's income for 2001 was about 1.37 times its income for 1993. If IBM's income was $62.7 billion in 1993, what was its income in 2001, to the nearest tenth of a billion dollars?

A $8.6 billion
B $45.8 billion
(C) $85.9 billion
D $860 billion

6. In 2002, an estimated 5.3 million households in the United States had broadband connections. This number is expected to increase by about 4.7 times by 2006. About how many homes are expected to have broadband connections in 2006?

F 1.6 million homes
G 2.5 million homes
H 10 million homes
(J) 25 million homes

7. Nauru and Gibraltar are among the smallest countries in the world. Nauru has about 3.28 times the area as Gibraltar does. Gibraltar is 2.5 square miles. What is the area of Nauru?

A 0.78 sq mi
B 0.82 sq mi
C 5.78 sq mi
(D) 8.2 sq mi

8. From 1999 to 2008, the United States Mint will issue a series of 50 quarters representing each of the 50 states. What is the cost of collecting 10 of each quarter?

F $100
(G) $125
H $150
J $250

Lesson Quiz

Multiply.

1. $9 \cdot 0.7$ 6.3

2. $1.6 \cdot 1.5$ 2.4

Multiply. Estimate to check whether each answer is reasonable.

3. $3.4 \cdot 4.1$ 13.94

4. $7.62 \cdot (-5.4)$ −41.148

5. Dennis runs 7.2 miles per day. How far does he run in 5 days? 36 miles

Available on Daily Transparency in CRB

4-4 Organizer

Pacing: Traditional 1 day
Block $\frac{1}{2}$ day

Objective: Students divide decimals by integers.

Warm Up

Multiply or divide.

1.	3.4 × 2.6	**8.84**
2.	6.25 × 5	**31.25**
3.	8.14 × 1.1	**8.954**
4.	825 ÷ 15	**55**
5.	756 ÷ 12	**63**

Problem of the Day

Divide 60 by $\frac{1}{2}$ and add 10. What is your answer? **130**

Available on Daily Transparency in CRB

Dad, will you do my math homework for me tonight?

No, it wouldn't be right.

Well, you could try.

4-4 Dividing Decimals by Integers

Learn to divide decimals by integers.

Elena received scores of 6.85, 6.95, 7.2, 7.1, and 6.9 on the balance beam at a gymnastics meet. To find her average score, add her scores and then divide by 5.

6.85 + 6.95 + 7.2 + 7.1 + 6.9 = 35

35 ÷ 5 = 7

Elena's average score was 7, or 7.0.

Notice that the sum of Elena's scores is an integer. But what if the sum is not an integer? You can find the average score by dividing a decimal by a whole number.

Remember!

Division can undo multiplication.
0.2 · 4 = 0.8 and
0.8 ÷ 4 = 0.2

0.8 ÷ 4 — *0.8 divided into 4 equal groups.*

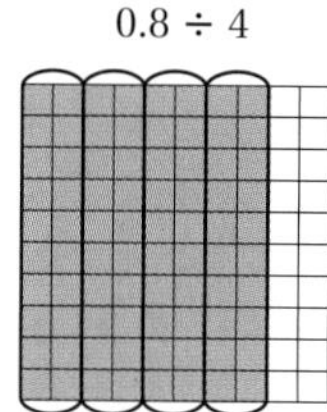

0.8 ÷ 4 = 0.2 — *The size of each group is the answer. Each group is 2 columns, or 0.2.*

EXAMPLE 1 Dividing Decimals by Integers

Divide. Estimate to check whether each answer is reasonable.

A 48.78 ÷ 6

```
   8.13
6)48.78
 -48
   07
   -6
    18
   -18
     0
```

Place the decimal point for the answer directly above the decimal point under the division symbol.

Divide as with whole numbers.

Estimate

48 ÷ 6 = 8 — *8.13 is a reasonable answer.*

1 Introduce

Alternate Opener

EXPLORATION

4-4 Dividing Decimals by Integers

Estimate each quotient. Then use a calculator to calculate the actual answer.

1. George averages 11 miles each hour he cycles.

		Estimate	Actual
a.	How long will it take him to go 64.9 miles?		
b.	How long will it take him to go 101.75 miles?		

Each of the following answers needs a decimal point. Use estimation to complete each quotient and to decide where to put the decimal point. Check your work with a calculator.

2. 280.5 ÷ 25 = 1 1 2 2
3. 100.4 ÷ 16 = 6 2 7 5
4. 17.35 ÷ 5 = 3 4 7
5. 16.2 ÷ 12 = 1 3 5

Think and Discuss

6. **Discuss** the estimation strategies you used.
7. **Explain** how you know where to place the decimal point in a quotient when you estimate and when you calculate the answer.

Motivate

To prepare students to estimate the quotients of decimals divided by integers, review the use of compatible numbers in estimation. Encourage students to explain what compatible numbers are and how they can be used to estimate quotients (e.g., they are numbers that divide evenly and are close to the original numbers). Ask volunteers to explain how they would estimate the following quotients: 39 ÷ 8 and 429 ÷ 7 (e.g., 40 ÷ 8 = 5 and 420 ÷ 7 = 60).

Exploration worksheet and answers on Chapter 4 Resource Book pp. 34 and 134

2 Teach

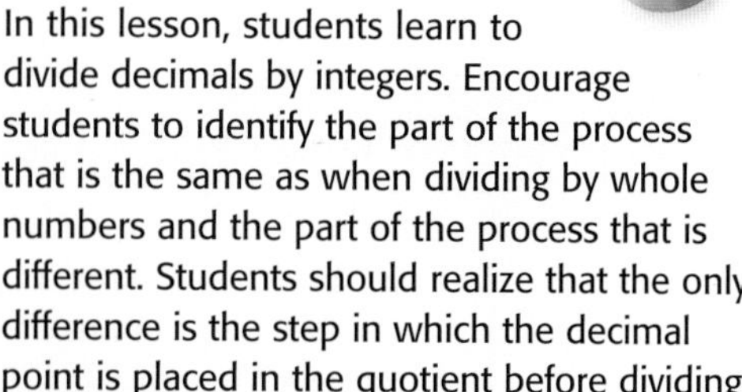

Guided Instruction

In this lesson, students learn to divide decimals by integers. Encourage students to identify the part of the process that is the same as when dividing by whole numbers and the part of the process that is different. Students should realize that the only difference is the step in which the decimal point is placed in the quotient before dividing.

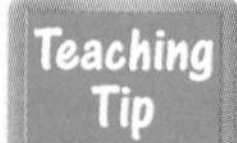

Show students how to use zeros as placeholders to continue dividing until there is no remainder. Remind the students that zeros can be written to the right of the last decimal place without changing the value of the decimal.

Divide. Estimate to check whether each answer is reasonable.

B 0.18 ÷ 2

$$\begin{array}{r} 0.09 \\ 2\overline{)0.18} \\ -18 \\ \hline 0 \end{array}$$

Place the decimal point for the answer directly above the decimal point under the division symbol.

Estimate

0.2 ÷ 2 = 0.1 — *0.09 is a reasonable answer.*

C 71.06 ÷ (−34)

$$\begin{array}{r} 2.09 \\ 34\overline{)71.06} \\ -68 \\ \hline 3\ 06 \\ -3\ 06 \\ \hline 0 \end{array}$$

The signs are different. Think: 71.06 ÷ 34. Place the decimal point for the answer directly above the decimal point under the division symbol.

71.06 ÷ (−34) = −2.09

Estimate

68 ÷ (−34) = −2 — *−2.09 is a reasonable answer.*

Remember!

When you divide two numbers with different signs, the answer is negative.

EXAMPLE 2 ***Money Application***

For Mrs. Deece's birthday, her class bought her a pendant for \$76.50 and a card for \$2.25. If there are 25 students in the class, what is the average amount each student owes for the gift?

First find the total cost of the gift. Then divide by the number of students.

76.50 + 2.25 = 78.75 — *The gift cost a total of \$78.75.*

$$\begin{array}{r} 3.15 \\ 25\overline{)78.75} \\ -75 \\ \hline 3\ 7 \\ -2\ 5 \\ \hline 1\ 25 \\ -1\ 25 \\ \hline 0 \end{array}$$

Place the decimal point for the answer directly above the decimal point under the division symbol.

Each student owes an average of \$3.15 for the gift.

Think and Discuss

1. **Describe** how to place the decimal point in the quotient when you divide a decimal by an integer.
2. **Explain** how to divide a positive decimal by a negative integer.

COMMON ERROR ALERT

Some students misalign the digits and therefore write the decimal point in the wrong place. Consider having them use graph paper to correctly align the decimal point in the quotient, as shown below.

		9 •	0	3	
6)	5	4 •	1	8	
−5	4				
	0	1	8		
	−	1	8		
			0		

Additional Examples

Example 1

Divide. Estimate to check whether each answer is reasonable.

A. 36.75 ÷ 7 **5.25**

Estimate: 35 ÷ 7 = 5

B. 0.87 ÷ 3 **0.29**

Estimate: 0.9 ÷ 3 = 0.3

C. 82.08 ÷ (−27) **−3.04**

Estimate: 90 ÷ −30 = −3

Example 2

You can buy juice by the bottle or by the case. Either way, it costs the same for each bottle. A case of 24 bottles of juice costs \$23.52. Kevin bought a bag of peanuts for 75¢ and 1 bottle of juice. How much did Kevin spend in all?

Kevin spent \$1.73.

3 Close

Reaching All Learners

Through Home Connection

Demonstrate to students how to measure the height of a person to the nearest quarter inch. Write the measurement in decimal form (e.g., $63\frac{1}{4}$ in. = 63.25 in.) Then ask students to measure the height of each of their family members to the nearest quarter inch and find the average height in their family.

Summarize

Have students list the steps to divide a decimal by an integer.

Possible answer: 1) Place the decimal point in the correct place in the quotient. 2) Divide as with whole numbers. 3) Check that the sign of the quotient is correct. 4) Estimate to check that the answer is reasonable.

Answers to Think and Discuss

Possible answers:

1. Before dividing, place the decimal point in the quotient directly above the decimal point that is in the dividend.
2. First place the decimal point in the quotient directly above the decimal point that is in the dividend. Next divide as with whole numbers. Then determine the sign of the quotient. When dividing numbers with different signs, the quotient is negative, so place a negative sign in front of the quotient.

4-4 PRACTICE & ASSESS

Students may want to refer back to the lesson examples.

Assignment Guide

If you finished Example 1 assign:
Core 1–6, 8–19, 23–39 odd, 47–56
Enriched 1–5 odd, 9–19 odd, 23–39, 46, 47–56

If you finished Example 2 assign:
Core 1–22, 23–43 odd, 47–56
Enriched 1–21 odd, 23–56

Notes

4-4 Exercises

FOR EXTRA PRACTICE see page 662

internet connect
Homework Help Online
go.hrw.com Keyword: MS4 4-4

GUIDED PRACTICE

See Example 1
Divide. Estimate to check whether each answer is reasonable.

1. $42.98 \div 7$ **6.14** **2.** $24.48 \div 8$ **3.06** **3.** $64.89 \div (-21)$ **−3.09**

4. $-94.72 \div 37$ **−2.56** **5.** $0.136 \div 8$ **0.017** **6.** $1.404 \div 6$ **0.234**

See Example 2
7. Members of a reading group order books for $89.10 and bookmarks for $10.62. If there are 18 people in the reading group, how much does each person owe on average? **$5.54**

INDEPENDENT PRACTICE

See Example 1
Divide. Estimate to check whether each answer is reasonable.

8. $12.8 \div 4$ **3.2** **9.** $80.1 \div (-9)$ **−8.9** **10.** $14.58 \div 3$ **4.86**

11. $-62.44 \div 7$ **−8.92** **12.** $7.2 \div 12$ **0.6** **13.** $33.6 \div (-7)$ **−4.8**

14. $0.108 \div 6$ **0.018** **15.** $65.28 \div 32$ **2.04** **16.** $-0.152 \div 8$ **−0.019**

17. $21.47 \div 19$ **1.13** **18.** $0.148 \div 4$ **0.037** **19.** $79.82 \div (-26)$ **−3.07**

See Example 2
20. Cheryl ran three laps during her physical education class. If her times were 1.23 minutes, 1.04 minutes, and 1.18 minutes, what was her average lap time? **1.15 minutes**

21. Randall spent $61.25 on some CDs and a set of headphones. All of the CDs were on sale for the same price. The set of headphones cost $12.50. If he bought 5 CDs, what was the sale price of each CD? **$9.75**

22. In qualifying for an auto race, one driver had lap speeds of 195.3 mi/h, 190.456 mi/h, 193.557 mi/h, and 192.575 mi/h. What was the driver's average speed for these four laps? **192.972 mi/h**

PRACTICE AND PROBLEM SOLVING

Divide. Estimate to check whether each answer is reasonable.

23. $-9.36 \div (-6)$ **1.56** **24.** $48.1 \div (-13)$ **−3.7** **25.** $20.95 \div 5$ **4.19**

26. $0.84 \div 12$ **0.07** **27.** $-39.2 \div 14$ **−2.8** **28.** $9.45 \div (-9)$ **−1.05**

29. $47.75 \div (-25)$ **−1.91** **30.** $-94.86 \div (-31)$ **3.06** **31.** $-0.399 \div 21$ **−0.019**

Evaluate.

32. $6.95 \div 5 \cdot 3 - 1.6$ **2.57** **33.** $0.29 + 18.6 \div 3$ **6.49**

34. $1 - 7.28 \div 4 + 0.9$ **0.08** **35.** $(19.2 \div 16)^2$ **1.44**

36. $-6.8 \div 4 \cdot (-2.5)$ **4.25** **37.** $-63.93 \cdot (-12.3) \div (-3)$ **−262.113**

38. $-2.7 \div 9 \div 12$ **−0.025** **39.** $-99.25 \div (-5) \cdot 4.7$ **93.295**

Math Background

Two names associated with division are Adam Ries and Johann Rahn. Adam Ries is noted for an explanation of division in his textbook published in 1550. What was remarkable about this was that at the time, division could be learned only at the University of Altdorf in Germany. Even most scientists did not know how to divide, yet Ries explained the process in a textbook meant for everyone. Johann Rahn was the first mathematician to use the division symbol ÷, which was introduced in his algebra book published in 1659.

RETEACH 4-4

LESSON 4-4 **Reteach**
Dividing Decimals by Integers

You can use models to divide decimals by integers.

Divide 0.35 ÷ 5.

Represent 0.35 by shading 35 out of 100 squares.

Divide the shaded area into 5 equal parts.

Each part is made up of 7 squares. This represents 0.07.

0.35 ÷ 5 = 0.07 or $5\overline{)0.35}$ = 0.07

Notice that the decimal point in the quotient is directly above the decimal point in the dividend.

Use the model to divide.

1. 0.48 ÷ 4 **0.12** 2. 1.8 ÷ 3 **0.6** 3. 0.16 ÷ 4 **0.04**

Divide. Draw models to help you.

4. 0.56 ÷ 8 **0.07** 5. 0.75 ÷ 5 **0.15** 6. 7.2 ÷ 9 **0.8**

7. 10.5 ÷ 5 **2.1** 8. 6.4 ÷ 16 **0.4** 9. 7.08 ÷ 6 **1.18**

PRACTICE 4-4

LESSON 4-4 **Practice B**
Dividing Decimals by Integers

Divide. Estimate to check whether your answer is reasonable.

1. 20.8 ÷ 8 **2.6** 2. 54.4 ÷ 5 **10.88** 3. 0.876 ÷ 6 **0.146**

4. 65.6 ÷ 4 **16.4** 5. −96.88 ÷ 7 **−13.84** 6. 50.4 ÷ 18 **2.8**

7. 67.42 ÷ 4 **16.855** 8. 88.65 ÷ (−3) **−29.55** 9. 77.25 ÷ 5 **15.45**

10. −0.18 ÷ 4 **−0.045** 11. 41.17 ÷ (−23) **−1.79** 12. 74.55 ÷ 25 **2.982**

13. 0.144 ÷ 4 **0.036** 14. 5.36 ÷ (−8) **−0.67** 15. 27.6 ÷ 12 **2.3**

16. 22.08 ÷ (−3) **−7.36** 17. 1.976 ÷ 13 **0.152** 18. 25.56 ÷ (−5) **−5.112**

19. 0.504 ÷ 9 **0.056** 20. 170.1 ÷ 27 **6.3** 21. 5.25 ÷ (−3) **−1.75**

22. Doris collects wicker baskets. She spent $9.56 on 3 baskets at the flea market. Then she found 4 more baskets at a garage sale. She paid $10.67 for those baskets. What was the average price per basket for all 7 baskets?

$2.89

23. As of January 2002, 3 top college football coaches had the following winning percentages in bowl games: 0.740, 0.692, and 0.683. What was their average winning percentage?

0.705

40. ***BUSINESS*** A ticket broker bought two dozen concert tickets for \$455.76. To resell the tickets, he will include a service charge of \$3.80 for each ticket. What is the resale price of each ticket? **\$22.79**

41. ***RECREATION*** The graph shows the number of visitors to the three most visited U.S. national parks in 2000. What was the average number of visitors to these three parks? Round your answer to the nearest hundredth. **14.53 million people**

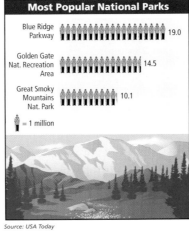

Most Popular National Parks

Park	Visitors (millions)
Blue Ridge Parkway	19.0
Golden Gate Nat. Recreation Area	14.5
Great Smoky Mountains Nat. Park	10.1

(icon) = 1 million

Source: USA Today

42. ***NUTRITION*** On average, each American consumed 261.1 lb of red meat and poultry in 2000. How many pounds of red meat and poultry did the average American eat during each month of 2000? Round your answer to the nearest tenth. **21.8 lb**

43. Jonathan wants a new mountain bike that costs \$216.99. If Jonathan can save enough money, his parents and grandparents have agreed to split the cost equally three ways with him. How much money must Jonathan save to get the mountain bike? **\$72.33**

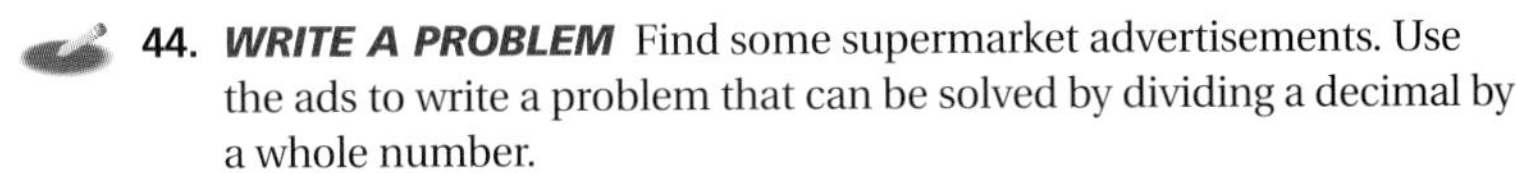

44. ***WRITE A PROBLEM*** Find some supermarket advertisements. Use the ads to write a problem that can be solved by dividing a decimal by a whole number.

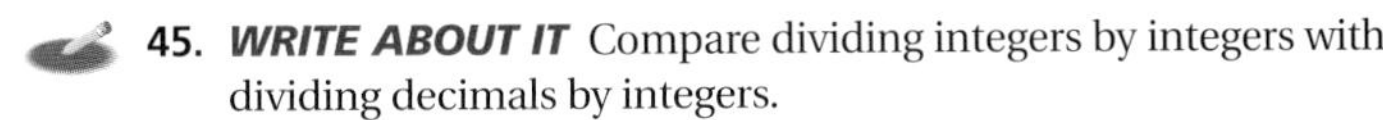

45. ***WRITE ABOUT IT*** Compare dividing integers by integers with dividing decimals by integers.

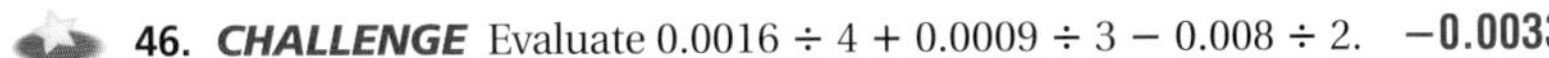

46. ***CHALLENGE*** Evaluate $0.0016 \div 4 + 0.0009 \div 3 - 0.008 \div 2$. **−0.0033**

Spiral Review

Add. (Lesson 3-3)

47. $-15 + 10$ **−5**
48. $8 + (-1)$ **7**
49. $97 + (-59)$ **38**
50. $-7 + (-25)$ **−32**

Subtract. (Lesson 3-4)

51. $-19 - 4$ **−23**
52. $-3 - (-61)$ **58**
53. $19 - (-12)$ **31**
54. $4 - 18$ **−14**

55. **TEST PREP** Simplify $(-5)^3$. (Lesson 3-5) **A**

A −125 **B** −15 **C** 15 **D** 125

56. **TEST PREP** Place these terms in order from least to greatest: 0.8, $\frac{1}{4}$, $\frac{1}{2}$, 0.3. (Lesson 3-10) **G**

F 0.8, $\frac{1}{4}$, $\frac{1}{2}$, 0.3 **G** $\frac{1}{4}$, 0.3, $\frac{1}{2}$, 0.8 **H** $\frac{1}{2}$, $\frac{1}{4}$, 0.3, 0.8 **J** $\frac{1}{2}$, 0.3, $\frac{1}{4}$, 0.8

Answers

44. Possible answer: It costs \$12.95 for 5 pounds of mixed nuts. What is the cost of 1 pound of mixed nuts?

45. Possible answer: The division process is the same. You must remember to place the decimal point in the quotient when dividing decimals by integers.

Journal

Ask students to describe a shopping situation in which they would need to divide a decimal by an integer.

Test Prep Doctor

For Exercise 55, students can eliminate **C** and **D** since the cube of any negative number is always negative.

CHALLENGE 4-4

LESSON 4-4 **Challenge**
Code to Order

Simplify each expression. Write the answers in order from least to greatest on the rules below. Then write the letter that corresponds to each answer in the same order to see a secret message.

1. $5.43 + 8(6 - 2.7) - 0.3^2 \div 9 + 12.6$ **44.42** [O]
2. $4^2(2 - 0.5) - 6.08 \div 2^3 + 13 \cdot 4.2$ **77.84** [O]
3. $(7.4 + 2.1) \div 5 + 1.2 \cdot (9 \div 0.3) - 8.4$ **29.5** [E]
4. $126 \div 12 \cdot 2 - 8(0.2 + 5) \div 2$ **0.2** [A]
5. $4 \div 0.2^3 \div 5 + (-5.95 + 5.45)^2$ **100.25** [B]
6. $72.32 \div 4 - 0.2^2 + 2.1 \div 0.3$ **25.04** [W]
7. $(0.2 \cdot 40 \div 2^2 + 10) \div 0.2^2 \cdot 0.5^2$ **75** [J]
8. $8(32 \div 1.6) \div 0.8 \cdot (0.7^2 + 1) \div 2.5$ **40** [S]
9. $54.18 + 2.34 \div 3.9 - 2.1 \cdot 1.2$ **52.26** [M]
10. $8.35 \div 5 + 5(4.86 \div 1.8)^2 \cdot 2$ **74.57** [E]

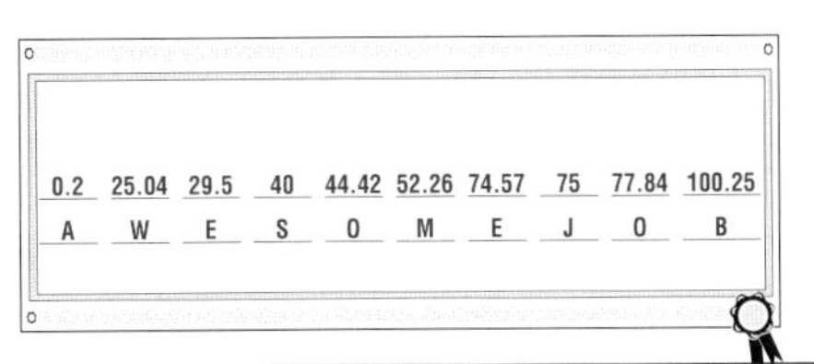

0.2	25.04	29.5	40	44.42	52.26	74.57	75	77.84	100.25
A	W	E	S	O	M	E	J	O	B

PROBLEM SOLVING 4-4

LESSON 4-4 **Problem Solving**
Dividing Decimals by Integers

Write the correct answer.

1. Teri collects loose change in 3 cans placed near cash registers at the mall. One can holds \$37.18. The second can holds \$44.25. The third can holds \$50.84. If Teri divides the money equally among 3 charities, how much money will each charity get?

\$44.09

2. In 2000, there were an estimated 5.28 million digital cable subscribers in the United States. The expected increase is 2.61 million by 2006. On average, over each of those 6 years how many new digital cable subscribers per year would be expected?

0.435 million per year

3. The longest life expectancies are found for Okinawa (81.2 years), Japan (79.9 years), and Hong Kong (79.1 years). Life expectancy in the United States is 76.8 years. About how much lower is that than the average life expectancy in the top 3 countries, to the nearest tenth?

3.3 years

4. The Ralstons are driving from Washington, D.C., to Los Angeles. The trip is 4,234.185 kilometers. The Ralstons want to make the trip in 5 days, driving the same distance each day. About how far will they drive each day? Round your answer to the nearest whole number.

about 847 km per day

Choose the letter of the best answer.

5. A top-grossing rock concert sold \$121.2 million worth of tickets over the course of 60 shows. What was the average value of the tickets sold at each of the shows?
   A \$20.2 million
   (B) \$2.02 million
   C \$0.202 million
   D \$7.27 million

6. A pizza parlor sells an 8-slice pizza for \$9.20. If the pizza parlor charges a total of \$1.20 more for a pizza it sells by the slice than for a pizza pie it sells whole, how much does a slice cost?
   F \$1.15
   G \$1.25
   (H) \$1.30
   J \$1.50

7. Bill orders 3 copies of a book from a book club. The cost is \$8.00, which includes \$0.50 for handling. How much does the book cost?
   A \$2.66 C \$0.25
   (B) \$2.50 D \$4.00

8. An apple pie has 27.6 grams of fat. It is cut into 6 slices. How many grams of fat are in 2 slices?
   F 4.6 grams H 13.8 grams
   (G) 9.2 grams J 92.0 grams

Lesson Quiz

Divide. Estimate to check whether each answer is reasonable.

1. $15.5 \div 5$ **3.1**
2. $22.8 \div (-6)$ **−3.8**
3. $72.48 \div 24$ **3.02**
4. $8.4 \div 12$ **0.7**
5. Allison swam 5 sprint laps in the pool. If her times were 17.5, 19.3, 20.6, 17.4, and 16.7 seconds per lap, what was her average lap time? **18.3 s**

Available on Daily Transparency in CRB

4-5 Organizer

Pacing: Traditional 1 day
Block $\frac{1}{2}$ day

Objective: Students divide decimals and integers by decimals.

Warm Up

Divide.

1. 24.5 ÷ 7 **3.5** **2.** 50.4 ÷ 6 **8.4**

3. 19.2 ÷ (−2) **−9.6** **4.** 128.1 ÷ 21 **6.1**

Problem of the Day

Place 20 pennies in a row on a table. Replace every fourth coin with a nickel. Now replace every third coin with a dime. Then replace every sixth coin with a quarter. What is the value of the 20 coins now on the table? **$1.35**

Available on Daily Transparency in CRB

Math Fact !

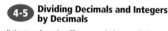

Engineers have built a tiny submarine that's just 0.16 inches long with a diameter of only 0.025 inches. It will be used to travel inside human blood vessels to repair damage. (*Source: Guinness World Records 2001*)

4-5 Dividing Decimals and Integers by Decimals

Learn to divide decimals and integers by decimals.

How many groups of 0.3 are in 0.6?

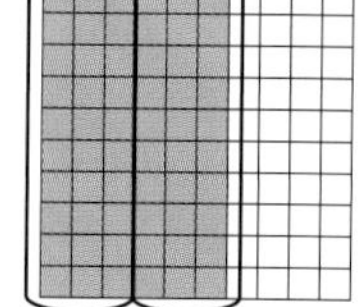

This problem is equivalent to 0.6 ÷ 0.3. You can use a grid to model this division by circling groups of 0.3 and counting the number of groups.

There are 2 groups of 0.3 in 0.6, so 0.6 ÷ 0.3 = 2.

When you divide two numbers, you can multiply *both numbers* by the same power of ten without changing the final answer.

Multiply both 0.6 and 0.3 by 10: **0.6 · 10 = 6** and **0.3 · 10 = 3**

$$0.6 \div 0.3 = 2 \quad \text{and} \quad 6 \div 3 = 2$$

By multiplying both numbers by the same power of ten, you can make the divisor an integer. Dividing by an integer is much easier than dividing by a decimal.

EXAMPLE 1 **Dividing Decimals by Decimals**

Helpful Hint

Multiply both numbers by the least power of ten that will make the divisor an integer.

Divide.

A **4.32 ÷ 3.6**

4.32 ÷ 3.6 = 43.2 ÷ 36 *Multiply both numbers by 10.*

```
     1.2
36)43.2        Divide as with whole numbers.
  −36
    7 2
   −7 2
      0
```

B **12.95 ÷ (−1.25)**

12.95 ÷ (−1.25) = 1295 ÷ (−125) *Multiply both numbers by 100.*

```
       10.36
125)1295.00     Use zeros as placeholders.
   −125         Divide as with whole numbers.
       45 0
      −37 5
        7 50
       −7 50
           0
```

12.95 ÷ (−1.25) = −10.36 *The signs are different.*

1 Introduce

Alternate Opener

EXPLORATION

4-5 Dividing Decimals and Integers by Decimals

Estimate each quotient. Then use a calculator to calculate the actual answer.

1. Mila averages 5.5 miles each hour she runs.

		Estimate	Actual
a.	How long will it take her to run 9 miles?		
b.	How long will it take her to run 15 miles?		

Think about real-world situations to find each quotient. For example, the division in number 2 could be expressed as "How many dimes are in $3.00?"

2. 3 ÷ 0.10 = ____
3. 3.75 ÷ 1.25 = ____
4. 3 ÷ 0.75 = ____
5. 7.2 ÷ 0.2 = ____

Think and Discuss

6. **Tell** whether the quotient of 10 divided by a decimal between 1 and 0 is greater than or less than 10.
7. **Explain** what it means to divide 3 by 2 (an integer by an integer) and 3 by 0.2 (an integer by a decimal). How are these divisions similar, and how are they different?

Motivate

Point out that dividing amounts of money by amounts of money is often an example of dividing decimals by decimals. Encourage students to describe a situation in which they would need to divide amounts of money by amounts of money. Then ask them to explain whether or not the quotient is an amount of money. For example, if students had $25.50 to spend on party favors and each favor cost $1.50, they could divide $25.50 by $1.50. The quotient would not be money, it would be the *number* of favors they could buy.

Exploration worksheet and answers on Chapter 4 Resource Book pp. 43 and 136

2 Teach

Lesson Presentation

Guided Instruction

In this lesson, students learn to divide decimals and integers by decimals. Emphasize that if the dividend and divisor are both multiplied by the same value, the quotient will remain the same. You may want to use Teaching Transparency T18 in the Chapter 4 Resource Book. To demonstrate this, have students multiply both numbers in Example 1B by 1,000 instead of 100. The final answer is the same as when both numbers are multiplied by 100.

EXAMPLE 2 Dividing Integers by Decimals

Divide. Estimate to check whether each answer is reasonable.

A $9 \div 1.25$

$9.00 \div 1.25 = 900 \div 125$ *Multiply both numbers by 100.*

$$\begin{array}{r} 7.2 \\ 125\overline{)900.0} \\ -875 \\ \hline 25\,0 \\ -25\,0 \\ \hline 0 \end{array}$$

Use zero as a placeholder. Divide as with whole numbers.

Estimate $9 \div 1 = 9$ *7.2 is a reasonable answer.*

B $-12 \div (-1.6)$

$-12.0 \div (-1.6) = -120 \div (-16)$ *Multiply both numbers by 10.*

$$\begin{array}{r} 7.5 \\ 16\overline{)120.0} \\ -112 \\ \hline 8\,0 \\ -8\,0 \\ \hline 0 \end{array}$$

Divide as with whole numbers.

$-12 \div (-1.6) = 7.5$ *The signs are the same.*

Estimate $-12 \div (-2) = 6$ *7.5 is a reasonable answer.*

EXAMPLE 3 *Transportation Application*

Helpful Hint

To calculate gas mileage, divide the number of miles driven by the number of gallons of gas used.

If Sandy used 15.45 gallons of gas to drive her car 370.8 miles, what was her car's gas mileage?

$370.80 \div 15.45 = 37080 \div 1545$ *Multiply both numbers by 100.*

$$\begin{array}{r} 24 \\ 1545\overline{)37080} \\ -3090 \\ \hline 6180 \\ -6180 \\ \hline 0 \end{array}$$

Divide as with whole numbers.

Sandy's car's gas mileage was 24 miles per gallon.

Think and Discuss

1. **Explain** whether $4.27 \div 0.7$ is the same as $427 \div 7$.
2. **Explain** how to divide an integer by a decimal.

COMMON ERROR ALERT

Some students interchange the divisor and dividend when translating a problem of the form $a \div b$ into the form $b\overline{)a}$. Remind students that the number after the division sign, ÷, is always the divisor, or the number outside the division house, $\overline{)}$.

Additional Examples

Example 1

Divide.

A. $8.28 \div 4.6$ **1.8**

B. $18.48 \div (-1.75)$ **−10.56**

Example 2

Divide. Estimate to check whether each answer is reasonable.

A. $4 \div 1.25$ **3.2**

Estimate: $4 \div 1 = 4$

B. $-24 \div (-2.5)$ **9.6**

Estimate: $-24 \div (-3) = 8$

Example 3

Eric paid $229.25 to rent a car. The fee to rent the car was $32.75 per day. For how long did Eric rent the car? 7 days

3 Close

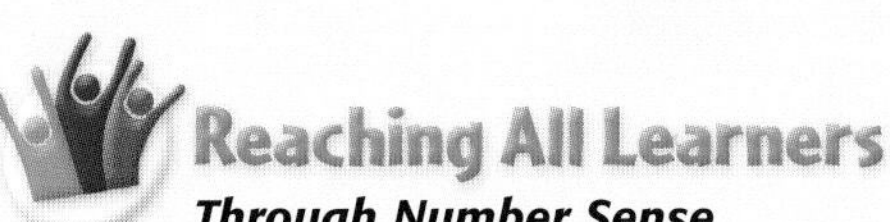

Reaching All Learners

Through Number Sense

Ask students to generate and test hypotheses about dividing decimals by different values. Present the following example:

Hypothesis: If the divisor is less than the dividend and both are positive, the quotient is always greater than 1.

Test: $12.5 \div 5 = 2.5$ (greater than 1)

Encourage students to test this hypothesis with other numbers. Then have students write another hypothesis and test it (e.g., if the divisor is greater than the dividend and both are positive, the quotient is always less than 1).

Summarize

Ask students to write what they believe are the two most important rules to follow when dividing decimals or integers by decimals. Have them share and compare their responses.

Possible answer: 1) To divide decimals by decimals, always multiply the divisor and dividend by a multiple of ten so that the divisor is a whole number. 2) The sign of the quotient is positive if the divisor and dividend have the same signs, and it is negative if the signs are different.

Answers to Think and Discuss

Possible answers:

1. They are not the same. To change 4.27 to a whole number, you must multiply by 100. You must also multiply 0.7 by 100, resulting in 70, not 7.
2. First multiply the divisor by a power of ten to make it a whole number, and multiply the integer by the same power of ten. Then divide as you would with whole numbers.

4-5 PRACTICE & ASSESS

Students may want to refer back to the lesson examples.

Assignment Guide

If you finished Example 1 assign:
- **Core** 1–6, 14–19, 31, 35–43 odd, 50–59
- **Enriched** 1–5 odd, 15–19 odd, 30, 31, 34–40, 42, 43, 50–59

If you finished Example 2 assign:
- **Core** 1–12, 14–25, 29–43 odd, 50–59
- **Enriched** 1–11 odd, 15–25 odd, 28–43, 50–59

If you finished Example 3 assign:
- **Core** 1–27, 29–47 odd, 50–59
- **Enriched** 1–27 odd, 28–59

Notes

4-5 Exercises

FOR EXTRA PRACTICE see page 662

internet connect — Homework Help Online go.hrw.com Keyword: MS4 4-5

GUIDED PRACTICE

See Example 1 **Divide.**

1. $3.78 \div 4.2$ **0.9** **2.** $13.3 \div (-0.38)$ **−35** **3.** $14.49 \div 3.15$ **4.6**

4. $1.06 \div 0.2$ **5.3** **5.** $-9.76 \div 3.05$ **−3.2** **6.** $263.16 \div (-21.5)$ **−12.24**

See Example 2 **Divide. Estimate to check whether each answer is reasonable.**

7. $3 \div 1.2$ **2.5** **8.** $84 \div 2.4$ **35** **9.** $36 \div (-2.25)$ **−16**

10. $24 \div (-1.2)$ **−20** **11.** $-18 \div 3.75$ **−4.8** **12.** $189 \div 8.4$ **22.5**

See Example 3 **13.** Samuel used 14.35 gallons of gas to drive his car 401.8 miles. What was his car's gas mileage? **28 mi/gal**

INDEPENDENT PRACTICE

See Example 1 **Divide.**

14. $81.27 \div 0.03$ **2,709** **15.** $-0.408 \div 3.4$ **−0.12** **16.** $38.5 \div (-5.5)$ **−7**

17. $-1.12 \div 0.08$ **−14** **18.** $27.82 \div 2.6$ **10.7** **19.** $14.7 \div 3.5$ **4.2**

See Example 2 **Divide. Estimate to check whether each answer is reasonable.**

20. $35 \div (-2.5)$ **−14** **21.** $361 \div 7.6$ **47.5** **22.** $63 \div (-4.2)$ **−15**

23. $5 \div 1.25$ **4** **24.** $14 \div 2.5$ **5.6** **25.** $-78 \div 1.6$ **−48.75**

See Example 3 **26.** Lonnie used 26.75 gallons of gas to drive his truck 508.25 miles. What was his truck's gas mileage? **19 mi/gal**

27. Mitchell walked 8.5 laps in 20.4 minutes. If he walked each lap at the same pace, how long did it take him to walk one full lap? **2.4 min**

PRACTICE AND PROBLEM SOLVING

Divide. Estimate to check whether each answer is reasonable.

28. $-24 \div 0.32$ **−75** **29.** $153 \div 6.8$ **22.5** **30.** $-2.58 \div (-4.3)$ **0.6**

31. $4.12 \div (-10.3)$ **−0.4** **32.** $-17.85 \div 17$ **−1.05** **33.** $64 \div 2.56$ **25**

Evaluate.

34. $11.5 \div 4.6 - 5.8$ **−3.3** **35.** $2 \cdot 6.8 \div 3.4 + 1.9$ **5.9**

36. $12 - 6.4 \div 2.56 - 1.2$ **8.3** **37.** $(11.7 \div 2.6 - 0.5)^2$ **16**

38. $(1.8 + 2.34) \div 0.75$ **5.52** **39.** $(-7.9 - 12.4) \div 3.5$ **−5.8**

40. $1.6 \div 3.2 \cdot 1.6$ **0.8** **41.** $127 \div (-12.7) \cdot (-25.32)$ **253.2**

42. $-24.63 \cdot (-3.9) \div 0.03$ **3,201.9** **43.** $96.3 \cdot 0.3 \div (-1.07)$ **−27**

Math Background

The decimal system was invented in India, but the exact time and place are unknown. However, it is known that the Hindu-Arabic numerals 1 through 9 are based on the Brahmi symbols, which were written as early as 250 B.C. and used to write Sanskrit. By A.D. 595, all numbers were written using the symbols for 1 through 9. The place in which the symbol was written was what gave the number its value. The symbol that was written in an empty place was believed to be first used in A.D. 876. This is the symbol we know today as zero.

RETEACH 4-5

LESSON 4-5 **Reteach**
Dividing Decimals and Integers by Decimals

To divide a decimal by a decimal:

Step 1: Make the divisor a whole number by moving the decimal point to the right.

Step 2: Move the decimal point in the dividend the same number of places. Remember to place the decimal in the quotient directly above the decimal point in the dividend.

Step 3: Divide.

Divide: $1.68 \div 0.3 \rightarrow 0.3\overline{)1.68} \rightarrow 3\overline{)16.8}$

$$\begin{array}{r} 5.6 \\ 3\overline{)16.8} \\ -15\downarrow \\ 18 \\ -18 \end{array}$$

The divisor, 0.3, has 1 decimal place. Move the decimal point 1 place to the right in both the divisor and the dividend.

Complete.

1. $5.6\overline{)4.48}$ **0.8**

a. How many decimal places are in the divisor? **1**

b. How many places do you need to move each decimal point? **1**

c. Rewrite the division. **$56\overline{)44.8}$**

d. Complete the division. What is the quotient? **0.8**

Divide.

2. $5.2\overline{)3.64}$ **0.7** 3. $0.09\overline{)36.45}$ **405** 4. $0.59\overline{)0.708}$ **1.2**

PRACTICE 4-5

LESSON 4-5 **Practice B**
Dividing Decimals and Integers by Decimals

Divide. Estimate to check whether your answer is reasonable.

1. $6 \div 0.25$ **24** 2. $78.74 \div 12.7$ **6.2** 3. $734.8 \div 1.67$ **440**

4. $347.25 \div 23.15$ **15** 5. $44.22 \div (-6.7)$ **−6.6** 6. $6.46 \div 0.034$ **190**

7. $550.44 \div (-13.9)$ **−39.6** 8. $89.886 \div (-21.3)$ **−4.22** 9. $927 \div 2.5$ **370.8**

10. $6.222 \div 10.2$ **0.61** 11. $56.525 \div 0.85$ **66.5** 12. $48.306 \div 16.6$ **2.91**

13. Freddie used 6.75 gallons of gas to drive 155.25 miles. What was his car's gas mileage? **23 miles per gallon**

14. The members of a book club met at a restaurant for dinner. The total bill was $112.95 and they shared the bill equally. Each person paid $12.55. How many members are there in the book club? **9 members**

Earth Science LINK

A glacier in Col Ferret, a pass in the Swiss Alps

44. Glaciers form when snow accumulates faster than it melts and thus becomes compacted into ice under the weight of more snow. Once the ice reaches a thickness of about 18 m, it begins to flow. If ice were to accumulate at a rate of 0.0072 m per year, how long would it take to start flowing? **2,500 years**

45. An alpine glacier is estimated to be flowing at a rate of 4.75 m per day. At this rate, how long will it take for a marker placed on the glacier by a researcher to move 1,140 m? **240 days**

46. If the Muir Glacier in Glacier Bay, Alaska, retreats at an average speed of 0.73 m per year, how long will it take to retreat a total of 7.9 m? Round your answer to the nearest year. **11 years**

47. The table shows the thickness of a glacier as measured at five different points using radar. What is the average thickness of the glacier? **202.228 m**

Location	Thickness (m)
A	180.23
B	160.5
C	210.19
D	260
E	200.22

48. The Harvard Glacier in Alaska is advancing at a rate of about 0.055 m per day. At this rate, how long will it take the glacier to advance 20 m? Round your answer to the nearest hundredth. **363.64 days**

49. ***CHALLENGE*** Hinman Glacier, on Mount Hinman, in Washington State, had an area of 1.3 km^2 in 1958. The glacier has lost an average of 0.06875 km^2 of area each year. In what year was the total area 0.2 km^2? **1974**

go.hrw.com
KEYWORD: MS4 Ice

Spiral Review

Find the prime factorization of each number. (Lesson 2-4)

50. 54 $2 \cdot 3^3$ **51.** 88 $2^3 \cdot 11$ **52.** 92 $2^2 \cdot 23$ **53.** 225 $3^2 \cdot 5^2$

Multiply. Estimate to check whether each answer is reasonable. (Lesson 4-3)

54. $1.8 \cdot (-0.7)$ **−1.26** **55.** $-3.2 \cdot 1.04$ **−3.328** **56.** $4.17 \cdot 36$ **150.12** **57.** $-0.09 \cdot (-5.34)$ **0.4806**

58. TEST PREP Kay swims every 4 days, Nathan every 3 days, and Julia every 6 days. They all swam on May 1. On what day will they all swim again? (Lesson 2-6) **C**

A May 6 **C** May 13
B May 9 **D** May 16

59. TEST PREP Jamison owes his sister $15. He pays her back $4 one day and $7 the next day. How much does he still owe his sister? (Lesson 3-3) **J**

F $26 **H** $8
G $11 **J** $4

CHALLENGE 4-5

LESSON 4-5 **Challenge**
Go For the Gold

A **golden rectangle** is a rectangle with a special relationship between the length and the width. The ancient Greeks believed that the shape of the golden rectangle was especially pleasing to the eye.

Discover the relationship between the length and width that makes a rectangle a golden rectangle.

1. The length of a golden rectangle is 5.26 centimeters and the width is 3.25 centimeters. Use a centimeter ruler to draw the rectangle.

   Check students' drawings; Rectangle should be about 5.3 cm long and 3.3 cm wide.

2. The **golden ratio** is a value that characterizes the relationship between the length and width of a golden rectangle. Use the dimensions of the golden rectangle above. Divide the length by the width to find the golden ratio. Round to the nearest hundredth.

   1.62

For each length given below, use the golden ratio to find the width to make a golden rectangle. Round your answers to the nearest hundredth.

3. length = 8 meters **4.94 meters**
4. length = 4.85 inches **2.99 inches**
5. length = 6.09 feet **3.76 feet**
6. length = 12 yards **7.41 yards**
7. length = 16.5 centimeters **10.19 centimeters**
8. length = 24.6 meters **15.19 meters**
9. length = 55 inches **33.95 inches**
10. length = 83.2 feet **51.36 feet**
11. length = 98.2 yards **60.62 yards**
12. length = 116 centimeters **71.60 centimeters**
13. length = 220.5 inches **136.11 inches**
14. length = 348.7 meters **215.25 meters**

PROBLEM SOLVING 4-5

LESSON 4-5 **Problem Solving**
Dividing Decimals and Integers by Decimals

Write the correct answer.

1. Fran has a plank of wood 4.65 meters long. She wants to cut it into pieces 0.85 meters long. How many pieces of wood that length can she cut from the plank?

   5 pieces

2. Jeremy has a box of 500 nails that weighs 1.35 kilograms. He uses 60 nails to build a birdhouse. How much do the nails in the birdhouse weigh?

   0.162 kilograms

3. Rhosanda is downloading a file from the Internet. The size of the file is 7.45 MB. The file is downloading at the rate of 0.095 MB per second. How many seconds will it take to download the entire file? Round your answer to the nearest second.

   79 seconds

4. Sean has a piece of poster board with an area of 476.28 square centimeters. He cuts it into equal-sized squares, each with an area of 39.69 square centimeters. How many squares can he cut from the piece of poster board?

   12 squares

Choose the letter for the best answer.

5. Mount McKinley, in Alaska, is about 3.848 miles high. If a mountain climber can climb 0.25 miles per day, about how long, to the nearest day, would it take to climb Mount McKinley?
   - A about 5 days
   - B about 8 days
   - C about 12 days
   - (D) about 16 days

6. In 2000, a production worker in Japan who worked 38.5 hours in a week would have earned an average of $847. What was the hourly wage?
   - F $2.20 per hour
   - G $3.20 per hour
   - (H) $22.00 per hour
   - J $32.00 per hour

7. In the 2000 Summer Olympics, Michael Johnson ran the 400-meter race in 43.84 seconds. To the nearest hundredth, what was his speed in meters per second?
   - (A) 9.12 meters per second
   - B 10.96 meters per second
   - C 1.09 meters per second
   - D 91.24 meters per second

8. In the 2000 Summer Olympics, the United States relay team ran the 1,600-meter relay in 2 minutes, 56.35 seconds. To the nearest hundredth, what was the speed for the relay race in meters per second?
   - F 2.83 meters per second
   - G 6.24 meters per second
   - (H) 9.07 meters per second
   - J 28.39 meters per second

Interdisciplinary LINK

Earth Science

Exercises 44–49 involve using information about glaciers. Glaciers are studied in middle school Earth science programs, such as *Holt Science & Technology.*

Journal

Ask students to describe a real-world situation in which knowing how to divide by decimals would be useful.

Test Prep Doctor

For Exercise 59, students can eliminate **F** since it is more money than Jamison owes to begin with. They can eliminate **G** since that is how much he will owe after the first payment, and they know he made another payment. He must owe less than $11.

Lesson Quiz

Divide. Estimate to check whether each answer is reasonable.

1. 78.2 ÷ 0.04 **1,955**
2. −9.72 ÷ 2.7 **−3.6**
3. 18.88 ÷ 1.6 **11.8**
4. 19.5 ÷ 3.25 **6**
5. Jordan used 32.46 gallons of gas to drive his van 584.28 miles. How many miles did Jordan get per gallon? **18**

Available on Daily Transparency in CRB

4-6 Organizer

Pacing: Traditional 1 day
Block $\frac{1}{2}$ day

Objective: Students solve one-step equations that contain decimals.

Warm Up

Solve.

1. $x - 17 = 32$ $\quad x = 49$
2. $y + 11 = 41$ $\quad y = 30$
3. $\frac{w}{5} = 18$ $\quad w = 90$
4. $12x = 108$ $\quad x = 9$
5. $x - 9 = 20$ $\quad x = 29$

Problem of the Day

A bowling league has 156 players evenly distibuted on 39 teams. If 40 players switch to another league and the number of teams is reduced to 29, will there still be the same number of players on each team? yes; 4

Available on Daily Transparency in CRB

Math Fact !

Chinese mathematicians had developed a decimal system by 100 B.C. It included fractions, zero, and negative numbers.

4-6 Solving Equations Containing Decimals

Learn to solve one-step equations that contain decimals.

Students in a physical education class were running 40-yard dashes as part of a fitness test. The slowest time in the class was 3.84 seconds slower than the fastest time of 7.2 seconds.

You can write an equation to represent this situation. The slowest time s minus 3.84 is equal to the fastest time of 7.2 seconds.

$$s - 3.84 = 7.2$$

EXAMPLE 1 Solving Equations by Adding or Subtracting

Remember!
You can solve an equation by performing the same operation on both sides of the equation to isolate the variable.

Solve.

A $s - 3.84 = 7.2$

$$\begin{aligned} s - 3.84 &= 7.20 \\ +3.84 \quad &\quad +3.84 \\ s &= 11.04 \end{aligned}$$

Add to isolate s.

B $y + 20.51 = 26$

$$\begin{aligned} y + 20.51 &= \overset{5\ 9\ 10}{26.00} \\ -20.51 \quad &\quad -20.51 \\ y &= 5.49 \end{aligned}$$

Subtract to isolate y.

EXAMPLE 2 Solving Equations by Multiplying or Dividing

Solve.

A $\frac{w}{3.9} = 1.2$

$$\frac{w}{3.9} = 1.2$$

$$\frac{w}{3.9} \cdot 3.9 = 1.2 \cdot 3.9$$ *Multiply to isolate w.*

$$w = 4.68$$

B $4 = 1.6c$

$$4 = 1.6c$$

$$\frac{4}{1.6} = \frac{1.6c}{1.6}$$ *Divide to isolate c.*

$$\frac{4}{1.6} = c$$ *Think: 4 ÷ 1.6 = 40 ÷ 16.*

$$2.5 = c$$

1 Introduce

Alternate Opener

EXPLORATION

4-6 Solving Equations Containing Decimals

For each equation, use mental math to find the missing number.

1. $24.75 + \_\_\_\_ = 50$
2. $20 - \_\_\_\_ = 15.5$
3. $6 \cdot \_\_\_\_ = 15$
4. $\_\_\_\_ \div 0.25 = 10$

For each equation, use a calculator to find the value of x.

5. $24.75 + x = 50$
6. $20 - x = 15.5$
7. $6x = 15$
8. $x \div 0.25 = 10$

Think and Discuss

9. **Discuss** what you notice about the equations in numbers 1–4 and 5–8.
10. **Write** a real-world situation for each equation in numbers 5–8. For example, the equation in number 5 could represent this situation: "After depositing $24.75 in his savings account, Pablo has a balance of $50. What was Pablo's balance before the deposit?"

Motivate

Present a one-step equation such as $x + 7 = 25$. Have students identify what they would do first to solve the equation (i.e., subtract 7 from both sides). Review with students the importance of isolating the variable when solving equations. Have students predict the first step in solving each of the following equations:

$3.2 + x = 6.8 \qquad x - 3.2 = 6.8$

$3.2 \cdot x = 6.8 \qquad x \div 3.2 = 6.8$

List students' predictions next to each equation, and check them for accuracy at the end of the lesson.

Exploration worksheet and answers on Chapter 4 Resource Book pp. 53 and 138

2 Teach

Lesson Presentation

Guided Instruction

In this lesson, students learn to solve one-step equations that contain decimals. Review the following rules for computing with decimals:

Example 1A: When adding decimals, align the decimal point.

Example 1B: When subtracting a decimal from a whole number, add zeros as placeholders before subtracting the decimal number.

Example 2A: When multiplying decimals, be sure the product has the same number of decimal places as the combined total of decimal places in the factors.

Example 2B: When dividing decimals, change the divisor to a whole number.

EXAMPLE  **PROBLEM SOLVING APPLICATION**

Yancey wants to buy a new snowboard that costs \$396.00. If she earns \$8.25 per hour at work, how many hours must she work to earn enough money to buy the snowboard?

1 Understand the Problem

Rewrite the question as a statement.

- Find the number of hours Yancey must work to earn \$396.00.

List the **important information**:

- Yancey earns \$8.25 per hour.
- Yancey needs \$396.00 to buy a snowboard.

2 Make a Plan

Yancey's pay is equal to her hourly pay times the number of hours she works. Since you know how much money she needs to earn, you can write an equation with h being the number of hours.

$8.25h = 396$

3 Solve

$8.25h = 396$

$\frac{8.25h}{8.25} = \frac{396}{8.25}$ *Divide to isolate h.*

$h = 48$

Yancey must work 48 hours.

4 Look Back

You can round 8.25 to 8 and 396 to 400 to estimate how many hours Yancey needs to work.

$400 \div 8 = 50$

So 48 hours is a reasonable answer.

Think and Discuss

1. **Describe** how to solve the equation $-1.25 + x = 1.25$. Then solve.
2. **Explain** how you can tell if 1.01 is a solution of $10s = -10.1$ without solving the equation.

COMMON ERROR ALERT

Some students might use the wrong operation to isolate a variable. Before students solve an equation, have them record the operation used and then record its inverse.

Additional Examples

Example 1

Solve.

A. $n - 2.75 = 8.3$ **$n = 11.05$**

B. $a + 32.66 = 42$ **$a = 9.34$**

Example 2

Solve.

A. $\frac{x}{4.8} = 5.4$ **$x = 25.92$**

B. $9 = 3.6d$ **$2.5 = d$**

Example 3

A board-game box is 2.5 inches tall. A toy store has shelving space measuring 15 inches vertically in which to store the boxes. How many boxes can be stacked in the space?

6

Example 3 note: For students who have difficulty understanding how to solve the problem, have them rewrite it using smaller whole numbers instead of decimals and then solve it.

3 Close

Summarize

Have students explain how to solve each type of decimal equation: addition, subtraction, multiplication, and division.

Possible answers:

Addition equation: Isolate the variable by subtracting from both sides of the equation.

Subtraction equation: Isolate the variable by adding to both sides.

Multiplication equation: Isolate the variable by dividing on both sides.

Division equation: Isolate the variable by multiplying on both sides.

Reaching All Learners
Through Modeling

Have students use graph paper to solve addition equations that contain decimals. Let each square on the graph paper represent 0.1. To solve $3.2 + x = 5.5$, have students outline an area representing 5.5 on the graph paper (55 squares). Next, have them lightly shade an area representing 3.2 (32 squares) within the outlined area. Finally, have students count the unshaded squares within the outlined area (23 squares) and label it x. The unshaded part is the solution to the equation $3.2 + x = 5.5$, so $x = 2.3$. Repeat the activity for other equations.

Answers to Think and Discuss

Possible answers:

1. Isolate x by adding 1.25 to each side. $x = 2.5$.
2. Because the product of $10s$ is a negative number, s must be negative because 10 is positive. Therefore, s cannot equal 1.01. $10 \cdot 1.01 = 10.1$, not -10.1.

4-6 PRACTICE & ASSESS

Students may want to refer back to the lesson examples.

Assignment Guide

If you finished Example 1 assign:
Core 1–4, 10–15, 27, 35, 45–53
Enriched 1, 3, 11–15 odd, 26–28, 30, 34, 35, 45–53

If you finished Example 2 assign:
Core 1–8, 10–21, 24–27, 36, 37, 45–53
Enriched 1–7 odd, 11–21 odd, 24–37, 45–53

If you finished Example 3 assign:
Core 1–29, 39, 40, 45–53
Enriched 1–23 odd, 24–53

Notes

4-6 Exercises

FOR EXTRA PRACTICE
see page 662

internet connect
Homework Help Online
go.hrw.com Keyword: MS4 4-6

GUIDED PRACTICE

See Example 1 Solve.

1. $w - 5.8 = 1.2$ **$w = 7$**
2. $x + 9.15 = 17$ **$x = 7.85$**
3. $k + 3.91 = 28$ **$k = 24.09$**
4. $n - 1.35 = 19.9$ **$n = 21.25$**

See Example 2

5. $\frac{b}{1.4} = 3.6$ **$b = 5.04$**
6. $\frac{x}{0.8} = 7.2$ **$x = 5.76$**
7. $3.1t = 27.9$ **$t = 9$**
8. $7.5 = 5y$ **$y = 1.5$**

See Example 3

9. Jeff bought a sandwich and a salad for lunch. His total bill was \$7.10. The salad cost \$2.85. How much did the sandwich cost? **\$4.25**

INDEPENDENT PRACTICE

See Example 1 Solve.

10. $v + 0.84 = 6$ **$v = 5.16$**
11. $c - 32.56 = 12$ **$c = 44.56$**
12. $d - 14.25 = -23.9$ **$d = -9.65$**
13. $3.52 + a = 8.6$ **$a = 5.08$**
14. $w - 9.01 = 12.6$ **$w = 21.61$**
15. $p + 30.34 = -22.87$ **$p = -53.21$**

See Example 2

16. $3.2c = 8$ **$c = 2.5$**
17. $72 = 4.5z$ **$z = 16$**
18. $21.8x = -124.26$ **$x = -5.7$**
19. $\frac{w}{2.8} = 4.2$ **$w = 11.76$**
20. $\frac{m}{0.19} = 12$ **$m = 2.28$**
21. $\frac{a}{21.23} = -3.5$ **$a = -74.305$**

See Example 3

22. At the fair, a pack of 25 food tickets costs \$31.25. What is the cost of each ticket? **\$1.25**
23. To climb the rock wall at the fair, you must have 5 ride tickets. If each ticket costs \$1.50, how much does it cost to climb the rock wall? **\$7.50**

PRACTICE AND PROBLEM SOLVING

Solve.

24. $1.2y = -1.44$ **$y = -1.2$**
25. $\frac{n}{8.2} = -0.6$ **$n = -4.92$**
26. $w - 4.1 = -5$ **$w = -0.9$**
27. $r + 0.48 = 1.2$ **$r = 0.72$**
28. $x - 5.2 = -7.3$ **$x = -2.1$**
29. $1.05 = -7m$ **$m = -0.15$**
30. $a + 0.81 = -6.3$ **$a = -7.11$**
31. $60k = 54$ **$k = 0.9$**
32. $\frac{h}{-7.1} = 0.62$ **$h = -4.402$**
33. $\frac{t}{-0.18} = -5.2$ **$t = 0.936$**
34. $7.9 = d + 12.7$ **$d = -4.8$**
35. $-1.8 + v = -3.8$ **$v = -2$**
36. $-k = 287.658$ **$k = -287.658$**
37. $-n = -12.254$ **$n = 12.254$**
38. The Drama Club at Smith Valley Middle School is selling cookie dough in order to raise money for costumes. If each tub of cookie dough costs \$4.75, how many tubs must members sell to make \$570.00? **120 tubs**

Math Background

The set of numbers that a variable may represent in an equation is called the *domain* of the variable. For equations that were solved in earlier chapters, the domain was the set of integers. That is, all solutions to equations were integers. In this lesson, the domain is extended to include all rational numbers. If the decimals are included, then the fractions with denominators of a power of 10 are also included. Recall that a rational number is a number that can be expressed as a ratio of two integers, $\frac{p}{q}$, with $q \neq 0$.

All rational numbers are included only if nonterminating decimals are part of the domain.

RETEACH 4-6

LESSON 4-6 **Reteach**
Solving Equations Containing Decimals

You can solve equations with decimals the same way you solve equations with whole numbers. Remember to always perform the same calculation on both sides of the equation to keep the two sides equal.

- You can use addition to solve a subtraction equation involving decimals.

$$x - 1.45 = 6.7$$
$$x - 1.45 + \mathbf{1.45} = 6.7 + \mathbf{1.45}$$
$$x = 8.15$$

Addition undoes subtraction

- You can use subtraction to solve an addition equation involving decimals.

$$n + 24.8 = -15.2$$
$$n + 24.8 - \mathbf{24.8} = -15.2 - \mathbf{24.8}$$
$$n = -40$$

Subtraction undoes addition

Solve.

1. $e + 7.1 = 9.3$
   $e + 7.1 - 7.1 = 9.3 - 7.1$
   $e =$ **2.2**
2. $x - 1.9 = 5.4$
   $x - 1.9 +$ **1.9** $= 5.4 +$ **1.9**
   $x =$ **7.3**
3. $w - 8.3 = -4.12$
   $w - 8.3$ **+ 8.3** $= -4.12$ **+ 8.3**
   $w =$ **4.18**
4. $b + 5.75 = -6.2$
   $b + 5.75$ **− 5.75** $= -6.2$ **− 5.75**
   $b =$ **−11.95**
5. $t + 39.5 = 54.1$ **$t = 14.6$**
6. $p - 29.4 = 3.7$ **$p = 33.1$**
7. $r - 6.25 = -17.3$ **$r = -11.05$**
8. $k + 9.8 = -11.9$ **$k = -21.7$**

PRACTICE 4-6

LESSON 4-6 **Practice B**
Solving Equations Containing Decimals

Solve.

1. $t + 0.77 = 9.3$ **$t = 8.53$**
2. $p - 1.34 = -11.8$ **$p = -10.46$**
3. $r + 2.14 = 7.8$ **$r = 5.66$**
4. $3.65 + e = -1.4$ **$e = -5.05$**
5. $w - 16.7 = 8.27$ **$w = 24.97$**
6. $z - 17.2 = 7.13$ **$z = 24.33$**
7. $p - 67.5 = 24.81$ **$p = 92.31$**
8. $h + 26.9 = 12.74$ **$h = -14.16$**
9. $k + 89.2 = -47.62$ **$k = -136.82$**
10. $x - 0.45 = 5.97$ **$x = 6.42$**
11. $1.08 + n = 15.72$ **$n = 14.64$**
12. $y - 6.32 = 0.73$ **$y = 7.05$**
13. $4.3p = 28.81$ **$p = 6.7$**
14. $7.7j = 76.23$ **$j = 9.9$**
15. $3.8g = -104.12$ **$g = -27.4$**
16. $18.36 = 2.7y$ **$y = 6.8$**
17. $99.96 = 6.8x$ **$x = 14.7$**
18. $293.92 = 17.6c$ **$c = 16.7$**
19. $\frac{e}{7.4} = 6.9$ **$e = 51.06$**
20. $\frac{f}{12.7} = 15.6$ **$f = 198.12$**
21. $\frac{d}{9.7} = 20.8$ **$d = 201.76$**
22. $\frac{w}{-0.2} = 15.4$ **$w = -3.08$**
23. $\frac{m}{9.8} = 1.7$ **$m = 16.66$**
24. $\frac{s}{14.35} = -5.2$ **$s = -74.62$**
25. Jeff paid a flat fee of \$269.50 for a year's worth of vet visits for his 4 cats. He made 14 visits during the year. What was the average cost per visit?
    \$19.25

Social Studies LINK

From 1892 to 1924, more than 22 million immigrants came to Ellis Island, New York.

go.hrw.com
KEYWORD: MS4 Ellis

CNN Student News

39. ***SOCIAL STUDIES*** The table shows the most common European ancestral origins of Americans (in millions), according to a Census 2000 supplementary survey. In addition, 19.6 million people stated that their ancestry was "American."

Ancestral Origins of Americans	
European Ancestry	**Number (millions)**
English	28.3
French	9.8
German	46.5
Irish	33.1
Italian	15.9
Polish	9.1
Scottish	5.4

a. How many people claimed ancestry from the countries listed, according to the survey? **148.1 million**

b. If the data were placed in order from greatest to least, between which two nationalities would "American" ancestry be placed? **between English and Italian**

40. ***CONSUMER MATH*** Gregory bought a computer desk at a thrift store for \$38. The regular price of a similar desk at a furniture store is 4.5 times as much. What is the regular price of the desk at the furniture store? **\$171**

41. ***SOCIAL STUDIES*** Pennies made before 1982 are made mostly of copper and have a density of 8.85 g/cm^3. Because of an increase in the cost of copper, the density of pennies made after 1982 is 1.71 g/cm^3 less. What is the density of pennies minted today? **7.14 g/cm^3**

42. ***WHAT'S THE ERROR?*** A student's solution to the equation $m + 0.63 = 5$ was $m = 5.63$. What is the error? What is the correct solution?

43. ***WRITE A PROBLEM*** Using the fact that 2.54 cm = 1 in., write a problem, an equation to represent the problem, and the solution.

44. ***CHALLENGE*** Solve the equation $-2.8 + (b - 1.7) = -0.6 \cdot 9.4$. **$b = -1.14$**

Spiral Review

Evaluate the expression $y^2 - 3$ for each given value of the variable. (Lesson 2-7)

45. $y = 3$ **6** 46. $y = 7$ **46** 47. $y = 12$ **141** 48. $y = 20$ **397**

Order the numbers from least to greatest. (Lesson 3-10)

49. $\frac{3}{5}$, 3.5, −3 **$-3, \frac{3}{5}, 3.5$** 50. −0.9, −6, $-\frac{1}{2}$ 51. 1.4, −2, $-1\frac{1}{4}$ **$-2, -1\frac{1}{4}, 1.4$**

52. **TEST PREP** Which of the following is **not** equal to −12? (Lesson 3-3) **A**

A $-7 + 5$ B $-8 + (-4)$ C $-6 + (-6)$ D $-18 + 6$

53. **TEST PREP** Mandy earned \$79.90 for working 8.5 hours. How much did she earn per hour? (Lesson 4-5) **F**

F \$9.40 G \$9.04 H \$8.90 J \$8.09

COMMON ERROR ALERT

For Exercises 36 and 37, point out that $-k$ is actually $-1k$, and $-n$ is $-1n$. Students then can divide both sides of the equation by -1 to isolate the variable and correctly solve the equation.

Answers

42. Possible answer: The student subtracted 0.63 on the side of the equation with the variable but added 0.63 on the side with 5 instead of subtracting; $m = 4.37$.

43. Possible answer: How many inches is 16.51 cm? $16.51 = 2.54x$; $x = 6.5$ in.

50. $-6, -0.9, -\frac{1}{2}$

Journal

Ask students to describe similarities and differences between solving equations with whole numbers and solving equations with decimals.

Test Prep Doctor

For Exercise 53, students can estimate $80 \div 8 = 10$ and $81 \div 9 = 9$; therefore, the answer will be between \$9 and \$10. Students can eliminate choices **H** and **J.**

CHALLENGE 4-6

LESSON 4-6 **Challenge**
The Pairs Event

When you solve a system of equations, you solve 2 different equations at once. The solution to a system of equations is an ordered pair (x, y).

Example: $2.5x = 50$
$x + y = 10.5$

First, solve the first equation for x: $x = 20$

Then use the solution from the first equation to solve for y in the second equation.

$x = 20$ ○ ○ ○ $x + y = 10.5$
$20 + y = 10.5$
$y = -9.5$

The solution to the system of equations is the ordered pair (20, −9.5).

Solve each system of equations.

1. $x - 5.4 = 7.3$; $2x + y = 10$ **(12.7, −15.4)**
2. $1.4x = 2.8$; $\frac{y}{x} = 9.6$ **(2, 19.2)**
3. $\frac{x}{3.9} = 0.8$; $4y = x$ **(3.12, 0.78)**
4. $x + 9.25 = 10.1$; $y - 3x = 1.7$ **(0.85, 4.25)**
5. $6.4x = 2.56$; $x = 2y$ **(0.4, 0.2)**
6. $x + 3.02 = 5$; $\frac{y}{3.5} = x$ **(1.98, 6.93)**
7. $6x = -7.2$; $y - x = 3.4$ **(−1.2, 2.2)**
8. $\frac{x}{0.3} = -9$; $y + x = 0.6$ **(−2.7, 3.3)**
9. $x - 4.7 = -9$; $\frac{y}{x} = 0.5$ **(−4.3, −2.15)**
10. $x + 8.4 = -2$; $2x + y = 1.1$ **(−10.4, 21.9)**
11. $2.6x = 3.64$; $-3x = y$ **(1.4, −4.2)**
12. $\frac{x}{0.4} = -3.2$; $x + y = 0.35$ **(−1.28, 1.63)**

PROBLEM SOLVING 4-6

LESSON 4-6 **Problem Solving**
Solving Equations Containing Decimals

Write the correct answer.

1. The diameter of the secondary mirror in NASA's Hubble telescope is 0.3 meters. The primary mirror is 8 times as large. What is the diameter of the primary mirror? **2.4 meters**

2. A cubic centimeter of titanium weighs 4.507 grams. The same volume of gold weighs 19.3 grams. How much more does a cubic centimeter of gold weigh? **14.793 grams**

3. Brianna drives 3.35 miles to work everyday. This is 1.75 miles less than Darius drives to work everyday. How far does Darius drive to work? **5.1 miles**

4. The weight of an object on Mars is 0.38 times its weight on Earth. How much would a 125-pound person weigh on Mars? **47.5 pounds**

Choose the letter for the best answer.

The table shows the orbital velocity of the planets.

Planets' Orbital Velocity

Planet	Orbital Velocity (miles per second)
Mercury	29.74
Venus	21.76
Earth	18.5
Mars	14.99
Jupiter	8.12
Saturn	6.02
Uranus	4.23
Neptune	3.37
Pluto	2.93

5. How much greater is the orbital velocity of Mercury than Pluto?
A 32.67 miles per second
(B) 26.81 miles per second
C 7.98 miles per second
D 2.93 miles per second

6. How many miles does Mercury travel in an hour?
F 1,784.4 miles
(G) 107,064 miles
H 10,706.4 miles
J 17,844 miles

7. How many miles does Jupiter travel in a minute?
A 8.12 miles
B 81.2 miles
C 48.72 miles
(D) 487.2 miles

8. During the time it takes Saturn to travel 32,508 miles, how much time has elapsed on Earth?
F 5,400 minutes
G 1,757.19 minutes
H 195,698 seconds
(J) 90 minutes

Lesson Quiz

Solve.

1. $x - 14.23 = 19.5$ **$x = 33.73$**
2. $12.6c = -103.32$ **$c = -8.2$**
3. $\frac{x}{9.3} = 6.1$ **$x = 56.73$**
4. $m + 12.97 = -14.35$ **$m = -27.32$**
5. The French Club is selling coupon books for \$8.25 each. How many books must be sold to bring in \$5,940? 720 books

Available on Daily Transparency in CRB

Chapter 4 Mid-Chapter Quiz

Purpose: *To assess students' mastery of concepts and skills in Lessons 4-1 through 4-6*

Assessment Resources

Section 4A Quiz

Assessment Resources .... p. 13

***Test and Practice Generator* CD-ROM**

Additional mid-chapter assessment items in both multiple-choice and free-response format may be generated for any objective in Lessons 4-1 through 4-6.

Chapter 4 Mid-Chapter Quiz

Mid-Chapter Quiz

LESSON 4-1 (pp. 192–195)

Estimate. **Possible answers:**

1. $163.2 \cdot 5.4$ **800**
2. $37.19 + 100.94$ **138**
3. $376.82 - 139.28$ **238**
4. $33.19 \div 8.18$ **4**
5. $-6.66 \cdot 5.17$ **−35**
6. $67.78 + 85.76$ **154**
7. $-65.63 - 24.12$ **−90**
8. $29.05 \div 3.73$ **10**

LESSON 4-2 (pp. 196–199)

Add or subtract.

9. $4.73 + 29.68$ **34.41**
10. $-6.89 - (-29.4)$ **22.51**
11. $23.58 - 8.36$ **15.22**
12. $-15 + (-9.44)$ **−24.44**
13. $66.84 + (-75.13)$ **−8.29**
14. $-6.48 + 2.3$ **−4.18**
15. $-5.21 - 3.64$ **−8.85**
16. $-81.6 - (-17.02)$ **−64.58**

LESSON 4-3 (pp. 202–205)

Multiply.

17. $3.4 \cdot 9.6$ **32.64**
18. $-2.66 \cdot 0.9$ **−2.394**
19. $-7 \cdot (-0.06)$ **0.42**
20. $6.94 \cdot (-24)$ **−166.56**
21. $-49.7 \cdot (-9.6)$ **477.12**
22. $7.55 \cdot (-31.21)$ **−235.6355**
23. $-35.3 \cdot (-8.6)$ **303.58**
24. $67.1 \cdot 7.35$ **493.185**

LESSON 4-4 (pp. 206–209)

Divide.

25. $10.8 \div (-4)$ **−2.7**
26. $6.5 \div 2$ **3.25**
27. $-45.6 \div 12$ **−3.8**
28. $-99.36 \div (-4)$ **24.84**
29. $31.08 \div (-8)$ **−3.885**
30. $12.5 \div 5$ **2.5**
31. $-52.6 \div 8$ **−6.575**
32. $48.01 \div 2$ **24.005**

LESSON 4-5 (pp. 210–213)

Divide.

33. $10.4 \div (-0.8)$ **−13**
34. $18 \div 2.4$ **7.5**
35. $-3.3 \div 0.11$ **−30**
36. $-36 \div (-0.9)$ **40**
37. $55 \div 12.5$ **4.4**
38. $46.134 \div (-6.6)$ **−6.99**
39. $-130 \div 1.6$ **−81.25**
40. $-126.45 \div (-4.5)$ **28.1**

LESSON 4-6 (pp. 214–217)

Solve.

41. $3.4 + n = 8$ **$n = 4.6$**
42. $x - 1.75 = -19$ **$x = -17.25$**
43. $-3.5 = -5x$ **$x = 0.7$**
44. $10.1 = \frac{s}{8}$ **$s = 80.8$**
45. Pablo earns $5.50 per hour. His friend Raymond earns 1.2 times as much. How much does Raymond earn per hour? **$6.60**

Focus on Problem Solving

Look Back

- **Does your solution answer the question in the problem?**

Sometimes, before you solve a problem, you first need to use the given data to find additional information. Any time you find a solution for a problem, you should ask yourself if your solution answers the question being asked, or if it just gives you the information you need to find the final answer.

Read each problem, and determine whether the given solution answers the question in the problem. Explain your answer.

1. At one store, a new CD costs $15.99. At a second store, the same CD costs 0.75 as much. About how much does the second store charge?

   Solution: The second store charges about $12.00.

2. Bobbie is 1.4 feet shorter than her older sister is. If Bobbie's sister is 5.5 feet tall, how tall is Bobbie?

   Solution: Bobbie is 4.1 feet tall.

3. Juanita ran the 100-yard dash 1.12 seconds faster than Kellie. Kellie's time was 0.8 seconds faster than Rachel's. If Rachel's time was 15.3 seconds, what was Juanita's time?

   Solution: Kellie's time was 14.5 seconds.

4. The playscape at a local park is located in a triangular sandpit. Side A of the sandpit is 2 meters longer than side B. Side B is twice as long as side C. If the side C is 6 meters long, how long is side A?

   Solution: Side B is 12 meters long.

5. Both Tyrone and Albert walk to and from school every day. Albert has to walk 1.25 miles farther than Tyrone does each way. If Tyrone's house is 0.6 mi from school, how far do the two boys walk altogether?

   Solution: Albert lives 1.85 mi from school.

Answers

1. $0.75 \cdot \$15.99 = \$11.99$
2. $5.5 - 1.4 = 4.1$ ft
3. $15.3 - 0.8 - 1.12 = 13.38$ s
4. side C = 6 m, side B = 12 m, side A = 14 m
5. Albert: 3.7 mi; Tyrone 1.2 mi; altogether: 4.9 mi

Focus on Problem Solving

Purpose: *To focus on determining whether the solution answers the question in the problem*

Problem Solving Resources

Interactive Problem Solving . pp. 32–43

Math: Reading and Writing in the Content Area . . . . pp. 32–43

Problem Solving Process

This page focuses on the last step of the problem-solving process: **Look Back**

Discuss

Have students discuss why they think the given solution does or does not answer the question in the problem.

Possible answers:

1. The answer appears to be correct. The price at the second store must be lower than the price at the first store.
2. The answer appears to be correct. Bobbie is shorter than her sister.
3. The answer is not correct. The question asks for Juanita's time.
4. The answer is not correct. The question asks for the length of side A.
5. The answer is not correct. The question asks how far the two boys walk altogether. You have to find how far Albert walks, how far Tyrone walks, and then the total distance that both walk.

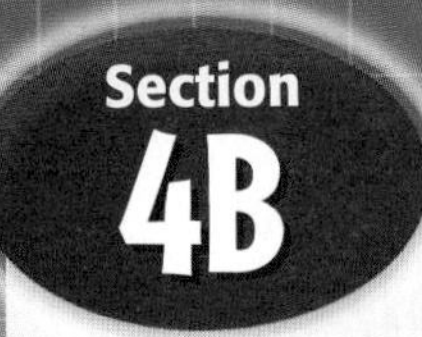

Fraction Operations

One-Minute Section Planner

Lesson	Materials	Resources
Hands-On Lab 4B Model Fraction Multiplication and Division **NCTM:** Number and Operations, Algebra, Geometry, Representation **NAEP:** Number Properties 1b ☐ SAT-9 ☐ SAT-10 ☐ ITBS ☐ CTBS ☐ MAT ☐ CAT	**Required** Pattern blocks *(MK)*	• *Hands-On Lab Activities,* pp. 24–26
Lesson 4-7 Multiplying Fractions and Mixed Numbers **NCTM:** Number and Operations, Communication **NAEP:** Number Properties 3a ☑ SAT-9 ☑ SAT-10 ☑ ITBS ☑ CTBS ☑ MAT ☑ CAT	**Optional** Colored pencils *(MK)* Calculators	• *Chapter 4 Resource Book,* pp. 63–71 • Daily Transparency T26, CRB • Additional Examples Transparencies T27–T29, CRB • *Alternate Openers: Explorations,* p. 38
Lesson 4-8 Dividing Fractions and Mixed Numbers **NCTM:** Number and Operations, Communication **NAEP:** Number Properties 3a ☑ SAT-9 ☑ SAT-10 ☑ ITBS ☑ CTBS ☑ MAT ☑ CAT	**Optional** Calculators Teaching Transparency T31 *(CRB)*	• *Chapter 4 Resource Book,* pp. 72–80 • Daily Transparency T30, CRB • Additional Examples Transparencies T32–T34, CRB • *Alternate Openers: Explorations,* p. 39
Lesson 4-9 Estimate with Fractions **NCTM:** Number and Operations, Problem Solving, Communication **NAEP:** Number Properties 3g ☑ SAT-9 ☑ SAT-10 ☐ ITBS ☐ CTBS ☑ MAT ☑ CAT		• *Chapter 4 Resource Book,* pp. 81–89 • Daily Transparency T35, CRB • Additional Examples Transparencies T36–T38, CRB • *Alternate Openers: Explorations,* p. 40
Hands-On Lab 4C Model Fraction Addition and Subtraction **NCTM:** Number and Operations, Algebra, Geometry, Reasoning and Proof, Representation **NAEP:** Number Properties 1b ☐ SAT-9 ☐ SAT-10 ☐ ITBS ☐ CTBS ☐ MAT ☐ CAT	**Required** Fraction bars *(MK)*	• *Hands-On Lab Activities,* pp. 27–30, 131
Lesson 4-10 Adding and Subtracting Fractions **NCTM:** Number and Operations, Communication **NAEP:** Number Properties 3a ☑ SAT-9 ☑ SAT-10 ☑ ITBS ☑ CTBS ☑ MAT ☑ CAT	**Optional** Teaching Transparency T40 *(CRB)*	• *Chapter 4 Resource Book,* pp. 90–98 • Daily Transparency T39, CRB • Additional Examples Transparencies T41–T43, CRB • *Alternate Openers: Explorations,* p. 41
Lesson 4-11 Adding and Subtracting Mixed Numbers **NCTM:** Number and Operations, Communication **NAEP:** Number Properties 3a ☑ SAT-9 ☑ SAT-10 ☐ ITBS ☐ CTBS ☑ MAT ☑ CAT	**Optional** Index cards	• *Chapter 4 Resource Book,* pp. 99–108 • Daily Transparency T44, CRB • Additional Examples Transparencies T45–T47, CRB • *Alternate Openers: Explorations,* p. 42
Lesson 4-12 Solving Equations Containing Fractions **NCTM:** Number and Operations, Algebra, Communication **NAEP:** Algebra 4a ☐ SAT-9 ☐ SAT-10 ☐ ITBS ☐ CTBS ☑ MAT ☑ CAT	**Optional** Calculators Recording Sheet for Reaching All Learners *(CRB, p. 127)*	• *Chapter 4 Resource Book,* pp. 109–118 • Daily Transparency T48, CRB • Additional Examples Transparencies T49–T51, CRB • *Alternate Openers: Explorations,* p. 43
Section 4B Assessment		• Section 4B Quiz, AR p. 14 • *Test and Practice Generator* CD-ROM

SAT = *Stanford Achievement Tests* **ITBS** = *Iowa Test of Basic Skills* **CTBS** = *Comprehensive Test of Basic Skills/Terra Nova*
MAT = *Metropolitan Achievement Test* **CAT** = *California Achievement Test*

NCTM—Complete standards can be found on pages T27–T33. **NAEP**—Complete standards can be found on pages A35–A39.

SE = *Student Edition* **TE** = *Teacher's Edition* **AR** = *Assessment Resources* **CRB** = *Chapter Resource Book* **MK** = *Manipulatives Kit*

Section Overview

Multiplying and Dividing Fractions *Hands-On Lab 4B, Lessons 4-7, 4-8*

Why? Division of fractions is defined in terms of multiplication, so it is important to be able to multiply fractions or mixed numbers before learning to divide fractions.

$$\frac{3}{4} \cdot \frac{3}{5} = \frac{3 \cdot 3}{4 \cdot 5} = \frac{9}{20}$$

Multiply the **numerators** and multiply the **denominators.**

$$\frac{5}{6} \div \frac{1}{3} = \frac{5}{6} \cdot \frac{3}{1} = \frac{5}{2} = 2\frac{1}{2}$$

Rewrite division by a fraction as **multiplication by its reciprocal.**

Estimating with Fractions *Lesson 4-9*

Why? Estimation can be used to determine whether answers are reasonable.

Round each fraction in a sum or difference to a benchmark, and then add or subtract. To round, compare the numerator to the denominator.

$\frac{9}{50}$ rounds to **0**.

The numerator is much smaller than the denominator.

$\frac{9}{20}$ rounds to $\frac{1}{2}$.

The numerator is about one half the denominator.

$\frac{9}{11}$ rounds to **1**.

The numerator is close to the denominator.

Benchmarks are 0, $\frac{1}{2}$, 1, and so on.

Adding and Subtracting Fractions *Hands-On Lab 4C, Lessons 4-10, 4-11*

Why? Adding and subtracting fractions occurs in many real contexts.

To add or subtract fractions, first write equivalent fractions with common denominators, and then add or subtract the numerators.

$$\frac{1}{3} + \frac{2}{5}$$
$$= \frac{5}{15} + \frac{6}{15}$$
$$= \frac{5+6}{15}$$
$$= \frac{11}{15}$$

Equivalent fractions with a **common denominator**

$$5 - \frac{2}{3}$$
$$= 4\frac{3}{3} - \frac{2}{3}$$
$$= 4\frac{1}{3}$$

Rewrite 5 as $4\frac{3}{3}$.

Solving Equations Containing Fractions *Lesson 4-12*

Why? Equations can be used to represent real-world situations. Solving equations containing fractions enables you to solve many real-world problems.

To solve one-step equations with fractions, apply the rules for computing with fractions when isolating the variable with inverse operations.

4B Model Fraction Multiplication and Division

Pacing: Traditional 1 day
Block $\frac{1}{2}$ day

Objective: To use pattern blocks to model multiplying fractions

Materials: Pattern blocks

Lab Resources

Hands-On Lab Activities .... pp. 24–26

Using the Pages

Discuss with students how to use pattern blocks to represent and multiply fractions.

Model with pattern blocks using the following as one whole:

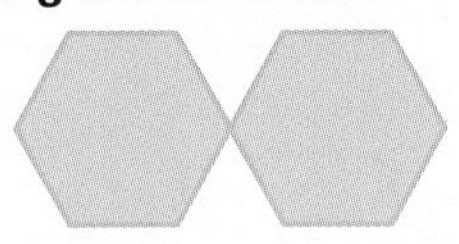

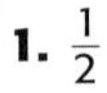

1. $\frac{1}{2}$

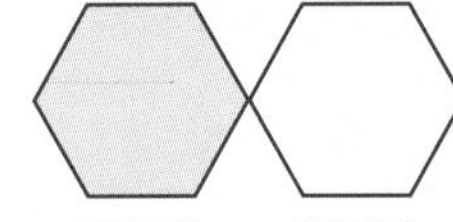

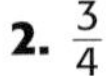

2. $\frac{3}{4}$

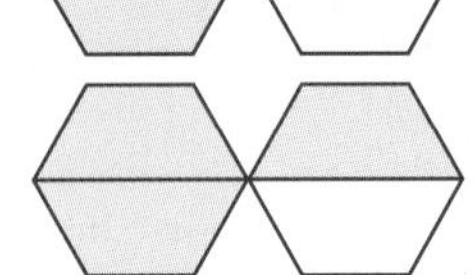

Answers

Activity

1. a. $\frac{1}{4}$

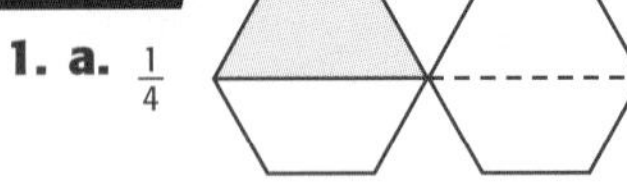

b. $\frac{1}{6}$

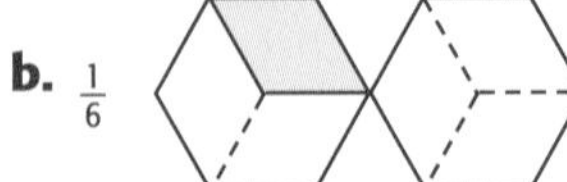

c. $\frac{1}{12}$

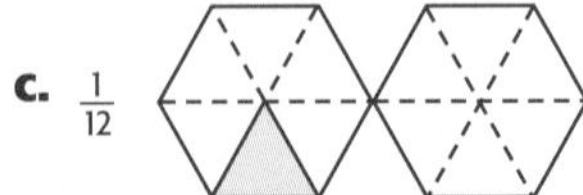

d. $\frac{1}{2}$

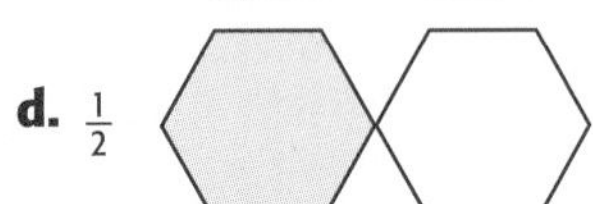

e. $\frac{2}{6} = \frac{1}{3}$

2. a. $= 1$

b. $= \frac{2}{6} = \frac{1}{3}$

c. $= \frac{4}{6} = \frac{2}{3}$

d. $= \frac{6}{12} = \frac{1}{2}$

Model Fraction Multiplication and Division

Use with Lessons 4-7 and 4-8

KEY

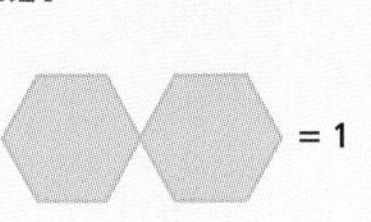

$= 1$

REMEMBER

- The multiplication sign can mean "of."

internet connect
Lab Resources Online
go.hrw.com
KEYWORD: MS4 Lab4B

You can use pattern blocks to model multiplying and dividing fractions.

Activity

1 Determine the fraction that each shape represents. Draw a sketch to explain your answer.

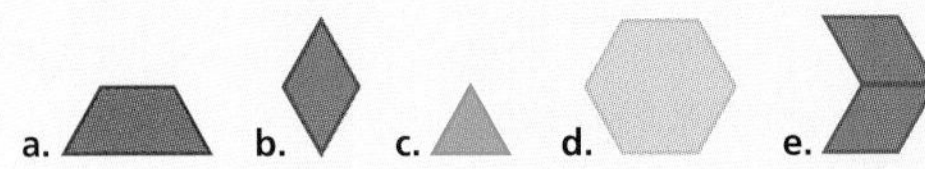

You can use pattern blocks to model multiplying a fraction by a whole number.

To evaluate $\frac{1}{12} \cdot 5$, arrange pattern blocks as shown.

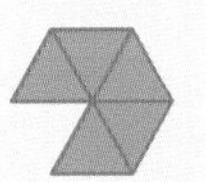

$\frac{1}{12} \cdot 5 = \frac{5}{12}$

2 Use pattern blocks to evaluate each expression.

a. $\frac{1}{2} \cdot 2$ **1** **b.** $\frac{1}{6} \cdot 2$ $\mathbf{\frac{1}{3}}$ **c.** $\frac{1}{3} \cdot 2$ $\mathbf{\frac{2}{3}}$ **d.** $\frac{2}{12} \cdot 3$ $\mathbf{\frac{6}{12} = \frac{1}{2}}$

When you multiply two fractions that are each less than 1, the product will always be less than either fraction.

To evaluate $\frac{1}{8} \cdot \frac{2}{3}$, arrange pattern blocks as shown.

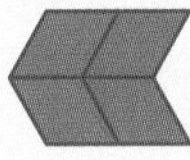

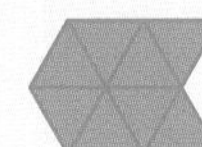

Show $\frac{2}{3}$. Find which shape uses 8 blocks to exactly cover $\frac{2}{3}$.

$\frac{1}{8}$ of $\frac{2}{3}$ is $\frac{1}{12}$. $\frac{1}{8} \cdot \frac{2}{3} = \frac{1}{12}$

3 Use pattern blocks to evaluate each expression.

a. $\frac{1}{4} \cdot \frac{1}{3}$ **$\frac{1}{12}$** b. $\frac{1}{2} \cdot \frac{2}{3}$ **$\frac{1}{3}$** c. $\frac{1}{3} \cdot \frac{1}{2}$ **$\frac{1}{6}$** d. $\frac{5}{6} \cdot \frac{1}{2}$ **$\frac{5}{12}$**

You can use pattern blocks to model dividing fractions.

To evaluate $\frac{1}{2} \div \frac{1}{4}$, arrange pattern blocks as shown.

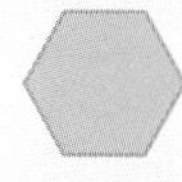

Show $\frac{1}{2}$.

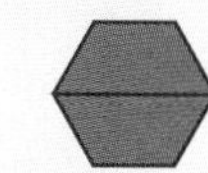

Find the number of $\frac{1}{4}$'s that cover $\frac{1}{2}$ exactly.

$\frac{1}{2} \div \frac{1}{4} = 2$

4 Use pattern blocks to evaluate each expression.

a. $\frac{1}{3} \div \frac{1}{6}$ **2** b. $\frac{1}{2} \div \frac{1}{12}$ **6** c. $1 \div \frac{1}{4}$ **4** d. $\frac{1}{2} \div \frac{1}{6}$ **3**

Think and Discuss

1. Are $\frac{1}{4} \cdot \frac{1}{3}$ and $\frac{1}{3} \cdot \frac{1}{4}$ modeled the same way? Explain. **No. The order of the factors differs so the models differ.**
2. If you used [hexagon] to model one whole, what would be the value

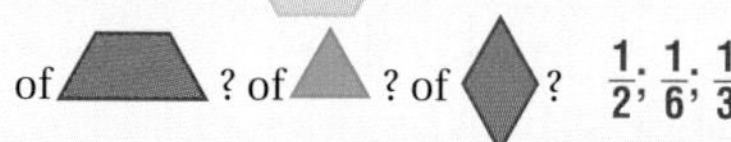

of [trapezoid]? of [triangle]? of [rhombus]? **$\frac{1}{2}, \frac{1}{6}, \frac{1}{3}$**

3. Use pattern blocks to order the fractions from least to greatest.

$\frac{1}{3}$ $\frac{1}{6}$ $\frac{1}{4}$ $\frac{1}{2}$ $\frac{1}{12}$ **$\frac{1}{12}, \frac{1}{6}, \frac{1}{4}, \frac{1}{3}, \frac{1}{2}$; Fractions with lesser**

What do you notice? **denominators represent greater numbers.**

Try This

Model each expression with pattern blocks using

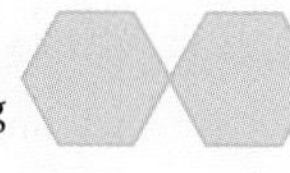

as one whole.

1. $\frac{3}{4} \cdot 1$ **$\frac{3}{4}$**
2. $\frac{1}{2} \cdot \frac{1}{6}$ **$\frac{1}{12}$**
3. $\frac{1}{2} \div \frac{1}{2}$ **1**
4. $\frac{2}{3} \cdot \frac{3}{6}$ **$\frac{1}{3}$**
5. $\frac{3}{4} \cdot \frac{1}{3}$ **$\frac{1}{4}$**
6. $2 \div \frac{1}{4}$ **8**
7. $\frac{1}{4} \cdot \frac{2}{3}$ **$\frac{1}{6}$**
8. $\frac{2}{3} \div \frac{1}{6}$ **4**
9. It took $\frac{1}{2}$ hour for your sister to drive to your aunt's house. If she was in traffic for $\frac{1}{3}$ of that time, how long was she in traffic? **$\frac{1}{6}$ hour**

Answers

Activity

3. a. $\frac{1}{4}$ of $\frac{1}{3}$ is $\frac{1}{12}$.

b. $\frac{1}{2}$ of $\frac{2}{3}$ is $\frac{1}{3}$.

c. $\frac{1}{3}$ of $\frac{1}{2}$ is $\frac{1}{6}$.

d. $\frac{5}{6}$ of $\frac{1}{2}$ is $\frac{5}{12}$.

4. a. It takes 2 pattern blocks representing $\frac{1}{6}$ to cover $\frac{1}{3}$ exactly.

b. It takes 6 pattern blocks representing $\frac{1}{12}$ to cover $\frac{1}{2}$ exactly.

c. It takes 4 pattern blocks representing $\frac{1}{4}$ to cover 1 exactly.

d. It takes 3 pattern blocks representing $\frac{1}{6}$ to cover $\frac{1}{2}$ exactly.

Answers

Try This

Check students' models.

1.

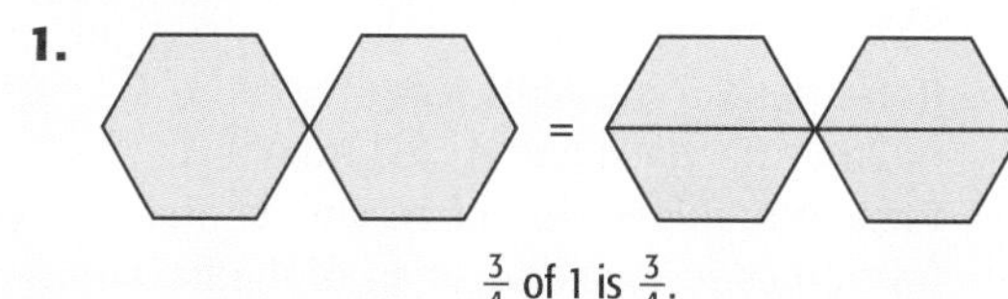

$\frac{3}{4}$ of 1 is $\frac{3}{4}$.

2. $\frac{1}{2}$ of $\frac{1}{6}$ is $\frac{1}{12}$.

3. It takes 1 pattern block representing $\frac{1}{2}$ to cover $\frac{1}{2}$ exactly.

4.

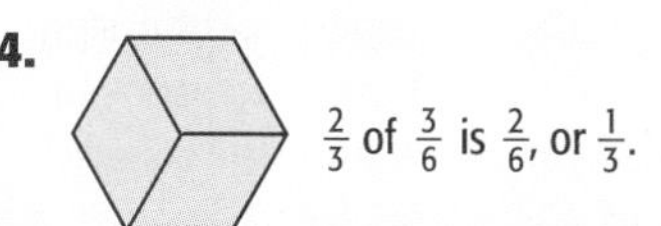

$\frac{2}{3}$ of $\frac{3}{6}$ is $\frac{2}{6}$, or $\frac{1}{3}$.

5. $\frac{3}{4}$ of $\frac{1}{3}$ is $\frac{3}{12}$, or $\frac{1}{4}$.

6.

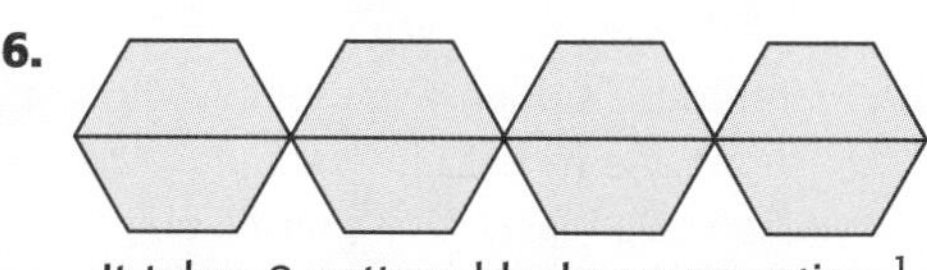

It takes 8 pattern blocks representing $\frac{1}{4}$ to cover 2 exactly.

7.

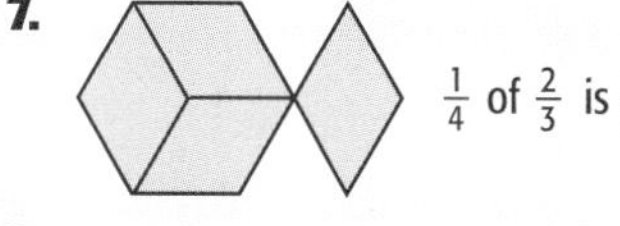

$\frac{1}{4}$ of $\frac{2}{3}$ is $\frac{1}{6}$.

8. It takes 4 pattern blocks representing $\frac{1}{6}$ to cover $\frac{2}{3}$ exactly.

4-7 Organizer

Pacing: Traditional 1 day
Block $\frac{1}{2}$ day

Objective: Students multiply fractions and mixed numbers.

Warm Up

1. What is $\frac{1}{2}$ of 24? 12
2. What is $\frac{1}{2}$ of 16? 8
3. What is $\frac{1}{2}$ of 30? 15
4. What is $\frac{1}{4}$ of 28? 7

Problem of the Day

Caitlin was watching television. In a weather forecast at midnight the forecaster indicated that it would be cloudy for exactly 72 hours and then would be sunny. Caitlin called the station to tell the forecaster he was wrong. How did she know?
There are 24 hours in a day, so 72 hours equals 3 days. In 3 days it would be midnight again, not sunny.

Available on Daily Transparency in CRB

Math Humor

Did you hear about the teenagers who stayed out until 3 A.M. because their parents told them to be home by a quarter of 12?

4-7 Multiplying Fractions and Mixed Numbers

Learn to multiply fractions and mixed numbers.

The San Francisco–Oakland Bay Bridge, which opened in 1936, is a toll bridge used by drivers traveling between the two cities. In 1977, the toll for a car crossing the bridge was $\frac{3}{8}$ of the toll in 2001. To find the toll in 1977, you will need to multiply the toll in 2001 by a fraction.

EXAMPLE 1 ***Transportation Application***

In 2001, the Bay Bridge toll for a car was \$2.00. In 1977, the toll was $\frac{3}{8}$ of the toll in 2001. What was the toll in 1977?

$2 \cdot \frac{3}{8} = \frac{3}{8} + \frac{3}{8}$

$= \frac{6}{8}$

$= \frac{3}{4}$ *Simplify.*

$= 0.75$ *Write the fraction as a decimal.*

$\frac{1}{8}\ \frac{1}{8}\ \frac{1}{8} + \frac{1}{8}\ \frac{1}{8}\ \frac{1}{8}$

$\frac{1}{8}\ \frac{1}{8}\ \frac{1}{8}\ \frac{1}{8}\ \frac{1}{8}\ \frac{1}{8}$

$\frac{1}{4}\ \frac{1}{4}\ \frac{1}{4}$

The Bay Bridge toll for a car was \$0.75 in 1977.

To multiply fractions, multiply the numerators to find the product's numerator. Then multiply the denominators to find the product's denominator.

EXAMPLE 2 **Multiplying Fractions**

Multiply. Write each answer in simplest form.

> **Remember!**
> You can write any integer as a fraction with a denominator of 1.

A $-15 \cdot \frac{2}{3}$

$-15 \cdot \frac{2}{3} = -\frac{15}{1} \cdot \frac{2}{3}$ *Write −15 as a fraction.*

$= -\frac{{}^{5}\cancel{15} \cdot 2}{1 \cdot \cancel{3}_{1}}$ *Simplify.*

$= -\frac{10}{1} = -10$ *Multiply numerators. Multiply denominators.*

1 Introduce

Alternate Opener

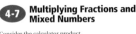

EXPLORATION

4-7 Multiplying Fractions and Mixed Numbers

Consider the calculator product.

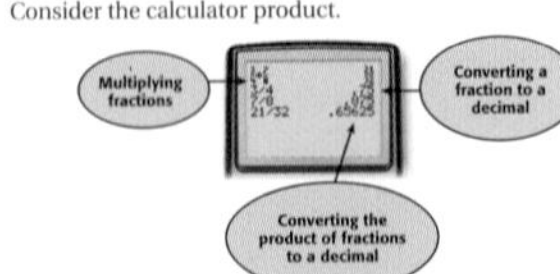

1. Why is the product 0.65625 smaller than its factors 0.75 and 0.875?
2. Why is the product $6\frac{11}{40}$ smaller than the mixed-number factor $7\frac{2}{3}$?

Think and Discuss

3. **Explain** how you know that the product of $\frac{23}{47} \cdot \frac{15}{17}$ is less than either factor.
4. **Demonstrate** that the product of $\frac{23}{47} \cdot \frac{15}{17}$ is less than either factor by converting to decimals on your calculator.

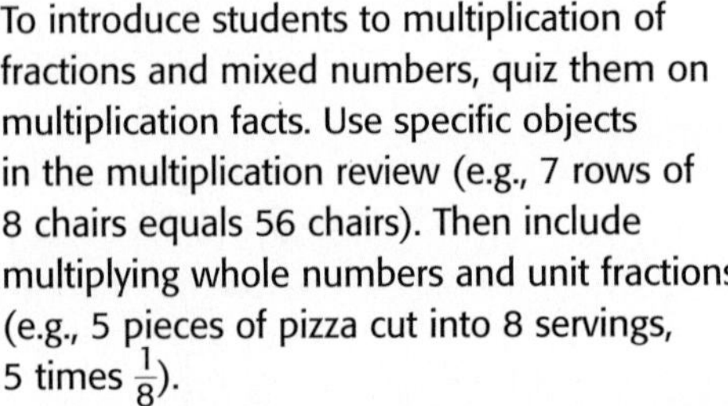

Motivate

To introduce students to multiplication of fractions and mixed numbers, quiz them on multiplication facts. Use specific objects in the multiplication review (e.g., 7 rows of 8 chairs equals 56 chairs). Then include multiplying whole numbers and unit fractions (e.g., 5 pieces of pizza cut into 8 servings, 5 times $\frac{1}{8}$).

Exploration worksheet and answers on Chapter 4 Resource Book pp. 64 and 140

2 Teach

Lesson Presentation

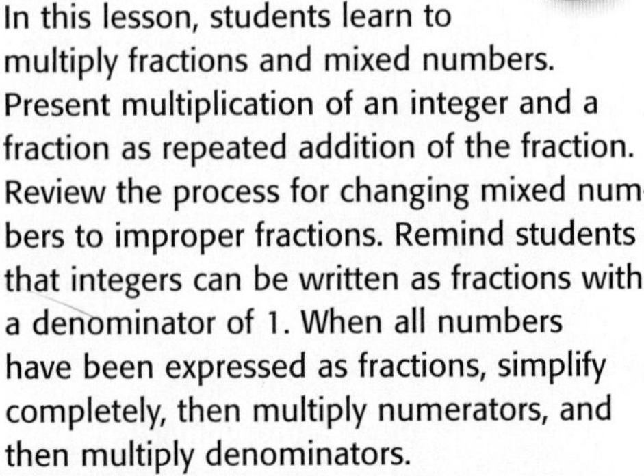

Guided Instruction

In this lesson, students learn to multiply fractions and mixed numbers. Present multiplication of an integer and a fraction as repeated addition of the fraction. Review the process for changing mixed numbers to improper fractions. Remind students that integers can be written as fractions with a denominator of 1. When all numbers have been expressed as fractions, simplify completely, then multiply numerators, and then multiply denominators.

Teaching Tip Reading the multiplication sign as "of" may help students estimate answers and understand the process. $\frac{1}{2}$ of $\frac{1}{4}$ is $\frac{1}{8}$, and $\frac{1}{4}$ of $\frac{4}{5}$ is $\frac{1}{5}$.

Helpful Hint

The product of two proper fractions is less than either fraction.

Multiply. Write each answer in simplest form.

B $\frac{1}{4} \cdot \frac{4}{5}$

$\frac{1}{4} \cdot \frac{4}{5} = \frac{1 \cdot \cancel{4}^{1}}{{}_{1}\cancel{4} \cdot 5}$ — *Simplify.*

$= \frac{1}{5}$ — *Multiply numerators. Multiply denominators.*

C $\frac{3}{4} \cdot \left(-\frac{1}{2}\right)$

$\frac{3}{4} \cdot \left(-\frac{1}{2}\right) = -\frac{3 \cdot 1}{4 \cdot 2}$ — *The signs are different, so the answer will be negative.*

$= -\frac{3}{8}$ — *Multiply numerators. Multiply denominators.*

EXAMPLE 3 Multiplying Mixed Numbers

Multiply. Write each answer in simplest form.

A $\frac{1}{3} \cdot 4\frac{1}{2}$

$\frac{1}{3} \cdot 4\frac{1}{2} = \frac{1}{3} \cdot \frac{9}{2}$ — *Write the mixed number as an improper fraction.*

$= \frac{1 \cdot \cancel{9}^{3}}{{}_{1}\cancel{3} \cdot 2}$ — *Simplify.*

$= \frac{3}{2}$ or $1\frac{1}{2}$ — *Multiply numerators. Multiply denominators.*

B $3\frac{3}{5} \cdot 1\frac{1}{12}$

$3\frac{3}{5} \cdot 1\frac{1}{12} = \frac{18}{5} \cdot \frac{13}{12}$ — *Write mixed numbers as improper fractions.*

$= \frac{{}^{3}\cancel{18} \cdot 13}{5 \cdot \cancel{12}_{2}}$ — *Simplify.*

$= \frac{39}{10}$ or $3\frac{9}{10}$ — *Multiply numerators. Multiply denominators.*

C $5\frac{1}{7} \cdot 2\frac{3}{4}$

$5\frac{1}{7} \cdot 2\frac{3}{4} = \frac{36}{7} \cdot \frac{11}{4}$ — *Write mixed numbers as improper fractions.*

$= \frac{{}^{9}\cancel{36} \cdot 11}{7 \cdot \cancel{4}_{1}}$ — *Simplify.*

$= \frac{99}{7}$ or $14\frac{1}{7}$ — *Multiply numerators. Multiply denominators.*

Think and Discuss

1. **Describe** how to multiply a mixed number and a fraction.
2. **Explain** why $\frac{1}{2} \cdot \frac{1}{3} \cdot \frac{1}{4} = \frac{1}{24}$ is or is not correct.
3. **Explain** why you may want to simplify before multiplying $\frac{2}{3} \cdot \frac{3}{4}$. What answer will you get if you don't simplify first?

COMMON ERROR ALERT

Students might simplify only the numerator or only the denominator. Remind them that simplifying requires dividing both the numerator and the denominator by the same factor.

Additional Examples

Example 1

In 2001, the car toll on the George Washington Bridge was \$6.00. In 1995, the toll was $\frac{2}{3}$ of the toll in 2001. What was the toll in 1995?

The toll was \$4.

Example 2

Multiply. Write each answer in simplest form.

A. $-12 \cdot \frac{3}{4}$ — **−9**

B. $\frac{1}{3} \cdot \frac{3}{8}$ — $\frac{1}{8}$

C. $-\frac{2}{3} \cdot \frac{4}{5}$ — $-\frac{8}{15}$

Example 3

Multiply. Write each answer in simplest form.

A. $\frac{2}{5} \cdot 1\frac{2}{3}$ — $\frac{2}{3}$

B. $4\frac{1}{5} \cdot 2\frac{1}{7}$ — **9**

C. $6\frac{2}{3} \cdot 4\frac{2}{5}$ — $\frac{88}{3}$ **or** $29\frac{1}{3}$

Example 1 note: Encourage students to use mental math when multiplying a fraction by an integer. Suggest that students use unit fractions (e.g., $\frac{1}{3}$ of 6 is 2, so $\frac{2}{3}$ of 6 is 4).

3 Close

Reaching All Learners

Through Modeling

To illustrate the concept that the product of two proper fractions is less than either of the factors, have students model $\frac{1}{2} \cdot \frac{2}{3}$ using paper and colored pencils. Direct students to fold a sheet of paper vertically into thirds and shade $\frac{2}{3}$ of the paper. Then have students fold the paper in half horizontally and use a second color to shade $\frac{1}{2}$ of the shaded $\frac{2}{3}$. Students should see that the doubled-shaded portion is $\frac{1}{3}$ of the whole sheet, so $\frac{1}{2} \cdot \frac{2}{3} = \frac{1}{3}$. Have students compare the product $\frac{1}{3}$ to the two factors, $\frac{1}{2}$ and $\frac{2}{3}$: $\frac{1}{3} < \frac{1}{2}$ and $\frac{1}{3} < \frac{2}{3}$. You may wish to have students repeat the activity with two other fractions.

Summarize

Ask students to list the steps for multiplying mixed numbers. Discuss when and how to determine the sign of the product.

Possible answer: (1) Change mixed numbers to improper fractions. (2) Simplify. (3) Multiply numerators. (4) Multiply denominators. (5) Simplify if needed. The rules for the sign of the product are the same as for integer products.

Answers to Think and Discuss

Possible answers:

1. Change the mixed number to an improper fraction, simplify completely, multiply numerators, and multiply denominators.
2. $\frac{1}{2} \cdot \frac{1}{3} \cdot \frac{1}{4} = \frac{1}{24}$ is correct since $1 \cdot 1 \cdot 1 = 1$ and $2 \cdot 3 \cdot 4 = 24$.
3. $\frac{2}{3} \cdot \frac{3}{4} = \frac{6}{12} = \frac{1}{2}$; If you simplify before multiplying, you will not have to simplify the answer.

4-7 PRACTICE & ASSESS

Students may want to refer back to the lesson examples.

Assignment Guide

If you finished Example 1 assign:
Core 1, 8, 9, 45–48, 52–59
Enriched 1, 8, 9, 45–48, 52–59

If you finished Example 2 assign:
Core 1–4, 8–17, 27–43 odd, 52–59
Enriched 1, 3, 9–17 odd, 26–48, 52–59

If you finished Example 3 assign:
Core 1–25, 27–47 odd, 52–59
Enriched 1–25 odd, 26–59

Answers

19. $\frac{222}{5}$ or $44\frac{2}{5}$

21. $\frac{35}{2}$ or $17\frac{1}{2}$

27. $\frac{155}{42}$ or $3\frac{29}{42}$

34. $\frac{35}{2}$ or $17\frac{1}{2}$

36. $\frac{30}{7}$ or $4\frac{2}{7}$

4-7 Exercises

FOR EXTRA PRACTICE see page 663

internet connect
Homework Help Online
go.hrw.com Keyword: MS4 4-7
go.hrw.com

GUIDED PRACTICE

See Example 1

1. On average, people spend $\frac{1}{4}$ of the time they sleep in a dream state. If Maxwell slept 10 hours last night, how much time did he spend dreaming? Write your answer in simplest form. **$2\frac{1}{2}$ hr**

See Example 2

Multiply. Write each answer in simplest form.

2. $-8 \cdot \frac{3}{4}$ **-6**
3. $\frac{2}{3} \cdot \frac{3}{5}$ **$\frac{2}{5}$**
4. $\frac{1}{4} \cdot \left(-\frac{2}{3}\right)$ **$-\frac{1}{6}$**

See Example 3

5. $4 \cdot 3\frac{1}{2}$ **14**
6. $\frac{4}{9} \cdot 5\frac{2}{5}$ **$\frac{12}{5}$ or $2\frac{2}{5}$**
7. $1\frac{1}{2} \cdot 1\frac{5}{9}$ **$\frac{7}{3}$ or $2\frac{1}{3}$**

INDEPENDENT PRACTICE

See Example 1

8. Sherry spent 4 hours exercising last week. If $\frac{5}{6}$ of the time was spent jogging, how much time did she spend jogging? Write your answer in simplest form. **$3\frac{1}{3}$ hr**

9. A cookie recipe calls for $\frac{1}{3}$ tsp of salt for 1 batch. Doreen is making cookies for a school bake sale and wants to bake 5 batches. How much salt does she need? Write your answer in simplest form. **$1\frac{2}{3}$ tsp**

See Example 2

Multiply. Write each answer in simplest form.

10. $5 \cdot \frac{1}{8}$ **$\frac{5}{8}$**
11. $4 \cdot \frac{1}{8}$ **$\frac{1}{2}$**
12. $3 \cdot \frac{5}{8}$ **$\frac{15}{8}$ or $1\frac{7}{8}$**
13. $6 \cdot \frac{2}{3}$ **4**
14. $\frac{2}{5} \cdot \frac{5}{7}$ **$\frac{2}{7}$**
15. $\frac{3}{8} \cdot \frac{2}{3}$ **$\frac{1}{4}$**
16. $\frac{1}{2} \cdot \left(-\frac{4}{9}\right)$ **$-\frac{2}{9}$**
17. $-\frac{5}{6} \cdot \frac{2}{3}$ **$-\frac{5}{9}$**

See Example 3

18. $7\frac{1}{2} \cdot 2\frac{2}{5}$ **18**
19. $6 \cdot 7\frac{2}{5}$
20. $2\frac{4}{7} \cdot \frac{1}{6}$ **$\frac{3}{7}$**
21. $2\frac{5}{8} \cdot 6\frac{2}{3}$
22. $\frac{2}{3} \cdot 2\frac{1}{4}$ **$\frac{3}{2}$ or $1\frac{1}{2}$**
23. $1\frac{1}{2} \cdot 1\frac{5}{9}$ **$\frac{7}{3}$ or $2\frac{1}{3}$**
24. $7 \cdot 5\frac{1}{8}$ **$\frac{287}{8}$ or $35\frac{7}{8}$**
25. $3\frac{3}{4} \cdot 2\frac{1}{5}$ **$\frac{33}{4}$ or $8\frac{1}{4}$**

PRACTICE AND PROBLEM SOLVING

Multiply. Write each answer in simplest form.

26. $\frac{5}{8} \cdot \frac{4}{5}$ **$\frac{1}{2}$**
27. $4\frac{3}{7} \cdot \frac{5}{6}$
28. $-\frac{2}{3} \cdot 6$ **-4**
29. $2 \cdot \frac{1}{6}$ **$\frac{1}{3}$**
30. $\frac{1}{8} \cdot 5$ **$\frac{5}{8}$**
31. $-\frac{3}{4} \cdot \frac{2}{9}$ **$-\frac{1}{6}$**
32. $4\frac{2}{3} \cdot 2\frac{4}{7}$ **12**
33. $-\frac{4}{9} \cdot \left(-\frac{3}{16}\right)$ **$\frac{1}{12}$**
34. $3\frac{1}{2} \cdot 5$
35. $\frac{1}{2} \cdot \frac{2}{3} \cdot \frac{3}{5}$ **$\frac{1}{5}$**
36. $\frac{6}{7} \cdot 5$
37. $1\frac{1}{2} \cdot \frac{3}{5} \cdot \frac{7}{9}$ **$\frac{7}{10}$**
38. $-\frac{2}{3} \cdot 1\frac{1}{2} \cdot \frac{2}{3}$ **$-\frac{2}{3}$**
39. $\frac{8}{9} \cdot \frac{3}{11} \cdot \frac{33}{40}$ **$\frac{1}{5}$**
40. $\frac{1}{6} \cdot 6 \cdot 8\frac{2}{3}$ **$\frac{26}{3}$ or $8\frac{2}{3}$**
41. $-\frac{8}{9} \cdot \left(-1\frac{1}{8}\right)$ **1**

Complete each multiplication sentence.

42. $\frac{1}{2} \cdot \frac{\blacksquare}{8} = \frac{3}{16}$ **3**
43. $\frac{\blacksquare}{7} \cdot \frac{2}{3} = \frac{10}{21}$ **5**
44. $\frac{2}{3} \cdot \frac{\blacksquare}{4} = \frac{1}{2}$ **3**

Math Background

Because mixed numbers can be represented as sums of integers and fractions, multiplication of mixed numbers can be viewed as an application of the Distributive Property. While this interpretation sometimes can lead to far more complex arithmetic than the standard algorithm, it can be a helpful technique. For example:

$$\begin{aligned}\frac{1}{3} \cdot 6\frac{9}{10} &= \frac{1}{3} \cdot \left(6 + \frac{9}{10}\right) \\ &= \frac{1}{3} \cdot 6 + \frac{1}{3} \cdot \frac{9}{10} \\ &= 2 + \frac{3}{10} \\ &= 2\frac{3}{10}\end{aligned}$$

RETEACH 4-7

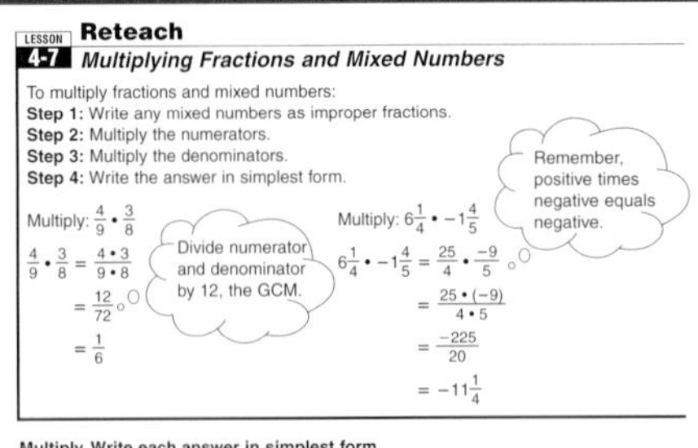

LESSON 4-7 **Reteach**
Multiplying Fractions and Mixed Numbers

To multiply fractions and mixed numbers:
Step 1: Write any mixed numbers as improper fractions.
Step 2: Multiply the numerators.
Step 3: Multiply the denominators.
Step 4: Write the answer in simplest form.

Multiply: $\frac{4}{9} \cdot \frac{3}{8}$

$\frac{4}{9} \cdot \frac{3}{8} = \frac{4 \cdot 3}{9 \cdot 8} = \frac{12}{72} = \frac{1}{6}$

Divide numerator and denominator by 12, the GCM.

Multiply: $6\frac{1}{4} \cdot -1\frac{4}{5}$

$6\frac{1}{4} \cdot -1\frac{4}{5} = \frac{25}{4} \cdot \frac{-9}{5} = \frac{25 \cdot (-9)}{4 \cdot 5} = \frac{-225}{20} = -11\frac{1}{4}$

Remember, positive times negative equals negative.

Multiply. Write each answer in simplest form.

1. $6 \cdot \frac{1}{9} = \frac{6 \cdot 1}{9} = \frac{6}{9} = \frac{2}{3}$
2. $-\frac{4}{5} \cdot \frac{5}{7} = -\frac{4 \cdot 5}{5 \cdot 7} = -\frac{20}{35} = -\frac{4}{7}$
3. $3\frac{1}{3} \cdot 9 = \frac{10}{3} \cdot 9 = \frac{10 \cdot 9}{3} = \frac{90}{3} = 30$
4. $\frac{3}{10} \cdot 2\frac{1}{2} = \frac{3}{10} \cdot \frac{5}{2} = \frac{3 \cdot 5}{10 \cdot 2} = \frac{15}{20} = \frac{3}{4}$
5. $\frac{2}{7} \cdot \frac{7}{8}$ **$\frac{1}{4}$**
6. $-\frac{5}{9} \cdot \frac{3}{4}$ **$-\frac{5}{12}$**
7. $\frac{9}{10} \cdot \left(-\frac{2}{3}\right)$ **$-\frac{3}{5}$**
8. $2\frac{5}{8} \cdot \frac{2}{3}$ **$1\frac{3}{4}$**
9. $\frac{1}{2} \cdot 4\frac{1}{4}$ **$2\frac{1}{8}$**
10. $-\frac{2}{3} \cdot 1\frac{3}{4}$ **$-1\frac{1}{6}$**
11. $5\frac{1}{5} \cdot \left(-1\frac{2}{3}\right)$ **$-8\frac{2}{3}$**
12. $4\frac{1}{2} \cdot 1\frac{1}{9}$ **5**
13. $-2\frac{3}{4} \cdot \left(-1\frac{1}{3}\right)$ **$3\frac{2}{3}$**

PRACTICE 4-7

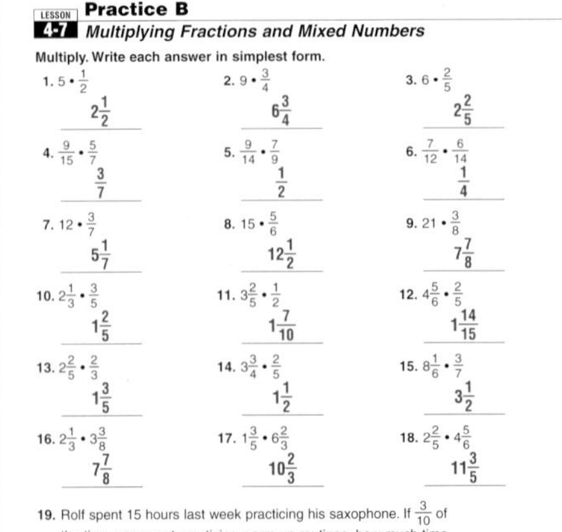

LESSON 4-7 **Practice B**
Multiplying Fractions and Mixed Numbers

Multiply. Write each answer in simplest form.

1. $5 \cdot \frac{1}{2}$ **$2\frac{1}{2}$**
2. $9 \cdot \frac{3}{4}$ **$6\frac{3}{4}$**
3. $6 \cdot \frac{2}{5}$ **$2\frac{2}{5}$**
4. $\frac{9}{15} \cdot \frac{5}{7}$ **$\frac{3}{7}$**
5. $\frac{9}{14} \cdot \frac{7}{9}$ **$\frac{1}{2}$**
6. $\frac{7}{12} \cdot \frac{6}{14}$ **$\frac{1}{4}$**
7. $12 \cdot \frac{3}{7}$ **$5\frac{1}{7}$**
8. $15 \cdot \frac{5}{6}$ **$12\frac{1}{2}$**
9. $21 \cdot \frac{3}{8}$ **$7\frac{7}{8}$**
10. $2\frac{1}{3} \cdot \frac{3}{5}$ **$1\frac{2}{5}$**
11. $3\frac{2}{5} \cdot \frac{1}{2}$ **$1\frac{7}{10}$**
12. $4\frac{5}{6} \cdot \frac{2}{5}$ **$1\frac{14}{15}$**
13. $2\frac{2}{5} \cdot \frac{2}{3}$ **$1\frac{3}{5}$**
14. $3\frac{3}{4} \cdot \frac{2}{5}$ **$1\frac{1}{2}$**
15. $8\frac{1}{6} \cdot \frac{3}{7}$ **$3\frac{1}{2}$**
16. $2\frac{1}{3} \cdot 3\frac{3}{8}$ **$7\frac{7}{8}$**
17. $1\frac{3}{5} \cdot 6\frac{2}{3}$ **$10\frac{2}{3}$**
18. $2\frac{2}{5} \cdot 4\frac{5}{6}$ **$11\frac{3}{5}$**

19. Rolf spent 15 hours last week practicing his saxophone. If $\frac{3}{10}$ of the time was spent practicing warm-up routines, how much time did he spend practicing warm-up routines?
$4\frac{1}{2}$ hours

20. A muffin recipe calls for $\frac{2}{5}$ tablespoon of vanilla extract for 6 muffins. Arthur is making 18 muffins. How much vanilla extract does he need?
$1\frac{1}{5}$ T

45. ***PHYSICAL SCIENCE*** The weight of an object on the moon is $\frac{1}{6}$ its weight on Earth. If a bowling ball weighs $12\frac{1}{2}$ pounds on Earth, how much would it weigh on the moon? **$2\frac{1}{12}$ lb**

46. ***CONSUMER*** In a survey, 200 students were asked what most influenced them to buy their latest CD. The results are shown in the circle graph.

Influences for Buying CDs

Radio $\frac{9}{20}$; Friend/relative $\frac{3}{20}$; Heard/saw in store $\frac{1}{10}$; Music video channel $\frac{2}{25}$; Live performance $\frac{7}{100}$; Other $\frac{3}{20}$

a. How many students said radio most influenced them? **90 students**

b. How many more were influenced by radio than by a music video channel? **74 students**

c. How many said a friend or relative influenced them or they heard the CD in a store? **50 students**

47. The Mississippi River flows at a rate of 2 miles per hour. If Eduardo floats down the river in a boat for $5\frac{2}{3}$ hours, how far will he travel? **$11\frac{1}{3}$ mi**

48. ***MEASUREMENT*** A standard paper clip is $1\frac{1}{4}$ in. long. If you laid 75 paper clips end to end, how long would the line of paper clips be? **$93\frac{3}{4}$ in.**

49. ***CHOOSE A STRATEGY*** What is the product of $\frac{1}{2} \cdot \frac{2}{3} \cdot \frac{3}{4} \cdot \frac{4}{5}$? **A**

A $\frac{1}{5}$ B 5 C $\frac{1}{20}$ D $\frac{3}{5}$

50. ***WRITE ABOUT IT*** Explain why the product of two positive proper fractions is always less than either fraction.

51. ***CHALLENGE*** Write three multiplication problems to show that the product of two fractions can be less than, equal to, or greater than 1.

Answers

50. Anytime you multiply a positive number by a number between 0 and 1, you get an answer that is smaller than the number you started with.

51. Possible answer: $\frac{1}{2} \cdot \frac{1}{2}, \frac{2}{1} \cdot \frac{1}{2}, \frac{5}{2} \cdot \frac{1}{2}$

Journal

Have students describe or draw a picture of a situation that requires finding a fraction of a fraction.

Spiral Review

Write each number in scientific notation. (Lesson 2-2)

52. 54,000 **5.4×10^4** 53. 3,430,000 **3.43×10^6** 54. 863 **8.63×10^2**

Find each product or quotient. (Lesson 3-5)

55. $3 \cdot (-9)$ **−27** 56. $(-8) \div (-4)$ **2** 57. $6 \cdot (-2) \cdot (-5)$ **60**

58. **TEST PREP** Which is the solution of the equation $x + 3 = -4$? (Lesson 3-6) **D**

A $x = 7$ C $x = -1$

B $x = 1$ D $x = -7$

59. **TEST PREP** Which is the product of 0.8 and 0.02? (Lesson 4-3) **G**

F 0.0016 H 0.16

G 0.016 J 1.6

Test Prep Doctor

In Exercise 59, remind students to look ahead at the answer choices. The question does not require multiplication, only correct placement of the decimal point. There should be 1 + 2, or 3, decimal digits, so choices **F**, **H**, and **J** can be eliminated.

CHALLENGE 4-7

LESSON 4-7 **Challenge**

Weigh Out in Space

How much do you think you would weigh on Mars? You can calculate anyone's weight on any of the planets by multiplying his or her weight times the planet's gravitational pull. Use the table to calculate what each animal listed below would weigh on different planets. Write your answers in simplest form.

Gravitational Pull of the Planets

Planet	Mercury	Venus	Mars	Jupiter	Saturn	Uranus	Neptune
Gravitational Pull	$\frac{19}{50}$	$\frac{9}{10}$	$\frac{19}{50}$	$2\frac{1}{2}$	$\frac{19}{20}$	$\frac{4}{5}$	$1\frac{1}{5}$

	Animal	Weight on Earth	Planet	Weight on Other Planet
1.	Mouse	$\frac{1}{16}$ pound	Neptune	**$\frac{3}{40}$ pounds**
2.	Cat	$5\frac{1}{4}$ pounds	Mercury	**$1\frac{199}{200}$ pounds**
			Jupiter	**$13\frac{1}{8}$ pounds**
3.	Dog	$50\frac{1}{2}$ pounds	Saturn	**$47\frac{39}{40}$ pounds**
			Neptune	**$60\frac{3}{5}$ pounds**
4.	Gorilla	200 pounds	Mars	**76 pounds**
			Uranus	**160 pounds**
5.	Cow	1,000 pounds	Venus	**900 pounds**
			Jupiter	**2,500 pounds**
6.	Small parrot	$\frac{7}{8}$ pound	Mercury	**$\frac{133}{400}$ pounds**
			Neptune	**$1\frac{1}{20}$ pounds**
7.	Macaw	$3\frac{1}{2}$ pounds	Neptune	**$4\frac{1}{5}$ pounds**
8.	Elephant	10,700 pounds	Uranus	**8,560 pounds**

PROBLEM SOLVING 4-7

LESSON 4-7 **Problem Solving**

Multiplying Fractions and Mixed Numbers

Write the correct answer.

1. Ariel's English homework is to read 24 pages. She reads $\frac{1}{8}$ of the assignment on the bus ride home. How many pages does she read on the bus?

3 pages

2. When a group of 14 friends goes to the movies at a multiplex, $\frac{1}{5}$ of the group decides to watch a science fiction movie. How many of the group see the science fiction movie?

8 friends

3. As of 1990, the American Indian population was about 2,000,000. About $\frac{1}{5}$ were Cherokee. About how many members of the Cherokee tribe were there in 1990?

400,000 members

4. Ron spends 3 hours painting a picture. Ashley spends $2\frac{2}{3}$ as long creating a sculpture. How long does Ashley work on her sculpture?

8 hours

Choose the letter for the best answer.

5. One cup of dry dog food weighs $1\frac{4}{5}$ ounces. A K9 dog eats $6\frac{1}{3}$ cups of food a day. How many ounces of food does the dog eat each day?

A $4\frac{8}{15}$ ounces (C) $11\frac{2}{5}$ ounces

B $8\frac{2}{15}$ ounces D $3\frac{14}{27}$ ounces

6. Max has enough chicken to make $8\frac{1}{2}$ servings of salad. He needs $\frac{1}{8}$ pound of chicken per serving. How much chicken does he have?

F 8 pounds H $8\frac{5}{8}$ pounds

(G) $1\frac{1}{16}$ pounds J $2\frac{1}{2}$ pounds

7. A meteorite found in Willamette, Oregon, weighed $\frac{7}{10}$ as much as one found in Armanti, Western Mongolia. The meteorite found in Armanti weighed 22 tons. How much did the one in Oregon weigh?

A $31\frac{1}{5}$ tons

B $21\frac{3}{10}$ tons

C $22\frac{7}{10}$ tons

(D) $15\frac{2}{5}$ tons

8. Nicole takes part in a $12\frac{1}{2}$-mile walk-a-thon to raise money for charity. She stops $\frac{1}{2}$ of the way to rest. How much farther must Nicole walk to finish the walk-a-thon?

(F) $6\frac{1}{4}$ miles

G $6\frac{1}{2}$ miles

H 12 miles

J 25 miles

Lesson Quiz

Multiply. Write each answer in simplest form.

1. $\frac{1}{8} \cdot \frac{5}{6}$ **$\frac{5}{48}$**

2. $5\frac{5}{6} \cdot \frac{1}{2}$ **$\frac{35}{12}$ or $2\frac{11}{12}$**

3. $5\frac{1}{10} \cdot 1\frac{2}{3}$ **$\frac{17}{2}$ or $8\frac{1}{2}$**

4. $\frac{3}{16} \cdot 4\frac{2}{3}$ **$\frac{7}{8}$**

5. A recipe for clam chowder calls for $2\frac{1}{4}$ pounds of butter. If you prepare one-half of the recipe, how much butter do you need? $1\frac{1}{8}$ pounds

Available on Daily Transparency in CRB

4-8 Organizer

Pacing: Traditional 1 day
Block $\frac{1}{2}$ day

Objective: Students divide fractions and mixed numbers.

Warm Up

Multiply.

1. $\frac{7}{9} \cdot \frac{3}{6}$ $\frac{7}{18}$
2. $\frac{9}{8} \cdot \frac{6}{5}$ $\frac{27}{20}$ or $1\frac{7}{20}$
3. $2\frac{1}{5} \cdot 7$ $\frac{77}{5}$ or $15\frac{2}{5}$
4. $2\frac{1}{2} \cdot 1\frac{1}{4}$ $\frac{25}{8}$ or $3\frac{1}{8}$

Problem of the Day

The Jeffers family is putting in a new fence around their yard. The yard is in the shape of a square. If they put nine fence posts on each side of the square, how many posts will be used? **32**

Available on Daily Transparency in CRB

Math Humor

If 3 people share $5\frac{1}{2}$ pizzas equally, what will each person get?

A stomachache

4-8 Dividing Fractions and Mixed Numbers

Learn to divide fractions and mixed numbers.

Vocabulary
reciprocal

When you divide 8 by 4, you find how many 4's there are in 8. Similarly, when you divide 2 by $\frac{1}{3}$, you find how many $\frac{1}{3}$'s there are in 2.

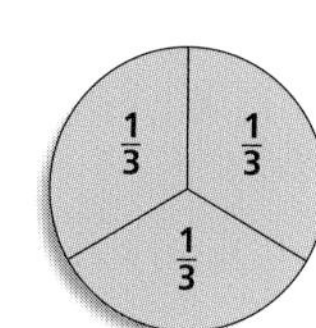

There are six $\frac{1}{3}$'s in 2.

Reciprocals can help you divide by fractions. Two numbers are **reciprocals** if their product is 1. The reciprocal of $\frac{1}{3}$ is 3 because

$\frac{1}{3} \cdot 3 = \frac{1}{3} \cdot \frac{3}{1} = \frac{3}{3} = 1.$

To divide by a fraction, find its reciprocal and then multiply.

$$2 \div \frac{1}{3} = 2 \cdot 3 = 6$$

EXAMPLE 1 Dividing Fractions

Divide. Write each answer in simplest form.

A $\frac{2}{3} \div \frac{1}{5}$

$\frac{2}{3} \div \frac{1}{5} = \frac{2}{3} \cdot \frac{5}{1}$ *Multiply by the reciprocal of $\frac{1}{5}$.*

$= \frac{2 \cdot 5}{3 \cdot 1}$

$= \frac{10}{3}$ or $3\frac{1}{3}$

B $\frac{3}{5} \div 6$

$\frac{3}{5} \div 6 = \frac{3}{5} \cdot \frac{1}{6}$ *Multiply by the reciprocal of 6.*

$= \frac{\overset{1}{\cancel{3}} \cdot 1}{5 \cdot \cancel{6}_{2}}$ *Simplify.*

$= \frac{1}{10}$

EXAMPLE 2 Dividing Mixed Numbers

Divide. Write each answer in simplest form.

A $4\frac{1}{3} \div 2\frac{1}{2}$

$4\frac{1}{3} \div 2\frac{1}{2} = \frac{13}{3} \div \frac{5}{2}$ *Write mixed numbers as improper fractions.*

$= \frac{13}{3} \cdot \frac{2}{5}$ *Multiply by the reciprocal of $\frac{5}{2}$.*

$= \frac{26}{15}$ or $1\frac{11}{15}$

1 Introduce

Alternate Opener

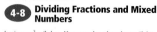

EXPLORATION

4-8 Dividing Fractions and Mixed Numbers

Jamie runs $\frac{3}{4}$-mile laps. How many laps does she run if she runs 6 miles?

Use the number line model to find how many $\frac{3}{4}$-mile laps are in 6 miles. (Find the quotient of $6 \div \frac{3}{4}$.)

Jamie runs 8 laps.

1. Use the number line model to find the quotient of $7 \div 2\frac{1}{3}$.

= $2\frac{1}{3}$
0 1 2 3 4 5 6 7

2. Use the number line model to find the quotient of $6\frac{1}{2} \div \frac{1}{2}$.

= $\frac{1}{2}$
0 1 2 3 4 5 6 7

Think and Discuss

3. **Explain** why the quotient of $7 \div 2\frac{1}{3}$ is less than 7, and the quotient of $6\frac{1}{2} \div \frac{1}{2}$ is greater than $6\frac{1}{2}$.
4. **Demonstrate** the results of the division in number **3** by computing with your calculator.

Motivate

To introduce students to dividing fractions and mixed numbers, ask them to use mental math to divide first with integers and then with fractions (e.g., How many 4's are in 24? How many $\frac{1}{3}$'s are in 2?). Point out that dividing by a fraction less than one produces a quotient greater than the dividend.

Exploration worksheet and answers on Chapter 4 Resource Book pp. 73 and 142

2 Teach

Lesson Presentation

Guided Instruction

In this lesson, students learn to divide fractions and mixed numbers. Mixed numbers are converted to improper fractions, and the division is changed to multiplication by the reciprocal of the divisor. Use division by a unit fraction to help explain the change to the reciprocal (e.g., when dividing by $\frac{1}{3}$, there are 3 thirds in each whole). Review the steps for multiplying by a fraction.

Teaching Tip Stress proper mathematical language to avoid confusion regarding the change to multiplication by the reciprocal. The dividend *divided* by the *divisor* becomes the dividend *multiplied* by the *reciprocal of the divisor.*

Divide. Write each answer in simplest form.

B $\frac{5}{6} \div 7\frac{1}{7}$

$\frac{5}{6} \div 7\frac{1}{7} = \frac{5}{6} \div \frac{50}{7}$ *Write $7\frac{1}{7}$ as an improper fraction.*

$= \frac{5}{6} \cdot \frac{7}{50}$ *Multiply by the reciprocal of $\frac{50}{7}$.*

$= \frac{{}^{1}\cancel{5} \cdot 7}{6 \cdot \cancel{50}_{10}}$ *Simplify.*

$= \frac{7}{60}$

C $4\frac{4}{5} \div \frac{6}{7}$

$4\frac{4}{5} \div \frac{6}{7} = \frac{24}{5} \div \frac{6}{7}$ *Write $4\frac{4}{5}$ as an improper fraction.*

$= \frac{24}{5} \cdot \frac{7}{6}$ *Multiply by the reciprocal of $\frac{6}{7}$.*

$= \frac{{}^{4}\cancel{24} \cdot 7}{5 \cdot \cancel{6}_{1}}$ *Simplify.*

$= \frac{28}{5}$ or $5\frac{3}{5}$

EXAMPLE 3 *Social Studies Application*

Social Studies LINK

The German mark plummeted in value following World War I. By November 1923, a single loaf of bread cost 2,000,000,000 marks. People used the worthless paper money for many unusual purposes, such as building kites.

Use the bar graph to determine how many times longer a $100 bill is expected to stay in circulation than a $1 bill.

Life Spans of Bills

	Years
$1	1.5
$5	2
$10	3
$20	4
$50	9
$100	9

The life span of a $1 bill is $1\frac{1}{2}$ years. The life span of a $100 bill is 9 years.

Think: How many $1\frac{1}{2}$'s are there in 9?

$9 \div 1\frac{1}{2} = \frac{9}{1} \div \frac{3}{2}$ *Write both numbers as improper fractions.*

$= \frac{9}{1} \cdot \frac{2}{3}$ *Multiply by the reciprocal of $\frac{3}{2}$.*

$= \frac{{}^{3}\cancel{9} \cdot 2}{1 \cdot \cancel{3}_{1}}$ *Simplify.*

$= \frac{6}{1}$ or 6

A $100 bill is expected to stay in circulation 6 times longer than a $1 bill.

Think and Discuss

1. **Explain** whether $\frac{1}{2} \div \frac{2}{3}$ is the same as $2 \cdot \frac{2}{3}$.
2. **Compare** the steps used in multiplying mixed numbers with those used in dividing mixed numbers.

COMMON ERROR ALERT

The language of dividing one number "into" another may be confusing. "Divided by" is a less confusing term. Remind students to use the reciprocal of the divisor, the number they are dividing by.

Additional Examples

Example 1

Divide. Write each answer in simplest form.

A. $\frac{3}{7} \div \frac{2}{5}$ — $\frac{15}{14}$ or $1\frac{1}{14}$

B. $\frac{3}{8} \div 12$ — $\frac{1}{32}$

Example 2

Divide. Write each answer in simplest form.

A. $5\frac{2}{3} \div 1\frac{1}{4}$ — $\frac{68}{15}$ or $4\frac{8}{15}$

B. $\frac{3}{4} \div 2\frac{1}{2}$ — $\frac{3}{10}$

C. $8\frac{2}{3} \div \frac{13}{27}$ — 18

Example 3

The life span of a golden dollar coin is 30 years, while paper currency lasts an average of $1\frac{1}{2}$ years. How many times longer will the golden dollar stay in circulation?

about 20 times longer

Example 3 note: Encourage students to check the answer by using the graph. Have them compare the answer with how many times longer the bar for the $100 bill is than the bar for the $1 bill.

3 Close

Reaching All Learners

Through Number Sense

Encourage students to notice that for non-negative numbers, multiplying a number by a proper fraction gives a product less than the original number and dividing a number by a proper fraction gives a quotient greater than the original number. Challenge students to make similar observations about mixed numbers and the number 1.

Possible answer: Multiplying by a mixed number yields a product greater than the original number, and dividing by a mixed number yields a quotient less than the original number. Multiplying by 1 or dividing by 1 leaves the number unchanged.

Summarize

Ask students to review the steps in dividing by a fraction or mixed number. Discuss whether the same steps would work for dividing by an integer. Ask students to give examples to support their opinions. Stress that division by a number is equivalent to multiplication by its reciprocal.

Possible answer: To divide by a mixed number, first change it to an improper fraction. Next, to divide by any fraction, multiply by its reciprocal. Then simplify the product to simplest form. Any integer can be written with a denominator of 1, so the rule works for integers $\left(\text{e.g., } 4 \div 2 = 4 \div \frac{2}{1} = 4 \cdot \frac{1}{2}\right)$.

Answers to Think and Discuss

Possible answers:

1. The wrong number has been replaced by its reciprocal. The reciprocal of the divisor, not the dividend, should be used.
2. When multiplying and dividing, mixed numbers are changed to improper fractions first. Fractions are simplified and then multiplied. The major difference is the change from division by a divisor to multiplication by its reciprocal prior to simplification and multiplication.

4-8 PRACTICE & ASSESS

Students may want to refer back to the lesson examples.

Assignment Guide

If you finished Example 1 assign:
Core 1–3, 8–13, 23, 24, 34, 36, 44–48
Enriched 1–3, 8–13, 23, 24, 34, 36, 44–48

If you finished Example 2 assign:
Core 1–6, 8–19, 23–35 odd, 44–48
Enriched 1–5 odd, 9–19 odd, 22–36, 44–48

If you finished Example 3 assign:
Core 1–21, 23–41 odd, 44–48
Enriched 1–21 odd, 22–48

Notes

4-8 Exercises

FOR EXTRA PRACTICE see page 663

internet connect
Homework Help Online
go.hrw.com Keyword: MS4 4-8

GUIDED PRACTICE

See Example 1 — Divide. Write each answer in simplest form.

1. $6 \div \frac{1}{3}$ **18**
2. $\frac{3}{5} \div \frac{3}{4}$ **$\frac{4}{5}$**
3. $\frac{3}{4} \div 8$ **$\frac{3}{32}$**

See Example 2

4. $\frac{5}{6} \div 3\frac{1}{3}$ **$\frac{1}{4}$**
5. $5\frac{5}{8} \div 4\frac{1}{2}$ **$\frac{5}{4}$ or $1\frac{1}{4}$**
6. $10\frac{4}{5} \div 5\frac{2}{5}$ **2**

See Example 3

7. Kareem has $12\frac{1}{2}$ yards of material. A cape for a play takes $3\frac{5}{6}$ yards. How many capes can Kareem make with the material? **3 capes**

INDEPENDENT PRACTICE

See Example 1 — Divide. Write each answer in simplest form.

8. $2 \div \frac{7}{8}$ **$\frac{16}{7}$ or $2\frac{2}{7}$**
9. $10 \div \frac{5}{9}$ **18**
10. $\frac{3}{4} \div \frac{6}{7}$ **$\frac{7}{8}$**
11. $\frac{8}{9} \div \frac{1}{4}$ **$\frac{32}{9}$ or $3\frac{5}{9}$**
12. $\frac{4}{9} \div 12$ **$\frac{1}{27}$**
13. $\frac{9}{10} \div 6$ **$\frac{3}{20}$**

See Example 2

14. $\frac{7}{11} \div 4\frac{1}{5}$ **$\frac{5}{33}$**
15. $\frac{3}{4} \div 2\frac{1}{10}$ **$\frac{5}{14}$**
16. $22\frac{1}{2} \div 4\frac{2}{7}$ **$\frac{21}{4}$ or $5\frac{1}{4}$**
17. $3\frac{5}{7} \div 9\frac{1}{7}$ **$\frac{13}{32}$**
18. $14\frac{2}{3} \div 1\frac{1}{6}$ **$\frac{88}{7}$ or $12\frac{4}{7}$**
19. $7\frac{7}{10} \div 2\frac{2}{5}$ **$\frac{77}{24}$ or $3\frac{5}{24}$**

See Example 3

20. A juicer holds $43\frac{3}{4}$ pints of juice. How many $2\frac{1}{2}$-pint bottles can be filled with that much juice? **17 bottles**
21. How many $24\frac{1}{2}$ in. pieces of ribbon can be cut from a roll of ribbon that is 147 in. long? **6 pieces**

PRACTICE AND PROBLEM SOLVING

33. $\frac{21}{2}$ or $10\frac{1}{2}$

Evaluate. Write each answer in simplest form.

22. $9 \div 1\frac{2}{3}$ **$\frac{27}{5}$ or $5\frac{2}{5}$**
23. $\frac{2}{3} \div \frac{8}{9}$ **$\frac{3}{4}$**
24. $-1\frac{7}{11} \div \left(-\frac{9}{11}\right)$ **2**
25. $6\frac{2}{3} \div \frac{7}{9}$ **$\frac{60}{7}$ or $8\frac{4}{7}$**
26. $\frac{1}{2} \div 4\frac{3}{4}$ **$\frac{2}{19}$**
27. $\frac{4}{21} \div 3\frac{1}{2}$ **$\frac{8}{147}$**
28. $4\frac{1}{2} \div 3\frac{1}{2}$ **$\frac{9}{7}$ or $1\frac{2}{7}$**
29. $1\frac{3}{5} \div 2\frac{1}{2}$ **$\frac{16}{25}$**
30. $\frac{7}{8} \div 2\frac{1}{10}$ **$\frac{5}{12}$**
31. $1\frac{3}{5} \div \left(2\frac{2}{9}\right)$ **$\frac{18}{25}$**
32. $\left(\frac{1}{2} + \frac{2}{3}\right) \div 1\frac{1}{2}$ **$\frac{7}{9}$**
33. $\left(2\frac{3}{4} + 3\frac{2}{3}\right) \div \frac{11}{18}$
34. $\frac{4}{5} \cdot \frac{3}{8} \div \frac{9}{10}$ **$\frac{1}{3}$**
35. $-\frac{12}{13} \cdot \frac{13}{18} \div 1\frac{1}{2}$ **$-\frac{4}{9}$**
36. $\frac{3}{7} \div \frac{15}{28} \div \left(-\frac{4}{5}\right)$ **−1**
37. Three friends are driving round-trip to an amusement park that is $102\frac{3}{4}$ mi from their town. If each friend drives the same distance, how far does each drive? **$68\frac{1}{2}$ mi**
38. How many $\frac{1}{4}$ lb hamburger patties can be made from a $10\frac{1}{4}$ lb package and an $11\frac{1}{2}$ lb package of ground meat? **87 hamburger patties**

Math Background

Division is defined as multiplication by the reciprocal. However, the sharing, or partitioning, analogy of division has a concrete basis that is useful for students. Physically dividing an object, such as a piece of paper, into fractional portions may help students understand why division by a fraction results in a quotient greater than the dividend.

RETEACH 4-8

LESSON 4-8 **Reteach**
Dividing Fractions and Mixed Numbers

Dividing fractions and mixed numbers is very much like multiplying fractions and mixed numbers. Just follow these steps:

Step 1: Write any mixed numbers as improper fractions.
Step 2: Invert the divisor.
Step 3: Multiply and write the quotient in simplest form.

Divide: $1\frac{1}{8} \div \frac{1}{3}$
Step 1: $1\frac{1}{8} \div \frac{1}{3} = \frac{9}{8} \div \frac{1}{3}$
Step 2: $\frac{9}{8} \div \frac{1}{3} = \frac{9}{8} \cdot \frac{3}{1}$
Step 3: $\frac{9}{8} \cdot \frac{3}{1} = \frac{27}{8} = 3\frac{3}{8}$

Divide: $1\frac{1}{4} \div 3\frac{1}{3}$
Step 1: $1\frac{1}{4} \div 3\frac{1}{3} = \frac{5}{4} \div \frac{10}{3}$
Step 2: $\frac{5}{4} \div \frac{10}{3} = \frac{5}{4} \cdot \frac{3}{10}$
Step 3: $\frac{5}{4} \cdot \frac{3}{10} = \frac{15}{40} = \frac{3}{8}$

Divide. Write each answer in simplest form.

1. $\frac{4}{5} \div \frac{1}{2} = \frac{4}{5} \cdot \frac{2}{1} = \frac{8}{5} = 1\frac{3}{5}$
2. $\frac{5}{8} \div \frac{5}{6} = \frac{5}{8} \cdot \frac{6}{5} = \frac{30}{40} = \frac{3}{4}$
3. $2\frac{1}{2} \div 1\frac{3}{4} = \frac{5}{2} \div \frac{7}{4} = \frac{5}{2} \cdot \frac{4}{7} = \frac{20}{14} = \frac{10}{7} = 1\frac{3}{7}$
4. $2\frac{2}{3} \div 1\frac{1}{5} = \frac{8}{3} \div \frac{6}{5} = \frac{8}{3} \cdot \frac{5}{6} = \frac{40}{18} = \frac{20}{9} = 2\frac{2}{9}$
5. $\frac{3}{5} \div \frac{3}{10}$ **2**
6. $\frac{7}{8} \div \frac{1}{3}$ **$2\frac{5}{8}$**
7. $\frac{5}{12} \div \frac{1}{2}$ **$\frac{5}{6}$**
8. $4\frac{1}{3} \div 1\frac{1}{9}$ **$3\frac{9}{10}$**
9. $2\frac{1}{3} \div 1\frac{3}{4}$ **$1\frac{1}{3}$**
10. $5\frac{5}{8} \div 2\frac{1}{2}$ **$2\frac{1}{4}$**

PRACTICE 4-8

LESSON 4-8 **Practice B**
Dividing Fractions and Mixed Numbers

Divide. Write each answer in simplest form.

1. $4 \div \frac{1}{2}$ **8**
2. $\frac{1}{5} \div \frac{1}{4}$ **$\frac{4}{5}$**
3. $\frac{1}{3} \div \frac{3}{5}$ **$\frac{5}{9}$**
4. $\frac{8}{9} \div \frac{2}{3}$ **$1\frac{1}{3}$**
5. $\frac{3}{8} \div \frac{3}{4}$ **$\frac{1}{2}$**
6. $\frac{7}{10} \div \frac{3}{5}$ **$1\frac{1}{6}$**
7. $\frac{5}{12} \div \frac{2}{5}$ **$1\frac{1}{24}$**
8. $\frac{3}{4} \div \frac{4}{9}$ **$1\frac{11}{16}$**
9. $\frac{7}{12} \div \frac{3}{4}$ **$\frac{7}{9}$**
10. $4\frac{1}{6} \div \frac{1}{3}$ **$12\frac{1}{2}$**
11. $3\frac{1}{4} \div \frac{2}{5}$ **$8\frac{1}{8}$**
12. $6\frac{1}{9} \div \frac{1}{6}$ **$36\frac{2}{3}$**
13. $2\frac{1}{4} \div 1\frac{3}{4}$ **$1\frac{2}{7}$**
14. $3\frac{3}{4} \div 2\frac{5}{6}$ **$1\frac{11}{34}$**
15. $5\frac{1}{3} \div 1\frac{4}{5}$ **$2\frac{26}{27}$**
16. $2\frac{1}{2} \div 2\frac{1}{3}$ **$1\frac{1}{14}$**
17. $1\frac{3}{4} \div 1\frac{1}{4}$ **$1\frac{2}{5}$**
18. $7\frac{2}{3} \div 1\frac{1}{5}$ **$6\frac{7}{18}$**
19. Burger Barn has $46\frac{2}{3}$ pounds of ground beef. How many $\frac{1}{3}$-pound burgers can be made using all the ground beef? **140 burgers**
20. Roberto needs some roofing tiles to be cut from a large tile. How many tiles that are each $14\frac{3}{8}$ inches in length can he cut from a larger piece of tile that is $100\frac{5}{8}$ inches long? **7 tiles**

Industrial Arts LINK

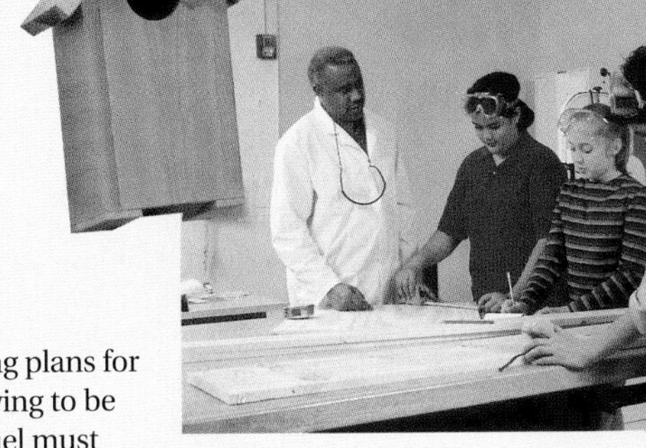

39. The students in Mr. Park's woodworking class are making birdhouses as one of their projects. The plans call for the side pieces of the birdhouses to be $7\frac{1}{4}$ inches long. If Mr. Park has 6 boards that are $50\frac{3}{4}$ inches long, how many side pieces can be cut? **42 side pieces**

40. For his drafting class, Manuel is drawing plans for a bookcase. Because he wants his drawing to be $\frac{1}{4}$ the actual size of the bookcase, Manuel must divide each measurement of the bookcase by 4. If the bookcase will be $3\frac{2}{3}$ feet wide, how wide will Manuel's drawing be? **$\frac{11}{12}$ foot or 11 in.**

41. The table shows the total number of hours that the students in each of Mrs. Anwar's 5 industrial arts classes took to complete their final projects. If the third-period class has 17 students, how many hours did each student in that class work on average? **$11\frac{3}{4}$ hours**

Period	Hours
1st	$200\frac{1}{2}$
2nd	$179\frac{2}{5}$
3rd	$199\frac{3}{4}$
5th	$190\frac{3}{4}$
6th	$180\frac{1}{4}$

42. Brandy is stamping circles from a strip of aluminum. If each circle is $1\frac{1}{4}$ inches tall, how many circles can she get from an $8\frac{3}{4}$-inch by $1\frac{1}{4}$-inch strip of aluminum? **7 circles**

43. ***CHALLENGE*** Alexandra is cutting wood stencils to spell her first name with capital letters. Her first step is to cut squares of wood that are $3\frac{1}{2}$ in. long on a side for each letter in her name. Will Alexandra be able to make all of the letters of her name from a single piece of wood that is $7\frac{1}{2}$ in. wide and 18 in. long? Explain your answer. **Yes. There are 9 letters in *Alexandra*. $7\frac{1}{2} \div 3\frac{1}{2} = 2\frac{1}{7}$ and $18 \div 3\frac{1}{2} = 5\frac{1}{7}$, so she can make 2 rows with 5 letters each.**

Spiral Review

Write the prime factorization of each number. (Lesson 2-4)

44. 102 **$2 \cdot 3 \cdot 17$** **45.** 320 **$2^6 \cdot 5$** **46.** 150 **$2 \cdot 3 \cdot 5^2$**

47. TEST PREP What is the GCF of 18 and 12? (Lesson 2-5) **B**

A 1 B 6 C 36 D 216

48. TEST PREP Order $\frac{1}{2}$, 0.4, −0.8, $-\frac{2}{3}$, and 0.04 from least to greatest. (Lesson 3-10) **J**

F $\frac{1}{2}$, 0.4, 0.04, $-\frac{2}{3}$, −0.8
H $-\frac{2}{3}$, −0.8, 0.04, 0.4, $\frac{1}{2}$
G −0.8, $-\frac{2}{3}$, 0.4, 0.04, $\frac{1}{2}$
J −0.8, $-\frac{2}{3}$, 0.04, 0.4, $\frac{1}{2}$

CHALLENGE 4-8

LESSON 4-8 **Challenge**
Animal Senior Citizens

The value of each division expression will show the average life expectancy of an animal. Complete the chart. Then use the information to fill in the blanks below.

	Animal	Division Expression	Life Expectancy (yr)
1.	Black Bear	$2\frac{1}{2} \div \frac{5}{36}$	18
2.	Chimpanzee	$40\frac{2}{5} \div 2\frac{1}{50}$	20
3.	Dog	$15\frac{1}{2} \div 1\frac{7}{24}$	12
4.	Hippopotamus	$4\frac{3}{8} \div \frac{7}{64}$	40
5.	Mouse	$\frac{5}{6} \div \frac{5}{18}$	3
6.	Guinea Pig	$\frac{2}{3} \div \left(-\frac{3}{5}\right) \div \left(-\frac{5}{18}\right)$	4
7.	Tiger	$-2\frac{1}{4} \div 3\frac{1}{2} \div \left(-\frac{9}{224}\right)$	16
8.	Kangaroo	$\left(\frac{3}{4} + \frac{7}{8}\right) \div \frac{13}{56}$	7

9. If you divide the average life span of a guinea pig by **$\frac{1}{10}$**, you get the average life span of a hippopotamus.

10. If you divide the average life span of a kangaroo by $\frac{7}{20}$, you find the average life span of a horse, which is **20 years**.

11. A **hippopotamus** can live 37 years longer than a **mouse**. This is $5\frac{1}{2} \div 2\frac{3}{4}$ years longer than the life expectancy of an African elephant, which is **35 years**.

12. (average life expectancy of a dog) $\div \frac{3}{8} \div 6\frac{2}{5}$ = (average life expectancy of a rabbit) = **5 years**.

PROBLEM SOLVING 4-8

LESSON 4-8 **Problem Solving**
Dividing Fractions and Mixed Numbers

Write the correct answer.

1. The Wheeling Bridge in West Virginia is about $307\frac{4}{5}$ meters long. If you walk with a stride of about $\frac{3}{10}$ meter, how many steps would it take you to cross this suspension bridge?
about 1,026 steps

2. The Flathead Rail Tunnel in Montana is about $7\frac{3}{4}$ miles long. If a train travels through the tunnel at a speed of about $1\frac{1}{2}$ miles per minute, how long will it take to pass from one end of the tunnel to the other?
$5\frac{1}{6}$ minutes

3. A hiking trail is $6\frac{2}{3}$ miles long. It has 4 exercise stations, spaced evenly along the trail. What is the distance between each exercise station?
$1\frac{1}{3}$ miles

4. Jamal buys a strip of 25 postage stamps. The strip of stamps is $21\frac{7}{8}$ inches long. How long is each stamp?
$\frac{7}{8}$ inch

Choose the letter for the best answer.

5. Matt wants to decorate his skateboard with decals. His skateboard is $28\frac{3}{4}$ inches long. The decals are $5\frac{1}{2}$ inches long. If Matt arranges them in a line from the front to the back, how many decals will fit?
(A) 5 decals
B 6 decals
C 7 decals
D 8 decals

6. A square floor tile measures $\frac{3}{4}$ square feet. How many tiles are required to cover a 200 square foot floor?
F 150 tiles
(G) 267 tiles
H 275 tiles
J 300 tiles

7. Bev buys a sleeve of ball bearings for her skateboard. Each of the bearings is $1\frac{1}{5}$ inches wide. The sleeve is $9\frac{3}{5}$ inches long. How many bearings are in the sleeve?
A 5 bearings
(B) 8 bearings
C 9 bearings
D 12 bearings

8. The average hamster weighs about $\frac{1}{4}$ pound. The total weight of all the hamsters in a cage in a pet store is $1\frac{1}{2}$ pounds. How many hamsters are in the cage?
F 3 hamsters
G 4 hamsters
H 5 hamsters
(J) 6 hamsters

Interdisciplinary LINK

Industrial Arts

Exercises 39–43 focus on the application of mathematics in industrial arts, such as woodworking and drafting.

Journal

Have students describe a real-world situation that required them to divide by a fraction (e.g., to find the number of quarters or halves in a certain number).

Test Prep Doctor

In Exercise 47, eliminate both choices **C** and **D** as multiples, not factors, of 18 and 12. As both numbers are even, choice **A** is quickly eliminated as well.

Lesson Quiz

Divide. Write each answer in simplest form.

1. $8 \div \frac{4}{5}$ **10** **2.** $\frac{5}{9} \div \frac{1}{8}$ **$\frac{40}{9}$ or $4\frac{4}{9}$**

3. $\frac{3}{5} \div 6$ **$\frac{1}{10}$** **4.** $2\frac{1}{2} \div 3\frac{1}{7}$ **$\frac{35}{44}$**

5. There are $5\frac{1}{4}$ yards of silk in a roll. If it takes $\frac{3}{4}$ of a yard to make one designer scarf, how many scarves can be made from the roll? **7**

Available on Daily Transparency in CRB

4-9 Organizer

Pacing: Traditional 1 day
Block $\frac{1}{2}$ day

Objective: Students estimate sums and differences of fractions and mixed numbers.

Warm Up

Divide. Write each answer in simplest form.

1. $4 \div \frac{3}{10}$ $\quad \frac{40}{3}$ or $13\frac{1}{3}$

2. $\frac{3}{4} \div \frac{6}{5}$ $\quad \frac{5}{8}$

3. $15\frac{2}{3} \div \frac{5}{6}$ $\quad \frac{94}{5}$ or $18\frac{4}{5}$

Problem of the Day

Fill in the square using the numbers 5–13 so that all sums (rows, columns, and main diagonals) are the same.

8	13	6
7	9	11
12	5	10

Available on Daily Transparency in CRB

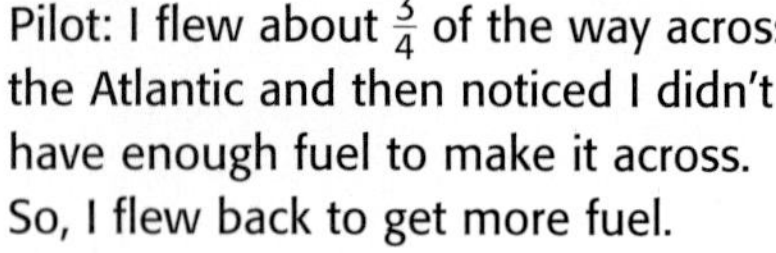

Pilot: I flew about $\frac{3}{4}$ of the way across the Atlantic and then noticed I didn't have enough fuel to make it across. So, I flew back to get more fuel.

4-9 Estimate with Fractions

Problem Solving Skill

Learn to estimate sums and differences of fractions and mixed numbers.

One of the largest lobsters ever caught was found off the coast of Nova Scotia, Canada, and weighed $44\frac{3}{8}$ lb. About how much heavier was this than an average lobster, which may weigh $3\frac{1}{4}$ lb?

Sometimes, when solving problems, you may not need an exact answer. To estimate sums and differences of fractions and mixed numbers, round each fraction to 0, $\frac{1}{2}$, or 1. You can use a number line to help.

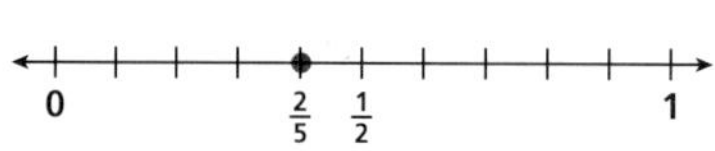

$\frac{2}{5}$ is closer to $\frac{1}{2}$ than to 0.

You can also round fractions by comparing numerators with denominators.

Guidelines for Rounding Fractions		
Round to **0** if the numerator is much smaller than the denominator. Examples: $\frac{1}{9}, \frac{3}{20}, \frac{2}{11}$	Round to $\frac{1}{2}$ if the numerator is about half the denominator. Examples: $\frac{2}{5}, \frac{5}{12}, \frac{7}{13}$	Round to **1** if the numerator is nearly equal to the denominator. Examples: $\frac{8}{9}, \frac{23}{25}, \frac{97}{100}$

EXAMPLE  1 ***Measurement Application***

One of the largest lobsters ever caught weighed $44\frac{3}{8}$ lb. Estimate how much more this lobster weighed than an average $3\frac{1}{4}$ lb lobster.

$44\frac{3}{8} - 3\frac{1}{4}$

$44\frac{3}{8} \longrightarrow 44\frac{1}{2}$ $\quad 3\frac{1}{4} \longrightarrow 3\frac{1}{2}$ *Round each mixed number.*

$44\frac{1}{2} - 3\frac{1}{2} = 41$ *Subtract.*

The lobster weighed about 41 lb more than an average lobster.

Remember!

Round $\frac{1}{4}$ to $\frac{1}{2}$ and $\frac{3}{4}$ to 1.

1 Introduce

Alternate Opener

EXPLORATION

4-9 Estimate with Fractions

The dimensions of a picture frame are $39\frac{7}{16}$ inches by $24\frac{3}{8}$ inches. Phyllis estimates that the distance around the frame is 80 + 50 = 130 inches.

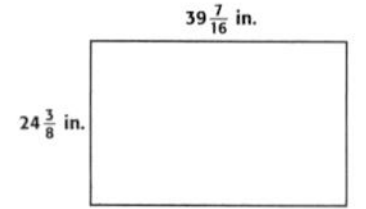

1. Is Phyllis's estimate reasonable? Why or why not?

Estimate each sum or difference.

2. $43\frac{1}{2} - 19\frac{27}{32}$
3. $21\frac{1}{2} + 19\frac{3}{8} - 12\frac{1}{4}$
4. $77\frac{7}{8} + 99\frac{1}{10}$
5. $14\frac{1}{8} - 8\frac{3}{10} + 32\frac{1}{4}$

Think and Discuss

6. **Discuss** the estimation strategies you used in numbers **2–5**.
7. **Explain** what you do to avoid underestimating or overestimating.

Motivate

To introduce estimating with fractions, ask students to explain how to round a whole number to a specified place. Discuss that rounding helps them locate the number between an upper and a lower limit and shows which limit is closer. Ask students to suggest how they could round a fraction. What numbers would they use for benchmarks (e.g., 0, $\frac{1}{2}$, 1)?

Exploration worksheet and answers on Chapter 4 Resource Book pp. 82 and 144

2 Teach

Lesson Presentation

Guided Instruction

In this lesson, students learn to estimate sums and differences of fractions and mixed numbers. A mixed number can be expressed as the sum of an integer and a fraction. To help students estimate the sum or difference of each part, focus the discussion on rounding fractions. Look at the relative size of the numerator and denominator to round each fraction to 0, $\frac{1}{2}$, or 1. Use the result of the fraction estimate to adjust the integer estimate.

Point out certain words that can tell students that an estimate is sufficient, such as *about, almost,* and *approximately.*

EXAMPLE 2 Estimating Sums and Differences

Estimate each sum or difference.

A $\frac{4}{7} - \frac{13}{16}$

$\frac{4}{7} \longrightarrow \frac{1}{2}$ $\quad \frac{13}{16} \longrightarrow 1$ *Round each fraction.*

$\frac{1}{2} - 1 = -\frac{1}{2}$ *Subtract.*

B $3\frac{3}{8} + 3\frac{2}{9}$

$3\frac{3}{8} \longrightarrow 3\frac{1}{2}$ $\quad 3\frac{2}{9} \longrightarrow 3$ *Round each mixed number.*

$3\frac{1}{2} + 3 = 6\frac{1}{2}$ *Add.*

C $5\frac{7}{8} + \left(-\frac{2}{5}\right)$

$5\frac{7}{8} \longrightarrow 6$ $\quad -\frac{2}{5} \longrightarrow -\frac{1}{2}$ *Round each number.*

$6 + \left(-\frac{1}{2}\right) = 5\frac{1}{2}$ *Add.*

When exact answers are not needed for a problem, you can use estimation. When exact answers are needed, an estimate can help you decide if your answer is reasonable.

EXAMPLE 3 Deciding If an Estimate Is Enough

Decide if you need an exact answer or if an estimate is enough.

A **In 1988, the population of Phoenix, Arizona, was $1\frac{1}{5}$ million and the population of New York City was $7\frac{2}{5}$ million. About how many more people lived in New York City than in Phoenix?**

The question asks *about* how many more people lived in New York City than in Phoenix, so an estimate is enough. The problem does not ask for an exact answer.

B **A concert hall pays a musician $\frac{1}{5}$ of the total amount collected from ticket sales plus a flat fee of $1,000. If 2,532 people attend the concert and pay $15 each, how much money does the musician receive?**

Since the problem is asking for the exact amount of money the musician will receive, an estimate would not be appropriate.

Helpful Hint

Words like *about* and *around* signal that an exact answer is not necessary.

Think and Discuss

1. **Demonstrate** how to round $\frac{5}{12}$ and $5\frac{1}{5}$.
2. **Give an example** of a problem using fractions or mixed numbers in which an exact answer is not needed.

Additional Examples

Example 1

A blue whale can grow to $33\frac{3}{5}$ m long, while the great white shark may be as long as $4\frac{1}{2}$ m. About how much longer is the blue whale?

about 29 m longer

Example 2

Estimate each sum or difference.

A. $\frac{7}{9} - \frac{2}{5}$ $\quad \frac{1}{2}$

B. $4\frac{5}{9} + 3\frac{1}{8}$ $\quad 7\frac{1}{2}$

C. $-2\frac{1}{8} + \frac{7}{12}$ $\quad -1\frac{1}{2}$

Example 3

Decide if you need an exact answer or if an estimate is enough.

A. Michael knows there will be 18 people at his party. He plans to give each person about a $1\frac{2}{3}$ cups serving of popcorn. If he can buy popcorn in 10-cup bags, how many bags should he buy?
estimate

B. For a soccer team celebration, Ellie buys rolls for $5.29 and $3\frac{1}{4}$ pounds of barbequed ham for $9 per pound. How much does she spend for the food?
exact

3 Close

Summarize

Have students explain how they would estimate a sum or a difference involving fractions. Discuss why fractions are rounded to 0, $\frac{1}{2}$, or 1 and not just to 0 or 1.

Possible answers: Round each fraction to 0, $\frac{1}{2}$, or 1, and then add or subtract whole numbers and adjust for any halves. Rounding to the nearest half is more accurate.

Reaching All Learners
Through Critical Thinking

Conduct a class discussion about which of the following is the proper way to round $-3\frac{7}{8}$.

- $\frac{7}{8}$ rounds to 1, and $-3 + 1 = -2$, so $-3\frac{7}{8}$ rounds to -2.
- $\frac{7}{8}$ is more than $\frac{1}{2}$, so round up. $-3\frac{7}{8}$ round to -4.
- -4 is less than $-3\frac{7}{8}$, so to round *up*, $-3\frac{7}{8}$ should be rounded to -3.

Answers to Think and Discuss

Possible answers:

1. $\frac{5}{12}$ is between 0 and $\frac{1}{2}$, or $\frac{6}{12}$. Since $\frac{5}{12}$ would be closer to $\frac{6}{12}$ than to $\frac{0}{12}$, it should be rounded to $\frac{1}{2}$. To round $5\frac{1}{5}$, students should focus on the $\frac{1}{5}$. Since it is closer to 0 than to $\frac{1}{2}$, $5\frac{1}{5}$ should be rounded to 5.
2. total mileage to a destination (it's about $3\frac{1}{2}$ miles to the store); time required for a trip (it takes about $\frac{1}{2}$ hour to walk home)

4-9 PRACTICE & ASSESS

Students may want to refer back to the lesson examples.

Assignment Guide

If you finished Example 1 assign:
Core 1, 7, 28–30, 34–39
Enriched 1, 7, 28–30, 34–39

If you finished Example 2 assign:
Core 1–4, 7–13, 17–27 odd, 28–30, 34–39
Enriched 1, 3, 7–13 odd, 16–30, 34–39

If you finished Example 3 assign:
Core 1–15, 17–27 odd, 28–30, 34–39
Enriched 1–15 odd, 16–39

Notes

4-9 Exercises

FOR EXTRA PRACTICE
see page 663

internet connect
Homework Help Online
go.hrw.com Keyword: MS4 4-9

GUIDED PRACTICE

See Example 1

1. The length of a large SUV is $18\frac{9}{10}$ feet, and the length of a small SUV is $15\frac{1}{8}$ feet. Estimate how much longer the large SUV is than the small SUV. **about 4 feet**

See Example 2

Estimate each sum or difference.

2. $\frac{5}{6} + \frac{5}{12}$ **$1\frac{1}{2}$**
3. $\frac{15}{16} - \frac{4}{5}$ **0**
4. $2\frac{1}{6} + 3\frac{6}{11}$ **$5\frac{1}{2}$**

See Example 3

Decide if you need an exact answer or if an estimate is enough.

5. If cashews cost \$6.75 per pound, how much does $\frac{3}{4}$ pound of cashews cost? **exact**
6. Kevin has $3\frac{3}{4}$ pounds of pecans and $6\frac{2}{3}$ pounds of walnuts. About how many more pounds of walnuts than pecans does Kevin have? **estimate**

INDEPENDENT PRACTICE

See Example 1

7. Sarah's bedroom is $14\frac{5}{6}$ feet long and $12\frac{1}{4}$ feet wide. Estimate the difference between the length and width of Sarah's bedroom. **3 feet**

See Example 2

Estimate each sum or difference.

8. $\frac{4}{9} + \frac{3}{5}$ **1**
9. $2\frac{5}{9} + 1\frac{7}{8}$ **$4\frac{1}{2}$**
10. $8\frac{3}{4} - 6\frac{2}{5}$ **$2\frac{1}{2}$**
11. $\frac{7}{8} - \frac{2}{5}$ **$\frac{1}{2}$**
12. $15\frac{1}{7} - 10\frac{8}{9}$ **4**
13. $8\frac{7}{15} + 2\frac{7}{8}$ **$11\frac{1}{2}$**

See Example 3

Decide if you need an exact answer or if an estimate is enough.

14. Ellen uses about $\frac{3}{4}$ of a bag of bird seed a week to feed her birds. About how many bags of bird seed does she use in one month? **estimate**
15. Jamil needs $7\frac{1}{2}$ cups of flour for a bread recipe. If he has $3\frac{3}{4}$ cups of flour, how much more does he need? **exact**

PRACTICE AND PROBLEM SOLVING

Estimate each sum or difference.

16. $\frac{7}{9} - \frac{3}{8}$ **$\frac{1}{2}$**
17. $\frac{3}{5} + \frac{6}{7}$ **$1\frac{1}{2}$**
18. $8\frac{11}{20} - 4\frac{9}{11}$ **$3\frac{1}{2}$**
19. $3\frac{7}{8} + \frac{2}{15}$ **4**
20. $23\frac{5}{11} - 16\frac{9}{10}$ **$6\frac{1}{2}$**
21. $5\frac{3}{5} - 4\frac{1}{3}$ **1**
22. $\frac{3}{8} + 3\frac{5}{7} + 6\frac{7}{8}$ **11**
23. $8\frac{4}{5} + 6\frac{1}{12} + 3\frac{2}{5}$ **$18\frac{1}{2}$**
24. $5\frac{6}{13} + 7\frac{1}{7} + 2\frac{7}{8}$ **$15\frac{1}{2}$**
25. $10\frac{1}{3} + \left(-\frac{8}{15}\right)$ **10**
26. $7\frac{3}{8} + 8\frac{5}{11}$ **16**
27. $14\frac{2}{3} + 1\frac{7}{9} - 11\frac{14}{29}$ **5**

Math Background

Rounding a fraction to 0 will feel uncomfortable for some students who may feel they are ignoring part of the problem. A discussion of the relative size of the numbers and the effect each has on the result may help. Approximations are important in mathematics, not only as a check on calculations but also as a means to understand patterns and trends. From arithmetic to calculus, the ability to account for the effect of a very small number will be important.

RETEACH 4-9

LESSON 4-9 **Reteach**
Estimate with Fractions

You can estimate with fractions and mixed numbers by rounding the fraction or mixed number to the nearest $\frac{1}{2}$. Use a number line to help.

Estimate $\frac{3}{8} + \frac{9}{10}$

$\frac{3}{8}$ is about $\frac{1}{2}$.

$\frac{9}{10}$ is about 1.

So, $\frac{3}{8} + \frac{9}{10}$ is about $\frac{1}{2} + 1 = 1\frac{1}{2}$.

Estimate each sum or difference.

1. $\frac{5}{9} + \frac{1}{6}$

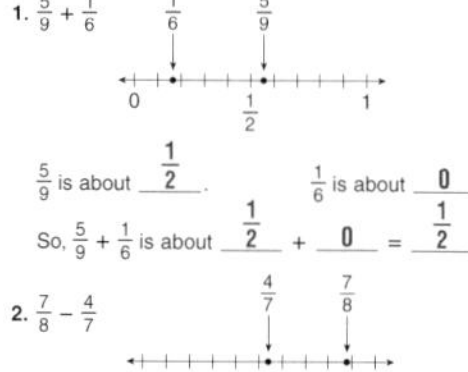

$\frac{5}{9}$ is about $\frac{1}{2}$. $\frac{1}{6}$ is about 0.

So, $\frac{5}{9} + \frac{1}{6}$ is about $\frac{1}{2}$ + 0 = $\frac{1}{2}$.

2. $\frac{7}{8} - \frac{4}{7}$

$\frac{7}{8}$ is about 1. $\frac{4}{7}$ is about $\frac{1}{2}$.

So, $\frac{7}{8} - \frac{4}{7}$ is about 1 − $\frac{1}{2}$ = $\frac{1}{2}$.

3. $\frac{11}{12} + \frac{2}{5}$ $1\frac{1}{2}$
4. $\frac{4}{9} - \frac{1}{3}$ 0
5. $\frac{13}{16} - \frac{2}{9}$ 1
6. $5\frac{8}{9} + 3\frac{2}{3}$ $9\frac{1}{2}$
7. $6\frac{5}{8} - 4\frac{5}{6}$ $1\frac{1}{2}$
8. $7\frac{1}{5} - 3\frac{9}{10}$ 3

PRACTICE 4-9

LESSON 4-9 **Practice B**
Estimate with Fractions

Estimate each sum or difference.

1. $\frac{5}{11} + \frac{4}{9}$ 1
2. $\frac{9}{17} + \frac{1}{13}$ $\frac{1}{2}$
3. $\frac{6}{13} + \frac{19}{20}$ $1\frac{1}{2}$
4. $\frac{2}{11} + \frac{3}{13}$ 0
5. $\frac{8}{15} + \frac{7}{10}$ 1
6. $\frac{7}{17} + \frac{7}{12}$ 1
7. $4\frac{5}{16} + 2\frac{9}{10}$ $7\frac{1}{2}$
8. $3\frac{5}{13} + 9\frac{8}{15}$ 13
9. $8\frac{9}{11} + 6\frac{11}{13}$ 16
10. $\frac{9}{10} - \frac{2}{9}$ 1
11. $\frac{7}{10} - \frac{4}{7}$ 0
12. $\frac{6}{11} - \frac{2}{7}$ 0
13. $\frac{8}{9} - \frac{5}{6}$ 0
14. $\frac{8}{11} - \frac{3}{15}$ $\frac{1}{2}$
15. $\frac{15}{16} - \frac{4}{21}$ 1
16. $3\frac{4}{7} - 1\frac{1}{9}$ $2\frac{1}{2}$
17. $11\frac{3}{7} - 5\frac{5}{6}$ $5\frac{1}{2}$
18. $13\frac{1}{4} - 3\frac{8}{11}$ $9\frac{1}{2}$

Decide if you need an exact answer or if an estimate is enough.

19. The school cafeteria uses about $\frac{5}{6}$ of a case of raviolis every month. About how many cases will it use during the school year?
estimate
20. The cost of a math textbook was \$24.95 last year. The cost has increased by $\frac{1}{8}$ this year. How much does a math textbook cost this year?
exact

28. ***BUSINESS*** October 19, 1987, is known as Black Monday because the stock market fell 508 points. Xerox stock began the day at $\$70\frac{1}{8}$ and finished at $\$56\frac{1}{4}$. Approximately how far did Xerox's stock price fall during the day? **\$14**

29. ***RECREATION*** While on a camping trip, Monica and Paul hiked $5\frac{3}{8}$ miles on Saturday and $4\frac{9}{10}$ miles on Sunday. Estimate the number of miles Monica and Paul hiked while camping. **$10\frac{1}{2}$ miles**

30. ***LIFE SCIENCE*** The diagram shows the wingspans of different species of birds.

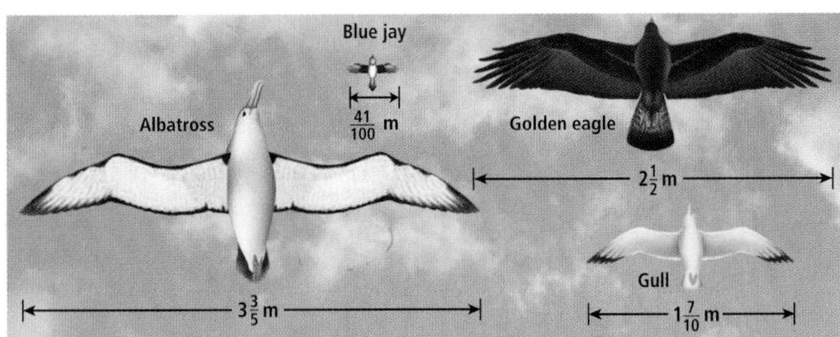

a. Approximately how much longer is the wingspan of an albatross than the wingspan of a gull? **2 m**

b. Approximately how much longer is the wingspan of a golden eagle than the wingspan of a blue jay? **2 m**

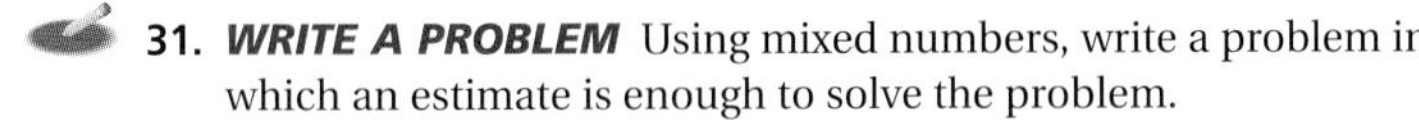

31. ***WRITE A PROBLEM*** Using mixed numbers, write a problem in which an estimate is enough to solve the problem.

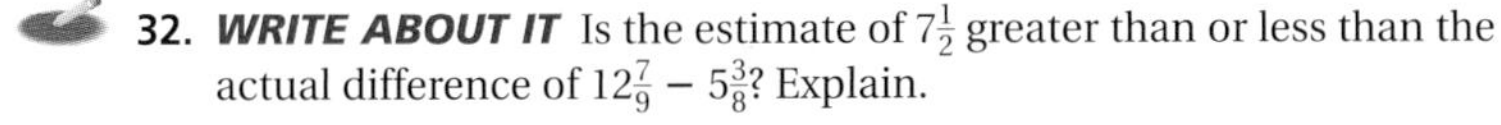

32. ***WRITE ABOUT IT*** Is the estimate of $7\frac{1}{2}$ greater than or less than the actual difference of $12\frac{7}{9} - 5\frac{3}{8}$? Explain.

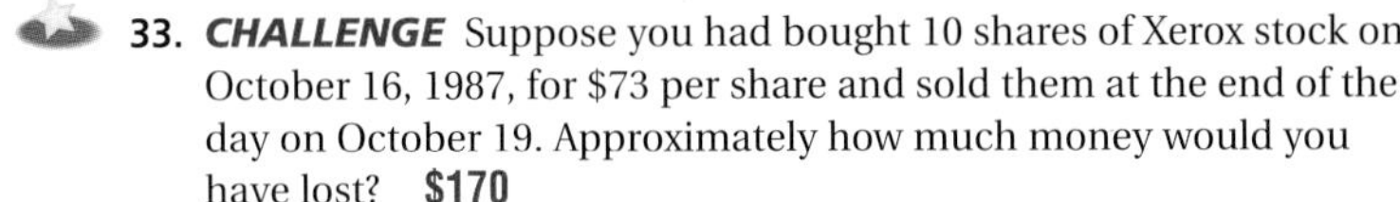

33. ***CHALLENGE*** Suppose you had bought 10 shares of Xerox stock on October 16, 1987, for \$73 per share and sold them at the end of the day on October 19. Approximately how much money would you have lost? **\$170**

Spiral Review

Combine like terms. (Lesson 2-9)

34. $3x + 5x - x$ **$7x$**

35. $5b - 5a + 7a$ **$5b + 2a$**

36. $5(p + 3) - 4p$ **$p + 15$**

37. $-2y + 6z - 3y$ **$6z - 5y$**

38. **TEST PREP** Which is the decimal form of $\frac{7}{8}$? (Lesson 3-9) **D**

A 675
C 0.675
B $87.\overline{5}$
D 0.875

39. **TEST PREP** Which is the value of $3\frac{1}{8} \div \frac{5}{8}$? (Lesson 4-8) **G**

F $\frac{64}{125}$
H $1\frac{61}{64}$
G 5
J $\frac{1}{5}$

CHALLENGE 4-9

LESSON 4-9 **Challenge**
Don't Underestimate the Answer to a Joke!

Circle the fractions whose estimated sums or differences equal the given solution. To find the answer to each joke, write the letters below the circled fractions in order in the blanks.

Why did the student go to school in an airplane?

1. $\frac{7}{8} + \left[1\frac{6}{11} \text{ or } 4\frac{4}{5}\right] - \left[3\frac{7}{8} \text{ or } -\frac{9}{10}\right] \approx 3\frac{1}{2}$
H E M I

2. $5\frac{11}{12} + \left[6\frac{3}{8} \text{ or } -4\frac{5}{6}\right] \approx 1$
P G

3. $\left[\frac{6}{11} \text{ or } \frac{6}{7}\right] + \left[5\frac{9}{10} \text{ or } \frac{4}{19}\right] - \left[7\frac{2}{3} \text{ or } -4\frac{16}{19}\right] \approx 5\frac{1}{2}$
H T Y E S R

ANSWER: She wanted to get a **H I G H E R** education!

What kind of hair does the Atlantic Ocean have?

4. $3\frac{1}{10} + \left[\frac{9}{10} \text{ or } 4\frac{5}{12}\right] - \left[-6\frac{1}{20} \text{ or } -6\frac{9}{10}\right] \approx 11$
W H U A

5. $8\frac{4}{7} - \left[-6\frac{5}{9} \text{ or } -6\frac{1}{8}\right] \approx 15$
V R

6. $\left[2\frac{1}{3} \text{ or } 1\frac{6}{13}\right] - 4\frac{1}{10} \approx -2$
Y T

ANSWER: **W A V Y**

What can go across the country and still stay in its corner?

7. $5\frac{4}{5} - \left[\frac{7}{16} \text{ or } \frac{10}{11}\right] + \left[-2\frac{1}{9} \text{ or } \frac{7}{9}\right] \approx 6$
T S R T

8. $\left[\frac{7}{15} \text{ or } \frac{13}{15}\right] + \left[\frac{1}{16} \text{ or } -\frac{4}{5}\right] \approx 1$
U A M C

9. $\left[4\frac{5}{6} \text{ or } -1\frac{11}{13}\right] - \left(-6\frac{1}{5}\right) \approx 4$
K P

ANSWER: A **S T A M P**

PROBLEM SOLVING 4-9

LESSON 4-9 **Problem Solving**
Estimate with Fractions

Write the correct answer.

1. At the beach, Richard rides the waves on a boogie board that is $3\frac{2}{3}$ feet long. Laura rides a $7\frac{1}{2}$-foot surfboard. Estimate the difference in length of the 2 boards.
about $3\frac{1}{2}$ feet

2. Jorgé had $5\frac{1}{3}$ jugs of apple cider. He used $2\frac{5}{6}$ jugs for a party. About how much apple cider does he have left?
about $2\frac{1}{2}$ jugs

3. Sari jogs $2\frac{3}{4}$ miles on Monday, $3\frac{5}{6}$ miles on Wednesday, and $2\frac{1}{3}$ miles on Friday. Estimate her total distance for the week.
about 9 miles

4. Luis is following a recipe that calls for $5\frac{1}{2}$ cups of flour, $2\frac{1}{4}$ cups of white sugar, and $2\frac{2}{3}$ cups of brown sugar. About how many cups of dry ingredients is he using?
about $10\frac{1}{2}$ cups

Choose the letter for the best answer.

This table shows the total amount of snow to fall in 5 cities during 2000.

Snowfall During 2000

City	Amount of Snow (in.)
Asheville, NC	$14\frac{2}{5}$
Indianapolis, IN	$37\frac{1}{2}$
Marquette, MI	251
Raleigh, NC	$28\frac{1}{10}$
St. Louis, MO	$25\frac{7}{10}$

5. About how much snow all together fell in the two cities in North Carolina?
A 38 inches
C 46 inches
(B) 42 inches
D 50 inches

6. About how much more snow fell in Indianapolis than in Asheville?
F 12 inches
H 18 inches
G 15 inches
(J) 23 inches

7. Which city had about 10 times as much snow as St. Louis?
A Asheville
(C) Marquette
B Indianapolis
D Raleigh

8. About how much more snow fell in St. Louis than in Asheville?
F 6 inches
H 18 inches
(G) 12 inches
J 24 inches

Answers

31. Possible answer: Anna slept for $9\frac{5}{12}$ hours on Friday night and $7\frac{7}{12}$ hours on Saturday night. Estimate how much she slept for those two nights.

32. The estimate is greater than the actual difference because each number in the equation was rounded up to get the estimate.

Journal

Have students describe a situation in which they might estimate the sum or difference of fractions.

Test Prep Doctor

In Exercise 38, remind students that they can eliminate **A** and **B** immediately since both are greater than 1. Then it is necessary to check only the first digit of the quotient to choose between the remaining answers. Exercise 39 is a perfect place for students to use estimation skills. $3\frac{1}{8} \div \frac{5}{8} \approx 3 \div \frac{1}{2}$, or 6. Only **G** is close to 6.

Lesson Quiz

1. The new show arena being built in Franklin County is $150\frac{3}{4}$ feet long and $110\frac{1}{2}$ feet wide. Estimate the difference between the length and width. **40 ft**

Estimate each sum or difference.

2. $\frac{5}{9} + \frac{4}{5}$ **$1\frac{1}{2}$**

3. $\frac{7}{8} - \frac{3}{7}$ **$\frac{1}{2}$**

4. $9\frac{3}{4} - 6\frac{1}{5}$ **4**

5. Decide if you need an exact answer or if an estimate is sufficient. Janet needs $4\frac{1}{2}$ quarts of oil for her car. If she has $2\frac{1}{2}$ quarts, how much more does she need? An estimate is sufficient.

Available on Daily Transparency in CRB

4C
Model Fraction Addition and Subtraction

Pacing: Traditional 1 day
Block $\frac{1}{2}$ day

Objective: To use fraction bars to model adding and subtracting fractions

Materials: Fraction bars

Lab Resources

Hands-On Lab Activities .... pp. 27–30, 131

Using the Pages

Discuss with students how to represent an addition problem and how to represent a subtraction problem.

Use fraction bars to model each expression.

1. $\frac{1}{4} + \frac{2}{3}$

$\frac{1}{4}$	$\frac{1}{3}$	$\frac{1}{3}$

$\frac{1}{12}$ $\frac{1}{12}$ $\frac{1}{12}$ $\frac{1}{12}$ $\frac{1}{12}$ $\frac{1}{12}$ $\frac{1}{12}$ $\frac{1}{12}$ $\frac{1}{12}$ $\frac{1}{12}$ $\frac{1}{12}$

$\frac{11}{12}$

2. $\frac{7}{8} - \frac{1}{2}$

$\frac{1}{8}$ $\frac{1}{8}$ $\frac{1}{8}$ $\frac{1}{8}$ $\frac{1}{8}$ $\frac{1}{8}$ $\frac{1}{8}$

$\frac{1}{2}$ $\frac{1}{8}$ $\frac{1}{8}$ $\frac{1}{8}$

$\frac{3}{8}$

Model Fraction Addition and Subtraction

Use with Lesson 4-10

internet connect
Lab Resources Online
go.hrw.com
KEYWORD: MS4 Lab4C

Fraction bars can be used to model and evaluate addition and subtraction of fractions.

Activity

You can use fraction bars to evaluate $\frac{3}{8} + \frac{2}{8}$.

Place the fraction bars side by side.

$\frac{1}{8}$	$\frac{1}{8}$	$\frac{1}{8}$	$\frac{1}{8}$	$\frac{1}{8}$

$\frac{3}{8} + \frac{2}{8} = \frac{5}{8}$

1 Use fraction bars to evaluate each expression.

a. $\frac{1}{3} + \frac{1}{3}$ $\mathbf{\frac{2}{3}}$ **b.** $\frac{2}{4} + \frac{1}{4}$ $\mathbf{\frac{3}{4}}$ **c.** $\frac{3}{12} + \frac{2}{12}$ $\mathbf{\frac{5}{12}}$ **d.** $\frac{1}{5} + \frac{2}{5}$ $\mathbf{\frac{3}{5}}$

You can use fraction bars to evaluate $\frac{1}{3} + \frac{1}{4}$.

Place the fraction bars side by side. Which kind of fraction bar placed side by side will exactly fill the space below? (*Hint:* What is the LCM of 3 and 4?)

$\frac{1}{3}$	$\frac{1}{4}$

$\frac{1}{12}$ $\frac{1}{12}$ $\frac{1}{12}$ $\frac{1}{12}$ $\frac{1}{12}$ $\frac{1}{12}$ $\frac{1}{12}$

$\frac{1}{3} + \frac{1}{4} = \frac{7}{12}$

2 Use fraction bars to evaluate each expression.

a. $\frac{1}{2} + \frac{1}{3}$ $\mathbf{\frac{5}{6}}$ **b.** $\frac{1}{2} + \frac{1}{4}$ $\mathbf{\frac{3}{4}}$ **c.** $\frac{1}{3} + \frac{1}{6}$ $\mathbf{\frac{1}{2}}$ **d.** $\frac{1}{4} + \frac{1}{6}$ $\mathbf{\frac{5}{12}}$

You can use fraction bars to evaluate $\frac{1}{3} + \frac{5}{6}$.

Place the fraction bars side by side. Which kind of fraction bar placed side by side will exactly fill the space below? (*Hint:* What is the LCM of 3 and 6?)

$\frac{1}{3}$	$\frac{1}{6}$	$\frac{1}{6}$	$\frac{1}{6}$	$\frac{1}{6}$	$\frac{1}{6}$

$\frac{1}{6}$ $\frac{1}{6}$ $\frac{1}{6}$ $\frac{1}{6}$ $\frac{1}{6}$ $\frac{1}{6}$ $\frac{1}{6}$

$\frac{1}{3} + \frac{5}{6} = \frac{7}{6}$

Teacher to Teacher

Elsie Newman
Bowling Green, Ohio

Students can create color-coded fraction tiles. Cut 8.5 in. × 11 in. sheets of colored paper into strips 1 in. wide so that the strips are 11 in. long. Use a different color for each unit fraction you want to model. Give each student one strip of each color. Students can fold one strip of paper in half to show that it takes two halves to make a whole strip. Fold another color strip in thirds, and so on. Equivalent fractions can be found by matching up fraction tiles of the same length (e.g., $\frac{2}{4}$ and $\frac{1}{2}$). The strips can also be used to model various addition and subtraction problems. If the students all use the same colors for each type of unit fraction, models can be checked at a glance.

When the sum is an improper fraction, you can use the 1 bar along with fraction bars to find the mixed-number equivalent.

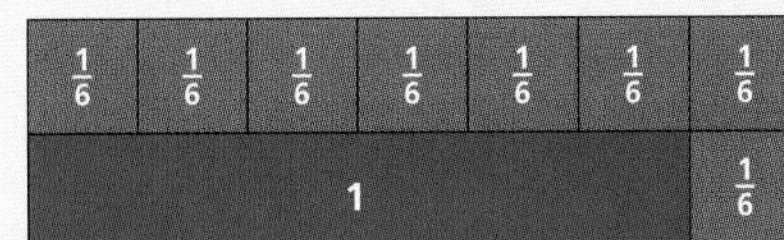

$\frac{7}{6} = 1\frac{1}{6}$

3 Use fraction bars to evaluate each expression.

a. $\frac{3}{4} + \frac{3}{4}$ **$1\frac{1}{2}$** b. $\frac{2}{3} + \frac{1}{2}$ **$1\frac{1}{6}$** c. $\frac{5}{6} + \frac{1}{4}$ **$1\frac{1}{12}$** d. $\frac{3}{8} + \frac{3}{4}$ **$1\frac{1}{8}$**

You can use fraction bars to evaluate $\frac{2}{3} - \frac{1}{2}$.

Place a $\frac{1}{2}$ bar beneath bars that show $\frac{2}{3}$, and find which fraction fills in the remaining space.

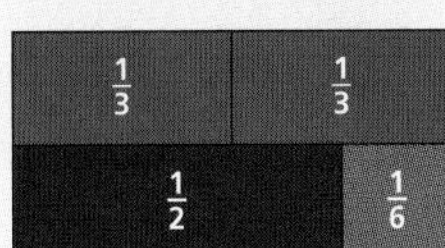

$\frac{2}{3} - \frac{1}{2} = \frac{1}{6}$

4 Use fraction bars to evaluate each expression.

a. $\frac{2}{3} - \frac{1}{3}$ **$\frac{1}{3}$** b. $\frac{1}{4} - \frac{1}{6}$ **$\frac{1}{12}$** c. $\frac{1}{2} - \frac{1}{3}$ **$\frac{1}{6}$** d. $\frac{3}{4} - \frac{2}{3}$ **$\frac{1}{12}$**

Think and Discuss

1. Model and solve $\frac{3}{4} - \frac{1}{6}$. Explain your steps.
2. Two students solved $\frac{1}{4} + \frac{1}{3}$ in different ways. One got $\frac{7}{12}$ for the answer, and the other got $\frac{2}{7}$. Use models to show which student is correct.
3. Find three different ways to model $\frac{1}{2} + \frac{1}{4}$.

Try This

Use fraction bars to evaluate each expression.

1. $\frac{1}{2} + \frac{1}{2}$ **1**
2. $\frac{2}{3} + \frac{1}{6}$ **$\frac{5}{6}$**
3. $\frac{1}{4} + \frac{1}{6}$ **$\frac{5}{12}$**
4. $\frac{1}{3} + \frac{7}{12}$ **$\frac{11}{12}$**
5. $\frac{5}{12} - \frac{1}{3}$ **$\frac{1}{12}$**
6. $\frac{1}{2} - \frac{1}{4}$ **$\frac{1}{4}$**
7. $\frac{3}{4} - \frac{1}{6}$ **$\frac{7}{12}$**
8. $\frac{2}{3} - \frac{1}{4}$ **$\frac{5}{12}$**
9. You ate $\frac{1}{4}$ of a pizza for lunch and $\frac{5}{8}$ of the pizza for dinner. How much of the pizza did you eat in all? **$\frac{7}{8}$ pizza**
10. It is $\frac{5}{6}$ mile from your home to the library. After walking $\frac{3}{4}$ mile, you stop to visit a friend on your way to the library. How much farther do you have left to walk to reach the library? **$\frac{1}{12}$ mi**

Answers

Think and Discuss

1. Possible answer: Model $\frac{3}{4}$. Place a $\frac{1}{6}$ bar beneath bars that show $\frac{3}{4}$, and find which fraction fills in the remaining space. The fraction that fits is $\frac{7}{12}$.

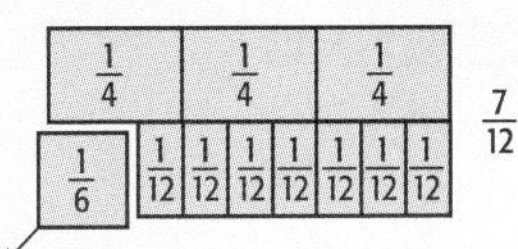

2.

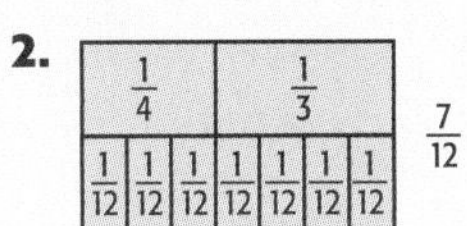

3. Possible answer:

1/2	1/4

1/4	1/4	1/4

1/8	1/8	1/8	1/8	1/8	1/8

4-10 Organizer

Pacing: Traditional 1 day
Block $\frac{1}{2}$ day

Objective: Students add and subtract fractions.

Warm Up

Find the LCM for each set of numbers.

1. 8 and 12 **24** **2.** 12 and 18 **36**
3. 10 and 12 **60** **4.** 12 and 24 **24**

Problem of the Day

Let *A* through *I* represent the digits of a number. Replace the letters *A* through *I* with the digits 1 through 9, respectively, and verify that the statement is true.

$$\left(\frac{E}{CD}\right) + \left(\frac{I}{AB}\right) + \left(\frac{G}{FH}\right) = 1$$

$$\mathbf{\frac{5}{34} + \frac{9}{12} + \frac{7}{68} = \frac{60 + 306 + 42}{408} = 1}$$

Available on Daily Transparency in CRB

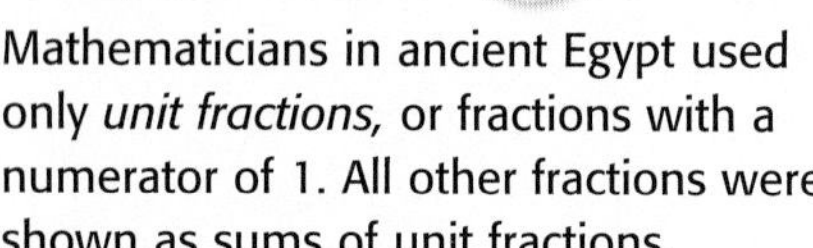

Mathematicians in ancient Egypt used only *unit fractions,* or fractions with a numerator of 1. All other fractions were shown as sums of unit fractions.

4-10 Adding and Subtracting Fractions

Learn to add and subtract fractions.

From January 1 to March 14 of any given year, Earth completes approximately $\frac{1}{5}$ of its orbit around the Sun, while Venus completes approximately $\frac{1}{3}$ of its orbit. The illustration shows what the positions of the planets would be on March 14 if they started at the same place on January 1 and their orbits were circular. To find out how much more of its orbit Venus completes than Earth, you need to subtract fractions.

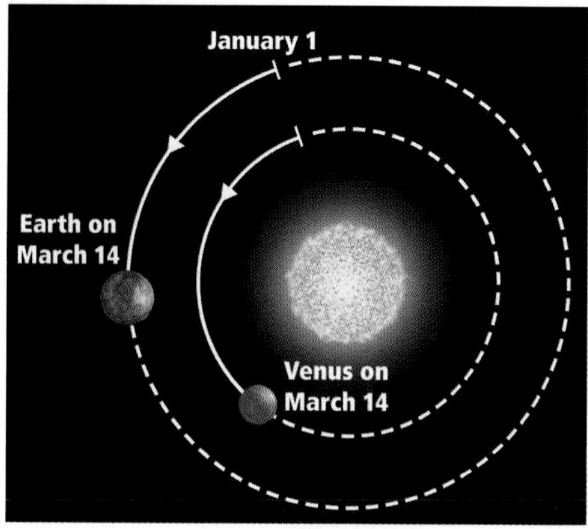

EXAMPLE 1 Adding and Subtracting Fractions with Like Denominators

Add or subtract. Write each answer in simplest form.

A $\frac{3}{10} + \frac{1}{10}$

$\frac{3}{10} + \frac{1}{10} = \frac{3 + 1}{10}$ *Add the numerators and keep the common denominator.*

$= \frac{4}{10} = \frac{2}{5}$ *Simplify.*

B $\frac{7}{9} - \frac{4}{9}$

$\frac{7}{9} - \frac{4}{9} = \frac{7 - 4}{9}$ *Subtract the numerators and keep the common denominator.*

$= \frac{3}{9} = \frac{1}{3}$ *Simplify.*

To add or subtract fractions with different denominators, you must rewrite the fractions with a common denominator.

Helpful Hint

The LCM of two denominators is the lowest common denominator (LCD) of the fractions.

Two Ways to Find a Common Denominator
• Find the LCM (least common multiple) of the denominators. • Multiply the denominators.

1 Introduce

Alternate Opener

EXPLORATION

4-10 Adding and Subtracting Fractions

Suzanne runs $\frac{3}{4}$ mile and then $\frac{1}{2}$ mile.

$\frac{3}{4} + \frac{1}{2} =$

$\frac{3}{4} + \frac{2}{4} = \frac{5}{4} =$

1 mile $1 + \frac{1}{4} = 1\frac{1}{4}$

1. Explain how the model shows that $\frac{3}{4} + \frac{1}{2} = 1\frac{1}{4}$.
2. Draw a model to show that $\frac{1}{2} + \frac{1}{3} = \frac{5}{6}$.

Draw a model to solve each addition problem. Write each answer as a mixed number.

3. $\frac{3}{10} + \frac{4}{5}$ **4.** $\frac{3}{5} + \frac{1}{2}$
5. $\frac{1}{2} + \frac{2}{3}$ **6.** $\frac{5}{6} + \frac{1}{3}$

Think and Discuss

7. Explain how you wrote the answers for numbers 3–6 as mixed numbers.

Motivate

To introduce addition and subtraction of fractions, ask students to estimate what fraction of the day they spend in common activities: school, meals, travel, sleep, sports. When all activities are listed, discuss how students could determine how much "spare time" they have each day. (Add the fractions and subtract the total from one whole day.)

Exploration worksheet and answers on Chapter 4 Resource Book pp. 91 and 146

2 Teach

Lesson Presentation

Guided Instruction

In this lesson, students learn to add and subtract fractions. Addition and subtraction of fractions with like denominators requires students to combine only the numerators. Remind students of the process for finding equivalent fractions, and review the fact that multiplying the numerator and denominator by the same number does not change the value. Once students have fractions with like denominators, they can add or subtract the numerators, and then simplify.

Teaching Tip While the LCM method will reduce the need to simplify later, both methods should be presented as equally acceptable.

EXAMPLE 2 Adding and Subtracting Fractions with Unlike Denominators

Add or subtract. Write each answer in simplest form.

A $\frac{3}{8} + \frac{5}{12}$

$\frac{3}{8} + \frac{5}{12} = \frac{3 \cdot 3}{8 \cdot 3} + \frac{5 \cdot 2}{12 \cdot 2}$ *The LCM of the denominators is 24.*

$= \frac{9}{24} + \frac{10}{24}$ *Write equivalent fractions using the common denominator.*

$= \frac{19}{24}$ *Add.*

B $\frac{1}{10} - \frac{5}{8}$

$\frac{1}{10} - \frac{5}{8} = \frac{1 \cdot 8}{10 \cdot 8} - \frac{5 \cdot 10}{8 \cdot 10}$ *Multiply the denominators.*

$= \frac{8}{80} - \frac{50}{80}$ *Write equivalent fractions using the common denominator.*

$= -\frac{42}{80} = -\frac{21}{40}$ *Subtract. Then simplify.*

C $-\frac{2}{3} + \frac{5}{8}$

$-\frac{2}{3} + \frac{5}{8} = -\frac{2 \cdot 8}{3 \cdot 8} + \frac{5 \cdot 3}{8 \cdot 3}$ *Multiply the denominators.*

$= -\frac{16}{24} + \frac{15}{24}$ *Write equivalent fractions using the common denominator.*

$= -\frac{1}{24}$ *Add.*

EXAMPLE 3 *Astronomy Application*

From January 1 to March 14, Earth completes about $\frac{1}{5}$ of its orbit, while Venus completes about $\frac{1}{3}$ of its orbit. How much more of its orbit does Venus complete than Earth?

$\frac{1}{3} - \frac{1}{5} = \frac{1 \cdot 5}{3 \cdot 5} - \frac{1 \cdot 3}{5 \cdot 3}$ *The LCM of the denominators is 15.*

$= \frac{5}{15} - \frac{3}{15}$ *Write equivalent fractions.*

$= \frac{2}{15}$ *Subtract.*

Venus completes $\frac{2}{15}$ more of its orbit than Earth does.

Think and Discuss

1. **Describe** the process for subtracting fractions with different denominators.
2. **Explain** whether $\frac{3}{4} + \frac{2}{3} = \frac{5}{7}$ is correct.

COMMON ERROR ALERT

Be alert for students who reverse subtraction problems to fit the *greater – lesser* pattern to avoid negative differences. Encourage students to identify exercises that will have negative differences.

Additional Examples

Example 1

Add or subtract. Write each answer in simplest form.

A. $\frac{5}{8} + \frac{1}{8}$ $\frac{3}{4}$

B. $\frac{9}{11} - \frac{4}{11}$ $\frac{5}{11}$

Example 2

Add or subtract. Write each answer in simplest form.

A. $\frac{5}{6} + \frac{7}{8}$ $\frac{41}{24}$ or $1\frac{17}{24}$

B. $\frac{2}{3} - \frac{3}{4}$ $-\frac{1}{12}$

C. $-\frac{2}{7} + \frac{1}{3}$ $\frac{1}{21}$

Example 3

In one Earth year, Jupiter completes about $\frac{1}{12}$ of its orbit around the Sun, while Mars completes about $\frac{1}{2}$ of its orbit. How much more of its orbit does Mars complete than Jupiter?

Mars completes $\frac{5}{12}$ more of its orbit than Jupiter.

Example 3 note: Point out that the LCM of the two denominators is found by multiplying the denominators, since the denominators have no factors in common.

3 Close

Reaching All Learners

Through World Math

Review the Math Fact about the ancient Egyptians. Share this additional information: To multiply fractions, the Egyptians used a table to convert multiples of a unit fraction into the sum of unit fractions. However, they did not repeat unit fractions. For example, $\frac{2}{5}$ would not have been written as $\frac{1}{5} + \frac{1}{5}$. Instead, it would have been written as $\frac{1}{3} + \frac{1}{15}$.

Have students write each of the following fractions as the sum of unit fractions: $\frac{3}{4}, \frac{5}{6}, \frac{7}{12}$, and $\frac{2}{3}$.

Possible answers: $\frac{3}{4} = \frac{1}{2} + \frac{1}{4}$; $\frac{5}{6} = \frac{1}{2} + \frac{1}{3}$; $\frac{7}{12} = \frac{1}{3} + \frac{1}{4}$; $\frac{2}{3} = \frac{1}{2} + \frac{1}{6}$

Summarize

Ask students to explain the process of finding a common denominator. Discuss the merits of each method.

Possible answer: The LCM method produces the least common denominator, so all the numbers in the problem are as small as possible, reducing chances of errors and the need to simplify. However, the LCM method may be difficult or time-consuming. Finding the product of the denominators always gives a usable common denominator quickly but may result in greater than necessary numbers.

Answers to Think and Discuss

Possible answers:

1. Find a common denominator and write fractions in that form. Numerators are subtracted, but the denominator stays the same.
2. $\frac{3}{4} + \frac{2}{3} = \frac{5}{7}$ is not correct. Adding numerators and denominators is not the correct way to add fractions. The correct way to add fractions is to write the fractions with common denominators and add the numerators: $\frac{9}{12} + \frac{8}{12} = \frac{17}{12}$.

4-10 PRACTICE & ASSESS

Students may want to refer back to the lesson examples.

Assignment Guide

If you finished Example 1 assign:
Core 1–3, 8–13, 46–50
Enriched 1–3, 8–13, 46–50

If you finished Example 2 assign:
Core 1–6, 8–19, 23–35 odd, 46–50
Enriched 1–5 odd, 9–19 odd, 22–36, 46–50

If you finished Example 3 assign:
Core 1–21, 23–35 odd, 37–42, 46–50
Enriched 1–21 odd, 22–50

Notes

4-10 Exercises

FOR EXTRA PRACTICE see page 663

internet connect
Homework Help Online
go.hrw.com Keyword: MS4 4-10

GUIDED PRACTICE

See Example 1 — Add or subtract. Write each answer in simplest form.

1. $\frac{2}{3} - \frac{1}{3}$ $\frac{1}{3}$
2. $\frac{1}{12} + \frac{1}{12}$ $\frac{1}{6}$
3. $\frac{16}{21} - \frac{7}{21}$ $\frac{3}{7}$

See Example 2
4. $\frac{1}{6} + \frac{1}{3}$ $\frac{1}{2}$
5. $\frac{9}{10} - \frac{3}{4}$ $\frac{3}{20}$
6. $\frac{2}{3} + \frac{1}{8}$ $\frac{19}{24}$

See Example 3
7. Parker spends $\frac{1}{4}$ of his earnings on rent and $\frac{1}{6}$ on entertainment. How much more of his earnings does Parker spend on rent than on entertainment? $\frac{1}{12}$

INDEPENDENT PRACTICE

See Example 1 — Add or subtract. Write each answer in simplest form.

8. $\frac{2}{3} + \frac{1}{3}$ 1
9. $\frac{3}{20} + \frac{7}{20}$ $\frac{1}{2}$
10. $\frac{5}{8} + \frac{7}{8}$ $\frac{3}{2}$ or $1\frac{1}{2}$
11. $\frac{7}{12} - \frac{5}{12}$ $\frac{1}{6}$
12. $\frac{5}{6} - \frac{1}{6}$ $\frac{2}{3}$
13. $\frac{8}{9} - \frac{5}{9}$ $\frac{1}{3}$

See Example 2
14. $\frac{1}{5} + \frac{2}{3}$ $\frac{13}{15}$
15. $\frac{1}{6} + \frac{1}{12}$ $\frac{1}{4}$
16. $\frac{5}{6} + \frac{3}{4}$ $\frac{19}{12}$ or $1\frac{7}{12}$
17. $\frac{21}{24} - \frac{1}{2}$ $\frac{3}{8}$
18. $\frac{3}{4} - \frac{11}{12}$ $-\frac{1}{6}$
19. $\frac{1}{2} - \frac{2}{7}$ $\frac{3}{14}$

See Example 3
20. Seana picked $\frac{3}{4}$ quart of blackberries. She ate $\frac{1}{12}$ quart. How much was left? $\frac{2}{3}$ qt
21. Armando lives $\frac{2}{3}$ mi from his school. If he has walked $\frac{1}{2}$ mi already this morning, how much farther must he walk to get to his school? $\frac{1}{6}$ mi

PRACTICE AND PROBLEM SOLVING

Find each sum or difference. Write your answer in simplest form.

22. $\frac{4}{5} + \frac{6}{7}$ $\frac{58}{35}$ or $1\frac{23}{35}$
23. $\frac{5}{6} - \frac{1}{9}$ $\frac{13}{18}$
24. $\frac{1}{2} - \frac{3}{4}$ $-\frac{1}{4}$
25. $\frac{5}{7} + \frac{1}{3}$ $\frac{22}{21}$ or $1\frac{1}{21}$
26. $\frac{1}{2} - \frac{7}{12}$ $-\frac{1}{12}$
27. $\frac{3}{4} + \frac{2}{5}$ $\frac{23}{20}$ or $1\frac{3}{20}$
28. $\frac{7}{8} + \frac{2}{3} + \frac{5}{6}$ $\frac{19}{8}$ or $2\frac{3}{8}$
29. $\frac{3}{5} + \frac{1}{10} - \frac{3}{4}$ $-\frac{1}{20}$
30. $\frac{3}{10} + \frac{5}{8} + \frac{1}{5}$ $\frac{9}{8}$ or $1\frac{1}{8}$
31. $-\frac{1}{2} + \frac{3}{8} + \frac{2}{7}$ $\frac{9}{56}$
32. $\frac{1}{3} + \frac{3}{7} - \frac{1}{9}$ $\frac{41}{63}$
33. $\frac{2}{9} - \frac{7}{18} + \frac{1}{6}$ 0
34. $\frac{9}{35} - \frac{4}{7} - \frac{5}{14}$ $-\frac{47}{70}$
35. $\frac{1}{3} - \frac{5}{7} + \frac{8}{21}$ 0
36. $-\frac{2}{9} - \frac{1}{12} - \frac{7}{18}$ $-\frac{25}{36}$
37. ***COOKING*** One fruit salad recipe calls for $\frac{1}{2}$ cup of sugar. Another recipe calls for 2 tablespoons of sugar. Since 1 tablespoon is $\frac{1}{16}$ cup, how much more sugar does the first recipe require? $\frac{3}{8}$ cup
38. It took Earl $\frac{1}{2}$ hour to do his science homework and $\frac{1}{3}$ hour to do his math homework. How long did Earl work on homework? $\frac{5}{6}$ hour

Math Background

Adding and subtracting fractions with like denominators will be fairly straightforward if students remember that the denominator shows the *kind* of fraction and the numerator shows *how many.* The word *denominator* comes from the same root as *denomination;* the word *numerator* from the same root as *number* and *enumerate.*

Working with different denominators is less straightforward for students. There is the additional step of finding the common denominator. Students need to grasp that when there are different denominators, the fractions cannot be directly combined because they are different parts of a whole.

RETEACH 4-10

LESSON 4-10 **Reteach**
Adding and Subtracting Fractions

To add or subtract fractions with different denominators:

Step 1: Find the least common multiple of the denominators.

Step 2: Write both fractions with the least common multiple (LCM) as the denominator.

Step 3: Add or subtract the numerators, keeping the denominator the same. Write the answer in simplest form.

$\frac{1}{4} + \frac{5}{6}$

The LCM of 4 and 6 is 12.

$\frac{1}{4} = \frac{3}{12}$ and $\frac{5}{6} = \frac{10}{12}$

$\frac{1}{4} + \frac{5}{6} = \frac{3}{12} + \frac{10}{12} = \frac{3+10}{12} = \frac{13}{12} = 1\frac{1}{12}$

$\frac{2}{3} - \frac{1}{2}$

The LCM of 3 and 2 is 6.

$\frac{2}{3} = \frac{4}{6}$ and $\frac{1}{2} = \frac{3}{6}$

$\frac{2}{3} - \frac{1}{2} = \frac{4}{6} - \frac{3}{6} = \frac{4-3}{6} = \frac{1}{6}$

Add or subtract. Write each answer in simplest form.

1. $\frac{3}{5} + \frac{1}{3} = \frac{9}{15} + \frac{5}{15} = \frac{9+5}{15} = \frac{14}{15}$
2. $\frac{8}{9} - \frac{1}{3} = \frac{8}{9} - \frac{3}{9} = \frac{8-3}{9} = \frac{5}{9}$
3. $\frac{2}{5} + \frac{1}{2} = \frac{4}{10} + \frac{5}{10} = \frac{4+5}{10} = \frac{9}{10}$
4. $\frac{3}{4} - \frac{1}{3} = \frac{9}{12} - \frac{4}{12} = \frac{9-4}{12} = \frac{5}{12}$
5. $\frac{2}{3} + \frac{3}{4} = \frac{8}{12} + \frac{9}{12} = \frac{8+9}{12} = \frac{17}{12} = 1\frac{5}{12}$
6. $\frac{5}{8} - \frac{1}{4} = \frac{5}{8} - \frac{2}{8} = \frac{5-2}{8} = \frac{3}{8}$
7. $\frac{1}{4} + \frac{2}{3}$ $\frac{11}{12}$
8. $\frac{9}{10} - \frac{1}{2}$ $\frac{2}{5}$
9. $\frac{7}{10} + \frac{2}{5}$ $1\frac{1}{10}$
10. $\frac{11}{12} - \frac{2}{3}$ $\frac{1}{4}$
11. $\frac{7}{10} - \frac{1}{4}$ $\frac{9}{20}$
12. $\frac{3}{4} + \frac{4}{5}$ $1\frac{11}{20}$

PRACTICE 4-10

LESSON 4-10 **Practice B**
Adding and Subtracting Fractions

Add or subtract. Write each answer in simplest form.

1. $\frac{1}{5} + \frac{2}{5}$ $\frac{3}{5}$
2. $\frac{4}{15} + \frac{8}{15}$ $\frac{4}{5}$
3. $\frac{7}{12} - \frac{5}{12}$ $\frac{1}{6}$
4. $\frac{9}{10} - \frac{7}{10}$ $\frac{1}{5}$
5. $\frac{11}{12} - \frac{7}{12}$ $\frac{1}{3}$
6. $\frac{2}{7} + \frac{6}{7}$ $1\frac{1}{7}$
7. $\frac{11}{15} + \frac{7}{15}$ $1\frac{1}{5}$
8. $\frac{3}{16} - \frac{1}{16}$ $\frac{1}{8}$
9. $\frac{8}{21} + \frac{5}{21}$ $\frac{13}{21}$
10. $\frac{4}{5} - \frac{3}{4}$ $\frac{1}{20}$
11. $\frac{3}{8} + \frac{1}{2}$ $\frac{7}{8}$
12. $\frac{21}{25} - \frac{2}{5}$ $\frac{11}{25}$
13. $\frac{11}{12} + \frac{5}{6}$ $1\frac{3}{4}$
14. $\frac{7}{8} - \frac{5}{12}$ $\frac{11}{24}$
15. $\frac{9}{10} + \frac{5}{6}$ $1\frac{11}{15}$
16. $\frac{7}{8} - \frac{2}{5}$ $\frac{19}{40}$
17. $\frac{5}{6} + \frac{11}{15}$ $1\frac{17}{30}$
18. $\frac{3}{4} - \frac{8}{15}$ $\frac{13}{60}$
19. The school track is $\frac{7}{8}$ mile in length. Sherri ran $\frac{2}{3}$ mile. How much farther does she have to go to get all the way around the track? $\frac{5}{24}$ mile
20. The Millers budget $\frac{1}{2}$ of their income for fixed expenses and $\frac{1}{8}$ of their income for savings. What fraction of their income is left? $\frac{3}{8}$

39. ***MUSIC*** In music written in $^4/_4$ time, a half note lasts for $\frac{1}{2}$ measure and an eighth note lasts for $\frac{1}{8}$ measure. In terms of a musical measure, what is the difference in the duration of the two notes? **$\frac{3}{8}$ measure**

40. ***STATISTICS*** The circle graph shows what the chances would be of having different numbers of boys and girls in a four-child family if gender were determined by chance rather than genetics.

Four-Child Family Probabilities

4 boys $\frac{1}{16}$; 2 girls, 2 boys $\frac{3}{8}$; 1 girl, 3 boys $\frac{1}{4}$; 3 girls, 1 boy $\frac{1}{4}$; 4 girls $\frac{1}{16}$

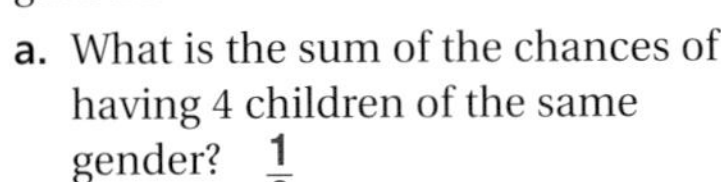

a. What is the sum of the chances of having 4 children of the same gender? **$\frac{1}{8}$**

b. What is the sum of the chances of having only 1 child of a certain gender? **$\frac{1}{2}$**

c. What is the difference in the chances of having 2 boys and 2 girls and of having 4 girls? **$\frac{5}{16}$**

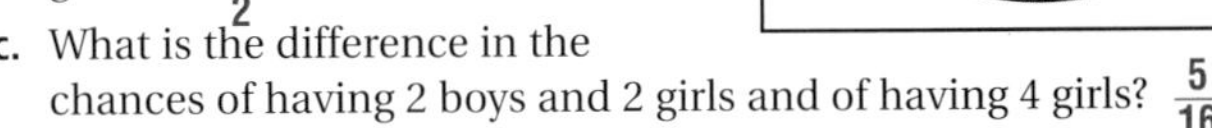

41. ***LIFE SCIENCE*** A shrew weighs $\frac{3}{16}$ lb. A hamster weighs $\frac{1}{4}$ lb.

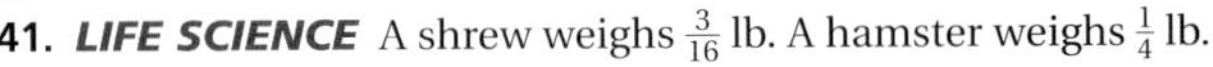

a. How many more pounds does a hamster weigh than a shrew? **$\frac{1}{16}$ lb**

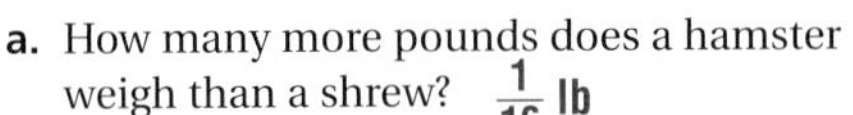

b. There are 16 oz in 1 lb. How many more ounces does the hamster weigh than the shrew? **1 oz**

42. To make $\frac{3}{4}$ lb of mixed nuts, how many pounds of cashews would you add to $\frac{1}{8}$ lb of almonds and $\frac{1}{4}$ lb of peanuts? **$\frac{3}{8}$ lb of cashews**

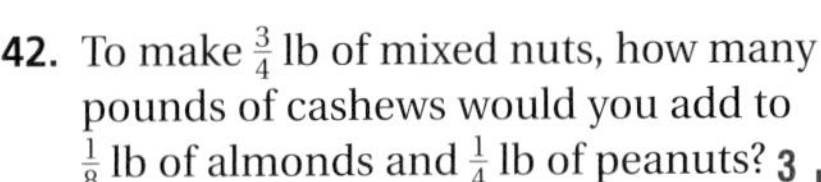

43. ***WRITE A PROBLEM*** Use facts you find in a newspaper or magazine to write a problem that can be solved using addition or subtraction of fractions.

44. ***WRITE ABOUT IT*** Explain the steps you use to add or subtract fractions that have different denominators.

45. ***CHALLENGE*** The sum of two fractions is 1. If one fraction is $\frac{3}{8}$ greater than the other, what are the two fractions? **$\frac{5}{16}, \frac{11}{16}$**

Spiral Review

Evaluate. (Lesson 2-3)

46. $12^2 \div (6 + 3) \cdot 2$ **32**

47. $4 + (8 - 2)^2 \div 9$ **8**

Solve each equation. Check your answers. (Lesson 2-11 and 2-12)

48. $x + 8 = 12$ **$x = 4$**

49. $5y = 35$ **$y = 7$**

50. **TEST PREP** Which of the following expressions is equal to 0.6? (Lesson 4-5) **C**

A $36 \div 0.6$　　B $3.6 \div 0.6$　　C $3.6 \div 6$　　D $0.36 \div 6$

COMMON ERROR ALERT

When combining three or more fractions, students may want to work with two at a time; however, this not only makes more work but could also introduce errors in the order of subtraction. Encourage students to find a common denominator for all fractions and then follow the order of operations.

Answers

43. Possible answer: of the people surveyed, $\frac{1}{3}$ prefer driving cars, $\frac{1}{4}$ prefer driving SUVs, and $\frac{1}{3}$ prefer driving trucks. If the rest of the people prefer riding the bus, what fraction of the people prefer riding the bus?

44. Write the fractions with a common denominator, and then write the sum or the difference of the numerators over the common denominator.

Journal

Ask students to describe a real-world situation in which they needed to find a common denominator. It could be a literal example of adding or subtracting fractions or a case of the "common denominator" taking on a more figurative meaning.

Test Prep Doctor

In Exercise 50, point out that the focus of the question is placement of the decimal point. Write each answer so that the divisor is a whole number, and then compare. Students can eliminate **A, B,** and **D** because **A** and **B** are too big, **D** is too small.

CHALLENGE 4-10

LESSON 4-10 **Challenge**
Fraction Tic-Tac-Toe

Find each sum or difference. Write the answer in simplest terms. Cross off the answers in the tic-tac-toe board to win.

1. $\frac{3}{8} + \frac{1}{2} + \frac{3}{4} =$ **$1\frac{5}{8}$**

2. $-\frac{6}{7} + \frac{2}{3} + \left(-\frac{11}{21}\right) =$ **$-\frac{5}{7}$**

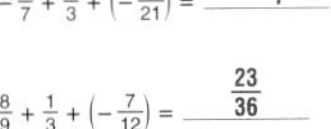

3. $\frac{8}{9} + \frac{1}{3} + \left(-\frac{7}{12}\right) =$ **$\frac{23}{36}$**

$\frac{1}{2}$	$\frac{1}{7}$	$\frac{23}{36}$
$\frac{2}{12}$	$-\frac{5}{7}$	$\frac{5}{7}$
$1\frac{5}{8}$	$-\frac{1}{6}$	$\frac{7}{8}$

4. $\frac{1}{6} + -\frac{2}{3} - \left(-\frac{5}{12}\right) =$ **$-\frac{1}{12}$**

5. $-\frac{7}{9} - \frac{5}{6} + \frac{1}{3} =$ **$-1\frac{5}{18}$**

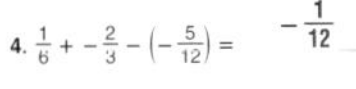

6. $\frac{7}{10} - \left(-\frac{1}{2}\right) + \left(-\frac{3}{5}\right) =$ **$\frac{3}{5}$**

$\frac{1}{12}$	1	$-\frac{3}{5}$
$\frac{5}{12}$	$1\frac{5}{18}$	$\frac{4}{5}$
$-\frac{1}{12}$	$-1\frac{5}{18}$	$\frac{3}{5}$

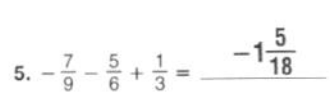

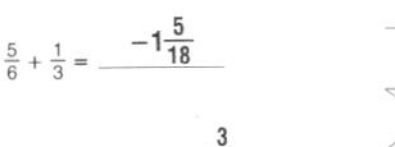

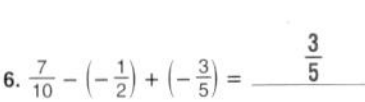

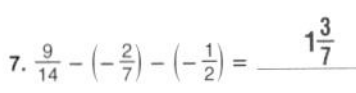

7. $\frac{9}{14} - \left(-\frac{2}{7}\right) - \left(-\frac{1}{2}\right) =$ **$1\frac{3}{7}$**

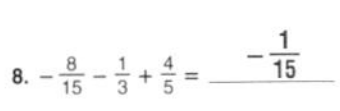

8. $-\frac{8}{15} - \frac{1}{3} + \frac{4}{5} =$ **$-\frac{1}{15}$**

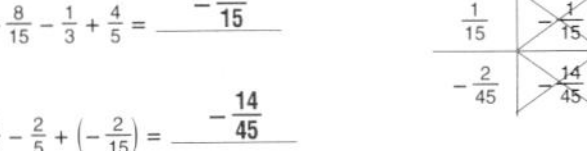

9. $\frac{2}{9} - \frac{2}{5} + \left(-\frac{2}{15}\right) =$ **$-\frac{14}{45}$**

$-\frac{1}{7}$	$1\frac{3}{7}$	1
$\frac{1}{15}$	$-\frac{1}{15}$	$\frac{1}{7}$
$-\frac{2}{45}$	$-\frac{14}{45}$	$\frac{2}{45}$

PROBLEM SOLVING 4-10

LESSON 4-10 **Problem Solving**
Adding and Subtracting Fractions

Write the correct answer.

1. During the recycling drive, $\frac{1}{5}$ of the items collected was bottles and $\frac{1}{4}$ was paper. Cardboard boxes made up $\frac{1}{10}$ of the items. How much of the total do these three items represent?
$\frac{11}{20}$ of the total

2. Decorations for school dances take $\frac{1}{5}$ of the student council's budget. Entertainment takes $\frac{3}{10}$ of the budget. What fraction of the budget is left?
$\frac{1}{2}$ of the budget

3. The school environmental club made a poster to celebrate Earth Day. The poster is $\frac{7}{8}$ yard long and $\frac{2}{3}$ yard wide. What is the difference in the length and width of the poster?
$\frac{5}{24}$ yard

4. Three students ran for president of the student council. Eddie received $\frac{1}{5}$ of the votes. Tamara received $\frac{3}{8}$ of the votes. Levi received the rest. Which student won the election?
Levi

Choose the letter for the best answer.

5. The Reeds budget $\frac{1}{3}$ of their income for rent and $\frac{1}{4}$ for food. How much of their budget is left?
A $\frac{1}{2}$　　Ⓒ $\frac{5}{12}$
B $\frac{3}{4}$　　D $\frac{7}{12}$

6. Jasmine's CD collection is $\frac{3}{8}$ jazz, $\frac{1}{4}$ classical, and the rest is rock music. What fraction of her CDs is rock music?
F $\frac{1}{4}$　　H $\frac{1}{2}$
Ⓖ $\frac{3}{8}$　　J $\frac{5}{8}$

7. Wong has 2 boxes of salt water taffy. One box contains $\frac{3}{4}$ pound, and the other box contains $\frac{7}{10}$ pound. How much taffy does he have altogether?
A $\frac{9}{10}$ pound
Ⓑ $1\frac{9}{20}$ pounds
C $1\frac{1}{2}$ pounds
D $1\frac{13}{20}$ pounds

8. In 1992, about $\frac{43}{100}$ people voted for Bill Clinton for President. About $\frac{1}{5}$ voted for Ross Perot and the rest voted for George Bush. About how many voted for George Bush?
Ⓕ about $\frac{37}{100}$
G about $\frac{52}{100}$
H about $\frac{57}{100}$
J about $\frac{3}{5}$

Lesson Quiz

Add or subtract. Write each answer in simplest form.

1. $\frac{5}{7} - \frac{3}{7}$ **$\frac{2}{7}$**　　**2.** $\frac{3}{8} + \frac{5}{8}$ **1**

3. $\frac{5}{12} + \frac{1}{2}$ **$\frac{11}{12}$**　　**4.** $\frac{1}{3} - \frac{1}{12}$ **$\frac{1}{4}$**

5. You need a nail to go through a $\frac{7}{8}$-inch door and extend an extra $\frac{1}{4}$ inch. How long should the nail be? **$1\frac{1}{8}$ in.**

Available on Daily Transparency in CRB

4-11 Organizer

Pacing: Traditional 1 day
Block $\frac{1}{2}$ day

Objective: Students add and subtract mixed numbers.

Warm Up

Add or subtract.

1. $\frac{3}{8} + \frac{4}{8}$ $\frac{7}{8}$ **2.** $\frac{11}{12} - \frac{7}{12}$ $\frac{1}{3}$

3. $\frac{2}{3} - \frac{1}{12}$ $\frac{7}{12}$ **4.** $\frac{1}{3} + \frac{1}{6} - \frac{3}{10}$ $\frac{1}{5}$

Problem of the Day

Which of these four expressions is the largest value? d

a. $13{,}579 + \frac{1}{2{,}468}$

b. $13{,}579 - \frac{1}{2{,}468}$

c. 13579.2468

d. $13{,}579 \div \frac{1}{2{,}468}$

Available on Daily Transparency in CRB

Math Fact !

Until 2000, prices of stocks on the New York Stock Exchange were given as fractions and mixed numbers. In August 2000, the system began to change over to decimals. The conversion to decimals was completed on January 29, 2001.

4-11 Adding and Subtracting Mixed Numbers

Learn to add and subtract mixed numbers.

On average, adult males who live in the Netherlands are $1\frac{4}{5}$ inches taller than those who live in the United States. The average height of an adult male in the United States is $70\frac{4}{5}$ inches. To find the average height of an adult male in the Netherlands, you can add $70\frac{4}{5}$ and $1\frac{4}{5}$.

(Source: USA Today)

Netherlands

Bicyclists rest at a windmill in the Netherlands.

EXAMPLE 1 *Measurement Application*

What is the average height of an adult male in the Netherlands?

$70\frac{4}{5} + 1\frac{4}{5} = 71 + \frac{8}{5}$ *Add the integers and add the fractions.*

$= 71 + 1\frac{3}{5}$ *Rewrite the improper fraction as a mixed number.*

$= 72\frac{3}{5}$ *Add.*

The average height of an adult male in the Netherlands is $72\frac{3}{5}$ in.

Helpful Hint

A mixed number is the sum of an integer and a fraction: $3\frac{4}{5} = 3 + \frac{4}{5}$.

EXAMPLE 2 Adding Mixed Numbers

Add. Write each answer in simplest form.

A $3\frac{4}{5} + 4\frac{2}{5}$

$3\frac{4}{5} + 4\frac{2}{5} = 7 + \frac{6}{5}$ *Add the integers and add the fractions.*

$= 7 + 1\frac{1}{5}$ *Rewrite the improper fraction as a mixed number.*

$= 8\frac{1}{5}$ *Add.*

B $1\frac{2}{15} + 7\frac{1}{6}$

$1\frac{2}{15} + 7\frac{1}{6} = 1\frac{4}{30} + 7\frac{5}{30}$ *Find a common denominator.*

$= 8 + \frac{9}{30}$ *Add the integers and add the fractions.*

$= 8\frac{9}{30} = 8\frac{3}{10}$ *Add. Then simplify.*

1 Introduce

Alternate Opener

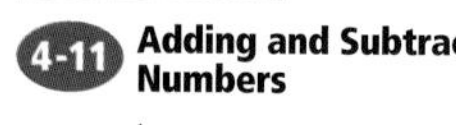

EXPLORATION

4-11 Adding and Subtracting Mixed Numbers

Bob had a $2\frac{1}{4}$-foot-long board. He cut a $1\frac{1}{2}$-foot piece. How much is left? Bob solves this problem by adding up to the next whole number.

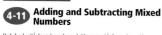

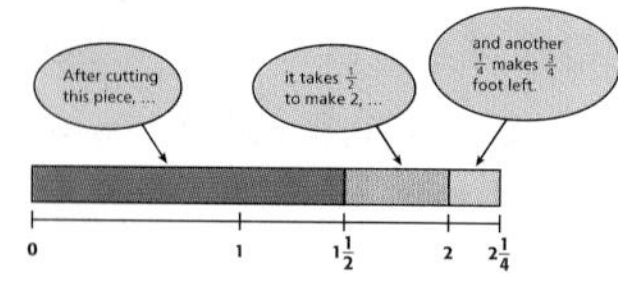
After cutting this piece, ...
it takes $\frac{1}{2}$ to make 2, ...
and another $\frac{1}{4}$ makes $\frac{3}{4}$ foot left.
0
1
$1\frac{1}{2}$
2
$2\frac{1}{4}$

Bob has a $\frac{3}{4}$-foot board left.

Use mental math and adding up to solve each subtraction problem.

1. $3 - 1\frac{3}{4}$
2. $4 - 2\frac{1}{2}$
3. $5\frac{1}{2} - 3\frac{3}{4}$
4. $7\frac{1}{8} - 6\frac{1}{4}$

Think and Discuss

5. **Discuss** your method for subtracting mixed numbers.
6. **Explain** how you can subtract mentally by adding up.

Motivate

To introduce students to adding and subtracting mixed numbers, present a recipe that calls for dry ingredients to be mixed together (e.g., a recipe for trail mix: $1\frac{1}{3}$ c raisins, $2\frac{1}{4}$ c peanuts, $\frac{7}{8}$ c coconut, $2\frac{2}{3}$ c sunflower seeds, and $\frac{3}{4}$ c chocolate chips). Ask students how they would determine what size bowl to use. Encourage students to regroup whole number and fraction parts and to use estimation skills.

Exploration worksheet and answers on Chapter 4 Resource Book pp. 100 and 148

2 Teach

Lesson Presentation

Guided Instruction

In this lesson, students learn to add and subtract mixed numbers. The lesson extends students' experience with fractions to mixed numbers. Teach students to regroup, putting whole numbers together and fractions together. Tell students to focus on the fractions, remembering to find common denominators and to simplify answers.

Teaching Tip If addition of fractions results in a mixed number, instruct students to regroup the whole number portion. Likewise, if necessary for subtraction, one whole may be regrouped as a fraction with a common denominator to be combined with the fraction.

Sometimes, when you subtract mixed numbers, the fraction portion of the first number is less than the fraction portion of the second number. In these cases, you must regroup before subtracting.

Remember!

Any fraction in which the numerator and denominator are the same is equal to 1.

REGROUPING MIXED NUMBERS

Words	Numbers
Regroup.	$7\frac{1}{8} = 6 + 1 + \frac{1}{8}$
Rewrite 1 as a fraction with a common denominator.	$= 6 + \frac{8}{8} + \frac{1}{8}$
Add.	$= 6\frac{9}{8}$

EXAMPLE 3 **Subtracting Mixed Numbers**

Subtract. Write each answer in simplest form.

A $10\frac{7}{9} - 4\frac{2}{9}$

$10\frac{7}{9} - 4\frac{2}{9} = 6 + \frac{5}{9}$ *Subtract the integers and subtract the fractions.*

$= 6\frac{5}{9}$ *Add.*

B $12\frac{7}{8} - 5\frac{17}{24}$

$12\frac{7}{8} - 5\frac{17}{24} = 12\frac{21}{24} - 5\frac{17}{24}$ *Find a common denominator.*

$= 7 + \frac{4}{24}$ *Subtract the integers and subtract the fractions.*

$= 7\frac{4}{24}$ *Add.*

$= 7\frac{1}{6}$ *Simplify.*

C $72\frac{3}{5} - 63\frac{4}{5}$

$72\frac{3}{5} - 63\frac{4}{5} = 71\frac{8}{5} - 63\frac{4}{5}$ *Regroup. $72\frac{3}{5} = 71 + \frac{5}{5} + \frac{3}{5}$*

$= 8 + \frac{4}{5}$ *Subtract the integers and subtract the fractions.*

$= 8\frac{4}{5}$ *Add.*

Think and Discuss

1. **Describe** the process for subtracting mixed numbers.
2. **Explain** whether $2\frac{3}{5} + 1\frac{3}{5} = 3\frac{6}{5}$ is correct. Is there another way to write the answer?
3. **Demonstrate** how to regroup to simplify $6\frac{2}{5} - 4\frac{3}{5}$.

COMMON ERROR ALERT

In subtraction problems, students might subtract the lesser fraction from the greater without regard to order. For example, students might treat $12\frac{1}{4} - 8\frac{3}{4}$ as $12 - 8$ and $\frac{3}{4} - \frac{1}{4}$. Remind students that order is significant in subtraction.

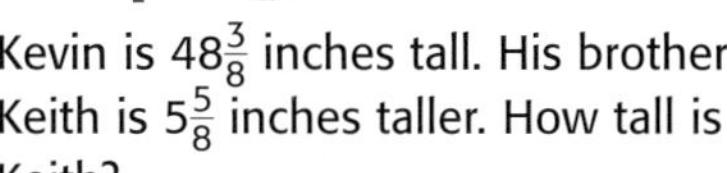

Additional Examples

Example 1

Kevin is $48\frac{3}{8}$ inches tall. His brother Keith is $5\frac{5}{8}$ inches taller. How tall is Keith?

Keith is 54 inches tall.

Example 2

Add. Write each answer in simplest form.

A. $9\frac{2}{3} + 12\frac{2}{3}$ — $22\frac{1}{3}$

B. $5\frac{1}{8} + 3\frac{5}{6}$ — $8\frac{23}{24}$

Example 3

Subtract. Write each answer in simplest form.

A. $4\frac{2}{3} - 2\frac{1}{3}$ — $2\frac{1}{3}$

B. $12\frac{8}{9} - 8\frac{2}{3}$ — $4\frac{2}{9}$

C. $17\frac{1}{8} - 12\frac{3}{8}$ — $4\frac{3}{4}$

Example 2 note: Students might subtract whole numbers as indicated but lose their concentration while finding common denominators and mistakenly add the fractions incorrectly. Encourage students to change to a common denominator before adding or subtracting.

3 Close

Reaching All Learners

Through Grouping Strategies

Have students work in groups of four. Each student needs ten index cards numbered 1 to 10. Students mix their own cards and place them in piles face down. Each player turns over one card, and the students make two fractions. The first player in the group to find the correct sum takes all of the cards. The player with the most cards after ten rounds of play wins. Vary the game by using mixed numbers as well as fractions or by subtracting.

Summarize

Ask students to compare and contrast addition and subtraction of mixed numbers with addition and subtraction of fractions. Discuss why it is often possible to deal with the whole numbers and fractions separately.

Possible answers: There is an extra step when adding or subtracting the whole number parts. Sometimes regrouping is necessary.

Answers to Think and Discuss

Possible answers:

1. Write each fraction with a common denominator. Subtract whole numbers from whole numbers and fractions from fractions. It also may be necessary to regroup before subtracting the fractions.
2. Yes, it is correct. The answer could also be written as either the mixed number $4\frac{1}{5}$ or the improper fraction $\frac{21}{5}$.
3. Rewrite $6\frac{2}{5}$ as $5 + 1 + \frac{2}{5}$. Write 1 as $\frac{5}{5}$. Add $\frac{5}{5}$ and $\frac{2}{5}$ to make $\frac{7}{5}$. Then subtract.

4-11 PRACTICE & ASSESS

Students may want to refer back to the lesson examples.

Assignment Guide

If you finished Example 1 assign:
Core 1, 8, 37–39, 43–51
Enriched 1, 8, 37–39, 43–51

If you finished Example 2 assign:
Core 1–4, 8–14, 21–29 odd, 37, 39, 43–51
Enriched 1, 3, 7–13 odd, 21, 23–25, 27–30, 34, 37-39, 43-51

If you finished Example 3 assign:
Core 1–20, 21–39 odd, 43–51
Enriched 1–19 odd, 21–51

Notes

4-11 Exercises

FOR EXTRA PRACTICE
see page 663

internet connect
Homework Help Online
go.hrw.com Keyword: MS4 4-11
go.hrw.com

GUIDED PRACTICE

See Example 1

1. Chrystelle's mother is $1\frac{2}{3}$ ft taller than Chrystelle is. If Chrystelle is $3\frac{1}{2}$ ft tall, how tall is her mother? $5\frac{1}{6}$ ft

See Example 2 Add. Write each answer in simplest form.

2. $3\frac{2}{5} + 4\frac{1}{5}$ $7\frac{3}{5}$
3. $2\frac{7}{8} + 3\frac{3}{4}$ $6\frac{5}{8}$
4. $1\frac{8}{9} + 4\frac{4}{9}$ $6\frac{1}{3}$

See Example 3 Subtract. Write each answer in simplest form.

5. $6\frac{2}{3} - 5\frac{1}{3}$ $1\frac{1}{3}$
6. $8\frac{1}{6} - 2\frac{5}{6}$ $5\frac{1}{3}$
7. $3\frac{2}{3} - 2\frac{3}{4}$ $\frac{11}{12}$

INDEPENDENT PRACTICE

See Example 1

8. The track at Daytona International Speedway is $\frac{24}{25}$ mi longer than the track at Atlanta Motor Speedway. If the track at Atlanta is $1\frac{27}{50}$ mi long, how long is the track at Daytona? $2\frac{1}{2}$ mi

See Example 2 Add. Write each answer in simplest form.

9. $6\frac{1}{4} + 8\frac{3}{4}$ 15
10. $3\frac{3}{5} + 7\frac{4}{5}$ $11\frac{2}{5}$
11. $3\frac{5}{6} + 1\frac{5}{6}$ $5\frac{2}{3}$
12. $2\frac{3}{10} + 4\frac{1}{2}$ $6\frac{4}{5}$
13. $6\frac{1}{8} + 8\frac{9}{10}$ $15\frac{1}{40}$
14. $6\frac{1}{6} + 5\frac{3}{10}$ $11\frac{7}{15}$

See Example 3 Subtract. Write each answer in simplest form.

15. $2\frac{1}{14} - 1\frac{3}{14}$ $\frac{6}{7}$
16. $4\frac{5}{12} - 1\frac{7}{12}$ $2\frac{5}{6}$
17. $8 - 2\frac{3}{4}$ $5\frac{1}{4}$
18. $8\frac{3}{4} - 6\frac{2}{5}$ $2\frac{7}{20}$
19. $3\frac{1}{3} - 2\frac{5}{8}$ $\frac{17}{24}$
20. $4\frac{2}{5} - 3\frac{1}{2}$ $\frac{9}{10}$

PRACTICE AND PROBLEM SOLVING

Add or subtract. Write each answer in simplest form.

21. $7\frac{1}{3} + 8\frac{1}{5}$ $15\frac{8}{15}$
22. $14\frac{3}{5} - 8\frac{1}{2}$ $6\frac{1}{10}$
23. $9\frac{1}{6} + 4\frac{6}{9}$ $13\frac{5}{6}$
24. $3\frac{5}{8} + 2\frac{7}{12}$ $6\frac{5}{24}$
25. $25\frac{1}{3} + 3\frac{5}{6}$ $29\frac{1}{6}$
26. $1\frac{7}{9} - \frac{17}{18}$ $\frac{5}{6}$
27. $3\frac{1}{2} + 5\frac{1}{4}$ $8\frac{3}{4}$
28. $6\frac{3}{4} + 2\frac{3}{4}$ $9\frac{1}{2}$
29. $1\frac{7}{15} + 2\frac{7}{10}$ $4\frac{1}{6}$
30. $4\frac{2}{3} + 1\frac{7}{8} + 3\frac{1}{2}$ $10\frac{1}{24}$
31. $5\frac{1}{6} + 8\frac{2}{3} - 9\frac{1}{2}$ $4\frac{1}{3}$
32. $12\frac{1}{2} - 3\frac{3}{4} - 6\frac{1}{3}$ $2\frac{5}{12}$

Compare. Write <, >, or =.

33. $12\frac{1}{4} - 10\frac{3}{4}$ ▒ $5\frac{1}{2} - 3\frac{7}{10}$ <
34. $4\frac{1}{2} + 3\frac{4}{5}$ ▒ $4\frac{5}{7} + 3\frac{1}{2}$ >
35. $13\frac{3}{4} - 2\frac{3}{8}$ ▒ $5\frac{5}{6} + 4\frac{2}{9}$ >
36. $4\frac{1}{3} - 2\frac{1}{4}$ ▒ $3\frac{1}{4} - 1\frac{1}{6}$ =

Math Background

The basic properties of commutativity and associativity are at the heart of the rules for adding and subtracting mixed numbers. For students who question the regrouping necessary when adding and subtracting mixed numbers, it may be worthwhile to verify that the same result is obtained by rewriting the mixed numbers as improper fractions, computing, and then rewriting them as mixed numbers. Though this is a longer process, it can help clarify things for some students.

RETEACH 4-11

LESSON 4-11 **Reteach**
Adding and Subtracting Mixed Numbers

You can write mixed numbers as improper fractions before adding.

Add: $4\frac{5}{8} + 2\frac{7}{8}$

- Write improper fractions.

  $4\frac{5}{8} = \frac{37}{8}$ and $2\frac{7}{8} = \frac{23}{8}$

- The denominators are the same. Add and simplify.

  $\frac{37}{8} + \frac{23}{8} = \frac{60}{8} = 7\frac{4}{8} = 7\frac{1}{2}$

Add: $1\frac{2}{5} + 3\frac{3}{4}$

- Write improper fractions.

  $1\frac{2}{5} = \frac{7}{5}$ and $3\frac{3}{4} = \frac{15}{4}$

- Find a common denominator. The LCD is 20.

  $\frac{7}{5} = \frac{28}{20}$ and $\frac{15}{4} = \frac{75}{20}$

- Add and simplify.

  $\frac{28}{20} + \frac{75}{20} = \frac{103}{20} = 5\frac{3}{20}$

Add. Write each answer in simplest form.

1. $4\frac{7}{10} + 2\frac{9}{10} = \frac{47}{10} + \frac{29}{10} = \frac{76}{10} = 7\frac{6}{10} = 7\frac{3}{5}$
2. $2\frac{1}{2} + 1\frac{3}{8} = \frac{5}{2} + \frac{11}{8} = \frac{20}{8} + \frac{11}{8} = \frac{31}{8} = 3\frac{7}{8}$
3. $3\frac{1}{5} + 2\frac{1}{3} = \frac{16}{5} + \frac{7}{3} = \frac{48}{15} + \frac{35}{15} = \frac{83}{15} = 5\frac{8}{15}$
4. $1\frac{2}{7} + 5\frac{3}{7}$ $6\frac{5}{7}$
5. $5\frac{3}{8} + 3\frac{7}{8}$ $9\frac{1}{4}$
6. $4\frac{4}{9} + 2\frac{2}{3}$ $7\frac{1}{9}$
7. $2\frac{3}{5} + 3\frac{7}{10}$ $6\frac{3}{10}$
8. $2\frac{3}{4} + 1\frac{5}{6}$ $4\frac{7}{12}$
9. $4\frac{1}{3} + 2\frac{1}{2}$ $6\frac{5}{6}$

PRACTICE 4-11

LESSON 4-11 **Practice B**
Adding and Subtracting Mixed Numbers

Add. Write each answer in simplest form.

1. $7\frac{2}{7} + 6\frac{5}{7}$ 14
2. $5\frac{4}{9} + 3\frac{7}{9}$ $9\frac{2}{9}$
3. $4\frac{1}{3} + 8\frac{1}{4}$ $12\frac{7}{12}$
4. $2\frac{7}{15} + 3\frac{11}{15}$ $6\frac{1}{5}$
5. $6\frac{9}{10} + 1\frac{2}{5}$ $8\frac{3}{10}$
6. $2\frac{3}{5} + 1\frac{11}{20}$ $4\frac{3}{20}$
7. $5\frac{9}{10} + 2\frac{5}{8}$ $8\frac{21}{40}$
8. $2\frac{11}{12} + 3\frac{7}{8}$ $6\frac{19}{24}$
9. $1\frac{2}{3} + 5\frac{7}{9}$ $7\frac{4}{9}$

Subtract. Write each answer in simplest form.

10. $7\frac{7}{9} - 3\frac{5}{9}$ $4\frac{2}{9}$
11. $9\frac{7}{10} - 5\frac{3}{10}$ $4\frac{2}{5}$
12. $4\frac{13}{15} - 1\frac{7}{15}$ $3\frac{2}{5}$
13. $6\frac{2}{3} - 3\frac{3}{5}$ $3\frac{1}{15}$
14. $10\frac{3}{4} - 6\frac{1}{3}$ $4\frac{5}{12}$
15. $2\frac{3}{10} - 1\frac{7}{8}$ $\frac{17}{40}$
16. $8\frac{7}{12} - 6\frac{1}{3}$ $2\frac{1}{4}$
17. $5\frac{7}{8} - 3\frac{9}{10}$ $1\frac{39}{40}$
18. $7\frac{6}{7} - 6\frac{3}{4}$ $1\frac{3}{28}$

19. Tucker ran $5\frac{3}{8}$ miles on Monday and $3\frac{3}{4}$ miles on Tuesday. How far did he run on both days?
    $9\frac{1}{8}$ miles

The Netherlands produces more than 3 billion tulips each year.

37. ***AGRICULTURE*** From January through September of 2001, the United States imported $\frac{49}{50}$ of its tulip bulbs from the Netherlands and $\frac{1}{100}$ of its tulip bulbs from New Zealand. What fraction more of tulip imports came from the Netherlands? **$\frac{97}{100}$**

38. ***TRAVEL*** The table shows the distances in miles between four cities. To find the distance between two cities, locate the square where the row for one city and the column for the other city intersect.

	Atherton	Baily	Charleston	Dixon
Atherton	X	$40\frac{2}{3}$	$100\frac{5}{6}$	$16\frac{1}{2}$
Baily	$40\frac{2}{3}$	X	$210\frac{3}{8}$	$30\frac{2}{3}$
Charleston	$100\frac{5}{6}$	$210\frac{3}{8}$	X	$98\frac{3}{4}$
Dixon	$16\frac{1}{2}$	$30\frac{2}{3}$	$98\frac{3}{4}$	X

a. How much farther is it from Charleston to Dixon than from Atherton to Baily? **$58\frac{1}{12}$ mi**

b. If you drove from Charleston to Atherton and then from Atherton to Dixon, how far would you drive? **$117\frac{1}{3}$ mi**

39. ***RECREATION*** Kathy wants to hike to Candle Lake. The waterfall trail is $1\frac{2}{3}$ miles long, and the meadow trail is $1\frac{5}{6}$ miles long. Which route is shorter and by how much? **the waterfall trail; $\frac{1}{6}$ mi**

40. ***CHOOSE A STRATEGY*** Spiro needs to draw a 6-inch-long line. He does not have a ruler, but he has sheets of notebook paper that are $8\frac{1}{2}$ inches wide and 11 inches long. Describe how Spiro can use the notebook paper to measure 6 inches.

41. ***WRITE ABOUT IT*** Explain why it is sometimes necessary to regroup a mixed number when subtracting.

42. ***CHALLENGE*** Todd had d pounds of nails. He sold $3\frac{1}{2}$ pounds on Monday and $5\frac{2}{3}$ pounds on Tuesday. Write an expression to show how many pounds he had left and then simplify it.

$d - \left(3\frac{1}{2} + 5\frac{2}{3}\right) = d - 9\frac{1}{6}$

Answers

40. Possible answer: The difference between 11 in. and $8\frac{1}{2}$ in. is $2\frac{1}{2}$ in. He can hold the $8\frac{1}{2}$ in. side along the 11 in. side and mark the $2\frac{1}{2}$ in. length. Then he can hold the $2\frac{1}{2}$ in. length along the $8\frac{1}{2}$ in. side and mark it on the $8\frac{1}{2}$ in. side. The remaining length is 6 in. $\left(8\frac{1}{2} - 2\frac{1}{2} = 6\right)$.

41. Possible answer: It is necessary to rename a mixed number if the fraction part being subtracted is greater than the fraction it is being subtracted from.

Journal

Have students describe a real-world situation in which they needed to regroup something (e.g., numbers, objects, people).

Spiral Review

Add. (Lesson 3-3)

43. $-3 + 8$ **5**
44. $-2 + (-7)$ **−9**
45. $8 + (-12)$ **−4**

Write each fraction as a decimal. (Lesson 3-9)

46. $\frac{3}{4}$ **0.75**
47. $\frac{5}{8}$ **0.625**
48. $\frac{3}{16}$ **0.1875**
49. $\frac{2}{9}$ **$0.\overline{2}$**

50. **TEST PREP** What is 154,000,000,000,000 written in scientific notation? (Lesson 2-2) **C**

A 15.4×10^{13} B 1.54×10^{13} C 1.54×10^{14} D 0.154×10^{15}

51. **TEST PREP** Which number is a solution of $2.2b = 1.1$? (Lesson 4-6) **G**

F 0.05 G 0.5 H 5 J 50

Test Prep Doctor

In Exercise 50, remind students that scientific notation is defined as a number *greater than or equal to 1 and less than 10* multiplied by a power of 10. This immediately eliminates **A** and **D.** In Exercise 51, **H** and **J** can be eliminated because dividing 1.1 by the larger 2.2 should yield a number less than 1.

CHALLENGE 4-11

LESSON 4-11 **Challenge**
Mixed Number Magic

In a magic square, each row, column, and diagonal has the same sum. Fill in the missing numbers to complete each magic square below.

Magic Square #1

$4\frac{1}{3}$	$9\frac{3}{4}$	$2\frac{1}{6}$
$3\frac{1}{4}$	$5\frac{5}{12}$	$7\frac{7}{12}$
$8\frac{2}{3}$	$1\frac{1}{12}$	$6\frac{1}{2}$

Magic Square #1 sum: **$16\frac{1}{4}$**

Magic Square #2

$2\frac{1}{6}$	$4\frac{7}{8}$	$1\frac{1}{12}$
$1\frac{5}{8}$	$2\frac{17}{24}$	$3\frac{19}{24}$
$4\frac{1}{3}$	$\frac{13}{24}$	$3\frac{1}{4}$

Magic Square #2 sum: **$8\frac{1}{8}$**

What is the difference between these two magic sums? **$8\frac{1}{8}$**

Magic Square #3

6	$13\frac{1}{2}$	3
$4\frac{1}{2}$	$7\frac{1}{2}$	$10\frac{1}{2}$
12	$1\frac{1}{2}$	9

Magic Square #3 sum: **$22\frac{1}{2}$**

Magic Square #4

$1\frac{1}{2}$	$3\frac{3}{8}$	$\frac{3}{4}$
$1\frac{1}{8}$	$1\frac{7}{8}$	$2\frac{5}{8}$
3	$\frac{3}{8}$	$2\frac{1}{4}$

Magic Square #4 sum: **$5\frac{5}{8}$**

What is the difference between these two magic sums? **$16\frac{7}{8}$**

PROBLEM SOLVING 4-11

LESSON 4-11 **Problem Solving**
Adding and Subtracting Mixed Numbers

Write the correct answer.

1. A female gray whale is $45\frac{1}{4}$ feet long. A male gray whale is $43\frac{1}{2}$ feet long. How much longer is the female than the male gray whale?
$1\frac{3}{4}$ feet

2. At birth, a pilot whale is $4\frac{3}{5}$ feet long. A newborn gray whale is $15\frac{1}{4}$ feet long. How much longer is the newborn gray whale?
$10\frac{13}{20}$ feet

3. A manatee weighs $\frac{1}{2}$ ton. A walrus weighs $1\frac{3}{4}$ tons. A narwhal weighs $1\frac{1}{2}$ tons. What is the total weight of all 3 animals?
$3\frac{3}{4}$ tons

4. A bottle-nosed dolphin can leap $15\frac{1}{8}$ feet out of the water. The world record high jump for a human is $8\frac{1}{24}$ feet. How much higher can a dolphin leap than a human?
$7\frac{1}{12}$ feet

Choose the letter for the best answer.

5. At a wildlife park, the killer whale show lasts $\frac{5}{8}$ of an hour. The guided tour of the park takes $2\frac{1}{2}$ hours. How long will it take to do both activities?
(A) $3\frac{1}{8}$ hours
B $2\frac{5}{8}$ hours
C $3\frac{5}{8}$ hours
D $1\frac{7}{8}$ hours

6. Jeremy walks $3\frac{1}{2}$ miles while visiting a wildlife park. Shawna hikes a $4\frac{3}{8}$-mile long nature trail. How much farther does Shawna walk?
F $\frac{3}{8}$ of a mile
G $\frac{5}{8}$ of a mile
(H) $\frac{7}{8}$ of a mile
J $1\frac{1}{8}$ of a mile

7. Dog food comes in $5\frac{7}{8}$-pound bags and $12\frac{3}{4}$-pound bags. Find the total weight of 2 small and 1 large bags.
A $22\frac{7}{8}$ pounds
B $23\frac{1}{2}$ pounds
(C) $24\frac{1}{2}$ pounds
D $25\frac{3}{4}$ pounds

8. A movie lasts $2\frac{1}{6}$ hours. A baseball game lasts $3\frac{2}{3}$ hours. How much longer does the game last?
F $\frac{5}{6}$ hours
G $1\frac{1}{6}$ hours
H $1\frac{1}{3}$ hours
(J) $1\frac{1}{2}$ hours

Lesson Quiz

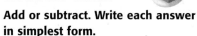

Add or subtract. Write each answer in simplest form.

1. $5\frac{1}{4} + 5\frac{1}{6}$ **$10\frac{5}{12}$**
2. $9\frac{2}{3} + 10\frac{7}{12}$ **$20\frac{1}{4}$**
3. $7\frac{7}{8} - 2\frac{3}{4}$ **$5\frac{1}{8}$**
4. $10\frac{2}{9} - 4\frac{5}{6}$ **$5\frac{7}{18}$**
5. A single roll of wallpaper unrolls to $15\frac{1}{2}$ yards. You hang $13\frac{7}{8}$ yards from the roll. How much wallpaper remains? **$1\frac{5}{8}$ yards**

Available on Daily Transparency in CRB

4-12 Organizer

Pacing: Traditional 1 day
Block $\frac{1}{2}$ day

Objective: Students solve one-step equations that contain fractions.

Warm Up

Solve.

1. $x - 16 = 8$ $x = 24$
2. $7a = 35$ $a = 5$
3. $\frac{x}{12} = 11$ $x = 132$
4. $y + 21 = 31$ $y = 10$

Problem of the Day

Write 15 positive integers less than 1,000 with digits that, when added together, total 4. **4, 13, 22, 31, 40, 103, 112, 121, 130, 202, 211, 220, 301, 310, 400**

Available on Daily Transparency in CRB

Math Humor

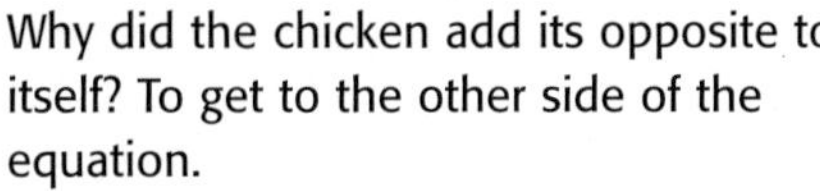

Why did the chicken add its opposite to itself? To get to the other side of the equation.

4-12 Solving Equations Containing Fractions

Learn to solve one-step equations that contain fractions.

Gold classified as 24 karat is pure gold, while gold classified as 18 karat is only $\frac{3}{4}$ pure. The remaining $\frac{1}{4}$ of 18-karat gold is made up of one or more different metals, such as silver, copper, or zinc. The color of gold varies, depending on the type and amount of each metal added to the pure gold.

Equations can help you determine the amounts of metals in different kinds of gold. The goal when solving equations that contain fractions is the same as when working with other kinds of numbers—*to isolate the variable* on one side of the equation.

EXAMPLE 1 Solving Equations by Adding or Subtracting

Solve. Write each answer in simplest form.

A $x - \frac{1}{5} = \frac{3}{5}$

$$x - \frac{1}{5} = \frac{3}{5}$$

$$x - \frac{1}{5} + \frac{1}{5} = \frac{3}{5} + \frac{1}{5} \quad \text{Add to isolate } x.$$

$$x = \frac{4}{5} \quad \text{Add.}$$

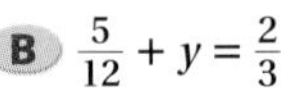

B $\frac{5}{12} + y = \frac{2}{3}$

$$\frac{5}{12} + y = \frac{2}{3}$$

$$\frac{5}{12} + y - \frac{5}{12} = \frac{2}{3} - \frac{5}{12} \quad \text{Subtract to isolate } y.$$

$$y = \frac{8}{12} - \frac{5}{12} \quad \text{Find a common denominator.}$$

$$y = \frac{3}{12} = \frac{1}{4} \quad \text{Subtract. Then simplify.}$$

Helpful Hint

You can also isolate the variable y by adding the opposite of $\frac{5}{12}$, $-\frac{5}{12}$, to both sides.

C $\frac{7}{18} + u = -\frac{14}{27}$

$$\frac{7}{18} + u = -\frac{14}{27}$$

$$\frac{7}{18} + u - \frac{7}{18} = -\frac{14}{27} - \frac{7}{18} \quad \text{Subtract to isolate } u.$$

$$u = -\frac{28}{54} - \frac{21}{54} \quad \text{Find a common denominator.}$$

$$u = -\frac{49}{54} \quad \text{Subtract.}$$

1 Introduce

Alternate Opener

EXPLORATION

4-12 Solving Equations Containing Fractions

For each equation, use mental math to find the missing number.

1. $2\frac{1}{2} + \_\_\_\_ = 10$
2. $20 - \_\_\_\_ = 4\frac{3}{4}$
3. $2 \cdot \_\_\_\_ = 3\frac{4}{5}$
4. $20 \div \_\_\_\_ = \frac{1}{4}$

For each equation, use a calculator to find the value of x.

5. $2\frac{1}{2} + x = 10$
6. $20 - x = 4\frac{3}{4}$
7. $2x = 3\frac{4}{5}$
8. $\frac{20}{x} = \frac{1}{4}$

Think and Discuss

9. **Discuss** what you notice about the equations in numbers **1–4** and **5–8.**
10. **Write** a real-world situation for each equation in numbers **5–8.** For example, the equation in number **5** could represent this situation: "After $2\frac{1}{2}$ more hours, the total number of hours that Elisa will have slept will be 10. How many hours has she slept so far?

Motivate

To introduce solving equations with fractions, ask students to review the process of solving one-step equations and to propose examples. Then discuss how solving similar equations containing fractions would be similar or different.

$$x + 3 = 7 \qquad x + \frac{3}{10} = \frac{7}{10}$$

Remind students that the process of solving one-step equations does not change.

Exploration worksheet and answers on Chapter 4 Resource Book pp. 110 and 151

2 Teach

Lesson Presentation

Guided Instruction

In this lesson, students learn to solve one-step equations that contain fractions. Because students are familiar with solving equations and with operations with fractions and mixed numbers, they may not give the work the care it needs. Encourage students to take their time and show each step in the solution, even though each solution may require several steps.

Teaching Tip Ask students to estimate the solution before solving. In addition to giving important practice estimating with fractions, this will give students an easy check of their work.

EXAMPLE 2 Solving Equations by Multiplying

Solve. Write each answer in simplest form.

Remember!

To undo multiplying by $\frac{2}{3}$, you can divide by $\frac{2}{3}$ or multiply by its reciprocal, $\frac{3}{2}$.

A $\frac{2}{3}x = \frac{4}{5}$

$$\frac{2}{3}x = \frac{4}{5}$$

$$\frac{2}{3}x \cdot \frac{3}{2} = \frac{\cancel{4}^{2}}{5} \cdot \frac{3}{\cancel{2}_{1}}$$ *Multiply by the reciprocal of $\frac{2}{3}$. Then simplify.*

$$x = \frac{6}{5} \text{ or } 1\frac{1}{5}$$

B $3y = \frac{6}{7}$

$$3y = \frac{6}{7}$$

$$3y \cdot \frac{1}{3} = \frac{\cancel{6}^{2}}{7} \cdot \frac{1}{\cancel{3}_{1}}$$ *Multiply by the reciprocal of 3. Then simplify.*

$$y = \frac{2}{7}$$

EXAMPLE 3 *Physical Science Application*

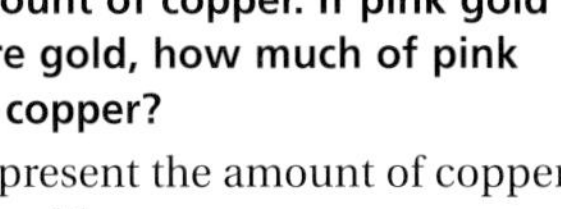

Pink gold is made up of gold, silver, and copper. The amount of pure gold in pink gold is $\frac{11}{20}$ more than the amount of copper. If pink gold is $\frac{3}{4}$ pure gold, how much of pink gold is copper?

Let c represent the amount of copper in pink gold.

$$c + \frac{11}{20} = \frac{3}{4}$$ *Write an equation.*

$$c + \frac{11}{20} - \frac{11}{20} = \frac{3}{4} - \frac{11}{20}$$ *Subtract to isolate c.*

$$c = \frac{15}{20} - \frac{11}{20}$$ *Find a common denominator.*

$$c = \frac{4}{20}$$ *Subtract.*

$$c = \frac{1}{5}$$ *Simplify.*

The amount of copper in pink gold is $\frac{1}{5}$.

Think and Discuss

1. **Show** the first step you would use to solve $m + 3\frac{5}{8} = 12\frac{1}{2}$.
2. **Describe** how to decide if $\frac{2}{3}$ is a solution of $\frac{7}{8}y = \frac{3}{5}$.
3. **Explain** why solving $\frac{2}{5}c = \frac{8}{9}$ by multiplying both sides by $\frac{5}{2}$ is the same as solving it by dividing both sides by $\frac{2}{5}$.

COMMON ERROR ALERT

When required to use several skills in solving an equation, some students might become distracted and skip steps. Watch for students who forget to find common denominators or who try to divide without the use of the reciprocal. If necessary, reteach these critical skills and strategies.

Additional Examples

Example 1

Solve. Write each answer in simplest form.

A. $x - \frac{3}{7} = \frac{5}{7}$ — $x = \frac{8}{7}$ or $1\frac{1}{7}$

B. $\frac{3}{4} + y = \frac{1}{8}$ — $y = -\frac{5}{8}$

C. $\frac{5}{12} + t = -\frac{3}{8}$ — $t = -\frac{19}{24}$

Example 2

Solve. Write each answer in simplest form.

A. $\frac{3}{8}x = \frac{1}{4}$ — $x = \frac{2}{3}$

B. $4y = \frac{8}{9}$ — $y = \frac{2}{9}$

Example 3

The amount of copper in brass is $\frac{3}{4}$ of the total weight. If a sample contains $4\frac{1}{5}$ ounces of copper, what is the total weight of the sample?

The sample weighs $5\frac{3}{5}$ ounces.

Example 1 note: Remind students to keep the sign for negative numbers with the numerator to make computation easier.

3 Close

Reaching All Learners

Through Critical Thinking

The following is a famous riddle from around A.D. 500. The riddle is supposed to tell about the life of Diophantus, an early mathematician. Challenge students to solve the riddle and find out how old Diophantus lived to be.

"His boyhood lasted $\frac{1}{6}$ of his life, he married after $\frac{1}{7}$ more, his beard grew after $\frac{1}{12}$ more, and his son was born 5 years later. The son lived to be half his father's age, and the father died 4 years after the son."

A recording sheet is available on CRB p. 127.

Summarize

Ask students to list the skills they used in this lesson. Did they learn any new skills? Did any skills they learned previously change? Have students summarize the process of solving an equation that involves mixed numbers.

Possible answers: The skills from the lesson were using inverse operations to solve equations, and adding, subtracting, multiplying, and dividing fractions. The skills were not new, but it was new to use the skills together. To solve an equation with mixed numbers, perform the inverse operation on both sides to isolate the variable.

Answers to Think and Discuss

Possible answers:

1. Use the inverse operation, subtraction, and subtract $3\frac{5}{8}$ from both sides.
2. Substitute $\frac{2}{3}$ for y and multiply, which will show that $\frac{7}{8} \cdot \frac{2}{3} \neq \frac{3}{5}$.
3. Dividing by a fraction is the same as multiplying by its reciprocal. Since $\frac{5}{2}$ is the reciprocal of $\frac{2}{5}$, the results will be the same.

4-12 PRACTICE & ASSESS

Students may want to refer back to the lesson examples.

Assignment Guide

If you finished Example 1 assign:
Core 1–3, 8–13, 22, 24, 30, 33, 36, 48–55
Enriched 1, 3, 9–13 odd, 22–30 even, 31–33, 36, 37, 48–55

If you finished Example 2 assign:
Core 1–6, 8–19, 21–26, 36–38, 48–55
Enriched 1–5 odd, 9–19 odd, 21–38, 48–55

If you finished Example 3 assign:
Core 1–26, 36–43, 48–55
Enriched 1–19 odd, 21–55

Answers

11. $x = \frac{53}{24}$ or $2\frac{5}{24}$
22. $m = \frac{7}{6}$ or $1\frac{1}{6}$
27. $n = \frac{12}{5}$ or $2\frac{2}{5}$
28. $z = \frac{103}{30}$ or $3\frac{13}{30}$
30. $m = -\frac{9}{26}$
33. $h = -\frac{1}{12}$
34. $t = \frac{9}{4}$ or $2\frac{1}{4}$
39. $11\frac{3}{16}$ lb
40. $3\frac{17}{100}$ in.

4-12 Exercises

FOR EXTRA PRACTICE
see page 663

internet connect
Homework Help Online
go.hrw.com Keyword: MS4 4-12

GUIDED PRACTICE

See Example 1 Solve. Write each answer in simplest form.

1. $a - \frac{1}{2} = \frac{1}{4}$ **$a = \frac{3}{4}$**
2. $m + \frac{1}{6} = \frac{5}{6}$ **$m = \frac{2}{3}$**
3. $p - \frac{2}{3} = \frac{5}{6}$ **$p = \frac{3}{2}$ or $1\frac{1}{2}$**

See Example 2

4. $\frac{1}{5}x = 8$ **$x = 40$**
5. $\frac{2}{3}r = \frac{3}{5}$ **$r = \frac{9}{10}$**
6. $3w = \frac{3}{7}$ **$w = \frac{1}{7}$**

See Example 3

7. Kara has $\frac{3}{8}$ cup less oatmeal than she needs for a cookie recipe. If she has $\frac{3}{4}$ cup of oatmeal, how much oatmeal does she need? **$\frac{9}{8}$ c or $1\frac{1}{8}$ c**

INDEPENDENT PRACTICE

See Example 1 Solve. Write each answer in simplest form.

8. $n - \frac{1}{5} = \frac{3}{5}$ **$n = \frac{4}{5}$**
9. $t - \frac{3}{8} = \frac{1}{4}$ **$t = \frac{5}{8}$**
10. $s - \frac{7}{24} = \frac{1}{3}$ **$s = \frac{5}{8}$**
11. $x + \frac{2}{3} = 2\frac{7}{8}$
12. $h + \frac{7}{10} = \frac{7}{10}$ **$h = 0$**
13. $y + \frac{5}{6} = \frac{19}{20}$ **$y = \frac{7}{60}$**

See Example 2

14. $\frac{1}{5}x = 4$ **$x = 20$**
15. $\frac{1}{4}w = \frac{1}{8}$ **$w = \frac{1}{2}$**
16. $5y = \frac{3}{10}$ **$y = \frac{3}{50}$**
17. $6z = \frac{1}{2}$ **$z = \frac{1}{12}$**
18. $\frac{5}{8}x = \frac{2}{5}$ **$x = \frac{16}{25}$**
19. $\frac{5}{8}n = 1\frac{1}{5}$ **$n = \frac{48}{25}$ or $1\frac{23}{25}$**

See Example 3

20. Carbon-14 has a half-life of 5,730 years. After 17,190 years, $\frac{1}{8}$ of the carbon-14 in a sample will be left. If 5 grams of carbon-14 are left after 17,190 years, how much was in the original sample? **40 g**

PRACTICE AND PROBLEM SOLVING

Solve. Write each answer in simplest form.

21. $\frac{4}{5}t = \frac{1}{5}$ **$t = \frac{1}{4}$**
22. $m - \frac{1}{2} = \frac{2}{3}$
23. $\frac{1}{8}w = \frac{3}{4}$ **$w = 6$**
24. $\frac{8}{9} + t = \frac{17}{18}$ **$t = \frac{1}{18}$**
25. $\frac{5}{3}x = 1$ **$x = \frac{3}{5}$**
26. $j + \frac{5}{8} = \frac{11}{16}$ **$j = \frac{1}{16}$**
27. $\frac{4}{3}n = 3\frac{1}{5}$
28. $z + \frac{1}{6} = 3\frac{9}{15}$
29. $\frac{3}{4}y = \frac{3}{8}$ **$y = \frac{1}{2}$**
30. $-\frac{5}{26} + m = -\frac{7}{13}$
31. $-\frac{8}{77} + r = -\frac{1}{11}$ **$r = \frac{1}{77}$**
32. $y - \frac{3}{4} = -\frac{9}{20}$ **$y = \frac{3}{10}$**
33. $h - \frac{3}{8} = -\frac{11}{24}$
34. $-\frac{5}{36}t = -\frac{5}{16}$
35. $-\frac{8}{13}v = -\frac{6}{13}$ **$v = \frac{3}{4}$**
36. $4\frac{6}{7} + p = 5\frac{1}{4}$ **$p = \frac{11}{28}$**
37. $d - 5\frac{1}{8} = 9\frac{3}{10}$ **$d = \frac{577}{40}$ or $14\frac{17}{40}$**
38. $6\frac{8}{21}k = 13\frac{1}{3}$ **$k = \frac{140}{67}$ or $2\frac{6}{67}$**
39. ***FOOD*** Each person in Finland drinks an average of $24\frac{1}{4}$ lb of coffee per year. This is $13\frac{1}{16}$ lb more than the average person in Italy consumes. On average, how much coffee does an Italian drink each year?
40. ***WEATHER*** Yuma, Arizona, receives $102\frac{1}{100}$ fewer inches of rain each year than Quillayute, Washington, which receives $105\frac{9}{50}$ inches per year. (*Source:* National Weather Service). How much rain does Yuma get in one year?

Math Background

Solving equations with fractions and mixed numbers brings together ideas about inverses and operations. Students should be able to connect *additive inverse* with *opposite* and *multiplicative inverse* with *reciprocal.* Furthermore, students should understand that subtraction may be defined as adding the opposite and, likewise, division as multiplication by the reciprocal. It may be useful to point out that every fraction is a division statement, with the *vinculum,* or fraction bar, serving as the division sign. In fact, the traditional division symbol (÷) is a representation of a fraction, with the dots taking the places of the numerator and denominator.

RETEACH 4-12

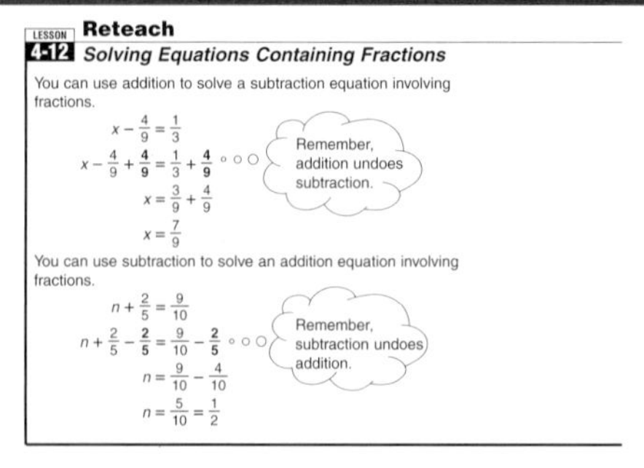

LESSON 4-12 **Reteach**
Solving Equations Containing Fractions

You can use addition to solve a subtraction equation involving fractions.

$$x - \frac{4}{9} = \frac{1}{3}$$
$$x - \frac{4}{9} + \frac{4}{9} = \frac{1}{3} + \frac{4}{9}$$
$$x = \frac{3}{9} + \frac{4}{9}$$
$$x = \frac{7}{9}$$

Remember, addition undoes subtraction.

You can use subtraction to solve an addition equation involving fractions.

$$n + \frac{2}{5} = \frac{9}{10}$$
$$n + \frac{2}{5} - \frac{2}{5} = \frac{9}{10} - \frac{2}{5}$$
$$n = \frac{9}{10} - \frac{4}{10}$$
$$n = \frac{5}{10} = \frac{1}{2}$$

Remember, subtraction undoes addition.

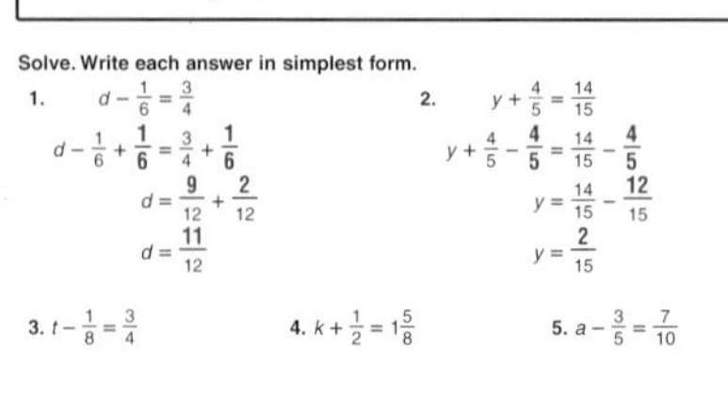

Solve. Write each answer in simplest form.

1. $d - \frac{1}{6} = \frac{3}{4}$
$d - \frac{1}{6} + \frac{1}{6} = \frac{3}{4} + \frac{1}{6}$
$d = \frac{9}{12} + \frac{2}{12}$
$d = \frac{11}{12}$

2. $y + \frac{4}{5} = \frac{14}{15}$
$y + \frac{4}{5} - \frac{4}{5} = \frac{14}{15} - \frac{4}{5}$
$y = \frac{14}{15} - \frac{12}{15}$
$y = \frac{2}{15}$

3. $t - \frac{1}{8} = \frac{3}{4}$ **$t = \frac{7}{8}$**
4. $k + \frac{1}{2} = 1\frac{5}{8}$ **$k = 1\frac{1}{8}$**
5. $a - \frac{3}{5} = \frac{7}{10}$ **$a = 1\frac{3}{10}$**

PRACTICE 4-12

LESSON 4-12 **Practice B**
Solving Equations Containing Fractions

Solve. Write each answer in simplest form.

1. $t - \frac{3}{7} = \frac{4}{7}$ **$t = 1$**
2. $g - \frac{5}{16} = \frac{3}{16}$ **$g = \frac{1}{2}$**
3. $k - \frac{3}{10} = \frac{2}{5}$ **$k = \frac{7}{10}$**
4. $n + \frac{1}{7} = \frac{2}{3}$ **$n = \frac{11}{21}$**
5. $j + \frac{5}{6} = \frac{17}{18}$ **$j = \frac{1}{9}$**
6. $f + \frac{5}{12} = \frac{3}{4}$ **$f = \frac{1}{3}$**
7. $\frac{1}{4}s = \frac{3}{4}$ **$s = 3$**
8. $\frac{1}{5}a = \frac{1}{2}$ **$a = 2\frac{1}{2}$**
9. $\frac{4}{5}h = \frac{8}{9}$ **$h = 1\frac{1}{9}$**
10. $p - \frac{2}{3} = \frac{5}{8}$ **$p = 1\frac{7}{24}$**
11. $d - \frac{3}{5} = \frac{7}{10}$ **$d = 1\frac{3}{10}$**
12. $y - \frac{2}{7} = 3\frac{1}{4}$ **$y = 3\frac{15}{28}$**
13. $c + \frac{5}{12} = 2\frac{1}{6}$ **$c = 1\frac{3}{4}$**
14. $w + \frac{4}{15} = 3\frac{1}{3}$ **$w = 3\frac{1}{15}$**
15. $z + \frac{6}{7} = 2\frac{3}{5}$ **$z = 1\frac{26}{35}$**
16. $\frac{5}{6}m = \frac{8}{9}$ **$m = 1\frac{1}{15}$**
17. $\frac{1}{2}x = 3\frac{7}{15}$ **$x = 6\frac{14}{15}$**
18. $\frac{1}{5}r = 2\frac{2}{3}$ **$r = 13\frac{1}{3}$**
19. Sarabeth ran $1\frac{2}{5}$ miles on a path around the park. This was $\frac{5}{8}$ of the distance around the park. What is the distance around the park?
$2\frac{6}{25}$ miles
20. An interior decorator bought $12\frac{1}{2}$ yards of material to make drapes. He used $8\frac{2}{3}$ yards on 1 pair of drapes. How much material does he have left?
$3\frac{5}{6}$ yards

41. **15 million species**

41. ***LIFE SCIENCE*** Scientists have discovered $1\frac{1}{2}$ million species of animals. This is estimated to be $\frac{1}{10}$ the total number of species thought to exist. About how many species do scientists think exist?

42. ***HISTORY*** The circle graph shows the birthplaces of some of the first presidents of the United States.

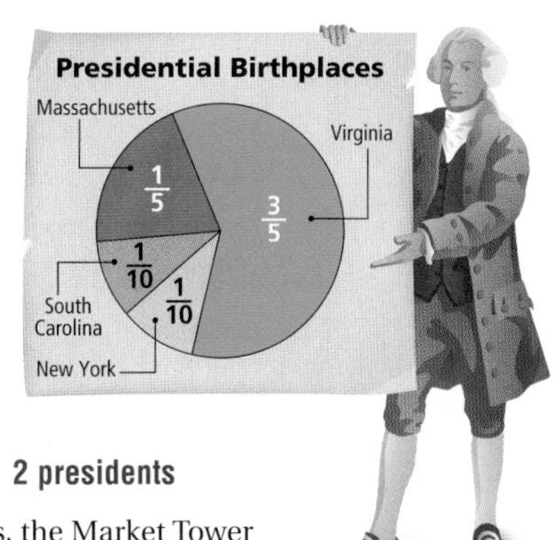

42a. **10 presidents**

a. If six of the presidents represented in the graph were born in Virginia, how many presidents are represented in the graph?

b. Based on your answer to **a**, how many of the presidents were born in Massachusetts? **2 presidents**

43. ***ARCHITECTURE*** In Indianapolis, the Market Tower has $\frac{2}{3}$ as many stories as the Bank One Tower. If the Market Tower has 32 stories, how many stories does the Bank One Tower have? **48 stories**

44. ***BUDGET*** Each week, Jennifer saves $\frac{1}{5}$ of her allowance and spends some of the rest on lunches. This week, she had $\frac{2}{15}$ of her allowance left after buying her lunch each day. What fraction of her allowance did she spend on lunches? $\mathbf{\frac{2}{3}}$

45. ***WHAT'S THE ERROR?*** A student solved $\frac{3}{5}x = \frac{2}{3}$ and got $x = \frac{2}{5}$. Find the error.

46. ***WRITE ABOUT IT*** Solve $3\frac{1}{3}z = 1\frac{1}{2}$. Explain why you need to write mixed numbers as improper fractions when multiplying and dividing.

47. ***CHALLENGE*** Solve $\frac{3}{5}w = 0.9$. Write your answer as a fraction and as a decimal. $\mathbf{w = 1\frac{1}{2}}$ **or 1.5**

Spiral Review

Write each improper fraction as a mixed number in simplest form. (Lesson 3-8)

48. $\frac{20}{3}$ $\mathbf{6\frac{2}{3}}$

49. $\frac{11}{5}$ $\mathbf{2\frac{1}{5}}$

50. $\frac{19}{4}$ $\mathbf{4\frac{3}{4}}$

51. $\frac{39}{9}$ $\mathbf{4\frac{1}{3}}$

52. $\frac{47}{4}$ $\mathbf{11\frac{3}{4}}$

53. $\frac{22}{14}$ $\mathbf{1\frac{4}{7}}$

54. **TEST PREP** Simplify $14 + 12 \cdot 3 - 8^2$. (Lesson 2-3) **B**

A 14 **B** −14 **C** 4,900 **D** −1,586

55. **TEST PREP** What is the sum of 3.9 and 0.35? (Lesson 4-2) **H**

F 3.25 **G** 0.425 **H** 4.25 **J** 3.55

COMMON ERROR ALERT

Understanding relative size of quantities in a problem is difficult for some students, particularly when fractions are involved. If the Market Tower has $\frac{2}{3}$ as many stories as the Bank One Tower, which is taller? Encourage students to take the time to understand relationships before trying to write equations.

Answers

45. Possible answer: $\frac{2}{3}$ was multiplied by the fraction $\frac{3}{5}$ instead of by its reciprocal, $\frac{5}{3}$.

46. Write both mixed numbers as fractions, and then multiply both sides by the reciprocal of $\frac{10}{3}$.

Journal

Ask students to compare solving equations with mixed numbers to solving equations with integers.

Test Prep Doctor

In Exercise 54, choices **C** and **D** can be quickly eliminated. The greatest term is $12 \cdot 3$, or 36, so 4,900 is too large. The only negative term is -8^2, or -64, so $-1,586$ is unreasonable. In Exercise 55, estimation will eliminate all but the correct answer because adding anything greater than 0.1 to 3.9 will yield an answer greater than 4.

CHALLENGE 4-12

LESSON 4-12 **Challenge**
Shopping List Equation

On the right is the list of ingredients for a recipe for bean and cheese tacos. The recipe serves 4 people. You are making bean and cheese tacos for 18 people.

Use the ingredients to answer the questions and solve the equations.

BEAN AND CHEESE TACOS
$\frac{1}{2}$ pound kidney beans
1 clove garlic, chopped
4 flour tortillas
1 cup ricotta cheese
$\frac{1}{4}$ cup parmesan cheese
$\frac{1}{4}$ cup green onions, chopped
Serves 4.

1. By what factor do you need to multiply each ingredient to serve 18 people? Solve the equation to find out. $4x = 18$
$x = 4\frac{1}{2}$

2. How many pounds of kidney beans do you need to serve 18 people?
$\mathbf{2\frac{1}{4}}$ **pounds**

3. Kidney beans come in $\frac{3}{4}$-pound cans. How many cans do you need to serve 18 people? Write and solve an equation.
$\mathbf{\frac{3}{4}x = 2\frac{1}{4};\ x = 3}$ **cans**

4. Ricotta cheese is on sale in $1\frac{1}{4}$-cup tubs. How many tubs do you need to serve 18 people? Write and solve an equation.
$\mathbf{1\frac{1}{4}x = 4\frac{1}{2};\ x = 3\frac{3}{5};}$ **you need 4 tubs.**

5. You need $1\frac{1}{8}$ cup of Parmesan cheese. You have $\frac{1}{4}$ cup. Write and solve an equation to find how much more you need.
$\mathbf{\frac{1}{4} + x = 1\frac{1}{8};\ x = \frac{7}{8}}$ **cup**

6. There are 4 green onions in $\frac{1}{4}$ cup. Write and solve an equation to find how many green onions you need.
$\mathbf{4\frac{1}{2} = \frac{1}{4}x;\ x = 18}$ **green onions**

7. You have 8 cloves of garlic and you need $4\frac{1}{2}$. How many cloves of garlic will you have left? Write and solve an equation.
$\mathbf{8 - x = 4\frac{1}{2};\ x = 3\frac{1}{2}}$ **cloves left**

PROBLEM SOLVING 4-12

LESSON 4-12 **Problem Solving**
Solving Equations Containing Fractions

Write the correct answer.

1. At the 2002 Winter Olympics, Austria won 2 gold medals. This was $\frac{1}{8}$ of the total medals Austria won. How many medals did Austria win?
16 medals

2. At the 2002 Winter Olympics, Germany won 35 medals, of which 16 were silver. They won $1\frac{1}{3}$ times as many silver medals as gold medals. How many gold medals did Germany win?
12 gold medals

3. Jesse plays ice hockey. He is on the ice $\frac{2}{5}$ of each game. A game lasts 45 minutes, divided into 3 periods. How many minutes is Jesse on the ice during each game?
18 minutes

4. Amelia's soccer team won $\frac{3}{4}$ of its games. The team won 18 games. How many games did the team play?
24 games

Choose the letter for the best answer.

5. At the 2002 Winter Olympics, China won 8 medals. The United States won $4\frac{1}{4}$ times as many medals as China did. How many medals did the United States win?
A 24 medals (**C**) 34 medals
B 32 medals **D** 40 medals

6. Juanita's water bottle contains $1\frac{7}{8}$ liters. She uses her bottle to fill Felix's. When she is done, her bottle contains $\frac{1}{4}$ liter. How many liters can Felix's bottle hold?
F $\frac{7}{8}$ liters (**H**) $1\frac{5}{8}$ liters
G $1\frac{1}{8}$ liters **J** $2\frac{1}{8}$ liters

7. Yoriko ran $6\frac{1}{2}$ laps of the track. Each lap is $\frac{1}{4}$ of a mile. How many miles did she run?
A $6\frac{5}{8}$ miles **C** 2 miles
B $4\frac{1}{2}$ miles (**D**) $1\frac{5}{8}$ miles

8. Rocky runs $3\frac{1}{2}$ miles each week. Leroy runs $5\frac{1}{3}$ miles each week. How much farther does Leroy run?
F $1\frac{1}{2}$ miles **H** $2\frac{1}{6}$ miles
(**G**) $1\frac{5}{6}$ miles **J** $2\frac{1}{4}$ miles

Lesson Quiz

Solve. Write each answer in simplest form.

1. $x - \frac{3}{8} = \frac{5}{8}$ **1**

2. $y + \frac{7}{16} = \frac{19}{32}$ $\mathbf{\frac{5}{32}}$

3. $\frac{x}{4} = \frac{3}{7}$ $\mathbf{\frac{12}{7}}$ **or** $\mathbf{1\frac{5}{7}}$

4. $\frac{3}{4}x = 1\frac{1}{3}$ $\mathbf{\frac{16}{9}}$ **or** $\mathbf{1\frac{7}{9}}$

5. Over the course of a week, Marissa ate some apples from a basket on the table. She left 20 apples in the basket. This was five-eighths the number of apples her mother had picked earlier in the week. How many apples did her mother pick? **32**

Available on Daily Transparency in CRB

Problem Solving on Location

North Carolina

Purpose: *To provide additional practice for problem-solving skills in Chapters 1–4*

Farmers' Markets

- After problem 2, ask students to explain how they found how much the owner of the market pays for each ear of corn.

  Possible answer: The number of ears of corn in $4\frac{1}{2}$ dozen is 54. The total price, $20.50, divided by 54 is $0.38.
- After problem 5, have students express the answer in millions, in billions, and in standard form. 1,141.3 million; 1.1413 billion; 1,141,300,000

Extension Have students express the answers to problems 3, 5, and 6 in scientific notation.

Problem 3: 3.59×10^7;

Problem 5: 1.1413×10^9;

Problem 6: 7.17×10^7

Problem Solving on Location

NORTH CAROLINA

Farmers' Markets

Agriculture is North Carolina's top industry. More sweet potatoes are grown in North Carolina than in any other state, and it ranks ninth in apple production. Cucumbers, beans, blueberries, eggplants, watermelons, peaches, and grapes are among the other fruits and vegetables produced in the state. Produce is sold in farmers' markets throughout the state.

1. The wholesale price of bananas is $12.50 for 40 pounds. What is the wholesale price of a pound of bananas to the nearest cent? **$0.31**

2. A crate of $4\frac{1}{2}$ dozen ears of corn is sold to the farmers' market for $20.50. At the market, the price of corn sold to the public is 5 ears for $2.00. How much money does the owner of the market make on every ear of corn, to the nearest cent? **$0.02**

The graph shows the pounds of produce grown in one year in North Carolina. Use the graph for 3–6.

3. How many more pounds of apples than watermelons were grown in the year? **35.9 million pounds**

4. To the nearest tenth, how many times as many pounds of sweet potatoes as apples were grown in the year? **2.3 times**

5. Find the total number of pounds of these fruits and vegetables grown in the year shown. **1,141.3 million pounds**

6. In the year shown, about 2.3 times as many pounds of apples were grown as tomatoes. How many pounds of tomatoes were grown, to the nearest tenth? **71.7 million pounds**

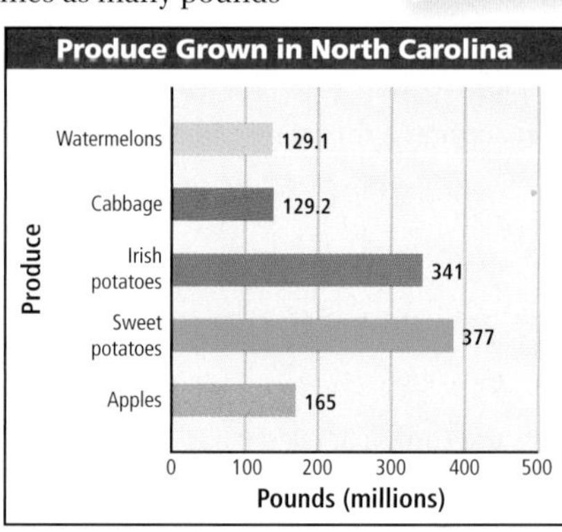

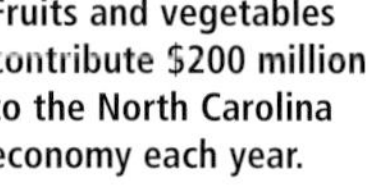

Fruits and vegetables contribute $200 million to the North Carolina economy each year.

Wright Brothers National Memorial

The Wright brothers were not born in North Carolina. But when the time came to make the first flights in their plane, they consulted the Weather Bureau and chose a site near Kitty Hawk. They made four flights that day.

Orville and Wilbur Wright flew the first heavier-than-air plane on December 17, 1903, near Kitty Hawk, North Carolina.

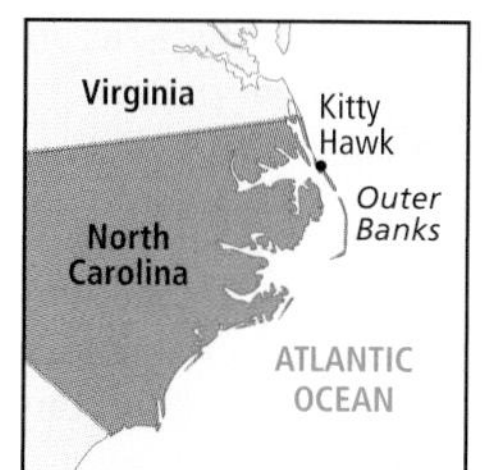

1. Orville piloted the plane 40 yards. This first flight lasted $\frac{1}{5}$ minute. The longest flight that day lasted $\frac{59}{60}$ minute. How much longer did this flight last than the first? **$\frac{47}{60}$ min**
2. On September 9, 1908, Orville made a flight that lasted $1\frac{1}{30}$ hours. About how many times as long as the first flight was the 1908 flight? **310 times**
3. Orville's flight was 40 yards long. Wilbur made the longest flight, which was 284 yards. How many times as far did Wilbur fly as Orville? **7.1 times**
4. On October 5, 1905, the Wright brothers' plane flew 24.2 miles in about 38 minutes.
   a. To the nearest tenth, what was their speed per minute? **0.6 mi/min**
   b. What was the plane's speed in miles per hour? **38.2 mi/h**

The first plane to fly across the English Channel was flown by Louis Bleriot of France. He made this flight in 1909 in a plane that was 8 meters long.

It took Louis Bleriot 37 minutes to fly across the English Channel.

5. The Wright brothers' first plane was 6.43 meters long. How much longer was the plane that flew across the Channel than the Wright brothers' first plane? **1.57 m**

Wright Brothers National Memorial

- After problem 1, have students consider the following problems: What was the length in seconds of Orville's first flight? 12 seconds What was Orville's speed in yards per second? Express the answer as a mixed number. $3\frac{1}{3}$ yards per second
- After problem 2, ask students to explain how they changed $1\frac{1}{30}$ hours into minutes.

  Possible answer: Since 1 hour = 60 minutes and $\frac{1}{30}$ hour = 2 minutes, $1\frac{1}{30}$ hours is equivalent to 62 minutes.

Extension Encourage students to write a problem about the Wright Brothers using the information from the problems.

Possible answer: On October 5, 1905, the Wright brothers' plane flew 24.2 miles in about 38 minutes. What was the speed of the plane in feet per second? about 56.0 ft/s

MATH-ABLES

Game Resources

Puzzles, Twisters & Teasers
Chapter 4 Resource Book

Number Patterns

Purpose: *To apply the skill of finding a pattern to a fun math event*

Discuss: Ask students to explain the relationship between each word or number and the word or number to which it points. If necessary, give students a hint by telling them to count the number of letters in each word.

Possible answer: The arrows point to the word names for the number of letters in each word.

Extend: Ask students if they think the product of 7 · 142857 fits the cyclic pattern. Have students explain their answers.

Possible answer:
7 · 142,857 = 999,999. The product of 7 · 142,857 does not fit the cyclic pattern because it must be larger than 6 · 142,857, but 857,142 is the largest possible number in the cyclic pattern.

Fraction Action

Purpose: *To practice adding fractions in a game format*

Discuss: Before playing the game, ask students to discuss strategies for forming fractions that have a sum close to 1.

Possible answer: Do not form improper fractions.

Extend: Have students form fractions whose difference is close to zero. To determine a player's score, find the difference between the difference of the fractions and zero. The winner is the player with the lowest score at the end of the game.

MATH-ABLES

Number Patterns

The numbers one through ten form the pattern below. Each arrow indicates some kind of relationship between the two numbers. Four relates to itself. Can you figure out what the pattern is?

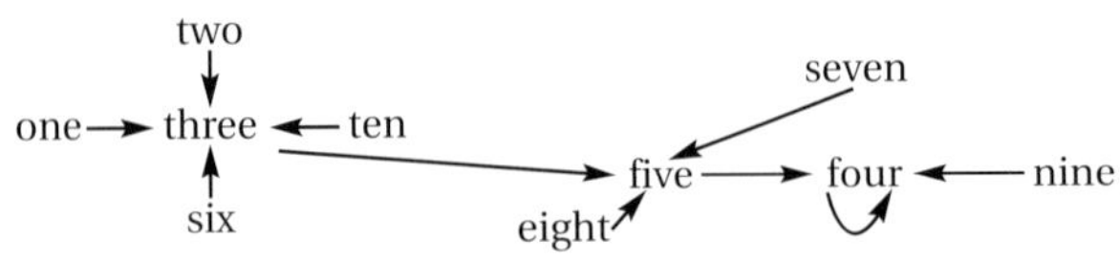

The Spanish numbers *uno* through *diez* form a similar pattern. In this case, *cinco* relates to itself.

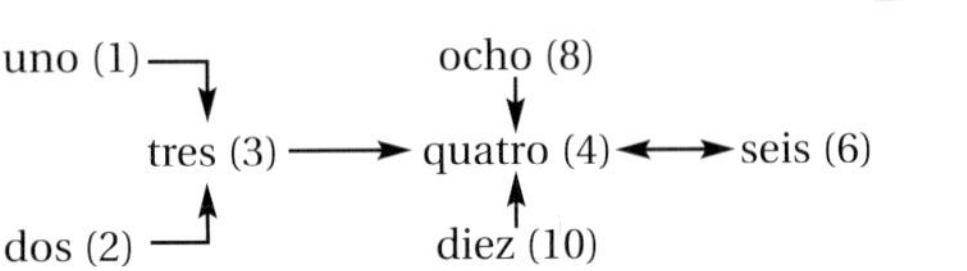

Other interesting number patterns involve cyclic numbers. Cyclic numbers sometimes occur when a fraction converts to a repeating nonterminating decimal. One of the most interesting cyclic numbers is produced by converting the fraction $\frac{1}{7}$ to a decimal.

$\frac{1}{7} = 0.142857142857142\ldots$

Multiplying 142857 by the numbers 1–6 produces the same digits in a different order.

1 · 142857 = 142857	3 · 142857 = 428571	5 · 142857 = 714285
2 · 142857 = 285714	4 · 142857 = 571428	6 · 142857 = 857142

Fraction Action

Roll four 1–6 number cubes and use the numbers to form two fractions. Add the fractions and try to get a sum as close to 1 as possible. To determine your score on each turn, find the difference between the sum of your fractions and 1. Keep a running total of your score as you play. The winner is the player with the lowest score at the end of the game.

internet connect
For a complete copy of the rules, go to *go.hrw.com*
KEYWORD: MS4 Game4

Fraction Operations

You can use a calculator to complete fraction operations.

internet connect
Lab Resources Online
go.hrw.com
KEYWORD: MS4 TechLab4

Activity

Many calculators will not display fractions with the numerator above the denominator. On these calculators, enter the fraction as a division expression.

1 Evaluate $\frac{2}{3} + \frac{4}{7}$ using a calculator.

2 Evaluate $\frac{1}{2} \cdot \frac{5}{6}$ using a calculator.

Think and Discuss

1. A mixed number is the sum of an integer and a fraction. How would you enter the mixed number $7\frac{9}{11}$ on a calculator?

Try This

Evaluate each expression using a calculator.

1. $\frac{9}{10} + \frac{8}{15}$ **2.** $\frac{12}{13} \cdot \frac{1}{6}$ **3.** $1\frac{9}{11} + 8\frac{2}{3}$ **4.** $2\frac{1}{8} \cdot 4\frac{1}{6}$

Answers

Try This

1. 1.433333333

2. 0.1538461538

3. 10.48484848

4. 8.854166667

Think and Discuss

1. 7 [+] 9 [÷] 11

Fraction Operations

Objective: To use a graphing calculator to perform operations with fractions

Materials: Graphing calculator

Lab Resources

Using the Page

This technology activity shows students how to enter fractions and mixed numbers and add or multiply fractions and mixed numbers on a graphing calculator. Specific keystrokes may vary, depending on the make and model of the graphing calculator used. The keystrokes given are for a TI-83 model.

The Think and Discuss problem can be used to assess students' understanding of the meaning of a mixed number. While Try This problems 1–4 can be done without a calculator, they are meant to help students become familiar with adding and multiplying fractions and mixed numbers on a calculator.

Assessment

Evaluate each expression using a calculator.

1. $\frac{5}{8} + \frac{3}{5}$ 1.225

2. $\frac{4}{9} \cdot \frac{3}{20}$ 0.0666666667

3. $1\frac{3}{4} + 3\frac{7}{9}$ 5.527777778

4. $2\frac{1}{3} \cdot 1\frac{7}{11}$ 3.818181818

Chapter 4

Study Guide and Review

Purpose: *To help students review and practice concepts and skills presented in Chapter 4*

Assessment Resources

Chapter Review

Chapter 4 Resource Book . pp. 119–121

***Test and Practice Generator* CD-ROM**

Additional review assessment items in both multiple-choice and free-response format may be generated for any objective in Chapter 4.

Answers

1. compatible numbers
2. reciprocals
3. 110
4. 5
5. 75
6. 4
7. 27.88
8. −51.2
9. 6.22
10. 52.902
11. 14.095
12. 35.88
13. 3.5
14. −38.7
15. 40.495
16. 60.282
17. 77.348
18. −18.81

Chapter 4

Study Guide and Review

Vocabulary

compatible numbers 192

reciprocal 226

Complete the sentences below with vocabulary words from the list above.

1. When estimating products or quotients, you can use __?__ that are close to the original numbers.
2. The fractions $\frac{3}{8}$ and $\frac{8}{3}$ are __?__ because they multiply to give 1.

Study Guide and Review

4-1 Estimate with Decimals (pp. 192–195)

EXAMPLE

■ Estimate.

$$\begin{array}{rcr} 43.55 & \longrightarrow & 40 \\ \times\ 8.65 & \longrightarrow & \times\ 9 \\ \hline & & 360 \end{array}$$

EXERCISES

Estimate by rounding or using compatible numbers.

3. 54.4 + 55.99
4. 11.48 − 5.6
5. 24.77 · 3.45
6. 37.8 ÷ 9.3

4-2 Adding and Subtracting Decimals (pp. 196–199)

EXAMPLE

■ Add.

5.67 + 22.44

$$\begin{array}{r} 5.67 \\ +\ 22.44 \\ \hline 28.11 \end{array}$$

EXERCISES

Add or subtract.

7. 4.99 + 22.89
8. −6.7 + (−44.5)
9. 18.09 − 11.87
10. 47 + 5.902
11. 23 − 8.905
12. 4.68 + 31.2

4-3 Multiplying Decimals (pp. 202–205)

EXAMPLE

■ Multiply.

1.44 · 0.6

$$\begin{array}{r} 1.44 \\ \times\ 0.6 \\ \hline 0.864 \end{array}$$

EXERCISES

Multiply.

13. 7 · 0.5
14. −4.3 · 9
15. 4.55 · 8.9
16. 7.88 · 7.65
17. 63.4 · 1.22
18. −9.9 · 1.9

4-4 Dividing Decimals by Integers (pp. 206–209)

EXAMPLE

■ Divide.

$2.8 \div 7$

$$\begin{array}{r} 0.4 \\ 7\overline{)2.8} \\ -2\,8 \\ \hline 0 \end{array}$$

EXERCISES

Divide.

19. $16.1 \div 7$ **20.** $102.9 \div (-21)$

21. $0.48 \div 6$ **22.** $17.4 \div (-3)$

23. $8.25 \div (-5)$ **24.** $81.6 \div 24$

4-5 Dividing Decimals and Integers by Decimals (pp. 210–213)

EXAMPLE

■ Divide.

$0.96 \div 1.6$

$$\begin{array}{r} 0.6 \\ 16\overline{)9.6} \\ -9\,6 \\ \hline 0 \end{array}$$

EXERCISES

Divide.

25. $7.65 \div 1.7$ **26.** $9.483 \div (-8.7)$

27. $126.28 \div (-8.2)$ **28.** $2.5 \div (-0.005)$

29. $9 \div 4.5$ **30.** $13 \div 3.25$

4-6 Solving Equations Containing Decimals (pp. 214–217)

EXAMPLE

■ Solve.

$$\begin{aligned} n - 4.77 &= 8.60 \\ +4.77 &\quad +4.77 \\ n &= 13.37 \end{aligned}$$

EXERCISES

Solve.

31. $x + 40.44 = 30$ **32.** $\frac{s}{1.07} = 100$

33. $0.8n = 0.0056$ **34.** $k - 8 = 0.64$

4-7 Multiplying Fractions and Mixed Numbers (pp. 222–225)

EXAMPLE

■ Multiply. Write the answer in simplest form.

$4\frac{1}{2} \cdot 5\frac{3}{4} = \frac{9 \cdot 23}{2 \cdot 4}$

$= \frac{207}{8}$ or $25\frac{7}{8}$

EXERCISES

Multiply. Write each answer in simplest form.

35. $1\frac{2}{3} \cdot 4\frac{1}{2}$ **36.** $\frac{4}{5} \cdot 2\frac{3}{10}$

37. $4\frac{6}{7} \cdot 3\frac{5}{9}$ **38.** $3\frac{4}{7} \cdot 1\frac{3}{4}$

4-8 Dividing Fractions and Mixed Numbers (pp. 226–229)

EXAMPLE

■ Divide.

$\frac{3}{4} \div \frac{2}{5} = \frac{3}{4} \cdot \frac{5}{2}$

$= \frac{15}{8}$ or $1\frac{7}{8}$

EXERCISES

Divide. Write each answer in simplest form.

39. $\frac{1}{3} \div 6\frac{1}{4}$ **40.** $\frac{1}{2} \div 3\frac{3}{4}$

41. $\frac{11}{13} \div \frac{11}{13}$ **42.** $2\frac{7}{8} \div 1\frac{1}{2}$

Study Guide and Review

Answers

19. 2.3

20. −4.9

21. 0.08

22. −5.8

23. −1.65

24. 3.4

25. 4.5

26. −1.09

27. −15.4

28. −500

29. 2

30. 4

31. $x = -10.44$

32. $s = 107$

33. $n = 0.007$

34. $k = 8.64$

35. $7\frac{1}{2}$

36. $1\frac{21}{25}$

37. $17\frac{17}{63}$

38. $6\frac{1}{4}$

39. $\frac{4}{75}$

40. $\frac{2}{15}$

41. 1

42. $1\frac{11}{12}$

Answers

43. 24

44. $2\frac{1}{2}$

45. -8

46. $22\frac{1}{2}$

47. 3

48. 1

49. $\frac{5}{12}$

50. $\frac{17}{20}$

51. $\frac{5}{11}$

52. $\frac{1}{9}$

53. $6\frac{5}{24}$

54. $3\frac{1}{3}$

55. $6\frac{1}{4}$

56. $1\frac{5}{12}$

57. $1\frac{2}{3}$

58. $\frac{1}{15}$

59. $1\frac{5}{7}$

60. $\frac{13}{28}$

Notes

Study Guide and Review

4-9 Estimate with Fractions (pp. 230–233)

EXAMPLE

■ Estimate the difference.

$7\frac{3}{4} - 4\frac{1}{3}$

$7\frac{3}{4} \longrightarrow 8,\ 4\frac{1}{3} \longrightarrow 4\frac{1}{2}$

$8 - 4\frac{1}{2} = 3\frac{1}{2}$

EXERCISES

Estimate each sum or difference.

43. $11\frac{1}{7} + 12\frac{3}{4}$

44. $5\frac{2}{3} - 3\frac{1}{5}$

45. $5\frac{5}{7} - 13\frac{10}{17}$

46. $8\frac{1}{6} + 14\frac{6}{11}$

47. $9\frac{7}{8} + \left(-7\frac{1}{13}\right)$

48. $11\frac{8}{9} - 11\frac{1}{20}$

4-10 Adding and Subtracting Fractions (pp. 236–239)

EXAMPLE

■ Add.

$\frac{1}{3} + \frac{2}{5} = \frac{5}{15} + \frac{6}{15}$

$= \frac{11}{15}$

EXERCISES

Add or subtract. Write each answer in simplest form.

49. $\frac{3}{4} - \frac{1}{3}$

50. $\frac{1}{4} + \frac{3}{5}$

51. $\frac{4}{11} + \frac{4}{44}$

52. $\frac{4}{9} - \frac{1}{3}$

4-11 Adding and Subtracting Mixed Numbers (pp. 240–243)

EXAMPLE

■ Add.

$1\frac{1}{3} + 2\frac{1}{2} = 1\frac{2}{6} + 2\frac{3}{6}$

$= 3 + \frac{5}{6}$

$= 3\frac{5}{6}$

EXERCISES

Add or subtract. Write each answer in simplest form.

53. $3\frac{7}{8} + 2\frac{1}{3}$

54. $2\frac{1}{4} + 1\frac{1}{12}$

55. $8\frac{1}{2} - 2\frac{1}{4}$

56. $11\frac{3}{4} - 10\frac{1}{3}$

4-12 Solving Equations Containing Fractions (pp. 244–247)

EXAMPLE

■ Solve. Write the answer in simplest form.

$\frac{1}{4}x = \frac{1}{6}$

$\frac{4}{1} \cdot \frac{1}{4}x = \frac{1}{6} \cdot \frac{4}{1}$

$x = \frac{4}{6} = \frac{2}{3}$

EXERCISES

Solve. Write each answer in simplest form.

57. $\frac{1}{5}x = \frac{1}{3}$

58. $\frac{1}{3} + y = \frac{2}{5}$

59. $\frac{1}{6}x = \frac{2}{7}$

60. $\frac{2}{7} + x = \frac{3}{4}$

Chapter Test

Chapter 4

Estimate. **Possible answers:**

1. $19.95 + 21.36$ **41**
2. $49.17 - 5.88$ **43**
3. $3.21 \cdot 16.78$ **51**
4. $49.1 \div 5.6$ **8**

Add or subtract.

5. $3.086 + 6.152$ **9.238**
6. $5.91 + 12.8$ **18.71**
7. $3.1 - 2.076$ **1.024**
8. $14.75 - 6.926$ **7.824**

Multiply.

9. $3.25 \cdot 24$ **78**
10. $1.4 \cdot 2.5$ **3.5**
11. $-3.79 \cdot 0.9$ **−3.411**
12. $-4.79 \cdot 7.2$ **−34.488**

Divide.

13. $1.8 \div (-6)$ **−0.3**
14. $3.2 \div 16$ **0.2**
15. $3.57 \div (-0.7)$ **−5.1**
16. $5.88 \div 0.6$ **9.8**

Solve.

17. $w - 5.3 = 7.6$ **$w = 12.9$**
18. $4.9 = c + 3.7$ **$c = 1.2$**
19. $b \div 1.8 = 2.1$ **$b = 3.78$**
20. $4.3h = 81.7$ **$h = 19$**

Multiply. Write each answer in simplest form.

21. $4 \cdot \frac{5}{8}$ **$\frac{5}{2}$ or $2\frac{1}{2}$**
22. $5 \cdot 4\frac{1}{3}$ **$\frac{65}{3}$ or $21\frac{2}{3}$**
23. $2\frac{7}{10} \cdot 2\frac{2}{3}$ **$\frac{36}{5}$ or $7\frac{1}{5}$**
24. $\frac{3}{5} \cdot \frac{1}{2}$ **$\frac{3}{10}$**

Divide. Write each answer in simplest form.

25. $\frac{3}{10} \div \frac{4}{5}$ **$\frac{3}{8}$**
26. $2\frac{1}{5} \div 1\frac{5}{6}$ **$\frac{6}{5}$ or $1\frac{1}{5}$**
27. $\frac{1}{4} \div \frac{1}{4}$ **1**
28. $3 \div 1\frac{4}{5}$ **$\frac{5}{3}$ or $1\frac{2}{3}$**

Estimate each sum or difference.

29. $\frac{3}{4} + \frac{3}{8}$ **1**
30. $5\frac{7}{8} + 3\frac{3}{4}$ **10**
31. $6\frac{5}{7} - 2\frac{2}{9}$ **5**
32. $8\frac{1}{2} - 3\frac{9}{10}$ **$4\frac{1}{2}$**

Add or subtract. Write each answer in simplest form.

33. $\frac{3}{10} + \frac{2}{5}$ **$\frac{7}{10}$**
34. $\frac{11}{16} - \frac{7}{8}$ **$-\frac{3}{16}$**
35. $7\frac{1}{3} + 5\frac{11}{12}$ **$13\frac{1}{4}$**
36. $9 - 3\frac{2}{5}$ **$5\frac{3}{5}$**

Solve. Write each answer in simplest form.

37. $\frac{1}{5}a = \frac{1}{8}$ **$a = \frac{5}{8}$**
38. $\frac{1}{4}c = 980$ **$c = 3{,}920$**
39. $-\frac{7}{9} + w = \frac{2}{3}$ **$w = \frac{13}{9}$ or $1\frac{4}{9}$**
40. $z - \frac{5}{13} = \frac{6}{7}$ **$z = \frac{113}{91}$ or $1\frac{22}{91}$**

41. Alan finished his homework in $1\frac{1}{2}$ hours. It took Jimmy $\frac{3}{4}$ of an hour longer than Alan to finish his homework. How long did it take Jimmy to finish his homework? **$2\frac{1}{4}$ hr**

Chapter Test

Chapter Test

Chapter 4

Purpose: *To assess students' mastery of concepts and skills in Chapter 4*

Assessment Resources

Chapter 4 Tests (Levels A, B, C)
Assessment Resources ..... pp. 51–56

***Test and Practice Generator* CD-ROM**

Additional assessment items in both multiple-choice and free-response format may be generated for any objective in Chapter 4.

Chapter 4

Performance Assessment

Purpose: *To assess students' understanding of concepts in Chapter 4 and combined problem-solving skills*

Assessment Resources ✓

Performance Assessment
Assessment Resources .... p. 112

Performance Assessment Teacher Support
Assessment Resources .... p. 111

Answers

1. See p. A2.
4. See Level 3 work sample below.

Scoring Rubric for Problem Solving Item 4

Level 3
Accomplishes the purpose of the task.
Student gives clear explanations, shows understanding of mathematical ideas and processes, and computes accurately.

Level 2
Purposes of the task not fully achieved.
Student demonstrates satisfactory but limited understanding of the mathematical ideas and processes.

Level 1
Purposes of the task not accomplished.
Student shows little evidence of understanding the mathematical ideas and processes and makes computational and/or procedural errors.

Chapter 4

Performance Assessment

Performance Assessment

Show What You Know

Create a portfolio of your best work from this chapter. Complete this page and include it with the four best pieces of your work from Chapter 4. Choose from your homework or lab assignments, mid-chapter quiz, or any journals you have done. Put them together using any design you want. Make your portfolio represent what you consider your best work.

Short Response

1. Amanda earns \$18.41 per hour. Tina earns \$12.07 per hour. Find the difference between their yearly salaries. Assume that they both work 40 hours each week for 52 weeks each year. Show your work.
2. A building proposal calls for 6 acres of land to be divided into $\frac{3}{4}$-acre lots. How many lots can be made? Explain your answer. **8 lots; the 6 acres of land divided into eight $\frac{3}{4}$-acre lots; $\frac{6}{1} \div \frac{3}{4} = 8$**
3. Mari bought 3 packages of colored paper. She used $\frac{3}{4}$ of a package to make greeting cards, used $1\frac{1}{6}$ packages for an art project, and gave $\frac{2}{3}$ of a package to her brother. How much colored paper does Mari have left? Show the steps that you used to find the answer. **$\frac{5}{12}$ of a package**

Extended Problem Solving

4. A high school is hosting a triple-jump competition. In this event, athletes make three leaps in a row—a hop, a skip, and a jump—and try to cover the greatest distance.
   a. Tony's first two jumps were $11\frac{2}{3}$ ft and $11\frac{1}{2}$ ft. His total distance was 44 ft. Write and solve an equation to find the length of his final jump.
   b. Candice's three jumps were all the same length. Her total distance was 38 ft. What was the length of each of her jumps?
   c. The lengths of Davis's jumps were 11.6 ft, $11\frac{1}{4}$ ft, and $11\frac{2}{3}$ ft. Plot these distances on a number line. What is the average distance of the jumps?

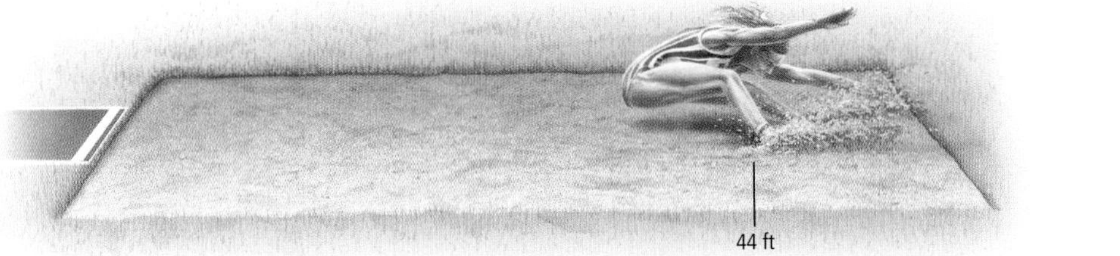

44 ft

Student Work Samples for Item 4

Level 3

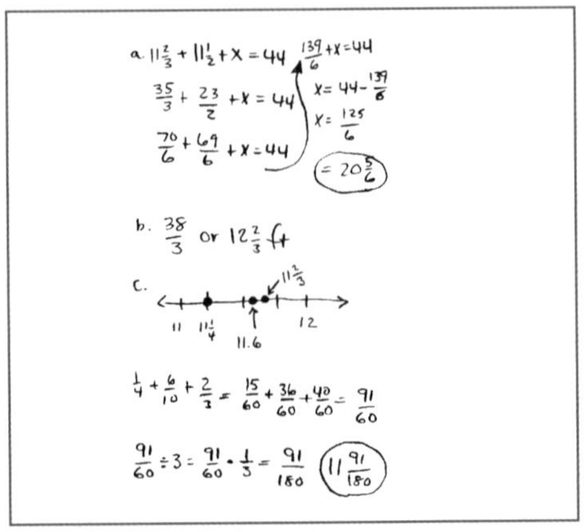

a. 11 2/3 + 11 1/2 + x = 44
35/3 + 23/2 + x = 44
70/6 + 69/6 + x = 44
139/6 + x = 44
x = 44 − 139/6
x = 125/6
= 20 5/6
b. 38/3 or 12 2/3 ft
c.
11 11 1/4 11.6 11 2/3 12
1/4 + 6/10 + 2/3 = 15/60 + 36/60 + 40/60 = 91/60
91/60 ÷ 3 = 91/60 · 1/3 = 91/180
11 91/180

The student correctly wrote and solved the equation, identified points on the number line, and found the exact average in part **c**.

Level 2

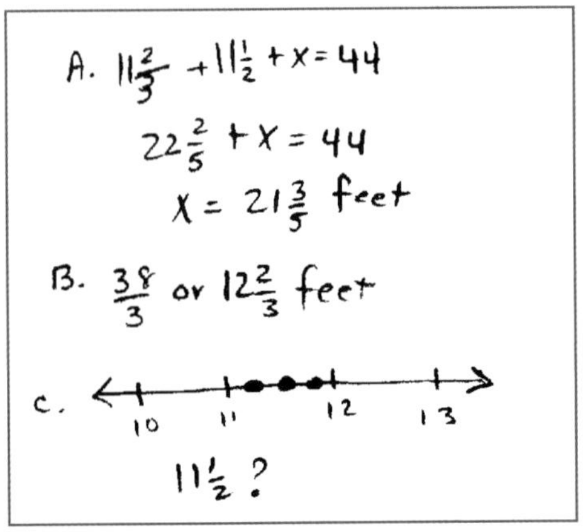

A. 11 2/3 + 11 1/2 + x = 44
22 2/5 + x = 44
x = 21 3/5 feet
B. 38/3 or 12 2/3 feet
c.
10 11 12 13
11 1/2 ?

The student did not find a common denominator in part **a** but correctly answered part **b**. The number line in part **c** is not clear, and the average is only an estimate.

Level 1

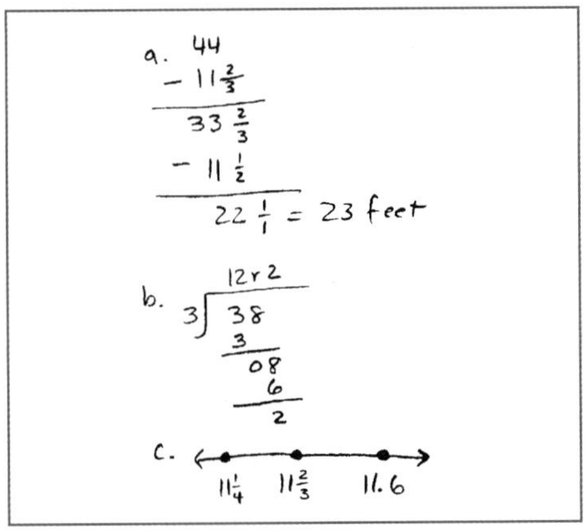

a. 44
− 11 2/3
33 2/3
− 11 1/2
22 1/1 = 23 feet
b. 12 r 2
3)38
3
08
6
2
c.
11 1/4 11 2/3 11.6

The student did not write a proper equation or perform operations correctly. The values on the number line are incorrectly placed, and there is no scale.

internet connect
State-Specific Test Practice Online
go.hrw.com Keyword: MS4 TestPrep

Standardized Test Prep

Chapter 4

Cumulative Assessment, Chapters 1–4

1. On a baseball field, the distance from home plate to the pitcher's mound is $60\frac{1}{2}$ feet. The distance from home plate to second base is about $127\frac{7}{24}$ feet. What is the difference between the two distances? **C**
   - (A) $61\frac{1}{3}$ ft
   - (B) $66\frac{5}{6}$ ft
   - (C) $66\frac{19}{24}$ ft
   - (D) $66\frac{5}{24}$ ft

2. Which number when rounded to the nearest whole number is 8? **G**
   - (F) $8\frac{7}{10}$
   - (G) $8\frac{4}{9}$
   - (H) $8\frac{11}{16}$
   - (J) $8\frac{8}{15}$

3. Evaluate $3\frac{1}{2} \div \frac{1}{8}$. **B**
   - (A) $24\frac{1}{16}$
   - (B) 28
   - (C) $\frac{7}{16}$
   - (D) $3\frac{1}{16}$

4. Evaluate $4 \cdot (3^2 + 7)$. **F**
   - (F) 64
   - (G) 52
   - (H) 43
   - (J) 40

TEST TAKING TIP!
Eliminate choices by estimating the quotient.

5. What is $0.12 \div 0.03$? **C**
   - (A) 0.04
   - (B) 0.4
   - (C) 4
   - (D) 40

6. Which is the GCF of 54 and 81? **J**
   - (F) 3
   - (G) 6
   - (H) 9
   - (J) 27

7. Use compatible numbers to estimate $98.4 \div 19.2$. **B**
   - (A) 5.1
   - (B) 5
   - (C) 4
   - (D) 4.75

8. Which word phrase best describes the expression $x + 2$? **H**
   - (F) a number plus itself
   - (G) a number plus another number
   - (H) a number more than two
   - (J) twice a number

9. ***SHORT RESPONSE*** The graph shows the number of boys and the number of girls who tried out for a talent show. Write a statement giving a reasonable conclusion that could be drawn from the graph.

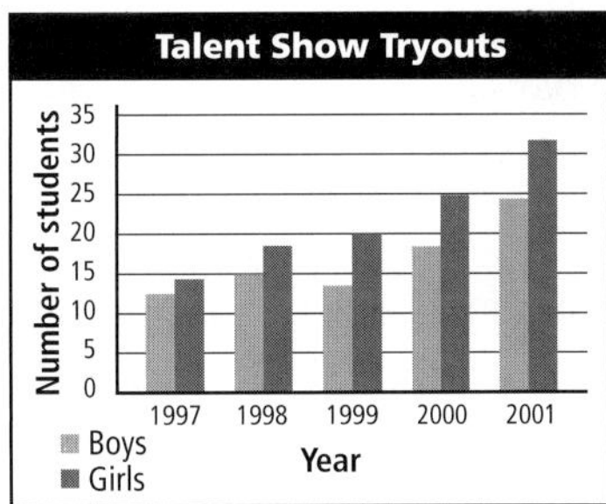

10. ***SHORT RESPONSE*** Write $\frac{3}{12}$ and $\frac{1}{3}$ as fractions with a common denominator. Explain your method. Then tell whether the fractions are equivalent.

Standardized Test Prep

Answers

9. Possible answer: More than 20 students tried out for the talent show every year.
10. $\frac{3}{12}$ and $\frac{4}{12}$; 12 is the least common multiple of the denominators, so $\frac{1}{3}$ can be written as the equivalent fraction $\frac{4}{12}$. $\frac{3}{12}$ and $\frac{4}{12}$ are not equivalent.

Standardized Test Prep

Chapter 4

Purpose: *To provide review and practice for Chapters 1–4 and standardized tests*

Assessment Resources 

Cumulative Tests (Levels A, B, C)
Assessment Resources . . . pp. 165–176

State-Specific Test Practice Online
KEYWORD: MS4 TestPrep

Test Prep Doctor 

Expand on the test-taking tip for item 5 by reminding students that before they can divide decimals, they must change the divisor to a whole number.

Point out that to change 0.03 to a whole number, students must multiply it by 100, and then they must do the same to the dividend. The result will be $12 \div 3$, which eliminates **A, B,** and **D.**

Chapter 5 Proportional Reasoning

Section 5A: Numerical Proportions	Section 5B: Graphical Proportions
Lesson 5-1 Ratios and Rates	**Hands-On Lab 5A** Make Similar Figures
Lesson 5-2 Identifying and Writing Proportions	**Lesson 5-5** Similar Figures and Proportions
Lesson 5-3 Solving Proportions	**Lesson 5-6** Using Similar Figures
Lesson 5-4 Dimensional Analysis	**Lesson 5-7** Scale Drawings and Scale Models

Pacing Guide for 45-Minute Classes

Chapter 5

DAY 66	DAY 67	DAY 68	DAY 69	DAY 70
Lesson 5-1	Lesson 5-2	Lesson 5-3	Lesson 5-4	Mid-Chapter Quiz Hands-On Lab 5A
DAY 71	**DAY 72**	**DAY 73**	**DAY 74**	**DAY 75**
Lesson 5-5	Lesson 5-6	Lesson 5-7	Chapter 5 Review	Chapter 5 Assessment

Pacing Guide for 90-Minute Classes

Chapter 5

DAY 33	DAY 34	DAY 35	DAY 36	DAY 37
Chapter 4 Assessment Lesson 5-1	Lesson 5-2 Lesson 5-3	Lesson 5-4 Hands-On Lab 5A	Mid-Chapter Quiz Lesson 5-5 Lesson 5-6	Lesson 5-7 Chapter 5 Review
DAY 38				
Chapter 5 Assessment Lesson 6-1				

Across the Series

COURSE 1

- Write ratios and rates to find unit rates.
- Write and solve proportions, and use them to make conversions within the customary system and to find unknown measures.
- Identify similar figures.
- Read and use map scales and scale drawings.

COURSE 2

- **Identify, write, and compare ratios and rates.**
- **Solve proportions by using cross products.**
- **Convert units using dimensional analysis.**
- **Identify similar figures.**
- **Find measures indirectly.**
- **Use scale drawings and scale models.**

COURSE 3

- Create and solve proportions, work with rates and ratios, and use conversion factors.
- Make and identify similar figures.
- Find measures indirectly.
- Make and use scale drawings and scale models.
- Use trigonometric ratios to find missing lengths in right triangles.

Across the Curriculum

LANGUAGE ARTS LINK

Math: Reading and Writing in the Content Area . . . . pp. 44–50

Focus on Problem Solving

Make a Plan . . . . SE p. 277

Journal . . . . TE, last page of each lesson

Write About It. . . . . SE pp. 267, 271, 275, 283, 287

SOCIAL STUDIES LINK

Social Studies . . . . SE p. 267

History . . . . SE p. 291

SCIENCE LINK

Life Science. . . . . SE pp. 265, 271, 275

Earth Science. . . . . SE pp. 271, 275, 287

Physical Science . . . . SE pp. 263, 275

Ecology . . . . SE p. 266

Chemistry . . . . SE p. 271

TE = *Teacher's Edition* **SE** = *Student Edition*

Interdisciplinary Bulletin Board

Life Science

A model is a representation of an object or system. Ratios and proportions are used to create scale models in order to accurately portray an actual size. Given a scale drawing of a 10 cm tall Giant Sequoia tree, what is the scale if the actual height of the tree is 100 meters? 1 cm = 10 m

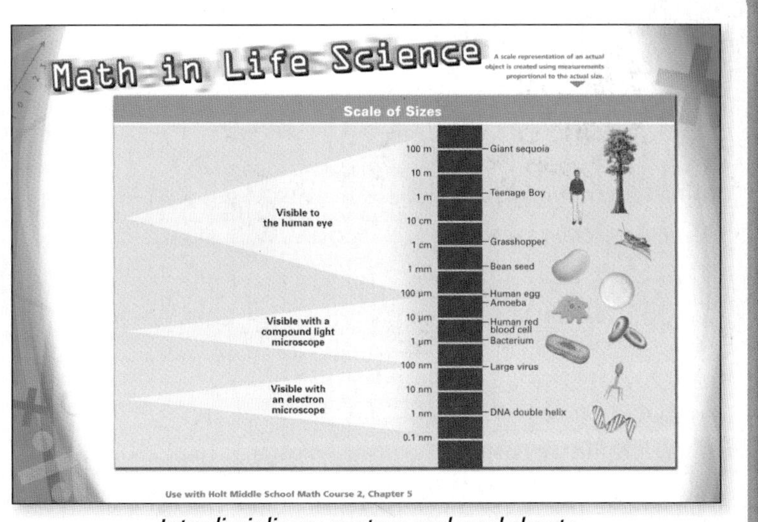

Interdisciplinary posters and worksheets are provided in your resource material.

Chapter 5

Resource Options

Chapter 5 Resource Book

Student Resources

Practice (Levels A, B, C). . . . . pp. 8–10, 18–20, 27–29, 37–39, 47–49, 56–58, 65–67
Reteach. . . . . pp. 11–12, 21, 30–31, 40, 50, 59, 68
Challenge . . . . pp. 13, 22, 32, 41, 51, 60, 69
Problem Solving . . . . pp. 14, 23, 33, 42, 52, 61, 70
Puzzles, Twisters & Teasers. . . . . pp. 15, 24, 34, 43, 53, 62, 71
Recording Sheets. . . . . . pp. 3, 7, 17, 26, 36, 46, 55, 64, 74, 77
Chapter Review . . . . pp. 72–73

Teacher and Parent Resources

Chapter Planning and Pacing Guide. . . . . p. 4
Section Planning Guides . . . . pp. 5, 44
Parent Letter . . . . pp. 1–2
Teaching Tools . . . . pp. 77–79
Teacher Support for Chapter Project . . . . p. 75
Transparencies . . . . pp. T1–T30
- Daily Transparencies
- Additional Examples Transparencies
- Teaching Transparencies

Reaching All Learners

English Language Learners

Success for English Language Learners . . . . pp. 87–100
Math: Reading and Writing in the Content Area . . . . pp. 44–50
Spanish Homework and Practice . . . . pp. 44–50
Spanish Interactive Study Guide . . . . pp. 44–50
Spanish Family Involvement Activities. . . . . pp. 41–48
Multilingual Glossary

Individual Needs

Are You Ready? Intervention and Enrichment . pp. 105–112, 185–188, 245–248, 413–414
Alternate Openers: Explorations . . . . pp. 44–50
Family Involvement Activities . . . . pp. 41–48
Interactive Problem Solving. . . . . pp. 44–50
Interactive Study Guide . . . . pp. 44–50
Readiness Activities . . . . pp. 9–10
Math: Reading and Writing in the Content Area . . . . pp. 44–50
Challenge . . . . CRB pp. 13, 22, 32, 41, 51, 60, 69

Hands-On

Hands-On Lab Activities. pp. 31–39
Technology Lab Activities. . . . . pp. 22–30
Alternate Openers: Explorations . . . . pp. 44–50
Family Involvement Activities . . . . pp. 41–48

Applications and Connections

Consumer and Career Math. . . . . pp. 17–20
Interdisciplinary Posters . . . . Poster 5, TE p. 258B
Interdisciplinary Poster Worksheets. . . . . pp. 13–15

Transparencies

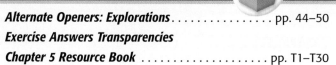

Alternate Openers: Explorations. . . . . pp. 44–50
Exercise Answers Transparencies
Chapter 5 Resource Book . . . . pp. T1–T30
- Daily Transparencies
- Additional Examples Transparencies
- Teaching Transparencies

Technology

Teacher Resources

***Lesson Presentations* CD-ROM**. . . . . Chapter 5
***Test and Practice Generator* CD-ROM** . . . . Chapter 5
***One-Stop Planner* CD-ROM** . . . . Chapter 5

Student Resources

***Are You Ready? Intervention* CD-ROM**
Skills 24, 25, 44, 59

internet connect

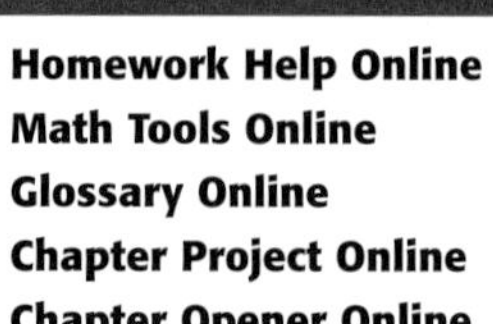

Homework Help Online	**KEYWORD:** MS4 HWHelp5
Math Tools Online	**KEYWORD:** MS4 Tools
Glossary Online	**KEYWORD:** MS4 Glossary
Chapter Project Online	**KEYWORD:** MS4 PSProject5
Chapter Opener Online	**KEYWORD:** MS4 C5

KEYWORD: MS4 CNN5

SE = *Student Edition* **TE** = *Teacher's Edition* **AR** = *Assessment Resources* **CRB** = *Chapter Resource Book* **MK** = *Manipulatives Kit*

Chapter 5

Assessment Options

Assessing Prior Knowledge

Determine whether students have the required prerequisite concepts and skills.

Are You Ready? . . . . SE p. 259
Inventory Test . . . . AR pp. 1–4

Test Preparation

Provide review and practice for chapter and standardized tests.

Standardized Test Prep . . . . SE p. 301
Spiral Review with Test Prep . . . . . SE, last page of each lesson
Study Guide and Review . . . . SE pp. 296–298
Test Prep Tool Kit

Technology

***Test and Practice Generator* CD-ROM**

internet connect

State-Specific Test Practice Online KEYWORD: MS4 TestPrep

Performance Assessment

Assess students' understanding of chapter concepts and combined problem-solving skills.

Performance Assessment . . . . SE p. 300
Includes scoring rubric in TE
Performance Assessment . . . . AR p. 114
Performance Assessment Teacher Support . . . . AR p. 113

Portfolio

Portfolio opportunities appear throughout the Student and Teacher's Editions.

Suggested work samples:

Problem Solving Project . . . . TE p. 258
Performance Assessment . . . . SE p. 300
Portfolio Guide . . . . AR p. xxxv
Journal . . . . TE, last page of each lesson
Write About It . . . . SE pp. 267, 271, 275, 283, 287

Daily Assessment

Obtain daily feedback on students' understanding of concepts.

Spiral Review and Test Prep . . . . . . SE, last page of each lesson

Also Available on Transparency In Chapter 5 Resource Book

Warm Up . . . . TE, first page of each lesson
Problem of the Day . . . . TE, first page of each lesson
Lesson Quiz . . . . TE, last page of each lesson

Student Self-Assessment

Have students evaluate their own work.

Group Project Evaluation . . . . AR p. xxxii
Individual Group Member Evaluation . . . . AR p. xxxiii
Portfolio Guide . . . . AR p. xxxv
Journal . . . . TE, last page of each lesson

Formal Assessment

Assess students' mastery of concepts and skills.

Section Quizzes . . . . AR pp. 15–16
Mid-Chapter Quiz . . . . SE p. 276
Chapter Test . . . . SE p. 299
Chapter Tests (Levels A, B, C) . . . . AR pp. 57–62
Cumulative Tests (Levels A, B, C) . . . . AR pp. 177–188
Standardized Test Prep
Cumulative Assessment . . . . SE p. 301
End-of-Year Test . . . . AR pp. 273–276

Technology

***Test and Practice Generator* CD-ROM**

Make tests electronically. This software includes:

- Dynamic practice for Chapter 5
- Customizable tests
- Multiple-choice items for each objective
- Free-response items for each objective
- Teacher management system

SE = *Student Edition* **TE** = *Teacher's Edition* **AR** = *Assessment Resources* **CRB** = *Chapter Resource Book* **MK** = *Manipulatives Kit*

Chapter 5

Chapter 5 Tests

Three levels (A,B,C) of tests are available for each chapter in the *Assessment Resources.*

LEVEL A

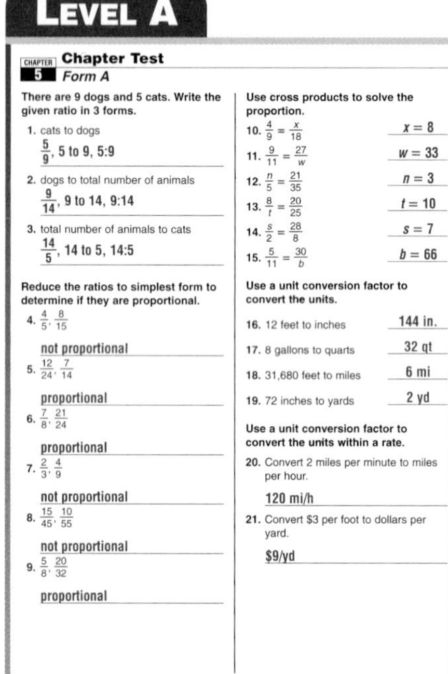

Chapter Test CHAPTER 5 *Form A*

There are 9 dogs and 5 cats. Write the given ratio in 3 forms.

1. cats to dogs — $\frac{5}{9}$, 5 to 9, 5:9
2. dogs to total number of animals — $\frac{9}{14}$, 9 to 14, 9:14
3. total number of animals to cats — $\frac{14}{5}$, 14 to 5, 14:5

Reduce the ratios to simplest form to determine if they are proportional.

4. $\frac{4}{5}, \frac{8}{15}$ — not proportional
5. $\frac{12}{24}, \frac{7}{14}$ — proportional
6. $\frac{7}{8}, \frac{21}{24}$ — proportional
7. $\frac{2}{3}, \frac{4}{9}$ — not proportional
8. $\frac{15}{45}, \frac{10}{55}$ — not proportional
9. $\frac{5}{8}, \frac{20}{32}$ — proportional

Use cross products to solve the proportion.

10. $\frac{4}{9} = \frac{x}{18}$ — $x = 8$
11. $\frac{9}{11} = \frac{27}{w}$ — $w = 33$
12. $\frac{n}{5} = \frac{21}{35}$ — $n = 3$
13. $\frac{8}{t} = \frac{20}{25}$ — $t = 10$
14. $\frac{s}{2} = \frac{28}{8}$ — $s = 7$
15. $\frac{5}{11} = \frac{30}{b}$ — $b = 66$

Use a unit conversion factor to convert the units.

16. 12 feet to inches — 144 in.
17. 8 gallons to quarts — 32 qt
18. 31,680 feet to miles — 6 mi
19. 72 inches to yards — 2 yd

Use a unit conversion factor to convert the units within a rate.

20. Convert 2 miles per minute to miles per hour. — 120 mi/h
21. Convert \$3 per foot to dollars per yard. — \$9/yd

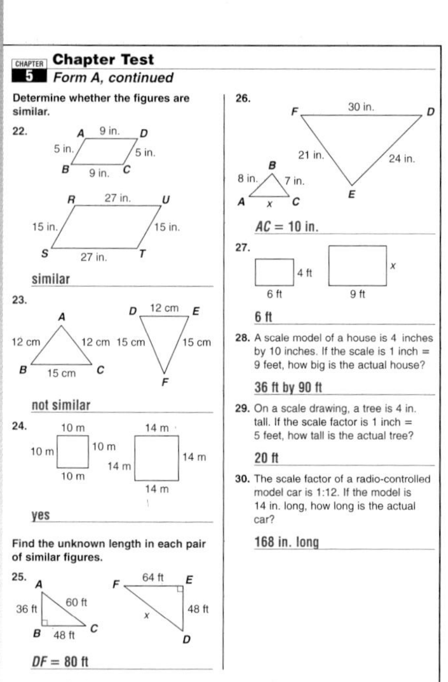

Chapter Test CHAPTER 5 *Form A, continued*

Determine whether the figures are similar.

22. similar
23. not similar
24. yes

Find the unknown length in each pair of similar figures.

25. $DF = 80$ ft
26. $AC = 10$ in.
27. 6 ft
28. A scale model of a house is 4 inches by 10 inches. If the scale is 1 inch = 9 feet, how big is the actual house? — 36 ft by 90 ft
29. On a scale drawing, a tree is 4 in. tall. If the scale factor is 1 inch = 5 feet, how tall is the actual tree? — 20 ft
30. The scale factor of a radio-controlled model car is 1:12. If the model is 14 in. long, how long is the actual car? — 168 in. long

LEVEL B

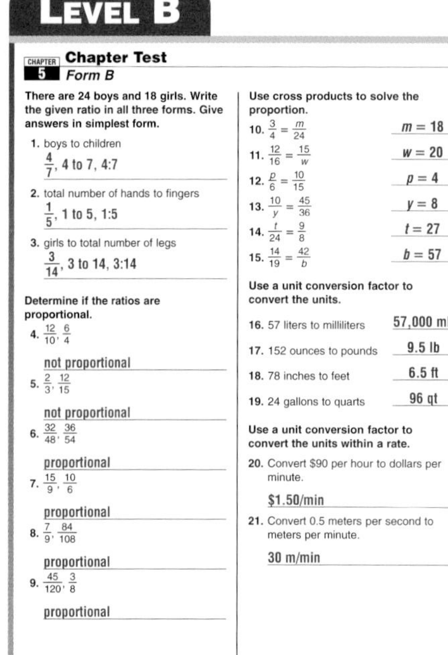

Chapter Test CHAPTER 5 *Form B*

There are 24 boys and 18 girls. Write the given ratio in all three forms. Give answers in simplest form.

1. boys to children — $\frac{4}{7}$, 4 to 7, 4:7
2. total number of hands to fingers — $\frac{1}{5}$, 1 to 5, 1:5
3. girls to total number of legs — $\frac{3}{14}$, 3 to 14, 3:14

Determine if the ratios are proportional.

4. $\frac{12}{10}, \frac{6}{4}$ — not proportional
5. $\frac{2}{3}, \frac{12}{15}$ — not proportional
6. $\frac{32}{48}, \frac{36}{54}$ — proportional
7. $\frac{15}{9}, \frac{10}{6}$ — proportional
8. $\frac{7}{9}, \frac{84}{108}$ — proportional
9. $\frac{45}{120}, \frac{3}{8}$ — proportional

Use cross products to solve the proportion.

10. $\frac{3}{4} = \frac{m}{24}$ — $m = 18$
11. $\frac{12}{16} = \frac{15}{w}$ — $w = 20$
12. $\frac{p}{6} = \frac{10}{15}$ — $p = 4$
13. $\frac{10}{y} = \frac{45}{36}$ — $y = 8$
14. $\frac{t}{24} = \frac{9}{8}$ — $t = 27$
15. $\frac{14}{19} = \frac{42}{b}$ — $b = 57$

Use a unit conversion factor to convert the units.

16. 57 liters to milliliters — 57,000 mL
17. 152 ounces to pounds — 9.5 lb
18. 78 inches to feet — 6.5 ft
19. 24 gallons to quarts — 96 qt

Use a unit conversion factor to convert the units within a rate.

20. Convert \$90 per hour to dollars per minute. — \$1.50/min
21. Convert 0.5 meters per second to meters per minute. — 30 m/min

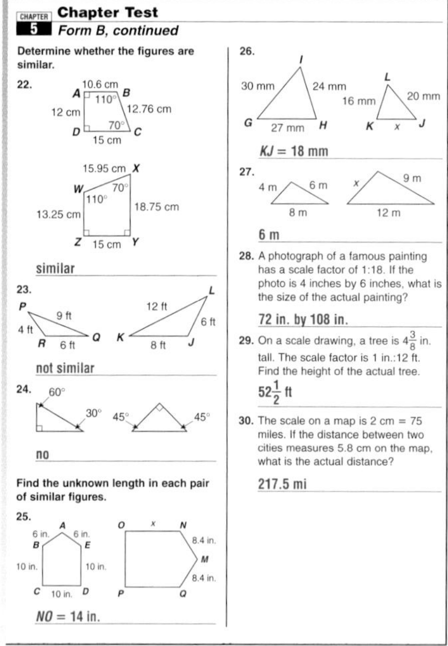

Chapter Test CHAPTER 5 *Form B, continued*

Determine whether the figures are similar.

22. similar
23. not similar
24. no

Find the unknown length in each pair of similar figures.

25. $NO = 14$ in.
26. $KJ = 18$ mm
27. 6 m
28. A photograph of a famous painting has a scale factor of 1:18. If the photo is 4 inches by 6 inches, what is the size of the actual painting? — 72 in. by 108 in.
29. On a scale drawing, a tree is $4\frac{3}{8}$ in. tall. The scale factor is 1 in.:12 ft. Find the height of the actual tree. — $52\frac{1}{2}$ ft
30. The scale on a map is 2 cm = 75 miles. If the distance between two cities measures 5.8 cm on the map, what is the actual distance? — 217.5 mi

LEVEL C

Chapter Test CHAPTER 5 *Form C*

There are 3 squares, 5 triangles, and 4 pentagons. Write the given ratio in all three forms. Give answers in simplest form.

1. pentagons to total number of figures — $\frac{1}{3}$, 1 to 3, 1:3
2. total number of figures to sides of squares — $\frac{1}{1}$, 1 to 1, 1:1
3. total number of figures to total number of sides — $\frac{12}{47}$, 12 to 47, 12:47

Determine if the ratios are proportional.

4. $\frac{3}{5}, \frac{18}{35}$ — not proportional
5. $\frac{4}{12}, \frac{18}{54}$ — proportional
6. $\frac{6}{7}$, 14:6 — not proportional
7. 2:12, 6 to 36 — proportional
8. $\frac{9}{4}, \frac{8}{18}$ — not proportional
9. $\frac{6}{7}$, 24:28 — proportional

Use cross products to solve the proportion.

10. $\frac{3}{200} = \frac{z}{840}$ — $z = 12.6$
11. $\frac{k}{7.5} = \frac{0.5}{0.3}$ — $k = 12.5$
12. $\frac{m}{8} = \frac{350}{40}$ — $m = 70$
13. $\frac{115}{w} = \frac{207}{64.8}$ — $w = 36$
14. $\frac{a}{64} = \frac{300}{960}$ — $a = 20$
15. $\frac{8.7}{4.9} = \frac{13.05}{b}$ — $b = 7.35$

Use a unit conversion factor to convert the units.

16. 8.3 meters to kilometers — 0.0083 km
17. 322 pints to quarts — 161 qt
18. 4.2 yards to inches — 151.2 in.
19. 8.6 kilograms to grams — 8,600 g

Use a unit conversion factor to convert the units within a rate.

20. Convert \$58.20 per hour to cents per minute. — \$0.97/min
21. Convert 0.25 meters per second to meters per hour. — 900 m/h

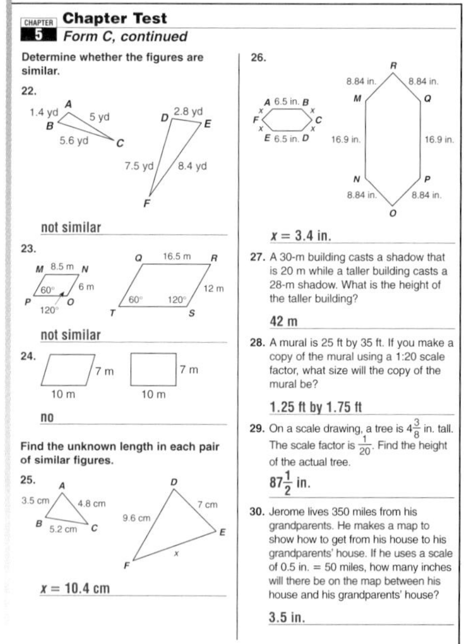

Chapter Test CHAPTER 5 *Form C, continued*

Determine whether the figures are similar.

22. not similar
23. not similar
24. no

Find the unknown length in each pair of similar figures.

25. $x = 10.4$ cm
26. $x = 3.4$ in.
27. A 30-m building casts a shadow that is 20 m while a taller building casts a 28-m shadow. What is the height of the taller building? — 42 m
28. A mural is 25 ft by 35 ft. If you make a copy of the mural using a 1:20 scale factor, what size will the copy of the mural be? — 1.25 ft by 1.75 ft
29. On a scale drawing, a tree is $4\frac{3}{8}$ in. tall. The scale factor is $\frac{1}{20}$. Find the height of the actual tree. — $87\frac{1}{2}$ in.
30. Jerome lives 350 miles from his grandparents. He makes a map to show how to get from his house to his grandparents' house. If he uses a scale of 0.5 in. = 50 miles, how many inches will there be on the map between his house and his grandparents' house? — 3.5 in.

***Test and Practice Generator* CD-ROM**

Create and customize multiple versions of the same tests with corresponding answers for any chosen chapter objectives.

Chapter 5 State and Standardized Test Preparation

Test Taking Skill Builder and Standardized Test Practice are provided for each chapter in the *Test Prep Tool Kit.*

TEST TAKING SKILL BUILDER

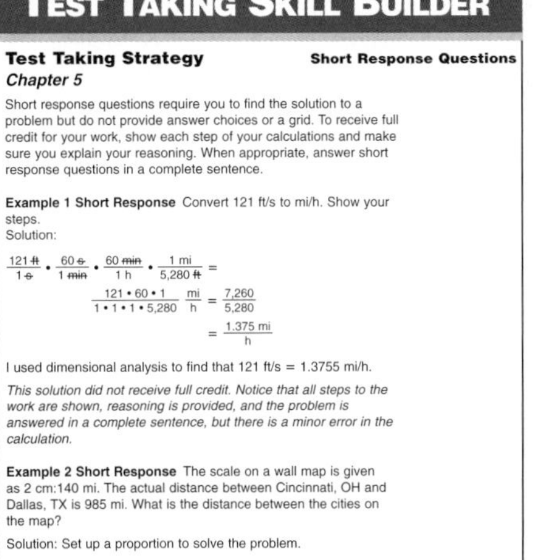

Test Taking Strategy — **Short Response Questions**

Chapter 5

Short response questions require you to find the solution to a problem but do not provide answer choices or a grid. To receive full credit for your work, show each step of your calculations and make sure you explain your reasoning. When appropriate, answer short response questions in a complete sentence.

Example 1 Short Response Convert 121 ft/s to mi/h. Show your steps.

Solution:

$$\frac{121 \text{ ft}}{1 \text{ s}} \cdot \frac{60 \text{ s}}{1 \text{ min}} \cdot \frac{60 \text{ min}}{1 \text{ h}} \cdot \frac{1 \text{ mi}}{5{,}280 \text{ ft}} = \frac{121 \cdot 60 \cdot 1}{1 \cdot 1 \cdot 1 \cdot 5{,}280} \frac{\text{mi}}{\text{h}} = \frac{7{,}260}{5{,}280} = \frac{1.375 \text{ mi}}{\text{h}}$$

I used dimensional analysis to find that 121 ft/s = 1.3755 mi/h.

This solution did not receive full credit. Notice that all steps to the work are shown, reasoning is provided, and the problem is answered in a complete sentence, but there is a minor error in the calculation.

Example 2 Short Response The scale on a wall map is given as 2 cm:140 mi. The actual distance between Cincinnati, OH and Dallas, TX is 985 mi. What is the distance between the cities on the map?

Solution: Set up a proportion to solve the problem.

$\frac{2 \text{ cm}}{140 \text{ mi}} = \frac{x \text{ cm}}{980 \text{ mi}}$

$980 \cdot 2 = 140 \cdot x$

$1{,}960 = 140x$

$\frac{1{,}960}{140} = \frac{140x}{140}$

$14 = x$

The distance between the cities on the map is 14 cm.

This solution received full credit. Notice that all steps to the work are shown, reasoning is provided, and the problem is answered in a complete sentence.

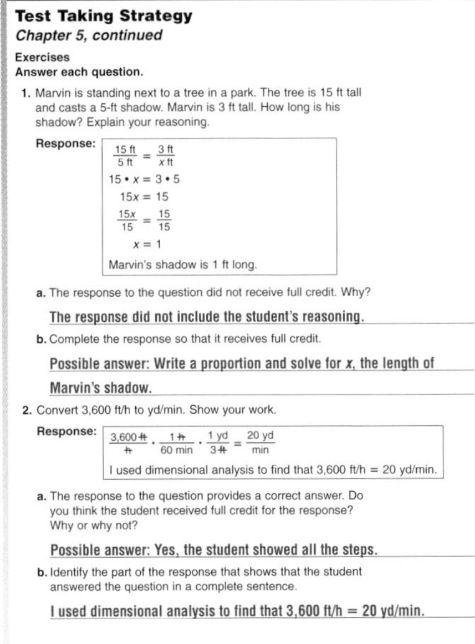

Test Taking Strategy

Chapter 5, continued

Exercises

Answer each question.

1. Marvin is standing next to a tree in a park. The tree is 15 ft tall and casts a 5-ft shadow. Marvin is 3 ft tall. How long is his shadow? Explain your reasoning.

Response:

$\frac{15 \text{ ft}}{5 \text{ ft}} = \frac{3 \text{ ft}}{x \text{ ft}}$

$15 \cdot x = 3 \cdot 5$

$15x = 15$

$\frac{15x}{15} = \frac{15}{15}$

$x = 1$

Marvin's shadow is 1 ft long.

a. The response to the question did not receive full credit. Why?

The response did not include the student's reasoning.

b. Complete the response so that it receives full credit.

Possible answer: Write a proportion and solve for *x*, the length of Marvin's shadow.

2. Convert 3,600 ft/h to yd/min. Show your work.

Response: $\frac{3{,}600 \text{ ft}}{\text{h}} \cdot \frac{1 \text{ h}}{60 \text{ min}} \cdot \frac{1 \text{ yd}}{3 \text{ ft}} = \frac{20 \text{ yd}}{\text{min}}$

I used dimensional analysis to find that 3,600 ft/h = 20 yd/min.

a. The response to the question provides a correct answer. Do you think the student received full credit for the response? Why or why not?

Possible answer: Yes, the student showed all the steps.

b. Identify the part of the response that shows that the student answered the question in a complete sentence.

I used dimensional analysis to find that 3,600 ft/h = 20 yd/min.

STANDARDIZED TEST PRACTICE

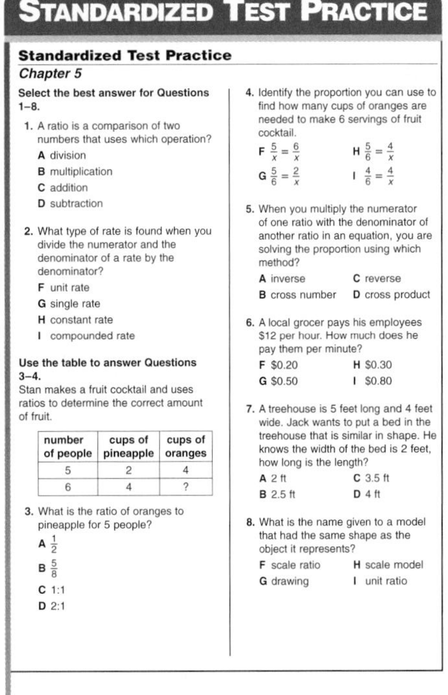

Standardized Test Practice

Chapter 5

Select the best answer for Questions 1–8.

1. A ratio is a comparison of two numbers that uses which operation?
   - **A** division
   - **B** multiplication
   - **C** addition
   - **D** subtraction

2. What type of rate is found when you divide the numerator and the denominator of a rate by the denominator?
   - **F** unit rate
   - **G** single rate
   - **H** constant rate
   - **I** compounded rate

Use the table to answer Questions 3–4.

Stan makes a fruit cocktail and uses ratios to determine the correct amount of fruit.

number of people	cups of pineapple	cups of oranges
5	2	4
6	4	?

3. What is the ratio of oranges to pineapple for 5 people?
   - **A** $\frac{1}{2}$
   - **B** $\frac{5}{8}$
   - **C** 1:1
   - **D** 2:1

4. Identify the proportion you can use to find how many cups of oranges are needed to make 6 servings of fruit cocktail.
   - **F** $\frac{5}{x} = \frac{6}{x}$
   - **G** $\frac{5}{6} = \frac{2}{x}$
   - **H** $\frac{5}{6} = \frac{4}{x}$
   - **I** $\frac{4}{6} = \frac{4}{x}$

5. When you multiply the numerator of one ratio with the denominator of another ratio in an equation, you are solving the proportion using which method?
   - **A** inverse
   - **B** cross number
   - **C** reverse
   - **D** cross product

6. A local grocer pays his employees $12 per hour. How much does he pay them per minute?
   - **F** $0.20
   - **G** $0.50
   - **H** $0.30
   - **I** $0.80

7. A treehouse is 5 feet long and 4 feet wide. Jack wants to put a bed in the treehouse that is similar in shape. He knows the width of the bed is 2 feet, how long is the length?
   - **A** 2 ft
   - **B** 2.5 ft
   - **C** 3.5 ft
   - **D** 4 ft

8. What is the name given to a model that had the same shape as the object it represents?
   - **F** scale ratio
   - **G** drawing
   - **H** scale model
   - **I** unit ratio

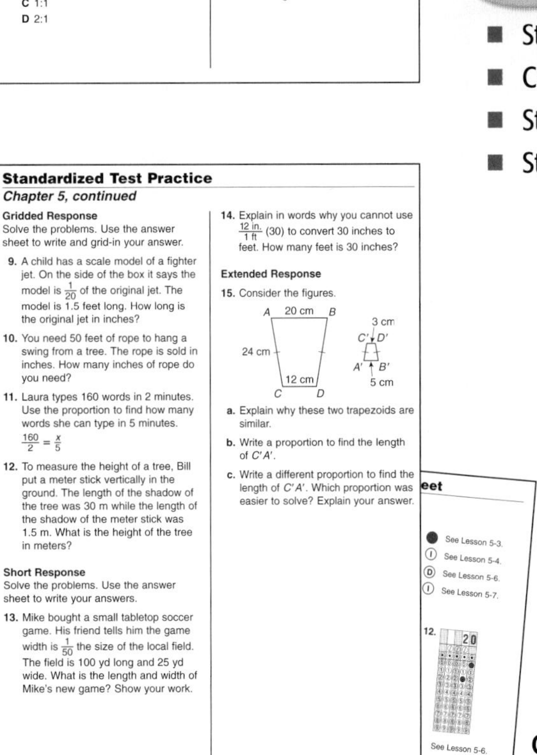

Standardized Test Practice

Chapter 5, continued

Gridded Response

Solve the problems. Use the answer sheet to write and grid-in your answer.

9. A child has a scale model of a fighter jet. On the side of the box it says the model is $\frac{1}{20}$ of the original jet. The model is 1.5 feet long. How long is the original jet in inches?

10. You need 50 feet of rope to hang a swing from a tree. The rope is sold in inches. How many inches of rope do you need?

11. Laura types 160 words in 2 minutes. Use the proportion to find how many words she can type in 5 minutes. $\frac{160}{2} = \frac{x}{5}$

12. To measure the height of a tree, Bill put a meter stick vertically in the ground. The length of the shadow of the tree was 30 m while the length of the shadow of the meter stick was 1.5 m. What is the height of the tree in meters?

Short Response

Solve the problems. Use the answer sheet to write your answers.

13. Mike bought a small tabletop soccer game. His friend tells him the game width is $\frac{1}{50}$ the size of the local field. The field is 100 yd long and 25 yd wide. What is the length and width of Mike's new game? Show your work.

14. Explain in words why you cannot use $\frac{12 \text{ in.}}{1 \text{ ft}}$ (30) to convert 30 inches to feet. How many feet is 30 inches?

Extended Response

15. Consider the figures.

a. Explain why these two trapezoids are similar.

b. Write a proportion to find the length of *C′A′*.

c. Write a different proportion to find the length of *C′A′*. Which proportion was easier to solve? Explain your answer.

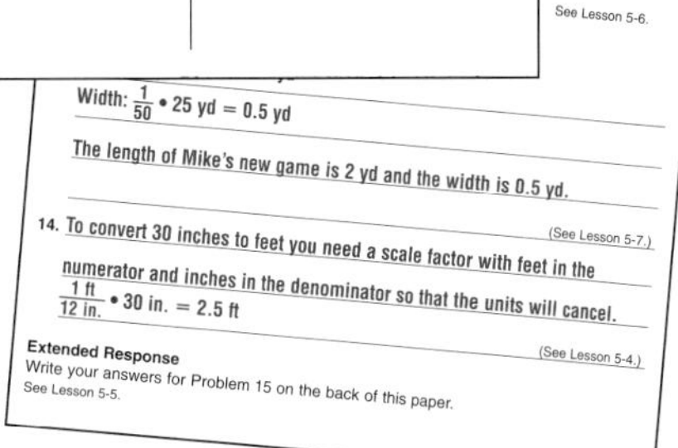

Width: $\frac{1}{50} \cdot 25 \text{ yd} = 0.5 \text{ yd}$

The length of Mike's new game is 2 yd and the width is 0.5 yd.

14. To convert 30 inches to feet you need a scale factor with feet in the numerator and inches in the denominator so that the units will cancel. (See Lesson 5-7.)

$\frac{1 \text{ ft}}{12 \text{ in.}} \cdot 30 \text{ in.} = 2.5 \text{ ft}$

Extended Response (See Lesson 5-4.)

Write your answers for Problem 15 on the back of this paper.

See Lesson 5-5.

internet connect

State-Specific Test Practice Online

KEYWORD: MS4 TestPrep

Test Prep Tool Kit

- Standardized Test Prep Workbook
- Countdown to Testing transparencies
- State Test Prep CD-ROM
- Standardized Test Prep Video

Customized answer sheets give students realistic practice for actual standardized tests.

Proportional Reasoning

Why Learn This?

Tell students that a scale factor is used to describe the relationship between an actual object and a scale model of the object. Scale models are used in many different careers. Architects build scale models of houses and buildings. Automobile manufacturers build scale models of cars that will be produced in the future. Toy manufacturers build scale models of trucks and cars for children to play with. Ask students to name another career in which scale models are used.

Possible answer: Scientists build scale models of the solar system.

Using Data

To begin the study of this chapter, have students:

- Multiply the length of the *Santa Maria* by $\frac{1}{65}$. **0.56 m** Ask students to change 0.56 m to millimeters. **560 mm**
- Express the lengths of the models for the *Golden Hind*, the HMS *Bounty*, and the *Mayflower* in meters. **0.360 m, 0.980 m, 0.605 m**

Chapter 5

Proportional Reasoning

TABLE OF CONTENTS

internet connect
Chapter Opener Online
go.hrw.com
KEYWORD: MS4 Ch5

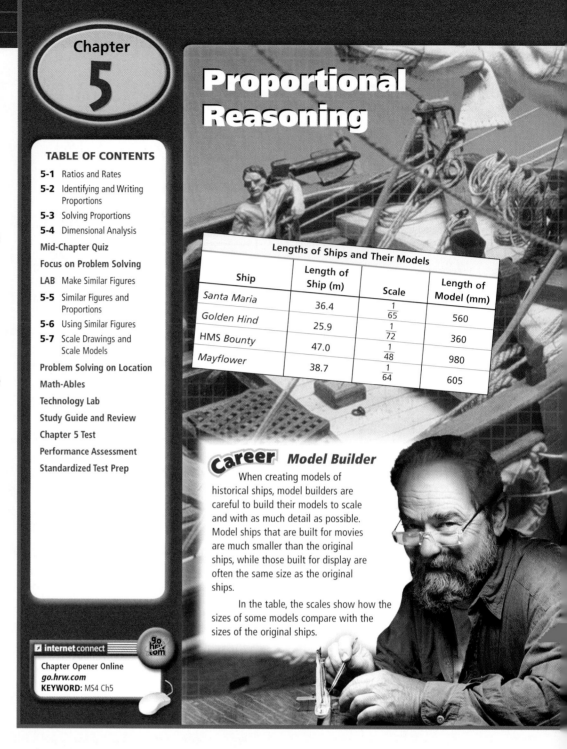

Lengths of Ships and Their Models

Ship	Length of Ship (m)	Scale	Length of Model (mm)
Santa Maria	36.4	$\frac{1}{65}$	560
Golden Hind	25.9	$\frac{1}{72}$	360
HMS Bounty	47.0	$\frac{1}{48}$	980
Mayflower	38.7	$\frac{1}{64}$	605

Career ***Model Builder***

When creating models of historical ships, model builders are careful to build their models to scale and with as much detail as possible. Model ships that are built for movies are much smaller than the original ships, while those built for display are often the same size as the original ships.

In the table, the scales show how the sizes of some models compare with the sizes of the original ships.

Problem Solving Project

Physical Science and Social Studies Connection

Purpose: To solve problems by using proportional reasoning to find the relationships between real objects and their scale models.

Materials: Scale Model Ships worksheet, modeling and art materials, video recorder, videotape

internet connect
Chapter Project Online: ***go.hrw.com***
KEYWORD: MS4 PSProject5

Understand, Plan, Solve, and Look Back

Have students:

- ✔ Complete the Scale Model Ships worksheet to discover relationships between similar objects.
- ✔ Research the historical role of one of the ships in the table and the people who sailed on it.
- ✔ Visit a store that sells models. Tell students to pick a machine other than a ship and to make a chart comparing the size of the actual object to the size of the model. What scale was used to make the model? If one of your objects were in a movie scene with one of the ships, what scale should be used?
- ✔ Check students' work.

ARE YOU READY?

Choose the best term from the list to complete each sentence.

1. A(n) __?__ is a number that represents a part of a whole. **fraction**
2. A closed figure with three sides is called a(n) __?__. **triangle**
3. Two fractions are __?__ if they represent the same number. **equivalent**
4. One way to compare two fractions is to first find a(n) __?__ between them. **common denominator**

common denominator
equivalent
fraction
quadrilateral
triangle

Complete these exercises to review skills you will need for this chapter.

✓ Write Equivalent Fractions

Find two fractions that are equivalent to each fraction. **Possible answers:**

5. $\frac{2}{5}$ **$\frac{4}{10}, \frac{6}{15}$**
6. $\frac{7}{11}$ **$\frac{14}{22}, \frac{28}{44}$**
7. $\frac{25}{100}$ **$\frac{1}{4}, \frac{5}{20}$**
8. $\frac{4}{6}$ **$\frac{2}{3}, \frac{8}{12}$**
9. $\frac{5}{17}$ **$\frac{10}{34}, \frac{15}{51}$**
10. $\frac{15}{23}$ **$\frac{30}{46}, \frac{45}{69}$**
11. $\frac{24}{78}$ **$\frac{12}{39}, \frac{4}{13}$**
12. $\frac{150}{325}$ **$\frac{30}{65}, \frac{6}{13}$**

✓ Compare Fractions

Compare. Write $<$ or $>$.

13. $\frac{5}{6} \square \frac{2}{3}$ **$>$**
14. $\frac{3}{8} \square \frac{2}{5}$ **$<$**
15. $\frac{6}{11} \square \frac{1}{4}$ **$>$**
16. $\frac{5}{8} \square \frac{11}{12}$ **$<$**
17. $\frac{8}{9} \square \frac{12}{13}$ **$<$**
18. $\frac{5}{11} \square \frac{7}{21}$ **$>$**
19. $\frac{4}{10} \square \frac{3}{7}$ **$<$**
20. $\frac{3}{4} \square \frac{2}{9}$ **$>$**

✓ Solve Multiplication Equations

Solve each equation.

21. $3x = 12$ **$x = 4$**
22. $15t = 75$ **$t = 5$**
23. $2y = 14$ **$y = 7$**
24. $7m = 84$ **$m = 12$**
25. $25c = 125$ **$c = 5$**
26. $16f = 320$ **$f = 20$**
27. $11n = 121$ **$n = 11$**
28. $53y = 318$ **$y = 6$**

✓ Multiply Fractions

Solve. Write each answer in simplest form.

29. $\frac{2}{3} \cdot \frac{5}{7}$ **$\frac{10}{21}$**
30. $\frac{12}{16} \cdot \frac{3}{9}$ **$\frac{1}{4}$**
31. $\frac{4}{9} \cdot \frac{18}{24}$ **$\frac{1}{3}$**
32. $\frac{1}{56} \cdot \frac{50}{200}$ **$\frac{1}{224}$**
33. $\frac{1}{5} \cdot \frac{5}{9}$ **$\frac{1}{9}$**
34. $\frac{7}{8} \cdot \frac{4}{3}$ **$\frac{7}{6}$ or $1\frac{1}{6}$**
35. $\frac{25}{100} \cdot \frac{30}{90}$ **$\frac{1}{12}$**
36. $\frac{46}{91} \cdot \frac{3}{6}$ **$\frac{23}{91}$**

Assessing Prior Knowledge

INTERVENTION 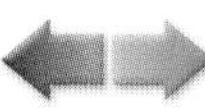

Diagnose and Prescribe

Evaluate your students' performance on this page to determine whether intervention is necessary or whether enrichment is appropriate. Options that provide instruction, practice, and a check are listed below.

Resources for Are You Ready?

- ***Are You Ready? Intervention and Enrichment***
- **Recording Sheet for Are You Ready?** *Chapter 5 Resource Book* ...... p. 3

 ***Are You Ready? Intervention*** **CD-ROM**

internet connect 

Are You Ready? Intervention
go.hrw.com
KEYWORD: MS4 AYR

ARE YOU READY?

Were students successful with Are You Ready?

NO **INTERVENE**

YES **ENRICH**

✓Write Equivalent Fractions
Are You Ready? Intervention, Skill 24
Blackline Masters, Online, and
 **CD-ROM** Intervention Activities

✓Compare Fractions
Are You Ready? Intervention, Skill 25
Blackline Masters, Online, and
 **CD-ROM** Intervention Activities

✓Solve Multiplication Equations
Are You Ready? Intervention, Skill 59
Blackline Masters, Online, and
 **CD-ROM** Intervention Activities

✓Multiply Fractions
Are You Ready? Intervention, Skill 44
Blackline Masters, Online, and
 **CD-ROM** Intervention Activities

Are You Ready? Enrichment, pp. 415–416

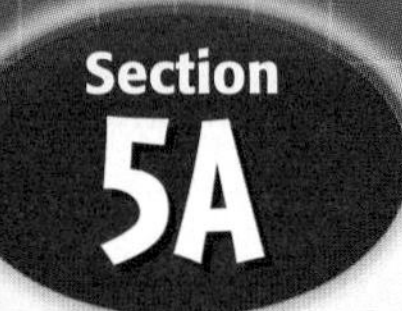

Numerical Proportions

One-Minute Section Planner

Lesson	Materials	Resources
Lesson 5-1 Ratios and Rates **NCTM:** Number and Operations, Communication, Connections **NAEP:** Number Properties 4a ☑ SAT-9 ☑ SAT-10 ☑ ITBS ☑ CTBS ☑ MAT ☑ CAT		• *Chapter 5 Resource Book,* pp. 6–15 • Daily Transparency T1, CRB • Additional Examples Transparencies T2–T4, CRB • *Alternate Openers: Explorations,* p. 44
Lesson 5-2 Identifying and Writing Proportions **NCTM:** Number and Operations, Communication, Connections **NAEP:** Number Properties 4b ☑ SAT-9 ☑ SAT-10 ☑ ITBS ☑ CTBS ☑ MAT ☑ CAT		• *Chapter 5 Resource Book,* pp. 16–24 • Daily Transparency T5, CRB • Additional Examples Transparencies T6–T8, CRB • *Alternate Openers: Explorations,* p. 45
Lesson 5-3 Solving Proportions **NCTM:** Number and Operations, Problem Solving, Communication **NAEP:** Number Properties 4c ☑ SAT-9 ☑ SAT-10 ☑ ITBS ☑ CTBS ☑ MAT ☑ CAT	**Optional** Teaching Transparency T10 *(CRB)* Measuring tape *(MK)*	• *Chapter 5 Resource Book,* pp. 25–34 • Daily Transparency T9, CRB • Additional Examples Transparencies T11–T13, CRB • *Alternate Openers: Explorations,* p. 46
Lesson 5-4 Dimensional Analysis **NCTM:** Measurement, Communication, Connections, Representation **NAEP:** Measurement 2b ☑ SAT-9 ☑ SAT-10 ☐ ITBS ☐ CTBS ☑ MAT ☑ CAT	**Optional** Teaching Transparency T15 *(CRB)*	• *Chapter 5 Resource Book,* pp. 35–43 • Daily Transparency T14, CRB • Additional Examples Transparencies T16–T18, CRB • *Alternate Openers: Explorations,* p. 47
Section 5A Assessment		• Mid-Chapter Quiz, SE p. 276 • Section 5A Quiz, AR p. 15 • *Test and Practice Generator* CD-ROM

SAT = *Stanford Achievement Tests* **ITBS** = *Iowa Test of Basic Skills* **CTBS** = *Comprehensive Test of Basic Skills/Terra Nova*
MAT = *Metropolitan Achievement Test* **CAT** = *California Achievement Test*

NCTM—Complete standards can be found on pages T27–T33. **NAEP**—Complete standards can be found on pages A35–A39.

SE = *Student Edition* **TE** = *Teacher's Edition* **AR** = *Assessment Resources* **CRB** = *Chapter Resource Book* **MK** = *Manipulatives Kit*

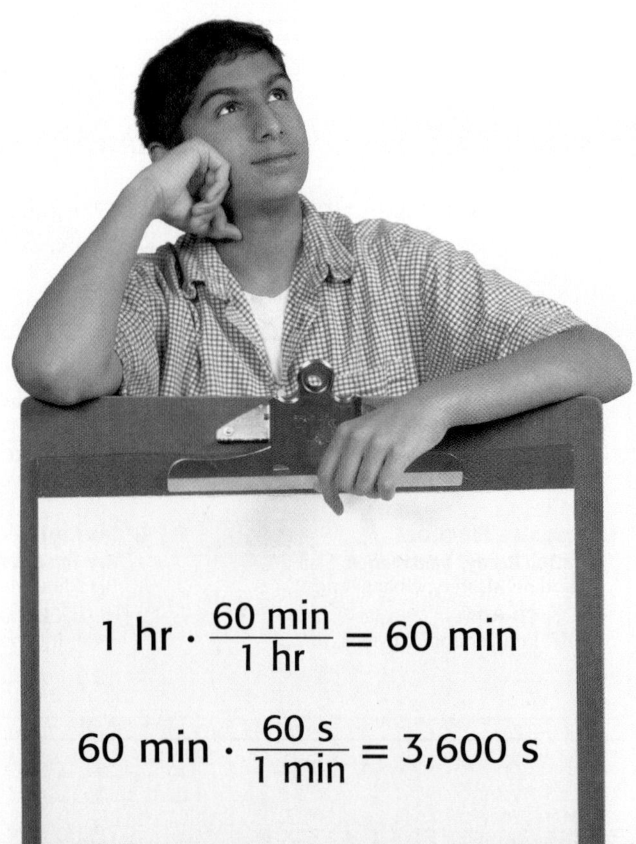

$1 \text{ hr} \cdot \frac{60 \text{ min}}{1 \text{ hr}} = 60 \text{ min}$
$60 \text{ min} \cdot \frac{60 \text{ s}}{1 \text{ min}} = 3{,}600 \text{ s}$

Section Overview

Ratios and Rates — Lesson 5-1

Why? Ratios are used to solve proportions, to find missing lengths in similar figures, and to interpret the scale in scale drawings or scale models.

A ratio compares two numbers. A **rate** is a ratio that compares two measurement values that have different units.

A **unit rate** has a denominator of 1. The fraction bar may be read as *per* in a rate.

Denise ran 5 miles in 40 minutes.

Rate: $\frac{5 \text{ mi}}{40 \text{ min}}$ or $\frac{40 \text{ min}}{5 \text{ mi}}$

Unit Rate: $\frac{0.125 \text{ mi}}{1 \text{min}}$ or $\frac{8 \text{ min}}{1 \text{ mi}}$

Proportions — Lessons 5-2, 5-3

Why? You can solve problems involving similar figures and scale drawings or models by writing and solving proportions.

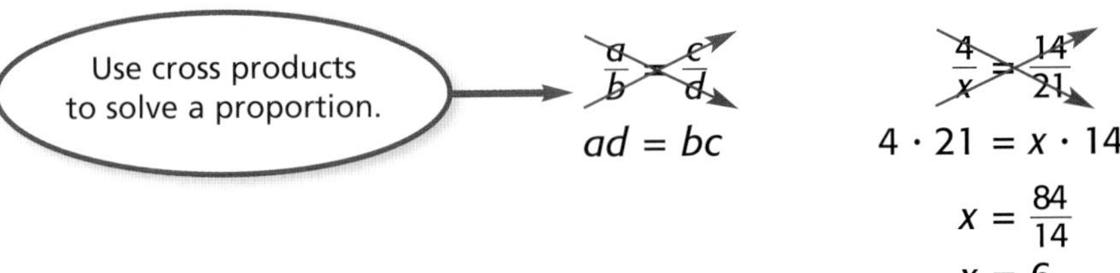

You can also use cross products to check whether ratios are equivalent.

$\frac{2}{5} \stackrel{?}{=} \frac{5}{12}$ $2 \cdot 12 \stackrel{?}{=} 5 \cdot 5$ $24 \neq 25$, so the ratios $\frac{2}{5}$ and $\frac{5}{12}$ are not equivalent.

Dimensional Analysis — Lesson 5-4

Why? You can use dimensional analysis to convert from one unit to another when solving equations and real-world problems involving situations such as recipes and timetables.

- Convert 6 hours to seconds.

$$6 \cancel{\text{hr}} \cdot \frac{60 \cancel{\text{min}}}{1 \cancel{\text{hr}}} \cdot \frac{60 \text{ s}}{1 \cancel{\text{min}}} = 6 \cdot 60 \cdot 60 \text{ s} = 21{,}600 \text{ s}$$

Be sure to carefully record the units when setting up conversion factors.

- Convert 3 gallons to pints.

$$3 \cancel{\text{gal}} \cdot \frac{4 \cancel{\text{qt}}}{1 \cancel{\text{gal}}} \cdot \frac{2 \text{ pt}}{1 \cancel{\text{qt}}} = 3 \cdot 4 \cdot 2 \text{ pt} = 24 \text{ pt}$$

5-1 Organizer

Pacing: Traditional 1 day
Block $\frac{1}{2}$ day

Objective: Students identify, write, and compare ratios and rates.

Warm Up

Write each fraction in simplest form.

1. $\frac{36}{40}$ $\frac{9}{10}$
2. $\frac{21}{35}$ $\frac{3}{5}$
3. $\frac{8}{12}$ $\frac{2}{3}$
4. $\frac{42}{90}$ $\frac{7}{15}$
5. $\frac{15}{80}$ $\frac{3}{16}$
6. $\frac{56}{84}$ $\frac{2}{3}$

Problem of the Day

If June 1 falls on a Tuesday, on which day of the week does September 1 fall? Wednesday

Available on Daily Transparency in CRB

Math Fact !

The word *rational,* which means "having reason or understanding," comes from the word *ratio,* which was used in the Middle Ages to mean "computation" or "reasoning through the problem."

5-1 Ratios and Rates

Learn to identify, write, and compare ratios and rates.

Vocabulary
ratio
rate
unit rate

In basketball practice, Kathlene made 17 baskets in 25 attempts. She compared the number of baskets she made to the total number of attempts she made by using the *ratio* $\frac{17}{25}$. A **ratio** is a comparison of two quantities by division.

Kathlene can write her ratio of baskets made to attempts in three different ways.

$\frac{17}{25}$ 17 to 25 17:25

EXAMPLE 1 Writing Ratios

A recipe for homemade ice cream calls for 6 cups of cream, 1 cup of sugar, and 2 cups of fruit. Write each ratio in all three forms.

A **cups of fruit to cups of cream**

$\frac{2}{6}$, 2 to 6, 2:6 — *For every 2 cups of fruit there are 6 cups of cream.*

The fraction $\frac{2}{6}$ can be simplified to $\frac{1}{3}$, so you can also write the following ratios:

$\frac{1}{3}$, 1 to 3, 1:3 — *For each cup of fruit there are 3 cups of cream.*

B **cups of sugar to total cups of ice cream mixture**

$6 + 1 + 2 = 9$ — *Find the total number of cups in the mixture.*

$\frac{1}{9}$, 1 to 9, 1:9 — *For each cup of sugar there are 9 cups of mixture.*

A ratio that compares two quantities measured in different units is a **rate**. Suppose Ms. Latocki drove 75 miles in 3 hours. Her rate of travel was 75 miles in 3 hours, or $\frac{75 \text{ mi}}{3 \text{ hr}}$.

If the measure of the second quantity in a rate is one unit, then the rate is a **unit rate**. To change a rate to a unit rate, divide both the numerator and the denominator by the number in the denominator.

$$\frac{75 \text{ mi}}{3 \text{ hr}} = \frac{75 \text{ mi} \div 3}{3 \text{ hr} \div 3} = \frac{25 \text{ mi}}{1 \text{ hr}}$$

The unit rate 25 miles per hour expresses the average number of miles Ms. Latocki drove each hour.

Reading Math

The unit rate $\frac{25 \text{ miles}}{1 \text{ hour}}$ is read as "twenty-five miles per hour."

1 Introduce

Alternate Opener

EXPLORATION

5-1 Ratios and Rates

Use number 1 as a guide to solve 2–5.

1.	A one-hour exam has 40 problems. How many problems per minute must the students complete to finish the test in time?	Compare 40 problems and 60 minutes. Divide $\frac{\text{number of problems}}{\text{number of minutes}}$. $\frac{40}{60} = \frac{4}{6} = \frac{2}{3} \rightarrow \frac{2}{3}$ of a problem per minute
2.	A cake that serves 10 people has 1,200 calories. How many calories per serving does the cake have?	
3.	A school has 500 students and 20 teachers. How many students are there per teacher?	
4.	A restaurant owner ordered 15 tables and 75 chairs for her new restaurant. How many chairs are there per table?	
5.	A car completed a 150-mile trip on 13 gallons of gasoline. How many miles per gallon of gasoline did the car travel?	

Think and Discuss

6. **Explain** why division is used to compare two numbers in a ratio.

Motivate

To introduce students to ratios and rates, ask them to give examples of ways to compare two numbers. Organize the examples into comparisons by addition or subtraction (e.g., 7 is 4 more than 3) and comparisons by multiplication or division (e.g., 12 is twice as much as 6). Point out that sometimes when quantities are compared using division, the units are the same (e.g., 3 red apples out of a dozen apples) and sometimes different (e.g., 120 miles in 3 hours).

Exploration worksheet and answers on Chapter 5 Resource Book pp. 7 and 80

2 Teach

Lesson Presentation

Guided Instruction

In this lesson, students learn to identify, write, and compare ratios and rates. The quantities to be compared can be written as a fraction or separated by the word "to" or a colon. A ratio that compares values with different units is called a *rate*, and if the denominator is 1, it is a *unit rate*.

Teaching Tip Point out that ratios can compare two separate quantities. Often students tend to think only in terms of part to whole comparisons. Be sure to examine ratios greater than 1.

EXAMPLE 2 Writing Rates and Unit Rates

Find the unit rates and write them in both fraction and word form.

A **Belinda biked 36 miles in 4 hours.**

$\frac{36 \text{ mi}}{4 \text{ hr}}$ *Rate in fraction form*

$\frac{36 \text{ mi} \div 4}{4 \text{ hr} \div 4} = \frac{9 \text{ mi}}{1 \text{ hr}}$ *Unit rate in fraction form*

She rode 9 miles per hour. *Unit rate in word form*

B **A recipe for a garden weed killer involves mixing 11 tablespoons of liquid soap with 2 quarts of water.**

$\frac{11 \text{ tbsp}}{2 \text{ qt}}$ *Rate in fraction form*

$\frac{11 \text{ tbsp} \div 2}{2 \text{ qt} \div 2} = \frac{5.5 \text{ tbsp}}{1 \text{ qt}}$ *Unit rate in fraction form*

The recipe calls for 5.5 tablespoons of soap per quart of water. *Unit rate in word form*

It is often easy to compare ratios when they are written as fractions in simplest form—especially when they have a common denominator.

EXAMPLE 3 Simplifying Ratios to Make Comparisons

Tell which cookie has the greater ratio of protein to serving size.

	Fruit Cookie	Chocolate Cookie
Serving size	30 grams	45 grams
Protein	2 grams	3 grams
Fat	0 grams	9 grams
Energy	90 calories	200 calories

Fruit cookie: $\frac{\text{protein grams}}{\text{serving grams}} = \frac{2}{30} = \frac{1}{15}$ *Simplify the ratio.*

Chocolate cookie: $\frac{\text{protein grams}}{\text{serving grams}} = \frac{3}{45} = \frac{1}{15}$ *Simplify the ratio.*

Both cookies have the same ratio of protein to serving size.

Think and Discuss

1. **Tell** how to identify whether a ratio is a rate.
2. **Give an example** of a ratio that can be written as a unit rate.
3. **Explain** why the ratio in Example 1B is considered a "part-to-whole" ratio.

Additional Examples

Example 1

The recommended fuel for Suzanne's snow blower is made from 80 quarts of gasoline and 1 quart of motor oil. Write each ratio in all three forms.

A. quarts of gasoline to quarts of oil

$\frac{80}{1}$, 80 to 1, 80:1

B. quarts of oil to quarts of fuel mixture

$\frac{1}{81}$, 1 to 81, 1:81

Example 2

Find the unit rates and write them in both fraction and word form.

A. Gordon memorized 560 vocabulary words in 28 days.

$\frac{20 \text{ words}}{1 \text{ day}}$

Gordon memorized 20 words per day.

B. Pete added 12 ounces of chocolate chips to a recipe that yielded 48 cookies.

$\frac{0.25 \text{ oz}}{1 \text{ cookie}}$

There is 0.25 ounce of chocolate chips per cookie.

Example 3

Honey lemon cough drops come in packages of 30 drops per 10-ounce bag. Cherry cough drops come in packages of 24 drops per 6-ounce box. Tell which package has the greater ratio of drops to ounces.

cherry cough drops

3 Close

Reaching All Learners

Through Critical Thinking

Instruct students to draw two right triangles whose sides have the same ratio (e.g., a right triangle with sides of 3, 4, and 5 units and another with sides of 9, 12, and 15 units). Ask them to find the ratios for the corresponding sides, their perimeters, and their areas ($A = \frac{1}{2}bh$). Ask students to tell whether any of the ratios are NOT the same and why.

Perimeters will have the same ratio as sides, but areas will not. Explanations may mention multiplying dimensions or the use of different units. Units of area are squared, so the corresponding ratio of areas should also be squared.

Summarize

Have students give examples of ratios and rates in each form. Ask students to explain when a ratio is called a rate and to summarize ways to compare ratios and rates.

Possible answers: $\frac{2}{5}$; 2 to 5; 2:5; 20 miles in 2 hours; $\frac{20 \text{ mi}}{2 \text{ hr}}$, $\frac{10 \text{ mi}}{1 \text{ hr}}$. A ratio is called a rate when the numerator and denominator are measured in different units. It is possible to compare rates by changing both rates to unit rates and to compare ratios by simplifying them.

Answers to Think and Discuss

1. A ratio is a rate if the two quantities being compared have different units.
2. Possible answer: $\frac{150 \text{ miles}}{3 \text{ hours}} = \frac{50 \text{ miles}}{1 \text{ hour}}$
3. Sugar is only part of the ice cream mixture.

5-1 PRACTICE & ASSESS

Students may want to refer back to the lesson examples.

Assignment Guide

If you finished Example 1 assign:
Core 1, 2, 6–9, 16, 18–30
Enriched 1, 7, 9, 14–16, 21, 18–30

If you finished Example 2 assign:
Core 1–4, 6–12, 16, 18–30
Enriched 1, 3, 7–11 odd, 14–16, 18–30

If you finished Example 3 assign:
Core 1–15, 18–30
Enriched 1–13 odd, 14–30

Answers

6. $\frac{25}{30}$, 25 to 30, 25:30, or $\frac{5}{6}$, 5 to 6, 5:6
7. $\frac{25}{70}$, 25 to 70, 25:70, or $\frac{5}{14}$, 5 to 14, 5:14
8. $\frac{30}{15}$, 30 to 15, 30:15, or $\frac{2}{1}$, 2 to 1, 2:1
9. $\frac{45}{25}$, 45 to 25, 45:25, or $\frac{9}{5}$, 9 to 5, 9:5
10. $\frac{12.5 \text{ mi}}{1 \text{ hr}}$; 12.5 miles per hour
11. $\frac{\$7}{1 \text{CD}}$; $7 per CD
12. $\frac{5 \text{ oz}}{1 \text{ qt}}$; 5 ounces per quart
14. $\frac{\$0.29}{12 \text{ oz}}$, $\frac{\$0.43}{24.8 \text{ oz}}$, $\frac{\$0.59}{33.8 \text{ oz}}$, $\frac{\$1.29}{128 \text{ oz}}$; the 128-ounce bottle

5-1 Exercises

FOR EXTRA PRACTICE see page 644

internet connect
Homework Help Online
go.hrw.com Keyword: MS4 5-1

GUIDED PRACTICE

See Example 1 **Sun-Li has 10 blue marbles, 3 red marbles, and 17 white marbles. Write each ratio in all three forms.**

1. blue marbles to red marbles **$\frac{10}{3}$, 10 to 3, 10:3**
2. red marbles to total marbles **$\frac{3}{30}$, 3 to 30, 3:30, or $\frac{1}{10}$, 1 to 10, 1:10**

See Example 2 **Find the unit rates and write them in both fraction and word form.**

3. Helena runs 10 miles in 2 hours. **$\frac{5 \text{ mi}}{1 \text{ hr}}$; 5 miles per hour**
4. Geoff scores 96 points in 8 games. **$\frac{12 \text{ points}}{1 \text{ game}}$; 12 points per game**

See Example 3

5. A 5-lb box of soap powder costs \$4.65. A 10-lb box of the same powder costs \$8.90. Which is the better price? Explain.
The 10-lb box is a better price because the unit price for a 10-lb box is lower than for a 5-lb box.

INDEPENDENT PRACTICE

See Example 1 **A soccer league has 25 sixth-graders, 30 seventh-graders, and 15 eighth-graders. Write each ratio in all three forms.**

6. 6th-graders to 7th-graders
7. 6th-graders to total students
8. 7th-graders to 8th-graders
9. 7th- and 8th-graders to 6th-graders

See Example 2 **Find the unit rates and write them in both fraction and word form.**

10. Sam bikes 100 miles in 8 hours.
11. Kendra spends \$21 for 3 CDs.
12. A recipe calls for 15 fl oz of punch mix per 3 qt of water.

See Example 3

13. Jonie paid \$10.70 for 10 gallons of gasoline. André paid \$15.60 for 12 gallons of gasoline. Who paid the higher price per gallon? Explain.
André paid the higher price per gallon, \$1.30. Jonie's price per gallon was \$1.07.

PRACTICE AND PROBLEM SOLVING

14. ***CONSUMER MATH*** Bottles of water are sold in various sizes. Write the ratios of price per volume for each size of bottled water. Which size is the best value?

$0.29
12 oz

$0.43
24.8 oz

$0.59
33.8 oz

$1.29
128 oz

Math Background

Although today we think of ratios as an arithmetic or algebraic topic, ancient mathematicians used ratios primarily in geometry—for the comparison of lengths of segments and of areas.

The Golden Ratio, equal to $\frac{1 + \sqrt{5}}{2} \approx 1.618$, was considered by the ancient Greeks to be an ideal, pleasing ratio for the length and width of a rectangle. Rectangles with dimensions in this ratio appear throughout Greek art and architecture. The overall dimensions of the Parthenon are in the Golden Ratio, and the same ratio is repeated many times throughout the structure.

RETEACH 5-1

LESSON 5-1 **Reteach**
Ratios and Rates

A **ratio** is a comparison of two numbers.

Tamara has 2 dogs and 8 fish. The ratio of dogs to fish can be written in three different ways.

	Ratio	Ratio in simplest form
• using the word *to*	2 to 8	1 to 4
• using a colon (:)	2:8	1:4
• writing a fraction	$\frac{2}{8}$	$\frac{1}{4}$

You can read the ratios as *2 to 8* or *1 to 4*.

In a basket of fruit, there are 8 apples, 3 bananas, and 5 oranges. Write the given ratio in all three forms.

1. apples to bananas
There are **8** apples and **3** bananas. So, the ratio of apples to bananas is **8** to **3**, or **8** : **3**, or $\frac{8}{3}$.
2. oranges to apples
There are **5** oranges and **8** apples. So, the ratio of oranges to apples is **5** to **8**, or **5** : **8**, or $\frac{5}{8}$.
3. bananas to oranges
There are **3** bananas and **5** oranges. So, the ratio of bananas to oranges is **3** to **5**, or **3** : **5**, or $\frac{3}{5}$.
4. apples to all pieces of fruit
There are **8** apples and **16** pieces of fruit in all. So, the ratio of apples to all pieces of fruit is **1** to **2**, or **1** : **2**, or $\frac{1}{2}$.

A large bouquet of flowers is made up of 18 roses, 16 daisies, and 24 iris. Write the given ratio in all three forms.

5. roses to iris
3 to 4; 3:4; $\frac{3}{4}$
6. daisies to roses
8 to 9; 8:9; $\frac{8}{9}$
7. iris to daisies
3 to 2; 3:2; $\frac{3}{2}$
8. roses to daisies
9 to 8; 9:8; $\frac{9}{8}$

PRACTICE 5-1

LESSON 5-1 **Practice B**
Ratios and Rates

The annual dog show has 22 collies, 28 boxers, and 18 poodles. Write the given ratio in all three forms.

1. collies to poodles
$\frac{11}{9}$; 11 to 9; 11:9
2. boxers to collies
$\frac{14}{11}$; 14 to 11; 14:11
3. poodles to boxers
$\frac{9}{14}$; 9 to 14; 9:14
4. poodles to collies
$\frac{9}{11}$; 9 to 11; 9:11

The Franklin School District has 15 art teachers, 27 math teachers, and 18 Spanish teachers. Write the given ratio in all three forms.

5. art teachers to math teachers
$\frac{5}{9}$; 5 to 9; 5:9
6. math teachers to Spanish teachers
$\frac{3}{2}$; 3 to 2, 3:2

Find the unit rates and write them in both fraction and word form.

7. Gabrielle bikes 78 miles in 6 hours.
$\frac{13}{1}$; 13 mi/h
8. A store sells 15 pears for \$5.
$\frac{3}{1}$; 3 pears for \$1
9. A class trip consists of 36 students and 6 teachers.
$\frac{6}{1}$; 6 students for each teacher
10. A landscaper plants 28 bushes and 4 trees.
$\frac{7}{1}$; 7 bushes for each tree
11. Carmen spends \$64 for 4 hats.
$\frac{16}{1}$; \$16 per hat
12. A car travels 330 miles in 6 hours.
$\frac{55}{1}$; 55 mi/h
13. Glen has 18 rock CDs and 15 classical CDs in his collection. He bought 10 of the rock CDs and 12 of the classical CDs. The rest were gifts. Compare the ratio of the number of rock CDs that he bought to the number of rock CDs in his collection with the ratio of the number of classical CDs that he bought to the number of classical CDs in his collection.
They are not the same ratio; 5:9 and 4:5.

Physical Science LINK

The pressure of water at different depths can be measured in *atmospheres*, or atm. The water pressure on a scuba diver increases as the diver descends below the surface. Use the table for Exercises 15–17.

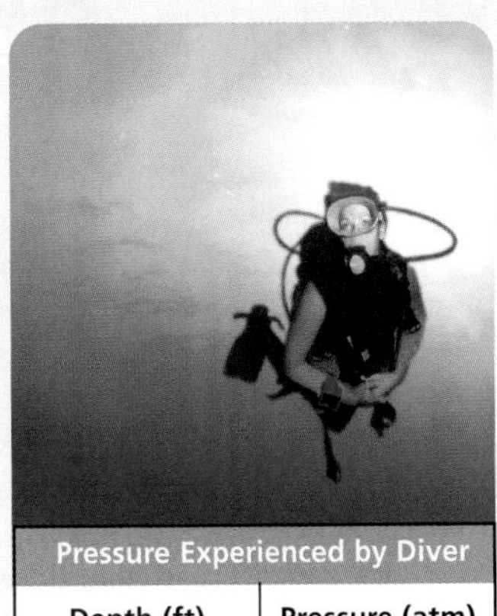

Pressure Experienced by Diver

Depth (ft)	Pressure (atm)
0	1
−33	2
−66	3
−99	4

15. Write each ratio in all three forms.
- **a.** pressure at −33 ft to pressure at surface
- **b.** pressure at −66 ft to pressure at surface
- **c.** pressure at −99 ft to pressure at surface
- **d.** pressure at −66 ft to pressure at −33 ft
- **e.** pressure at −99 ft to pressure at −66 ft

16. A scuba diver descends 33 feet below the surface.
- **a.** Write a rate in fraction form that shows the relation between the change in water pressure and the change in the diver's depth.
- **b.** Tell how you would write this rate as a unit rate. Then write the unit rate in word form.

17. ***CHALLENGE*** The ratio of the beginning pressure and the new pressure when a scuba diver goes from −33 ft to −66 ft is less than the ratio of pressures when the diver goes from the surface to −33 ft. The ratio of pressures is even less when the diver goes from −66 ft to −99 ft. Use the ratios that you wrote in Exercise 15 to explain why this is true.

go.hrw.com
KEYWORD: MS4 Pressure
CNN Student News.

Spiral Review

Solve each equation. (Lesson 2-12)

18. $3n = 18$ **$n = 6$** **19.** $15c = 225$ **$c = 15$** **20.** $8b = 120$ **$b = 15$** **21.** $19m = 95$ **$m = 5$**

Find three fractions equivalent to each given fraction. (Lesson 3-8) **Possible answers:**

22. $\frac{1}{2}$ $\mathbf{\frac{2}{4}, \frac{3}{6}, \frac{4}{8}}$ **23.** $\frac{3}{5}$ $\mathbf{\frac{6}{10}, \frac{9}{15}, \frac{12}{20}}$ **24.** $\frac{1}{9}$ $\mathbf{\frac{2}{18}, \frac{3}{27}, \frac{4}{36}}$ **25.** $\frac{4}{7}$ $\mathbf{\frac{8}{14}, \frac{12}{21}, \frac{16}{28}}$

Write each fraction in simplest form. (Lesson 3-8)

26. $\frac{8}{12}$ $\mathbf{\frac{2}{3}}$ **27.** $\frac{15}{18}$ $\mathbf{\frac{5}{6}}$ **28.** $\frac{21}{24}$ $\mathbf{\frac{7}{8}}$ **29.** $\frac{18}{36}$ $\mathbf{\frac{1}{2}}$

30. TEST PREP Which is the product of $3.68 \cdot 7.1$? (Lesson 4-3) **B**

A 2.6128 B 26.128 C 261.28 D 2,612.8

CHALLENGE 5-1

LESSON 5-1 Challenge
The Rate Maze

Contestants A–H must make their way through the maze to the Winners' Circle. To reach the Winners' Circle, each contestant must find a path from his or her current location through sections containing equivalent unit prices or rates. The contestants can move only through sections that share a corner.

Find each unit price or rate. Circle the two contestants who will *not* be able to get to the Winners' Circle.

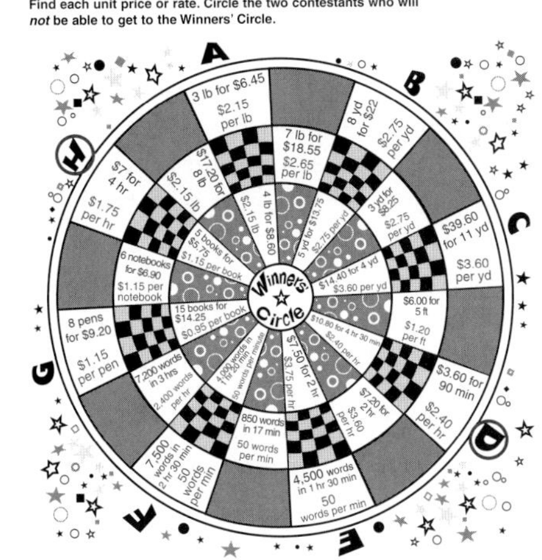

PROBLEM SOLVING 5-1

LESSON 5-1 Problem Solving
Ratios and Rates

Write the correct answer.

1. A truck driver drives from Chicago to Cincinnati in 14 hours. The distance traveled is 840 miles. Write the average speed as a unit rate in fraction form.
   $\frac{60 \text{ mi}}{1 \text{ hr}}$

2. During the 2001 WNBA season, the Los Angeles Sparks had 28 wins and only 4 losses. Write the ratio of wins to games played in simplest form three ways.
   7 to 8; 7:8; $\frac{7}{8}$

3. For every 300 people surveyed in 2002, 186 said their favorite Winter Olympic sport was figure skating. Write this ratio in simplest form three ways.
   50 to 31; 50:31; $\frac{50}{31}$

4. In 2000, George W. Bush received 271 electoral votes, Al Gore received 266, and 1 elector abstained from voting. Write the ratio of Bush's electoral votes to total electoral votes in simplest form three ways.
   271 to 538; 271:538; $\frac{271}{538}$

Choose the letter for the best answer.

5. There are 62 girls in the seventh grade and 58 boys in the eighth grade. Each grade has 120 students. Which statement correctly compares the ratios of boys to total students in each grade?
   A The eighth-grade ratio is greater.
   B The seventh-grade ratio is greater.
   C The eighth-grade ratio is lesser.
   (D) Both ratios are equal.

6. Matt has 6 video racing games and 8 video sports games. Which ratio is the ratio of racing games to total video games in simplest form?
   F $\frac{3}{4}$ (G) $\frac{3}{7}$ H $\frac{4}{3}$ J $\frac{4}{7}$

7. What is 20 pounds per 5 gallons as a unit rate?
   A $\frac{20 \text{ lb}}{1 \text{ gal}}$ B $\frac{5 \text{ lb}}{1 \text{ gal}}$ (C) $\frac{4 \text{ lb}}{1 \text{ gal}}$ D $\frac{20 \text{ lb}}{5 \text{ gal}}$

8. Last year Yeh grew 4 inches in 8 months. How much did she grow per month?
   (F) $\frac{1}{2}$ inch G 1 inch H 4 inches J 2 inches

Answers

15. 2:1, $\frac{2}{1}$, 2 to 1; 3:1, $\frac{3}{1}$, 3 to 1; 4:1, $\frac{4}{1}$, 4 to 1; 3:2, $\frac{3}{2}$, 3 to 2; 4:3, $\frac{4}{3}$, 4 to 3

16. **a.** $\frac{1 \text{ atm}}{33 \text{ ft}}$
b. Divide both the numerator and the denominator by 33; $\frac{1}{33}$ atmospheres per foot.

17. $\frac{3}{2} < \frac{2}{1}$ and $\frac{4}{3} < \frac{3}{2}$; therefore, the ratios of water pressures is less at greater depths.

Journal

Have students write about everyday situations in which ratios are used (e.g., adapting recipes or mixing colors of paint).

Test Prep Doctor

For Exercise 30, encourage students to estimate the answer before looking at the answer choices. The product of $3.68 \cdot 7.1$ can be estimated as $4 \cdot 7 = 28$, so eliminate **A** as too small and **C** and **D** as too large.

Lesson Quiz

A coin bank contains 16 quarters, 12 dimes, and 8 nickels. Write the given ratio in all three forms.

1. nickels to quarters **$\frac{8}{16}$, 8 to 16, 8:16, or $\frac{1}{2}$, 1 to 2, 1:2**

2. dimes to nickels **$\frac{12}{8}$, 12 to 8, 12:8, or $\frac{3}{2}$, 3 to 2, 3:2**

3. nickels and dimes to quarters **$\frac{20}{16}$, 20 to 16, 20:16, or $\frac{5}{4}$, 5 to 4, 5:4**

Find the unit rate and write it in both fraction and word form.

4. There are 220 calories in 5 crackers. $\frac{44 \text{ calories}}{1 \text{ cracker}}$, 44 calories per cracker

5. Kim and Ted work out on treadmills together at the gym. Kim walked 3.0 miles in 21 minutes, while Ted walked 4.5 miles in 42 minutes. Who walked at a faster rate? Kim

Available on Daily Transparency in CRB

5-2 Organizer

Pacing: Traditional 1 day
Block $\frac{1}{2}$ day

Objective: Students find equivalent ratios and identify proportions.

Warm Up

Write each fraction in simplest form.

1. $\frac{9}{21}$ $\frac{3}{7}$
2. $\frac{6}{18}$ $\frac{1}{3}$
3. $\frac{20}{25}$ $\frac{4}{5}$
4. $\frac{21}{36}$ $\frac{7}{12}$
5. $\frac{12}{18}$ $\frac{2}{3}$

Problem of the Day

Bob made a square tabletop with 100 white square tiles. He painted the tiles along the edges of the table red. How many tiles are red? **36**

Available on Daily Transparency in CRB

The professional athlete needed a huge helping of mashed potatoes, so he ordered a pro-portion.

5-2 Identifying and Writing Proportions

Learn to find equivalent ratios and to identify proportions.

Vocabulary
equivalent ratios
proportion

Students in Mr. Howell's math class are measuring the width w and the length ℓ of their heads. The ratio of ℓ to w is 10 inches to 6 inches for Jean and 25 centimeters to 15 centimeters for Pat.

Calipers have adjustable arms that are used to measure the thickness of objects.

These ratios can be written as the fractions $\frac{10}{6}$ and $\frac{25}{15}$. Since both ratios simplify to $\frac{5}{3}$, they are equivalent. **Equivalent ratios** are ratios that name the same comparison.

An equation stating that two ratios are equivalent is called a **proportion** . The equation, or proportion, below states that the ratios $\frac{10}{6}$ and $\frac{25}{15}$ are equivalent.

Reading Math

Read the proportion $\frac{10}{6} = \frac{25}{15}$ by saying "ten is to six as twenty-five is to fifteen."

$$\frac{10}{6} = \frac{25}{15}$$

If two ratios are equivalent, they are said to be *proportional* to each other, or *in proportion.*

EXAMPLE 1 Comparing Ratios in Simplest Form

Determine whether the ratios are proportional.

A $\frac{2}{7}, \frac{6}{21}$

$\frac{2}{7}$ — *$\frac{2}{7}$ is already in simplest form.*

$\frac{6}{21} = \frac{6 \div 3}{21 \div 3} = \frac{2}{7}$ — *Simplify $\frac{6}{21}$.*

Since $\frac{2}{7} = \frac{2}{7}$, the ratios are proportional.

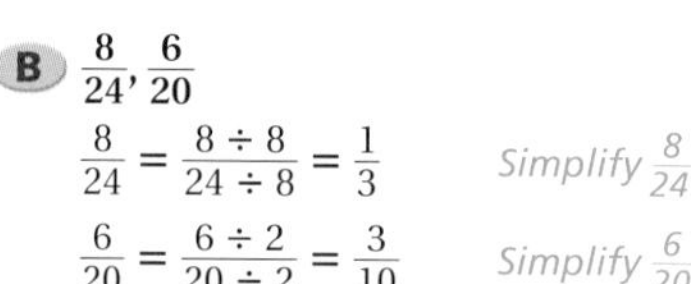

B $\frac{8}{24}, \frac{6}{20}$

$\frac{8}{24} = \frac{8 \div 8}{24 \div 8} = \frac{1}{3}$ — *Simplify $\frac{8}{24}$.*

$\frac{6}{20} = \frac{6 \div 2}{20 \div 2} = \frac{3}{10}$ — *Simplify $\frac{6}{20}$.*

Since $\frac{1}{3} \neq \frac{3}{10}$, the ratios are *not* proportional.

1 Introduce

Alternate Opener

EXPLORATION

5-2 Identifying and Writing Proportions

LaShonda is training to run a local 10-kilometer race. She keeps a record of her training runs in a table.

	Mon	Tue	Wed	Thu	Fri	Sat	Sun
Minutes (min)	50	20	25	off	40	32	40
Kilometers (km)	10	5	5		10	8	8

The two ratios $\frac{50 \text{ min}}{10 \text{ km}}$ and $\frac{25 \text{ min}}{5 \text{ km}}$ are equivalent because they have the same unit rate, $\frac{5 \text{ min}}{1 \text{ km}}$.

1. Identify the equivalent ratios in the table.
2. Find the smaller ratio. What does this ratio indicate?
3. Find the larger ratio. What does this ratio indicate?
4. Determine whether the following ratios are equivalent.
   a. $\frac{40 \text{ min}}{8 \text{ km}}, \frac{22 \text{ min}}{4 \text{ km}}$ b. $\frac{36 \text{ min}}{8 \text{ km}}, \frac{54 \text{ min}}{12 \text{ km}}$

Think and Discuss

5. **Describe** how you can determine whether two ratios are equivalent.
6. **Explain** why 30 out of 120 is the same as 40 out of 160.

Motivate

To introduce students to proportions, discuss situations in which they have heard the words *proportion*, *proportions*, or *in proportion* used. Discuss the common meanings of these words. Students may talk about a part or a share, about dimensions, or about balance. Ask students to explain what it means to say that two things are in proportion (e.g., that they are in the correct relationship to each other).

Exploration worksheet and answers on Chapter 5 Resource Book pp. 17 and 82

2 Teach

Lesson Presentation

Guided Instruction

In this lesson, students learn to find equivalent ratios and to identify proportions. Begin by defining a proportion as a statement that two ratios are equal. Since ratios can be written as fractions, proportions show equal fractions. Ask students to recall how to determine whether fractions are equal. If necessary, demonstrate how to find the common denominator and to determine whether the fractions are equal. Demonstrate that some ratios can be simplified to make comparison easier, while others must be changed to have a common denominator.

EXAMPLE 2 Comparing Ratios Using a Common Denominator

Use the data in the table to determine whether the ratios of oats to water are proportional for both servings of oatmeal.

Servings of Oatmeal	Cups of Oats	Cups of Water
8	2	4
12	3	6

Write the ratios of oats to water for 8 servings and for 12 servings.

Ratio of oats to water, 8 servings: $\frac{2}{4}$ *Write the ratio as a fraction.*

Ratio of oats to water, 12 servings: $\frac{3}{6}$ *Write the ratio as a fraction.*

$\frac{2}{4} = \frac{2 \cdot 6}{4 \cdot 6} = \frac{12}{24}$ *Write the ratios with a common denominator, such as 24.*

$\frac{3}{6} = \frac{3 \cdot 4}{6 \cdot 4} = \frac{12}{24}$

Since both ratios are equal to $\frac{12}{24}$, they are proportional.

You can find an equivalent ratio by multiplying or dividing the numerator and the denominator of a ratio by the same number.

EXAMPLE 3 Finding Equivalent Ratios and Writing Proportions

Find a ratio equivalent to each ratio. Then use the ratios to write a proportion.

A $\frac{8}{14}$

$\frac{8}{14} = \frac{8 \cdot 20}{14 \cdot 20} = \frac{160}{280}$ *Multiply both the numerator and denominator by any number, such as 20.*

$\frac{8}{14} = \frac{160}{280}$ *Write a proportion.*

B $\frac{4}{18}$

$\frac{4}{18} = \frac{4 \div 2}{18 \div 2} = \frac{2}{9}$ *Divide both the numerator and denominator by a common factor, such as 2.*

$\frac{4}{18} = \frac{2}{9}$ *Write a proportion.*

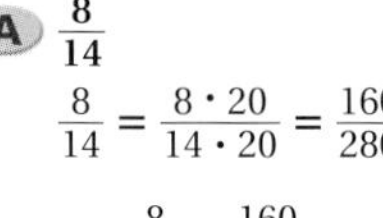

Life Science LINK

The ratios of the sizes of the segments of a nautilus shell are approximately equal to the *golden ratio*, 1.618. . . . This ratio can be found in many places in nature.

go.hrw.com KEYWORD: MS4 Golden

CNN Student News

Think and Discuss

1. Explain why the ratios in Example 1B are not proportional.

2. Describe what it means for ratios to be proportional.

3. Give an example of a proportion. Then tell how you know it is a proportion.

COMMON ERROR ALERT

When simplifying ratios to determine whether they are proportional, some students might check only the denominators or only the numerators. For example, for $\frac{3}{4}$ and $\frac{8}{12}$, the student might think $12 \div 3 = 4$ and decide that the ratios are proportional. Remind students to check both the denominators and the numerators.

Additional Examples

Example 1

Determine whether the ratios are proportional.

A. $\frac{24}{51}, \frac{72}{128}$

The ratios are not proportional.

B. $\frac{150}{105}, \frac{90}{63}$

The ratios are proportional.

Example 2

Directions for making 12 servings of rice call for 3 cups of rice and 6 cups of water. For 40 servings, the directions call for 10 cups of rice and 19 cups of water. Determine whether the ratios of rice to water are proportional for both servings of rice.

The ratios are not proportional.

Example 3

Find an equivalent ratio. Then write the proportion.

A. $\frac{3}{5}$ $\frac{3}{5} = \frac{6}{10}$ **B.** $\frac{28}{16}$ $\frac{28}{16} = \frac{7}{4}$

3 Close

Reaching All Learners

Through Curriculum Integration

Language Arts Discuss everyday objects that are proportional (e.g., different sizes of the same product and shoes or clothing in different sizes). Ask students to explain why they think the mathematical idea of "in proportion" came to mean "balance" or "harmony."

Possible answer: If objects were enlarged or reduced so that dimensions were not in proportion, the objects would seem distorted. When quantities are in proportion, all the parts are changed in the same way.

Summarize

Have students make up pairs of ratios that are not in simplest form. On the chalkboard, list some of the pairs that students suggest. Then select some of the pairs of ratios and have students explain how to determine whether the ratios are proportional.

Write the ratios in simplest form and see whether they are equal.

Answers to Think and Discuss

Possible answers:

1. The ratios in Example 1B can be simplified to different fractions. Ratios are proportional if they can be simplified to the same fraction.
2. A ratio is a relationship between two quantities. When two ratios are proportional, they show the same relationship.
3. $\frac{10}{4} = \frac{20}{8}$. The ratios reduce to the same fraction, $\frac{5}{2}$.

5-2 PRACTICE & ASSESS

Students may want to refer back to the lesson examples.

Assignment Guide

If you finished Example 1 assign:
Core 1–4, 13–16, 35–38, 46–58
Enriched 1–4, 13–16, 35–38, 46–58

If you finished Example 2 assign:
Core 1–8, 13–20, 35–38, 40, 46–58
Enriched 1–8, 13–20, 35–38, 40, 46–58

If you finished Example 3 assign:
Core 1–28, 29–41 odd, 46–58
Enriched 1–27 odd, 29–58

5-2 Exercises

FOR EXTRA PRACTICE see page 664

internet connect
Homework Help Online
go.hrw.com Keyword: MS4 5-2

GUIDED PRACTICE

See Example 1 Determine whether the ratios are proportional.

1. $\frac{2}{3}, \frac{4}{6}$ yes
2. $\frac{5}{10}, \frac{8}{18}$ no
3. $\frac{9}{12}, \frac{15}{20}$ yes
4. $\frac{3}{4}, \frac{8}{12}$ no

See Example 2

5. $\frac{10}{12}, \frac{15}{18}$ yes
6. $\frac{6}{9}, \frac{8}{12}$ yes
7. $\frac{3}{4}, \frac{5}{6}$ no
8. $\frac{4}{6}, \frac{6}{9}$ yes

See Example 3 Find a ratio equivalent to each ratio. Then use the ratios to write a proportion. **Possible answers:**

9. $\frac{1}{3}$ $\frac{1}{3} = \frac{2}{6}$
10. $\frac{9}{21}$ $\frac{9}{21} = \frac{3}{7}$
11. $\frac{8}{3}$ $\frac{8}{3} = \frac{16}{6}$
12. $\frac{10}{4}$ $\frac{10}{4} = \frac{5}{2}$

INDEPENDENT PRACTICE

See Example 1 Determine whether the ratios are proportional.

13. $\frac{5}{8}, \frac{7}{14}$ no
14. $\frac{8}{24}, \frac{10}{30}$ yes
15. $\frac{18}{20}, \frac{81}{180}$ no
16. $\frac{15}{20}, \frac{27}{35}$ no

See Example 2

17. $\frac{2}{3}, \frac{4}{9}$ no
18. $\frac{18}{12}, \frac{15}{10}$ yes
19. $\frac{7}{8}, \frac{14}{24}$ no
20. $\frac{18}{54}, \frac{10}{30}$ yes

See Example 3 Find a ratio equivalent to each ratio. Then use the ratios to write a proportion. **Possible answers:**

21. $\frac{5}{9}$ $\frac{5}{9} = \frac{10}{18}$
22. $\frac{27}{60}$ $\frac{27}{60} = \frac{9}{20}$
23. $\frac{6}{15}$ $\frac{6}{15} = \frac{2}{5}$
24. $\frac{121}{99}$ $\frac{121}{99} = \frac{11}{9}$
25. $\frac{11}{13}$ $\frac{11}{13} = \frac{55}{65}$
26. $\frac{5}{22}$ $\frac{5}{22} = \frac{15}{66}$
27. $\frac{78}{104}$ $\frac{78}{104} = \frac{39}{52}$
28. $\frac{27}{72}$ $\frac{27}{72} = \frac{3}{8}$

PRACTICE AND PROBLEM SOLVING

Complete each table of equivalent ratios.

29. 8 angelfish to 6 tiger fish

angelfish	4			20
tiger fish		6	18	

3 8 24 15

30. 4 squares to 16 circles

squares	2	4	6	8
circles				

8 16 24 32

Find two ratios equivalent to each given ratio. **Possible answers:**

31. 3 to 7 **6 to 14, 9 to 21**
32. 6:2 **3:1, 9:3**
33. $\frac{5}{12}$ $\frac{10}{24}, \frac{15}{36}$
34. 8:4 **2:1, 4:2**
35. 6 to 9 **2 to 3, 12 to 18**
36. $\frac{10}{50}$ $\frac{1}{5}, \frac{2}{10}$
37. 10:4 **5:2, 20:8**
38. 1 to 10 **2 to 20, 3 to 30**

39. ***ECOLOGY*** If you recycle one aluminum can, you save enough energy to run a TV for four hours.
   a. Write the ratio of cans to hours. $\frac{\text{1 can}}{\text{4 hours}}$
   b. Marti's class recycled enough aluminum cans to run a TV for 2,080 hours. Did the class recycle 545 cans? Justify your answer using equivalent ratios. **No, 1:4 = x:2,080; the class recycled 520 cans.**

Math Background

Arithmetically, ratios look and behave like fractions, but often they are not the same as fractions. With fractions, there is a part-to-whole relationship between the numerator and the denominator. That relationship may be present in ratios; however, since a ratio is a comparison of two numbers (not necessarily integers) that uses division, it should not be confused with a fraction, for example, the ratio 1.67 to 2.37 or the ratio $\frac{22}{7}$ to π.

A proportion is defined as a statement that two given ratios are equal. Proportions have the following property:

Let $\frac{a}{b} = \frac{c}{d}$, $b \neq 0$, $d \neq 0$, be any two ratios. Then $\frac{a}{b} = \frac{c}{d}$ if and only if $ad = bc$.

RETEACH 5-2

LESSON 5-2 **Reteach**
Identifying and Writing Proportions

Two ratios that are equal form a **proportion.** To determine whether two ratios are proportional, find the cross products of the ratios. If the cross products are equal, then the ratios are proportional.

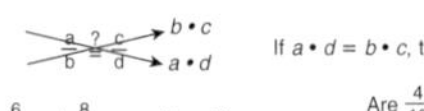

If $a \cdot d = b \cdot c$, then $\frac{a}{b} = \frac{c}{d}$.

Are $\frac{6}{9}$ and $\frac{8}{12}$ proportional?
Find the cross products.
$6 \cdot 12 = 72$ and $9 \cdot 8 = 72$
Since the cross products are equal, $\frac{6}{9}$ and $\frac{8}{12}$ are proportional.
So, $\frac{6}{9} = \frac{8}{12}$.

Are $\frac{4}{10}$ and $\frac{3}{8}$ proportional?
Find the cross products.
$4 \cdot 8 = 32$ and $10 \cdot 3 = 30$
Since the cross products are not equal, $\frac{4}{10}$ and $\frac{3}{8}$ are not proportional.
So, $\frac{4}{10} \neq \frac{3}{8}$.

Find the cross products to determine if the ratios are proportional.

1. $\frac{15}{21}, \frac{5}{7}$
   $15 \cdot$ **7** = **105** $21 \cdot$ **5** = **105**
   Are the ratios proportional? **yes**
2. $\frac{6}{9}, \frac{9}{15}$
   $6 \cdot$ **15** = **90** **9** $\cdot$ **9** = **81**
   Are the ratios proportional? **no**
3. $\frac{15}{6}, \frac{9}{4}$ **60, 54, no**
4. $\frac{12}{24}, \frac{5}{10}$ **120, 120, yes**
5. $\frac{20}{12}, \frac{15}{9}$ **180, 180, yes**

You can write a proportion from a given ratio. Multiply or divide the numerator and denominator of the ratio by the same number.

$\frac{9}{12} = \frac{9 \div 3}{12 \div 3} = \frac{3}{4}$ So, $\frac{9}{12} = \frac{3}{4}$. $\frac{9}{12} = \frac{9 \cdot 4}{12 \cdot 4} = \frac{36}{48}$ So, $\frac{9}{12} = \frac{36}{48}$.

Find an equivalent ratio. Then write the proportion. **Possible answers given.**

6. $\frac{6}{10}$ $\frac{6}{10} = \frac{3}{5}$
7. $\frac{10}{15}$ $\frac{10}{15} = \frac{20}{30}$
8. $\frac{18}{24}$ $\frac{18}{24} = \frac{3}{4}$

PRACTICE 5-2

LESSON 5-2 **Practice B**
Identifying and Writing Proportions

Determine if the ratios are proportional by reducing them to simplest form and comparing them.

1. $\frac{3}{4}, \frac{24}{32}$ $\frac{3}{4}, \frac{3}{4}$; yes
2. $\frac{5}{6}, \frac{15}{18}$ $\frac{5}{6}, \frac{5}{6}$; yes
3. $\frac{10}{12}, \frac{20}{32}$ $\frac{5}{6}, \frac{5}{8}$; no
4. $\frac{7}{10}, \frac{22}{30}$ $\frac{7}{10}, \frac{11}{15}$; no
5. $\frac{9}{6}, \frac{21}{14}$ $\frac{3}{2}, \frac{3}{2}$; yes
6. $\frac{7}{9}, \frac{24}{27}$ $\frac{7}{9}, \frac{8}{9}$; no

Determine if the ratios are proportional by finding a common denominator.

7. $\frac{4}{10}, \frac{6}{15}$ $\frac{12}{30}, \frac{12}{30}$; yes
8. $\frac{7}{12}, \frac{13}{20}$ $\frac{35}{60}, \frac{39}{60}$; no
9. $\frac{4}{9}, \frac{6}{12}$ $\frac{16}{36}, \frac{8}{36}$; no
10. $\frac{7}{8}, \frac{14}{16}$ $\frac{14}{16}, \frac{14}{16}$; yes
11. $\frac{9}{10}, \frac{45}{50}$ $\frac{45}{50}, \frac{45}{50}$; yes
12. $\frac{3}{7}, \frac{10}{21}$ $\frac{9}{21}, \frac{10}{21}$; no

Find an equivalent ratio. Then write the proportion. Answers may vary. Possible answers given.

13. $\frac{7}{9}$ $\frac{7}{9} = \frac{70}{90}$
14. $\frac{11}{12}$ $\frac{11}{12} = \frac{110}{120}$
15. $\frac{14}{15}$ $\frac{14}{15} = \frac{28}{30}$
16. $\frac{35}{55}$ $\frac{35}{55} = \frac{70}{110}$
17. $\frac{14}{10}$ $\frac{14}{10} = \frac{7}{5}$
18. $\frac{25}{18}$ $\frac{25}{18} = \frac{100}{72}$

40. ***SOCIAL STUDIES*** Population density is the average number of people per unit of area.

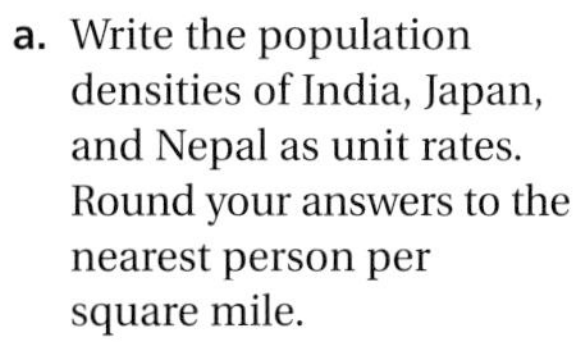

a. Write the population densities of India, Japan, and Nepal as unit rates. Round your answers to the nearest person per square mile.

b. Which country has the greatest population density? Explain.

Nepal
Population = 23,698,000
Area = 56,827 mi^2

Japan
Population = 125,932,000
Area = 145,834 mi^2

ASIA

India
Population = 984,004,000
Area = 1,269,346 mi^2

Source: 1999 World Almanac

41. Last year in Kerry's school, the ratio of students to teachers was 22:1. Write an equivalent ratio to show how many students there were if the school had only 8 teachers. **176:8; 176 students**

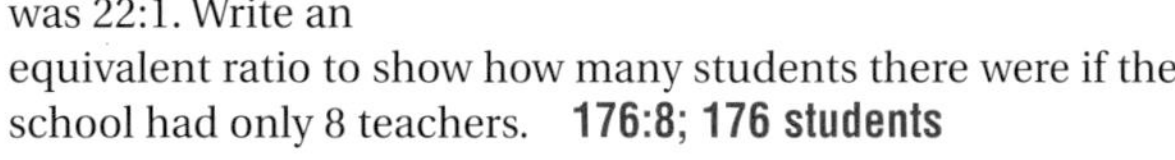

42. Marcus earned $230 for 40 hours of work. Phillip earned $192 for 32 hours of work. Are these pay rates proportional? Explain. **No, Marcus earned $5.75 per hour and Phillip earned $6.00 per hour.**

43. ***WHAT'S THE ERROR?*** A student wrote the proportion $\frac{13}{20} = \frac{26}{60}$. What did the student do wrong?

44. ***WRITE ABOUT IT*** Explain two different ways to determine if two ratios are proportional. **Write them with a common denominator or reduce them both to simplest form.**

45. ***CHALLENGE*** Write all possible proportions using only the numbers 1, 2, and 4. **1:2 = 2:4, 2:1 = 4:2, 1:1 = 2:2, 1:1 = 4:4, 2:2 = 4:4**

Spiral Review

Write the prime factorization of each number. (Lesson 2-4)

46. 16 **2^4** **47.** 120 **$2^3 \cdot 3 \cdot 5$** **48.** 18 **$2 \cdot 3^2$** **49.** 48 **$2^4 \cdot 3$**

Evaluate each algebraic expression for $x = 2$ and $y = 3$. (Lesson 2-7)

50. $2x$ **4** **51.** $5 - y$ **2** **52.** $3x + 2y$ **12** **53.** $4y^2 - 3$ **33**

Add. (Lesson 3-3)

54. $8 + (-2)$ **6** **55.** $-9 + 3$ **−6** **56.** $-7 + (-2)$ **−9** **57.** $11 + (-6)$ **5**

58. TEST PREP The best estimate of $\frac{1}{16} + \frac{1}{9}$ is __?__ . (Lesson 4-9) **A**

A 0 **B** $\frac{1}{2}$ **C** 1 **D** $1\frac{1}{2}$

Answers

40. a. 775 people/mi^2; 864 people/mi^2; 417 people/mi^2

b. Japan, because it has the largest number of people per square mile

43. The student multiplied the numerator by 2 and the denominator by 3. The multipliers should have been the same.

Journal

Have students describe real-world objects that seem to be proportional to each other and others that do not seem to be proportional. Invite students to include sketches with their descriptions if appropriate or helpful.

Test Prep Doctor

In Exercise 58, students are asked to estimate with fractions. Since the fractions being added both round to 0, the answer is **A.**

CHALLENGE 5-2

LESSON 5-2 **Challenge**
What's in the Set?

The ratios below describe a set of polygons. Use the ratios to find the number of each type of polygon in the set. All ratios are written in simplest form.

- Equilateral triangles to isosceles triangles is 2 to 3
- Isosceles triangles to scalene triangles is 6:5
- Triangles to rectangles is $\frac{5}{4}$
- Parallelograms to triangles is $\frac{4}{3}$

1. What is the fewest number of each polygon that can be in the set?
   a. Equilateral triangles **4**
   b. Isosceles triangles **6**
   c. Scalene triangles **5**
   d. All triangles **15**
   e. Rectangles **12**
   f. Parallelograms **20**
2. Explain the order in which you determined the number of each polygon in the set.
   Answers will vary. Possible answer: Find the number of triangles first. There must be at least 5 scalene triangles. Then use the ratios.
3. Other sets of polygons with the same ratios are possible. Find the number of polygons in another set that has the same ratios.
   Answers will vary. Possible answers given.
   a. Equilateral triangles **12**
   b. Isosceles triangles **18**
   c. Scalene triangles **15**
   d. All triangles **45**
   e. Rectangles **36**
   f. Parallelograms **60**

PROBLEM SOLVING 5-2

LESSON 5-2 **Problem Solving**
Identifying and Writing Proportions

Write the correct answer.

1. In 2000, the average price for a gallon of gasoline in Mexico was $2.02. Write a ratio equivalent to 2.02:1 to find out how many gallons of gasoline could have been purchased for $24.24.
   24.24:12; 12 gal
2. In 1999, the population density of the United States was approximately 76 people per square mile. If the area of the United States is about 3.7 million square miles, what was the population to the nearest million?
   281 million people
3. The ratio of the population of California to that of Wyoming is about 68 to 1. If there were about 494,000 people in Wyoming in 2001, about how many were there in California, to the nearest million?
   about 34 million
4. There are 3 atoms of hydrogen for every 1 atom of nitrogen in each molecule of ammonia. Write a ratio to show how many atoms of hydrogen there are in 15 molecules of ammonia in three ways.
   45:15; 45 to 15; $\frac{45}{15}$
5. During one month, it rained 24 out of 30 days. Write an equivalent ratio.
   Possible answer: 48:60
6. There are 52 computers for every 200 students in Fairway Middle School. Write an equivalent ratio.
   Possible answer: 13:50

Choose the letter for the best answer.

7. A clothing store stocks 5 blouses for every 3 pairs of pants. Which ratio is proportional for the number of pairs of pants to blouses?
   A 15:9 (C) 12:20
   B 3:8 D 18:25
8. To make lemonade, you can mix 4 teaspoons of lemonade powder with 16 ounces of water. What is the ratio of powder to water?
   F 4:32 H 24:64
   G 32:8 (J) 32:128
9. The town library is open 4 days per week. If you write this as a ratio and then find an equivalent ratio, how could you write a proportion?
   A $\frac{4}{7} = \frac{20}{25}$ C $\frac{4}{7} = \frac{20}{28}$
   B $\frac{7}{4} = \frac{21}{12}$ (D) $\frac{4}{7} = \frac{20}{35}$
10. The ratio of cars to residents on a small island is 1:112. There are 2,912 residents on the island. How many cars are there on the island?
    F 2,800 cars H 112 cars
    (G) 26 cars J 52 cars

Lesson Quiz

Determine whether the rates are proportional by writing them in simplest form and comparing them.

1. $\frac{9}{30}, \frac{12}{40}$ $\frac{3}{10}, \frac{3}{10}$; proportional

2. $\frac{12}{21}, \frac{10}{15}$ $\frac{4}{7}, \frac{2}{3}$; not proportional

Determine if the ratios are proportional by finding a common denominator.

3. $\frac{3}{8}, \frac{2}{5}$ $\frac{15}{40}, \frac{16}{40}$; not proportional

4. $\frac{3}{7}, \frac{9}{21}$ $\frac{9}{21}, \frac{9}{21}$; proportional

5. In a local pre-school, there are 5 children for every teacher. Write an equivalent ratio to show how many children there would be if there were 4 teachers. $\frac{5}{1}, \frac{20}{4}$

Available on Daily Transparency in CRB

5-3 Organizer

Pacing: Traditional 1 day
Block $\frac{1}{2}$ day

Objective: Students solve proportions by using cross products.

Warm Up

Determine whether the ratios are proportional.

1. $\frac{5}{8}, \frac{15}{24}$ proportional
2. $\frac{12}{15}, \frac{16}{25}$ not proportional
3. $\frac{15}{10}, \frac{20}{16}$ not proportional
4. $\frac{14}{18}, \frac{42}{54}$ proportional
5. $\frac{30}{36}, \frac{20}{24}$ proportional

Problem of the Day

If $A = 1, B = 2, C = 3, D = 4$, and so on, all the way to $Z = 26$, then what is $A + B + C + D + \ldots + Z = ?$ (*Hint*: $A + Z = B + Y$.) **351**

Available on Daily Transparency in CRB

Math Fact !

The daily recommended dietary allowance for protein is described in proportion to a person's weight. It is given as 0.8 g/kg per day. Using that proportion, a dietitian would recommend that an adult weighing 120 pounds consume 44 grams of protein a day.

5-3 Solving Proportions

Learn to solve proportions by using cross products.

Vocabulary
cross product

The tall stack of Jenga® blocks is 25.8 cm tall. How tall is the shorter stack of blocks? To find the answer, you will need to solve a proportion.

For two ratios, the product of the numerator in one ratio and the denominator in the other is a **cross product**. If the cross products of the ratios are equal, then the ratios form a proportion.

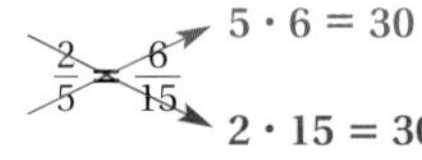

CROSS PRODUCT RULE

In the proportion $\frac{a}{b} = \frac{c}{d}$, the cross products, $a \cdot d$ and $b \cdot c$, are equal.

You can use the cross product rule to solve proportions with variables.

EXAMPLE 1 Solving Proportions Using Cross Products

Use cross products to solve the proportion $\frac{p}{6} = \frac{10}{3}$.

$\frac{p}{6} = \frac{10}{3}$

$p \cdot 3 = 6 \cdot 10$ *The cross products are equal.*

$3p = 60$ *Multiply.*

$\frac{3p}{3} = \frac{60}{3}$ *Divide each side by 3 to isolate the variable.*

$p = 20$

When setting up a proportion to solve a problem, use a variable to represent the number you want to find. In proportions that include different units of measurement, either the units in the numerators must be the same and the units in the denominators must be the same or the units within each ratio must be the same.

$$\frac{16 \text{ mi}}{4 \text{ hr}} = \frac{8 \text{ mi}}{x \text{ hr}} \qquad \frac{16 \text{ mi}}{8 \text{ mi}} = \frac{4 \text{ hr}}{x \text{ hr}}$$

1 Introduce

Alternate Opener

EXPLORATION

5-3 Solving Proportions

Kyle runs 5 kilometers in 25 minutes at a constant pace. Use this information to solve each problem.

Minutes: 0 10 20 30 40 50 60 70 80 90 100
Kilometers: 0 2 4 6 8 10 12 14 16 18 20

		Using a Proportion	Using the Number Line
1.	How long does it take him to run 10 kilometers?	$\frac{5}{25} = \frac{10}{x}$ $5x = (25)(10)$ $x = \frac{(25)(10)}{5} = 50$ It takes him 50 minutes.	The number line shows that 10 kilometers can be run in **50 minutes.**
2.	How long does it take him to run 1 kilometer?		
3.	How far does he go in 30 minutes?		
4.	How far does he go in 40 minutes?		

Think and Discuss

5. **Discuss** what a proportion is.
6. **Explain** how you can use number lines to write proportions.

Motivate

To introduce solving proportions, ask students to give examples of equal ratios (e.g., $\frac{1}{4}$ and $\frac{4}{16}$). Introduce a pair of ratios with a variable in place of one number, such as $\frac{3}{8}$ and $\frac{x}{16}$. Tell students that the ratios are equal, and ask them to think of ways to determine the value of the variable.

Exploration worksheet and answers on Chapter 5 Resource Book pp. 26 and 84

2 Teach

Lesson Presentation

Guided Instruction

In this lesson, students learn to solve proportions by using cross products. Use examples to show that cross products of proportions are equal (Teaching Transparency, T10, CRB). Stress that this is true only for proportions. Discuss a proportion with a variable term, and find the cross products. Ask students to explain how they could use the knowledge that cross products are equal to find the value of the variable.

Teaching Tip In problem solving, help students organize information to create correct proportions. Use units or descriptive models such as $\frac{\text{ounces}}{\text{grams}} = \frac{\text{ounces}}{\text{grams}}$ or $\frac{\text{big}}{\text{little}} = \frac{\text{big}}{\text{little}}$ to help them set up equal ratios.

EXAMPLE 2 PROBLEM SOLVING APPLICATION

A stack of 18 Jenga blocks is about 25.8 cm tall. What is the height, to the nearest tenth of a centimeter, of a stack of 11 Jenga blocks?

1 Understand the Problem

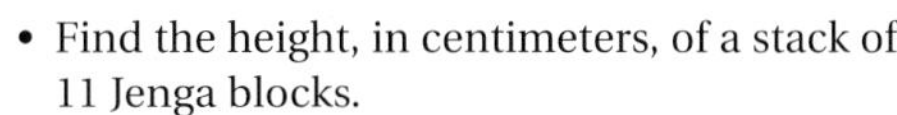

Rewrite the question as a statement.

- Find the height, in centimeters, of a stack of 11 Jenga blocks.

List the **important information:**

- A stack of 18 Jenga blocks is about 25.8 cm tall.

2 Make a Plan

Set up a proportion using the given information.

$\frac{18 \text{ blocks}}{25.8 \text{ cm}} = \frac{11 \text{ blocks}}{h}$ *Let h be the unknown height.*

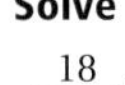

3 Solve

$\frac{18}{25.8} = \frac{11}{h}$	*Write the proportion.*
$18 \cdot h = 25.8 \cdot 11$	*The cross products are equal.*
$18h = 283.8$	*Multiply.*
$\frac{18h}{18} = \frac{283.8}{18}$	*Divide each side by 18 to isolate the variable.*
$h \approx 15.7\overline{6}$	
$h \approx 15.8$	*Round to the nearest tenth.*

The stack of 11 Jenga blocks is about 15.8 cm.

4 Look Back

Since the height of the smaller stack of blocks was rounded, the cross products of the proportion are not equal.

$\frac{18}{25.8} \quad \frac{11}{15.8}$ $\quad 11 \cdot 25.8 = 283.8$

$18 \cdot 15.8 = 284.4$

However, the cross products are close in value, so 15.8 cm is a reasonable answer.

Think and Discuss

1. **Describe** the error in these steps: $\frac{2}{3} = \frac{x}{12}$; $2x = 36$; $x = 18$.
2. **Show** how to use cross products to decide whether the ratios 6:45 and 2:15 are proportional.

COMMON ERROR ALERT

Caution students to take the time to write the equal cross products before solving. Some students might try to do both the cross multiplication and the division mentally, which can lead to errors both in calculation and in the position of the numbers.

Additional Examples

Example 1

Use cross products to solve the proportion. $\frac{9}{15} = \frac{m}{5}$

$m = 3$

Example 2

If 3 volumes of Jennifer's encyclopedia take up 4 inches of space on her shelf, how much space will she need for all 26 volumes?

She needs $34\frac{2}{3}$ inches for all 26 volumes.

Example 2 note: Point out the importance of including the units when setting up proportions (e.g., $\frac{18 \text{ blocks}}{25.8 \text{ cm}}$, rather than $\frac{18}{25.8}$). This will help students write the correct proportion.

3 Close

Reaching All Learners

Through Curriculum Integration

Art American artist Chuck Close (1940–) specializes in giant, highly realistic portraits. In 1978, he created a self-portrait more than 11 feet high and 9 feet wide. Have the students measure the height and width of their faces. Have students determine how wide a portrait of their faces would be if they made the portrait 11 ft tall. Then have students find the dimensions that their eyes, nose, and mouth would be on the portrait.

Summarize

Ask students to explain how to solve a proportion and whether it matters where the variable is located. Discuss how cross products are related to the techniques of solving equations that students have learned.

Possible answer: To solve a proportion, find cross products by multiplying the numerator of one ratio by the denominator of the other. Write the equal cross products, and solve the equation. The steps are the same regardless of where the variable is. Using cross products is a shortcut for multiplying both sides of the equation first by the denominator of one ratio, and then by the denominator of the other.

Answers to Think and Discuss

Possible answers:

1. The error was in multiplying the numerators and multiplying the denominators rather than cross multiplying the numerator of one ratio by the denominator of the other.
2. To decide whether 6:45 and 2:15 form a proportion, first write both in fraction form, $\frac{6}{45} \stackrel{?}{=} \frac{2}{15}$. Then multiply $6 \cdot 15$ and $45 \cdot 2$. Since both equal 90, the ratios form a proportion.

5-3 PRACTICE & ASSESS

Students may want to refer back to the lesson examples.

Assignment Guide

If you finished Example 1 assign:
Core 1–4, 6–13, 17–33 odd, 43–50
Enriched 1, 6, 10, 16–33, 43–50

If you finished Example 2 assign:
Core 1–15, 17–39 odd, 43–50
Enriched 1, 5, 6, 10, 14, 16–50

Answers

6. $x = 20$
7. $h = 144$
8. $r = 6.5$
9. $v = 336$
10. $x = 9$
11. $t = 36$
12. $s = 4.8$
13. $n = 22.4$

16–27. Possible answers:

16. $h = 8; \frac{1}{2}$
17. $x = 2; \frac{4}{30}$
18. $t = 117; \frac{78}{8}$
19. $w = 18; \frac{11}{12}$
20. $y = 8.5; \frac{2}{6}$
21. $x = 90; \frac{2}{10}$
22. $m = 35; \frac{70}{8}$
23. $q = 17.4; \frac{26.1}{6}$
24. $r = 15; \frac{30}{168}$
25. $k = 324; \frac{1}{4}$
26. $p = 45; \frac{18}{1{,}000}$
27. $j = 16.5; \frac{10}{33}$

5-3 Exercises

FOR EXTRA PRACTICE see page 664

GUIDED PRACTICE

See Example 1 **Use cross products to solve each proportion.**

1. $\frac{6}{10} = \frac{36}{x}$ **x = 60**
2. $\frac{4}{7} = \frac{5}{p}$ **p = 8.75**
3. $\frac{12.3}{m} = \frac{75}{100}$ **m = 16.4**
4. $\frac{t}{42} = \frac{1.5}{3}$ **t = 21**

See Example 2

5. A stack of 2,450 one dollar bills weighs 5 pounds. How much does a stack of 1,470 one dollar bills weigh? **3 lb**

INDEPENDENT PRACTICE

See Example 1 **Use cross products to solve each proportion.**

6. $\frac{4}{36} = \frac{x}{180}$
7. $\frac{7}{84} = \frac{12}{h}$
8. $\frac{3}{24} = \frac{r}{52}$
9. $\frac{5}{140} = \frac{12}{v}$
10. $\frac{45}{x} = \frac{15}{3}$
11. $\frac{t}{6} = \frac{96}{16}$
12. $\frac{2}{5} = \frac{s}{12}$
13. $\frac{14}{n} = \frac{5}{8}$

See Example 2

14. Euro coins come in eight denominations. One denomination is the one-euro coin, which is worth 100 cents. A stack of 10 one-euro coins is 21.25 millimeters tall. How tall would a stack of 45 one-euro coins be? Round your answer to the nearest hundredth of a millimeter. **95.63 mm**

15. There are 18.5 ounces of soup in a can. This is equivalent to 524 grams. If Jenna has 8 ounces of soup, how many grams does she have? Round your answer to the nearest whole gram. **227 grams**

PRACTICE AND PROBLEM SOLVING

Solve each proportion. Then find another equivalent ratio.

16. $\frac{4}{h} = \frac{12}{24}$
17. $\frac{x}{15} = \frac{12}{90}$
18. $\frac{39}{4} = \frac{t}{12}$
19. $\frac{5.5}{6} = \frac{16.5}{w}$
20. $\frac{1}{3} = \frac{y}{25.5}$
21. $\frac{18}{x} = \frac{1}{5}$
22. $\frac{m}{4} = \frac{175}{20}$
23. $\frac{8.7}{2} = \frac{q}{4}$
24. $\frac{r}{84} = \frac{32.5}{182}$
25. $\frac{76}{304} = \frac{81}{k}$
26. $\frac{9}{500} = \frac{p}{2{,}500}$
27. $\frac{5}{j} = \frac{6}{19.8}$

Arrange each set of numbers to form a proportion. **Possible answers:**

28. 10, 6, 30, 18 $\frac{6}{18} = \frac{10}{30}$
29. 4, 6, 10, 15 $\frac{4}{10} = \frac{6}{15}$
30. 12, 21, 7, 4 $\frac{4}{12} = \frac{7}{21}$
31. 75, 4, 3, 100 $\frac{3}{75} = \frac{4}{100}$
32. 30, 42, 5, 7 $\frac{5}{30} = \frac{7}{42}$
33. 5, 90, 108, 6 $\frac{5}{6} = \frac{90}{108}$

34. If you put an object that weighs 8 grams on one side of a balance scale, you would have to put about 20 paper clips on the other side to balance the weight. How many paper clips would balance the weight of a 10-gram object? **25 paper clips**

35. Sandra drove 126.2 miles in 2 hours at a constant speed. Use a proportion to find how long it would take her to drive 189.3 miles at the same speed. **3 hours**

Math Background

The method of cross multiplying is sometimes stated as the Means-Extremes Property. The name comes from the labels given to the terms of the proportion based upon their positions. In the proportion $a:b = c:d$, a and d are called the *extremes,* and b and c the *means*. With these labels, the cross products become the product of the means and the product of the extremes, and the Means-Extremes Property states that the product of the means is equal to the product of the extremes.

RETEACH 5-3

LESSON 5-3 **Reteach**
Solving Proportions

Solving a proportion is like solving an equation involving fractions.

- Multiply both sides of the equation by the denominator of the fraction containing the variable.
- If the variable is in the denominator, invert both fractions in the proportion.

$\frac{n}{7} = \frac{20}{28}$

$7 \cdot \frac{n}{7} = 7 \cdot \frac{20}{28}$

$n = \frac{7 \cdot 20}{28} = \frac{140}{28}$

$n = 5$

$\frac{12}{x} = \frac{9}{6}$

$\frac{x}{12} = \frac{6}{9}$ (Invert both fractions.)

$12 \cdot \frac{x}{12} = 12 \cdot \frac{6}{9}$

$x = \frac{12 \cdot 6}{9} = \frac{72}{9}$

$x = 8$

Solve the proportion.

1. $\frac{a}{2} = \frac{27}{18}$
   $\underline{2} \cdot \frac{a}{2} = \frac{27}{18} \cdot \underline{2}$
   $a = \frac{27 \cdot 2}{18}$
   $a = \frac{54}{18}$
   $a = \underline{3}$
2. $\frac{8}{12} = \frac{n}{9}$
   $\underline{9} \cdot \frac{8}{12} = \frac{n}{9} \cdot \underline{9}$
   $\frac{9 \cdot 8}{12} = n$
   $\frac{72}{12} = n$
   $n = \underline{6}$
3. $\frac{10}{t} = \frac{4}{6}$
   $\frac{t}{10} = \frac{6}{4}$
   $\underline{10} \cdot \frac{t}{10} = \frac{6}{4} \cdot \underline{10}$
   $t = \frac{6 \cdot 10}{4}$
   $t = \frac{60}{4}$
   $t = \underline{15}$
4. $\frac{x}{15} = \frac{8}{10}$ $x = 12$
5. $\frac{7}{3} = \frac{w}{18}$ $w = 42$
6. $\frac{3}{2} = \frac{15}{c}$ $c = 10$

PRACTICE 5-3

LESSON 5-3 **Practice B**
Solving Proportions

Use cross products to solve the proportion.

1. $\frac{2}{5} = \frac{x}{35}$ $x = 14$
2. $\frac{7}{r} = \frac{1}{4}$ $r = 28$
3. $\frac{k}{75} = \frac{9}{15}$ $k = 45$
4. $\frac{1}{3} = \frac{z}{27}$ $z = 9$
5. $\frac{2}{11} = \frac{12}{d}$ $d = 66$
6. $\frac{24}{s} = \frac{4}{12}$ $s = 72$
7. $\frac{w}{42} = \frac{6}{7}$ $w = 36$
8. $\frac{t}{54} = \frac{2}{9}$ $t = 12$
9. $\frac{3}{8} = \frac{a}{64}$ $a = 24$
10. $\frac{17}{34} = \frac{7}{f}$ $f = 14$
11. $\frac{15}{h} = \frac{5}{6}$ $h = 18$
12. $\frac{4}{15} = \frac{36}{c}$ $c = 135$
13. $\frac{z}{25} = \frac{12}{5}$ $z = 60$
14. $\frac{36}{k} = \frac{9}{4}$ $k = 16$
15. $\frac{5}{14} = \frac{n}{42}$ $n = 15$
16. $\frac{8}{9} = \frac{40}{m}$ $m = 45$
17. $\frac{7}{c} = \frac{63}{54}$ $c = 6$
18. $\frac{24}{21} = \frac{s}{35}$ $s = 40$
19. $\frac{e}{22} = \frac{6}{15}$ $e = 8.8$
20. $\frac{3}{v} = \frac{12}{17}$ $v = 4.25$
21. $\frac{5}{14} = \frac{4}{a}$ $a = 11.2$
22. Eight oranges cost \$1.00. How much will 5 dozen oranges cost? $7.50
23. A recipe calls for 2 eggs to make 10 pancakes. How many eggs will you need to make 35 pancakes? 7 eggs

36a. Within the Tuesday sample of 100 fish, 4 had been part of the Monday sample.

36c. $\frac{4}{100} = \frac{50}{n}$; $n = 1{,}250$ fish

36. ***LIFE SCIENCE*** On Monday a marine biologist took a random sample of 50 fish from a pond and tagged them. On Tuesday she took a new sample of 100 fish. Among them were 4 fish that had been tagged on Monday.
    a. What does the ratio $\frac{4}{100}$ show?
    b. How can you show the ratio of fish tagged on Monday to n, the estimated total number of fish in the pond? **$\frac{50}{n}$**
    c. Use a proportion to estimate the number of fish in the pond.

37. ***CHEMISTRY*** The table shows the type and number of atoms in one molecule of citric acid. Use a proportion to find the number of oxygen atoms in 15 molecules of citric acid. **105 oxygen atoms**

Composition of Citric Acid	
Type of Atom	**Number of Atoms**
Carbon	6
Hydrogen	8
Oxygen	7

38. A certain shade of paint is made by mixing 5 parts blue paint with 2 parts white paint. To get the correct shade, how many quarts of white paint should be mixed with 8.5 quarts of blue paint? **3.4 quarts**

39. ***EARTH SCIENCE*** You can find your distance from a thunderstorm by counting the number of seconds between a lightning flash and the thunder. For example, if the time difference is 21 s, then the storm is 7 km away. How far away is a storm if the time difference is 9 s? **3 km**

40. ***WHAT'S THE QUESTION?*** There are 20 grams of protein in 3 ounces of sautéed fish. If the answer is 9 ounces, what is the question? **What amount of sautéed fish, in ounces, contains 60 grams of protein?**

41. ***WRITE ABOUT IT*** Give an example from your own life that can be described using a ratio. Then tell how a proportion can give you additional information.

42. ***CHALLENGE*** How can you use the proportion $\frac{a}{b} = \frac{c}{d}$ to show why the cross product rule works?

Spiral Review

Solve. (Lesson 3-6)

43. $y - 5 = -2$ **$y = 3$**
44. $9 + n = -4$ **$n = -13$**
45. $5 = x - 8$ **$x = 13$**

Subtract. (Lesson 4-2)

46. $9.2 - 3.76$ **5.44**
47. $17 - 1.97$ **15.03**
48. $4.235 - 1.407$ **2.828**

49. **TEST PREP** Solve $x + 1.6 = -4.87$. (Lesson 4-6) **D**
    A 6.47 C −5.47
    B 3.27 D −6.47

50. **TEST PREP** Find the sum in simplest form: $\frac{3}{8} + \frac{5}{24}$. (Lesson 4-10) **F**
    F $\frac{7}{12}$ H $\frac{1}{3}$
    G $\frac{14}{24}$ J $\frac{1}{6}$

Answers

41. Possible answer: I got 9 out of 12 questions correct on a test. I can find out my score by using the proportion $\frac{9}{12} = \frac{x}{100}$. My score is 75.

42. Multiply both ratios by b and simplify. Then multiply both by d and simplify.
$\frac{a}{b} \cdot b = \frac{c}{d} \cdot b$ or $a = \frac{cb}{d}$;
$a \cdot d = \frac{cb}{d} \cdot d$ or $ad = cb$,
which shows that the cross products are equal.

Journal

Have students think of and write real-world situations in which algebraic expressions are used. Have them describe how to work through the problem. For example, you buy a shirt on sale for half price and a sweater that costs \$20. The expression is $\frac{1}{2}s + 20$.

Test Prep Doctor

Remind students that Exercise 49 can be solved by subtracting 1.6 from both sides of the equation. Subtracting a positive from a negative will yield a negative, so choices **A** and **B,** both of which are positive, can be eliminated. Encourage students to read directions carefully in Exercise 50. The sum appears as both $\frac{14}{24}$ and $\frac{7}{12}$, but the instruction is to find the sum "in simplest form," so only choice **F** is correct.

CHALLENGE 5-3

LESSON 5-3 Challenge
Directly Speaking

Two quantities vary directly if they change in the same direction.
- If one quantity increases, then the other increases.
- If one quantity decreases, then the other decreases.

Here are some examples of direct variation.
- Amount bought and total cost
- Number of inches on a map and number of actual miles

If Farmer Jones plants 8 acres that produce 144 bushels of melons, how many acres will produce 1,152 bushels of melons?

Use the following proportion to solve.

$$\frac{\text{acres for 144 bushels}}{\text{144 bushels}} = \frac{\text{acres for 1,152 bushels}}{\text{1,152 bushels}}$$

$$\frac{8}{144} = \frac{x}{1{,}152} \qquad 144x = 9{,}216 \qquad x = 64$$

It will take 64 acres to produce 1,152 bushels of melons.

Complete the proportion to find the answer.

		Do quantities increase or decrease?	Proportion	Answer
1.	If a furnace uses 40 gallons of oil in 8 days, how many gallons does it use in 10 days?	**both increase**	$\frac{40 \text{ gal}}{8 \text{ d}} = \frac{x \text{ gal}}{10 \text{ d}}$	**50 gallons**
2.	If 20 yards of wire weigh 80 pounds, what is the weight of 2 yards of the same wire?	**both decrease**	$\frac{20 \text{ yd}}{80 \text{ lb}} = \frac{2 \text{ yd}}{x \text{ lb}}$	**8 pounds**
3.	A cookie recipe calls for 2.5 cups of sugar and 4 eggs. If 6 eggs are used, how much sugar is needed?	**both increase**	$\frac{2.5 \text{ c}}{4} = \frac{x \text{ c}}{6}$	**3.75 cups**
4.	The scale on a map is 1 inch = 60 miles. What distance on the map represents 300 miles?	**both increase**	$\frac{1 \text{ in.}}{60 \text{ mi}} = \frac{x \text{ in.}}{300 \text{ mi}}$	**5 inches**
5.	At the market, 4 limes cost \$1.50. How much will 10 limes cost?	**both increase**	$\frac{4}{\$1.50} = \frac{10}{x}$	**\$3.75**

PROBLEM SOLVING 5-3

LESSON 5-3 Problem Solving
Solving Proportions

Write the correct answer.

1. Euros are currency used in several European countries. On one day in February 2002, you could exchange \$6 for about 6.9 euros. How many euros could you have gotten for \$20?
   23 euros

2. A 3-ounce serving of tuna fish provides 24 grams of protein. How many grams of protein are in a 10-ounce serving of tuna fish?
   80 grams

3. Hooke's law states that the distance a spring is stretched is directly proportional to the force applied. If 20 pounds of force stretches a spring 4 inches, how much will the spring stretch if 80 pounds of force is applied?
   16 inches

4. Beeswax used in making candles is produced by honeybees. The honeybees produce 7 pounds of honey for each pound of wax they produce. How many pounds of honey is produced if 145 pounds of beeswax?
   1,015 pounds of honey

Choose the letter for the best answer.

5. For every 5 books her students read, Mrs. Fenway gives them a free homework pass for 4 days. Juan has accumulated homework passes for 12 days so far. What proportion would you write to find how many books Juan has read?
   A $\frac{4}{12} = \frac{x}{5}$
   B $\frac{4}{5} = \frac{x}{12}$
   (C) $\frac{4}{5} = \frac{12}{x}$
   D $\frac{5}{12} = \frac{4}{x}$

6. In his last 13 times at bat in the township baseball league, Santiago got 8 hits. If he is at bat 65 times for the season, how many hits will he get if his average stays the same?
   F $\frac{8}{65} = \frac{x}{13}$
   G $\frac{x}{65} = \frac{13}{8}$
   H $\frac{8}{x} = \frac{65}{13}$
   (J) $\frac{8}{13} = \frac{x}{65}$

7. A 12-pack of 8-ounce juice boxes costs \$5.40. How much would an 18-pack of juice boxes cost if it is proportionate in price?
   A \$9.40 C \$3.60
   (B) \$8.10 D \$12.15

8. Jeanette can swim 105 meters in 70 seconds. How far can she probably swim in 30 seconds?
   F 20 meters (H) 45 meters
   G 245 meters J 55 meters

Lesson Quiz

Use cross products to solve the proportion.

1. $\frac{25}{20} = \frac{45}{t}$ $t = 36$
2. $\frac{x}{9} = \frac{19}{57}$ $x = 3$
3. $\frac{2}{3} = \frac{r}{36}$ $r = 24$
4. $\frac{n}{10} = \frac{28}{8}$ $n = 35$
5. Carmen bought 3 pounds of bananas for \$1.08. June paid \$1.80 for her purchase of bananas. If they paid the same price per pound, how many pounds did June buy? 5 pounds

Available on Daily Transparency in CRB

5-4 Organizer

Pacing: Traditional 1 day
Block $\frac{1}{2}$ day

Objective: Students use dimensional analysis to make unit conversions.

Warm Up

Use cross products to solve the proportions.

1. $\frac{6}{10} = \frac{15}{n}$ $\quad n = 25$
2. $\frac{3}{8} = \frac{r}{64}$ $\quad r = 24$
3. $\frac{9}{17} = \frac{k}{68}$ $\quad k = 36$
4. $\frac{30}{9} = \frac{40}{x}$ $\quad x = 12$

Problem of the Day

The sum of four consecutive integers is 182. What are the four numbers?
44, 45, 46, and 47

Available on Daily Transparency in CRB

Why is the meterstick such a difficult ruler? Because it won't give an inch.

5-4 Dimensional Analysis

Learn to use dimensional analysis to make unit conversions.

Vocabulary
unit conversion factor

In 1999, NASA's *Climate Observer* was destroyed by the atmosphere of Mars. This happened because one NASA team used customary units (feet, pounds, etc.), while another team used metric units (meters, grams, etc.). The problem could have been avoided by changing the units of measurement used by one team to match those of the other team.

You can use a *unit conversion factor* to change, or convert, measurements from one unit to another. A **unit conversion factor** is a fraction in which the numerator and denominator represent the same quantity, but in different units. The fraction below is a unit conversion factor that can be used to convert miles to feet. Notice that it can be simplified to 1.

$$\frac{5{,}280 \text{ ft}}{1 \text{ mi}} = \frac{5{,}280 \text{ ft}}{5{,}280 \text{ ft}} = 1$$

Multiplying a quantity by a unit conversion factor changes only its units, not its value. The process of choosing an appropriate conversion factor is called dimensional analysis.

EXAMPLE  1 Making Unit Conversions

A bucket holds 16 quarts. How many gallons of water will fill the bucket? Use a unit conversion factor to convert the units.

One gallon equals 4 quarts, so use the unit conversion factor $\frac{1 \text{ gal}}{4 \text{ qt}}$ or $\frac{4 \text{ qt}}{1 \text{ gal}}$. Choose the first one so that the quart units will "cancel."

$16 \cancel{\text{qt}} \cdot \frac{1 \text{ gal}}{4 \cancel{\text{qt}}} = \frac{16 \text{ gal}}{4}$ *Multiply.*

$= 4 \text{ gal}$

Four gallons will fill the 16-quart bucket.

Helpful Hint

When choosing a unit conversion factor, choose the one that cancels the units you want to change and replaces them with the units you want.

1 Introduce

Alternate Opener

EXPLORATION

5-4 Dimensional Analysis

1. Five miles is about eight kilometers. Complete the number line to show how miles compare with kilometers in longer distances.
   Miles: 0 5
   Kilometers: 0 8
2. Use the completed number line from number 1 to find each of the following approximate comparisons.
   a. 20 mi ≈ ___ km b. 7.5 mi ≈ ___ km
   c. 16 km ≈ ___ mi d. 40 km ≈ ___ mi
3. Four quarts is equal to 1 gallon. Complete the number line to show how quarts compare with gallons in larger quantities.
   Quarts: 0 4
   Gallons: 0 1
4. Use the completed number line from number 3 to find each of the following comparisons.
   a. 8 quarts = ___ gallons b. 4 gallons = ___ quarts
   c. 10 quarts = ___ gallons d. 6.5 gallons = ___ quarts

Think and Discuss

5. **Explain** how you can convert kilometers to miles or miles to kilometers.
6. **Explain** how you can convert quarts to gallons or gallons to quarts.

Motivate

To introduce students to dimensional analysis, ask them how they would find the number of seconds in a year (i.e., 365 days = 31,536,000 seconds). Students might find it hard to keep track of the steps involved. List the necessary conversions:

1 year = 365 days
1 day = 24 hours
1 hour = 60 minutes
1 minute = 60 seconds

You may want to use Teaching Transparency T15 in the Chapter 5 Resource Book.

Exploration worksheet and answers on Chapter 5 Resource Book pp. 36 and 86

2 Teach

Lesson Presentation

Guided Instruction

In this lesson, students learn to use dimensional analysis to make unit conversions. Emphasize the similarities to operations with fractions: multiplying by a unit conversion factor to change the appearance. Discuss how to choose the correct unit conversion factor and how to set up the problem when more than one conversion factor is needed.

Teaching Tip When converting rates, encourage students to begin with a rate that includes one of the units they want and to use unit conversion factors to eliminate units they do not want. Direct students to the Table of Measures on the inside back cover of the book.

EXAMPLE 2 Making Rate Conversions

Use a unit conversion factor to convert the units within each rate.

A **Convert 80 miles per hour to feet per hour.**

There are 5,280 feet per mile, so use $\frac{5,280 \text{ ft}}{1 \text{ mi}}$ to cancel the miles.

$$\frac{80 \cancel{\text{mi}}}{1 \text{ hr}} \cdot \frac{5,280 \text{ ft}}{1 \cancel{\text{mi}}} = \frac{80 \cdot 5,280 \text{ ft}}{1 \text{ hr}} \quad \textit{Multiply.}$$

$$= \frac{422,400 \text{ ft}}{1 \text{ hr}}$$

80 miles per hour is 422,400 feet per hour.

B **A phone service in the United States charges $1.99 per minute for a call to Australia. How many dollars per hour is the phone service charging?**

There are 60 minutes per hour, so use $\frac{60 \text{ min}}{1 \text{ hr}}$ to cancel the minutes.

$$\frac{\$1.99}{1 \cancel{\text{min}}} \cdot \frac{60 \cancel{\text{min}}}{1 \text{ hr}} = \frac{\$1.99 \cdot 60}{1 \text{ hr}} \quad \textit{Multiply.}$$

$$= \frac{\$119.40}{1 \text{ hr}}$$

$1.99 per minute is $119.40 per hour.

EXAMPLE 3 *Measurement Application*

The *Climate Observer* missed its target altitude of about 145 km above Mars during its entry into orbit. Instead, its altitude was 57 km, where it was destroyed by the Martian atmosphere. How many feet above Mars is 145 km?

Use the unit conversion factors that convert kilometers to miles, and then miles to feet. One kilometer is equivalent to 0.62 mile.

$$145 \cancel{\text{km}} \cdot \frac{0.62 \cancel{\text{mi}}}{1 \cancel{\text{km}}} \cdot \frac{5,280 \text{ ft}}{1 \cancel{\text{mi}}} = \frac{145 \cdot 0.62 \cdot 5,280 \text{ ft}}{1}$$

$$= 474,672 \text{ ft}$$

145 km is 474,672 ft.

Think and Discuss

1. **Explain** why you cannot use the unit conversion factor $\frac{100 \text{ cm}}{1 \text{ m}}$ to convert 50 centimeters to meters.
2. **Tell** whether you get an equivalent rate when you multiply a rate by a conversion factor. Explain.
3. **Compare** the process of converting feet to inches with the process of converting feet per minute to inches per second.

COMMON ERROR ALERT

Particularly when more than one conversion factor is involved, students might get confused and use the reciprocal of the rate they want. Encourage students to begin with a rate that contains the unit they want in the numerator, then work at converting to the correct denominator.

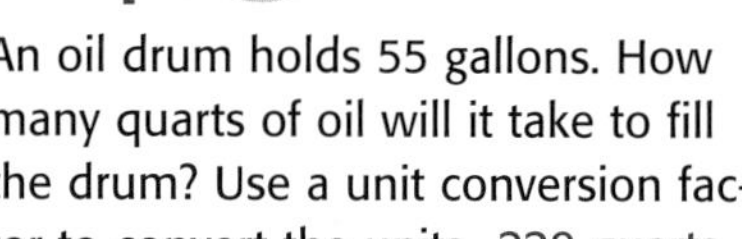

Additional Examples

Example 1

An oil drum holds 55 gallons. How many quarts of oil will it take to fill the drum? Use a unit conversion factor to convert the units. 220 quarts

Example 2

Use a unit conversion factor to convert the units within each rate.

A. If orange juice sells for $1.28 per gallon, what is the cost per ounce?
$0.01 per ounce

B. Convert 80 miles per hour to miles per minute.
about 1.33 miles per minute

Example 3

The Mare Orientale crater on the Moon is more than 620 miles across. How many meters is this?
about 1,000,000

Reaching All Learners
Through Home Connection

Have students work with their families to estimate their family consumption of some common food or drink (e.g., bread, milk, juice) for a day. Then use the estimate to calculate the amount consumed in a year by the family. If possible, give students an estimate of the number of families in the community and have students extend their calculations to find the approximate consumption of the food product by the community in one year.

3 Close

Summarize

Have the students explain what is meant by a unit conversion factor. Discuss why multiplying by a conversion factor changes the appearance without changing the value of the expression. Ask students to explain how to choose the correct form of the conversion factor.

Possible answers: A unit conversion factor is the ratio of a unit of measurement to its equivalent in different units. A unit can be crossed out if it appears in the numerator of one fraction and the denominator of another fraction. Choose the form of the conversion factor that allows you to eliminate units you do not want in your answer.

Answers to Think and Discuss

Possible answers:

1. Multiplying 50 cm by $\frac{100 \text{ cm}}{1 \text{ m}}$ would not allow units to be crossed out. Centimeters appear in the numerator twice.
2. Since the values of both the numerator and the denominator of a conversion factor are the same, multiplying the numerator and denominator of a rate by the same value gives an equivalent rate.
3. The former requires one conversion factor; the latter requires two conversion factors.

5-4 PRACTICE & ASSESS

Students may want to refer back to the lesson examples.

Assignment Guide

If you finished Example 1 assign:
Core 1, 2, 6, 7, 12–19, 28–36
Enriched 1, 2, 6, 7, 12–19, 28–36

If you finished Example 2 assign:
Core 1–4, 6–9, 13–19 odd, 28–36
Enriched 1, 3, 7, 9, 12–19, 28–36

If you finished Example 3 assign:
Core 1–11, 13–23 odd, 28–36
Enriched 1–11 odd, 12–36

Answers

4. $\frac{\$1.75}{1 \text{ ft}} \cdot \frac{3 \text{ ft}}{1 \text{ yd}} = \frac{\$5.25}{1 \text{ yd}}$

9. $\frac{\$9}{1 \text{ hr}} \cdot \frac{1 \text{ hr}}{60 \text{ min}} = \frac{\$0.15}{1 \text{ min}}$

5-4 Exercises

FOR EXTRA PRACTICE see page 664

internet connect — Homework Help Online go.hrw.com Keyword: MS4 5-4 go.hrw.com

GUIDED PRACTICE

See Example 1 **Use a unit conversion factor to convert the units.** $64 \text{ oz} \cdot \frac{1 \text{ lb}}{16 \text{ oz}} = 4 \text{ lb}$

1. A bag of apples weighs 64 ounces. How many pounds does it weigh?
2. Dario drank 2 liters of water. How many milliliters of water did he drink? $2 \text{ L} \cdot \frac{1{,}000 \text{ mL}}{1 \text{ L}} = 2{,}000 \text{ mL}$

See Example 2 **Use a unit conversion factor to convert the units within each rate.**

3. Convert 32 feet per second to inches per second. $\frac{32 \text{ ft}}{1 \text{ s}} \cdot \frac{12 \text{ in.}}{1 \text{ ft}} = \frac{384 \text{ in.}}{1 \text{ s}}$
4. A craft store charges $1.75 per foot for lace. How much per yard is this?

See Example 3
5. Pluto has a diameter of about 1,423 miles. What is the planet's diameter in meters? (There are about 1.61 kilometers in 1 mile.) $1{,}423 \text{ mi} \cdot \frac{1.61 \text{ km}}{1 \text{ mi}} \cdot \frac{1{,}000 \text{ m}}{1 \text{ km}} = 2{,}291{,}030 \text{ m}$

INDEPENDENT PRACTICE

See Example 1 **Use a unit conversion factor to convert the units.**

6. A soup recipe calls for 3.5 quarts of water. How many pints of water are needed? $3.5 \text{ qt} \cdot \frac{2 \text{ pt}}{1 \text{ qt}} = 7 \text{ pt}$
7. You need 48 inches of ribbon. How many feet of ribbon do you need? $48 \text{ in.} \cdot \frac{1 \text{ ft}}{12 \text{ in.}} = 4 \text{ ft}$

See Example 2 **Use a unit conversion factor to convert the units within each rate.**

8. Convert 63,360 feet per hour to miles per hour. $\frac{63{,}360 \text{ ft}}{1 \text{ hr}} \cdot \frac{1 \text{ mi}}{5{,}280 \text{ ft}} = \frac{12 \text{ mi}}{1 \text{ hr}}$
9. A company rents boats for $9 per hour. How much per minute is this?

See Example 3
10. Andy is 5.25 feet tall. What is Andy's height to the nearest centimeter? (There are about 2.54 centimeters in 1 inch.) **160 centimeters**

PRACTICE AND PROBLEM SOLVING

Write the appropriate unit conversion factor for each conversion.

11. inches to feet $\frac{1 \text{ ft}}{12 \text{ in.}}$
12. meters to centimeters $\frac{100 \text{ cm}}{1 \text{ m}}$
13. minutes to hours $\frac{1 \text{ hr}}{60 \text{ min}}$
14. yards to feet $\frac{3 \text{ ft}}{1 \text{ yd}}$

Convert each quantity to the given units.

15. 42 inches to feet **3.5 ft**
16. 1 hour to seconds **3,600 s**
17. 2 kilometers to meters **2,000 m**
18. 7 weeks to minutes **70,560 min**
19. 36 pints to gallons **4.5 gal**
20. 500 milliliters to liters **0.5 L**

Math Background

In dimensional analysis, proportional reasoning is used to convert the units in which a dimension is measured. The use of proportion may not be apparent, since we see only the multiplication of ratios. However, the pattern of multiplication derives from cross multiplication of a proportion where one ratio is a unit rate. For example, $\frac{12 \text{ ft}}{x \text{ yd}} = \frac{3 \text{ ft}}{1 \text{ yd}}$ becomes $3 \text{ ft} \cdot x \text{ yd} = 12 \text{ ft} \cdot 1 \text{ yd}$ and then, $x \text{ yd} = \frac{12 \text{ ft} \cdot 1 \text{ yd}}{3 \text{ ft}}$.

RETEACH 5-4

LESSON 5-4 **Reteach**
Dimensional Analysis

A **unit conversion factor** is a fraction whose numerator and denominator are equivalent measures. Some common unit conversion factors are given below. You can also use the reciprocals of each unit conversion factor.

$\frac{1 \text{ ft}}{12 \text{ in.}}$	$\frac{1 \text{ yd}}{3 \text{ ft}}$	$\frac{1 \text{ mi}}{5{,}280 \text{ ft}}$	$\frac{1 \text{ lb}}{16 \text{ oz}}$	$\frac{1 \text{ pt}}{2 \text{ c}}$	$\frac{1 \text{ qt}}{2 \text{ pt}}$	$\frac{1 \text{ gal}}{4 \text{ qt}}$	$\frac{1 \text{ hr}}{60 \text{ min}}$	$\frac{1 \text{ min}}{60 \text{ s}}$	$\frac{1 \text{ m}}{100 \text{ cm}}$	$\frac{1 \text{ km}}{1{,}000 \text{ m}}$

Convert 8 yards to feet. Use the unit conversion factor $\frac{3 \text{ ft}}{1 \text{ yd}}$.

$8 \text{ yd} \cdot \frac{3 \text{ ft}}{1 \text{ yd}} = 8 \text{ yd} \cdot \frac{3 \text{ ft}}{1 \text{ yd}} = \frac{8 \cdot 3 \text{ ft}}{1} = 24 \text{ ft}$

So, 8 yards is equivalent to 24 feet.

Convert 60 mi/h to mi/min. Use the unit conversion factor $\frac{1 \text{ hr}}{60 \text{ min}}$.

$\frac{60 \text{ mi}}{1 \text{ hr}} \cdot \frac{1 \text{ hr}}{60 \text{ min}} = \frac{60 \text{ mi}}{1 \text{ hr}} \cdot \frac{1 \text{ hr}}{60 \text{ min}} = \frac{60 \text{ mi}}{60 \text{ min}} = \frac{1 \text{ mi}}{\text{min}}$

So, 60 mi/h is equivalent to 1 mi/min.

Use a unit conversion factor to convert the units.

1. Mitchell is 72 inches tall. What is his height in feet? $72 \text{ in.} \cdot \frac{1 \text{ ft}}{12 \text{ in.}} = \frac{72}{12} = \underline{6} \text{ ft}$
2. Julia made 3 gallons of soup. How many quarts of soup did she make? $3 \text{ gal} \cdot \frac{4 \text{ qt}}{1 \text{ gal}} = \frac{3 \cdot 4}{1} = \underline{12} \text{ qt}$
3. The classroom is 9.5 meters wide. How many centimeters wide is the classroom? **950 cm**
4. A gift box holds 48 ounces of cherries. How many pounds of cherries does the box hold? **3 lb**

Use a unit conversion factor to convert the units within a rate.

5. Convert 5 inches per minute to inches per hour. $\frac{5 \text{ in.}}{1 \text{ min}} \cdot \frac{60 \text{ min}}{1 \text{ hr}} = \frac{5 \cdot 60}{1} = \frac{300 \text{ in.}}{1 \text{ hr}}$
6. Convert 8,000 meters per hour to kilometers per hour. $\frac{8{,}000 \text{ m}}{1 \text{ hr}} \cdot \frac{1 \text{ km}}{1{,}000 \text{ m}} = \frac{8{,}000}{1{,}000} = \frac{8 \text{ km}}{1 \text{ hr}}$
7. Convert 5 feet per minute to inches per second. **1 in. per second**
8. Convert a monthly rate of $13 to a yearly rate. **$156 per year**

PRACTICE 5-4

LESSON 5-4 **Practice B**
Dimensional Analysis

Use a unit conversion factor to convert the units.

1. A bag of pecans weighs 48 ounces. How many pounds is that? $48 \text{ oz} \cdot \frac{1 \text{ lb}}{16 \text{ oz}} = 3 \text{ pounds}$
2. A watermelon weighs 4.2 kilograms. How many grams is that? $4.2 \text{ kg} \cdot \frac{1{,}000 \text{ g}}{1 \text{ kg}} = 4{,}200 \text{ grams}$
3. You need 156 inches of wrapping paper. How many feet of wrapping paper do you need? $156 \text{ in.} \cdot \frac{1 \text{ ft}}{12 \text{ in.}} = 13 \text{ ft}$
4. The ceiling in the school is 376 centimeters high. How high is the ceiling in meters? $376 \text{ cm} \cdot \frac{1 \text{ m}}{100 \text{ cm}} = 3.76 \text{ m}$
5. An insulated jug holds 4.5 quarts of water. How many pints is that? $4.5 \text{ qt} \cdot \frac{2 \text{ pt}}{1 \text{ qt}} = 9 \text{ pt}$
6. Ahmed is 5.25 feet tall. How tall is he in inches? $5.25 \text{ ft} \cdot \frac{12 \text{ in.}}{1 \text{ ft}} = 63 \text{ in.}$
7. Raquel goes to a school that is 13.27 kilometers from her home. How far is that in meters? $13.27 \text{ km} \cdot \frac{1{,}000 \text{ m}}{1 \text{ km}} = 13{,}270 \text{ m}$
8. The baseball team drank 3.5 gallons of water during the game. How many quarts of water did they drink? $3.5 \text{ gal} \cdot \frac{4 \text{ qt}}{1 \text{ gal}} = 14 \text{ qt}$

Use a unit conversion factor to convert the units within a rate.

9. Convert a jogging rate of 23,760 feet per hour to miles per hour. $\frac{23{,}760 \text{ ft}}{1 \text{ hr}} \cdot \frac{1 \text{ mi}}{5{,}280 \text{ ft}} = \frac{4.5 \text{ mi}}{1 \text{ hr}}$
10. The pool fills at a rate of 20 gallons per minute. What is the rate in gallons per hour? $\frac{20 \text{ gal}}{1 \text{ min}} \cdot \frac{60 \text{ min}}{1 \text{ hr}} = \frac{1{,}200 \text{ gal}}{1 \text{ hr}}$
11. A dose of a children's medicine is 33 milliliters per kilogram. What is the dose in milliliters per pound? Use 1 kilogram = 2.2 pounds. $\frac{33 \text{ mL}}{1 \text{ kg}} \cdot \frac{1 \text{ kg}}{2.2 \text{ lb}} = \frac{15 \text{ mL}}{1 \text{ lb}}$
12. You can rent a recording studio for $1,275 per day. What is the rate per week? $\frac{\$1{,}275}{1 \text{ day}} \cdot \frac{7 \text{ days}}{1 \text{ wk}} = \frac{\$8{,}925}{1 \text{ wk}}$

Life Science LINK

Whales communicate with each other by singing. Their songs are made up of moans, grunts, blasts, and shrieks, and the sound can travel up to 10,000 miles through the ocean.

21. ***PHYSICAL SCIENCE*** It takes 5 seconds for sound to travel 1 mile through air. It takes only 1 second for sound to travel 1 mile through water. How many minutes faster will a sound 90 miles away travel through water than through air? **6 minutes faster**

22. ***EARTH SCIENCE*** The amount of time it takes for a planet to revolve around the Sun is called a period of revolution. The period of revolution for Earth is one Earth year, and the period of revolution for any other planet is one year on that planet.

Periods of Revolution Compared to Earth's

Planet	One Revolution in Earth Years
Venus	0.615
Mars	1.88
Neptune	164.79

a. How many Earth years does it take Venus to revolve around the Sun? **0.615 Earth years**

b. Use a unit conversion factor to find the number of Venus years equivalent to three Earth years. Round to the nearest tenth. **4.9 Venus years**

c. Find your age on each planet to the nearest year.

23. In England, a commonly used unit of measure is the stone. One stone is equivalent to 14 pounds. If Jo weighs 95 pounds, about how many stone does she weigh? Round your answer to the nearest tenth of a stone. **6.8 stone**

24. ***MONEY*** Fencing costs \$3.75 per foot. Harris wants to enclose his rectangular garden, which measures 6 yards by 4 yards. How much will fencing for the garden cost? **\$225**

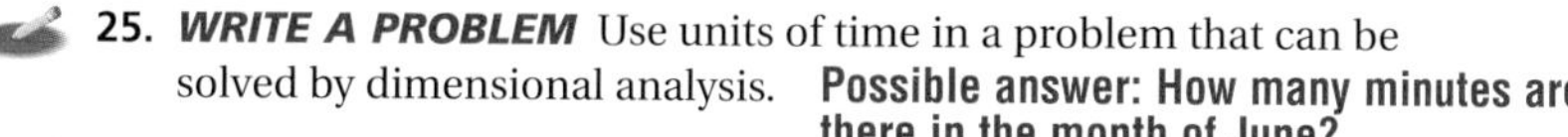

25. ***WRITE A PROBLEM*** Use units of time in a problem that can be solved by dimensional analysis. **Possible answer: How many minutes are there in the month of June?**

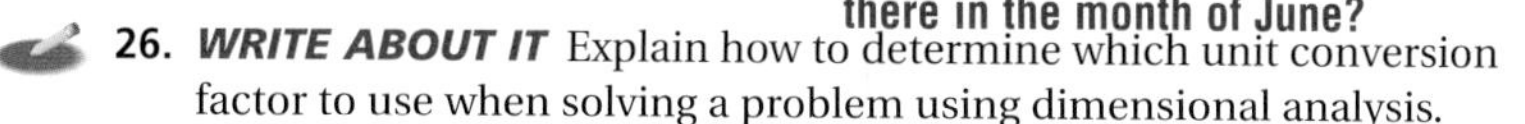

26. ***WRITE ABOUT IT*** Explain how to determine which unit conversion factor to use when solving a problem using dimensional analysis.

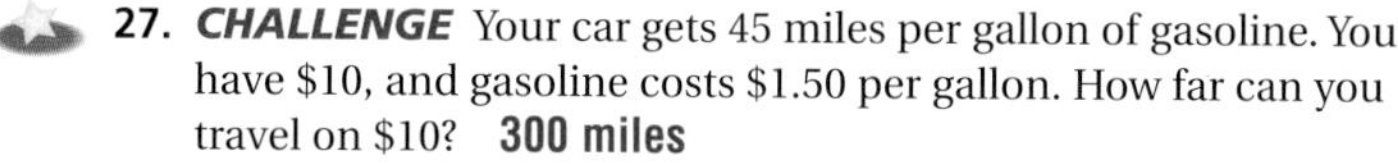

27. ***CHALLENGE*** Your car gets 45 miles per gallon of gasoline. You have \$10, and gasoline costs \$1.50 per gallon. How far can you travel on \$10? **300 miles**

Spiral Review

Use compatible numbers to estimate. (Lesson 4-1) **Possible answers:**

28. $4.08 \cdot 31.17$ **120**
29. $-6.19 \cdot 88.5$ **−540**
30. $53.7 \div 8.89$ **6**

Find each product. (Lesson 4-7)

31. $\frac{1}{3} \cdot 7$ $\mathbf{\frac{7}{3}}$ **or** $\mathbf{2\frac{1}{3}}$
32. $2 \cdot \frac{5}{6}$ $\mathbf{\frac{5}{3}}$ **or** $\mathbf{1\frac{2}{3}}$
33. $1\frac{4}{9} \cdot \frac{1}{3}$ $\mathbf{\frac{13}{27}}$
34. $2\frac{1}{2} \cdot 9\frac{1}{3}$ $\mathbf{\frac{70}{3}}$ **or** $\mathbf{23\frac{1}{3}}$

35. **TEST PREP** Solve $\frac{1}{8} \cdot x = 7$. (Lesson 4-12) **D**

A $6\frac{7}{8}$ C 54
B 49 D 56

36. **TEST PREP** Solve $w - \frac{4}{9} = \frac{2}{9}$. (Lesson 4-12) **H**

F 6 H $\frac{2}{3}$
G 2 J $\frac{2}{9}$

CHALLENGE 5-4

LESSON 5-4 **Challenge**
Is It Reasonable?

If someone tells you a car can travel 50 kilometers in 5 minutes, you have to decide if that is reasonable.

Since 5 min = $\frac{1}{12}$ hr, 50 km in 5 min = 600 km in 1 hr.
A kilometer is less than a mile, but more than $\frac{1}{2}$ mile.

If a car travels 50 kilometers in 5 minutes, then it would travel more than 300 miles per hour. This is too fast, so the statement is unreasonable.

Use your knowledge of distance, weight, time, and other measures to decide which of the following statement are reasonable. If you are unsure, you can research the topic. Write R for Reasonable and U for Unreasonable.

1. The tallest buildings in the world are more than 1,000 feet high. **R**
2. The tallest mountain in the world is more than 500 miles high. **U**
3. The world's longest railway tunnel is more than 30 miles long. **R**
4. The smallest state, Rhode Island, has an area of 100,000 square feet. **U**
5. The longest river in the United States is more than 1,000 miles long. **R**
6. The deepest well in the United States is more than 10,000 feet deep. **R**
7. Los Angeles has a population of about 60,000 people. **U**
8. The Pacific Ocean is more than 3,000 meters deep. **R**
9. A baby elephant weighs about 2,000 grams. **U**
10. A full-grown elephant can weigh as much as 16,000 pounds. **R**
11. An eagle's wingspan is about 225 centimeters. **R**
12. An elephant might eat 100 pounds of food per day. **R**
13. A whale measures as long as 1,000 meters. **U**
14. There are over 50 billion dogs in the United States. **U**

PROBLEM SOLVING 5-4

LESSON 5-4 **Problem Solving**
Dimensional Analysis

Write the correct answer.

1. Pittsburgh, Pennsylvania, is 452 miles from Chicago, Illinois. Find the distance between the two cities to the nearest kilometer. Use 1 mile ≈ 1.6 kilometers.

723 km

2. In the Olympic marathon race event, the distance was standardized in 1908 as 26 miles, 385 yards. Express this distance in feet. *Hint:* First convert miles, then yards.

138,435 ft

3. The ideal weight for a woman with a small frame who is 65 inches tall is between 117 and 130 pounds. Express her height in centimeters. Use 1 inch = 2.54 centimeters.

165.1 cm

4. Last night, Harry slept a total of 30,600 seconds. How many hours did Harry sleep last night?

8.5 hours

Choose the letter for the best answer.

5. Mt. Everest, in Nepal-Tibet, is the world's highest mountain at 29,035 feet, which was determined in 1999 using satellite-based technology. What is the mountain's height to the nearest tenth of a mile?

A 2.9 miles C 6.2 miles
(B) 5.5 miles D 6.8 miles

6. The Green Landscape Company needs 48 meters of fencing to enclose a plot. The cost of fencing is \$3.95 per running foot. What is the cost of the fence to the nearest dollar? Use 1 meter ≈ 1.09 yards.

(F) \$620 H \$207
G \$52 J \$190

7. The school cafeteria buys juice in 6-gallon jugs. The workers pour the juice into cups that each holds 6 ounces. How many cups of juice will they pour from each jug?

A 32 cups
B 28 cups
(C) 128 cups
D 768 cups

8. The track team jogs 5 miles every day. About how many kilometers do they jog each week? Use 1 mile ≈ 1.6 kilometers.

F $\frac{5\text{ mi}}{1\text{ day}} \cdot \frac{1\text{ mi}}{1.6\text{ km}} \cdot \frac{7\text{ days}}{1\text{ wk}}$
G $\frac{5\text{ mi}}{1\text{ day}} \cdot \frac{1.6\text{ km}}{1\text{ mi}} \cdot \frac{1\text{ wk}}{7\text{ days}}$
(H) $\frac{5\text{ mi}}{1\text{ day}} \cdot \frac{1.6\text{ km}}{1\text{ mi}} \cdot \frac{7\text{ days}}{1\text{ wk}}$
J $\frac{5\text{ mi}}{1\text{ day}} \cdot \frac{1\text{ mi}}{1.6\text{ km}} \cdot \frac{1\text{ wk}}{7\text{ days}}$

COMMON ERROR ALERT

It is important to write conversion factors and verify that units can be crossed out when solving problems like those in Exercise 22. Often, when asked to find their age on other planets, students will think that a shorter year will make them "younger." Actually, the opposite is true.

Answers

22. c. Possible answers: 12 years old on Earth is about 20 Venus years, 0 Neptune years, 6 Mars years; 13 years old on Earth is about 21 Venus years, 0 Neptune years, 7 Mars years.

26. Choose the unit conversion factor that, when multiplied, will eliminate the units you want to change and will substitute them for the ones that will solve the problem.

Journal

Have students write about a situation in which changing the units of measurement would help them to understand the size of something.

Test Prep Doctor

Students should recognize that Exercise 35 can be solved by multiplying both sides by 8. Since this will give an integer result, **A** can be eliminated. Of the remaining choices, **B** and **C** are both common mistakes for the product of 7 · 8.

Lesson Quiz

Use a unit conversion factor to convert the units.

1. Football fields are 100 yards long. How many feet is that? **300 feet**
2. In a biology lab you measure a grasshopper's wingspan to be 3 inches long. How many centimeters is this? **7.62 cm**

Use a unit conversion factor to convert the units within a rate.

3. On a freeway, a car's speed is 62 miles per hour. What speed is that in feet per hour? **327,360 ft/h**
4. If you are paid \$7.50 per hour to watch your neighbor's children, how much are you paid per minute? 12.5 cents per minute

Available on Daily Transparency in CRB

Mid-Chapter Quiz

Purpose: To assess students' mastery of concepts and skills in Lessons 5-1 through 5-4

Assessment Resources

Section 5A Quiz

Assessment Resources .... p. 15

***Test and Practice Generator* CD-ROM**

Additional mid-chapter assessment items in both multiple-choice and free-response format may be generated for any objective in Lessons 5-1 through 5-4.

Answers

1. $\frac{16}{14}$, 16 to 14, 16:14, or $\frac{8}{7}$, 8 to 7, 8:7
2. $\frac{14}{16}$, 14 to 16, 14:16, or $\frac{7}{8}$, 7 to 8, 7:8
3. $\frac{14}{30}$, 14 to 30, 14:30, or $\frac{7}{15}$, 7 to 15, 7:15
4. $\frac{30}{16}$, 30 to 16, 30:16, or $\frac{15}{8}$, 15 to 8, 15:8

Chapter 5

Mid-Chapter Quiz

Mid-Chapter Quiz

LESSON 5-1 (pp. 260–263)

There are 16 boys and 14 girls on the bus. Write each ratio in all three forms.

1. boys to girls
2. girls to boys
3. girls to total students
4. total students to boys

Find the unit rates and write them in both fraction and word form.

5. Sean walked 7 miles in 2 hours. **$\frac{3.5 \text{ mi}}{1 \text{ hr}}$; 3.5 miles per hour**
6. Kara made juice using 12 fluid ounces of concentrate for 3 quarts of water. **$\frac{4 \text{ oz.}}{1 \text{ qt}}$, 4 ounces per quart**
7. Last month Mr. Oliver used 21 gallons of gasoline to drive 525 miles. This month he used 20 gallons to drive 480 miles. During which month did he get better gas mileage? **last month**

LESSON 5-2 (pp. 264–267)

Determine whether the ratios are proportional.

8. $\frac{6}{8}, \frac{9}{12}$ **yes**
9. $\frac{16}{36}, \frac{20}{30}$ **no**
10. $\frac{7}{10}, \frac{21}{30}$ **yes**
11. $\frac{21}{49}, \frac{15}{35}$ **yes**

Find a ratio equivalent to each ratio. Then use the ratios to write a proportion. **Possible answers:**

12. $\frac{10}{16}$ **$\frac{10}{16} = \frac{5}{8}$**
13. $\frac{21}{28}$ **$\frac{21}{28} = \frac{3}{4}$**
14. $\frac{12}{25}$ **$\frac{12}{25} = \frac{24}{50}$**
15. $\frac{40}{48}$ **$\frac{40}{48} = \frac{10}{12}$**

LESSON 5-3 (pp. 268–271)

Use cross products to solve each proportion.

16. $\frac{n}{8} = \frac{15}{4}$ **$n = 30$**
17. $\frac{20}{t} = \frac{2.5}{6}$ **$t = 48$**
18. $\frac{6}{11} = \frac{0.12}{z}$ **$z = 0.22$**
19. $\frac{15}{24} = \frac{x}{10}$ **$x = 6.25$**
20. The average life expectancy of a dog is 12 to 14 years. One dog year is said to equal 7 human years. If Cliff's dog is 5.5 years old in dog years, what is his dog's age in human years? **38.5 years**

LESSON 5-4 (pp. 272–275)

Use a unit conversion factor to convert the units.

21. 8 gallons to quarts **32 qt**
22. 7,920 feet to miles **1.5 mi**
23. 18 minutes to seconds **1,080 s**
24. 450 grams to kilograms **0.45 kg**

Use a unit conversion factor to convert the units within each rate.

25. 15 miles per hour to feet per hour **$\frac{79,200 \text{ ft}}{1 \text{ hr}}$**
26. \$720 per hour to dollars per minute **$\frac{\$12}{1 \text{ min}}$**

Focus on Problem Solving

Make a Plan

• Choose a problem-solving strategy

The following are strategies that you might choose to help you solve a problem:

- Make a table
- Find a pattern
- Make an organized list
- Work backward
- Draw a diagram
- Guess and test
- Use logical reasoning
- Solve a simpler problem

Tell which strategy from the list above you would use to solve each problem. Explain your choice.

1. A recipe for blueberry muffins calls for 1 cup of milk and 1.5 cups of blueberries. Ashley wants to make more muffins than the recipe yields. In Ashley's muffin batter, there are 4.5 cups of blueberries. If she is using the recipe as a guide, how many cups of milk will she need?

2. One side of a triangle is 3 cm long. Another side is 1 cm longer than the first side, and the third side is 1 cm longer than the second side. On a similar triangle, the side that corresponds to the 3 cm side of the first triangle is 6 m long. How long is the third side of the similar triangle?

3. Jeremy is the oldest of four brothers. Each of the four boys gets an allowance for doing chores at home each week. The amount of money each boy receives depends on his age. Jeremy is 13 years old, and he gets $7.05. His 11-year-old brother gets $6.11, and his 9-year-old brother gets $5.17. How much money does his 7-year-old brother get?

4. Jorge lives in Santa Fe, New Mexico, and is going to see his grandparents in Tucson, Arizona. By using his map, he found that he will travel 375 miles. The scale of Jorge's map is 1 inch = 120 miles. What other information did Jorge use to find the distance in miles that he will travel?

Focus on Problem Solving

Purpose: *To focus on making a plan to solve a problem*

Problem Solving Resources

Interactive Problem Solving . . pp. 44–50

Math: Reading and Writing in the Content Area . . . . pp. 44–50

Problem Solving Process

This page focuses on the second step of the problem-solving process: **Make a Plan**

Discuss

Have students discuss how they might use the strategy they chose to solve each problem.

Possible answers:

1. Write an equation. Write a proportion comparing the number of cups of milk with the number of cups of blueberries.
2. Draw a diagram. Draw a diagram of the first triangle and label the lengths of the sides. Draw the second triangle.
3. Find a pattern. Determine the relationship between the increase in allowance and the age of the boys.
4. Write an equation. Write a proportion using the scale and the actual distance between Santa Fe and Tucson.

Answers

1. 3 cups
2. 10 m
3. $4.23
4. Jorge used the distance in inches ($3\frac{1}{8}$ inches) on the map between Santa Fe and Tucson to find the distance that he will travel.

Section 5B Graphical Proportions

One-Minute Section Planner

Lesson	Materials	Resources
Hands-On Lab 5A Make Similar Figures **NCTM:** Algebra, Geometry, Measurement, Reasoning and Proof, Connections, Representation **NAEP:** Geometry 1f ☐ SAT-9 ☐ SAT-10 ☐ ITBS ☐ CTBS ☐ MAT ☐ CAT	**Required** Square tiles *(MK)*	• *Hands-On Lab Activities,* pp. 33–35
Lesson 5-5 Similar Figures and Proportions **NCTM:** Geometry, Measurement, Reasoning and Proof, Communication, Connections **NAEP:** Geometry 2e ☑ SAT-9 ☑ SAT-10 ☑ ITBS ☑ CTBS ☑ MAT ☑ CAT	**Optional** Teaching Transparency T20 *(CRB)* Recording Sheet for Reaching All Learners *(CRB, p. 77)*	• *Chapter 5 Resource Book,* pp. 45–53 • Daily Transparency T19, CRB • Additional Examples Transparencies T21–T22, CRB • *Alternate Openers: Explorations,* p. 48
Lesson 5-6 Using Similar Figures **NCTM:** Number and Operations, Measurement, Communication, Connections **NAEP:** Geometry 2f ☐ SAT-9 ☑ SAT-10 ☐ ITBS ☐ CTBS ☐ MAT ☑ CAT	**Optional** Rulers *(MK)*	• *Chapter 5 Resource Book,* pp. 54–62 • Daily Transparency T23, CRB • Additional Examples Transparencies T24–T26, CRB • *Alternate Openers: Explorations,* p. 49
Lesson 5-7 Scale Drawings and Scale Models **NCTM:** Number and Operations, Measurement, Communication, Connections, Representation **NAEP:** Measurement 2f ☑ SAT-9 ☑ SAT-10 ☐ ITBS ☐ CTBS ☑ MAT ☐ CAT	**Optional** Social studies textbooks Reference books or encyclopedia	• *Chapter 5 Resource Book,* pp. 63–71 • Daily Transparency T27, CRB • Additional Examples Transparencies T28–T30, CRB • *Alternate Openers: Explorations,* p. 50
Section 5B Assessment		• Section 5B Quiz, AR p. 16 • *Test and Practice Generator* CD-ROM

SAT = *Stanford Achievement Tests* **ITBS** = *Iowa Test of Basic Skills* **CTBS** = *Comprehensive Test of Basic Skills/Terra Nova*
MAT = *Metropolitan Achievement Test* **CAT** = *California Achievement Test*

NCTM—Complete standards can be found on pages T27–T33. **NAEP**—Complete standards can be found on pages A35–A39.

SE = *Student Edition* **TE** = *Teacher's Edition* **AR** = *Assessment Resources* **CRB** = *Chapter Resource Book* **MK** = *Manipulatives Kit*

Section Overview

Similar Figures

Hands-On Lab 5A, Lessons 5-5, 5-6

Why? You can use facts about similar figures to solve problems involving indirect measurement, such as finding the height of a tall building without physically measuring it.

The triangle formed by the height of the man and his shadow and the triangle formed by the height of the building and its shadow are similar. Find the height of the building.

$$\frac{6}{2} = \frac{h}{40}$$

$$2 \cdot h = 6 \cdot 40$$

$$2 \cdot h = 240$$

$$h = 120$$

The height of the building is 120 feet.

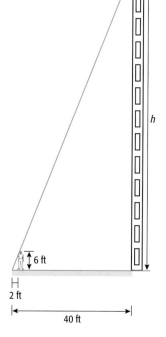

Similar figures are figures that have the same shape.
- Corresponding pairs of sides of similar figures are proportional.
- Pairs of corresponding sides have equal ratios.
- All corresponding angles of similar figures are congruent.

Scale Drawings and Scale Models

Lesson 5-7

Why? Scales are used in maps, blueprints, and other scale drawings.

Scale drawings and scale models have the same shape but not the same size as the objects they represent.

A **scale** is a ratio between two sets of measurements.

Using the scale and a proportion, you can find the actual measurement of an object pictured on a scale drawing or represented by a scale model.

Map scale: **1** in. = **50** mi

Map measurement between points *A* and *B*:**4.5** in.

Use a proportion to find the actual distance between points *A* and *B*.

$$\frac{\mathbf{1}}{\mathbf{50}} = \frac{\mathbf{4.5}}{d}$$

$$d = 50 \cdot 4.5$$

$$d = 225$$

The actual distance between points *A* and *B* is 225 miles.

5A Make Similar Figures

Pacing: Traditional 1 day
Block $\frac{1}{2}$ day

Objective: To use square tiles to make similar figures by increasing or decreasing each dimension of a rectangle by the same scale factor

Materials: Square tiles

Lab Resources

Hands-On Lab Activities . . . . . pp. 33–35

Using the Pages

Discuss with students how to model each rectangle with square tiles. Be sure students understand that to make the similar rectangle, they must increase or decrease both the length and the width.

Use square tiles to model making similar figures with given dimensions.

1. The original rectangle is 3 tiles wide by 2 tiles long. The similar rectangle is 9 tiles wide.

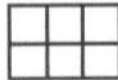

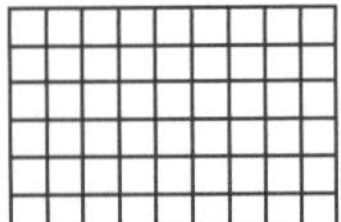

2. The original rectangle is 12 tiles wide by 8 tiles long. The similar rectangle is 4 tiles long.

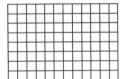

Make Similar Figures

Use with Lesson 5-5

REMEMBER
- The ratios of the lengths of the corresponding sides of similar figures are proportional.
- All of the angles of a rectangle have the same measure.

You can make similar figures by increasing or decreasing each dimension of a rectangle while keeping the ratios of the lengths of the corresponding sides proportional. Modeling similar figures using square tiles can help you solve proportions.

Activity

A rectangle made of square tiles measures 5 tiles long and 2 tiles wide. What is the length of a similar rectangle whose width is 6 tiles?

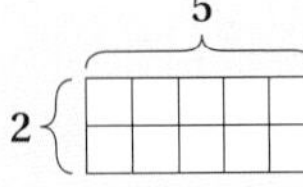

Use tiles to make a 5 × 2 rectangle.

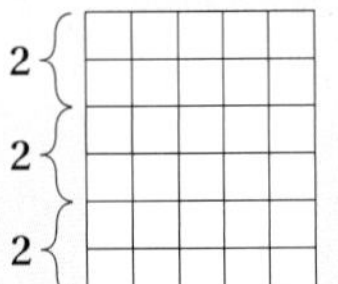

Add tiles to increase the width of the rectangle to 6 tiles.

Notice that there are now 3 sets of 2 tiles along the width of the rectangle because 2 × 3 = 6.

The width of the new rectangle is three times greater than the width of the original rectangle. To keep the ratios of the side measures proportional, the length must also be three times greater than the length of the original rectangle.

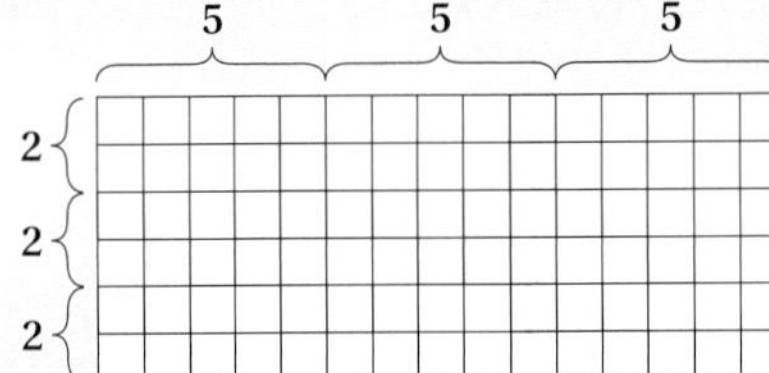

5 × 3 = 15

Add tiles to increase the length of the rectangle to 15 tiles.

The length of the similar rectangle is 15 tiles.

Teacher to Teacher

Stacie Tarbet
Prince William County, Virginia

My students were having great difficulty with the concept of similar figures. Despite their knowledge of ratios, they believed that it was impossible for two figures to be similar if the lengths of their sides were different. I decided to relate the concept of similar figures with that of a movie set. I asked students how they thought large creatures could walk around destroying large cities in movies without hurting the actual cities. Students suggested that perhaps the cities were smaller models of the real cities. We discussed how all the angles must remain the same for the buildings to look the same, however the actual length, width and height have to be scaled to create the smaller version. This was a nice bridge to the investigation of similar figures.

To check your answer, you can use ratios.

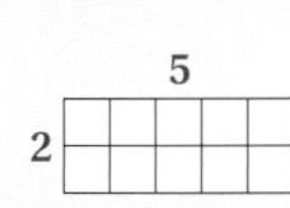
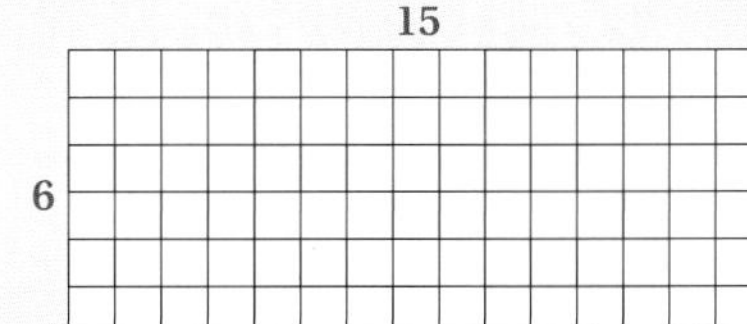

$\frac{2}{6} \stackrel{?}{=} \frac{5}{15}$ *Write ratios using the corresponding side lengths.*

$\frac{1}{3} \stackrel{?}{=} \frac{1}{3}$ *Simplify each ratio.*

1. Use square tiles to model similar figures with the given dimensions.
   a. The original rectangle is 4 tiles wide by 3 tiles long. The similar rectangle is 8 tiles wide. **8 tiles wide by 6 tiles long**
   b. The original rectangle is 8 tiles wide by 10 tiles long. The similar rectangle is 15 tiles long. **12 tiles wide by 15 tiles long**

Think and Discuss

1. In a backyard, a plot of land that is 5 yd × 8 yd is used to grow corn. The homeowner wants to decrease this plot to 5 yd × 4 yd. Will the new plot be similar to the original? Why or why not?
2. The homeowner wants to make the new plot similar to the original that is 5 yd × 8 yd by decreasing the longer side to 4 yd. What should the measure of the shorter side be? **2.5 yd**
3. What other dimensions could the homeowner have used for the new plot to make it similar to the old plot? **Possible answer: 10 yd by 16 yd**

Try This

1. A rectangle is 3 feet long and 7 feet wide. What is the width of a similar rectangle whose length is 9 feet? **21 feet**
2. A rectangle is 6 feet long and 12 feet wide. What is the length of a similar rectangle whose width is 4 feet? **2 feet**

Use square tiles to model similar rectangles to solve each proportion.

3. $\frac{4}{5} = \frac{8}{x}$ **$x = 10$** 4. $\frac{5}{9} = \frac{h}{18}$ **$h = 10$** 5. $\frac{2}{y} = \frac{6}{18}$ **$y = 6$** 6. $\frac{1}{t} = \frac{4}{16}$ **$t = 4$**

7. $\frac{2}{3} = \frac{8}{m}$ **$m = 12$** 8. $\frac{9}{12} = \frac{p}{4}$ **$p = 3$** 9. $\frac{6}{r} = \frac{9}{15}$ **$r = 10$** 10. $\frac{k}{12} = \frac{7}{6}$ **$k = 14$**

Answers

Activity

1. a.

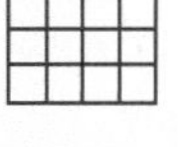
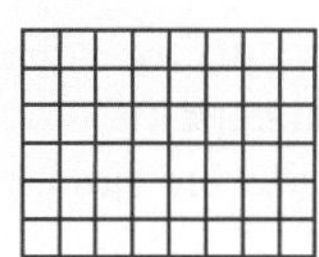

b.

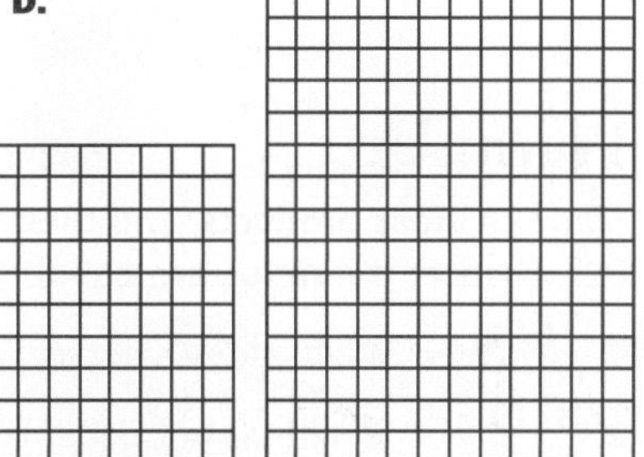

Think and Discuss

1. No, the 2 plots will not be similar. The ratios of corresponding side lengths are not proportional because $\frac{5}{8} \neq \frac{5}{4}$.

5-5 Organizer

Pacing: Traditional 1 day
Block $\frac{1}{2}$ day

Objective: Students use ratios to determine if two figures are similar.

Warm Up

Find the cross products, and then tell whether the ratios are equal.

1. $\frac{16}{6}, \frac{40}{15}$ 240 = 240; equal
2. $\frac{3}{8}, \frac{18}{46}$ 138 ≠ 144; not equal
3. $\frac{8}{9}, \frac{24}{27}$ 216 = 216; equal
4. $\frac{28}{12}, \frac{42}{18}$ 504 = 504; equal

Problem of the Day

Every 8th telephone pole along a road has a red band painted on it. Every 14th pole has an emergency call phone on it. If pole 1 has neither, what is the number of the first pole with both a red band and a call phone? pole 56

Available on Daily Transparency in CRB

What did the little acorn say when she grew up? Geometry! (Gee, I'm a tree!)

5-5 Similar Figures and Proportions

Learn to use ratios to determine if two figures are similar.

Vocabulary
similar
corresponding sides
corresponding angles

Octahedral fluorite is a crystal found in nature. It grows in the shape of an octahedron, which is a solid figure with eight triangular faces. The triangles in different-sized fluorite crystals are *similar* figures. **Similar** figures have the same shape but not necessarily the same size.

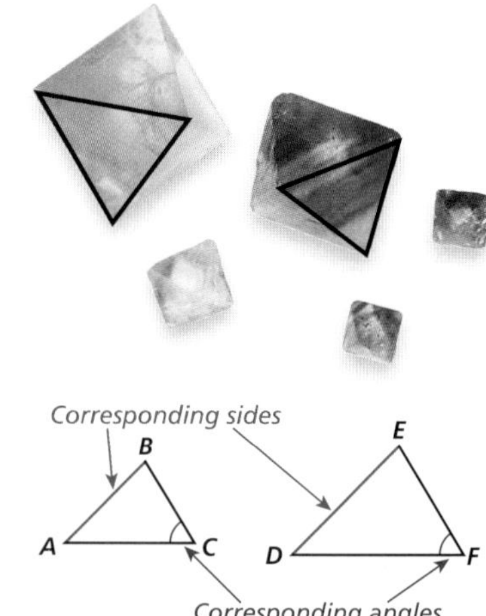

Matching sides of two or more polygons are called **corresponding sides**, and matching angles are called **corresponding angles**.

Corresponding sides: triangle ABC and triangle DEF
Corresponding angles

SIMILAR FIGURES

If two figures are similar, then the measures of the corresponding angles are equal and the ratios of the lengths of the corresponding sides are proportional.

To find out if triangles are similar, determine whether the ratios of the lengths of their corresponding sides are proportional. If the ratios are proportional, then the corresponding angles must have equal measures.

EXAMPLE 1 Determining Whether Two Triangles Are Similar

Identify the corresponding sides in the pair of triangles. Then use ratios to determine whether the triangles are similar.

Triangle DEF: DE = 7 in., EF = 8 in., DF = 12 in. Triangle QRS: QR = 21 in., RS = 24 in., QS = 36 in.

$\overline{DE}$ corresponds to $\overline{QR}$.
$\overline{EF}$ corresponds to $\overline{RS}$.
$\overline{DF}$ corresponds to $\overline{QS}$.

$\frac{DE}{QR} \stackrel{?}{=} \frac{EF}{RS} \stackrel{?}{=} \frac{DF}{QS}$ *Write ratios using the corresponding sides.*

$\frac{7}{21} \stackrel{?}{=} \frac{8}{24} \stackrel{?}{=} \frac{12}{36}$ *Substitute the lengths of the sides.*

$\frac{1}{3} \stackrel{?}{=} \frac{1}{3} \stackrel{?}{=} \frac{1}{3}$ *Simplify each ratio.*

Since the ratios of the corresponding sides are equivalent, the triangles are similar.

Reading Math

A side of a figure can be named by its endpoints, with a bar above.
$\overline{AB}$
Without the bar, the letters indicate the *length* of the side.

1 Introduce

Alternate Opener

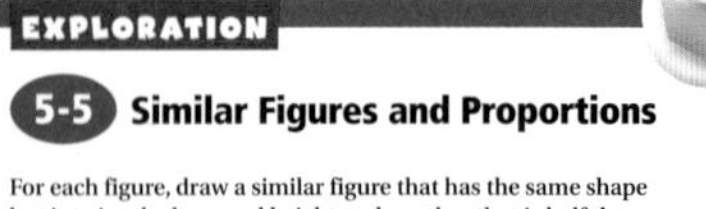

For each figure, draw a similar figure that has the same shape but is twice the base and height and another that is half the base and height.

	Twice the base and height	Half the base and height
1.		
2.		
3.		

Think and Discuss
4. **Explain** how you can recognize similar figures.

Motivate

Ask students to suggest definitions for the word *similar* as it is used in everyday conversation. Have students consider what characteristics are used to determine whether two objects are similar to each another. Brainstorm with students a list of ways that objects can be similar (e.g., having the same shape, color, size, or function).

Exploration worksheet and answers on Chapter 5 Resource Book pp. 46 and 88

2 Teach

Lesson Presentation

Guided Instruction

In this lesson, students learn to use ratios to determine if two figures are similar. Direct students' attention to the symbols used in the examples:

In Example 1, read $\overline{DE}$ as "side DE."

Be sure students understand that the symbol $\stackrel{?}{=}$ is used before it is certain that the ratios are equal to each other.

In Example 2, encourage students to identify the corresponding angles:
$\angle E$ corresponds to $\angle L$;
$\angle F$ corresponds to $\angle M$;
$\angle G$ corresponds to $\angle N$; and
$\angle H$ corresponds to $\angle O$.

In figures with four or more sides, it is possible for the corresponding side lengths to be proportional and the figures to have different shapes. To find out if these figures are similar, first check that their corresponding angles have equal measures.

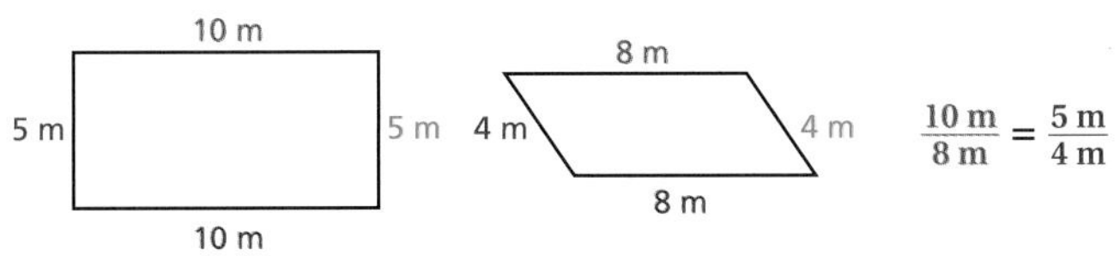

$\frac{10\text{ m}}{8\text{ m}} = \frac{5\text{ m}}{4\text{ m}}$

EXAMPLE 2 **Determining Whether Two Four-Sided Figures Are Similar**

Use the properties of similarity to determine whether the figures are similar.

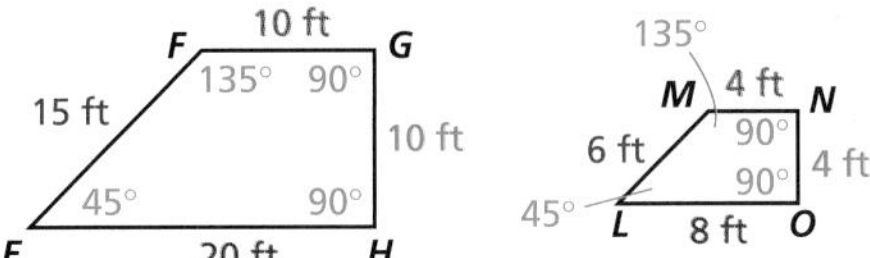

The corresponding angles of the figures have equal measure.
Write each set of corresponding sides as a ratio.

$\frac{EF}{LM}$ $\overline{EF}$ corresponds to $\overline{LM}$.

$\frac{FG}{MN}$ $\overline{FG}$ corresponds to $\overline{MN}$.

$\frac{GH}{NO}$ $\overline{GH}$ corresponds to $\overline{NO}$.

$\frac{EH}{LO}$ $\overline{EH}$ corresponds to $\overline{LO}$.

Determine whether the ratios of the lengths of the corresponding sides are proportional.

$\frac{EF}{LM} \stackrel{?}{=} \frac{FG}{MN} \stackrel{?}{=} \frac{GH}{NO} \stackrel{?}{=} \frac{EH}{LO}$ *Write ratios using the corresponding sides.*

$\frac{15}{6} \stackrel{?}{=} \frac{10}{4} \stackrel{?}{=} \frac{10}{4} \stackrel{?}{=} \frac{20}{8}$ *Substitute the lengths of the sides.*

$\frac{5}{2} \stackrel{?}{=} \frac{5}{2} \stackrel{?}{=} \frac{5}{2} \stackrel{?}{=} \frac{5}{2}$ *Simplify each ratio.*

Since the ratios of the corresponding sides are equivalent, the figures are similar.

Think and Discuss

1. **Identify** the corresponding angles of the triangles in Example 1.
2. **Explain** whether all rectangles are similar. Give specific examples to justify your answer.

Additional Examples

Example 

Identify the corresponding sides in the pair of triangles. Then use ratios to determine whether the triangles are similar.

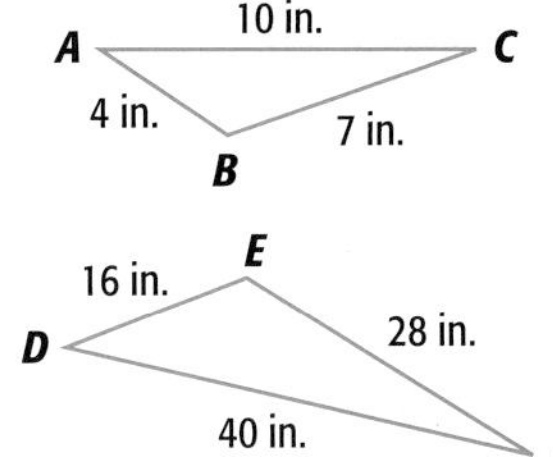

$\overline{AC}$ corresponds to $\overline{DF}$, $\overline{AB}$ corresponds to $\overline{DE}$, $\overline{BC}$ corresponds to $\overline{EF}$; similar

Example 2

Use the properties of similarity to determine whether the figures are similar.

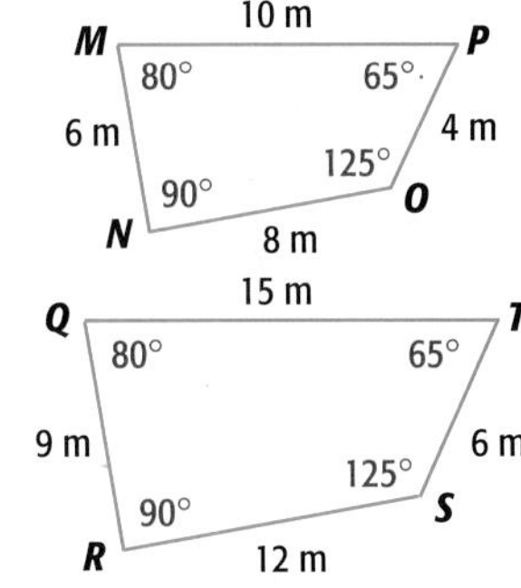

The figures are similar.

3 Close

Reaching All Learners

Through Modeling

Have students draw a figure similar to a given quadrilateral. A recording sheet and answers are available on Chapter 5 Resource Book pp. 77 and 95.

Have students count the units on each corresponding side to draw figures that have sides with double and/or half the size of the original figure.

Summarize

Ask students to describe the characteristics of corresponding angles and corresponding sides in similar figures. Then have students tell how they would decide whether two shapes are similar.

Possible answer: Corresponding angles must be the same measure, but corresponding sides need to be only proportional. In order to decide whether two shapes are similar, it is necessary to identify the corresponding sides, to measure the lengths of the sides, and to determine whether the lengths are proportional.

Answers to Think and Discuss

1. $\angle F$ corresponds to $\angle S$, $\angle E$ corresponds to $\angle R$, and $\angle D$ corresponds to $\angle Q$.
2. Possible answer: All rectangles are not similar. For example, a square with side lengths of 5 inches and a rectangle with a length of 10 inches and a width of 4 inches are both rectangles but are different shapes. All the sides on the square are equal, so they could not be proportional to all the sides of the rectangle.

5-5 PRACTICE & ASSESS

Students may want to refer back to the lesson examples.

Assignment Guide

If you finished Example 1 assign:
Core 1, 2, 5, 6, 9, 10, 20–26
Enriched 1, 2, 5, 6, 9, 10, 20–26

If you finished Example 2 assign:
Core 1–16, 20–26
Enriched 1–7 odd, 9–26

Answers

1. $\frac{AB}{DE} = \frac{BC}{EF} = \frac{AC}{DF}$; $\frac{9}{3} = \frac{12}{4} = \frac{6}{2} = 3$
2. $\frac{RQ}{VT} \neq \frac{QS}{TW}$; $\frac{3}{15} \neq \frac{5}{20}$; $60 \neq 75$
3. Corresponding sides are proportional. Corresponding angles have equal measures.
4. Corresponding sides are not proportional.
5. $\frac{JK}{PQ} \neq \frac{JL}{PR}$; $\frac{18}{48} \neq \frac{12}{28}$; $\frac{3}{8} \neq \frac{3}{7}$
6. $\frac{CD}{JL} = \frac{DE}{LK} = \frac{CE}{JK}$; $\frac{60}{36} = \frac{40}{24} = \frac{50}{30}$; $\frac{5}{3} = \frac{5}{3} = \frac{5}{3}$
7. Corresponding sides are proportional; corresponding angles have equal measures.
8. Corresponding angles do not have equal measures.
9. 4 in. × 6 in., 16 in. × 24 in., 20 in. × 30 in.

5-5 Exercises

FOR EXTRA PRACTICE
see page 665

internet connect
Homework Help Online
go.hrw.com Keyword: MS4 5-5

GUIDED PRACTICE

See Example 1 Identify the corresponding sides in each pair of triangles. Then use ratios to determine whether the triangles are similar.

1. 2.

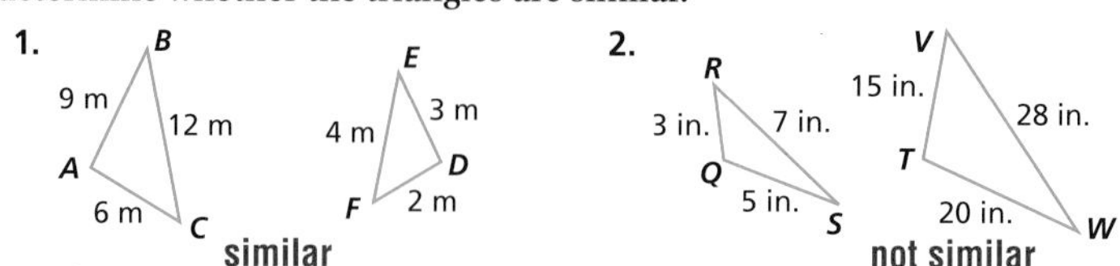

See Example 2 Use the properties of similarity to determine whether the figures are similar.

3. 4.

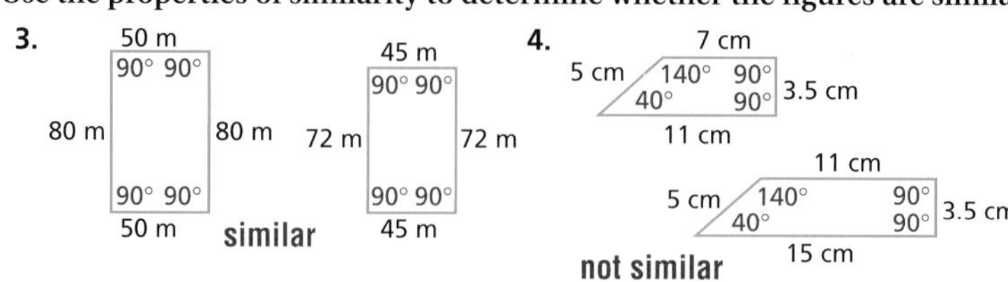

INDEPENDENT PRACTICE

See Example 1 Identify the corresponding sides in each pair of triangles. Then use ratios to determine whether the triangles are similar.

5. 6.

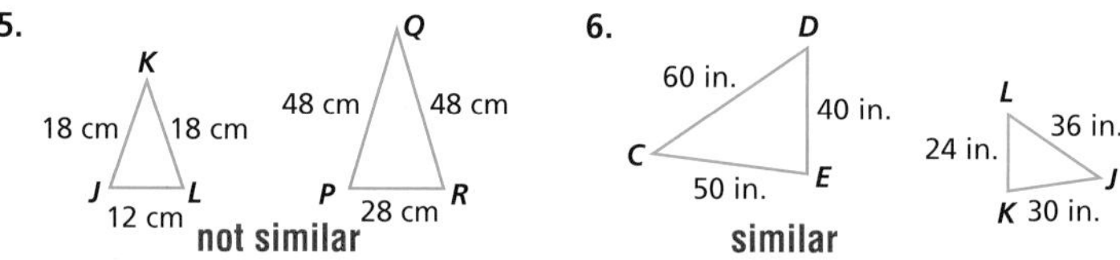

See Example 2 Use the properties of similarity to determine whether the figures are similar.

7. 8.

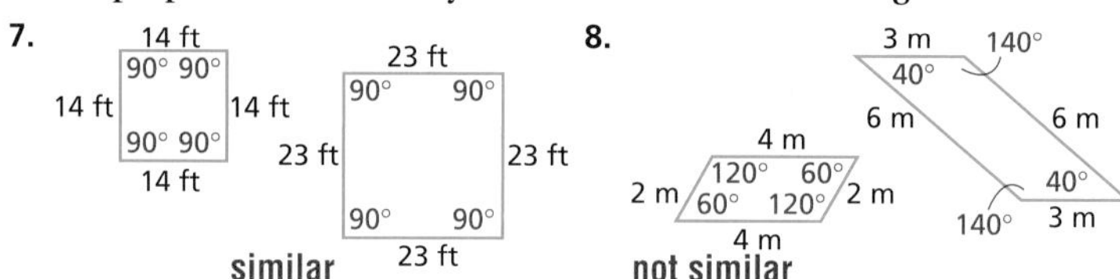

PRACTICE AND PROBLEM SOLVING

9. ***HOBBIES*** Michelle wants similar prints made in various sizes, both small and large, of a favorite photograph. The photo lab offers prints in these sizes: 3 in. × 5 in., 4 in. × 6 in., 8 in. × 18 in., 9 in. × 20 in., 16 in. × 24 in., and 20 in. × 30 in. Which could she order to get similar prints?

Math Background

A *fractal* is a special geometric object that exhibits self-similarity. Self-similarity means that every subdivision of a figure has a structure similar to the structure of the whole. Fractals are created by *iteration*—repeating the same procedure over and over. The following fractal began as a triangle.

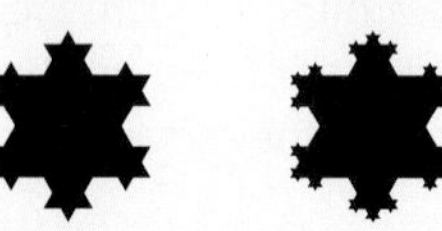

Any part of a fractal is a miniature copy of the original figure.

RETEACH 5-5

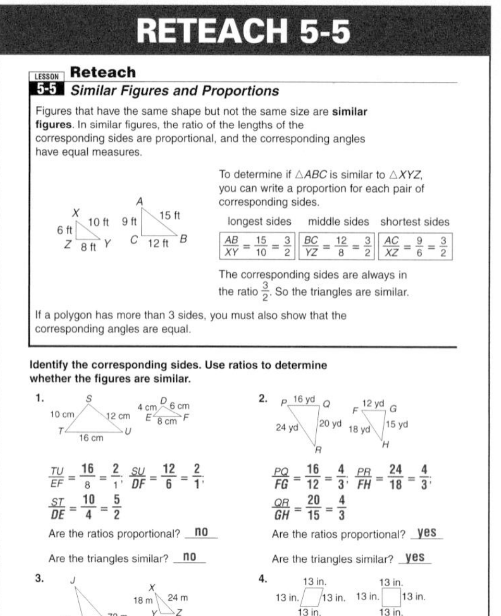

LESSON 5-5 **Reteach**
Similar Figures and Proportions

Figures that have the same shape but not the same size are **similar figures**. In similar figures, the ratio of the lengths of the corresponding sides are proportional, and the corresponding angles have equal measures.

To determine if $\triangle ABC$ is similar to $\triangle XYZ$, you can write a proportion for each pair of corresponding sides.

longest sides	middle sides	shortest sides
$\frac{AB}{XY} = \frac{15}{10} = \frac{3}{2}$	$\frac{BC}{YZ} = \frac{12}{8} = \frac{3}{2}$	$\frac{AC}{XZ} = \frac{9}{6} = \frac{3}{2}$

The corresponding sides are always in the ratio $\frac{3}{2}$. So the triangles are similar.

If a polygon has more than 3 sides, you must also show that the corresponding angles are equal.

Identify the corresponding sides. Use ratios to determine whether the figures are similar.

1.

$\frac{TU}{EF} = \frac{16}{8} = \frac{2}{1}$; $\frac{SU}{DF} = \frac{12}{6} = \frac{2}{1}$;
$\frac{ST}{DE} = \frac{10}{4} = \frac{5}{2}$

Are the ratios proportional? __no__

Are the triangles similar? __no__

2.

$\frac{PQ}{FG} = \frac{16}{12} = \frac{4}{3}$; $\frac{PR}{FH} = \frac{24}{18} = \frac{4}{3}$;
$\frac{QR}{GH} = \frac{20}{15} = \frac{4}{3}$

Are the ratios proportional? __yes__

Are the triangles similar? __yes__

3.

__similar__

4.

__not similar; angles not equal measure__

PRACTICE 5-5

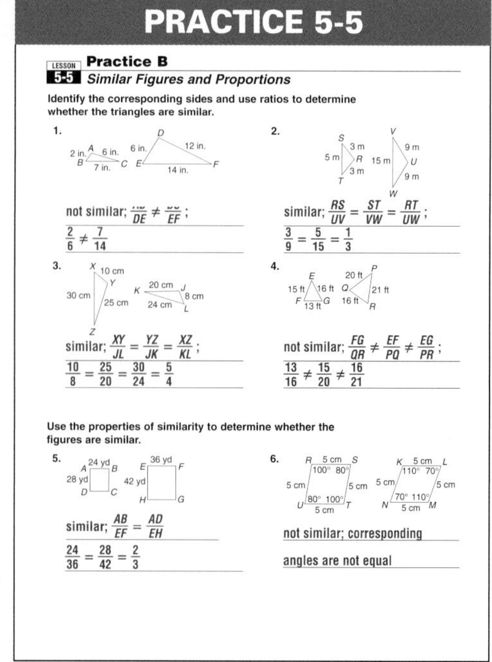

LESSON 5-5 **Practice B**
Similar Figures and Proportions

Identify the corresponding sides and use ratios to determine whether the triangles are similar.

1.

not similar; $\frac{AB}{DE} \neq \frac{BC}{EF}$;
$\frac{2}{6} \neq \frac{7}{14}$

2.

similar; $\frac{RS}{UV} = \frac{ST}{VW} = \frac{RT}{UW}$;
$\frac{3}{9} = \frac{5}{15} = \frac{1}{3}$

3.

similar; $\frac{XY}{JL} = \frac{YZ}{JK} = \frac{XZ}{KL}$;
$\frac{10}{8} = \frac{25}{20} = \frac{30}{24} = \frac{5}{4}$

4.

not similar; $\frac{FG}{QR} \neq \frac{EF}{PQ} \neq \frac{EG}{PR}$;
$\frac{13}{16} \neq \frac{15}{20} \neq \frac{16}{21}$

Use the properties of similarity to determine whether the figures are similar.

5.

similar; $\frac{AB}{EF} = \frac{AD}{EH}$
$\frac{24}{36} = \frac{28}{42} = \frac{2}{3}$

6.

not similar; corresponding angles are not equal

Identify the corresponding sides in each pair of triangles. Then use ratios to determine whether the triangles are similar.

10. 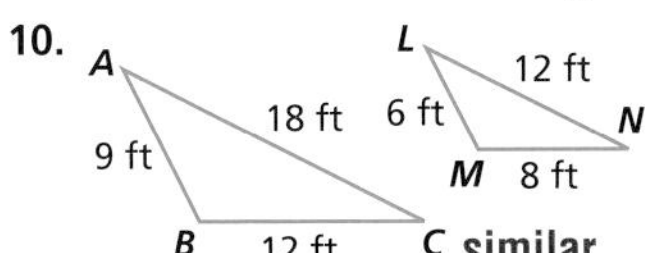

similar

11. 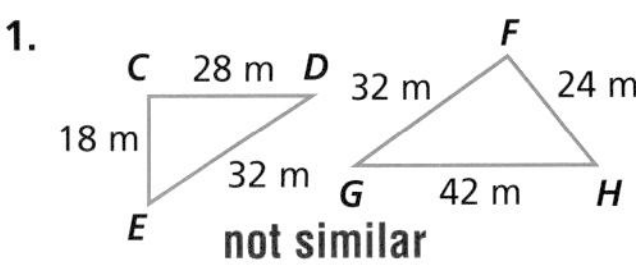

not similar

12. Tell whether the parallelogram and trapezoid could be similar. Explain your answer. **No, corresponding angles are not congruent.**

120° 60° / 60° 120°   120° 120° / 60° 60°

13. The figure at right shows a rectangular piece of paper that has been cut into four rectangular parts. Tell whether the rectangles in each pair are similar. Explain your answers.

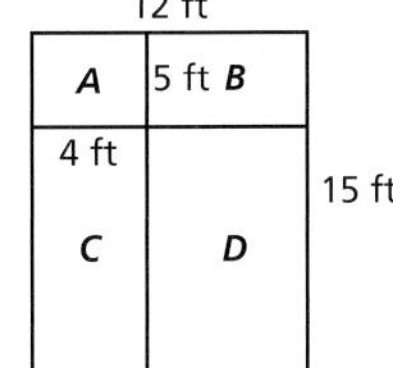

a. rectangle A and the original rectangle
b. rectangle C and rectangle B
c. the original rectangle and rectangle D

13a. Yes; $\frac{4}{12} = \frac{5}{15}$, $60 = 60$

13b. No; $\frac{4}{5} \neq \frac{10}{8}$, $32 \neq 50$

13c. Yes; $\frac{12}{8} = \frac{15}{10}$, $120 = 120$

For Exercises 14–16, justify your answers using words or drawings.

14. Are all squares similar? **Yes; the side ratios are equivalent because all the sides of a square are the same and squares all have four right angles.**
15. Are all parallelograms similar? **No; parallelograms do not all have the same angle measures.**
16. Are all right triangles similar? **No; the acute angles of a right triangle are not the same in every right triangle.**
17. ***CHOOSE A STRATEGY*** What number gives the same result when multiplied by 6 as it does when 6 is added to it? $\frac{6}{5}$ **or** $1\frac{1}{5}$
18. ***WRITE ABOUT IT*** Tell how to decide whether two triangles are similar.
19. ***CHALLENGE*** Two triangles are similar. The ratio of the lengths of the corresponding sides is $\frac{5}{4}$. If the length of one side of the larger triangle is 40 feet, what is the length of the corresponding side of the smaller triangle? **32 ft**

Spiral Review

Add or subtract. (Lesson 4-2)

20. $29 - 4.63$ **24.37**
21. $9.6 - 0.47$ **9.13**
22. $-14.7 + (-5.06) + (-0.9)$ **−20.66**

Write each as a unit rate in fraction and word form. (Lesson 5-1)

23. $\frac{48 \text{ min}}{6 \text{ mi}}$ $\frac{8 \text{ min}}{1 \text{ mi}}$; **8 minutes per mile**
24. $\frac{78 \text{ m}}{4 \text{ s}}$ $\frac{19.5 \text{ m}}{1 \text{ s}}$; **19.5 meters per second**
25. 8 cups per 4 servings

26. **TEST PREP** A store receives a delivery of 112 quarts of milk. How many gallons of milk does the store receive? (Lesson 5-4) **B**

A 14 gal   B 28 gal   C 56 gal   D 448 gal

CHALLENGE 5-5

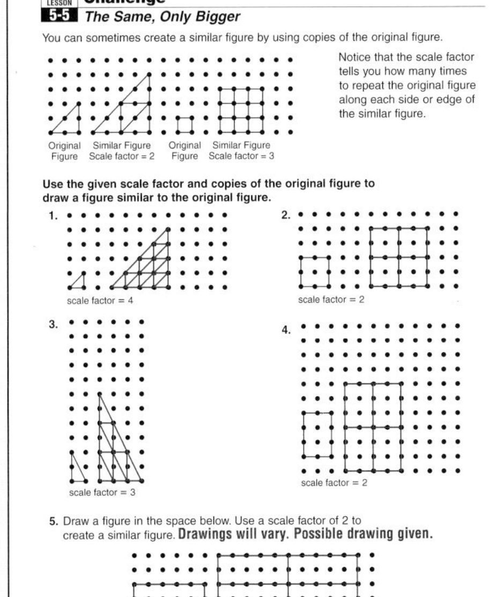
LESSON 5-5 **Challenge**
The Same, Only Bigger

You can sometimes create a similar figure by using copies of the original figure.

Notice that the scale factor tells you how many times to repeat the original figure along each side or edge of the similar figure.

Original Figure   Similar Figure Scale factor = 2   Original Figure   Similar Figure Scale factor = 3

Use the given scale factor and copies of the original figure to draw a figure similar to the original figure.

1. scale factor = 4
2. scale factor = 2
3. scale factor = 3
4. scale factor = 2
5. Draw a figure in the space below. Use a scale factor of 2 to create a similar figure. **Drawings will vary. Possible drawing given.**

PROBLEM SOLVING 5-5

LESSON 5-5 **Problem Solving**
Similar Figures and Proportions

Use the information in the table to solve problems 1–3.

Painting	Artist	Original Size (in.)
Mona Lisa	Leonardo da Vinci	30 by 21
The Dance Class	Edgar Degas	33 by 30
The Blue Vase	Paul Cézanne	22 by 18

1. A small reproduction of one of the paintings in the list is similar in size. The reproduction measures 11 inches by 10 inches. Of which painting is this a reproduction?
The Dance Class

2. A local artist painted a reproduction of Cézanne's painting. It measures 88 inches by 72 inches. Is the reproduction similar to the original? What is the ratio of corresponding sides?
yes; 1:4

3. A poster company made a poster of da Vinci's painting. The poster is 5 feet long and 3.5 feet wide. Is the poster similar to the original *Mona Lisa*? What is the ratio of corresponding sides?
yes; 1:2

Choose the letter for the best answer.

4. Triangle ABC has sides of 15 cm, 20 cm, and 25 cm. Which triangle could be similar to triangle ABC?
   (A) A triangle with sides of 3 cm, 4 cm, and 5 cm
   B A triangle with sides of 5 cm, 6 cm, and 8 cm
   C A triangle with sides of 30 cm, 40 cm, and 55 cm
   D A triangle with sides of 5 cm, 10 cm, and 30 cm

5. A rectangular picture frame is 14 inches long and 4 inches wide. Which dimensions could a similar picture frame have?
   F Length = 21 in.; width = 8 in.
   G Length = 35 in.; width = 15 in.
   (H) Length = 49 in.; width = 14 in.
   J Length = 7 in.; width = 3 in.

6. A rectangle is 12 meters long and 21 meters wide. Which dimensions correspond to a nonsimilar rectangle?
   A 4 m; 7 m   C 20 m; 35 m
   B 8 m; 14 m   (D) 24 m; 35 m

7. A parallelogram is 6 feet long and 15 feet wide. Which dimensions correspond to a similar parallelogram?
   F 8 ft; 24 ft   H 15 ft; 35 ft
   (G) 10 ft; 25 ft   J 18 ft; 40 ft

Answers

10. $\frac{AB}{LM} = \frac{AC}{LN} = \frac{BC}{MN}; \frac{9}{6} = \frac{18}{12} = \frac{12}{8}$

11. $\frac{CD}{FG} \neq \frac{CE}{FH} \neq \frac{ED}{HG}; \frac{28}{32} \neq \frac{18}{24} \neq \frac{32}{42}; \frac{7}{8} \neq \frac{3}{4} \neq \frac{16}{21}$

18. Possible answer: To find out whether triangles are similar, determine whether the ratios of their corresponding sides are proportional.

25. $\frac{2 \text{ c}}{1 \text{ serving}}$; 2 cups per serving

Journal

Have students describe the two methods they have learned to determine if corresponding sides of two figures are proportional: using cross products and simplifying ratios.

Test Prep Doctor

For Exercise 26, students can quickly eliminate **D** because the answer must be less than 112. Using compatible numbers 100 and 120 to estimate, students can then determine that the answer lies between 25 and 30, eliminating **A** and **C.**

Lesson Quiz

Identify the corresponding sides in the pair of triangles, and use ratios to determine whether the triangles are similar.

1.

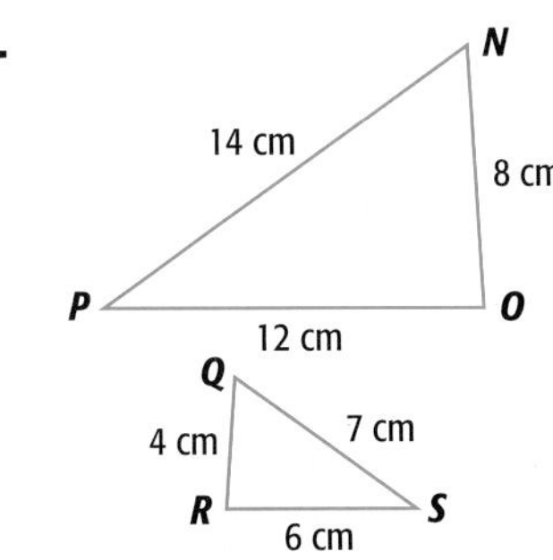

$\overline{NO}$ corresponds to $\overline{QR}$;
$\overline{PO}$ corresponds to $\overline{SR}$;
$\overline{PN}$ corresponds to $\overline{SQ}$; similar.

Use properties of similarity to determine whether the figures are similar.

2.

13 m, 18 m, 14 m, 26 m
52 m, 31 m, 60 m, 104 m

not similar

Available on Daily Transparency in CRB

5-6 Organizer

Pacing: Traditional 1 day
Block $\frac{1}{2}$ day

Objective: Students use similar figures to find unknown lengths.

Warm Up

Solve each proportion.

1. $\frac{k}{4} = \frac{75}{25}$ $\quad k = 12$

2. $\frac{6}{19} = \frac{24}{x}$ $\quad x = 76$

Triangles *JNZ* and *KOA* are similar. Identify the side that corresponds to the given side of the similar triangles.

3.

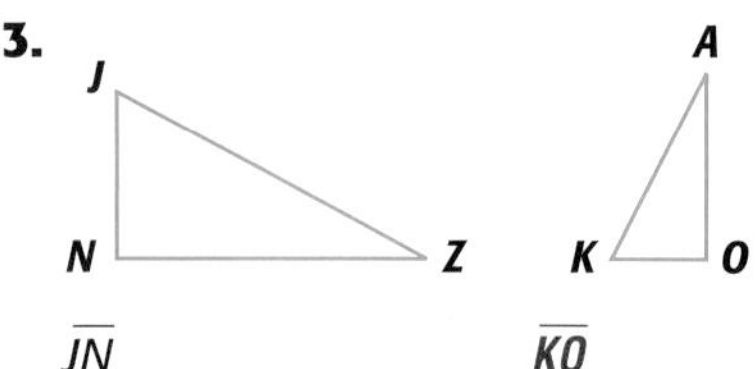

$\overline{JN}$ $\quad \overline{KO}$

Problem of the Day

Harvey starts to fill a 3-gallon tank from a hose that delivers 1 gallon per minute. However, the tank leaks 1 quart per minute. In how many minutes will the tank begin to overflow? 4 minutes

Available on Daily Transparency in CRB

5-6 Using Similar Figures

Learn to use similar figures to find unknown lengths.

Vocabulary

indirect measurement

Native Americans of the Northwest, such as the Tlingit tribe of Alaska, carved totem poles out of tree trunks. These poles, sometimes painted with bright colors, could stand up to 80 feet tall. Totem poles include carvings of animal figures, such as bears and eagles, which symbolize traits of the family or clan who built them.

Measuring the heights of tall objects, like some totem poles, cannot be done by using a ruler or yardstick. Instead, you can use *indirect measurement*.

Indirect measurement is a method of using proportions to find an unknown length or distance in similar figures.

EXAMPLE 1 Finding Unknown Lengths in Similar Figures

Find the unknown length in the similar figures.

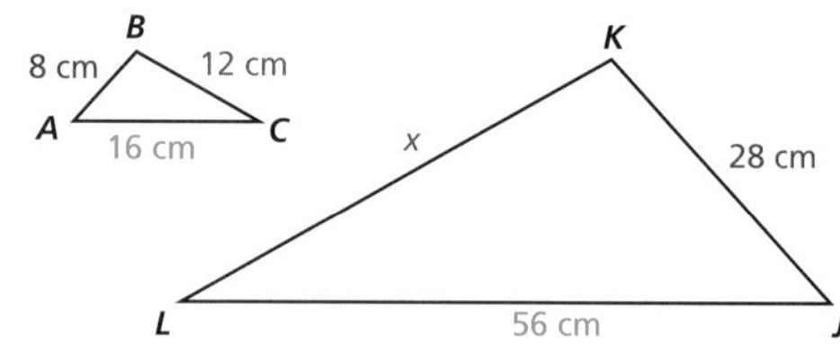

$\frac{AB}{JK} = \frac{BC}{KL}$	*Write a proportion using corresponding sides.*
$\frac{8}{28} = \frac{12}{x}$	*Substitute the lengths of the sides.*
$8 \cdot x = 28 \cdot 12$	*Find the cross products.*
$8x = 336$	*Multiply.*
$\frac{8x}{8} = \frac{336}{8}$	*Divide each side by 8 to isolate the variable.*
$x = 42$	

KL is 42 centimeters.

1 Introduce

Alternate Opener

5-6 Using Similar Figures

1. Draw this Egyptian symbol, which stands for *H*, on graph paper, and measure the length and width of each colored section.

2. Redraw the Egyptian symbol, but this time make it larger by lengthening each section by 1 square. The first two sections are shown as an example. Is the resulting symbol similar to the original?

3. Redraw the Egyptian symbol again, but this time double the width and length of each section. Is the resulting symbol similar to the original?

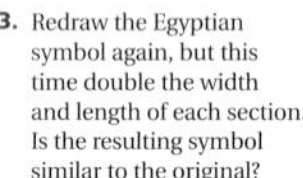

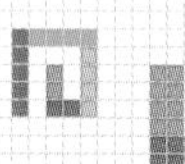

Think and Discuss

4. Explain how to create similar figures.

Motivate

Pose the following problem to students:

How can the principal determine the height of the flagpole without taking it down?

Discuss the difficulties of measuring tall objects. Point out that measuring an object with a ruler or a yardstick is direct measurement. Explain that students can use what they know about similar figures to measure tall objects indirectly, that is, without having to measure the object itself.

Exploration worksheet and answers on Chapter 5 Resource Book pp. 55 and 90

2 Teach

Guided Instruction

In this lesson, students learn to use similar figures to find unknown lengths. Some students may not understand why the triangles in Example 3 are similar. Explain that similar triangles are formed when shadows are cast of objects that are near each other. Point out that a person's shadow is always proportional to his or her height. Ask students to recall how to determine whether two triangles are similar.

Review solving proportions with students before they begin finding missing lengths.

EXAMPLE 2 ***Measurement Application***

A volleyball court is a rectangle that is similar in shape to an Olympic-sized pool. Find the width of the pool.

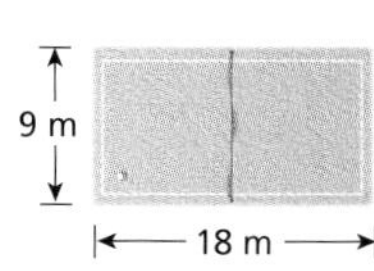

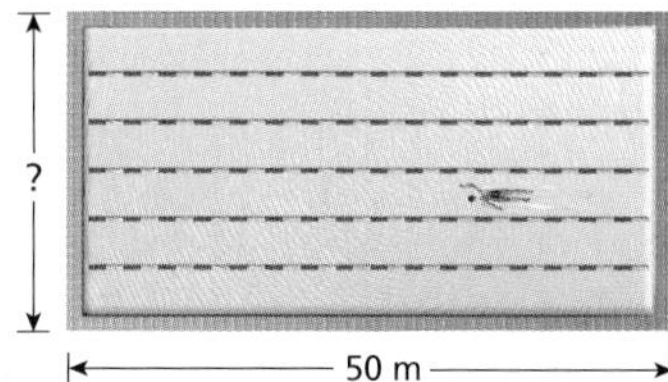

Let w = the width of the pool.

$\frac{18}{50} = \frac{9}{w}$	*Write a proportion using corresponding side lengths.*
$18 \cdot w = 50 \cdot 9$	*Find the cross products.*
$18w = 450$	*Multiply.*
$\frac{18w}{18} = \frac{450}{18}$	*Divide each side by 18 to isolate the variable.*
$w = 25$	

The pool is 25 meters wide.

EXAMPLE 3 **Using Indirect Measurement**

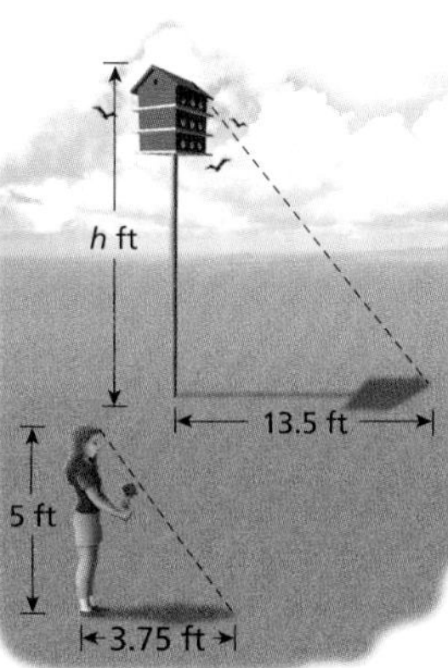

The birdhouse in Chantal's yard casts a shadow that is 13.5 ft long. Chantal casts a shadow that is 3.75 ft long. What is the height of the birdhouse?

Let h = the height of the birdhouse.

$\frac{h}{5} = \frac{13.5}{3.75}$	*Write a proportion.*
$3.75h = 5 \cdot 13.5$	*Find the cross products.*
$3.75h = 67.5$	
$\frac{3.75h}{3.75} = \frac{67.5}{3.75}$	*Divide each side by 3.75 to isolate the variable.*
$h = 18$	

The birdhouse is 18 feet tall.

Think and Discuss

1. **Write** another proportion that could be used to find the value of x in Example 1.
2. **Name** two objects that would make sense to measure using indirect measurement.

Additional Examples

Example 1

Find the unknown length in the similar figures.

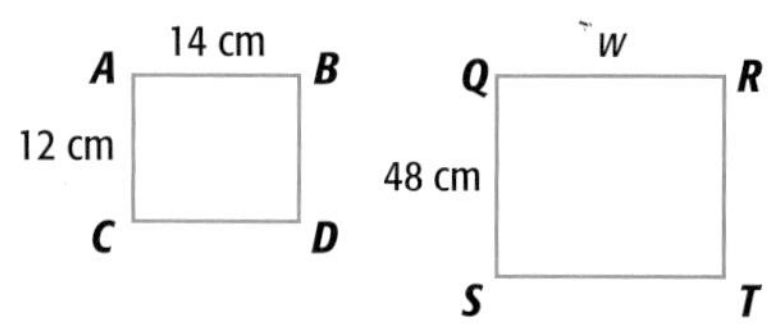

56 cm

Example 2

The inside triangle is similar in shape to the outside triangle. Find the length of the base of the inside triangle.

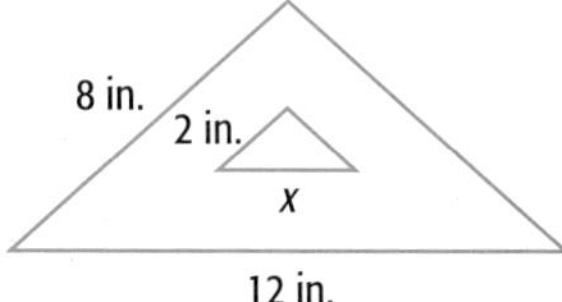

3 in.

Example 3

City officials want to know the height of a traffic light. Use indirect measurement to find the height of the traffic light.

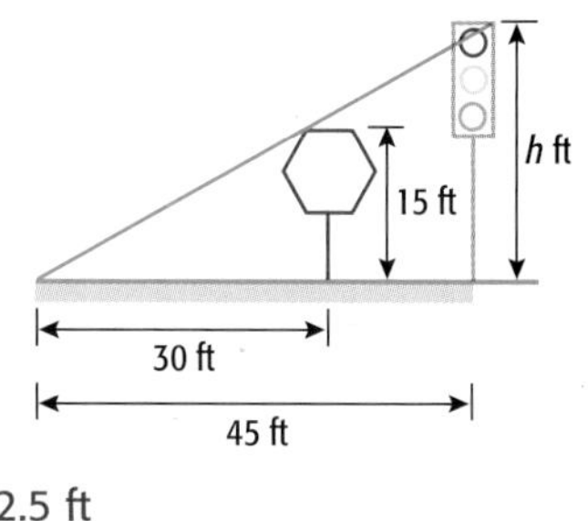

22.5 ft

3 Close

Reaching All Learners
Through Grouping Strategies

Have partners work together to draw two similar triangles with the ratio of the lengths of corresponding sides being 3:1. Encourage students to discuss their method before they begin to draw. Students should use a ruler to measure and to draw the first triangle and then use the ratio 3:1 to determine the length of the corresponding sides of the similar triangle.

Summarize

Ask students to explain in their own words how to find a missing measure for one of two similar figures.

Possible answer: To find a missing measure, create a proportion using one ratio of the lengths of two corresponding sides and another ratio of the missing measure and the lengths of its corresponding side. Use a variable as the missing measure in the second ratio. Solve the proportion.

Answers to Think and Discuss

Possible answers:

1. $\frac{16}{56} = \frac{12}{x}$
2. You could stand next to a tree and measure your shadow and the shadow of the tree to find the height of the tree. You could do the same with a basketball goal.

5-6 PRACTICE & ASSESS

Students may want to refer back to the lesson examples.

Assignment Guide

If you finished Example 1 assign:
Core 1, 2, 5, 6, 9, 14–22
Enriched 1, 2, 5, 6, 9, 14–22

If you finished Example 2 assign:
Core 1–3, 5–7, 9, 10, 14–22
Enriched 1–3, 5–7, 9, 10, 14–22

If you finished Example 3 assign:
Core 1–10, 14–22
Enriched 1–22

Notes

5-6 Exercises

FOR EXTRA PRACTICE see page 665

internet connect
Homework Help Online
go.hrw.com Keyword: MS4 5-6

GUIDED PRACTICE

See Example 1 Find the unknown length in each pair of similar figures.

1.
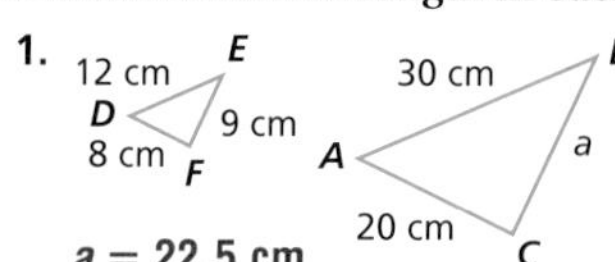

$a = 22.5$ cm

2.
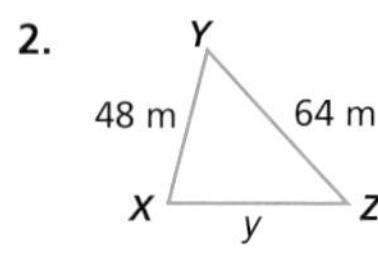

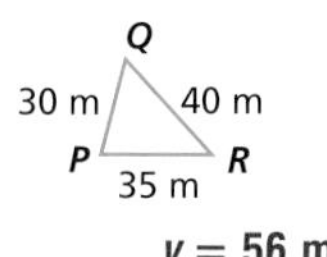

$y = 56$ m

See Example 2

3. The rectangular gardens at right are similar in shape. How wide is the smaller garden? **28 ft**

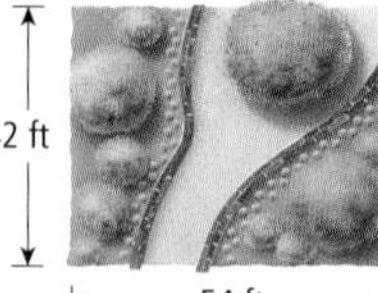

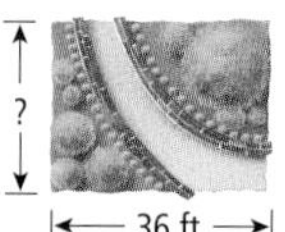

See Example 3

4. A water tower casts a shadow that is 20 ft long. A tree casts a shadow that is 8 ft long. What is the height of the water tower? **25 ft**

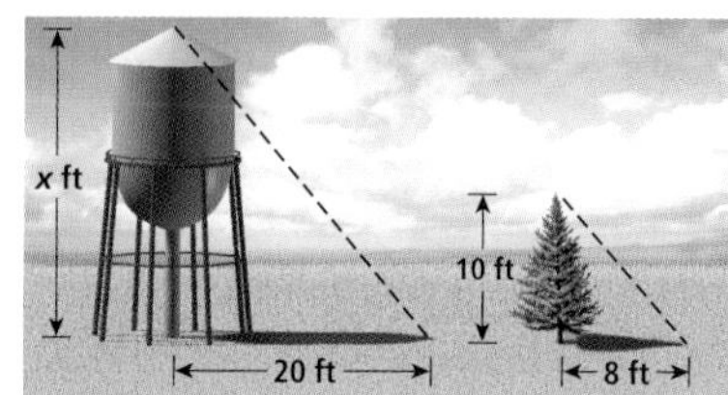

INDEPENDENT PRACTICE

See Example 1 Find the unknown length in each pair of similar figures.

5.
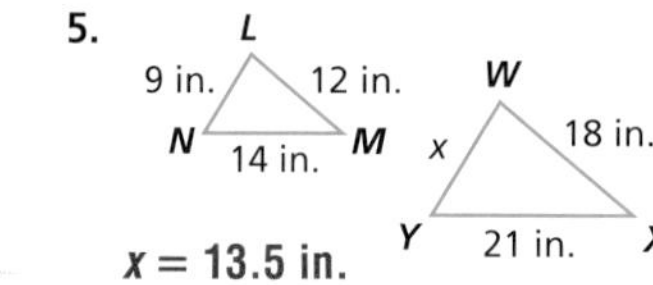

$x = 13.5$ in.

6.
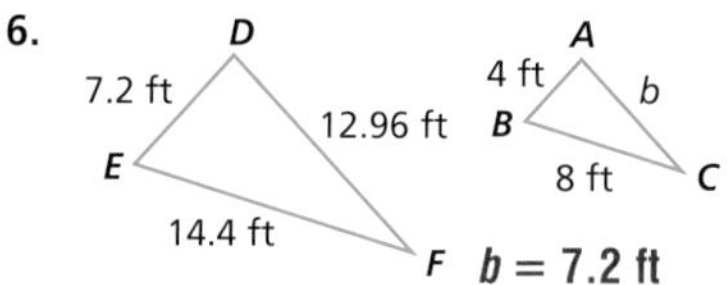

$b = 7.2$ ft

See Example 2

7. The two rectangular windows at right are similar. What is the height of the bigger window? **3.9 ft**

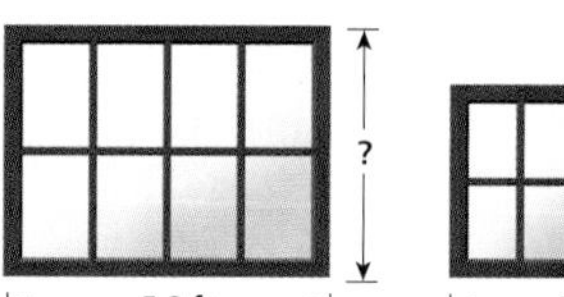

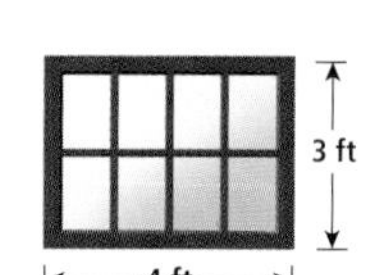

See Example 3

8. A cactus casts a shadow that is 11.25 ft long. A gate nearby casts a shadow that is 5 ft long. What is the height of the cactus? **9 ft**

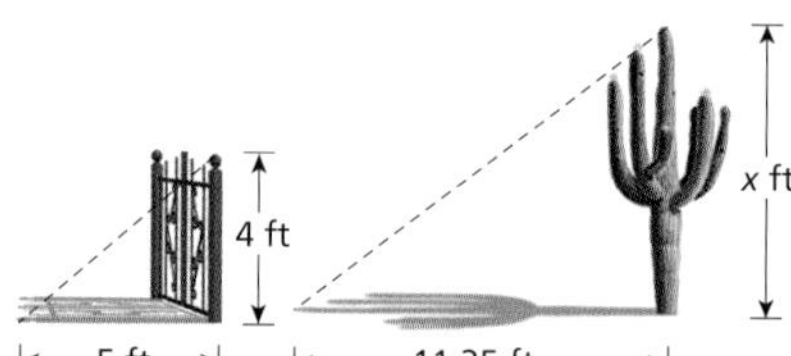

Math Background

In their formal study of geometry, students will learn a postulate and two theorems that allow shortcuts for determining triangle similarity. The AA (Angle-Angle) Triangle Similarity Postulate states: If two angles of one triangle are congruent to two angles of another triangle, then the triangles are similar. The SSS (Side-Side-Side) Similarity Theorem states: If the three sides of one triangle are proportional to the three sides of another triangle, then the triangles are similar. The SAS (Side-Angle-Side) Similarity Theorem states: If two sides of one triangle are proportional to two sides of another triangle and their included angles are congruent, then the triangles are similar.

RETEACH 5-6

LESSON 5-6 **Reteach**
Using Similar Figures

If you know that 2 figures are similar, you can use proportions to find unknown lengths of sides.

The triangles are similar.

Side AC corresponds to side DF.
Side AB corresponds to side DE.
Side BC corresponds to side EF.

Write a proportion comparing the lengths of a pair of corresponding sides.

$$\frac{AC}{DF} = \frac{BC}{EF}$$
$$\frac{5}{15} = \frac{3}{n}$$
$$5 \cdot n = 15 \cdot 3$$
$$5n = 45$$
$$\frac{5n}{5} = \frac{45}{5}$$
$$n = 9$$

The length of the missing side is 9 in.

Find the unknown length in each pair of similar figures.

1. $\frac{UW}{MO} = \frac{UV}{MN}$; $\frac{20}{x} = \frac{12}{6}$
$x = 10$ cm

2. $\frac{WZ}{AD} = \frac{WX}{AB}$; $\frac{9}{5} = \frac{y}{15}$
$y = 27$ m

3. $k = 16$ ft

4. $s = 8$ in.

PRACTICE 5-6

LESSON 5-6 **Practice B**
Using Similar Figures

Find the unknown length in each pair of similar figures.

1. $x = 60$ cm

2. $x = 21$ ft

3. $x = 11$ yd

4. $x = 28$ m

5. Raul is 5 feet tall and casts a shadow that is 7 feet long. The flagpole in front of the school casts a shadow that is 17.5 feet long. Use indirect measurement to find the height of the flagpole.
12.5 feet

6. A palm tree casts a shadow that is 44 feet long. A 6-foot ladder casts a shadow that is 16 feet long. Use indirect measurement to find the height of the palm tree.
16.5 feet

PRACTICE AND PROBLEM SOLVING

9. A building casts a shadow that is 16 m long while a taller building casts a 24 m long shadow. What is the height of the taller building? **36 m**

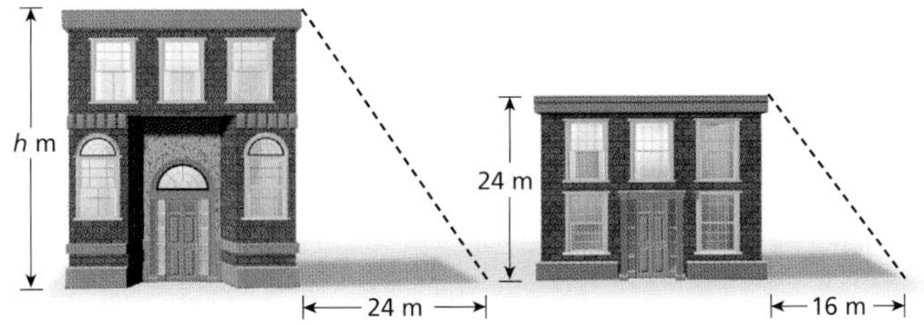

10. ***EARTH SCIENCE*** An art class is painting a wall mural of the solar system. The table shows the distances of three planets from the Sun in astronomical units (AU) and the corresponding distances planned for the mural. Find the missing distances in the table. Round your answers to the nearest tenth.

Planet	Distance from Sun (AU)	Distance on Mural (yd)
Venus	0.72	■ **1.8**
Earth	1.0	2.5
Mars	■ **1.5**	3.8

11. ***WRITE A PROBLEM*** Write a problem that can be solved using indirect measurement.

12. ***WRITE ABOUT IT*** Assume you know the side lengths of one triangle and the length of one side of a second similar triangle. Explain how to use the rules of similar figures to find the unknown lengths in the second triangle.

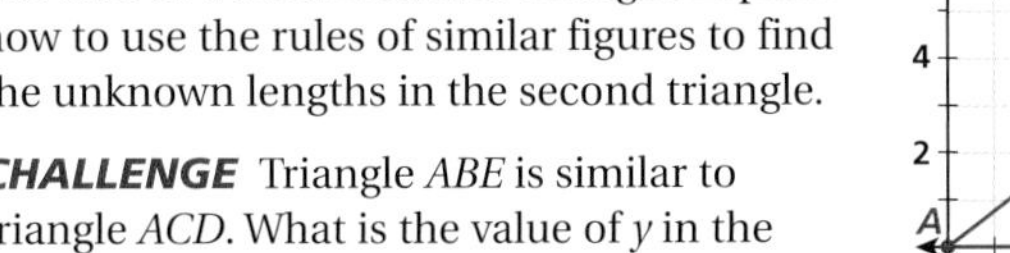

13. ***CHALLENGE*** Triangle ABE is similar to triangle ACD. What is the value of y in the diagram? **3.75**

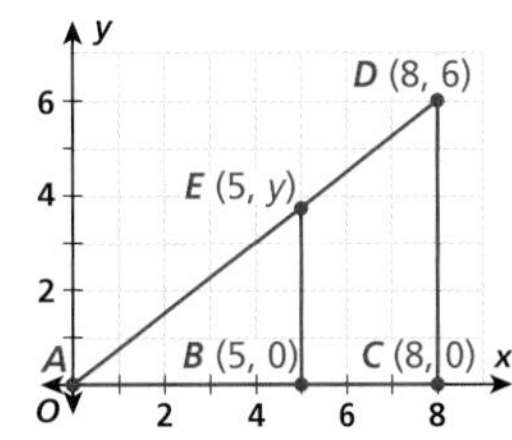

Spiral Review

Solve. (Lesson 3-6)

14. $w + 8 = -5$ **$w = -13$**
15. $y - 12 = -1$ **$y = 11$**
16. $4 + m = 51$ **$m = 47$**
17. $a - 23 = -23$ **$a = 0$**

Multiply. (Lesson 4-3)

18. $8.6 \cdot 0.13$ **1.118**
19. $-5.12 \cdot 6$ **−30.72**
20. $-7.2 \cdot (-1.9)$ **13.68**
21. $0.45 \cdot 0.23$ **0.1035**

22. **TEST PREP** Andreas needs $\frac{2}{3}$ cup of cornmeal to make one batch of corn muffins. He needs to make six batches of muffins for a picnic. How many cups of cornmeal will he need? (Lesson 4-7) **A**

A 4 cups　**B** $4\frac{1}{3}$ cups　**C** $6\frac{2}{3}$ cups　**D** $12\frac{2}{3}$ cups

Answers

11. Possible answer: A pole casts a shadow that is 4 feet long. At the same time, a tree casts a shadow that is 2 feet long. The tree is 6 feet tall. How tall is the pole? 12 ft

12. Possible answer: Write proportions using the lengths of corresponding sides. Solve the proportions for the missing lengths.

Journal

Ask students to tell what tall structures in their own neighborhoods they could find the height of using indirect measurement.

Test Prep Doctor

For Exercise 22, students can estimate that $6 \cdot \frac{2}{3}$ is less than $6 \cdot 1 = 6$. They can use this estimate to eliminate **C** and **D**.

Lesson Quiz

Find the unknown length in each pair of similar figures.

1.

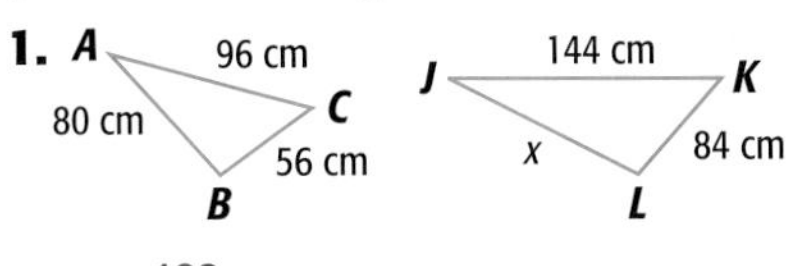

$x = 120$ cm

2.

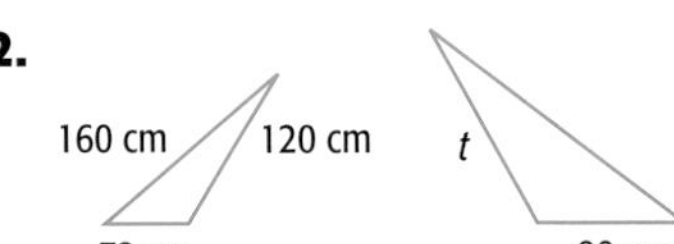

$t = 150$ cm

3. These two rectangular cakes are similar in shape. How long is the larger cake?

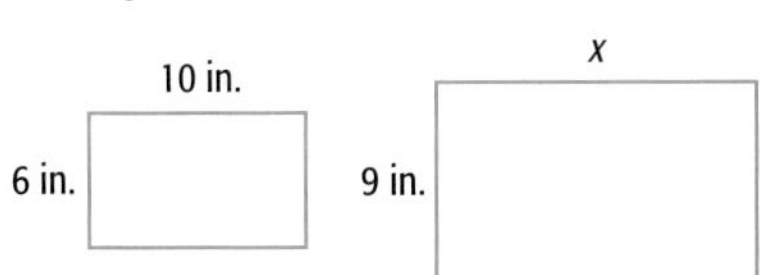

$x = 15$ inches

Available on Daily Transparency in CRB

CHALLENGE 5-6

LESSON 5-6 Challenge
You Be the Artist

Your club is planning a poster to advertise the school's international dinner. The poster will be enlarged and used as a mural on the school cafeteria wall. The poster will also be reduced and used as flyers. The mural will be 10 feet high and 15 feet long. The flyers will be printed on $8\frac{1}{2}$-by-11-inch paper.

Plan the size of the poster so that the enlargement and reduction will be easy to make.

1. What is the width-to-length ratio for the wall mural? Write the ratio in simplest terms.
10:15; 2:3
2. What is the width-to-length ratio for the flyer? Write the ratio in simplest terms.
8.5:11; 17:22
3. Do you want your artwork to fill the entire page for the flyer?
No, you need to leave room to print information about the dinner.
4. What are some possible dimensions for your poster?
2 feet by 3 feet or 1 foot by 1.5 feet
5. Will your poster fill the wall space when it is enlarged for the mural? Explain.
Yes, the ratios are equal.
6. What would be a good size for the artwork on the flyer?
6 inches by 9 inches

PROBLEM SOLVING 5-6

LESSON 5-6 Problem Solving
Using Similar Figures

Write the correct answer.

1. An architect is building a model of a tennis court for a new client. On the model, the court is 6 inches wide and 13 inches long. An official tennis court is 36 feet wide. What is the length of a tennis court?
78 feet long
2. Mr. Hemley stands next to the Illinois Centennial Monument at Logan Square in Chicago and casts a shadow that is 18 feet long. The shadow of the monument is 204 feet long. If Mr. Hemley is 6 feet tall, how tall is the monument?
68 feet tall
3. The official size of a basketball court in the NBA is 94 feet by 50 feet. The basketball court in the school gym is 47 feet long. How wide must it be to be similar to an NBA court?
25 feet wide
4. Two rectangular desks are similar. The larger one is 42 inches long and 18 inches wide. The smaller one is 35 inches long. What is the width of the smaller desk?
15 inches wide

Choose the letter for the best answer.

5. An isosceles triangle has two sides that are equal in length. Isosceles triangle ABC is similar to isosceles triangle XYZ. What proportion would you use to find the length of the third side of triangle XYZ?

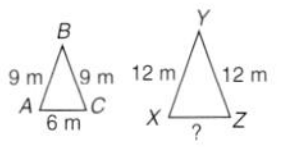

(Figure: triangle ABC with $AB = 9$ m, $BC = 9$ m, $AC = 6$ m; triangle XYZ with $XY = 12$ m, $YZ = 12$ m, $XZ = ?$)

A $\frac{BC}{XZ} = \frac{AB}{XY}$　**Ⓒ** $\frac{AB}{XY} = \frac{AC}{XZ}$
B $\frac{AC}{XY} = \frac{BC}{XZ}$　**D** $\frac{AB}{XY} = \frac{BC}{YZ}$

6. The dining room at Monticello, Thomas Jefferson's home in Virginia, is 216 inches by 222 inches. Of the following, which size rug would be similar in shape to the dining room?
Ⓕ 72 inches by 74 inches
G 108 inches by 110 inches
H 118 inches by 111 inches
J 84 inches by 96 inches

7. A 9-foot street sign casts a 12-foot shadow. The lamppost next to it casts a 24-foot shadow. How tall is the lamppost?
A 24 feet
B 15 feet
Ⓒ 18 feet
D 36 feet

5-7 Organizer

Pacing: Traditional 1 day
Block $\frac{1}{2}$ day

Objective: Students understand ratios and proportions in scale drawings and use ratios and proportions with scale.

Warm Up

Write each fraction in simplest form.

1. $\frac{4}{48}$ $\frac{1}{12}$ **2.** $\frac{9}{135}$ $\frac{1}{15}$

Convert the following measurements.

3. 192 inches = ▢ feet 16

4. 18.5 feet = ▢ inches 222

5. 324 inches = ▢ feet 27

Problem of the Day

A toy model of a 200 ft dinosaur is 3 in. long. How many times as long as the model is the dinosaur?
800 times as long

Available on Daily Transparency in CRB

Math Humor

The draftsman bought a raffle ticket. When he heard that first prize was an expensive weighing device, he couldn't wait for the *scale drawing.*

5-7 Scale Drawings and Scale Models

Learn to understand ratios and proportions in scale drawings. Learn to use ratios and proportions with scale.

Vocabulary
scale model
scale factor
scale
scale drawing

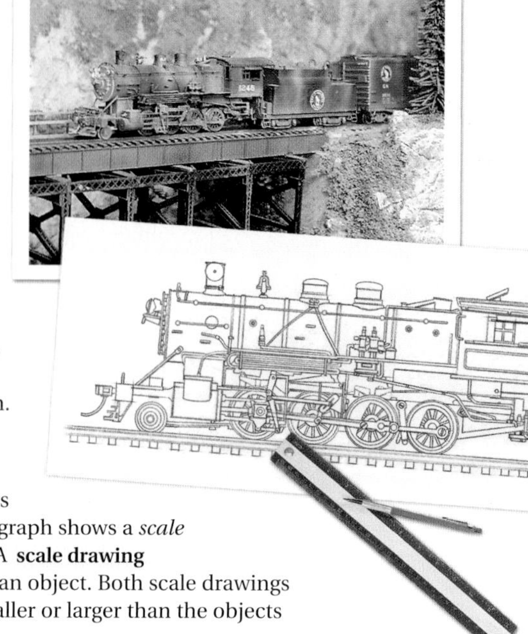

This HO gauge model train is a *scale model* of a historic train. A **scale model** is a proportional model of a three-dimensional object. Its dimensions are related to the dimensions of the actual object by a ratio called the **scale factor** . The scale factor of an HO gauge model train is $\frac{1}{87}$. This means that each dimension of the model is $\frac{1}{87}$ of the corresponding dimension of the actual train.

A **scale** is the ratio between two sets of measurements. Scales can use the same units or different units. The photograph shows a *scale drawing* of the model train. A **scale drawing** is a proportional drawing of an object. Both scale drawings and scale models can be smaller or larger than the objects they represent.

EXAMPLE  **1 Finding a Scale Factor**

Identify the scale factor.

	Race Car	Model
Length (in.)	132	11
Height (in.)	66	5.5

$\frac{\text{model length}}{\text{race car length}} = \frac{11}{132}$ *Write a ratio using one of the dimensions.*

$= \frac{1}{12}$ *Simplify.*

The scale factor is $\frac{1}{12}$.

1 Introduce

Alternate Opener

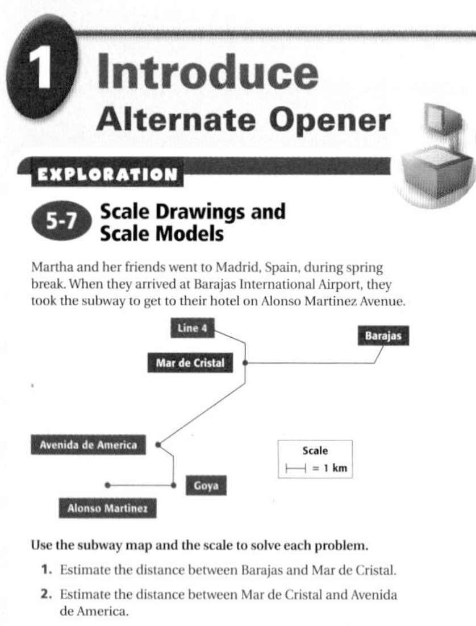
EXPLORATION

5-7 Scale Drawings and Scale Models

Martha and her friends went to Madrid, Spain, during spring break. When they arrived at Barajas International Airport, they took the subway to get to their hotel on Alonso Martinez Avenue.

Use the subway map and the scale to solve each problem.

1. Estimate the distance between Barajas and Mar de Cristal.
2. Estimate the distance between Mar de Cristal and Avenida de America.
3. How far is Alonso Martinez station, their destination, from Avenida de America?
4. Estimate the total distance from the airport to the destination.

Think and Discuss

5. Discuss other applications of scale drawings.

Motivate

Have students look through their social studies textbooks to find maps. Ask each student to display a map and tell why (or how) it is useful. Encourage students to be specific about what they can learn from maps. Discuss how maps are similar to the real places that they represent.

Exploration worksheet and answers on Chapter 5 Resource Book pp. 64 and 92

2 Teach

Lesson Presentation

Guided Instruction

In this lesson, students learn to understand ratios and proportions in scale drawings and to use ratios and proportions with scale. As you read through the examples, be sure students understand that scale drawings can be either larger or smaller than a real object.

Demonstrate how to use multiplication in Example 2 to find the actual size of the painting: 6.13 · 15 = 92, and 4.90 · 15 = 73.5.

EXAMPLE 2 Using Scale Factors to Find Unknown Lengths

A photograph of Vincent van Gogh's painting *Still Life with Irises Against a Yellow Background* has dimensions 6.13 cm and 4.90 cm. The scale factor is $\frac{1}{15}$. Find the size of the actual painting, to the nearest tenth of a centimeter.

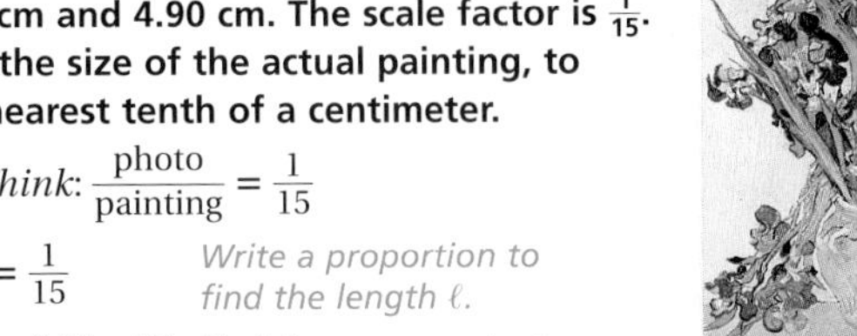

Think: $\frac{\text{photo}}{\text{painting}} = \frac{1}{15}$

$\frac{6.13}{\ell} = \frac{1}{15}$ *Write a proportion to find the length ℓ.*

$\ell = 6.13 \cdot 15$ *Find the cross products.*

$\ell = 92.0$ *Multiply and round to the nearest tenth.*

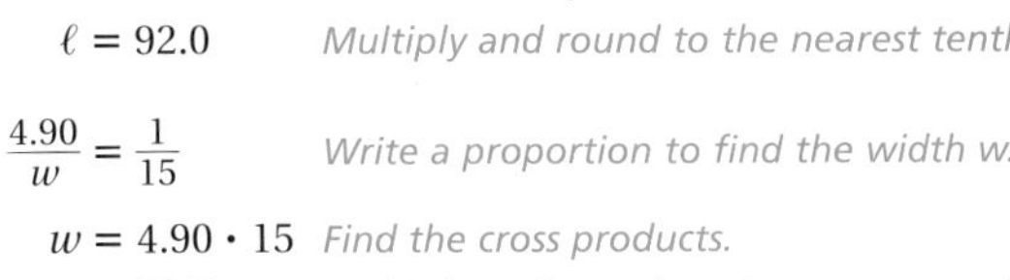

$\frac{4.90}{w} = \frac{1}{15}$ *Write a proportion to find the width w.*

$w = 4.90 \cdot 15$ *Find the cross products.*

$w = 73.5$ *Multiply and round to the nearest tenth.*

The painting is 92.0 cm long and 73.5 cm wide.

EXAMPLE 3 *Measurement Application*

On a map of Florida, the distance between Hialeah and Tampa is 10.5 cm. What is the actual distance between the cities if the map scale is 3 cm = 80 mi?

Let d be the actual distance between the cities.

$\frac{3}{80} = \frac{10.5}{d}$ *Write a proportion.*

$3 \cdot d = 80 \cdot 10.5$ *Find the cross products.*

$3d = 840$

$\frac{3d}{3} = \frac{840}{3}$ *Divide.*

$d = 280$

The distance between the cities is 280 miles.

Think and Discuss

1. **Given** a scale factor of $\frac{5}{3}$, explain how you can tell whether a model is bigger or smaller than the original object.
2. **Describe** how to find the scale factor if an antenna is 60 feet long and a scale drawing shows the length as 1 foot long.

COMMON ERROR ALERT

Some students might have difficulty recalling that if the scale factor is greater than 1, then the new figure is bigger than the original. To remind students, write the following ratio on the board: A scale factor is $\frac{\text{model}}{\text{original}}$.

Additional Examples

Example 1

Identify the scale factor.

	Room	Blueprint
Length (in.)	144	18
Width (in.)	108	13.5

$\frac{1}{8}$

Example 2

A photograph was enlarged and made into a poster. The poster is 20.5 inches by 36 inches. The scale factor is $\frac{5}{1}$. Find the size of the original photograph.

4.1 in. by 7.2 in.

Example 3

On a road map with a scale of 1.5 inches = 60 miles, the distance between Pittsburgh and Philadelphia measures 7.5 inches. What is the actual distance between the two cities?

300 miles

Reaching All Learners
Through World Math

Have students choose a photograph of a famous structure, such as the Great Sphinx in Egypt, from a reference book. Have students find the actual dimensions of the structure. Then ask them to determine the scale factor for the photograph. Encourage students to share their photographs with the class and to explain how they found the scale factor.

3 Close

Summarize

Ask students to describe how they would find the actual height of an object whose scale drawing is smaller than the object, and the actual height of an object whose scale drawing is larger.

Possible answer: Write a proportion of the ratio of the height of the drawing to x and the scale factor, and cross multiply.

Answers to Think and Discuss

Possible answers:

1. The model is bigger because its scale factor is greater than 1. A model with a scale factor of 1 is the same size as the original object, and a model with a scale factor less than 1 is smaller than the original object.
2. To find the scale of the drawing, divide the length of the drawing by the actual length of the antenna. The scale factor is $\frac{1}{60}$.

5-7 PRACTICE & ASSESS

Students may want to refer back to the lesson examples.

Assignment Guide

If you finished Example 1 assign:
Core 1, 4, 7–11, 16–23
Enriched 1, 4, 7–11, 16–23

If you finished Example 2 assign:
Core 1, 2, 4, 5, 7–11, 14, 16–23
Enriched 1, 2, 4, 5, 7–11, 14, 16–23

If you finished Example 3 assign:
Core 1–6, 7–13 odd, 16–23
Enriched 1–5 odd, 7–23

Answers

7. 16 in.
8. 5 in. $\left(\frac{5}{12}\text{ ft}\right)$
9. height: $2\frac{2}{3}$ in., length: $5\frac{3}{4}$ in.
10. height: 75 cm, width: 141 cm, length: 240 cm
11. $4\frac{7}{24}$ in.

5-7 Exercises

FOR EXTRA PRACTICE see page 665

internet connect
Homework Help Online
go.hrw.com Keyword: MS4 5-7

GUIDED PRACTICE

See Example 1 — Identify the scale factor.

1.

	Grizzly Bear	Model
Height (in.)	84	6

$\frac{1}{14}$

See Example 2 — 2. In a photograph, a sculpture is 4.2 cm tall and 2.5 cm wide. The scale factor is $\frac{1}{16}$. Find the size of the actual sculpture. **67.2 cm tall, 40 cm wide**

See Example 3 — 3. Ms. Jackson is driving from South Bend to Indianapolis. She measures a distance of 4.3 cm between the cities on her Indiana road map. What is the actual distance between the cities if the map scale is 1 cm = 30 mi? **129 mi**

INDEPENDENT PRACTICE

See Example 1 — Identify the scale factor.

4.

	Eagle	Model
Wingspan (in.)	90	6

$\frac{1}{15}$

See Example 2 — 5. On a scale drawing, a tree is $6\frac{3}{4}$ inches tall. The scale factor is $\frac{1}{20}$. Find the height of the actual tree. **135 in.**

See Example 3 — 6. On a road map of Virginia, the distance from Alexandria to Roanoke is 7.6 cm. What is the actual distance between the cities if the map scale is 2 cm = 50 mi? **190 mi**

PRACTICE AND PROBLEM SOLVING

The scale factor of each model is 1:12. Find the missing dimensions.

	Item	Actual Dimensions	Model Dimensions
7.	Lamp	Height: ▢	Height: $1\frac{1}{3}$ in.
8.	Grandfather clock	Height: 5 ft	Height: ▢
9.	Couch	Height: 32 in. Length: 69 in.	Height: ▢ Length: ▢
10.	Table	Height: ▢ Width: ▢ Length: ▢	Height: 6.25 cm Width: 11.75 cm Length: 20 cm
11.	Chair	Height: $51\frac{1}{2}$ in.	Height: ▢

Math Background

A *dilation* is a proportional shrinking or enlargement of a figure. The figure is reduced or enlarged by a scale factor. Photographers and artists use dilations to reduce or enlarge photographs or other pictures. When the size of a figure is reduced by a dilation, the dilation is called a *contraction.* When the size of a figure is enlarged by a dilation, the dilation is called an *expansion.*

RETEACH 5-7

LESSON 5-7 **Reteach**
Scale Drawings and Scale Models

The dimensions of a scale model or scale drawing are related to the actual dimensions by a *scale factor.* The **scale factor** is a ratio.

The length of a model car is 9 in.
The length of the actual car is 162 in. → $\frac{9\text{ in.}}{162\text{ in.}} = \frac{9 \div 9}{162 \div 9} = \frac{1}{18}$

$\frac{9}{162}$ can be simplified to $\frac{1}{18}$. — The scale factor is $\frac{1}{18}$.

If you know the scale factor, you can use a proportion to find the dimensions of an actual object or of a scale model or drawing.

- The scale factor of a model train set is $\frac{1}{87}$. A piece of track in the model train set is 8 in. long. What is the actual length of the track?

  $\frac{\text{model length}}{\text{actual length}} = \frac{8}{x}$ $\quad \frac{8}{x} = \frac{1}{87}$ $\quad x = 696$

  The actual length of track is 696 inches.

- The distance between 2 cities on a map is 4.5 centimeters. The scale on the map is 1 cm = 40 miles.

  $\frac{\text{distance on map}}{\text{actual distance}} = \frac{4.5\text{ cm}}{x\text{ mi}} = \frac{1\text{ cm}}{40\text{ mi}}$ $\quad \frac{4.5}{x} = \frac{1}{40}$ $\quad x = 180$

  The actual distance is 180 miles.

Identify the scale factor.

1. Photograph: height 3 in.
   Painting: height 24 in.
   $\frac{\text{photo height}}{\text{painting height}} = \frac{3\text{ in.}}{24\text{ in.}} = \frac{1}{8}$

2. Butterfly: wingspan 20 cm
   Silk butterfly: wingspan 4 cm
   $\frac{\text{silk butterfly}}{\text{butterfly}} = \frac{4\text{ cm}}{20\text{ cm}} = \frac{1}{5}$

3. On a scale drawing, the scale factor is $\frac{1}{12}$. A plum tree is 7 inches tall on the scale drawing. What is the actual height of the tree?
   84 inches

4. On a road map, the distance between 2 cities is 2.5 inches. The map scale is 1 inch = 30 miles. What is the actual distance between the cities?
   75 miles

PRACTICE 5-7

LESSON 5-7 **Practice B**
Scale Drawings and Scale Models

Identify the scale factor.

1.

	Alligator	Toy Alligator
Length (in.)	175	7

$\frac{1}{25}$

2.

	Airplane	Model
Length (ft)	24	3

$\frac{1}{8}$

3.

	Car	Toy Car
Length (ft)	13.5	1.5

$\frac{1}{9}$

4.

	Person	Action Figure
Height (in.)	66	6

$\frac{1}{11}$

5.

	Boat	Model
Length (in.)	128	8

$\frac{1}{16}$

6.

	Fish	Fishing Lure
Length (in.)	18	2

$\frac{1}{9}$

7.

	Tiger	Stuffed Animal
Length (in.)	70	14

$\frac{1}{5}$

8.

	House	Dollhouse
Height (ft)	39.2	2.8

$\frac{1}{14}$

9. On a scale drawing, a school is 1.6 feet tall. The scale factor is $\frac{1}{22}$. Find the height of the school. **35.2 feet**

10. On a road map of Pennsylvania, the distance from Philadelphia to Washington, D.C., is 6.8 centimeters. What is the actual distance between the cities if the map scale is 2 centimeters = 40 miles? **136 miles**

11. On a scale drawing, a bicycle is $6\frac{4}{5}$ inches tall. The scale factor is $\frac{1}{6}$. Find the height of the bicycle. **$40\frac{4}{5}$ inches**

History LINK

Use the map for Exercises 12 and 13. The map scale is 1 inch = 10 miles.

12. The battle at Gettysburg was the turning point of the American Civil War. It started when Confederate troops marched from Chambersburg into Gettysburg in search of badly needed shoes. There, they encountered Union troops. Use the ruler and the scale of the map to estimate how far the Confederate soldiers, many of whom were barefoot, marched. **about 25 mi**

13. Before the Civil War, the Mason-Dixon Line was considered the dividing line between the North and the South. If Gettysburg is about 8.1 miles north of the Mason-Dixon Line, how far apart in inches are Gettysburg and the Mason-Dixon Line on the map?

14. Uncle Toby is making a scale model of the battlefield at Fredericksburg. The area he wants to model measures about 11 mi by 7.5 mi. He plans to put the model on a 3.25 ft by 3.25 ft square table. On each side of the model he wants to leave at least 3 in. between the model and the table edges. What is the largest scale he can use? **1 mi = 0.25 ft or 1 ft = 4 mi**

This painting by H.A. Ogden depicts General Robert E. Lee at Fredericksburg in 1862.

15. ***CHALLENGE*** In a Civil War book, an original map of the Vicksburg, Mississippi, area has a scale of "1 mile to the inch." The map has been reduced so that 5 inches on the original map appears as 1.5 inches on the reduced map. If the distance between two points on the reduced map is 1.75 inches, what is the actual distance in miles? **about 5.8 mi**

Spiral Review

Write the numbers in order from least to greatest. (Lesson 3-10)

16. $\frac{4}{7}$, 0.41, 0.054 **0.054, 0.41, $\frac{4}{7}$**

17. $\frac{1}{4}$, 0.2, −1.2 **−1.2, 0.2, $\frac{1}{4}$**

18. 0.7, $\frac{7}{9}$, $\frac{7}{11}$ **$\frac{7}{11}$, 0.7, $\frac{7}{9}$**

Divide. (Lesson 4-4)

19. 0.32 ÷ 5 **0.064**

20. 78.57 ÷ 9 **8.73**

21. 40.5 ÷ 15 **2.7**

22. 29.68 ÷ 28 **1.06**

23. TEST PREP A spool has 21 meters of ribbon. The ribbon is cut into pieces that are each 0.6 meters long. How many pieces of ribbon are cut from the spool? (Lesson 4-5) **C**

A 3.5 **B** 12.6 **C** 35 **D** 126

Interdisciplinary LINK

History

Exercises 12–15 involve using a map scale from a historical map to estimate distances. Using maps is a skill learned in middle school social studies programs, such as Holt, Rinehart & Winston's *People, Places, and Change.*

Answers

13. 0.81 in., or about $\frac{13}{16}$ in.

Journal

Ask students to tell about a model or photograph they own and to explain how it is the same and how it is different from the actual object it shows.

Test Prep Doctor

For Exercise 23, students can estimate that 21 ÷ 1 = 21. Therefore, the answer will be greater than 21. They can use this estimate to eliminate **A** and **B.**

CHALLENGE 5-7

LESSON 5-7 **Challenge**

Balls of Sports

Each circle below is a scale drawing of a different type of ball used in a sport.

- Measure the diameter of each circle to the nearest tenth of a centimeter.
- Use the scale to find the actual diameter of the ball to the nearest tenth of a centimeter.
- Use the chart below to find the sport in which the ball is used.

Diameter of Balls Used in Various Sports	
Basketball	24.0 cm
Baseball	7.5 cm
Golf	4.2 cm
Table Tennis	3.8 cm
Tennis	6.4 cm
Volleyball	21.0 cm

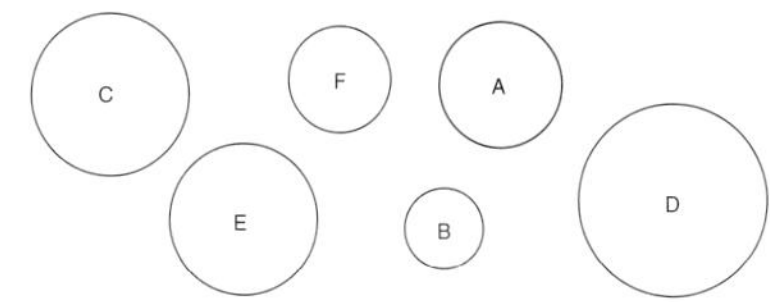

	Circle	Scale	Measured Diameter	Actual Diameter	Sport
1.	A	1 cm = 3 cm	**2.5 cm**	**7.5 cm**	**baseball**
2.	B	1 cm = 15 cm	**1.6 cm**	**24 cm**	**basketball**
3.	C	1 cm = 2 cm	**3.2 cm**	**6.4 cm**	**tennis**
4.	D	1 cm = 1 cm	**3.8 cm**	**3.8 cm**	**table tennis**
5.	E	1 cm = 1.4 cm	**3.0 cm**	**4.2 cm**	**golf**
6.	F	1 cm = 10 cm	**2.1 cm**	**21 cm**	**volleyball**

PROBLEM SOLVING 5-7

LESSON 5-7 **Problem Solving**

Scale Drawings and Scale Models

Write the correct answer.

1. The scale on a road map is 1 centimeter = 500 miles. If the distance on the map between New York City and Memphis is 2.2 centimeters, what is the actual distance between the two cities?

1,100 miles

2. There are several different scales in model railroading. Trains designated as O gauge are built to a scale factor of 1:48. To the nearest hundredth of a foot, how long is a model of a 50-foot boxcar in O gauge?

1.04 feet long

3. For a school project, LeeAnn is making a model of the Empire State Building. She is using a scale of 1 centimeter = 8 feet. The Empire State Building is 1,252 feet tall. How tall is her model?

156.5 centimeters tall

4. A model of the Eiffel Tower that was purchased in a gift shop is 29.55 inches tall. The actual height of the Eiffel Tower is 985 feet, or 11,820 inches. What scale factor was used to make the model?

1 inch = 400 inches

Choose the letter for the best answer.

5. The scale factor for Maria's dollhouse furniture is 1:8. If the sofa in Maria's dollhouse is $7\frac{1}{2}$ inches long, how long is the actual sofa?

A 54 inches
(B) 60 inches
C 84 inches
D $15\frac{1}{2}$ inches

6. The Painted Desert is a section of high plateau extending 150 miles in northern Arizona. On a map, the length of this desert is 5 centimeters. What is the map scale?

F 1 centimeter = 25 miles
G 5 centimeters = 100 miles
(H) 1 centimeter = 30 miles
J 1 centimeter = 50 miles

7. Josh wants to add a model of a tree to his model railroad layout. How big should the model tree be if the actual tree is 315 inches and the scale factor is 1:90?

A 395 inches
B 39.5 inches
C 35 inches
(D) 3.5 inches

8. The scale on a wall map is 1 inch = 55 miles. What is the distance on the map between two cities that are 99 miles apart?

F 44 inches
(G) 1.8 inches
H 2.5 inches
J 0.55 inches

Lesson Quiz

Identify the scale factor.

1.

	Statue of Liberty	Model
Height (in.)	1,824	8

$\frac{1}{228}$

2. On a scale drawing, a kitchen wall is 6 inches long. The scale factor is $\frac{1}{24}$. What is the length of the actual wall? **144 inches, or 12 feet**

3. On a road map, the distance from Green Bay to Chicago is 11 cm. What is the actual distance between the cities if the map scale is 3 cm = 90 km?

330 km

Available on Daily Transparency in CRB

Problem Solving on Location

Illinois

Purpose: *To provide additional practice for problem-solving skills in Chapters 1–5*

Melvin Price Locks and Dam

- After problem 2, have students tell how they found the number of inches in the length of the dam and the dimensions of the Tainter gates. Multiply the number of feet by 12 to change feet to inches.
- After problems 3 and 4, have students tell how they solved the problems. Possible answer: Write a proportion using the ratio of the average high temperature to the average low temperature and the average low temperature from the table for the given month. Use the proportion to solve for the average high temperature in the given month.

Extension Have students find the perimeter of the Tainter gates in feet and in inches and the area of the Tainter gates in square feet and square inches.

perimeter: 304 ft; 3,648 in.

area: 4,620 ft^2; 665,280 in^2

Problem Solving on Location

ILLINOIS

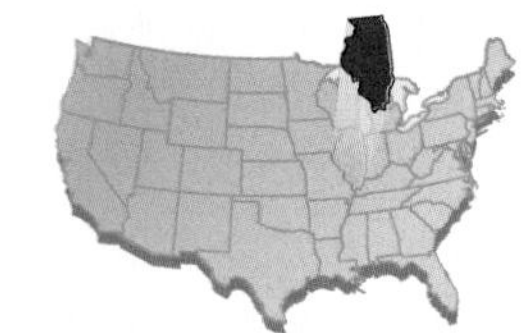

Melvin Price Locks and Dam

The Melvin Price Locks and Dam, in Alton, Illinois, are used to control the flow of the Mississippi River. The locks and the dam became operational in October of 1989. They are located 2 miles downstream from the location where Lock and Dam 26 previously stood.

1. The main lock chamber on the Melvin Price Locks and Dam is 1,200 feet long by 110 feet wide. The auxiliary lock chamber is 600 feet long by 110 feet wide. Write the ratio of length to width of each lock. Write the ratios in all three forms. Then simplify each ratio.

2. The dam is 1,160 feet long and has nine *tainter gates*. A tainter gate has a curved side that can pivot open to let water flow from the lake above the dam. Each tainter gate is 110 feet wide by 42 feet high. How many inches long is the dam? What are the dimensions in inches of each tainter gate? **13,920 in.; 1,320 in. wide by 504 in. high**

Use the table for 3 and 4.

3. The ratio of the average high temperature to the average low temperature in August in Chicago is 41°F to 31°F. What is the average high temperature in August? **82°F**

4. The ratio of the average low temperature to the average high temperature in December in Chicago is 4°F to 7°F. What is the average high temperature in December? **35°F**

Average Low Temperature, Chicago (°F)

Month	Temp
Jan	13
Feb	18
Mar	28
Apr	39
May	48
Jun	57
Jul	63
Aug	62
Sep	64
Oct	42
Nov	31
Dec	20

Answers

1. mainlock: 1,200:110, 1,200 to 110, $\frac{1,200}{110}$; 120:11, 120 to 11, $\frac{120}{11}$
   auxiliary lock: 600:110, 600 to 110, $\frac{600}{110}$; 60:11, 60 to 11, $\frac{60}{11}$

World's First Ferris Wheel

The Ferris wheel was invented by George W. Ferris. The original Ferris wheel had 36 cars that could each hold 60 people. At the time the Ferris wheel was built, its axle was the largest single piece of forged steel in the world.

The world's first Ferris wheel

1. During its operation at the World's Columbian Exposition in Chicago, the Ferris wheel brought in a total of \$726,805.50. Each ride cost \$0.50. How many people rode the Ferris wheel at the Exposition? **1,453,611 people**

2. The diameter of the wheel on the original Ferris wheel was 250 feet. Suppose that on a scale model of the original Ferris wheel, 1 inch equals 75 feet. What would be the diameter of the wheel on the scale model? **$3\frac{1}{3}$ in.**

3. The circumference of the wheel on the original Ferris wheel was about 785 feet. What would be the approximate circumference of the wheel on the scale model? **$10\frac{7}{15}$ in.**

4. The original Ferris wheel was 264 feet tall. What would be the height of the scale model? **3.52 in.**

Illinois is known as the Land of Lincoln. Lincoln, Illinois, was the only town named for Abraham Lincoln during his lifetime. The map shows Lincoln and its neighboring cities. Use a ruler and the map for 5–8.

5. What is the scale of the map? **Possible answer: 1 in. = 20 mi**
6. About how many miles is Peoria from Lincoln? **about 40 mi**
7. Approximate the distance in kilometers from Lincoln to Springfield. **about 40 km**
8. How many more miles is it to drive to Decatur than to Clinton from Bloomington? **about 20 mi**

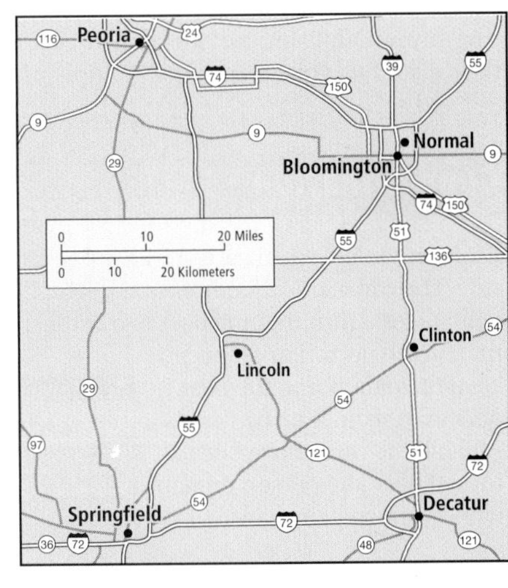

World's First Ferris Wheel

- After problem 1, ask students to describe two methods for finding the number of people who rode the Ferris wheel. Possible answer: Divide \$726,805.50 by \$0.50 or multiply 726,805.50 by 2. Ask which method is easier. Possible answer: Multiply 726,805.50 by 2.
- After problem 6, ask students to give the proportion problem they used to find the distance in miles between Peoria and Lincoln. Possible answer: $\frac{20}{1} = \frac{d}{2.25}$

Extension: Ask students to find the maximum number of people who could ride the Ferris wheel at the Exposition at one time. 2,160 people Have students find the amount of money made each time the Ferris wheel ran with maximum number of people riding. \$1,080 Ask students to find the least number of times the Ferris wheel could have run to generate the total amount made at the Exposition. 673 times

MATH-ABLES

Game Resources

Puzzles, Twisters & Teasers
Chapter 5 Resource Book

Water Works

Purpose: *To apply the skill of finding sums and differences to solve a fun puzzle*

Discuss: Ask students how they can keep track of the amount of water in each glass.
Possible answer: Make a table with three columns. After each pour from one glass to another, record the number of ounces in each glass in the table.

Extend: Challenge students to use a 3-ounce, an 8-ounce, and an 11-ounce glass to get exactly 6 ounces of water in one glass using only 3 pourings from one cup to another. They begin with the 11-ounce glass full of water and the other two empty. Have students record their results in a table.
Possible answer:

3-oz Glass	8-oz Glass	11-oz Glass
0	0	11
0	8	3
3	5	3
0	5	6

Concentration

Purpose: *To practice solving equations in a game format*

Discuss: When a matching pair of ratios is flipped over, have the student or team demonstrate why the ratios are equivalent. Discuss different methods to show that two ratios are equivalent.
Possible answer: 1. Cross multiply and see if the cross products are equal.
2. Find equivalent fractions with the same denominators.

Extend: For every pair of cards that does not show equivalent ratios, have the student or team demonstrate how you can tell that the ratios are not equivalent.
Possible answer: When you cross multiply two ratios that are not equivalent, you will get two different cross products.

MATH-ABLES

Water Works

You have three glasses: a 3-ounce glass, a 5-ounce glass, and an 8-ounce glass. The 8-ounce glass is full of water, and the other two glasses are empty. By pouring water from one glass to another, how can you get exactly 6 ounces of water in one of the glasses? The step-by-step solution is described below.

Step 1: Pour the water from the 8 oz glass into the 5 oz glass.

Step 2: Pour the water from the 5 oz glass into the 3 oz glass.

Step 3: Pour the water from the 3 oz glass into the 8 oz glass.

You now have 6 ounces of water in the 8-ounce glass.

Start again, but this time try to get exactly 4 ounces of water in one glass. (*Hint:* Find a way to get 1 ounce of water. Start by pouring water into the 3-ounce glass.)

Next, using 3-ounce, 8-ounce, and 11-ounce glasses, try to get exactly 9 ounces of water in one glass. Start with the 11-ounce glass full of water. (*Hint:* Start by pouring water into the 8-ounce glass.)

Look at the sizes of the glasses in the first and second problem and the sizes of the glasses in the third problem. The volume of the third glass is the sum of the volumes of the first two glasses:
$3 + 5 = 8$ and $3 + 8 = 11$.
Using any amounts for the two smaller glasses, and starting with the largest glass full, you can get any multiple of the smaller glass's volume. Try it and see.

Concentration

Each card in a deck of cards has a ratio printed on one side. The cards are laid out upside down. Each person or team takes a turn flipping over two cards. If the cards match, the person or team can keep the pair. If not, the next person or team flips two cards. After all the cards have been turned over, the person or team with the most pairs wins.

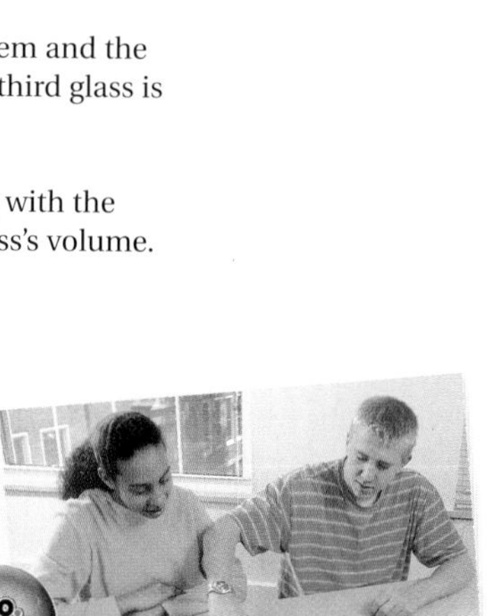

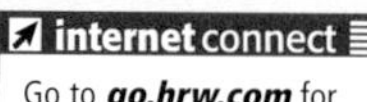

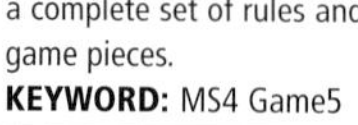

Go to **go.hrw.com** for a complete set of rules and game pieces.
KEYWORD: MS4 Game5

Answers

To get 4 oz:

3-oz Glass	5-oz Glass	8-oz Glass
0	0	8
3	0	5
0	3	5
3	3	2
1	5	2
1	0	7
0	1	7
3	1	4

To get 9 oz:

3-oz Glass	8-oz Glass	11-oz Glass
0	0	11
0	8	3
3	5	3
0	5	6
3	2	6
0	2	9

Model Similar Triangles

Similar triangles can be constructed by drawing one line across a single triangle.

Activity

1. Using geometry software, construct a triangle that resembles the one shown in the first window below. Label the vertices *A*, *B*, and *C*. Label a point *D* on $\overline{AB}$. Use the parallel line tool to draw a line parallel to $\overline{BC}$, through point *D*. Label point *E* where $\overline{AC}$ intersects the new line. Triangles *ABC* and *ADE* are similar.

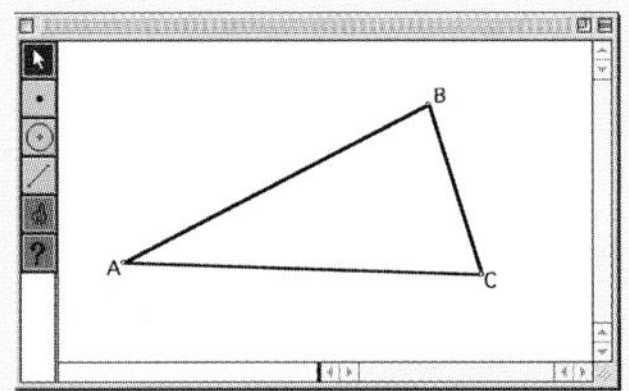

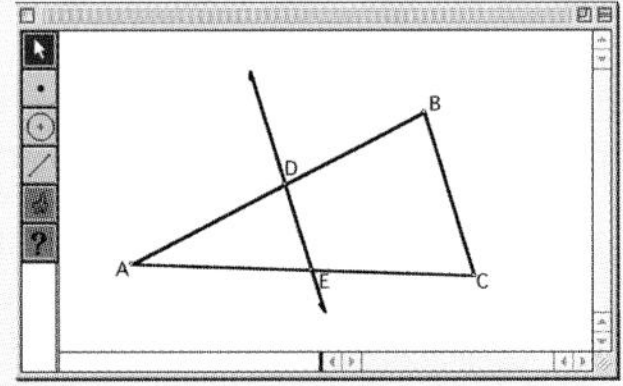

Select vertex *C* and drag it until your figure resembles the one shown in the first window below. Use your angle measure tool to measure $\angle ABC$ and $\angle ADE$. (Your measurements may differ from those shown.) Drag point *C* again. What do you notice about the measures of $\angle ABC$ and $\angle ADE$?

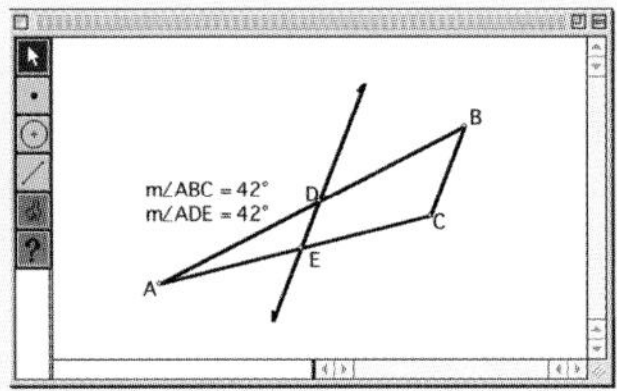

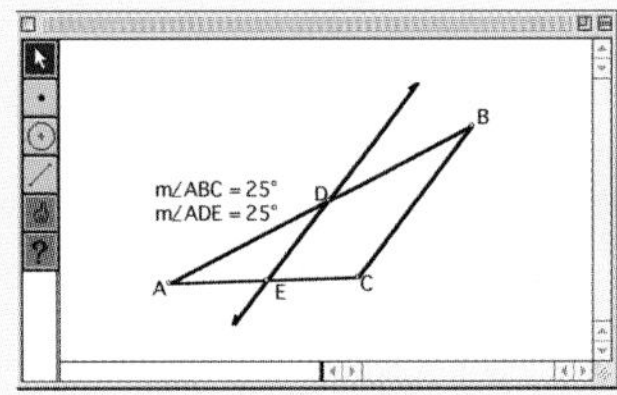

Think and Discuss

1. Notice quadrilateral *DBCE* that is formed when $\overline{DE}$ divides triangle *ABC*. Can such a quadrilateral ever be a rectangle? Explain.

Try This

1. Draw a quadrilateral *ABCD* that is *not* a rectangle. Connect vertices *A* and *C* with a line segment to form two triangles. Select and drag a point until $m\angle BAC$ is equal to $m\angle DCA$. Describe the new quadrilateral *ABCD*.

Answers

Think and Discuss

1. No, $\overline{DB}$ and $\overline{EC}$ could never be parallel because $\overline{AB}$ and $\overline{AC}$, which contain $\overline{DB}$ and $\overline{EC}$, intersect at *A*. Also, $\angle B$ and $\angle C$ cannot both be right angles because they belong to the same triangle.

Try This

1. Quadrilateral *ABCD* is a parallelogram.

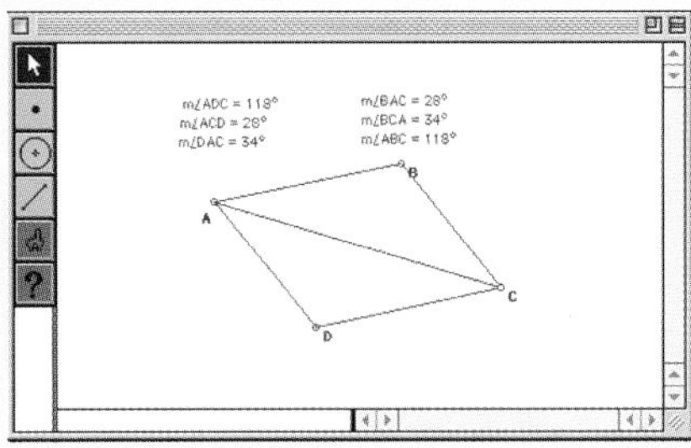

Objective: To use geometry software to construct similar triangles

Materials: Geometry software

Lab Resources

Technology Lab Activities . . . . p. 30

Using the Page

This technology activity shows students how to use geometry software to construct similar triangles. Be sure students understand how to use the geometry software.

The Think and Discuss problem can be used to assess students' understanding of triangles and quadrilaterals. The Try This problem can be used to assess students' understanding of using geometry software to construct similar triangles in a way that is different from constructing a parallel line.

Assessment

1. Draw a right triangle *ABC* and construct a similar triangle *DEC* by drawing one line across triangle *ABC*.

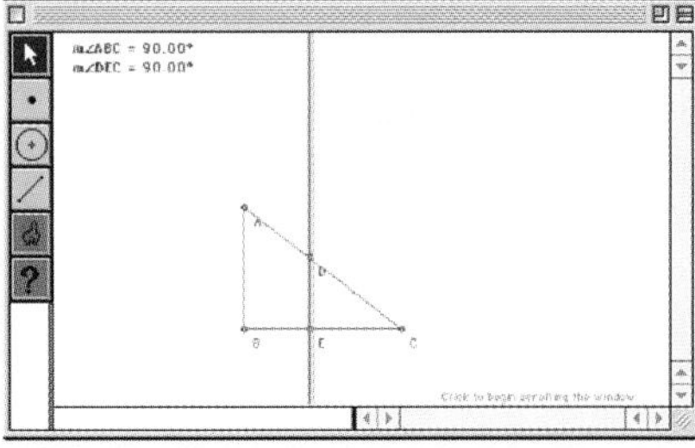

Chapter 5 **Study Guide and Review**

Purpose: *To help students review and practice concepts and skills presented in Chapter 5*

Assessment Resources

Chapter Review

Chapter 5 Resource Book . . . pp. 72–73

Test and Practice Generator **CD-ROM**

Additional review assessment items in both multiple-choice and free-response format may be generated for any objective in Chapter 5.

Answers

1. similar
2. ratio; rate or unit rate
3. scale factor
4. indirect measurement
5. $\frac{6}{10}$, 6 to 10, 6:10
6. $\frac{10}{16}$, 10 to 16, 10:16
7. $\frac{2 \text{ gal}}{1 \text{ min}}$; 2 gallons per minute
8. $\frac{3.5 \text{ mi}}{1 \text{ min}}$; 3.5 miles per minute

Chapter 5 Study Guide and Review

Study Guide and Review

Vocabulary

corresponding angles	280	scale	288
corresponding sides	280	scale drawing	288
cross product	268	scale factor	288
equivalent ratios	264	scale model	288
indirect measurement	284	similar	280
proportion	264	unit conversion factor	272
rate	260	unit rate	260
ratio	260		

Complete the sentences below with vocabulary words from the list above. Words may be used more than once.

1. __?__ figures have the same shape but not necessarily the same size.
2. A(n) __?__ is a comparison of two numbers, and a(n) __?__ is a ratio that compares two quantities measured in different units.
3. The ratio used to enlarge or reduce similar figures is a(n) __?__.
4. The process of using proportions to find an unknown length or distance in similar figures is called __?__.

5-1 Ratios and Rates (pp. 260–263)

EXAMPLE

■ **Write the ratio of 2 servings of bread to 4 servings of vegetables in all three forms.**

$\frac{2}{4}$, 2 to 4, 2:4 — *For every 2 servings of bread there are 4 servings of vegetables.*

The fraction $\frac{2}{4}$ can be simplified to $\frac{1}{2}$.

$\frac{1}{2}$, 1 to 2, 1:2 — *For each serving of bread there are 2 servings of vegetables.*

EXERCISES

There are 6 cats and 10 dogs. Write each ratio in all three forms.

5. cats to dogs
6. dogs to total animals

Find the unit rates and write them in both fraction and word form.

7. 8 gallons in 4 minutes
8. 35 miles in 10 minutes

5-2 Identifying and Writing Proportions (pp. 264–267)

EXAMPLE

- **Determine if the ratios are proportional.**

$\frac{5}{12}, \frac{3}{9}$

$\frac{5}{12}$ — *$\frac{5}{12}$ is already in simplest form.*

$\frac{3}{9} = \frac{1}{3}$ — *Simplify $\frac{3}{9}$.*

Since $\frac{5}{12} \neq \frac{1}{3}$, the ratios are not proportional.

EXERCISES

Determine if the ratios are proportional.

9. $\frac{15}{20}, \frac{20}{21}$
10. $\frac{2}{3}, \frac{64}{90}$
11. $\frac{16}{32}, \frac{4}{8}$
12. $\frac{9}{27}, \frac{6}{20}$
13. $\frac{15}{25}, \frac{20}{30}$
14. $\frac{21}{14}, \frac{18}{12}$

Find a ratio equivalent to each ratio. Then use the ratios to write a proportion.

15. $\frac{10}{12}$
16. $\frac{45}{50}$
17. $\frac{9}{15}$

5-3 Solving Proportions (pp. 268–271)

EXAMPLE

- **Use cross products to solve $\frac{p}{8} = \frac{10}{12}$.**

$$\frac{p}{8} = \frac{10}{12}$$
$$p \cdot 12 = 8 \cdot 10$$
$$12p = 80$$
$$\frac{12p}{12} = \frac{80}{12}$$
$$p = \frac{20}{3}, \text{ or } 6\frac{2}{3}$$

EXERCISES

Use cross products to solve each proportion.

18. $\frac{4}{6} = \frac{n}{3}$
19. $\frac{2}{a} = \frac{5}{15}$
20. $\frac{b}{1.5} = \frac{8}{3}$
21. $\frac{16}{11} = \frac{96}{x}$
22. $\frac{2}{y} = \frac{1}{11}$
23. $\frac{7}{10} = \frac{70}{k}$

5-4 Dimensional Analysis (pp. 272–275)

EXAMPLE

- **Use a unit conversion factor to convert 14 gallons to quarts.**

1 gal = 4 qt, so use $\frac{1 \text{ gal}}{4 \text{ qt}}$ or $\frac{4 \text{ qt}}{1 \text{ gal}}$.

Choose the second conversion factor so that the gallon units cancel.

$$14 \text{ gal} \cdot \frac{4 \text{ qt}}{1 \text{ gal}} = 56 \text{ qt}$$

EXERCISES

Use a unit conversion factor to convert the units.

24. 10 gallons to quarts
25. 6 quarts to gallons
26. 11,616 feet to miles
27. How many feet are there in 15 yards?

Answers

9. no
10. no
11. yes
12. no
13. no
14. yes
15. Possible answer: $\frac{10}{12} = \frac{5}{6}$
16. Possible answer: $\frac{45}{50} = \frac{9}{10}$
17. Possible answer: $\frac{9}{15} = \frac{3}{5}$
18. $n = 2$
19. $a = 6$
20. $b = 4$
21. $x = 66$
22. $y = 22$
23. $k = 100$
24. 40 qt
25. 1.5 gal
26. 2.2 mi
27. 45 ft

Answers

28. similar

29. not similar

30. $x = 100$ ft

31. 12.1 in.

32. 148 mi

5-5 Similar Figures and Proportions (pp. 280–283)

EXAMPLE

■ **Determine if the triangles are similar.**

$\frac{AB}{DE} \stackrel{?}{=} \frac{BC}{EF} \stackrel{?}{=} \frac{AC}{DF}$

$\frac{2}{6} \stackrel{?}{=} \frac{4}{12} \stackrel{?}{=} \frac{3}{9}$

$\frac{1}{3} \stackrel{?}{=} \frac{1}{3} \stackrel{?}{=} \frac{1}{3}$

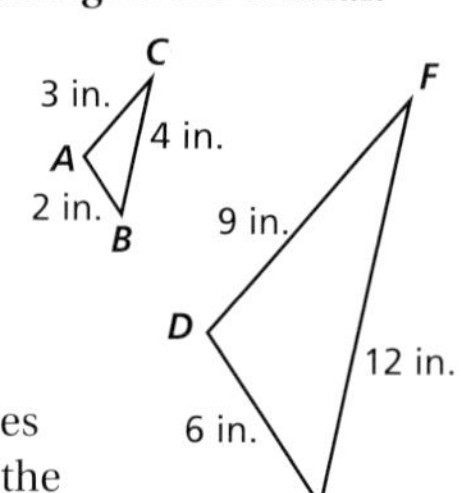

The ratios of the corresponding sides are equivalent, so the triangles are similar.

EXERCISES

Determine if the triangles are similar.

28.

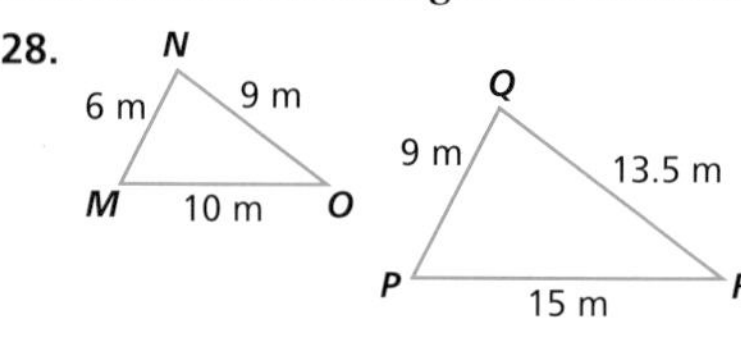

29.

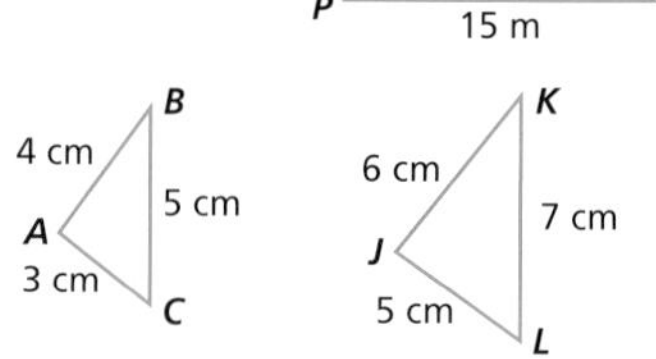

5-6 Using Similar Figures (pp. 284–287)

EXAMPLE

■ **Find the unknown length in the similar triangle.**

$\frac{AB}{LM} = \frac{AC}{LN}$

$\frac{8}{t} = \frac{11}{44}$

$8 \cdot 44 = t \cdot 11$

$352 = 11t$

$\frac{352}{11} = \frac{11t}{11}$

$32 \text{ in.} = t$

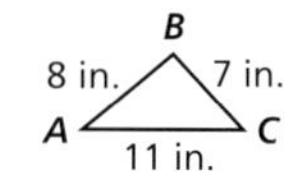

M
t
28 in.
L
N
44 in.

EXERCISES

Find the unknown length in the similar triangle.

30.

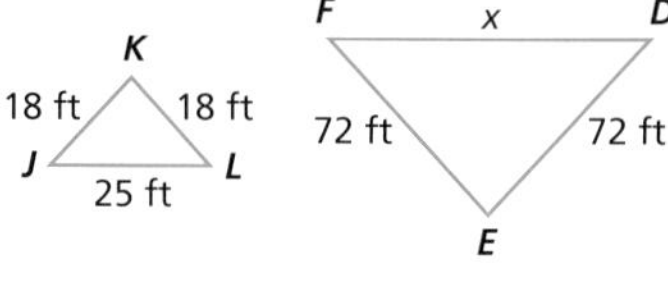

5-7 Scale Drawings and Scale Models (pp. 288–291)

EXAMPLE

■ **A model sailboat is 4 inches long. The scale factor is $\frac{1}{24}$. How long is the actual sailboat?**

$\frac{\text{model}}{\text{sailboat}} = \frac{1}{24}$

$\frac{4}{n} = \frac{1}{24}$ *Write a proportion.*

$4 \cdot 24 = n \cdot 1$ *Find the cross products.*

$96 = n$ *Solve.*

The sailboat is 96 inches long.

EXERCISES

Solve.

31. The Wright brothers' *Flyer* had a 484-inch wingspan. Carla bought a model of the plane with a scale factor of $\frac{1}{40}$. What is the model's wingspan?

32. Eduardo measured the distance from Asheville to Winston-Salem on a map to be 3.7 inches. The map scale is 1 inch = 40 miles. What is the actual distance?

Study Guide and Review

Chapter Test

Chapter 5

There are 20 wagons and 10 bicycles. Write each ratio in all three forms.

1. wagons to bicycles **$\frac{20}{10}$, 20 to 10, 20:10**
2. bicycles to total vehicles **$\frac{10}{30}$, 10 to 30, 10:30**
3. total vehicles to wagons **$\frac{30}{20}$, 30 to 20, 30:20**

Determine whether the ratios are proportional.

4. $\frac{5}{6}, \frac{20}{24}$ **yes**
5. $\frac{3}{4}, \frac{9}{16}$ **no**
6. $\frac{11}{33}, \frac{5}{15}$ **yes**

Solve each proportion. Then write a ratio equivalent to the ratios in the proportion.

7. $\frac{9}{12} = \frac{m}{6}$ **$m = 4.5$; Possible answer: $\frac{3}{4}$**
8. $\frac{x}{2} = \frac{18}{6}$ **$x = 6$; Possible answer: $\frac{12}{4}$**
9. $\frac{3}{7} = \frac{21}{t}$ **$t = 49$; Possible answer: $\frac{15}{35}$**

Use a unit conversion factor to convert the units.

10. 18 feet to inches **216 in.**
11. 6 gallons to quarts **24 qt**
12. 13,200 feet to miles **2.5 mi**

Use a unit conversion factor to convert the units within each rate.

13. 6 feet per second to feet per minute **360 feet per minute**
14. \$0.35 per ounce to dollars per pound **\$5.60 per pound**

Determine whether the figures are similar.

15. 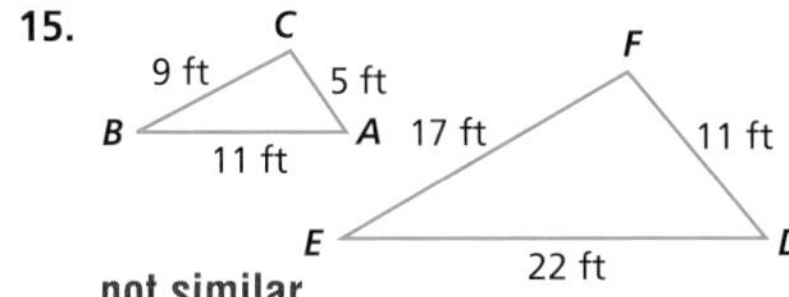

not similar

16. 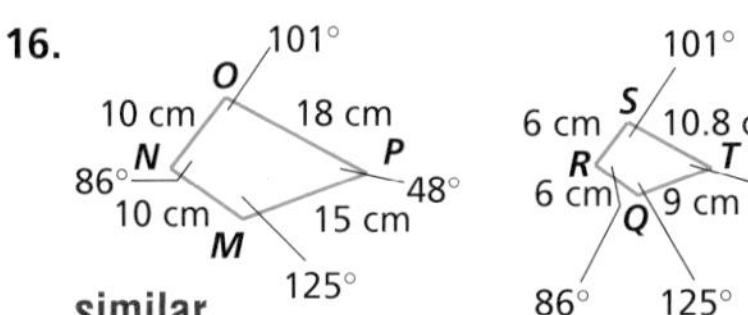

similar

Find the unknown length in each pair of similar figures.

17. 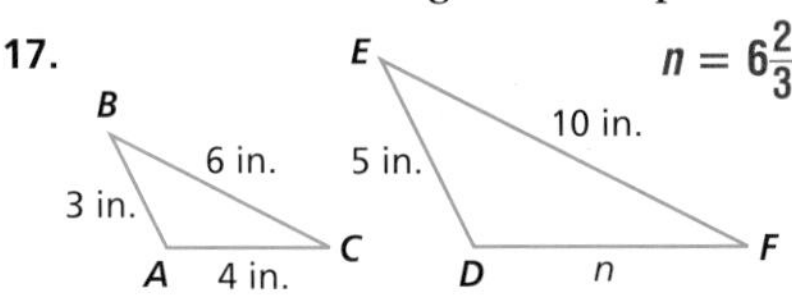

$n = 6\frac{2}{3}$ in.

18. 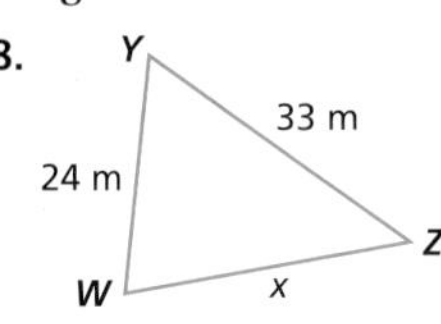

$x = 30$ m

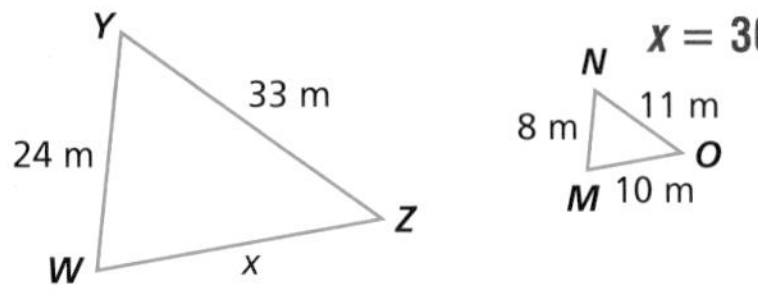

Solve.

19. A scale model of a building is 8 in. by 12 in. If the scale is 1 in. = 15 ft, what are the dimensions of the actual building? **120 ft by 180 ft**

20. The actual distance from Portland to Seaside is 75 mi. If the map scale is $1\frac{1}{4}$ in. = 25 mi, what is the distance in inches between the two towns on the map? **$3\frac{3}{4}$ in.**

Chapter Test

Chapter Test

Chapter 5

Purpose: *To assess students' mastery of concepts and skills in Chapter 5*

Assessment Resources

Chapter 5 Tests (Levels A, B, C)
Assessment Resources. . . . . . pp. 57–62

***Test and Practice Generator* CD-ROM**

Additional assessment items in both multiple-choice and free-response format may be generated for any objective in Chapter 5.

Chapter 5

Performance Assessment

Purpose: *To assess students' understanding of concepts in Chapter 5 and combined problem-solving skills*

Assessment Resources 

Performance Assessment
Assessment Resources . . . . p. 114

Performance Assessment Teacher Support
Assessment Resources . . . . p. 113

Answers

1. See p. A2.
4. See Level 3 work sample below.

Scoring Rubric for Problem Solving Item 4

Level 3
Accomplishes the purposes of the task.
Student gives clear explanations, shows understanding of mathematical ideas and processes, and computes accurately.

Level 2
Purposes of the task not fully achieved.
Student demonstrates satisfactory but limited understanding of the mathematical ideas and processes.

Level 1
Purposes of the task not accomplished.
Student shows little evidence of understanding the mathematical ideas and processes and makes computational and/or procedural errors.

Chapter 5

Performance Assessment

Show What You Know

Create a portfolio of your best work from this chapter. Complete this page and include it with your four best pieces of work from Chapter 5. Choose from your homework or lab assignments, mid-chapter quiz, or any journal entries you have done. Put them together using any design you want. Make your portfolio represent what you consider your best work.

Short Response

1. A tree casts a shadow 20 feet long. Monica is 5 feet tall, and her shadow is 4 feet long. Describe in words how to find the height of the tree. Then find the height, and show your work.
2. In the past, \$1 U.S. equaled \$1.575 Canadian. Find the approximate value of \$75 Canadian. Show the steps that you used to calculate the answer. **$\$75 \text{ Canadian} \cdot \frac{\$1 \text{ U.S.}}{\$1.575 \text{ Canadian}} \approx \$47.62 \text{ U.S.}$**
3. Adam is refilling his 10-gallon fish tank. He must add $\frac{1}{2}$ tsp of chemical solution for each quart of water. How much chemical solution will he need to treat the entire tank? Show your work.

$$10 \text{ gal} \cdot \frac{4 \text{ qt}}{1 \text{ gal}} = 40 \text{ qt} \cdot \frac{\frac{1}{2} \text{ tsp}}{1 \text{ qt}} = 20 \text{ tsp}$$

Extended Problem Solving

4. Casey and Jacqui are building a scale model of the state of Virginia. From east to west, the greatest distance across the state is about 430 mi. From north to south, the greatest distance is about 200 mi.
   a. What scale factor are Casey and Jacqui using to build their model? Explain how you found your answer.
   b. How wide will their model be? Show your work.
   c. If an airplane travels at a speed of 880 feet per second, how long will it take for the plane to fly east to west across the widest part of Virginia?

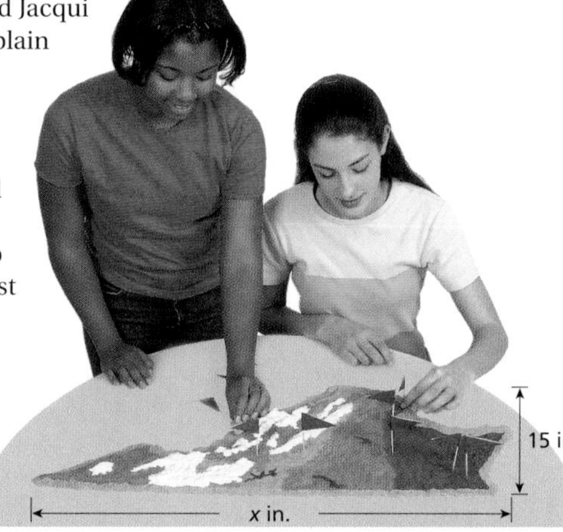

Student Work Samples for Item 4

Level 3

a. scale is 15 in / 200 mi
scale factor is 1/844,800
b. 15 in / 200 mi = x in / 430 mi
200 x 6,450
x = 32.25 in wide
c. 430 mi / 1 x 5280 ft / 1 mi = 2,270,400 ft
2,270,400 ÷ 880 = 2580 s or 43 min

The student correctly identified the scale and the scale factor, calculated the width of the model, and used dimensional analysis to solve part **c.**

Level 2

a. Scale factor is 15in = 200mi
b. 15/200 = x/430   200x/200 = 6450/200
x = 32in
c. 430/880 = .49 about half an hour

The student identified the scale but not the scale factor in part **a.** The answer to part **b** is correct, but the student showed little understanding of part **c.**

Level 1

a. Scale is 200mi = 15in.
b. 430 ÷ 15 = 28.6 in.
c. 880 - 430 = 450min.

The student reversed the scale in part **a,** gave an incorrect width in part **b,** and used the wrong operation in part **c.**

internet connect
State-Specific Test Practice Online
go.hrw.com Keyword: MS4 TestPrep

Standardized Test Prep

Chapter 5

Cumulative Assessment, Chapters 1–5

1. Find the difference: $-6 - (-3)$. **B**
   - (A) -9
   - (B) -3
   - (C) 3
   - (D) 9

TIP! TEST TAKING TIP!

Eliminate choices by using estimation.

2. Multiply $5\frac{1}{3} \cdot 3\frac{3}{4}$. Write the answer in simplest form. **J**
   - (F) $15\frac{1}{4}$
   - (G) $1\frac{19}{45}$
   - (H) $9\frac{1}{12}$
   - (J) 20

3. Find the mean of the numbers 6, 6, 8, 20, and 10. **C**
   - (A) 6
   - (B) 8
   - (C) 10
   - (D) 14

4. Find the solution to the equation $y + (-8) = 12$. **F**
   - (F) $y = 20$
   - (G) $y = -20$
   - (H) $y = -96$
   - (J) $y = 4$

5. Write 123,000 in scientific notation. **D**
   - (A) $123 \times 1{,}000$
   - (B) 123×10^3
   - (C) 0.123×10^6
   - (D) 1.23×10^5

6. Which of the following numbers is irrational? **F**
   - (F) π
   - (G) $3.\overline{8}$
   - (H) $6\frac{1}{2}$
   - (J) $\sqrt{4}$

7. Which is the LCM of 16 and 12? **C**
   - (A) 4
   - (B) 24
   - (C) 48
   - (D) 192

8. Which is the GCF of 32 and 18? **J**
   - (F) 9
   - (G) 6
   - (H) 18
   - (J) 2

9. Solve the proportion $\frac{m}{3} = \frac{18}{6}$. **D**
   - (A) $m = 36$
   - (B) $m = 18$
   - (C) $m = 1$
   - (D) $m = 9$

10. ***SHORT RESPONSE*** Write an expression to describe the phrase "sixteen less than a number m." Can you use your expression to find the value of m? Why or why not?

11. ***SHORT RESPONSE*** The box-and-whisker plot shows the scores on a quiz students took in Ms. Santini's class. Can you find the mean quiz score from the box-and-whisker plot? If so, find it. If not, explain why not.

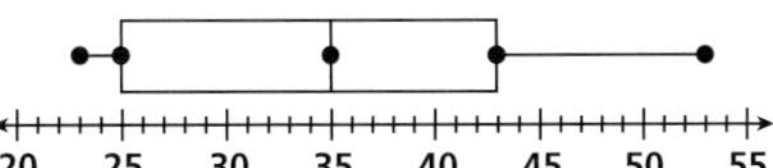

Standardized Test Prep

Chapter 5

Purpose: *To provide review and practice for Chapters 1–5 and standardized tests*

Assessment Resources

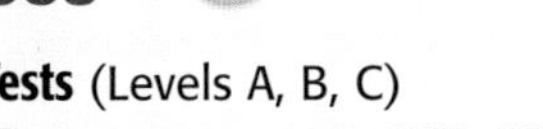

Cumulative Tests (Levels A, B, C)
Assessment Resources . . . pp. 177–188

State-Specific Test Practice Online
KEYWORD: MS4 TestPrep

Test Prep Doctor

Expand on the test-taking tip given for item 2 by reminding students that they can estimate products of mixed numbers by first rounding each mixed number to the nearest whole number. Point out that $5\frac{1}{3}$ rounds to 5 and $3\frac{3}{4}$ rounds to 4, so the estimate of the product is $5 \cdot 4 = 20$. This eliminates choices **G** and **H,** which are too low.

Answers

10. $m - 16$; no, you need to know the value of the expression in order to find the value of m.

11. No, the mean is the average of all the scores. The box-and-whisker plot does not show each individual score.

Chapter 6

Percents

Section 6A

Introduction to Percent

Lesson 6-1
Fractions, Decimals, and Percents

Lesson 6-2
Estimate with Percents

Lesson 6-3
Percent of a Number

Lesson 6-4
Solving Equations Containing Percents

Section 6B

Using Percents

Hands-On Lab 6A
Percent of Increase and Decrease

Lesson 6-5
Percent of Change

Lesson 6-6
Simple Interest

Pacing Guide for 45-Minute Classes

Chapter 6

DAY 76	DAY 77	DAY 78	DAY 79	DAY 80
Lesson 6-1	Lesson 6-2	Lesson 6-3	Lesson 6-4	Mid-Chapter Quiz Hands-On Lab 6A
DAY 81	**DAY 82**	**DAY 83**	**DAY 84**	
Lesson 6-5	Lesson 6-6	Chapter 6 Review	Chapter 6 Assessment	

Pacing Guide for 90-Minute Classes

Chapter 6

DAY 38	DAY 39	DAY 40	DAY 41	DAY 42
Chapter 5 Assessment Lesson 6-1	Lesson 6-2 Lesson 6-3	Lesson 6-4 Hands-On Lab 6A	Mid-Chapter Quiz Lesson 6-5 Lesson 6-6	Chapter 6 Review Lesson 7-1
DAY 43				
Chapter 6 Assessment Lesson 7-2				

Across the Series

COURSE 1

- Write equivalent percents, decimals, and fractions.
- Find the missing value in a percent problem.
- Solve percent problems involving discounts, sales tax, and tips.
- Find the amount of simple interest.

COURSE 2

- **Write equivalent fractions, decimals, and percents.**
- **Determine if answers need to be exact or can be estimated; estimate percents.**
- **Find the percent of a number.**
- **Solve one-step equations with percents.**
- **Find the percent of increase or decrease; find the amount of a discount or markup.**
- **Find the amount of simple interest.**

COURSE 3

- Write equivalent percents, decimals, and fractions.
- Estimate percents, and find the missing value in a percent problem.
- Find the percent of increase or decrease, and solve percent problems involving commission or taxes.
- Find the amount of simple or compound interest.

Across the Curriculum

LANGUAGE ARTS 

Math: Reading and Writing in the Content Area . . . . pp. 51–56
Focus on Problem Solving
Make a Plan. . . . . SE p. 321
Journal . . . . TE, last page of each lesson
Write About It. . . . . SE pp. 311, 315, 319, 331

SOCIAL STUDIES 

Geography . . . . SE p. 313
Social Studies . . . . SE pp. 307, 317
History . . . . SE p. 319
Economics. . . . . SE p. 327

SCIENCE 

Earth Science. . . . . SE p. 315
Physical Science. . . . . SE p. 315
Nutrition. . . . . SE p. 315
Health. . . . . SE p. 319

TE = *Teacher's Edition* **SE** = *Student Edition*

Interdisciplinary

Bulletin Board

Life Science

An important by-product of photosynthesis is oxygen, which living organisms need to survive. Air is made up primarily of nitrogen and oxygen. Oxygen, O_2, has a molecular weight of 32, and nitrogen, N_2, has a molecular weight about 12.5% less than that of oxygen. Find the molecular weight of nitrogen. **28**

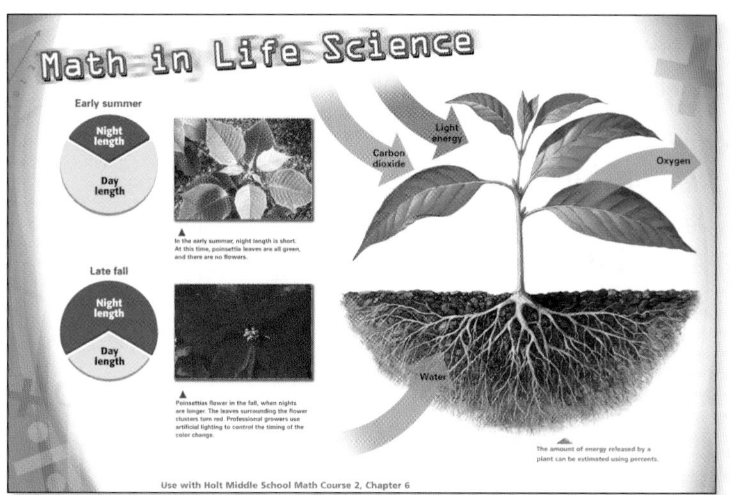

Interdisciplinary posters and worksheets are provided in your resource material.

Resource Options

Chapter 6 Resource Book

Student Resources

Practice (Levels A, B, C) .... pp. 8–10, 17–19, 27–29, 36–38, 46–48, 55–57
Reteach .... pp. 11, 20–21, 30, 39, 49, 58
Challenge .... pp. 12, 22, 31, 40, 50, 59
Problem Solving .... pp. 13, 23, 32, 41, 51, 60
Puzzles, Twisters & Teasers .... pp. 14, 24, 33, 42, 52, 61
Recording Sheets ..... pp. 3, 7, 16, 26, 35, 45, 54, 64, 67–68
Chapter Review .... pp. 62–63

Teacher and Parent Resources

Chapter Planning and Pacing Guide .... p. 4
Section Planning Guides .... pp. 5, 43
Parent Letter .... pp. 1–2
Teaching Tools .... pp. 67–69
Teacher Support for Chapter Project .... p. 65
Transparencies .... pp. T1–T26
- Daily Transparencies
- Additional Examples Transparencies
- Teaching Transparencies

Reaching All Learners

English Language Learners

Success for English Language Learners ...... pp. 101–112
Math: Reading and Writing in the Content Area .... pp. 51–56
Spanish Homework and Practice .... pp. 51–56
Spanish Interactive Study Guide .... pp. 51–56
Spanish Family Involvement Activities .... pp. 49–56
Multilingual Glossary

Individual Needs

Are You Ready? Intervention and Enrichment .. pp. 65–68, 113–116, 245–248, 269–272, 415–416
Alternate Openers: Explorations .... pp. 51–56
Family Involvement Activities .... pp. 49–56
Interactive Problem Solving .... pp. 51–56
Interactive Study Guide .... pp. 51–56
Readiness Activities .... pp. 11–12
Math: Reading and Writing in the Content Area .... pp. 51–56
Challenge .... CRB pp. 12, 22, 31, 40, 50, 59

Hands-On

Hands-On Lab Activities .... pp. 40–43
Technology Lab Activities .... pp. 31–35
Alternate Openers: Explorations .... pp. 51–56
Family Involvement Activities .... pp. 49–56

Applications and Connections

Consumer and Career Math .... pp. 21–24
Interdisciplinary Posters .... Poster 6, TE p. 302B
Interdisciplinary Poster Worksheets .... pp. 16–18

Transparencies

Alternate Openers: Explorations .... pp. 51–56
Exercise Answers Transparencies
Chapter 6 Resource Book .... pp. T1–T26
- Daily Transparencies
- Additional Examples Transparencies
- Teaching Transparencies

Technology

Teacher Resources

***Lesson Presentations* CD-ROM** .... Chapter 6
***Test and Practice Generator* CD-ROM** .... Chapter 6
***One-Stop Planner* CD-ROM** .... Chapter 6

Student Resources

***Are You Ready? Intervention* CD-ROM**
Skills 14, 26, 59, 65

internet connect (go.hrw.com)

Homework Help Online	**KEYWORD:** MS4 HWHelp6
Math Tools Online	**KEYWORD:** MS4 Tools6
Glossary Online	**KEYWORD:** MS4 Glossary
Chapter Project Online	**KEYWORD:** MS4 PSProject6
Chapter Opener Online	**KEYWORD:** MS4 Ch 6
CNN Student News™	**KEYWORD:** MS4 CNN6

SE = *Student Edition* **TE** = *Teacher's Edition* **AR** = *Assessment Resources* **CRB** = *Chapter Resource Book* **MK** = *Manipulatives Kit*

Chapter 6

Assessment Options

Assessing Prior Knowledge

Determine whether students have the required prerequisite concepts and skills.

Are You Ready? . . . . SE p. 303

Inventory Test . . . . AR pp. 1–4

Test Preparation

Provide review and practice for chapter and standardized tests.

Standardized Test Prep . . . . SE p. 341

Spiral Review with Test Prep . . . . . SE, last page of each lesson

Study Guide and Review . . . . SE pp. 336–338

Test Prep Tool Kit

Technology

***Test and Practice Generator* CD-ROM**

internet connect

State-Specific Test Practice Online KEYWORD: MS4 TestPrep

Performance Assessment

Assess students' understanding of chapter concepts and combined problem-solving skills.

Performance Assessment . . . . SE p. 340
Includes scoring rubric in TE

Performance Assessment . . . . AR p. 116

Performance Assessment Teacher Support . . . . AR p. 115

Portfolio

Portfolio opportunities appear throughout the Student and Teacher's Editions.

Suggested work samples:

Problem Solving Project . . . . TE p. 302

Performance Assessment . . . . SE p. 340

Portfolio Guide . . . . AR p. xxxv

Journal . . . . TE, last page of each lesson

Write About It . . . . SE pp. 311, 315, 319, 331

Daily Assessment

Obtain daily feedback on students' understanding of concepts.

Spiral Review and Test Prep . . . . . . SE, last page of each lesson

Also Available on Transparency In Chapter 6 Resource Book

Warm Up . . . . TE, first page of each lesson

Problem of the Day . . . . TE, first page of each lesson

Lesson Quiz . . . . TE, last page of each lesson

Student Self-Assessment

Have students evaluate their own work.

Group Project Evaluation . . . . AR p. xxxii

Individual Group Member Evaluation . . . . AR p. xxxiii

Portfolio Guide . . . . AR p. xxxv

Journal . . . . TE, last page of each lesson

Formal Assessment

Assess students' mastery of concepts and skills.

Section Quizzes . . . . AR pp. 17–18

Mid-Chapter Quizzes . . . . SE pp. 320

Chapter Test . . . . SE p. 339

Chapter Tests (Levels A, B, C) . . . . AR pp. 63–68

Cumulative Tests (Levels A, B, C) . . . . AR pp. 189–200

Standardized Test Prep
Cumulative Assessment . . . . SE p. 341

End-of-Year Test . . . . AR pp. 273–276

Technology

***Test and Practice Generator* CD-ROM**

Make tests electronically. This software includes:

- Dynamic practice for Chapter 6
- Customizable tests
- Multiple-choice items for each objective
- Free-response items for each objective
- Teacher management system

SE = *Student Edition* **TE** = *Teacher's Edition* **AR** = *Assessment Resources* **CRB** = *Chapter Resource Book* **MK** = *Manipulatives Kit*

Chapter 6

Chapter 6 Tests

Three levels (A,B,C) of tests are available for each chapter in the *Assessment Resources.*

LEVEL A

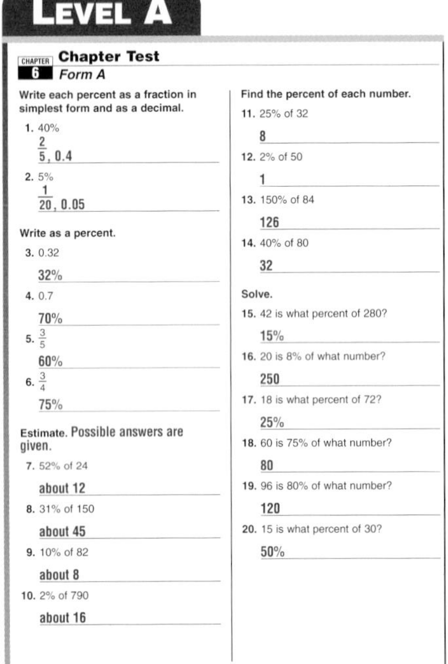

Chapter 6 Chapter Test
Form A

Write each percent as a fraction in simplest form and as a decimal.

1. 40% — $\frac{2}{5}$, 0.4
2. 5% — $\frac{1}{20}$, 0.05

Write as a percent.

3. 0.32 — 32%
4. 0.7 — 70%
5. $\frac{3}{5}$ — 60%
6. $\frac{3}{4}$ — 75%

Estimate. Possible answers are given.

7. 52% of 24 — about 12
8. 31% of 150 — about 45
9. 10% of 82 — about 8
10. 2% of 790 — about 16

Find the percent of each number.

11. 25% of 32 — 8
12. 2% of 50 — 1
13. 150% of 84 — 126
14. 40% of 80 — 32

Solve.

15. 42 is what percent of 280? — 15%
16. 20 is 8% of what number? — 250
17. 18 is what percent of 72? — 25%
18. 60 is 75% of what number? — 80
19. 96 is 80% of what number? — 120
20. 15 is what percent of 30? — 50%

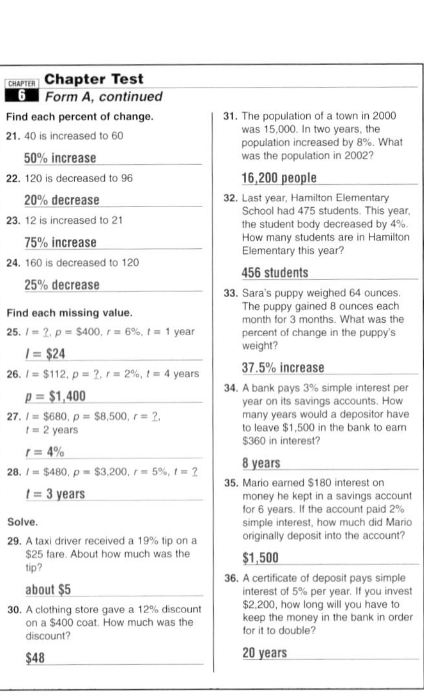

Chapter 6 Chapter Test
Form A, continued

Find each percent of change.

21. 40 is increased to 60 — 50% increase
22. 120 is decreased to 96 — 20% decrease
23. 12 is increased to 21 — 75% increase
24. 160 is decreased to 120 — 25% decrease

Find each missing value.

25. $I = ?$, $p = \$400$, $r = 6\%$, $t = 1$ year — $I = \$24$
26. $I = \$112$, $p = ?$, $r = 2\%$, $t = 4$ years — $p = \$1{,}400$
27. $I = \$680$, $p = \$8{,}500$, $r = ?$, $t = 2$ years — $r = 4\%$
28. $I = \$480$, $p = \$3{,}200$, $r = 5\%$, $t = ?$ — $t = 3$ years

Solve.

29. A taxi driver received a 19% tip on a $25 fare. About how much was the tip? — about $5
30. A clothing store gave a 12% discount on a $400 coat. How much was the discount? — $48
31. The population of a town in 2000 was 15,000. In two years, the population increased by 8%. What was the population in 2002? — 16,200 people
32. Last year, Hamilton Elementary School had 475 students. This year, the student body decreased by 4%. How many students are in Hamilton Elementary this year? — 456 students
33. Sara's puppy weighed 64 ounces. The puppy gained 8 ounces each month for 3 months. What was the percent of change in the puppy's weight? — 37.5% increase
34. A bank pays 3% simple interest per year on its savings accounts. How many years would a depositor have to leave $1,500 in the bank to earn $360 in interest? — 8 years
35. Mario earned $180 interest on money he kept in a savings account for 6 years. If the account paid 2% simple interest, how much did Mario originally deposit into the account? — $1,500
36. A certificate of deposit pays simple interest of 5% per year. If you invest $2,200, how long will you have to keep the money in the bank in order for it to double? — 20 years

LEVEL B

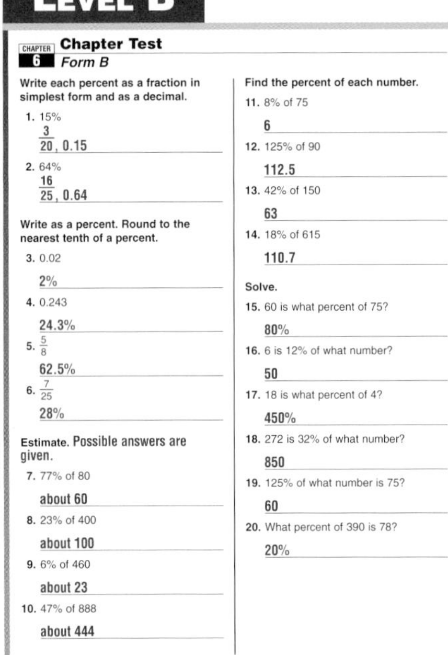

Chapter 6 Chapter Test
Form B

Write each percent as a fraction in simplest form and as a decimal.

1. 15% — $\frac{3}{20}$, 0.15
2. 64% — $\frac{16}{25}$, 0.64

Write as a percent. Round to the nearest tenth of a percent.

3. 0.02 — 2%
4. 0.243 — 24.3%
5. $\frac{5}{8}$ — 62.5%
6. $\frac{7}{25}$ — 28%

Estimate. Possible answers are given.

7. 77% of 80 — about 60
8. 23% of 400 — about 100
9. 6% of 460 — about 23
10. 47% of 888 — about 444

Find the percent of each number.

11. 8% of 75 — 6
12. 125% of 90 — 112.5
13. 42% of 150 — 63
14. 18% of 615 — 110.7

Solve.

15. 60 is what percent of 75? — 80%
16. 6 is 12% of what number? — 50
17. 18 is what percent of 4? — 450%
18. 272 is 32% of what number? — 850
19. 125% of what number is 75? — 60
20. What percent of 390 is 78? — 20%

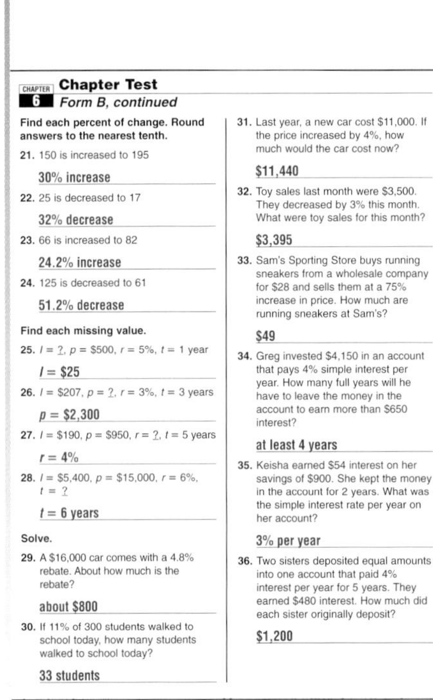

Chapter 6 Chapter Test
Form B, continued

Find each percent of change. Round answers to the nearest tenth.

21. 150 is increased to 195 — 30% increase
22. 25 is decreased to 17 — 32% decrease
23. 66 is increased to 82 — 24.2% increase
24. 125 is decreased to 61 — 51.2% decrease

Find each missing value.

25. $I = ?$, $p = \$500$, $r = 5\%$, $t = 1$ year — $I = \$25$
26. $I = \$207$, $p = ?$, $r = 3\%$, $t = 3$ years — $p = \$2{,}300$
27. $I = \$190$, $p = \$950$, $r = ?$, $t = 5$ years — $r = 4\%$
28. $I = \$5{,}400$, $p = \$15{,}000$, $r = 6\%$, $t = ?$ — $t = 6$ years

Solve.

29. A $16,000 car comes with a 4.8% rebate. About how much is the rebate? — about $800
30. If 11% of 300 students walked to school today, how many students walked to school today? — 33 students
31. Last year, a new car cost $11,000. If the price increased by 4%, how much would the car cost now? — $11,440
32. Toy sales last month were $3,500. They decreased by 3% this month. What were toy sales for this month? — $3,395
33. Sam's Sporting Store buys running sneakers from a wholesale company for $28 and sells them at a 75% increase in price. How much are running sneakers at Sam's? — $49
34. Greg invested $4,150 in an account that pays 4% simple interest per year. How many full years will he have to leave the money in the account to earn more than $650 interest? — at least 4 years
35. Keisha earned $54 interest on her savings of $900. She kept the money in the account for 2 years. What was the simple interest rate per year on her account? — 3% per year
36. Two sisters deposited equal amounts into one account that paid 4% interest per year for 5 years. They earned $480 interest. How much did each sister originally deposit? — $1,200

LEVEL C

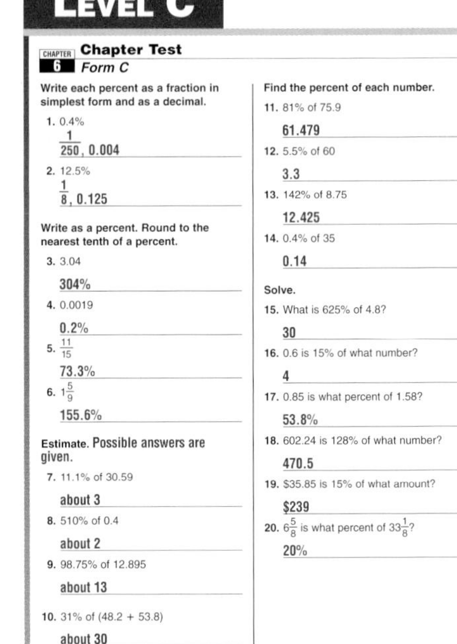

Chapter 6 Chapter Test
Form C

Write each percent as a fraction in simplest form and as a decimal.

1. 0.4% — $\frac{1}{250}$, 0.004
2. 12.5% — $\frac{1}{8}$, 0.125

Write as a percent. Round to the nearest tenth of a percent.

3. 3.04 — 304%
4. 0.0019 — 0.2%
5. $\frac{11}{15}$ — 73.3%
6. $1\frac{5}{9}$ — 155.6%

Estimate. Possible answers are given.

7. 11.1% of 30.59 — about 3
8. 510% of 0.4 — about 2
9. 98.75% of 12.895 — about 13
10. 31% of (48.2 + 53.8) — about 30

Find the percent of each number.

11. 81% of 75.9 — 61.479
12. 5.5% of 60 — 3.3
13. 142% of 8.75 — 12.425
14. 0.4% of 35 — 0.14

Solve.

15. What is 625% of 4.8? — 30
16. 0.6 is 15% of what number? — 4
17. 0.85 is what percent of 1.58? — 53.8%
18. 602.24 is 128% of what number? — 470.5
19. $35.85 is 15% of what amount? — $239
20. $6\frac{5}{8}$ is what percent of $33\frac{1}{8}$? — 20%

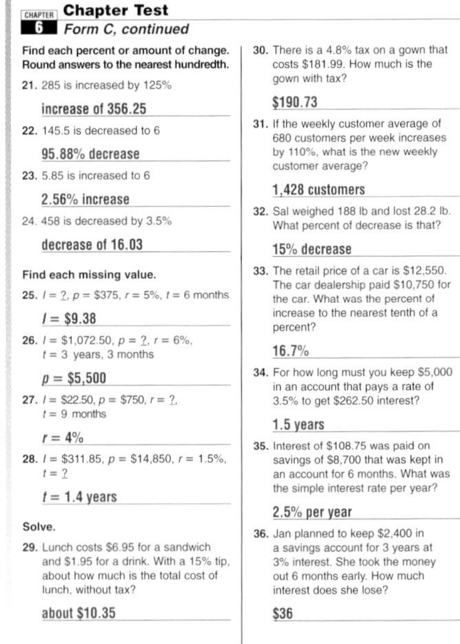

Chapter 6 Chapter Test
Form C, continued

Find each percent or amount of change. Round answers to the nearest hundredth.

21. 285 is increased by 125% — increase of 356.25
22. 145.5 is decreased to 6 — 95.88% decrease
23. 5.85 is increased to 6 — 2.56% increase
24. 458 is decreased by 3.5% — decrease of 16.03

Find each missing value.

25. $I = ?$, $p = \$375$, $r = 5\%$, $t = 6$ months — $I = \$9.38$
26. $I = \$1{,}072.50$, $p = ?$, $r = 6\%$, $t = 3$ years, 3 months — $p = \$5{,}500$
27. $I = \$22.50$, $p = \$750$, $r = ?$, $t = 9$ months — $r = 4\%$
28. $I = \$311.85$, $p = \$14{,}850$, $r = 1.5\%$, $t = ?$ — $t = 1.4$ years

Solve.

29. Lunch costs $6.95 for a sandwich and $1.95 for a drink. With a 15% tip, about how much is the total cost of lunch, without tax? — about $10.35
30. There is a 4.8% tax on a gown that costs $181.99. How much is the gown with tax? — $190.73
31. If the weekly customer average of 680 customers per week increases by 110%, what is the new weekly customer average? — 1,428 customers
32. Sal weighed 188 lb and lost 28.2 lb. What percent of decrease is that? — 15% decrease
33. The retail price of a car is $12,550. The car dealership paid $10,750 for the car. What was the percent of increase to the nearest tenth of a percent? — 16.7%
34. For how long must you keep $5,000 in an account that pays a rate of 3.5% to get $262.50 interest? — 1.5 years
35. Interest of $108.75 was paid on savings of $8,700 that was kept in an account for 6 months. What was the simple interest rate per year? — 2.5% per year
36. Jan planned to keep $2,400 in a savings account for 3 years at 3% interest. She took the money out 6 months early. How much interest does she lose? — $36

Test and Practice Generator CD-ROM

Create and customize multiple versions of the same tests with corresponding answers for any chosen chapter objectives.

Chapter 6 State and Standardized Test Preparation

Test Taking Skill Builder and Standardized Test Practice are provided for each chapter in the *Test Prep Tool Kit.*

TEST TAKING SKILL BUILDER

Test Taking Strategies — **Multiple Choice Questions—Elimination Method**
Chapter 6

Eliminating answer choices that you know are incorrect is an excellent test-taking strategy. If you must guess on a question, you will have a better chance of getting the question correct if you have eliminated some of the answer choices.

Example 1 Multiple Choice A portable CD player regularly costs \$63.99. It is on sale for 33% off. Find the sale price.

A \$21.12 **B** \$30.99 **C** \$40.00 **D** \$42.87

Use mental math to estimate the discount amount.

$33\% \approx \frac{1}{3}$

$\frac{1}{3}(\$60) \approx \$20$

$\$60 - \$20 = \$40$

Consider Choice A: \$21.12. Eliminate this choice because it is too small. \$21.12 is how much the CD player is discounted, not the sale price.

Consider Choice B: \$30.99. Eliminate this choice because it is also too small. The sale price is close to \$40.

The correct answer is Choice D. The sale price of the CD player is \$42.87. The exact calculations are as follows:

$0.33 \cdot 63.99 = 21.12$

$\$63.99 - \$21.12 = \$42.87$

Example 2 Multiple Choice You earned \$500. You put the money into a savings account that earns 6% simple interest. You plan to keep the money in the account for 7 years. How much will you have in your account at the end of 7 years?

F \$210 **G** \$542 **H** \$710 **I** \$2,100

Read over the answer choices. Two of the choices can be quickly eliminated.

Eliminate Choice F because it is too small. \$210 is the amount of interest you'll earn during the 7 years.

Eliminate Choice I because it is too large. The interest rate is not high enough and you are not keeping the money in the account long enough for you to have \$2,100 in your account after 7 years.

The correct answer is Choice H.

STANDARDIZED TEST PRACTICE

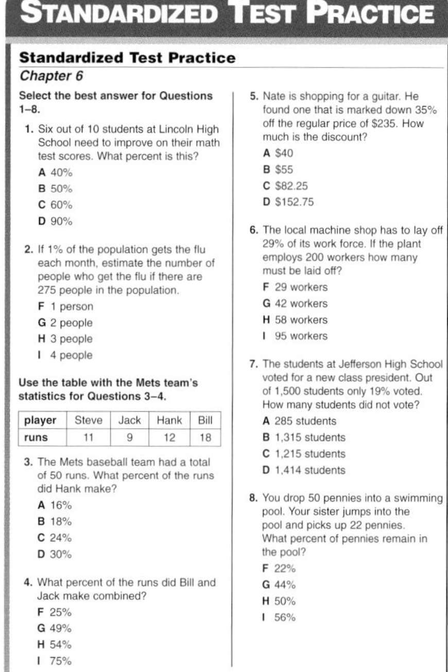

Standardized Test Practice
Chapter 6

Select the best answer for Questions 1–8.

1. Six out of 10 students at Lincoln High School need to improve on their math test scores. What percent is this?
   A 40%
   B 50%
   C 60%
   D 90%

2. If 1% of the population gets the flu each month, estimate the number of people who get the flu if there are 275 people in the population.
   F 1 person
   G 2 people
   H 3 people
   I 4 people

Use the table with the Mets team's statistics for Questions 3–4.

player	Steve	Jack	Hank	Bill
runs	11	9	12	18

3. The Mets baseball team had a total of 50 runs. What percent of the runs did Hank make?
   A 16%
   B 18%
   C 24%
   D 30%

4. What percent of the runs did Bill and Jack make combined?
   F 25%
   G 49%
   H 54%
   I 75%

5. Nate is shopping for a guitar. He found one that is marked down 35% off the regular price of \$235. How much is the discount?
   A \$40
   B \$55
   C \$82.25
   D \$152.75

6. The local machine shop has to lay off 29% of its work force. If the plant employs 200 workers how many must be laid off?
   F 29 workers
   G 42 workers
   H 58 workers
   I 95 workers

7. The students at Jefferson High School voted for a new class president. Out of 1,500 students only 19% voted. How many students did not vote?
   A 285 students
   B 1,315 students
   C 1,215 students
   D 1,414 students

8. You drop 50 pennies into a swimming pool. Your sister jumps into the pool and picks up 22 pennies. What percent of pennies remain in the pool?
   F 22%
   G 44%
   H 50%
   I 56%

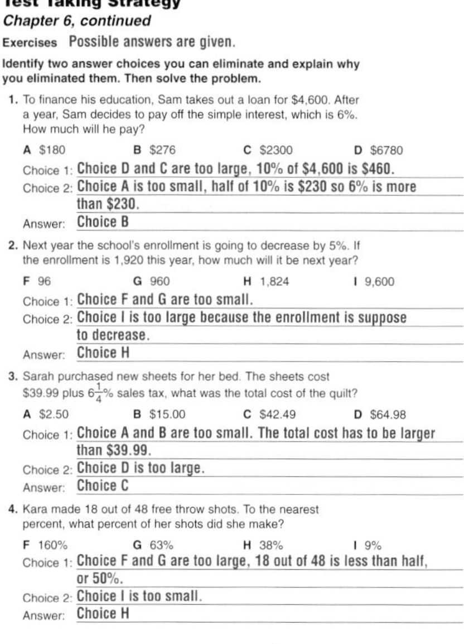

Test Taking Strategy
Chapter 6, continued

Exercises Possible answers are given.

Identify two answer choices you can eliminate and explain why you eliminated them. Then solve the problem.

1. To finance his education, Sam takes out a loan for \$4,600. After a year, Sam decides to pay off the simple interest, which is 6%. How much will he pay?
   A \$180 **B** \$276 **C** \$2300 **D** \$6780
   Choice 1: Choice D and C are too large, 10% of \$4,600 is \$460.
   Choice 2: Choice A is too small, half of 10% is \$230 so 6% is more than \$230.
   Answer: Choice B

2. Next year the school's enrollment is going to decrease by 5%. If the enrollment is 1,920 this year, how much will it be next year?
   F 96 **G** 960 **H** 1,824 **I** 9,600
   Choice 1: Choice F and G are too small.
   Choice 2: Choice I is too large because the enrollment is suppose to decrease.
   Answer: Choice H

3. Sarah purchased new sheets for her bed. The sheets cost \$39.99 plus $6\frac{1}{4}$% sales tax, what was the total cost of the quilt?
   A \$2.50 **B** \$15.00 **C** \$42.49 **D** \$64.98
   Choice 1: Choice A and B are too small. The total cost has to be larger than \$39.99.
   Choice 2: Choice D is too large.
   Answer: Choice C

4. Kara made 18 out of 48 free throw shots. To the nearest percent, what percent of her shots did she make?
   F 160% **G** 63% **H** 38% **I** 9%
   Choice 1: Choice F and G are too large, 18 out of 48 is less than half, or 50%.
   Choice 2: Choice I is too small.
   Answer: Choice H

Standardized Test Practice
Chapter 6, continued

Gridded Response
Solve the problems. Use the answer sheet to write and grid-in your answer.

9. Dan wants to know how much interest was paid to him over the last year on his bank account. He received \$546 at the end of the year and he deposited \$520 in the beginning of the year. The simple interest rate was ____%.

10. A diamond store buys diamonds and then increases the price by 175% to sell them to the public. If they buy a diamond for \$125, how much do they sell it for?

11. Thirty-eight percent of your class participated in the school fundraiser. If there are 1,850 students in your school, how many students participated in the fundraiser?

12. The soccer coach has every player attempt 30 goals. Barry made 12 goals. What percent of his attempts resulted in goals?

Short Response
Solve the problems. Use the answer sheet to write your answers.

13. Stan has \$500 that he wants to place in the bank. One bank offers a interest rate of 2.5%. His banker friend at another bank offers to give him 2% interest plus \$10 at the end of the year. Find the amount of money Stan will earn at both banks at the end of the year. Then determine in which bank Stan should deposit his money. Show your work.

14. In the 1992 presidential elections, approximately 63% of women of voting age cast their ballots. Write this percent as a fraction and as a decimal. Explain how you arrived at each answer.

Extended Response

15. For spirit day, students can buy a book cover, a mug with the school logo, or a school pennant. Of the 680 items that were sold, 15% were school pennants.
    a. Write and solve a proportion to find how many pennants were sold.
    b. Write and solve an equation to find how many pennants were sold. How does your answer differ from part a.?
    c. If 408 book covers were sold, what percent of the items sold were book covers?

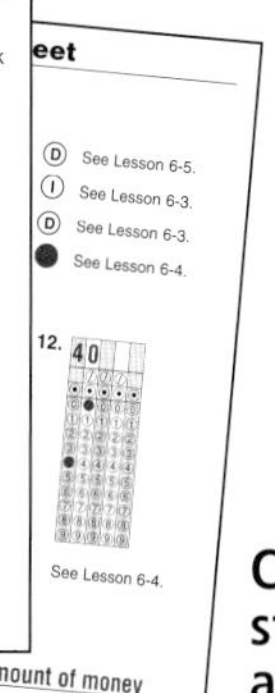

...eet

D See Lesson 6-5.
I See Lesson 6-3.
D See Lesson 6-3.
See Lesson 6-4.

12. 40
See Lesson 6-4.

... $P = IRT$ to find the amount of money Stan will earn at each bank. $P = 500(0.025) = 12.50$; Stan would receive \$12.50 in interest from the first bank. $P = 500(0.02) = 10$; Stan would receive \$10 in interest plus an additional \$10 from his friend's bank. Stan should deposit his money in his friend's bank. (See Lesson 6-6.)

14. $63\% = \frac{63}{100} = 0.63$; To write the percent as a fraction, write the number over 100 and then simplify. To write the percent as a decimal, divide the number by 100. (See Lesson 6-1.)

Extended Response
Write your answers for Problem 15 on the back of this paper.
See Lesson 6-4.

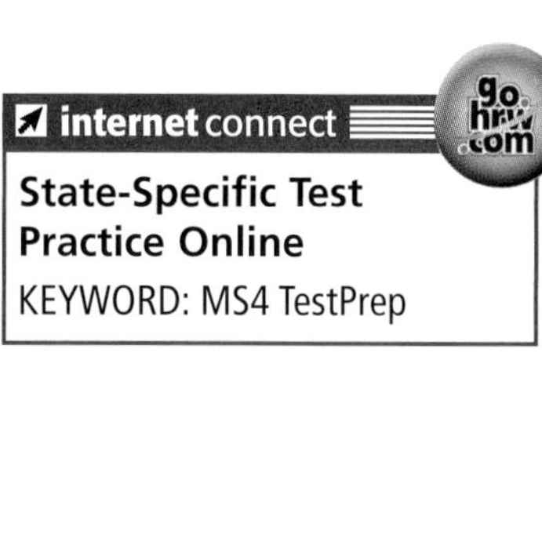

internet connect
State-Specific Test Practice Online
KEYWORD: MS4 TestPrep

Test Prep Tool Kit

- Standardized Test Prep Workbook
- Countdown to Testing transparencies
- State Test Prep CD-ROM
- Standardized Test Prep Video

Customized answer sheets give students realistic practice for actual standardized tests.

Percents

Why Learn This?

Tell students that percents are used to describe relationships. Ask students for possible meanings of the words *per* and *cent*. Possible answers: *Per* means "divide by," and *cent* is the French word for "one hundred." Discuss that each percent can be expressed as a ratio, a fraction, and a decimal. Have students write 80% as a fraction and decimal. $80\% = \frac{80}{100} = 0.80$

Using Data

To begin the study of this chapter, have students:

- Find the total amount of urban waste deposited annually in landfills in millions of tons. 250.4 million tons
- Write in fraction form the ratio of each type of urban waste to the total deposited urban waste.

  soil: $\frac{107.6}{250.4}$

  wood: $\frac{87.6}{250.4}$

  concrete: $\frac{22.5}{250.4}$

  household refuse: $\frac{32.7}{250.4}$

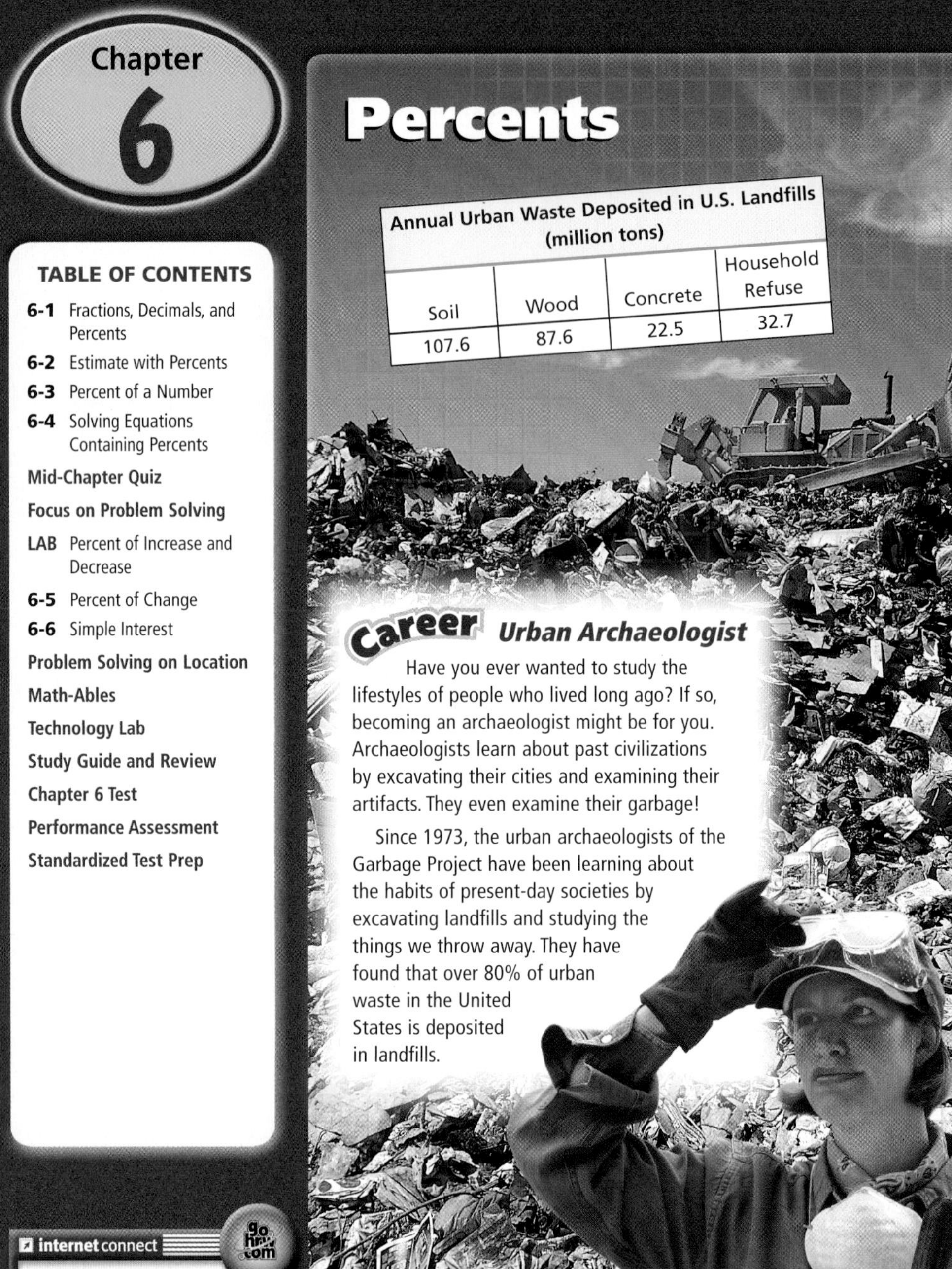

Chapter 6

Percents

TABLE OF CONTENTS

internet connect
Chapter Opener Online
go.hrw.com
KEYWORD: MS4 Ch6

Annual Urban Waste Deposited in U.S. Landfills (million tons)			
Soil	Wood	Concrete	Household Refuse
107.6	87.6	22.5	32.7

Career ***Urban Archaeologist***

Have you ever wanted to study the lifestyles of people who lived long ago? If so, becoming an archaeologist might be for you. Archaeologists learn about past civilizations by excavating their cities and examining their artifacts. They even examine their garbage!

Since 1973, the urban archaeologists of the Garbage Project have been learning about the habits of present-day societies by excavating landfills and studying the things we throw away. They have found that over 80% of urban waste in the United States is deposited in landfills.

Problem Solving Project

Earth Science Connection

Purpose: To solve problems using percents

Materials: Landfill Archaeology worksheet

internet connect
Chapter Project Online: ***go.hrw.com***
KEYWORD: MS4 PSProject6

Understand, Plan, Solve, and Look Back

Have students:

- ✓ Complete the Landfill Archaeology worksheet to learn about urban waste disposal in the United States.
- ✓ Determine the percent of soil, concrete, wood, and household refuse deposited in landfills.
- ✓ Take a poll of their classmates to discover which countries or cultures they might choose to study if they were an archaeologist. Then have them display the data they collected in a graph.
- ✓ Research to find out how urban archaeologists discover what is deposited in landfills. What techniques do they use?
- ✓ Check students' work.

ARE YOU READY?

Choose the best term from the list to complete each sentence.

	Terms
1. A statement that two ratios are equivalent is called a(n) __?__. proportion	decimal
2. To write $\frac{2}{3}$ as a(n) __?__, divide the numerator by the denominator. decimal	equation
3. A(n) __?__ is a comparison by division of two quantities. ratio	fraction
4. The __?__ of $\frac{9}{24}$ is $\frac{3}{8}$. simplest form	proportion
	ratio
	simplest form

Complete these exercises to review skills you will need for this chapter.

✔ Write Fractions as Decimals

Write each fraction as a decimal.

5. $\frac{8}{10}$ 0.8 **6.** $\frac{53}{100}$ 0.53 **7.** $\frac{739}{1,000}$ 0.739 **8.** $\frac{7}{100}$ 0.07

9. $\frac{2}{5}$ 0.4 **10.** $\frac{5}{8}$ 0.625 **11.** $\frac{7}{12}$ $0.58\overline{3}$ **12.** $\frac{13}{20}$ 0.65

✔ Write Decimals as Fractions

Write each decimal as a fraction in simplest form.

13. 0.05 $\frac{1}{20}$ **14.** 0.92 $\frac{23}{25}$ **15.** 0.013 $\frac{13}{1,000}$ **16.** 0.8 $\frac{4}{5}$

17. 0.006 $\frac{3}{500}$ **18.** 0.305 $\frac{61}{200}$ **19.** 0.0007 $\frac{7}{10,000}$ **20.** 1.04 $\frac{26}{25}$ or $1\frac{1}{25}$

✔ Solve Multiplication Equations

Solve each equation.

21. $100n = 300$ $n = 3$ **22.** $38 = 0.4x$ $x = 95$ **23.** $16p = 1,200$ $p = 75$

24. $9 = 72y$ $y = \frac{1}{8}$ **25.** $0.07m = 56$ $m = 800$ **26.** $25 = 100t$ $t = \frac{1}{4}$

✔ Solve Proportions

Solve each proportion.

27. $\frac{2}{3} = \frac{x}{12}$ $x = 8$ **28.** $\frac{x}{20} = \frac{3}{4}$ $x = 15$ **29.** $\frac{8}{15} = \frac{x}{45}$ $x = 24$

30. $\frac{16}{28} = \frac{4}{n}$ $n = 7$ **31.** $\frac{p}{100} = \frac{12}{36}$ $p = 33\frac{1}{3}$ **32.** $\frac{42}{12} = \frac{14}{n}$ $n = 4$

Assessing Prior Knowledge

INTERVENTION 

Diagnose and Prescribe

Evaluate your students' performance on this page to determine whether intervention is necessary or whether enrichment is appropriate. Options that provide instruction, practice, and a check are listed below.

Resources for Are You Ready?

- ***Are You Ready? Intervention and Enrichment***
- **Recording Sheet for Are You Ready?** *Chapter 6 Resource Book ...... p. 3*

 ***Are You Ready? Intervention*** **CD-ROM**

internet connect 

Are You Ready? Intervention
go.hrw.com
KEYWORD: MS4 AYR

ARE YOU READY?

Were students successful with Are You Ready?

YES
ENRICH

✔ Write Fractions as Decimals
Are You Ready? Intervention, Skill 26
Blackline Masters, Online, and
 **CD-ROM** Intervention Activities

✔ Write Decimals as Fractions
Are You Ready? Intervention, Skill 14
Blackline Masters, Online, and
CD-ROM Intervention Activities

✔ Solve Multiplication Equations
Are You Ready? Intervention, Skill 59
Blackline Masters, Online, and
 **CD-ROM** Intervention Activities

✔ Solve Proportions
Are You Ready? Intervention, Skill 65
Blackline Masters, Online, and
  **CD-ROM** Intervention Activities

Are You Ready? Enrichment, pp. 417–418

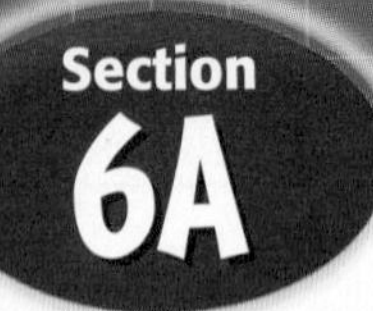

Introduction to Percent

One-Minute Section Planner

Lesson	Materials	Resources
Lesson 6-1 Fractions, Decimals, and Percents **NCTM:** Number and Operations, Communication, Connections, Representation **NAEP:** Number Properties 1e ☑ SAT-9 ☑ SAT-10 ☑ ITBS ☑ CTBS ☑ MAT ☑ CAT	**Optional** Teaching Transparency T2 *(CRB)* Dictionary	• *Chapter 6 Resource Book,* pp. 6–14 • Daily Transparency T1, CRB • Additional Examples Transparencies T3–T5, CRB • *Alternate Openers: Explorations,* p. 51
Lesson 6-2 Estimate with Percents **NCTM:** Number and Operations, Problem Solving, Communication, Connections **NAEP:** Number Properties 2b ☐ SAT-9 ☑ SAT-10 ☐ ITBS ☐ CTBS ☐ MAT ☑ CAT	**Optional** Teaching Transparency T7 *(CRB)* Recording Sheet for Reaching All Learners *(CRB, p. 67)*	• *Chapter 6 Resource Book,* pp. 15–24 • Daily Transparency T6, CRB • Additional Examples Transparencies T8–T9 CRB • *Alternate Openers: Explorations,* p. 52
Lesson 6-3 Percent of a Number **NCTM:** Number and Operations, Communication **NAEP:** Number Properties 4d ☑ SAT-9 ☑ SAT-10 ☑ ITBS ☑ CTBS ☑ MAT ☑ CAT	**Optional** Newspaper or magazine articles containing percents Recording Sheet for Reaching All Learners *(CRB, p. 68)*	• *Chapter 6 Resource Book,* pp. 25–33 • Daily Transparency T10, CRB • Additional Examples Transparencies T11–T13, CRB • *Alternate Openers: Explorations,* p. 53
Lesson 6-4 Solving Equations Containing Percents **NCTM:** Number and Operations, Algebra, Communication **NAEP:** Number Properties 4d ☐ SAT-9 ☐ SAT-10 ☐ ITBS ☐ CTBS ☐ MAT ☐ CAT	**Optional** Teaching Transparency T15 *(CRB)*	• *Chapter 6 Resource Book,* pp. 34–42 • Daily Transparency T14, CRB • Additional Examples Transparencies T16–T18, CRB • *Alternate Openers: Explorations,* p. 54
Section 6A Assessment		• Mid-Chapter Quiz, SE p. 320 • Section 6A Quiz, AR p. 17 • *Test and Practice Generator* CD-ROM

SAT = *Stanford Achievement Tests* **ITBS** = *Iowa Test of Basic Skills* **CTBS** = *Comprehensive Test of Basic Skills/Terra Nova*
MAT = *Metropolitan Achievement Test* **CAT** = *California Achievement Test*

NCTM—Complete standards can be found on pages T27–T33. **NAEP**—Complete standards can be found on pages A35–A39.

SE = *Student Edition* **TE** = *Teacher's Edition* **AR** = *Assessment Resources* **CRB** = *Chapter Resource Book* **MK** = *Manipulatives Kit*

Section Overview

Fractions, Decimals, and Percents — *Lessons 6-1, 6-2*

Why? When you are solving problems or making mental calculations it is helpful to write a fraction, decimal, or percent in an equivalent form.

Title To Come	
From Decimal to Percent	$0.86 = \frac{86}{100} = 86\%$
From Percent to Decimal	$23\% = \frac{23}{100} = 0.23$
From Percent to Fraction	$45\% = \frac{45}{100} = \frac{9}{20}$
From Fraction to Percent	$\frac{7}{8} = 0.875 = 87.5\%$

Remember: $\frac{7}{8}$ means $7 \div 8$.

Percent of a Number — *Lesson 6-3*

Why? Information is often given in percents. You need to be able to find the percent of a number to determine what the sales tax is on a purchase or what the savings is during a sale.

Two methods for finding the percent of a number are presented.

Proportion Method

Find 38% of 60.

Use a proportion.

$$\frac{38}{100} = \frac{n}{60}$$
$$100n = 38 \cdot 60$$
$$100n = 2{,}280$$
$$n = 22.8$$

38% of 60 is 22.8.

Equation Method

Find 53% of 12.

$$n = \mathbf{0.53} \cdot 12$$
$$n = 6.36$$

Use a decimal.

53% of 12 is 6.36.

Equations and Percents — *Lesson 6-4*

Why? Many real-world situations, such as figuring profit and loss, discounts, and taxes, involve solving equations with percents.

Either a proportion or a decimal can be used to solve percent problems.

Find the percent.

62 is what percent of 160?

Use a proportion.

$$\frac{n}{100} = \frac{62}{160}$$
$$160n = 62 \cdot 100$$
$$160n = 6{,}200$$
$$\frac{160n}{\mathbf{160}} = \frac{6{,}200}{\mathbf{160}}$$
$$n = 38.75$$

62 is 38.75% of 160.

Find the number.

28 is 32% of what number?

$$28 = \mathbf{0.32n}$$

Use a decimal.

$$\frac{28}{\mathbf{0.32}} = \frac{0.32n}{\mathbf{0.32}}$$
$$87.5 = n$$

28 is 32% of 87.5.

6-1 Organizer

Pacing: Traditional 1 day
Block $\frac{1}{2}$ day

Objective: Students write equivalent fractions, decimals, and percents.

Warm Up

Write each fraction in simplest form.

1.	$\frac{4}{10}$	$\frac{2}{5}$	**2.**	$\frac{8}{50}$	$\frac{4}{25}$
3.	$\frac{75}{100}$	$\frac{3}{4}$	**4.**	$\frac{12}{36}$	$\frac{1}{3}$
5.	$\frac{9}{15}$	$\frac{3}{5}$	**6.**	$\frac{18}{48}$	$\frac{3}{8}$

Problem of the Day

Use the clues to find the mystery percent. 83%

1. The product of its digits is 24.
2. It is greater than $\frac{1}{2}$.
3. The sum of its digits is a prime number.

Available on Daily Transparency in CRB

Math Fact !

Percent comes from the Latin *per centum*, or "per hundred." Consequently, a number such as 32% can be written as "32 per hundred" or the fraction $\frac{32}{100}$. This fraction is equivalent to the decimal 0.32.

6-1 Fractions, Decimals, and Percents

Learn to write equivalent fractions, decimals, and percents.

Vocabulary
percent

The students at Westview Middle School are collecting cans of food for the local food bank. Their goal is to collect 2,000 cans in one month. After 10 days, they have 800 cans of food. What *percent* of their goal have the students reached?

0 200 400 600 800 1,000 1,200 1,400 1,600 1,800 2,000

0 $\frac{1}{5}$ $\frac{2}{5}$ $\frac{3}{5}$ $\frac{4}{5}$ $\frac{5}{5}$

0 0.2 0.4 0.6 0.8 1.0

0 20% 40% 60% 80% 100%

Reading Math

The word *percent* means "per hundred." So 40% means "40 out of 100."

The number lines show that the students have reached 40% of their goal.

A **percent** is a ratio of a number to 100. The symbol % is used to indicate that a number is a percent. For example, 40% is the ratio 40 to 100, or $\frac{40}{100}$. Percents can be written as fractions or decimals.

EXAMPLE 1 Writing Percents as Fractions

Write 35% as a fraction in simplest form.

$35\% = \frac{35}{100}$ *Write the percent as a fraction with a denominator of 100.*

$= \frac{7}{20}$ *Simplify.*

EXAMPLE 2 Writing Percents as Decimals

Write 43% as a decimal.

$43\% = \frac{43}{100}$ *Write the percent as a fraction with a denominator of 100.*

$= 0.43$ *Write the fraction as a decimal.*

Notice that both 43% and 0.43 mean "43 hundredths." Another way to write a percent as a decimal is to delete the percent sign and move the decimal point two places to the left.

$43.\% = 0.43$

1 Introduce

Alternate Opener

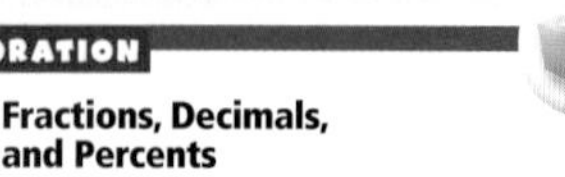

EXPLORATION

6-1 Fractions, Decimals, and Percents

The model below represents a recreation center. The swimming pool occupies 10 out of the 100 total squares of the recreation center. This can be written as a fraction ($\frac{10}{100} = \frac{1}{10}$), as a decimal (0.10), or as a percent (10%).

Count the number of squares to find each area as a fraction, a decimal, and a percent of the recreation center's total area.

Swimming pool
Wall climbing
Tennis courts
Cafeteria
Weight training
Cross training

		Fraction	Decimal	Percent
1.	Wall climbing			
2.	Weight training			
3.	Cross training			
4.	Tennis courts			
5.	Cafeteria			

Think and Discuss

6. **Explain** how you write a fraction as a decimal.
7. **Explain** how you write a decimal as a percent.

Motivate

Ask students to describe different ways they have seen percent used (e.g., a 25%-off sale, 12% of students walk to school). Have students discuss what they think these statements mean.

Exploration worksheet and answers on Chapter 6 Resource Book pp. 7 and 70

2 Teach

Lesson Presentation

Guided Instruction

In this lesson, students learn to write equivalent fractions, decimals, and percents. Work back and forth between percents and decimals or fractions by replacing % with $\frac{}{100}$, or $\frac{}{100}$ with %. After working several examples, select some students to work problems independently so that you can assess understanding.

Teaching Tip To help explain the tip below Example 2, tell students that moving the decimal point two places to the left is like dividing by 100, or per 100 (%).

EXAMPLE 3 Writing Decimals as Percents

Write each decimal as a percent.

A 0.07

$0.07 = \frac{7}{100}$ *Write the decimal as a fraction.*

$= 7\%$ *Write the fraction as a percent.*

B 0.2

$0.2 = \frac{2}{10}$ *Write the decimal as a fraction.*

$= \frac{20}{100}$ *Write an equivalent fraction with a denominator of 100.*

$= 20\%$ *Write the fraction as a percent.*

Both 0.07 and 7% mean "7 hundredths." You can write a decimal as a percent by moving the decimal point two places to the right and adding the percent sign.

0.07 = 7.%

EXAMPLE 4 Writing Fractions as Percents

Helpful Hint

The method shown in Example 4A works only if the given denominator is a factor or multiple of 100. The method shown in Example 4B works for any denominator.

Write each fraction as a percent.

A $\frac{4}{5}$

$\frac{4}{5} = \frac{4 \cdot 20}{5 \cdot 20}$

$= \frac{80}{100}$ *Write an equivalent fraction with a denominator of 100.*

$= 80\%$ *Write the fraction as a percent.*

B $\frac{3}{8}$

$\frac{3}{8} = 3 \div 8$

$= 0.375$ *Use division to write the fraction as a decimal.*

$= 37.5\%$ *Write the decimal as a percent.*

Think and Discuss

1. **Explain** how to write 5% as a decimal.
2. **Describe** two methods you could use to write $\frac{3}{4}$ as a percent.
3. **Write** the ratio 25:100 as a fraction in simplest form, as a decimal, and as a percent.

COMMON ERROR ALERT

When writing decimals as percents, some students might write a decimal such as 0.2 as 2%. Remind students to always write the decimal to the hundredths place before writing the percent.

Additional Examples

Example 1

Write 88% as a fraction in simplest form. $\frac{22}{25}$

Example 2

Write 51% as a decimal. **0.51**

Example 3

Write each decimal as a percent.

A. 0.08 **8%**

B. 0.7 **70%**

Example 4

Write each fraction as a percent.

A. $\frac{3}{5}$ **60%**

B. $\frac{7}{40}$ **17.5%**

Example 4 note: To help students understand why 0.375 = 37.5%, have them write 0.375 as the fraction $\frac{375}{1,000}$ and then divide both the numerator and denominator by 10 to yield a number divided by 100.

Reaching All Learners

Through Curriculum Integration

Language Arts Ask students to think of as many words as they can that contain the word *cent*, such as *centipede*, *cent* (penny), *centimeter*, *century*, and *centennial*. Have volunteers look up the words in the dictionary and share the definitions with the class. Discuss the connection with the number 100 that each word has.

3 Close

Summarize

Have students explain how to write a percent as a fraction or decimal and then how to write a decimal or fraction as a percent.

Possible answers: Write the number over 100 and then simplify, or divide by 100 by moving the decimal point two places to the left. Write the digits of the decimal over 100. Or write the fraction as an equivalent fraction with a denominator of 100. In either case, the numerator is the same as the percent.

Answers to Think and Discuss

1. Possible answer: Divide 5 by 100 and drop the percent sign.
2. Possible answers: Divide 3 by 4 and write the decimal as a percent. Write an equivalent fraction with a denominator of 100 and then write the equivalent percent.
3. $\frac{1}{4}$; 0.25; 25%

6-1 PRACTICE & ASSESS

Students may want to refer back to the lesson examples.

Assignment Guide

If you finished Example 1 assign:
Core 1–4, 17–20, 58–63
Enriched 1–4, 17–20, 58–63

If you finished Example 2 assign:
Core 1–8, 17–24, 33–39 odd, 53, 56, 58–63
Enriched 1–7 odd, 17–24, 33–40, 53, 56, 58–63

If you finished Example 3 assign:
Core 1–12, 17–28, 33–39, 45, 47, 53, 56, 58–63
Enriched 1–11 odd, 17–28, 33–40, 42, 45, 47, 53, 56, 58–63

If you finished Example 4 assign:
Core 1–32, 33–51 odd, 53–56, 58–63
Enriched 1–31 odd, 33–63

Answers

37. $\frac{3}{400}$, 0.0075

38. $\frac{4}{25}$, 0.16

39. $\frac{703}{1,000}$, 0.703

40. $\frac{12}{25}$, 0.48

6-1 Exercises

FOR EXTRA PRACTICE
see page 666

internet connect
Homework Help Online
go.hrw.com Keyword: MS4 6-1

GUIDED PRACTICE

See Example 1 Write each percent as a fraction in simplest form.

1. 10% $\frac{1}{10}$ **2.** 45% $\frac{9}{20}$ **3.** 60% $\frac{3}{5}$ **4.** 28% $\frac{7}{25}$

See Example 2 Write each percent as a decimal.

5. 85% **0.85** **6.** 30% **0.3** **7.** 9% **0.09** **8.** 100% **1.0**

See Example 3 Write each decimal as a percent.

9. 0.18 **18%** **10.** 0.4 **40%** **11.** 0.75 **75%** **12.** 0.03 **3%**

See Example 4 Write each fraction as a percent.

13. $\frac{2}{5}$ **40%** **14.** $\frac{1}{4}$ **25%** **15.** $\frac{7}{50}$ **14%** **16.** $\frac{1}{8}$ **12.5%**

INDEPENDENT PRACTICE

See Example 1 Write each percent as a fraction in simplest form.

17. 30% $\frac{3}{10}$ **18.** 50% $\frac{1}{2}$ **19.** 88% $\frac{22}{25}$ **20.** 2% $\frac{1}{50}$

See Example 2 Write each percent as a decimal.

21. 16% **0.16** **22.** 32% **0.32** **23.** 105% **1.05** **24.** 0.1% **0.001**

See Example 3 Write each decimal as a percent.

25. 0.21 **21%** **26.** 0.57 **57%** **27.** 0.08 **8%** **28.** 0.038 **3.8%**

See Example 4 Write each fraction as a percent.

29. $\frac{3}{10}$ **30%** **30.** $\frac{7}{8}$ **87.5%** **31.** $\frac{11}{40}$ **27.5%** **32.** $\frac{9}{1,000}$ **0.9%**

PRACTICE AND PROBLEM SOLVING

Write each percent as a fraction in simplest form and as a decimal.

33. 8% $\frac{2}{25}$, **0.08** **34.** 120% $\frac{6}{5}$, **1.2** **35.** 2.5% $\frac{1}{40}$, **0.025** **36.** 300% $\frac{3}{1}$, **3.00**

37. 0.75% **38.** 16% **39.** 70.3% **40.** 48%

Write as a percent. Round to the nearest tenth of a percent, if necessary.

41. $\frac{9}{10}$ **90%** **42.** 0.15 **15%** **43.** $\frac{1}{3}$ **33.3%** **44.** 5:8 **62.5%**

45. 0.001 **0.1%** **46.** 4 to 9 **44.4%** **47.** 2.7 **270%** **48.** $\frac{5}{2}$ **250%**

Compare. Write <, >, or =.

49. 45% ▒ $\frac{2}{5}$ $>$ **50.** 9% ▒ 0.9 $<$ **51.** $\frac{7}{12}$ ▒ 60% $<$ **52.** 1.5 ▒ 150% $=$

Math Background

There are four cases of conversion to consider:

1. **Percent to fraction** Use $n\% = \frac{n}{100}$, to write any percent as a number divided by 100.
2. **Percent to decimal** Drop the percent sign and move the decimal point two places to the left.
3. **Decimal to percent** Move the decimal point two places to the right and add the percent sign.
4. **Fraction to percent** Write the fraction in decimal form, and then the conversion in case 3 can be applied.

RETEACH 6-1

LESSON 6-1 **Reteach**
Fractions, Decimals, and Percents

To change a percent to a fraction:
- drop the percent symbol;
- write the percent as the numerator;
- write 100 as the denominator;
- simplify.

$45\% = \frac{45}{100} = \frac{9}{20}$

Write each percent as a fraction in simplest form.

1. 37% $\frac{37}{100}$ 2. 80% $\frac{4}{5}$ 3. 4% $\frac{1}{25}$ 4. 75% $\frac{3}{4}$

To change a fraction to a percent:
- use a proportion to find an equivalent fraction with a denominator of 100.

$\frac{7}{25} = \frac{x}{100}$
$25x = 700$
$x = 28$
$\frac{7}{25} = \frac{28}{100} = 28\%$

Write each fraction as a percent.

5. $\frac{1}{10}$ 10% 6. $\frac{3}{5}$ 60% 7. $\frac{11}{20}$ 55% 8. $\frac{1}{50}$ 2%

To change a percent to a decimal:
- drop the % symbol;
- move the decimal point two places to the left.

54% = 54. = 0.54

Write each percent as a decimal.

9. 33% 0.33 10. 15% 0.15 11. 97% 0.97 12. 20% 0.2

To change a decimal to a percent:
- move the decimal point two places to the right;
- write the % symbol after the number.

0.09 = .09 = 9%

Write each decimal as a percent.

13. 0.06 6% 14. 0.25 25% 15. 0.49 49% 16. 0.15 15%

PRACTICE 6-1

LESSON 6-1 **Practice B**
Fractions, Decimals, and Percents

Write each percent as a fraction in simplest form.

1. 25% $\frac{1}{4}$ 2. 70% $\frac{7}{10}$ 3. 96% $\frac{24}{25}$ 4. 8% $\frac{2}{25}$

5. 55% $\frac{11}{20}$ 6. 48% $\frac{12}{25}$ 7. 150% $\frac{3}{2}$ 8. 83% $\frac{83}{100}$

Write each percent as a decimal.

9. 71% 0.71 10. 9% 0.09 11. 235% 2.35 12. 0.1% 0.001

13. 47.3% 0.473 14. 0.05% 0.0005 15. 11% 0.11 16. 107% 1.07

Write each decimal as a percent.

17. 0.87 87% 18. 0.125 12.5% 19. 0.04 4% 20. 0.005 0.5%

21. 1.09 109% 22. 0.22 22% 23. 0.3 30% 24. 8.7 870%

Write each fraction as a percent.

25. $\frac{3}{5}$ 60% 26. $\frac{9}{25}$ 36% 27. $\frac{7}{100}$ 7% 28. $\frac{3}{1,000}$ 0.3%

29. $\frac{7}{10}$ 70% 30. $\frac{1}{8}$ 12.5% 31. $\frac{21}{50}$ 42% 32. $\frac{11}{500}$ 2.2%

Social Studies LINK

The table shows the results of a survey to determine the number of people who walk to work in five U.S. cities. Use the table for Exercises 53–55. **53.** $\frac{3}{50}$**; 0.06, 6%**

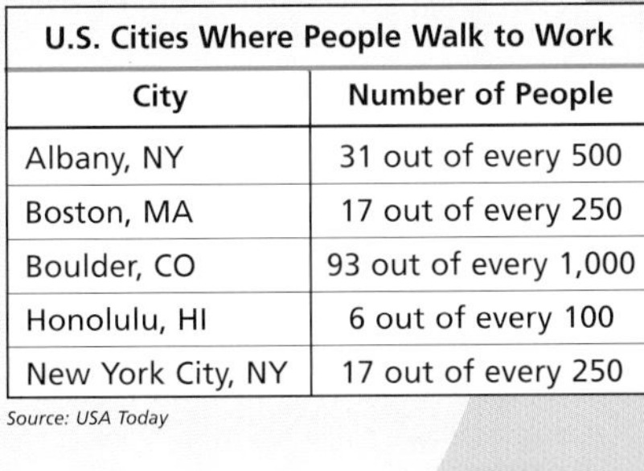

U.S. Cities Where People Walk to Work

City	Number of People
Albany, NY	31 out of every 500
Boston, MA	17 out of every 250
Boulder, CO	93 out of every 1,000
Honolulu, HI	6 out of every 100
New York City, NY	17 out of every 250

Source: USA Today

53. What fraction of people walk to work in Honolulu? Write the fraction as a decimal and as a percent.

54. What percent of people walk to work in Boulder? **9.3%**

55. Compare the percent of people who walk to work in New York City with the percent of people who walk to work in Albany. **6.8% > 6.2%**

56. In a survey, 35% of downtown workers in Ann Arbor, Michigan, reported that they had walked to work at least once in the past 5 years. Write this percent as a fraction in simplest form and as a decimal. $\frac{7}{20}$**, 0.35**

57. ***CHALLENGE*** According to the 1990 U.S. Census, $\frac{530,857}{814,548}$ of people in Los Angeles drove alone to work each day and $\frac{17,881}{116,364}$ carpooled. What is the total percent of people in Los Angeles who used a car to get to work? Round your answer to the nearest tenth of a percent. **80.5%**

Spiral Review

Find each value. (Lesson 2-1)

58. 5^3 **125** **59.** 12^2 **144** **60.** 30^2 **900** **61.** 8^3 **512**

62. TEST PREP A cookie recipe calls for $\frac{3}{4}$ cup brown sugar for 1 batch of cookies. If Jamie wants to make 3 batches of cookies, how much brown sugar does she need? (Lesson 4-7) **C**

A 1 cup **B** $1\frac{1}{2}$ cups **C** $2\frac{1}{4}$ cups **D** $3\frac{1}{4}$ cups

63. TEST PREP What is the solution to the proportion $\frac{2}{3} = \frac{6}{a}$? (Lesson 5-3) **H**

F 4 **G** 1 **H** 9 **J** 1.5

CHALLENGE 6-1

LESSON 6-1 **Challenge**
Climbing a Percent Pyramid

Begin by changing each ratio in the pyramid to a percent. Then climb to the top by comparing the percents as you go.

The percents must increase as you climb to the top. Each brick on your path must touch the previous brick. Circle the ratios in the path that leads to the top.

Possible path shown.

PROBLEM SOLVING 6-1

LESSON 6-1 **Problem Solving**
Fractions, Decimals, and Percents

Write the correct answer.

1. About 48 out of every 100 people in the United States owned a cell phone in 2001. In Italy, the rate was 864 for every 1,000 people. How many more people in Italy owned cell phones? Write your answer as a percent.

38.4% more people

2. In a survey, 46% of men said that they spend fewer than 5 hours shopping for gifts for holidays. Write this percent as a fraction in simplest form and as a decimal.

$\frac{23}{50}$**; 0.46**

3. When asked about their favorite Thanksgiving leftover, $\frac{1}{20}$ of the people said vegetables and $\frac{7}{100}$ said mashed potatoes. Which food was more popular and by what percent?

mashed potatoes, 2%

4. A group aged 18–29 was asked if they have enough time to do what they want, and 59% said they do not. How many people in this age group feel they *do* have enough time to do what they want? Write your answer as a percent, decimal, and fraction.

41%; 0.41; $\frac{41}{100}$

Choose the letter for the best answer.

The table shows the number of students in four schools who own computers.

Students Who Own Computers

School	Number of Students
Madison	90 out of 270
Hunter	56 out of 100
King	110 out of 150
Percy	125 out of 500

5. What percent of students at Percy owns computers?
   A 125% C 250%
   B 12.5% (D) 25%

6. In which school does about 73% of the students own computers?
   F Hunter H Percy
   G Madison (J) King

7. Express the number of students who own computers at Madison as a fraction.
   A $\frac{9}{10}$ (C) $\frac{1}{3}$
   B $\frac{9}{270}$ D $\frac{1}{27}$

8. Which school has the greatest percent of students who own computers?
   F Hunter H Percy
   G Madison (J) King

Interdisciplinary LINK

Social Studies

Exercises 53–57 involve using fractions, decimals, and percents to examine how people get to and from work each day.

Journal

Have students write a letter to a student who was absent that explains how to change fractions and decimals to percents.

Test Prep Doctor

For Exercise 62, encourage students to estimate the answer before looking at the answer choices. Students know that 3 batches will require about 3 cups of brown sugar, so they can eliminate **A** and **B.** Because students rounded up to estimate, the estimate will be high, so they can eliminate **D** as well.

For Exercise 63, students should realize that because the numerator of the second ratio is greater than the numerator of the first, the denominator of the second ratio will also be greater than the denominator of the first. So they can eliminate choices **G** and **J.** Because the denominator of the first ratio is greater than the numerator, the denominator of the second ratio will be greater than 6. So students can eliminate choice **F.**

Lesson Quiz

1. Write 40% as a fraction. $\frac{2}{5}$
2. Write 0.65 as a percent. **65%**
3. Write 72% as a decimal. **0.72**
4. Write $\frac{6}{10}$ as a percent. **60%**
5. About 95% of all animals are insects. Express this percent as a fraction. $\frac{19}{20}$

Available on Daily Transparency in CRB

6-2 Organizer

Pacing: Traditional 1 day
Block $\frac{1}{2}$ day

Objective: Students estimate percents.

Warm Up

Write each percent as a fraction and as a decimal.

1. 75% $\frac{3}{4}$, **0.75** **2.** 10% $\frac{1}{10}$, **0.1**

3. 32% $\frac{8}{25}$, **0.32** **4.** 17% $\frac{17}{100}$, **0.17**

Problem of the Day

You are biking to the library. When you are 75% of the way there, you realize you forgot a book. So you turn around and head back. When you are $\frac{1}{3}$ of the way back, you realize you don't need the book, so you turn around again and bike 3.2 miles to the library. How far do you live from the library? 6.4 miles

Available on Daily Transparency in CRB

A student asks a parent for some help finding an estimate for a percent problem. The parent replies, "Haven't they found that yet? They were looking for that when I was a kid!"

6-2 Estimate with Percents

Problem Solving Skill

Learn to estimate percents.

A hair dryer at Lester's Discount Haven costs \$14.99. Carissa's Corner is offering the same hair dryer at 20% off the regular price of \$19.99. To find out which store is offering the better deal on the hair dryer, you can use estimation.

The table shows common percents and their fraction equivalents. You can use fractions to estimate the percent of a number by choosing a fraction that is close to a given percent.

Percent	10%	20%	25%	$33\frac{1}{3}$%	50%	$66\frac{2}{3}$%
Fraction	$\frac{1}{10}$	$\frac{1}{5}$	$\frac{1}{4}$	$\frac{1}{3}$	$\frac{1}{2}$	$\frac{2}{3}$

EXAMPLE  1 **Using Fractions to Estimate Percents**

Use a fraction to estimate 48% of 79.

$48\% \text{ of } 79 \approx \frac{1}{2} \cdot 79$ *Think: 48% is about 50% and 50% is equivalent to $\frac{1}{2}$.*

$\approx \frac{1}{2} \cdot 80$ *Change 79 to a compatible number.*

≈ 40 *Multiply.*

48% of 79 is about 40.

Remember!
Compatible numbers are close to the numbers in the problem and are used to do math mentally.

EXAMPLE  2 ***Consumer Math Application***

Carissa's Corner is offering 20% off a hair dryer that costs \$19.99. If the same hair dryer costs \$14.99 at Lester's Discount Haven, which store offers the better deal?

First find the discount on the hair dryer at Carissa's Corner.

$20\% \text{ of } \$19.99 = \frac{1}{5} \cdot \$19.99$ *Think: 20% is equivalent to $\frac{1}{5}$.*

$\approx \frac{1}{5} \cdot \$20$ *Change \$19.99 to a compatible number.*

$\approx \$4$ *Multiply.*

The discount is approximately \$4. Since \$20 − \$4 = \$16, the \$14.99 hair dryer at Lester's Discount Haven is the better deal.

1 Introduce

Alternate Opener

EXPLORATION

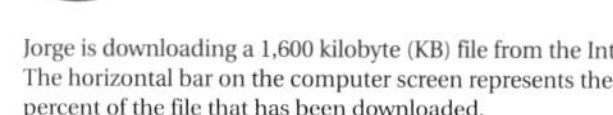

6-2 Estimate with Percents

Jorge is downloading a 1,600 kilobyte (KB) file from the Internet. The horizontal bar on the computer screen represents the percent of the file that has been downloaded.

The bar shows that approximately 50% of the file has been downloaded. This is about half of the 1,600 KB file, or 800 KB.

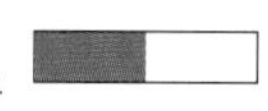

For each problem, look at the horizontal bar to estimate the answer. Then use a calculator to compute the actual answer.

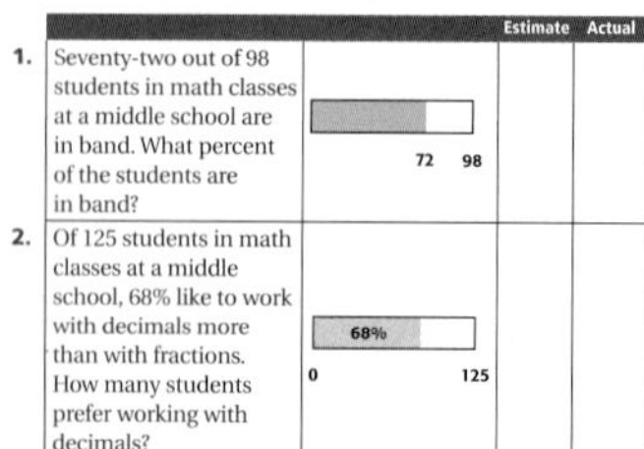

			Estimate	Actual
1.	Seventy-two out of 98 students in math classes at a middle school are in band. What percent of the students are in band?	72 98		
2.	Of 125 students in math classes at a middle school, 68% like to work with decimals more than with fractions. How many students prefer working with decimals?	68% 0 125		

Think and Discuss

3. Discuss the estimation strategies you used.

Motivate

To introduce estimating with percents, show the number line labeled with percents.

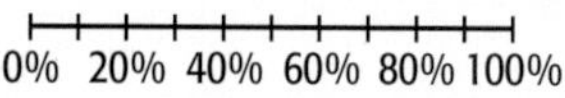

Discuss with students how to place some common fractions, such as $\frac{1}{2}$, $\frac{2}{5}$, and $\frac{3}{4}$, on the number line. Decide which percents are equivalent to the fractions and why. $\frac{1}{2} = 50\%$, $\frac{2}{5} = 40\%$, $\frac{3}{4} = 75\%$

Exploration worksheet and answers on Chapter 6 Resource Book pp. 16 and 72

2 Teach

Lesson Presentation

Guided Instruction

In this lesson, students learn to estimate percents. Compare the two methods of estimating developed in this lesson. Remind students that when they estimate, one goal is to make the computation easy to do mentally. Point out that in each problem-solving situation, students should choose the method they find easier to use.

Discuss how to decide which method of estimating works better for different percents. Give students sample percents, and ask them to describe how they would estimate that percent of a number.

Another way to estimate percents is to find 1% or 10% of a number. You can do this by moving the decimal point in the number.

1% of 45 = .45. 10% of 45 = 4.5.

To find 1% of a number, move the decimal point two places to the left.

To find 10% of a number, move the decimal point one place to the left.

EXAMPLE 3 Estimating with Simple Percents

Use 1% or 10% to estimate the percent of each number.

A 3% of 59

59 is about 60, so find 3% of 60.

1% of 60 = .60.

3% of 60 = 3 · 0.60 = 1.8 *3% equals 3 · 1%.*

3% of 59 is about 1.8.

B 18% of 45

18% is about 20%, so find 20% of 45.

10% of 45 = 4.5.

20% of 45 = 2 · 4.5 = 9.0 *20% equals 2 · 10%.*

18% of 45 is about 9.

EXAMPLE 4 *Consumer Math Application*

Eric and Selena spent $25.85 for their meals at a restaurant. About how much money should they leave for a 15% tip?

Since $25.85 is about $26, find 15% of $26.

15% = 10% + 5% *Think: 15% is 10% plus 5%.*

10% of $26 = $2.60

5% of $26 = $2.60 ÷ 2 = $1.30 *5% is $\frac{1}{2}$ of 10%, so divide $2.60 by 2.*

$2.60 + $1.30 = $3.90 *Add the 10% and 5% estimates.*

Eric and Selena should leave about $3.90 for a 15% tip.

Think and Discuss

1. **Describe** two ways to estimate 51% of 88.
2. **Explain** why you might divide by 7 or multiply by $\frac{1}{7}$ to estimate a 15% tip.
3. **Give an example** of a situation in which an estimate of a percent is sufficient. Then give an example of a situation in which an exact percent is necessary.

COMMON ERROR ALERT

Some students might try to estimate with numbers that are not compatible and end up with a problem that is as difficult to solve as the original problem. Encourage students to mentally review the multiplication and division facts and choose compatible numbers when estimating with percents.

Additional Examples

Example 1

Use a fraction to estimate 27% of 63. approximately 15

Example 2

Carey earns $9.88 per hour. He gets a bonus of 50% for each hour he works overtime. About how much is he paid per hour for overtime? about $15

Example 3

Use 1% or 10% to estimate the percent of each number.

A. 4% of 18 about 0.8

B. 29% of 80 about 24

Example 4

Tim spent $58 on dinner for his family. About how much should he leave for a 15% tip? about $9

Example 3 note: After you discuss Example 3, go back to Example 2 and have students solve it by finding 10% of $20 and multiplying that number by 2 to find the price at Carissa's Corner. Ask students to compare the two methods.

3 Close

Reaching All Learners

Through Number Sense

Have students work in small groups. Give all the groups the series of problems found on the recording sheet on Chapter 6 Resource Book p. 67. First, have the small groups discuss the best way to find an estimate, and then have them estimate an answer. Then have groups share and discuss their results.

Summarize

Place students with partners or in small groups, and then have them describe two ways to estimate with percents and tell when each is more appropriate to use.

Possible answer: You can estimate a percent by using a fraction that is close to the percent or by finding 1% or 10% and then multiplying the result by an integer. Using a fraction is appropriate when the percent is close to a fraction. Finding 1% or 10% works best with smaller percents such as 3% or when the percent is close to a multiple of 10.

Answers to Think and Discuss

Possible answers:

1. Find $\frac{1}{2}$ of 88, or find 10% of 88 and multiply by 5.
2. 15% is close to $\frac{1}{7}$ because $\frac{15}{100} = \frac{3}{20}$ is close to $\frac{1}{7}$ and because 100 ÷ 15 is about 7.
3. when you want to estimate the item's sale price or the sales tax on an item; when a store needs to collect sales tax on an item

6-2 PRACTICE & ASSESS

Students may want to refer back to the lesson examples.

Assignment Guide

If you finished Example 1 assign:
Core 1–4, 11–18, 29, 30, 33, 34, 46–51
Enriched 1–4, 11–18, 29, 30, 33, 34, 46–51

If you finished Example 2 assign:
Core 1–5, 11–19, 29, 34, 46–51
Enriched 1–5 odd, 11–19 odd, 29, 30, 33, 34, 46–51

If you finished Example 3 assign:
Core 1–9, 11–27, 29–35, 46–51
Enriched 1–27 odd, 29–36, 37, 39–41, 46–51

If you finished Example 4 assign:
Core 1–28, 29–41 odd, 46–51
Enriched 1–27 odd, 28–51

Notes

6-2 Exercises

FOR EXTRA PRACTICE see page 666

internet connect
Homework Help Online
go.hrw.com Keyword: MS4 6-2

GUIDED PRACTICE

See Example 1 — Use a fraction to estimate the percent of each number. **Possible answers:**

1. 30% of 86 **30** 2. 52% of 83 **40** 3. 10% of 48 **5** 4. 27% of 63 **15**

See Example 2

5. Darden has $35 to spend on a backpack. He finds one on sale for 35% off the regular price of $43.99. Does Darden have enough money to buy the backpack? Explain. **Yes; 35% of $43.99 is close to $\frac{1}{3}$ of $45, which is $15. Since $45 − $15 = $30, Darden will have enough money.**

See Example 3 — Use 1% or 10% to estimate the percent of each number. **Possible answers:**

6. 5% of 82 **4** 7. 39% of 19 **8** 8. 21% of 68 **14** 9. 7% of 109 **7.7**

See Example 4

10. Mrs. Coronado spent $23 on a manicure. About how much money should she leave for a 15% tip? **Possible answer: $3.45**

INDEPENDENT PRACTICE

See Example 1 — Use a fraction to estimate the percent of each number. **Possible answers:**

11. 8% of 261 **26** 12. 34% of 93 **31** 13. 53% of 142 **70** 14. 23% of 98 **25**

15. 51% of 432 **216** 16. 18% of 42 **8** 17. 11% of 132 **13** 18. 54% of 39 **20**

See Example 2

19. A pair of shoes at The Value Store costs $20. Betty's Boutique has the same shoes on sale for 25% off the regular price of $23.99. Which store offers the better price on the shoes? **Betty's Boutique**

See Example 3 — Use 1% or 10% to estimate the percent of each number. **Possible answers:**

20. 41% of 16 **6.4** 21. 8% of 310 **24** 22. 83% of 70 **56** 23. 2% of 634 **12**

24. 58% of 81 **48** 25. 24% of 49 **12** 26. 11% of 99 **10** 27. 63% of 39 **24**

See Example 4

28. Marc's lunch cost $8.92. He wants to leave a 15% tip for the service. About how much should his tip be? **Possible answer: $1.35**

PRACTICE AND PROBLEM SOLVING

Estimate. **Possible answers:**

29. 31% of 180 **60** 30. 18% of 150 **30** 31. 3% of 96 **3** 32. 2% of 198 **4**

33. 78% of 90 **72** 34. 52% of 234 **115** 35. 19% of 75 **15** 36. 4% of 311 **12**

37. The new package of Marti's Snacks contains 20% more snack mix than the old package. If there were 22 ounces of snack mix in the old package, about how many ounces are in the new package? **about 26 oz**

38. Frameworks charges $60.85 for framing. Including the 7% sales tax, about how much will it cost to have a painting framed? **$64.20**

Math Background

Estimating with percents requires the same skills as estimating with other kinds of numbers. Students can use rounding to make the computation easier. For example, when finding 3% of 59, rounding 59 to 60 makes multiplying by 1% and then by 3 simpler.

However, when estimating using fractions, students should use compatible numbers. For example, when estimating 48% of 79, they should first choose $\frac{1}{2}$ as the fraction closest to 48%. Then they should use 80, which is divisible by 2. Above all, students should choose numbers that make it possible to do the estimation mentally.

RETEACH 6-2

LESSON 6-2 **Reteach**
Estimate with Percents

To estimate the percent of a number, choose a fraction that is close to the given percent.

Percent	5%	10%	20%	25%	$33\frac{1}{3}$	40%	50%	60%	75%	80%
Fraction	$\frac{1}{20}$	$\frac{1}{10}$	$\frac{1}{5}$	$\frac{1}{4}$	$\frac{1}{3}$	$\frac{2}{5}$	$\frac{1}{2}$	$\frac{3}{5}$	$\frac{3}{4}$	$\frac{4}{5}$

Estimate 27% of 123.
27% is about 25%, which is equivalent to $\frac{1}{4}$.
123 rounded to the nearest ten is 120.
$\frac{1}{4} \cdot 120 = 30$
So, 27% of 123 is about 30.

Use a fraction to estimate the percent of each number. Possible answers:

1. 17% of 49
17% is about **20%**, which is **$\frac{1}{5}$**.
49 rounded to the nearest ten is **50**.
$\frac{1}{5}$ • **50** = **10**
So, 17% of 49 is about **10**.

2. 58% of 298
58% is about **60%**, which is **$\frac{3}{5}$**.
298 rounded to the nearest ten is **300**.
$\frac{3}{5}$ • **300** = **180**
So, 58% of 298 is about **180**.

3. 4% of 42
4% is about **5%**, which is **$\frac{1}{20}$**.
42 rounded to the nearest ten is **40**.
$\frac{1}{20}$ • **40** = **2**
So, 4% of 42 is about **2**.

4. 46% of 533
46% is about **50%**, which is **$\frac{1}{2}$**.
533 rounded to the nearest ten is **530**.
$\frac{1}{2}$ • **530** = **265**
So, 46% of 533 is about **265**.

5. 11% of 88 **9** 6. 74% of 203 **150** 7. 21% of 346 **70** 8. 79% of 55 **48**

PRACTICE 6-2

LESSON 6-2 **Practice B**
Estimate with Percent

Use a fraction to estimate the percent of each number. Answers will vary. Possible answers are given.

1. 21% of 82 **16** 2. 35% of 42 **14** 3. 47% of 164 **82** 4. 9% of 68 **7**

5. 65% of 78 **50** 6. 11% of 92 **9** 7. 26% of 124 **30** 8. 89% of 51 **45**

9. 77% of 198 **150** 10. 5% of 75 **4** 11. 31% of 148 **45** 12. 53% of 539 **270**

13. In 2000, about $39 out of every $100 spent on advertising was spent on television advertising. The amount spent on radio advertising was about 34% as much as was spent on television advertising. How much of every $100 spent on advertising was spent on radio advertising? **about $13**

Use 1% or 10% to estimate the percent of each number. Answers may vary. Possible answers are given.

14. 32% of 46 **15** 15. 81% of 36 **32** 16. 15% of 44 **6** 17. 21% of 62 **12**

18. 3% of 72 **2** 19. 62% of 88 **54** 20. 12% of 48 **5** 21. 65% of 124 **84**

22. 18% of 147 **30** 23. 5% of 837 **42** 24. 37% of 213 **84** 25. 2% of 188 **4**

26. The Fresh Acres Swim Club has a $35,000 budget for pool maintenance this year. The club members have agreed to raise the budget by 4%. Estimate the pool maintenance budget for next year. **$36,400**

39. ***SPORTS*** Last season, Ali had a hit 19.3% of the times he came to bat. If Ali batted 82 times last season, about how many hits did he have? **about 16 hits**

40. ***BUSINESS*** The table shows the results of a survey about the Internet. The number of people interviewed was 391.

Information People Are Willing to Give Out on the Internet

Information	Percent of People
E-mail address	78
Work phone number	53
Street address	49
Home phone number	35
Credit card number	33
Social Security number	11

Source: USA Today

a. Estimate the number of people willing to give out their e-mail address.

40a. Possible answer: 300 people

b. Estimate the number of people not willing to give out their credit card number. **Possible answer: 260 people**

41. ***SPORTS*** In a survey of 1,032 people, 58% said they got their information about the 2000 Summer Olympics by watching television. Estimate the number of people who got their information by watching television. **Possible answer: 600 people**

42. Sandi earns $43,000 per year. This year, she plans to spend about 27% of her income on rent. **Possible answer:**

a. About how much does Sandi plan to spend on rent this year? **$10,000**

b. About how much does she plan to spend on rent each month? **$1,000**

43. ***WRITE A PROBLEM*** Use information from the table in Exercise 40 to write a problem that can be solved by using estimation of a percent.

44. ***WRITE ABOUT IT*** Explain why it might be important to know whether your estimate of a percent is too high or too low. Give an example.

45. ***CHALLENGE*** Use the table from Exercise 40 to estimate how many more people will give out their work phone number than their Social Security number. Show your work using two different methods.
Possible answer: Estimate each percent and subtract, or subtract percents and then estimate the difference times 400; about 160 people.

Spiral Review

Find each product. (Lesson 4-3)

46. 0.8 · 96 **76.8** 47. 30 · 0.04 **1.2** 48. 1.6 · 900 **1,440** 49. 0.005 · 75 **0.375**

50. **TEST PREP** Brandi spent $15 on a new CD. If this was $\frac{1}{3}$ of her monthly allowance, how much is Brandi's allowance? (Lesson 4-12) **D**

A $5 **B** $30 **C** $35 **D** $45

51. **TEST PREP** What is the decimal equivalent of 4%? (Lesson 6-1) **H**

F 4 **G** 0.4 **H** 0.04 **J** 0.004

Answers

43. Possible answer: If 3,000 people are surveyed, about how many people are willing to give out their street address?

44. Possible answer: If you are checking to see if you have enough money to buy an item, it is important to know if your estimate is too high or too low.

Journal

Have students describe an advertisement they may have heard or seen that involves percent. Have them write about how they could use estimation in relation to the advertisement.

Test Prep Doctor

For Exercise 50, students should recognize that because $15 is a part of the allowance, the answer will be greater than $15. So they can eliminate choice **A.** Remembering that dividing by $\frac{1}{3}$ is the same as multiplying by 3 should lead students to choice **D.**

For Exercise 51, if students recall that the decimal equivalents of percents less than 100% are less than 1, they can eliminate choice **F.** Working backward by writing each of the other numbers as a percent should lead to choice **H.**

CHALLENGE 6-2

LESSON 6-2 **Challenge**
The Octagon Garden

Estimate each percent. Find your way through the octagon garden by moving to the neighboring octagon with the next greater value. Keep going until you find your way out.

Estimates may vary.

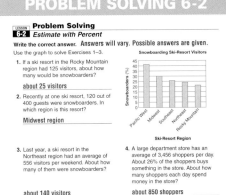

PROBLEM SOLVING 6-2

LESSON 6-2 **Problem Solving**
Estimate with Percent

Write the correct answer. **Answers will vary. Possible answers are given.**

Use the graph to solve Exercises 1–3.

Snowboarding Ski-Resort Visitors

Snowboarders (%)
45
40
35
30
25
20
15
10
5
0
Pacific West
Midwest
Southeast
Northeast
Rocky Mountain
Ski-Resort Region

1. If a ski resort in the Rocky Mountain region had 125 visitors, about how many would be snowboarders?

about 25 visitors

2. Recently at one ski resort, 120 out of 400 guests were snowboarders. In which region is this resort?

Midwest region

3. Last year, a ski resort in the Northeast region had an average of 556 visitors per weekend. About how many of them were snowboarders?

about 140 visitors

4. A large department store has an average of 3,456 shoppers per day. About 26% of the shoppers buys something in the store. About how many shoppers each day spend money in the store?

about 850 shoppers

Choose the letter for the best answer.

5. LaToya bought a new car for $29,000. She is entitled to an 11% rebate. About how much will the car cost after the rebate?

A $3,000 C $22,000
B $10,000 **(D)** $26,000

6. The cost of a video game is $29.95. Sales tax is 6%. About how much will the video game cost, including tax?

F about $29 **(H)** about $32
G about $30 J about $35

7. Toshi made 4.9% of his 3-point shots in basketball last season. He attempted 40 3-point shots. About how many points did he score from his 3-point shots?

A 2 points
(B) 6 points
C 9 points
D 12 points

8. In 1999, there were 1.8 million tons of electronic waste. Video equipment, such as TVs, VCRs, and camcorders, made up about 41% of the waste. About how many million tons of video equipment was this?

F about 0.18 million tons
G about 0.41 million tons
(H) about 0.72 million tons
J about 1.4 million tons

Lesson Quiz

Use a fraction to estimate the percent of each number.

Possible answers:

1. 48% of 72 **36**
2. 26% of 80 **20**

Use 1% or 10% to estimate the percent of each number.

Possible answers:

3. 4% of 220 **8.8**
4. 19% of 75 **15**
5. Mr. and Mrs. Dargen spent $46.25 on a meal. About how much should they leave for a 15% tip? **$7**

Available on Daily Transparency in CRB

6-3 Organizer

Pacing: Traditional 1 day
Block $\frac{1}{2}$ day

Objective: Students find the percent of a number.

Warm Up

Multiply.

1. 0.05 × 20 **1** **2.** 0.32 × 15 **4.8**
3. 0.06 × 25 **1.5** **4.** 0.75 × 18 **13.5**
5. 0.34 × 76 **25.84**

Problem of the Day

In a group of 60 triangular and square tiles, 25% are red, and 75% are blue. The ratio of triangles to squares is 1:2. Seventy percent of the squares are blue. Find the number of each kind of tile (red or blue squares or triangles).
3 red triangles, 17 blue triangles, 12 red squares, 28 blue squares

Available on Daily Transparency in CRB

If a number is 100% of another number, both numbers are the same. If a number is 1,000% of another number, it is 10 times as great as the other number.

6-3 Percent of a Number

Learn to find the percent of a number.

The human body is made up mostly of water. In fact, about 67% of a person's total (100%) body weight is water. If Cameron weighs 90 pounds, about how much of his weight is water?

Recall that a percent is a part of 100. Since you want to know the part of Cameron's body that is water, you can set up and solve a proportion to find the answer.

$$\text{Part} \rightarrow \frac{67}{100} = \frac{n}{90} \leftarrow \text{Part}; \quad \text{Whole} \rightarrow 100, \ 90 \leftarrow \text{Whole}$$

EXAMPLE 1 Using Proportions to Find Percents of Numbers

Find the percent of each number.

A 67% of 90

$\frac{67}{100} = \frac{n}{90}$	*Write a proportion.*
$67 \cdot 90 = 100 \cdot n$	*Set the cross products equal.*
$6{,}030 = 100n$	*Multiply.*
$\frac{6{,}030}{100} = \frac{100n}{100}$	*Divide each side by 100 to isolate the variable.*
$60.3 = n$	

67% of 90 is 60.3.

Helpful Hint

When solving a problem with a percent greater than 100%, the *part* will be greater than the *whole*.

B 145% of 210

$\frac{145}{100} = \frac{n}{210}$	*Write a proportion.*
$145 \cdot 210 = 100 \cdot n$	*Set the cross products equal.*
$30{,}450 = 100n$	*Multiply.*
$\frac{30{,}450}{100} = \frac{100n}{100}$	*Divide each side by 100 to isolate the variable.*
$304.5 = n$	

145% of 210 is 304.5.

1 Introduce

Alternate Opener

EXPLORATION

6-3 Percent of a Number

A survey of 125 volunteers shows their key characteristics and interests. This information will be used to assign volunteers to different kinds of volunteer work.

0, 25, 50, 75, 100, 125
0%, 20%, 40%, 60%, 80%, 100%

Use the number line to estimate the number of volunteers represented by each percent below. Then use a calculator to compute the actual number.

		Estimate	Actual
1.	48% are female.		
2.	28% enjoy working outdoors.		
3.	84% have a car.		
4.	60% are parents.		
5.	24% are younger than 25 years of age.		
6.	56% are good at math.		
7.	76% are good at reading.		

Think and Discuss

8. Discuss the estimation strategies you used.
9. Explain why the percents in numbers 1–7 do not add up to 100%.

Motivate

To introduce students to percent of a number, read a number of statements from newspapers or magazines, such as the following:

- 40% of people prefer Brand X juice.
- 35% of the students attending Grant School ride the bus to school.

Ask students to talk about what these statements mean.

Exploration worksheet and answers on Chapter 6 Resource Book pp. 26 and 74

2 Teach

Lesson Presentation

Guided Instruction

In this lesson, students learn to find the percent of a number. When they are writing a proportion to solve a percent problem, it is important for them to compare the same quantities in each ratio. In the ratio $\frac{67}{100}$, the part is compared to the whole. So in the second ratio, the part that is not known, or n, must be compared to the whole weight, or 90 pounds.

Teaching Tip Build on the last lesson by asking students to estimate the answer to the question "What is 67% of 90?" A reasonable estimate would be $\frac{2}{3}$ of 90, or 60.

In addition to using proportions, you can find the percent of a number by using decimal equivalents.

EXAMPLE 2 **Using Decimal Equivalents to Find Percents of Numbers**

Find the percent of each number. Estimate to check whether your answer is reasonable.

> **Helpful Hint**
>
> When you are solving problems with percents, *of* usually means "times."

A 8% of 50

8% of 50 = 0.08 · 50	*Write the percent as a decimal.*
= 4	*Multiply.*

Estimate

10% of 50 = 5, so 8% of 50 is less than 5. Thus 4 is a reasonable answer.

B 0.5% of 36

0.5% of 36 = 0.005 · 36	*Write the percent as a decimal.*
= 0.18	*Multiply.*

Estimate

1% of 36 = 0.36, so 0.5% of 36 is half of 0.36. Thus 0.18 is a reasonable answer.

EXAMPLE 3 ***Geography Application***

Earth's total land area is about 57,308,738 mi^2. The land area of Asia is about 30% of this total. What is the approximate land area of Asia to the nearest square mile?

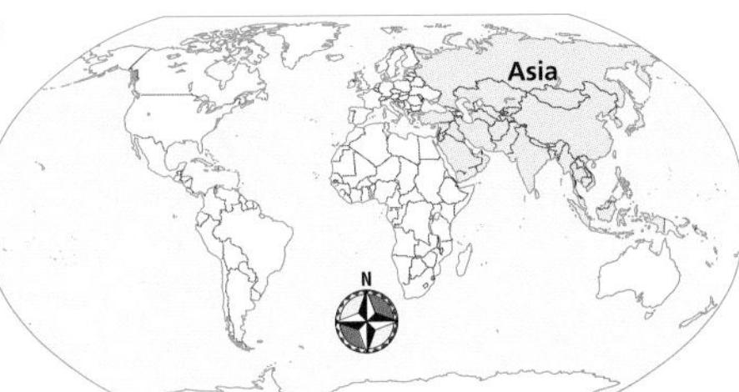

Find 30% of 57,308,738.

0.30 · 57,308,738	*Write the percent as a decimal.*
17,192,621.4	*Multiply.*

The land area of Asia is about 17,192,621 mi^2.

Think and Discuss

1. **Explain** how to set up a proportion to find 150% of a number. Describe how this proportion differs from the one used to find 50% of a number.
2. **Name** a situation in which you might need to find a percent of a number.

COMMON ERROR ALERT

Some students make mistakes when the percent is greater than 100. Point out that if the percent given is greater than 100, the part will always be greater than the whole.

When students use a proportion to solve, remind them to be sure they are comparing the part to the whole in both ratios.

Additional Examples

Example 1

Find the percent of each number.

A. 30% of 50 **15**

B. 200% of 24 **48**

Example 2

Find the percent of each number. Estimate to check whether your answer is reasonable.

A. 9% of 80 7.2

B. 3% of 12 **0.36**

Example 3

The estimated world population in 2001 was 6,157 million. About 40% of the people were 19 or younger. What was the approximate number of people 19 or younger, to the nearest million? 2,463 million

3 Close

Reaching All Learners

Through Grouping Strategies

Have students work in small groups to create diagrams to illustrate the percent problems in Examples 1–3. A recording sheet is provided on Chapter 6 Resource Book p. 68. The following diagram illustrates Example 1A:

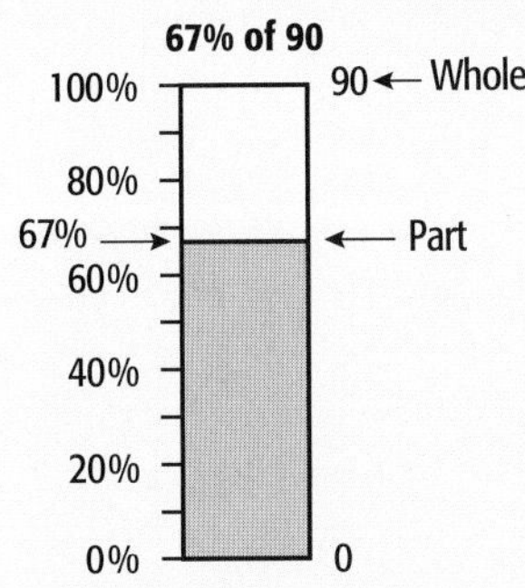

Summarize

Have students compare the two methods of finding a percent of a number: using a proportion and multiplying by a decimal.

Possible answers: To use a proportion, write two ratios comparing the part to the whole, and then solve the resulting proportion. To multiply by a decimal, write the decimal equivalent of the percent, and multiply it by the given whole.

Answers to Think and Discuss

Possible answers:

1. 150% means $\frac{150}{100}$, so use this ratio to set up the proportion. This proportion is different from the one used to find 50% of a number because, in this case, both numerators will be greater than the denominators.
2. finding the amount you save when something is on sale or finding the amount of sales tax on a purchase

6-3 PRACTICE & ASSESS

Students may want to refer back to the lesson examples.

Assignment Guide

If you finished Example 1 assign:
Core 1–4, 10–17, 27–33 odd, 51–58
Enriched 1, 3, 11–17 odd, 27–34, 51–58

If you finished Example 2 assign:
Core 1–8, 10–25, 27–41 odd, 51–58
Enriched 1–7, 11–25 odd, 27–42, 51–58

If you finished Example 3 assign:
Core 1–26, 27–47 odd, 51–58
Enriched 1–25 odd, 27–58

Answers

39. 0.61
40. 0.39
41. 4.21
42. 0.68

6-3 Exercises

FOR EXTRA PRACTICE
see page 666

internet connect
Homework Help Online
go.hrw.com Keyword: MS4 6-3

GUIDED PRACTICE

See Example 1 Find the percent of each number.

1. 30% of 80 **24**
2. 38% of 400 **152**
3. 200% of 10 **20**
4. 180% of 90 **162**

See Example 2 Find the percent of each number. Estimate to check whether your answer is reasonable.

5. 16% of 50 **8**
6. 7% of 200 **14**
7. 47% of 900 **423**
8. 40% of 75 **30**

See Example 3
9. Of the 450 students at Miller Middle School, 38% ride the bus to school. How many students ride the bus to school? **171 students**

INDEPENDENT PRACTICE

See Example 1 Find the percent of each number.

10. 80% of 35 **28**
11. 16% of 70 **11.2**
12. 150% of 80 **120**
13. 118% of 3,000 **3,540**
14. 5% of 58 **2.9**
15. 1% of 4 **0.04**
16. 103% of 50 **51.5**
17. 225% of 8 **18**

See Example 2 Find the percent of each number. Estimate to check whether your answer is reasonable.

18. 9% of 40 **3.6**
19. 20% of 65 **13**
20. 36% of 50 **18**
21. 2.9% of 60 **1.74**
22. 5% of 12 **0.6**
23. 220% of 18 **39.6**
24. 0.2% of 160 **0.32**
25. 155% of 8 **12.4**

See Example 3
26. In 1999, there were 4,652 Dalmatians registered by the American Kennel Club. Approximately 66% of this number were registered in 2000. About how many Dalmatians were registered in 2000? **3,070 Dalmatians**

PRACTICE AND PROBLEM SOLVING

Solve.

27. 60% of 10 is what number? **6**
28. What number is 25% of 160? **40**
29. What number is 15% of 30? **4.5**
30. 10% of 84 is what number? **8.4**
31. 25% of 47 is what number? **11.75**
32. What number is 59% of 20? **11.8**
33. What number is 125% of 4,100? **5,125**
34. 150% of 150 is what number? **225**

Find the percent of each number. If necessary, round to the nearest hundredth.

35. 160% of 50 **80**
36. 350% of 20 **70**
37. 480% of 25 **120**
38. 115% of 200 **230**
39. 18% of 3.4
40. 0.9% of 43
41. 98% of 4.3
42. 1.22% of 56

Math Background

There are three types of percent problems: 1) finding a percent of a number, 2) finding a number when a percent of it is known, and 3) finding the percent when the part and whole are known. This lesson develops the first type, finding a percent of a number.

Using a proportion is a standard method of solving each type of problem. The two ratios in the proportion are part to whole and n to 100, where n is the percent. Rewriting $\frac{n}{100}$ as n% and cross multiplying gives $n\% \cdot \text{whole} = \text{part}$, which is the percent equation. When using the percent equation, n% can be replaced by either its decimal or its fraction equivalent.

RETEACH 6-3

LESSON 6-3 **Reteach**
Percent of a Number

You can use this proportion to solve percent problems.

$$\frac{\text{part}}{\text{total}} = \frac{\text{percent}}{100}$$

Find 20% of 65.

20 is the **percent**, and 65 is the **total**. So, the **part** is unknown.

$\frac{x}{65} = \frac{20}{100}$

$100 \cdot x = 65 \cdot 20$ Find the cross products.

$100x = 1{,}300$

$\frac{100x}{100} = \frac{1{,}300}{100}$ Simplify.

$x = 13$

So, 20% of 65 is 13.

Find the percent of each number.

1. 40% of 90
   a. part = **x**
   b. total = **90**
   c. percent = **40**
   d. $\frac{x}{\mathbf{90}} = \frac{\mathbf{40}}{100}$
   e. $100x$ = **3,600**
   f. x = **36**

2. 85% of 520
   a. part = **x**
   b. total = **520**
   c. percent = **85**
   d. $\frac{x}{\mathbf{520}} = \frac{\mathbf{85}}{\mathbf{100}}$
   e. $100x$ = **44,200**
   f. x = **442**

3. 30% of 80 **24**
4. 47% of 300 **141**
5. 45% of 200 **90**
6. 120% of 70 **84**
7. 65% of 40 **26**
8. 25% of 76 **19**
9. 115% of 40 **46**
10. 275% of 12 **33**

PRACTICE 6-3

LESSON 6-3 **Practice B**
Percent of a Number

Find the percent of each number.

1. 25% of 56 **14**
2. 10% of 110 **11**
3. 5% of 150 **7.5**
4. 90% of 180 **162**
5. 125% of 48 **60**
6. 225% of 88 **198**
7. 2% of 350 **7**
8. 285% of 200 **570**
9. 150% of 125 **187.5**
10. 46% of 235 **108.1**
11. 78% of 410 **319.8**
12. 0.5% of 64 **0.32**

Find the percent of each number. Estimate to check whether your answer is reasonable.

13. 55% of 900 **495**
14. 140% of 50 **70**
15. 75% of 128 **96**
16. 3% of 600 **18**
17. 16% of 85 **13.6**
18. 22% of 105 **23.1**
19. 0.7% of 110 **0.77**
20. 95% of 500 **475**
21. 3% of 750 **22.5**
22. 162% of 250 **405**
23. 18% of 90 **16.2**
24. 23.2% of 125 **29**
25. 0.1% of 950 **0.95**
26. 11% of 300 **33**
27. 52% of 410 **213.2**
28. 250% of 12 **30**

29. The largest frog in the world is the goliath, found in West Africa. This type of frog can grow to be 12 inches long. The smallest frog in the world is about 4% as long as the goliath. What is the approximate length of the smallest frog in the world?

about 0.5 inch

Physical Science LINK

The mineral turquoise is often used as an ornamental stone in jewelry. Its color varies from greenish blue to sky-blue shades and can change from exposure to skin oils.

43. ***NUTRITION*** The United States Department of Agriculture recommends that women should eat 25 g of fiber each day. If a granola bar provides 9% of that amount, how many grams of fiber does it contain? **2.25 grams**

44. ***PHYSICAL SCIENCE*** The percent of pure gold in 14-karat gold is about 58.3%. If a 14-karat gold ring weighs 5.6 grams, about how many grams of pure gold are in the ring? **3.26 grams**

45. ***EARTH SCIENCE*** The apparent magnitude of the star Mimosa is 1.25. If Spica, another star, has an apparent magnitude that is 78.4% of Mimosa's, what is Spica's apparent magnitude? **0.98**

46. ***CONSUMER MATH*** Trahn purchased a pair of slacks for $39.95 and a jacket for $64.00. The sales tax rate on his purchases was 5.5%. **$5.72**
    a. Find the amount of sales tax Trahn paid, to the nearest cent. **$109.67**
    b. Find the total cost of the purchases, including sales tax.

47. The graph shows the results of a student survey about computers. Use the graph to predict how many students in your class have a computer at home.

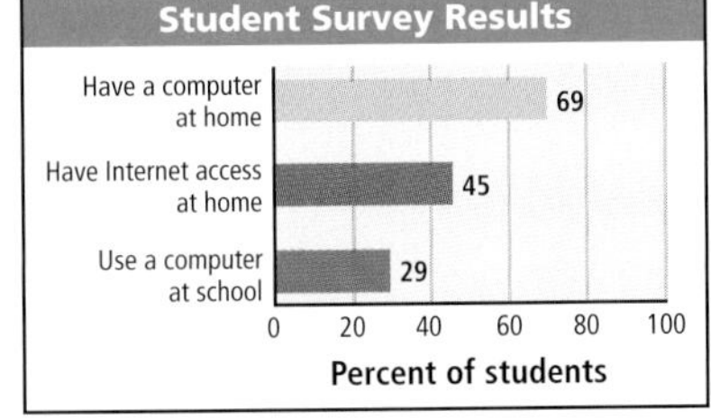

48. ***WHAT'S THE ERROR?*** A student used the proportion $\frac{n}{100} = \frac{5}{26}$ to find 5% of 26. What did the student do wrong?

49. ***WRITE ABOUT IT*** Describe two ways to find 18% of 40.

50. ***CHALLENGE*** François's starting pay was $6.25 per hour. During his annual review, he received a 5% raise. Find François's pay raise to the nearest cent and the amount he will earn with his raise. Then find 105% of $6.25. What can you conclude? **0.31; $6.56; $6.56; 105% of $6.25 is the same as $6.25 + 5% of $6.25.**

Spiral Review

Solve each equation. (Lesson 4-6)

51. $0.4x = 16$ **$x = 40$**
52. $c \div 1.25 = 4$ **$c = 5$**
53. $2.2b = 2.42$ **$b = 1.1$**
54. $\frac{x}{2.5} = 20$ **$x = 50$**

Find the unit rates and write them in both fraction and word form. (Lesson 5-1)

55. Monica buys 3 greeting cards for $5.25.
56. Kevin types 295 words in 5 minutes.

57. **TEST PREP** The decimal 0.0125 is equivalent to which percent? (Lesson 6-1) **B**
    A 0.125% C 12.5%
    B 1.25% D 125%

58. **TEST PREP** Which is the closest estimate of 150% of 83? (Lesson 6-2) **H**
    F 40 H 120
    G 80 J 160

Answers

47. Possible answer: In a class of 30 students, 21 students have computers at home.
48. Possible answers: The student set up the proportion incorrectly. The student should have used $\frac{5}{100} = \frac{n}{26}$.
49. Possible answer: Either write a proportion and solve, or write 18% as a decimal and multiply it by 40.
55. $\frac{\$1.75}{1 \text{ card}}$; $1.75 per card
56. $\frac{59 \text{ words}}{1 \text{ min}}$; 59 words per minute

Journal

Have students record which method they prefer for solving percent problems, using a proportion or using the decimal equivalent of the percent, and why.

Test Prep Doctor

For Exercise 57, students can eliminate **D** if they recall that a percent greater than 100% is associated with a decimal greater than 1. By observing that 0.0125 is close to 0.01, which is one-hundredth, or 1%, students can eliminate choices **A** and **C.**

For Exercise 58, remind students that 150% of a number is greater than the number, so they can eliminate choices **F** and **G.** Because choice **J** is 160, which is almost 2 times 83, it is too great and can be eliminated as well.

CHALLENGE 6-3

LESSON 6-3 **Challenge**
Percent Puzzler

Use the percent clues to find each number below.

1. This number is 8 more than $83\frac{1}{2}$% of 20. **24.7**
2. This number is 5 less than 28% of 292. **76.76**
3. This number is equal to the sum of 4% of 75 and $32\frac{1}{2}$% of 64. **23.8**
4. This number is 7.82 more than $15\frac{3}{4}$% of 320. **58.22**
5. This number is equal to the sum of 52% of 86 and 35% of 52. **62.92**
6. This number is equal to the product of 8% of 75 and 12% of 60. **43.2**
7. This number is equal to the sum of 5% of 125 and $55\frac{1}{2}$% of 20. **17.35**
8. This number is equal to the product of 24% of 225 and $3\frac{1}{5}$% of 45. **77.76**
9. This number is equal to the sum of $9\frac{3}{10}$% of 110 and $38\frac{1}{4}$% of 124. **57.66**
10. This number is 23.04 less than $14\frac{1}{2}$% of 768. **88.32**
11. This number is 50.21 more than the sum of $15\frac{1}{2}$% of 42 and 64% of 112. **128.4**
12. This number is equal to the difference of 150% of 85 and 280% of 0.3. **126.66**
13. This number is equal to the square of $7\frac{1}{2}$% of 160. **144**
14. This number is 6.8 less than the product of 5 and 8% of 517. **200**

PROBLEM SOLVING 6-3

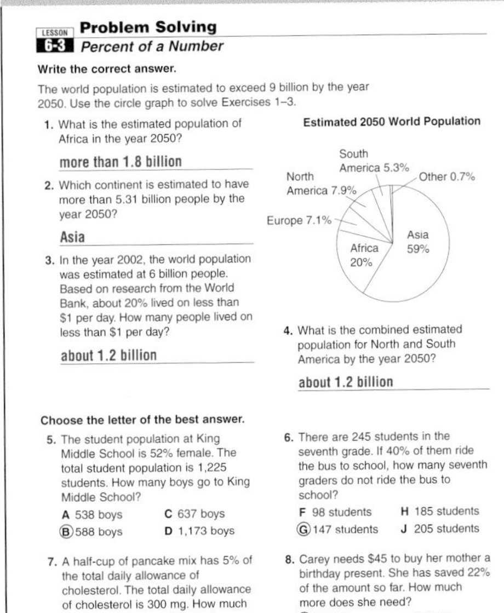

LESSON 6-3 **Problem Solving**
Percent of a Number

Write the correct answer.

The world population is estimated to exceed 9 billion by the year 2050. Use the circle graph to solve Exercises 1–3.

Estimated 2050 World Population

1. What is the estimated population of Africa in the year 2050?
   more than 1.8 billion
2. Which continent is estimated to have more than 5.31 billion people by the year 2050?
   Asia
3. In the year 2002, the world population was estimated at 6 billion people. Based on research from the World Bank, about 20% lived on less than $1 per day. How many people lived on less than $1 per day?
   about 1.2 billion
4. What is the combined estimated population for North and South America by the year 2050?
   about 1.2 billion

Choose the letter of the best answer.

5. The student population at King Middle School is 52% female. The total student population is 1,225 students. How many boys go to King Middle School?
   A 538 boys C 637 boys
   (B) 588 boys D 1,173 boys
6. There are 245 students in the seventh grade. If 40% of them ride the bus to school, how many seventh graders do not ride the bus to school?
   F 98 students H 185 students
   (G) 147 students J 205 students
7. A half-cup of pancake mix has 5% of the total daily allowance of cholesterol. The total daily allowance of cholesterol is 300 mg. How much cholesterol does a half-cup of pancake mix have?
   A 100 mg C 20 mg
   B 60 mg (D) 15 mg
8. Carey needs $45 to buy her mother a birthday present. She has saved 22% of the amount so far. How much more does she need?
   (F) $35.10 H $23.00
   G $44.01 J $9.90

Lesson Quiz

Find the percent of each number.

1. 25% of 8 **2**
2. 40% of 110 **44**
3. 150% of 96 **144**
4. 0.3% of 120 **0.36**
5. Whitmer Middle School has 850 students. If 42% of the students bought lunch on Monday, how many students bought lunch on Monday? **357**

Available on Daily Transparency in CRB

6-4 Organizer

Pacing: Traditional 1 day
Block $\frac{1}{2}$ day

Objective: Students solve one-step equations containing percents.

Warm Up

Solve.

1. $4x = 90$ $\quad x = 22.5$

2. $8x = 96$ $\quad x = 12$

3. $12x = 180$ $\quad x = 15$

4. $26x = 182$ $\quad x = 7$

Problem of the Day

Rearrange the digits in $\frac{2}{6} = \frac{1}{3}$. What fraction of the possible arrangements are true proportions? $\frac{1}{3}$

Available on Daily Transparency in CRB

Math Fact !

Sometimes the word *percentage* is used to mean "the part found by multiplying the percent by the whole". You could say that either a percent or a percentage of the students ride the bus, but it is not correct to say that 6 percentage of the students ride the bus.

6-4 Solving Equations Containing Percents

Learn to solve one-step equations containing percents.

Sloths may seem lazy, but their extremely slow movement helps to make them almost invisible to predators. Sloths sleep an average of 16.5 hours per day. To find out what percent of a 24-hour day 16.5 hours is, you can use a proportion or an equation.

Proportion method

Part → $\frac{n}{100} = \frac{16.5}{24}$ ← Part
Whole → ← Whole

$$n \cdot 24 = 100 \cdot 16.5$$
$$24n = 1{,}650$$
$$n = 68.75$$

Equation method

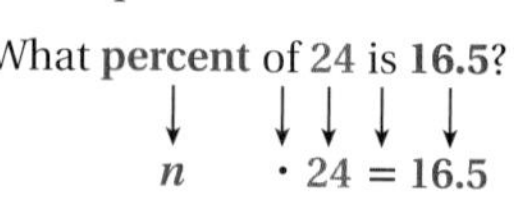

What **percent** of **24** is **16.5**?

$$n \cdot 24 = 16.5$$
$$n = 0.6875$$
$$n = 68.75\%$$

Sloths spend about **69%** of the day sleeping!

EXAMPLE 1 Using Proportions to Solve Problems with Percents

Solve.

A 45 is what percent of 90?

$\frac{n}{100} = \frac{45}{90}$ *Write a proportion.*

$n \cdot 90 = 100 \cdot 45$ *Set the cross products equal.*

$90n = 4{,}500$ *Multiply.*

$\frac{90n}{90} = \frac{4{,}500}{90}$ *Divide each side by 90 to isolate the variable.*

$n = 50$

45 is 50% of 90.

B 12 is 8% of what number?

$\frac{8}{100} = \frac{12}{n}$ *Write a proportion.*

$8 \cdot n = 100 \cdot 12$ *Set the cross products equal.*

$8n = 1{,}200$ *Multiply.*

$\frac{8n}{8} = \frac{1{,}200}{8}$ *Divide each side by 8 to isolate the variable.*

$n = 150$

12 is 8% of 150.

1 Introduce

Alternate Opener

EXPLORATION

6-4 Solving Equations Containing Percents

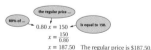

The sale price of a mountain bike is \$150.00. This is 80% of the regular price. What is the regular price?

80% of ... → $0.80x = 150$ ← is equal to 150.
(the regular price ... → x)

$$x = \frac{150}{0.80}$$
$x = 187.50$ The regular price is \$187.50.

Solve each equation.

		Sale Price	Regular Price	Equation
1.	An airline offers airfare at a 30% discount on weekdays. The discounted price of a ticket is \$125.00. What is the regular price?	\$125.00	x	$0.70x = 125$
2.	A computer is on sale for \$800.00. This is 90% of the regular price. What is the regular price?	\$800.00	x	$0.90x = 800$

Think and Discuss

3. Explain how you solved each equation.

4. Discuss what the equation would look like in a problem involving a markup instead of a discount.

Motivate

To introduce using an equation to solve different kinds of percent problems, write the percent proportion, $\frac{n}{100} = \frac{\text{part}}{\text{whole}}$, on the board. Then have students describe what they could find if they knew the percent and the part, the part and the whole, or the percent and the whole. (e.g., They could find the whole, the percent, and the part, respectively.)

You may want to remind students that they were able to derive an equation for finding the percent when they knew the part and the whole.

Exploration worksheet and answers on Chapter 6 Resource Book pp. 35 and 76

2 Teach

Lesson Presentation

Guided Instruction

In this lesson, students learn to solve one-step equations containing percents. As students discuss both the proportion method and the equation method of solving the example about sloths (Teaching Transparency T15, CRB), emphasize that the equation is related to the proportion. Point out that the 100 that is multiplied by 16.5 in the proportion method is also used in the last step of the equation method when 0.6785 is written as a percent.

Teaching Tip Discuss how to decide where in a percent proportion to write the numbers given in a proportion.

EXAMPLE 2 Using Equations to Solve Problems with Percents

Solve.

A 48 is 20% of what number?

$48 = 20\% \cdot n$ *Write an equation.*

$48 = 0.2 \cdot n$ *Write 20% as a decimal.*

$\frac{48}{0.2} = \frac{0.2 \cdot n}{0.2}$ *Divide each side by 0.2 to isolate the variable.*

$240 = n$

48 is 20% of 240.

B 105 is what percent of 75?

$105 = n \cdot 75$ *Write an equation.*

$\frac{105}{75} = \frac{n \cdot 75}{75}$ *Divide each side by 75 to isolate the variable.*

$1.4 = n$

$140\% = n$ *Write the decimal as a percent.*

105 is 140% of 75.

EXAMPLE 3 *Social Studies Application*

The table shows the average number of annual vacation days earned by workers with one year of service. What percent of the vacation days that workers in Finland earn do workers in Mexico earn?

Country	Vacation Days
Mexico	6
United States	10
Canada	10
Britain	20
Finland	30

Workers in Mexico earn 6 vacation days, and workers in Finland earn 30. Restate the question: What percent of 30 is 6?

$n \cdot 30 = 6$ *Write an equation.*

$\frac{n \cdot 30}{30} = \frac{6}{30}$ *Divide each side by 30 to isolate the variable.*

$n = 0.2$

$n = 20\%$ *Write the decimal as a percent.*

Workers in Mexico earn 20% of the number of vacation days that workers in Finland earn.

Think and Discuss

1. **Tell** what number is always used when you use a proportion to solve a percent problem. Explain.
2. **Write** and solve an equation to find the number that is 40% of 65.

COMMON ERROR ALERT

Remind students to identify what they are given in a problem and what they want to find before they begin working on it.

Additional Examples

Example 1

Solve.

A. 25 is what percent of 40? **62.5%**

B. 15 is 25% of what number? **60**

Example 2

Solve.

A. 35 is 28% of what number? **125**

B. 18 is what percent of 9? **200%**

Example 3

Workers in Canada earn 10 vacation days, and workers in Finland earn 30 vacation days. What percent of vacation days earned by workers in Canada do workers in Finland earn?

300%

Example 2 note: If students have difficulty using a percent equation, show them how using a proportion results in the same answer.

3 Close

Through Critical Thinking

Present the following problem to the class:

> In Mrs. Landau's math class, 18 students prefer to do their homework before dinner. In Mr. Toubassi's class, 20 students prefer to do their homework before dinner. Does that mean a higher percent of the students in Mr. Toubassi's class prefer to do homework before dinner? Explain your reasoning.

Not necessarily; percent is a ratio comparing two numbers, the part and the whole. The total number of students in each class must be given to compare the percentages.

Summarize

Have students write a general percent equation, percent · whole = part, and then describe how to solve it if they know the part and the whole or the percent and the part.

Possible answer: If the part and the whole are known, substitute the values and divide both sides by the whole. Write the resulting decimal as a percent. If the percent and the part are known, substitute the values and divide both sides by the percent written as a decimal.

Answers to Think and Discuss

Possible answers:

1. The number 100 is always used when you use a proportion to solve a percent problem because *percent* means "per 100".
2. $40\% \cdot 65 = p$; $0.40 \cdot 65 = 26$

6-4 PRACTICE & ASSESS

Students may want to refer back to the lesson examples.

Assignment Guide

If you finished Example 1 assign:
Core 1–4, 10–15, 24–27, 39–44
Enriched 1–4, 10–15, 24–27, 39–44

If you finished Example 2 assign:
Core 1–8, 10–21, 25–31 odd, 39–44
Enriched 1–7 odd, 11–21 odd, 24–31, 39–44

If you finished Example 3 assign:
Core 1–23, 25–35 odd, 39–44
Enriched 1–23 odd, 24–44

Notes

Math Background

The most frequently used way to solve any percent problem is to write a proportion. As in the last lesson, an equation can be derived from the proportion $\frac{n}{100} = \frac{\text{part}}{\text{whole}}$ when the ratio $\frac{n}{100}$ is written as $n\%$:

$$n\% = \frac{\text{part}}{\text{whole}}$$

$$n\% \cdot \text{whole} = \text{part}$$

Note that, when students are solving a proportion for n, the result will be the percent written without a percent sign, and students will simply add a percent sign to the answer. When students are solving a percent equation for n, the result will be a decimal that must be written as a percent by moving the decimal point two places to the right.

6-4 Exercises

FOR EXTRA PRACTICE see page 666

internet connect
Homework Help Online
go.hrw.com Keyword: MS4 6-4

GUIDED PRACTICE

See Example 1 **Solve.**

1. 25 is what percent of 100? **25%**
2. 8 is 20% of what number? **40**
3. 9 is what percent of 50? **18%**
4. 30 is 15% of what number? **200**

See Example 2

5. 6 is 10% of what number? **60**
6. 4 is what percent of 5? **80%**
7. 7 is 14% of what number? **50**
8. 27 is what percent of 30? **90%**

See Example 3

9. Each week, Sandler spends $10 of his allowance on school lunches. If his allowance is $25, what percent of his allowance does he spend on school lunches? **40%**

INDEPENDENT PRACTICE

See Example 1 **Solve.**

10. 56 is 140% of what number? **40**
11. 16 is what percent of 48? **$33\frac{1}{3}\%$**
12. 9 is what percent of 45? **20%**
13. 9 is 30% of what number? **30**
14. 210% of what number is 147? **70**
15. 12.4 is what percent of 12.4? **100%**

See Example 2

16. 40 is what percent of 60? **$66\frac{2}{3}\%$**
17. 45 is 20% of what number? **225**
18. 18 is 15% of what number? **120**
19. 18 is what percent of 6? **300%**
20. What percent of 80 is 10? **12.5%**
21. 8.8 is 40% of what number? **22**

See Example 3

22. On average, teens spend 4 hours a week using the Internet and 4 hours doing chores. They spend 10 hours listening to the radio. What percent of the total time teens spend using the Internet and doing chores is the time they spend listening to the radio? **125%**
23. Montrell saves 8% of each paycheck for his college fund. If Montrell saved $18.80 from his last paycheck, how much was he paid? **$235.00**

PRACTICE AND PROBLEM SOLVING

Solve. Round answers to the nearest tenth, if necessary.

24. 5 is what percent of 9? **55.6%**
25. What is 45% of 39? **17.6**
26. 55 is 80% of what number? **68.8**
27. 12 is what percent of 19? **63.2%**
28. What is 155% of 50? **77.5**
29. 5.8 is 0.9% of what number? **644.4**
30. 36% of what number is 57? **158.3**
31. What percent of 64 is 40? **62.5%**
32. Every night, Sean reads 12 pages of a 286-page novel. What percent of the book is this? Round to the nearest tenth of a percent. **4.2%**

RETEACH 6-4

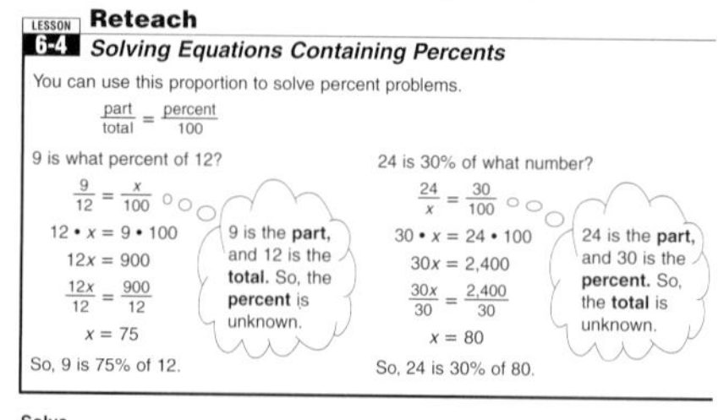

LESSON 6-4 **Reteach**
Solving Equations Containing Percents

You can use this proportion to solve percent problems.

$$\frac{\text{part}}{\text{total}} = \frac{\text{percent}}{100}$$

9 is what percent of 12?

$\frac{9}{12} = \frac{x}{100}$
$12 \cdot x = 9 \cdot 100$
$12x = 900$
$\frac{12x}{12} = \frac{900}{12}$
$x = 75$

9 is the **part,** and 12 is the **total.** So, the **percent** is unknown.

So, 9 is 75% of 12.

24 is 30% of what number?

$\frac{24}{x} = \frac{30}{100}$
$30 \cdot x = 24 \cdot 100$
$30x = 2{,}400$
$\frac{30x}{30} = \frac{2{,}400}{30}$
$x = 80$

24 is the **part,** and 30 is the **percent.** So, the **total** is unknown.

So, 24 is 30% of 80.

Solve.

1. What percent of 25 is 14?
   a. part = 14
   b. total = 25
   c. percent = x
   d. $\frac{14}{25} = \frac{x}{100}$
   e. 25 x = 1,400
   f. x = 56
   g. 14 is 56% of 25.
2. 80% of what number is 16?
   a. part = 16
   b. total = x
   c. percent = 80
   d. $\frac{16}{x} = \frac{80}{100}$
   e. 80 x = 1,600
   f. x = 20
   g. 16 is 80% of 20.
3. What percent of 20 is 11? 55%
4. 18 is 45% of what number? 40
5. 15 is what percent of 5? 300%
6. 75% of what number is 105? 140

PRACTICE 6-4

LESSON 6-4 **Practice B**
Solving Equations Containing Percents

Solve. Round answers to the nearest tenth, if necessary.

1. 50 is 40% of what number? 125
2. 12 is 25% of what number? 48
3. 18 is what percent of 60? 30%
4. 12 is what percent of 96? 12.5%
5. 4% of what number is 25? 625
6. 80% of what number is 160? 200
7. What percent of 55 is 22? 40%
8. What percent of 75 is 6? 8%
9. 15 is 30% of what number? 50
10. 8% of what number is 2? 25
11. 7 is what percent of 105? 6.7%
12. 24 is 40% of what number? 60
13. 10% of what number is 14? 140
14. 16 is what percent of 200? 8%
15. What percent of 32 is 4? 12.5%
16. What percent of 150 is 60? 40%
17. 1% of what number is 11? 1,100
18. 20% of what number is 14? 70
19. Kylie works part-time at a greenhouse. She spends 7 hours a week watering plants and 9 hours a week transplanting seedlings. She also spends 4 hours a week filing invoices. What percent of her time is spent watering plants? 35%
20. The Perez family saves 3% of their monthly income for their summer vacation. This past year, they saved $774 for their vacation. What is their monthly income? $2,150

The viola family is made up of the cello, violin, and viola. Of the three instruments, the cello is the largest. Originally, the cello was named *violoncello*, which means little big viola.

33. ***MUSIC*** Beethoven wrote 9 trios for the piano, violin, and cello. If 20% of the chamber music pieces Beethoven wrote are trios, how many pieces of chamber music did he write? **45 pieces**

34. ***HEALTH*** The circle graph shows the approximate distribution of blood types among people in the United States.

U.S. Blood Type Distribution

O 45%, AB 4%, B 11%, A 40%

a. In a survey, 126 people had type O blood. Predict how many people were surveyed. **280 people**

b. How many of the people surveyed had type AB blood? **about 11 people**

35. ***HISTORY*** The length of Abraham Lincoln's first inaugural speech was 3,635 words. The length of his second inaugural speech was about 19.3% of the length of his first speech. About how long was Lincoln's second speech? **about 700 words**

36. ***WHAT'S THE QUESTION?*** The first lap of an auto race is 2,500 m. This is 10% of the total race distance. The answer is 10. What is the question? **How many laps is the race?**

37. ***WRITE ABOUT IT*** If 35 is 110% of a number, is the number greater than or less than 35? Explain. **Less than 35; 110% is greater than 100%, so 35 is greater than the number.**

38. ***CHALLENGE*** Kayleen has been offered two jobs. The first job offers an annual salary of \$32,000. The second job offers an annual salary of \$10,000 plus 8% commission on all of her sales. How much money per month would Kayleen need to make in sales to earn enough commission to make more money at the second job? **She needs to make more than \$275,000 per month in sales.**

Spiral Review

39. What is the range of the data in the stem-and-leaf plot? (Lesson 1-2) **25**

Stems	Leaves
6	1 2 2 5 9
7	0 4 6 7 8
8	3 3 3 5 6

Key: 7|0 means 70

Write each fraction as a mixed number. (Lesson 3-8)

40. $\frac{28}{3}$ **$9\frac{1}{3}$**   41. $\frac{40}{7}$ **$5\frac{5}{7}$**   42. $\frac{19}{5}$ **$3\frac{4}{5}$**

43. **TEST PREP** The speed limit on a stretch of highway is 70 mi/h. What is this in miles per minute? (Lesson 5-4) **A**

A $1\frac{1}{6}$ mi/min   B 6,160 mi/min   C 369,600 mi/min   D 70 mi/min

44. **TEST PREP** Which proportion would you use to find 38% of 90? (Lesson 6-3) **F**

F $\frac{38}{100} = \frac{n}{90}$ G $\frac{100}{38} = \frac{n}{90}$ H $\frac{38}{100} = \frac{90}{n}$ J $\frac{38}{n} = \frac{90}{100}$

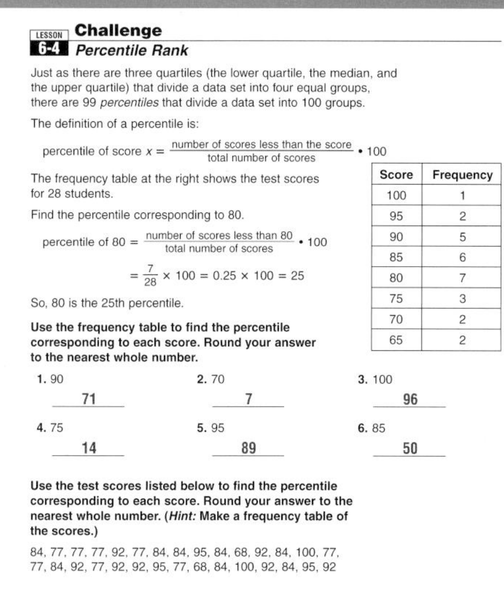

CHALLENGE 6-4

LESSON 6-4 **Challenge**
Percentile Rank

Just as there are three quartiles (the lower quartile, the median, and the upper quartile) that divide a data set into four equal groups, there are 99 *percentiles* that divide a data set into 100 groups.

The definition of a percentile is:

$$\text{percentile of score } x = \frac{\text{number of scores less than the score}}{\text{total number of scores}} \cdot 100$$

The frequency table at the right shows the test scores for 28 students.

Score	Frequency
100	1
95	2
90	5
85	6
80	7
75	3
70	2
65	2

Find the percentile corresponding to 80.

$$\text{percentile of } 80 = \frac{\text{number of scores less than 80}}{\text{total number of scores}} \cdot 100$$

$$= \frac{7}{28} \times 100 = 0.25 \times 100 = 25$$

So, 80 is the 25th percentile.

Use the frequency table to find the percentile corresponding to each score. Round your answer to the nearest whole number.

1. 90 **71**   2. 70 **7**   3. 100 **96**

4. 75 **14**   5. 95 **89**   6. 85 **50**

Use the test scores listed below to find the percentile corresponding to each score. Round your answer to the nearest whole number. (*Hint:* Make a frequency table of the scores.)

84, 77, 77, 77, 92, 77, 84, 84, 95, 84, 68, 92, 84, 100, 77, 77, 84, 92, 77, 92, 92, 95, 77, 68, 84, 100, 92, 84, 95, 92

7. 100 **93**   8. 95 **83**   9. 92 **60**

10. 84 **33**   11. 77 **7**   12. 68 **0**

PROBLEM SOLVING 6-4

LESSON 6-4 **Problem Solving**
Solving Equations Containing Percents

Write the correct answer.

1. At one time during 2001, for every 20 copies of *Harry Potter and the Sorcerer's Stone* that were sold, 13.2 copies of *Harry Potter and the Prisoner of Azkaban* were sold. Express the ratio of copies of *The Prisoner of Azkaban* sold to copies of *The Sorcerer's Stone* sold as a percent.
66%

2. According to the Department of Agriculture, the United States sold \$99 billion worth of livestock and poultry products in 1997. Of this, 19% was dairy products. What was the value of the dairy products sold by the United States in that year?
\$18.81 billion

3. Craig just finished reading 120 pages of his history assignment. If the assignment is 125 pages, what percent has Craig read so far?
96%

4. Hal's Sporting Goods had a 1-day sale. The original price of a mountain bike was \$325. On sale, it was \$276.25. What is the percent reduction for this sale?
15% off

Choose the correct letter for the best answer.

5. China's area is about 3.7 million square miles. It is on the continent of Asia, which has an area of about 17.2 million square miles. About what percent of the Asian continent does China cover?
A about 10%   C about 17%
B about 15%   **(D) about 22%**

6. After six weeks, the tomato plant that was given extra plant food and water was 26 centimeters tall. The tomato plant that was not given any extra plant food was only 74.5% as tall. How tall was the tomato plant that was not given extra plant food?
F 1.94 cm   H 34.89 cm
(G) 19.37 cm   J 48.5 cm

7. In a survey, 46 people, which was 20% of those surveyed, chose red as their favorite color. How many people were surveyed?
A 66 people   C 460 people
(B) 230 people   D 920 people

8. Of the 77 billion food and drink cans, bottles, and jars Americans throw away each year, about 65% of them are cans. How many food and drink cans, to the nearest billion, do Americans throw away each year?
F 12 billion   **(H) 50 billion**
G 17 billion   J 65 billion

COMMON ERROR ALERT

When the answer needs to be given as a percent, some students might report the answer as a decimal. Encourage students to avoid errors by noting how the answer needs to be reported and to estimate the answer before starting.

Journal

Ask students to think about the different types of percent problems they have learned to solve. Have them write about the type of problem they are most comfortable solving.

Test Prep Doctor

For Exercise 43, suggest that students estimate that 70 mi/h is about 1 mi/min because there are 60 minutes in an hour. This would eliminate choices **B, C,** and **D.** The reasonable answer is choice **A.**

For Exercise 44, students can eliminate choice **J** because 38 is not compared to 100 in the proportion. Choices **G** and **H** can be eliminated because the ratios in each answer choice do not have the whole and part in corresponding positions.

Lesson Quiz

1. 21 is 42% of what number? **50**
2. 73 is what percent of 292? **25%**
3. 112% of what number is 84? **75**
4. 13.4 is what percent of 1340? **1%**
5. An ad shows a DVD player on sale for 75% of its original price. If its original price was \$242, what is the sale price? **\$181.50**

Available on Daily Transparency in CRB

Mid-Chapter Quiz

Purpose: *To assess students' mastery of concepts and skills in Lessons 6-1 through 6-4*

Assessment Resources

Section 6A Quiz

Assessment Resources . . . . p. 17

***Test and Practice Generator* CD-ROM**

Additional mid-chapter assessment items in both multiple-choice and free-response format may be generated for any objective in Lessons 6-1 through 6-4.

Mid-Chapter Quiz

LESSON 6-1 (pp. 304–307)

Write each percent as a fraction in simplest form.

1. 9% $\frac{9}{100}$ **2.** 43% $\frac{43}{100}$ **3.** 5% $\frac{1}{20}$ **4.** 18% $\frac{9}{50}$

Write each percent as a decimal.

5. 22% **0.22** **6.** 90% **0.9** **7.** 29% **0.29** **8.** 5% **0.05**

Write each decimal as a percent.

9. 0.85 **85%** **10.** 0.026 **2.6%** **11.** 0.1111 **11.11%** **12.** 0.56 **56%**

Write each fraction as a percent. Round to the nearest tenth of a percent, if necessary.

13. $\frac{14}{81}$ **17.3%** **14.** $\frac{25}{52}$ **48.1%** **15.** $\frac{55}{78}$ **70.5%** **16.** $\frac{13}{32}$ **40.6%**

LESSON 6-2 (pp. 308–311)

Estimate. **Possible answers:**

17. 49% of 46 **23** **18.** 9% of 25 **2.5** **19.** 36% of 150 **50** **20.** 5% of 60 **3**

21. 18% of 80 **16** **22.** 26% of 115 **30** **23.** 91% of 300 **270** **24.** 42% of 197 **80**

25. The Carsons find a new video game system selling for $230.00 on the Internet. A local electronics store is selling the same system for 25% off the regular price of $299.99. Which is the better offer for the system? **the offer from the local electronics store**

LESSON 6-3 (pp. 312–315)

Find the percent of each number.

26. 25% of 84 **21** **27.** 52% of 300 **156** **28.** 0.5% of 40 **0.2** **29.** 160% of 450 **720**

30. 41% of 122 **50.02** **31.** 178% of 35 **62.3** **32.** 29% of 88 **25.52** **33.** 80% of 176 **140.8**

LESSON 6-4 (pp. 316–319)

Solve. Round to the nearest tenth, if necessary.

34. 14 is what percent of 280? **5%** **35.** 8 is 32% of what number? **25**

36. 14 is 44% of what number? **31.8** **37.** 22 is what percent of 900? **2.4%**

38. 99 is what percent of 396? **25%** **39.** 75 is 24% of what number? **312.5**

40. 36 is 18% of what number? **200** **41.** 16 is what percent of 34? **47.1%**

Focus on Problem Solving

Make a Plan

- **Estimate or find an exact answer**

Sometimes an estimate is sufficient when you are solving a problem. Other times you need to find an exact answer. Before you try to solve a problem, you should decide whether an estimate will be sufficient. Usually if a problem includes the word *about,* then you can estimate the answer.

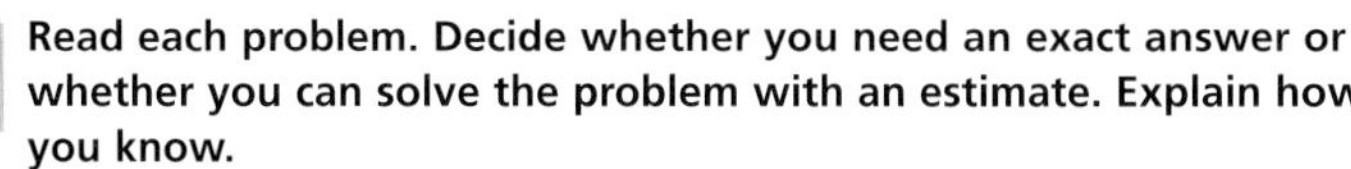

Read each problem. Decide whether you need an exact answer or whether you can solve the problem with an estimate. Explain how you know.

1. Barry has $21.50 left from his allowance. He wants to buy a book for $5.85 and a CD for $14.99. Assuming these prices include tax, does Barry have enough money left to buy both the book and the CD?
2. Last weekend Valerie practiced playing the drums for 3 hours. This is 40% of the total time she spent practicing last week. How much time did Valerie spend practicing last week?
3. Amber is shopping for a winter coat. She finds one that costs $157. The coat is on sale and is discounted 25% today only. About how much money will Amber save if she buys the coat today?
4. Marcus is planning a budget. He plans to spend less than 35% of his allowance each week on entertainment. Last week Marcus spent $7.42 on entertainment. If Marcus gets $20.00 each week, did he stay within his budget?
5. An upright piano is on sale for 20% off the original price. If the original price is $9,840, what is the sale price?
6. The Mapleton Middle School band has 41 students. If 6 of the students in the band play percussion instruments, do more than 15% of the students play percussion instruments?

Answers

1. Yes; round $5.85 to $6 and $14.99 to $15; the total cost for the book and CD is about $21.
2. 7.5 h
3. about $40; $39.25
4. No; $7.42 is 37.1% of Marcus' allowance.
5. $7,872
6. No; 6 out of 41 students is only about 14.6% of the students.

Focus on Problem Solving

Purpose: *To focus on deciding whether to estimate or find an exact answer*

Problem Solving Resources

Interactive Problem Solving . . pp. 51–56

Math: Reading and Writing in the Content Area . . . . pp. 51–56

Problem Solving Process

This page focuses on the second step of the problem-solving process: **Make a Plan**

Discuss

Have students discuss how they decided whether each problem needed an exact answer or whether they could solve the problem with an estimate.

Possible answers:

1. You can estimate the answer, since Barry needs to know if he has enough money, not an exact amount.
2. You need to find an exact answer because you need to find the number of hours Valerie practiced last week.
3. You can estimate the answer because it asks *about* how much Amber will save if she buys the coat today.
4. You need to find an exact answer to determine if Marcus stayed within his budget.
5. You need to find an exact answer to find the sale price.
6. You need to find an exact answer to determine if more than 15% of the students play percussion instruments.

Section

6B Using Percents

One-Minute Section Planner

Lesson	Materials	Resources
Hands-On Lab 6A Percent of Increase and Decrease **NCTM:** Number and Operations, Algebra, Geometry, Representation **NAEP:** Number Properties 4d ☐ SAT-9 ☐ SAT-10 ☐ ITBS ☐ CTBS ☑ MAT ☑ CAT	**Required** Geoboards *(MK)* Dot paper	• *Hands-On Lab Activities*, pp. 42–43
Lesson 6-5 Percent of Change **NCTM:** Number and Operations, Algebra, Communication, Connections **NAEP:** Number Properties 4d ☐ SAT-9 ☐ SAT-10 ☐ ITBS ☐ CTBS ☑ MAT ☑ CAT	**Optional** Play money *(MK, CRB p. 69)*	• *Chapter 6 Resource Book,* pp. 44–52 • Daily Transparency T19, CRB • Additional Examples Transparencies T20–T22, CRB • *Alternate Openers: Explorations,* p. 55
Lesson 6-6 Simple Interest **NCTM:** Number and Operations, Algebra, Problem Solving, Communication, Connections **NAEP:** Number Properties 4d ☐ SAT-9 ☐ SAT-10 ☐ ITBS ☑ CTBS ☐ MAT ☐ CAT		• *Chapter 6 Resource Book,* pp. 53–61 • Daily Transparency T23, CRB • Additional Examples Transparencies T24–T26, CRB • *Alternate Openers: Explorations,* p. 56
Section 6B Assessment		• Section 6B Quiz, AR p. 18 • *Test and Practice Generator* CD-ROM

SAT = *Stanford Achievement Tests* **ITBS** = *Iowa Test of Basic Skills* **CTBS** = *Comprehensive Test of Basic Skills/Terra Nova*
MAT = *Metropolitan Achievement Test* **CAT** = *California Achievement Test*

NCTM – Complete standards can be found on pages T27–T33. **NAEP** – Complete standards can be found on pages A35–A39.

SE = *Student Edition* **TE** = *Teacher's Edition* **AR** = *Assessment Resources* **CRB** = *Chapter Resource Book* **MK** = *Manipulatives Kit*

Section Overview

Percent of Change

Hands-On Lab 6A, Lesson 6-5

Why? Both discounts and markups are examples of percents of change.

$$\text{percent of change} = \frac{\textbf{amount of change}}{\text{original amount}}$$

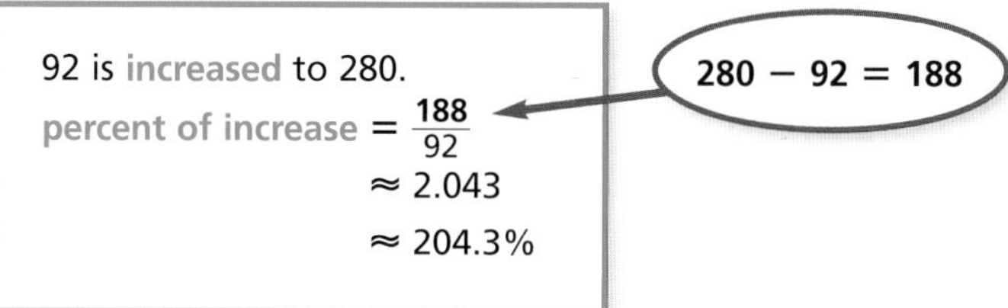

92 is increased to 280.
percent of increase = 188/92
≈ 2.043
≈ 204.3%
280 − 92 = 188
75 is decreased to 35.
percent of decrease = 40/75
≈ 0.533
≈ 53.3%
75 − 35 = 40

Simple Interest

Lesson 6-6

Why? Simple interest can be charged when you borrow money or paid when you loan or invest money.

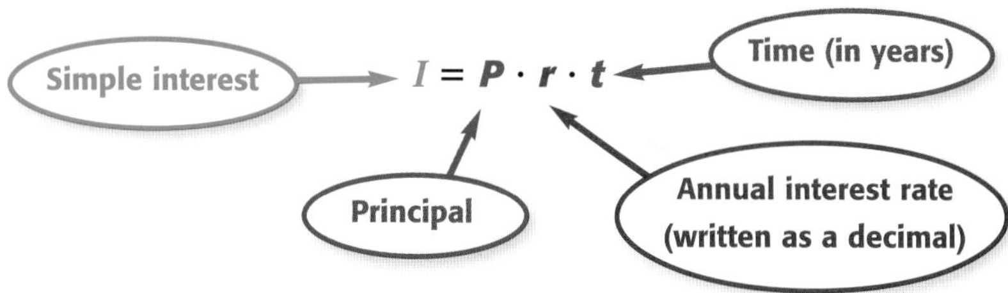

Find the interest rate if the simple interest earned on \$800 for 2 years is \$96.

$$I = P \cdot r \cdot t$$
$$96 = 800 \cdot r \cdot 2$$
$$\frac{96}{1{,}600} = \frac{1{,}600}{1{,}600} \cdot r$$
$$0.06 = r$$
$$6\% = r$$

The interest rate is 6%.

Find the simple interest if \$400 is invested for 18 months at 3.5%.

$$I = P \cdot r \cdot t$$
$$I = 400 \cdot 0.035 \cdot 1.5$$
$$I = \$21.00$$

The simple interest is \$21.00.

Change the rate from a percent to a decimal and the time from months to years.

6A
Percent of Increase and Decrease

Pacing: Traditional 1 day
Block $\frac{1}{2}$ day

Objective: To use a geoboard or dot paper to model percent of increase and percent of decrease

Materials: Geoboard, dot paper

Lab Resources

Hands-On Lab Activities . . . . . pp. 42–43

Using the Pages

Discuss with students how to use a geoboard or dot paper to model squares.

Model each figure on a geoboard or dot paper.

1. 3-by-3 square

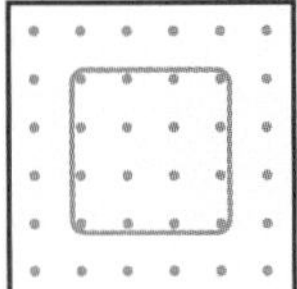

2. 4-by-4 square

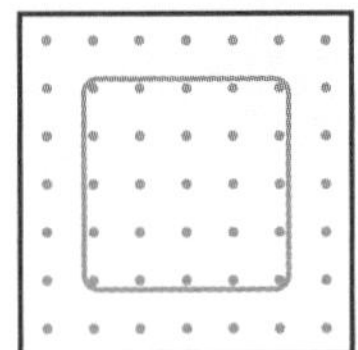

Percent of Increase and Decrease

Use with Lesson 6-5

You can use a geoboard or dot paper to help you understand the concepts of percent of increase and percent of decrease.

internet connect
Lab Resources Online
go.hrw.com
KEYWORD: MS4 Lab6A

Activity

1 Follow the steps to model a percent decrease.

a. Make a 4-by-4 square like the one shown at right.

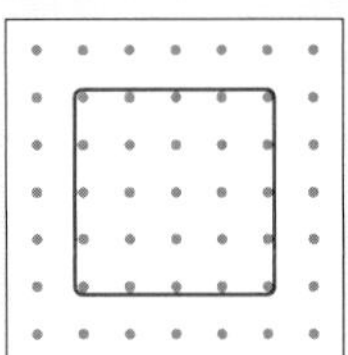

b. To decrease the area of the square by 25%, first divide the square into four equal parts. (Recall that 25% is equivalent to $\frac{1}{4}$.)

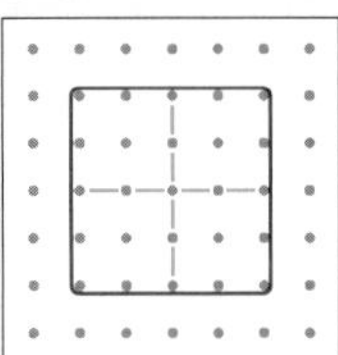

c. Remove one part, which represents 25%, or $\frac{1}{4}$, from the original square to model a decrease of 25%.

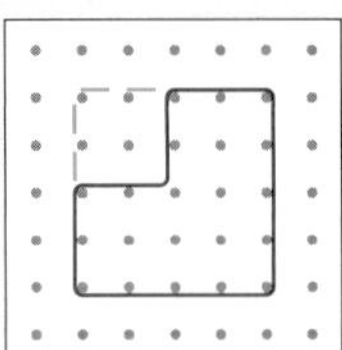

2 Follow the steps to model a percent increase.

a. Make a 3-by-3 square like the one shown at right.

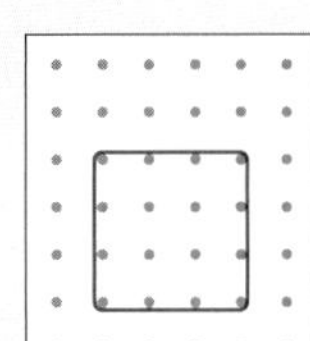

Teacher to Teacher

Toni Roland
Weatherford, TX

A great way to have students discover what a percent of increase means is through "grow creatures." At a local retail store I found toy reptiles advertised to increase 600% when soaked in water. The students measured and drew pictures of their creatures. They predicted what the increase would mean. Some actually computed 600 times the original measurements. Their computations seemed unreasonable, but they were not sure what would be a correct prediction. The measurements of the grown creatures were about six times the original. The students were able to see what a percent of increase actually represents.

b. To increase the area of the square by $33\frac{1}{3}\%$, first divide the square into three equal parts. (Recall that $33\frac{1}{3}\%$ is equivalent to $\frac{1}{3}$.)

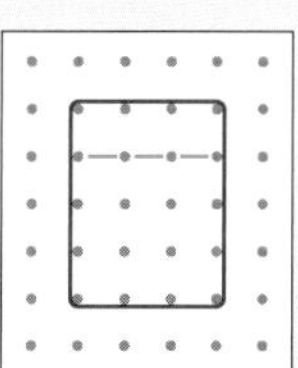

c. Add one part, which represents $33\frac{1}{3}\%$, or $\frac{1}{3}$, from the original square to model an increase of $33\frac{1}{3}\%$.

Think and Discuss

1. Explain why you divided the square in the first activity into four equal parts.
2. What percent of the 4-by-4 square remains after the 25% decrease? **75%**
3. Give an example of a figure that you might use to model a 40% increase. **Possible answer: a 1-by-5 rectangle since 40% is equivalent to $\frac{2}{5}$**
4. In the second activity, what is the ratio of the area of the new rectangle to the area of the original square? Write this ratio as a percent. Then explain what this percent means. **4:3; $133\frac{1}{3}\%$; this means the new rectangle is 100% plus an additional $33\frac{1}{3}\%$ of the size of the original square.**

Try This

1. Use a 2-by-2 square to model a 25% decrease. Then use the square to model a 25% increase.
2. Use a 3-by-3 square to model a $33\frac{1}{3}\%$ decrease.
3. Use a 4-by-4 square to model a 50% increase.
4. Use the figure at right to model a 50% decrease.
5. Choose a figure to use to model an increase of 10%. Explain why you chose that figure.
6. Look at the figures on the geoboard below. By what percent must you increase the area of the figure on the left to get the figure on the right? **100%**

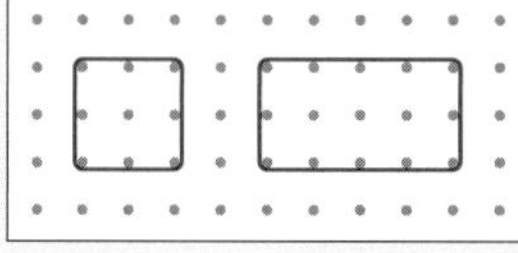

Answers

Think and Discuss

1. Possible answer: To decrease the area of the square by 25%, one-fourth of its area must be removed. So dividing the square into 4 parts makes it easy to remove one-fourth of the square.

Try This

Possible answers:

1. original; 25% decrease

25% increase

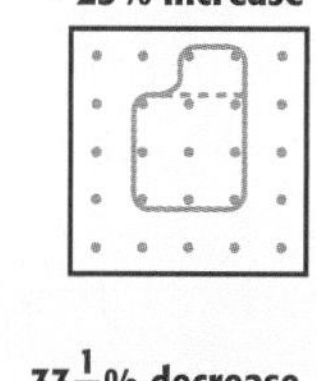

2. original; $33\frac{1}{3}\%$ decrease

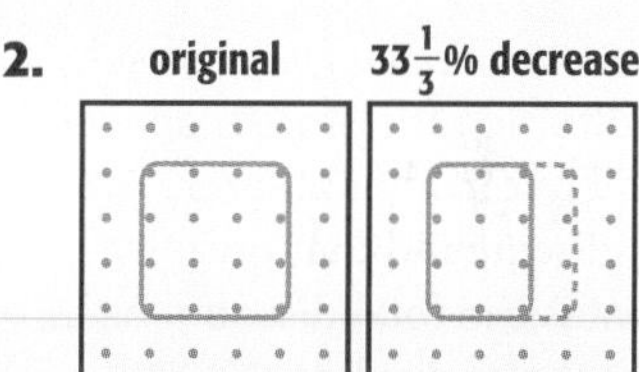

3. original

50% increase

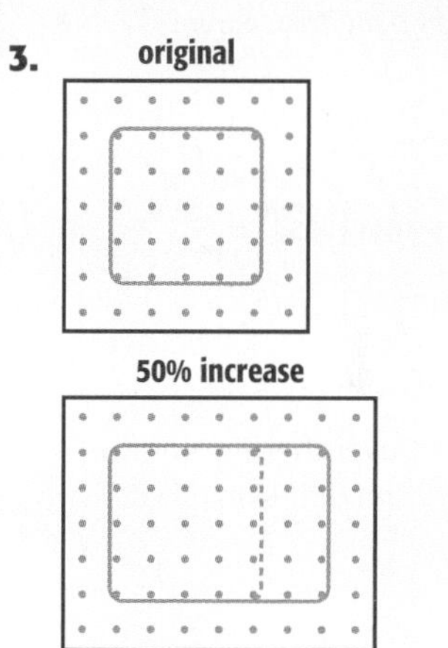

4. original

50% decrease

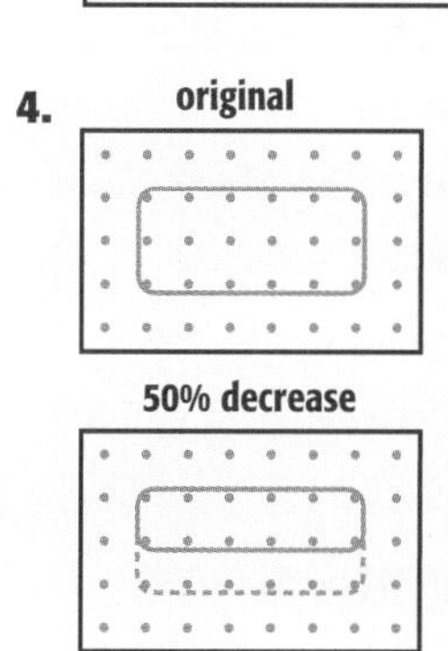

5. A 1-by-10 rectangle; increasing a 1-by-10 rectangle by 10% means adding one-tenth, which is equivalent to one square.

6-5 Organizer

Pacing: Traditional 1 day
Block $\frac{1}{2}$ day

Objective: Students solve problems involving percent of change.

Warm Up

Solve.

1. 10% of what number is 6? **60**
2. What percent of 20 is 8? **40%**
3. What is 80% of 60? **48**
4. 50 is what percent of 200? **25%**

Problem of the Day

A pair of $100 sneakers was on sale for 50% off. Then the store manager marked them down another 30%. She then discounted that price by 20%. What is the total discount as a percent of the original price? **72%**

Available on Daily Transparency in CRB

Customer: The sign says 20% off each book. If I pick out 5 books, do I get them for 100% off?

Clerk: No, but over there is another sign for you to read. It says, "Exit."

6-5 Percent of Change

Learn to solve problems involving percent of change.

Vocabulary
percent of change
percent of increase
percent of decrease

The U.S. Consumer Product Safety Commission has reported that, in 2000, 4,390 injuries related to motorized scooters were treated in hospital emergency rooms. This was a 230% increase from 1999's report of 1,330 injuries.

A percent can be used to describe an amount of change. The **percent of change** is the amount, stated as a percent, that a number increases or decreases. If the amount goes up, it is a **percent of increase**. If the amount goes down, it is a **percent of decrease**.

You can find the percent of change by using the following formula.

$$\text{percent of change} = \frac{\textbf{amount of change}}{\textbf{original amount}}$$

EXAMPLE 1 Finding Percent of Change

Find each percent of change. Round answers to the nearest tenth of a percent, if necessary.

Helpful Hint

When a number is decreased, subtract the new amount from the original amount to find the amount of change. When a number is increased, subtract the original amount from the new amount.

A 27 is decreased to 20.

$27 - 20 = 7$ *Find the amount of change.*

$\text{percent of change} = \frac{7}{27}$ *Substitute values into formula.*

≈ 0.259259 *Divide.*

$\approx 25.9\%$ *Write as a percent. Round.*

The percent of decrease is about 25.9%.

B 32 is increased to 67.

$67 - 32 = 35$ *Find the amount of change.*

$\text{percent of change} = \frac{35}{32}$ *Substitute values into formula.*

$= 1.09375$ *Divide.*

$\approx 109.4\%$ *Write as a percent. Round.*

The percent of increase is about 109.4%.

1 Introduce

Alternate Opener

EXPLORATION

6-5 Percent of Change

An electronics store has scratch-off cards that determine the discount on a calculator, a radio, and an alarm clock. Your cards reveal the discounts in the table below.

Complete the table using each percent of discount.

	Original Price	Scratch-off Discount	New Price	Price Change	$\frac{\text{Price Change}}{\text{Original Price}}$
1.	Calculator $80.00	50% Off			
2.	Radio $65.00	25% Off			
3.	Clock $45.00	15% Off			

Think and Discuss

4. **Explain** how you found the new price and the price change in the table.
5. **Discuss** the meaning of $\frac{\text{price change}}{\text{original price}}$, used in the last column of the table.

Motivate

To introduce students to percents of change, discuss how sales are advertised in different media (e.g., newspapers, television, store displays). If students do not mention such advertisements as "50% off" or "30% discount on all shirts," ask them whether they are familiar with such ads. Discuss both the appeal of such ads (the items cost less than the original price) and how students would compute the sale price. Mention that a discount is a *percent of change.*

Exploration worksheet and answers on Chapter 6 Resource Book pp. 45 and 78

2 Teach

Lesson Presentation

Guided Instruction

In this lesson, students learn to solve problems involving percent of change. For a percent of decrease, the new value is less than the original value. For a percent of increase, the new value is greater than the original value. A percent of change is always based on the original value. Always compute the percent of change relative to the original value.

Teaching Tip Discuss how merchandise in a store is priced. Stores buy merchandise at *wholesale prices.* They *markup* the price of the merchandise to get the *retail price.* To sell merchandise quickly, stores may decide to have a sale and to *discount* retail prices.

When you know the percent of change, you can use an equation to find the actual amount of change.

EXAMPLE 2 **Using Percent of Change**

The regular price of a portable CD player at Edwin's Electronics is $31.99. This week the CD player is on sale for 25% off.

A **Find the actual amount of the discount.**

$25\% \cdot 31.99 = d$ — *Think: 25% of $31.99 is what number?*
$0.25 \cdot 31.99 = d$ — *Write the percent as a decimal.*
$7.9975 = d$ — *Multiply.*
$\$8.00 \approx d$ — *Round to the nearest cent.*

The discount is $8.00.

B **Find the sale price.**

$\$31.99 - \$8.00 = \$23.99$ — *Subtract the discount from the regular price.*

The sale price is $23.99.

EXAMPLE 3 ***Business Application***

Helpful Hint

The retail price is the wholesale price from the manufacturer plus the amount of increase.

Winter Wonders buys snow globes from a manufacturer for $9.20 each and sells them at a 95% increase in price. What is the retail price of the snow globes?

First find the actual amount of increase.

Think: 95% of $9.20 is what number?

$95\% \cdot 9.20 = n$
$0.95 \cdot 9.20 = n$ — *Write the percent as a decimal.*
$8.74 = n$ — *Multiply.*

CHICAGO

The amount of increase is $8.74. Now find the retail price.

Think: retail price = wholesale price + amount of increase

$r = \$9.20 + \$8.74$
$r = \$17.94$

The retail price of the snow globes is $17.94 each.

Think and Discuss

1. **Explain** what is meant by a 100% decrease.
2. **Give an example** in which the amount of increase is greater than the original amount. What do you know about the percent of increase?

COMMON ERROR ALERT

Some students might get confused about which value to use in the denominator to find percent of change. One way to remember this is as follows:

$$\%\text{ change} = \frac{\text{from} - \text{to}}{\text{from}}.$$

The difference always goes over "from."

Additional Examples

Example 1

Find each percent of change. Round answers to the nearest tenth of a percent, if necessary.

A. 65 is decreased to 38. **41.5%**
B. 41 is increased to 92. **124.4%**

Example 2

The regular price of a bicycle helmet is $42.99. It is on sale for 20% off.

A. Find the actual amount of the discount. **$8.60**
B. Find the sale price. **$34.39**

Example 3

A boutique buys hand-painted T-shirts for $12.60 each and sells them after a price increase of 110%. What is the selling price of the T-shirts? **$26.46**

Example 3 note: The amount of increase is called the *markup.* The markup is added to the wholesale price to find the retail price.

3 Close

Reaching All Learners
Through Concrete Manipulatives

Use play money (provided in the Manipulatives Kit and on Chapter 6 Resource Book p. 69) to demonstrate the ideas of percent of increase and percent of decrease. Present small groups of students with ten $1 bills. Ask students to find 10% of the money. $1 Then ask if one dollar is added to the money, what percent is added? 10% Similarly, if one dollar is taken away from the $10, what percent is subtracted? 10% Similar questions can be formulated for other percents that are multiples of 10, such as 20% or 50%.

Summarize

You may wish to have students give definitions of *percent of increase* and *percent of decrease.* Have students give an example of each type of percent of change.

Possible answers: *Percent of increase* is the ratio of the amount of the increase to the original amount. A markup is a percent of increase. *Percent of decrease* is the ratio of the amount of the decrease to the original amount. A discount is a percent of decrease.

Answers to Think and Discuss

1. A 100% decrease is a decrease equal to the original amount. The difference between the original amount and a 100% decrease is zero.
2. Possible answer: 10 increased to 25 is a 150% increase of 10. The percent of increase must be greater than 100% for the amount of increase to exceed the original amount.

6-5 PRACTICE & ASSESS

Students may want to refer back to the lesson examples.

Assignment Guide

If you finished Example 1 assign:
Core 1–4, 7–12, 17–22, 27–34
Enriched 1–4, 7–12, 17–22, 27–34

If you finished Example 2 assign:
Core 1–5, 7–14, 17–23 odd, 27–34
Enriched 1–13 odd, 17–24, 27–34

If you finished Example 3 assign:
Core 1–16, 17–25 odd, 27–34
Enriched 1–15 odd, 17–34

Notes

6-5 Exercises

FOR EXTRA PRACTICE see page 667

internet connect
Homework Help Online
go.hrw.com Keyword: MS4 6-5

GUIDED PRACTICE

See Example 1 **Find each percent of change. Round answers to the nearest tenth of a percent, if necessary.**

1. 25 is decreased to 18. **28%**
2. 36 is increased to 84. **133.3%**
3. 62 is decreased to 52. **16.1%**
4. 28 is increased to 96. **242.9%**

See Example 2 **5.** The regular price of a sweater is $42.99. It is on sale for 20% off. Find the amount of the discount and the sale price. **$8.60, $34.39**

See Example 3 **6.** The retail price of a pair of shoes is a 98% increase from its wholesale price. If the wholesale price of the shoes is $12.50, what is the retail price? **$24.75**

INDEPENDENT PRACTICE

See Example 1 **Find each percent of change. Round answers to the nearest tenth of a percent, if necessary.**

7. 72 is decreased to 45. **37.5%**
8. 40 is increased to 95. **137.5%**
9. 12 is increased to 56. **366.7%**
10. 90 is decreased to 55. **38.9%**
11. 180 is decreased to 140. **22.2%**
12. 230 is increased to 250. **8.7%**

See Example 2 **13.** A skateboard that sells for $65 is on sale for 15% off. Find the amount of the discount and the sale price. **$9.75, $55.25**

14. A store is closing out its stock of sunglasses. The original price of the sunglasses was $44.95. The closeout price is 40% off the original price. Find the amount of the discount and the sale price. **$17.98, $26.97**

See Example 3 **15.** A jeweler buys a ring from an artisan for $85. He sells the ring in his store at a 135% increase in price. What is the retail price of the ring? **$199.75**

16. A water tank holds 45 gallons of water. A new water tank can hold 25% more water. What is the capacity of the new water tank? **56.25 gal**

PRACTICE AND PROBLEM SOLVING

Find each percent of change, amount of increase, or amount of decrease. Round answers to the nearest tenth, if necessary.

17. $8.80 is increased to $17.60. **100%**
18. 6.2 is decreased to 5.9. **4.8%**
19. 39.2 is increased to 56.3. **43.6%**
20. 28 is increased by 150%. **42**
21. 75 is decreased by 40%. **30**
22. $325 is decreased by 100%. **$325**

Math Background

It is important to be careful when combining percent changes. For example, if sales are up 25% one month and down 25% the second month, they are not back to where they started. Although it might appear that a 25% increase cancels a 25% decrease, it does not. The first 25% is a quarter of one amount, and the second 25% is a quarter of a different amount.

Similarly, a discount of a discount is not the same as the sum of the discounts. For example, suppose an item is discounted 30%. An additional discount of 10% on the discounted item would not be a 40% discount of the original price. Instead, it would be a 37% discount of the original price.

RETEACH 6-5

CHAPTER 6-5 **Reteach**
Percent of Change

A change in a quantity is often described as a percent increase or decrease. To calculate a percent increase or decrease, use this equation.

$$\text{percent of change} = \frac{\text{amount of increase or decrease}}{\text{original amount}} \cdot 100$$

Find the percent of change from 28 to 42.

- First, find the amount of the change. $42 - 28 = 14$
- What is the original amount? 28
- Use the equation. $\frac{14}{28} \cdot 100 = 50\%$

An increase from 28 to 42 represents a 50% increase.

Find each percent of change.

1. 8 is increased to 22
amount of change 22 − 8 = 14
original amount 8
$\frac{14}{8} \cdot 100 =$ 175 %

2. 90 is decreased to 81
amount of change 90 − 81 = 9
original amount 90
$\frac{9}{90} \cdot 100 =$ 10 %

3. 125 is increased to 200
amount of change 200 − 125 = 75
original amount 125
$\frac{75}{125} \cdot 100 =$ 60 %

4. 400 is decreased to 60
amount of change 400 − 60 = 340
original amount 400
$\frac{340}{400} \cdot 100 =$ 85 %

5. 64 is decreased to 48 25%

6. 140 is increased to 273 95%

7. 30 is decreased to 6 80%

8. 15 is increased to 21 40%

9. 7 is increased to 21 200%

10. 320 is decreased to 304 5%

PRACTICE 6-5

LESSON 6-5 **Practice B**
Percent of Change

Find each percent of change. Round answers to the nearest tenth, if necessary.

1. 20 is decreased to 11 45%
2. 24 is increased to 30 25%
3. 56 is decreased to 14 75%
4. 25 is increased to 100 300%
5. 18 is increased to 45 150%
6. 90 is decreased to 75 16.7%
7. 126 is decreased to 48 61.9%
8. 65 is increased to 144 121.5%
9. 42 is increased to 72 71.4%
10. 84 is decreased to 8 90.5%
11. 95 is increased to 145 52.6%
12. 248 is decreased to 200 19.4%
13. 105 is decreased to 32 69.5%
14. 75 is increased to 350 366.7%
15. 93 is decreased to 90 3.2%
16. 16 is decreased to 2 87.5%

17. A backpack that normally sells for $39 is on sale for 33% off. Find the amount of the discount and the sale price.
$12.87; $26.13

18. A sporting goods store is having a closeout on a certain style of running shoes. They are marked 55% off the regular price. The regular price is $79.95. Find the amount of the discount and the sale price.
$43.97; $35.98

19. A gallery owner purchased a very old painting for $3,000. The painting sells at a 325% increase in price. What is the retail price of the painting?
$12,750

20. In August, the Simons' water bill was $48. In September, it was 15% lower. What was the Simons' water bill in September?
$40.80

Economics LINK

23. The information at right shows the expenses for the Kramer family for one year.

a. If the Kramers spent $2,905 on auto expenses, what was their income for the year? **$41,500**

b. How much money was spent on household expenses? **$17,845**

c. The Kramers pay $14,400 per year on their mortgage. What percent of their household expenses is this? Round your answer to the nearest tenth. **80.7%**

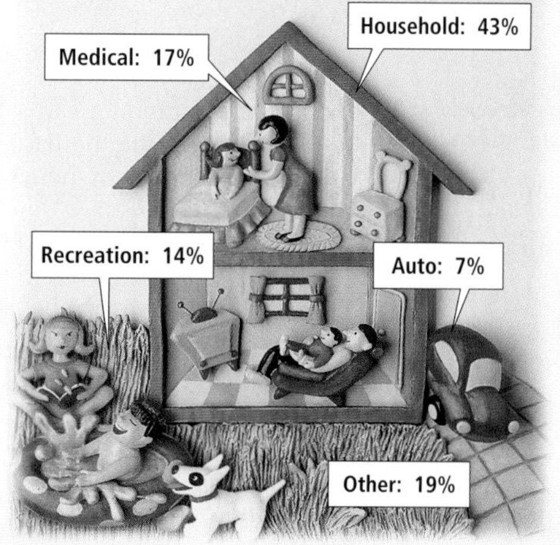

24. United States health expenses were $428.7 billion in 1985 and $991.4 billion in 1995. What was the percent of increase in health expenses during this ten-year period? Round your answer to the nearest tenth of a percent. **about 131.3%**

25. In 1990, the total amount of energy consumed for transportation in the United States was 22,540 trillion British thermal units (Btu).

a. From 1990 to 1991, there was a 1.8% decrease in energy consumed. About how many Btu of energy were consumed in 1991? **about 22,134 trillion Btu**

b. From 1950 to 1990, there was a 165% increase in energy consumed for transportation. About how many Btu of energy were consumed in 1950? **about 8,506 trillion Btu**

26. ***CHALLENGE*** In 1960, 21.5% of U.S. households did not have a telephone. This statistic decreased by 75.8% between 1960 and 1990. In 1990, what percent of U.S. households had a telephone? **94.8%**

Spiral Review

Convert using dimensional analysis. (Lesson 5-4)

27. 8 gallons to pints **64 pt** **28.** 3 weeks to minutes **30,240 min** **29.** 120 feet to yards **40 yd**

Write each percent as a fraction in simplest form. (Lesson 6-1)

30. 80% $\frac{4}{5}$ **31.** 2% $\frac{1}{50}$ **32.** 65% $\frac{13}{20}$ **33.** 48% $\frac{12}{25}$

34. TEST PREP Of the 765 people registered to run in a race, only 80% ran. How many people ran in the race? (Lesson 6-3) **B**

A 61 B 612 C 676 D 685

CHALLENGE 6-5

LESSON 6-5 **Challenge**
Double Percent Change

Solve.

1. Enrollment in the school soccer league was 340 last year. This year, it dropped 15%. What is the enrollment this year? If enrollment increases 15% next year, what will the enrollment be? Round to the nearest whole number.
289; 332

2. Enrollment in the Wilderness Club increased 8% for each of the last two years. Enrollment two years ago was 175. What was the enrollment for each of the following two years? Round to the nearest whole number.
189; 204

3. The toy store buys stuffed animals from the manufacturer for $2.40 each. The store then sells them at a 96% increase in price. What is the retail price of each animal? If the customer brings in a coupon for 20% off the retail price, how much will the stuffed animal cost?
$4.70; $3.76

4. Enrollment in the Jacksonville Township Basketball League was 425 last year. This year, the number enrolled increased 12%. If enrollment drops 12% next year, how many people will be enrolled in the league? Round to the nearest whole number.
419

5. The manager of a card store buys cards from the manufacturer for $0.65 each. The store regularly sells the cards at a markup of 130%. For a sale, the manager marks down half of the cards 15%. What is the price of the cards that are on sale?
$1.27

6. Leander wants to buy a video game. Two stores in the neighborhood offer the game at $49.95. Jamal has a coupon for 18% off the regular price at Fun Electronics. The other store, Gamers, is having a sale with 8% off everything in the store. Jamal also has a coupon for 10% off the sale price at Gamers. At which store should he buy the game? Explain.
Fun Electronics, since the game will cost $40.96; it will cost $41.36 at Gamers.

PROBLEM SOLVING 6-5

LESSON 6-5 **Problem Solving**
Percent of Change

Write the correct answer.

1. In 1999, U.S. consumers spent about $98 billion on new cars. In 2000, that amount increased by about 7%. How much did U.S. consumers spend on new cars in 2000 to the nearest billion dollars?
about $105 billion

2. In Union County, Florida, the 1990 census listed the population at 10,252. The 2000 census listed the population as 13,442. What percent increase is this to the nearest tenth of a percent?
31.1% increase

3. World production of motor vehicles increased from about 58 million in 1999 to 60 million in 2000. What was the percent increase to the nearest percent?
3% increase

4. Arthur's dog, Shep, used to weigh 158 pounds. The vet put him on a diet and he lost 13% of his weight. To the nearest pound, how much does Shep weigh now?
137 pounds

5. The number of volunteers rose from 47 on Monday to 64 on Tuesday. What is the percent increase to the nearest tenth of a percent?
36.2% increase

6. Coretta's bowling average decreased from 158 to 133. What is the percent decrease to the nearest tenth of a percent?
15.8% decrease

Choose the correct letter for the best answer.

7. Shandra scored 75 on her first math test. She scored 20% higher on her next math test. What did she score on the second test?
A 80 (C) 90
B 85 D 95

8. Jim's Gym had income of $20,350 last month. The total increased by $2,000 this month. What was the percent increase to the nearest percent?
F 11% H 7%
(G) 10% J 6%

9. Last year, the average number of absences in school was 8 students per day. This year, the absentee rate is down to 6 students per day. What is the percent decrease in student absences this year?
A 75% (C) 25%
B 33% D 66%

10. During the 1996–1997 ski season, snowboarding equipment had sales of $125 million. Sales had increased 88% by the 2000–2001 season. What were sales of snowboarding equipment during 2000–2001?
F $37 million H $213 million
G $110 million (J) $235 million

Interdisciplinary LINK

Economics

Exercises 23–26 involve using percents of change to learn more about consumption of goods and services in the United States.

Journal

Ask students to think of and write about a real-world situation in which they encountered a percent decrease. Have students describe how they recognized that the situation involved a percent decrease.

Test Prep Doctor

For Exercise 34, you may want to encourage students to estimate to find the answer. Since 10% of 765 is about 75, 20% is about 150, and 765 − 150 = 615. This eliminates all choices except the correct answer, **B.** Students who chose **C** or **D** probably made common multiplication errors. Students who selected **A** probably placed the decimal point incorrectly. (80% is not equal to 0.08.)

Lesson Quiz

Find each percent of change.

1. 10 is increased to 12. **20%**

2. 25 is increased to 45. **80%**

3. 10 is decreased to 1. **90%**

4. 120 is decreased to 90. **25%**

5. A backpack that sells for $42 is on sale for 25% off. Find the amount of discount and the sale price. **$10.50, $31.50**

Available on Daily Transparency in CRB

6-6 Organizer

Pacing: Traditional 1 day
Block $\frac{1}{2}$ day

Objective: Students solve problems involving simple interest.

Warm Up

Multiply.

1. 800 × 0.04 × 3 **96**
2. 1,700 × 2 × 0.25 **850**
3. 900 × 0.05 × 4 **180**
4. 1,200 × 6 × 0.35 **2,520**

Problem of the Day

Which number does not belong in the group?

0.75 75% $\frac{3}{4}$ $\frac{6}{8}$ $\frac{75}{1,000}$

$\frac{75}{1,000} = \frac{3}{40}$; the others equal $\frac{3}{4}$.

Available on Daily Transparency in CRB

Math Fact !

Most loans and savings accounts today use *compound interest*. This means that interest is paid not only on the principal but also on all of the interest earned up to that time.

6-6 Simple Interest

Learn to solve problems involving simple interest.

Vocabulary
interest
simple interest
principal

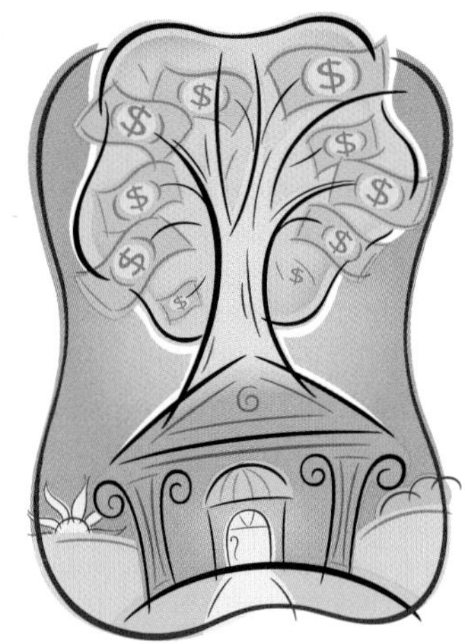

When you keep money in a savings account, your money earns *interest*. **Interest** is an amount that is collected or paid for the use of money. For example, the bank pays you interest to use your money to conduct its business. Likewise, when you borrow money from the bank, the bank collects interest on its loan to you.

One type of interest, called **simple interest**, is money paid only on the *principal*. The **principal** is the amount of money deposited or borrowed. To solve problems involving simple interest, you can use the following formula.

$$I = P \cdot r \cdot t$$

Interest → I
Principal → P
Rate of interest per year (as a decimal) → r
Time in years that the money earns interest → t

EXAMPLE 1 Using the Simple Interest Formula

Find each missing value.

A $I = \square$, $P = \$225$, $r = 3\%$, $t = 2$ years

$I = P \cdot r \cdot t$
$I = 225 \cdot 0.03 \cdot 2$ *Substitute. Use 0.03 for 3%.*
$I = 13.5$ *Multiply.*

The simple interest is $13.50.

B $I = \$300$, $P = \$1,000$, $r = \square$, $t = 5$ years

$I = P \cdot r \cdot t$
$300 = 1,000 \cdot r \cdot 5$ *Substitute.*
$300 = 5,000r$ *Multiply.*
$\frac{300}{5,000} = \frac{5,000r}{5,000}$ *Divide by 5,000 to isolate the variable.*
$0.06 = r$

The interest rate is 6%.

1 Introduce

Alternate Opener

1. Alicia has a summer job. She decides to save 10% of each paycheck. Complete the table to show how much Alicia will save.

	Paycheck	10% of Paycheck	Amount Alicia Saves
a.	$100	0.10 × 100 = 10	$10.00
b.	$200		
c.	$300		
d.	$500		

2. Alicia deposits the total amount she saved, $110.00, in a savings account that earns 4% simple interest each year. How much interest will she earn in 1 year? 2 years? 3 years? To complete the table, look at how the formula is used.

	Time	Formula	Substitute in Formula	Interest Earned
a.	$t = 1$ year	$I = P \cdot r \cdot t$	$I = 110 \cdot 0.04 \cdot 1 = 4.4$	$4.40
b.	$t = 2$ years			
c.	$t = 3$ years			

Think and Discuss

3. Explain why 4% is written as 0.04 when substituted into the formula in number **2**.

4. Discuss whether Alicia would have more or less money if she had saved 4% of her paychecks and the savings account paid 10% simple interest each year.

Motivate

Discuss different types of bank accounts with which students are familiar (e.g., checking accounts, savings accounts). Have students explain what they know about the different accounts and the benefits of such accounts. (For example., with a checking account, you can write a check to use the money; with a savings account, you earn interest, which increases the amount of money in the account.)

Exploration worksheet and answers on Chapter 6 Resource Book pp. 54 and 80

Lesson Presentation

Guided Instruction

In this lesson, students learn to solve problems involving simple interest. Emphasize that as long as any three values are known, the other value can be found using the formula for simple interest.

You may wish to share the other forms of the interest formula: $P = \frac{I}{r \cdot t}$, $r = \frac{I}{P \cdot t}$, and $t = \frac{I}{P \cdot r}$. Remind them to follow the order of operations after they substitute values in to the formulas.

Point out that the time in the simple interest formula must be in years. If time is given in months, the time will have to be converted to years.

EXAMPLE 2 PROBLEM SOLVING APPLICATION

PROBLEM SOLVING

Olivia deposits \$7,000 in an account that earns 7% simple interest. About how long will it take for her account balance to reach \$8,000?

1 Understand the Problem

Rewrite the question as a statement:

- Find the number of years it will take for Olivia's account balance to reach \$8,000.

List the **important information:**

- The principal is \$7,000.
- The interest rate is 7%.
- Her account balance will be \$8,000.

2 Make a Plan

Olivia's account balance A includes the principal plus the interest: $A = P + I$. Once you solve for I, you can use $I = P \cdot r \cdot t$ to find the time.

3 Solve

$A = P + I$

$8{,}000 = 7{,}000 + I$ — *Substitute.*

$\underline{-7{,}000} \quad \underline{-7{,}000}$ — *Subtract to isolate the variable.*

$1{,}000 = I$

$I = P \cdot r \cdot t$

$1{,}000 = 7{,}000 \cdot 0.07 \cdot t$ — *Substitute. Use 0.07 for 7%.*

$1{,}000 = 490t$ — *Multiply.*

$\frac{1{,}000}{490} = \frac{490t}{490}$ — *Divide to isolate the variable.*

$2.04 \approx t$ — *Round to the nearest hundredth.*

It will take just over 2 years.

4 Look Back

After exactly 2 years, Olivia's money will have earned \$980 in simple interest and her account balance will be \$7,980.

$$I = 7{,}000 \cdot 0.07 \cdot 2 = 980$$

So it will take just over 2 years for her account to reach \$8,000.

Think and Discuss

1. **Write** the value of t for a time period of 6 months.
2. **Show** how to find r if $I = \$10$, $P = \$100$, and $t = 2$ years.

COMMON ERROR ALERT

Some students might make errors when substituting values. Remind them to begin by writing the simple interest formula. Then they can systematically substitute values and decide how to solve for the missing value.

Additional Examples

Example 1

Find each missing value.

A. $I =$ ▒, $P = \$575$, $r = 8\%$, $t = 3$ years — **$I = \$138$**

B. $I = \$204$, $P = \$1{,}700$, $r =$ ▒, $t = 6$ years — **$r = 2\%$**

Example 2

Avery deposits \$6,000 in an account that earns 4% simple interest. How long will it take for the total amount in his account to reach \$6,800?

$3\frac{1}{3}$ years

Example 1 note: Remind students that the rates are expressed as percents. They must be written as decimals to be used in the formula. Remind students that decimals must be converted to percents when they are stating interest rates.

3 Close

Reaching All Learners

Through Home Connection

Have students work with family members to prepare a short description of some of the different ways in which interest affects savings, investments, and debts. Have students list some of the interest rates for different bank accounts, credit cards, or other loans.

Possible answers: Interest is money earned on savings and investments, but it can also be additional money paid while you are repaying a debt, such as a mortgage or car loan. Savings accounts, IRAs, and CDs are examples of investments that earn interest. Credit cards, mortgages, and car loans are examples of debt for which interest must be paid.

Summarize

Have students write the simple interest formula and explain what each variable in the simple interest formula represents. Then ask students how to find the time if the interest, principal, and interest rate are known.

$I = P \cdot r \cdot t$; I = interest, P = principal, r = rate, t = time (in years); Possible answer: Use the formula $I = P \cdot r \cdot t$. Substitute the values for I, P, and r. Then solve the equation for t.

Answers to Think and Discuss

1. Six months is one-half year. Possible answers: $t = 0.5, \frac{1}{2}$, or $\frac{6}{12}$
2. Possible answer: $I = P \cdot r \cdot t$

$10 = 100 \cdot r \cdot 2$

$10 = 200 \cdot r$

$\frac{10}{200} = \frac{200}{200} \cdot r$

$0.05 = r$

$5\% = r$

6-6 PRACTICE & ASSESS

Students may want to refer back to the lesson examples.

Assignment Guide

If you finished Example 1 assign:
Core 1–4, 6–11, 15, 17, 25–30
Enriched 1–4, 7–11 odd, 14–18, 25–30

If you finished Example 2 assign:
Core 1–13, 15–21 odd, 25–30
Enriched 1–13 odd, 14–30

Notes

6-6 Exercises

FOR EXTRA PRACTICE
see page 667

internet connect
Homework Help Online
go.hrw.com Keyword: MS4 6-6

GUIDED PRACTICE

See Example 1
Find each missing value.

1. $I =$ ▒, $P = \$300$, $r = 4\%$, $t = 2$ years **$I = \$24$**
2. $I =$ ▒, $P = \$500$, $r = 2\%$, $t = 1$ year **$I = \$10$**
3. $I = \$120$, $P =$ ▒, $r = 6\%$, $t = 5$ years **$P = \$400$**
4. $I = \$240$, $P = \$4{,}000$, $r =$ ▒, $t = 2$ years **$r = 3\%$**

See Example 2
5. Scott deposits \$8,000 in an account that earns 6% simple interest. How long will it be before the total amount is \$10,000? **just over 4 years**

INDEPENDENT PRACTICE

See Example 1
Find each missing value.

6. $I =$ ▒, $P = \$600$, $r = 7\%$, $t = 2$ years **$I = \$84$**
7. $I =$ ▒, $P = \$12{,}000$, $r = 3\%$, $t = 9$ years **$I = \$3{,}240$**
8. $I = \$364$, $P = \$1{,}300$, $r =$ ▒, $t = 7$ years **$r = 4\%$**
9. $I = \$440$, $P =$ ▒, $r = 5\%$, $t = 4$ years **$P = \$2{,}200$**
10. $I = \$455$, $P =$ ▒, $r = 7\%$, $t = 5$ years **$P = \$1{,}300$**
11. $I = \$231$, $P = \$700$, $r =$ ▒, $t = 3$ years **$r = 11\%$**

See Example 2
12. Broderick deposits \$6,000 in an account that earns 5.5% simple interest. How long will it be before the total amount is \$9,000? **just over 9 years**
13. Teresa deposits \$4,000 in an account that earns 7% simple interest. How long will it be before the total amount is \$6,500? **almost 9 years**

PRACTICE AND PROBLEM SOLVING

Complete the table.

	Principal	Interest Rate	Time	Simple Interest	
14.	\$2,455	3%	▒	\$441.90	**6 years**
15.	▒	4.25%	3 years	\$663	**\$5,200**
16.	\$18,500	▒	42 months	\$1,942.50	**3%**
17.	\$425.50	5%	10 years	▒	**\$212.75**
18.	▒	6%	3 years	\$2,952	**\$16,400**

19. ***FINANCE*** How many years will it take for \$4,000 to double at a simple interest rate of 5%? **20 years**

Math Background

Simple interest is interest that is paid only on the principal, or original amount borrowed or invested. The formula for simple interest is as follows:

$I = Prt$, where
I = the amount of interest earned or paid,
P = the principal,
r = the interest rate expressed as a decimal, and
t = the number of years the money is borrowed or invested.

As long as any three of the values in the simple interest formula are known, the fourth value can be calculated.

RETEACH 6-6

CHAPTER 6-6 **Reteach**
Simple Interest

When you put money into a bank account, you may receive simple interest for loaning the bank your money.

Interest = Principal • Rate • Time
$I = p \cdot r \cdot t$

You can use the expression $\frac{I}{p \cdot r \cdot t}$ to solve interest problems.

- To find interest (I), put your finger over I. Perform the operations for letters you see.
- To find principal (p), put your finger over p. Perform the operations for letters you see.
- To find interest rate (r), put your finger over r. Perform the operations for letters you see.

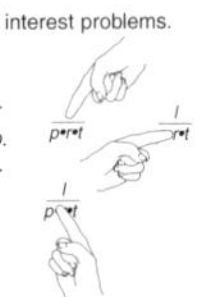

Find each missing value.

1. $p = \$400$, $r = 5\%$, $t = 3$ years
   $I = p \cdot r \cdot t$
   $I =$ **400** • **0.05** • **3**
   $I =$ **\$60**
2. $p = \$15{,}000$, $r = 6\%$, $t = 2$ years
   $I = p \cdot r \cdot t$
   $I =$ **\$15,000** • **0.06** • **2**
   $I =$ **\$1,800**
3. $I = \$350$, $r = 7\%$, $t = 2$ years
   $p = \frac{I}{r \cdot t}$
   $p = \frac{350}{0.07 \cdot 2}$
   $p =$ **\$2,500**
4. $I = \$168$, $p = \$1{,}400$, $t = 4$ years
   $r = \frac{I}{p \cdot t}$
   $r = \frac{168}{1{,}400 \cdot 4}$
   $r =$ **0.03** = **3%**
5. $I = \$57$, $p = \$380$, $t = 5$ years
   $r =$ **3%**
6. $p = \$4{,}800$, $r = 6\%$, $t = 2$ years
   $I =$ **\$576**
7. $I = \$1{,}200$, $r = 4\%$, $t = 4$ years
   $p =$ **\$7,500**
8. $p = \$750$, $r = 7\%$, $t = 3$ years
   $I =$ **\$157.50**

PRACTICE 6-6

LESSON 6-6 **Practice B**
Simple Interest

Find each missing value.

1. $p = \$1{,}500$, $r = 5\%$, $t = 3$ years
   $I =$ **\$225**
2. $p = \$6{,}000$, $r = 4\%$, $t = 2$ years
   $I =$ **\$480**
3. $I = \$30$, $r = 4\%$, $t = 2$ years
   $p =$ **\$375**
4. $I = \$180$, $r = 5\%$, $t = 3$ years
   $p =$ **\$1,200**
5. $I = \$20$, $p = \$250$, $t = 2$ years
   $r =$ **4%**
6. $I = \$144$, $p = \$800$, $t = 3$ years
   $r =$ **6%**
7. $p = \$525$, $r = 3\%$, $t = 1$ year
   $I =$ **\$15.75**
8. $p = \$3{,}200$, $r = 6\%$, $t = 4$ years
   $I =$ **\$768**
9. $I = \$450$, $r = 6\%$, $t = 4$ years
   $p =$ **\$1,875**
10. $I = \$1{,}440$, $r = 3\%$, $t = 5$ years
    $p =$ **\$9,600**
11. $I = \$1{,}275$, $p = \$5{,}100$, $t = 5$ years
    $r =$ **5%**
12. $I = \$3{,}920$, $p = \$14{,}000$, $t = 4$ years
    $r =$ **7%**
13. $p = \$1{,}300$, $r = 4.5\%$, $t = 6$ months
    $I =$ **\$29.25**
14. $I = \$47.25$, $r = 3.5\%$, $t = 1.5$ years
    $p =$ **\$900**
15. $I = \$891$, $p = \$2{,}700$, $t = 5.5$ years
    $r =$ **6%**
16. $I = \$126$, $p = \$400$, $t = 9$ years
    $r =$ **3.5%**
17. You deposit \$2,500 in an account that earns 4% simple interest. How long will it be before the total amount is \$3,000? **5 years**
18. You deposit \$5,000 in account that earns 6.5% simple interest. How much will be in the account after 3 years? **\$5,975**
19. A deposit of \$10,000 was made to an account the year you were born. After 12 years, the account is worth \$16,600. What simple interest rate did the account earn? **5.5%**
20. How long will it take for \$6,500 to double at a simple interest rate of 7%? Round to the nearest tenth of a year. **14.3 years**

The Flemish painter Marinus van Reymerswaele painted several portraits of bankers and tax collectors. His *The Money-Changer and His Wife* was finished in 1539 and is now in a museum in Madrid, Spain.

go.hrw.com KEYWORD: MS4 Reserve

CNN Student News

20. ***BANKING*** The graph shows interest rate returns for different types of investment as of July 2001.
    a. How much more interest was earned on \$8,000 deposited for 6 months in a statement savings account than in a passbook savings account? **\$4**
    b. How much money was lost on \$5,000 invested in S&P 500 stocks for one year? **\$525**
    c. Compare the returns on \$12,000 invested in the high-yield 1-year CD and the Dow Jones industrials for one year.

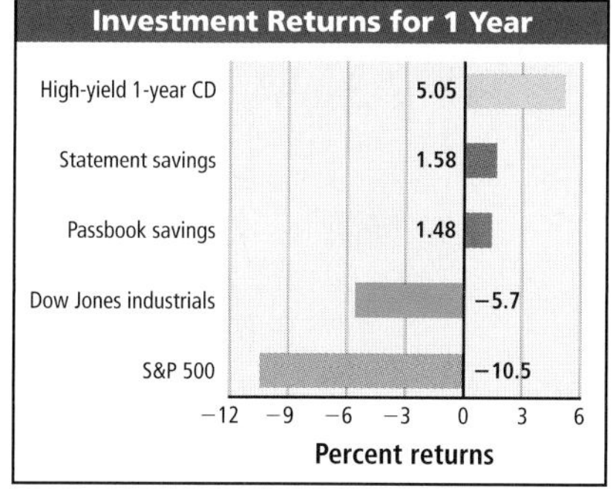

Source: USA Today

21. ***BANKING*** Alexis put \$400 in an account that earns 2% simple interest. At the end of the first year, the bank deposited the interest earned on the principal into her account. After that, the money in Alexis's account included both the principal and the interest, and the entire sum earned interest. How much will Alexis have in the account at the end of 2 years? **\$416.16**

22. ***WRITE A PROBLEM*** Use the graph in Exercise 20 to write a problem that can be solved by using the simple interest formula.

23. ***WRITE ABOUT IT*** Explain whether you would pay more simple interest on a loan if you used plan A or plan B.

    Plan A: \$1,500 for 8 years at 6%

    Plan B: \$1,500 for 6 years at 8%

24. ***CHALLENGE*** The Jacksons are opening a savings account for their child's college education. In 18 years, they will need about \$134,000. If the account earns 6% simple interest, how much money must the Jacksons invest now to cover the cost of the college education? **\$64,423.08**

Spiral Review

Write each fraction as a percent. (Lesson 6-1)

25. $\frac{1}{20}$ **5%** 26. $\frac{3}{5}$ **60%** 27. $\frac{7}{50}$ **14%** 28. $\frac{11}{25}$ **44%**

29. **TEST PREP** What percent of 150 is 48? (Lesson 6-4) **A**

    A 32% B 50% C 72% D 312.5%

30. **TEST PREP** The regular price of a helmet is \$36.50. It is on sale for 20% off. What is the sale price of the helmet? (Lesson 6-5) **H**

    F \$7.30 G \$16.50 H \$29.20 J \$35.77

COMMON ERROR ALERT

Caution students to read Exercise 21 carefully. The simple interest must be computed every year for each of the two years, with a different principal each time. Although the principal changes, the interest rate and the time ($t = 1$) remain the same.

Answers

20. c. high yield CD: gain \$606; Dow Jones: loss \$684; a difference of \$1,290

22. Possible answer: How much interest was earned on \$500 in a high-yield 1-year CD that was deposited for 1 year?

23. Since $1{,}500 \cdot 0.06 \cdot 8 = 720$ and $1{,}500 \cdot 0.08 \cdot 6 = 720$, the simple interest is the same.

Journal

Ask students to write about what they would consider if they were looking for a bank in which to deposit \$100 in a savings account. Have students explain their considerations.

Test Prep Doctor

For Exercise 29, estimation and mental math are good strategies: 48 is close to 50, and 50 is about one-third of 150. One-third of 150 is about 33%. With that estimate, students can eliminate choices **B, C,** and **D.**

CHALLENGE 6-6

LESSON 6-6 **Challenge**
Adding On

Simple interest is the amount of interest earned on the original principal. However, you can earn interest on the interest as well as on the principal. This is called **compound interest.**

Josef deposits \$400 in a bank that pays 5% interest, compounded annually. Find the amount of interest and principal in Josef's account after 3 years.

Interest and Principal

Year 1	Year 2	Year 3
$I = p \cdot r \cdot t$	$I = p \cdot r \cdot t$	$I = p \cdot r \cdot t$
$= 400 \cdot 0.05 \cdot 1$	$= 420 \cdot 0.05 \cdot 1$	$= 441 \cdot 0.05 \cdot 1$
= 20	= 21	= 22.05
Interest is \$20.	Interest is \$21.	Interest is \$22.05.
Principal is \$420.	Principal is \$441.	Principal is \$463.05.

The amount of interest earned after 3 years is \$20 + \$21 + \$22.05 = \$63.05.

The amount of principal plus interest after 3 years is \$400 + \$63.05 = \$463.05.

You can also find the total of principal and interest on \$400 for 3 years at 5% by multiplying on a calculator $400 \cdot 1.05 \cdot 1.05 \cdot 1.05$. This shows the amount of interest and principal in Josef's bank account after 3 years, or \$463.05.

Find the total amount of interest and principal if interest is compounded annually.

1. \$500 for 2 years at 4% **\$540.80**
2. \$1,200 for 3 years at 4.5% **\$1,369.40**
3. \$300 for 4 years at 5.5% **\$371.65**
4. \$750 for 2 years at 5.5% **\$834.77**
5. \$98 for 3 years at 6.5% **\$118.38**
6. \$1,056 for 4 years at 5.25% **\$1,295.84**
7. \$520 for 5 years at 4.75% **\$655.80**
8. \$873 for 6 years at 5.2% **\$1,183.34**

PROBLEM SOLVING 6-6

LESSON 6-6 **Problem Solving**
Simple Interest

Write the correct answer.

Use the graph to solve Exercises 1–3.

AEA Bank Simple Interest CDs

Term (days): over 270; 180–269; 90–179; 30–89; 14–29

Interest Rate (%): 2.2 2.4 2.6 2.8 3

1. How much more interest would be earned on a \$100,000 CD for 9 months than for 6 months? **\$775**
2. A customer earned \$3,262.50 interest on a 9-month CD. How much was the opening deposit? **\$150,000 deposit**
3. Mrs. Wallace bought a \$125,000 CD with a term of 3 years. How much will she earn in 3 years? **\$10,875**
4. Until June 2002, the simple interest rate on Stafford loans to college students was 5.39% while the student was still in college. How much interest would a student pay on a \$1,500 loan for 2 years? **\$161.70**
5. Diego deposits \$4,200 into a savings account that pays 5% simple interest. He decides not to touch the money until it doubles. How long will Diego have to keep the money in this account? **20 years**

Choose the letter of the best answer.

6. Scott took out a 4-year car loan for \$5,500. He paid back a total of \$7,370. What interest rate did he pay for this loan?
   A 9.5% B 9% (C) 8.5% D 7.5%
7. How much interest would you earn if you were to deposit \$575 for 3 months at 2.88% simple interest?
   (F) \$4.14 G \$4.83 H \$41.40 J \$48.30
8. How long would you need to keep \$775 in an account that pays 3% simple interest to earn \$93 interest?
   (A) 4 years B 2 years C 4 months D 2 months
9. If you borrow \$12,000 for 30 months at 6.5% simple interest, what is the total amount you will have to repay?
   F \$12,065 G \$12,780 (H) \$13,950 J \$21,500

Lesson Quiz

Find each missing value.

1. $I =$ ▢, $P = 800$, $r = 10\%$, $t = 3$ years **\$240**
2. $I = \$18$, $P = \$150$, $r =$ ▢, $t = 2$ years **6%**
3. $I = \$640$, $P =$ ▢, $r = 4\%$, $t = 8$ years **\$2,000**
4. $I = \$120$, $P = \$600$, $r = 5\%$, $t =$ ▢ **4 years**
5. Dennis deposits \$6,000 in an account that earns 5.5% simple interest. How long will it take before the total amount is \$8,000? **a little over 6 years**

Available on Daily Transparency in CRB

Problem Solving on Location

Michigan

Purpose: *To provide additional practice for problem-solving skills in Chapters 1–6*

Mackinac Island State Park

- After problem 1, have students find the percent of time, as of 2000, that Fort Mackinac (built in 1780) stood on Mackinac Island without being part of a national or state park. $\frac{95}{220} \approx 43.2\%$
- After problem 3, have students explain how to find percent increase. Divide the change in value by the original value. Then have students determine what the percent increase in the total length of the roads and trails in the park would be if 15 miles were added. $\approx 21.4\%$

Extension Have students research to find out which parks were the first 12 national parks and the years they were established. Then have students find the percent of these 12 parks established from 1875 to 1895.

National Park	Year Established
Yellowstone	1872
Mackinac	1875
Sequoia	1890
General Grant	1890
Yosemite	1890
Mount Rainier	1899
Crater Lake	1902
Wind Cave	1903
Sullys Hill	1904
Mesa Verde	1906
Platt	1906
Glacier	1910

$33\frac{1}{3}\%$ of the first 12 national parks were established during the 20-year period when Mackinac Island was part of a national park.

Problem Solving on Location

MICHIGAN

Mackinac Island State Park

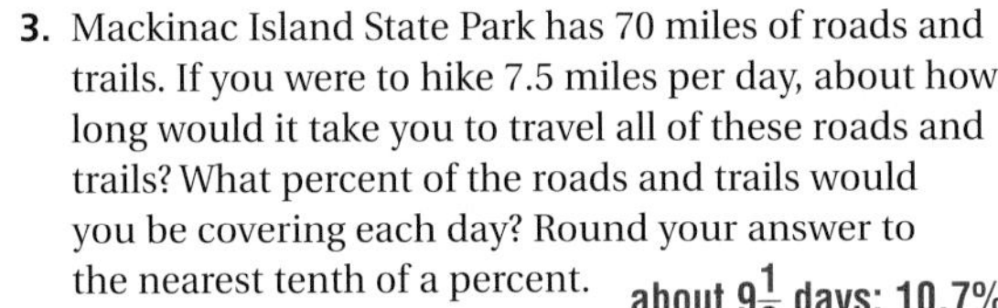

Located on Lake Huron between the Upper and Lower Peninsulas, Mackinac Island is the location of a British fort that was built during the Revolutionary War. Mackinac Island State Park began as Mackinac National Park in 1875 and was transferred to the state of Michigan in 1895.

1. As of 2000, there had been either a national or a state park on Mackinac Island for 125 years. What percent of that time was it a national park? Round your answer to the nearest whole percent. **16%**
2. Approximately 80% of Mackinac Island is covered by wooded parkland. To preserve this land, automobiles are not permitted on the island. If there are about 1,800 acres of wooded parkland, how large is Mackinac Island? **2,250 acres**
3. Mackinac Island State Park has 70 miles of roads and trails. If you were to hike 7.5 miles per day, about how long would it take you to travel all of these roads and trails? What percent of the roads and trails would you be covering each day? Round your answer to the nearest tenth of a percent. **about $9\frac{1}{3}$ days; 10.7%**

Michigan State University

Michigan State University is located in East Lansing. It was founded in 1855 and was the nation's first agricultural college.

1. In 2001, there were about 18,000 female students at Michigan State. Women made up about 53% of the student body, including full- and part-time students. Write and solve an equation to find how many students, to the nearest thousand, were at Michigan State in 2001.
   $0.53x = 18{,}000$; $x \approx 34{,}000$ students
2. Each year, about 22,700 students apply for admission to Michigan State University. Of these applicants, about 15,600 are accepted. What percent of applicants does Michigan State University accept? **about 69%**

First-Year Student's Annual Expenses at Michigan State University (2001)	
Application fee: $30	Room and board: $4,688
Tuition for Michigan residents: $5,686	Books and supplies: $870
Tuition for out-of-state residents: $13,614	Personal expenses: $990

For 3–6, use the table above.

3. Josh lives in Michigan. When Josh was a high school freshman, his parents put $4,000 in a bank account that earned 4.5% simple interest for 4 years. After withdrawing the total amount in the account, how much more will Josh need for his first year of tuition at Michigan State?
   He will still need $966.
4. What is the total annual cost for a first-year out-of-state resident to go to Michigan State University? About what percent of this cost will go toward room and board?
   $20,192; about 23% goes toward room and board.
5. If tuition for out-of-state residents increases by 2% for the next year, how much will the new tuition be to the nearest dollar? **$13,886**

6. Tyrone lives in New York but plans to go to Michigan State University. He has saved 35% of his first-year tuition so far. How much more money to the nearest dollar must Tyrone save to pay his tuition for his first year at Michigan State?
   He needs to save another $8,849.

Michigan State University

- After problem 2, have students find, to the nearest whole number, the percent of students who apply to Michigan State University and are not accepted. Ask students to explain how they got the answer. Possible answer: 31%; subtract the answer to problem 2 from 100%.
- After problem 4, have students find how much it would cost a first-year Michigan resident to live on campus and attend Michigan State. $12,264 About what percent of this cost will go toward room and board? $\approx$38.2%

Extension: Have students compare the cost of Michigan resident tuition with the cost of out-of-state tuition for a first-year student. Have them state the approximate cost for a Michigan resident as a percent of the cost for an out-of-state resident. about 42% Have students state the approximate cost for a Michigan resident living on campus as a percent of the total cost for a first-year out-of-state resident living on campus. about 61%

MATH-ABLES

Game Resources

Puzzles, Twisters & Teasers
Chapter 6 Resource Book

Lighten Up

Purpose: *To apply the problem-solving skill of making a list to perform a fun activity*

Discuss: Suggest that students draw the shapes for the numbers 3 through 9 and indicate which bulbs are needed to make up each of the numbers. Have students make a list showing the total number of times each bulb is used to produce the numbers 0 through 9.

Bulb	Frequency
a	8
b	6
c	8
d	7
e	4
f	9
g	7

Ask students to find the total number of bulbs needed to make all 10 digits simultaneously. 49 bulbs Which digit requires all 7 bulbs to be lit? 8

Extend: Have students pick a time of day and find how many of each bulb would be needed to light up the time.
Possible answer: 10:23; a: 3, b: 1, c: 4, d: 2, e: 2, f: 3, g: 3

Percent Bingo

Purpose: *To practice using percent in a game format*

Discuss: When a student gets bingo, have him or her demonstrate for the class how each winning solution was obtained.

Extend: Create new bingo cards in which there is a percent problem in each box. For example, the problem in the box might be "25% of 24." The caller calls out a solution to a percent problem. Players mark off the box containing the problem.

MATH-ABLES

Lighten Up

On a digital clock, up to seven light bulbs make up each digit on the display. You can label each light bulb as shown below.

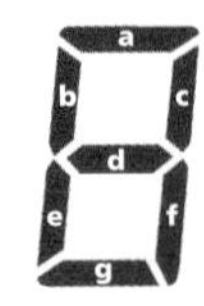

If each number were lit up for the same amount of time, you could find out which light bulb is lit the greatest percent of the time. You could also find out which light bulb is lit the least percent of the time.

For each number 0–9, list the letters of the light bulbs that are used when that number is showing. The first few numbers have been done for you.

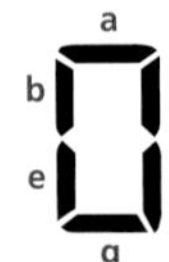

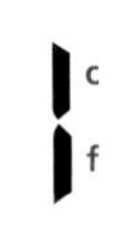

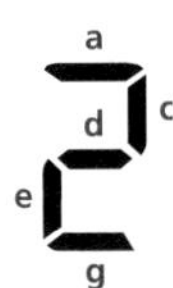

Once you have determined which bulbs are lit for each number, count how many times each bulb is lit. What percent of the time is each bulb lit? What does this tell you about which bulb will burn out first?

Percent Bingo

Each bingo card has numbers and percents on it. The caller has a collection of percent problems. The caller reads a problem. Then the players solve the problem, and the solution is a number or a percent. If players have the solution on their card, they mark it off. Normal bingo rules apply. You can win with a horizontal, vertical, or diagonal row.

Go to **go.hrw.com** for a complete set of rules and game pieces.
KEYWORD: MS4 Game6

Answers

The table shows the percent of time each bulb is lit, assuming each number is lit for the same amount of time.

Bulb	Percent
a	80%
b	60%
c	80%
d	70%
e	40%
f	90%
g	70%

Bulb f is most likely to burn out first.

Create Circle Graphs

internet connect
Lab Resources Online
go.hrw.com
KEYWORD: MS4 TechLab6

A circle graph shows the relationship of parts to a whole. You can use a spreadsheet to create circle graphs.

Activity

1. The table shows the number of videos rented in one week. Use a spreadsheet to create a circle graph of the data.

   Enter the data in the spreadsheet as shown below. Highlight the types and numbers of rentals by clicking on cell **A2** and dragging down to cell **B5.** Select the Graph Wizard tool and select the **Pie** option from the **Chart Type** list. Then click Finish to choose the first type of circle graph.

Videos Rented

Type	Number of Rentals
Classics	200
Comedy	250
Drama	250
Kids	300

	A	B
1	Type	Number of Rentals
2	Classics	200
3	Comedy	250
4	Drama	250
5	Kids	300

Classics 20%
Comedy 25%
Drama 25%
Kids 30%

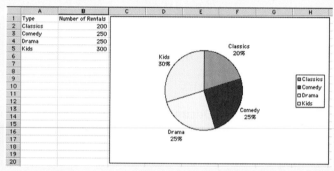

The graph shown uses an option that displays the types of movies and the percent each type is of the total.

Think and Discuss

1. Explain the advantages of using a circle graph rather than a bar graph to represent the data in the Activity.

Try This

1. The table shows the results of a survey to determine students' favorite subjects. Use a spreadsheet to make a circle graph of the data.

Subject	English	Health	History	Math	Science
Number of Students	179	108	234	242	184

Answers

Think and Discuss

1. Possible answer: with a circle graph you can compare the percent of one type of video rented with the percents of other types, as well as with the total number of videos rented.

Try This

1. **Students' Favorite Subjects**

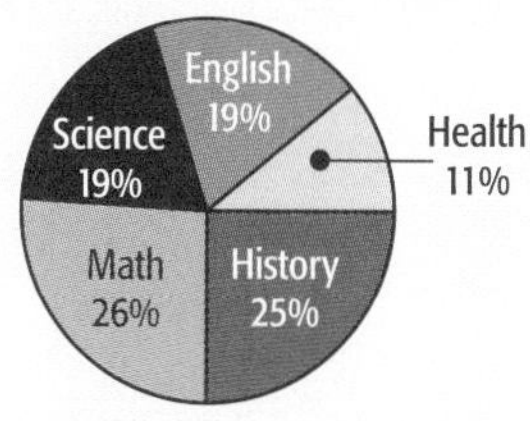

Create Circle Graphs

Objective: To use a spreadsheet to create a circle graph

Materials: Computer with spreadsheet software

Lab Resources

Technology Lab Activities .... p. 35

Using the Page

This technology activity shows students how to use a spreadsheet to create a circle graph. The instructions given are for Microsoft Excel.

The Think and Discuss problem can be used to assess students' understanding of the advantages of using a circle graph rather than a bar graph. While circle graphs can be drawn without a spreadsheet, Try This problem 1 helps students become familiar with using spreadsheet software to create a circle graph.

Assessment

1. The table shows the number of DVDs rented in one week. Use a spreadsheet to create a circle graph of the data.

DVDs Rented in a Week

Type	Number of Rentals
Classic	125
Comedy	150
Drama	175
Children's	50

Number of Rentals

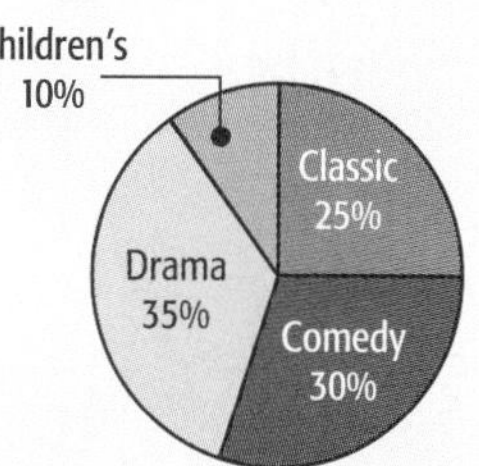

Chapter 6 **Study Guide and Review**

Purpose: *To help students review and practice concepts and skills presented in Chapter 6*

Assessment Resources

Chapter Review

Chapter 6 Resource Book . . . pp. 62–63

***Test and Practice Generator* CD-ROM**

Additional review assessment items in both multiple-choice and free-response format may be generated for any objective in Chapter 6.

Answers

1. interest, simple interest, principal
2. percent of increase
3. percent of decrease
4. percent
5. 0.78
6. 0.4
7. 0.05
8. 1.19
9. 60%
10. 16.7%
11. 66.7%
12. 8%

Chapter 6 **Study Guide and Review**

Study Guide and Review

Vocabulary

Complete the sentences below with vocabulary words from the list above. Words may be used more than once.

1. __?__ is an amount that is collected or paid for the use of money. The equation $I = P \cdot r \cdot t$ is used for calculating __?__. The letter P represents the __?__ and the letter r represents the annual rate.
2. The ratio of an amount of increase to the original amount is the __?__.
3. The ratio of an amount of decrease to the original amount is the __?__.
4. A(n) __?__ is a ratio whose denominator is 100.

6-1 Fractions, Decimals, and Percents (pp. 304–307)

EXAMPLE

- Write 12% as a decimal.

$12\% = \frac{12}{100}$
$= 0.12$

- Write $\frac{7}{8}$ as a percent.

$\frac{7}{8} = 7 \div 8$
$= 0.875$
$= 87.5\%$

EXERCISES

Write each percent as a decimal.

5. 78%
6. 40%
7. 5%
8. 119%

Write each fraction as a percent. Round to the nearest tenth of a percent, if necessary.

9. $\frac{3}{5}$
10. $\frac{1}{6}$
11. $\frac{2}{3}$
12. $\frac{2}{25}$

6-2 Estimate with Percents (pp. 308–311)

EXAMPLE

- **Estimate 26% of 77.**

$26\% \text{ of } 77 \approx \frac{1}{4} \cdot 77$

$\approx \frac{1}{4} \cdot 80$

≈ 20

26% of 77 is about 20.

EXERCISES

Estimate.

13. 22% of 44
14. 43% of 64
15. 49% of 82
16. 74% of 120
17. 31% of 97
18. 6% of 53

6-3 Percent of a Number (pp. 312–315)

EXAMPLE

- **Find the percent of the number.**

125% of 610

$\frac{125}{100} = \frac{n}{610}$

$125 \cdot 610 = 100 \cdot n$

$76{,}250 = 100n$

$\frac{76{,}250}{100} = \frac{100n}{100}$

$762.5 = n$

125% of 610 is 762.5.

EXERCISES

Find the percent of each number.

19. 16% of 425
20. 48% of 50
21. 7% of 63
22. 96% of 125
23. 130% of 21
24. 72% of 75

6-4 Solving Equations Containing Percents (pp. 316–319)

EXAMPLE

- **Solve.**

80 is 32% of what number?

$80 = 32\% \cdot n$

$80 = 0.32 \cdot n$

$\frac{80}{0.32} = \frac{0.32 \cdot n}{0.32}$

$250 = n$

80 is 32% of 250.

EXERCISES

Solve.

25. 20% of what number is 25?
26. 4 is what percent of 50?
27. 30 is 250% of what number?
28. What percent of 96 is 36?
29. 6 is 75% of what number?
30. 200 is what percent of 720?

Study Guide and Review

Answers

13. Possible answer: 8
14. Possible answer: 24
15. Possible answer: 40
16. Possible answer: 90
17. Possible answer: 32
18. Possible answer: 3
19. 68
20. 24
21. 4.41
22. 120
23. 27.3
24. 54
25. 125
26. 8%
27. 12
28. 37.5%
29. 8
30. 27.8%

Answers

31. 50%
32. 14.3%
33. 30%
34. 83.1%
35. 23.1%
36. 75%
37. \$36.75, \$208.25
38. I = \$15
39. t = 3 years
40. I = \$243
41. r = 3.9%
42. P = \$2,300
43. 7 years

Study Guide and Review

6-5 Percent of Change (pp. 324–327)

EXAMPLE

Find each percent of change. Round answers to the nearest tenth, if necessary.

- **25 is decreased to 16.**

$25 - 16 = 9$

$$\text{percent of change} = \frac{9}{25} = 0.36 = 36\%$$

The percent of decrease is 36%.

- **13.5 is increased to 27.**

$27 - 13.5 = 13.5$

$$\text{percent of change} = \frac{13.5}{13.5} = 1 = 100\%$$

The percent of increase is 100%.

EXERCISES

Find each percent of change. Round answers to the nearest tenth, if necessary.

31. 54 is increased to 81.
32. 14 is decreased to 12.
33. 110 is increased to 143.
34. 90 is decreased to 15.2.
35. 26 is increased to 32.
36. 84 is decreased to 21.
37. The regular price of a new pair of skis is \$245. This week the skis are on sale for 15% off. Find the amount of the discount and the sale price.

6-6 Simple Interest (pp. 328–331)

EXAMPLE

Find each missing value.

- **I = ▒, P = \$545, r = 1.5%, t = 2 years**

$I = P \cdot r \cdot t$

$I = 545 \cdot 0.015 \cdot 2$

$I = 16.35$

The simple interest is \$16.35.

- **I = \$825, P = ▒, r = 6%, t = 11 years**

$I = P \cdot r \cdot t$

$825 = P \cdot 0.06 \cdot 11$

$825 = P \cdot 0.66$

$\frac{825}{0.66} = \frac{P \cdot 0.66}{0.66}$

$1{,}250 = P$

The principal is \$1,250.

EXERCISES

Find each missing value.

38. I = ▒, P = \$1,000, r = 3%, t = 6 months
39. I = \$452.16, P = \$1,256, r = 12%, t = ▒
40. I = ▒, P = \$675, r = 4.5%, t = 8 years
41. I = \$555.75, P = \$950, r = ▒, t = 15 years
42. I = \$172.50, P = ▒, r = 5%, t = 18 months
43. Craig deposits \$1,000 in a savings account that earns 5% simple interest. How long will it take for the total amount in his account to reach \$1,350?

Chapter Test

Chapter 6

Write each percent as a fraction in simplest form and as a decimal.

1. 95% $\frac{19}{20}$, **0.95**
2. 37.5% $\frac{3}{8}$, **0.375**
3. 4% $\frac{1}{25}$, **0.04**
4. 0.01% $\frac{1}{10{,}000}$, **0.0001**

Write as a percent.

5. 0.75 **75%**
6. 0.06 **6%**
7. 0.8 **80%**
8. 0.0039 **0.39%**
9. $\frac{3}{10}$ **30%**
10. $\frac{9}{20}$ **45%**
11. $\frac{5}{16}$ **31.25%**
12. $\frac{21}{7}$ **300%**

Estimate. **Possible answers:**

13. 48% of 8 **4**
14. 3% of 119 **3.6**
15. 26% of 32 **8**
16. 76% of 280 **210**
17. The Pattersons spent $47.89 for a meal at a restaurant. About how much should they leave for a 15% tip? **about $7.20**

Find the percent of each number.

18. 90% of 200 **180**
19. 35% of 210 **73.5**
20. 16% of 85 **13.6**
21. 250% of 30 **75**
22. 38% of 11 **4.18**
23. 5% of 145 **7.25**

Solve.

24. 36 is what percent of 150? **24%**
25. 29 is what percent of 145? **20%**
26. 51 is what percent of 340? **15%**
27. 36 is 40% of what number? **90**
28. 70 is 14% of what number? **500**
29. 25 is 20% of what number? **125**
30. Hampton Middle School is expecting 376 seventh-graders next year. This is 40% of the expected school enrollment. How many students are expected to enroll in the school next year? **940 students**

Find each percent of change.

31. 30 is increased to 45. **50%**
32. 115 is decreased to 46. **60%**
33. 116 is increased to 145. **25%**
34. 128 is decreased to 32. **75%**
35. A community theater sold 8,500 tickets to performances during its first year. By its tenth year, ticket sales had increased by 34%. How many tickets did the theater sell during its tenth year? **11,390 tickets**

Find each missing value.

36. $I = \blacksquare$, $P = \$500$, $r = 5\%$, $t = 1$ year
37. $I = \$702$, $P = \$1{,}200$, $r = 3.9\%$, $t = \blacksquare$
38. $I = \$468$, $P = \$900$, $r = \blacksquare$, $t = 8$ years
39. $I = \$37.50$, $P = \blacksquare$, $r = 10\%$, $t = 6$ months
40. Kate invested $3,500 at a 5% simple interest rate. How many years will it take for the original amount to double? **20 years**

Chapter Test

Purpose: *To assess students' mastery of concepts and skills in Chapter 6*

Assessment Resources

Chapter 6 Tests (Levels A, B, C)
Assessment Resources ..... pp. 63–68

***Test and Practice Generator* CD-ROM**

Additional assessment items in both multiple-choice and free-response format may be generated for any objective in Chapter 6.

Answers

36. $I = \$25$
37. $t = 15$ years
38. $r = 6.5\%$
39. $P = \$750$

Chapter 6

Performance Assessment

Purpose: *To assess students' understanding of concepts in Chapter 6 and combined problem-solving skills*

Assessment Resources

Answers

4. See Level 3 work sample below.

Scoring Rubric for Problem Solving Item 4

Level 3

Accomplishes the purposes of the task.

Student gives clear explanations, shows understanding of mathematical ideas and processes, and computes accurately.

Level 2

Purposes of the task not fully achieved.

Student demonstrates satisfactory but limited understanding of the mathematical ideas and processes.

Level 1

Purposes of the task not accomplished.

Student shows little evidence of understanding the mathematical ideas and processes and makes computational and/or procedural errors.

Chapter 6

Performance Assessment

1. $I = Prt$
$2.75 = 150 \cdot r \cdot 0.5$
$2.75 = 75r$
$0.036 = r$
The bank pays about 3.7%.

Show What You Know

Create a portfolio of your work from this chapter. Complete this page and include it with your four best pieces of work from Chapter 6. Choose from your homework or lab assignments, mid-chapter quiz, or any journal entries you have done. Put them together using any design you want. Make your portfolio represent what you consider your best work.

2. $25\% \cdot \$7.00 = d;\ 0.25 \cdot 7 = d;\ d = 1.75;$
$7 - 1.75 = 5.25;\ 7.25\% \cdot 5.25 = p;\ 0.0725 \cdot 5.25 = p;$
$p = 0.380625;\ 5.25 + 0.38 = 5.63;\ 10 - 5.63 = \$4.37$

Short Response

1. A bank advertises that a deposit of $150.00 will earn $2.75 in 6 months. What simple interest rate does the bank pay? Show the work that you used to determine your answer.

2. You have a coupon for 25% off the price of a mystery novel that regularly sells for $7.00. The sales tax is 7.25%. If you gave the cashier $10.00, how much change would you expect in return? Show your work.

3. Amber's meal cost $15.70. She paid her server $18.76. Approximately what percent tip did Amber give the server? Show your calculations.

3. **$15.70 is increased to $18.76**
$\$18.76 - 15.70 = 3.06$
$\frac{3.06}{15.70} \approx 0.1949 \approx 19.5\%$

Extended Problem Solving

4. The table shows the results of a survey about favorite types of restaurants.
   a. Make a bar graph of the data in the table.
   b. Write each number as a percent. Show your work.
   c. What is the total of the four percents? How can you find this answer without adding the four percents?
   d. Explain how you can use the percents from part **b** to find how many more people prefer steak houses than prefer formal-dining restaurants. Then find this number.

Type of Restaurant	Number of People
Cafeteria	32
Fast food	63
Formal dining	38
Steak house	47

Student Work Samples for Item 4

Level 3

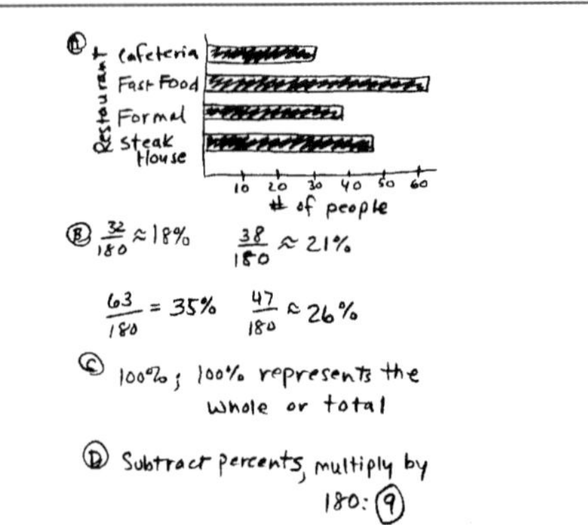

The student created an accurate graph, converted to percents, and explained the answers correctly.

Level 2

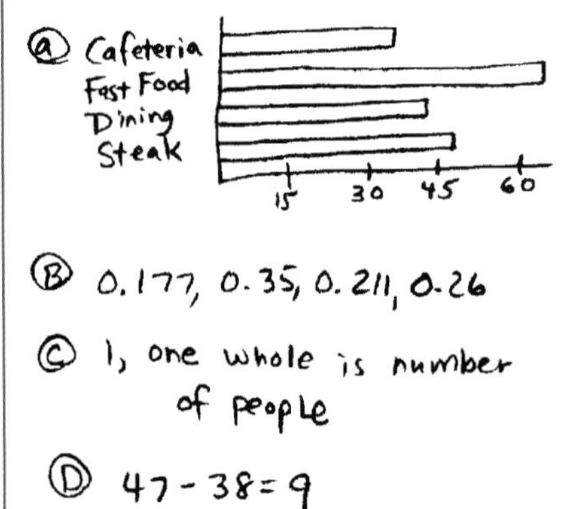

The student created an adequate graph but found decimals instead of percents. The student also did not provide a complete answer for part **d**.

Level 1

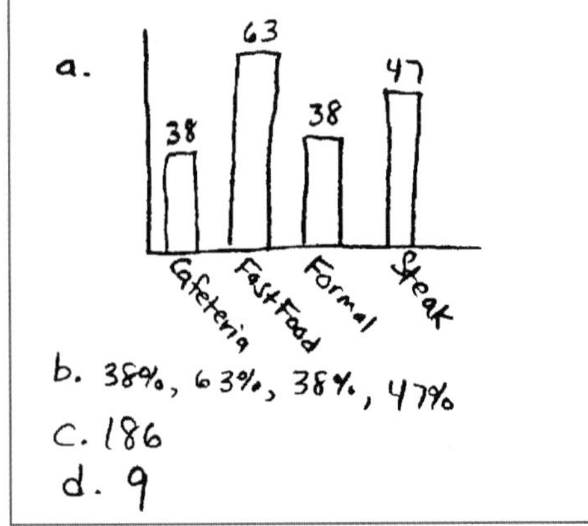

The student created a graph with no scale and mislabeled one of the bars. The student showed no understanding of percents.

internet connect
State-Specific Test Practice Online
go.hrw.com Keyword: MS4 TestPrep

Standardized Test Prep

Chapter 6

Cumulative Assessment, Chapters 1–6

1. You deposit $750 in an account that earns 5% simple interest. How much interest will your money earn in 6 months? **D**

   Ⓐ $375.00 Ⓒ $37.50
   Ⓑ $187.50 Ⓓ $18.75

2. What are all the factors of 15? **G**

   Ⓕ 3, 5 Ⓗ 3, 5, 15
   Ⓖ 1, 3, 5, 15 Ⓙ 3, 5, 10, 15

TEST TAKING TIP!
Try breaking a complex problem into smaller parts.

3. This year, 592 students said they recycle. Last year, only $\frac{5}{8}$ of that number said they recycled. How many more students recycle this year than last year? **B**

   Ⓐ 74 students Ⓒ 370 students
   Ⓑ 222 students Ⓓ 974 students

4. Which number is **not** equivalent to the other three? **J**

   Ⓕ $\frac{27}{8}$ Ⓗ $3\frac{3}{8}$
   Ⓖ 3.375 Ⓙ $\frac{61}{24}$

5. Which expression has the greatest value? **D**

   Ⓐ $-3(3) - 9$ Ⓒ $-3(-3) - 9$
   Ⓑ $-3(3) + 9$ Ⓓ $-3(-3) + 9$

6. In a survey, 28 students said that pizza is their favorite lunch. If 28 is 16% of the class, how many students are in the class? **G**

   Ⓕ 4 students Ⓗ 32 students
   Ⓖ 175 students Ⓙ 448 students

7. Divide $\frac{7}{10}$ by $2\frac{1}{2}$. **D**

   Ⓐ $1\frac{3}{4}$ Ⓒ $\frac{14}{25}$
   Ⓑ $1\frac{4}{10}$ Ⓓ $\frac{7}{25}$

8. The graph shows the results of a survey. Use the graph to determine which statement is false. **F**

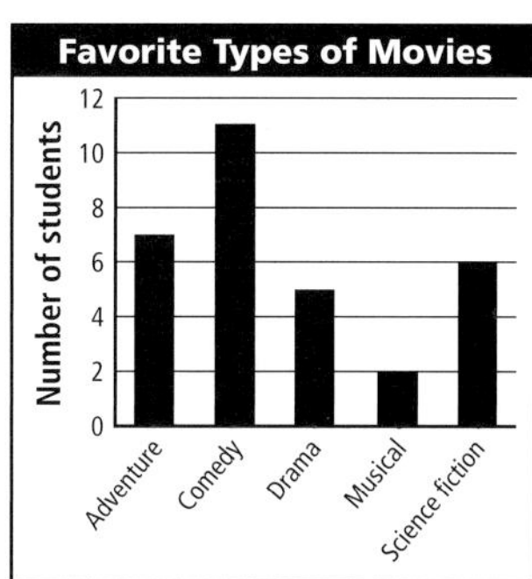

   Ⓕ More than half the students chose comedies.
   Ⓖ Musicals are less popular than dramas.
   Ⓗ Fewer than $\frac{1}{5}$ of the students chose dramas.
   Ⓙ Fewer than $\frac{1}{10}$ of the students chose musicals.

9. ***SHORT RESPONSE*** Set up a proportion to represent the following question: 50 is 125% of what number? Explain each term in your proportion. Then solve it, and show all of your steps.

10. ***SHORT RESPONSE*** Write and simplify an expression that represents the phrase "four times the difference of ten and three." Explain how you used the order of operations to simplify your expression.

Standardized Test Prep

Answers

9. $\frac{50}{x} = \frac{125}{100}$; the numerators represent the parts, and the denominators represent the wholes. 50 is part of x, and 125% is part of 100%.

$$50 \cdot 100 = x \cdot 125$$
$$\frac{5{,}000}{125} = \frac{125x}{125}$$
$$40 = x$$

10. $4(10 - 3) = 4(7) = 28$; perform operations within parentheses first, and then multiply.

Standardized Test Prep

Chapter 6

Purpose: *To provide review and practice for Chapters 1–6 and standardized tests*

Assessment Resources

Cumulative Tests (Levels A, B, C)
Assessment Resources. . . . pp. 189–200

State-Specific Test Practice Online
KEYWORD: MS4 TestPrep

Test Prep Doctor

For item 3, students should first multiply $\frac{5}{8}$ by 592 to find out how many students said they recycled last year. Since **C** is the number who recycled last year, it can be eliminated as an option. **D** can be eliminated because it is more than the number who recycled either year and cannot be the difference between them. Since 592 is about 200 more than 370, **A** can also be eliminated.

Plane Figures

Section 7A: Lines and Angles	Section 7B: Closed Figures	Section 7C: Closed Figure Relationships
Lesson 7-1 Points, Lines, and Planes	**Hands-On Lab 7C** Construct Perpendicular and Parallel Lines	**Lesson 7-9** Congruent Figures
Lesson 7-2 Angles	**Lesson 7-4** Circles	**Lesson 7-10** Transformations
Hands-On Lab 7A Explore Parallel Lines and Transversals	**Hands-On Lab 7D** Construct Circle Graphs	**Lesson 7-11** Symmetry
Lesson 7-3 Parallel and Perpendicular Lines	**Lesson 7-5** Polygons	**Hands-On Lab 7F** Create Tessellations
Hands-On Lab 7B Construct Bisectors and Congruent Angles	**Hands-On Lab 7E** Constructions with Polygons and Circles	
	Lesson 7-6 Triangles	
	Lesson 7-7 Quadrilaterals	
	Lesson 7-8 Angles in Polygons	

Pacing Guide for 45-Minute Classes

Chapter 7

DAY 85 Lesson 7-1	DAY 86 Lesson 7-2	DAY 87 Hands-On Lab 7A	DAY 88 Lesson 7-3	DAY 89 Hands-On Lab 7B
DAY 90 Mid-Chapter Quiz Hands-On Lab 7C	DAY 91 Lesson 7-4	DAY 92 Hands-On Lab 7D	DAY 93 Lesson 7-5	DAY 94 Hands-On Lab 7E
DAY 95 Lesson 7-6	DAY 96 Lesson 7-7	DAY 97 Lesson 7-8	DAY 98 Mid-Chapter Quiz Lesson 7-9	DAY 99 Lesson 7-10
DAY 100 Lesson 7-11	DAY 101 Hands-On Lab 7F	DAY 102 Chapter 7 Review	DAY 103 Chapter 7 Assessment	

Pacing Guide for 90-Minute Classes

Chapter 7

DAY 42 Chapter 6 Review Lesson 7-1	DAY 43 Chapter 6 Assessment Lesson 7-2	DAY 44 Hands-On Lab 7A Lesson 7-3	DAY 45 Hands-On Lab 7B Hands-On Lab 7C	DAY 46 Mid-Chapter Quiz Lesson 7-4 Hands-On Lab 7D

DAY 47 Lesson 7-5 Hands-On Lab 7E	DAY 48 Lesson 7-6 Lesson 7-7	DAY 49 Lesson 7-8 Lesson 7-9	DAY 50 Mid-Chapter Quiz Lesson 7-10 Lesson 7-11	DAY 51 Hands-On Lab 7F Chapter 7 Review	DAY 52 Chapter 7 Assessment Lesson 8-1

Across the Series

COURSE 1

- Identify, describe, measure, classify, and construct geometric plane figures.
- Identify angle relationships, including those formed by perpendicular lines and parallel lines with a transversal.
- Identify, classify, and compare polygons.
- Identify and use congruent figures.
- Understand and show transformations.

COURSE 2

- **Identify, describe, measure, classify, and construct geometric plane figures.**
- **Identify and use angle relationships, including those formed by perpendicular lines and parallel lines with a transversal.**
- **Find the measures of angles in polygons.**
- **Use congruent figures and symmetry.**
- **Recognize, describe, and show transformations and tessellations.**

COURSE 3

- Classify and construct geometric plane figures on a coordinate plane.
- Identify and use angle relationships, including those formed by perpendicular lines and parallel lines with a transversal.
- Find the measures of angles in polygons.
- Use congruent figures and symmetry.
- Understand, describe, and show transformations and their combinations.

Across the Curriculum

LANGUAGE ARTS LINK

Math: Reading and Writing in the Content Area . . . . pp. 57–67

Focus on Problem Solving
Understand the Problem . . . . SE p. 387

Journal . . . . TE, last page of each lesson

Write About It. . . SE pp. 347, 351, 357, 365, 377, 381, 385, 391, 395, 399

SOCIAL STUDIES LINK

Social Studies . . . . SE pp. 381, 395, 396

Geography . . . . SE p. 351

SCIENCE LINK

Life Science . . . . SE p. 399

Earth Science. . . . . SE p. 385

Geology . . . . SE p. 377

TE = *Teacher's Edition* **SE** = *Student Edition*

Interdisciplinary Bulletin Board

Art

Quilt designers can make unique designs with geometric figures. In a typical quilt, a block, a basic design unit, is repeated over and over to form the basic pattern of the quilt. Have students create a block and form a sample quilt design. Have students list all of the geometric figures they used in their design. Check students' work.

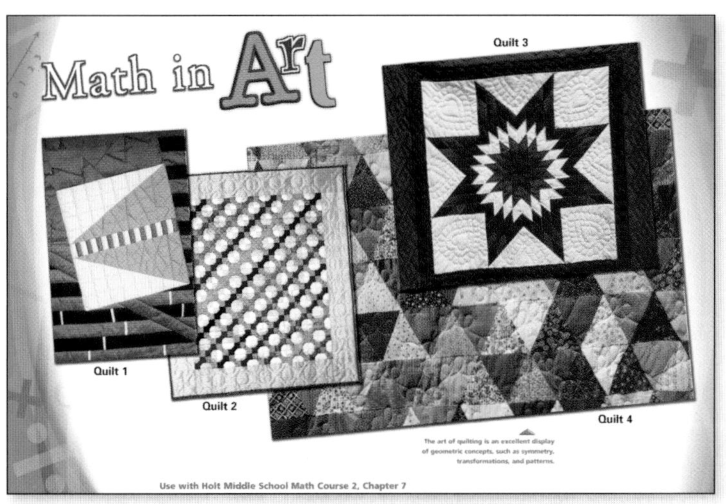

Interdisciplinary posters and worksheets are provided in your resource material.

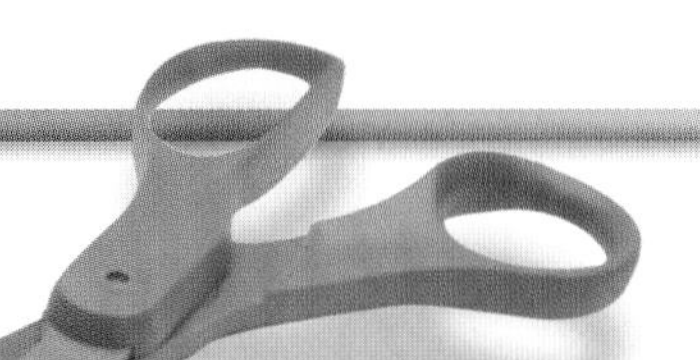

Chapter 7

Resource Options

Chapter 7 Resource Book

Student Resources

Practice (Levels A, B, C) .... pp. 9–11, 18–20, 27–29, 37–39, 46–48, 55–57, 64–66, 73–75, 83–85, 92–94, 102–104

Reteach ... pp. 12, 21, 30, 40, 49, 58, 67, 76, 86, 95–96, 105

Challenge ...... pp. 13, 22, 31, 41, 50, 59, 68, 77, 87, 97, 106

Problem Solving . pp. 14, 23, 32, 42, 51, 60, 69, 78, 88, 98, 107

Puzzles, Twisters & Teasers .... pp. 15, 24, 33, 43, 52, 61, 70, 79, 89, 99, 108

Recording Sheets .... pp. 3–4, 8, 17, 26, 36, 45, 54, 63, 72, 82, 91, 101, 112, 117–118, 121

Chapter Review .... pp. 109–111

Teacher and Parent Resources

Chapter Planning and Pacing Guide .... p. 5

Section Planning Guides .... pp. 6, 34, 80

Parent Letter .... pp. 1–2

Teaching Tools .... pp. 117–121

Teacher Support for Chapter Project .... p. 113

Transparencies .... pp. T1–T45

- Daily Transparencies
- Additional Examples Transparencies
- Teaching Transparencies

Reaching All Learners

English Language Learners

Success for English Language Learners ...... pp. 113–134

Math: Reading and Writing in the Content Area .... pp. 57–67

Spanish Homework and Practice .... pp. 57–67

Spanish Interactive Study Guide .... pp. 57–67

Spanish Family Involvement Activities .... pp. 57–68

Multilingual Glossary

Individual Needs

Are You Ready? Intervention and Enrichment pp. 129–132, 189–192, 269–272, 281–284, 417–418

Alternate Openers: Explorations .... pp. 57–67

Family Involvement Activities .... pp. 57–68

Interactive Problem Solving .... pp. 57–67

Interactive Study Guide .... pp. 57–67

Readiness Activities .... pp. 13–14

Math: Reading and Writing in the Content Area .... pp. 57–67

Challenge .... CRB pp. 13, 22, 31, 41, 50, 59, 68, 77, 87, 97, 106

Hands-On

Hands-On Lab Activities .... pp. 44–67

Technology Lab Activities .... pp. 36–40

Alternate Openers: Explorations .... pp. 57–67

Family Involvement Activities .... pp. 57–68

Applications and Connections

Consumer and Career Math .... pp. 25–28

Interdisciplinary Posters .... Poster 7, TE p. 342B

Interdisciplinary Poster Worksheets .... pp. 19–21

Transparencies

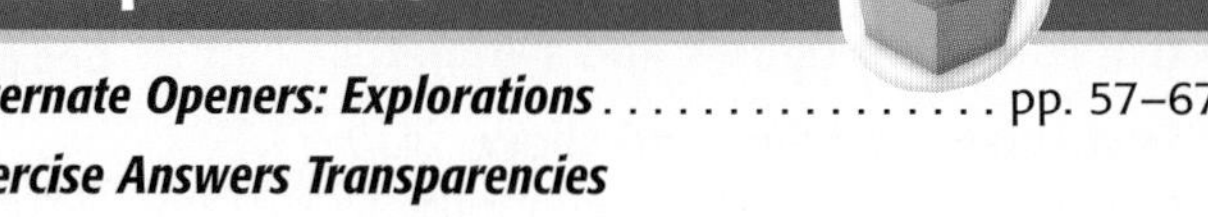

Alternate Openers: Explorations .... pp. 57–67

Exercise Answers Transparencies

Chapter 7 Resource Book .... pp. T1–T45

- Daily Transparencies
- Additional Examples Transparencies
- Teaching Transparencies

Technology

Teacher Resources

***Lesson Presentations* CD-ROM** .... Chapter 7

***Test and Practice Generator* CD-ROM** .... Chapter 7

***One-Stop Planner* CD-ROM** .... Chapter 7

Student Resources

***Are You Ready? Intervention* CD-ROM**
Skills 30, 45, 65, 68

internet connect

Homework Help Online	**KEYWORD:** MS4 HWHelp7
Math Tools Online	**KEYWORD:** MS4 Tools
Glossary Online	**KEYWORD:** MS4 Glossary
Chapter Project Online	**KEYWORD:** MS4 PSProject7
Chapter Opener Online	**KEYWORD:** MS4 Ch7
CNN Student News™	**KEYWORD:** MS4 CNN7

SE = *Student Edition* **TE** = *Teacher's Edition* **AR** = *Assessment Resources* **CRB** = *Chapter Resource Book* **MK** = *Manipulatives Kit*

Chapter 7

Assessment Options

Assessing Prior Knowledge

Determine whether students have the required prerequisite concepts and skills.

Are You Ready? . . . . SE p. 343
Inventory Test . . . . AR pp. 1–4

Test Preparation

Provide review and practice for chapter and standardized tests.

Standardized Test Prep . . . . SE p. 411
Spiral Review with Test Prep . . . . . SE, last page of each lesson
Study Guide and Review . . . . SE pp. 406–408
Test Prep Tool Kit

Technology

 ***Test and Practice Generator* CD-ROM**

internet connect

State-Specific Test Practice Online KEYWORD: MS4 TestPrep

Performance Assessment

Assess students' understanding of chapter concepts and combined problem-solving skills.

Performance Assessment . . . . SE p. 410
Includes scoring rubric in TE
Performance Assessment . . . . AR p. 118
Performance Assessment Teacher Support . . . . AR p. 117

Portfolio

Portfolio opportunities appear throughout the Student and Teacher's Editions.

Suggested work samples:

Problem Solving Project . . . . TE p. 342
Performance Assessment . . . . SE p. 410
Portfolio Guide . . . . AR p. xxxv
Journal . . . . TE, last page of each lesson
Write About It . . . . . . SE pp. 347, 351, 357, 365, 377, 381, 385, 391, 395, 399

Daily Assessment

Obtain daily feedback on students' understanding of concepts.

Spiral Review and Test Prep . . . . . . SE, last page of each lesson

Also Available on Transparency In Chapter 7 Resource Book

Warm Up . . . . TE, first page of each lesson
Problem of the Day . . . . TE, first page of each lesson
Lesson Quiz . . . . TE, last page of each lesson

Student Self-Assessment

Have students evaluate their own work.

Group Project Evaluation . . . . AR p. xxxii
Individual Group Member Evaluation . . . . AR p. xxxiii
Portfolio Guide . . . . AR p. xxxv
Journal . . . . TE, last page of each lesson

Formal Assessment

Assess students' mastery of concepts and skills.

Section Quizzes . . . . AR pp. 19–21
Mid-Chapter Quizzes . . . . SE pp. 360, 386
Chapter Test . . . . SE p. 409
Chapter Tests (Levels A, B, C) . . . . AR pp. 69–74
Cumulative Tests (Levels A, B, C) . . . . AR pp. 201–212
Standardized Test Prep
Cumulative Assessment . . . . SE p. 411
End-of-Year Test . . . . AR pp. 273–276

Technology

 ***Test and Practice Generator* CD-ROM**

Make tests electronically. This software includes:

- Dynamic practice for Chapter 7
- Customizable tests
- Multiple-choice items for each objective
- Free-response items for each objective
- Teacher management system

SE = *Student Edition* **TE** = *Teacher's Edition* **AR** = *Assessment Resources* **CRB** = *Chapter Resource Book* **MK** = *Manipulatives Kit*

Chapter 7 Tests

Three levels (A,B,C) of tests are available for each chapter in the *Assessment Resources.*

Level A

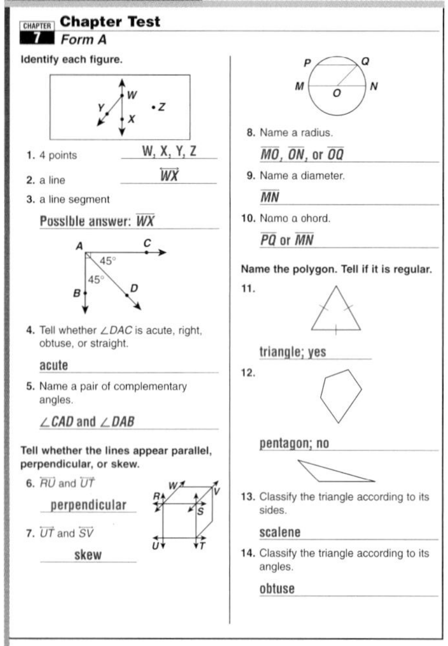

Chapter 7 Chapter Test
Form A

Identify each figure.

1. 4 points W, X, Y, Z
2. a line $\overleftrightarrow{WX}$
3. a line segment
   Possible answer: $\overline{WX}$
4. Tell whether ∠*DAC* is acute, right, obtuse, or straight.
   acute
5. Name a pair of complementary angles.
   ∠*CAD* and ∠*DAB*

Tell whether the lines appear parallel, perpendicular, or skew.

6. $\overleftrightarrow{RU}$ and $\overleftrightarrow{UT}$ perpendicular
7. $\overleftrightarrow{UT}$ and $\overleftrightarrow{SV}$ skew
8. Name a radius.
   $\overline{MO}$, $\overline{ON}$, or $\overline{OQ}$
9. Name a diameter.
   $\overline{MN}$
10. Name a chord.
    $\overline{PQ}$ or $\overline{MN}$

Name the polygon. Tell if it is regular.

11. triangle; yes
12. pentagon; no
13. Classify the triangle according to its sides.
    scalene
14. Classify the triangle according to its angles.
    obtuse

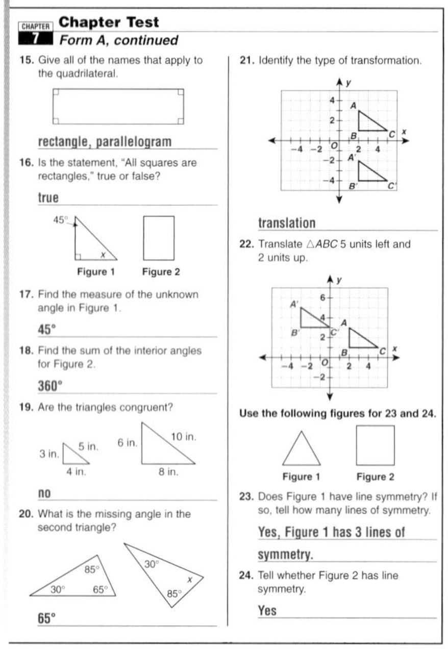

Chapter 7 Chapter Test
Form A, continued

15. Give all of the names that apply to the quadrilateral.
    rectangle, parallelogram
16. Is the statement, "All squares are rectangles," true or false?
    true
17. Find the measure of the unknown angle in Figure 1.
    45°
18. Find the sum of the interior angles for Figure 2.
    360°
19. Are the triangles congruent?
    no
20. What is the missing angle in the second triangle?
    65°
21. Identify the type of transformation.
    translation
22. Translate △*ABC* 5 units left and 2 units up.

Use the following figures for 23 and 24.

23. Does Figure 1 have line symmetry? If so, tell how many lines of symmetry.
    Yes, Figure 1 has 3 lines of symmetry.
24. Tell whether Figure 2 has line symmetry.
    Yes

Level B

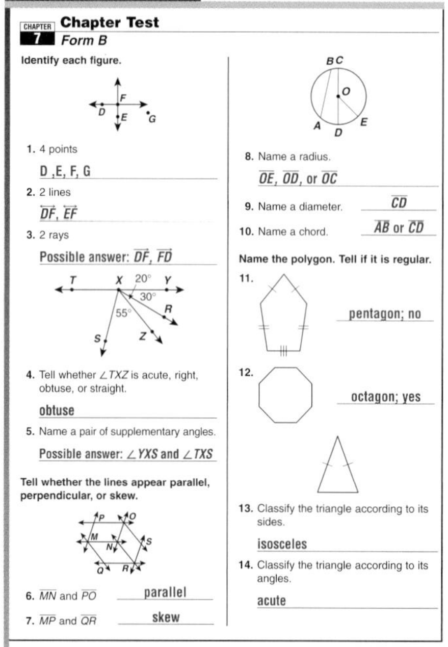

Chapter 7 Chapter Test
Form B

Identify each figure.

1. 4 points
   D, E, F, G
2. 2 lines
   $\overleftrightarrow{DF}$, $\overleftrightarrow{EF}$
3. 2 rays
   Possible answer: $\overrightarrow{DF}$, $\overrightarrow{FD}$
4. Tell whether ∠*TXZ* is acute, right, obtuse, or straight.
   obtuse
5. Name a pair of supplementary angles.
   Possible answer: ∠*YXS* and ∠*TXS*

Tell whether the lines appear parallel, perpendicular, or skew.

6. $\overleftrightarrow{MN}$ and $\overleftrightarrow{PO}$ parallel
7. $\overleftrightarrow{MP}$ and $\overleftrightarrow{QR}$ skew
8. Name a radius.
   $\overline{OE}$, $\overline{OD}$, or $\overline{OC}$
9. Name a diameter. $\overline{CD}$
10. Name a chord. $\overline{AB}$ or $\overline{CD}$

Name the polygon. Tell if it is regular.

11. pentagon; no
12. octagon; yes
13. Classify the triangle according to its sides.
    isosceles
14. Classify the triangle according to its angles.
    acute

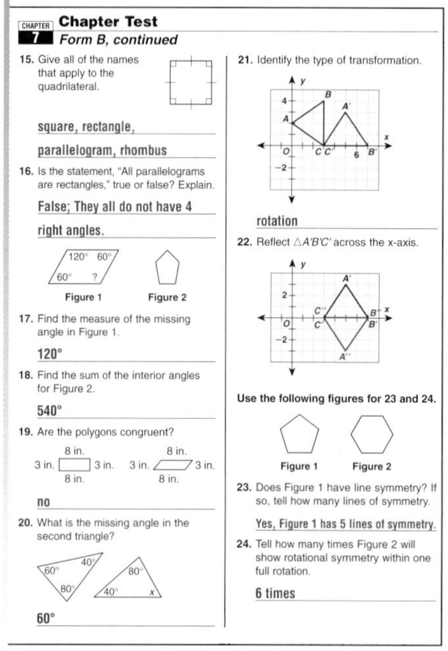

Chapter 7 Chapter Test
Form B, continued

15. Give all of the names that apply to the quadrilateral.
    square, rectangle, parallelogram, rhombus
16. Is the statement, "All parallelograms are rectangles," true or false? Explain.
    False; They all do not have 4 right angles.
17. Find the measure of the missing angle in Figure 1.
    120°
18. Find the sum of the interior angles for Figure 2.
    540°
19. Are the polygons congruent?
    no
20. What is the missing angle in the second triangle?
    60°
21. Identify the type of transformation.
    rotation
22. Reflect △*A'B'C'* across the x-axis.

Use the following figures for 23 and 24.

23. Does Figure 1 have line symmetry? If so, tell how many lines of symmetry.
    Yes, Figure 1 has 5 lines of symmetry.
24. Tell how many times Figure 2 will show rotational symmetry within one full rotation.
    6 times

Level C

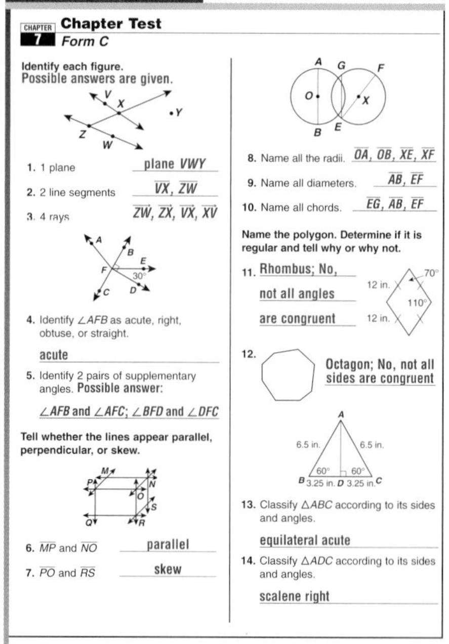

Chapter 7 Chapter Test
Form C

Identify each figure.
Possible answers are given.

1. 1 plane plane *VWY*
2. 2 line segments $\overline{VX}$, $\overline{ZW}$
3. 4 rays $\overrightarrow{ZW}$, $\overrightarrow{ZX}$, $\overrightarrow{VX}$, $\overrightarrow{XV}$
4. Identify ∠*AFB* as acute, right, obtuse, or straight.
   acute
5. Identify 2 pairs of supplementary angles. Possible answer:
   ∠*AFB* and ∠*AFC*; ∠*BFD* and ∠*DFC*

Tell whether the lines appear parallel, perpendicular, or skew.

6. $\overleftrightarrow{MP}$ and $\overleftrightarrow{NO}$ parallel
7. $\overleftrightarrow{PO}$ and $\overleftrightarrow{RS}$ skew
8. Name all the radii. $\overline{OA}$, $\overline{OB}$, $\overline{XE}$, $\overline{XF}$
9. Name all diameters. $\overline{AB}$, $\overline{EF}$
10. Name all chords. $\overline{EG}$, $\overline{AB}$, $\overline{EF}$

Name the polygon. Determine if it is regular and tell why or why not.

11. Rhombus; No, not all angles are congruent
12. Octagon; No, not all sides are congruent
13. Classify △*ABC* according to its sides and angles.
    equilateral acute
14. Classify △*ADC* according to its sides and angles.
    scalene right

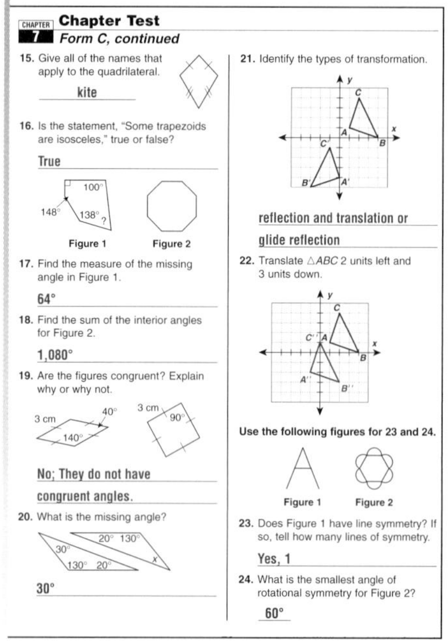

Chapter 7 Chapter Test
Form C, continued

15. Give all of the names that apply to the quadrilateral.
    kite
16. Is the statement, "Some trapezoids are isosceles," true or false?
    True
17. Find the measure of the missing angle in Figure 1.
    64°
18. Find the sum of the interior angles for Figure 2.
    1,080°
19. Are the figures congruent? Explain why or why not.
    No; They do not have congruent angles.
20. What is the missing angle?
    30°
21. Identify the types of transformation.
    reflection and translation or glide reflection
22. Translate △*ABC* 2 units left and 3 units down.

Use the following figures for 23 and 24.

23. Does Figure 1 have line symmetry? If so, tell how many lines of symmetry.
    Yes, 1
24. What is the smallest angle of rotational symmetry for Figure 2?
    60°

Test and Practice Generator CD-ROM

Create and customize multiple versions of the same tests with corresponding answers for any chosen chapter objectives.

Chapter 7 State and Standardized Test Preparation

Test Taking Skill Builder and Standardized Test Practice are provided for each chapter in the *Test Prep Tool Kit.*

TEST TAKING SKILL BUILDER

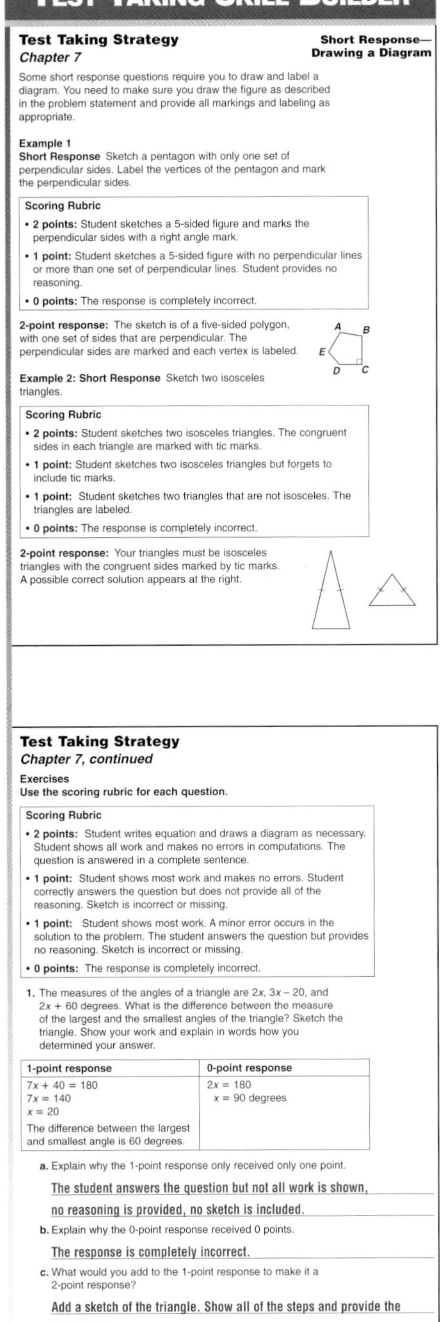

Test Taking Strategy **Short Response—Drawing a Diagram**

Chapter 7

Some short response questions require you to draw and label a diagram. You need to make sure you draw the figure as described in the problem statement and provide all markings and labeling as appropriate.

Example 1
Short Response Sketch a pentagon with only one set of perpendicular sides. Label the vertices of the pentagon and mark the perpendicular sides.

Scoring Rubric
- **2 points:** Student sketches a 5-sided figure and marks the perpendicular sides with a right angle mark.
- **1 point:** Student sketches a 5-sided figure with no perpendicular lines or more than one set of perpendicular lines. Student provides no reasoning.
- **0 points:** The response is completely incorrect.

2-point response: The sketch is of a five-sided polygon, with one set of sides that are perpendicular. The perpendicular sides are marked and each vertex is labeled.

Example 2: Short Response Sketch two isosceles triangles.

Scoring Rubric
- **2 points:** Student sketches two isosceles triangles. The congruent sides in each triangle are marked with tic marks.
- **1 point:** Student sketches two isosceles triangles but forgets to include tic marks.
- **1 point:** Student sketches two triangles that are not isosceles. The triangles are labeled.
- **0 points:** The response is completely incorrect.

2-point response: Your triangles must be isosceles triangles with the congruent sides marked by tic marks. A possible correct solution appears at the right.

Test Taking Strategy
Chapter 7, continued

Exercises
Use the scoring rubric for each question.

Scoring Rubric
- **2 points:** Student writes equation and draws a diagram as necessary. Student shows all work and makes no errors in computations. The question is answered in a complete sentence.
- **1 point:** Student shows most work and makes no errors. Student correctly answers the question but does not provide all of the reasoning. Sketch is incorrect or missing.
- **1 point:** Student shows most work. A minor error occurs in the solution to the problem. The student answers the question but provides no reasoning. Sketch is incorrect or missing.
- **0 points:** The response is completely incorrect.

1. The measures of the angles of a triangle are $2x$, $3x - 20$, and $2x + 60$ degrees. What is the difference between the measure of the largest and the smallest angles of the triangle? Sketch the triangle. Show your work and explain in words how you determined your answer.

1-point response	0-point response
$7x + 40 = 180$ $7x = 140$ $x = 20$ The difference between the largest and smallest angle is 60 degrees.	$2x = 180$ $x = 90$ degrees

a. Explain why the 1-point response only received only one point.
The student answers the question but not all work is shown, no reasoning is provided, no sketch is included.

b. Explain why the 0-point response received 0 points.
The response is completely incorrect.

c. What would you add to the 1-point response to make it a 2-point response?
Add a sketch of the triangle. Show all of the steps and provide the reasoning.

STANDARDIZED TEST PRACTICE

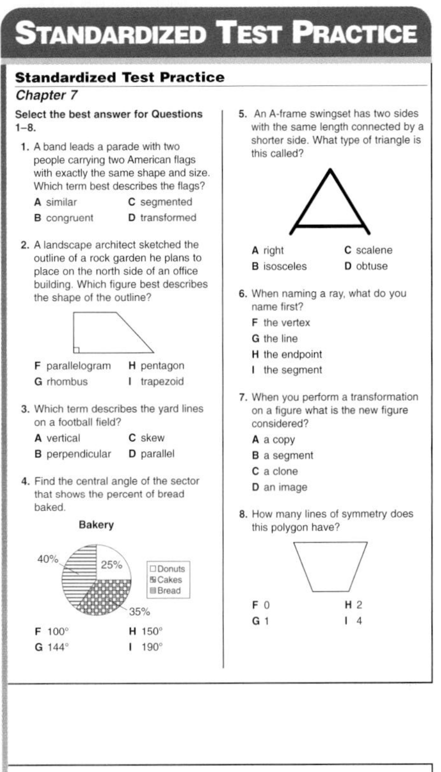

Standardized Test Practice
Chapter 7

Select the best answer for Questions 1–8.

1. A band leads a parade with two people carrying two American flags with exactly the same shape and size. Which term best describes the flags?
A similar C segmented
B congruent D transformed

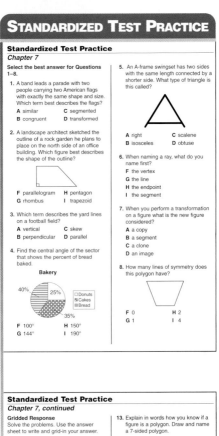

2. A landscape architect sketched the outline of a rock garden he plans to place on the north side of an office building. Which figure best describes the shape of the outline?
F parallelogram H pentagon
G rhombus I trapezoid

3. Which term describes the yard lines on a football field?
A vertical C skew
B perpendicular D parallel

4. Find the central angle of the sector that shows the percent of bread baked.
Bakery
40% 25% 35% Donuts Cakes Bread
F 100° H 150°
G 144° I 190°

5. An A-frame swingset has two sides with the same length connected by a shorter side. What type of triangle is this called?
A right C scalene
B isosceles D obtuse

6. When naming a ray, what do you name first?
F the vertex
G the line
H the endpoint
I the segment

7. When you perform a transformation on a figure what is the new figure considered?
A a copy
B a segment
C a clone
D an image

8. How many lines of symmetry does this polygon have?
F 0 H 2
G 1 I 4

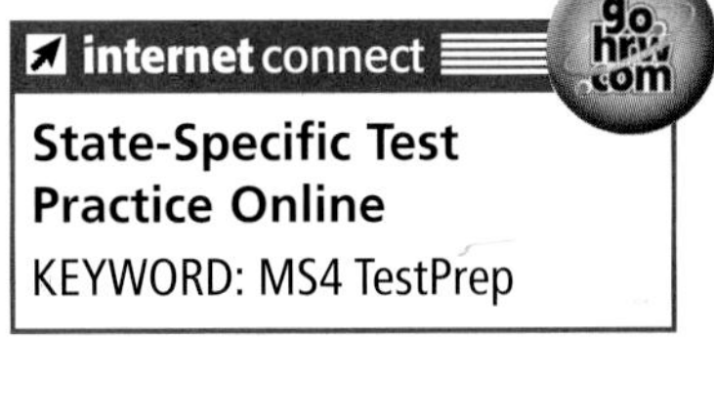

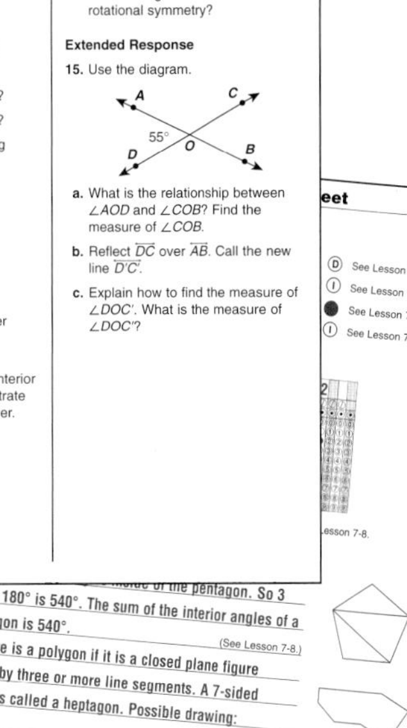

Standardized Test Practice
Chapter 7, continued

Gridded Response
Solve the problems. Use the answer sheet to write and grid-in your answer.

Use the figure to answer Questions 9–10.

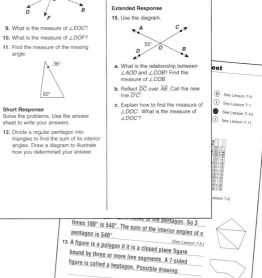

9. What is the measure of ∠EOC?
10. What is the measure of ∠DOF?
11. Find the measure of the missing angle.

Short Response
Solve the problems. Use the answer sheet to write your answers.

12. Divide a regular pentagon into triangles to find the sum of its interior angles. Draw a diagram to illustrate how you determined your answer.

13. Explain in words how you know if a figure is a polygon. Draw and name a 7-sided polygon.

14. Matt has drawn a figure according to the specifications given to him by his boss. His boss wants him to check that the figure has rotational symmetry. How can Matt check to see if the figure he has drawn has rotational symmetry?

Extended Response

15. Use the diagram.
a. What is the relationship between ∠AOD and ∠COB? Find the measure of ∠COB.
b. Reflect $\overline{DC}$ over $\overline{AB}$. Call the new line $\overline{D'C'}$.
c. Explain how to find the measure of ∠DOC'. What is the measure of ∠DOC'?

times 180° is 540°. The sum of the interior angles of a pentagon is 540°. (See Lesson 7-8.)

13. A figure is a polygon if it is a closed plane figure bound by three or more line segments. A 7-sided figure is called a heptagon. Possible drawing: (See Lesson 7-5.)

14. He must rotate the figure less than 360° and it must coincide with itself. (See Lesson 7-11.)

Extended Response
Write your answers for Problem 15 on the back of this paper.
See Lesson 7-2.

Test Prep Tool Kit

- Standardized Test Prep Workbook
- Countdown to Testing transparencies
- State Test Prep CD-ROM
- Standardized Test Prep Video

Customized answer sheets give students realistic practice for actual standardized tests.

Chapter 7

Plane Figures

Why Learn This?

Tell students that geometric figures are an important part of the design of a bridge. Have students look at the photographs and identify the geometric shapes that they see. Ask students why they think triangles are often used when designing bridges. Possible answer: The shape of a triangle cannot be changed by direct force.

Using Data

To begin the study of this chapter, have students:

- Find how much longer the main span of the Great Belt bridge is than the main span of the Tatara bridge. **734 m**

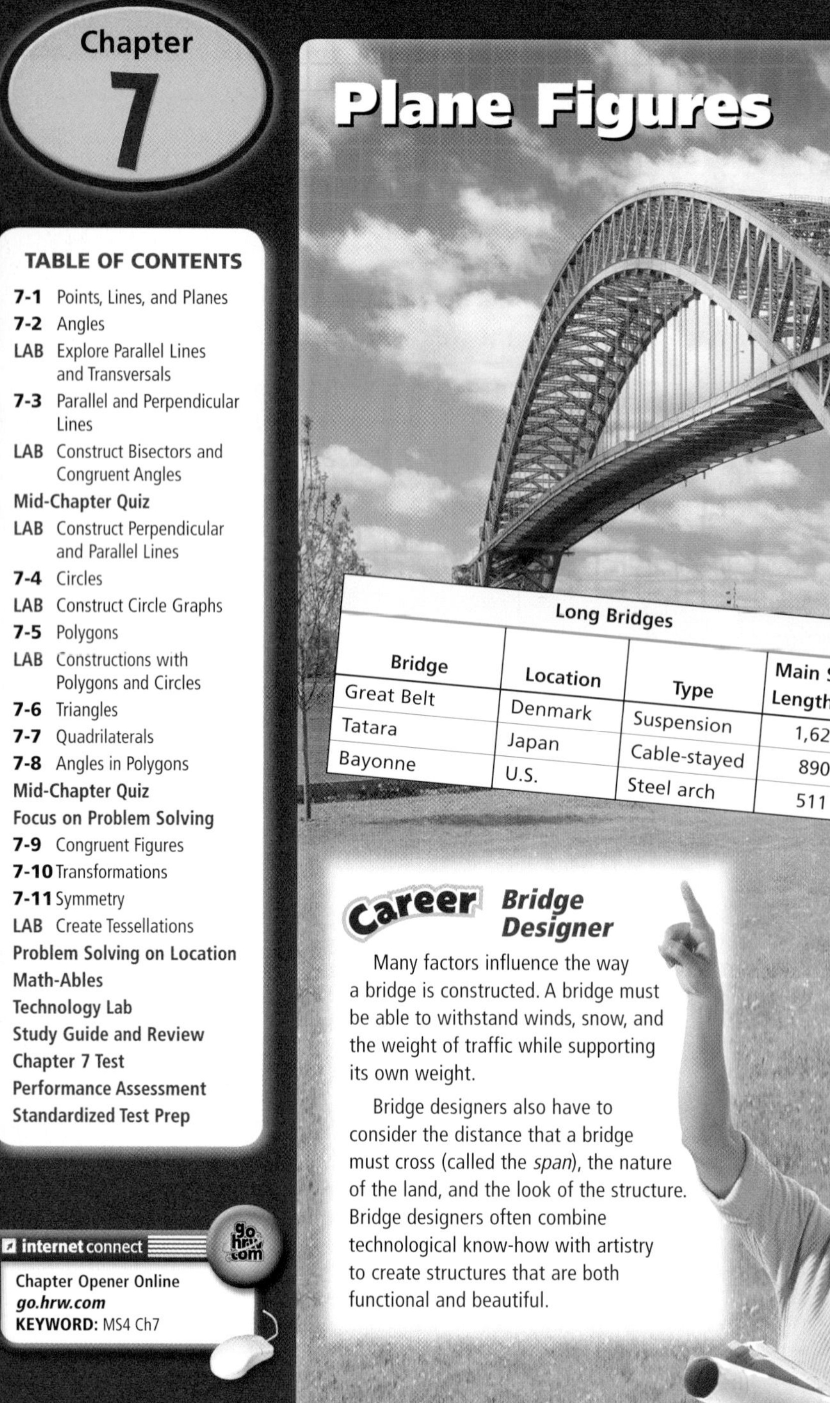

Chapter 7

Plane Figures

TABLE OF CONTENTS

internet connect
Chapter Opener Online
go.hrw.com
KEYWORD: MS4 Ch7

Long Bridges

Bridge	Location	Type	Main Span Length (m)
Great Belt	Denmark	Suspension	1,624
Tatara	Japan	Cable-stayed	890
Bayonne	U.S.	Steel arch	511

Career ***Bridge Designer***

Many factors influence the way a bridge is constructed. A bridge must be able to withstand winds, snow, and the weight of traffic while supporting its own weight.

Bridge designers also have to consider the distance that a bridge must cross (called the *span*), the nature of the land, and the look of the structure. Bridge designers often combine technological know-how with artistry to create structures that are both functional and beautiful.

Problem Solving Project

Physical Science Connection

Purpose: To solve problems using properties of plane figures

Materials: Bridge Designer worksheet

internet connect
Chapter Project Online: go.hrw.com
KEYWORD: MS4 PSProject7

Understand, Plan, Solve, and Look Back

Have students:

- Complete the Bridge Designer worksheet to see the close relationship between geometry and bridge designs.
- Look at some pictures of bridges. What kinds of plane geometric figures do you see? Which are the most common?
- Research to make a list of the longest bridges in the United States. Which type of bridge is each of the bridges on the list? What are the pros and cons of each type of bridge? Why are the longest bridges suspension bridges?
- Check students' work.

ARE YOU READY?

Choose the best term from the list to complete each sentence.

1. An equation showing that two ratios are equal is a(n) __?__. **proportion**	decimal
2. The coordinates of a point on a grid are written as a(n) __?__. **ordered pair**	difference
3. A(n) __?__ is a special ratio that compares a number to 100 and uses the symbol %. **percent**	integer
4. The number –3 is a(n) __?__. **integer**	percent
5. The __?__ between two numbers is found by subtracting one of the numbers from the other. **difference**	proportion
	ordered pair
	sum

Complete these exercises to review skills you will need for this chapter.

✔ Write Percents and Decimals

Write each decimal as a percent.

6. 0.77 **77%** **7.** 0.06 **6%** **8.** 0.9 **90%** **9.** 1.04 **104%**

Write each percent as a decimal.

10. 42% **0.42** **11.** 80% **0.8** **12.** 1% **0.01** **13.** 131% **1.31**

✔ Multiply with Fractions and Decimals

Find the percent of each number. Round to the nearest hundredth, if necessary.

14. 10% of 40 **4** **15.** 12% of 100 **12** **16.** 6% of 18 **1.08** **17.** 99% of 60 **59.4**

18. 100% of 81 **81** **19.** 150% of 20 **30** **20.** 45% of 360 **162** **21.** 55% of 1,024 **563.2**

✔ Solve Proportions

Solve each proportion.

22. $\frac{n}{30} = \frac{3}{15}$ **$n = 6$** **23.** $\frac{x}{50} = \frac{3}{75}$ **$x = 2$** **24.** $\frac{51}{17} = \frac{k}{3}$ **$k = 9$** **25.** $\frac{3}{45} = \frac{4}{y}$ **$y = 60$**

26. $\frac{s}{12} = \frac{4}{16}$ **$s = 3$** **27.** $\frac{8}{56} = \frac{t}{14}$ **$t = 2$** **28.** $\frac{5}{h} = \frac{4}{8}$ **$h = 10$** **29.** $\frac{9}{57} = \frac{3}{p}$ **$p = 19$**

✔ Graph Ordered Pairs

Graph each ordered pair on a coordinate plane.

30. $A(0, 2)$ **31.** $B(-6, 7)$ **32.** $C(4, -6)$ **33.** $D(-3, -5)$

34. $E(5, 0)$ **35.** $F(-5, 5)$ **36.** $G(6, 1)$ **37.** $H(0, -7)$

Assessing Prior Knowledge

INTERVENTION 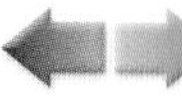

Diagnose and Prescribe

Evaluate your students' performance on this page to determine whether intervention is necessary or whether enrichment is appropriate. Options that provide instruction, practice, and a check are listed below.

Resources for Are You Ready?

- ***Are You Ready? Intervention and Enrichment***
- **Recording Sheet for Are You Ready?** *Chapter 7 Resource Book . . . . . . p. 3*

 ***Are You Ready? Intervention* CD-ROM**

Answers

30–37.

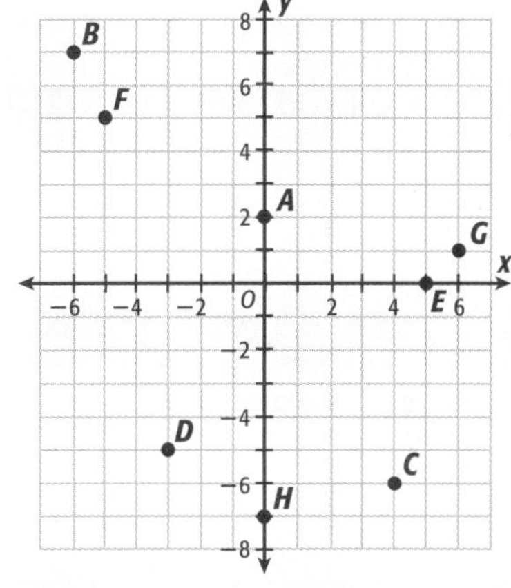

ARE YOU READY?

Were students successful with Are You Ready?

NO INTERVENE

YES ENRICH

✔Write Percents and Decimals
Are You Ready? Intervention, Skill 30
Blackline Masters, Online, and
 **CD-ROM** Intervention Activities

✔Multiply with Fractions and Decimals
Are You Ready? Intervention, Skill 45
Blackline Masters, Online, and
CD-ROM Intervention Activities

✔Solve Proportions
Are You Ready? Intervention, Skill 65
Blackline Masters, Online, and
 **CD-ROM** Intervention Activities

✔Graph Ordered Pairs
Are You Ready? Intervention, Skill 68
Blackline Masters, Online, and
 **CD-ROM** Intervention Activities

Are You Ready? Enrichment, pp. 419–420

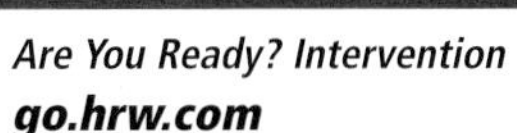

Are You Ready? Intervention
go.hrw.com
KEYWORD: MS4 AYR

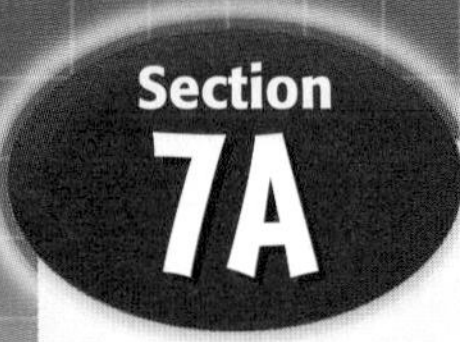

Section 7A

Lines and Angles

One-Minute Section Planner

Lesson	Materials	Resources
Lesson 7-1 Points, Lines, and Planes **NCTM:** Geometry, Communication **NAEP:** Geometry 1b ☑ SAT-9 ☑ SAT-10 ☐ ITBS ☐ CTBS ☑ MAT ☑ CAT	**Optional** Teaching Transparency T2 *(CRB)* Dot paper *(CRB, p. 115)*	• *Chapter 7 Resource Book,* pp. 7–15 • Daily Transparency T1, CRB • Additional Examples Transparencies T3–T4, CRB • *Alternate Openers: Explorations,* p. 57
Lesson 7-2 Angles **NCTM:** Geometry, Communication **NAEP:** Geometry 1b ☑ SAT-9 ☑ SAT-10 ☐ ITBS ☑ CTBS ☑ MAT ☑ CAT	**Optional** Teaching Transparency T6 *(CRB)* Rectangular prism model or box	• *Chapter 7 Resource Book,* pp. 16–24 • Daily Transparency T5, CRB • Additional Examples Transparencies T7–T8, CRB • *Alternate Openers: Explorations,* p. 58
Hands-On Lab 7A Explore Parallel Lines and Transversals **NCTM:** Geometry **NAEP:** Geometry 3g ☑ SAT-9 ☑ SAT-10 ☐ ITBS ☐ CTBS ☐ MAT ☑ CAT	**Required** Protractors *(MK)* Straightedges *(MK)*	• *Hands-On Lab Activities,* pp. 48–51
Lesson 7-3 Parallel and Perpendicular Lines **NCTM:** Geometry, Reasoning and Proof, Communication, Connections **NAEP:** Geometry 3g ☑ SAT-9 ☑ SAT-10 ☐ ITBS ☐ CTBS ☐ MAT ☑ CAT	**Optional** Teaching Transparency T10 *(CRB)*	• *Chapter 7 Resource Book,* pp. 25–33 • Daily Transparency T9, CRB • Additional Examples Transparencies T11–T12, CRB • *Alternate Openers: Explorations,* p. 59
Hands-On Lab 7B Construct Bisectors and Congruent Angles **NCTM:** Geometry **NAEP:** Geometry 1f ☐ SAT-9 ☐ SAT-10 ☐ ITBS ☐ CTBS ☐ MAT ☐ CAT	**Required** Compasses *(MK)* Straightedges *(MK)*	• *Hands-On Lab Activities,* pp. 52–53
Section 7A Assessment		• Mid-Chapter Quiz, SE p. 360 • Section 7A Quiz, AR p. 19 • *Test and Practice Generator* CD-ROM

SAT = *Stanford Achievement Tests* **ITBS** = *Iowa Test of Basic Skills* **CTBS** = *Comprehensive Test of Basic Skills/Terra Nova*
MAT = *Metropolitan Achievement Test* **CAT** = *California Achievement Test*

NCTM—Complete standards can be found on pages T27–T33. **NAEP**—Complete standards can be found on pages A35–A39.

SE = *Student Edition* **TE** = *Teacher's Edition* **AR** = *Assessment Resources* **CRB** = *Chapter Resource Book* **MK** = *Manipulatives Kit*

Section Overview

Identifying Geometric Figures — *Lesson 7-1*

Why? Familiarity with basic geometric figures is a prerequisite to understanding more complex geometric relationships. You can see many real-world examples of geometric figures; for example, telephone poles resemble parallel line segments.

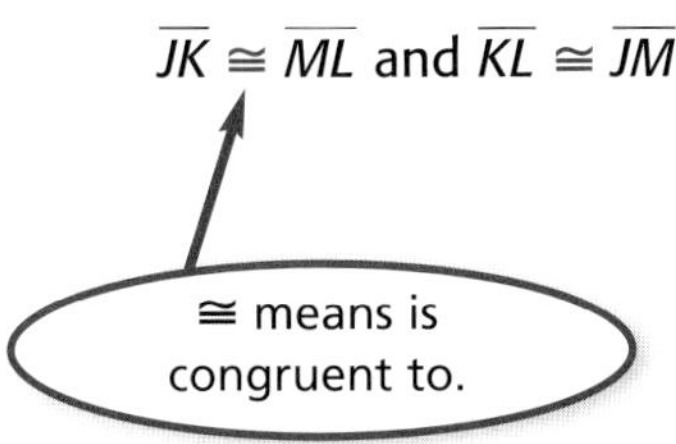

$\overline{JK} \cong \overline{ML}$ and $\overline{KL} \cong \overline{JM}$
≅ means is congruent to.

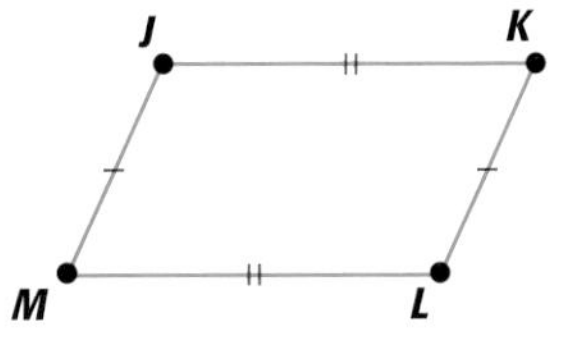

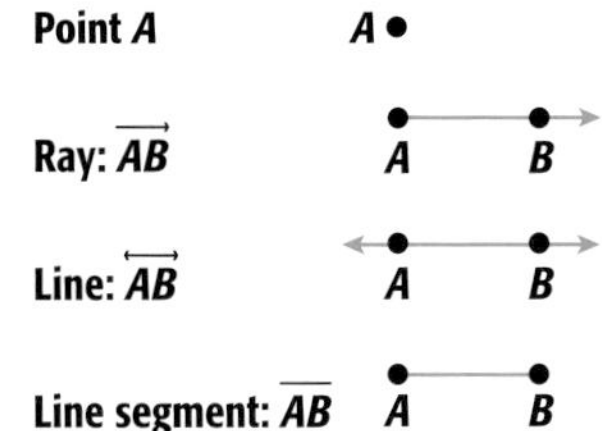

Angles — *Lesson 7-2*

Why? To understand special angle relationships, you must be able to distinguish different types of angles. These relationships are basic to the study of geometry.

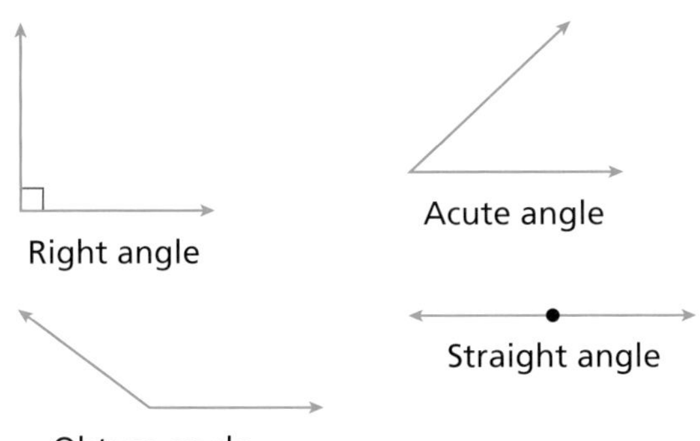

Special Angle Relationships

Complementary angles are angle pairs whose measures have a sum of 90°.

Supplementary angles are angle pairs whose measures have a sum of 180°.

Line and Angle Relationships — *Hands-On Labs 7A, 7B, Lesson 7-3*

Why? Special line and angle relationships are part of geometry. Some special angle relationships occur when lines intersect.

Vertical angles are the opposite angles formed by intersecting lines. **Vertical angles are congruent.**

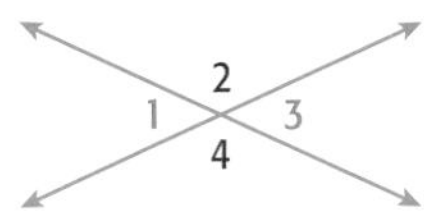

$\angle 1 \cong \angle 3$ and $\angle 2 \cong \angle 4$

When a **transversal** intersects parallel lines, all the acute angles formed are congruent, and all the obtuse angles formed are congruent.

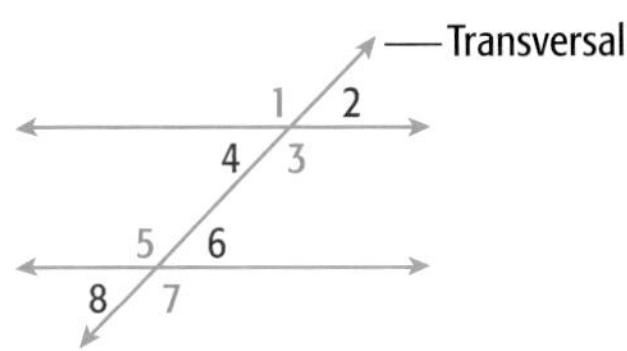

$\angle 1 \cong \angle 3 \cong \angle 5 \cong \angle 7$ and $\angle 2 \cong \angle 4 \cong \angle 6 \cong \angle 8$

7-1 Organizer

Pacing: Traditional 1 day
Block $\frac{1}{2}$ day

Objective: Students identify and describe geometric figures.

Warm Up

What geometry term might you associate with each object?

1. one edge of a cardboard box line segment or line
2. the floor plane or rectangle
3. the tip of a pen point

Problem of the Day

Remove 4 of the segments to leave 5 equal squares.

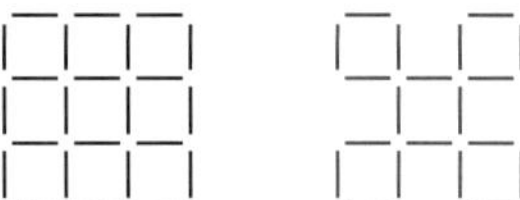

Available on Daily Transparency in CRB

Math Fact !!

Thales of Miletus was a mathematician born in 624 B.C. in what is now Turkey. He is believed to have introduced the study of geometry to Greece.

7-1 Points, Lines, and Planes

Learn to identify and describe geometric figures.

Vocabulary
point
line
ray
line segment
plane
congruent

Artists often use basic geometric figures when creating their works. For example, Wassily Kandinsky used *line segments* in his painting called *Red Circle,* which is shown at right.

Helpful Hint

A number line is an example of a line, and a coordinate plane is an example of a plane.

A **point** is an exact location in space. It is usually represented as a dot, but it has no size at all.	• A	point A *Use a capital letter to name a point.*
A **line** is a straight path that extends without end in opposite directions.	 X Y	$\overleftrightarrow{XY}$, or $\overleftrightarrow{YX}$ *Use two points on the line to name a line.*
A **ray** is a part of a line. It has one endpoint and extends without end in one direction.	 G H	$\overrightarrow{GH}$ *Name the endpoint first when naming a ray.*
A **line segment** is a part of a line or a ray that extends from one endpoint to another.	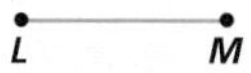 L M	$\overline{LM}$, or $\overline{ML}$ *Use the endpoints to name a line segment.*
A **plane** is a perfectly flat surface that extends infinitely in all directions.	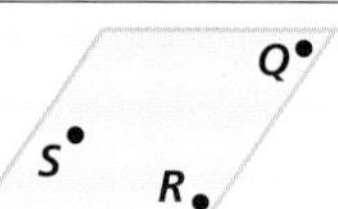	plane QRS *Use three points in any order, not on the same line, to name a plane.*

EXAMPLE 1 Identifying Points, Lines, and Planes

Identify the figures in the diagram.

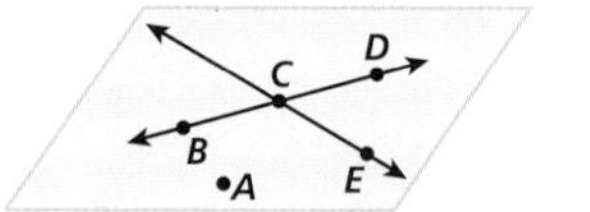

A three points
A, B, and C

B two lines
$\overleftrightarrow{BD}$, $\overleftrightarrow{CE}$ *Choose any two points on a line to name the line.*

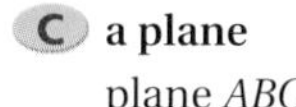

C a plane
plane ABC *Choose any three points on a plane to name the plane.*

1 Introduce

Alternate Opener

EXPLORATION

7-1 Points, Lines, and Planes

The table below shows different geometric figures by name and notation.

Geometric Figure	Name	Notation
A •	Point	Point A
B C	Line segment	$\overline{BC}$
D E	Ray	$\overrightarrow{DE}$
M N	Line	$\overleftrightarrow{MN}$

Look at the model of each figure to answer the following questions.

1. Is there a limit to the number of lines that can be drawn through point A?
2. Is there a limit to the number of points that are between the endpoints of line segment BC?
3. How are the line segment and the ray similar? How are they different?
4. How are the ray and the line similar? How are they different?

Think and Discuss

5. **Name** real-world objects that resemble points.
6. **Name** real-world objects that resemble line segments.

Motivate

Tell students they are going to learn about geometric figures with zero, one, or two dimensions. Discuss the term *dimension*. Have students suggest definitions. Then summarize by explaining that *dimension* refers to an object's measurements (i.e., length, width, height). Draw a point, line, and plane on the chalkboard. Ask students to tell which figure has each number of dimensions: zero, one, and two dimensions. a point has no dimensions or measurements; a line has one dimension—length; a plane has two dimensions—length and width

Exploration worksheet and answers on Chapter 7 Resource Book pp. 8 and 122

2 Teach

Lesson Presentation

Guided Instruction

In this lesson, students learn to identify and describe geometric figures. As you discuss the various figures, encourage students to name real-world objects of which the figures remind them.

Teaching Tip Draw the following figure on the chalkboard and ask students to decide whether the figure is a line and to explain why or why not:

Students should realize that the figure is not a straight path.

EXAMPLE 2 Identifying Line Segments and Rays

Identify the figures in the diagram.

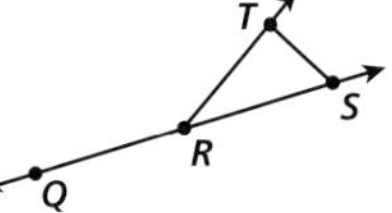

A three rays
$\overrightarrow{RQ}$, $\overrightarrow{RT}$, and $\overrightarrow{SQ}$ — *Name the endpoint of a ray first.*

B three line segments
$\overline{RQ}$, $\overline{QS}$, and $\overline{ST}$ — *Use the endpoints in any order to name a segment.*

Figures are **congruent** if they have the same shape and size. If you place one on top of the other, they match exactly. Line segments are congruent if they have the same length.

Tick marks are used to indicate congruent line segments. In the illustration below, segments that have the same number of tick marks are congruent. Line segments AB and BC are congruent (one tick mark), and line segments MN and OP are congruent (two tick marks).

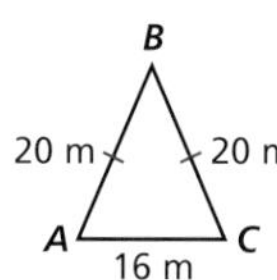

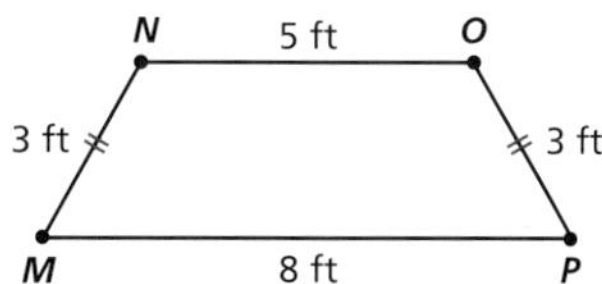

EXAMPLE 3 Identifying Congruent Line Segments

Reading Math

The symbol ≅ means "is congruent to."

Identify the line segments that are congruent.

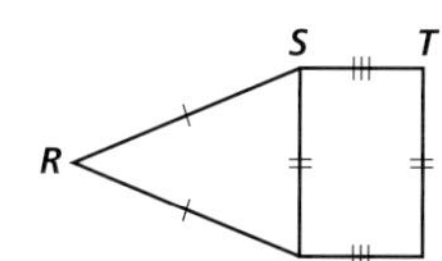

$\overline{QR} \cong \overline{SR}$ — *One tick mark*
$\overline{QS} \cong \overline{PT}$ — *Two tick marks*
$\overline{QP} \cong \overline{ST}$ — *Three tick marks*

Think and Discuss

1. **Explain** why a line and a plane can be named in more than two ways. How many ways can a line segment be named?
2. **Explain** why it is important to choose three points that are not on the same line when naming a plane.
3. **Tell** how you can determine whether two line segments are congruent without knowing their actual measures.

Additional Examples

Example 1

Identify the figures in the diagram.

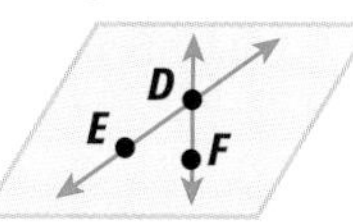

A. three points — *D*, *E*, and *F*
B. two lines — $\overleftrightarrow{DE}$, $\overleftrightarrow{DF}$
C. a plane — plane *DEF*

Example 2

Identify the figures in the diagram.

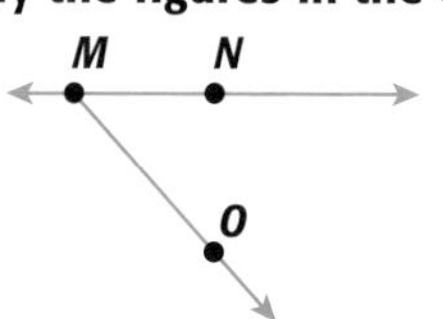

A. three rays — $\overrightarrow{MN}$, $\overrightarrow{NM}$, $\overrightarrow{MO}$
B. two line segments — $\overline{MN}$, $\overline{MO}$

Example 3

Identify the line segments that are congruent.

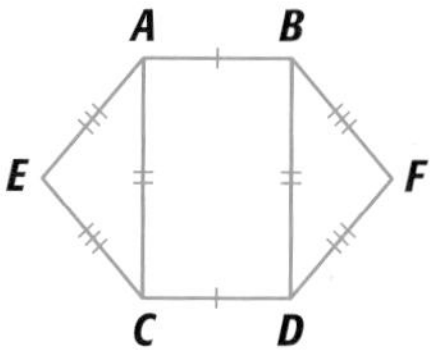

$\overline{AB} \cong \overline{CD}$; $\overline{AC} \cong \overline{BD}$;
$\overline{BF} \cong \overline{DF} \cong \overline{EC} \cong \overline{AE}$

Example 2 note: Point out that although some of the line segments and rays are named by the same letters, the notation above the letters distinguishes each as either a segment or a ray. Have students write the notation for line segment $\overline{AB}$ and ray $\overrightarrow{AB}$ and then draw each.

3 Close

Reaching All Learners

Through Modeling

Have students work in pairs. Have each partner use dot paper (provided on Chapter 7 Resource Book p. 115) to draw several line segments of different lengths.

Partners can exchange papers and draw a congruent line segment for each of their partner's line segments. Encourage students to discuss how to be sure their line segments are congruent.

Summarize

Draw three points on the chalkboard:

Have students use geometric notation to name a point, line, ray, line segment, and plane that can be drawn from one or more of these points. Then ask volunteers to come up to the chalkboard and draw each figure that is named.

Possible answers: point *D*, $\overrightarrow{DE}$, $\overleftrightarrow{EF}$, $\overline{DE}$, plane *DEF*

Answers to Think and Discuss

1. Possible answers: A line can be named using any two points on the line. A plane can be named by any of its three points that are not on the same line. A line segment can be named using only two particular points.
2. Possible answer: Since a line has only one dimension, you need three points not on the same line to show the two dimensions of a plane.
3. Possible answer: Copy one segment and place it on top of the other to see whether they are the same length.

7-1 PRACTICE & ASSESS

Students may want to refer back to the lesson examples.

Assignment Guide

If you finished Example **1** assign:
Core 1–3, 7–9, 13, 20–27
Enriched 1–3, 7–9, 13, 20–27

If you finished Example **2** assign:
Core 1–5, 7–11, 13, 20–27
Enriched 1–5, 7–11, 13, 20–27

If you finished Example **3** assign:
Core 1–12, 13, 15, 20–27
Enriched 1–11 odd, 13–27

Answers

8–11. Possible answers:

8. $\overleftrightarrow{DE}$, $\overleftrightarrow{EF}$

9. plane *DEF*

10. $\overrightarrow{DE}$, $\overrightarrow{FD}$, $\overrightarrow{EF}$

11. $\overline{DE}$, $\overline{EF}$, $\overline{DF}$

13. Plane *ABC* contains points *A, B,* and *C;* lines $\overleftrightarrow{AB}$ and $\overleftrightarrow{BC}$; line segments $\overline{AB}$, $\overline{AC}$, and $\overline{BC}$; and rays $\overrightarrow{AB}$, $\overrightarrow{BA}$, $\overrightarrow{BC}$, $\overrightarrow{CB}$, and $\overrightarrow{CA}$. Plane *ACD* contains points *A, C,* and *D;* line segments $\overline{AC}$, $\overline{AD}$, and $\overline{CD}$; and ray $\overrightarrow{CA}$.

7-1 Exercises

FOR EXTRA PRACTICE
see page 668

GUIDED PRACTICE

See Example 1 **Identify the figures in the diagram.** Possible answers:

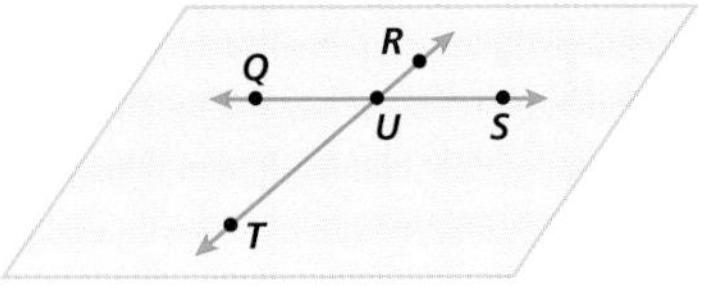

1. three points *Q, R, S*
2. two lines $\overleftrightarrow{QS}$, $\overleftrightarrow{RT}$
3. a plane plane *QRS*

See Example 2

4. three rays $\overrightarrow{UQ}$, $\overrightarrow{UT}$, $\overrightarrow{US}$
5. three line segments $\overline{QU}$, $\overline{RU}$, $\overline{SU}$

See Example 3

6. Identify the line segments that are congruent.
   $\overline{BA}$ and $\overline{BC}$, $\overline{AE}$ and $\overline{CE}$, $\overline{AD}$ and $\overline{CD}$

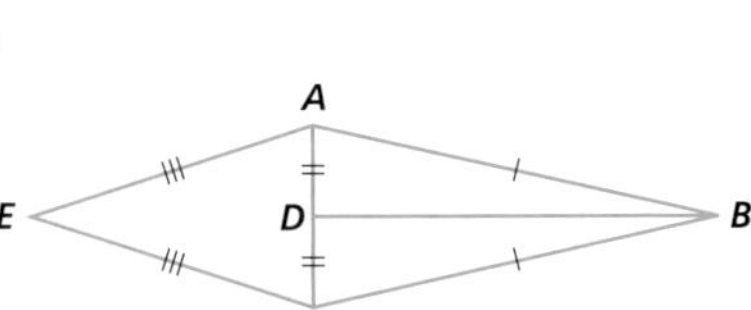

INDEPENDENT PRACTICE

See Example 1 **Identify the figures in the diagram.**

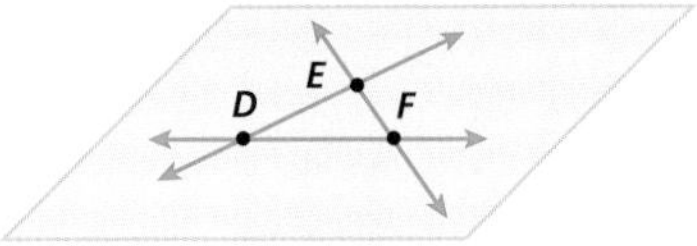

7. three points *D, E, F*
8. two lines
9. a plane

See Example 2

10. three rays
11. three line segments

See Example 3

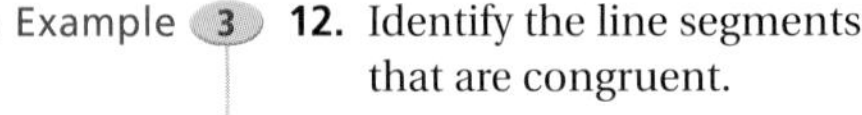

12. Identify the line segments that are congruent.
    $\overline{AF}$ and $\overline{BC}$, $\overline{AE}$ and $\overline{BD}$, $\overline{AB}$ and $\overline{ED}$, $\overline{FE}$ and $\overline{CD}$

PRACTICE AND PROBLEM SOLVING

13. Identify the points, lines, line segments, and rays that are represented in the illustration, and tell what plane each is in. Some figures may be in more than one plane.

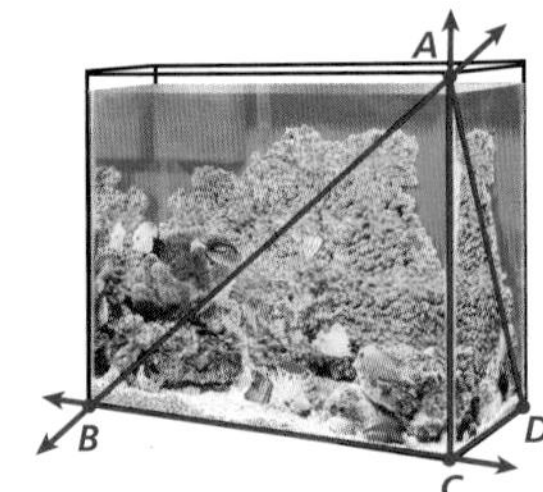

Math Background

Projective geometry is the basis for using perspective technique to create a painting or drawing that has the illusion of depth and distance. Linear perspective is based on the optical illusion that parallel lines appear to meet at a *vanishing point.* The illusion of depth is created by making more distant objects smaller and closer together than nearer objects.

RETEACH 7-1

LESSON 7-1 **Reteach**
Points, Lines, Planes

You can think of real-life objects to represent geometric terms.

Point: a polka dot — Point *A*

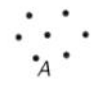

Line: a straight road in both directions — Line *BC*, or $\overleftrightarrow{BC}$

Ray: flashlight beam — Ray *PQ*, or $\overrightarrow{PQ}$

Line segment: a ruler — Line segment *GH*, or $\overline{GH}$

Part of a plane: table top — Plane *DEF*

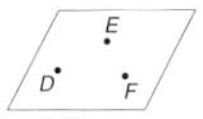

Congruent line segments: lines on an index card — $\overline{WX} \cong \overline{YZ}$

For 1–5, use geometry notation to identify the figures.

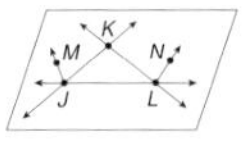

1. points
   J, K, L, M, N
2. lines
   $\overleftrightarrow{JK}$, $\overleftrightarrow{KL}$, $\overleftrightarrow{JL}$
3. planes
   Possible answer: plane *JMK*
4. rays
   $\overrightarrow{LN}$, $\overrightarrow{JM}$, $\overrightarrow{JK}$, $\overrightarrow{KJ}$, $\overrightarrow{KL}$, $\overrightarrow{LK}$, $\overrightarrow{JL}$, $\overrightarrow{LJ}$
5. line segments
   $\overline{JK}$, $\overline{KL}$, $\overline{JL}$, $\overline{JM}$, $\overline{LN}$
6. Identify the congruent line segments in the figure at the right.
   $\overline{AE} \cong \overline{AC}$; $\overline{CD} \cong \overline{DE}$

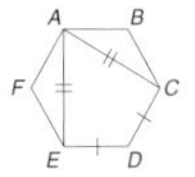

PRACTICE 7-1

LESSON 7-1 **Practice B**
Points, Lines, and Planes

Use geometry notation to identify the figures.

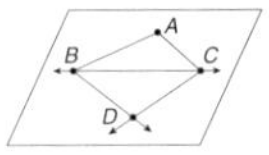

1. points *A, B, C, D*
2. lines $\overleftrightarrow{BC}$
3. planes Possible answer: plane *ABC*
4. rays $\overrightarrow{BD}$, $\overrightarrow{CD}$, $\overrightarrow{CB}$, $\overrightarrow{BC}$
5. line segments $\overline{AB}$, $\overline{AC}$, $\overline{BD}$, $\overline{CD}$, $\overline{BC}$

Use geometry notation to identify the figures.

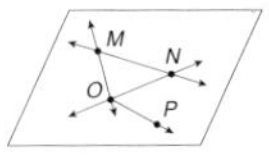

6. points *M, N, O, P*
7. lines $\overleftrightarrow{MN}$, $\overleftrightarrow{MO}$, $\overleftrightarrow{NO}$
8. planes Possible answer: plane *MNO*
9. rays $\overrightarrow{MO}$, $\overrightarrow{MN}$, $\overrightarrow{NM}$, $\overrightarrow{NO}$, $\overrightarrow{OM}$, $\overrightarrow{ON}$, $\overrightarrow{OP}$
10. line segments $\overline{MN}$, $\overline{MO}$, $\overline{NO}$, $\overline{OP}$

Use geometry notation to identify the figures.

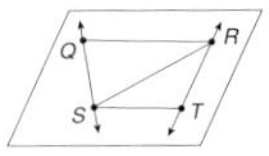

11. points *Q, R, S, T*
12. lines $\overleftrightarrow{QS}$, $\overleftrightarrow{RT}$
13. planes Possible answer: *QRS*
14. rays $\overrightarrow{QS}$, $\overrightarrow{SQ}$, $\overrightarrow{RT}$, $\overrightarrow{TR}$
15. line segments $\overline{QR}$, $\overline{RS}$, $\overline{QS}$, $\overline{ST}$, $\overline{RT}$
16. Identify which line segments are congruent.
    $\overline{AB}$ and $\overline{DE}$; $\overline{BC}$ and $\overline{EF}$;
    $\overline{AD}$, $\overline{BE}$, and $\overline{CF}$

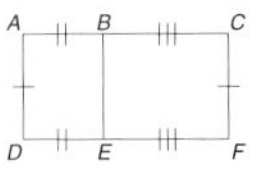

Art LINK

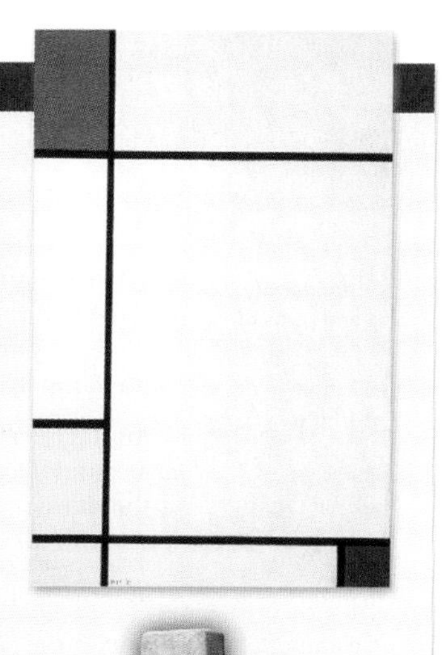

14. The painting at right, by Piet Mondrian, is called *Composition with Red, Yellow, and Blue.*
    a. Copy the line segments in the painting.
    b. Add tick marks to show congruent line segments.
    c. Label the endpoints of the segments, including the points of intersection. Then name five pairs of congruent line segments.
15. For each of the following, make an illustration.
    a. Show at least three sets of congruent line segments. Label the endpoints and use notation to tell which line segments are congruent.
    b. Show how one point could be shared by more than one line segment.
    c. Show how one point could be shared by more than one plane.
16. Can two endpoints be shared by two different line segments? Make a drawing to illustrate your answer.
17. Draw a diagram in which a plane, 5 points, 4 rays, and 2 lines can be identified. Then identify these figures.
18. ***WRITE ABOUT IT*** Explain the difference between a line, a line segment, and a ray. Is it possible to estimate the length of any of these figures? If so, tell which ones and why.
19. ***CHALLENGE*** The wooden sculpture at right, by Vantongerloo, is called *Interrelation of Volumes.* Explain whether two separate faces on the front of the sculpture could be on the same plane.

Spiral Review

Write each percent as a fraction in simplest form. (Lesson 6-1)

20. 24% $\frac{6}{25}$ **21.** 7% $\frac{7}{100}$ **22.** 95% $\frac{19}{20}$ **23.** 62% $\frac{31}{50}$

Find the percent of each number. (Lesson 6-3)

24. 12% of 30 **3.6** **25.** 9% of 50 **4.5** **26.** 0.5% of 8 **0.04**

27. TEST PREP Sixty people were expected at a reception. Only 45 people came. What percent of the people who were expected at the reception actually came? (Lesson 6-4) **C**

A 7.5% **B** 13.3% **C** 75% **D** 133.3%

CHALLENGE 7-1

LESSON 7-1 **Challenge**
Plane Drawings

You can use a drawing to represent a part of a plane.

The horizontal planes below do not intersect. They are *parallel.* The dashed lines show that one plane lies behind the other plane.

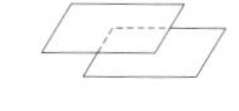

The steps below demonstrate how to sketch two intersecting planes.

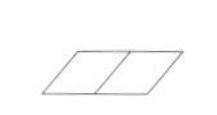

Draw a parallelogram.
Draw a line segment through its center.

Use the segment as one side of a new parallelogram.

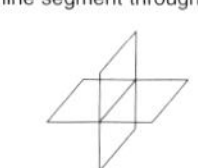

Draw the bottom part of a new plane.

Dash the invisible edges.

Make a sketch of the planes described below.

1. Draw a pair of vertical planes that do not intersect. **Answers will vary. Possible answer given.**

2. Draw a pair of planes that intersect at an angle different from the example sketched above. **Answers will vary. Possible answer given.**

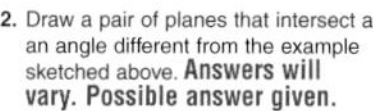

PROBLEM SOLVING 7-1

LESSON 7-1 **Problem Solving**
Points, Lines, and Planes

Write the correct answer. **Answers may vary. Possible answers are given.**

The drawing shows a section of the Golden Gate Bridge in San Francisco.

1. Identify two lines that are suggested by the bridge.
   $\overleftrightarrow{JK}$ **and** $\overleftrightarrow{LM}$
2. Identify a ray and a line segment that are suggested by the bridge.
   $\overrightarrow{RQ}$ **and** $\overline{ST}$
3. Identify two lines in the figure that are in the same plane.
   $\overleftrightarrow{JK}$ **and** $\overleftrightarrow{LM}$
4. Identify a plane in the figure.
   plane *RLM*

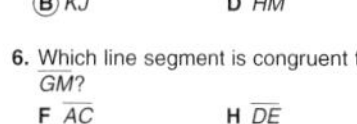

Choose the letter for the best answer.

The drawing is an artist's sketch for an abstract painting.

5. Which line segment is congruent to $\overline{BC}$?
   A $\overline{AB}$ C $\overline{AC}$
   (B) $\overline{KJ}$ D $\overline{HM}$
6. Which line segment is congruent to $\overline{GM}$?
   F $\overline{AC}$ H $\overline{DE}$
   G $\overline{DF}$ (J) $\overline{AB}$
7. Which line segment is congruent to $\overline{ED}$?
   (A) $\overline{AC}$ C $\overline{DF}$
   B $\overline{CD}$ D $\overline{GH}$
8. Which line segment is congruent to $\overline{DF}$?
   F $\overline{ED}$ H $\overline{CJ}$
   (G) $\overline{HM}$ J $\overline{FM}$

Interdisciplinary LINK

Art

Exercises 14–19 involve identifying geometric figures and congruence in pieces of art.

Answers

14–19. See p. A2.

Journal

Ask students to write about which method they prefer to use to determine whether lines are congruent and why they prefer that method.

Test Prep Doctor

For Exercise 27, students can estimate that since 50% of 60 is 30, then 45 people must be more than 50%. Therefore, students can eliminate **A** and **B.**

Lesson Quiz

Use geometric notation to identify the figures.

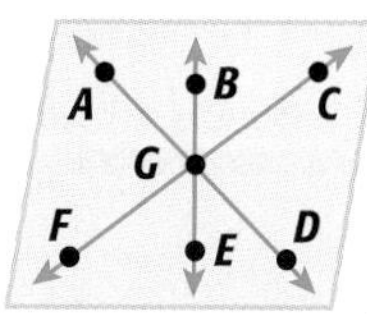

1. lines $\overleftrightarrow{AD}$, $\overleftrightarrow{BE}$, $\overleftrightarrow{CF}$
2. plane Possible answer: plane *ABG*
3. three rays Possible answer: $\overrightarrow{GA}$, $\overrightarrow{GB}$, $\overrightarrow{GC}$
4. four line segments Possible answer: $\overline{AG}$, $\overline{AD}$, $\overline{DG}$, $\overline{BG}$
5. How many planes, lines, and points are suggested by the sides, edges, and corners of an ordinary box? 6 planes, 12 lines, 8 points

Available on Daily Transparency in CRB

7-2 Organizer

Pacing: Traditional 1 day
Block $\frac{1}{2}$ day

Objective: Students identify angles and parts of angles.

Warm Up

Draw each figure.

1. line segment
2. line
3. ray
4. plane

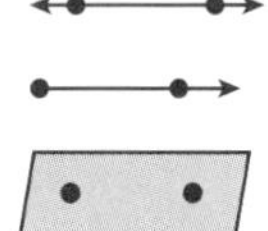

Problem of the Day

What is the measure of the smaller angle between the hour hand and the minute hand on a clock at eight o'clock? **120°**

Available on Daily Transparency in CRB

Math Fact !!

Using degrees to measure angles is thought to be based on the Babylonian number system, which was based on the number 60. The Babylonian year had 360 days, with 12 months of 30 days each.

7-2 Angles

Learn to identify angles and parts of angles.

Vocabulary
angle
vertex
right angle
acute angle
obtuse angle
straight angle
complementary angles
supplementary angles

When riding down a ramp on a skateboard, the speed you gain depends partly on the *angle* that the ramp makes with the ground.

An **angle** is formed by two rays with a common endpoint. The two rays are the sides of the angle. The common endpoint is the **vertex**.

You can name an angle in three ways:

- with the capital letter at the vertex: $\angle B$,
- with the number inside the angle: $\angle 1$,
- with three capital letters so that the letter at the vertex is in the middle: $\angle ABC$ or $\angle CBA$

Vertex A 1 B C

Angles are measured in degrees (°). You can use a protractor to measure an angle.

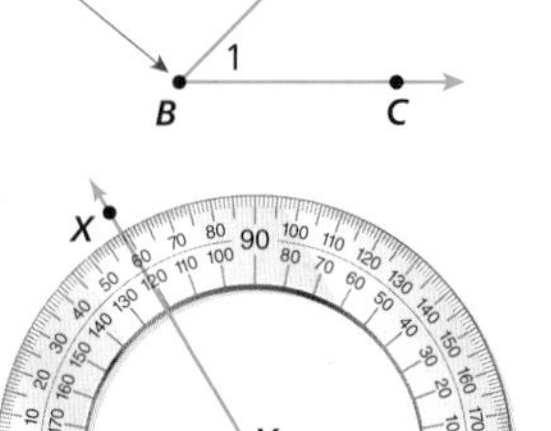

The measure of $\angle XYZ$ is 122°, or $m\angle XYZ = 122°$.

EXAMPLE 1 Identifying Angle Measures

Give the measure of each angle.

A $\angle EAD$
$m\angle EAD = 105°$

B $\angle CAB$
$m\angle CAB = 45°$

C $\angle DAB$
$m\angle DAB = 45° + 30°$
$m\angle DAB = 75°$

D $\angle FAC$
$m\angle FAC = 30° + 105° + 45°$
$m\angle FAC = 180°$

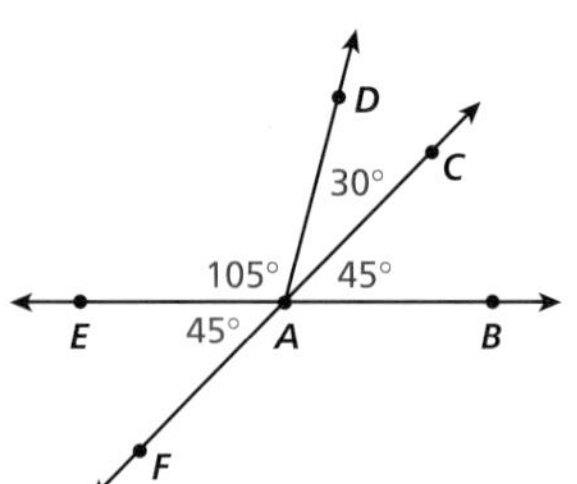

An angle's measure determines the type of angle it is.

1 Introduce

Alternate Opener

EXPLORATION

7-2 Angles

An envelope is made by cutting and folding a piece of paper at different angles.

Each corner of an envelope is a *right angle*. A right angle measures 90°.

Notice that four triangles are formed on the surface of the envelope. The sum of the measures of the angles in a triangle is 180°.

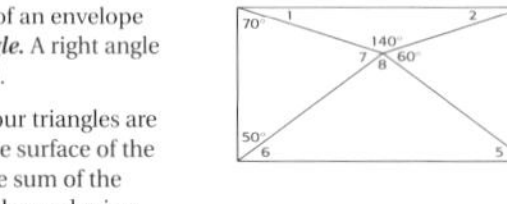

Find the measures of the numbered angles on the envelope.

1. m∠1 = ____
2. m∠2 = ____
3. m∠3 = ____
4. m∠4 = ____
5. m∠5 = ____
6. m∠6 = ____
7. m∠7 = ____
8. m∠8 = ____

Think and Discuss

9. **Explain** how you found the measure of ∠1.
10. **Explain** how you found the measure of ∠7.

Motivate

Display a box or other rectangular prism. Have students identify which parts of the box are representative of line segments, planes, and points. line segments—edges, planes—sides, points—vertices Point out that each vertex is a common endpoint for three edges, then lead into a discussion of the geometrical figures formed by the intersection of two rays—angles.

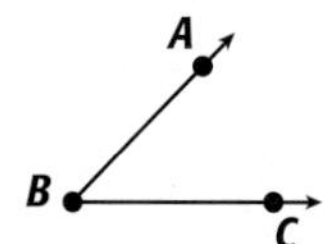

Exploration worksheet and answers on Chapter 7 Resource Book pp. 17 and 124

2 Teach

Lesson Presentation

Guided Instruction

In this lesson, students learn to identify angles and parts of angles. Help students grasp the difference between $\angle B$ and point B. Emphasize that the point is the place where the rays meet, but the angle includes the point and the rays. In Example 1, have students name the angles that were used to find the measure of $\angle DAB$. $m\angle DAB = m\angle CAB + m\angle DAC$

Point out that when students are naming angles such as $\angle ABC$, the vertex of the angle, B, should be written as the middle letter.

A **right angle** is an angle that measures exactly 90°. The symbol ⌝ indicates a right angle.

An **acute angle** is an angle that measures less than 90°.

An **obtuse angle** is an angle that measures more than 90° but less than 180°.

A **straight angle** is an angle that measures exactly 180°.

EXAMPLE 2 Classifying Angles

Tell whether each angle is acute, right, obtuse, or straight.

A 

Right angle

B 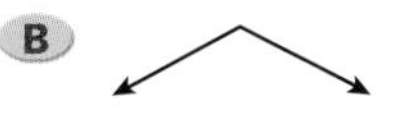

Obtuse angle

C 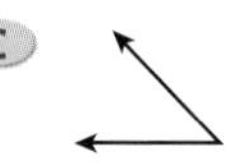

Acute angle

If the sum of the measures of two angles is 90°, then the angles are **complementary angles**. If the sum of the measures of two angles is 180°, then the angles are **supplementary angles**.

EXAMPLE 3 Identifying Complementary and Supplementary Angles

Use the figure to name the following.

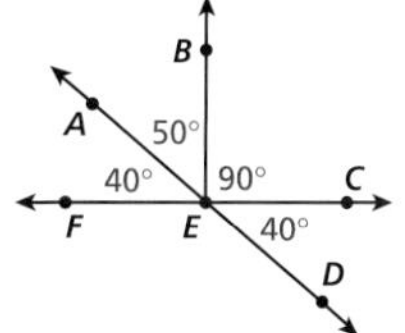

A one pair of complementary angles

$m\angle AEF = 40°$ and $m\angle AEB = 50°$

Since $40° + 50° = 90°$, $\angle AEF$ and $\angle AEB$ are complementary.

B one pair of supplementary angles

$m\angle AEB = 50°$ and $m\angle BED = 90° + 40° = 130°$

Since $50° + 130° = 180°$, $\angle AEB$ and $\angle BED$ are supplementary.

Think and Discuss

1. **Describe** three different ways to name an angle.
2. **Explain** how to find the measure of $\angle P$ if $\angle P$ and $\angle Q$ are complementary angles and $m\angle Q = 25°$.

Additional Examples

Example 1

Give the measure of each angle.

A. $\angle STV$ **55°** **B.** $\angle XTU$ **25°**

C. $\angle WTU$ **65°** **D.** $\angle STX$ **155°**

Example 2

Tell whether each angle is acute, right, obtuse, or straight.

A. right angle

B. obtuse angle

C. acute angle

Example 3

Use the figure to name the following.

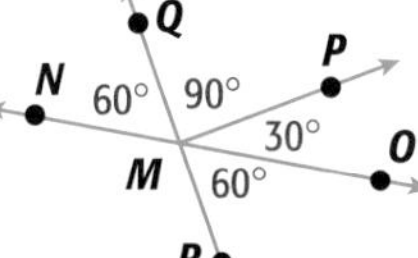

Possible answers:

A. Name one pair of complementary angles. $\angle OMP$ and $\angle QMN$

B. Name one pair of supplementary angles. $\angle NMQ$ and $\angle QMO$

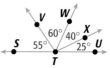

3 Close

Reaching All Learners

Through Grouping Strategies

Have students work in pairs to identify and list objects in the classroom that have right, acute, obtuse, and straight angles. Encourage pairs to share and compare their lists with the class.

Possible answers: The corner of a textbook forms a right angle. The chalkboard and the chalk ledge form a right angle. The edge of the desk forms a straight angle. A closed empty binder forms an acute angle. The pages of an open book form an obtuse angle.

Summarize

Write the vocabulary terms for this lesson on index cards. Place the cards face down on a desk. Have students in small groups take turns choosing a card and then do the following:

1. Orally define the term.
2. Draw an example of the term on the chalkboard.
3. Choose the next person to pick a card. After all the cards have been picked, have volunteers identify the examples drawn on the chalkboard using the correct vocabulary term.

Answers to Think and Discuss

1. Possible answer: Angles can be named using a point on each ray and the vertex, which is written in the middle: $\angle ABC$ or $\angle CBA$. An angle can also be named using only the vertex: $\angle B$. An angle can also be named by a number inside the angle.
2. The sum of the measures of complementary angles is 90°; therefore, the missing measure can be found using the equation $m\angle P + 25° = 90°$. $m\angle P = 65°$.

7-2 PRACTICE & ASSESS

Students may want to refer back to the lesson examples.

Assignment Guide

If you finished Example 1 assign:
Core 1–4, 10–13, 27–34
Enriched 1–4, 10–13, 22, 27–34

If you finished Example 2 assign:
Core 1–7, 10–16, 27–34
Enriched 1–7 odd, 10–16, 22, 23, 27–34

If you finished Example 3 assign:
Core 1–18, 19–23 odd, 27–34
Enriched 1–9 odd, 10–34

Answers

18. Possible answer: ∠*BAC* and ∠*CAE*; ∠*GAF* and ∠*GAC*

7-2 Exercises

FOR EXTRA PRACTICE
see page 668

GUIDED PRACTICE

See Example 1 Give the measure of each angle.

1. ∠*CAD* **60°**
2. ∠*EAF* **30°**
3. ∠*DAF* **120°**
4. ∠*BAE* **180°**

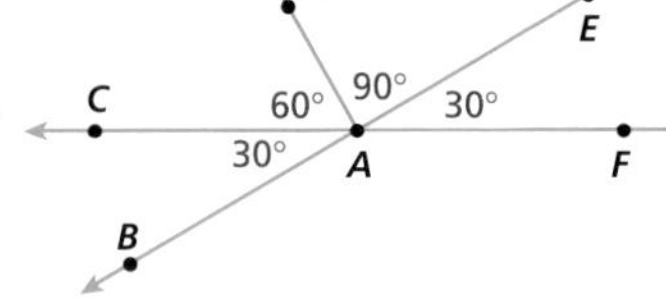

See Example 2 Tell whether each angle is acute, right, obtuse, or straight.

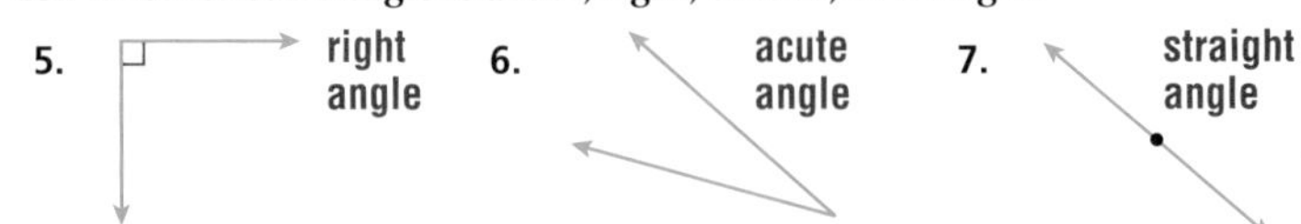

5. **right angle**
6. **acute angle**
7. **straight angle**

See Example 3 Use the figure to name the following.

8. two pairs of complementary angles
8. ∠*MNL* and ∠*ONP*, ∠*ONP* and ∠*PNQ*
9. two pairs of supplementary angles
Possible answers: ∠*PNQ* and ∠*MNP*, ∠*LNQ* and ∠*PNQ*

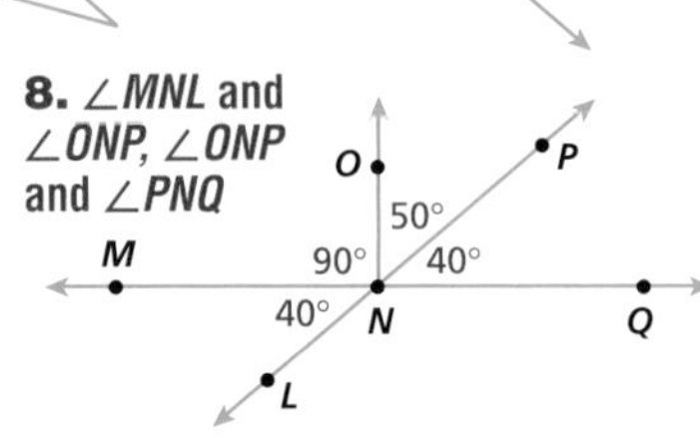

INDEPENDENT PRACTICE

See Example 1 Give the measure of each angle.

10. ∠*MJN* **80°**
11. ∠*LJK* **70°**
12. ∠*MJK* **130°**
13. ∠*MJO* **120°**

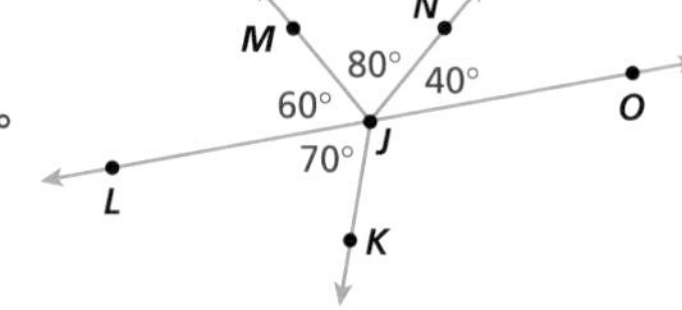

See Example 2 Tell whether each angle is acute, right, obtuse, or straight.

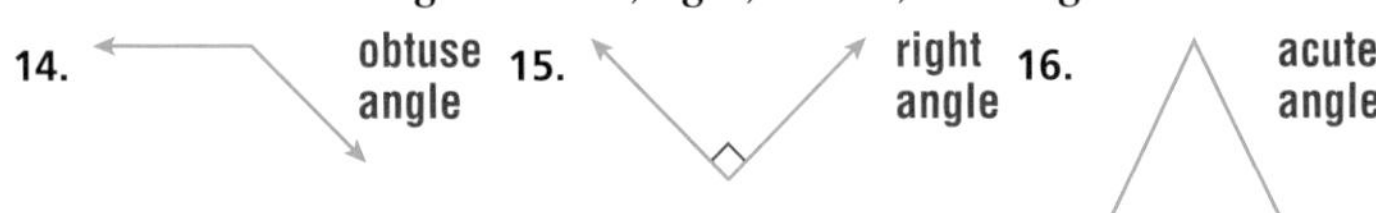

14. **obtuse angle**
15. **right angle**
16. **acute angle**

See Example 3 Use the figure to name the following.

17. two pairs of complementary angles
∠*BAC* and ∠*GAF*; ∠*EAF* and ∠*GAF*
18. two pairs of supplementary angles

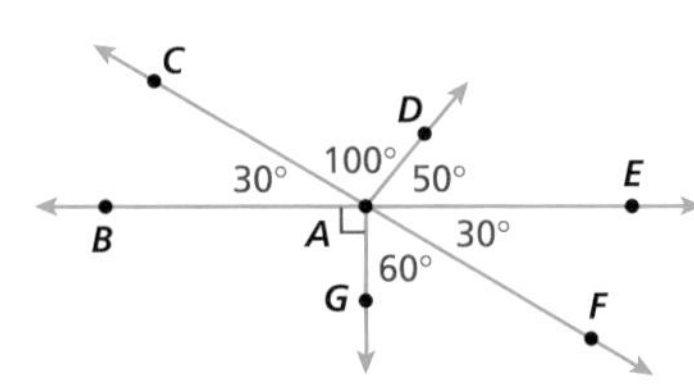

Math Background

The measurement of angles in degrees is a historical convention. A more natural mathematical unit for measuring angles is the *radian,* which is denoted as *rad.* The radian measure of an angle is equal to the length of the arc on a unit circle intercepted by the angle. Radians follow from the formula for the circumference of a circle:

$$C = 2\pi r.$$

To convert degrees to radians, multiply the number of degrees by $\frac{\pi}{180}$ radians. For example,

$$45° = 45 \cdot \frac{\pi}{180} \text{ rad} = \frac{\pi}{4} \text{ rad.}$$

Radians are commonly used in trigonometry.

RETEACH 7-2

LESSON 7-2 **Reteach**
Angles

Two rays with a common endpoint form an **angle.** The common endpoint is called the **vertex.** You can name an angle three ways:

- with the letter at the vertex: ∠*Y*.
- with a number written inside the angle: ∠1.
- with three letters: ∠*XYZ* or ∠*ZYX*. The letter of the vertex must be in the middle.

Angles are measured in degrees and classified by their measures.

Right angle: 90°
Acute angle: between 0° and 90°
Obtuse angle: between 90° and 180°
Straight angle: 180°

Two angles are **complementary** if their sum is 90°.
Two angles are **supplementary** if their sum is 180°.

Use the figure to complete the statements.

1. ∠*PQR* measures **90°**.
It is a **right** angle.
2. ∠*RQS* measures **60°**.
It is an **acute** angle.
3. ∠*UQR* measures 30° + 90°, or **120°**.
It is an **obtuse** angle.
4. ∠*PQT* measures 90° + 60° + 30°, or **180°**.
It is a **straight** angle.

Use the figure to complete the statements.

5. ∠*NKL* and ∠*LKO* are **complementary** angles since 70° + 20° = **90°**.
6. ∠*JKO* and ∠*OKL* are **supplementary** angles since 160° + 20° = **180°**.

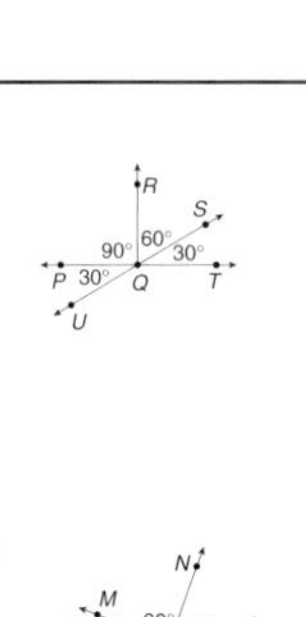

PRACTICE 7-2

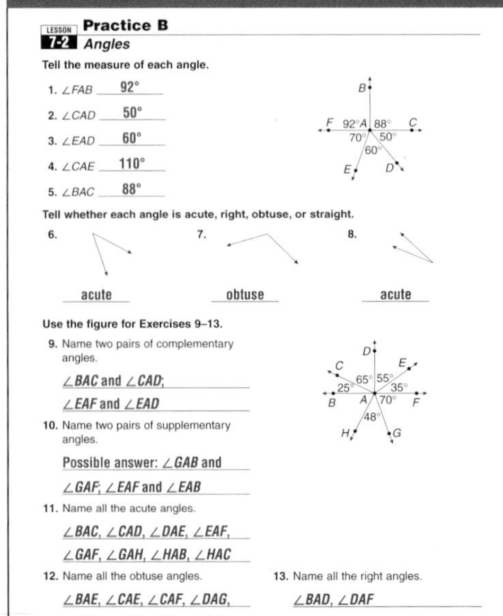

LESSON 7-2 **Practice B**
Angles

Tell the measure of each angle.

1. ∠*FAB* **92°**
2. ∠*CAD* **50°**
3. ∠*EAD* **60°**
4. ∠*CAE* **110°**
5. ∠*BAC* **88°**

Tell whether each angle is acute, right, obtuse, or straight.

6. **acute**
7. **obtuse**
8. **acute**

Use the figure for Exercises 9–13.

9. Name two pairs of complementary angles.
∠*BAC* and ∠*CAD*; ∠*EAF* and ∠*EAD*
10. Name two pairs of supplementary angles.
Possible answer: ∠*GAB* and ∠*GAF*; ∠*EAF* and ∠*EAB*
11. Name all the acute angles.
∠*BAC*, ∠*CAD*, ∠*DAE*, ∠*EAF*, ∠*GAF*, ∠*GAH*, ∠*HAB*, ∠*HAC*
12. Name all the obtuse angles.
∠*BAE*, ∠*CAE*, ∠*CAF*, ∠*DAG*, ∠*EAG*, ∠*EAH*, ∠*FAH*, ∠*GAB* ∠*GAC*, ∠*HAD*
13. Name all the right angles.
∠*BAD*, ∠*DAF*

PRACTICE AND PROBLEM SOLVING

Classify each pair of angles as complementary or supplementary. Then find the missing angle measure.

19. 

supplementary; 152°

20. 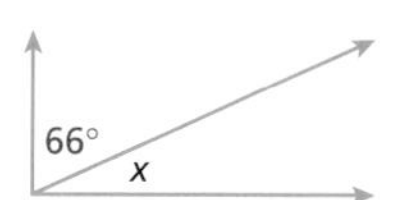

complementary; 24°

21. 

supplementary; 46°

22. The hands of a clock form an acute angle at 1:00. What type of angle is formed at 6:00? at 3:00? at 5:00? **straight; right; obtuse**

23. ***GEOGRAPHY*** Imaginary curves around Earth show distances in degrees from the equator and Prime Meridian. On a flat map, these curves are displayed as horizontal lines (latitude) and vertical lines (longitude).

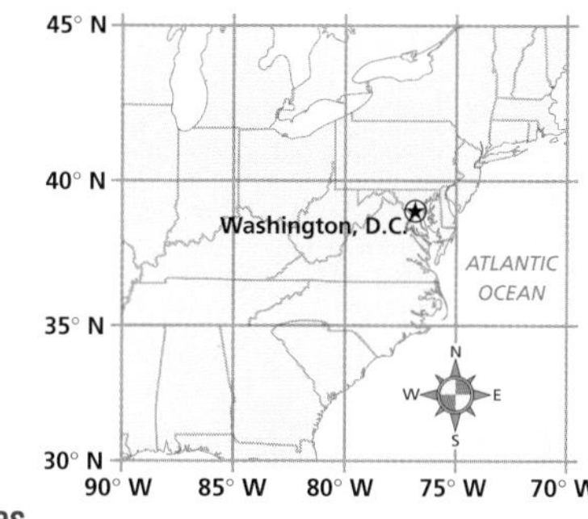

a. What type of angle is formed where a line of latitude and a line of longitude cross? **right angles**

b. Estimate the latitude and longitude of Washington, D.C. **about 39°N, 77°W**

24. ***WHAT'S THE ERROR?*** Jamal drew the pair of complementary angles at right. His classmate says that the angles are not complementary since they do not share a ray. Why is his classmate wrong?

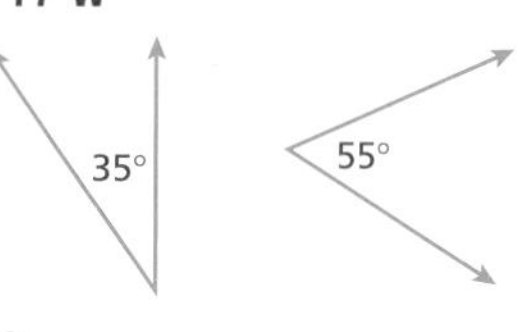

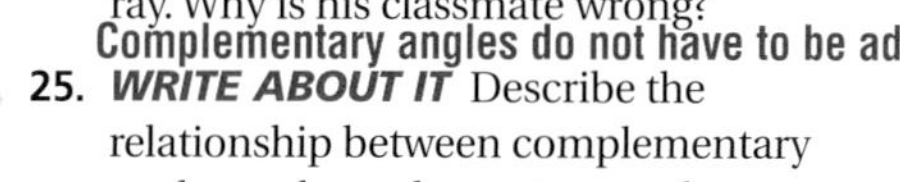

Complementary angles do not have to be adjacent.

25. ***WRITE ABOUT IT*** Describe the relationship between complementary angles and supplementary angles.

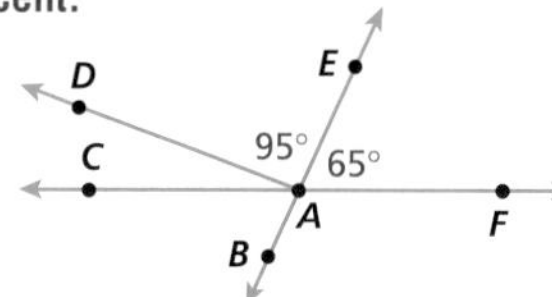

26. ***CHALLENGE*** Find m∠*BAC* in the figure. **65°**

Spiral Review

Write each decimal as a percent. (Lesson 6-1)

27. 0.7 **70%** **28.** 0.09 **9%** **29.** 1.45 **145%** **30.** 0.234 **23.4%**

Find each percent of change. Round your answer to the nearest tenth. (Lesson 6-5)

31. 35 is decreased to 15. **57.1%** **32.** 42 is increased to 98. **133.3%** **33.** 150 is decreased to 80. **46.7%**

34. TEST PREP Which geometric figure has one endpoint and extends infinitely in one direction? (Lesson 7-1) **B**

A Line **B** Ray **C** Line segment **D** Plane

CHALLENGE 7-2

LESSON 7-2 **Challenge**
Angling Clocks

The hands of a clock form an angle. At 9 o'clock, the hour hand points to 9, and the minute hand points to 12. The angle formed measures 90°.

But how do you measure the angle when both hands are between numbers?

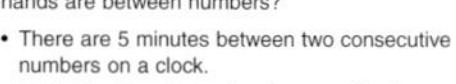

- There are 5 minutes between two consecutive numbers on a clock.
- Each time the minute hand moves 12 minutes, or $\frac{1}{5}$ the distance around the clock, the hour hand moves $\frac{1}{5}$ the distance between two consecutive numbers.

What is the angle between the hands at 7:24?

When the minute hand moves 24 minutes, the hour hand moves 2 sections. So, there are (7 • 5 + 2) − 24, or 13, sections between the hands. Each section is $\frac{1}{60}$ of an hour, and there are 360° on a clock face.

$13 \cdot \frac{1}{60} \cdot 360 = 13 \cdot 6 = 78$

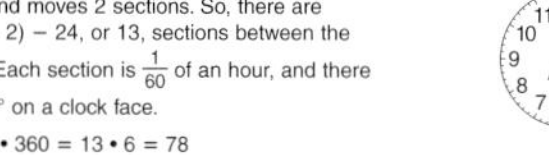

The angle between the hands measures 78°.

1. Draw the clock hands and find the angle between them at 5 o'clock.

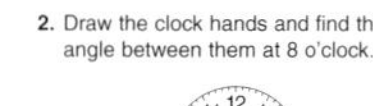

150°

2. Draw the clock hands and find the angle between them at 8 o'clock. **120°**

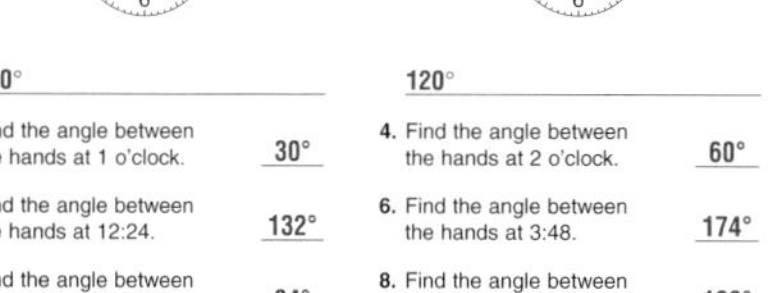

3. Find the angle between the hands at 1 o'clock. **30°**
4. Find the angle between the hands at 2 o'clock. **60°**
5. Find the angle between the hands at 12:24. **132°**
6. Find the angle between the hands at 3:48. **174°**
7. Find the angle between the hands at 3:12. **24°**
8. Find the angle between the hands at 1:36. **168°**

PROBLEM SOLVING 7-2

LESSON 7-2 **Problem Solving**
Angles

Write the correct answer.

The drawing shows a scene on a calendar.

1. ∠1 and ∠2 are complementary angles. If ∠1 measures 35°, what is the measure of ∠2? **55°**
2. ∠3 and ∠4 are supplementary angles. If ∠3 measures 50°, what is the measure of ∠4? **130°**
3. Which angle is an obtuse angle: ∠6 or ∠7? **∠6**
4. Which angle labeled on the drawing is a right angle? **∠5**

Choose the letter for the best answer.

The drawing shows the path a player runs to cross a sports field.

5. Which angle is an acute angle?
   A ∠1 Ⓒ ∠3
   B ∠2 D ∠4
6. Which two angles are supplementary angles?
   F ∠1 and ∠2 Ⓗ ∠1 and ∠3
   G ∠1 and ∠4 J ∠2 and ∠4
7. If ∠2 measures 115°, what is the measure of ∠4?
   Ⓐ 115° C 180°
   B 65° D 35°
8. If ∠2 measures 115°, what is the measure of ∠3?
   F 115° H 90°
   Ⓖ 65° J 30°
9. If ∠5 measures 78°, what is the measure of ∠1?
   A 98° C 78°
   Ⓑ 102° D 82°
10. If ∠4 measures 96°, what is the measure of ∠3?
   F 96° H 104°
   G 76° Ⓙ 84°

COMMON ERROR ALERT

You may wish to provide additional practice for students who still confuse acute and obtuse angles. Consider having those students use the phrase "a cute little angle" to remember that acute angles are less than 90°, or "little" angles.

Answers

25. Complementary angles are two angles whose sum is 90°. Supplementary angles are two angles whose sum is 180°.

Journal

Ask students to describe how angles are related to rays, points, and line segments.

Test Prep Doctor

For Exercise 34, students can eliminate **A** and **D** by using the fact that a line and plane both extend infinitely in more than one direction. Remind students that a segment is only part of something, therefore it is not a likely answer to a figure that extends infinitely. So **B** must be the correct answer.

Lesson Quiz

Give the measure of each angle, and tell whether it is acute, right, obtuse, or straight.

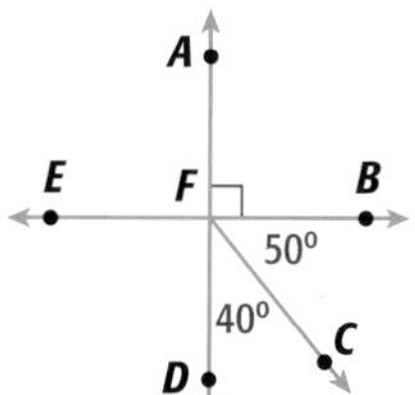

1. ∠*AFB* 90°; right

2. ∠*AFC* 140°; obtuse

3. ∠*DFC* 40°; acute

4. Name a pair of complementary angles. ∠*DFC* and ∠*CFB*

5. Name a pair of supplementary angles.
Possible answer: ∠*EFA* and ∠*AFB*

Available on Daily Transparency in CRB

7A Explore Parallel Lines and Transversals

Pacing: Traditional 1 day
Block $\frac{1}{2}$ day

Objective: To use a protractor to find relationships between the angles formed by parallel lines and transversals

Materials: Protractor

Lab Resources

Hands-On Lab Activities . . . . pp. 48–51

Using the Pages

Discuss with students the meaning of *transversal.* Make sure students understand the difference between interior angles and exterior angles.

Draw two parallel lines and a transversal.

1. Write the word *interior* in each of the interior angles. Write the word *exterior* in each of the exterior angles.

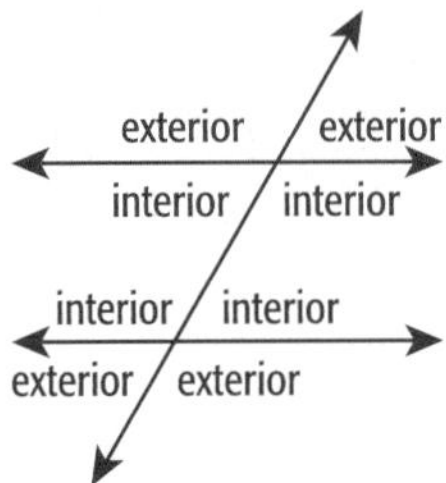

2. Use a protractor to find the measure of all of the angles. Possible answer: Acute angles measure 60°, and obtuse angles measure 120°.

Explore Parallel Lines and Transversals

Use with Lesson 7-3

REMEMBER
- Two angles are supplementary if the sum of their measures is 180°.
- Angles with measures less than 90° are acute.
- Angles with measures greater than 90° but less than 180° are obtuse.

Lab Resources Online
go.hrw.com
KEYWORD: MS4 Lab7A

Parallel lines are lines in the same plane that never cross. When two parallel lines are intersected by a third line, the angles formed have special relationships. This third line is called a *transversal.*

In San Francisco, California, many streets are parallel such as Lombard St. and Broadway.

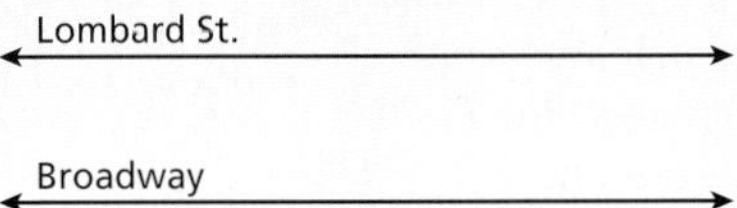

Columbus Ave. is a transversal that runs diagonally across them. The eight angles that are formed are labeled on the diagram below.

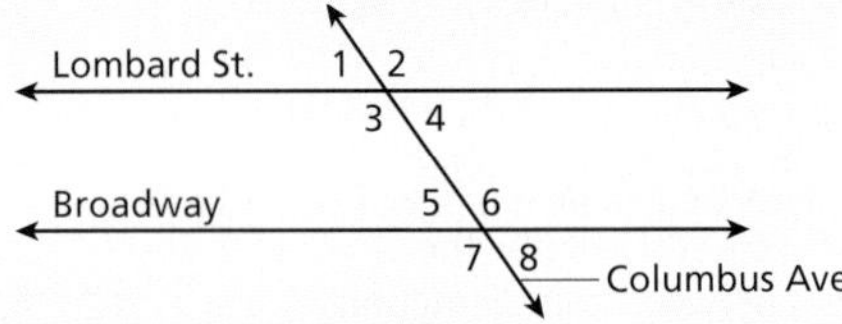

Activity

1. Copy the table below. Then measure angles 1–8 in the diagram below. Write these measures in your table.

Angle Number	Angle Measure
1	55°
2	125°
3	125°
4	55°
5	55°
6	125°
7	125°
8	55°

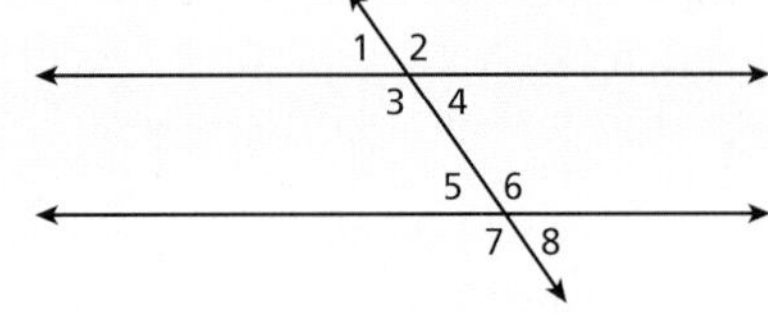

2 Use the table you completed and the corresponding diagram for the following problems.

a. Angles inside the parallel lines are *interior angles.* Name them.

b. Angles outside the parallel lines are *exterior angles.* Name them.

c. Angles 3 and 6 and angles 4 and 5 are *alternate interior angles.* What do you notice about angles 3 and 6? What do you notice about angles 4 and 5?

d. Angles 2 and 7 and angles 1 and 8 are *alternate exterior angles.* How do the measures of each pair of alternate exterior angles compare?

e. Angles 1 and 5 are *corresponding angles* because they are in the same position on each of the parallel lines. How do the measures of angles 1 and 5 compare? Name another set of corresponding angles.

f. Add the measures of angles 1 and 2. Now add the measures of angles 3 and 8. What can you say about the relationship of the angles in each of these sets? Name two other angles that have the same relationship.

Think and Discuss

1. $\overleftrightarrow{FG}$ and $\overleftrightarrow{LO}$ are parallel. Tell what you know about the angles that are labeled 1 through 8.
2. If angle 2 measures 125°, what are the measures of angles 1, 3, 4, 5, 6, 7, and 8? **55°; 125°; 55°; 55°; 125°; 125°; 55°**
3. If a transversal intersects two parallel lines and one of the angles formed measures 90°, discuss the relationship between all the angles. **Possible answer: All angles have a measure of 90°.**

Try This

Use a protractor to measure one angle in each diagram. Then find the measures of all the other angles without using a protractor. Tell how to find each angle measure.

1.

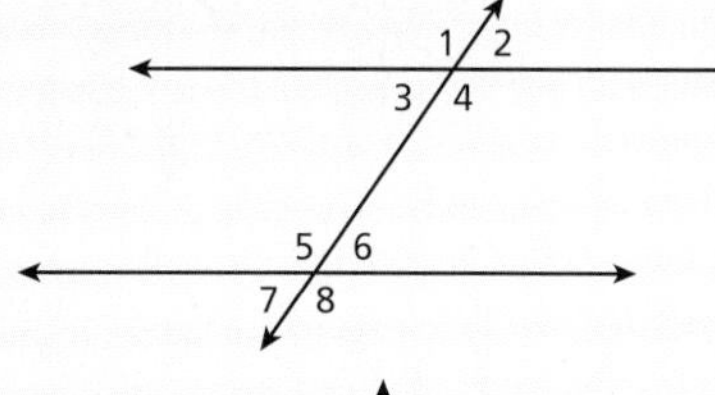

2.

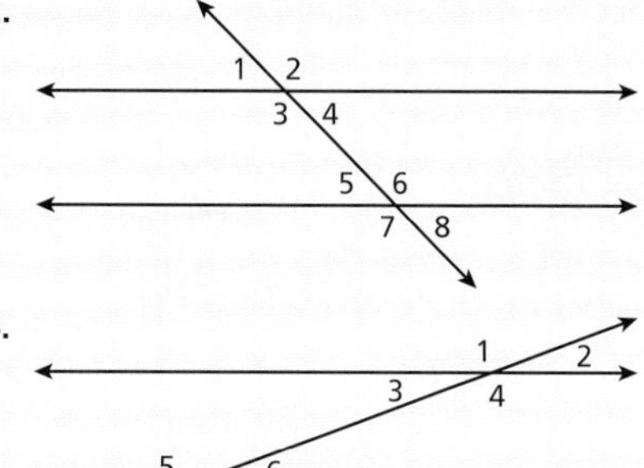

3.

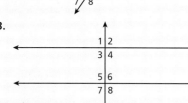

4.

Answers

Activity

2. **a.** interior angles: 3, 4, 5, and 6

b. exterior angles: 1, 2, 7, and 8

c. Angles 3 and 6 have the same measure; angles 4 and 5 have the same measure.

d. They have the same measure.

e. Possible answer: They have the same measure; angles 2 and 6 are corresponding angles.

f. Possible answer: They are supplementary angles; angles 4 and 6 are also supplementary.

Think and Discuss

1. Possible answer: The interior angles are 3, 4, 5, and 6. The exterior angles are 1, 2, 7, and 8. The alternate interior angles are 3 and 6, 4 and 5. The alternate exterior angles are 1 and 8, 2 and 7.

Try This

1. Possible answer: Angle 1 measures 125°. Angles 2, 3, 6, and 7 each have a measure of 55°, since a 55° angle is supplementary to a 125° angle. Angles 4, 5, and 8 each have a measure of 125°.
2. Possible answer: Angle 2 measures 135°. Angles 1, 4, 5, and 8 each have a measure of 45°, since a 45° angle is supplementary to a 135° angle. Angles 3, 6, and 7 each have a measure of 135°.
3. Possible answer: Angle 1 measures 90°. Since a 90° angle is supplementary to a 90° angle, all the angles must have measure 90°.
4. Possible answer: Angle 5 measures 160°. Angles 2, 3, 6, and 7 each has a measure of 20°, since a 20° angle is supplementary to a 160° angle. Angles 1, 4, and 8 each have a measure of 160°.

7-3 Organizer

Pacing: Traditional 1 day
Block $\frac{1}{2}$ day

Objective: Students identify parallel, perpendicular, and skew lines, and angles formed by a transversal.

Warm Up

Find the complement of each angle measure.

1. 30° **60°** **2.** 42° **48°**

Find the supplement of each angle measure.

3. 150° **30°** **4.** 82° **98°**

Problem of the Day

Draw three points that are not on the same line. Label them *A, B,* and *C.* How many lines can you draw that are determined by the points? Name the lines. 3; $\overleftrightarrow{AB}$, $\overleftrightarrow{AC}$, $\overleftrightarrow{BC}$

Available on Daily Transparency in CRB

Math Fact !!

Perpendicular lines are also known as *orthogonal lines.* A transversal is also known as a *semisecant.*

7-3 Parallel and Perpendicular Lines

Learn to identify parallel, perpendicular, and skew lines, and angles formed by a transversal.

Vocabulary
perpendicular lines
parallel lines
skew lines
vertical angles
transversal

When lines, segments, or rays intersect, they form angles. If the angles formed by two intersecting lines are equal to 90°, the lines are **perpendicular lines** . The red and yellow line segments in the photograph of the skyscraper are perpendicular because they form 90° angles.

Some lines in the same plane do not intersect at all. These lines are **parallel lines** . Segments and rays that are parts of parallel lines are also parallel. All of the vertical line segments in the photo appear to be parallel. Even if you extend the line segments, it seems that they will never cross. The same is true of the horizontal line segments.

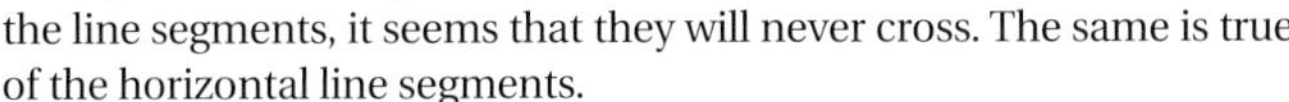

Skew lines do not intersect, and yet they are also not parallel. They lie in different planes. The orange line segments in the photograph are skew.

EXAMPLE 1 Identifying Parallel, Perpendicular, and Skew Lines

Tell whether the lines appear parallel, perpendicular, or skew.

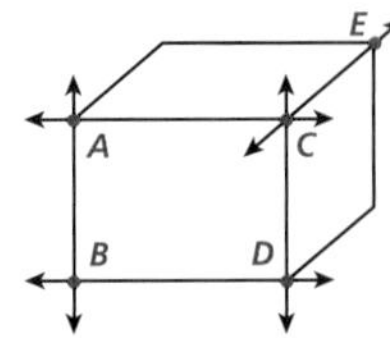

Reading Math

The symbol || means "is parallel to." The symbol ⊥ means "is perpendicular to."

A $\overleftrightarrow{AB}$ and $\overleftrightarrow{AC}$
$\overleftrightarrow{AB} \perp \overleftrightarrow{AC}$ — *The lines appear to intersect to form right angles.*

B $\overleftrightarrow{CE}$ and $\overleftrightarrow{BD}$
$\overleftrightarrow{CE}$ and $\overleftrightarrow{BD}$ are skew. — *The lines are in different planes and do not intersect.*

C $\overleftrightarrow{AC}$ and $\overleftrightarrow{BD}$
$\overleftrightarrow{AC} \parallel \overleftrightarrow{BD}$ — *The lines are in the same plane and do not intersect.*

1 Introduce

Alternate Opener

EXPLORATION

7-3 Parallel and Perpendicular Lines

Tell whether the lines in each diagram appear to be *parallel, perpendicular,* or *skew* by putting a check mark in the appropriate box.

	Parallel Lines (never cross each other)	Perpendicular Lines (cross each other at 90° angles)	Skew Lines (do not cross and are not parallel)
1.			
2.			
3.			
4.			

Think and Discuss

5. Discuss a major difference between the lines in numbers 1–3 and the lines in number 4.

Motivate

Draw a line on the chalkboard. Direct a volunteer to draw a second line on the chalkboard that will never cross the first line. Discuss with students what would need to be true for the lines to never cross. the lines would need to be the same distance apart everywhere

Exploration worksheet and answers on Chapter 7 Resource Book pp. 26 and 126

2 Teach

Lesson Presentation

Guided Instruction

In this lesson, students learn to identify parallel, perpendicular, and skew lines, and angles formed by a transversal. Skew lines are often confusing for students. Mention that since skew lines must be on different planes, they can be identified only in three dimensions. You may want to use Teaching Transparency T10 in the Chapter 7 Resource Book.

With Example 1, point out that perpendicular lines are intersecting lines, and the vertical angles formed are right angles. Have a volunteer draw an example on the chalkboard to show this.

Reading Math

Angles with the same number of tick marks are congruent. The tick marks are placed in arcs drawn inside the angles.

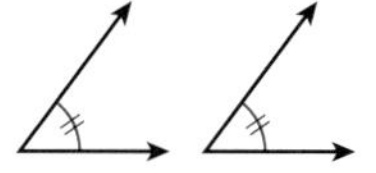

Vertical angles are the opposite angles formed by two intersecting lines. When two lines intersect, two pairs of vertical angles are formed. Vertical angles have the same measure, so they are congruent.

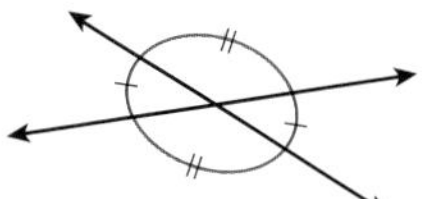

A **transversal** is a line that intersects two or more lines. Eight angles are formed when a transversal intersects two lines. When those two lines are parallel, all of the acute angles formed are congruent, and all of the obtuse angles formed are congruent. These obtuse and acute angles are supplementary.

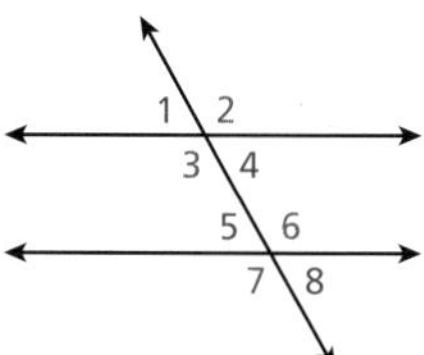

EXAMPLE 2 Using Angle Relationships to Find Angle Measures

Line $n \parallel$ line p. Find the measure of each angle.

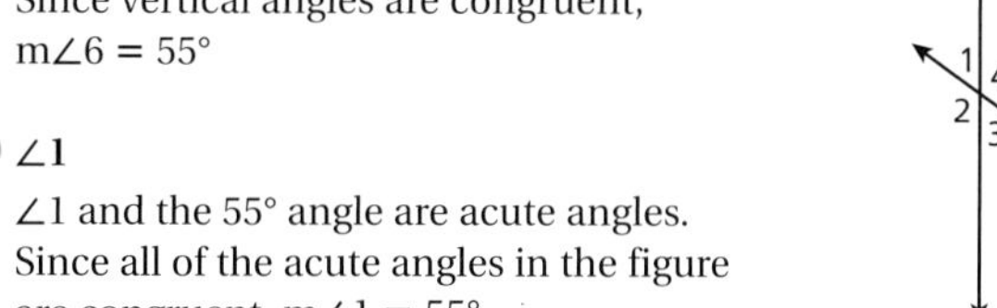

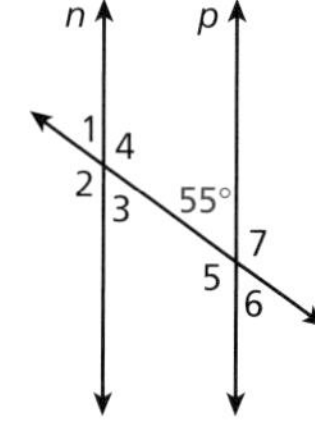

A $\angle 6$

$\angle 6$ and the 55° angle are vertical angles. Since vertical angles are congruent, $m\angle 6 = 55°$

B $\angle 1$

$\angle 1$ and the 55° angle are acute angles. Since all of the acute angles in the figure are congruent, $m\angle 1 = 55°$.

C $\angle 2$

$\angle 2$ is an obtuse angle.

$m\angle 1 + m\angle 2 = 180°$	*In the figure, the acute and obtuse angles are supplementary.*
$55° + m\angle 2 = 180°$	*Substitute for $m\angle 1$.*
$-55° \qquad -55°$	*Subtract 55° to isolate $m\angle 2$.*
$m\angle 2 = 125°$	

Think and Discuss

1. **Draw** a pair of parallel lines intersected by a transversal. Use tick marks to indicate the congruent angles.
2. **Give** some examples in which parallel, perpendicular, and skew relationships can be seen in the real world.

COMMON ERROR ALERT

Some students might assume that lines are perpendicular if they appear perpendicular in a drawing or picture. Remind students that perpendicular lines must be labeled at their intersection with a small square to show that they form right angles, or must be labeled as perpendicular, before they can be identified as perpendicular.

Additional Examples

Example 1

Tell whether the lines appear parallel, perpendicular, or skew.

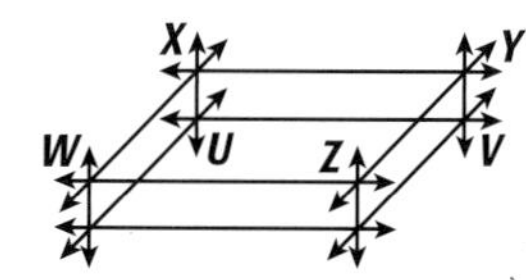

A. $\overleftrightarrow{UV}$ and $\overleftrightarrow{YV}$ — $\overleftrightarrow{UV} \perp \overleftrightarrow{YV}$

B. $\overleftrightarrow{XU}$ and $\overleftrightarrow{WZ}$ — $\overleftrightarrow{XU}$ and $\overleftrightarrow{WZ}$ are skew.

C. $\overleftrightarrow{XY}$ and $\overleftrightarrow{WZ}$ — $\overleftrightarrow{XY} \parallel \overleftrightarrow{WZ}$

Example 2

Line $n \parallel$ line p. Find the measure of each angle.

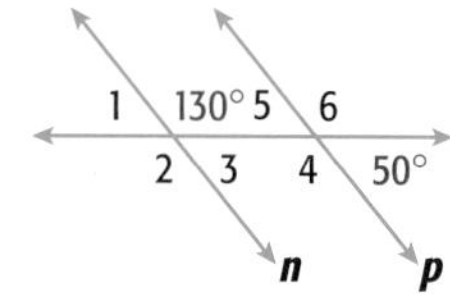

A. $\angle 2$ — $m\angle 2 = 130°$

B. $\angle 3$ — $m\angle 3 = 50°$

C. $\angle 4$ — $m\angle 4 = 130°$

3 Close

Reaching All Learners

Through Home Connection

Have each student work with his or her family to name streets that are parallel and perpendicular in their neighborhood. Have students sketch the streets they named, showing the parallel and perpendicular relationships.

Summarize

Have students tell whether each of the following statements is true sometimes, always, or never.

1. Parallel lines are intersecting lines.
2. Perpendicular lines are intersecting lines.
3. Skew lines are intersecting lines.
4. A transversal intersects perpendicular lines.
5. Vertical angles are right angles.
6. Parallel lines can never touch each other.
7. Vertical angles are straight angles.

1. never; **2.** always; **3.** never; **4.** sometimes; **5.** sometimes; **6.** always; **7.** never

Answers to Think and Discuss

1. Possible answer:

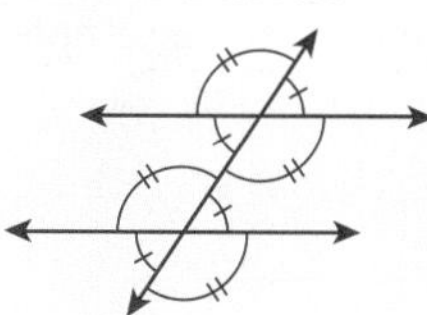

2. Possible answers: parallel—railroad tracks, sides of a ladder; perpendicular—rungs of a ladder and the sides of the ladder, windows with multiple panes; skew—a telephone pole and the edge of the curb of the sidewalk

7-3 PRACTICE & ASSESS

Students may want to refer back to the lesson examples.

Assignment Guide

If you finished Example 1 assign:
Core 1–3, 7–9, 13, 15, 19, 23–30
Enriched 1–3, 7–9, 13, 15, 19, 23–30

If you finished Example 2 assign:
Core 1–12, 13–19 odd, 23–30
Enriched 1–11 odd, 13–30

Notes

7-3 Exercises

FOR EXTRA PRACTICE see page 668

Homework Help Online
go.hrw.com Keyword: MS4 7-3

GUIDED PRACTICE

See Example 1 Tell whether the lines appear parallel, perpendicular, or skew.

1. $\overleftrightarrow{JL}$ and $\overleftrightarrow{KM}$ **parallel**
2. $\overleftrightarrow{LM}$ and $\overleftrightarrow{KN}$ **skew**
3. $\overleftrightarrow{LM}$ and $\overleftrightarrow{KM}$ **perpendicular**

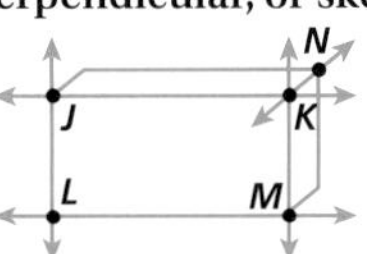

See Example 2 Line $r \parallel$ line s. Find the measure of each angle.

4. ∠5 **115°**
5. ∠2 **115°**
6. ∠7 **65°**

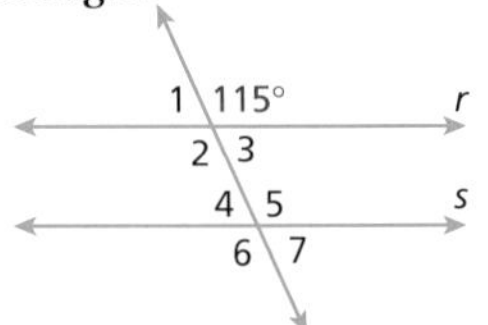

INDEPENDENT PRACTICE

See Example 1 Tell whether the lines appear parallel, perpendicular, or skew.

7. $\overleftrightarrow{UX}$ and $\overleftrightarrow{YZ}$ **skew**
8. $\overleftrightarrow{YZ}$ and $\overleftrightarrow{XY}$ **perpendicular**
9. $\overleftrightarrow{UX}$ and $\overleftrightarrow{VW}$ **parallel**

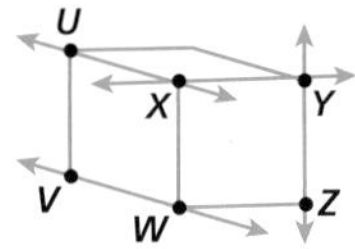

See Example 2 Line $k \parallel$ line m. Find the measure of each angle.

10. ∠1 **30°**
11. ∠3 **150°**
12. ∠6 **150°**

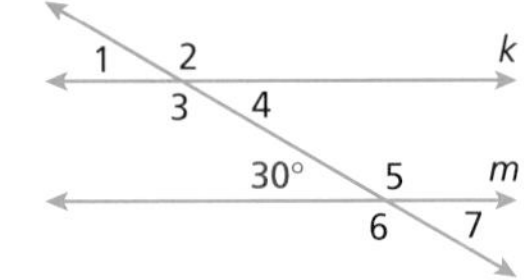

PRACTICE AND PROBLEM SOLVING

For Exercises 13–16, use the figure to complete each statement.

13. Lines x and y are __?__. **parallel**
14. ∠3 and ∠4 are __?__. **supplementary**
15. Lines u and x are __?__. **perpendicular**
16. ∠2 and ∠6 are __?__. They are also __?__. **acute; congruent**

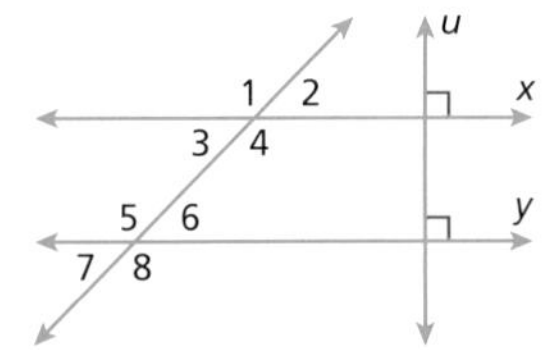

17. A pair of complementary angles are congruent. What is the measure of each angle? **45°**

Math Background

Some pairs of angles formed by a transversal that intersects parallel lines are congruent angles that have specific names. The diagram shows examples of these congruent angle pairs.

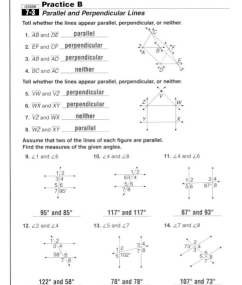

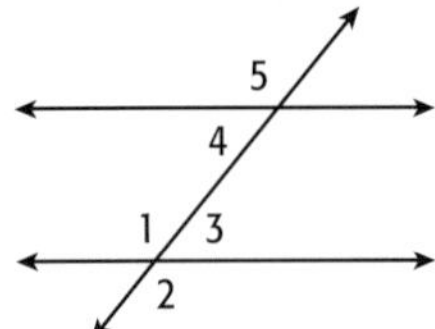

∠3 and ∠4 are alternate interior angles.
∠2 and ∠5 are alternate exterior angles.
∠1 and ∠5 are corresponding angles.

RETEACH 7-3

LESSON 7-3 **Reteach**
Parallel and Perpendicular Lines

Lines in the same plane that never meet are called **parallel** lines.

Two lines that intersect to form right angles are called **perpendicular** lines.

Lines that do not intersect and are not parallel are called **skew** lines. Skew lines are in different planes.

Use the figure to complete the statements.

1. $\overline{AB}$ and $\overline{DC}$ are **parallel** lines, since they never meet and lie in the same plane.
2. $\overline{DH}$ and $\overline{EH}$ are **perpendicular** lines, since they intersect to form right angles.
3. $\overline{AB}$ and $\overline{EH}$ are **skew** lines, since they do not intersect and are not parallel.

A **transversal** is a line that intersects two or more lines.
- When two parallel lines are intersected by a transversal, 8 angles are formed.
- The 4 acute angles are congruent, and the 4 obtuse angles are congruent.
- The sum of an acute angle and an obtuse angle is 180°.

Use the figure to answer the questions.

4. Which angles are acute angles? **∠2, ∠3, ∠6, ∠7**
5. Which angles are obtuse angles? **∠1, ∠4, ∠5, ∠8**
6. Find the measures of ∠1 and ∠2. **m∠1 = 140°; m∠2 = 40°**

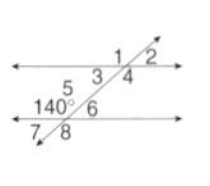

PRACTICE 7-3

LESSON 7-3 **Practice B**
Parallel and Perpendicular Lines

Tell whether the lines appear parallel, perpendicular, or neither.

1. $\overline{AB}$ and $\overline{DE}$ **parallel**
2. $\overline{EF}$ and $\overline{CF}$ **perpendicular**
3. $\overline{AB}$ and $\overline{AD}$ **perpendicular**
4. $\overline{BC}$ and $\overline{AC}$ **neither**

Tell whether the lines appear parallel, perpendicular, or neither.

5. $\overline{VW}$ and $\overline{VZ}$ **perpendicular**
6. $\overline{WX}$ and $\overline{XY}$ **perpendicular**
7. $\overline{VZ}$ and $\overline{WX}$ **neither**
8. $\overline{WZ}$ and $\overline{XY}$ **parallel**

Assume that two of the lines of each figure are parallel. Find the measures of the given angles.

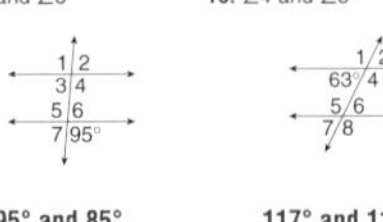

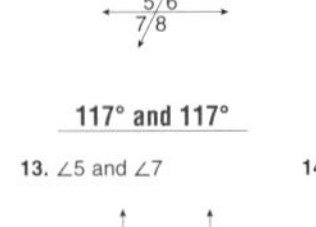

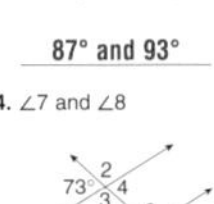

9. ∠1 and ∠6 **95° and 85°**
10. ∠4 and ∠8 **117° and 117°**
11. ∠4 and ∠6 **87° and 93°**
12. ∠2 and ∠4 **122° and 58°**
13. ∠5 and ∠7 **78° and 78°**
14. ∠7 and ∠8 **107° and 73°**

Construction workers use a special tool called a *square* to make sure that boards are perpendicular.

18. *CARPENTRY* In the diagram of a partial wall frame, the *ceiling joist*, $\overline{PQ}$, and the *soleplate*, $\overline{RS}$, are parallel.

a. How are $\angle RTP$ and $\angle TPQ$ related?

b. How is $\overline{PT}$ related to the vertical beams that it crosses?

c. How are $\angle 1$ and $\angle 2$ related?

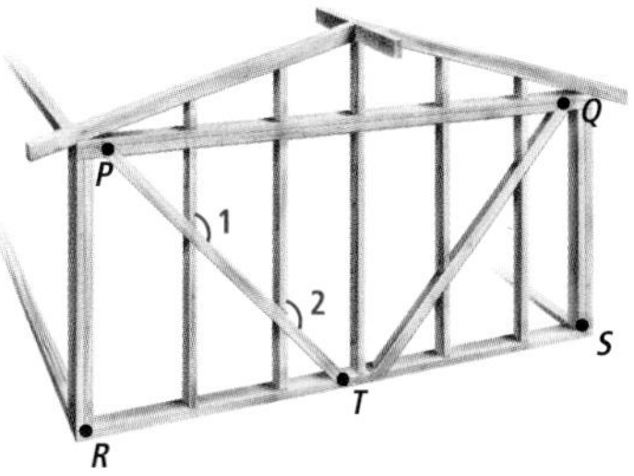

19. Tell whether the lines in each pair appear parallel, perpendicular, skew, or none of these.

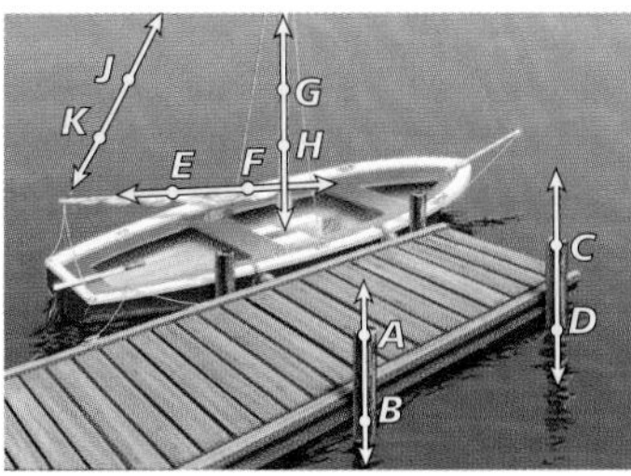

a. $\overleftrightarrow{AB}$ and $\overleftrightarrow{CD}$ **parallel**

b. $\overleftrightarrow{AB}$ and $\overleftrightarrow{JK}$ **skew**

c. $\overleftrightarrow{GH}$ and $\overleftrightarrow{EF}$ **perpendicular**

d. $\overleftrightarrow{EF}$ and $\overleftrightarrow{JK}$ **none**

20. *CHOOSE A STRATEGY* Trace the dots in the figure. Draw all the lines that connect three dots. How many pairs of perpendicular lines have you drawn? **C**

A 8 C 10
B 9 D 14

21. *WRITE ABOUT IT* Describe the relationship between the acute and obtuse angles formed when a transversal intersects two parallel lines.

22. *CHALLENGE* The lines in the parking lot appear to be parallel. How could you check that the lines are parallel? What would you have to assume to do this?

Spiral Review

Find the simple interest for each principal, interest rate, and time. (Lesson 6-6)

23. $550, 3%, 2 years **$33**
24. $900, 7%, 6 months **$31.50**
25. $1,200, 2.5%, 18 months **$45**

Give a real-world example of each type of line segment pair. (Lesson 7-1)

26. intersecting **27.** parallel **28.** skew **29.** congruent

30. TEST PREP $\angle 1$ and $\angle 2$ are complementary angles. What is the sum of their measures? (Lesson 7-2) **B**

A 45° B 90° C 180° D 360°

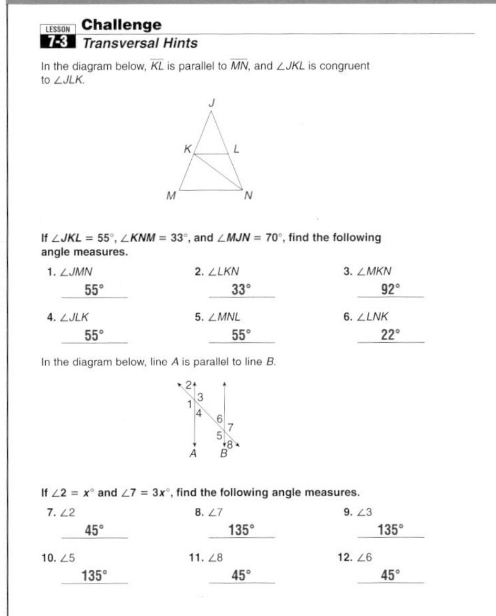

CHALLENGE 7-3

LESSON 7-3 **Challenge**
Transversal Hints

In the diagram below, $\overline{KL}$ is parallel to $\overline{MN}$, and $\angle JKL$ is congruent to $\angle JLK$.

If $\angle JKL = 55°$, $\angle KNM = 33°$, and $\angle MJN = 70°$, find the following angle measures.

1. $\angle JMN$ **55°**
2. $\angle LKN$ **33°**
3. $\angle MKN$ **92°**
4. $\angle JLK$ **55°**
5. $\angle MNL$ **55°**
6. $\angle LNK$ **22°**

In the diagram below, line *A* is parallel to line *B*.

If $\angle 2 = x°$ and $\angle 7 = 3x°$, find the following angle measures.

7. $\angle 2$ **45°**
8. $\angle 7$ **135°**
9. $\angle 3$ **135°**
10. $\angle 5$ **135°**
11. $\angle 8$ **45°**
12. $\angle 6$ **45°**

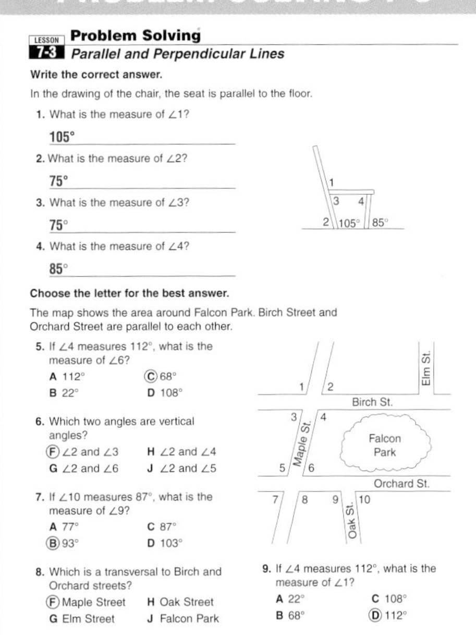

PROBLEM SOLVING 7-3

LESSON 7-3 **Problem Solving**
Parallel and Perpendicular Lines

Write the correct answer.

In the drawing of the chair, the seat is parallel to the floor.

1. What is the measure of $\angle 1$? **105°**
2. What is the measure of $\angle 2$? **75°**
3. What is the measure of $\angle 3$? **75°**
4. What is the measure of $\angle 4$? **85°**

Choose the letter for the best answer.

The map shows the area around Falcon Park. Birch Street and Orchard Street are parallel to each other.

5. If $\angle 4$ measures 112°, what is the measure of $\angle 6$?
A 112° **(C) 68°**
B 22° D 108°

6. Which two angles are vertical angles?
(F) $\angle 2$ and $\angle 3$ H $\angle 2$ and $\angle 4$
G $\angle 2$ and $\angle 6$ J $\angle 2$ and $\angle 5$

7. If $\angle 10$ measures 87°, what is the measure of $\angle 9$?
A 77° C 87°
(B) 93° D 103°

8. Which is a transversal to Birch and Orchard streets?
(F) Maple Street H Oak Street
G Elm Street J Falcon Park

9. If $\angle 4$ measures 112°, what is the measure of $\angle 1$?
A 22° C 108°
B 68° **(D) 112°**

Answers

18. a. $\angle RTP$ and $\angle TPQ$ are congruent.
b. $\overline{PT}$ is a transversal.
c. $\angle 1$ and $\angle 2$ are congruent.

21. Possible answer: When a transversal intersects two parallel lines, the acute angles all have the same measures, and the obtuse angles all have the same measures. An acute angle and an obtuse angle are supplementary.

22. Draw a transversal that intersects two or more lines in the parking lot, and measure a pair of angles that should be congruent, such as corresponding angles. If you can assume that your measurements are correct and the angles are congruent, then you can conclude that the lines in the parking lot are likely to be parallel.

26–29. Possible answers:
26. two streets crossing
27. two telephone poles
28. a light pole on one side of a street and a telephone wire on the other side of the street
29. two drum sticks

Journal

Ask students to explain which type of lines—parallel, perpendicular, or skew—they find most interesting and why.

Test Prep Doctor

For Exercise 30, students can use the definition of complementary angles to eliminate all choices except the correct one—**B.**

Lesson Quiz

Tell whether the lines appear parallel, perpendicular, or skew.

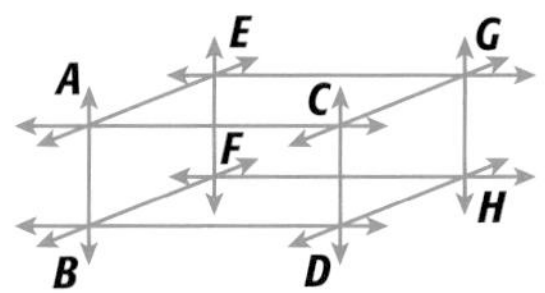

1. $\overleftrightarrow{AB}$ and $\overleftrightarrow{CD}$ parallel
2. $\overleftrightarrow{EF}$ and $\overleftrightarrow{FH}$ perpendicular
3. $\overleftrightarrow{AB}$ and $\overleftrightarrow{CG}$ skew
4. How are railroad tracks and two parallel lines alike, and how are they different? Both are always the same distance apart, but railroad tracks are not always straight.

Available on Daily Transparency in CRB

7B
Construct Bisectors and Congruent Angles

Pacing: Traditional 1 day
Block $\frac{1}{2}$ day

Objective: To use a compass and a straightedge to bisect a line segment, bisect an angle, and construct congruent angles

Materials: Compass, straightedge, protractor

Lab Resources

Hands-On Lab Activities. . . . . pp. 52–53

Using the Pages

Show students how to use a compass to draw an arc.

Use a compass and a straightedge.

1. Draw a line with the straightedge. Place your compass point on any point on the line. Draw an arc that intersects the line in two places.

   Possible answer:

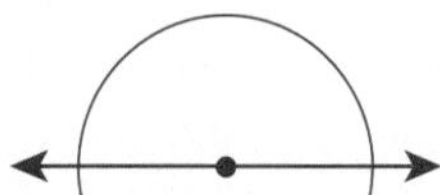

2. Draw an angle. Place your compass point on the vertex of the angle and draw an arc that intersects both sides of the angle.

   Possible answer:

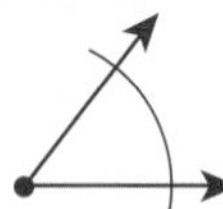

Construct Bisectors and Congruent Angles

Use with Lesson 7-3

REMEMBER
- To bisect a segment or an angle is to divide it into two congruent parts.
- Congruent angles have the same measure, and congruent segments are the same length.

internet connect
Lab Resources Online
go.hrw.com
KEYWORD: MS4 Lab7B

You can bisect segments and angles, and construct congruent angles without using a protractor or ruler. Instead, you can use a compass and a straightedge.

Activity

1 Bisect a line segment.

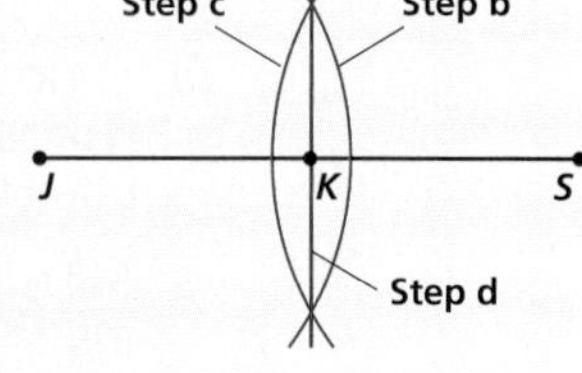

a. Draw a line segment $\overline{JS}$ on a piece of paper.

b. Place your compass on endpoint *J* and, using an opening that is greater than half the length of $\overline{JS}$, draw an arc that intersects $\overline{JS}$.

c. Place your compass on endpoint *S* and draw an arc using the same opening as you did in part **b.** The arc should intersect the first arc at both ends.

d. Draw a line to connect the intersections of the arcs. Label the intersection of $\overline{JS}$ and the line point *K*.

Measure $\overline{JS}$, $\overline{JK}$, and $\overline{KS}$. What do you notice?

The bisector of $\overline{JS}$ is a *perpendicular bisector* because all of the angles it forms with $\overline{JS}$ measure 90°.

2 Bisect an angle.

a. Draw an acute angle *GHE* on a piece of paper. Label the vertex *H*.

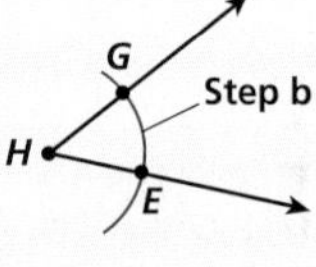

b. Place the point of your compass on *H* and draw an arc through both sides of the angle. Label points *G* and *E* where the arc crosses each side of the angle.

c. Without changing your compass opening, draw intersecting arcs from point *G* and point *E*. Label the point of intersection *D*.

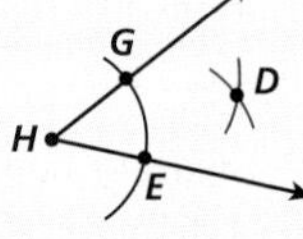

d. Draw $\overrightarrow{HD}$.

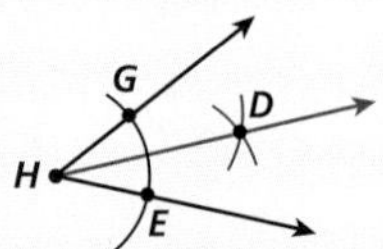

Use your protractor to measure angles *GHE*, *GHD*, and *DHE*. What do you notice?

3 Construct congruent angles.

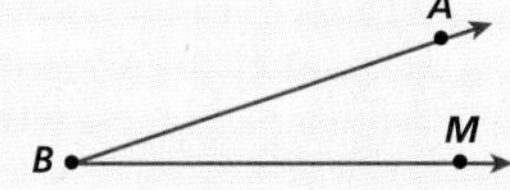

a. Draw angle *ABM* on your paper.

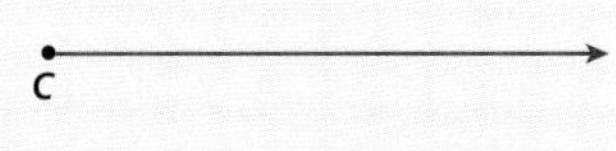

b. To construct an angle congruent to angle *ABM*, begin by drawing a ray, and label its endpoint *C*.

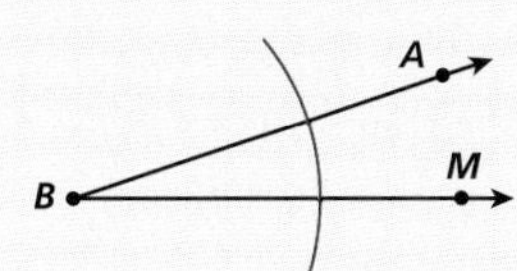

c. With your compass point on *B*, draw an arc through angle *ABM*.

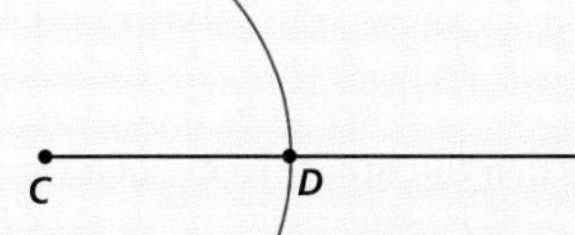

d. With the same compass opening, place the compass point on *C* and draw an arc through the ray. Label point *D* where the arc crosses the ray.

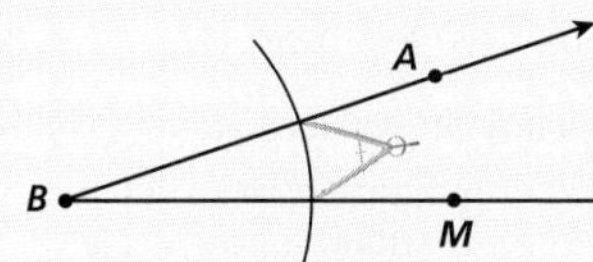

e. With your compass, measure the arc in angle *ABM*.

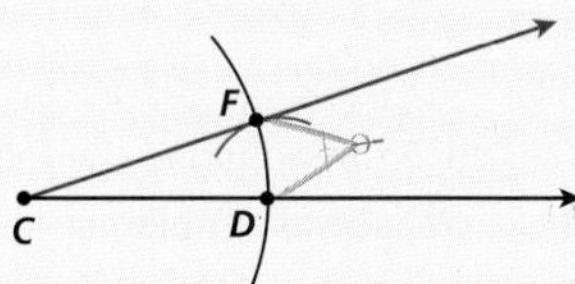

f. With the same opening, place your compass point on *D*, and draw another arc intersecting the first one. Label the intersection *F*. Draw $\overrightarrow{CF}$.

Use your protractor to measure angle *ABM* and angle *FCD*. What do you find?

Think and Discuss

1. How many bisectors would you use to divide an angle into four equal parts? **3 bisectors**
2. An 88° angle is bisected, and then each of the two angles formed are bisected. What is the measure of each of the smaller angles formed? **22°**

Try This

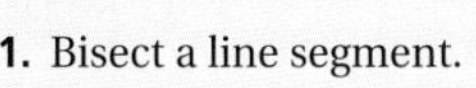

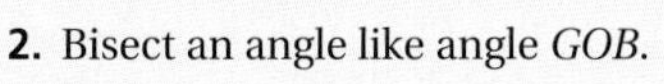

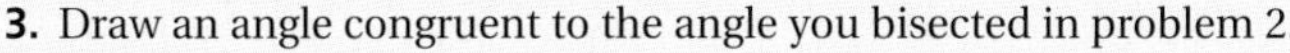

Use a compass and a straightedge to perform each construction.

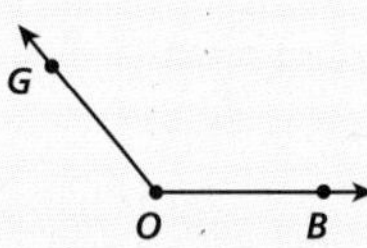

1. Bisect a line segment.
2. Bisect an angle like angle *GOB*.
3. Draw an angle congruent to the angle you bisected in problem 2.

Answers

Activity

1. The lengths of $\overline{JK}$ and $\overline{KS}$ are the same, and they are both exactly half the length of $\overline{JS}$.
2. Angles *GHD* and *DHE* have the same measure, and they both have exactly half the measure of angle *GHE*.
3. Angles *ABM* and *FCD* have the same measure.

Try This

Possible answers:

1.

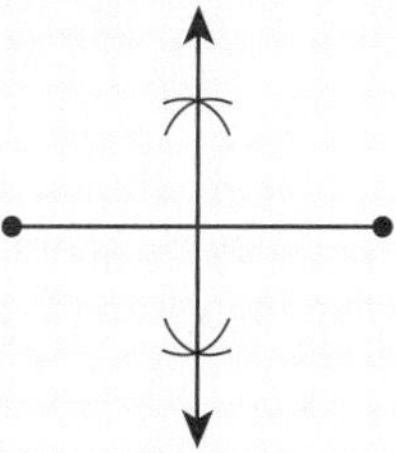

Check students' work.

2.

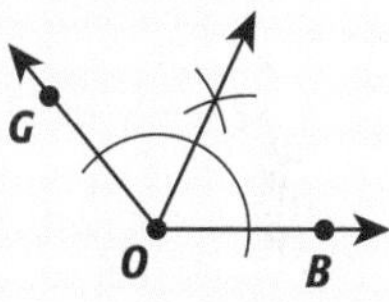

Check students' work.

3.

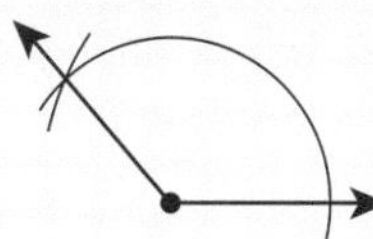

Check students' work.

Mid-Chapter Quiz

Purpose: *To assess students' mastery of concepts and skills in Lessons 7-1 through 7-3*

Assessment Resources

Section 7A Quiz

Assessment Resources . . . . p. 19

***Test and Practice Generator* CD-ROM**

Additional mid-chapter assessment items in both multiple-choice and free-response format may be generated for any objective in Lessons 7-1 through 7-3.

Chapter 7 Mid-Chapter Quiz

Mid-Chapter Quiz

LESSON 7-1 (pp. 344–347)

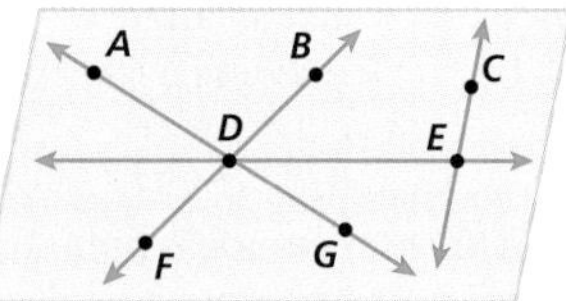

Identify the figures in the diagram. **Possible answers:**

1. three points **A, B, C**
2. three lines **$\overleftrightarrow{AG}, \overleftrightarrow{FB}, \overleftrightarrow{DE}$**
3. a plane **plane ABC**
4. three line segments **$\overline{AD}, \overline{DB}, \overline{EC}$**
5. three rays **$\overrightarrow{DA}, \overrightarrow{DB}, \overrightarrow{EC}$**

LESSON 7-2 (pp. 348–351)

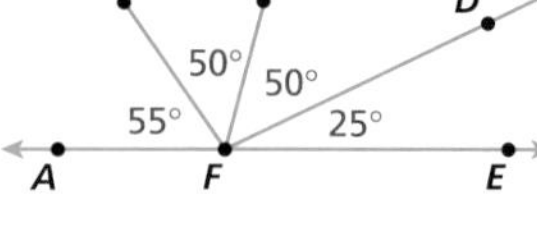

Give the measure of each angle.

6. $\angle DFE$ **25°**
7. $\angle BFC$ **50°**
8. $\angle AFE$ **180°**
9. $\angle AFD$ **155°**

Tell whether each angle is acute, right, obtuse, or straight.

10. **right**
11. **obtuse**
12. **acute**
13. **straight**

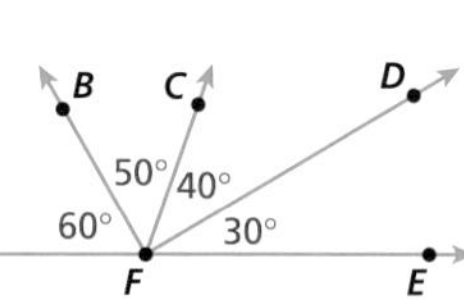

Use the figure to name the following in 14 and 15.

14. two pairs of supplementary angles **Possible answer: $\angle AFB$ and $\angle BFE$; $\angle DFE$ and $\angle AFD$**
15. two pairs of complementary angles **$\angle AFB$ and $\angle DFE$; $\angle BFC$ and $\angle CFD$**
16. Two supplementary angles are congruent. What is their measure? **90°**

LESSON 7-3 (pp. 354–357)

Tell whether the lines appear parallel, perpendicular, or skew.

17. $\overleftrightarrow{KL}$ and $\overleftrightarrow{MN}$ **skew**
18. $\overleftrightarrow{JL}$ and $\overleftrightarrow{MN}$ **parallel**
19. $\overleftrightarrow{KL}$ and $\overleftrightarrow{JL}$ **perpendicular**
20. $\overleftrightarrow{IJ}$ and $\overleftrightarrow{MN}$ **skew**

Line a || line b. Find the measure of each angle.

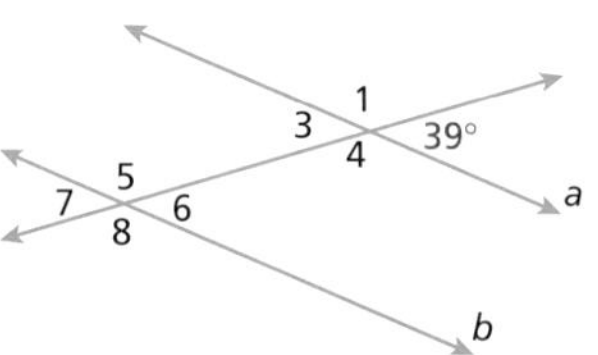

21. $\angle 3$ **39°**
22. $\angle 4$ **141°**
23. $\angle 8$ **141°**
24. $\angle 6$ **39°**
25. $\angle 1$ **141°**

Closed Figures

One-Minute Section Planner

Lesson	Materials	Resources
Hands-On Lab 7C Construct Perpendicular and Parallel Lines **NCTM:** Geometry, Reasoning and Proof **NAEP:** Geometry 1f ☐ SAT-9 ☐ SAT-10 ☐ ITBS ☐ CTBS ☐ MAT ☐ CAT	**Required** Compasses *(MK)* Straightedges *(MK)*	• *Hands-On Lab Activities,* pp. 54–55
Lesson 7-4 Circles **NCTM:** Geometry, Problem Solving, Communication, Connections **NAEP:** Geometry 1c ☑ SAT-9 ☑ SAT-10 ☑ ITBS ☑ CTBS ☑ MAT ☑ CAT	**Optional** Teaching Transparency T14 *(CRB)* Paper circles *(CRB, p. 116)* Analog clock	• *Chapter 7 Resource Book,* pp. 35–43 • Daily Transparency T13, CRB • Additional Examples Transparencies T15–T17, CRB • *Alternate Openers: Explorations,* p. 60
Hands-On Lab 7D Construct Circle Graphs **NCTM:** Geometry, Data Analysis and Probability, Reasoning and Proof **NAEP:** Data Analysis and Probability 1b ☑ SAT-9 ☐ SAT-10 ☑ ITBS ☑ CTBS ☐ MAT ☐ CAT	**Required** Compasses *(MK)* Straightedges *(MK)* Protractors *(MK)*	• *Hands-On Lab Activities,* pp. 56–57
Lesson 7-5 Polygons **NCTM:** Geometry, Reasoning and Proof, Communication, Connections **NAEP:** Geometry 1c ☑ SAT-9 ☑ SAT-10 ☑ ITBS ☑ CTBS ☑ MAT ☑ CAT	**Optional** Teaching Transparency T19 *(CRB)*	• *Chapter 7 Resource Book,* pp. 44–52 • Daily Transparency T18, CRB • Additional Examples Transparencies T20–T21, CRB • *Alternate Openers: Explorations,* p. 61
Hands-On Lab 7E Constructions with Polygons and Circles **NCTM:** Geometry **NAEP:** Geometry 1d ☐ SAT-9 ☐ SAT-10 ☐ ITBS ☐ CTBS ☐ MAT ☐ CAT	**Required** Compasses *(MK)* Straightedges *(MK)* **Optional** Rulers *(MK)*	• *Hands-On Lab Activities,* pp. 61–63, 127
Lesson 7-6 Triangles **NCTM:** Geometry, Communication, Connections **NAEP:** Geometry 3f ☑ SAT-9 ☑ SAT-10 ☑ ITBS ☑ CTBS ☑ MAT ☑ CAT	**Optional** Teaching Transparency T23 *(CRB)*	• *Chapter 7 Resource Book,* pp. 53–61 • Daily Transparency T22, CRB • Additional Examples Transparencies T24–T25, CRB • *Alternate Openers: Explorations,* p. 62
Lesson 7-7 Quadrilaterals **NCTM:** Geometry, Reasoning and Proof, Communication, Connections **NAEP:** Geometry 3f ☑ SAT-9 ☑ SAT-10 ☑ ITBS ☑ CTBS ☑ MAT ☑ CAT	**Optional** Teaching Transparency T27 *(CRB)* Recording Sheet for Reaching All Learners *(CRB, p. 117)*	• *Chapter 7 Resource Book,* pp. 62–70 • Daily Transparency T26, CRB • Additional Examples Transparencies T28–T29, CRB • *Alternate Openers: Explorations,* p. 63
Lesson 7-8 Angles in Polygons **NCTM:** Geometry, Reasoning and Proof, Communication, Connections **NAEP:** Geometry 3f ☐ SAT-9 ☑ SAT-10 ☐ ITBS ☑ CTBS ☐ MAT ☑ CAT	**Optional** Teaching Transparency T31 *(CRB)* Recording Sheet for Reaching All Learners *(CRB, p. 118)* Scissors *(MK)* Paper	• *Chapter 7 Resource Book,* pp. 71–79 • Daily Transparency T30, CRB • Additional Examples Transparency T32, CRB • *Alternate Openers: Explorations,* p. 64
Section 7B Assessment		• Mid-Chapter Quiz, SE p. 386 • Section 7B Quiz, AR p. 20 • *Test and Practice Generator* CD-ROM

SAT = *Stanford Achievement Tests* **ITBS** = *Iowa Test of Basic Skills* **CTBS** = *Comprehensive Test of Basic Skills/Terra Nova*
MAT = *Metropolitan Achievement Test* **CAT** = *California Achievement Test*

NCTM—Complete standards can be found on pages T27–T33. **NAEP**—Complete standards can be found on pages A35–A39.

SE = *Student Edition* **TE** = *Teacher's Edition* **AR** = *Assessment Resources* **CRB** = *Chapter Resource Book* **MK** = *Manipulatives Kit*

Section Overview

Circles

Hands-On Lab 7D, Lesson 7-4

Why? You need to know the parts of a circle to construct and interpret a circle graph and to find the circumference and area of a circle.

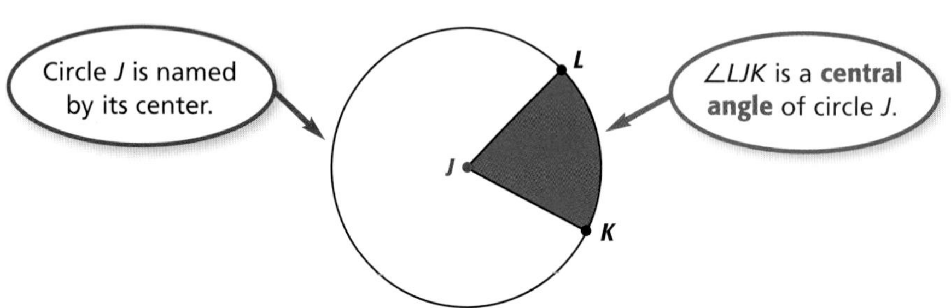

The sum of the measures of all the central angles of a circle is **360°**.

Find the measure of the central angle if the sector is 20% of the circle.

central angle measure = 20% of **360°**
= (0.20) · **360** = 72°

Polygons

Hands-On Lab 7E, Lessons 7-5, 7-6, 7-7

Why? When you are able to recognize polygons and distinguish between different types of polygons, it is easier to apply the properties of special features of polygons.

A **polygon** is a closed plane figure bounded by three or more line segments that intersect only at their endpoints.

Polygons

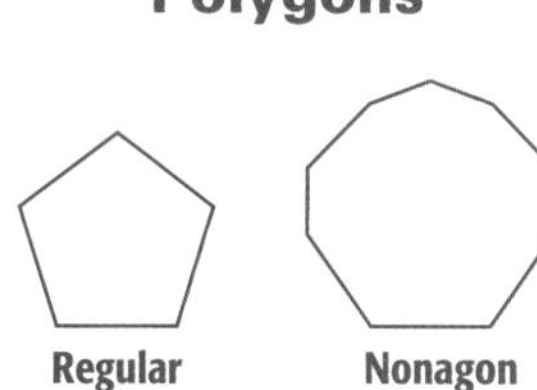

Not polygons

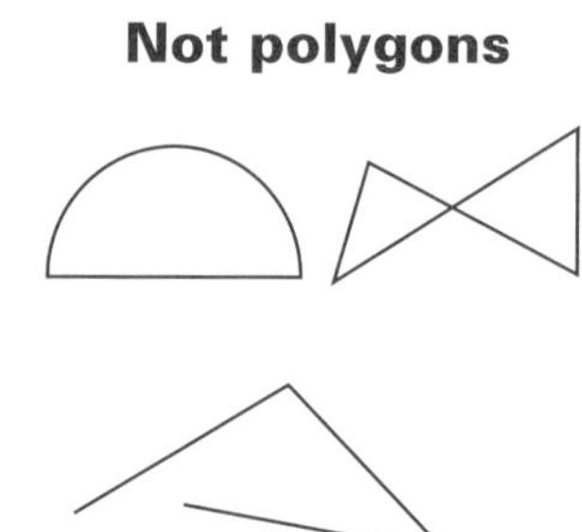

Angles in Polygons

Lesson 7-8

Why? When you know the sum of the interior angles of a polygon and all the angle measures but one, you can find the missing angle measure.

The sum of the interior angles of a triangle is **180°**.

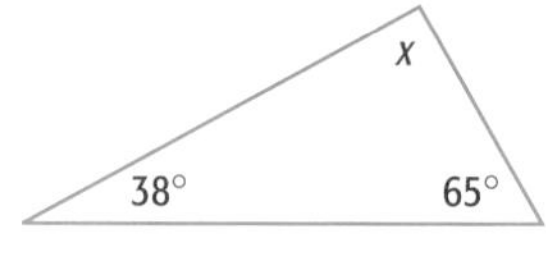

Find the measure of the unknown angle.

38° + 65° + *x* = 180°
103° + *x* = 180°
x = 77°

If you know the measure of two angles of a triangle, you can find the measure of the third angle.

Construct Perpendicular and Parallel Lines

Use with Lesson 7-3

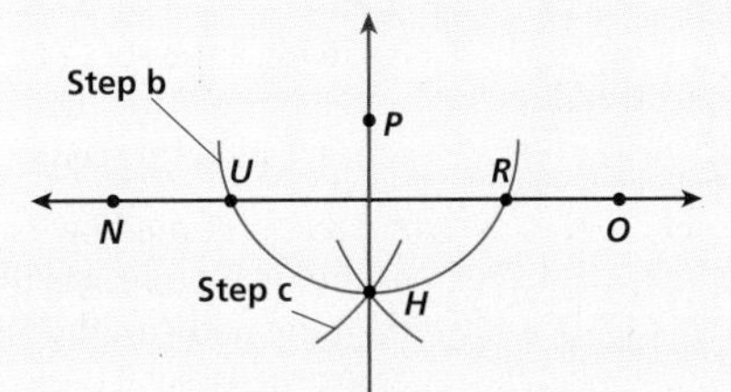

internet connect
Lab Resources Online
go.hrw.com
KEYWORD: MS4 Lab7C

Activity

1. Construct perpendicular lines.
   a. Draw $\overleftrightarrow{NO}$ and a point *P* above or below it.
   b. Put your compass point at *P* and draw an arc intersecting $\overleftrightarrow{NO}$. Label points *U* and *R*.
   c. Using the same compass opening, draw intersecting arcs from points *U* and *R*. Label the intersection *H*.
   d. Draw $\overleftrightarrow{PH}$.

What angle does $\overleftrightarrow{NO}$ make with $\overleftrightarrow{PH}$? **They appear to be perpendicular, so they make a 90° angle.**

2. Construct parallel lines.
   a. Draw $\overleftrightarrow{LR}$ and a point *S* above or below it.
   b. Draw a line that intersects point *S* and $\overleftrightarrow{LR}$. Label the intersection *T*.
   c. Use your compass to construct an angle *USW* at point *S* that is congruent to angle *STR*.
   d. Draw $\overleftrightarrow{SW}$.

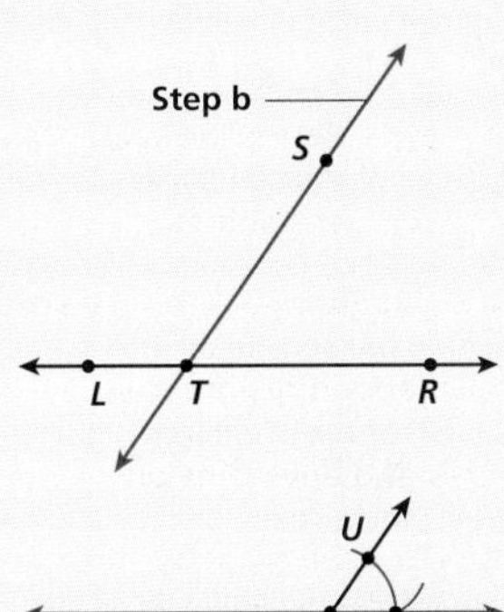

How do $\overleftrightarrow{SW}$ and $\overleftrightarrow{LR}$ relate to each other?
They appear to be parallel.

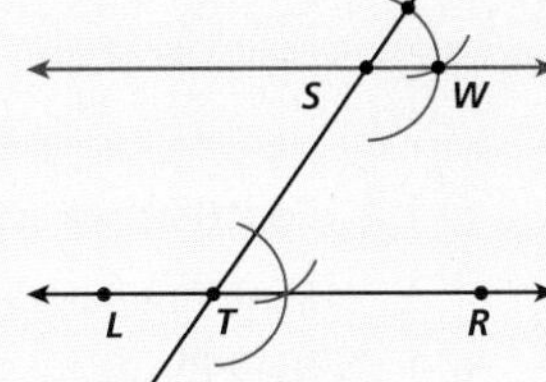

Think and Discuss

1. In 1, how would you confirm that $\overleftrightarrow{PH}$ and $\overleftrightarrow{NO}$ are perpendicular?
2. In 2, if $\overleftrightarrow{ST}$ is perpendicular to $\overleftrightarrow{LR}$, what can you say about angle *USW*?

Try This

1. Starting with $\overleftrightarrow{MT}$, construct a line segment parallel to $\overleftrightarrow{MT}$.
2. Starting with $\overleftrightarrow{PS}$, construct a line segment perpendicular to $\overleftrightarrow{PS}$.

Teacher to Teacher

Sandy R. Puckett
Taipei American School
Taipei, Taiwan

Students consider constructing parallel lines difficult, so I challenged them to find an easier method.

Construct parallel lines:

1. Start with a line *MA* and a point *T* above or below the line.
2. Begin by placing the point of the compass on point *M* and making an arc through point *T* so that it intersects line *MA*. Label the intersection *X*.
3. Now place the point of the compass on point *T* and make an arc to its right. Repeat with the point of the compass on point *X*. Label the arcs' intersection *H*.
4. Draw a line through points *T* and *H*.

7C Construct Perpendicular and Parallel Lines

Pacing: Traditional 1 day
Block $\frac{1}{2}$ day

Objective: To use a compass to construct perpendicular and parallel lines

Materials: Compass, protractor, straightedge

Lab Resources

Hands-On Lab Activities . . . . pp. 54–55

Using the Page

Discuss with students the difference between perpendicular and parallel lines. Review how to construct congruent angles.

Use a compass and a straightedge.

1. Draw an acute angle. Construct an angle congruent to this angle. Check students' work.
2. Draw an obtuse angle. Construct an angle congruent to this angle. Check students' work.

Answers

Think and Discuss

Possible answers:

1. Measure one of the angles formed by the intersection of $\overleftrightarrow{NO}$ and $\overleftrightarrow{PH}$. If the angle is 90°, the lines are perpendicular.
2. If $\overleftrightarrow{ST}$ is perpendicular to $\overleftrightarrow{LR}$, then angle *USW* is a right angle.

Try This

1.

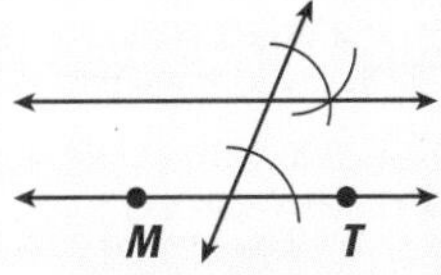

2.

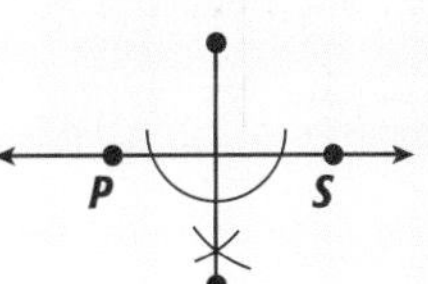

7-4 Organizer

Pacing: Traditional 1 day
Block $\frac{1}{2}$ day

Objective: Students identify and name different parts of a circle.

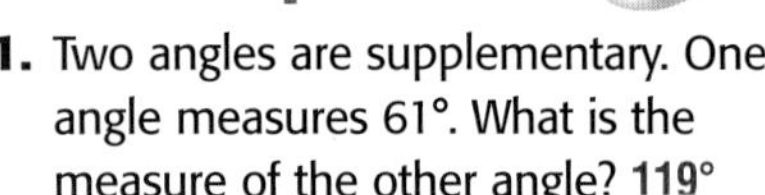

Warm Up

1. Two angles are supplementary. One angle measures 61°. What is the measure of the other angle? **119°**
2. Two angles are complementary. One angle measures 19°. What is the measure of the other angle? **71°**
3. Two angles are supplementary and equal in measure. What is the measure of each angle? **90°**

Problem of the Day

In a circle graph, three sectors representing 15%, 25%, and 30% are labeled. What percent does the fourth sector represent, and what is its measure in degrees? 30%; 108°

Available on Daily Transparency in CRB

Math Humor

A man tied a package using a diameter because it was the longest chord he could find.

7-4 Circles

Learn to identify parts of a circle and to find central angle measures.

Vocabulary
circle
center of a circle
radius
diameter
chord
arc
central angle
sector

The wheel is one of the most important inventions of all time. Vehicles with wheels—from ancient chariots to modern bicycles and cars—rely on the idea of a *circle*.

A **circle** is the set of all points in a plane that are the same distance from a given point, called the **center of a circle**.

A circle is named by its center. For example, if point A is the center of a circle, then the name of the circle is circle A. There are special names for the different parts of a circle.

This relief sculpture was made around 645 A.D., and shows King Ashurbanipal of Nineveh riding on his chariot.

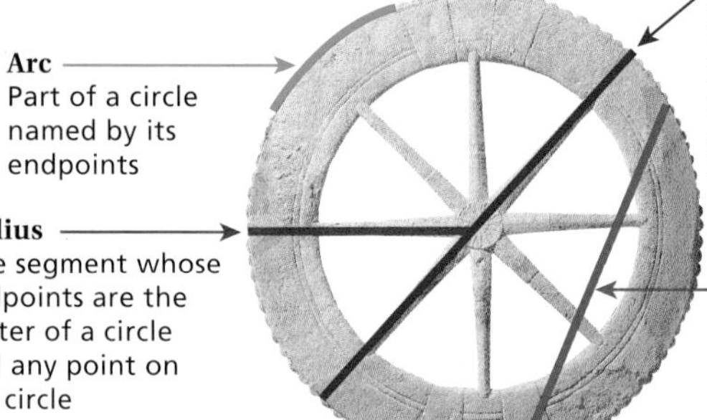
Arc
Part of a circle named by its endpoints
Radius
Line segment whose endpoints are the center of a circle and any point on the circle
Diameter
Line segment that passes through the center of a circle, and whose endpoints lie on the circle
Chord
Line segment whose endpoints are any two points on a circle

EXAMPLE 1 Identifying Parts of Circles

Reading Math
Radii is the plural form of *radius*.

Name the parts of circle P.

A radii
$\overline{PA}, \overline{PB}, \overline{PC}, \overline{PD}$

B diameter
$\overline{BD}$

C chords
$\overline{AD}, \overline{DC}, \overline{AB}, \overline{BC}, \overline{BD}$

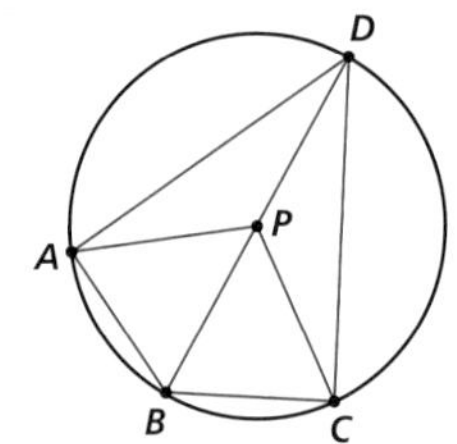
D
P
A
B
C

1 Introduce

Alternate Opener

EXPLORATION

7-4 Circles

According to the August 2000 U.S. Census Bureau Population Survey, there are 48,721,000 school-age children in the U.S.

Use the percents in the circle graph, the number of school-age children (48,721,000), and the number of degrees in a circle (360) to complete the table.

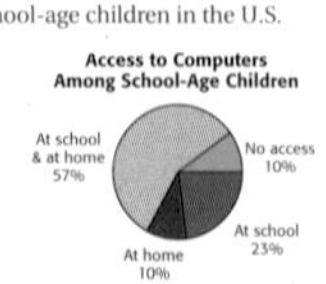
Access to Computers Among School-Age Children
At school & at home 57%
No access 10%
At school 23%
At home 10%

	Access	Percent	Portion of Graph (degrees)	Number of Children
	None	10%	$0.10 \cdot 360° = 36°$	$0.10 \cdot 48{,}721{,}000 =$ 4,872,100
1.	School	23%		
2.	Home	10%		
3.	School and home	57%		

Think and Discuss

4. **Explain** which percent should be eliminated and which should be increased if the goal is to provide access to computers.
5. **Discuss** other applications of a circle.

Motivate

Have students cut out a circle from paper (provided on Chapter 7 Resource Book p. 116). Have each student fold a circle in half. Then have each student open the circle and fold it in half again, but not in the same place. Have students repeat the folding activity several times. Then discuss the following questions:

1. How many different fold center lines can a circle have? infinitely many
2. What single point do all of the fold lines have in common? the center

Exploration worksheet and answers on Chapter 7 Resource Book pp. 36 and 128

2 Teach

Lesson Presentation

Guided Instruction

In this lesson, students learn to identify and name different parts of a circle. As students identify the different parts of a circle, encourage them to discuss the characteristics of each part. You may want to use Teaching Transparency T14 in the Chapter 7 Resource Book. Point out that a diameter divides a circle in half. A diameter is a straight line and therefore has a straight angle of 180°, which is one-half of 360°. So the diameter is a central angle of a circle.

Teaching Tip Before beginning Example 2, review the method of changing a percent to a decimal by moving the decimal point two places to the left.

A **central angle** of a circle is an angle formed by two radii. A **sector** of a circle is the part of the circle enclosed by two radii and an arc connecting them.

The sum of the measures of all of the central angles in a circle is 360°. We say that there are 360° in a circle.

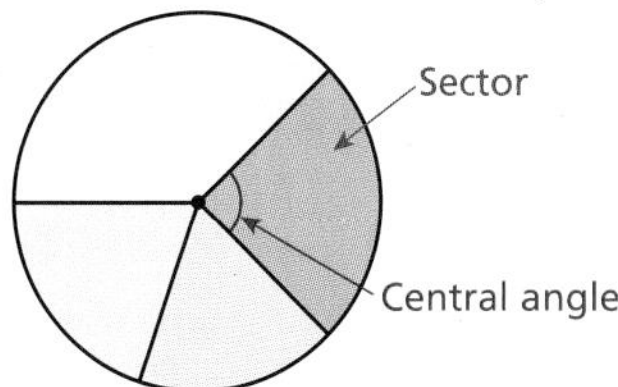

EXAMPLE 2 PROBLEM SOLVING APPLICATION

PROBLEM SOLVING

The circle graph shows the results of a survey to determine how people feel about keeping the penny. Find the central angle measure of the sector that shows the percent of people who are against keeping the penny.

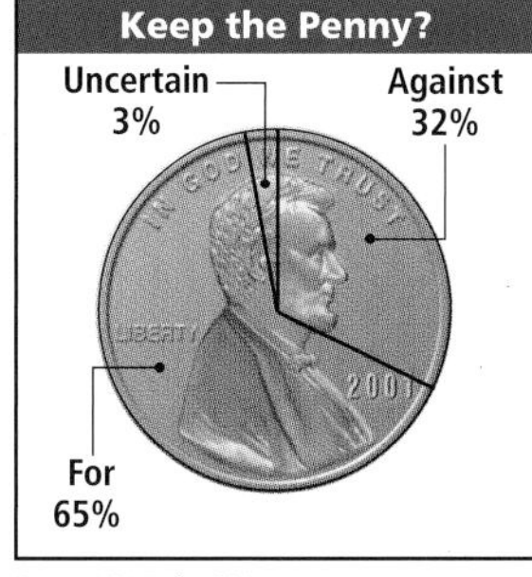

Source: USA Today, 2001

1 Understand the Problem

List the **important information:**

- The percent of people who are against keeping the penny is 32%.

2 Make a Plan

The central angle measure of the sector that represents those people against keeping the penny is 32% of the angle measure of the whole circle. The angle measure of a circle is 360°. Since the sector is 32% of the circle graph, the central angle measure is 32% of 360°.

32% of 360° = $0.32 \cdot 360°$

3 Solve

$0.32 \cdot 360° = 115.2°$ *Multiply.*

The central angle of the sector measures 115.2°.

4 Look Back

The 32% sector is about one-third of the graph, and 120° is one-third of 360°. Since 115.2° is close to 120°, the answer is reasonable.

Think and Discuss

1. **Explain** why a diameter is a chord but a radius is not.
2. **Draw** a circle with a central angle of 90°.

Additional Examples

Example 1

Name the parts of circle *M*.

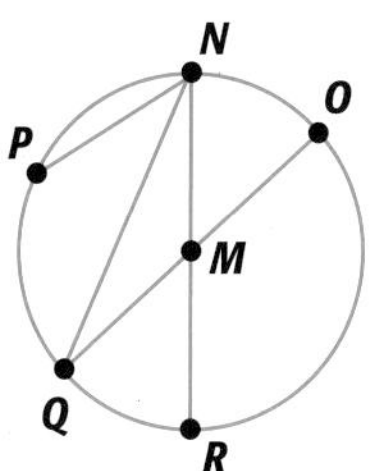

A. radii: $\overline{MN}, \overline{MR}, \overline{MQ}, \overline{MO}$

B. diameters: $\overline{NR}, \overline{QO}$

C. chords: $\overline{NR}, \overline{QO}, \overline{QN}, \overline{NP}$

Example 2

The circle graph shows the results of a survey about favorite types of muffins. Find the central angle of the sector that shows the percent of people whose favorite type of muffin is blueberry.

Favorite Types of Muffins

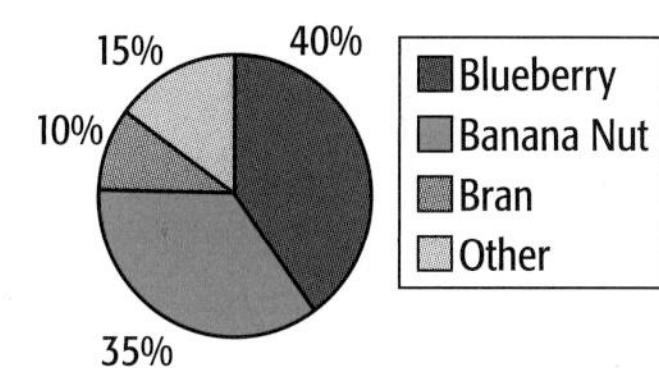

The central angle of the sector is 144°.

3 Close

Reaching All Learners

Through Visual Organizers

Use an analog clock to show central angles of sectors. Point out that there are 12 hours located equally around 360°. Therefore, at one o'clock the hands form a sector with a central angle measure of 30°, at two o'clock they form a sector with a central angle measure of 60°, and so on.

Summarize

Have students identify one major difference between each pair of parts of a circle:

1. radius and diameter
2. central angle and sector
3. arc and chord

1. A radius is a segment from the center to a point on the circle, whereas a diameter is a segment that passes through the center of the circle and connects two points on the circle.
2. A central angle is formed by two radii; the sector is the region enclosed by the radii that form the central angle and the arc connecting them.
3. An arc is a section of the circle; a chord is a line that connects two points on the circle.

Answers to Think and Discuss

1. A diameter is a chord because both of its endpoints lie on the circle. A radius has only one endpoint on the circle.
2.

7-4 PRACTICE & ASSESS

Students may want to refer back to the lesson examples.

Assignment Guide

If you finished Example 1 assign:
Core 1–3, 5–7, 17–25
Enriched 1–7 odd, 9, 10, 12, 17–25

If you finished Example 2 assign:
Core 1–8, 9–13 odd, 17–25
Enriched 1–7 odd, 9–25

Notes

7-4 Exercises

FOR EXTRA PRACTICE
see page 669

Homework Help Online
go.hrw.com Keyword: MS4 7-4

GUIDED PRACTICE

See Example 1 **Name the parts of circle *O*.**

1. radii **$\overline{OQ}$, $\overline{OR}$, $\overline{OS}$, $\overline{OT}$**
2. diameter **$\overline{RT}$**
3. chords **$\overline{RT}$, $\overline{RS}$, $\overline{ST}$, $\overline{TQ}$**

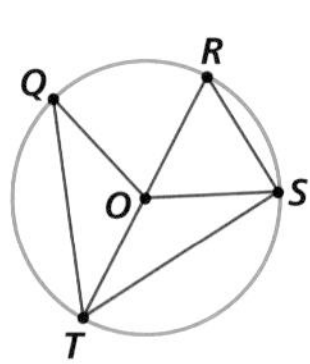

See Example 2

4. The circle graph shows the results of a 2001 survey in which the following question was asked: "If you had to describe your office environment as a type of television show, which would it be?" Find the central angle measure of the sector that shows the percent of people who described their workplace as a courtroom drama. **36°**

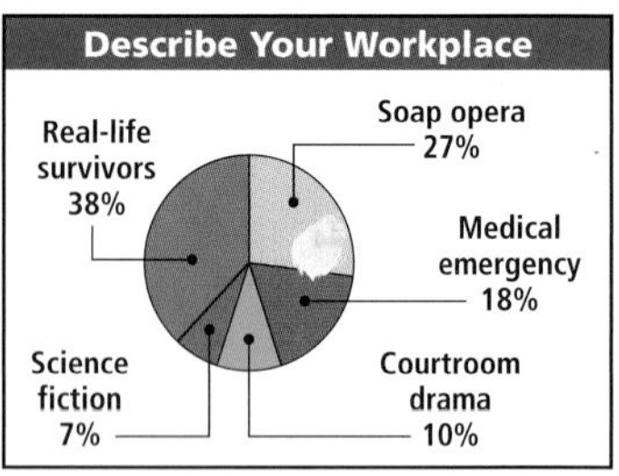

Source: USA Today

INDEPENDENT PRACTICE

See Example 1 **Name the parts of circle *C*.**

5. radii **$\overline{CA}$, $\overline{CB}$, $\overline{CD}$, $\overline{CE}$, $\overline{CF}$**
6. diameters **$\overline{AE}$, $\overline{BF}$**
7. chords **$\overline{GB}$, $\overline{BF}$, $\overline{DE}$, $\overline{FE}$, $\overline{AE}$**

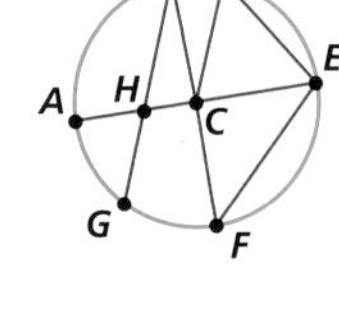

See Example 2

8. The circle graph shows the areas from which the United States imports bananas. Find the central angle measure of the sector that shows the percent of banana imports from South America. **156.6°**

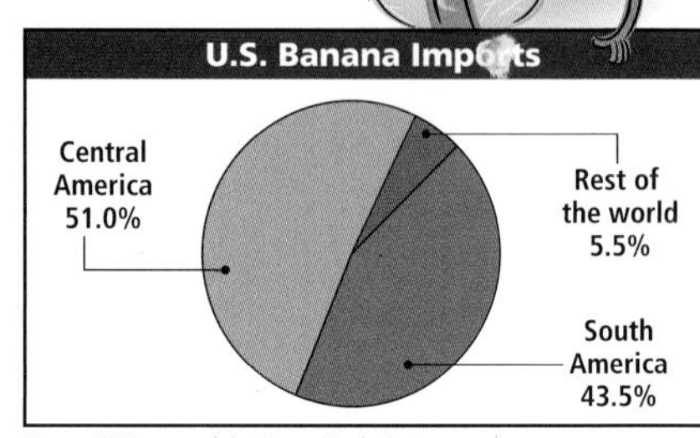

Source: US Bureau of the Census Trade Data

PRACTICE AND PROBLEM SOLVING

9. What is the distance between the centers of the circles? **10 cm**

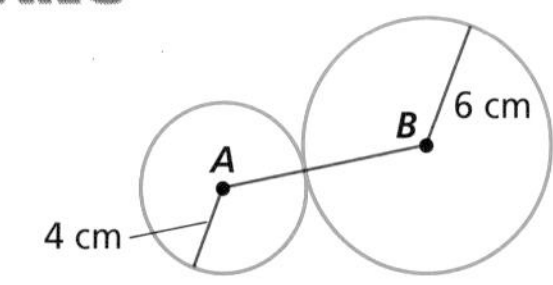

Math Background

Students probably have heard of magic squares, but they might not have heard of magic circles. Magic circles are intersecting circles, where the sum of all of the numbers at the intersections of each circle is the same constant. The circle below shows 3 magic circles with a magic constant of 14.

$5 + 6 + 2 + 1 = 14$

$5 + 3 + 2 + 4 = 14$

$1 + 3 + 6 + 4 = 14$

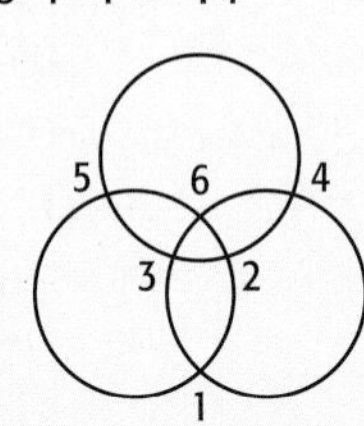

RETEACH 7-4

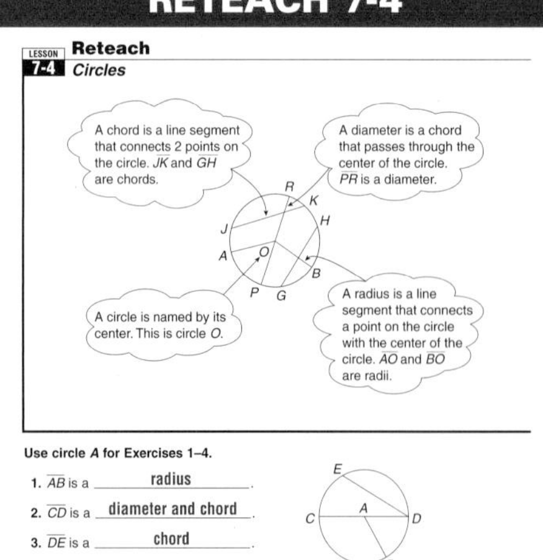

LESSON 7-4 **Reteach**
Circles

A chord is a line segment that connects 2 points on the circle. $\overline{JK}$ and $\overline{GH}$ are chords.
A diameter is a chord that passes through the center of the circle. $\overline{PR}$ is a diameter.
A circle is named by its center. This is circle O.
A radius is a line segment that connects a point on the circle with the center of the circle. $\overline{AO}$ and $\overline{BO}$ are radii.
R
K
H
J
A
O
B
P
G

Use circle *A* for Exercises 1–4.

1. $\overline{AB}$ is a radius.
2. $\overline{CD}$ is a diameter and chord.
3. $\overline{DE}$ is a chord.
4. $\overline{CA}$ is a radius.

Use circle *Z* for Exercises 5–7.

5. Name 3 radii of circle *Z*. $\overline{ZV}$, $\overline{ZW}$, $\overline{ZX}$
6. Name 2 chords of circle *Z*. $\overline{YU}$, $\overline{VX}$
7. Name the diameter of circle *Z*. $\overline{VX}$

PRACTICE 7-4

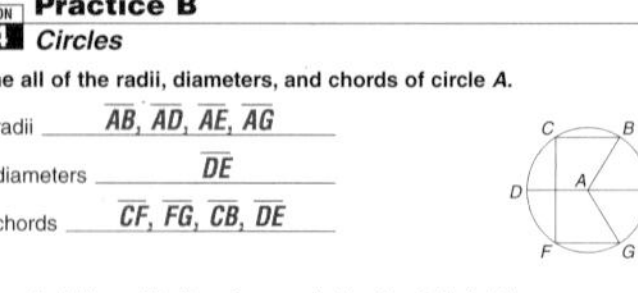

LESSON 7-4 **Practice B**
Circles

Name all of the radii, diameters, and chords of circle *A*.

1. radii $\overline{AB}$, $\overline{AD}$, $\overline{AE}$, $\overline{AG}$
2. diameters $\overline{DE}$
3. chords $\overline{CF}$, $\overline{FG}$, $\overline{CB}$, $\overline{DE}$

Name all of the radii, diameters, and chords of circle *H*.

4. radii $\overline{HP}$, $\overline{HJ}$, $\overline{HK}$, $\overline{HL}$, $\overline{HM}$
5. diameters $\overline{JM}$
6. chords $\overline{OQ}$, $\overline{NR}$, $\overline{JM}$

Name all of the radii, diameters, and chords of circle *C*.

7. radii $\overline{CA}$, $\overline{CB}$, $\overline{CF}$, $\overline{CJ}$, $\overline{CH}$
8. diameters $\overline{AH}$, $\overline{FB}$
9. chords $\overline{AB}$, $\overline{FH}$, $\overline{AH}$, $\overline{FB}$

Name all of the radii, diameters, and chords of circle *Z*.

10. radii $\overline{ZY}$, $\overline{ZT}$, $\overline{ZU}$, $\overline{ZV}$, $\overline{ZW}$, $\overline{ZX}$
11. diameters $\overline{TW}$, $\overline{YV}$, $\overline{XU}$
12. chords $\overline{YT}$, $\overline{WV}$, $\overline{TW}$, $\overline{YV}$, $\overline{XU}$

Use the circle graph.

13. The circle graph shows the distribution of ethnic groups in New Zealand. Find the central angle measure of the sector that shows the percent of New Zealanders who are Maori. 34.92°

New Zealand Population: Maori 9.7%, Asian/other 7.4%, Other European 4.6%, Pacific Islander 3.8%, New Zealand European 74.5%

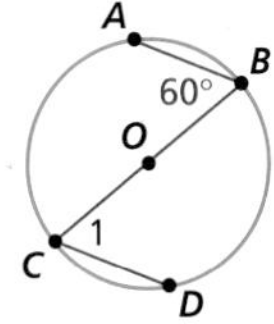

10. a. Name all of the chords of the circle at right.
b. If $\overline{AB} \parallel \overline{CD}$, what is the measure of $\angle 1$? Explain your answer.

11. A circle is divided into five equal sectors. Find the measure of the central angle of each sector. **72°**

12. What is the measure of the central angle of a quarter of a circle? **90°**

13c. Possible answer: While more people favored *God Bless America* as a song, they still preferred *The Star-Spangled Banner* as the national anthem.

13. ***MUSIC*** The circle graphs show the results of a music survey.
a. Find the central angle measure of the sector that shows the percent of people who chose *The Star-Spangled Banner* as the song they prefer. **133.2°**
b. Find the central angle measure of the sector that shows the percent of people who prefer *God Bless America* as the national anthem. **122.4°**
c. What point is made by showing the two circle graphs together?

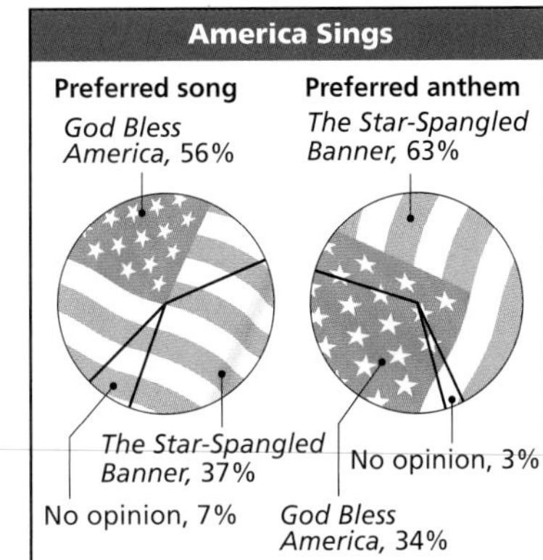

Source: USA Today

14. ***WRITE A PROBLEM*** Find a circle graph in your science or social studies textbook. Use the graph to write a problem that can be solved by finding the central angle measure of one of the sectors of the circle.

15. ***WRITE ABOUT IT*** Compare central angles of a circle with sectors of a circle.

16. ***CHALLENGE*** Find the angle measure between the minute and hour hands on the clock at right. **120°**

Spiral Review

Solve. (Lesson 4-6)

17. $w - 7.3 = 12$ **$w = 19.3$**
18. $x + 0.5 = 3.1$ **$x = 2.6$**
19. $y - 1.06 = 0.9$ **$y = 1.96$**
20. $a + 9.6 = 10$ **$a = 0.4$**

Tell whether each angle is acute, obtuse, right, or straight. (Lesson 7-2)

21.  **acute**
22.  **obtuse**
23.  **straight**
24. 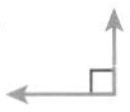 **right**

25. **TEST PREP** Which best describes the relationship between the obtuse angles that are formed when a transversal intersects two parallel lines? (Lesson 7-3) **A**

A Congruent
B Intersecting
C Complementary
D Supplementary

Answers

10. a. $\overline{AB}$, $\overline{CD}$, $\overline{CB}$
b. 60°; all acute angles made by a transversal and two parallel lines are congruent.

14. Possible answer: A circle graph shows a population distribution of males and females. What is the measure of the central angle of the sector that shows the population distribution of females?

15. Possible answer: A central angle is an angle formed by two radii. A sector is the region inside the circle formed by a central angle and an arc.

Journal

Have students find a circle graph in a textbook or a newspaper. Ask them to write about the graph and describe the central angles.

Test Prep Doctor

For Exercise 25, students who answered **B** did not understand that angles do not intersect, lines intersect. Students who answered **C** did not understand that obtuse angles are greater than 90 degrees, and therefore two obtuse angles could not be complementary. Students who answered **D** likely did not understand how to identify the obtuse angles when a transversal intersects two parallel lines. The answer is **A.**

CHALLENGE 7-4

LESSON 7-4 **Challenge**
Arc Length

An *arc* is a portion of the circumference of a circle. On the circle below, arc *QR* corresponds to the part of the circumference whose endpoints are the radii forming central angle *QCR*.

A *minor arc* is less than 180° and is named by its endpoints. Arc *QR* is a minor arc. A *major arc* is greater than 180° and is named by its endpoints and one other point that lies on the arc. Arc *QSR* is a major arc.

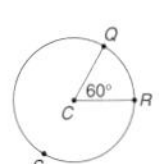

The degree measure of a minor arc is the measure of its central angle. The degree measure of a major arc is 360° minus the degree measure of the minor arc.

For circle *C* above, the measure of arc *QR* is 60°, and the measure of arc *QSR* is 360° − 60°, or 300°.

Find the degree measure of each arc.

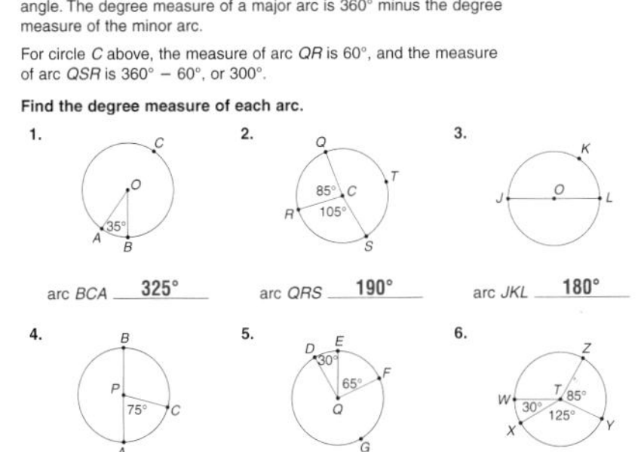

1. arc *BCA* **325°**
2. arc *QRS* **190°**
3. arc *JKL* **180°**
4. arc *BC* **105°**
5. arc *DGF* **265°**
6. arc *WZ* **120°**

PROBLEM SOLVING 7-4

LESSON 7-4 **Problem Solving**
Circles

Write the correct answer.

The circle graph shows the results of a survey in which people were asked to name their hobbies.

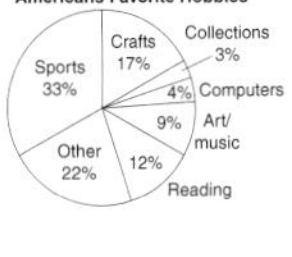

Americans Favorite Hobbies

Sports 33%
Crafts 17%
Collections 3%
Computers 4%
Art/music 9%
Reading 12%
Other 22%

1. If 1,000 people were surveyed, how many said that collecting things is their favorite hobby?
30 people

2. Find the central angle measure of the sector that shows the percent of people who named sports as their favorite hobby.
118.8°

3. Find the central angle measure of the sector that shows the percent of people who named reading as their favorite hobby.
43.2°

4. Find the central angle measure of the sector that shows the percent of people who like to do crafts as their favorite hobby.
61.2°

Choose the letter for the best answer.

The circle graph shows the age breakdown of people who most enjoy snowboarding.

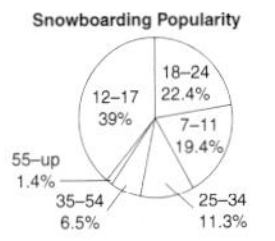

Snowboarding Popularity

12–17 39%
18–24 22.4%
7–11 19.4%
25–34 11.3%
35–54 6.5%
55–up 1.4%

5. What is the central angle measure that shows the percent of 35–54-year-olds?
A 5.1° (C) 23.4°
B 6.5° D 40.7°

6. With which age group is snowboarding least popular?
F 7–11 years H 25–34 years
G 12–17 years (J) 55–up

7. With which age group is snowboarding most popular?
A 7–11 years C 18–24 years
(B) 12–17 years D 25–34 years

8. What is the central angle measure that shows the percent of 12–17-year-olds?
F 39° H 108°
(G) 140.4° J 180°

Lesson Quiz

Name the parts of circle *B*.

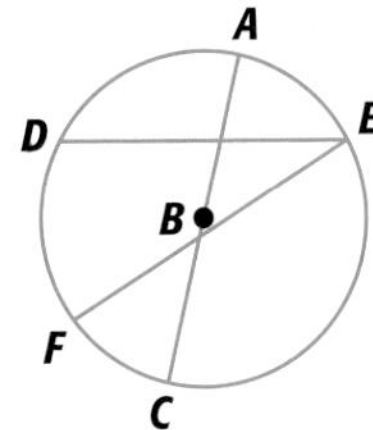

1. radii **$\overline{BA}$, $\overline{BC}$**
2. diameter(s) **$\overline{AC}$**
3. chord(s) **$\overline{DE}$, $\overline{FE}$, $\overline{AC}$**
4. A pie is cut into 8 equal sectors. What is the measure of the central angle of one slice of pie? **45°**

Available on Daily Transparency in CRB

7D Construct Circle Graphs

Pacing: Traditional 1 day
Block $\frac{1}{2}$ day

Objective: To use a compass, a straightedge, and a protractor to make a circle graph

Materials: Compass, straightedge, protractor

Lab Resources

Hands-On Lab Activities . . . . pp. 56–57

Using the Pages

Discuss with students how to use a protractor to draw an angle. Make sure that students realize that they use the ray of one central angle to create the next central angle in a circle graph.

Use a protractor to draw each angle.

1. 60°

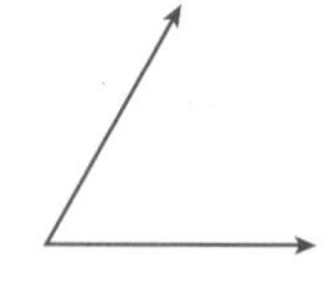

2. 140°

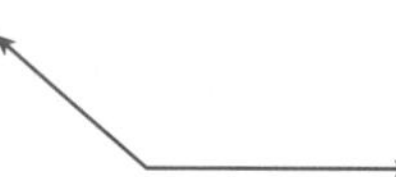

Construct Circle Graphs

Use with Lesson 7-4

REMEMBER

- There are 360° in a circle.
- A radius is a line segment with one endpoint at the center of a circle and the other endpoint on the circle.

internet connect
Lab Resources Online
go.hrw.com
KEYWORD: MS4 Lab7D

A circle graph can be used to compare data that are parts of a whole.

Activity

You can make a circle graph using information from a table.

At Booker Middle School, a survey was conducted to find the percent of students who favor certain types of books. The results are shown in the table below.

To make a circle graph, you need to find the size of each part of your graph. Each part is a *sector*.

To find the size of a sector, you must find the measure of its angle. You do this by finding what percent of the whole circle that sector represents.

1 Find the size of each sector.

a. Copy the table at right.

b. Find a decimal equivalent for each percent given, and fill in the decimal column of your table.

c. Find the fraction equivalent for each percent given, and fill in the fraction column of your table.

d. Find the angle measure of each sector by multiplying each fraction or decimal by 360°. Fill in the last column of your table.

Students Favorite Types of Books

Type of Book	Percent	Decimal	Fraction	Degrees
Mysteries	35%	**0.35**	$\frac{7}{20}$	**126°**
Science Fiction	25%	**0.25**	$\frac{1}{4}$	**90°**
Sports	20%	**0.20**	$\frac{1}{5}$	**72°**
Biographies	15%	**0.15**	$\frac{3}{20}$	**54°**
Humor	5%	**0.05**	$\frac{1}{20}$	**18°**

2 Follow the steps below to draw a circle graph.

a. Using a compass, draw a circle. Using a straightedge, draw one radius.

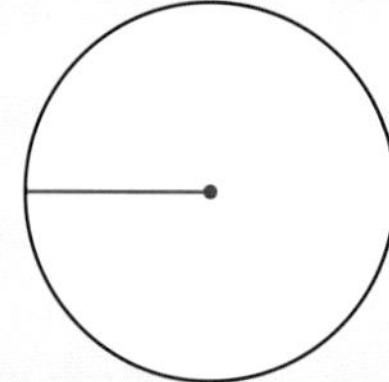

b. Use a protractor to measure the angle of the first sector. Draw the angle.

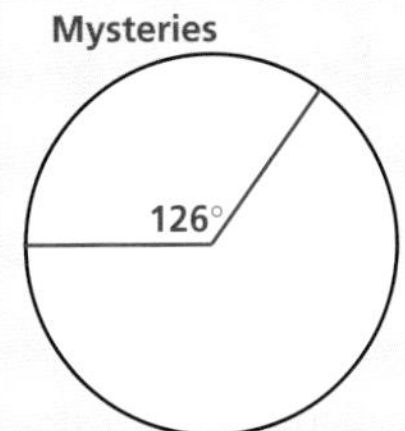

c. Use a protractor to measure the angle of the next sector. Draw the angle.

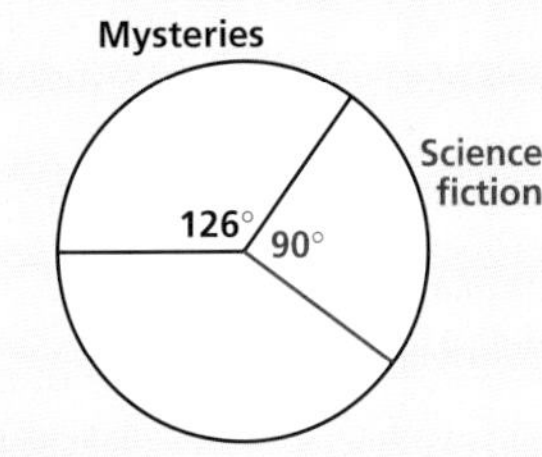

d. Continue until your graph is complete. Label each sector with its name and percent.

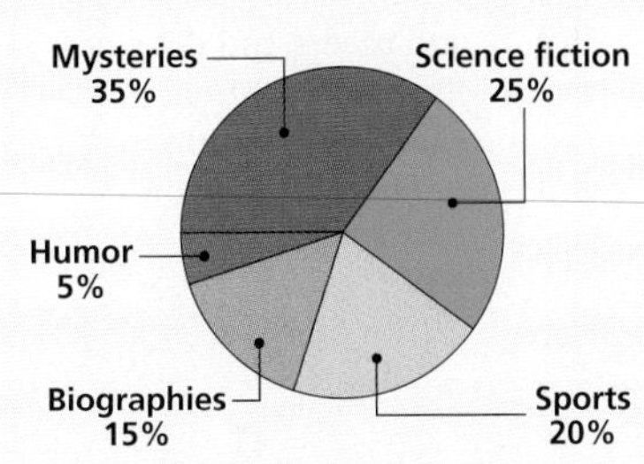

Think and Discuss

1. Total each column in the table from the beginning of the activity. What do you notice? **100%; 1; 1; 360°; All column totals are equivalent to one whole.**
2. What type of data would you want to display using a circle graph? **categories that represent all the parts of a whole**
3. How does the size of each sector of your circle graph relate to the percent, the decimal, and the fraction in your table? **The larger the sector, the larger the percent, decimal, and fraction.**

Try This

1. Complete the table below and use the information to make a circle graph.

   On a typical Saturday, Alan divides his leisure time and spends it in the following ways:

Time Spent for Leisure				
Activity	**Percent**	**Decimal**	**Fraction**	**Degrees**
Reading	30%	**0.30**	$\frac{3}{10}$	**108°**
Playing sports	25%	**0.25**	$\frac{1}{4}$	**90°**
Working on computer	40%	**0.40**	$\frac{2}{5}$	**144°**
Watching TV	5%	**0.05**	$\frac{1}{20}$	**18°**

Answers

Try This

1.

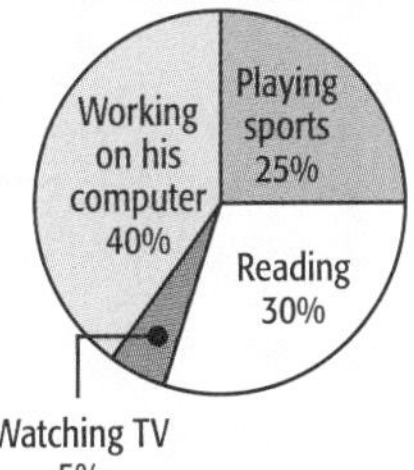

7-5 Organizer

Pacing: Traditional 1 day
Block $\frac{1}{2}$ day

Objective: Students identify and name polygons.

Warm Up

1. How do you name a ray? Under the ray symbol, name first the endpoint and then any other point on the ray.
2. What is the measure of an obtuse angle? between 90° and 180°
3. How do you name a line? Under the line symbol, name any two points on a line.
4. What is true of supplementary angles? The sum of their measures is 180°.

Problem of the Day

Draw a polygon with 10 congruent sides. Make 5 of the angles acute angles and the other 5 reflex angles (greater than 180°). Possible answer:

Available on Daily Transparency in CRB

7-5 Polygons

Learn to identify and name polygons.

Vocabulary
polygon
side
vertex of a polygon
regular polygon

From the earliest recorded time, geometric shapes, such as triangles and rectangles, have been used to decorate buildings and works of art.

Triangles and rectangles are examples of *polygons.* A **polygon** is a closed plane figure formed by three or more line segments. Each line segment forms a **side** of the polygon, and meets, but does not cross, another line segment at a common point. This common point is a **vertex of a polygon**.

The Paracas were an ancient native culture of Peru. Among the items that have been excavated from their lands are color tapestries, such as this one.

Vertices is plural for *vertex.*

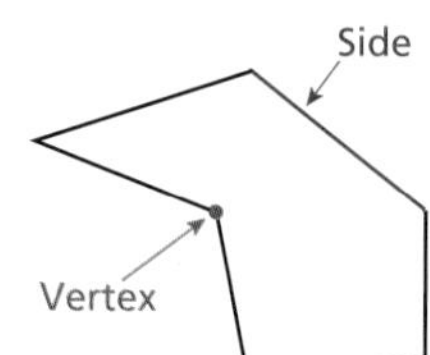

The polygon at left has six sides and six vertices.

EXAMPLE 1 Identifying Polygons

Determine whether each figure is a polygon. If it is not, explain why not.

A

The figure is a polygon.
It is a closed figure with 5 sides.

B

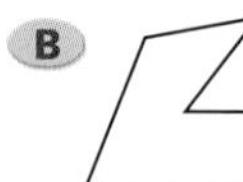

The figure is not a polygon.
It is not a closed figure.

C

The figure is not a polygon.
Not all of the sides of the figure are line segments.

D

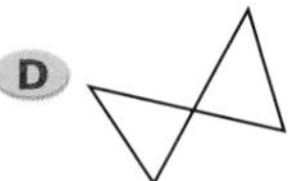

The figure is not a polygon.
There are line segments in the figure that cross.

1 Introduce

Alternate Opener

7-5 Polygons

A *polygon* is a closed figure bounded by line segments.

For each polygon, draw a line segment from each vertex (corner) to the next vertex with which it does not share a side. Use the first example as a guide.

	Polygon	Polygon with Connected Vertices	Figure Formed Inside	Name of Figure Formed Inside
	Pentagon			Pentagon
1.	Hexagon			
2.	Heptagon			
3.	Octagon			

Think and Discuss________

4. **Compare** the figure that was formed inside each polygon with the original polygon.

Motivate

On the chalkboard, write the following prefixes, without the numbers, in alphabetical order. Tell students that each prefix corresponds to a number from 3 to 10. Have students work in pairs to match each prefix with its number.

deca (10), *hepta* (7), *hexa* (6), *nona* (9), *octa* (8), *penta* (5), *quadri* (4), *tri* (3)

Explain that students will use these prefixes in identifying the figures in this lesson.

Exploration worksheet and answers on Chapter 7 Resource Book pp. 45 and 130

2 Teach

Lesson Presentation

Guided Instruction

In this lesson, students learn to identify and name polygons. List the characteristics of a polygon on the chalkboard:

closed, plane figure, bounded by three or more line segments that intersect only at endpoints.

Refer to the list as students study the figures in Example 1.

Discuss similarities and differences among regular polygons. For example, ask students in what ways all regular pentagons are alike and are different. they are all the same shape but not all the same size

Polygons are classified by the number of sides and angles they have.

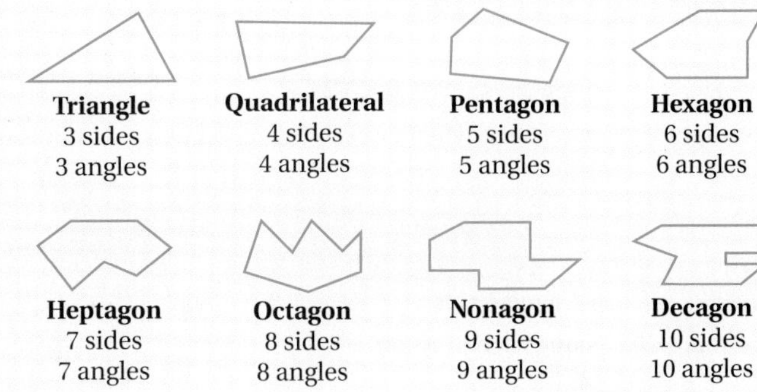

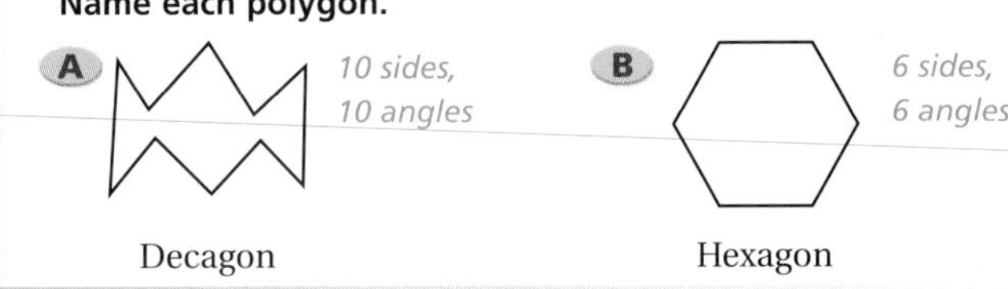

EXAMPLE 2 **Classifying Polygons**

Name each polygon.

A 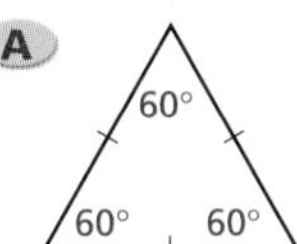

Decagon

B 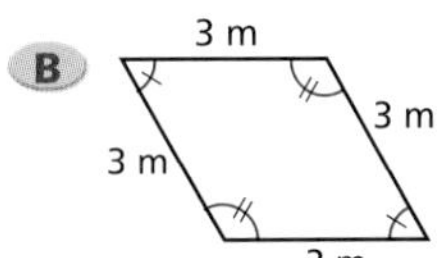

Hexagon

A **regular polygon** is a polygon in which all sides are congruent and all angles are congruent.

EXAMPLE 3 **Identifying and Classifying Regular Polygons**

Name each polygon, and tell whether it is a regular polygon. If it is not, explain why not.

A 60° 60° 60°

The figure is a regular triangle.

B 3 m 3 m 3 m 3 m

The figure is a quadrilateral. It is not a regular polygon because all of the angles are not congruent.

Think and Discuss

1. **Explain** why a circle is not a polygon.
2. **Draw** a dodecagon, which is a polygon with 12 sides and 12 angles.

Additional Examples

Example 1

Determine whether each figure is a polygon. If it is not, explain why not.

A. 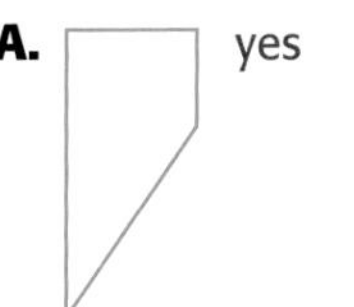 yes

B. No; it is not closed.

C.  No; the sides are not line segments.

D. No; the sides of a polygon cannot intersect except at endpoints.

Example 2

Name each polygon.

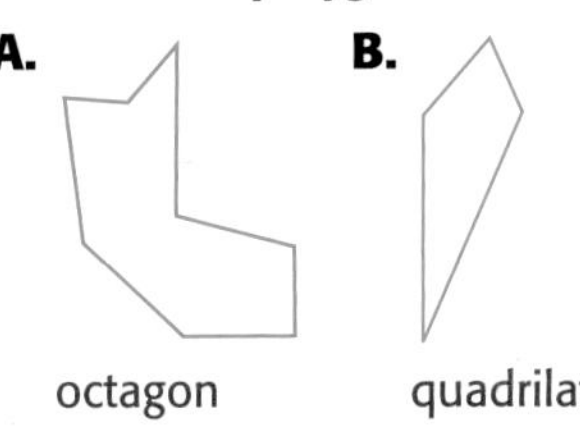

A. octagon **B.** quadrilateral

Example 3

Name each polygon, and tell whether it is a regular polygon. If it is not, explain why not.

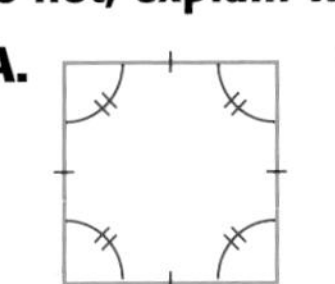

A. Quadrilateral; the figure is a regular polygon.

B. Quadrilateral; all the sides are not congruent.

3 Close

Reaching All Learners

Through World Math

Have students work in small groups. Challenge each group to research buildings or structures around the world that were designed with different polygons (e.g., the Pentagon in Washington, D.C., the pyramids in Egypt and Mexico, the Parthenon in Greece). Encourage groups to include pictures and make a visual presentation of their findings to the class.

Summarize

Have students, without looking at their textbooks, list and define as many different kinds of polygons as they can in three minutes. Record the names and definitions as volunteers read from their lists.

Answers to Think and Discuss

1. Possible answer: Although a circle is a closed figure, it does not contain only line segments, so it cannot be a polygon.
2. Possible answer:

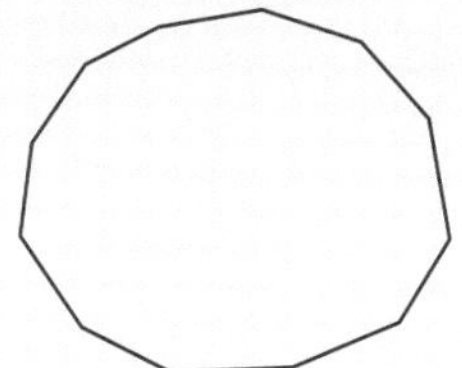

7-5 PRACTICE & ASSESS

Students may want to refer back to the lesson examples.

Assignment Guide

If you finished Example 1 assign:
Core 1–3, 10–12, 24–31
Enriched 1–3, 10–12, 24–31

If you finished Example 2 assign:
Core 1–6, 10–15, 24–31
Enriched 1–6, 10–15, 24–31

If you finished Example 3 assign:
Core 1–22, 24–31
Enriched 1–31

7-5 Exercises

FOR EXTRA PRACTICE see page 669

GUIDED PRACTICE

See Example 1 Determine whether each figure is a polygon. If it is not, explain why not.

1.  no; curved side
2.  yes
3. 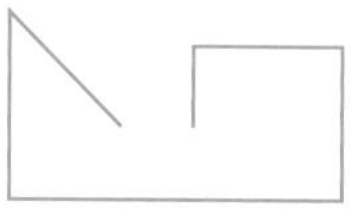 no; open figure

See Example 2 Name each polygon.

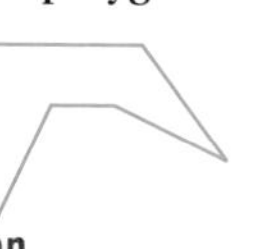

4. octagon
5. 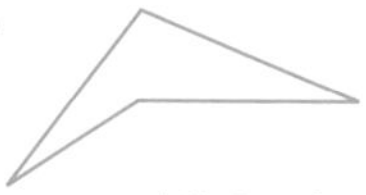 quadrilateral
6.  nonagon

See Example 3 Name each polygon, and tell whether it is a regular polygon. If it is not, explain why not.

7. 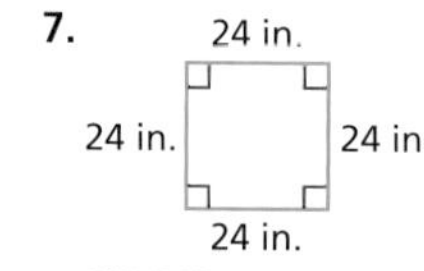

square; yes

8. 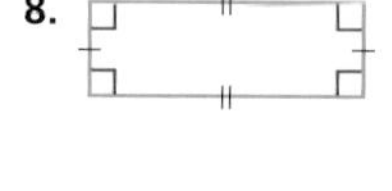
rectangle; no; all sides not congruent

9. 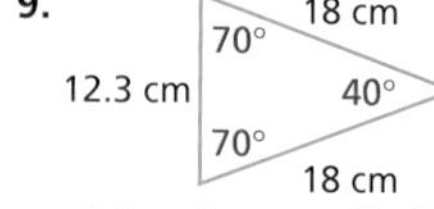

triangle; no; all sides and all angles not congruent

INDEPENDENT PRACTICE

See Example 1 Determine whether each figure is a polygon. If it is not, explain why not.

10. 
no; line segments cross

11. 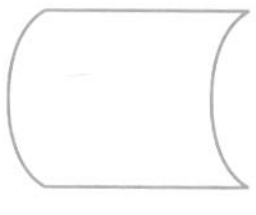 no; curved sides

12. 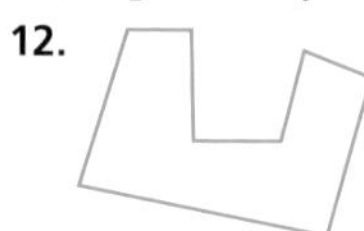
yes

See Example 2 Name each polygon.

13. 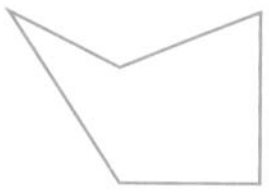 pentagon
14.  triangle
15.  heptagon

See Example 3 Name each polygon, and tell whether it is a regular polygon. If it is not, explain why not.

16. 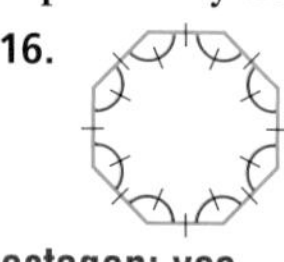
octagon; yes

17. 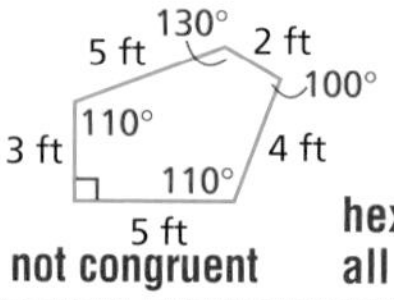
5 ft, 130°, 2 ft, 100°, 110°, 3 ft, 4 ft, 110°, 5 ft
pentagon; no; all sides and all angles are not congruent

18. 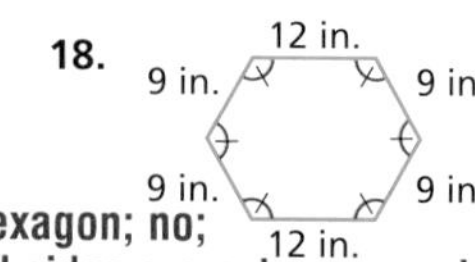

hexagon; no; all sides are not congruent

Math Background

You are probably familiar with different types of game boards. There is a mathematical definition for the term *board:* "a subset of the polygons determined by a number of lines." On a board, the lines are usually regularly spaced and oriented. The polygons are the spaces in which the game pieces can be placed and moved.

Some common boards are shown.

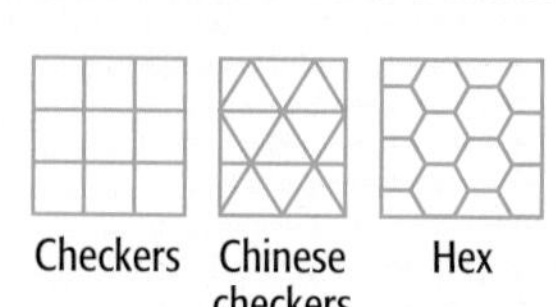

RETEACH 7-5

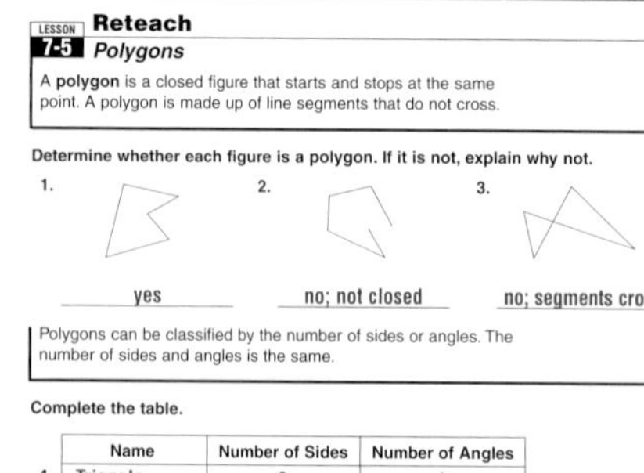

LESSON 7-5 **Reteach**
Polygons

A **polygon** is a closed figure that starts and stops at the same point. A polygon is made up of line segments that do not cross.

Determine whether each figure is a polygon. If it is not, explain why not.

1. yes
2. no; not closed
3. no; segments cross

Polygons can be classified by the number of sides or angles. The number of sides and angles is the same.

Complete the table.

	Name	Number of Sides	Number of Angles
4.	Triangle	3	3
5.	Quadrilateral	4	4
6.	Pentagon	5	5
7.	Hexagon	6	6
8.	Heptagon	7	7
9.	Octagon	8	8
10.	Nonagon	9	9
11.	Decagon	10	10

All the sides of a **regular polygon** have the same length, and all the angles have the same measure.

Determine whether each is a regular polygon. If it is not, explain why not.

12. 110°, 8 cm, 70°, 8 cm, 8 cm, 70°, 8 cm, 110°
no; angles not equal

13. 120°, 2 in., 120°, 2 in., 2 in., 120°, 120°, 2 in., 2 in., 120°, 2 in., 120°
yes

14. 9 in., 4 in., 90°, 90°, 90°, 90°
no; sides not equal

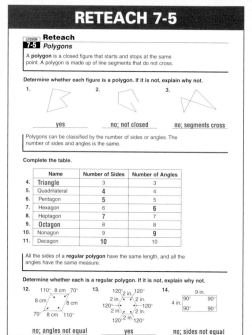

PRACTICE 7-5

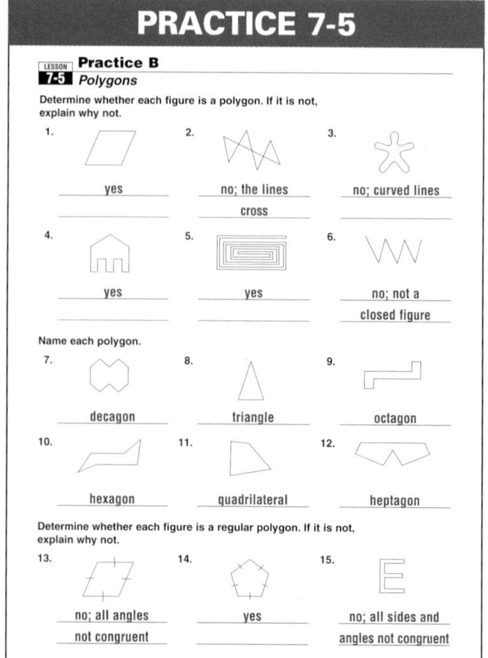

LESSON 7-5 **Practice B**
Polygons

Determine whether each figure is a polygon. If it is not, explain why not.

1. yes
2. no; the lines cross
3. no; curved lines
4. yes
5. yes
6. no; not a closed figure

Name each polygon.

7. decagon
8. triangle
9. octagon
10. hexagon
11. quadrilateral
12. heptagon

Determine whether each figure is a regular polygon. If it is not, explain why not.

13. no; all angles not congruent
14. yes
15. no; all sides and angles not congruent

Art LINK

19. The design of the quilt at right is made up of triangles.
    a. What other polygons can you find in the pattern?
    b. Which of the polygons in the pattern appear to be regular?

Use the photograph of the star quilt for Exercises 20 and 21.

20. The large star in the quilt pattern is made of smaller shapes stitched together. These smaller shapes are all the same type of polygon. What type of polygon are the smaller shapes? **quadrilaterals**

21. A polygon can be named by the number of its sides followed by *-gon*. For example, a polygon with 14 sides is called a 14-gon. What is the name of the large star-shaped polygon on the quilt? **16-gon**

22. The pattern on the quilt at right is called a bow tie pattern.
    a. Name the polygons that are used in the bow tie pattern.
    b. Do regular polygons appear to be used in the pattern? Explain.

23. ***CHALLENGE*** The quilt at right has a modern design. Copy one of each type of polygon, from a triangle to a decagon, onto your paper from the design. Write the name of each polygon next to its drawing. **Check students' answers.**

go.hrw.com
KEYWORD: MS4 Quilt
CNN Student News

Spiral Review

∠1 and ∠2 are complementary angles. Find m∠2. (Lesson 7-2)

24. m∠1 = 50° **40°**
25. m∠1 = 25° **65°**
26. m∠1 = 12° **78°**
27. m∠1 = 66° **24°**

Line *a* || line *b*. Use the diagram to find each angle measure. (Lesson 7-3)

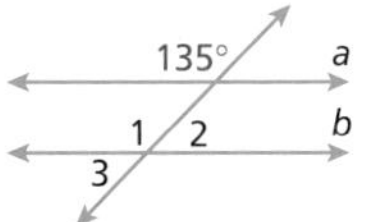

28. ∠1 **135°**
29. ∠2 **45°**
30. ∠3 **45°**

31. **TEST PREP** Which is a chord of a circle? (Lesson 7-4) **B**

A Radius **B** Diameter **C** Sector **D** Central angle

Interdisciplinary LINK

Art

Exercises 19–23 focus on identifying polygons in quilt patterns.

Answers

19. a. Possible answer: quadrilaterals, hexagons, heptagons, and octagons
b. triangles and hexagons

22. a. Possible answer: quadrilaterals, pentagons, octagons, and decagons
b. Yes; the quadrilaterals are regular.

Journal

Ask each student to sketch a polygon in his or her journal and write a short poem describing it.

Test Prep Doctor

For Exercise 31, students can eliminate **C** and **D** since a chord is a line segment, and a sector and a central angle are not.

CHALLENGE 7-5

LESSON 7-5 **Challenge**
The Diagonal Count

Consecutive vertices connect the sides of a polygon. A *diagonal* of a polygon is a segment that connects two nonconsecutive vertices.

The figure below shows two diagonals of a pentagon.

Other diagonals can be drawn in the pentagon from other vertices.

diagonals

For each polygon below, find the total number of diagonals from all the vertices. Do not count the same diagonal more than once. *Hint:* Draw each figure and then draw all possible diagonals. Use different colors to distinguish the diagonals as the number of sides of the polygons increases.

1. Triangle 0 diagonals
2. Quadrilateral 2 diagonals
3. Pentagon 5 diagonals
4. Hexagon 9 diagonals
5. Heptagon 14 diagonals
6. Octagon 20 diagonals

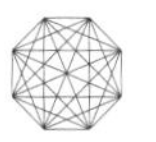

PROBLEM SOLVING 7-5

LESSON 7-5 **Problem Solving**
Polygons

Write the correct answer.

The drawing shows a crown designed by a child in an arts and crafts class. The crown is composed of 4 different figures.

1. Name the polygon in figure 1.
   decagon
2. Name the polygon in figure 4.
   hexagon
3. Name the polygon in figure 3.
   pentagon
4. Is the crown a regular polygon? Explain.
   No, sides and angles not congruent.
5. Name the polygon formed by figures 2, 3, and 4.
   pentagon

Choose the letter for the best answer.

The box shows some basic shapes from a word processing tool bar.

6. Which figure is *not* a quadrilateral?
   A Figure 2 C Figure 4
   B Figure 3 (D) Figure 5
7. Which figure is *not* a polygon?
   F Figure 3 H Figure 11
   (G) Figure 9 J Figure 12
8. Which figure is a pentagon?
   A Figure 4 C Figure 10
   B Figure 5 (D) Figure 12
9. Which figure is a regular polygon?
   F Figure 1 (H) Figure 7
   G Figure 2 J Figure 8
10. Which figure is an octagon?
    (A) Figure 6 C Figure 11
    B Figure 10 D Figure 12

Lesson Quiz

Determine whether each statement is true or false.

1. Every polygon is a closed figure. true
2. Every open figure is a polygon. false
3. A pentagon with sides lengths of 10 units and angles measuring 108° is a regular polygon. true
4. A quadrilateral with sides lengths 10, 12, 10, and 12 units is a regular polygon. false
5. What is the name of a five-sided polygon? pentagon

Available on Daily Transparency in CRB

7E Constructions with Polygons and Circles

Pacing: Traditional 1 day
Block $\frac{1}{2}$ day

Objective: To use a compass and a straightedge to inscribe polygons in circles

Materials: Compass, straightedge

Lab Resources

Hands-On Lab Activities . pp. 61–63, 127

Using the Pages

Discuss with students the difference between inscribing a polygon in a circle and inscribing a circle in a polygon. Make sure students understand that when a figure is inscribed in a circle, all the vertices of the figure must lie on the circle.

Draw the following figures on the chalkboard and ask students to identify the figure inscribed in each circle.

1.  triangle

2. 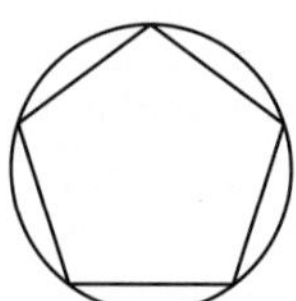 pentagon

3. 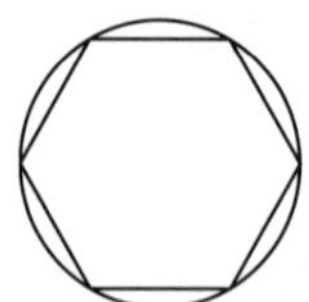 hexagon

Constructions with Polygons and Circles

Use with Lesson 7-5

REMEMBER
- An equilateral triangle has three congruent sides and three congruent angles.
- A square has four congruent sides and four congruent angles.
- A regular hexagon has six congruent sides and six congruent angles.
- A perpendicular bisector of a line segment is a line that intersects the segment at its midpoint at a right angle.
- The diameter of a circle is a line segment that passes through the center of the circle and whose endpoints are on the circle.

internet connect
Lab Resources Online
go.hrw.com
KEYWORD: MS4 Lab7E

A regular polygon is inscribed in a circle when all of its vertices lie on a circle that surrounds it.

Activity

1 Inscribe an equilateral triangle in a circle.

a. Draw a circle using a compass. Make the circle at least an inch in diameter.

b. Draw a diameter anywhere inside the circle.

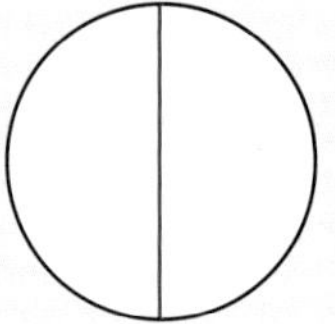

c. Place the point of your compass at one end of the diameter. Using the same compass opening that was used to make the circle, draw two arcs, one on each side of the point, that intersect the circle.

d. Label the points where the arcs intersect the circle as A and B. Label point C where the diameter meets the circle farthest from the arcs.

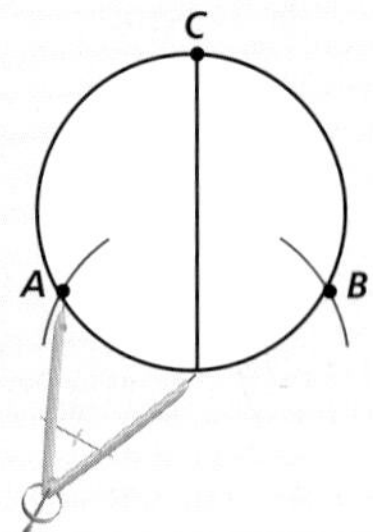

e. Draw line segments to connect the points to form an equilateral triangle.

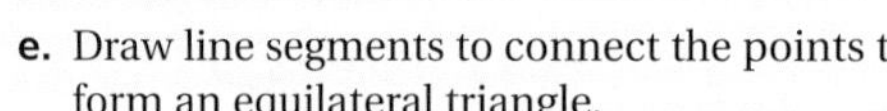

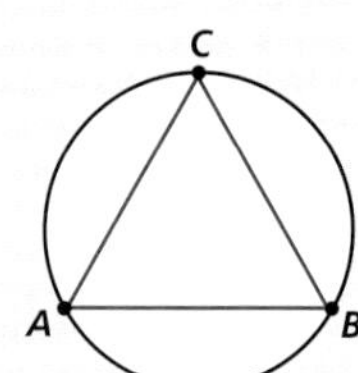

2 Inscribe a square in a circle.

a. Repeat steps **a** and **b** from **1**.

b. Construct a perpendicular bisector of the diameter. Then label points *D, E, F,* and *G* where the diameter and its bisector intersect the circle.

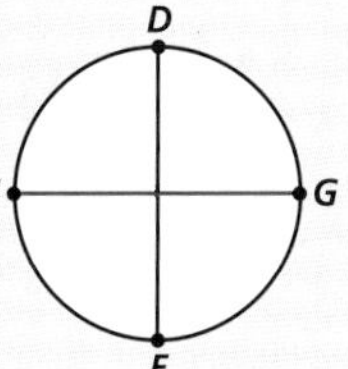

c. Draw line segments to connect the points to form a square.

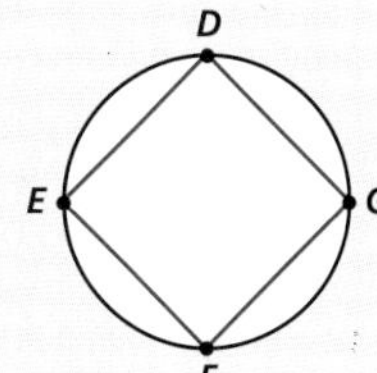

3 Inscribe a regular hexagon in a circle.

a. Repeat steps **a, b,** and **c** from **1**.

b. Draw two diameters that each include one of the points where the arcs intersect the circle. Then label the points *L, M, N, O, P,* and *Q* where the diameters meet the circle.

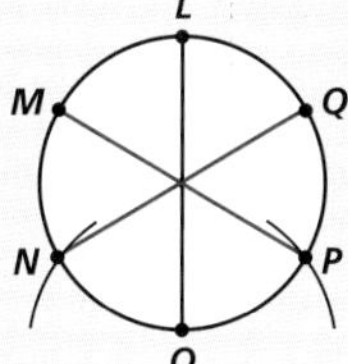

c. Draw line segments to connect the points to form a regular hexagon.

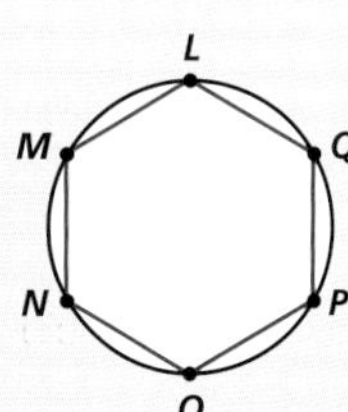

Think and Discuss

1. Do you have to keep the compass opening the same at all times when inscribing an equilateral triangle in a circle? Explain.
2. Do you have to keep the compass opening the same at all times when inscribing a square in a circle? Explain.
3. When you are inscribing a regular hexagon in a circle, how can you tell that all of the sides of the hexagon are congruent? How does the length of each side of the hexagon compare with the radius of the circle?
4. When you are inscribing a square in a circle, do the sides of the square have the same length as the radius of the circle? Explain.

Try This

1. Inscribe an equilateral triangle in a circle with a 3-inch diameter.
2. Inscribe a square in a circle with a 2-inch diameter.
3. Inscribe a regular hexagon in a circle with a 1.5-inch diameter.
4. Inscribe an equilateral triangle, a square, and a regular hexagon in the same circle with a 4-inch diameter.

Answers

Think and Discuss

1. Yes; the sides of an equilateral triangle are congruent.
2. No; when bisecting the diameter of a circle, you must use a compass opening that is greater than the radius of the circle. When drawing the circle, however, you must use a compass opening equal to the radius of the circle.
3. They were all constructed using the same opening on the compass; the radius of the circle and the sides of the hexagon have the same measure.
4. No; each side of a square inscribed in a circle is equal in length to the compass opening used to construct the perpendicular bisector of the diameter, which must be greater than the radius of the circle.

Try This

Check students' work.

1.

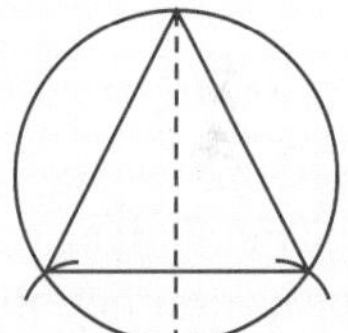

2.

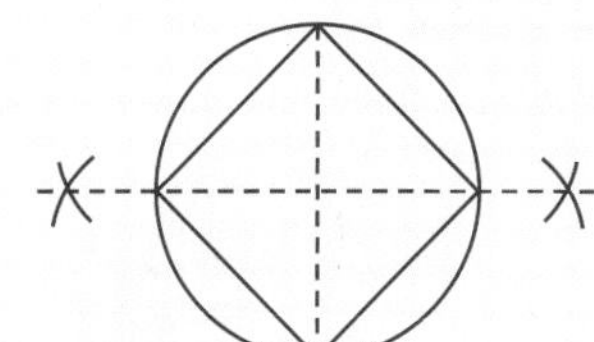

3.

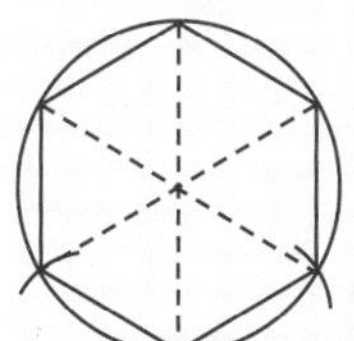

4.

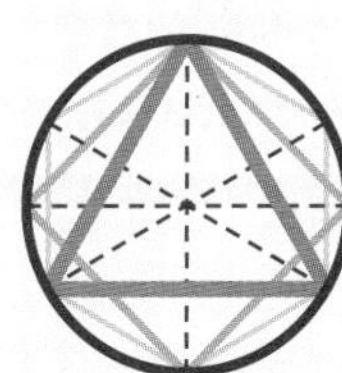

7-6 Organizer

Pacing: Traditional 1 day
Block $\frac{1}{2}$ day

Objective: Students classify triangles by their side lengths and angle measures.

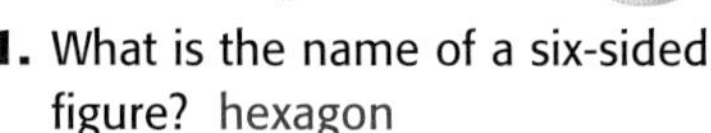

Warm Up

1. What is the name of a six-sided figure? hexagon
2. What is the definition of an acute angle? an angle that measures less than 90°
3. The measure of one angle of two supplementary angles is 32°. What is the measure of the other angle? 148°

Problem of the Day

Use 6 congruent line segments to form 4 equilateral triangles. (*Hint:* Use toothpicks or other objects to model the segments.) Place the segments so they form a pyramid.

Available on Daily Transparency in CRB

Math Humor

What do you call an adorable three-sided figure? acute triangle

7-6 Triangles

Learn to classify triangles by their side lengths and angle measures.

Vocabulary
scalene triangle
isosceles triangle
equilateral triangle
acute triangle
obtuse triangle
right triangle

How many different kinds of triangles can you find in the origami butterfly at right? To answer this question, you must first have ways of classifying the triangles. One way to classify them is by the lengths of their sides. Another way is by the measures of their angles.

Triangles classified by sides

A **scalene triangle** has no congruent sides.

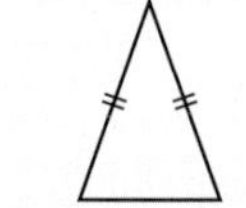

An **isosceles triangle** has at least 2 congruent sides.

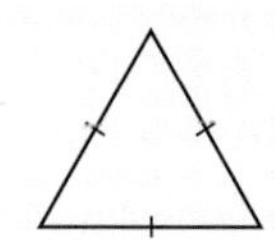

In an **equilateral triangle**, all of the sides are congruent.

Triangles classified by angles

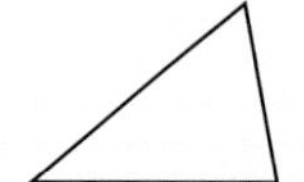

In an **acute triangle**, all of the angles are acute.

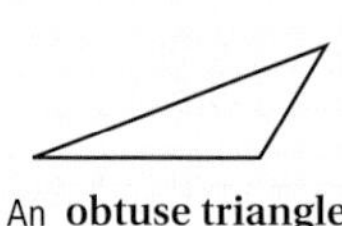

An **obtuse triangle** has one obtuse angle.

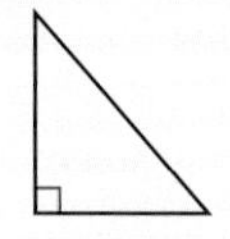

A **right triangle** has one right angle.

EXAMPLE 1 Classifying Triangles

Classify each triangle according to its sides and angles.

A

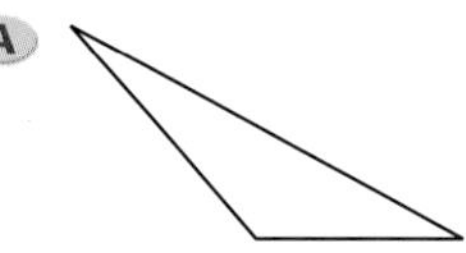

scalene *No congruent sides*
obtuse *One obtuse angle*

This is a scalene obtuse triangle.

B

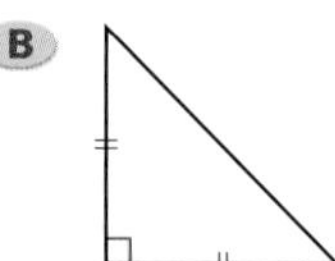

isosceles *Two congruent sides*
right *One right angle*

This is an isosceles right triangle.

Writing Math

When classifying a triangle according to its sides and angles, use the word that describes the sides first, and use the word that describes the angles second.

1 Introduce

Alternate Opener

EXPLORATION

7-6 Triangles

Draw triangles that match the descriptions in the first column of the table below. Then measure the angles of each triangle and describe the relationships between the number of congruent sides and the number of congruent angles.

	Triangle	Drawing	Angle Measures	Relationship between Number of Congruent Sides and Number of Congruent Angles
1.	Three congruent sides			
2.	Two congruent sides			
3.	All three sides unequal			

Think and Discuss

4. **Discuss** the relationship between the number of congruent sides and the number of congruent angles.

Motivate

To review acute, obtuse, right, and straight angles, have volunteers draw an example of each on the chalkboard.

Change the acute, obtuse, and right angles into acute, obtuse, and right triangles. Then have students name the types of angles within each triangle (i.e., acute triangle—all acute angles; obtuse triangle—one obtuse angle and two acute angles; right triangle—one right angle, two acute angles).

Exploration worksheet and answers on Chapter 7 Resource Book pp. 54 and 132

2 Teach

Lesson Presentation

Guided Instruction

In this lesson, students learn to classify triangles by their side lengths and angle measures. Point out that every triangle has two classifications, one by the lengths of its sides and one by the measures of the angles. Even though obtuse and right triangles contain acute angles, they are not acute triangles because an acute triangle must have three acute angles. You may want to use Teaching Transparency T23 in the Chapter 7 Resource Book.

Teaching Tip Point out that the angle classifications are mutually exclusive, but the side classifications are not because an equilateral triangle is also isosceles.

Classify each triangle according to its sides and angles.

C

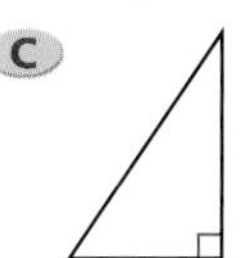

scalene *No congruent sides*
right *One right angle*

This is a scalene right triangle.

D

isosceles *Two congruent sides*
obtuse *One obtuse angle*

This is an isosceles obtuse triangle.

EXAMPLE 2 Identifying Triangles

Identify the different types of triangles in the figure, and determine how many of each there are.

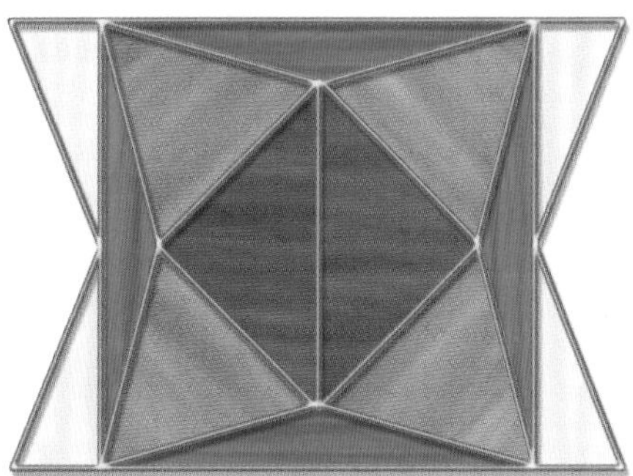

Type	How Many	Colors	Type	How Many	Colors
Scalene	4	Yellow	Right	6	Purple, yellow
Isosceles	10	Green, pink, purple	Obtuse	4	Green
Equilateral	4	Pink	Acute	4	Pink

Think and Discuss

1. **Draw** an isosceles acute triangle and an isosceles obtuse triangle.
2. **Draw** a triangle that is right and scalene.
3. **Explain** why an equilateral triangle is also an isosceles triangle but an isosceles triangle is not always an equilateral triangle.

Additional Examples

Example 1

Classify each triangle according to its sides and angles.

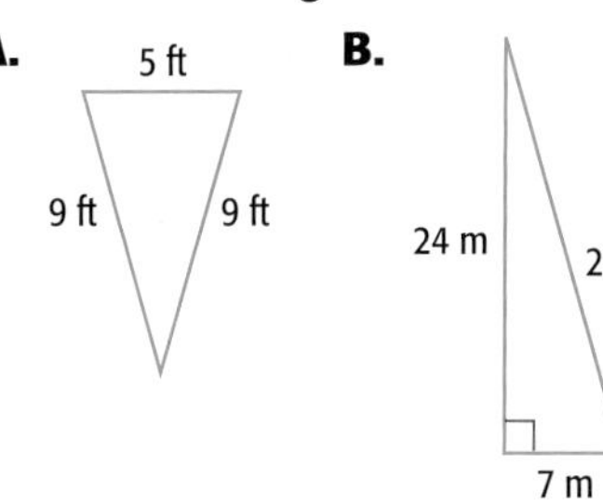

isosceles acute scalene right

Example 2

Identify the different types of triangles in the figure and determine how many of each there are.

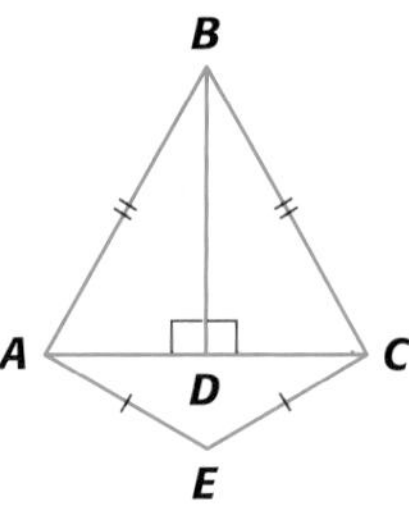

2 right triangles: $\triangle ABD$, $\triangle CBD$

2 isosceles triangles: $\triangle ACE$, $\triangle ABC$

1 acute triangle: $\triangle ABC$

2 scalene triangles: $\triangle ABD$, $\triangle BDC$

1 obtuse triangle: $\triangle ACE$

3 Close

Reaching All Learners

Through Curriculum Integration

Language Arts Have students work with partners to look up the origins of the words *scalene, isosceles, equilateral, acute, obtuse,* and *right.* Let students use those origins to justify the classifications in this lesson.

Scalene means "uneven." *Isosceles* means "having two equal sides." *Equilateral* means "equal lines." *Acute* means "sharp." *Obtuse* means "not pointed" or "blunt." *Right* means "to lead straight."

Summarize

Have students name six ways to classify triangles, and record them on the chalkboard. Then ask each student to draw an example of each type of triangle. Let students share their drawings and name each triangle they have drawn using two names. For example, an acute triangle may also be an isosceles triangle.

scalene triangle, isosceles triangle, equilateral triangle, acute triangle, obtuse triangle, right triangle

Answers to Think and Discuss

Possible answers:

1.

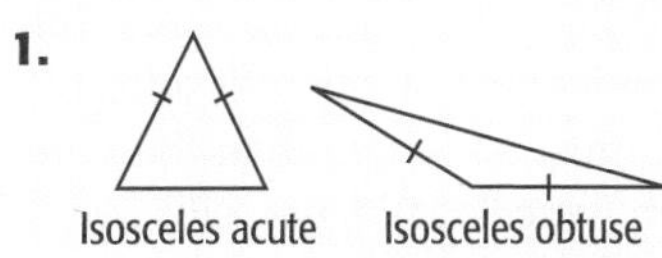

2.

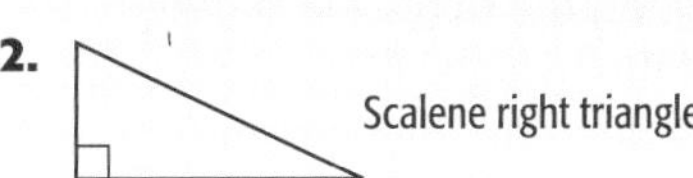

3. Since at least two of the sides of an equilateral triangle are congruent, it is also isosceles. A triangle with exactly two congruent sides is an isosceles triangle, but it is not equilateral, because all of its sides are not congruent.

7-6 PRACTICE & ASSESS

Students may want to refer back to the lesson examples.

Assignment Guide

If you finished Example 1 assign:
Core 1–3, 5–7, 9–21 odd, 28–36
Enriched 1, 5, 9–21, 28–36

If you finished Example 2 assign:
Core 1–20, 23, 28–36
Enriched 1–7 odd, 9–36

Notes

7-6 Exercises

FOR EXTRA PRACTICE
see page 669

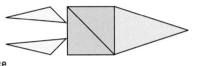

internet connect
Homework Help Online
go.hrw.com Keyword: MS4 7-6

GUIDED PRACTICE

See Example 1 Classify each triangle according to its sides and angles.

1. isosceles right
2. scalene obtuse
3. isosceles acute

See Example 2
4. Identify the different types of triangles in the figure, and determine how many of each there are. **2 isosceles right; 1 isosceles acute; 2 scalene obtuse**

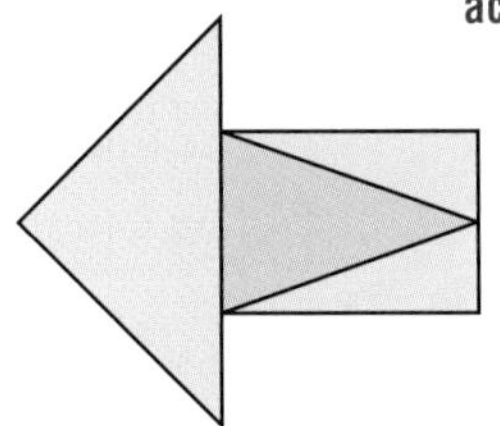

INDEPENDENT PRACTICE

See Example 1 Classify each triangle according to its sides and angles.

5. scalene right
6. isosceles obtuse
7. equilateral acute

See Example 2
8. Identify the different types of triangles in the figure, and determine how many of each there are.
1 isosceles right; 1 isosceles acute; 2 scalene right

PRACTICE AND PROBLEM SOLVING

Classify each triangle according to the lengths of its sides.

9. 3 cm, 5 cm, 3 cm **isosceles**
10. 3 ft, 4 ft, 5 ft **scalene**
11. 4 m, 4 m, 4 m **equilateral**
12. 6 ft, 9 ft, 12 ft **scalene**
13. 2 in., 2 in., 2 in. **equilateral**
14. 7.4 mi, 7.4 mi, 4 mi **isosceles**

Classify each triangle according to the measures of its angles.

15. 60°, 60°, 60° **acute**
16. 105°, 38°, 37° **obtuse**
17. 79°, 11°, 90° **right**
18. 30°, 120°, 30° **obtuse**
19. 45°, 90°, 45° **right**
20. 40°, 60°, 80° **acute**

Math Background

Triangles are polygons with three sides. A triangle can also be defined as the figure formed by connecting three non-collinear points with line segments. The sum of the lengths of any two sides of a triangle must be longer than the third side. In an isosceles triangle with two equal sides, the third side is called the *base* of the triangle. In a right triangle, the side opposite the right angle is called the *hypotenuse,* and the other two sides are called the *legs.* An *oblique triangle* is a triangle with no right angles; thus, acute and obtuse triangles are oblique.

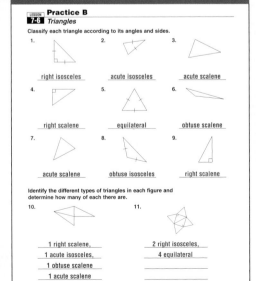

RETEACH 7-6

LESSON 7-6 **Reteach**
Triangles

All triangles have at least two acute angles.

If the third angle is acute, the triangle is an **acute triangle.**

acute

If the third angle is right, the triangle is a **right triangle.**

If the third angle is obtuse, the triangle is an **obtuse triangle.**

obtuse

A triangle is **scalene** if each side is a different length.

4 in. 5 in. 6 in.

A triangle is **isosceles** if two sides are the same length.

7 cm 7 cm 3 cm

A triangle is **equilateral** if all three sides are the same length.

2 m 2 m 2 m

Use the figure to complete the statements.

5 ft 60° 5 ft 60° 60° 5 ft

1. Each of the 3 angles is less than 90°, so the triangle is an acute triangle.
2. The triangle has 3 sides that have the same length, so it is an equilateral triangle.

Use the figure to complete the statements.

10 cm 45° 14 cm 90° 45° 10 cm

3. The triangle has a 90° angle, so it is a right triangle.
4. The triangle has 2 sides that have the same length, so it is an isosceles triangle.

Use the figure to complete the statements.

14 in. 30° 10 in. 40° 110° 8 in.

5. The triangle has an angle that measures more than 90°, so it is an obtuse triangle.
6. Each side of the triangle has a different length, so it is a scalene triangle.

PRACTICE 7-6

LESSON 7-6 **Practice B**
Triangles

Classify each triangle according to its angles and sides.

1. right isosceles
2. acute isosceles
3. acute scalene
4. right scalene
5. equilateral
6. obtuse scalene

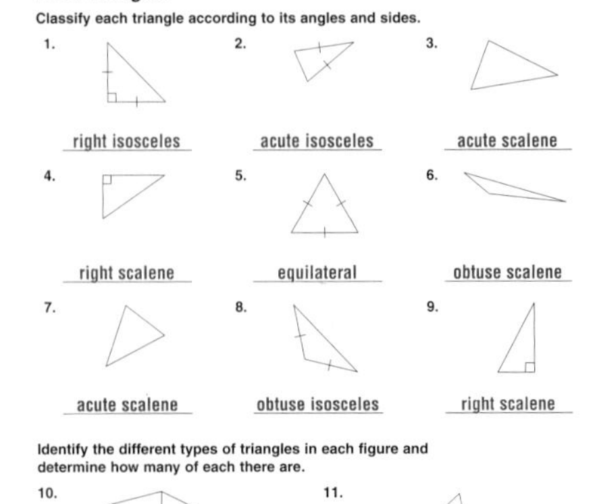

7. acute scalene
8. obtuse isosceles
9. right scalene

Identify the different types of triangles in each figure and determine how many of each there are.

10. 1 right scalene, 1 acute isosceles, 1 obtuse scalene 1 acute scalene

11. 2 right isosceles, 4 equilateral

The Devil's Postpile in California is an area where lava once cooled and solidified to form hexagonal structures.

21. The sum of the lengths of the sides of triangle ABC is 25 in. The lengths of sides $\overline{AB}$ and $\overline{BC}$ are 9 inches and 8 inches. Find the length of side $\overline{AC}$ and classify the triangle. **8 in., isosceles**

22. Draw a square. Divide it into two triangles. Describe the triangles. **2 isosceles right triangles**

23. ***GEOLOGY*** Each face of a topaz crystal is a triangle whose sides are all different lengths. What kind of triangle is each face of a topaz crystal? **scalene triangle**

24. ***ARCHITECTURE*** The Washington Monument is an obelisk, the top of which is a pyramid. The pyramid has four triangular faces. The bottom edge of each face measures 10.5 m. The other edges measure 17.0 m. What kind of triangle is each face of the pyramid? **isosceles triangles**

25. ***CHOOSE A STRATEGY*** How many triangles are in the figure? **D**

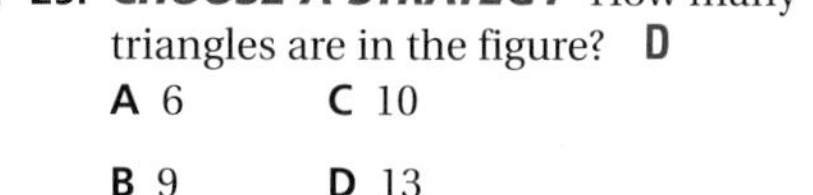

A 6 C 10

B 9 D 13

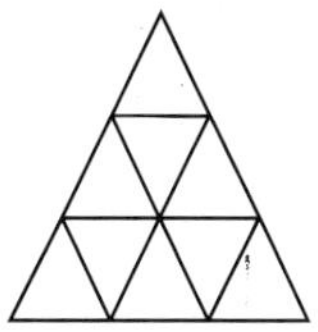

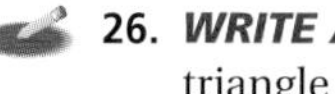

26. ***WRITE ABOUT IT*** Is it possible for an equilateral triangle to be obtuse? Explain your answer.

27. ***CHALLENGE*** The centers of circles A, B, C, D, and E are connected by line segments as shown. Classify each triangle that is formed in the figure according to its side lengths, given the following information:

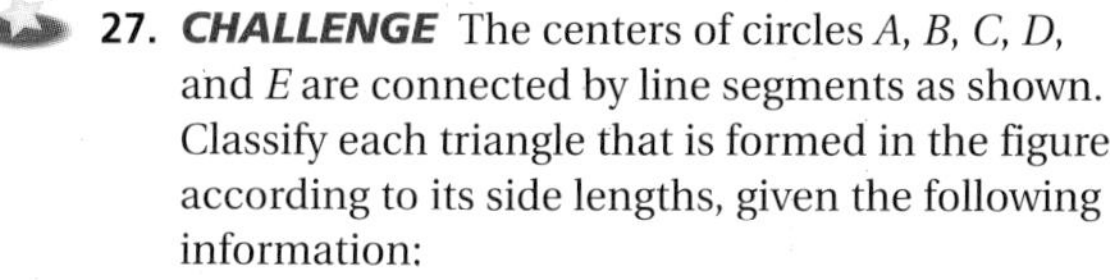

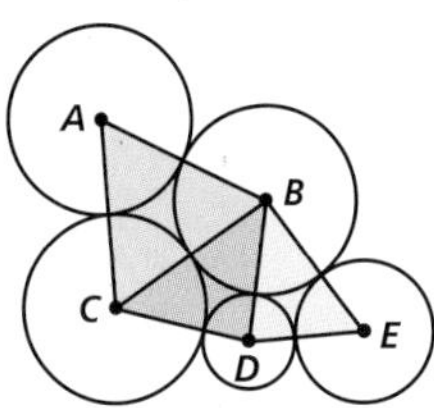

$DE = 5$ $BD = 6$

$CB = 8$ $AC = 8$

The diameter of circle D is 4.

Spiral Review

Multiply. (Lesson 4-3)

28. $0.2 \cdot 10^3$ **200**
29. $3.84 \cdot 10^2$ **384**
30. $0.006 \cdot 10^4$ **60**
31. $0.0056 \cdot 10^2$ **0.56**

Solve. (Lesson 5-3)

32. $\frac{6}{a} = \frac{15}{10}$ **$a = 4$**
33. $\frac{h}{9} = \frac{10}{15}$ **$h = 6$**
34. $\frac{4}{17} = \frac{k}{34}$ **$k = 8$**
35. $\frac{12}{5} = \frac{24}{m}$ **$m = 10$**

36. **TEST PREP** What percent of 15 is 5? (Lesson 6-4) **D**

A 300% B 3% C $\frac{1}{3}\%$ D $33\frac{1}{3}\%$

CHALLENGE 7-6

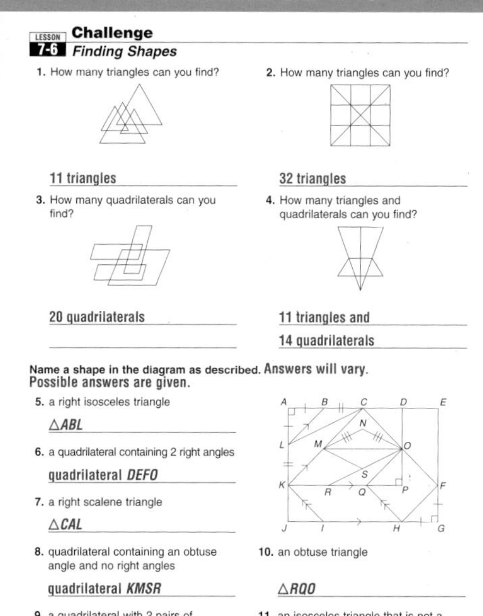

LESSON 7-6 **Challenge**
Finding Shapes

1. How many triangles can you find? **11 triangles**
2. How many triangles can you find? **32 triangles**
3. How many quadrilaterals can you find? **20 quadrilaterals**
4. How many triangles and quadrilaterals can you find? **11 triangles and 14 quadrilaterals**

Name a shape in the diagram as described. **Answers will vary. Possible answers are given.**

5. a right isosceles triangle **$\triangle ABL$**
6. a quadrilateral containing 2 right angles **quadrilateral $DEFO$**
7. a right scalene triangle **$\triangle CAL$**
8. quadrilateral containing an obtuse angle and no right angles **quadrilateral $KMSR$**
9. a quadrilateral with 2 pairs of equal sides **quadrilateral $KQHI$**
10. an obtuse triangle **$\triangle RQO$**
11. an isosceles triangle that is not a right triangle **$\triangle MNO$**

PROBLEM SOLVING 7-6

LESSON 7-6 **Problem Solving**
Triangles

Write the correct answer.

Brian made the following drawing of his kite.

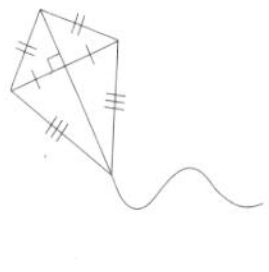

1. How many triangles are in the figure? **8 triangles**
2. How many acute triangles are in the figure? **2 acute triangles**
3. How many right triangles are in the figure? **4 right triangles**
4. How many scalene triangles are in the figure? **6 scalene triangles**
5. How many isosceles triangles are in the figure? **2 isosceles triangles**

Choose the letter for the best answer.

The figure shows an architect's design for a large window.

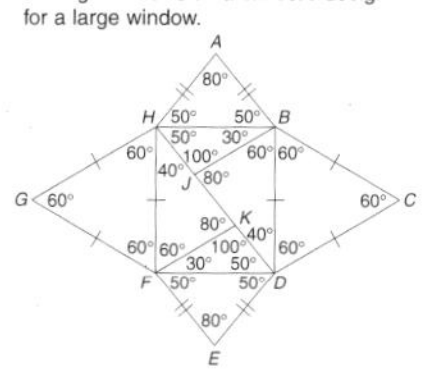

6. Which triangle is an equilateral triangle?
   A $\triangle ABH$ Ⓒ $\triangle FGH$
   B $\triangle BDH$ D $\triangle DHF$
7. Which triangle is a right triangle?
   F $\triangle FHK$ H $\triangle DKF$
   G $\triangle DEF$ Ⓙ $\triangle DBH$
8. Which triangle is an isosceles triangle?
   A $\triangle DBJ$ C $\triangle HBJ$
   Ⓑ $\triangle DEF$ D $\triangle DHF$
9. Which triangle is a scalene triangle?
   F $\triangle ABH$ H $\triangle BCD$
   Ⓖ $\triangle HBJ$ J $\triangle DEF$
10. Which triangle is an obtuse triangle?
   Ⓐ $\triangle DKF$ C $\triangle JBD$
   B $\triangle HKF$ D $\triangle ABH$

Answers

26. No; the angles in an equilateral triangle are all acute, and a triangle must have one obtuse angle to be classified as an obtuse triangle.

27. $\triangle ABC$ is equilateral; $\triangle BCD$ is isosceles; $\triangle BDE$ is scalene.

Journal

Ask students to find and write about several real-world examples of the triangles defined in this lesson. Suggest that students look around the classroom or their homes.

Test Prep Doctor

For Exercise 36, students can eliminate **A** because 5 is less than 15. They can also eliminate **B** and **C** because 5 is a little less than half of 15, which would be 50%. The correct answer is **D.**

Lesson Quiz

Classify each triangle according to its side or angle measures.

1. 7 ft, 8 ft, 12 ft — scalene
2. 45°, 90°, 45° — right
3. 12, 9, 12 — isosceles
4. 120°, 20°, 40° — obtuse
5. Identify the different types of triangles in the figure, and determine how many of each there are.

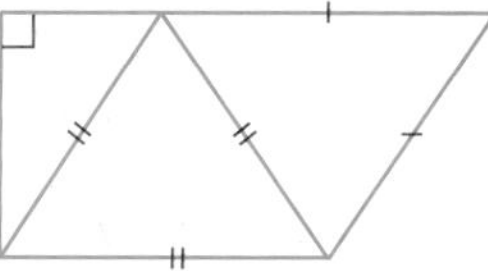

1 isosceles acute triangle, 1 equilateral triangle, 1 scalene right triangle

Available on Daily Transparency in CRB

7-7 Organizer

Pacing: Traditional 1 day
Block $\frac{1}{2}$ day

Objective: Students name and identify types of quadrilaterals.

Warm Up

Identify the triangle based on the given measurements.

1. 3 ft, 4 ft, 6 ft — scalene
2. 46°, 90°, 44° — right
3. 7 in., 7 in., 10 in. — isosceles

Problem of the Day

One angle of a parallelogram measures 90°. What are the measures of the other angles? all 90°

Available on Daily Transparency in CRB

The girl had an enormous collection of CD-ROMs, so when she took them to her friend's house, she had to rent a CD-ROMbus.

7-7 Quadrilaterals

Learn to name and identify types of quadrilaterals.

Vocabulary
parallelogram
rhombus
rectangle
square
trapezoid
kite

College campuses are often built around an open space called a "quad" or "quadrangle." A quadrangle is a four-sided enclosure, or a quadrilateral.

Some quadrilaterals have properties that classify them as *special quadrilaterals.* The figures below are six major special quadrilaterals.

A quad at Cornell University in Ithaca, NY

A **parallelogram** has two pairs of parallel sides.

A **rhombus** has four congruent sides.

A **rectangle** has four right angles.

A **square** has four congruent sides and four right angles.

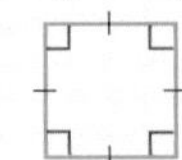

A **trapezoid** has exactly one pair of parallel sides.

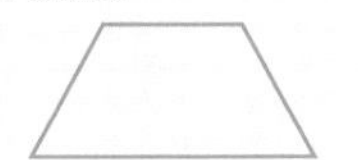

A **kite** has exactly two pairs of congruent, adjacent sides.

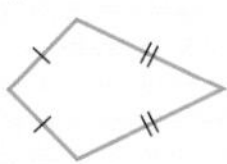

Quadrilaterals can have more than one name because the special quadrilaterals sometimes share properties.

EXAMPLE 1 Identifying Types of Quadrilaterals

Give all of the names that apply to each quadrilateral.

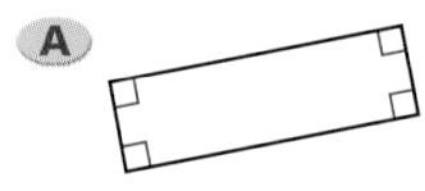

The figure has two pairs of parallel sides, so it is a **parallelogram**. It has four right angles, so it is also a **rectangle**.

1 Introduce

Alternate Opener

7-7 Quadrilaterals

A *quadrilateral* is a four-sided polygon.

Write the letter of the quadrilateral that matches each definition.

1. Square: four right angles, four congruent sides — a. ____
2. Rectangle: four right angles — b. ____
3. Rhombus: four congruent sides — c. ____
4. Parallelogram: two pairs of parallel sides, two pairs of congruent sides — d. ____
5. Trapezoid: only one pair of parallel sides — e. ____

Think and Discuss

6. Discuss how the quadrilaterals are similar and different.
7. Explain why a square is a rectangle.

Motivate

To introduce special types of quadrilaterals, begin by asking students to think of as many words as they can that use the prefix *quad* and to explain how each word is related to the word *four.* (For example, a set of quadruplets is four children.) Point out that *quadrilateral* comes from words meaning "four" and "lines." Then have students find as many examples of quadrilateral figures in your classroom as they can.

Exploration worksheet and answers on Chapter 7 Resource Book pp. 63 and 134

2 Teach

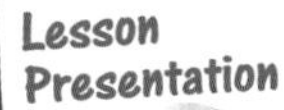

Guided Instruction

In this lesson, students learn to name and identify types of quadrilaterals. To help students understand the properties of quadrilaterals, have them consider why a square is also a parallelogram, why a trapezoid is not a parallelogram, and why all rectangles are not squares. a square has all the properties of a parallelogram; a trapezoid does not have two sets of parallel sides; all rectangles do not have four congruent sides Point out that the opposite sides of a kite are not parallel.

To identify a special quadrilateral, students should look for pairs of congruent sides, for parallel sides, and for right angles.

Give all of the names that apply to each quadrilateral.

The figure has exactly one pair of parallel sides, so it is a **trapezoid**. It does not fit the definitions of any of the other special quadrilaterals.

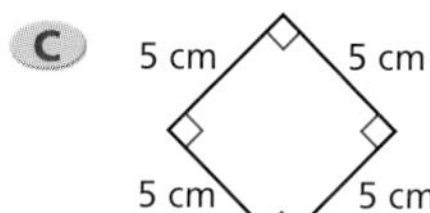

The figure has two pairs of parallel sides, so it is a **parallelogram**. It has four right angles, so it is also a **rectangle**. It has four congruent sides, so it is also a **rhombus** and a **square**.

EXAMPLE 2 Recognizing Relationships Between Quadrilaterals

Tell whether each statement is true or false. Explain your answer.

A All squares are rhombuses.

Any quadrilateral that has four congruent sides is a rhombus. Because a square has four congruent sides, it is a rhombus. The statement is true.

B All kites are parallelograms.

The opposite sides of a kite are not parallel, but the opposite sides of a parallelogram are parallel. The statement is false.

C All rhombuses are rectangles.

A rhombus may or may not have right angles, but a rectangle must have four right angles. The statement is false.

Think and Discuss

1. **Compare** a parallelogram with a trapezoid.
2. **Describe** how you can decide whether a rhombus is also a square. Use drawings to justify your answer.
3. **Discuss** why a rhombus is not a kite.

Additional Examples

Example 1

Give all of the names that apply to each quadrilateral.

A. 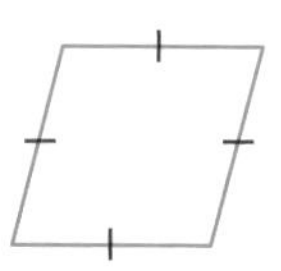 parallelogram, rhombus

B. 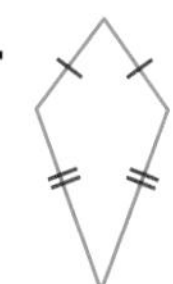 kite

C. 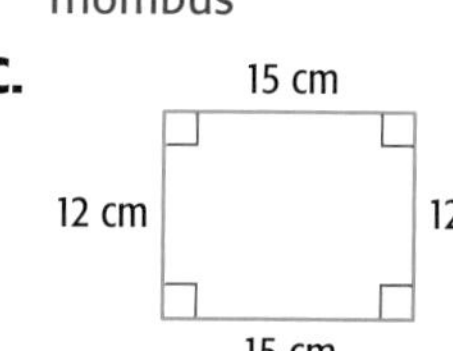

parallelogram, rectangle

Example 2

Tell whether each statement is true or false. Explain your answer.

A. All rhombuses are squares.

False; a rhombus has four congruent sides, but some do not have right angles.

B. Not all squares are rectangles.

False; squares have four right angles, so they are rectangles.

C. Some parallelograms are squares.

True; a square has all the properties of a parallelogram, so some parallelograms do have equal sides and right angles, while some do not.

3 Close

Summarize

Have students write brief descriptions of each type of special quadrilateral studied in this lesson.

Possible answers: A parallelogram is a quadrilateral with opposite sides parallel. A rectangle is a quadrilateral with four right angles. A square is a quadrilateral with four congruent sides and four right angles. A trapezoid has only one pair of parallel sides. A kite has two pairs of adjacent, congruent sides. A rhombus has four congruent sides.

Reaching All Learners
Through Critical Thinking

Allow students to work in groups to determine what properties they can discover about the diagonals of special quadrilaterals. Then have each group complete a table such as the one shown here. (You may use the Recording Sheet on Chapter 7 Resource Book p. 117.)

Quadrilateral	Congruent Diagonals	Perpendicular Diagonals
Parallelogram	No	No
Rectangle	Yes	No
Square	Yes	Yes
Rhombus	No	Yes
Kite	No	Yes

Answers to Think and Discuss

Possible answers:

1. A parallelogram has two pairs of parallel sides, but a trapezoid has only one pair of parallel sides.
2. If the angles of a rhombus are right angles, then the rhombus is also a square. If the diagonals of a rhombus are congruent, then the rhombus is also a square.
3. A kite has exactly two pairs of congruent, adjacent sides, but a rhombus has exactly four pairs of congruent, adjacent sides.

7-7 PRACTICE & ASSESS

Students may want to refer back to the lesson examples.

Assignment Guide

If you finished Example 1 assign:

Core 1–3, 6–11, 17, 19, 27–35

Enriched 1, 3, 7–11 odd, 16–20, 27–35

If you finished Example 2 assign:

Core 1–15, 17–23 odd, 27–35

Enriched 1–15 odd, 16–35

Answers

20. trapezoid

7-7 Exercises

FOR EXTRA PRACTICE
see page 669

internet connect
Homework Help Online
go.hrw.com Keyword: MS4 7-7

GUIDED PRACTICE

See Example 1 Give all of the names that apply to each quadrilateral.

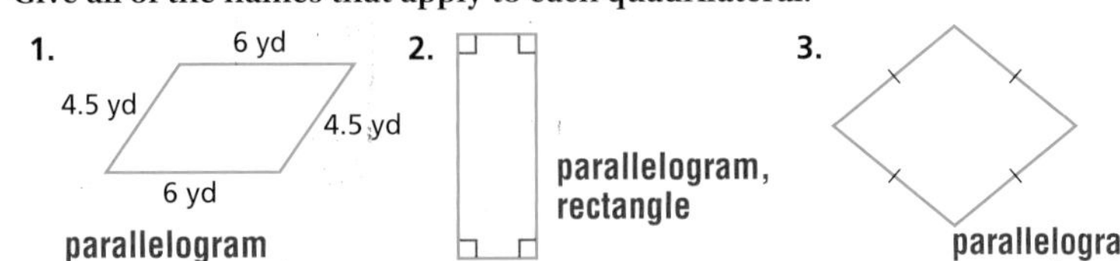

1. parallelogram
2. parallelogram, rectangle
3. parallelogram, rhombus

See Example 2 Tell whether each statement is true or false. Explain your answer.

4. All rhombuses are squares. False; a rhombus may have four right angles or not; if it does not, it is not a square.
5. All rectangles are parallelograms. True; opposite sides are parallel in a rectangle.

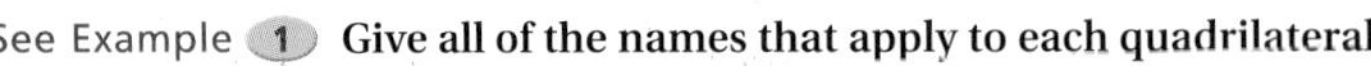

INDEPENDENT PRACTICE

See Example 1 Give all of the names that apply to each quadrilateral.

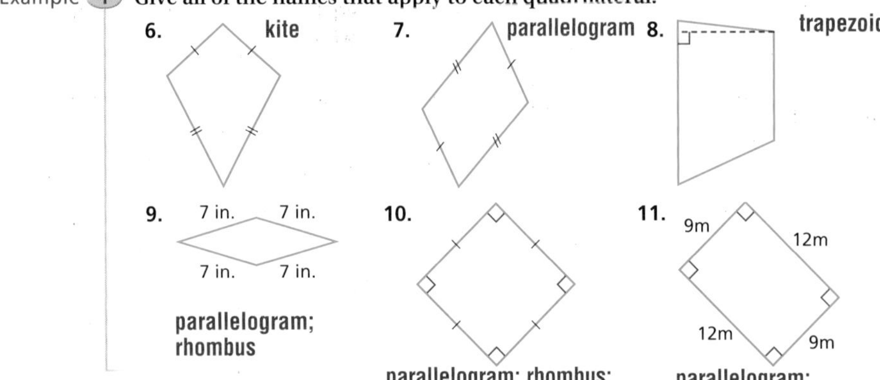

6. kite
7. parallelogram
8. trapezoid
9. parallelogram; rhombus
10. parallelogram; rhombus; rectangle; square
11. parallelogram; rectangle

See Example 2 Tell whether each statement is true or false. Explain your answer.

12. All squares are rectangles. True; squares have four right angles.
13. All rectangles are squares. False; some rectangles do not have all sides equal.
14. Some rectangles are squares. True; those with four equal sides are squares.
15. Some trapezoids are squares. False; a square has two sets of parallel sides, but a trapezoid has only one set.

PRACTICE AND PROBLEM SOLVING

Name the types of quadrilaterals with each feature.

16. four right angles
 square, rectangle
17. two pairs of opposite, parallel sides
 parallelogram, rectangle, rhombus, square
18. four congruent sides
 rhombus, square
19. opposite sides are congruent
 parallelogram, rhombus, rectangle, square
20. Graph the points $A(-2, -2)$, $B(4, 1)$, $C(3, 4)$, and $D(-1, 2)$, and draw line segments to connect the points. What kind of quadrilateral did you draw?

Math Background

The following concept map can be used to show relationships. For example, you can see that a rhombus is a kite, and a quadrilateral, and also a parallelogram, but that kites are not parallelograms. The concept map also shows that no trapezoids are parallelograms and that all squares are rectangles.

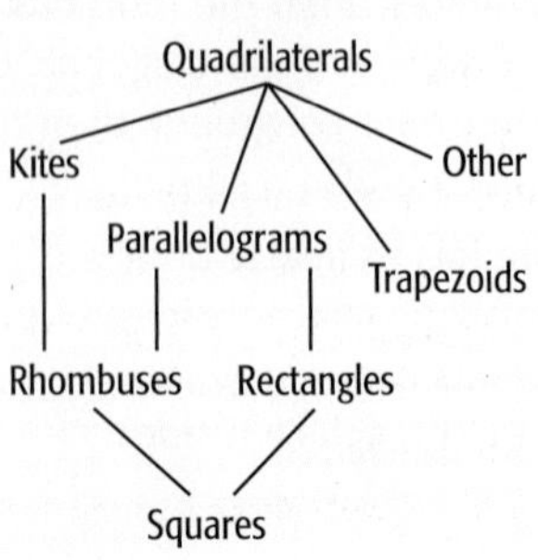

RETEACH 7-7

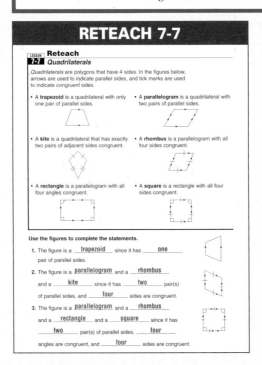

LESSON 7-7 **Reteach**
Quadrilaterals

Quadrilaterals are polygons that have 4 sides. In the figures below, arrows are used to indicate parallel sides, and tick marks are used to indicate congruent sides.

- A **trapezoid** is a quadrilateral with only one pair of parallel sides.
- A **parallelogram** is a quadrilateral with two pairs of parallel sides.
- A **kite** is a quadrilateral that has exactly two pairs of adjacent sides congruent.
- A **rhombus** is a parallelogram with all four sides congruent.
- A **rectangle** is a parallelogram with all four angles congruent.
- A **square** is a rectangle with all four sides congruent.

Use the figures to complete the statements.

1. The figure is a trapezoid since it has one pair of parallel sides.
2. The figure is a parallelogram and a rhombus and a kite since it has two pair(s) of parallel sides, and four sides are congruent.
3. The figure is a parallelogram and a rhombus and a rectangle and a square since it has two pair(s) of parallel sides, four angles are congruent, and four sides are congruent.

PRACTICE 7-7

LESSON 7-7 **Practice B**
Quadrilaterals

Give all of the names that apply to each quadrilateral.

1. parallelogram, rectangle
2. parallelogram
3. kite
4. trapezoid
5. parallelogram, rhombus
6. parallelogram, square, rectangle rhombus

Tell if each statement is true or false. Explain your answer.

7. Some rhombuses are parallelograms. Possible answers:
 False; All rhombuses are parallelograms that have four congruent sides.
8. All trapezoids are rhombuses.
 False; A trapezoid does not have four congruent sides.
9. Some parallelograms are squares.
 True; All squares have two pairs of parallel sides.
10. All kites are rhombuses.
 False; A kite does not have four congruent sides.

Native fruits of the Bahamas include guavas, pineapples, coconuts, bananas, and plantains.

go.hrw.com KEYWORD: MS4 Bahamas

CNN Student News

21. ***SOCIAL STUDIES*** Name the polygons made by each color in the flag of the Bahamas. Give the specific names of any quadrilaterals you find.
1 triangle, 1 pentagon, and 2 trapezoids

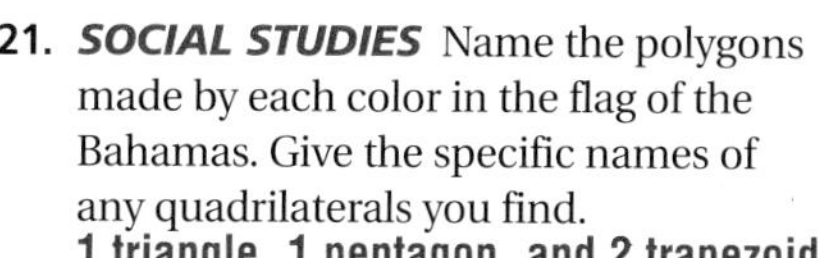

22. Describe how to construct a parallelogram from the figure at right, then complete the construction.

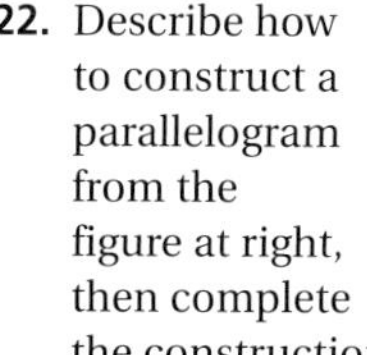

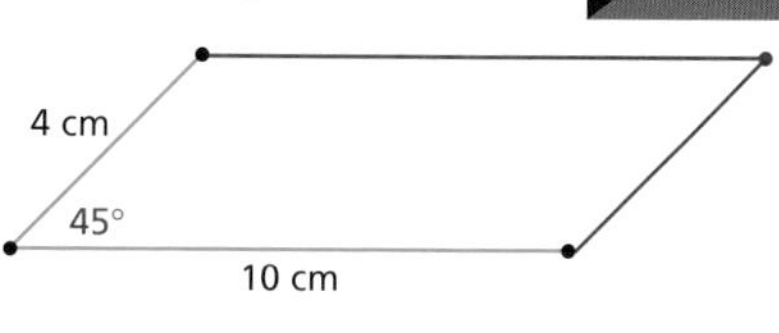

23. Bandon Highway is being built perpendicular to Avenue A and Avenue B, which are parallel. What kinds of polygons could be made by adding a fourth road?

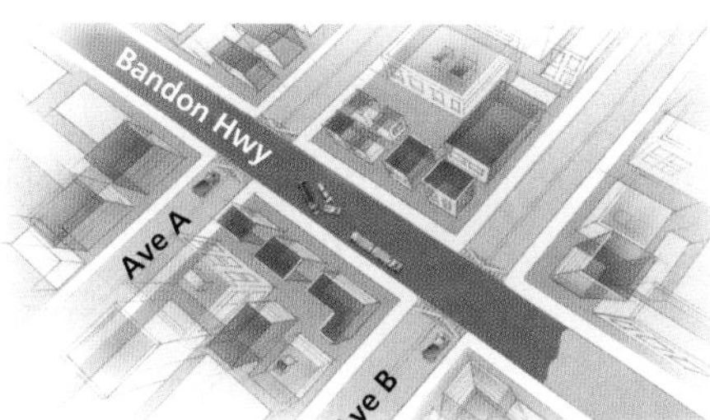

24. ***WRITE A PROBLEM*** Draw a design, or find one in a book, and then write a problem about the design that involves identifying quadrilaterals.

25. ***WRITE ABOUT IT*** Compare a kite with a parallelogram.

26. ***CHALLENGE*** The diagonals of a parallelogram bisect each other, and the diagonals of a rectangle are congruent. Given this information, what type of quadrilateral is figure *BCFD* if *ABFE* is a rectangle? Be specific, and explain your answer. **rhombus; $\overline{BC}$ and $\overline{CF}$ are congruent. Since the diagonals of *BCFD* bisect each other, it must be a parallelogram and $\overline{BD} \cong \overline{CF}$ and $\overline{DF} \cong \overline{BC}$.**

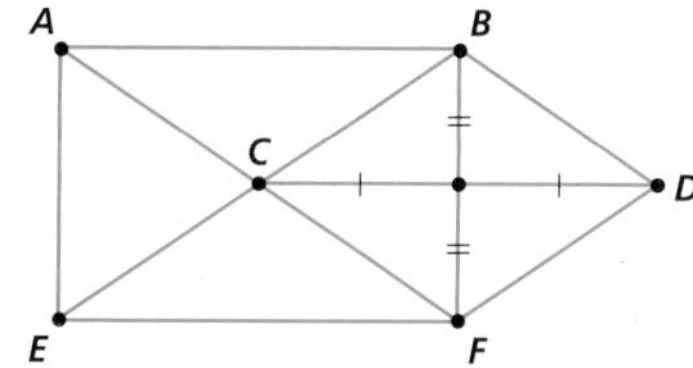

Spiral Review

Find the GCF of each set of numbers. (Lesson 2-5)

27. 16, 32 **16** **28.** 8, 28 **4** **29.** 15, 35 **5** **30.** 19, 21 **1**

Find each sum or difference. (Lessons 3-3, 3-4)

31. $5 + (-8)$ **−3** **32.** $-9 - 2$ **−11** **33.** $17 - 22$ **−5** **34.** $-4 + 6$ **2**

35. TEST PREP What is the solution to $45 \div 0.009$? (Lesson 4-5) **A**

A 5,000 **B** 500 **C** 50 **D** 5

Answers

22. Draw lines parallel to the 4 cm and 10 cm sides. Their point of intersection is the remaining vertex.

23. parallelogram, rhombus, square, rectangle, trapezoid, right triangle

24.

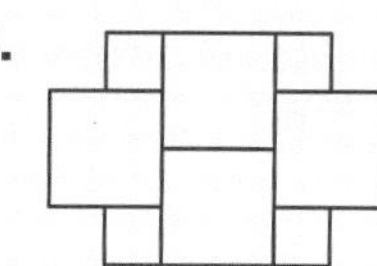

Possible answer: How many squares are in the design?

25. The opposite sides of a kite are not parallel, but opposite sides of a parallelogram are parallel. Also, two pairs of adjacent sides of a kite are congruent, while opposite sides of a parallelogram are congruent.

Journal

Ask students to think of five real-world places where they see different special quadrilaterals and to describe these in their journal.

Test Prep Doctor

For Exercise 35, students should recognize that the divisor is much smaller than 1, so the answer will be much greater than 45; thus, they can eliminate **C** and **D.** By thinking of the problem as "45 divided by 9 thousandths," students can rewrite it as $(45 \div 9) \cdot 1{,}000$, or $5 \cdot 1{,}000$, **A.**

Lesson Quiz

1. Give all the names that apply to the quadrilateral.
rhombus, quadrilateral, parallelogram

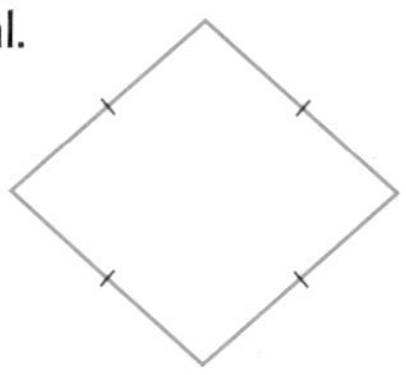

Identify the quadrilateral described.

2. 4 right angles, 4 congruent sides
square

3. only one pair of parallel sides
trapezoid

Tell if each statement is true or false. Explain.

4. All quadrilaterals are parallelograms. False; a quadrilateral is any 4-sided figure.

5. Every parallelogram is a rectangle. False; a rectangle is a specific kind of parallelogram.

Available on Daily Transparency in CRB

CHALLENGE 7-7

LESSON 7-7 **Challenge**
It's Only a Quadrilateral!

Match each picture with the list showing which quadrilaterals are found in the picture.

1.

2.

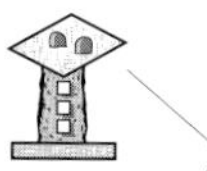

3.

List A:
kite
rhombus
trapezoid
rectangle

List B:
trapezoid
rectangle
square
parallelogram

List C:
rhombus
rectangle
square
parallelogram

4. Draw a design on the rug using only the following quadrilaterals: trapezoid, rectangle, and rhombus. You can use as many of each figure as you like, but all must be used at least once. **Answers will vary, but student's designs should include only trapezoids, rectangles, and rhombi, no kites, or parallelograms that are not rectangles.**

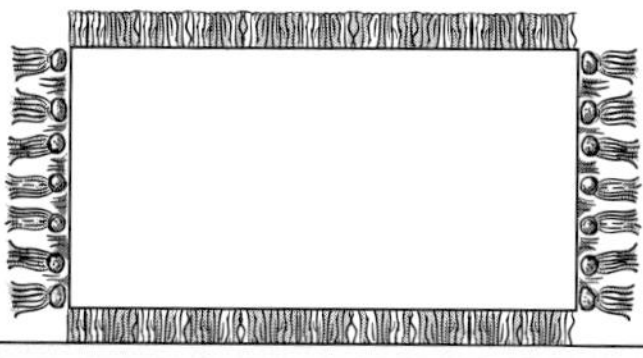

PROBLEM SOLVING 7-7

LESSON 7-7 **Problem Solving**
Quadrilaterals

Write the correct answer.

1. A garden has 2 pairs of congruent sides. The congruent sides are not adjacent, and the angles are not all congruent. What is the shape of the garden?
parallelogram

2. A poster advertising an art show has 1 pair of parallel sides. All the angles are different, and none of the sides are congruent. What is the shape of this poster?
trapezoid

3. In a math report, Ming said that since a rhombus has 4 equal sides and a square has 4 equal sides, all rhombuses are squares. Is she correct? Explain.
No, a rhombus does not always have 4 right angles.

4. A student was asked to give an example of a polygon that is not a quadrilateral and an example of a quadrilateral that is not a polygon. Is this possible? Why or why not?
No, all quadrilaterals are polygons.

Choose the letter for the best answer.

This is a drawing of Piet Mondrian's painting *Composition 8.*

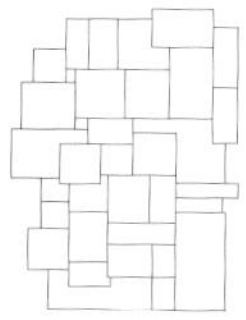

5. Which type of quadrilateral do you see most in the painting?
A kite
B trapezoid
(C) rectangle
D square

6. Which type of quadrilateral does not appear to be in the painting?
F rectangle
G parallelogram
H square
(J) trapezoid

7. Which statement is true about the painting?
A There are no parallelograms.
B There are only rectangles.
C There are only quadrilaterals.
(D) None of the above

8. Which statement is true about the painting?
(F) There are no triangles.
G There are only squares.
H There are no squares.
J None of the above

7-8 Organizer

Pacing: Traditional 1 day
Block $\frac{1}{2}$ day

Objective: Students find the measures of angles in polygons.

Warm Up

Solve.

1. $72 + 18 + x = 180$ $\quad$ **$x = 90$**
2. $80 + 70 + x = 180$ $\quad$ **$x = 30$**
3. $x + 42 + 90 = 180$ $\quad$ **$x = 48$**
4. $120 + x + 32 = 180$ $\quad$ **$x = 28$**

Problem of the Day

How many different rectangles are in the figure shown? **100**

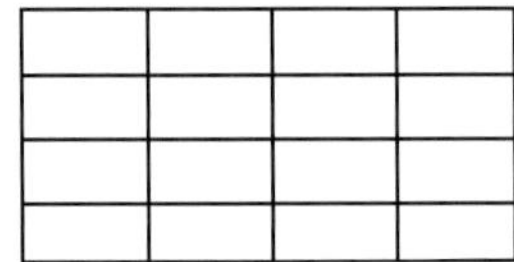

Available on Daily Transparency in CRB

Math Fact !

A *concave polygon* is a polygon with at least one interior angle that measures greater than 180°. Interior angles greater than 180° are called *re-entrant angles.*

7-8 Angles in Polygons

Learn to find the measures of angles in polygons.

Vocabulary
diagonal

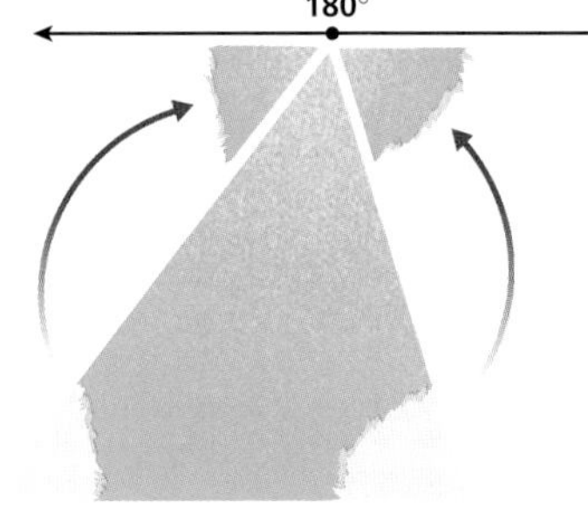

If you tear off the corners of a triangle and put them together, you will find that they form a straight angle. This suggests that the sum of the measures of the angles in a triangle is 180°.

You can prove mathematically that the angle measures in a triangle add up to 180° by drawing a diagram using the following steps.

a. Draw a triangle.

b. Extend the sides of the triangle.

c. Draw a line through the vertex opposite the base so that the line is parallel to the base.

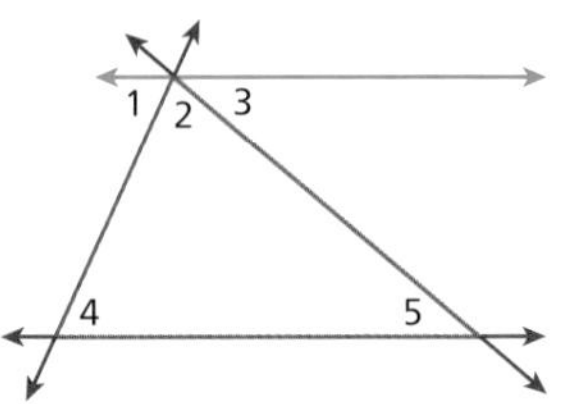

Notice that ∠1, ∠2, and ∠3 together form a straight angle. That is, the sum of their measures is 180°.

Notice also that the figure you have drawn consists of two parallel lines cut by two transversals. So if you were to tear off ∠4 and ∠5 from the triangle, they would fit exactly over ∠1 and ∠3. This shows that the sum of the measures of the angles in the triangle is 180°.

EXAMPLE 1 Determining the Measure of an Unknown Interior Angle

Find the measure of the unknown angle.

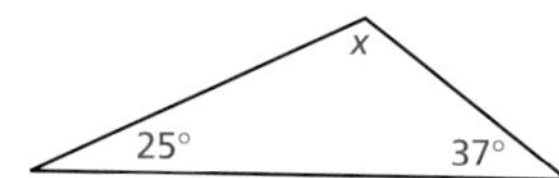

$25° + 37° + x = 180°$ *The sum of the measures of the angles is 180°.*

$62° + x = 180°$ *Combine like terms.*

$\underline{-62°} \quad \underline{-62°}$ *Subtract 62° from both sides.*

$x = 118°$

The measure of the unknown angle is 118°.

1 Introduce

Alternate Opener

EXPLORATION

7-8 Angles in Polygons

You can use measurement to discover an interesting property of triangles.

1. Draw a triangle and measure the three angles.
   a. What is the sum of the measures of the three angles?
   b. Cut out the triangle and cut off the bottom two corners. Attach the two corners as shown. What is the sum of the measures of the three adjacent angles?

Think and Discuss

2. **Explain** how you know that the sum of the angles in a triangle is 180°.
3. **Explain** how you know that the sum of the angles in a rectangle is 360°.

Motivate

Review the concepts of parallel lines and transversals from Lesson 7-3. When a transversal intersects two parallel lines

1. eight angles are formed,
2. all the acute angles formed are congruent,
3. and all the obtuse angles formed are congruent.

To introduce the measures of angles in polygons, start with a square and a rectangle, and ask students to speculate on the total number of degrees in each figure.

Exploration worksheet and answers on Chapter 7 Resource Book pp. 72 and 136

2 Teach

Lesson Presentation

Guided Instruction

In this lesson, students learn to identify and find the measures of angles in polygons. To help students understand the results presented for the triangle, have students cut out their own triangles and replicate the experiment. You may want to use Teaching Transparency T31 in the Chapter 7 Resource Book.

Teaching Tip Before discussing the first example, ask students to write an equation that shows the relationship of the measures in triangle *ABC*. Students can then use that equation in writing an equation to solve Example 1.

The sum of the angle measures in other polygons can be found by dividing the polygons into triangles. A polygon can be divided into triangles by drawing all of the *diagonals* from one of its vertices.

A **diagonal** of a polygon is a segment that is drawn from one vertex to another and is not one of the sides of the polygon. You can divide a polygon into triangles by using diagonals only if all of the diagonals of that polygon are inside the polygon. The sum of the angle measures in the polygon is then found by combining the sums of the angle measures in the triangles.

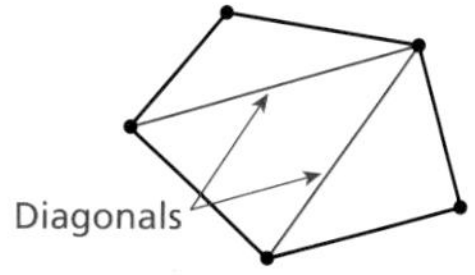

Number of triangles in pentagon		Sum of angle measures in each triangle		Sum of angle measures in pentagon
3	·	180°	=	540°

EXAMPLE 2 Drawing Triangles to Find the Sum of Interior Angles

Divide each polygon into triangles to find the sum of its angle measures.

A

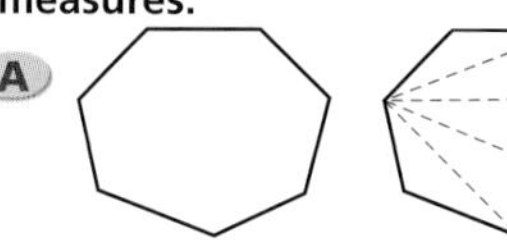

There are 5 triangles.

$5 \cdot 180° = 900°$

The sum of the angle measures of a heptagon is 900°.

B

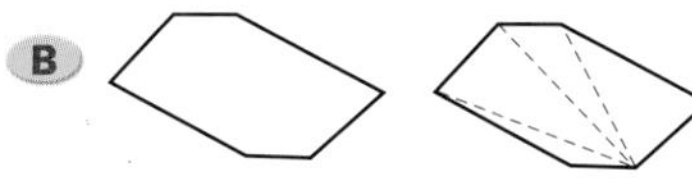

There are 4 triangles.

$4 \cdot 180° = 720°$

The sum of the angle measures of a hexagon is 720°.

Think and Discuss

1. **Explain** how to find the measure of an angle in a triangle when the measures of the two other angles are known.
2. **Determine** for which polygon the sum of the angle measures is greater, a pentagon or an octagon.
3. **Explain** how the measure of each angle in a regular polygon changes as the number of sides increases.

COMMON ERROR ALERT

Some students might multiply the number of sides of the polygon by 180°. Caution students to be sure they have the correct number of triangles before they multiply.

Additional Examples

Example 1

Find the measure of the unknown angle.

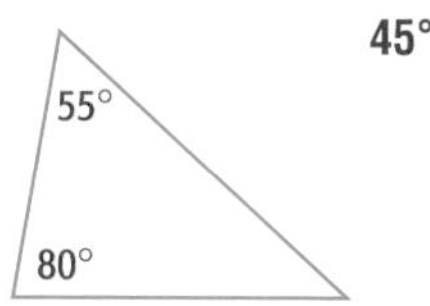

45°

Example 2

Divide each polygon into triangles to find the sum of its angle measures.

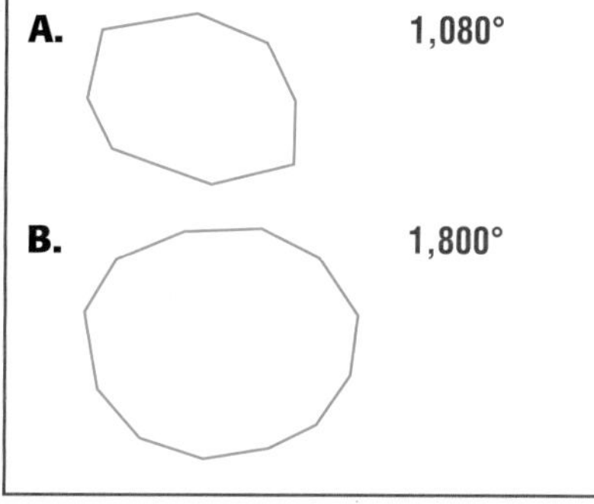

Example 1 note: Point out that students could also solve by subtracting 25 from 180 and then subtracting 37 from that result.

3 Close

Reaching All Learners
Through Critical Thinking

Let students complete the table and use it to determine a formula for finding the sum of the angles in a polygon. $(n - 2)180°$ A recording sheet is provided on Chapter 7 Resource Book p. 118.

Hint: Think about how the number of sides in each figure relates to the number of triangles in each figure.

Figure	Number of Triangles	Total Number of Degrees
Triangle	1	180°
Quadrilateral	2	360°
Pentagon	3	540°

Summarize

Have students describe the steps they would use to find the number of degrees in the angles of an octagon.

Possible answer: Draw the diagonals in the octagon and count the number of triangles. There will be 6. Multiply 6 by 180° to find the total number of degrees. The number of degrees in an octagon is 1,080°.

Answers to Think and Discuss

1. Subtract the sum of the measures of the two angles from 180°.
2. The octagon has more triangles when the diagonals are drawn. Since there are more triangles, there are more degrees. The octagon has 1,080°, while the pentagon has only 540°.
3. Possible answer: The size of each angle in a regular polygon increases as the number of sides increases. For example, each angle of an equilateral triangle is 60°, and each angle of a square is 90°.

7-8 PRACTICE & ASSESS

Students may want to refer back to the lesson examples.

Assignment Guide

If you finished Example 1 assign:

Core 1–3, 7–9, 13–17 odd, 21, 26–32

Enriched 1, 3, 7, 9, 13–18, 20, 21, 26–32

If you finished Example 2 assign:

Core 1–12, 13–21 odd, 26–32

Enriched 1–11 odd, 13–32

Notes

7-8 Exercises

FOR EXTRA PRACTICE see page 669

GUIDED PRACTICE

See Example 1 Find the measure of each unknown angle.

1. **77°** (60°, 43°, x)
2. **110°** (40°, x, 30°)
3. **55°** (x, 35°, right angle)

See Example 2 Divide each polygon into triangles to find the sum of its angle measures.

4. **720°**
5. **540°**
6. **360°**

INDEPENDENT PRACTICE

See Example 1 Find the measure of each unknown angle.

7. **60°** (x, 60°, 60°)
8. **37°** (78°, 65°, x)
9. **32°**

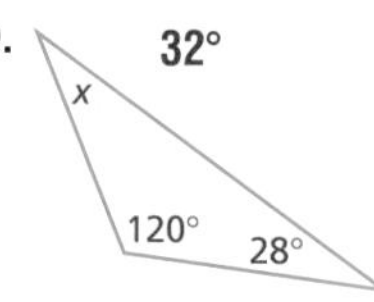

See Example 2 Divide each polygon into triangles to find the sum of its angle measures.

10. 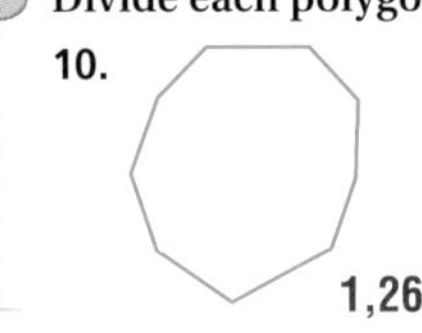 **1,260°**
11. 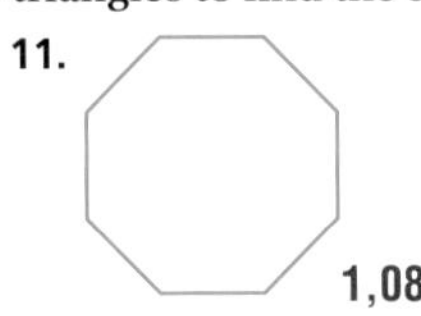 **1,080°**
12. 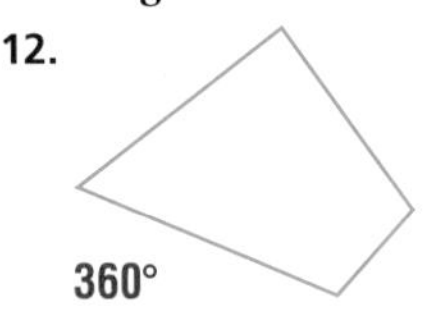 **360°**

PRACTICE AND PROBLEM SOLVING

Find the measure of the third angle in each triangle, given two angle measures.

13. 56°, 101° **23°**
14. 18°, 63° **99°**
15. 62°, 58° **60°**

Decide whether the angle measures can form a triangle. If they can, classify the triangle.

16. 54°, 68°, 58° **acute**
17. 120°, 59°, 30° **no**
18. 110°, 30°, 40° **obtuse**

Math Background

Since it is not possible to draw a diagonal from a vertex of a polygon to either of the adjacent vertices, a polygon with n sides will always have $n - 3$ diagonals from any one vertex. These $n - 3$ diagonals divide the interior of the polygon into $n - 2$ triangles, so the formula for the sum of the measures of the angles in any polygon is $(n - 2) \cdot 180°$. From that formula, it is possible to derive the formula for the measure of an interior angle in a regular polygon: $\frac{(n-2) \cdot 180}{n}$.

RETEACH 7-8

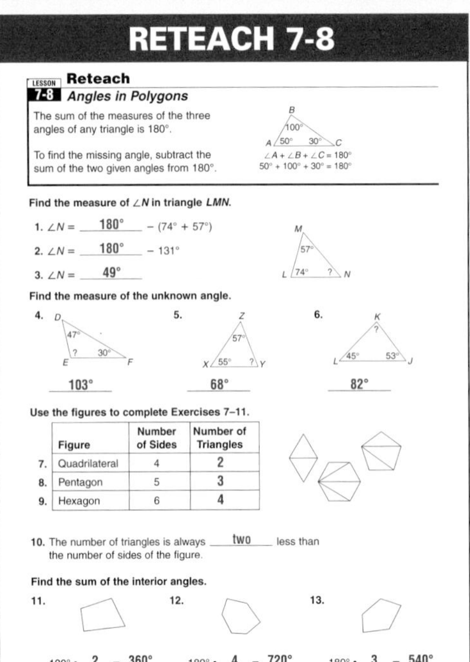

LESSON 7-8 **Reteach**

Angles in Polygons

The sum of the measures of the three angles of any triangle is 180°.

To find the missing angle, subtract the sum of the two given angles from 180°.

$\angle A + \angle B + \angle C = 180°$

$50° + 100° + 30° = 180°$

Find the measure of $\angle N$ in triangle LMN.

1. $\angle N =$ **180°** $- (74° + 57°)$
2. $\angle N =$ **180°** $- 131°$
3. $\angle N =$ **49°**

Find the measure of the unknown angle.

4. **103°**
5. **68°**
6. **82°**

Use the figures to complete Exercises 7–11.

	Figure	Number of Sides	Number of Triangles
7.	Quadrilateral	4	2
8.	Pentagon	5	3
9.	Hexagon	6	4

10. The number of triangles is always **two** less than the number of sides of the figure.

Find the sum of the interior angles.

11. 180° • **2** = **360°**
12. 180° • **4** = **720°**
13. 180° • **3** = **540°**

PRACTICE 7-8

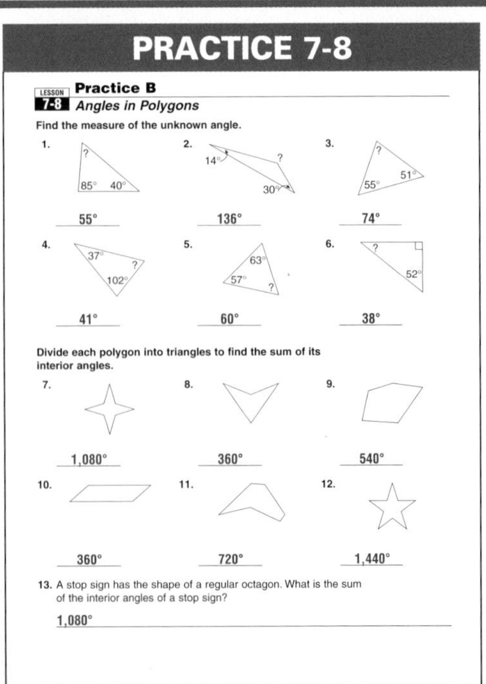

LESSON 7-8 **Practice B**

Angles in Polygons

Find the measure of the unknown angle.

1. **55°**
2. **136°**
3. **74°**
4. **41°**
5. **60°**
6. **38°**

Divide each polygon into triangles to find the sum of its interior angles.

7. **1,080°**
8. **360°**
9. **540°**
10. **360°**
11. **720°**
12. **1,440°**

13. A stop sign has the shape of a regular octagon. What is the sum of the interior angles of a stop sign?

1,080°

19. ***ARCHITECTURE*** Each outer wall of the Pentagon in Washington, D.C., measures 921 feet.

a. What is the sum of the angle measures in the shape made by the Pentagon's outer walls? **540°**

b. What is the measure of each angle in this shape? **108°**

20. ***EARTH SCIENCE*** A sundial consists of a circular base and a right triangle mounted upright on the base. If one acute angle in the right triangle is 52°, what is the measure of the other acute angle? **38°**

21. ***NAVIGATION*** The angle between the lines of sight from a lighthouse to a tugboat and to a cargo ship is 27°. The angle between the lines of sight at the cargo ship is twice the angle between the lines of sight at the tugboat. What are the angles at the tugboat and at the cargo ship? **51° and 102°**

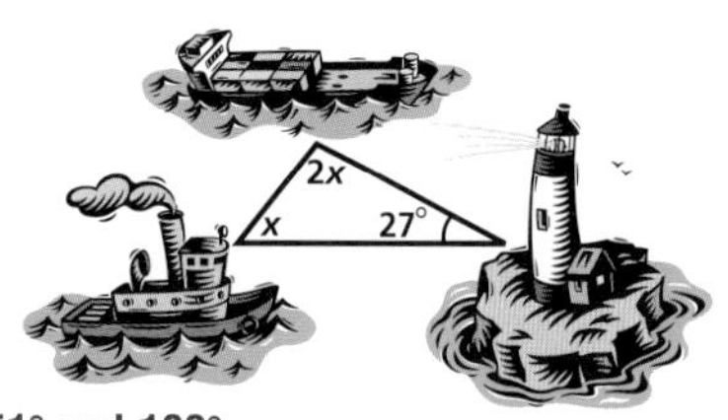

22. ***CONSTRUCTION*** A truss bridge is supported by frames called trusses. Each truss consists of steel or wooden parts connected to form triangles. If every triangle in a truss bridge is an isosceles right triangle, what is the measure of each angle in one of the triangles? **45°, 45°, 90°**

23. ***WHAT'S THE ERROR?*** If you try to find the sum of the angle measures in an octagon by multiplying 7 · 180°, what is your error? **Possible answer: Six triangles can be drawn inside an octagon, not seven.**

24. ***WRITE ABOUT IT*** Describe how you would find the sum of the angle measures in a polygon with diagonals that are all inside the polygon. **Count the number of sides, subtract 2, and multiply the result by 180°.**

25. ***CHALLENGE*** Write a formula for the measure of each angle in a regular polygon with n sides. $\frac{(n-2)180°}{n}$

Spiral Review

Use the graph for Exercises 26–28. (Lesson 1-4)

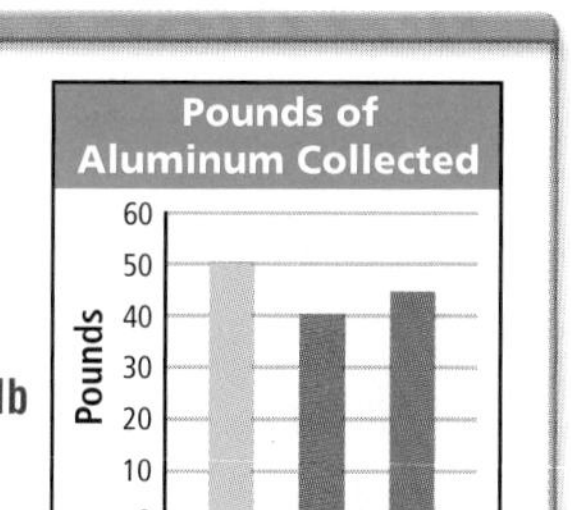

26. Which grade collected the most aluminum? **seventh grade**

27. About how many more pounds of aluminum did the ninth grade collect than the eighth grade? **about 5 lb**

28. About how many pounds were collected by all three grades? **135 lb**

Find each sum. (Lesson 4-2)

29. 4.2 + 3.68 **7.88**

30. 16.8 + 7.02 **23.82**

31. 431.025 + 14.86 **445.885**

32. **TEST PREP** What is 0.4% written as a fraction? (Lesson 6-1) **C**

A $\frac{4}{10}$ B $\frac{4}{100}$ C $\frac{4}{1,000}$ D $\frac{4}{10,000}$

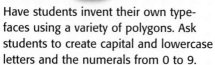

CHALLENGE 7-8

LESSON 7-8 **Challenge**
Shape Up

Draw a polygon based on each description. Label the measures of all angles. Name the polygon. Answers may vary. Possible answers are given.

1. A figure has vertices A, B, C, D, and E. Sides AB and BC are 8 units in length. $\angle A = \angle C = 130°$. Side CD is parallel to AE, and each side is 10 units in length. $\angle D = \angle E = 90°$

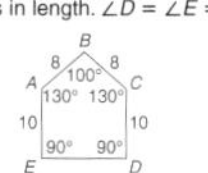
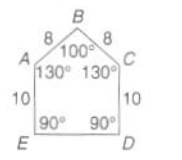

pentagon

2. A figure has vertices W, X, Y, and Z. Sides WZ, WX, and XY are each 12 units in length. Sides WX and YZ are parallel but are not the same length. $\angle W = \angle X = 120°$

W 12 X; 120° 120°; 12 12; 60° 60°; Z 24 Y

trapezoid

3. A figure has vertices M, N, O, P, Q, and R. Sides MN and QP are parallel, and each is 15 units in length. $\angle M = \angle N = \angle P = \angle Q = 150°$

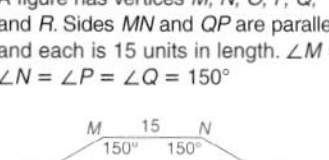

hexagon

4. A figure has vertices A, B, C, and D. $AB = BC = CD = AD$. Side AB is parallel to CD, and side AD is parallel to BC. $\angle B$ and $\angle D = 125°$

A B; 55° 125°; 125° 55°; D C

rhombus

5. A figure with vertices E, F, and G has perpendicular sides EF and FG. $\angle E = \angle G$

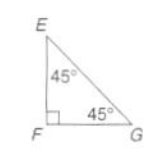

right triangle

6. A figure has vertices Q, R, S, T. Side QR is parallel to ST, and side QT is parallel to RS. $\angle Q = 113°$

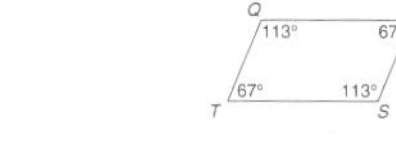

parallelogram

PROBLEM SOLVING 7-8

LESSON 7-8 **Problem Solving**
Angles in Polygons

Write the correct answer.

These are some common street signs.

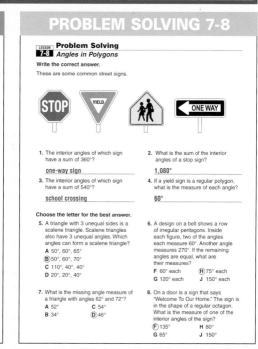

1. The interior angles of which sign have a sum of 360°? **one-way sign**

2. What is the sum of the interior angles of a stop sign? **1,080°**

3. The interior angles of which sign have a sum of 540°? **school crossing**

4. If a yield sign is a regular polygon, what is the measure of each angle? **60°**

Choose the letter for the best answer.

5. A triangle with 3 unequal sides is a scalene triangle. Scalene triangles also have 3 unequal angles. Which angles can form a scalene triangle?
   A 50°, 60°, 65°
   (B) 50°, 60°, 70°
   C 110°, 40°, 40°
   D 20°, 20°, 40°

6. A design on a belt shows a row of irregular pentagons. Inside each figure, two of the angles each measure 60°. Another angle measures 270°. If the remaining angles are equal, what are their measures?
   F 60° each (H) 75° each
   G 120° each J 150° each

7. What is the missing angle measure of a triangle with angles 62° and 72°?
   A 52° C 54°
   B 34° (D) 46°

8. On a door is a sign that says "Welcome To Our Home." The sign is in the shape of a regular octagon. What is the measure of one of the interior angles of the sign?
   (F) 135° H 80°
   G 65° J 150°

Journal 

Have students invent their own typefaces using a variety of polygons. Ask students to create capital and lowercase letters and the numerals from 0 to 9.

Test Prep Doctor 

For Exercise 32, students can eliminate **A** and **B** by writing the percent equivalents of each. Then by using the definition of percent, students can determine that **C** is correct.

Lesson Quiz 

Find the measure of the unknown angle for the following.

1. a triangle with angle measures of 66° and 77° **37°**

2. a right triangle with one angle measure of 36° **54°**

3. an obtuse triangle with angle measures of 32° and 42° **106°**

4. Divide a seven-sided polygon into triangles to find the sum of its interior angles. **900°**

Available on Daily Transparency in CRB

Chapter 7 Mid-Chapter Quiz

Purpose: *To assess students' mastery of concepts and skills in Lessons 7-1 through 7-8*

Assessment Resources

Section 7B Quiz

Assessment Resources . . . . p. 20

***Test and Practice Generator* CD-ROM**

Additional mid-chapter assessment items in both multiple-choice and free-response format may be generated for any objective in Lessons 7-1 through 7-8.

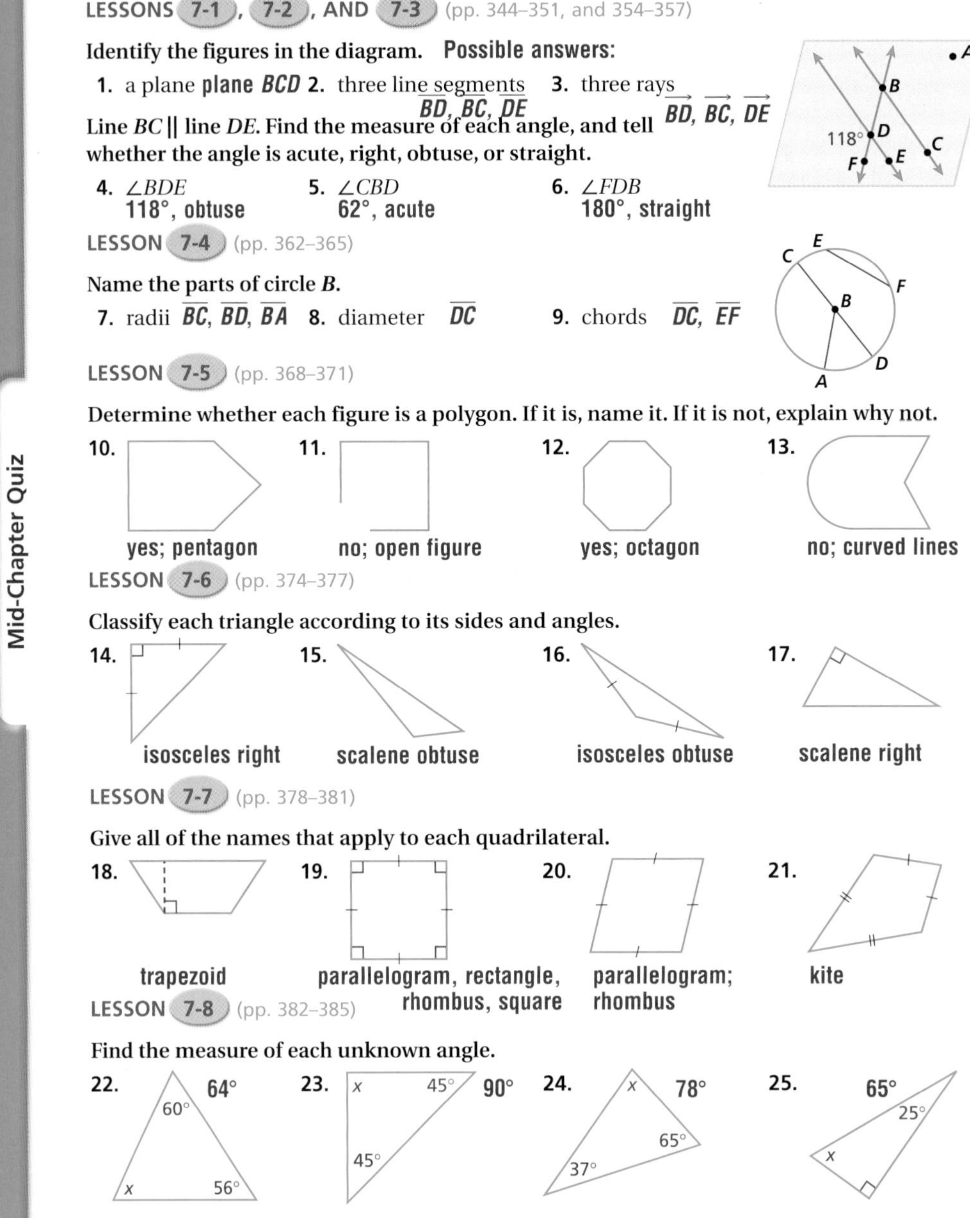

Chapter 7 Mid-Chapter Quiz

Mid-Chapter Quiz

LESSONS 7-1, 7-2, AND 7-3 (pp. 344–351, and 354–357)

Identify the figures in the diagram. **Possible answers:**

1. a plane **plane *BCD***
2. three line segments **$\overline{BD}$, $\overline{BC}$, $\overline{DE}$**
3. three rays **$\overrightarrow{BD}$, $\overrightarrow{BC}$, $\overrightarrow{DE}$**

Line *BC* || line *DE*. Find the measure of each angle, and tell whether the angle is acute, right, obtuse, or straight.

4. ∠*BDE* **118°, obtuse**
5. ∠*CBD* **62°, acute**
6. ∠*FDB* **180°, straight**

LESSON 7-4 (pp. 362–365)

Name the parts of circle *B*.

7. radii **$\overline{BC}$, $\overline{BD}$, $\overline{BA}$**
8. diameter **$\overline{DC}$**
9. chords **$\overline{DC}$, $\overline{EF}$**

LESSON 7-5 (pp. 368–371)

Determine whether each figure is a polygon. If it is, name it. If it is not, explain why not.

10. **yes; pentagon**
11. **no; open figure**
12. **yes; octagon**
13. **no; curved lines**

LESSON 7-6 (pp. 374–377)

Classify each triangle according to its sides and angles.

14. **isosceles right**
15. **scalene obtuse**
16. **isosceles obtuse**
17. **scalene right**

LESSON 7-7 (pp. 378–381)

Give all of the names that apply to each quadrilateral.

18. **trapezoid**
19. **parallelogram, rectangle, rhombus, square**
20. **parallelogram; rhombus**
21. **kite**

LESSON 7-8 (pp. 382–385)

Find the measure of each unknown angle.

22. **64°**

23. **90°**

24. **78°**

25. **65°**

Focus on Problem Solving

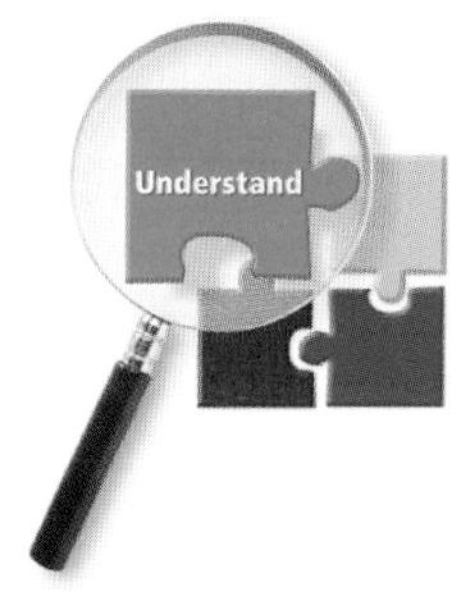

Understand the Problem

• Understand the words in the problem

Words that you do not understand can sometimes make a simple problem seem difficult. Some of those words, such as the names of things or persons, may not even be necessary to solve the problem. If a problem contains an unfamiliar name, or one that you cannot pronounce, you can substitute another word for it. If a word that you don't understand is necessary to solve the problem, look the word up to find its meaning.

Read each problem, and make a list of unusual or unfamiliar words. If a word is not necessary to solve the problem, replace it with a familiar one. If a word is necessary, look up the word and write its meaning.

1. Using a pair of calipers, Mr. Papadimitriou measures the diameter of an ancient Greek amphora to be 17.8 cm at its widest point. What is the radius of the amphora at this point?

2. Joseph wants to plant gloxinia and hydrangeas in two similar rectangular gardens. The length of one garden is 5 ft, and the width is 4 ft. The other garden's length is 20 ft. What is the width of the second garden?

3. Mr. Manityche is sailing his catamaran from Kaua'i to Ni'ihau, a distance of about 12 nautical miles. If his speed averages 10 knots, how long will the trip take him?

4. Aimee's lepidoptera collection includes a butterfly with dots that appear to form a scalene triangle on each wing. What is the sum of the angles of each triangle on the butterfly's wings?

5. Students in a physics class use wire and resistors to build a Wheatstone bridge. Each side of their rhombus-shaped design is 2 cm long. What angle measures would the design have to have for its shape to be a square?

Answers

1. 8.9 cm
2. 16 ft
3. about 1.2 h
4. 180°
5. 90°

Focus on Problem Solving

Purpose: *To focus on understanding the problem*

Problem Solving Resources

Interactive Problem Solving . . pp. 57–67

Math: Reading and Writing in the Content Area . . . . pp. 57–67

Problem Solving Process

This page focuses on the first step of the problem-solving process: **Understand the Problem**

Discuss

Have students discuss the unusual or unfamiliar words and the replacement words they used in each exercise.

Possible answers:

1. Mr. Papadimitriou: He, A man, Mr. P
   calipers: scientific instrument
   amphora: vase
2. gloxinia: tropical plant
   hydrangeas: shrubs
3. Mr. Manityche: He, A man, Mr. M
   catamaran: sailboat
   Kaua'i to Ni'ihau: K to N
   nautical mile: 6,080 ft
   knot: a speed of 1 nautical mile per hour
4. lepidoptera: butterfly
5. resistors: electric devices
   Wheatstone: model

Section 7C

Closed Figure Relationships

One-Minute Section Planner

Lesson	Materials	Resources
Lesson 7-9 Congruent Figures **NCTM:** Geometry, Communication, Connections **NAEP:** Geometry 2e ☐ SAT-9 ☐ SAT-10 ☐ ITBS ☑ CTBS ☑ MAT ☑ CAT	**Optional** Teaching Transparency T34 *(CRB)*	• *Chapter 7 Resource Book,* pp. 81–89 • Daily Transparency T33, CRB • Additional Examples Transparencies T35–T36, CRB • *Alternate Openers: Explorations,* p. 65
Lesson 7-10 Transformations **NCTM:** Geometry, Reasoning and Proof, Communication, Connections **NAEP:** Geometry 2c ☑ SAT-9 ☑ SAT-10 ☐ ITBS ☑ CTBS ☐ MAT ☑ CAT	**Optional** Teaching Transparency T38 *(CRB)* Tranparency of coordinate plane T39 *(CRB)* Cutout figures *(CRB, p. 119)* Scissors	• *Chapter 7 Resource Book,* pp. 90–99 • Daily Transparency T37, CRB • Additional Examples Transparencies T40–T42, CRB • *Alternate Openers: Explorations,* p. 66
Lesson 7-11 Symmetry **NCTM:** Geometry, Communication, Connections **NAEP:** Geometry 2a ☑ SAT-9 ☑ SAT-10 ☑ ITBS ☑ CTBS ☑ MAT ☑ CAT	**Optional** Cutout shapes *(CRB, p. 120)* Scissors **Required** Recording Sheet for Exercises 1–6 and 10–15 *(CRB, p. 121)* Dot paper *(CRB, p. 115)*	• *Chapter 7 Resource Book,* pp. 100–108 • Daily Transparency T43, CRB • Additional Examples Transparencies T44–T45, CRB • *Alternate Openers: Explorations,* p. 67
Hands-On Lab 7F Create Tessellations **NCTM:** Algebra, Geometry, Connections **NAEP:** Geometry 1f ☐ SAT-9 ☐ SAT-10 ☐ ITBS ☐ CTBS ☐ MAT ☐ CAT	**Required** Straightedges *(MK)*	• *Hands-On Lab Activities,* pp. 66–67
Section 7C Assessment		• Section 7C Quiz, AR p. 21 • *Test and Practice Generator* CD-ROM

SAT = *Stanford Achievement Tests* **ITBS** = *Iowa Test of Basic Skills* **CTBS** = *Comprehensive Test of Basic Skills/Terra Nova*
MAT = *Metropolitan Achievement Test* **CAT** = *California Achievement Test*

NCTM—Complete standards can be found on pages T27–T33. **NAEP**—Complete standards can be found on pages A35–A39.

SE = *Student Edition* **TE** = *Teacher's Edition* **AR** = *Assessment Resources* **CRB** = *Chapter Resource Book*
MK = *Manipulatives Kit*

Section Overview

Congruent Figures — Lesson 7-9

Why? You can use the properties of congruent figures in many proofs in geometry.

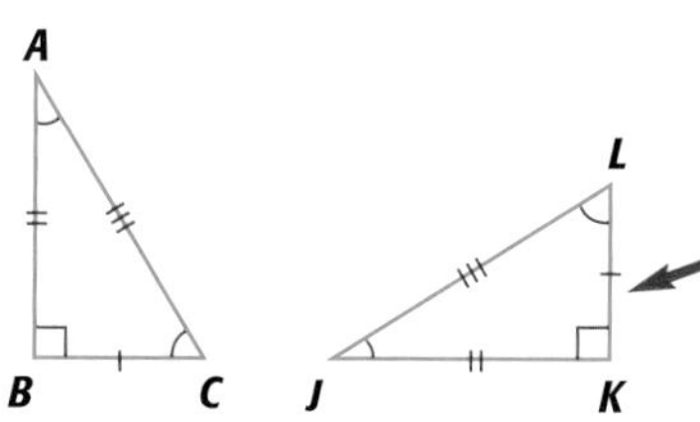

Two figures are **congruent** when their corresponding sides and corresponding angles are congruent.

Congruent
$\triangle ABC \cong \triangle JKL$
Their positions are different, but the triangles are the same size and shape.

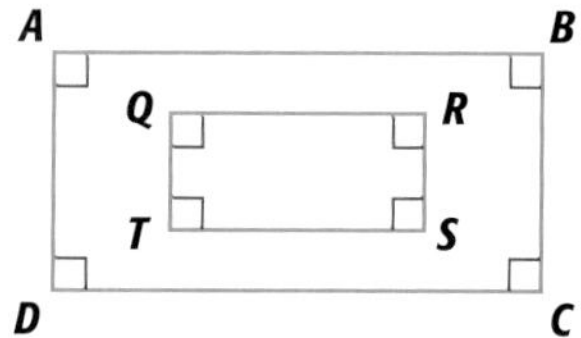

Not congruent
$ABCD \ncong QRST$
The rectangles are not the same size.

Transformations and Symmetry — Hands-On Lab 7E, Lessons 7-10, 7-11

Why? Transformations of, and symmetry in, geometric figures occurs often in art, architecture, and engineering.

Translation

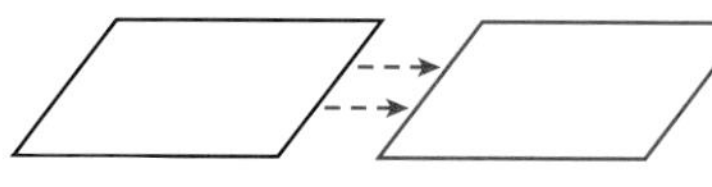

Reflection

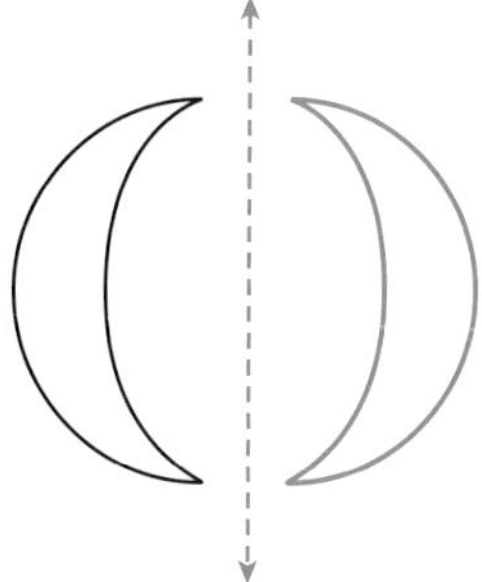

Line of symmetry

Rotation

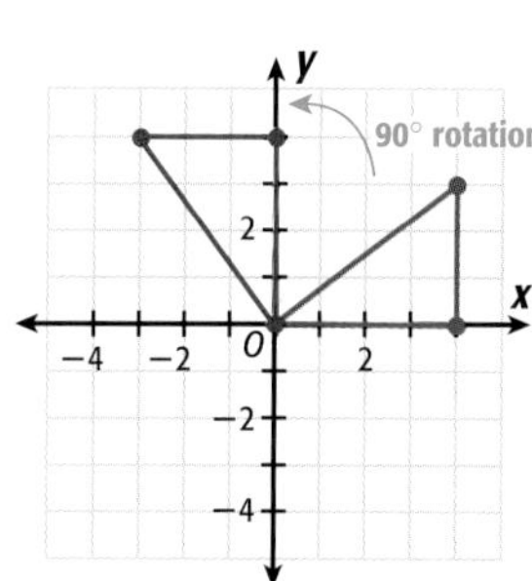

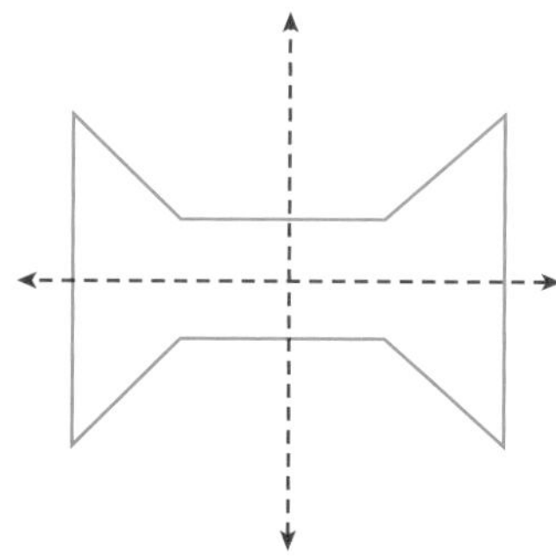

A figure has **line symmetry** if it can be folded so that its halves coincide. This figure has both vertical and horizontal line symmetry.

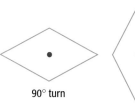

Center of rotation

90° turn

180° turn

A figure has **rotational symmetry** if it can be rotated a specific measure less than 360° and still look like the original figure. This figure has rotational symmetry with a 180° rotation.

7-9 Organizer

Pacing: Traditional 1 day
Block $\frac{1}{2}$ day

Objective: Students identify congruent figures and use congruence to solve problems.

Warm Up

Find the measure of the third angle in the triangle, given two angle measures.

1. 58°, 104° **18°** **2.** 32°, 63° **85°**
3. 90°, 38° **52°** **4.** 42°, 88° **50°**

Problem of the Day

Draw triangles *ABC* and *DEF* so that
a. *AB* = *DE* and *BC* = *EF*.
b. angle *A* is congruent to angle *D*.
c. the triangles are not congruent.

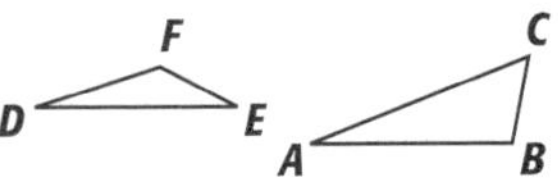

Available on Daily Transparency in CRB

Math Fact !

The word *congruent* comes from the Latin *congruere,* which means "to coincide."

7-9 Congruent Figures

Learn to identify congruent figures and to use congruence to solve problems.

Vocabulary
Side-Side-Side Rule

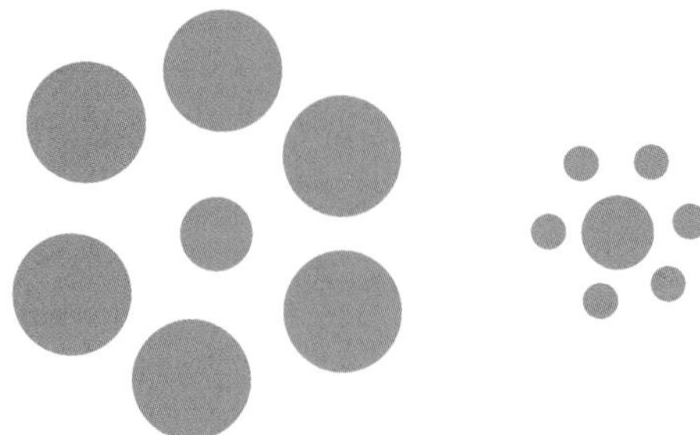

Look at the two patterns. Which center circle do you think is bigger? In spite of appearances, the two center circles are congruent. Their apparent differences are optical illusions. One way to determine whether figures are congruent is to see if one figure will fit exactly over the other one.

EXAMPLE 1 Identifying Congruent Figures in the Real World

Identify any congruent figures.

A

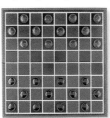

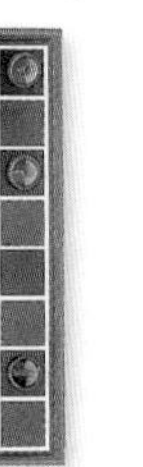

The squares on a checkerboard are congruent. The checkers are also congruent.

B

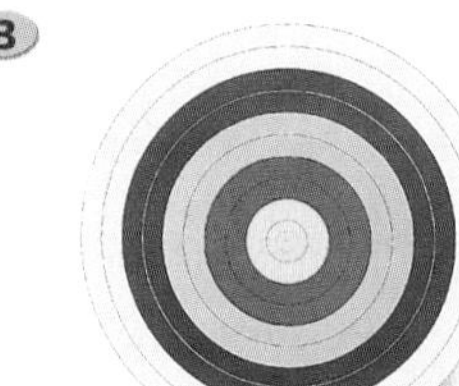

The rings on a target are not congruent. Each ring is larger than the one inside of it.

If all of the corresponding sides and angles of two polygons are congruent, then the polygons are congruent. For triangles in particular, the corresponding angles will always be congruent if the corresponding sides are congruent. This is called the **Side-Side-Side Rule**. Because of this rule, when determining whether triangles are congruent, you only need to determine whether the sides are congruent.

1 Introduce

Alternate Opener

7-9 Congruent Figures

Congruent figures are exactly the same shape and size.

Tell whether the figures are congruent.

1.

2.

3.

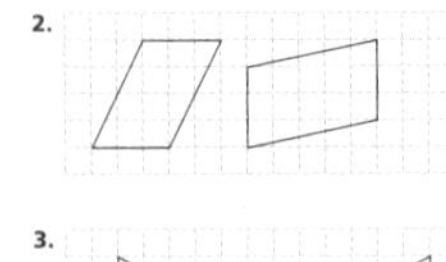

Think and Discuss

4. Explain how you know whether two figures are congruent.

Motivate

To introduce congruent figures, ask students to identify shapes in the classroom that are alike. Then talk about which of these shapes are exactly the same size and shape.

You may want to mention that when one figure is congruent to another, you can move one figure over the other and they will be identical. Some examples are identical textbooks and sheets of paper.

Exploration worksheet and answers on Chapter 7 Resource Book pp. 82 and 138

2 Teach

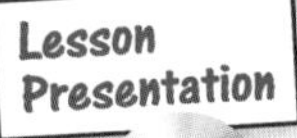

Guided Instruction

In this lesson, students learn to identify congruent figures and to use congruence to solve problems. The optical illusion at the top of the page (Teaching Transparency T34 in the Chapter 7 Resource Book) shows that it is not always possible to determine whether figures are congruent without measuring. Point out that figures do not have to have the same orientation to be congruent.

Point out that for circles, the determining factor for congruence is that they have congruent diameters.

EXAMPLE 2 Identifying Congruent Triangles

Determine whether the triangles are congruent.

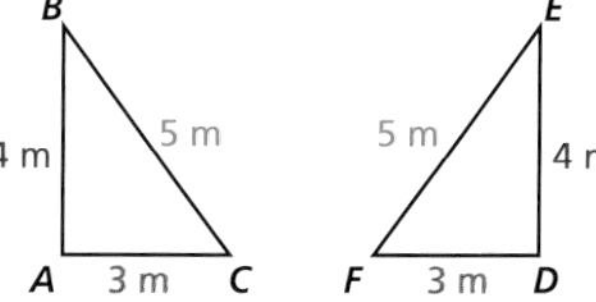

$AC = 3$ m $DF = 3$ m
$AB = 4$ m $DE = 4$ m
$BC = 5$ m $EF = 5$ m

By the Side-Side-Side Rule, $\triangle ABC$ is congruent to $\triangle DEF$, or $\triangle ABC \cong \triangle DEF$. If you flip one triangle, it will fit exactly over the other.

Reading Math

The notation $\triangle ABC$ is read "triangle *ABC*."

For polygons with more than three sides, it is not enough to compare the measures of their sides. For example, the corresponding sides of the figures below are congruent, but the figures are not congruent.

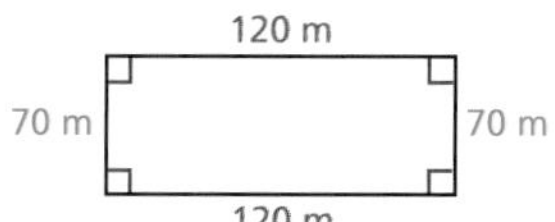

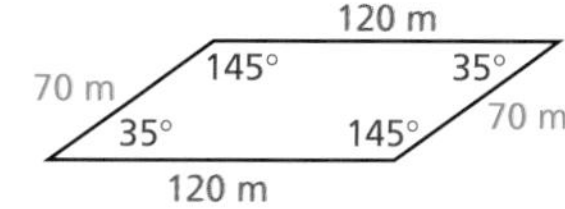

If you know that two figures are congruent, you can find missing measures in the figures.

EXAMPLE 3 Using Congruence to Find Missing Measures

Determine the missing measure in each set of congruent polygons.

A

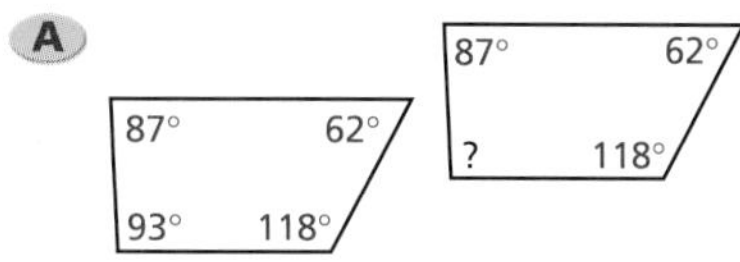

The corresponding angles of congruent polygons are congruent.

The missing angle measure is 93°.

B

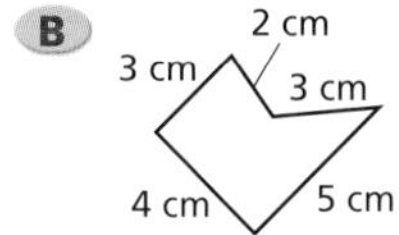

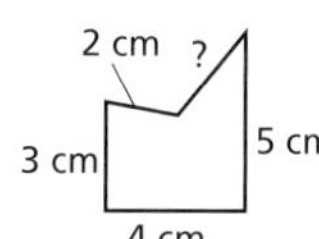

The corresponding sides of congruent polygons are congruent.

The missing side measure is 3 cm.

Think and Discuss

1. **Draw** an illustration to explain whether an isosceles triangle can be congruent to a right triangle.
2. **Explain** whether an isosceles triangle can be congruent to a scalene triangle.

Additional Examples

Example 1

Identify any congruent figures.

None; the sides of the octagons are not congruent.

Example 2

Determine whether the triangles are congruent.

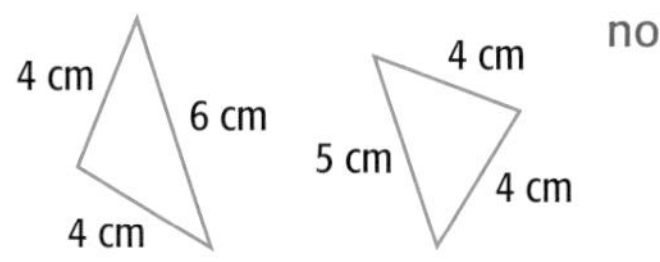

no

Example 3

Determine the missing measure in the congruent polygons.

28 mm

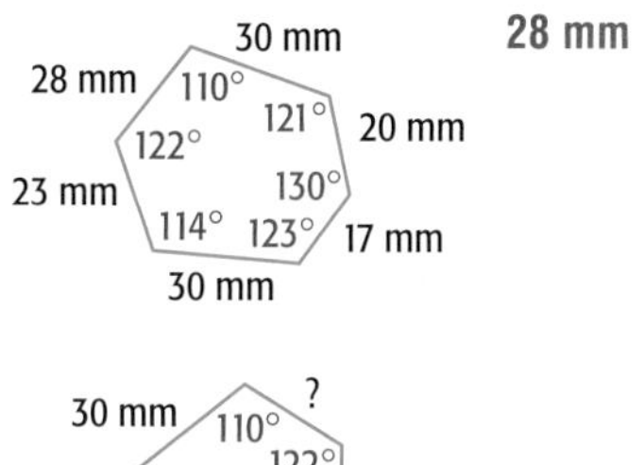

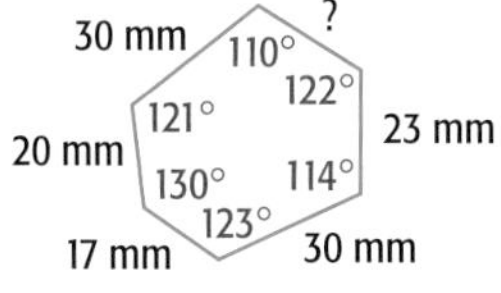

3 Close

Reaching All Learners

Through Home Connection

Ask students to work with family members to find as many examples of congruent figures in their homes as they can. Have each student make a list of the congruent figures found and report his or her findings to the class.

Students might find, for example, congruent knives, plates, windows, doors, cereal box fronts and backs, or rectangles forming drawer or cabinet fronts.

Summarize

Have students describe in their own words what it means for two circles to be congruent and for two polygons to be congruent.

Possible answers: Two circles are congruent if their diameters are congruent, and two polygons are congruent if they are the same size and shape.

Answers to Think and Discuss

1. Possible answer: yes, if the sides and angles of the isosceles triangle are congruent to the sides and angles of the right triangle

2. Isosceles triangles must have two congruent sides, but scalene triangles do not have any congruent sides.

7-9 PRACTICE & ASSESS

Students may want to refer back to the lesson examples.

Assignment Guide

If you finished Example 1 assign:
Core 1–3, 8–10, 15, 17, 25–32
Enriched 1, 3, 7, 9, 15–18, 25–32

If you finished Example 2 assign:
Core 1–5, 8–12, 15, 17, 19, 25–32
Enriched 1–5 odd, 9, 11, 15–19, 21, 22, 25–32

If you finished Example 3 assign:
Core 1–14, 15–21 odd, 25–32
Enriched 1–13 odd, 15–32

Answers

1. The triangles on the game board are congruent, and the holes on the game board are also congruent.
2. The triangles in the kite's design are not congruent.
3. The bowling pins are congruent.
8. The gears are not congruent.
9. The triangles in the kite's design are congruent.
10. The pink and blue triangles that make up the kite are congruent.

7-9 Exercises

FOR EXTRA PRACTICE see page 670

internet connect
Homework Help Online
go.hrw.com Keyword: MS4 7-9

GUIDED PRACTICE

See Example 1 Identify any congruent figures.

1. 

2. 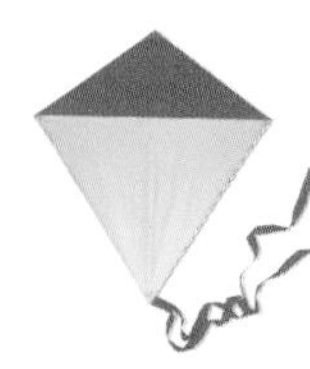

3. 

See Example 2 Determine whether the triangles are congruent.

4. 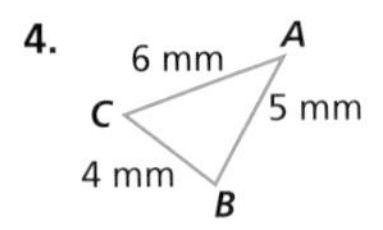

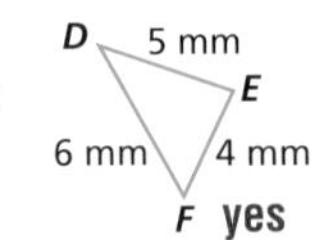

yes

5. 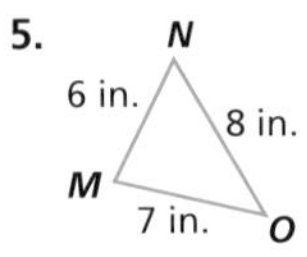

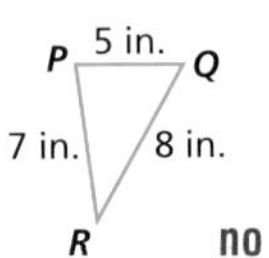

no

See Example 3 Determine the missing measure in each set of congruent polygons.

6. 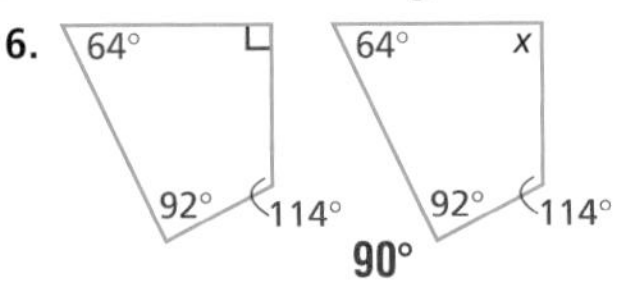

90°

7. 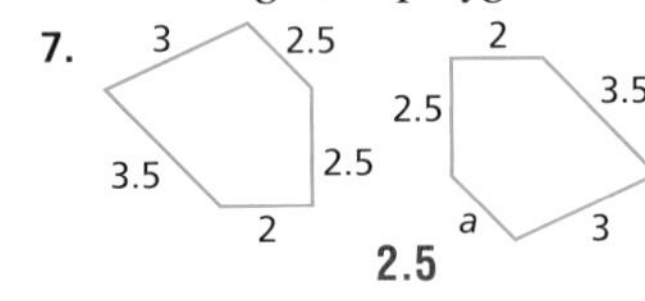

2.5

INDEPENDENT PRACTICE

See Example 1 Identify any congruent figures.

8.

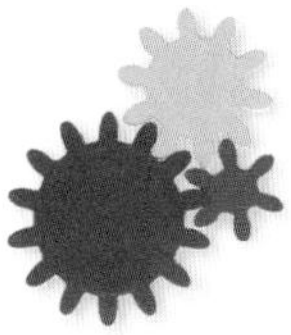

9. 

10. 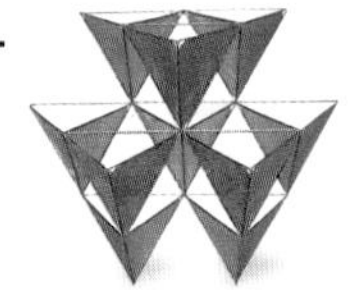

See Example 2 Determine whether the triangles are congruent.

11. 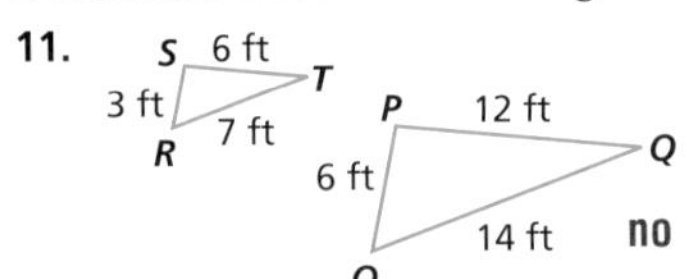

no

12. 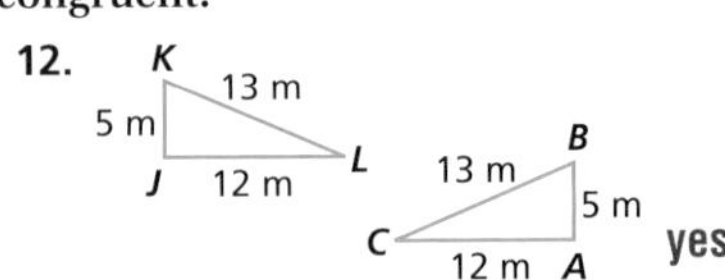

yes

See Example 3 Determine the missing measures in each set of congruent polygons.

13. 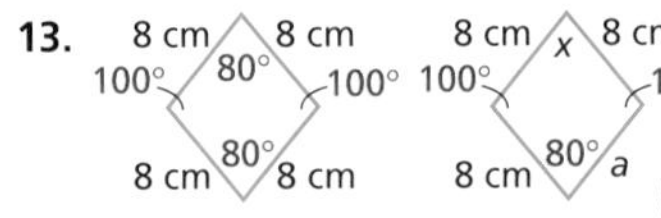

80°; 8 cm

14. 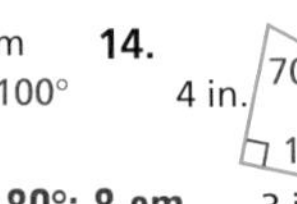

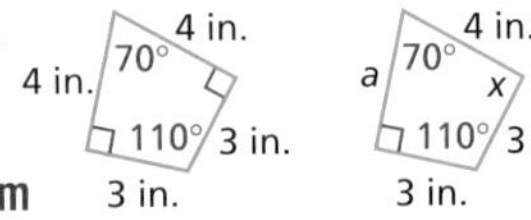

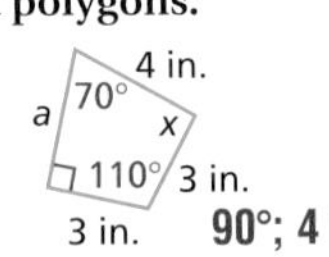

90°; 4 in.

Math Background

There are several ways to prove that two triangles are congruent.

- If three sides of one triangle are congruent to three sides of another triangle, the triangles are congruent.
- If two sides and the included angle of one triangle are congruent to two sides and the included angle of another triangle, the triangles are congruent.
- If two angles and the included side of one triangle are congruent to two angles and the included side of another triangle, the triangles are congruent.

These rules do not translate to other polygons, however.

RETEACH 7-9

LESSON 7-9 **Reteach**
Congruent Figures

When two polygons are congruent, the angles and the sides of one polygon are equivalent to the corresponding angles and sides of the other polygon.

Find the corresponding side or angle. $ABCD \cong EFGH$

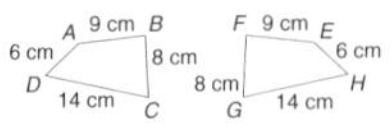

1. $\overline{AB} \cong$ $\overline{EF}$
2. $\angle DAB \cong$ $\angle HEF$
3. $\overline{GH} \cong$ $\overline{CD}$
4. $\angle GFE \cong$ $\angle CBA$

To show that two triangles are congruent, you can show that the three sides of one triangle are congruent to the three sides of the other triangle. This is called the *Side-Side-Side* rule.

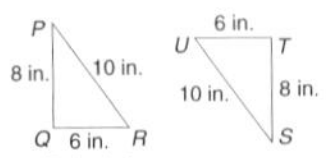

$\overline{PQ} \cong \overline{ST}$ since both are 8 inches.
$\overline{QR} \cong \overline{TU}$ since both are 6 inches.
$\overline{PR} \cong \overline{SU}$ since both are 10 inches.
So, $\triangle PQR \cong \triangle STU$.

If you know that two figures are congruent, you can find missing measures in the figures.

- The corresponding angles are in the same position.
- The corresponding sides are in the same position.

Complete.

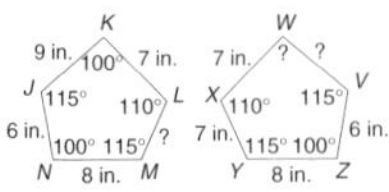

5. $JKLMN \cong VWXYZ$
$\angle K \cong \angle W$, so the measure of $\angle W$ is 100°.

6. $JKLMN \cong VWXYZ$
$\overline{LM} \cong \overline{XY}$, so the length of $\overline{LM}$ is 7 in.

7. What is the length of $\overline{VW}$? 9 in.

PRACTICE 7-9

LESSON 7-9 **Practice B**
Congruent Figures

Determine whether the figures in each set are congruent.

1. 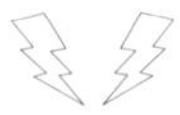 yes
2.  yes
3. 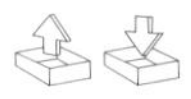 no

Are the triangles congruent?

4. 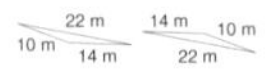 yes
5. 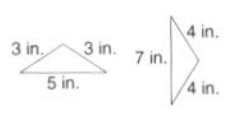 no
6. 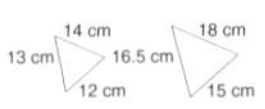 no
7. 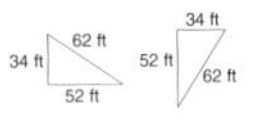 yes

Determine the missing measure or measures in each set of congruent polygons.

8. 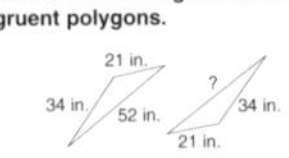 52 in.
9. 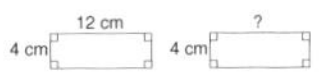 12 cm
10. 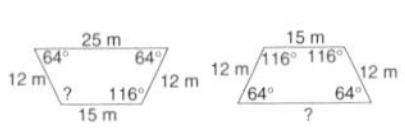 116°; 25 m
11. 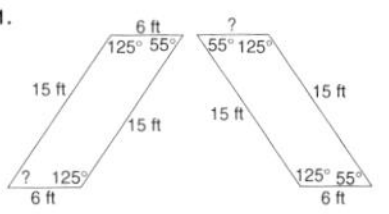 55°; 6 ft

PRACTICE AND PROBLEM SOLVING

Tell the minimum amount of information needed to determine whether the figures are congruent.

15. two triangles **16.** two squares **17.** two rectangles **18.** two pentagons

19. The diagonals of rectangle $ABCD$ bisect each other at point E. Explain why $\triangle CED \cong \triangle AEB$.

20. ***SURVEYING*** In the figure, trees A and B are on opposite sides of the stream. Jamil wants to string a rope from one tree to the other. If triangles ABC and DEC are congruent, what is the distance between the trees? **40 m**

21. ***HOBBIES*** In the quilt block, which figures appear congruent?

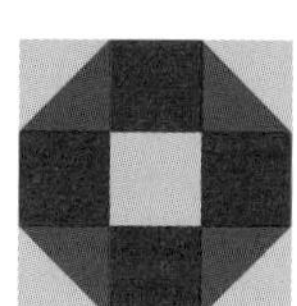

The squares appear to be congruent and the triangles appear to be congruent.

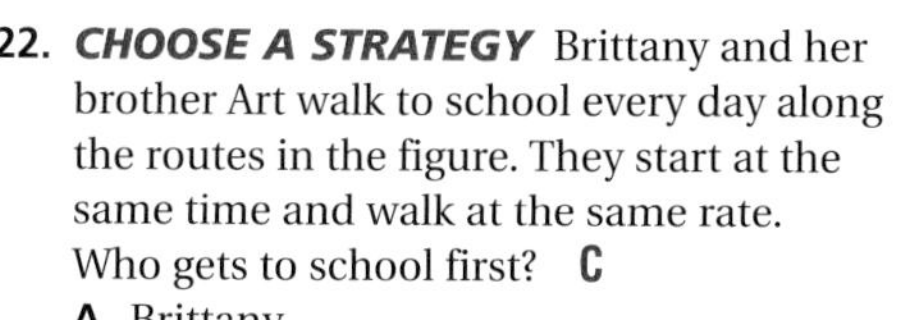

22. ***CHOOSE A STRATEGY*** Brittany and her brother Art walk to school every day along the routes in the figure. They start at the same time and walk at the same rate. Who gets to school first? **C**

A Brittany

B Art

C They arrive at the same time.

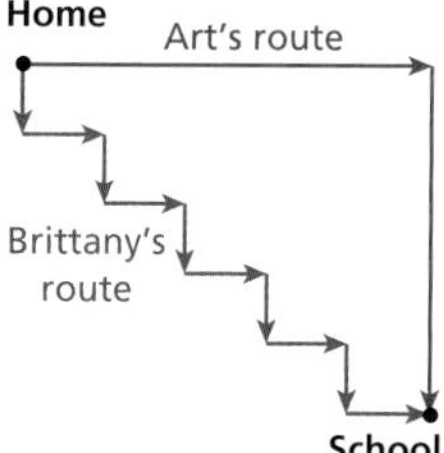

23. ***WRITE ABOUT IT*** Explain how you can determine whether two triangles are congruent.

24. ***CHALLENGE*** If all of the angles in two triangles have the same measure, are the triangles necessarily congruent?

No. The three sides in each triangle are congruent, but the sides in one triangle can be of different length than those in the other triangle.

Spiral Review

Round each decimal to the nearest tenth. (Lesson 4-1)

25. 8.032 **8.0** **26.** 0.985 **1.0** **27.** 1.246 **1.2** **28.** 18.872 **18.9**

Find each value. (Lesson 6-4)

29. 28 is what percent of 40? **70%** **30.** 30% of what number is 12? **40** **31.** 8% of what number is 4? **50**

32. TEST PREP An angle that measures 148° is what kind of angle? (Lesson 7-2) **A**

A Obtuse **B** Right **C** Congruent **D** Acute

CHALLENGE 7-9

LESSON 7-9 **Challenge**
Congruent Presidents?

Find the figures in each row that appear to be congruent. Write their letters on the line next to the figures. Unscramble the letters to name the president.

1. K L A N T E — **KNE**
2. E D O N A Y — **EN, DY**
3. This president had a pony named Macaroni. **Kennedy**
4. B R A R T E O H — **RR, AH**
5. A N C O I E S T — **NO, IS**
6. This president had a goat named Old Whiskers who used to pull the president's grandchildren in a cart. **Harrison**
7. O A L O E C N R — **OO, CL**
8. O E P I L G A D — **ED, IG**
9. This president walked his raccoon named Rebecca on a leash at the White House. **Coolidge**

PROBLEM SOLVING 7-9

LESSON 7-9 **Problem Solving**
Congruent Figures

Write the correct answer.

The table shows the dimensions of regulation NBA and NCAA basketball courts, which are rectangular in shape.

Basketball Court and Lane Sizes

	NBA	NCAA
Court	94 ft by 50 ft	94 ft by 50 ft
Lane	16 ft by 19 ft	12 ft by 19 ft

1. Is an NBA court congruent to an NCAA court? Why or why not?
Yes, they are both rectangles and both 94 ft by 50 ft.

2. If the lane on an NBA court is the same shape as the lane on an NCAA court, are they congruent? Explain.
No, they are not the same size.

3. The lane on a WNBA court is 12 feet by 19 feet. If the lane is the same shape as that of the NBA lane, are they congruent? Why or why not?
No, they are not the same size.

Choose the letter for the best answer.

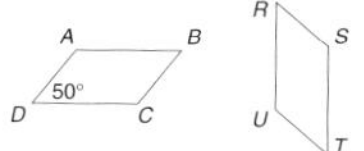

4. The parallelograms above are congruent. What is the measure of $\angle U$?
A 50° (B) 130° C 100° D 260°

5. The Mexican flag is a rectangle divided into three vertical stripes of identical measures. Which of the following statements is true about the Mexican flag?
(F) It has 3 congruent rectangles.
G It has 3 rectangles that are not congruent.
H It has 4 congruent rectangles.
J It has 4 rectangles and none are congruent.

6. In $\triangle ABC$, $m\angle A = m\angle B$, and $m\angle C = 100°$. What are the measures of the angles in $\triangle DEF$ if it is congruent to $\triangle ABC$?
A 60°, 60°, 100° C 30°, 60°, 100°
B 20°, 60°, 100° (D) 40°, 40°, 100°

7. $\triangle JKL$ is congruent to $\triangle RST$. $\angle L$ and $\angle T$ are right angles. Which statement about the two triangles is *not* true?
F $m\angle K = m\angle S$
G $\overline{JK} \cong \overline{RS}$
(H) $m\angle J = m\angle L$
J $m\angle R + m\angle S = 90°$

Answers

15. the lengths of all the sides

16. the length of one side in each square

17. the length of adjacent sides in each rectangle

18. the length of each side and the measure of each angle in each pentagon

19. Sides $\overline{AE}$ and $\overline{CE}$ are congruent, $\overline{EB}$ and $\overline{ED}$ are congruent, and $\overline{AB}$ and $\overline{CD}$ are congruent. So the triangles are congruent.

23. Compare the measures of the three sides. If corresponding sides are congruent, the triangles are congruent.

Journal

Have students draw examples of congruent figures and explain why they are congruent.

Test Prep Doctor

For Exercise 32, students can eliminate **B** and **D** because 148° > 90°. Students can eliminate **C** because it is not a type of angle. Students might also find it helpful to remember that *acute* means "pointed" or "sharp," which describes an angle less than 90°.

Lesson Quiz

1. Are the triangles congruent? **no**

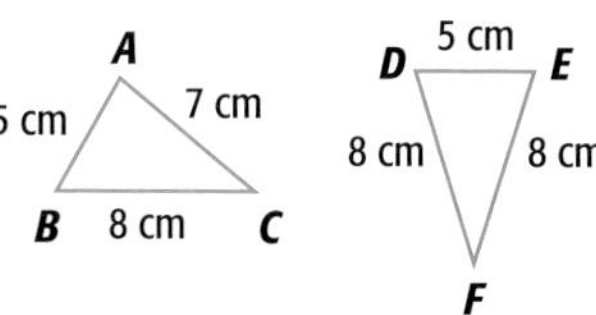

2. Determine the missing measures for the set of congruent polygons.

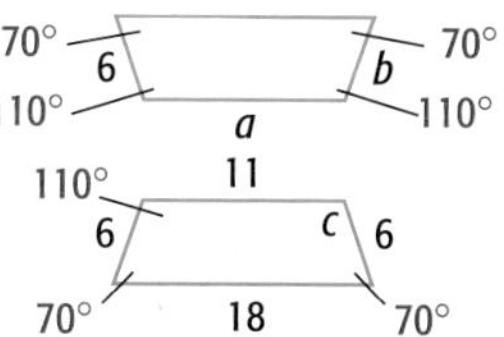

$a = 11$, $b = 6$, $c = 110°$

Available on Daily Transparency in CRB

7-10 Organizer

Pacing: Traditional 1 day
Block $\frac{1}{2}$ day

Objective: Students recognize, describe, and show transformations.

Warm Up

1. Subtract 3 from the *x*-coordinate and 2 from the *y*-coordinate in (7, −4). **(4, −6)**
2. Multiply each coordinate by 3 in (4, 9). **(12, 27)**
3. Subtract 4 from the *x*-coordinate and add 3 to the *y*-coordinate in (−2, −1). **(−6, 2)**

Problem of the Day

Some numbers appear as different numbers when rotated or reflected. Name as many as you can.

Possible answers: 6 and 9; 6999 and 6669; IV and VI; IX and XI

Available on Daily Transparency in CRB

Math Humor

What did the triangle say when it looked in the mirror? Wow, what a transformation!

7-10 Transformations

Learn to recognize, describe, and show transformations.

Vocabulary
transformation
image
translation
rotation
reflection
line of reflection

In the photograph, Kristi Yamaguchi is performing a *layback spin*. She is holding her body in one position while she rotates. This is an example of a *transformation*.

In mathematics, a **transformation** changes the position or orientation of a figure. The resulting figure is the **image** of the original. Images resulting from the transformations described below are congruent to the original figures.

Types of Transformations

Translation
The figure slides along a straight line without turning.

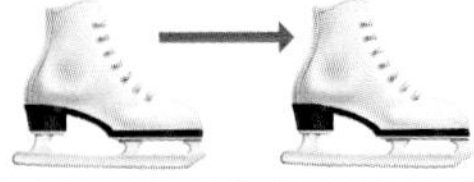

Rotation
The figure turns around a fixed point.

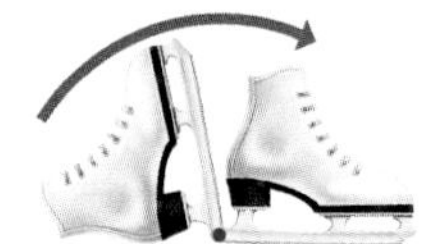

Reflection
The figure flips across a **line of reflection**, creating a mirror image.

EXAMPLE 1 Identifying Types of Transformations

Identify each type of transformation.

Helpful Hint
The point that a figure rotates around may be on the figure or away from the figure.

A

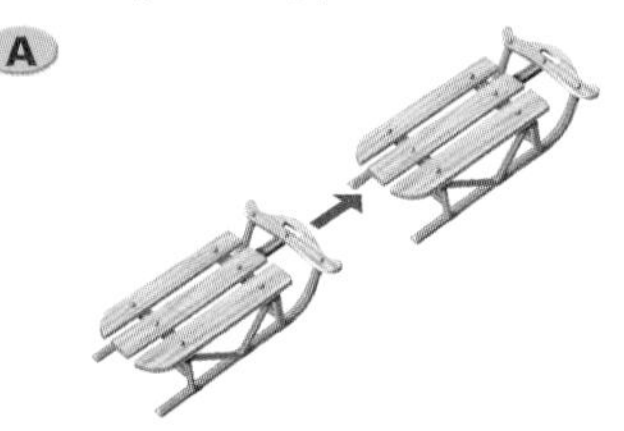

Translation

B

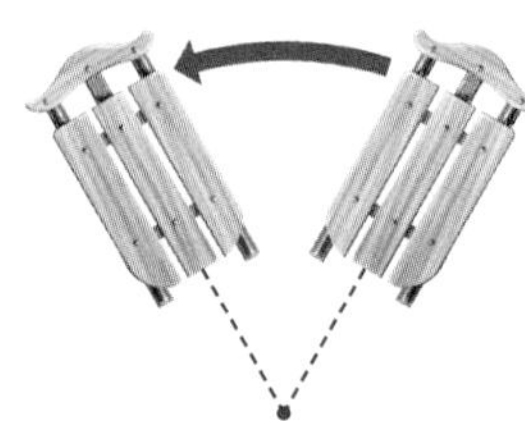

Rotation

1 Introduce

Alternate Opener

EXPLORATION

7-10 Transformations

You can transform figures by *translating* (sliding), *rotating* (turning), or *reflecting* (flipping) them.

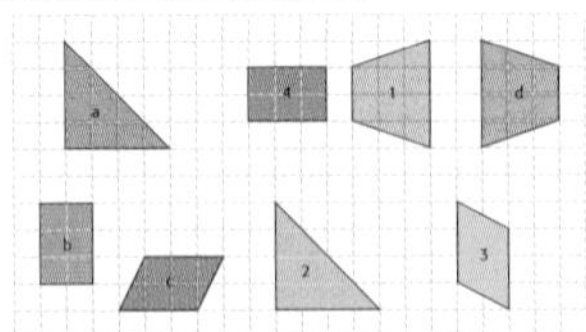

1. The figures with letters are transformations of the figures with numbers.
   a. Match the congruent figures (same shape and size).
   b. Which pairs of figures represent translations?
   c. Which pairs of figures represent rotations?
   d. Which pairs of figures represent reflections?

Think and Discuss

2. **Describe** a real-world example of a translation.
3. **Describe** a real-world example of a rotation.

Motivate

To introduce students to transformations, ask them to describe the movements of pieces in checkers, chess, or a similar game. After students describe the moves, have them explain how the moves affect the sizes and shapes of the pieces. Point out that the pieces do not change despite the moves in the game.

You may want to have students describe other ways to move shapes without changing their sizes or shapes, such as flipping them over or rotating them.

Exploration worksheet and answers on Chapter 7 Resource Book pp. 91 and 140

2 Teach

Lesson Presentation

Guided Instruction

In this lesson, students learn to recognize, describe, and show transformations. To help students understand the different types of transformations, continue to relate each type to real-world situations, such as sliding down a slide, looking in a mirror, and turning around. You may want to use Teaching Transparency T38 in the Chapter 7 Resource Book.

EXAMPLE 2 Graphing Transformations on a Coordinate Plane

Graph each transformation.

Reading Math

A' is read "A prime" and is used to represent the point on the image that corresponds to point *A* of the original figure.

A Translate $\triangle ABC$ 6 units right and 4 units down.

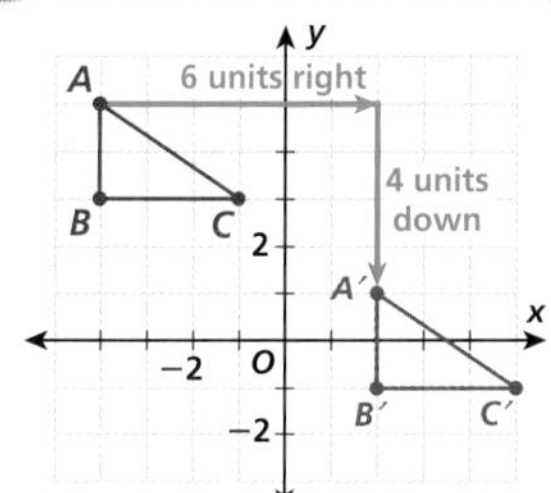

Each vertex is moved 6 units right and 4 units down.

B Rotate $\triangle JKL$ 90° counterclockwise around the vertex *J*.

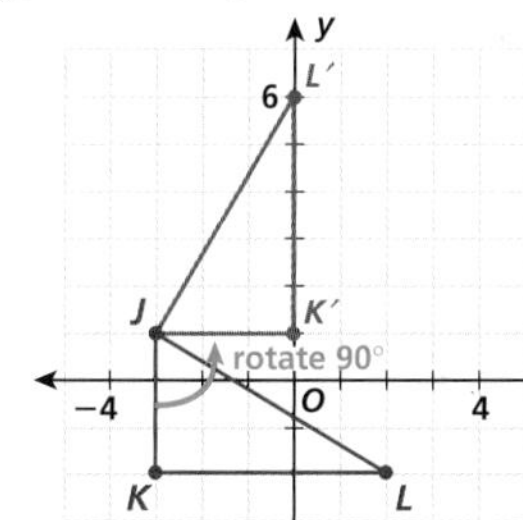

The corresponding sides, $\overline{JK}$ and $\overline{JK'}$, make a 90° angle.

Notice that vertex K is 3 units below vertex J, and vertex K' is 3 units to the right of vertex J.

C Reflect the figure across the *y*-axis.

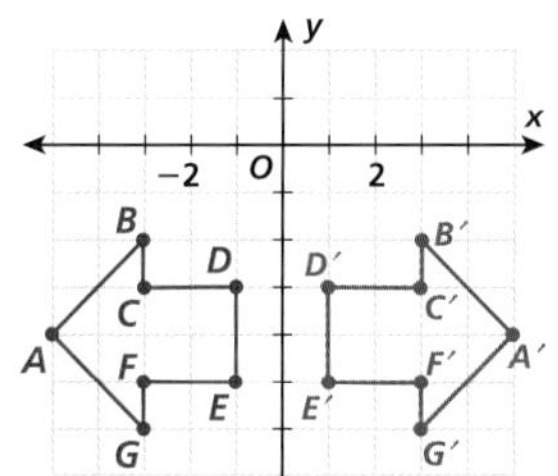

The y-coordinates of the corresponding vertices are the same, and the x-coordinates of the corresponding vertices are opposites.

Think and Discuss

1. **Describe** a classroom situation that illustrates a translation.
2. **Explain** how a figure skater might perform a translation and a rotation at the same time.
3. **Draw** a rectangle, and place a dot in one corner. Show the rectangle after a translation, a reflection, and a rotation.

Additional Examples

Example 1

Identify each type of transformation.

A. 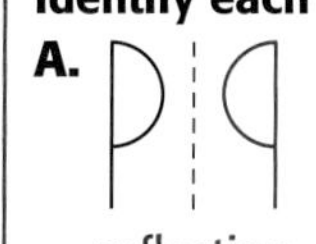 **B.** 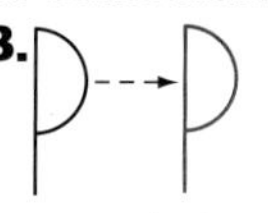

reflection translation

Example 2

Graph each transformation.

A. Translate quadrilateral *ABCD* 4 units left and 2 down.

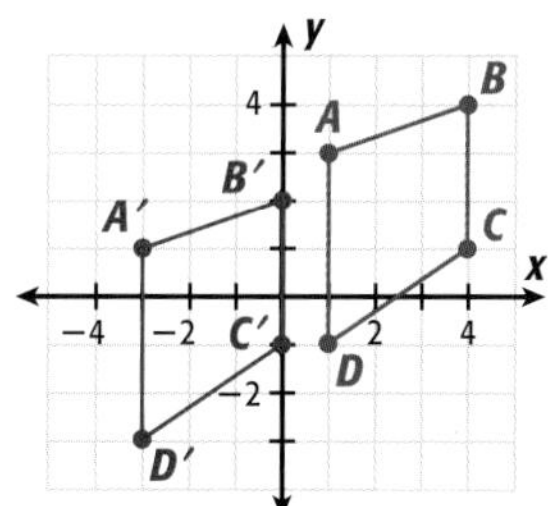

B. Rotate $\triangle ABC$ 180° around the vertex *A*.

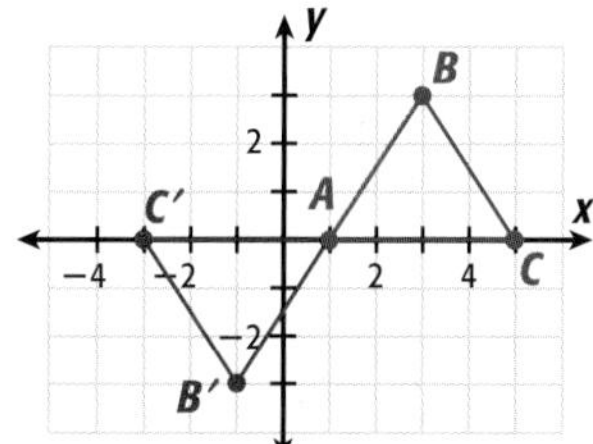

C. Reflect the figure across the *x*-axis.

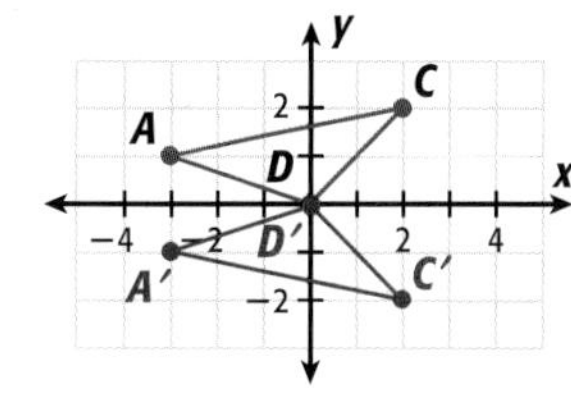

3 Close

Reaching All Learners

Through Hands-On Experience

Use cutout figures (provided on Chapter 7 Resource Book p. 119) to illustrate types of transformations from the examples in the lesson. This will help emphasize that the sizes and shapes of the figures do not change under the transformations in this lesson. For Example 2B, rotate the cutout figures on the coordinate plane (Transparency of Coordinate plane T39 in the Chapter 7 Resource Book).

Summarize

Ask students to describe each of the transformations introduced in this lesson and explain how to do each one.

Possible answers: A translation is a slide along a straight line with no turns. A rotation is a turn around a fixed point, and a reflection is a flip across a line of reflection.

Answers to Think and Discuss

Possible answers:

1. sliding a desk, without turning it, from one row to another
2. if the skater outlines on the ice the shape of a lowercase *d*
3. 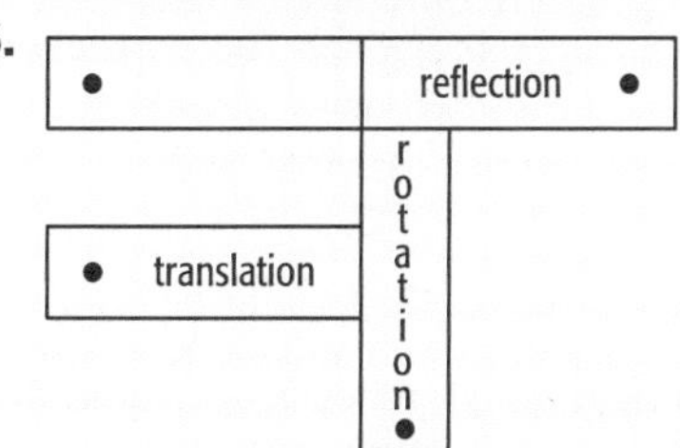

7-10 PRACTICE & ASSESS

Students may want to refer back to the lesson examples.

Assignment Guide

If you finished Example 1 assign:
Core 1, 2, 6, 7, 14–19
Enriched 1, 2, 6, 7, 14–19

If you finished Example 2 assign:
Core 1–11, 14–19
Enriched 1, 3–5, 7–19

Answers

3–5, 8–10. See pp. A2–A3.

7-10 Exercises

FOR EXTRA PRACTICE see page 670

internet connect
Homework Help Online
go.hrw.com Keyword: MS4 7-10

GUIDED PRACTICE

See Example 1 Identify each type of transformation.

1. reflection

2. 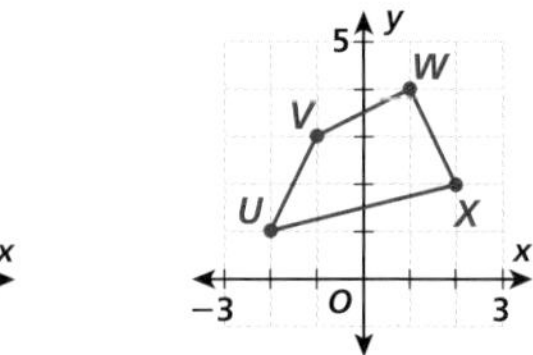
translation

See Example 2 Graph each transformation.

3. Translate $\triangle ABC$ 2 units left and 3 units up.

4. Rotate $\triangle LMN$ 180° around the vertex L.

5. Reflect the figure across the x-axis.

INDEPENDENT PRACTICE

See Example 1 Identify each type of transformation.

6. reflection

7. rotation

See Example 2 Graph each transformation.

8. Rotate $\triangle MNL$ 90° counterclockwise around the vertex L.

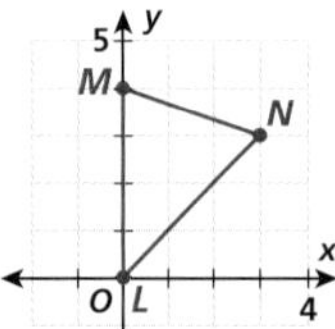

9. Translate $\triangle XYZ$ 5 units right and 1 unit down.

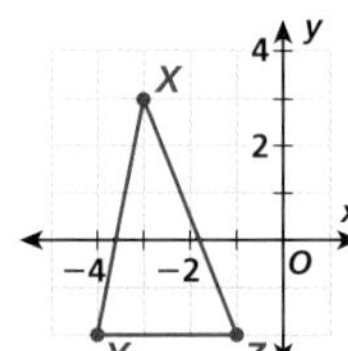

10. Reflect the figure across the y-axis.

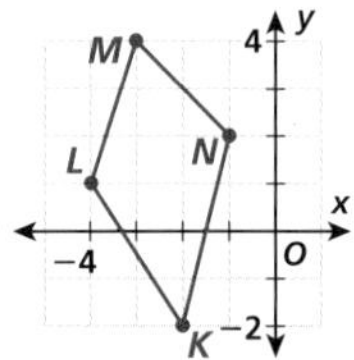

Math Background

Transformations in a plane affect the points being transformed in a consistent manner. For example, a translation described by the rule "move 3 units right and 4 units down" can be described by the rule $(x, y) \rightarrow (x + 3, y - 4)$, so that (5, 6) translates to (8, 2). In general, in a translation, $(x, y) \rightarrow (x + a, y + b)$. The translation can also be shown using a sum of matrices. For the example given,

$$\begin{bmatrix}5\\6\end{bmatrix} + \begin{bmatrix}3\\-4\end{bmatrix} = \begin{bmatrix}8\\2\end{bmatrix}.$$

For a point (x, y), reflecting it across the y-axis gives $(-x, y)$. Reflecting it across the x-axis gives $(x, -y)$. Reflecting it across the line $y = x$ gives (y, x).

RETEACH 7-10

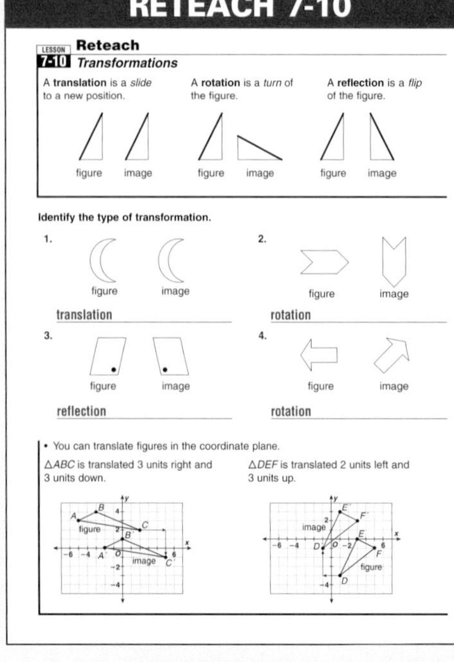

LESSON 7-10 Reteach
Transformations

A **translation** is a *slide* to a new position. A **rotation** is a *turn* of the figure. A **reflection** is a *flip* of the figure.

figure image figure image figure image

Identify the type of transformation.

1. figure image — translation
2. figure image — rotation
3. figure image — reflection
4. figure image — rotation

• You can translate figures in the coordinate plane.

$\triangle ABC$ is translated 3 units right and 3 units down.

$\triangle DEF$ is translated 2 units left and 3 units up.

PRACTICE 7-10

LESSON 7-10 Practice B
Transformations

Identify the type of transformation.

1. original image — translation
2. original image — rotation
3. original image — reflection
4. original image — translation

Graph each transformation.

5. Rotate $\triangle DEF$ 90° counter clockwise around vertex E.

6. Translate $\triangle TUV$ 5 units to the left and 2 units up.

7. Reflect $\triangle HJK$ across the x-axis.

8. Rotate rectangle $ABCD$ 180° around vertex D.

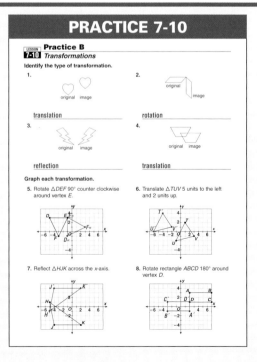

Social Studies 

Native Americans often use transformations in their art. The art pieces in the photos show combinations of transformations. Use the photos for Exercises 11–13.

11. The bowl at right was made by Maria Martinez, a Native American potter from the San Ildefonso pueblo in New Mexico. Are translations, rotations, and reflections all shown in the design? If not, which transformations are not shown?

12. ***WRITE ABOUT IT*** The Navajo blanket in the photo has a design based on a sand painting. The two people in the design are standing next to a stalk of corn, which the Native Americans called *maize*. The red, white, and black stripes represent a rainbow.

a. Tell how the figure shows reflections. Also explain what parts of the design do not show reflections.

b. A *glide reflection* is a combination of a reflection and a translation. Tell where the design shows a glide reflection.

13. ***CHALLENGE*** The bead design in the saddle bag at right shows different types of transformations. What part of the design can be described as three separate transformations? Draw diagrams to illustrate your answer. **Possible answer: The stick figures are a reflection of each other, but they are also a 180° rotation of each other. One is also a translated image of the other.**

Spiral Review

Find the mode of each data set. (Lesson 1-2)

14. 1, 3, 8, 2, 7, 1, 8, 4, 5 **1, 8**

15. 6.2, 3.8, 4.1, 9.5, 6.3, 5.4 **none**

Solve each equation. (Lesson 2-12)

16. $2x = 8$ **$x = 4$**

17. $\frac{y}{2} = 12$ **$y = 24$**

18. $5m = 170$ **$m = 34$**

19. TEST PREP What is the percent of increase from 120 to 300? (Lesson 6-5) **A**

A 150% **B** 40% **C** 250% **D** 60%

Interdisciplinary 

Social Studies

Exercises 11–13 focus on identifying various transformations of figures found in Native American art.

Answers

11. Rotation is shown, but not translation or reflection.

12. a. Possible answer: The two people are the same shape and size, but they are holding different objects, and their skirts are slightly different.

b. A glide reflection can be seen on the cornstalk where the leaves on one side are reflected and translated to the other side of the stalk.

Journal 

Ask students to find a design and describe any rotations, translations, or reflections they see in the design.

Test Prep Doctor 

For Exercise 19, students should use the fact that 300 is more than twice as large as 120 to eliminate **B** and **D.** Observing that an increase of 100% would yield 240 leads to **A,** which can be verified by computation.

CHALLENGE 7-10

LESSON 7-10 Challenge
Follow That Transformation

You alone know the location of the secret treasure. You want to draw a map to direct your friend to the treasure, but you must do so in code. Use transformations to make the code.

First, draw a triangle on the coordinate plane below.

Next, list in order 5 transformations that must be done to the original figure. The treasure is located in the image of the last transformed triangle.

Then exchange your map with another student. Follow the directions and draw a triangle to show the location of the treasure. **Possible answer given.**

1. **reflect across x-axis**
2. **rotate 180° about point (2, −3)**
3. **translate 4 units left and 10 units up**
4. **reflect across y-axis**
5. **translate 7 units left and 6 units down**

PROBLEM SOLVING 7-10

LESSON 7-10 Problem Solving
Transformations

Write the correct answer.

Clock 1

Clock 2

1. If you reflect the hands of clock 1 across a line from 9 to 3, what time will it show? **5:30**
2. If you rotate the hands on clock 2 by 90° clockwise, what time will it be? **6:15**
3. The hands on clock 1 show 7:30 after a transformation. What was the transformation? **180° rotation**
4. The hands on clock 2 show 9:00 after a transformation. What was the transformation? **reflection across a line from 12 to 6**

Choose the letter for the best answer.

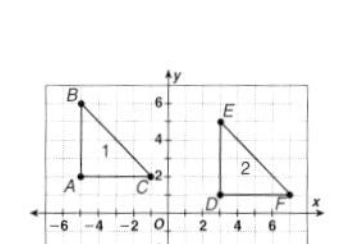

5. What transformation of triangle 1 created triangle 2?
   - A translation 3 units right and 1 unit down
   - **(B)** translation 8 units right and 1 unit down
   - C rotation of 180° about the origin
   - D reflection across the y-axis
6. If you rotate triangle 2 90° clockwise about vertex D, what will be the coordinates of the new triangle?
   - **(F)** $D'(3, 1)$, $E'(7, 1)$, $F'(3, -3)$
   - G $D'(3, 1)$, $E'(3, -3)$, $F'(7, 1)$
   - H $D'(3, 1)$, $E'(-4, 1)$, $F'(-3, 3)$
   - J $D'(3, 1)$, $E'(-3, 3)$, $F'(-7, 1)$
7. If you reflect triangle 1 across the x-axis, what will be the coordinates of the new triangle?
   - A $A'(5, 2)$, $B'(5, 6)$, $C'(1, 2)$
   - B $A'(-5, 0)$, $B'(-5, -4)$, $C'(-1, 0)$
   - C $A'(5, -2)$, $B'(5, -6)$, $C'(1, -2)$
   - **(D)** $A'(-5, -2)$, $B'(-5, -6)$, $C'(-1, -2)$

Lesson Quiz 

1. Identify the type of transformation.

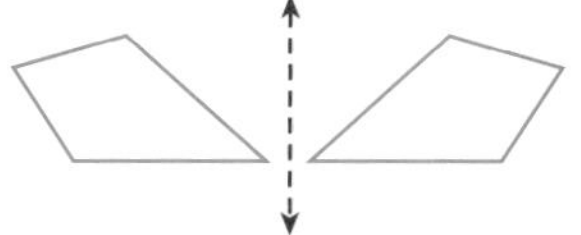

reflection

2. The figure formed by (−5, −6), (−1, −6), and (3, 2) is transformed 6 units right and 2 units up. What are the coordinates of the new figure?

(1, −4), (5, −4), (9, 4)

Available on Daily Transparency in CRB

7-11 Organizer

Pacing: Traditional 1 day
Block $\frac{1}{2}$ day

Objective: Students identify symmetry in figures.

Warm Up

1. Give the coordinates of triangle *ABC* with vertices (7, 2), (1, 2), (4, −5) reflected across the *y*-axis. **(−7, 2), (−1, 2), (−4, −5)**
2. Give the coordinates of triangle *ABC* translated 3 units left and 2 units down. **(4, 0), (−2, 0), (1, −7)**

Problem of the Day

There are some capital letters in our alphabet that have both horizontal and vertical lines of symmetry. Which of the 50 states can you spell using only letters from that group? OHIO

Available on Daily Transparency in CRB

Math Fact !!

Another type of symmetry is point symmetry. Any figure that has 180° rotational symmetry around a point is said to have point symmetry.

7-11 Symmetry

Learn to identify symmetry in figures.

Vocabulary
- line symmetry
- line of symmetry
- asymmetry
- rotational symmetry
- center of rotation

Many architects and artists use symmetry in their buildings and artwork because symmetry is pleasing to the eye.

When you can draw a line through a plane figure so that the two halves are mirror images of each other, the figure has **line symmetry**, or is symmetrical. The line along which the figure is divided is called the **line of symmetry**.

The Taj Mahal in Agra, India is an example of Mughal architecture.

When a figure is not symmetrical, then it has **asymmetry**, or is asymmetrical.

The image of the Taj Mahal is symmetrical. You can draw a line of symmetry down the center of the building. Also, each window in the image has its own line of symmetry.

EXAMPLE 1 Identifying Line Symmetry

Decide whether each figure has line symmetry. If it does, draw all the lines of symmetry.

A

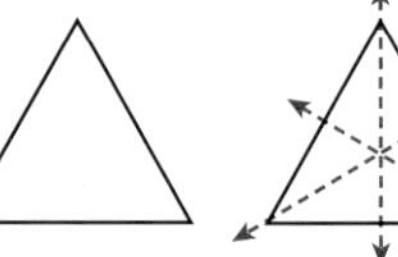

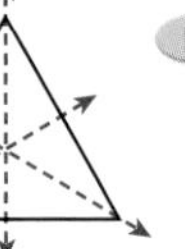

3 lines of symmetry

B

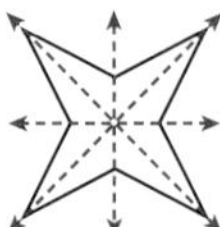

4 lines of symmetry

EXAMPLE 2 *Social Studies Application*

Find all the lines of symmetry in each flag.

A

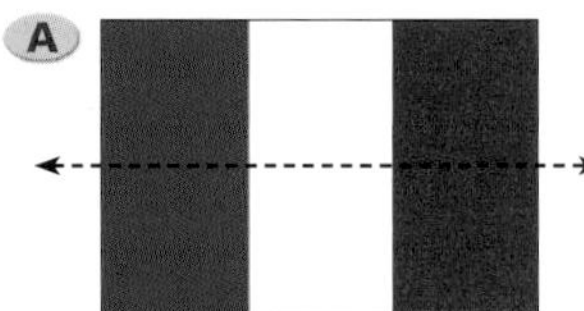

There is 1 line of symmetry.

B

There are no lines of symmetry.

1 Introduce

Alternate Opener

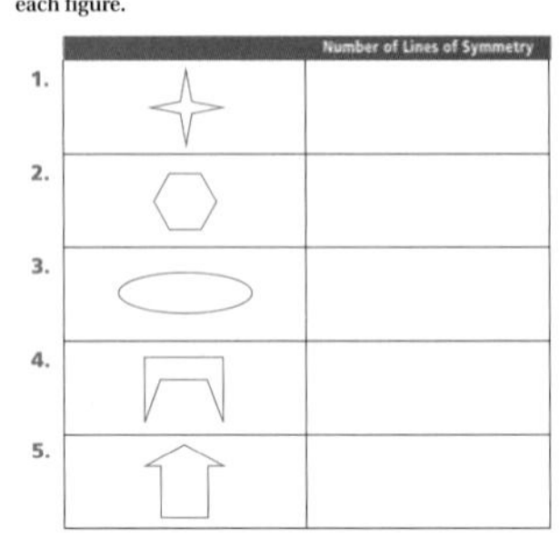

EXPLORATION

7-11 Symmetry

A shape has *line symmetry* if you can draw a line through it to form two congruent shapes that are reflections of each other.

Draw as many lines of symmetry as possible through each figure.

		Number of Lines of Symmetry
1.		
2.		
3.		
4.		
5.		

Think and Discuss

6. Give examples of real-world objects that have line symmetry.

Motivate

To introduce students to symmetry, show them several symmetrical and asymmetrical cutout shapes (provided on Chapter 7 Resource Book p. 120). Ask students to describe how the figures are different from one another. You may wish to have students experiment with folding the cutouts to clarify their thinking.

Once students have described the symmetrical shapes, have them look for other symmetrical shapes in the classroom.

Exploration worksheet and answers on Chapter 7 Resource Book pp. 101 and 142

2 Teach

Lesson Presentation

Guided Instruction

In this lesson, students learn to identify symmetry in figures. Point out that if a figure has line symmetry, it can be folded along the line of symmetry, and the halves will be identical. Also mention that if a figure has one or more lines of symmetry that intersect, it will have rotational symmetry.

Teaching Tip Remind students to double-check that they have found all the possible lines when determining the number of lines of rotational symmetry. It is easy to overlook one or two lines.

A figure has **rotational symmetry** if, when it is rotated less than 360° around a central point, it coincides with itself. The central point is called the **center of rotation**.

If the stained glass window at right is rotated 90°, as shown, the image looks the same as the original stained glass window. Therefore the window has rotational symmetry.

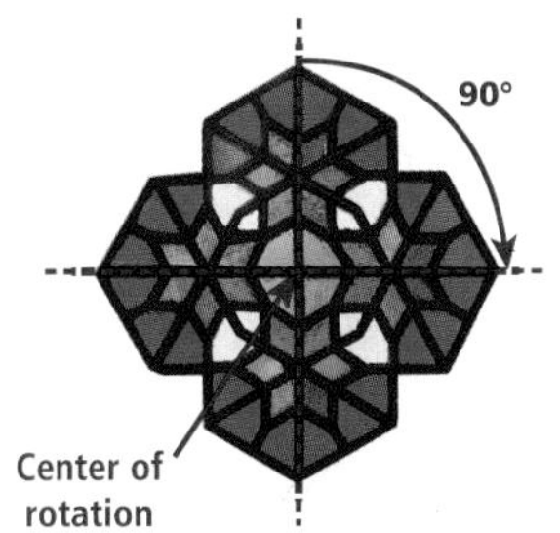

EXAMPLE 3 **Identifying Rotational Symmetry**

Tell how many times each figure will show rotational symmetry within one full rotation.

A

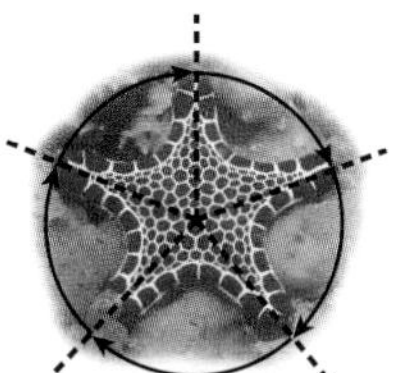

Draw lines from the center of the figure out through identical places in the figure.

The starfish will show rotational symmetry 5 times within a 360° rotation.

Count the number of lines drawn.

B

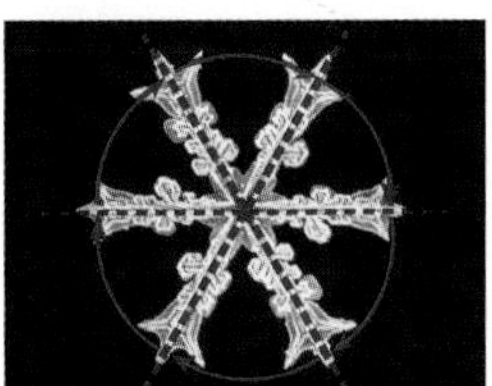

Draw lines from the center of the figure out through identical places in the figure.

The snowflake will show rotational symmetry 6 times within a 360° rotation.

Count the number of lines drawn.

Think and Discuss

1. **Draw** a figure that has no rotational symmetry.
2. **Determine** whether an equilateral triangle has rotational symmetry. If so, tell how many times it shows rotational symmetry within one full rotation.

Additional Examples

Example 1

Decide whether each of the figures has line symmetry. If it does, draw all the lines of symmetry.

A.  **B.** 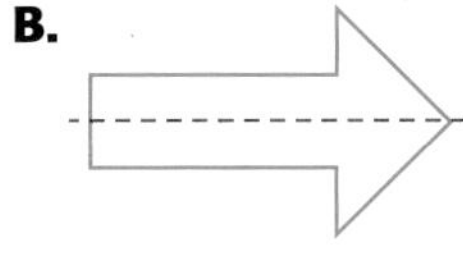

none

Example 2

Find all the lines of symmetry in each figure.

A. 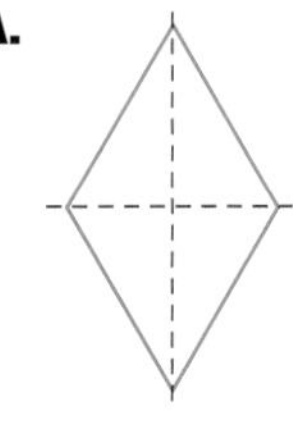 **B.**

none

Example 3

Tell how many times each figure will show rotational symmetry within one full rotation.

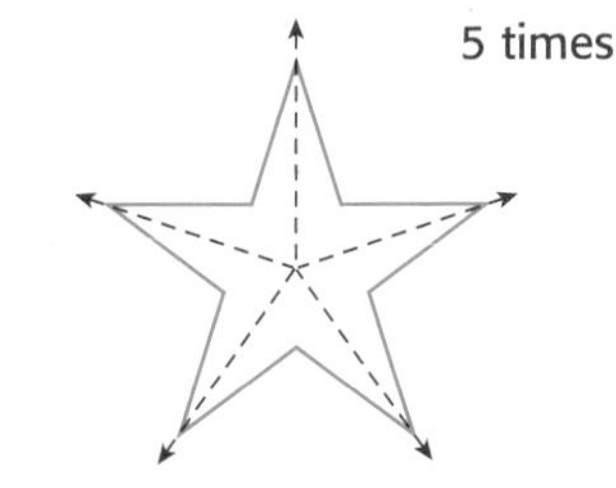

5 times

3 Close

Reaching All Learners

Through Critical Thinking

Provide students with dot paper (Chapter 7 Resource Book p. 115), and have them draw a quadrilateral with the following numbers of lines of symmetry:

- exactly one — isosceles trapezoid or kite
- exactly two — non-square rectangle
- exactly three — not possible
- exactly four — square

Summarize

Have students provide brief descriptions of line and rotational symmetry and then tell how to find the degrees of rotational symmetry.

Possible answers: A figure has line symmetry if two halves are mirror images of each other. The figure has rotational symmetry if, when rotated less than 360° around a central point, it coincides with itself. To find the degree of rotational symmetry, divide 360° by the number of lines in the figure.

Answers to Think and Discuss

1. Possible answer:

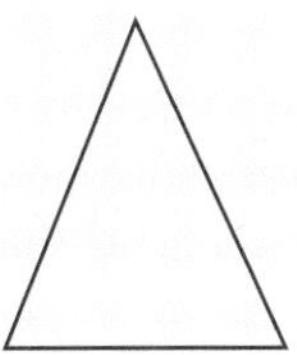

2. Yes, an equilateral triangle has rotational symmetry. It shows rotational symmetry three times within a 360° rotation.

7-11 PRACTICE & ASSESS

Students may want to refer back to the lesson examples.

Assignment Guide

If you finished Example 1 assign:
Core 1–3, 10–12, 27–34
Enriched 1, 3, 11, 19, 21, 27–34

If you finished Example 2 assign:
Core 1–6, 10–15, 19, 27–34
Enriched 1–5 odd, 10–15, 19, 21, 27–34

If you finished Example 3 assign:
Core 1–18, 19–23 odd, 27–34
Enriched 1–17 odd, 19–34

A recording sheet for Exercises 1–6 and 10–15 is available on Chapter 7 Resource Book p. 121.

Notes

Math Background

Any figure coincides with itself if you rotate it 360° around a central point. A figure has rotational symmetry only if it coincides with itself when it is rotated a specific measure less than 360° around a central point. In fact, rotational symmetry must always be through an angle of 180° or less. A figure that has no rotational symmetry between 0° and 180° will not have rotational symmetry between 180° and 360°.

7-11 Exercises

FOR EXTRA PRACTICE
see page 670

internet connect
Homework Help Online
go.hrw.com Keyword: MS4 7-11

GUIDED PRACTICE

See Example 1 Decide whether each figure has line symmetry. If it does, draw all the lines of symmetry.

1. 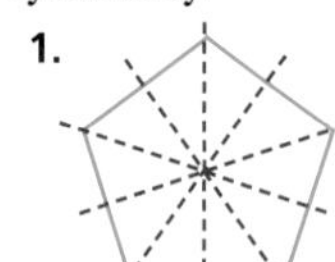
2. 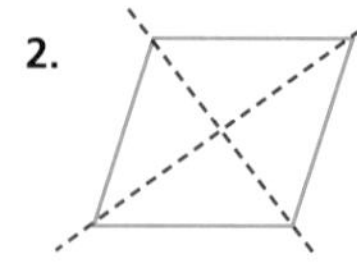
3. 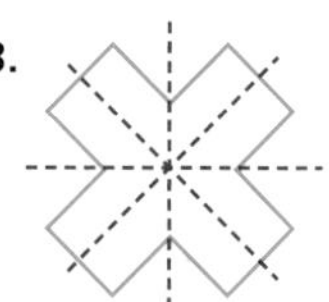

See Example 2 Find all the lines of symmetry in each flag.

4. 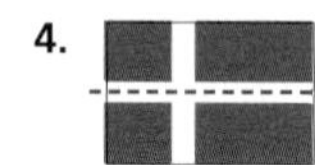
5.  none
6. 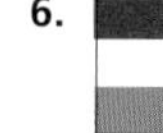

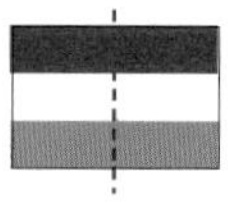

See Example 3 Tell how many times each figure will show rotational symmetry within one full rotation.

7.  6 times
8. 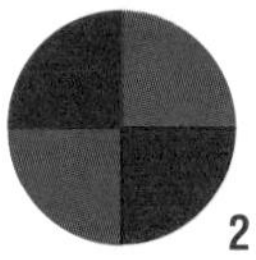 2 times
9. 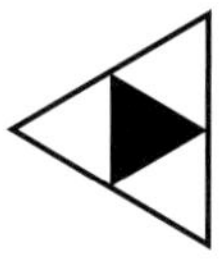 3 times

INDEPENDENT PRACTICE

See Example 1 Decide whether each figure has line symmetry. If it does, draw all the lines of symmetry.

10. 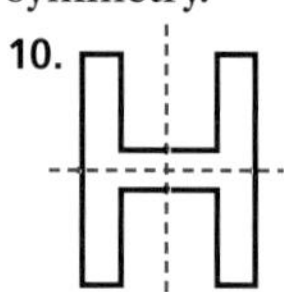
11. 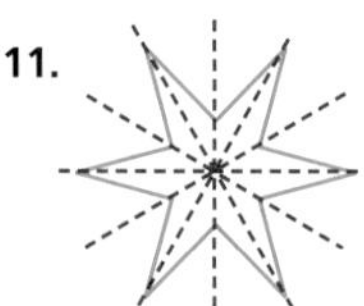
12. 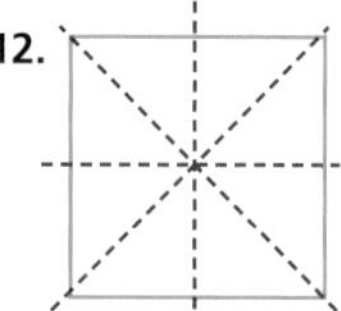

See Example 2 Find all the lines of symmetry in each flag.

13.  none
14. 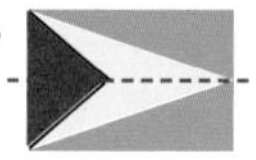
15. 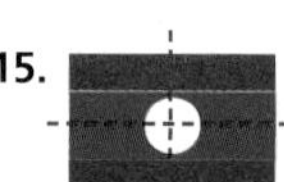

See Example 3 Tell how many times each figure will show rotational symmetry within one full rotation.

16. 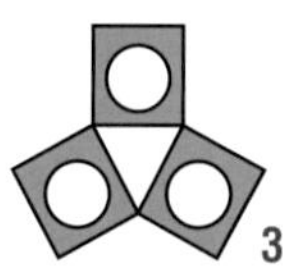 3 times
17.  8 times
18. 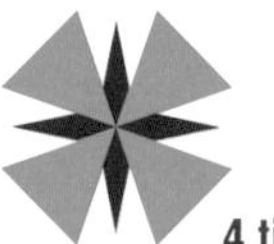 4 times

RETEACH 7-11

LESSON 7-11 **Reteach**
Symmetry

A figure has **line symmetry** if it can be folded along a line so that the two halves match exactly. The fold line of a figure is called a **line of symmetry**. A figure can have more than one line of symmetry.

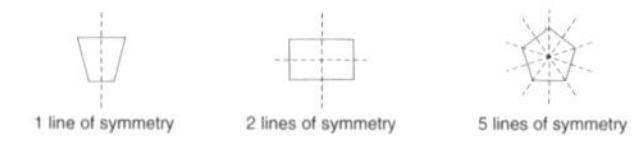

1 line of symmetry 2 lines of symmetry 5 lines of symmetry

Trace each figure and cut it out. Fold the figure on each line of symmetry. Tell how many lines of symmetry each figure has.

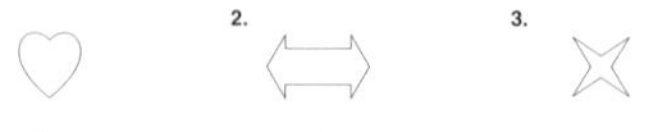

1. 1
2. 2
3. 4

A figure has **rotational symmetry** if it can be turned less than a full turn (360°) and look exactly like the original figure.

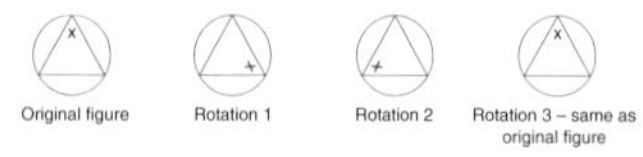

Original figure Rotation 1 Rotation 2 Rotation 3 – same as original figure

Trace each figure. Mark an X at the top of the tracing. Put the tracing on top of the figure and rotate it until it matches. Tell the number of rotations until the X is at the top again. Then find the smallest angle of rotation.

4. 4 rotations
360° ÷ 4 = 90°

5. 6 rotations
360° ÷ 6 = 60°

6. 3 rotations
360° ÷ 3 = 120°

PRACTICE 7-11

LESSON 7-11 **Practice B**
Symmetry

Tell whether each of the following flags has line symmetry.

1. Iceland — yes
2. Nauru — no
3. Burundi — yes

How many times will each figure show rotational symmetry within one full rotation?

4. 2
5. 5
6. 3
7. 4
8. 5
9. 6

Describe the smallest angle of rotational symmetry for each figure.

10. 90°
11. 120°
12. 72°

PRACTICE AND PROBLEM SOLVING

19. Draw a figure with at least two lines of symmetry.

20. Which regular polygon shows rotational symmetry 9 times within one full rotation? **regular nonagan**

21. ***LIFE SCIENCE*** How many lines of symmetry does the image of the moth have? **1 line**

22. Fold a piece of paper in half vertically and then in half horizontally. Cut or tear a design into one of the folded edges. Then unfold the paper. Does the design have a vertical or horizontal line of symmetry? rotational symmetry? Explain your answer.

23. ***ART*** Tell how many times the stained glass image at right shows rotational symmetry in one full rotation if you do one of the following:
    a. consider only the shape of the design and **4 times**
    b. consider both the shape and the colors in the design. **none**

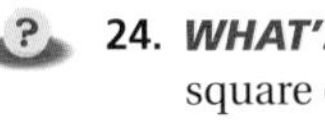

24. ***WHAT'S THE QUESTION?*** Marla drew a square on the chalkboard. As an answer to Marla's question about symmetry, Rob said "90°." What question did Marla ask? **Possible answer: What is the smallest angle of rotational symmetry for the square?**

25. ***WRITE ABOUT IT*** Explain why an angle of rotation must be less than 360° for a figure to have rotational symmetry.

26. ***CHALLENGE*** Print a word in capital letters, using only letters that have horizontal lines of symmetry. Print another word with capital letters that have vertical lines of symmetry. **Possible answers: BED and MOM**

Spiral Review

Find each sum. (Lesson 4-10)

27. $\frac{3}{8}+\frac{3}{8}$ **$\frac{3}{4}$** 28. $\frac{5}{9}+\frac{2}{9}$ **$\frac{7}{9}$** 29. $\frac{7}{10}+\frac{3}{10}$ **1** 30. $\frac{5}{6}+\frac{5}{6}$ **$1\frac{2}{3}$**

Solve each equation. (Lesson 4-12)

31. $\frac{2}{3}x = 12$ **$x = 18$** 32. $y-\frac{3}{4}=\frac{3}{8}$ **$y = 1\frac{1}{8}$** 33. $\frac{5}{9}+m=\frac{2}{3}$ **$m=\frac{1}{9}$**

34. **TEST PREP** What is the annual interest on $8,000 at 4.5% for 6 months? (Lesson 6-6) **D**

A $3,600 **B** $720 **C** $360 **D** $180

Answers

19. Possible answer:

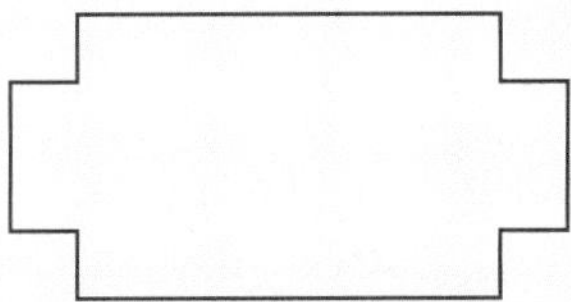

22. yes, because the design was cut along a vertical line; yes, because the same design was cut into both halves

25. In order to have rotational symmetry, a figure must match itself at least once before rotating completely around; otherwise, all figures would have rotational symmetry.

Journal

Ask students to describe what is meant by symmetry and why they think it is so pleasing to the eye.

Test Prep Doctor

For Exercise 34, students can note that 10% a year would give $800, so **A** and **B** are too great. Using estimation, 4.5% a year would be about $400, so students can eliminate **C.**

CHALLENGE 7-11

LESSON 7-11 **Challenge**
Design Your Own Quilt

This quilt will be a collection of individual squares. In each square, draw a different figure that has the given rotational symmetry.

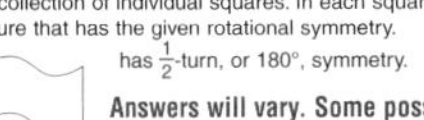

For example, [figure] has $\frac{1}{2}$-turn, or 180°, symmetry.

Answers will vary. Some possible answers given.

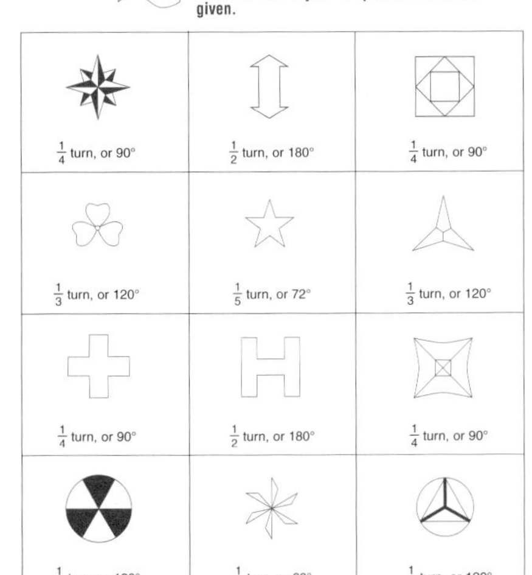

$\frac{1}{4}$ turn, or 90°	$\frac{1}{2}$ turn, or 180°	$\frac{1}{4}$ turn, or 90°
$\frac{1}{3}$ turn, or 120°	$\frac{1}{5}$ turn, or 72°	$\frac{1}{3}$ turn, or 120°
$\frac{1}{4}$ turn, or 90°	$\frac{1}{2}$ turn, or 180°	$\frac{1}{4}$ turn, or 90°
$\frac{1}{3}$ turn, or 120°	$\frac{1}{6}$ turn, or 60°	$\frac{1}{3}$ turn, or 120°

PROBLEM SOLVING 7-11

LESSON 7-11 **Problem Solving**
Symmetry

Write the correct answer.

Use the logo of an Australian TV station for Exercises 1 and 2.

1. How many lines of symmetry do the dots in the Channel 9 logo have?
   4

2. How many times will the dots show rotational symmetry in 1 rotation of 360°? What is the smallest angle of rotational symmetry for the dots?
   4 times; 90°

3. The figure on an emblem will show rotational symmetry 8 times within a single rotation. What is the smallest angle of rotational symmetry for the emblem?
   45°

4. Draw a figure that shows rotational symmetry 5 times within a 360° rotation.
   Possible answer:

Choose the letter for the best answer.

5. Which is a true statement about the stained glass window?
   A It is asymmetrical.
   (B) It has 1 line of symmetry.
   C It will show rotational symmetry 4 times within a full rotation.
   D It has 2 lines of symmetry.

6. Which is a true statement about the time shown on the clocks?
   F Only clocks 1 and 2 have a line of symmetry.
   G All of the clocks have at least 1 line of symmetry.
   H All of the clocks are asymmetrical.
   (J) Only clocks 1 and 4 have a line of symmetry.

3:08	4:00	6:13	1:30
1	2	3	4

Lesson Quiz

Does the figure described have symmetry?

1. a regular hexagon with a line drawn through the middle and two vertices yes
2. a square with a diagonal line drawn in yes
3. a heart with a horizontal line drawn through the middle no
4. Tell how many times the figure will have rotational symmetry within one full rotation.

8

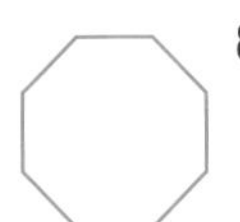

Available on Daily Transparency in CRB

7F Tessellations

Pacing: Traditional 1 day
Block $\frac{1}{2}$ day

Objective: To use geometric shapes to create tessellations

Materials: Paper, straightedge

Lab Resources

Hands-On Lab Activities . . . . . pp. 66–67

Using the Pages

Discuss with students why certain shapes can be used for tessellations. Make sure students understand that when the figures meet at the corners, the sum of the angles must be 360°. If the sum of the angles is not 360°, there will be gaps.

Tell whether each figure can be used for a tessellation.

1. equilateral triangle yes
2. square yes
3. rectangle yes
4. regular pentagon no
5. regular hexagon yes

Create Tessellations

Use with Lesson 7-10

internet connect
Lab Resources Online
go.hrw.com
KEYWORD: MS4 Lab7F

Tessellations are patterns of identical shapes that completely cover a plane with no gaps or overlaps. The artist M. C. Escher created many fascinating tessellations.

Activity

1. Create a translation tessellation.

The tessellation by M. C. Escher shown at right is an example of a *translation tessellation*. To create your own translation tessellation, follow the steps below.

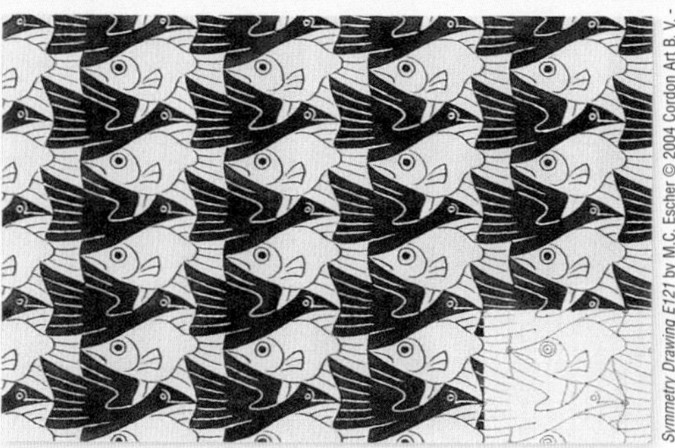

a. Start by drawing a square, rectangle, or other parallelogram. Replace one side of the parallelogram with a curve, as shown.

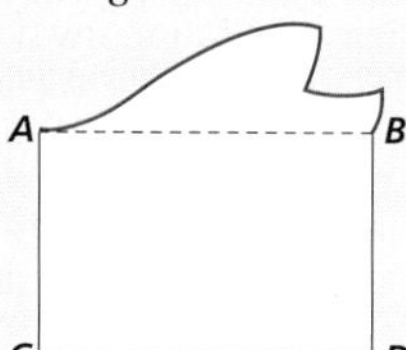

b. Translate the curve to the opposite side of the parallelogram.

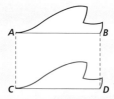

c. Repeat steps **a** and **b** for the other two sides of your parallelogram.

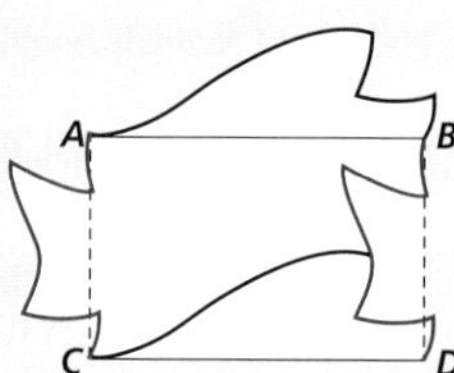

d. The figure can be translated to create an interlocking design, or tessellation. You can add details to your figure or divide it into two or more parts, as shown below.

❷ Create a rotation tessellation.

The tessellation by M. C. Escher shown at right is an example of a *rotation tessellation*. To create your own rotation tessellation, follow the steps below.

a. Start with a regular hexagon. Replace one side of the hexagon with a curve. Rotate the curve about point B so that the endpoint at point A is moved to point C.

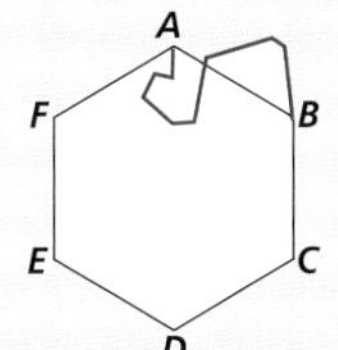

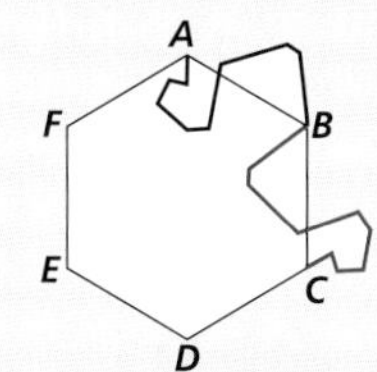

b. Replace side $\overline{CD}$ with a new curve, and rotate it about point D to replace side $\overline{DE}$.

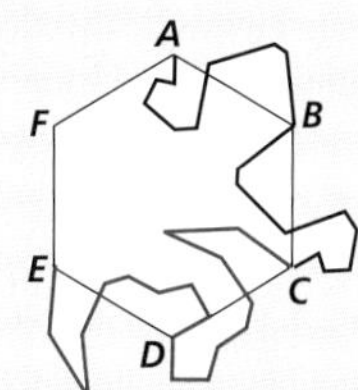

c. Replace side $\overline{EF}$ with a new curve, and rotate it about point F to replace side $\overline{FA}$.

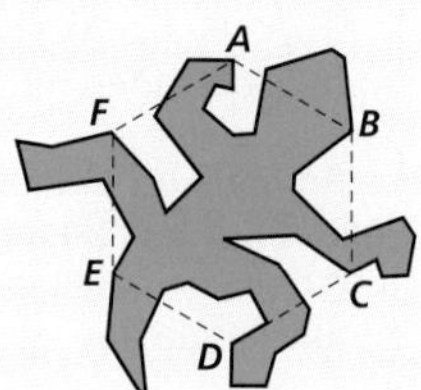

The figure can be rotated and fitted together with copies of itself to create an interlocking design, or tessellation. You can add details to your figure, if desired.

Think and Discuss

1. Explain why the two types of tessellations in this activity are known as translation and rotation tessellations. **Translation tessellations use translated images to create a pattern, and rotation tessellations use rotated images to create a pattern.**

Try This

1. Create your own design for a translation or rotation tessellation.
2. Cut out copies of your design from **1** and fit them together to fill a space with your pattern.

Answers

Try This

Possible answers:

1. Check students' work.

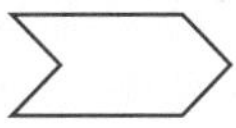

2. Check students' work.

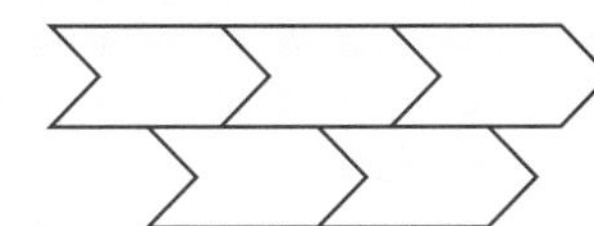

Problem Solving on Location

Pennsylvania

Purpose: *To provide additional practice for problem-solving skills in Chapters 1–7*

Philadelphia

- After problem 3, ask students to identify a figure in the photo that is made up of a rectangle and semicircle. Possible answer: center window above the main door
- After problem 5, have students describe another tessellation in the photo. Possible answer: rectangular fence along roof

Extension Have students look at a photo of the Washington Monument in Washington, D.C. Ask students to identify the plane figures that make up a side of the Washington Monument. trapezoid and triangle

Problem Solving on Location

PENNSYLVANIA

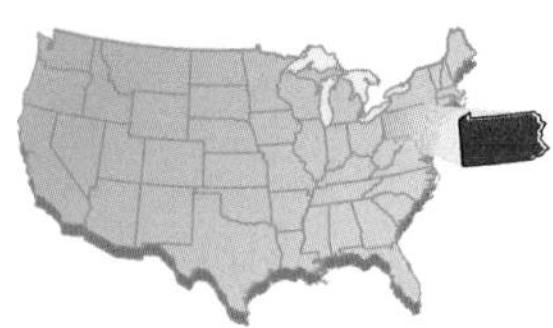

Philadelphia

Washington, D.C., has not always been the capital of the United States. Our nation's first capital was Philadelphia.

William Penn, a Quaker, founded Philadelphia in 1682. The Declaration of Independence and the U.S. Constitution were both adopted in Independence Hall in Philadelphia. The Liberty Bell is near Independence Hall.

Philadelphia was the capital of the American Colonies from 1775 to 1783 and the capital of the United States from 1790 to 1800.

For 1–7, use the photo of Independence Hall.

1. Identify a circle on Independence Hall. **the clock**
2. Identify a rectangle on Independence Hall. **Possible answer: the main door**
3. Identify a triangle on Independence Hall. What kind of triangle does it appear to be?
4. Describe two transformations that could be used to visually move a window on the first floor to one above it on the second floor.
5. Describe a tessellation appearing on Independence Hall. **the square grid on the windows**
6. Find two congruent figures on the building. **Possible answer: the two small windows above the main doors**
7. Does the image of Independence Hall appear to have a line of symmetry? Explain.

Answers

Possible answers:

3. The pediment above the circular window is an obtuse isosceles triangle.
4. a vertical translation; a reflection over a horizontal line halfway between the top and bottom row of windows.
7. Yes; disregarding the clock's numbers and the position of the hands, Independence Hall has a vertical line of symmetry down the middle of its front side.

Pittsburgh

Pittsburgh is the nation's largest port that is not on a coast. Two large rivers meet in the city at a place known as the Point. These rivers make it possible for imports from overseas to reach inland to Pittsburgh.

The map shows an area of downtown Pittsburgh where the Monongahela and Allegheny Rivers join to form the Ohio River. Streets fan out from the Golden Triangle to form many geometric patterns. For 1–8, use the map.

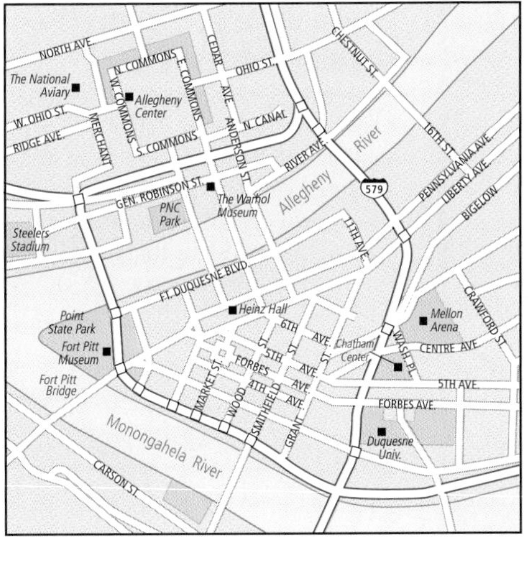

1. Name two streets on the map that appear to be parallel.
   Possible answer: Forbes Ave. and 5th Ave.
2. Describe the shape of the area on the map that includes Allegheny Center, which is bound by North and South Commons and East and West Commons. **rectangle**
3. How many lines of symmetry does the area in problem 2 have? **two; horizontal and vertical**
4. What shape describes the area where Chatham Center is located? **quadrilateral**
5. Name two streets that appear to be perpendicular.
   Possible answer: 16th St. and Pennsylvania Ave.
6. Describe the figure formed by 6th Avenue, Liberty Avenue, 5th Avenue, Wood St., and Market St. **pentagon**
7. Which streets appear to form an acute triangle? **Highway 579, Washington Pl., and 5th Ave.**
8. Which streets appear to form a right triangle? **5th Ave., Liberty Ave., and Grant St.**

Pittsburgh

- After problem 1 ask students to identify a street that is a transversal of the parallel streets that they named. Possible answer: Highway 579
- After problem 7 have students name sets of streets that appear to form similar triangles. Highway 579, Centre Ave., and Washington Pl.; Highway 579, 5th Ave., and Washington Pl.

Extension Encourage students to use the map to write a problem about a visit to Pittsburgh. Then have students exchange problems and solve. Check students' work.

MATH-ABLES

Game Resources

Puzzles, Twisters & Teasers
Chapter 7 Resource Book

Networks

Purpose: *To extend the study of plane figures to networks*

Discuss: A good example of a network that students can examine is a road map. What on a road map corresponds to the vertices of a network? cities What corresponds to the segments of a network? streets and highways To help students identify all the possible routes on a network, encourage them to organize the routes in a list or table.

Extend: Challenge students to use road maps to create real-world networks of their own. Have students trade networks with a partner and find all possible routes on the network.

Color Craze

Purpose: *To extend the problem-solving skill of translating geometric patterns into math to perform a fun activity*

Discuss: Have students count the number of tiles needed for each figure. **6** Ask students if they can perform this activity with polygons consisting of more than 6 tiles. yes Have students demonstrate figures that have line symmetry or rotational symmetry.

Extend: Have students build their own designs and then challenge other students to build each design with the tiles. Have students use the tiles to create a design that is a tessellation.

MATH-ABLES

Networks

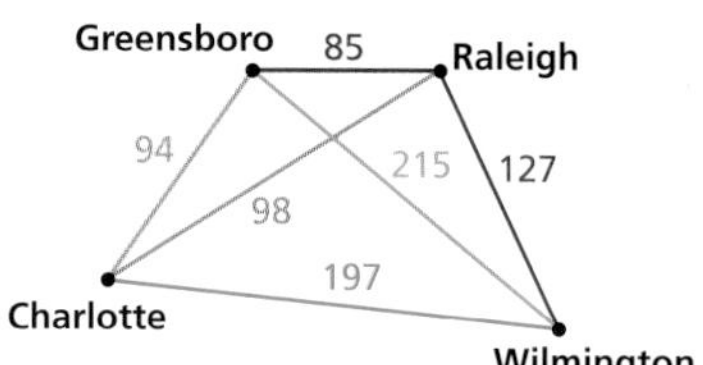

A network is a figure that uses vertices and segments to show how objects are connected. You can use a network to show distances between cities. In the network at right, the vertices identify four cities in North Carolina, and the segments show the distances in miles between the cities.

You can use the network to find the shortest route from Charlotte to the other three cities and back to Charlotte. First find all the possible routes. Then find the distance in miles for each route. One route has been identified below.

CGRWC $94 + 85 + 127 + 197 = 503$

Which is the shortest route, and what is the distance? **CGRWC or CWRGC; 503 mi**

Color Craze

You can use rhombus-shaped tiles to build a variety of polygons. Each side of a tile is a different color. Build each design by matching the same-colored sides of tiles. Then see if you can create your own designs with the tiles. Try to make designs that have line or rotational symmetry.

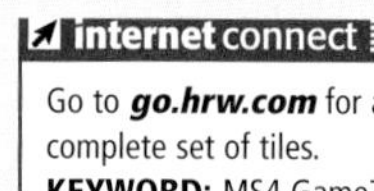

Go to ***go.hrw.com*** for a complete set of tiles.
KEYWORD: MS4 Game7

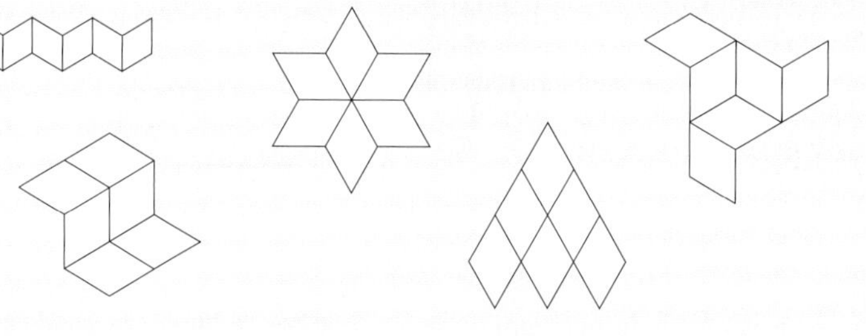

Transformations

You can use geometry software to perform transformations of geometric figures.

internet connect
Lab Resources Online
go.hrw.com
KEYWORD: MS4 TechLab7

Activity

1 Use your dynamic geometry software to construct a 5-sided polygon like the one below. Label the vertices *A, B, C, D,* and *E.* Use the translation tool to translate the polygon 2 units right and $\frac{1}{2}$ unit up.

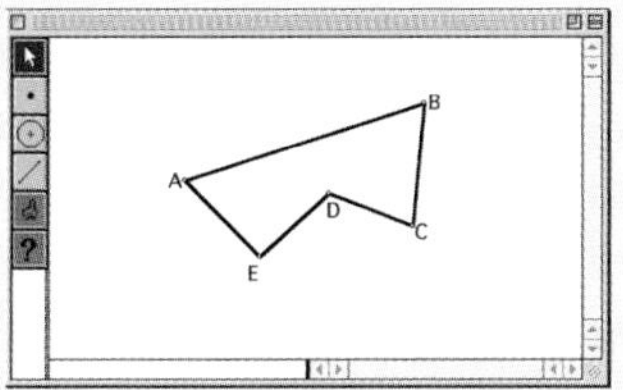

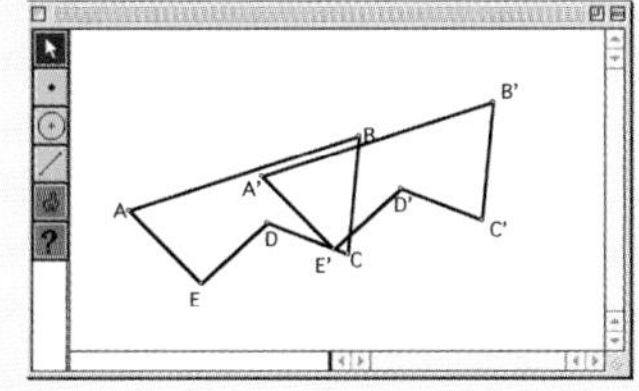

2 Start with the polygon from **1**. Use the rotation tool to rotate the polygon 30° and then 150°, both about the vertex *C.*

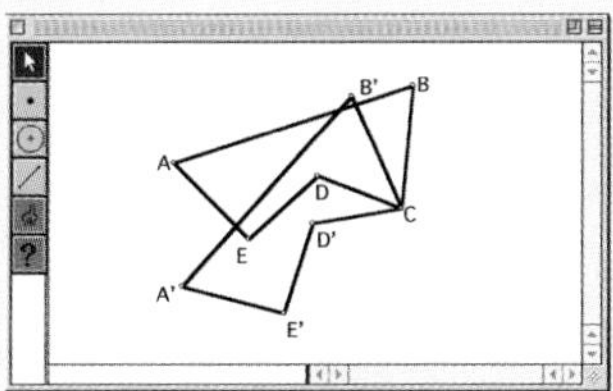

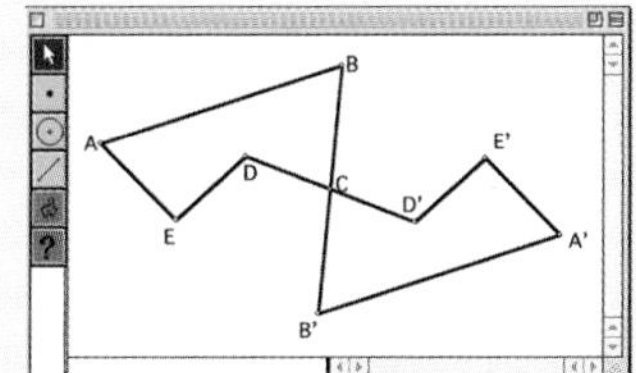

Think and Discuss

1. Rotate a triangle 30° about a point outside the triangle. Can this image be found by combining a vertical translation (slide up or down) and a horizontal translation (slide left or right) of the original triangle?
2. After what angle of rotation will the rotated image of a figure have the same orientation as the original figure? **360°**

Try This

1. Construct a quadrilateral *ABCD* using the geometry software.
   a. Translate the figure 2 units right and 1 unit up.
   b. Rotate the figure 30°, 45°, and 60°.

Transformations

Objective: To use geometry software to translate and rotate polygons

Materials: Geometry software

Lab Resources

Technology Lab Activities .... p. 40

Using the Page

This technology activity shows students how to use geometry software to translate and rotate polygons.

The first Think and Discuss problem can be used to assess students' understanding of whether a set of translations is equivalent to a rotation. The second Think and Discuss problem can be used to assess students' understanding of which rotations will produce a figure with the same orientation as the original figure. Have students try this with different figures. While Try This problem 1 can be done without geometry software, it is meant to help students become familiar with using geometry software to translate and rotate polygons.

Assessment

Use geometry software to construct a triangle *ABC*.

1. Translate the figure 2 units left and 3 units down.

   Possible answer:

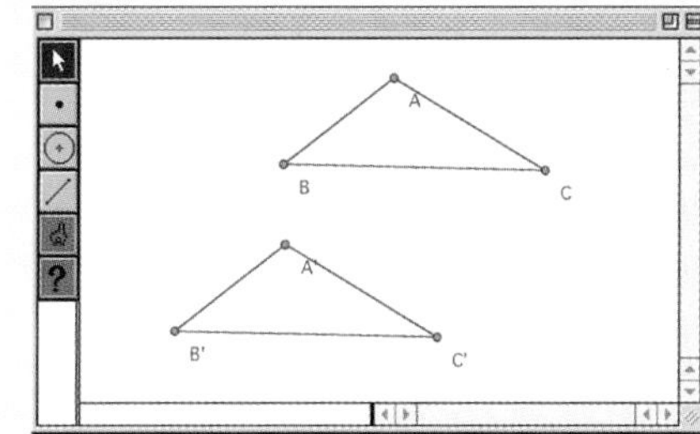

2. Rotate the figure 90°.

   Possible answer:

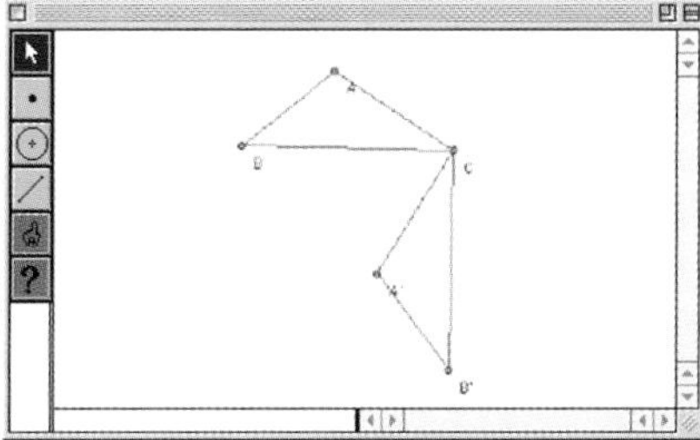

Answers

Think and Discuss

1. No; no matter which direction the triangle is translated, the vertices of the triangle will always have the same orientation.

Try This

1. a.

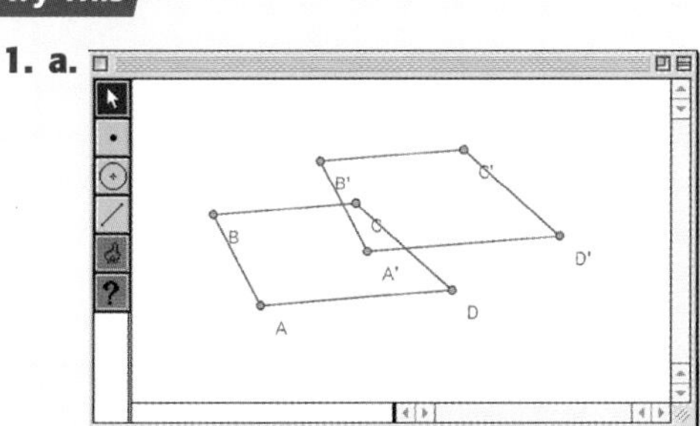

b.

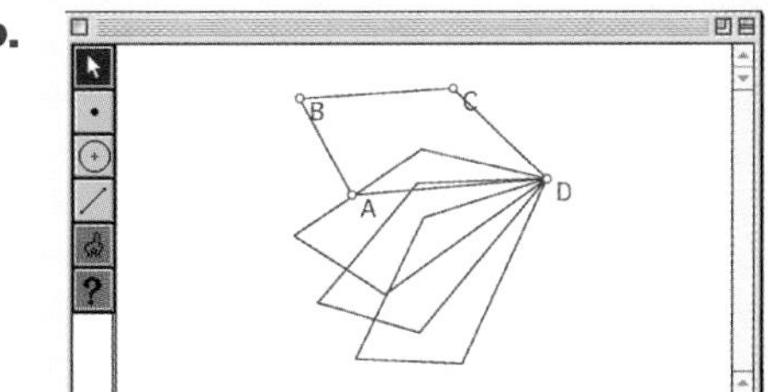

Study Guide and Review

Purpose: *To help students review and practice concepts and skills presented in Chapter 7*

Assessment Resources 

Chapter Review
Chapter 7 Resource Book . pp. 109–111

***Test and Practice Generator* CD-ROM**

Additional review assessment items in both multiple-choice and free-response format may be generated for any objective in Chapter 7.

Answers

1. acute or isosceles
2. parallel lines
3. *D, E, F*
4. $\overleftrightarrow{DF}$
5. plane *DEF*
6. $\overrightarrow{ED}$, $\overrightarrow{FD}$, $\overrightarrow{DF}$
7. $\overline{DE}$, $\overline{DF}$, $\overline{EF}$

Chapter 7

Study Guide and Review

Study Guide and Review

Vocabulary

acute angle 349
acute triangle 374
angle 348
arc 362
asymmetry 396
center of a circle 362
center of rotation 397
central angle 363
chord 362
circle 362
complementary angles 349
congruent 345
diagonal 383
diameter 362
equilateral triangle 374
image 392
isosceles triangle 374
kite 378
line 344
line of reflection 392
line of symmetry 396
line segment 344
line symmetry 396
obtuse angle 349
obtuse triangle 374
parallel lines 354
parallelogram 378
perpendicular lines 354
plane 344
point 344
polygon 368
radius 362
ray 344
rectangle 378
reflection 392
regular polygon 369
rhombus 378
right angle 349
right triangle 374
rotation 392
rotational symmetry 397
scalene triangle 374
sector 363
side 368
Side-Side-Side Rule 388
skew lines 354
square 378
straight angle 349
supplementary angles 349
transformation 392
translation 392
transversal 355
trapezoid 378
vertex 348
vertex of a polygon 368
vertical angles 355

Complete the sentences below with vocabulary words from the list above.

1. Every equilateral triangle is also a(n) __?__ triangle.
2. Lines in the same plane that do not intersect are __?__.

7-1 Points, Lines, and Planes (pp. 344–347)

EXAMPLE

Identify each figure in the diagram.

- points: *A, B, C*
- lines: $\overleftrightarrow{AB}$
- planes: *ABC*
- rays: $\overrightarrow{BA}$; $\overrightarrow{AB}$
- line segments: $\overline{AB}$; $\overline{BC}$

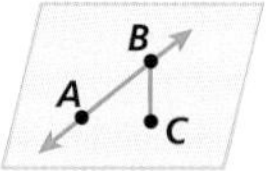

B
A
C

EXERCISES

Identify each figure in the diagram.

3. points
4. lines
5. planes
6. rays
7. line segments

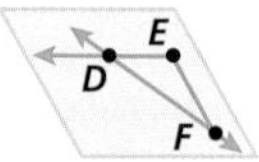

E
D
F

7-2 Angles (pp. 348–351)

EXAMPLE

- **Tell whether the angle is acute, right, obtuse, or straight.**

The angle is a right angle.

EXERCISES

Tell whether each angle is acute, right, obtuse, or straight.

8.

9.

7-3 Parallel and Perpendicular Lines (pp. 354–357)

EXAMPLE

- **Tell whether the lines appear parallel, perpendicular, or skew.**

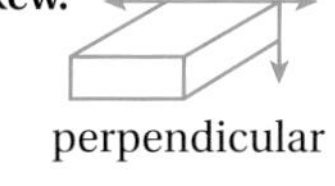

perpendicular

EXERCISES

Tell whether the lines appear parallel, perpendicular, or skew.

10.

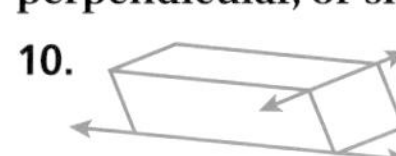

7-4 Circles (pp. 362–365)

EXAMPLE

Name the parts of circle *D*.

- radii: $\overline{DB}, \overline{DC}, \overline{DE}$
- diameter: $\overline{EB}$
- chords: $\overline{AB}, \overline{EB}, \overline{EF}$

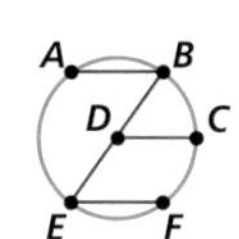

EXERCISES

Name the parts of circle *F*.

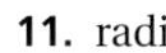

11. radii
12. diameter
13. chords

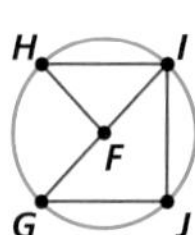

7-5 Polygons (pp. 368–371)

EXAMPLE

- **Tell whether the figure is a regular polygon. If it is not, explain why not.**
  No, all the angles in the polygon are not congruent.

EXERCISES

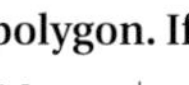

Tell whether each figure is a regular polygon. If it is not, explain why not.

14.

15.

7-6 Triangles (pp. 374–377)

EXAMPLE

- **Classify the triangle according to its sides and angles.**

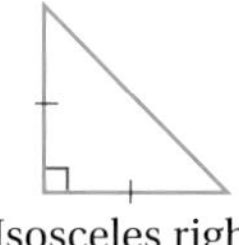

Isosceles right

EXERCISES

Classify each triangle according to its sides and angles.

16.

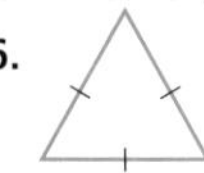

17.

Study Guide and Review

Answers

8. acute
9. straight
10. skew
11. $\overline{HF}, \overline{FI}, \overline{FG}$
12. $\overline{GI}$
13. $\overline{HI}, \overline{GI}, \overline{GJ}, \overline{JI}$
14. Square; all sides are congruent and all angles are congruent.
15. No; all sides are not congruent.
16. equilateral acute
17. scalene right

Answers

18. parallelogram, rhombus

19. parallelogram, rectangle

20. 53°

21. 133°

22.

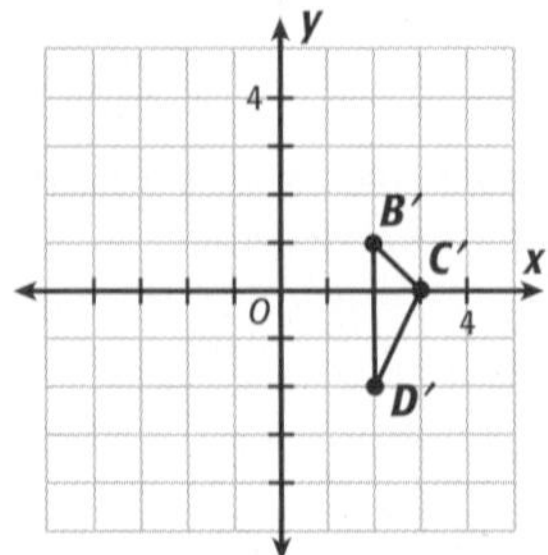

23. 1 vertical line through center of flag

Study Guide and Review

7-7 Quadrilaterals (pp. 378–381)

EXAMPLE

- **Give all of the names that apply to the quadrilateral.**

trapezoid

EXERCISES

Give all of the names that apply to each quadrilateral.

18. 

19.

7-8 Angles in Polygons (pp. 382–385)

EXAMPLE

- **Find the measure of the unknown angle.**

$62° + 45° + x = 180°$
$107° + x = 180°$
$x = 73°$

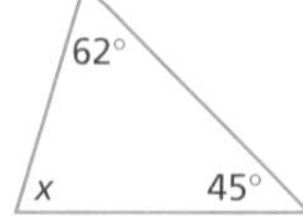

EXERCISES

Find the measure of the unknown angle.

20.

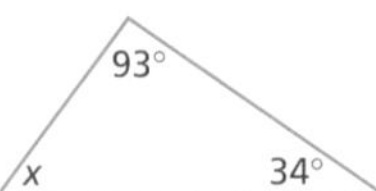

7-9 Congruent Figures (pp. 388–391)

EXAMPLE

- **Determine the missing measure in the set of congruent polygons.**

The angle measures 53°.

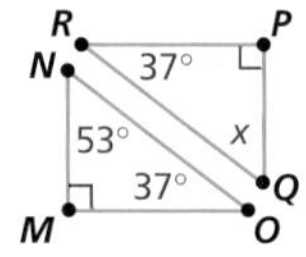

EXERCISES

21. Determine the missing measure in the set of congruent polygons.

7-10 Transformations (pp. 392–395)

EXAMPLE

- **Graph the translation.**

Translate $\triangle ABC$ 1 unit right and 3 units down.

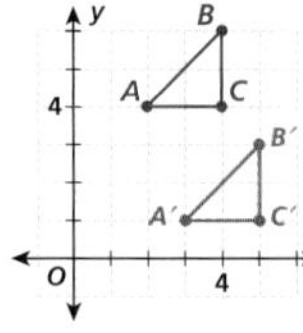

EXERCISES

Graph the translation.

22. Translate $\triangle BCD$ 2 units left and 4 units down.

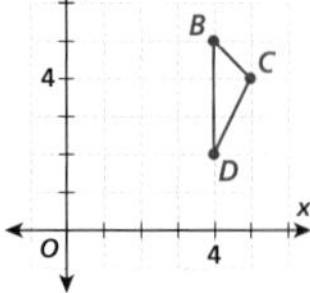

7-11 Symmetry (pp. 396–399)

EXAMPLE

- **Find all the lines of symmetry in the flag.**

The flag has four lines of symmetry.

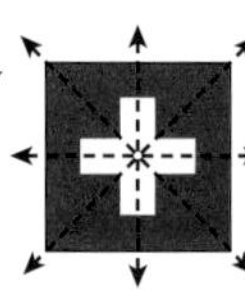

EXERCISES

23. Find all the lines of symmetry in the flag.

Chapter Test

Identify the figures in the diagram. **Possible answers:**

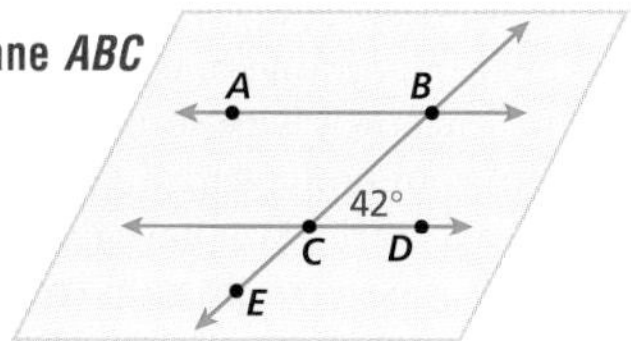

1. 5 points
2. 3 lines **$\overleftrightarrow{AB}$, $\overleftrightarrow{CD}$, $\overleftrightarrow{CB}$**
3. a plane **plane *ABC***
4. 5 line segments **$\overline{AB}$, $\overline{CD}$, $\overline{EC}$, $\overline{EB}$, $\overline{CB}$**
5. 6 rays **$\overrightarrow{AB}$, $\overrightarrow{BA}$, $\overrightarrow{BC}$, $\overrightarrow{CB}$, $\overrightarrow{CD}$, $\overrightarrow{DC}$**

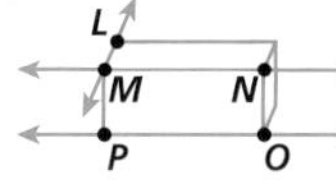

Line *AB* || line *CD*. Find the measure of each angle and tell whether the angle is acute, right, obtuse, or straight.

6. $\angle ABC$ **42°, acute angle**
7. $\angle BCE$ **180°, straight angle**
8. $\angle DCE$ **138° obtuse angle**

Tell whether the lines appear parallel, perpendicular, or skew.

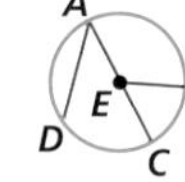

9. $\overleftrightarrow{MN}$ and $\overleftrightarrow{PO}$ **parallel**
10. $\overleftrightarrow{LM}$ and $\overleftrightarrow{PO}$ **skew**
11. $\overleftrightarrow{NO}$ and $\overleftrightarrow{MN}$ **perpendicular**

Name the parts of circle *E*.

12. radii **$\overline{AE}$, $\overline{EC}$, $\overline{BE}$**
13. chords **$\overline{AD}$, $\overline{AC}$**
14. diameter **$\overline{AC}$**

Tell whether each figure is a regular polygon. If it is not, explain why not.

15.  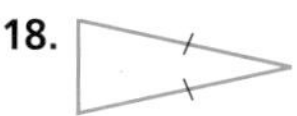 **No; all the interior angles are not congruent.**
16.  **No; one side is curved.**
17. 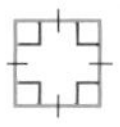 **yes**

Classify each triangle according to its sides and angles.

18. **isosceles acute**
19.  **equilateral acute**
20.  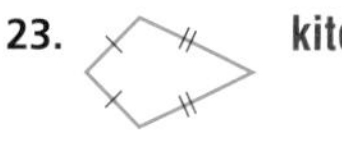 **scalene right**

Give all the names that apply to each quadrilateral.

21. 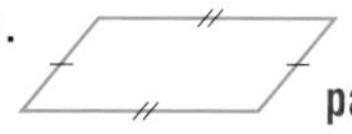 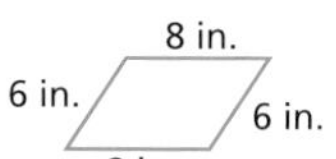 **parallelogram**
22. 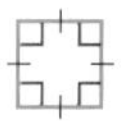 **parallelogram, rectangle, rhombus, square**
23. **kite**

Find the measure of each unknown angle.

24. **90°** 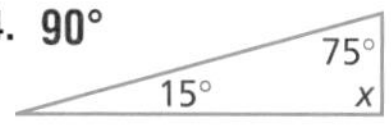
25. 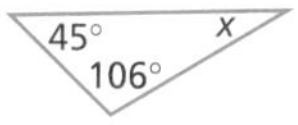 **29°**
26.  **110°**

27. Determine the missing measure in the congruent polygons. **6 in.**

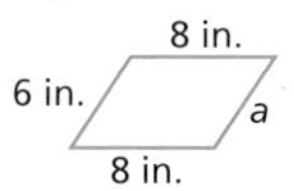

28. The vertices of a triangle have the coordinates (−1, −3), (−4, −1), and (−1, −1). Graph the triangle after a translation 3 units left.

Find all the lines of symmetry in each flag.

29. 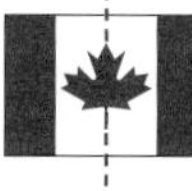
30.  **none**

Chapter Test

Chapter Test

Purpose: *To assess students' mastery of concepts and skills in Chapter 7*

Assessment Resources

Chapter 7 Tests (Levels A, B, C)
Assessment Resources ..... pp. 69–74

***Test and Practice Generator* CD-ROM**

Additional assessment items in both multiple-choice and free-response format may be generated for any objective in Chapter 7.

Answers

1. *A, B, C, D,* and *E*

28.

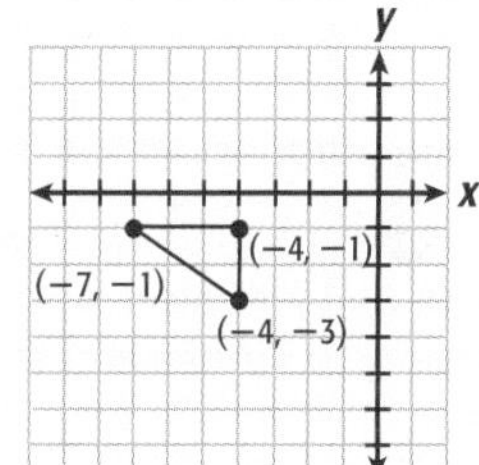

Chapter 7 Performance Assessment

***Purpose:** To assess students' understanding of concepts in Chapter 7 and combined problem-solving skills*

Assessment Resources

Performance Assessment
Assessment Resources .... p. 118

Performance Assessment Teacher Support
Assessment Resources .... p. 117

Answers

5. See Level 3 work sample below.

Scoring Rubric for Problem Solving Item 5

Level 3

Accomplishes the purposes of the task.

Student gives clear explanations, shows understanding of mathematical ideas and processes, and computes accurately.

Level 2

Purposes of the task not fully achieved.

Student demonstrates satisfactory but limited understanding of the mathematical ideas and processes.

Level 1

Purposes of the task not accomplished.

Student shows little evidence of understanding the mathematical ideas and processes and makes computational and/or procedural errors.

Chapter 7

Performance Assessment

Performance Assessment

Show What You Know

Create a portfolio of your work from this chapter. Complete this page and include it with your four best pieces of work from Chapter 7. Choose from your homework or lab assignments, mid-chapter quizzes, or any journal entries you have done. Put them together using any design you want. Make your portfolio represent what you consider your best work.

Short Response

1. The vertices of a triangle are $A(6, 4)$, $B(6, 2)$, and $C(8, 2)$. Translate triangle ABC left 7 units, and list the coordinates of the translated image. **$A'(-1, 4)$, $B'(-1, 2)$, $C'(1, 2)$**
2. According to a circle graph, 55% of the people who responded to a survey eat cereal for breakfast. Find the central angle measure of the sector that shows this percent. Show your work. **55% of 360°; $0.55 \cdot 360° = 198°$**
3. Jacob drew a pair of parallel lines intersected by a transversal. One of the angles formed by one of the parallel lines and the transversal is a right angle. What can you conclude about the other angles? Explain your answer.

3. Since one of the angles is a right angle, the transversal must be perpendicular to the two parallel lines. Therefore all of the angles are right angles.

4. Barry drew a quadrilateral. One angle measures 80°, and another angle measures 130°. The fourth angle is twice as large as the third angle. Write and solve an equation to find the measures of the third and fourth angles. Show your work. **$80° + 130° + x + 2x = 360°$; $x = 50°$, $2x = 100°$**

Extended Problem Solving

5. Use the tapestry for the following problems.
   a. Identify as many places as possible where the line symmetry is broken.
   b. Identify a rotation in the tapestry.
   c. Identify a reflection in the tapestry.
   d. Identify a combination of a rotation and a translation in the tapestry.

Student Work Samples for Item 5

Level 3

a) white triangles in the lower right corner face wrong way; small white triangles near center are reversed; large tan arrows point opposite directions; Colored diamonds that make up large diamond are in different orders

b) The gold diamonds can rotate around the center 2 times.

c) The red and green rectangle is a horizontal and vertical reflection.

d) The tan arrow near upper left corner can be rotated and translated to match the arrow in right corner.

The student identified several examples and included descriptive details about the types of symmetry involved.

Level 2

A. Arrows at top center and bottom center point different directions. White triangles near center are switched.

B. The large diamond can rotate.

C. The purple diamonds are reflections.

D. The white triangles at the top left can be rotated and moved to the top right.

The student identified some examples, but failed to include significant details. The answer to part **d** is also inaccurate.

Level 1

a. purple diamonds, gold diamonds, orange diamonds, 4 corners

b. yes, it is a rotation

c. no, it's not a reflection because of the white triangles

d.

The student provided some vague examples in part **a,** but did not identify specific examples in parts **b** and **c.** Part **d** was left incomplete.

internet connect
State-Specific Test Practice Online
go.hrw.com Keyword: MS4 TestPrep

Standardized Test Prep

Chapter 7

Cumulative Assessment, Chapters 1–7

1. Which statement about the figure is true? **D**

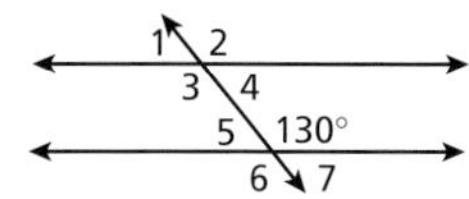

Ⓐ ∠1 and ∠6 are congruent.
Ⓑ The measure of ∠7 is 85°.
Ⓒ ∠4 and ∠6 are complementary angles.
Ⓓ ∠2 and ∠3 are vertical angles.

2. Find the median of −47, 25, −10, 7, −24, and −29. **H**

Ⓕ 17 Ⓗ −17
Ⓖ −10 Ⓙ −24

3. A pair of shoes that normally cost \$18.50 are on sale for \$14.80. What is the percent of decrease? **C**

Ⓐ 125% Ⓒ 20%
Ⓑ 80% Ⓓ 10%

4. Which number is **not** expressed in scientific notation? **J**

Ⓕ 1.7×10^{34} Ⓗ 2.354×10^{1}
Ⓖ 3×10^{2} Ⓙ 10.3×10^{5}

5. The mean of a set of five numbers is 8.8. If the number 7 is added to the set, what is the new mean? **B**

Ⓐ 8 Ⓒ 9
Ⓑ 8.5 Ⓓ 9.5

6. What is 65 mi/h expressed in ft/min?

Ⓕ 0.74 ft/min Ⓗ 4,874 ft/min
Ⓖ 1,907 ft/min Ⓙ 5,720 ft/min

J

7. Solve $\frac{2}{3}x = \frac{5}{6}$. **A**

Ⓐ $x = \frac{5}{4}$ Ⓒ $x = \frac{4}{5}$
Ⓑ $x = \frac{5}{9}$ Ⓓ $x = \frac{9}{5}$

8. What is the prime factorization of 1,000? **H**

Ⓕ $2^3 \cdot 3 \cdot 5^2$ Ⓗ $2^3 \cdot 5^3$
Ⓖ $2^2 \cdot 5^4$ Ⓙ $2^2 \cdot 5^3 \cdot 7$

9. ***SHORT RESPONSE*** The triangles are congruent. What is the value of x? How do you know?

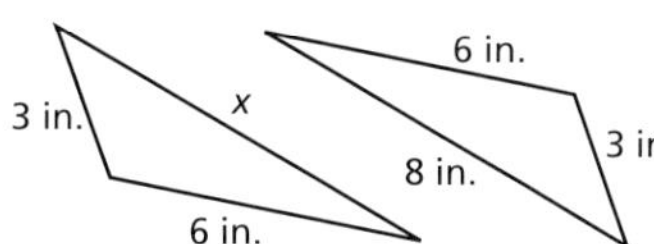

TEST TAKING TIP!
When solving a geometry word problem, draw a diagram to illustrate the problem.

10. ***SHORT RESPONSE*** Four of the angles in a pentagon measure 81°, 115°, 139°, and 90°. What is the measure of the fifth angle? Explain how you determined your answer.

Standardized Test Prep

Answers

9. The value of x is 8 inches, because if the triangles are congruent, they have exactly the same shape and size.

10. The measure of the fifth angle in the pentagon is 115°. The sum of the measures of the angles in a pentagon is 540°. To find the measure of the fifth angle in the pentagon, add the other four angle measures and subtract from 540°.
540° − (81° + 115° + 139° + 90°) = 115°

Standardized Test Prep

Purpose: *To provide review and practice for Chapters 1–7 and standardized tests*

Assessment Resources

Cumulative Tests (Levels A, B, C)
Assessment Resources . . . pp. 201–212

State-Specific Test Practice Online
KEYWORD: MS4 TestPrep

Test Prep Doctor

Point out that for item 5, if a number that is lesser than the mean is added to a set of numbers, the new mean will be lesser. Therefore, **C** and **D** can be eliminated.

Chapter 8

Perimeter, Circumference, and Area

Section 8A	Section 8B	Section 8C
Measurement, Perimeter, and Circumference	**Area**	**The Pythagorean Theorem**
Lesson 8-1 Customary and Metric Measurements	**Lesson 8-4** Area of Parallelograms	**Lesson 8-7** Powers and Roots
Hands-On Lab 8A Measure Objects	**Lesson 8-5** Area of Triangles and Trapezoids	**Hands-On Lab 8B** Explore the Pythagorean Theorem
Lesson 8-2 Accuracy and Precision	**Lesson 8-6** Area of Circles	**Lesson 8-8** The Pythagorean Theorem
Lesson 8-3 Perimeter and Circumference		**Hands-On Lab 8C** Graph Irrational Numbers
		Extension Area of Irregular Figures

Pacing Guide for 45-Minute Classes

Chapter 8

DAY 104	DAY 105	DAY 106	DAY 107	DAY 108
Lesson 8-1	Hands-On Lab 8A	Lesson 8-2	Lesson 8-2	Lesson 8-3
DAY 109	**DAY 110**	**DAY 111**	**DAY 112**	**DAY 113**
Mid-Chapter Quiz Lesson 8-4	Lesson 8-5	Lesson 8-6	Mid-Chapter Quiz Lesson 8-7	Hands-On Lab 8B
DAY 114	**DAY 115**	**DAY 116**	**DAY 117**	**DAY 118**
Lesson 8-8	Hands-On Lab 8C	Extension	Chapter Review	Chapter 8 Assessment

Pacing Guide for 90-Minute Classes

Chapter 8

DAY 52	DAY 53	DAY 54	DAY 55	DAY 56
Chapter 7 Assessment Lesson 8-1	Hands-On Lab 8A Lesson 8-2	Lesson 8-2 Lesson 8-3	Mid-Chapter Quiz Lesson 8-4 Lesson 8-5	Lesson 8-6 Lesson 8-7
DAY 57	**DAY 58**	**DAY 59**	**DAY 60**	
Mid-Chapter Quiz Hands-On Lab 8B Lesson 8-8	Hands-On Lab 8C Extension	Chapter 8 Review Hands-On Lab 9A	Chapter 8 Assessment Lesson 9-1	

Across the Series

COURSE 1

- Convert measurements within the customary system.
- Find the perimeter, circumference, and area of geometric figures.
- Express and evaluate with exponents.
- Estimate the area of irregular figures.

COURSE 2

- **Convert measurements within the customary and metric measurement systems.**
- **Compare the precision of measurements and determine acceptable levels of accuracy.**
- **Find the perimeter, circumference, and area of geometric figures.**
- **Express and evaluate powers and roots.**
- **Use the Pythagorean Theorem.**
- **Graph irrational numbers.**
- **Find the areas of irregular figures.**

COURSE 3

- Convert measurements.
- Find the perimeter, circumference, and area of geometric figures.
- Express and evaluate powers and roots.
- Use the Pythagorean Theorem.
- Identify and classify real numbers.

Across the Curriculum

LANGUAGE ARTS

Math: Reading and Writing in the Content Area .... pp. 68–75

Focus on Problem Solving

Understand the Problem .... SE pp. 429, 443

Journal .... TE, last page of each lesson

Write About It .... SE pp. 417, 427, 433, 437, 441, 447, 453

Literature .... SE p. 417

SOCIAL STUDIES

Geography .... SE pp. 427, 437

History .... SE p. 453

Social Studies .... SE p. 439

SCIENCE

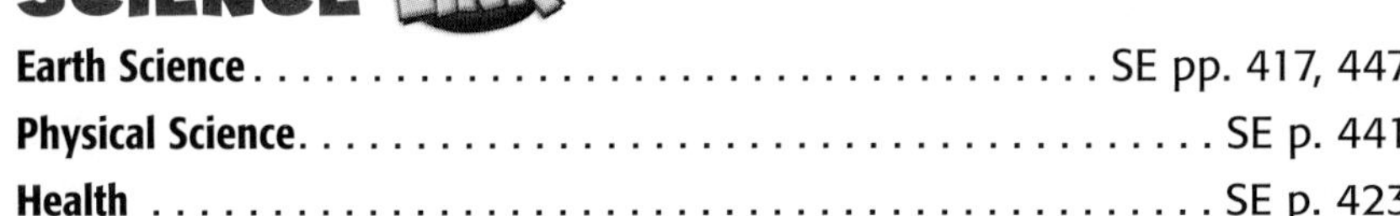

Earth Science .... SE pp. 417, 447

Physical Science .... SE p. 441

Health .... SE p. 423

TE = *Teacher's Edition* **SE** = *Student Edition*

Interdisciplinary Bulletin Board

Design

The London Eye is the largest Ferris wheel ever built; its height is 135 m, and it weighs 1,600 tons. It was built as a landmark for London as a welcome to the new millennium. How many feet tall is the Ferris wheel (1 m ≈ 3.3 ft)? Round your answer to the nearest tenth. 445.5

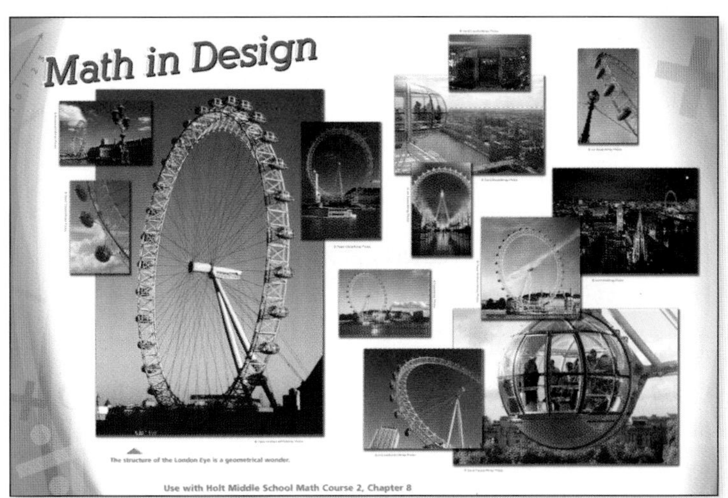

Math in Design
Use with Holt Middle School Math Course 2, Chapter 8

Interdisciplinary posters and worksheets are provided in your resource material.

Chapter 8

Resource Options

Chapter 8 Resource Book

Student Resources

Practice (Levels A, B, C) . . . . pp. 8–10, 17–19, 26–28, 37–39, 46–48, 56–58, 66-68, 75–77

Reteach . . . . pp. 11, 20, 29–30, 40, 49–50, 59, 69, 78

Challenge . . . . pp. 12, 21, 31, 41, 51, 60, 70, 79

Problem Solving . . . . pp. 13, 22, 32, 42, 52, 61, 71, 80

Puzzles, Twisters & Teasers . . pp. 14, 23, 33, 43, 53, 62, 72, 81

Recording Sheets . . pp. 3, 7, 16, 25, 36, 45, 55, 65, 74, 84, 87

Chapter Review . . . . pp. 82–83

Teacher and Parent Resources

Chapter Planning and Pacing Guide . . . . p. 4

Section Planning Guides . . . . pp. 5, 34, 63

Parent Letter . . . . pp. 1–2

Teaching Tools . . . . pp. 87–91

Teacher Support for Chapter Project . . . . p. 85

Transparencies . . . . pp. T1–T37

- Daily Transparencies
- Additional Examples Transparencies
- Teaching Transparencies

Reaching All Learners

English Language Learners

Success for English Language Learners . . . . . . pp. 135–150

Math: Reading and Writing in the Content Area . . . . pp. 68–75

Spanish Homework and Practice . . . . pp. 68–75

Spanish Interactive Study Guide . . . . pp. 68–75

Spanish Family Involvement Activities . . . . pp. 69–80

Multilingual Glossary

Individual Needs

Are You Ready? Intervention and Enrichment . . . pp. 21–24, 73–76, 169–172, 213–216, 313–316, 419–420

Alternate Openers: Explorations . . . . pp. 68–75

Family Involvement Activities . . . . pp. 69–80

Interactive Problem Solving . . . . pp. 68–75

Interactive Study Guide . . . . pp. 68–75

Readiness Activities . . . . pp. 15–16

Math: Reading and Writing in the Content Area . . . . pp. 68–75

Challenge . . . . CRB pp. 12, 21, 31, 41, 51, 60, 70, 79

Hands-On

Hands-On Lab Activities . . . . pp. 68–84

Technology Lab Activities . . . . pp. 41–45

Alternate Openers: Explorations . . . . pp. 68–75

Family Involvement Activities . . . . pp. 69–80

Applications and Connections

Consumer and Career Math . . . . pp. 29–32

Interdisciplinary Posters . . . . Poster 8, TE p. 412B

Interdisciplinary Poster Worksheets . . . . pp. 22–24

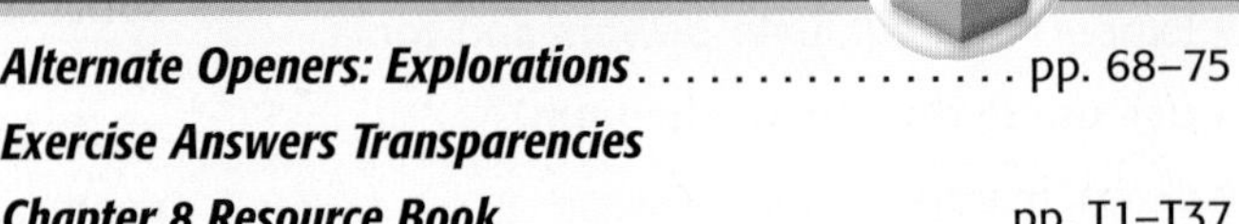

Transparencies

Alternate Openers: Explorations . . . . pp. 68–75

Exercise Answers Transparencies

Chapter 8 Resource Book . . . . pp. T1–T37

- Daily Transparencies
- Additional Examples Transparencies
- Teaching Transparencies

Technology

Teacher Resources

Lesson Presentations **CD-ROM** . . . . Chapter 8

Test and Practice Generator **CD-ROM** . . . . Chapter 8

One-Stop Planner **CD-ROM** . . . . Chapter 8

Student Resources

Are You Ready? Intervention **CD-ROM**
Skills 3, 16, 40, 51, 76

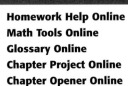

internet connect

go.hrw.com

Homework Help Online	**KEYWORD:** MS4 HWHelp8
Math Tools Online	**KEYWORD:** MS4 Tools
Glossary Online	**KEYWORD:** MS4 Glossary
Chapter Project Online	**KEYWORD:** MS4 PSProject8
Chapter Opener Online	**KEYWORD:** MS4 Ch8
	**KEYWORD:** MS4 CNN8

SE = *Student Edition* **TE** = *Teacher's Edition* **AR** = *Assessment Resources* **CRB** = *Chapter Resource Book* **MK** = *Manipulatives Kit*

Chapter 8

Assessment Options

Assessing Prior Knowledge

Determine whether students have the required prerequisite concepts and skills.

Are You Ready? . . . . . . SE p. 413
Inventory Test . . . . . . AR pp. 1–4

Test Preparation

Provide review and practice for chapter and standardized tests.

Standardized Test Prep . . . . . . SE p. 467
Spiral Review with Test Prep . . . . . SE, last page of each lesson
Study Guide and Review . . . . . . SE pp. 462–464
Test Prep Tool Kit

Technology 

 ***Test and Practice Generator* CD-ROM**

internet connect 

State-Specific Test Practice Online KEYWORD: MS4 TestPrep

Performance Assessment

Assess students' understanding of chapter concepts and combined problem-solving skills.

Performance Assessment . . . . . . SE p. 466
Includes scoring rubric in TE
Performance Assessment . . . . . . AR p. 120
Performance Assessment Teacher Support . . . . . . AR p. 119

Portfolio

Portfolio opportunities appear throughout the Student and Teacher's Editions.

Suggested work samples:

Problem Solving Project . . . . . . TE p. 412
Performance Assessment . . . . . . SE p. 466
Portfolio Guide . . . . . . AR p. xxxv
Journal . . . . . . TE, last page of each lesson
Write About It . . . . . . SE pp. 417, 427, 433, 437, 441, 447, 453

Daily Assessment

Obtain daily feedback on students' understanding of concepts.

Spiral Review and Test Prep . . . . . . SE, last page of each lesson

Also Available on Transparency In Chapter 8 Resource Book

Warm Up . . . . . . TE, first page of each lesson
Problem of the Day . . . . . . TE, first page of each lesson
Lesson Quiz . . . . . . TE, last page of each lesson

Student Self-Assessment

Have students evaluate their own work.

Group Project Evaluation . . . . . . AR p. xxxii
Individual Group Member Evaluation . . . . . . AR p. xxxiii
Portfolio Guide . . . . . . AR p. xxxv
Journal . . . . . . TE, last page of each lesson

Formal Assessment

Assess students' mastery of concepts and skills.

Section Quizzes . . . . . . AR pp. 22–24
Mid-Chapter Quizzes . . . . . . SE pp. 428, 442
Chapter Test . . . . . . SE p. 465
Chapter Tests (Levels A, B, C) . . . . . . AR pp. 75–80
Cumulative Tests (Levels A, B, C) . . . . . . AR pp. 213–224
Standardized Test Prep
Cumulative Assessment . . . . . . SE p. 467
End-of-Year Test . . . . . . AR pp. 273–276

Technology 

 ***Test and Practice Generator* CD-ROM**

Make tests electronically. This software includes:

- Dynamic practice for Chapter 8
- Customizable tests
- Multiple-choice items for each objective
- Free-response items for each objective
- Teacher management system

SE = *Student Edition* **TE** = *Teacher's Edition* **AR** = *Assessment Resources* **CRB** = *Chapter Resource Book* **MK** = *Manipulatives Kit*

Chapter 8

Chapter 8 Tests

Three levels (A,B,C) of tests are available for each chapter in the *Assessment Resources.*

LEVEL A

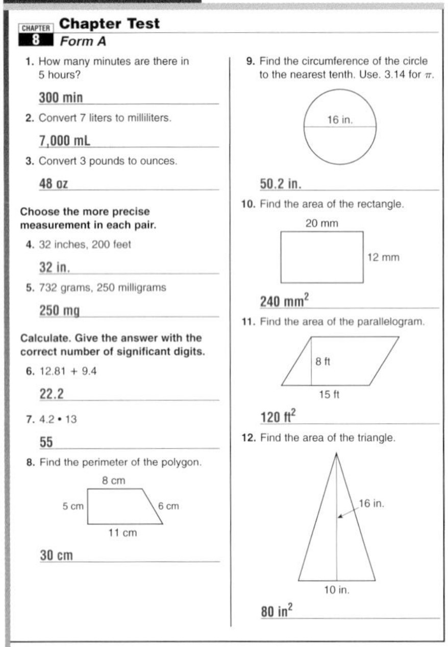

CHAPTER 8 Chapter Test
Form A

1. How many minutes are there in 5 hours?
   300 min
2. Convert 7 liters to milliliters.
   7,000 mL
3. Convert 3 pounds to ounces.
   48 oz

Choose the more precise measurement in each pair.

4. 32 inches, 200 feet
   32 in.
5. 732 grams, 250 milligrams
   250 mg

Calculate. Give the answer with the correct number of significant digits.

6. 12.81 + 9.4
   22.2
7. 4.2 • 13
   55
8. Find the perimeter of the polygon.
   8 cm, 5 cm, 6 cm, 11 cm
   30 cm
9. Find the circumference of the circle to the nearest tenth. Use 3.14 for π.
   16 in.
   50.2 in.
10. Find the area of the rectangle.
    20 mm, 12 mm
    240 mm^2
11. Find the area of the parallelogram.
    8 ft, 15 ft
    120 ft^2
12. Find the area of the triangle.
    16 in., 10 in.
    80 in^2

CHAPTER 8 Chapter Test
Form A, continued

13. Find the area of the triangle.
    42 cm, 38 cm
    798 cm^2
14. Find the area of the trapezoid.
    6 yd, 10 yd, 11 yd
    85 yd^2
15. Find the area of the circle to the nearest tenth. Use 3.14 for π.
    6.5 m
    132.7 m^2
16. Find the area of the circle. Use $\frac{22}{7}$ for π.
    35 cm
    3,850 cm^2
17. Evaluate 12^2. 144
18. Evaluate 15^2. 225

For 19–20, estimate each square root to the nearest whole number.

19. $\sqrt{18}$ about 4
20. $\sqrt{70}$ about 8
21. Use the Pythagorean Theorem to find the missing length.
    A, B, C; 20 cm, 15 cm, ?
    25 cm

Solve.

22. Alison leans a 15-foot board against a wall. The spot where the top of the board touches the wall is 9 feet above the ground. How far away from the wall is the bottom of the board?
    12 ft
23. Paul and Chris leave the train station at the same time. Paul travels 12 miles north. Chris travels 16 miles west. How far away from each other are Paul and Chris now?
    20 mi

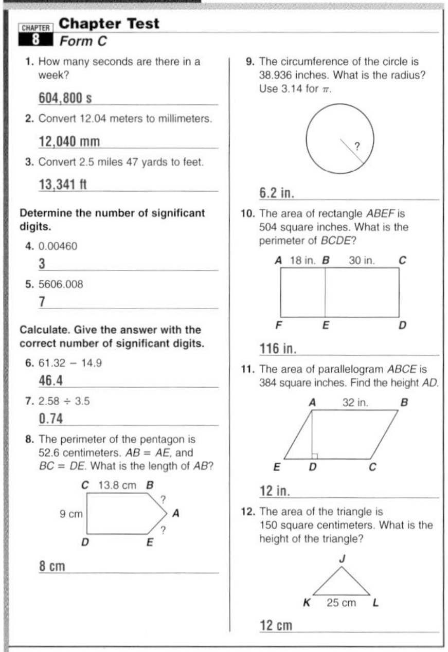

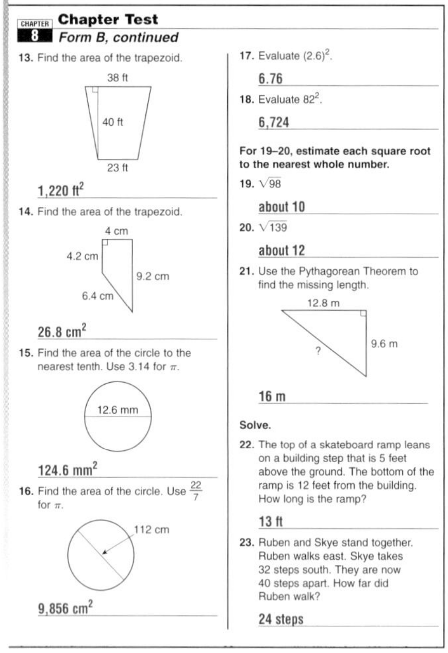

LEVEL B

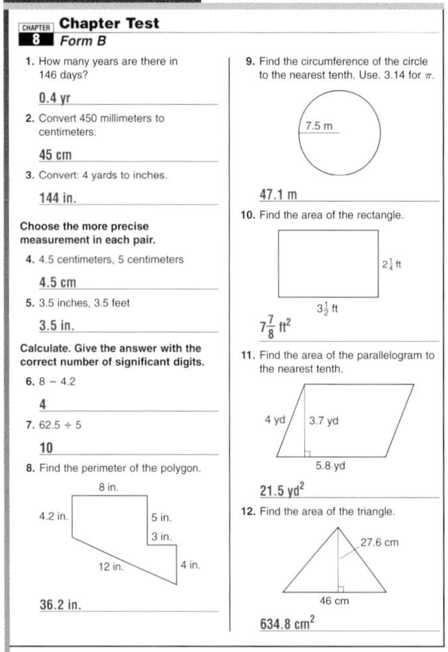

CHAPTER 8 Chapter Test
Form B

1. How many years are there in 146 days?
   0.4 yr
2. Convert 450 millimeters to centimeters.
   45 cm
3. Convert: 4 yards to inches.
   144 in.

Choose the more precise measurement in each pair.

4. 4.5 centimeters, 5 centimeters
   4.5 cm
5. 3.5 inches, 3.5 feet
   3.5 in.

Calculate. Give the answer with the correct number of significant digits.

6. 8 − 4.2
   4
7. 62.5 ÷ 5
   10
8. Find the perimeter of the polygon.
   8 in., 4.2 in., 5 in., 3 in., 12 in., 4 in.
   36.2 in.
9. Find the circumference of the circle to the nearest tenth. Use 3.14 for π.
   7.5 m
   47.1 m
10. Find the area of the rectangle.
    $2\frac{1}{4}$ ft, $3\frac{1}{2}$ ft
    $7\frac{7}{8}$ ft^2
11. Find the area of the parallelogram to the nearest tenth.
    4 yd, 3.7 yd, 5.8 yd
    21.5 yd^2
12. Find the area of the triangle.
    27.6 cm, 46 cm
    634.8 cm^2

CHAPTER 8 Chapter Test
Form B, continued

13. Find the area of the trapezoid.
    38 ft, 40 ft, 23 ft
    1,220 ft^2
14. Find the area of the trapezoid.
    4 cm, 4.2 cm, 9.2 cm, 6.4 cm
    26.8 cm^2
15. Find the area of the circle to the nearest tenth. Use 3.14 for π.
    12.6 mm
    124.6 mm^2
16. Find the area of the circle. Use $\frac{22}{7}$ for π.
    112 cm
    9,856 cm^2
17. Evaluate $(2.6)^2$.
    6.76
18. Evaluate 82^2.
    6,724

For 19–20, estimate each square root to the nearest whole number.

19. $\sqrt{98}$
    about 10
20. $\sqrt{139}$
    about 12
21. Use the Pythagorean Theorem to find the missing length.
    12.8 m, 9.6 m, ?
    16 m

Solve.

22. The top of a skateboard ramp leans on a building step that is 5 feet above the ground. The bottom of the ramp is 12 feet from the building. How long is the ramp?
    13 ft
23. Ruben and Skye stand together. Ruben walks east. Skye takes 32 steps south. They are now 40 steps apart. How far did Ruben walk?
    24 steps

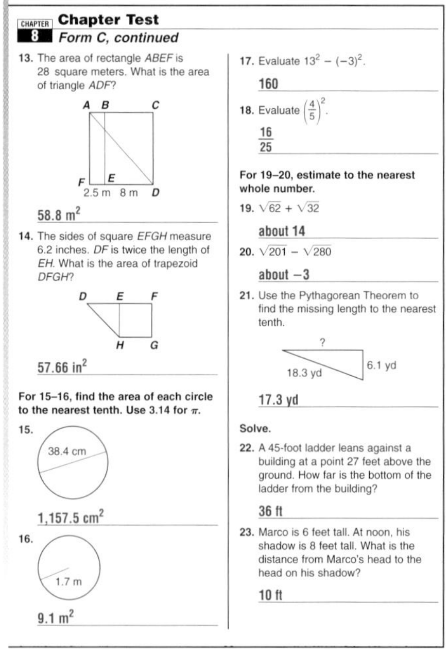

LEVEL C

CHAPTER 8 Chapter Test
Form C

1. How many seconds are there in a week?
   604,800 s
2. Convert 12.04 meters to millimeters.
   12,040 mm
3. Convert 2.5 miles 47 yards to feet.
   13,341 ft

Determine the number of significant digits.

4. 0.00460
   3
5. 5606.008
   7

Calculate. Give the answer with the correct number of significant digits.

6. 61.32 − 14.9
   46.4
7. 2.58 ÷ 3.5
   0.74
8. The perimeter of the pentagon is 52.6 centimeters. $AB = AE$, and $BC = DE$. What is the length of $\overline{AB}$?
   C 13.8 cm B, 9 cm, A, D, E, ?
   8 cm
9. The circumference of the circle is 38.936 inches. What is the radius? Use 3.14 for π.
   6.2 in.
10. The area of rectangle *ABEF* is 504 square inches. What is the perimeter of *BCDE*?
    A 18 in. B 30 in. C; F E D
    116 in.
11. The area of parallelogram *ABCE* is 384 square inches. Find the height *AD*.
    A 32 in. B; E D C
    12 in.
12. The area of the triangle is 150 square centimeters. What is the height of the triangle?
    J; K 25 cm L
    12 cm

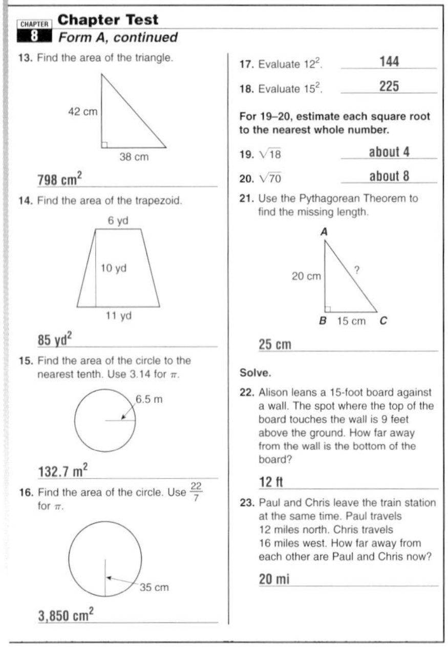

CHAPTER 8 Chapter Test
Form C, continued

13. The area of rectangle *ABEF* is 28 square meters. What is the area of triangle *ADF*?
    A B C; F E D; 2.5 m, 8 m
    58.8 m^2
14. The sides of square *EFGH* measure 6.2 inches. *DF* is twice the length of *EH*. What is the area of trapezoid *DFGH*?
    D E F; H G
    57.66 in^2

For 15–16, find the area of each circle to the nearest tenth. Use 3.14 for π.

15. 38.4 cm
    1,157.5 cm^2
16. 1.7 m
    9.1 m^2
17. Evaluate $13^2 - (-3)^2$.
    160
18. Evaluate $\left(\frac{4}{5}\right)^2$.
    $\frac{16}{25}$

For 19–20, estimate to the nearest whole number.

19. $\sqrt{62} + \sqrt{32}$
    about 14
20. $\sqrt{201} - \sqrt{280}$
    about −3
21. Use the Pythagorean Theorem to find the missing length to the nearest tenth.
    ?, 6.1 yd, 18.3 yd
    17.3 yd

Solve.

22. A 45-foot ladder leans against a building at a point 27 feet above the ground. How far is the bottom of the ladder from the building?
    36 ft
23. Marco is 6 feet tall. At noon, his shadow is 8 feet tall. What is the distance from Marco's head to the head on his shadow?
    10 ft

Test and Practice Generator
CD-ROM

Create and customize multiple versions of the same tests with corresponding answers for any chosen chapter objectives.

Chapter 8 State and Standardized Test Preparation

Test Taking Skill Builder and Standardized Test Practice are provided for each chapter in the *Test Prep Tool Kit*.

TEST TAKING SKILL BUILDER

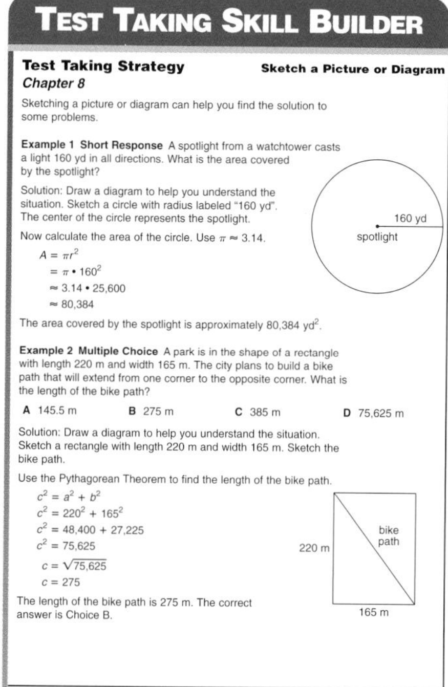

Test Taking Strategy — **Sketch a Picture or Diagram**
Chapter 8

Sketching a picture or diagram can help you find the solution to some problems.

Example 1 Short Response A spotlight from a watchtower casts a light 160 yd in all directions. What is the area covered by the spotlight?

Solution: Draw a diagram to help you understand the situation. Sketch a circle with radius labeled "160 yd". The center of the circle represents the spotlight.

Now calculate the area of the circle. Use $\pi \approx 3.14$.

$A = \pi r^2$
$= \pi \cdot 160^2$
$\approx 3.14 \cdot 25{,}600$
$\approx 80{,}384$

The area covered by the spotlight is approximately 80,384 yd^2.

Example 2 Multiple Choice A park is in the shape of a rectangle with length 220 m and width 165 m. The city plans to build a bike path that will extend from one corner to the opposite corner. What is the length of the bike path?

A 145.5 m **B** 275 m **C** 385 m **D** 75,625 m

Solution: Draw a diagram to help you understand the situation. Sketch a rectangle with length 220 m and width 165 m. Sketch the bike path.

Use the Pythagorean Theorem to find the length of the bike path.

$c^2 = a^2 + b^2$
$c^2 = 220^2 + 165^2$
$c^2 = 48{,}400 + 27{,}225$
$c^2 = 75{,}625$
$c = \sqrt{75{,}625}$
$c = 275$

The length of the bike path is 275 m. The correct answer is Choice B.

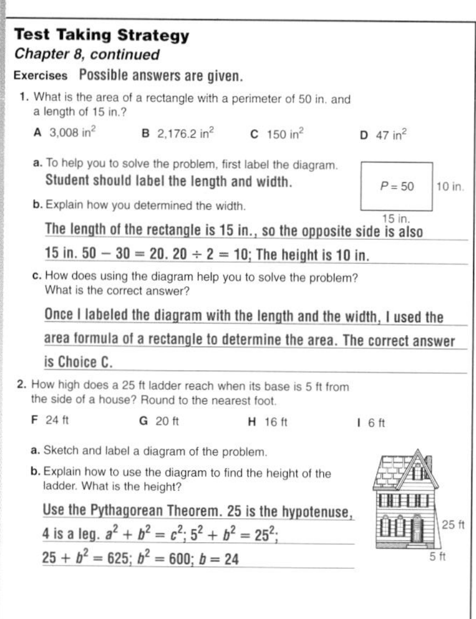

Test Taking Strategy
Chapter 8, continued

Exercises Possible answers are given.

1. What is the area of a rectangle with a perimeter of 50 in. and a length of 15 in.?

   A 3,008 in^2 **B** 2,176.2 in^2 **C** 150 in^2 **D** 47 in^2

   a. To help you to solve the problem, first label the diagram.
   Student should label the length and width.

   b. Explain how you determined the width.
   The length of the rectangle is 15 in., so the opposite side is also 15 in. $50 - 30 = 20$. $20 \div 2 = 10$; The height is 10 in.

   c. How does using the diagram help you to solve the problem? What is the correct answer?
   Once I labeled the diagram with the length and the width, I used the area formula of a rectangle to determine the area. The correct answer is Choice C.

2. How high does a 25 ft ladder reach when its base is 5 ft from the side of a house? Round to the nearest foot.

   F 24 ft **G** 20 ft **H** 16 ft **I** 6 ft

   a. Sketch and label a diagram of the problem.

   b. Explain how to use the diagram to find the height of the ladder. What is the height?
   Use the Pythagorean Theorem. 25 is the hypotenuse, 4 is a leg. $a^2 + b^2 = c^2$; $5^2 + b^2 = 25^2$; $25 + b^2 = 625$; $b^2 = 600$; $b = 24$

STANDARDIZED TEST PRACTICE

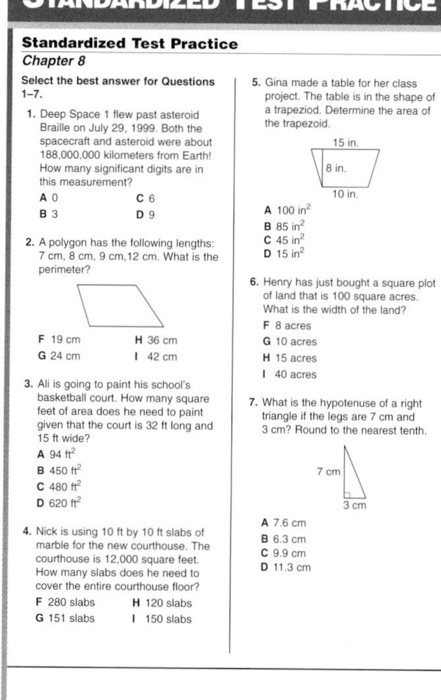

Standardized Test Practice
Chapter 8

Select the best answer for Questions 1–7.

1. Deep Space 1 flew past asteroid Braille on July 29, 1999. Both the spacecraft and asteroid were about 188,000,000 kilometers from Earth! How many significant digits are in this measurement?

   A 0 **C** 6
   B 3 **D** 9

2. A polygon has the following lengths: 7 cm, 8 cm, 9 cm, 12 cm. What is the perimeter?

   F 19 cm **H** 36 cm
   G 24 cm **I** 42 cm

3. Ali is going to paint his school's basketball court. How many square feet of area does he need to paint given that the court is 32 ft long and 15 ft wide?

   A 94 ft^2
   B 450 ft^2
   C 480 ft^2
   D 620 ft^2

4. Nick is using 10 ft by 10 ft slabs of marble for the new courthouse. The courthouse is 12,000 square feet. How many slabs does he need to cover the entire courthouse floor?

   F 280 slabs **H** 120 slabs
   G 151 slabs **I** 150 slabs

5. Gina made a table for her class project. The table is in the shape of a trapeziod. Determine the area of the trapezoid.

   A 100 in^2
   B 85 in^2
   C 45 in^2
   D 15 in^2

6. Henry has just bought a square plot of land that is 100 square acres. What is the width of the land?

   F 8 acres
   G 10 acres
   H 15 acres
   I 40 acres

7. What is the hypotenuse of a right triangle if the legs are 7 cm and 3 cm? Round to the nearest tenth.

   A 7.6 cm
   B 6.3 cm
   C 9.9 cm
   D 11.3 cm

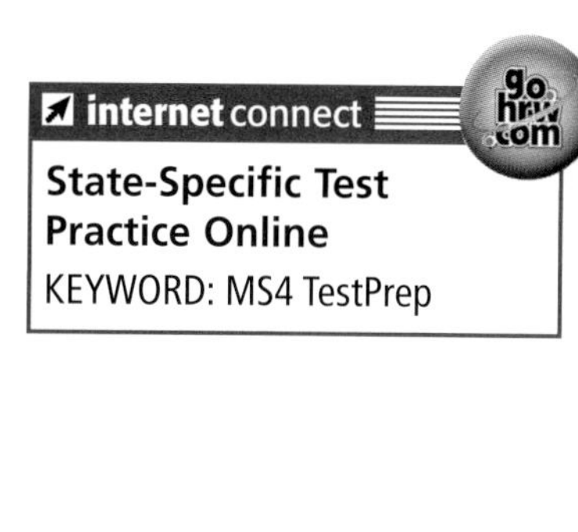

State-Specific Test Practice Online
KEYWORD: MS4 TestPrep

Test Prep Tool Kit

- Standardized Test Prep Workbook
- Countdown to Testing transparencies
- State Test Prep CD-ROM
- Standardized Test Prep Video

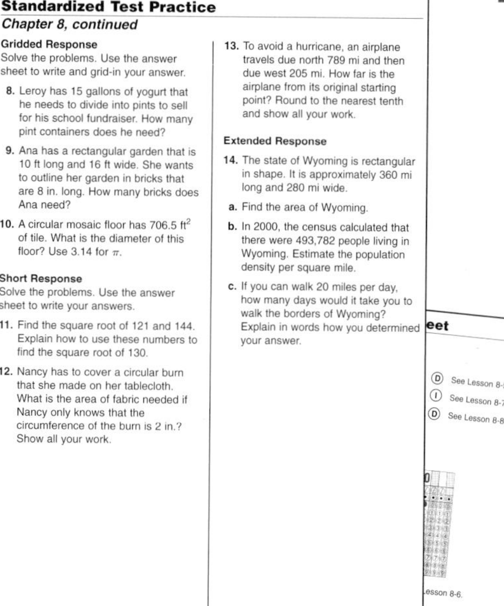

Standardized Test Practice
Chapter 8, continued

Gridded Response
Solve the problems. Use the answer sheet to write and grid-in your answer.

8. Leroy has 15 gallons of yogurt that he needs to divide into pints to sell for his school fundraiser. How many pint containers does he need?

9. Ana has a rectangular garden that is 10 ft long and 16 ft wide. She wants to outline her garden in bricks that are 8 in. long. How many bricks does Ana need?

10. A circular mosaic floor has 706.5 ft^2 of tile. What is the diameter of this floor? Use 3.14 for π.

Short Response
Solve the problems. Use the answer sheet to write your answers.

11. Find the square root of 121 and 144. Explain how to use these numbers to find the square root of 130.

12. Nancy has to cover a circular burn that she made on her tablecloth. What is the area of fabric needed if Nancy only knows that the circumference of the burn is 2 in.? Show all your work.

13. To avoid a hurricane, an airplane travels due north 789 mi and then due west 205 mi. How far is the airplane from its original starting point? Round to the nearest tenth and show all your work.

Extended Response

14. The state of Wyoming is rectangular in shape. It is approximately 360 mi long and 280 mi wide.

    a. Find the area of Wyoming.

    b. In 2000, the census calculated that there were 493,782 people living in Wyoming. Estimate the population density per square mile.

    c. If you can walk 20 miles per day, how many days would it take you to walk the borders of Wyoming? Explain in words how you determined your answer.

...eet

Ⓓ See Lesson 8-5.
Ⓘ See Lesson 8-7.
Ⓓ See Lesson 8-8.

...esson 8-6.

...between 121 and 144 so the square root of 130 is between 11 and 12. Since 130 is closer to 121 than 144, the square root of 130 is approximately 11.4.

12. $C = 2\pi r = 2$; $r = \frac{1}{\pi}$; $A = \left(\frac{1}{\pi}\right)^2 \pi = \frac{1}{\pi} \approx 0.32$. The area of the burn is approximately 0.32 in^2. (See Lesson 8-7.)

13. $789^2 + 205^2 = \sqrt{664{,}546} = 815.2$; The airplane is 815.2 miles from its original starting point. (See Lesson 8-6.)

(See Lesson 8-8.)

Extended Response
Write your answers for Problem 14 on the back of this paper.
See Lesson 8-4.

Customized answer sheets give students realistic practice for actual standardized tests.

Chapter 8

Perimeter, Circumference, and Area

Why Learn This?

Tell students that the geometric concepts of perimeter, circumference, and area are used in many careers. Have students look at the photograph. Discuss why it is important for fruit tree growers to be able to calculate perimeter, circumference, and area.

Possible answer: Fruit tree growers need to know how to find perimeter or circumference if they want to fence in a grove. They need to know how to calculate area to determine how many trees they can plant.

Using Data

To begin the study of this chapter, have students:

- Look up the number of square feet in an acre. 43,560 square feet
- Find the number of acres to the nearest acre planted with grapefruit, lemon, lime, and orange trees in Florida. grapefruit: 81,497 acres; lemon: 1,034 acres; lime: 3,160 acres; orange: 657,813 acres

Chapter 8

TABLE OF CONTENTS

internet connect
Chapter Opener Online
go.hrw.com
KEYWORD: MS4 Ch8

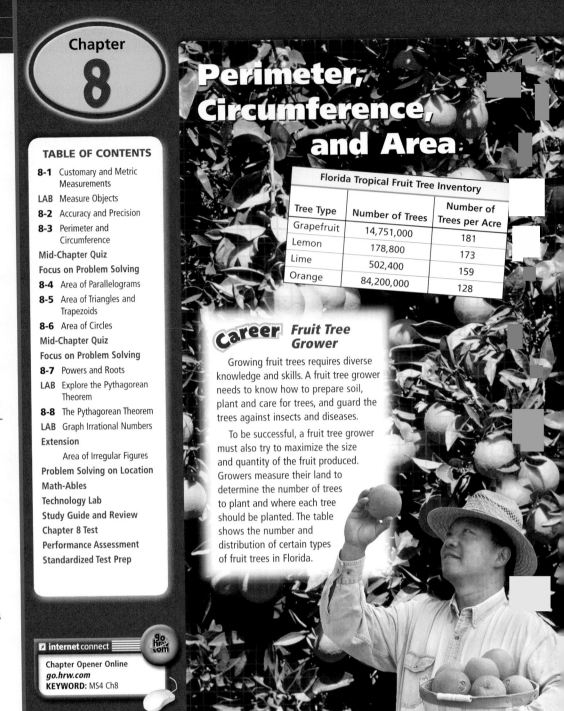

Perimeter, Circumference, and Area

Florida Tropical Fruit Tree Inventory

Tree Type	Number of Trees	Number of Trees per Acre
Grapefruit	14,751,000	181
Lemon	178,800	173
Lime	502,400	159
Orange	84,200,000	128

Career ***Fruit Tree Grower***

Growing fruit trees requires diverse knowledge and skills. A fruit tree grower needs to know how to prepare soil, plant and care for trees, and guard the trees against insects and diseases.

To be successful, a fruit tree grower must also try to maximize the size and quantity of the fruit produced. Growers measure their land to determine the number of trees to plant and where each tree should be planted. The table shows the number and distribution of certain types of fruit trees in Florida.

Problem Solving Project

Purpose: To solve problems using information about area, circumference, and perimeter

Materials: Got a Lemon? Make Lemonade worksheet

internet connect
Chapter Project Online: go.hrw.com
KEYWORD: MS4 PSProject8
go.hrw.com

Understand, Plan, Solve, and Look Back

Have students:

✔ Complete the Got a Lemon? Make Lemonade worksheet with measurement and area calculations.

✔ Research to find the proper amount of soil needed by each type of tree to remain healthy. What are some of the other concerns tree growers must consider to keep their trees healthy? Which states grow large numbers of citrus fruits? Does your state? If so, how does it compare with Florida?

✔ Check students' work.

ARE YOU READY?

Choose the best term from the list to complete each sentence.

diameter	parallelogram
radius	right triangle
trapezoid	

1. A(n) __?__ is a quadrilateral with exactly one pair of parallel sides. **trapezoid**
2. A(n) __?__ is a four-sided figure with opposite sides that are congruent and parallel. **parallelogram**
3. The __?__ of a circle is one-half the __?__ of the circle. **radius; diameter**

Complete these exercises to review skills you will need for this chapter.

✔ Round Whole Numbers

Round each number to the nearest ten and nearest hundred.

4. 1,535 **1,540; 1,500**
5. 294 **290; 300**
6. 30,758 **30,760; 30,800**
7. 497 **500; 500**

✔ Round Decimals

Round each number to the nearest whole number and nearest tenth.

8. 6.18 **6; 6.2**
9. 10.50 **11; 10.5**
10. 513.93 **514; 513.9**
11. 29.06 **29; 29.1**

✔ Multiply with Decimals

Multiply.

12. $5.63 \cdot 8$ **45.04**
13. $9.67 \cdot 4.3$ **41.581**
14. $8.34 \cdot 16$ **133.44**
15. $6.08 \cdot 0.56$ **3.4048**

✔ Order of Operations

Evaluate each expression.

16. $2 \cdot 9 + 2 \cdot 6$ **30**
17. $2(15 + 8)$ **46**
18. $4 \cdot 6.8 + 7 \cdot 9.3$ **92.3**
19. $14(25.9 + 13.6)$ **553**

✔ Identify Polygons

Name each figure.

20.  **trapezoid**

21.  **triangle**

22. 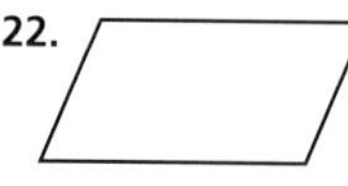 **parallelogram**

Assessing Prior Knowledge

INTERVENTION 

Diagnose and Prescribe

Evaluate your students' performance on this page to determine whether intervention is necessary or whether enrichment is appropriate. Options that provide instruction, practice, and a check are listed below.

Resources for Are You Ready?

- ***Are You Ready? Intervention and Enrichment***
- **Recording Sheet for Are You Ready?** *Chapter 8 Resource Book ...... p. 3*

 ***Are You Ready? Intervention* CD-ROM**

internet connect 

Are You Ready? Intervention
go.hrw.com
KEYWORD: MS4 AYR

ARE YOU READY?

Were students successful with Are You Ready?

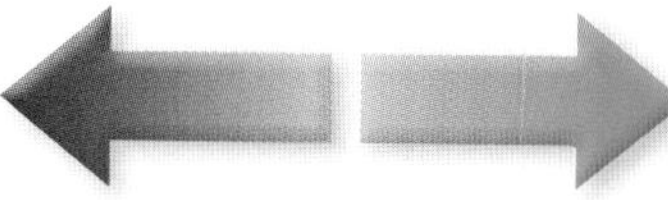

NO INTERVENE | **YES ENRICH**

✔Round Whole Numbers
Are You Ready? Intervention, Skill 3
Blackline Masters, Online, and
 **CD-ROM** Intervention Activities

✔Round Decimals
Are You Ready? Intervention, Skill 16
Blackline Masters, Online, and
 **CD-ROM** Intervention Activities

✔Multiply with Decimals
Are You Ready? Intervention, Skill 40
Blackline Masters, Online, and
  **CD-ROM** Intervention Activities

✔Order of Operations
Are You Ready? Intervention, Skill 51
Blackline Masters, Online, and
 **CD-ROM** Intervention Activities

✔Identify Polygons
Are You Ready? Intervention, Skill 76
Blackline Masters, Online, and
 **CD-ROM** Intervention Activities

Are You Ready? Enrichment, pp. 421–422

Section

8A Measurement, Perimeter, and Circumference

One-Minute Section Planner

Lesson	Materials	Resources
Lesson 8-1 Customary and Metric Measurements **NCTM:** Measurement, Problem Solving, Communication, Representation **NAEP:** Measurement 2b ☑ SAT-9 ☑ SAT-10 ☑ ITBS ☑ CTBS ☑ MAT ☑ CAT	**Optional** Calculator Recording sheet to summarize lesson (*CRB,* p. 87) Teaching Transparency T2 (*CRB*)	• *Chapter 8 Resource Book,* pp. 6–14 • Daily Transparency T1, CRB • Additional Examples Transparencies T3–T4, CRB • *Alternate Openers: Explorations,* p. 68
Hands-On Lab 8A Measure Objects **NCTM:** Measurement, Connections, Representation **NAEP:** Measurement 1b ☐ SAT-9 ☐ SAT-10 ☑ ITBS ☑ CTBS ☐ MAT ☐ CAT	**Required** Standard and metric rulers (*MK, CRB, p. 88*)	• *Hands-On Lab Activities,* pp. 73–74, 127
Lesson 8-2 Accuracy and Precision **NCTM:** Number and Operations, Measurement, Communication **NAEP:** Measurement 2e ☐ SAT-9 ☐ SAT-10 ☑ ITBS ☐ CTBS ☐ MAT ☐ CAT	**Optional** Pencils Standard and metric rulers (*MK, CRB, p. 88*) Teaching Transparency T6 (*CRB*)	• *Chapter 8 Resource Book,* pp. 15–23 • Daily Transparency T5, CRB • Additional Examples Transparencies T7–T8, CRB • *Alternate Openers: Explorations,* p. 69
Lesson 8-3 Perimeter and Circumference **NCTM:** Measurement, Communication, Connections **NAEP:** Measurement 1h ☑ SAT-9 ☑ SAT-10 ☑ ITBS ☑ CTBS ☑ MAT ☑ CAT	**Optional** Standard and metric rulers (*MK, CRB, p. 88*) String Various circular objects	• *Chapter 8 Resource Book,* pp. 24–33 • Daily Transparency T9, CRB • Additional Examples Transparencies T10–T12, CRB • *Alternate Openers: Explorations,* p. 70
Section 8A Assessment		• Mid-Chapter Quiz, SE p. 428 • Section 8A Quiz, AR p. 22 • *Test and Practice Generator* CD-ROM

SAT = *Stanford Achievement Tests* **ITBS** = *Iowa Test of Basic Skills* **CTBS** = *Comprehensive Test of Basic Skills/Terra Nova*
MAT = *Metropolitan Achievement Test* **CAT** = *California Achievement Test*

NCTM—Complete standards can be found on pages T27–T33. **NAEP**—Complete standards can be found on pages A35–A39.

SE = *Student Edition* **TE** = *Teacher's Edition* **AR** = *Assessment Resources* **CRB** = *Chapter Resource Book* **MK** = *Manipulatives Kit*

Section Overview

Customary and Metric Measurements — Lesson 8-1

Why? In real-life situations, you often need to use measurements and calculations with measurements in order to find perimeter, area, and volume. Skill with unit conversion factors will help students with biology, chemistry, and physics.

Multiply by unit conversion factors.
4 quarts = 1 gallon
2 pints = 1 quart

Convert 3 gallons to pints.

$3\ \cancel{gal} \cdot \frac{4\ \cancel{qt}}{1\ \cancel{gal}} \cdot \frac{2\ pt}{1\ \cancel{qt}} = 24\ pt$ There are 24 pints in 3 gallons.

Accuracy and Precision — Hands-On Lab 8A, Lesson 8-2

Why? Accuracy, precision, and significant digits are important concepts in science; however, you should recognize that no measurement is exact and that a measurement depends on the tool used to measure.

Identifying Significant Digits		
• Nonzero digits	58.92	4 significant digits
• Zeros between significant digits	90.207	5 significant digits
• Zeros after the last nonzero digit and to the right of the decimal point	0.0060	2 significant digits

Perimeter and Circumference — Lesson 8-3

Why? To find the distance around an athletic field, you need to be able to calculate perimeter. The perimeter of a circle is called the circumference of the circle. Being able to find the distances around figures will prepare students for finding the areas of like figures.

Find the circumference of the circle to the nearest tenth.

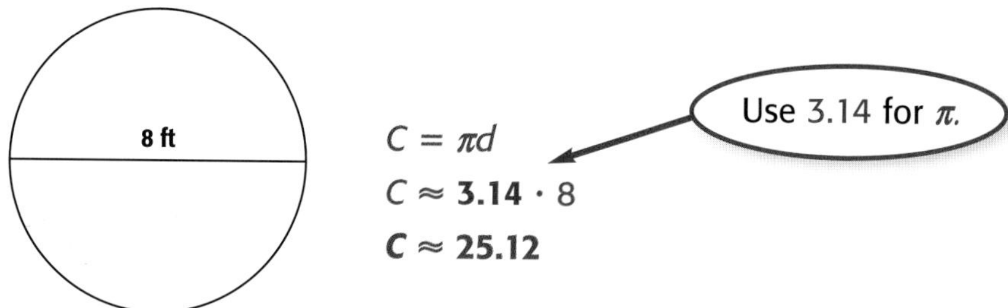

The circumference is about 25.1 ft.

8-1 Organizer

Pacing: Traditional 1 day
Block $\frac{1}{2}$ day

Objective: Students convert measurements within the customary and metric systems.

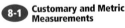

Warm Up

1. How many days are in 1 week? **7**
2. How many seconds are in 1 minute? **60**
3. How many inches are in 1 foot? **12**
4. How many hours are in 1 day? **24**
5. How many inches are in 1 yard? **36**

Problem of the Day

It takes a driver about $\frac{3}{4}$ second to begin braking after seeing something on the road. How many feet does a car travel in that time if it is going 10 mi/h? 20 mi/h? 30 mi/h?
11 ft; 22 ft; 33 ft

Available on Daily Transparency in CRB

Math Fact !!

Jewelers measure diamonds in carats. One metric carat weighs 200 milligrams.

8-1 Customary and Metric Measurements

Learn to convert measurements within the customary and metric systems.

To conserve energy and to avoid the heat of the day, lions spend much of their time resting—usually up to 20 hours a day. This means that in one year, a lion spends about 7,300 hours resting.

You can use *unit conversion*, which you explored in Lesson 5-4, to find out how many days there are in 7,300 hours. Recall that a *unit conversion factor* is a fraction whose numerator and denominator represent the same quantity but in different units.

EXAMPLE 1 Converting Between Units of Time

Remember!
60 s = 1 min
60 min = 1 hr
24 hr = 1 day
365 days = 1 yr

About how many days are there in 7,300 hours?

There are 24 hours in 1 day, so the possible conversion factors are $\frac{1 \text{ day}}{24 \text{ hr}}$ or $\frac{24 \text{ hr}}{1 \text{ day}}$. Choose the first factor so that hour units will cancel.

$$7{,}300 \cancel{\text{hr}} \cdot \frac{1 \text{ day}}{24 \cancel{\text{hr}}} = \frac{7{,}300 \text{ days}}{24}$$

$$\approx 304 \text{ days}$$

There are about 304 days in 7,300 hours.

We use two systems of measurement: customary and metric. The customary system is based on measurements from old English law, and the metric system is based on powers of ten. Each system has its own units.

Measure	Customary System	Metric System
Length/distance	12 inches (in.) = 1 foot (ft) 3 feet = 1 yard (yd) 5,280 feet = 1 mile (mi)	10 millimeters (mm) = 1 centimeter (cm) 100 centimeters = 1 meter (m) 1,000 meters = 1 kilometer (km)
Volume/capacity	8 fluid ounces (fl oz) = 1 cup (c) 2 cups = 1 pint (pt) 2 pints = 1 quart (qt) 4 quarts = 1 gallon (gal)	1,000 milliliters (mL) = 1 liter (L)
Weight/mass	16 ounces (oz) = 1 pound (lb) 2,000 pounds = 1 ton	1,000 milligrams (mg) = 1 gram (g) 1,000 grams = 1 kilogram (kg)

1 Introduce

Alternate Opener

EXPLORATION

8-1 Customary and Metric Measurements

1. Is it possible that the average person's heart beats 3 billion times in his or her lifetime? To answer this question, use a calculator to perform the following steps.
   a. Count the number of times your heart beats in several 15-second intervals and find the average.
   b. How many heartbeats do you average per minute? (Multiply the average in part **a** by 4.)
   c. How many heartbeats do you average per hour? (Multiply the average in part **b** by 60.)
   d. How many heartbeats do you average per day? (Multiply the average in part **c** by 24.)
   e. How many heartbeats do you average per year? (Multiply the average in part **d** by 365.)
   f. Suppose you live until you are 80 years old. How many total heartbeats could you expect to have in your lifetime? (Multiply the average in part **e** by 80.)

Think and Discuss

2. **Explain** why you were asked to multiply the average by 4 in number **1b**.
3. **Discuss** whether it is possible that the average person's heart beats 3 billion times in his or her lifetime.

Motivate

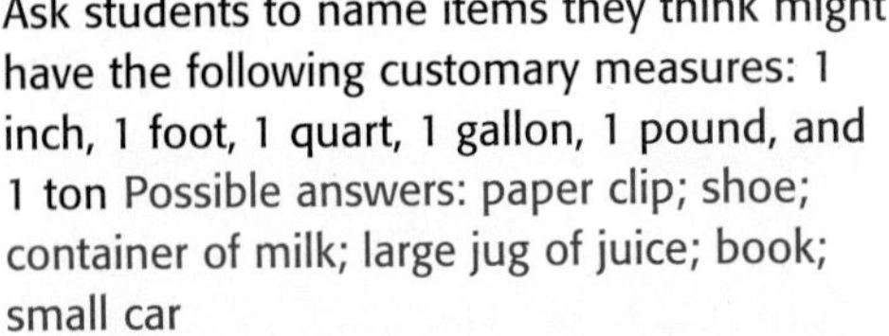

Ask students to name items they think might have the following customary measures: 1 inch, 1 foot, 1 quart, 1 gallon, 1 pound, and 1 ton Possible answers: paper clip; shoe; container of milk; large jug of juice; book; small car

Repeat the same activity using the following metric measures: 1 meter, 1 liter, and 1 gram Possible answers: length of an adult's arm; bottle of spring water; thumbtack

Exploration worksheet and answers on Chapter 8 Resource Book pp. 7 and 92

2 Teach

Lesson Presentation

Guided Instruction

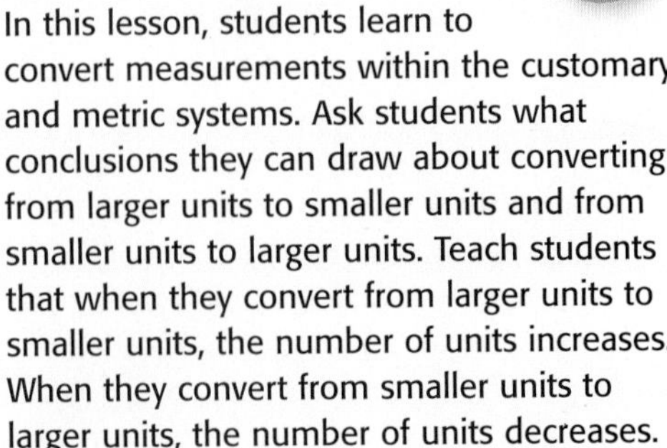

In this lesson, students learn to convert measurements within the customary and metric systems. Ask students what conclusions they can draw about converting from larger units to smaller units and from smaller units to larger units. Teach students that when they convert from larger units to smaller units, the number of units increases. When they convert from smaller units to larger units, the number of units decreases.

Teaching Tip Guide students to realize that they will multiply when working from larger to smaller units and divide when working from smaller to larger units.

EXAMPLE 2 **Making One-Step Unit Conversions**

Convert 25 kilometers to meters.

There are 1,000 meters in 1 kilometer.

$$25 \cancel{\text{km}} \cdot \frac{1{,}000 \text{ m}}{1 \cancel{\text{km}}} = \frac{25 \cdot 1{,}000 \text{ m}}{1}$$ *Use a unit conversion factor.*

$$= 25{,}000 \text{ m}$$

So 25 kilometers is equal to 25,000 meters.

EXAMPLE 3 **PROBLEM SOLVING APPLICATION**

Selena is selling juice during the intermission of a school play. If she has 6 quarts of juice, how many 1-cup servings of juice can she pour?

1 Understand the Problem

Rewrite the question as a statement:

- Find the number of cups in 6 quarts.

List the **important information:**

- Selena has 6 quarts of juice.

2 Make a Plan

Use unit conversion factors to convert quarts to pints and then pints to cups.

3 Solve

$$6 \cancel{\text{qt}} \cdot \frac{2 \cancel{\text{pt}}}{1 \cancel{\text{qt}}} \cdot \frac{2 \text{ c}}{1 \cancel{\text{pt}}} = 6 \cdot 2 \cdot 2 \text{ c}$$ *Use two conversion factors.*

$$= 24 \text{ c}$$

Since 6 quarts is equal to 24 cups, Selena can pour 24 one-cup servings of juice.

4 Look Back

A cup is a smaller unit than a quart, so the answer should be greater than 6. So 24 is a reasonable answer.

Think and Discuss

1. **Describe** how you could use mental math to convert measurements within the metric system.
2. **Write** a unit conversion factor that relates ounces to tons.

COMMON ERROR ALERT

Remind students to be sure they are using the correct unit conversion factors, especially when more than one is needed, as in Example 3.

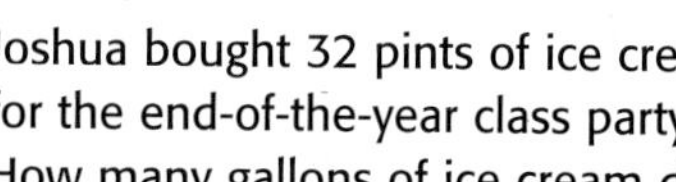

Additional Examples

Example 1

How many hours are there in 102 days? 2,448 hours

Example 2

Convert 2,500 centimeters to meters. 25 meters

Example 3

Joshua bought 32 pints of ice cream for the end-of-the-year class party. How many gallons of ice cream did he buy for the party? 4 gallons

Example 3 note: Discuss how to choose the correct conversion factors when using more than one. After students share ideas, point out that you should always begin with a conversion factor that has the unit of measure from which you are converting; then use others as needed to get to the unit to which you are converting.

3 Close

Reaching All Learners

Through Grouping Strategies

Let students work in groups. Tell them to make up riddles about classroom objects. Each riddle should include customary or metric measures and a conversion question. Have groups exchange riddles, convert the measures in the riddles, and solve the riddles.

Possible answer: Riddle: I am yellow, found in the classroom, and about 6 inches long. What am I, and how many feet long am I? Answer: pencil; $\frac{1}{2}$ ft

Summarize

Have students complete a three-column table with the customary and metric units for length, inch, foot, yard, mile, millimeter, centimeter, meter, kilometer volume/capacity, cup, pint, quart, gallon, milliliter, liter and weight/mass. ounce, pound, ton, milligram, gram, kilogram A recording sheet for this activity can be found on p. 87 of the Chapter 8 Resource Book.

Answers to Think and Discuss

1. Possible answer: You can convert larger units, such as kilometers, to smaller units, such as meters, by mentally multiplying by a power of 10; you can convert smaller units to larger units by mentally dividing by a power of 10.
2. Possible answer: $\frac{32{,}000 \text{ ounces}}{1 \text{ ton}}$

8-1 PRACTICE & ASSESS

Students may want to refer back to the lesson examples.

Assignment Guide

If you finished Example 1 assign:
Core 1, 2, 10–13, 30, 32, 46–51
Enriched 1, 2, 10–13, 30, 32, 46–51

If you finished Example 2 assign:
Core 1–8, 10–22, 30, 32, 46–51
Enriched 1–7 odd, 11–21 odd, 25–36, 46–51

If you finished Example 3 assign:
Core 1–24, 25–41 odd, 46–51
Enriched 1–23 odd, 25–51

Notes

8-1 Exercises

FOR EXTRA PRACTICE
see page 671

internet connect
Homework Help Online
go.hrw.com Keyword: MS4 8-1

GUIDED PRACTICE

See Example 1
1. How many hours are there in 24 days? **576 hr**
2. How many minutes are there in 450 seconds? **7.5 min**

See Example 2
Convert.

3. 5 gal = ___ qt **20 qt**
4. 600 min = ___ hr **10 hr**
5. 3,700 mg = ___ g **3.7 g**
6. 100 m = ___ cm **10,000 cm**
7. 8 mi = ___ ft **42,240 ft**
8. 72 oz = ___ lb **4.5 lb**

See Example 3
9. Roger has 48 pints of strawberries. How many gallon containers would he need to hold all of the strawberries? **6 gallon containers**

INDEPENDENT PRACTICE

See Example 1
10. How many days are there in 9 years? **3,285 days**
11. How many seconds are there in 45 minutes? **2,700 s**
12. How many years are there in 292 days? **0.8 yr**
13. How many minutes are there in 8.3 hours? **498 min**

See Example 2
Convert.

14. 4.2 kg = ___ g **4,200 g**
15. 0.5 ton = ___ lb **1,000 lb**
16. 3.8 mm = ___ cm **0.38 cm**
17. 217 cm = ___ m **2.17 m**
18. 48 oz = ___ lb **3 lb**
19. 10 qt = ___ gal **2.5 gal**
20. 3.5 qt = ___ pt **7 pt**
21. $8\frac{1}{3}$ yd = ___ ft **25 ft**
22. 2.2 mi = ___ ft **11,616 ft**

See Example 3
23. Cassie is planning a 2-day nonstop Valentine's Day tribute on her radio show. If each person can give a 1-minute tribute, how many tributes can Cassie play? **2,880 tributes**
24. In 1998, a 2,505-gallon ice cream float was made in Atlanta, Georgia. How many 1-pint servings did the float contain? **20,040 servings**

PRACTICE AND PROBLEM SOLVING

Convert.

25. 64 oz = ___ lb **4 lb**
26. 7.9 m = ___ km **0.0079 km**
27. 2 mi = ___ yd **3,520 yd**
28. 4 gal = ___ c **64 c**
29. 1.6 m = ___ mm **1,600 mm**
30. 2,160 min = ___ days **1.5 days**

Compare. Write <, >, or =.

31. 6 yd ___ 12 ft **>**
32. 70 s ___ 1 min **>**
33. 80 oz ___ 5 lb **=**
34. 40 cm ___ 40 mm **>**
35. 25 m ___ 250 cm **>**
36. 18 in. ___ 3 ft **<**

Math Background

The customary system was inherited from the British imperial system. This system was preferred in the United States until 1988. The Trade Act of 1988 states that the metric system is the preferred system to use in the United States for trade and commerce.

The metric system is made up of a combination of prefixes and basic unit names. For example, *kilo-* is the prefix for thousandfold, and the meter is the basic unit of length. Thus, a kilometer is 1,000 meters. Some other prefixes used with basic units are as follows:

giga = billionfold *milli* = thousandth
mega = millionfold *micro* = millionth
centi = hundredth *nano* = billionth

RETEACH 8-1

LESSON 8-1 **Reteach**
Customary and Metric Measurements

To convert between units of time, you need to recall these facts:

1 min = 60 s 1 hr = 60 min 1 day = 24 hr 1 yr = 365 days

How many minutes are in 4 hours?
An hour is a larger unit than a minute.
Use the conversion fact: 1 hr = 60 min.
To change from hours to minutes, multiply by 60.
4 hr = 4 • 60 = 240 min

To change from a larger unit to a smaller unit, multiply.

How many days are in 168 hours?
A day is a larger unit than an hour.
Use the conversion fact: 1 day = 24 hr.
To change from hours to days, divide by 24.
168 hr = 168 ÷ 24 = 7 days

To change from a smaller unit to a larger unit, divide.

Convert.

1. 3,400 cm = ? m
Smaller unit → larger unit
Fact: **100** cm = **1** m
Operation: **divide**
3,400 cm = 3,400 **÷ 100** = **34** m

2. 5 lb = ? oz
Larger unit → smaller unit
Fact: **1** lb = **16** oz
Operation: **multiply**
5 lb = 5 **• 16** = **80** oz

3. 10 qt = ? gal
Smaller unit → larger unit
Fact: **4** qt = **1** gal
Operation: **divide**
10 qt = 10 **÷ 4** = **2.5** gal

4. 420 s = ? min
Smaller unit → larger unit
Fact: **1** min = **60** s
Operation: **divide**
420 s = 420 **÷ 60** = **7** min

PRACTICE 8-1

LESSON 8-1 **Practice B**
Customary and Metric Measurements

1. How many hours are there in 28 days? **672 hr**
2. How many minutes are there in 510 seconds? **8.5 min**
3. How many days are there in 7 years? **2,555 days**
4. How many seconds are there in 35 minutes? **2,100 s**
5. How many years are there in 219 days? **0.6 yr**
6. How many minutes are there in 6.2 hours? **372 min**

Convert.

7. 7 gal = **28** qt
8. 540 min = **9** hr
9. 5,200 mg = **5.2** g
10. 200 m = **20,000** cm
11. 3 mi = **15,840** ft
12. 56 oz = **3.5** lb
13. $17\frac{1}{2}$ hr = **1,050** min
14. $6\frac{1}{3}$ yd = **19** ft
15. 5.6 kg = **5,600** g
16. 144 hr = **6** days
17. 3.5 tons = **7,000** lb
18. 2.7 cm = **27** mm
19. 14 qt = **3.5** gal
20. 45 ft = **15** yd
21. 1.5 mi = **7,920** ft
22. 365 cm = **3.65** m
23. 252 min = **4.2** hr
24. 6.5 qt = **13** pt
25. 2.7 L = **2,700** mL
26. 740 m = **0.74** km

Solve.

27. Althea bought 5.5 gallons of fruit punch for the class picnic. How many pints of fruit punch did she buy?
44 pt
28. The 2002 New York City Marathon was won by Tesfaye Jifar of Ethiopia. He finished the race in 2 hours, 7 minutes, 42 seconds. How many seconds is this?
7,662 s
29. Lake Superior is the deepest of the Great Lakes. The deepest point is 1,333 feet. Write the depth in miles rounded to the nearest hundredth.
0.25 mi

37. ***EARTH SCIENCE*** The average depth of the Pacific Ocean is 12,925 feet. How deep is this, rounded to the nearest tenth of a mile? **2.4 mi**

The owner of this 1,009.6 lb pumpkin won the New England Giant Pumpkin Weigh-Off in September 2000.

go.hrw.com
KEYWORD: MS4 Pumpkin
CNN Student News

38. ***AGRICULTURE*** In one year, the United States produced nearly 895 million pounds of pumpkins. How many ounces were produced by the state with the lowest production shown in the table? **1,744 million oz**

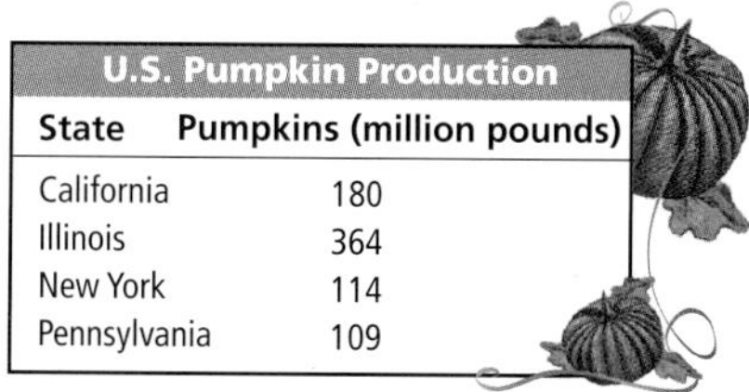

U.S. Pumpkin Production

State	Pumpkins (million pounds)
California	180
Illinois	364
New York	114
Pennsylvania	109

39. How many milliliters are there in a 2.2-liter container of juice? **2,200 mL**

40. ***MUSIC*** The shortest published opera is *The Sands of Time*, which lasted 4 minutes 9 seconds when it was first performed in 1993. How many seconds long was the performance? **249 s**

41. ***LITERATURE*** The novel *Twenty Thousand Leagues Under the Sea* was written by Jules Verne in 1873. One league is approximately 3.45 miles. How many miles are in 20,000 leagues? **about 69,000 mi**

42. ***SPORTS*** A marathon is a race that is 26 miles 385 yards long.
    a. Write a unit conversion factor that can be used to convert miles to yards. $\frac{1{,}760 \text{ yd}}{1 \text{ mi.}}$
    b. What is the length of a marathon in yards? **46,145 yd**

43. ***WHAT'S THE ERROR?*** A student used the following method to convert 85 centimeters to meters. What did the student do wrong?

$$85 \text{ cm} \cdot \frac{100 \text{ cm}}{1 \text{ m}} = 8{,}500 \text{ m}$$

44. ***WRITE ABOUT IT*** Explain how to convert 12,000 milligrams to kilograms.

45. ***CHALLENGE*** Chen's heart beats once per second. How many times does it beat in a year? **31,536,000 times**

Spiral Review

Find each sum or difference. (Lesson 4-2)

46. 3.8 + 4.02 **7.82** 47. 8 − 6.18 **1.82** 48. 18.4 − 13.61 **4.79** 49. 15.07 + 3.08 **18.15**

50. **TEST PREP** Eighty-four is 12% of what number? (Lesson 6-4) **A**

A 700
B 70
C 10.08
D 14.3

51. **TEST PREP** Describe the transformation shown. (Lesson 7-10) **H**

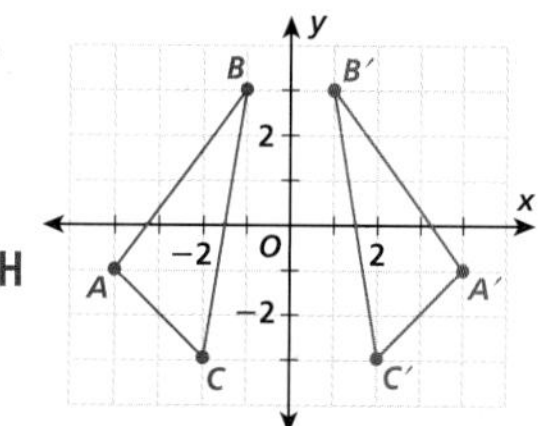

F Rotation
G Translation
H Reflection
J Glide reflection

Answers

43. Possible answer: The student multiplied by the wrong conversion factor. The student should have multiplied by $\frac{1 \text{ m}}{100 \text{ cm}}$.

44. Multiply by the conversion factor $\frac{1\text{g}}{1{,}000 \text{ mg}}$ and then by the conversion factor $\frac{1 \text{ kg}}{1{,}000 \text{ g}}$.

Journal 

Have students describe a situation in their own life in which they might need to convert from one customary or metric unit to another.

Test Prep Doctor 

For Exercise 50, encourage students to estimate the answer to eliminate choices. Students should realize that since 84 is 10% of 840, the answer should be a little less than 840. **A** is the correct answer. Students who chose **B** made an error when moving the decimal point. Students who chose **C** have taken 12% of 84. Students who chose **D** moved the decimal point in 84 instead of in 12.

For Exercise 51, have students consider the definition of each kind of transformation. In a rotation, the two figures would share at least one point. In a translation, the corresponding points would be in the same relative positions. Since the corresponding points are the same distance from the y-axis, **H** is the correct answer.

CHALLENGE 8-1

LESSON 8-1 **Challenge**
Conversion Diversion

The table shows data about some of the most famous baseball parks in the United States. Use the table to answer the questions.

Baseball Field	Team	Year Opened	Year Closed	Cost	Dimensions of the Center Field Line
Ebbets Field	Brooklyn Dodgers	1913	1957	$750,000	393 ft
Forbes Field	Pittsburgh Pirates	1909	1970	$1 million	400 ft
Tiger Stadium	Detroit Tigers	1912	1999	$8 million	440 ft
Yankee Stadium	New York Yankees	1923		$50 million	408 ft
L.A. Coliseum	Los Angeles Dodgers	1958	1961	$950,000	420 ft

1. How many inches was the center field line in Tiger Stadium? **5,280 in.**
2. How many thousands of dollars did it cost to build Yankee Stadium? **50,000 thousands**
3. For about how many months was the L.A. Coliseum open? **about 36 months**
4. How many quarters (25¢) would it have taken to build the L.A. Coliseum? **3,800,000 quarters**
5. How many inches longer was center field in Forbes Field than in Ebbets Field? **84 in. longer**
6. How many miles to the nearest hundredth of a mile was the center field line in the L.A. Coliseum? **0.08 mi**
7. For about how many months was Forbes Field open? **about 732 months**
8. How many yards is the center field line in Yankee Stadium? **136 yd**

PROBLEM SOLVING 8-1

LESSON 8-1 **Problem Solving**
Customary and Metric Measurements

Write the correct answer.

1. During NASA space shuttle missions, crewmembers must live together in tight quarters. A mission typically lasts about 11 days. How many minutes is that? **15,840 min**
2. As of January 1998, the total space flight experience of the United States was about 5,768 days. How many years of experience to the nearest tenth of a year is that? **15.8 yr**
3. Mr. Juarez bought 6 bottles of orange juice. Each bottle contained 1,200 milliliters of juice. How many liters of juice did he buy? **7.2 L**
4. Latrell and Lamar are twins. Latrell is 2 hours and 4 minutes older than Lamar. How many seconds older is Latrell than Lamar? **7,440 s older**

Choose the letter of the correct answer.

5. Jim drinks at least 2 cups of juice per day. If he does this every day for a year, about how many gallons of juice he will drink in a year?
   A about 182 gal (C) about 46 gal
   B about 91 gal D about 11 gal
6. One of the oldest actresses to win the "Best Actress" Oscar was Jessica Tandy in 1989. She was 960 months old. How old was she in years?
   F 90 years old H 60 years old
   (G) 80 years old J 40 years old
7. One of the tallest trees in the United States is a Coast Douglas fir located in Coos County, Oregon. It is 3,948 inches tall. How many feet tall is it?
   (A) 329 ft C 1,316 ft
   B 109.7 ft D 11,844 ft
8. There is 0.25 kilometer between Paul's house and his next-door neighbor's house. How many centimeters are there between the two houses?
   F 250,000 cm H 2,500 cm
   (G) 25,000 cm J 250 cm
9. Rainfall in Pago Pago averages about 4,990 millimeters each year. How many centimeters of rainfall does Pago Pago average per year?
   A 499,000 cm C 4,990 cm
   B 49,900 cm (D) 499 cm
10. If a kitten weighs 2.5 pounds, how many ounces does it weigh?
   F 250 oz (H) 40 oz
   G 48 oz J 20 oz

Lesson Quiz 

1. How many minutes are there in 5.5 hours? **330 min**
2. How many seconds are in 2 hours? **7,200 s**

Convert.

3. 320 cm = ______m **3.2**
4. 64 oz = ______lb **4**
5. How many gallons of oil are needed to fill a 40-quart barrel? **10 gal**

Available on Daily Transparency in CRB

8A
Measure Objects

Pacing: Traditional 1 day
Block $\frac{1}{2}$ day

Objective: To use metric rulers to estimate measurements to a given degree of accuracy

Materials: Metric ruler

Lab Resources

Hands-On Lab Activities. pp. 73–74, 127

Using the Pages

Discuss with students the difference between a standard ruler and a metric ruler. Discuss the number of sections, or millimeters, into which each centimeter is divided.

Measure each length to the nearest centimeter and to the nearest tenth of a centimeter.

1. the length of your thumb
   Possible answer: 4 cm, 4.1 cm
2. the length of your foot
   Possible answer: 22 cm, 21.8 cm

Give an appropriate unit of measurement for each.

3. the height of a door
   Possible answer: meter
4. the weight of a dictionary
   Possible answer: kilogram

Answers

Activity 1

Think and Discuss

1. 18.1 cm; the measurement to the nearest tenth best represents the actual length because it gives more-exact information about the length of the pencil.
2. Possible answer: No; the measurement to the nearest tenth of a centimeter is more exact than a measurement in inches because the centimeter is a smaller unit than the inch.

Measure Objects

Use with Lesson 8-2

To measure the length in inches of an object, you can use a standard ruler. To measure the length in centimeters of an object, you can use a metric ruler.

Activity 1

1. Use a metric ruler to measure the length of the pencil to the nearest centimeter and to the nearest tenth of a centimeter.

On a metric ruler, the numbered divisions represent centimeters. Since the tip of the pencil is between the 18 cm mark and the 19 cm mark, the pencil is between 18 cm and 19 cm. The tip of the pencil is closest to the 18 cm mark, so to the nearest centimeter it is 18 cm long.

Each centimeter on the ruler is divided into tenths. Since the tip of the pencil is between the 18.1 cm mark and the 18.2 cm mark, the pencil is between 18.1 cm and 18.2 cm. The tip of the pencil is closest to the 18.1 cm mark, so to the nearest tenth of a centimeter it is 18.1 cm long.

Think and Discuss

1. Which measurement, 18 cm or 18.1 cm, best represents the actual length of the pencil? Explain.
2. Suppose you used a standard ruler to measure the pencil in inches. Would this measurement better represent the length of the pencil? Explain.

Try This

Measure each length to the nearest centimeter and to the nearest tenth of a centimeter.

1. 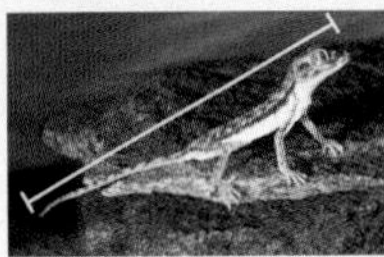 **3 cm; 3.3 cm**

2. 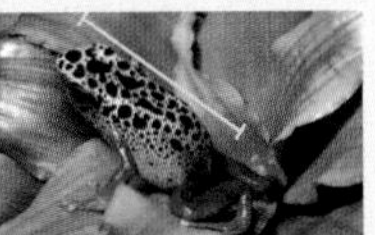 **2 cm; 1.8 cm**

Activity 2

1 Use a standard ruler to measure the lengths of the sides of the rectangle.

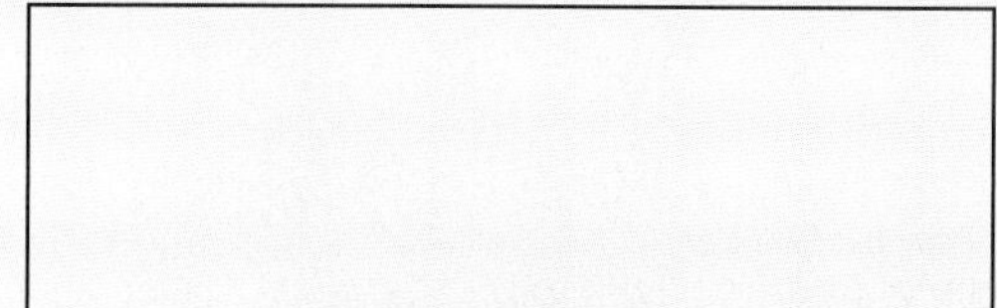

A standard ruler is 12 inches long, and each inch is divided into sixteenths. Therefore, each division on a ruler represents $\frac{1}{16}$ inch. The length of one of the longer sides of the rectangle is halfway between the 3-inch and 4-inch marks. So the length is $3\frac{8}{16}$ in., or $3\frac{1}{2}$ in. The length of one of the shorter sides is just over 1 inch. Since the side ends at the second mark after the 1-inch mark, the length is $1\frac{2}{16}$ in., or $1\frac{1}{8}$ in.

2 Find the distance around the rectangle.

$3\frac{8}{16} + 3\frac{8}{16} + 1\frac{2}{16} + 1\frac{2}{16} = 8 + \frac{20}{16}$ *Add the whole numbers. Then add the fractions.*

$= 8 + 1\frac{4}{16}$ *Write the fraction as a mixed number.*

$= 9\frac{4}{16}$ *Add the whole numbers.*

$= 9\frac{1}{4}$ *Write the fraction in simplest form.*

The distance around the rectangle is $9\frac{1}{4}$ inches.

Think and Discuss

1. Use a metric ruler to measure the length of each side of the rectangle in **1** to the nearest tenth of a centimeter. What can you conclude about the relationship between an inch and a centimeter?

Try This

Use a standard ruler to measure the lengths of the sides of each rectangle. Then find the distance around each rectangle.

1.

2.

Use a metric ruler to measure the lengths of the sides of each rectangle. Then find the distance around each rectangle.

3.

4.

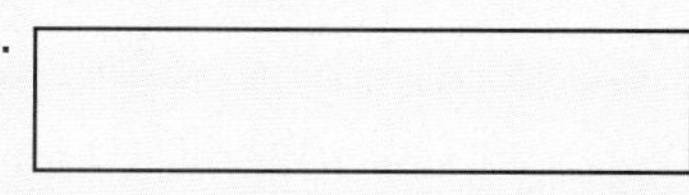

Answers

Activity 2

Think and Discuss

1. 2.9 cm; 8.9 cm; 1 inch is about 2.6 cm.

Try This

1. length: $\frac{3}{4}$ in.; width: $\frac{3}{4}$ in.; perimeter: 3 in.
2. length: $\frac{1}{4}$ in.; width: $2\frac{3}{4}$ in.; perimeter: 6 in.
3. length: $\frac{7}{8}$ in.; width: $2\frac{1}{4}$ in.; perimeter: $6\frac{1}{4}$ in.
4. length: $\frac{1}{2}$ in.; width: $2\frac{3}{8}$ in.; perimeter: $5\frac{3}{4}$ in.

8-2 Organizer

Pacing: Traditional 2 days
Block 1 day

Objective: Students compare the precision of measurements and determine acceptable levels of accuracy.

Warm Up

Convert.

1. 216 hr = _____ days 9

2. 3.7 kg = _____ g 3,700

3. 4.5 qt = _____ pt 9

4. 7.2 mm = _____ cm 0.72

Problem of the Day

Polly found that an empty bird cage weighs 18 oz. With a bird in it, the cage weighs 24 oz. Polly calculated that that bird must weigh 6 oz. How far off might that calculation be?
1 oz in either direction; each weight might be off by 0.5 oz in either direction.

Available on Daily Transparency in CRB

Math Humor

A new agency was formed to study how carefully surgeons used their scalpels. It was called the *Division of Incision Precision.*

8-2 Accuracy and Precision

Learn to compare the precision of measurements and to determine acceptable levels of accuracy.

Vocabulary
precision
accuracy
significant digits

At the University of Texas McDonald Observatory, a laser is used to measure the distance from Earth to the Moon.

Ancient Greeks used measurements taken during lunar eclipses to determine that the Moon was 240,000 miles from Earth. In 1969, the distance was measured as 221,463 miles.

There is a difference between these measurements because modern scientists conducted the measurement with greater *precision*. **Precision** is the level of detail an instrument can measure.

The smaller the unit an instrument can measure, the more precise its measurements will be. For example, a millimeter ruler has greater precision than a centimeter ruler because it can measure smaller units.

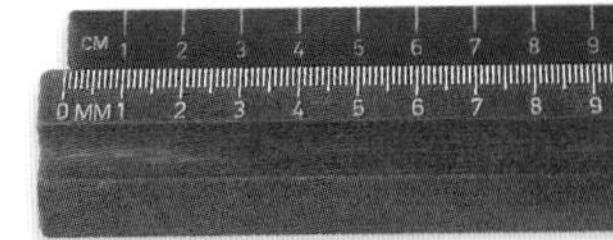

EXAMPLE  1 **Judging Precision of Measurements**

Choose the more precise measurement in each pair.

A **37 in., 3 ft**
Since an inch is a smaller unit than a foot, 37 in. is more precise.

B **5 km, 5.8 km**
Since tenths are smaller than ones, 5.8 km is more precise.

In the real world, no measurement is exact. The relative exactness of a measurement is its **accuracy**. In a measured value, all the digits that are known with certainty are called **significant digits**. Zeros at the end of a whole number are assumed to be nonsignificant. The table shows the rules for identifying significant digits.

Rule	Example	Number of Significant Digits
• Nonzero digits	45.7	3 significant digits
• Zeros between significant digits	78,002	5 significant digits
• Zeros after the last nonzero digit and to the right of a decimal point	0.0040	2 significant digits

1 Introduce

Alternate Opener

EXPLORATION

 **8-2 Accuracy and Precision**

The unit of measurement you choose determines the precision with which you measure.

Measure two different pencils using the following units of measurement.

1. Measure the length of the first pencil to the nearest
   - **a.** inch.
   - **b.** $\frac{1}{2}$ inch.
   - **c.** $\frac{1}{4}$ inch.
   - **d.** $\frac{1}{8}$ inch.
   - **e.** $\frac{1}{16}$ inch.
2. Measure the length of the second pencil to the nearest
   - **a.** centimeter.
   - **b.** $\frac{1}{2}$ centimeter.
   - **c.** millimeter.

Think and Discuss

3. **Discuss** which approximation in **1a–1e** gives you a measurement that is closest to the actual length of the pencil.
4. **Explain** whether measuring to the closest inch, as in **1a**, gives you a closer approximation to the actual length of a pencil than measuring to the closest centimeter, as in **2a**.

Motivate

Have small groups of students measure lengths of common classroom objects, such as a piece of chalk, an eraser, a book, and a pencil. Be sure each group measures the same objects. Do not tell groups which unit of measure to use or how precise to be. Ask each group to make a chart of its findings. Then have the groups share and compare their results. Discuss why everyone's results are not exactly the same (e.g., students measured to different levels of precision).

Exploration worksheet and answers on Chapter 8 Resource Book pp. 16 and 94

2 Teach

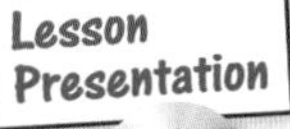

Lesson Presentation

Guided Instruction

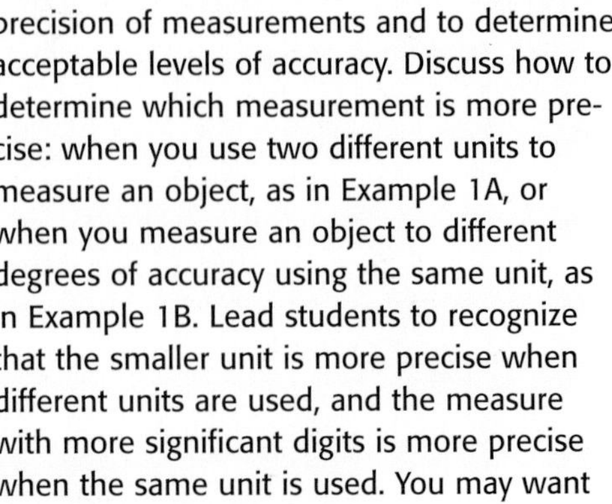

In this lesson, students learn to compare the precision of measurements and to determine acceptable levels of accuracy. Discuss how to determine which measurement is more precise: when you use two different units to measure an object, as in Example 1A, or when you measure an object to different degrees of accuracy using the same unit, as in Example 1B. Lead students to recognize that the smaller unit is more precise when different units are used, and the measure with more significant digits is more precise when the same unit is used. You may want to use Teaching Transparency T6 in the Chapter 8 Resource Book.

EXAMPLE 2 Identifying Significant Digits

Determine the number of significant digits in each measurement.

A 120.1 mi

The digits 1 and 2 are nonzero digits, and 0 is between two nonzero digits.

So 120.1 mi has 4 significant digits.

B 0.0350 kg

The digits 3 and 5 are nonzero digits, and 0 is to the right of the decimal after the last nonzero digit.

So 0.0350 kg has 3 significant digits.

When you are adding and subtracting measurements, the answer should have the same number of digits to the right of the decimal point as the measurement with the least number of digits to the right of the decimal point.

EXAMPLE 3 Using Significant Digits in Addition or Subtraction

Calculate 45 mi − 0.9 mi. Use the correct number of significant digits in the answer.

45	*0 digits to the right of the decimal point*
− 0.9	*1 digit to the right of the decimal point*
44.1 ≈ 44 mi	*Round the difference so that it has no digits to the right of the decimal point.*

When you are multiplying and dividing measurements, the answer must have the same number of significant digits as the measurement with the least number of significant digits.

EXAMPLE 4 Using Significant Digits in Multiplication or Division

Calculate 32.8 m · 1.5 m. Use the correct number of significant digits in the answer.

32.8	*3 significant digits*
× 1.5	*2 significant digits*
49.2 ≈ 49 m	*Round the product so that it has 2 significant digits.*

Think and Discuss

1. **Tell** how many significant digits there are in 380.102.
2. **Choose** the more precise measurement: 18 oz or 1 lb. Explain.

COMMON ERROR ALERT

Some students may have difficulty identifying significant digits when zeros are involved. Remind students that a zero to the left of the decimal point can be significant only if it is between two significant digits. Provide additional practice for students who still get confused.

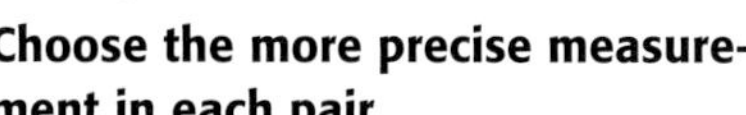

Additional Examples

Example 1

Choose the more precise measurement in each pair.

A. 13 oz, 1 lb — **13 oz**

B. 52 cm, 52.3 cm — **52.3 cm**

Example 2

Determine the number of significant digits in each measurement.

A. 304.7 km — 4 significant digits

B. 0.0760 L — 3 significant digits

Example 3

Calculate 67 ft − 0.8 ft. Use the correct number of significant digits in the answer. **66**

Example 4

Calculate 19.8 mm · 1.4 mm. Use the correct number of significant digits in the answer. **28**

3 Close

Reaching All Learners
Through Home Connection

Have students measure five items at home, each to two different levels of precision. Encourage students to share their findings with the class and explain which unit of measure was more precise for each item and why.

Possible answer: Measurement of the height of a lamp: 22 inches or 2 feet. The measure of 22 inches is more precise because inches are smaller than feet.

Summarize

Have students discuss the following: Which digits in a measurement are significant? nonzero digits, zeros between significant digits, and zeros after the last nonzero digit and to the right of the decimal point How many digits should a sum or difference of measurements have? the same number of digits to the right of the decimal point as the measurement with the least number of digits to the right of the decimal point How many significant digits should a product or quotient of measurements have? the same amount of significant digits as the measurement with the least number of significant digits

Answers to Think and Discuss

1. There are 6 significant digits: 4 nonzero digits and 2 zeros between significant digits.
2. 18 ounces is more precise because an ounce is smaller than a pound.

8-2 PRACTICE & ASSESS

Students may want to refer back to the lesson examples.

Assignment Guide

If you finished Example 1 assign:
Core 1–3, 13–18, 37, 39, 48, 52–61
Enriched 1, 3, 13–17 odd, 37–40, 48, 52–61

If you finished Example 2 assign:
Core 1–6, 13–24, 37, 39, 47, 48, 52–61
Enriched 1–5 odd, 13–24, 37–40, 47, 48, 52–61

If you finished Example 3 assign:
Core 1–9, 13–30, 37, 39, 43–47 odd, 52–61
Enriched 1–9 odd, 13–30, 37–40, 42, 43, 45, 47, 48, 52–61

If you finished Example 4 assign:
Core 1–36, 37–49 odd, 52–61
Enriched 1–11 odd, 19–61

8-2 Exercises

FOR EXTRA PRACTICE see page 671

internet connect
Homework Help Online
go.hrw.com Keyword: MS4 8-2

GUIDED PRACTICE

See Example 1 Choose the more precise measurement in each pair.

1. 4 ft, 1 yd **4 ft** **2.** 2 cm, 21 mm **21 mm** **3.** $5\frac{1}{2}$ in., $5\frac{1}{4}$ in. **$5\frac{1}{4}$ in.**

See Example 2 Determine the number of significant digits in each measurement.

4. 2.703 g **4** **5.** 0.02 km **1** **6.** 28,000 lb **2**

See Example 3 Calculate. Use the correct number of significant digits in each answer.

7. 16 − 3.8 **12** **8.** 3.5 + 0.66 **4.2** **9.** 11.3 − 4 **7**

See Example 4 **10.** 47.9 · 3.8 **180** **11.** 7.0 · 3.6 **25** **12.** 50.2 ÷ 8.0 **6.3**

INDEPENDENT PRACTICE

See Example 1 Choose the more precise measurement in each pair.

13. 11 in., 1 ft **11 in.** **14.** 7.2 m, 6.2 cm **6.2 cm** **15.** 14.2 km, 14 km **14.2 km**

16. $4\frac{3}{8}$ in., $4\frac{7}{16}$ in. **$4\frac{7}{16}$ in.** **17.** 2.8 m, 3 m **2.8 m** **18.** 37 g, 37.0 g **37.0 g**

See Example 2 Determine the number of significant digits in each measurement.

19. 0.00002 kg **1** **20.** 10,000,000 lb **1** **21.** 200.060 m **6**

22. 4.003 L **4** **23.** 0.230 cm **3** **24.** 940.0 ft **4**

See Example 3 Calculate. Use the correct number of significant digits in each answer.

25. 6.2 + 8.93 **15.1** **26.** 7.02 + 15 **22** **27.** 8 − 6.6 **1**

28. 29.1 − 13.204 **15.9** **29.** 8.6 + 9.43 **18.0** **30.** 43.5 + 876.23 **919.7**

See Example 4 **31.** 17 · 104 **1,800** **32.** 21.8 · 10.9 **238** **33.** 7.0 ÷ 3.11 **2.3**

34. 1,680 ÷ 5.025 **334** **35.** 14.2 ÷ 0.05 **300** **36.** 5.22 · 6.3 **33**

PRACTICE AND PROBLEM SOLVING

Which unit is more precise?

37. foot or mile **foot** **38.** centimeter or millimeter **millimeter**

39. liter or milliliter **milliliter** **40.** minute or second **second**

Calculate. Use the correct number of significant digits in each answer.

41. 38,000 · 4.8 **180,000** **42.** 2.879 + 113.6 **116.5** **43.** 290 − 6.1 **280**

44. 5.6 ÷ 0.6 **9** **45.** 40.29 − 18.5 **21.8** **46.** 24 ÷ 6.02 **4.0**

Math Background

Significant digits are often used in calculations for scientific experiments. Most of the confusion in counting significant digits results from a misunderstanding of how to count the zeros. One way to avoid this confusion is to use scientific notation. Writing numbers in scientific notation makes identifying significant digits less confusing because all the digits in a number written in scientific notation are significant. Here are some examples.

Number	Scientific Notation	Significant Digits
3,400	$3.4 \cdot 10^3$	2
341,000	$3.41 \cdot 10^5$	3
0.0403	$4.03 \cdot 10^{-2}$	3
0.080	$8.0 \cdot 10^{-2}$	2

RETEACH 8-2

LESSON 8-2 **Reteach**
Accuracy and Precision

A measurement is more **precise** than another measurement if its unit of measure is smaller.

1. Which measurement is more precise, 14 cm or 140 mm?
   a. 14 cm means the measure is to the nearest **centimeter**.
   b. 140 mm means the measure is to the nearest **millimeter**.
   c. Since a millimeter is a smaller measurement, **140 mm** is more precise.

2. Which measurement is more precise, 5 ft or 50.1 ft?
   a. 5 ft means the measure is to the nearest **foot**.
   b. 50.1 ft means the measure is to the nearest tenth of a **foot**.
   c. Since a tenth of a foot is a smaller measurement, **50.1 ft** is more precise.

Choose the more precise measurement in each pair.

3. 7.5 m or 75 cm **75 cm** 4. 11.0 in. or 11 in. **11.0 in.** 5. 8.4 lb or 8 oz **8 oz**

You can find the number of **significant digits,** or all the digits that are known to be exact, by dividing a measurement by its smallest place value. The number of digits in the quotient is the number of significant digits.

Measurement	Smallest Place Value	Measurement ÷ Smallest Place Value	Number of Significant Digits
14 ft	1	14 ÷ 1 = 14	2
0.043 in.	0.001	0.043 ÷ 0.001 = 43	2
50.1 m	0.1	50.1 ÷ 0.1 = 501	3

Zeros to the left of a decimal point are not significant if there are no digits to the right of the decimal point.

910 contains 2 significant digits: 9 and 1.

Zeros after digits to the right of a decimal point are significant.

64.9500 contains 6 significant digits: 6, 4, 9, 5, and the two zeros.

Determine the number of significant digits.

6. 41.25 **4** 7. 30.6 **3** 8. 0.085 **2**

9. 1,207,000 **4** 10. 38.600 **5** 11. 4.00020 **6**

PRACTICE 8-2

LESSON 8-2 **Practice B**
Accuracy and Precision

Choose the more precise measurement in each pair.

1. 2 tons, 3,700 lb **3,700 lb** 2. 4 weeks, 27 days **27 days** 3. 3.5 m, 3.03 m **3.03 m**

4. 3 ft, 32 in. **32 in.** 5. 4.6 mL, 2.8 L **4.6 mL** 6. 15.8 km, 15 km **15.8 km**

Determine the number of significant digits in each measurement.

7. 5.801 **4** 8. 0.06 **1** 9. 75,000 **2**

10. 0.00007 **1** 11. 100,000,000 **1** 12. 300.080 **6**

13. 9.007 **4** 14. 0.840 **3** 15. 0.0050 **2**

Calculate. Give the answer with the correct number of significant digits.

16. 21 − 8.6 = **12** 17. 47.6 + 8 = **56** 18. 9.8 − 3 = **7**

19. 31.3 − 24.78 = **6.5** 20. 9.63 + 3.4 = **13.0** 21. 15.7 + 0.82 = **16.5**

22. 0.54 + 0.104 = **0.64** 23. 102 − 2.77 = **99.2** 24. 62 + 0.319 = **62**

25. 52.7 • 2.3 = **120** 26. 8.0 • 1.7 = **14** 27. 20.5 ÷ 6.0 = **3.4**

28. 23.9 • 14.4 = **344** 29. 19.2 ÷ 0.03 = **600** 30. 1,240 ÷ 4.025 = **308**

31. 0.18 • 6.2 = **1.1** 32. 95 ÷ 32 = **3.0** 33. 74.3 • 0.22 = **16**

Health LINK

The food labels at right give information about two types of soup: cream of tomato and minestrone. Use the labels for Exercises 47–49.

Cream of Tomato

Nutrition Facts
Serving size 1 cup (240mL)
Servings per container about 2

Amount per Serving	
Calories 100	Calories from Fat 20
	% Daily Value*
Total Fat 2 g	3%
Saturated Fat 1.5 g	6%
Cholesterol 10 mg	3%
Sodium 690 mg	29%
Total Carbohydrate 17 g	6%
Dietary Fiber 4 g	18%
Sugars 11 g	
Protein 2 g	
Vitamin A 20% —	Vitamin C 20%
Calcium 0% —	Iron 8%

*Percent daily values are based on a 2,000 calorie diet.

Minestrone

Nutrition Facts
Serving size 1 cup (240mL)
Servings per container about 2

Amount per Serving	
Calories 90	Calories from Fat 10
	% Daily Value*
Total Fat 1.5 g	2%
Saturated Fat 0 g	0%
Cholesterol 0 mg	0%
Sodium 540 mg	22%
Total Carbohydrate 17 g	6%
Dietary Fiber 3 g	14%
Sugars 5 g	
Protein 3 g	
Vitamin A 30% —	Vitamin C 10%
Calcium 2% —	Iron 6%

*Percent daily values are based on a 2,000 calorie diet.

47. In one serving of minestrone, how many significant digits are there in the number of milligrams of sodium? **2**

48. Which measurement is more precise, the total amount of fat in cream of tomato soup or the total amount in minestrone? Explain.

49. One serving of cream of tomato soup contains 29% of the recommended daily value of sodium for a 2,000-calorie diet. What is the recommended daily value for sodium, in milligrams? Express your answer with the appropriate number of significant digits. **2,400 mg**

50. One-half of a medium-sized grapefruit, or 154 grams, counts as one serving of fruit. How many servings of fruit are in 1 kilogram of grapefruit? Express your answer with the appropriate number of significant digits. **6 servings of fruit**

51. ***CHALLENGE*** The greatest possible error of any measurement is half of the smallest unit used in the measurement. For example, 1 pt of juice may actually measure between $\frac{1}{2}$ pt and $1\frac{1}{2}$ pt. What is the range of possible actual weights for a watermelon that was weighed at $19\frac{1}{4}$ lb? **$19\frac{1}{8}$ lb to $19\frac{3}{8}$ lb**

The food pyramid can be used as a guide for meeting daily balanced nutrition needs.

Spiral Review

Write each mixed number as an improper fraction. (Lesson 3-8)

52. $3\frac{1}{2}$ $\frac{7}{2}$ **53.** $7\frac{3}{4}$ $\frac{31}{4}$ **54.** $16\frac{1}{3}$ $\frac{49}{3}$ **55.** $10\frac{2}{5}$ $\frac{52}{5}$

Solve. (Lesson 4-6)

56. $2.7 + y = 9.3$ **$y = 6.6$** **57.** $\frac{m}{0.2} = 16$ **$m = 3.2$** **58.** $0.5t = 28$ **$t = 56$** **59.** $n - 8.01 = 16.2$ **$n = 24.21$**

60. TEST PREP What is 0.2 written as a percent? (Lesson 6-1) **A**

A 20% C 0.02%
B 2% D 0.002%

61. TEST PREP What is 137% of 52? (Lesson 6-3) **H**

F 7.124 H 71.24
G 19.24 J 123.24

Interdisciplinary LINK

Health

Exercises 47–51 involve using the measurements found on Nutrition Facts labels. Nutrition is studied in health courses as well as in middle school life science programs, such as *Holt Science & Technology.*

Answers

48. The amount in minestrone is more accurate because 1.5 has the smaller decimal place.

Journal 

Have students describe a real-world situation in which measuring to a less precise level makes more sense than measuring to a more precise level.

Test Prep Doctor 

For Exercise 60, remind students that the value of the numbers that make up a percent is greater than the value of the numbers that make up the equivalent decimal, so they can eliminate choices **C** and **D.**

For Exercise 61, encourage students to estimate the answer to eliminate choices. Students should realize that 137% of 52 is more than 100% of 52, so the answer must be more than 52. Therefore they can eliminate **F** and **G. J** is more than 200% of 52, so it cannot be the correct answer.

CHALLENGE 8-2

LESSON 8-2 **Challenge**
The Significance of a Riddle

Write a solution for each of the following riddles. Your answer must include all of the information in the riddle, but all of the information about each number is not always given in the riddle. **Possible answers are given.**

1. I am a number with *only* the digits 1, 2, and 3. I have four significant digits and no decimal places. What number could I be? **1,231**
2. I am a number with *only* the digits 2, 4, and 0. I have one decimal place and four significant digits. What number could I be? **240.2**
3. I am a number with *only* the digits 6 and 0. I have three significant digits and four decimal places. What number could I be? **0.0660**
4. I am the greatest number with *only* the digits 1, 2, and 3. I have five significant digits. What number am I? **33,321**
5. I have no significant digits. What number am I? **0**
6. What number could I be with two significant digits and five decimal places? **0.00050**
7. I am the least number with *only* the digits 1, 2, and 3, with five significant digits and six decimal places. What number am I? **0.010123**
8. I am a number with two significant digits and four decimal places. I begin and end with 0. What number could I be? **0.0070**
9. I am a number between 155 and 1,555. I have five significant digits and two decimal places. What number could I be? **200.05**
10. I am a number between 0 and 2 with *only* the digits 1 and 4. I have five significant digits and four decimal places. What number could I be? **1.1414**
11. I have four digits, but only three are significant. I have three decimal places. What number could I be? **0.120**
12. I have six digits, but only two are significant. I have no decimal places. What number could I be? **450,000**

PROBLEM SOLVING 8-2

LESSON 8-2 **Problem Solving**
Accuracy and Precision

Write the correct answer.

1. Normal rainfall in Hilo, Hawaii, is 2.36 feet per year. Yearly rainfall in Honolulu, Hawaii, is 7.77 inches. Which measurement is more precise? Explain. **An inch is a smaller unit than a foot, so 7.77 in. is more precise than 2.36 ft.**
2. The Seismosaurus was about 5.5 meters high. The Troodon, considered the smartest dinosaur, was only about 1.75 meters high. Write the difference in height of the two dinosaurs using the correct number of significant digits. **3.8 m difference**
3. Esther drives a total of 120 miles to and from work each day. She works 5 days per week. How many significant digits are there in the number of miles Esther drives to and from work each week? **1 significant digit**
4. Big Al weighs 256.8 pounds. His brother, Little Lou, weighs 125 pounds. What is their combined weight? Express your answer with the appropriate number of significant digits. **382 lb**

Choose the letter of the correct answer.

5. A square picture frame measures 50.1 centimeters on each side. How many significant digits are there in the perimeter of the frame?
   A 2 (C) 4
   B 3 D 1
6. Four students each measured his or her own height. The measures below show each student's results. Which is the most precise measure?
   F 5 ft H 62 in.
   G 5.5 ft (J) 64.5 in.
7. Before the year 2000, Harvard University had 12,877,360 books in its library. How many significant digits are there in the number of books in the Harvard Library?
   A 5 (C) 7
   B 6 D 8
8. In 1996, Tokyo Disneyland had an estimated 16.98 million visitors. Disneyland in Anaheim, California, had 15 million visitors. What is the estimated total number of visitors for both parks using the correct number of significant digits?
   (F) 32 million H 31.9 million
   G 31.98 million J 31 million

Lesson Quiz 

1. Which measurement is more precise, 10 in. or 1 ft? **10 in.**

Determine the number of significant digits in each measurement.

2. 6.004 **4**
3. 0.070 **2**

Calculate. Give the answer with the correct number of significant digits.

4. 72 − 0.8 **71**
5. 18.3 · 4.1 **75**
6. A veterinarian's assistant finds that a dog weighs 11 kg. What is the least and the most the dog might really weigh? **10.5 kg to 11.5 kg**

Available on Daily Transparency in CRB

8-3 Organizer

Pacing: Traditional 1 day
Block $\frac{1}{2}$ day

Objective: Students find the perimeter of a polygon and the circumference of a circle.

Warm Up

Add or multiply.

1. 8.2 + 5.6 + 8.2 + 5.6 **27.6**
2. 12.4 + 15.8 + 9.3 **37.5**
3. 4 · 8.5 **34**
4. 22 · 3.14 **69.08**

Problem of the Day

A rectangular piece of sheet metal measures 5 in. by 6 in. A rectangular notch 1 in. deep and $\frac{7}{64}$ in. wide is cut out of the middle of each side. What is the perimeter of the piece after the cuts have been made? (*Hint:* You don't have to use fractions.)

30 in. (the original 6 in. by 5 in. sheet plus 8 in. for the eight 1 in. cuts)

Available on Daily Transparency in CRB

In 1999, Dr. Yasumasa Kanada of the University of Tokyo computed pi to 206,158,430,000 decimal places.

8-3 Perimeter and Circumference

Learn to find the perimeter of a polygon and the circumference of a circle.

Vocabulary
perimeter
circumference

The distance around a geometric figure is its **perimeter**. To find the perimeter P of a polygon, you can add the lengths of its sides.

If a ball hits the perimeter of a tennis court with chalked lines, a mark will show that it landed in the court. To find the perimeter of a tennis court, add the lengths of each baseline and each sideline.

EXAMPLE 1 Finding the Perimeter of a Polygon

Find the perimeter of each polygon.

A

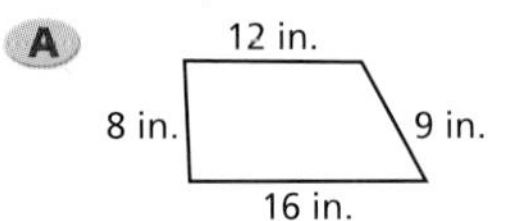

$P = 8 + 12 + 9 + 16$ *Use the side lengths.*

$P = 45$ *Add.*

The perimeter of the trapezoid is 45 in.

B

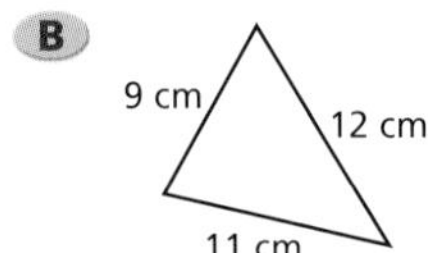

$P = 9 + 12 + 11$ *Use the side lengths.*

$P = 32$ *Add.*

The perimeter of the triangle is 32 cm.

You can find the perimeter of a rectangle by adding the lengths of its sides. Or, since opposite sides of a rectangle are equal in length, you can find the perimeter by using the formula $P = 2\ell + 2w$.

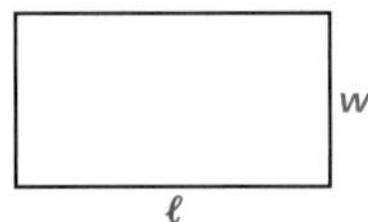

EXAMPLE 2 Using Properties of a Rectangle to Find Perimeter

Find the perimeter of the rectangle.

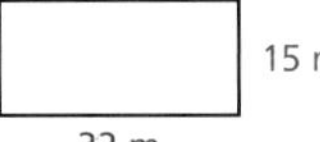

$P = 2\ell + 2w$ *Use the formula.*

$P = (2 \cdot 32) + (2 \cdot 15)$ *Substitute for ℓ and w.*

$P = 64 + 30$ *Multiply.*

$P = 94$ *Add.*

The perimeter of the rectangle is 94 m.

1 Introduce

Alternate Opener

EXPLORATION

8-3 Perimeter and Circumference

Circumference is the distance around a circle, and *perimeter* is the distance around a figure that is not a circle. You can estimate the distance around the circle below by measuring the perimeters of the hexagons directly inside and outside the circle.

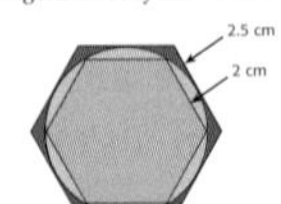

1. Use the figure above to estimate the circumference of the circle.
   a. Find the perimeter of the orange hexagon.
   b. Find the perimeter of the blue hexagon.
   c. Average the two perimeters in parts **a** and **b** to estimate the circumference of the circle.

Think and Discuss

2. **Explain** why you were asked to average the two perimeters of the hexagons to estimate the circumference of the circle.
3. **Explain** the difference between a perimeter and a circumference.

Motivate

Ask students to share ideas about how to measure the distance around a circle. Then provide groups of students with string, a ruler, and various sizes of circles. Tell groups to measure and record the diameter of each circle, using the ruler and to measure and record the circumference, using the string. Have groups record the measurements for each circle in a table.

Exploration worksheet and answers on Chapter 8 Resource Book pp. 25 and 96

2 Teach

Lesson Presentation

Guided Instruction

In this lesson, students learn to find the perimeter of a polygon and the circumference of a circle. After completing Example 3, have students add another column to the table they made in the Motivate section and use the heading "Calculated Circumference." Ask students to use the formula to calculate the circumference for each circle. Discuss the accuracy of using a formula for measurement versus using measuring tools.

Explain that $\frac{22}{7}$ and 3.14 are approximations for π. Using them gives the approximate circumference of a circle.

The distance around a circle is called **circumference**. For every circle, the ratio of circumference C to diameter d is the same. This ratio, $\frac{C}{d}$, is represented by the symbol π, called *pi*. *Pi* is approximately equal to 3.14 or $\frac{22}{7}$. By multiplying both sides of the equation $\frac{C}{d} = \pi$ by d, you get the formula for circumference, $C = \pi d$, or $C = 2\pi r$.

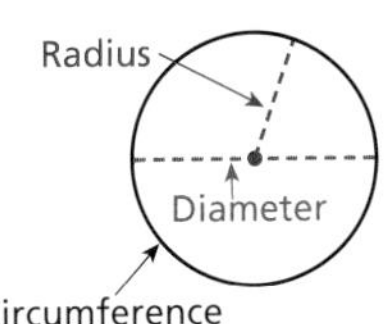

EXAMPLE 3 Finding the Circumference of a Circle

Find the circumference of each circle to the nearest tenth. Use 3.14 for π.

A

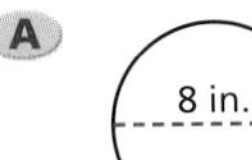

$C = \pi d$ — *You know the diameter.*

$C \approx 3.14 \cdot 8$ — *Substitute for π and d.*

$C \approx 25.12$ — *Multiply.*

The circumference of the circle is about 25.1 in.

B

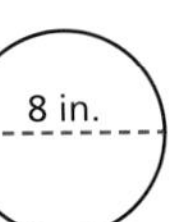

$C = 2\pi r$ — *You know the radius.*

$C \approx 2 \cdot 3.14 \cdot 10$ — *Substitute for π and r.*

$C \approx 62.8$ — *Multiply.*

The circumference of the circle is about 62.8 cm.

EXAMPLE 4 *Art Application*

Melanie is drawing plans for a circular fountain. If the diameter of the fountain is 21 ft, what is its circumference? Use $\frac{22}{7}$ for π.

$C = \pi d$ — *You know the diameter.*

$C \approx \frac{22}{7} \cdot 21$ — *Substitute $\frac{22}{7}$ for π and 21 for d.*

$C \approx \frac{22}{7} \cdot \frac{21}{1}$ — *Write 21 as a fraction.*

$C \approx \frac{22}{\cancel{7}_1} \cdot \frac{\cancel{21}^3}{1}$ — *Simplify.*

$C \approx 66$ — *Multiply.*

The circumference of the fountain is about 66 ft.

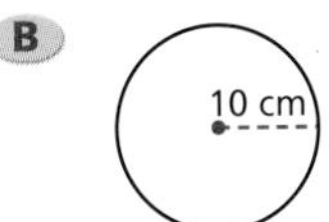

Think and Discuss

1. **Describe** two ways to find the perimeter of a rectangle.
2. **Explain** how to use the formula $C = \pi d$ to find the circumference of a circle if you know the radius.

Additional Examples

Example 1

Find the perimeter of each polygon.

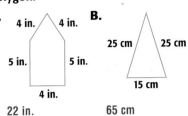

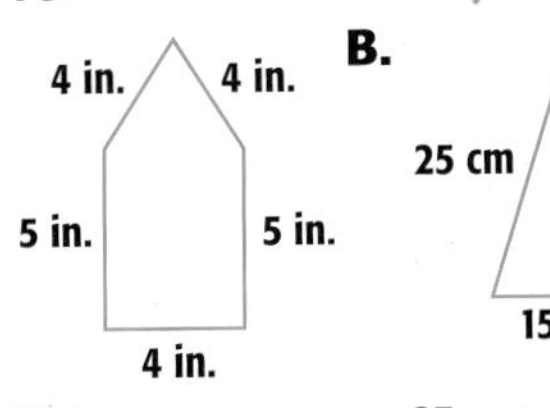

A. 22 in. B. 65 cm

Example 2

Find the perimeter of the rectangle.

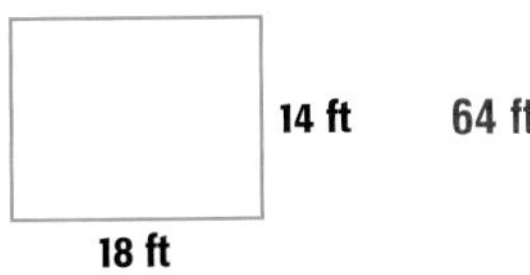

64 ft

Example 3

Find the circumference of each circle to the nearest tenth. Use 3.14 for π.

A.

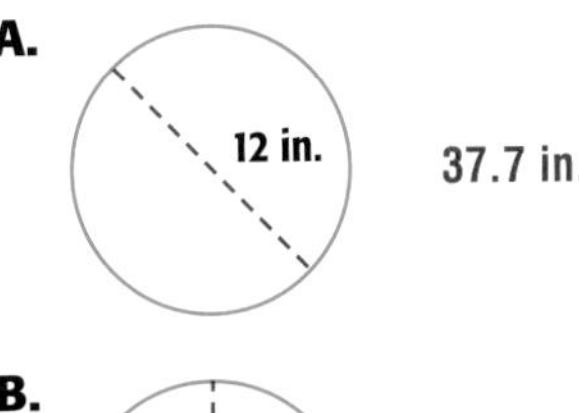

37.7 in.

B.

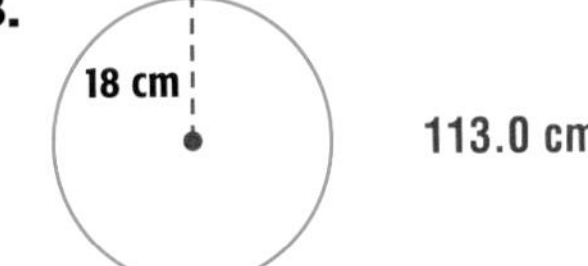

113.0 cm

Example 4

The diameter of a circular pond is 42 m. What is its circumference? Use $\frac{22}{7}$ for π. 132 m

3 Close

Reaching All Learners

Through Critical Thinking

Challenge students to write a formula for the perimeter of a semicircle. Then have students apply the formula to a semicircle with a diameter of 4 inches and write their answers to the nearest tenth.

Circumference of a semicircle $= \frac{1}{2}\pi d + d$

The perimeter of the semicircle is approximately 10.3 in. Students might simply find the circumference of the whole circle, multiply by one-half, and give the answer as 6.3. One-half the circumference of the whole circle gives only the length of the arc of the semicircle.

Summarize

Ask students to write a brief paragraph describing how the circumference of a circle and the perimeter of a polygon are alike and how they are different. Have students share and compare paragraphs.

Possible answer: The circumference of a circle and the perimeter of a polygon are alike in that both are distances around a plane figure. They are different in that the circumference measures the distance around a circle, while the perimeter is the sum of the lengths of the sides of a polygon.

Answers to Think and Discuss

1. Possible answers: Add the lengths of the four sides. Or multiply twice the length and twice the width, and then find the sum of the products.
2. Multiply the radius by 2 to find the diameter, and then substitute the value for the diameter into the formula.

8-3 PRACTICE & ASSESS

Students may want to refer back to the lesson examples.

Assignment Guide

If you finished Example 1 assign:
Core 1–3, 11–13, 25–27, 33–41
Enriched 1–3, 11–13, 25–27, 33–41

If you finished Example 2 assign:
Core 1–6, 11–16, 25–28, 33–41
Enriched 1–6, 11–16, 25–28, 33–41

If you finished Example 3 assign:
Core 1–9, 11–19, 21–27 odd, 33–41
Enriched 1–9 odd, 11–19, 21–28, 33–41

If you finished Example 4 assign:
Core 1–20, 21–29 odd, 33–41
Enriched 1–19 odd, 21–41

Notes

8-3 Exercises

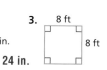

FOR EXTRA PRACTICE see page 671

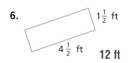

internet connect
Homework Help Online
go.hrw.com Keyword: MS4 8-3

GUIDED PRACTICE

See Example 1 Find the perimeter of each polygon.

1. 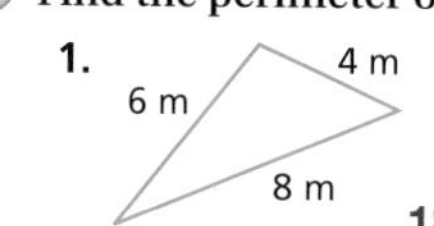

18 m

2. 7 in., 5 in., 5 in., 7 in. **24 in.**

3. 8 ft, 8 ft **32 ft**

See Example 2 Find the perimeter of each rectangle.

4. 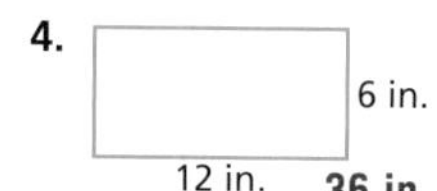

36 in.

5. 8 m, 2 m **20 m**

6. $1\frac{1}{2}$ ft, $4\frac{1}{2}$ ft **12 ft**

See Example 3 Find the circumference of each circle to the nearest tenth. Use 3.14 for π.

7. 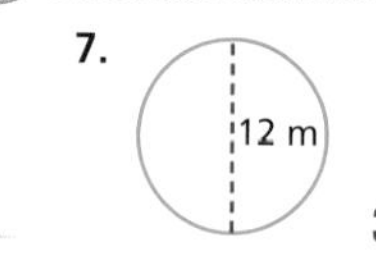

37.7 m

8. 3 ft **9.4 ft**

9. 8 in. **50.2 in.**

See Example 4 **10.** A Ferris wheel has a diameter of 140 feet. What is the circumference of the Ferris wheel? Use $\frac{22}{7}$ for π. **440 ft**

INDEPENDENT PRACTICE

See Example 1 Find the perimeter of each polygon.

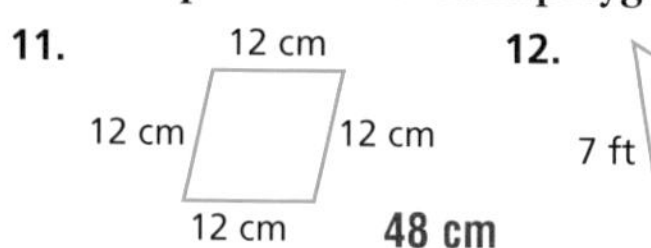

11. 12 cm, 12 cm, 12 cm, 12 cm **48 cm**

12. 7 ft, 13 ft, 10 ft **30 ft**

13. 10 m, 8 m, 10 m, 16 m **44 m**

See Example 2 Find the perimeter of each rectangle.

14. 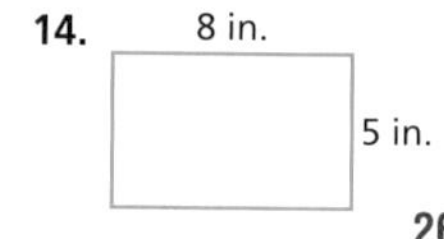

26 in.

15. 3 ft, 1 ft **8 ft**

16. 8 cm, 10.2 cm **36.4 cm**

See Example 3 Find the circumference of each circle to the nearest tenth. Use 3.14 for π.

17. 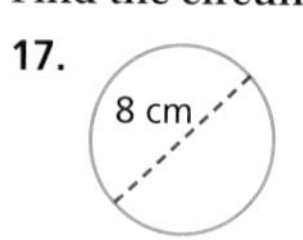

25.1 cm

18. 3 m **18.8 m**

19. 5.1 in. **32.0 in.**

See Example 4 **20.** The diameter of Kayla's bicycle wheel is 28 inches. What is the circumference of her bicycle wheel? Use $\frac{22}{7}$ for π. **88 in.**

Math Background

Eratosthenes of Cyrene, who lived around 275–194 B.C., used measurements taken in the cities of Syene and Alexandria at noon during a summer solstice to estimate the circumference of Earth. At noon he noticed that a vertical post cast no shadow in Syene, while a vertical post in Alexandria did cast a shadow. The angle of the shadow was $\frac{1}{50}$ of 360°. Eratosthenes reasoned that the angle was equal to the angle at Earth's center, formed by the radii to the two towns. By multiplying the distance between the two towns by 50, he estimated that the circumference of Earth was 250,000 *stadia* (about 40,000 kilometers). Today, we know that the circumference of Earth is 40,070 km.

RETEACH 8-3

LESSON 8-3 **Reteach**
Perimeter and Circumference

The **perimeter** of any figure is the distance around the figure. Think of *perimeter* as "going around the rim" of a figure. Find the perimeter of a figure by adding the measures of the sides.

The word perimeter has the word **rim** in it.

Find the perimeter of each polygon.

Triangle: 5 in., 9 in., 6 in.
$P = 6 + 5 + 9$
$P = 20$
The perimeter of the triangle is 20 in.

Quadrilateral: 10 cm, 7cm, 8 cm, 11 cm
$P = 7 + 11 + 10 + 8$
$P = 36$
The perimeter of the quadrilateral is 36 cm.

To find the perimeter of a rectangle, you can add the length and the width and multiply the sum by 2. The formula for the perimeter of a rectangle is $P = 2(\ell + w)$.

Rectangle: 8 ft, 5 ft, 5 ft, 8 ft
$P = 2(\ell + w)$
$P = 2(8 + 5)$
$P = 2(13)$
$P = 26$
The perimeter of the rectangle is 26 feet.

Find the perimeter of each polygon.

1. 11m, 15m, 13 m
$P =$ 11 + 13 + 15
$P =$ 39 m

2. 23 ft, 21 ft, 24 ft, 30 ft
$P =$ 21 + 23 + 24 + 30
$P =$ 98 ft

3. 16 cm, 8 cm
$P = 2($16 + 8$)$
$P =$ 48 cm

PRACTICE 8-3

LESSON 8-3 **Practice B**
Perimeter and Circumference

Find the perimeter of each polygon.

1. 11 in., 7 in., 9 in., 16 in. — 43 in.
2. 17 cm, 13 cm, 15 cm — 45 cm
3. 9 ft, 6 ft, 6 ft, 9 ft — 30 ft

Find the perimeter of each rectangle.

4. 12 mm, 9 mm, 9 mm, 12 mm — 42 mm
5. 3 m, 10 m, 10 m, 3 m — 26 m
6. $2\frac{1}{2}$ yd, $7\frac{1}{2}$ yd, $7\frac{1}{2}$ yd, $2\frac{1}{2}$ — 20 yd

Find the circumference of each circle to the nearest tenth. Use 3.14 for π.

7. 6 in. — 18.8 in.
8. 9 cm — 56.5 cm
9. 1.5 ft — 4.7 ft

10. A circular swimming pool is 21 feet in diameter. What is the circumference of the swimming pool? Use $\frac{22}{7}$ for π. — 66 ft

11. A jar lid has a diameter of 42 millimeters. What is the circumference of the lid? Use $\frac{22}{7}$ for π. — 132 mm

12. A frying pan has a radius of 14 centimeters. What is the circumference of the frying pan? Use $\frac{22}{7}$ for π. — 88 cm

PRACTICE AND PROBLEM SOLVING

Find each missing measurement to the nearest tenth. Use 3.14 for π.

21. $r = $ ▒; $d = $ ▒; $C = 17.8$ m **2.8 m; 5.7 m**
22. $r = 6.7$ yd; $d = $ ▒; $C = $ ▒ **13.4 yd; 42.1 yd**
23. $r = $ ▒; $d = 10.6$ in.; $C = $ ▒ **5.3 in.; 33.3 in.**
24. $r = $ ▒; $d = $ ▒; $C = \pi$ $\mathbf{\frac{1}{2}; 1}$

Find the perimeter of each polygon.

25. a parallelogram with side lengths 0.23 m and 0.76 m **1.98 m**
26. a regular hexagon with side lengths $4\frac{2}{3}$ in. **28 in.**
27. ***GEOGRAPHY*** The map shows the distances in miles between the airports on the Big Island of Hawaii. If Dembe, a pilot, flies from Kailua-Kona to Waimea to Hilo and back to Kailua-Kona, how far does he travel? **141 mi**

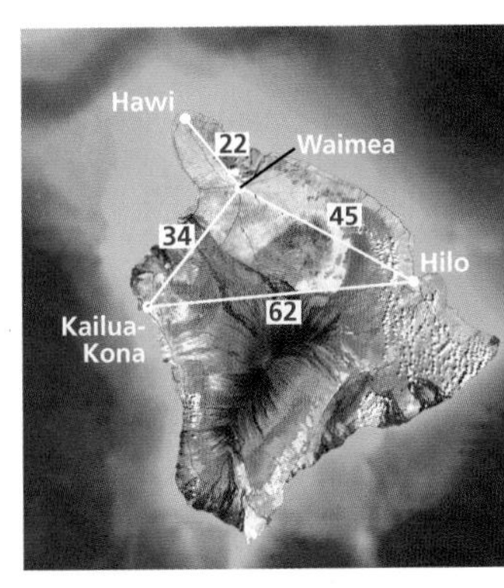

28. ***SPORTS*** In baseball, each of the two batter's boxes, on opposite sides of home plate, is 1.8 meters long and 1.2 meters wide. How many meters must be chalked to outline both boxes? **12 m**
29. ***ARCHITECTURE*** The Capitol Rotunda connects the House and Senate sides of the U.S. Capitol. The rotunda is 180 feet tall and has a circumference of about 301.5 feet. What is its approximate diameter, to the nearest foot? **96 ft**

30. ***WRITE A PROBLEM*** Write a problem about finding the perimeter or circumference of an object in your school or classroom.

31. ***WRITE ABOUT IT*** Explain how to find the width of a rectangle if you know its perimeter and length. **Subtract twice the length from the perimeter and divide the result by 2.**
32. ***CHALLENGE*** The perimeter of a regular nonagon is $25\frac{1}{2}$ in. What is the length of one side of the nonagon? $\mathbf{2\frac{5}{6}}$ **in.**

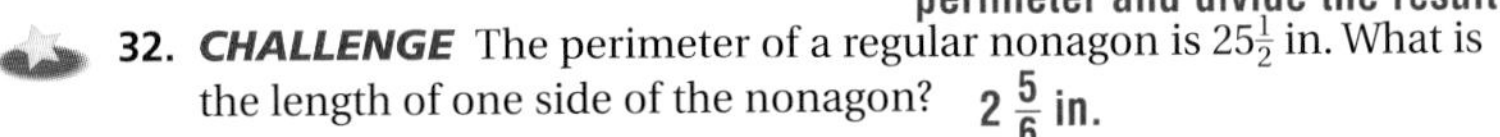

Spiral Review

Multiply or divide. (Lesson 3-5)

33. $4 \cdot (-3)$ **−12**
34. $-18 \div 9$ **−2**
35. $6 \cdot 9$ **54**
36. $45 \div (-5)$ **−9**

Divide. (Lesson 4-5)

37. $9.8 \div 0.4$ **24.5**
38. $0.02 \div 0.5$ **0.04**
39. $30 \div 2.5$ **12**
40. $1.752 \div 1.2$ **1.46**

41. **TEST PREP** How many millimeters are there in 4.2 cm? (Lesson 8-1) **C**

A 0.042 mm **B** 0.42 mm **C** 42 mm **D** 420 mm

Answers

30. Possible answer: How many feet of ribbon would be needed to trim the edge of the bulletin board?

Journal

Have students describe how they would determine how many times they would have to run around the gym to run a mile. Remind students that a mile equals 5,280 feet.

Test Prep Doctor

For Exercise 41, encourage students to estimate the answer to eliminate choices. Students should realize that since a millimeter is smaller than a centimeter, there will be more than 4.2 millimeters in 4.2 cm. Thus, students can eliminate **A** and **B.** If students answered **A** or **B,** they do not understand that as you move to smaller units, the number must get larger.

Lesson Quiz

Find the perimeter of each polygon.

1. 8 m, 12 m, 10 m, 9 m, 6 m

45 m

2.

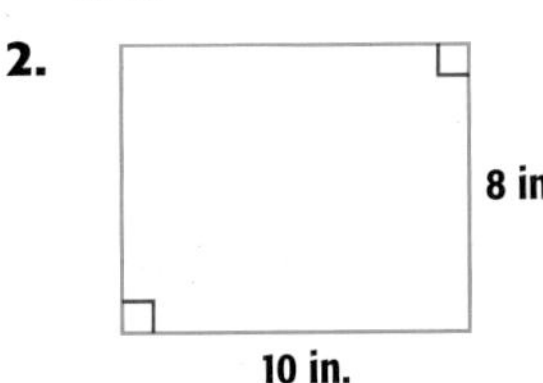

36 in.

3. What is the circumference of a circle with a radius of 8 in.? Use 3.14 for π. **50.24 in.**
4. If a guardrail is to be placed around the edge of a circular swimming pool with a diameter of 21 ft, how many feet of railing would be needed? Use $\frac{22}{7}$ for π. **66 ft**

Available on Daily Transparency in CRB

CHALLENGE 8-3

LESSON 8-3 **Challenge**
All-Around Formulas

Use the first figure in each row to write a formula for the perimeter of the combined figure next to it. Use your formulas in Exercises 5–8.

	Original Figure	Combined Figure	Perimeter
1.	A regular octagon:		$P = 26m$
2.	An isosceles triangle:		$P = 2s + 6b$
3.	A parallelogram:		$P = 4\ell + 4w$
4.	A semicircle:		$P = 3(\frac{1}{2}\pi d + d)$

5. What is the perimeter of the combined figure in Exercise 1 if $m = 4$ in.? **104 in.**
6. What is the perimeter of the combined figure in Exercise 2 if $s = 4.5$ m and $b = 5.2$ m? **40.2 m**
7. What is the length of the original figure in Exercise 3 if the width is 6 in. and the perimeter of the combined figure is 56 in.? **8 in.**
8. What is the perimeter of the combined figure in Exercise 4 if $d = 10$ cm? **77.1 cm**

PROBLEM SOLVING 8-3

LESSON 8-3 **Problem Solving**
Perimeter and Circumference

Write the correct answer.

1. Mr. Marcos, the gym teacher, had the seventh graders run around the perimeter of the gym 3 times. The gym has a length of 34 feet and a width of 58 feet. What was the total distance the students ran? **552 ft**
2. The distance between bases on a baseball field is 90 feet. If 3 players hit home runs during a game and each runs around all 4 bases, what is the total distance the players run? **1,080 ft**
3. Basketball rims have a diameter of 18 inches. If you want to put a band around a basketball rim, how much material to the nearest tenth of an inch will you need? **56.5 in.**
4. A pizza cutter has a diameter of 2.5 inches. To cut a pizza in half, the cutter makes two complete revolutions. What is the diameter of the pizza? **15.7 in.**
5. A round stained-glass window has a circumference of 195 inches. What is the radius of the window to the nearest inch? **31 in.**
6. A planter full of pansies has a diameter of 14 inches. What is the circumference of the planter to the nearest inch? **44 in.**

Choose the letter of the correct answer.

7. A welcome mat on the front porch is a semicircle. The straight side of the mat is 36 inches. What is the perimeter of the mat?
   (A) 92.52 in. **C** 56.52 in.
   B 64.26 in. **D** 28.26 in.
8. The radius of the planet Jupiter is about 44,368 miles. What is the approximate circumference of Jupiter to the nearest mile?
   F 557,262 mi **H** 139,316 mi
   (G) 278,631 mi **J** 69,658 mi
9. Four square tables with sides of 48 inches each are placed end to end to form one big table. What is the perimeter of the table that is formed?
   A 192 in. (C) 480 in.
   B 384 in. **D** 768 in.
10. Three sides of the Great Pyramid at Giza, Egypt, each measure 756 feet in length to the nearest foot. If the perimeter of the pyramid is 3,023 feet, what is the length of the fourth side of the pyramid?
   F 754 ft **H** 756 ft
   (G) 755 ft **J** 757 ft

Purpose: *To assess students' mastery of concepts and skills in Lessons 8-1 through 8-3*

Assessment Resources

Section 8A Quiz
Assessment Resources .... p. 22

***Test and Practice Generator* CD-ROM**

Additional mid-chapter assessment items in both multiple-choice and free-response format may be generated for any objective in Lessons 8-1 through 8-3.

Chapter 8

Mid-Chapter Quiz

Mid-Chapter Quiz

LESSON **8-1** (pp. 414–417)

Convert.

1. 336 hr = ___ days **14** **2.** 3,500 cm = ___ m **35** **3.** 1,500 s = ___ min **25**

4. 47 kg = ___ g **47,000** **5.** 21,120 ft = ___ mi **4** **6.** 324 in. = ___ yd **9**

7. 248 oz = ___ lb **15.5** **8.** 675 km = ___ mm **675,000,000** **9.** 12 gal = ___ pt **96**

10. How many ounces are there in 16 pounds? **256 oz**

LESSON **8-2** (pp. 420–423)

Choose the more precise measurement in each pair.

11. 5 in., 56 ft **5 in.** **12.** 46 cm, 46.2 cm **46.2 cm** **13.** 24 g, 2 kg **24 g**

Determine the number of significant digits in each measurement.

14. 305.7 km **4** **15.** 0.0840 g **3** **16.** 6,030.0 mi **5**

Calculate. Use the correct number of significant digits in each answer.

17. 13 + 2.5 **16** **18.** 5.6 • 2.59 **15** **19.** 27.1 − 4 **23**

20. 82.5 ÷ 16 **5.2** **21.** 329 + 640 **970** **22.** 205.0 • 0.009 **2**

LESSON **8-3** (pp. 424–427)

Find the perimeter of each polygon.

23. **24.** **25.**

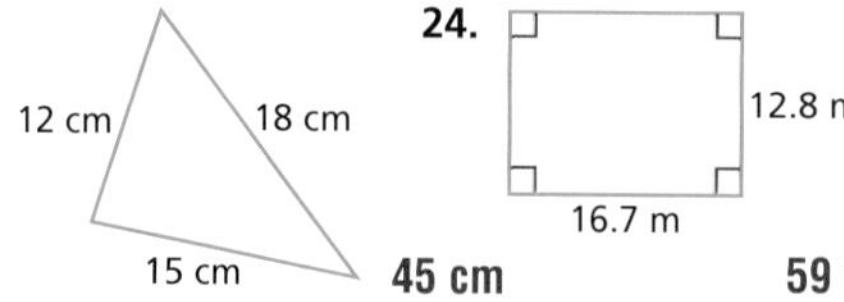

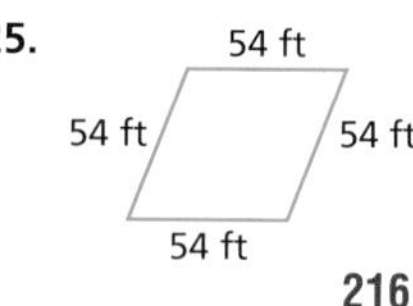

45 cm **59 m** **216 ft**

Find the circumference of each circle to the nearest tenth. Use 3.14 for π.

26. **27.** **28.**

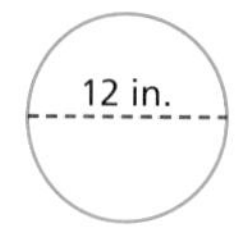

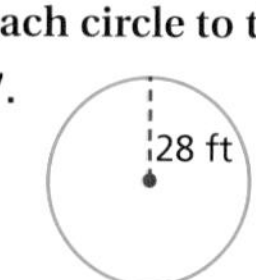

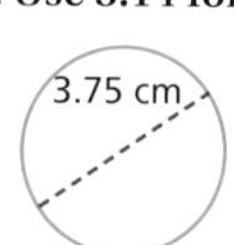

37.7 in. **175.8 ft** **11.8 cm**

29. The diameter of a circle is 56 centimeters. What is the circumference of the circle? Use $\frac{22}{7}$ for π. **176 cm**

Focus on Problem Solving

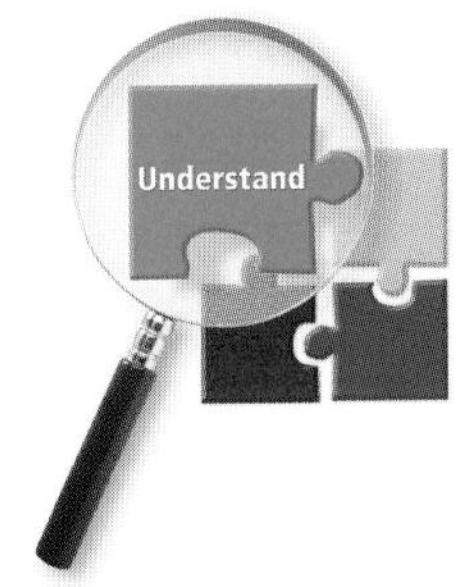

Understand the Problem

• Restate the problem in your own words

By writing a problem in your own words, you may understand it better. Before writing the problem, you may need to reread it several times, perhaps aloud so that you can hear yourself saying the words.

Once you have written the problem in your own words, check to make sure you included all of the necessary information to solve it.

Write each problem in your own words. Check to make sure you have included all of the information needed to solve the problem.

1. College basketball is played on a court that measures 94 feet in length and 50 feet in width. The gym crew needs to paint a stripe around the court. What is the distance around the court?

2. The tallest living tree in the world is a redwood in Montgomery State Reserve in California. The tree is 112 meters tall and has a diameter of 3.14 meters. It is estimated to be over 1,000 years old. What is the circumference of this tree?

3. The shape of a raindrop varies, depending on its size and the air resistance as it falls. The smallest raindrop produced during a drizzle has a mass of about 0.004 milligrams. The largest raindrop produced during a heavy storm has a mass of about 300 milligrams. How many significant digits are in the mass of the smallest raindrop?

4. The volume of blood in an average human adult is between 4.7 and 5 liters. People who live at high altitudes, where the air contains less oxygen, may have up to 1.9 liters more blood than people who live at low altitudes. The extra blood delivers additional oxygen to body cells. How many more milliliters of blood do people at high altitudes have?

Focus on Problem Solving

Purpose: *To focus on understanding the problem*

Problem Solving Resources

Problem Solving Process

This page focuses on the first step of the problem-solving process: **Understand the Problem**

Discuss

Have students tell how they restated the problem in their own words. Possible answers:

1. A basketball court measures 94 feet by 50 feet. What is the perimeter of the basketball court?
2. The tallest living tree has a diameter of 3.14 meters. What is the circumference of this tree?
3. The smallest raindrop has a mass of about 0.004 milligrams. How many significant digits are in the mass of the smallest raindrop?
4. People who live at high altitudes may have up to 1.9 liters more blood than people who live at low altitudes. How many more milliliters of blood do people at high altitudes have?

Answers

1. 288 ft
2. about 9.86 m
3. one significant digit
4. 1,900 mL

Section 8B Area

One-Minute Section Planner

Lesson	Materials	Resources
Lesson 8-4 Area of Parallelograms **NCTM:** Measurement, Reasoning and Proof, Communication, Connections **NAEP:** Measurement 1h ☑ SAT-9 ☑ SAT-10 ☑ ITBS ☑ CTBS ☑ MAT ☑ CAT	**Optional** Teaching Transparency T14 *(CRB)* Graph paper *(CRB, p. 89)* Scissors Parallelogram cutouts *(CRB p. 90)* Glue or tape	• *Chapter 8 Resource Book,* pp. 35–43 • Daily Transparency T13, CRB • Additional Examples Transparencies T15–T16, CRB • *Alternate Openers: Explorations,* p. 71
Lesson 8-5 Area of Triangles and Trapezoids **NCTM:** Measurement, Reasoning and Proof, Communication, Connections **NAEP:** Measurement 1h ☑ SAT-9 ☑ SAT-10 ☑ ITBS ☑ CTBS ☑ MAT ☑ CAT	**Optional** Teaching Transparency T18 *(CRB)* Graph paper *(CRB p. 89)* Scissors	• *Chapter 8 Resource Book,* pp. 44–53 • Daily Transparency T17, CRB • Additional Examples Transparencies T19–T20, CRB • *Alternate Openers: Explorations,* p. 72
Lesson 8-6 Area of Circles **NCTM:** Measurement, Reasoning and Proof, Communication, Connections **NAEP:** Measurement 1h ☑ SAT-9 ☑ SAT-10 ☑ ITBS ☑ CTBS ☑ MAT ☑ CAT	**Optional** Teaching Transparency T22 *(CRB)* Reference books Calculators	• *Chapter 8 Resource Book,* pp. 54–62 • Daily Transparency T21, CRB • Additional Examples Transparencies T23–T25, CRB • *Alternate Openers: Explorations,* p. 73
Section 8B Assessment		• Mid-Chapter Quiz, SE p. 442 • Section 8B Quiz, AR p. 23 • *Test and Practice Generator* CD-ROM

SAT = *Stanford Achievement Tests* **ITBS** = *Iowa Test of Basic Skills* **CTBS** = *Comprehensive Test of Basic Skills/Terra Nova*
MAT = *Metropolitan Achievement Test* **CAT** = *California Achievement Test*

NCTM—Complete standards can be found on pages T27–T33. **NAEP**—Complete standards can be found on pages A35–A39.

SE = *Student Edition* **TE** = *Teacher's Edition* **AR** = *Assessment Resources* **CRB** = *Chapter Resource Book* **MK** = *Manipulatives Kit*

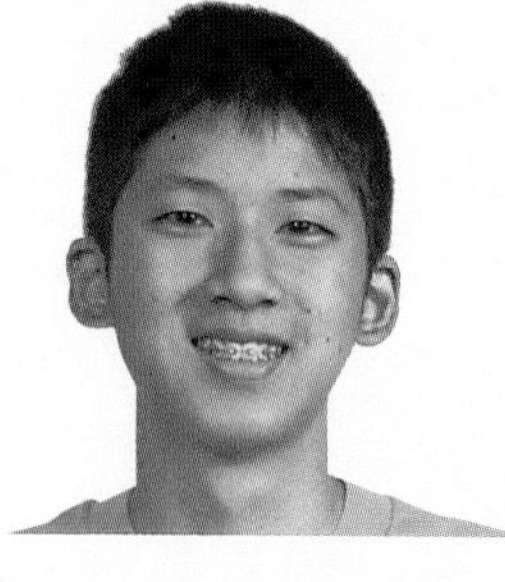

$$A = \pi r^2$$

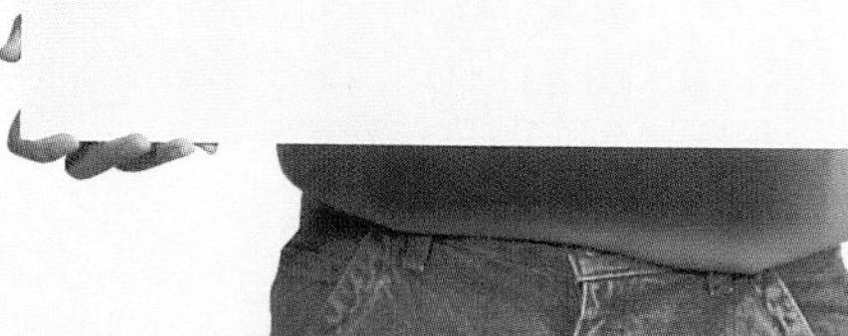

Section Overview

Area of Parallelograms — Lesson 8-4

Why? To find the amount of carpet needed in a room, you may need to know how to find the area of a parallelogram. When students understand how to find areas of parallelograms, including squares and rectangles, they then can apply this understanding to finding areas of the other figures introduced in this section.

Find the area of the parallelogram.

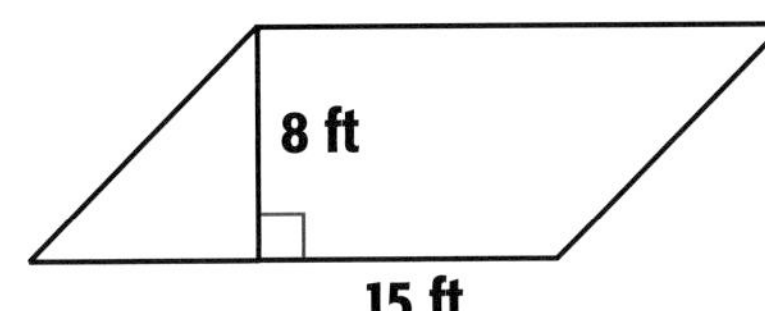

$A = bh$

$A = (15)(8)$

$A = 120 \text{ ft}^2$

The area of the parallelogram is 120 ft^2.

Area of Triangles and Trapezoids — Lesson 8-5

Why? You must be able to find the areas of a variety of basic shapes before you can find the areas of irregular shapes. Students will encounter both basic and irregular shapes in the real world.

Find the area of each figure.

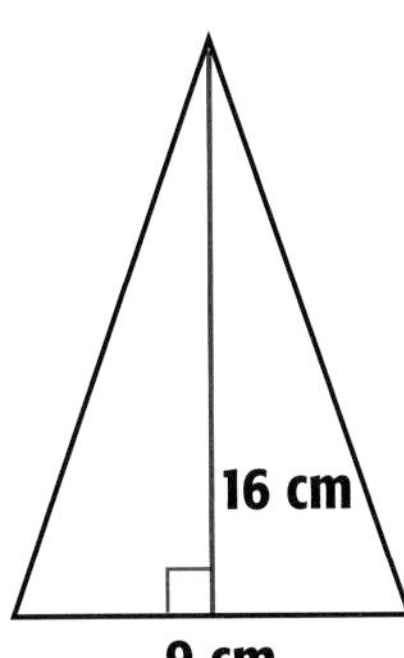

$A = \frac{1}{2}bh$

$A = \frac{1}{2}(9)(16)$

$A = 72 \text{ cm}^2$

The area of the triangle is 72 cm^2.

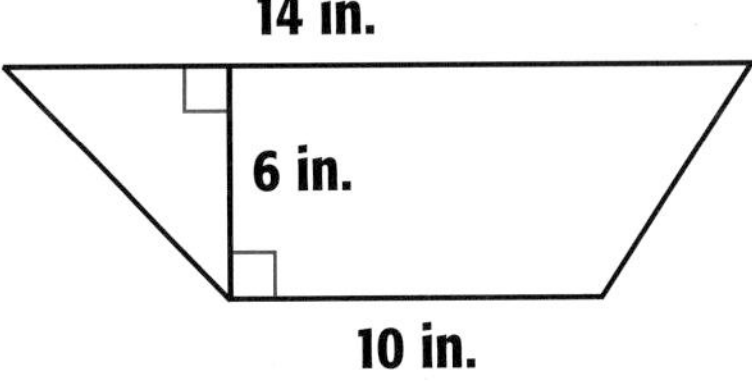

$A = \frac{1}{2}h(b_1 + b_2)$

$A = \frac{1}{2}(6)(10 + 14)$

$A = \frac{1}{2}(6)(24)$

$A = 72 \text{ in}^2$

The area of the trapezoid is 72 in^2.

Area of Circles — Lesson 8-6

Why? In addition to being able to solve problems involving circles, if you know how to find the area of a circle, you can also find the volume or the surface area of a cylinder.

Find the area of the circle to the nearest tenth.

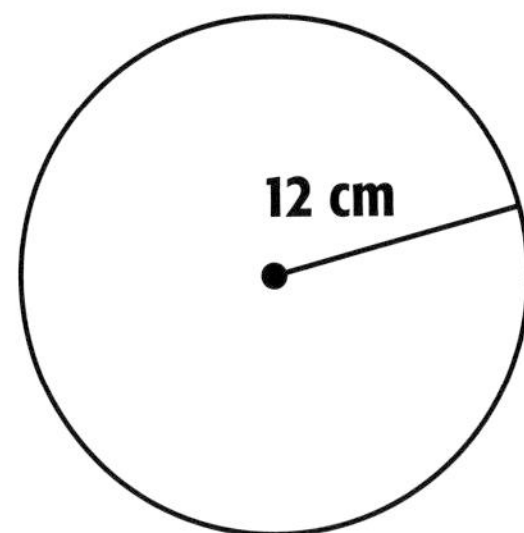

$A = \pi r^2$

$A \approx 3.14(12)^2$

$A \approx 3.14(144)$

$A \approx 452.16 \text{ cm}^2$

The area of the circle is about 452.2 cm^2.

8-4 Organizer

Pacing: Traditional 1 day
Block $\frac{1}{2}$ day

Objective: Students find the area of rectangles and other parallelograms.

Warm Up

Find each product.

1. 8×12 **96**
2. $3\frac{1}{2} \times 5\frac{1}{3}$ **$\frac{56}{3}$ or $18\frac{2}{3}$**
3. 9.4×6.3 **59.22**
4. 3.5×7 **24.5**

Problem of the Day

How many 3 ft by 2 ft rectangles can you cut from one 8 ft by 4 ft rectangle? How much will be left over?
5 pieces; 2 ft^2 left over

Available on Daily Transparency in CRB

Math Fact !

A *rhombus* is an equilateral parallelogram. A rhombus with two acute angles of 45° is called a *lozenge*.

8-4 Area of Parallelograms

Learn to find the area of rectangles and other parallelograms.

Vocabulary
area

The **area** of a figure is the number of unit squares needed to cover the figure. Area is measured in square units. For example, the area of a chessboard can be measured in square inches. The area of a lawn chessboard is much larger, so it can be measured in square feet or square yards.

AREA OF A RECTANGLE

The area A of a rectangle is the product of its length ℓ and its width w.	$A = \ell w$	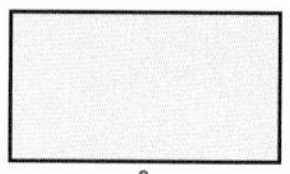 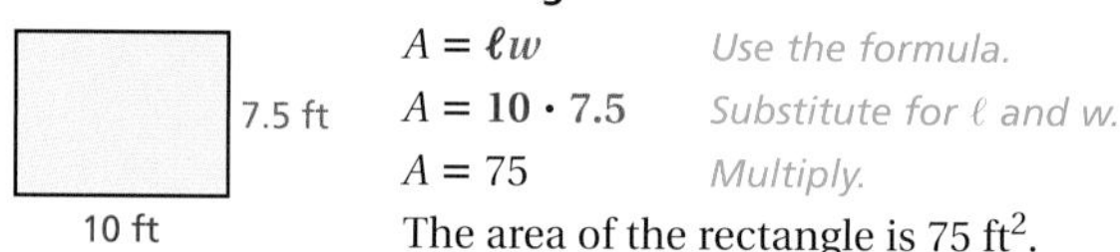

EXAMPLE 1 Finding the Area of a Rectangle

Find the area of the rectangle.

(Rectangle: 10 ft by 7.5 ft)

$A = \ell w$ — *Use the formula.*
$A = \mathbf{10} \cdot \mathbf{7.5}$ — *Substitute for ℓ and w.*
$A = 75$ — *Multiply.*
The area of the rectangle is 75 ft^2.

Helpful Hint

The *base* of the parallelogram is the length of the rectangle. The *height* of the parallelogram is the width of the rectangle.

For any parallelogram that is not a rectangle, you can cut a right triangle-shaped piece from one side and move it to the other side to form a rectangle.

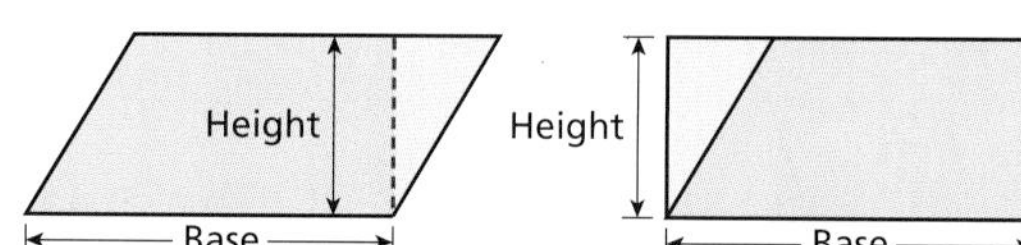

The base of a parallelogram is the length of one side. The height of a parallelogram is the perpendicular distance from the base to the opposite side.

1 Introduce

Alternate Opener

EXPLORATION

8-4 Area of Parallelograms

The *area* of a figure on a grid is the number of squares needed to cover the figure. Area is measured in square units.

Count the number of squares in each figure to find its area.

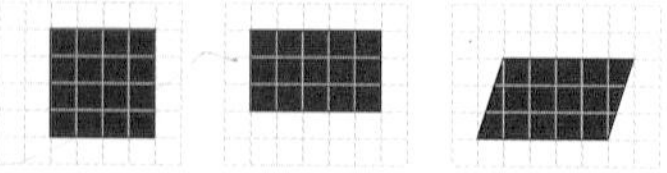

Square — Rectangle — Parallelogram

1. Area = ______
2. Area = ______
3. Area = ______
4. Draw a rectangle and a parallelogram that each have an area of 6 square units.

Rectangle — Parallelogram

Think and Discuss

5. **Explain** how you found the area of the parallelogram in number 3.
6. **Discuss** how you can find the area of any parallelogram, using your explanation from number 5.

Motivate

Discuss real-world situations that require knowledge of perimeter and/or area (e.g., making a border for a bulletin board, buying carpet for a room). Encourage students to share ideas about the differences between area and perimeter. Point out that perimeter is a one-dimensional measure and is measured in linear units, whereas area is two-dimensional and is measured in square units.

Exploration worksheet and answers on Chapter 8 Resource Book pp. 36 and 98

2 Teach

Lesson Presentation

Guided Instruction

In this lesson, students learn to find the area of rectangles and other parallelograms. Have students use graph paper (Chapter 8 Resource Book p. 89) to demonstrate the solution to Example 3.

Teaching Tip Remind students that although many quadrilaterals are parallelograms, not all are. For example, a rectangle, a square, and a rhombus are parallelograms, but a trapezoid is not. The formula for finding the area of a parallelogram will work for any of the special parallelograms: square, rectangle, and rhombus. However, the formula does not work for the trapezoid.

AREA OF A PARALLELOGRAM

The area A of a parallelogram is the product of its base b and its height h.	$A = bh$	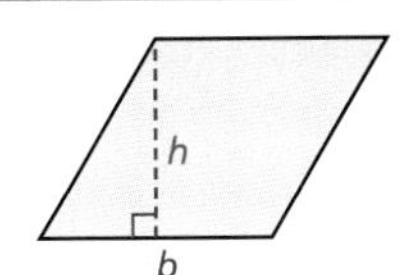

EXAMPLE 2 Finding the Area of a Parallelogram

Find the area of the parallelogram.

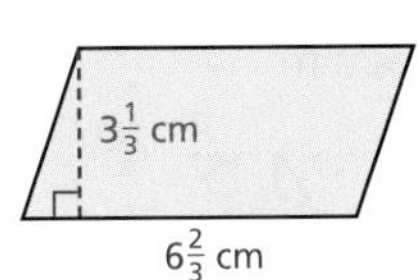

$A = bh$ *Use the formula.*

$A = 6\frac{2}{3} \cdot 3\frac{1}{3}$ *Substitute for b and h.*

$A = \frac{20}{3} \cdot \frac{10}{3}$

$A = \frac{200}{9}$ or $22\frac{2}{9}$

The area of the parallelogram is $22\frac{2}{9}$ cm^2.

EXAMPLE 3 *Measurement Application*

Teesha and Justin are using 4 ft by 8 ft plywood sheets to build a rectangular stage for an outdoor concert. If the area of the stage is 200 ft^2, what is the least number of sheets they need?

First find the area of each sheet of plywood.

$A = \ell w$ *Use the formula for the area of a rectangle.*

$A = 8 \cdot 4$ *Substitute 8 for ℓ, and 4 for w.*

$A = 32$ *Multiply.*

The area of each sheet of plywood is 32 ft^2.

To find the number of plywood sheets needed, divide the area of the stage by the area of one sheet.

$\frac{200 \text{ ft}^2}{32 \text{ ft}^2} = 6.25$

Since building the stage requires more than 6 sheets of plywood, Teesha and Justin need at least 7 sheets.

Think and Discuss

1. **Write** a formula for the area of a square, using an exponent. Explain your answer.
2. **Explain** why the area of a nonrectangular parallelogram with side lengths 5 in. and 3 in. is not 15 in^2.

COMMON ERROR ALERT

Some students might incorrectly try to find the area of a parallelogram by multiplying the side lengths rather than the height and base.

Additional Examples

Example 1

Find the area of the rectangle. 33.3 in^2

Example 2

Find the area of the parallelogram. 128 m^2

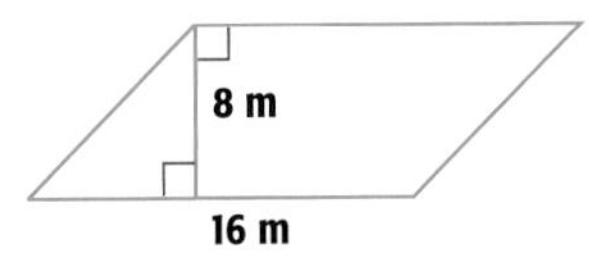

Example 3

A carpenter is covering a 150 ft^2 floor with square tiles that are each 2 ft in length. What is the least number of tiles the carpenter will need to cover the floor? at least 38 tiles

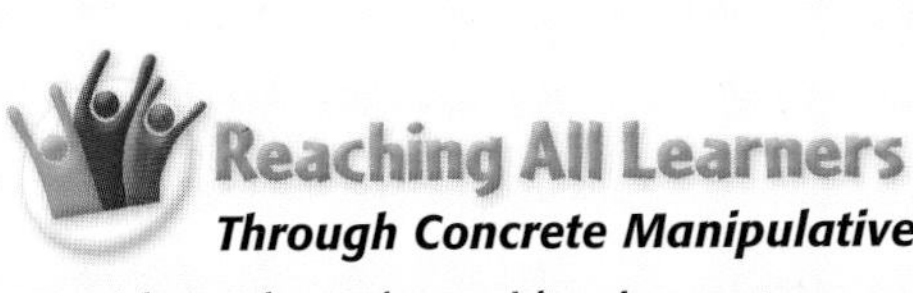

Reaching All Learners

Through Concrete Manipulatives

Provide each student with scissors, tape or glue, and a parallelogram cutout (Chapter 8 Resource Book p. 90). Tell each student to measure the height and base of the parallelogram and to use the formula to find its area. Have each student cut up the parallelogram and rearrange the parts to form a rectangle. Have each student tape or glue the parts onto construction paper to show the rectangle and then find the area of the rectangle.

The finished rectangles should be formed by cutting a triangle from one side of the parallelogram and gluing it to the other side to form a rectangle. Both areas should be equal.

3 Close

Summarize

Have students explain the difference between the formulas $A = \ell w$ and $A = bh$.

Possible answer: In the formula $A = \ell w$, the ℓ and w stand for the side lengths of the rectangle, but in $A = bh$, only the b stands for the length of a side. The h stands for the height of the figure, not necessarily its side length.

Answers to Think and Discuss

Possible answers:

1. All of the sides of a square are equal, so when you multiply the length times the width, you are multiplying the same number by itself. This means you are squaring the number, so $A = s^2$.
2. When a parallelogram is nonrectangular, you have to multiply the height and the base, not the side lengths, to find the area.

8-4 PRACTICE & ASSESS

Students may want to refer back to the lesson examples.

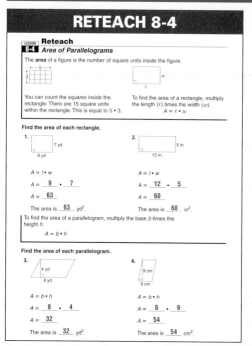

Assignment Guide

If you finished Example 1 assign:
Core 1–3, 8–10, 15, 20, 26, 30–38
Enriched 1, 3, 9, 15, 17, 19, 20, 25, 26, 30–38

If you finished Example 2 assign:
Core 1–6, 8–13, 15, 16, 20, 21, 30–38
Enriched 1–5 odd, 9–13 odd, 15–22, 30–38

If you finished Example 3 assign:
Core 1–14, 16, 17, 21–25 odd, 30–38
Enriched 1–13 odd, 15–38

Notes

Math Background

Parallelograms of different shapes can have the same perimeter. Of all possibile parallelograms with a given perimeter, the one with the largest area is a square.

The shortest distance between a point and a line is along the line connecting the point and the line perpendicularly. This means that the height of a nonrectangular parallelogram will be less than the side length. In a rectangle, the height is the same as the side length (or width).

8-4 Exercises

FOR EXTRA PRACTICE
see page 672

internet connect
Homework Help Online
go.hrw.com Keyword: MS4 8-4

GUIDED PRACTICE

See Example 1 Find the area of each rectangle.

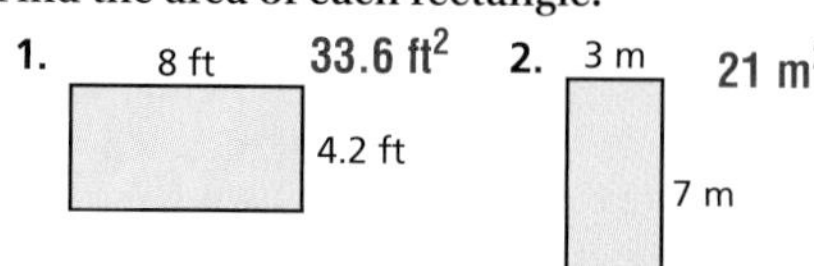

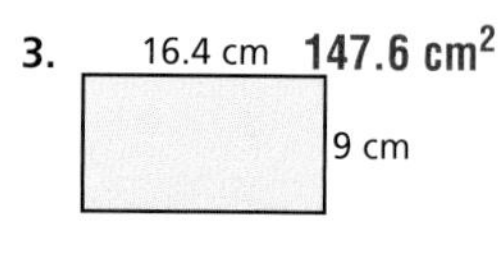

See Example 2 Find the area of each parallelogram.

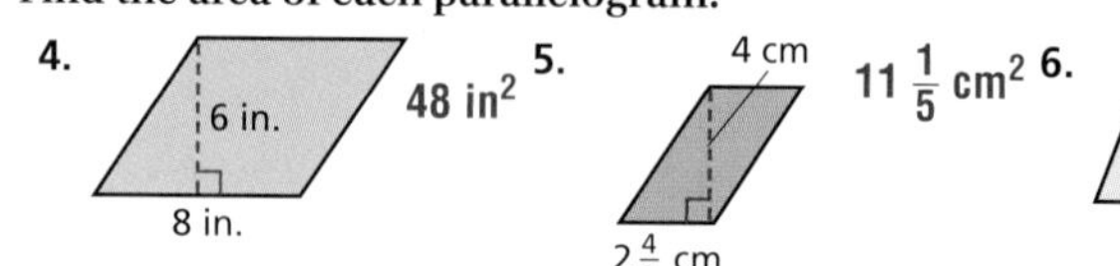

See Example 3 7. Leanne is using 1.5 ft by 1 ft tiles to tile her kitchen floor. If her floor is 10 ft by 6 ft, what is the least number of tiles she will need? **40 tiles**

INDEPENDENT PRACTICE

See Example 1 Find the area of each rectangle.

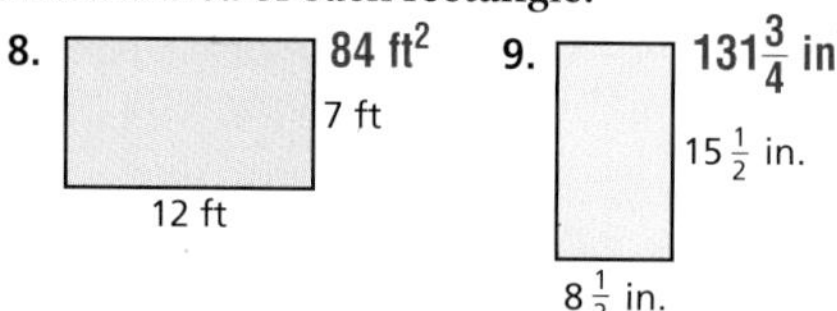

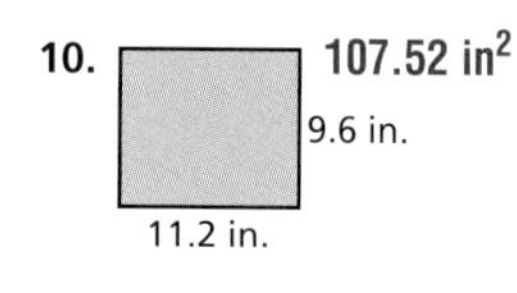

See Example 2 Find the area of each parallelogram.

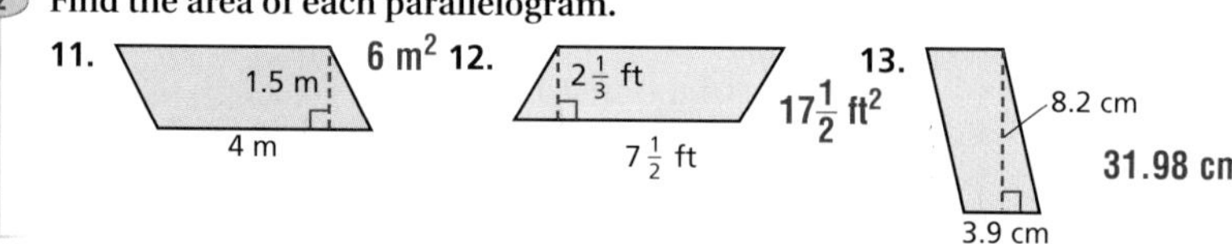

See Example 3 14. Roberto has four 4 ft by 6 ft carpet remnants that he will use to cover a game room floor. If the floor is 9 ft by 12 ft, does he have enough carpet to cover the floor? Explain. **no; The carpet remnants will cover 96 ft^2, but the floor is 108 ft^2.**

PRACTICE AND PROBLEM SOLVING

Find the area of each polygon.

15. rectangle: $\ell = 9$ yd; $w = 8$ yd **72 yd^2**
16. parallelogram: $b = 7$ m; $h = 4.2$ m **29.4 m^2**
17. rectangle: $\ell = 16$ cm; $w = 12$ cm **192 cm^2**
18. parallelogram: $b = 2\frac{1}{2}$ ft; $h = \frac{2}{5}$ ft **1 ft^2**

RETEACH 8-4

LESSON 8-4 **Reteach**
Area of Parallelograms

The **area** of a figure is the number of square units inside the figure.

You can count the squares inside the rectangle. There are 15 square units within the rectangle. This is equal to 5 • 3.

To find the area of a rectangle, multiply the length (ℓ) times the width (w).
$A = \ell \cdot w$

Find the area of each rectangle.

1. 7 yd, 9 yd
$A = l \cdot w$
$A =$ 9 • 7
$A =$ 63
The area is 63 yd^2.

2. 5 in., 12 in.
$A = l \cdot w$
$A =$ 12 • 5
$A =$ 60
The area is 60 in^2.

To find the area of a parallelogram, multiply the base b times the height h.
$A = b \cdot h$

Find the area of each parallelogram.

3. 4 yd, 8 yd
$A = b \cdot h$
$A =$ 8 • 4
$A =$ 32
The area is 32 yd^2.

4. 9 cm, 6 cm
$A = b \cdot h$
$A =$ 6 • 9
$A =$ 54
The area is 54 cm^2.

PRACTICE 8-4

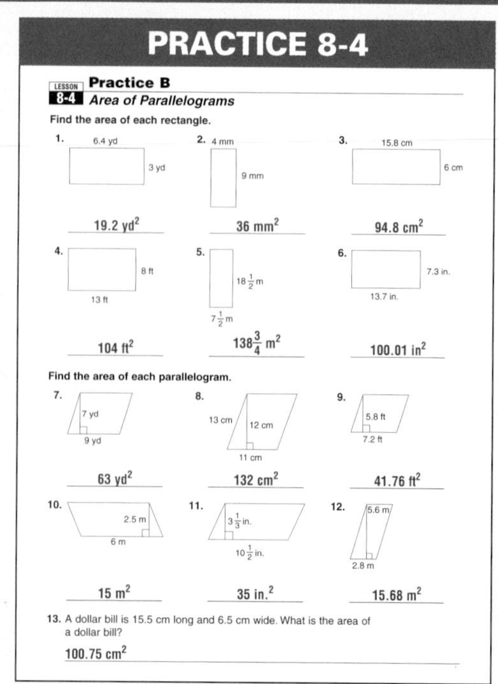

LESSON 8-4 **Practice B**
Area of Parallelograms

Find the area of each rectangle.

1. 6.4 yd, 3 yd — 19.2 yd^2
2. 4 mm, 9 mm — 36 mm^2
3. 15.8 cm, 6 cm — 94.8 cm^2
4. 8 ft, 13 ft — 104 ft^2
5. $18\frac{1}{2}$ m, $7\frac{1}{2}$ m — $138\frac{3}{4}$ m^2
6. 7.3 in., 13.7 in. — 100.01 in^2

Find the area of each parallelogram.

7. 7 yd, 9 yd — 63 yd^2
8. 13 cm, 12 cm, 11 cm — 132 cm^2
9. 5.8 ft, 7.2 ft — 41.76 ft^2
10. 2.5 m, 6 m — 15 m^2
11. $3\frac{1}{3}$ in., $10\frac{1}{2}$ in. — 35 in.^{2}
12. 5.6 m, 2.8 m — 15.68 m^2

13. A dollar bill is 15.5 cm long and 6.5 cm wide. What is the area of a dollar bill?
100.75 cm^2

Graph the polygon with the given vertices. Then find the area of the polygon.

19. (2, 0), (2, −2), (9, 0), (9, −2) **14 units²** 20. (−3, 1), (−3, 6), (1, 1), (1, 6) **20 units²**

21. (1, 2), (3, 5), (7, 2), (9, 5) **18 units²** 22. (4, 1), (4, 7), (8, 4), (8, 10) **24 units²**

23. What is the height of a parallelogram with an area of 66 in² and a base of 11 in.? **h = 6 in.**

24. What is the width of a rectangle with an area of 105 cm² and a length of 7.5 cm? **w = 14 cm**

25. ***ART*** Without the frame, the painting *Girl of Tehuantepec* by Diego Rivera measures about 23 in. by 31 in. The width of the frame is 3 in.
    a. What is the area of the painting? **713 in²**
    b. What is the perimeter of the painting? **108 in.**
    c. What is the total area covered by the painting and the frame? **1,073 in²**

Girl of Tehuantepec by Diego Rivera

26. A local grocery store has diagonal parking spaces that are shaped like parallelograms. If a space is 9 ft wide and 24 ft long, what is its area? **216 ft²**

27. ***CHOOSE A STRATEGY*** The area of a parallelogram is 84 cm². If the base is 5 cm longer than the height, what is the length of the base? **C**

    A 5 cm B 7 cm C 12 cm D 14 cm

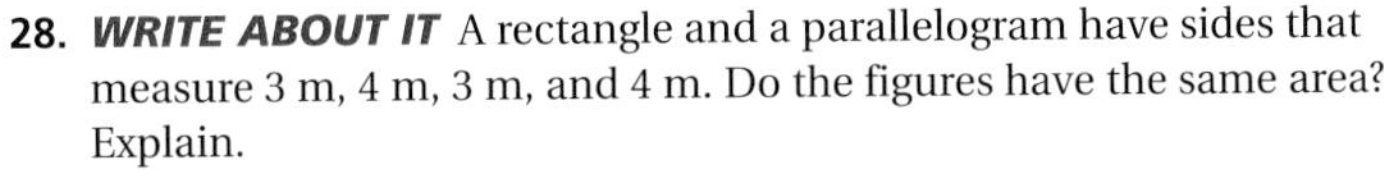

28. ***WRITE ABOUT IT*** A rectangle and a parallelogram have sides that measure 3 m, 4 m, 3 m, and 4 m. Do the figures have the same area? Explain.

28. No, the parallelogram could have a height less than 3 m, but the height of the rectangle is 3 m.

29. ***CHALLENGE*** Two parallelograms have the same base length, but the height of the first is half that of the second. What is the ratio of the area of the first parallelogram to that of the second? What would the ratio be if both the height and the base of the first parallelogram were half those of the second? **1:2; 1:4**

Spiral Review

Solve each equation. (Lesson 3-6)

30. $n - 8 = 16$ **$n = 24$** 31. $-12d = -96$ **$d = 8$** 32. $\frac{t}{-6} = 5$ **$t = -30$** 33. $5 + b = 1$ **$b = -4$**

Find the percent of each number. (Lesson 6-3)

34. 25% of 48 **12** 35. 72% of 60 **43.2** 36. 4% of 35 **1.4** 37. 30% of 115 **34.5**

38. **TEST PREP** What is an angle that measures less than 90° called? (Lesson 7-2) **B**

A Right B Acute C Obtuse D Straight

Answers

19–22. Complete answers on p. A3

Journal

Have students describe how to determine how much paint they would need to paint the classroom ceiling if 1 gallon of paint covers 200 square feet.

Test Prep Doctor

For Exercise 38, encourage students to recall the definitions of *right angle* and *straight angle* to help eliminate **A** and **D.**

Lesson Quiz

Find the area of each figure.

1. 3.5 ft; 7 ft **24.5 ft²**

2.

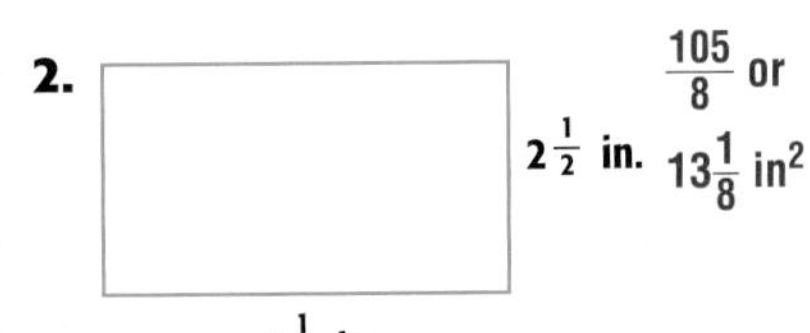

$2\frac{1}{2}$ in.; $5\frac{1}{4}$ in. $\frac{105}{8}$ or $13\frac{1}{8}$ in²

3.

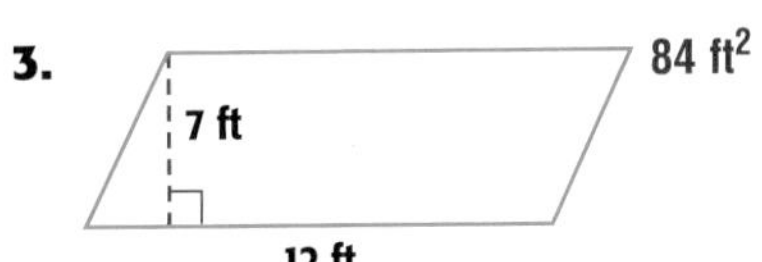

7 ft; 12 ft **84 ft²**

4.

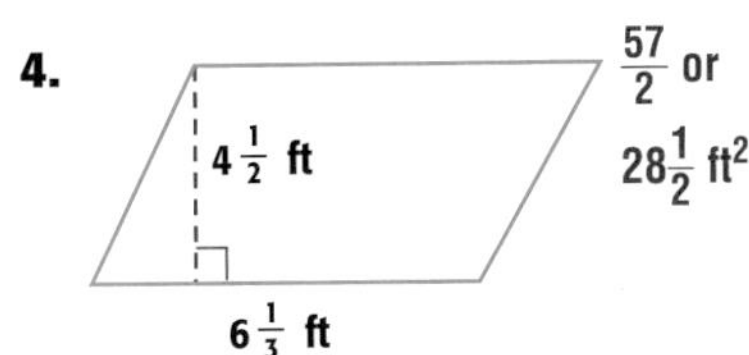

$4\frac{1}{2}$ ft; $6\frac{1}{3}$ ft $\frac{57}{2}$ or $28\frac{1}{2}$ ft²

5. Suzanne is planning to use 1 ft by 0.5 ft tiles to finish her bathroom floor. If her floor is 7 ft by 10 ft, how many tiles will she need?
140 tiles

Available on Daily Transparency in CRB

CHALLENGE 8-4

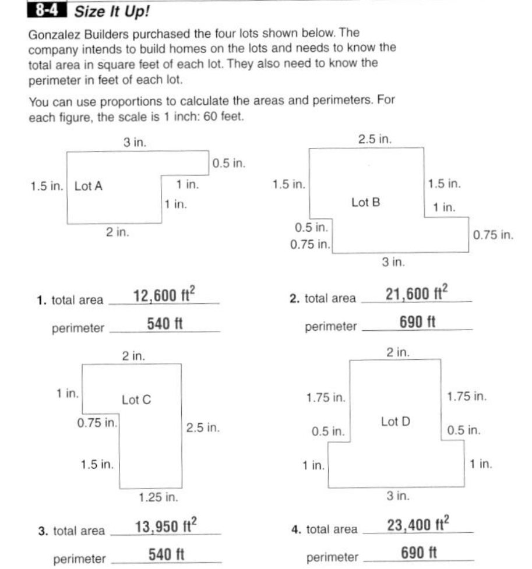

LESSON 8-4 **Challenge**
Size It Up!

Gonzalez Builders purchased the four lots shown below. The company intends to build homes on the lots and needs to know the total area in square feet of each lot. They also need to know the perimeter in feet of each lot.

You can use proportions to calculate the areas and perimeters. For each figure, the scale is 1 inch: 60 feet.

1. total area **12,600 ft²**
   perimeter **540 ft**
2. total area **21,600 ft²**
   perimeter **690 ft**

3. total area **13,950 ft²**
   perimeter **540 ft**
4. total area **23,400 ft²**
   perimeter **690 ft**
5. What is the combined area of all four lots? **71,550 ft²**
6. What length of fencing would be needed to enclose all four lots during construction? **2,460 ft**

PROBLEM SOLVING 8-4

LESSON 8-4 **Problem Solving**
Area of Parallelograms

Write the correct answer.

1. A dollar bill has an area of 15.86 square inches. If a dollar bill is 2.6 inches long, how wide is it?
   6.1 in.
2. On an official United States flag, the ratio of width to length is exactly 1 to 1.9. What is the area of a United States flag whose width is 2 feet?
   7.6 ft²
3. A back yard is shaped like a parallelogram with a height of 32 feet and a base of 100 feet. One bag of grass seed covers 125 square feet. What is the least number of bags of seed needed to seed the lawn?
   26 bags of seed
4. The art club is painting a mural on a school wall. The mural is in the shape of a parallelogram. If the base of the mural is 10.5 feet long and the mural covers 89.25 square feet, how high is the mural?
   8.5 ft high

Choose the letter of the correct answer.

5. In baseball, the area of each base is 225 square inches. Each base is a square. What is the length of each side of a base on a baseball field?
   A 12 in. C 25 in.
   B 22.5 in. (D) 15 in.
6. The area of a parallelogram is 632.1 square centimeters. Its base is 24.5 centimeters. What is the height of the parallelogram?
   (F) 25.8 cm H 21.9 cm
   G 705.6 cm J 11.8 cm
7. The official rules for volleyball were developed in 1897. The rules state that the court or floor space must be 25 feet wide and 50 feet long. An official basketball court is 94 feet by 50 feet. How much larger is the area of a basketball court than the area of a volleyball court?
   A 69 ft² larger
   (B) 3,450 ft² larger
   C 1,250 ft² larger
   D 4,700 ft² larger
8. Two parallelograms each have an area of 288 square inches. One has a height of 12 inches, and the other has a height of 18 inches. What are the bases of each parallelogram?
   F 40 in. and 30 in.
   G 22 in. and 15 in.
   (H) 24 in. and 16 in.
   J 26 in. and 20 in.

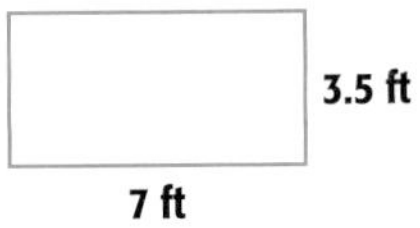

8-5 Organizer

Pacing: Traditional 1 day
Block $\frac{1}{2}$ day

Objective: Students find the area of triangles and trapezoids.

Warm Up

Evaluate.

1. $\frac{1}{2} \cdot 6 \cdot 8$ **24**
2. $\frac{1}{2} \cdot 5.4 \cdot 7.2$ **19.44**
3. $4(7 + 10)$ **68**
4. $3.5(12 + 8.2)$ **70.7**

Problem of the Day

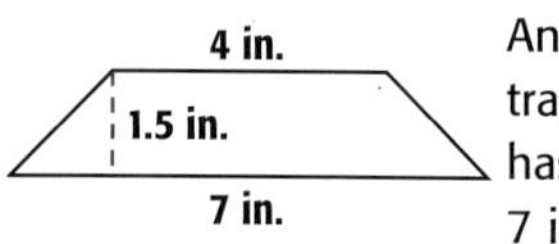

An isosceles trapezoid has bases 7 in. and 4 in. and height 1.5 in. Find its area by using only the formula for the area of a parallelogram.
$(5.5)(1.5) = 8.25 \text{ in}^2$

Available on Daily Transparency in CRB

Math Fact

The line connecting the midpoints of the two nonparallel segments of a trapezoid is called the *midsegment*.

8-5 Area of Triangles and Trapezoids

Learn to find the area of triangles and trapezoids.

The Bermuda Triangle is a triangular region between Bermuda, Florida, and Puerto Rico. To find the area of this region, you could use the formula for the area of a triangle, which is related to the formula for the area of a parallelogram.

A diagonal of a parallelogram divides the parallelogram into two congruent triangles. So the area of each triangle is half the area of the parallelogram.

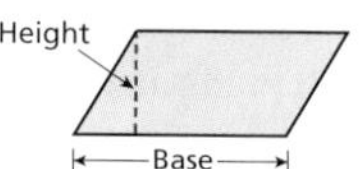

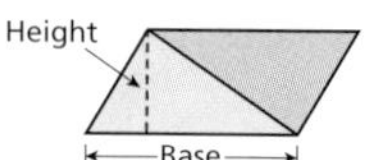

The base of a triangle can be any side. The height of a triangle is the perpendicular distance from the base to the opposite vertex.

AREA OF A TRIANGLE		
The area A of a triangle is half the product of its base b and its height h.	$A = \frac{1}{2}bh$	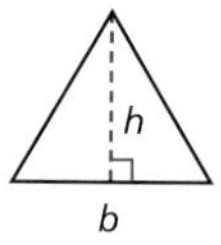 (triangle with h and b)

EXAMPLE 1 Finding the Area of a Triangle

Find the area of each triangle.

A

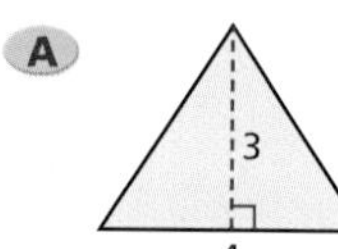

$A = \frac{1}{2}bh$ *Use the formula.*

$A = \frac{1}{2}(4 \cdot 3)$ *Substitute 4 for b and 3 for h.*

$A = 6$

The area of the triangle is 6 square units.

B

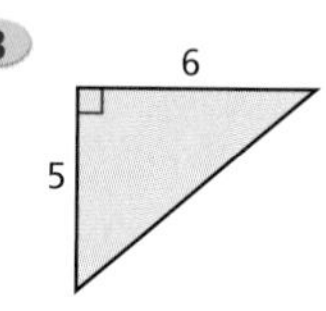

$A = \frac{1}{2}bh$ *Use the formula.*

$A = \frac{1}{2}(6 \cdot 5)$ *Substitute 6 for b and 5 for h.*

$A = 15$

The area of the triangle is 15 square units.

1 Introduce

Alternate Opener

EXPLORATION

8-5 Area of Triangles and Trapezoids

You can use rectangles and parallelograms to help you find the areas of triangles and trapezoids.

Count the number of squares inside each figure to find its area. (*Hint:* What portion of the green quadrilateral is each red figure?)

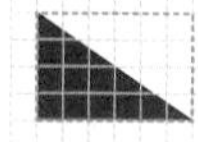

Right triangle

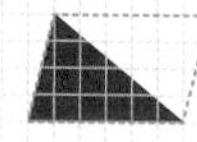

Triangle

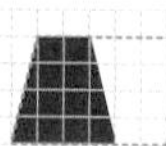

Trapezoid

1. Area = ______ 2. Area = ______ 3. Area = ______
4. Use the grids below to draw two different triangles, each with an area of 6 square units.

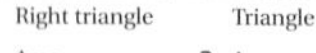

Think and Discuss

5. **Explain** how you used the green quadrilaterals in numbers 1–3 to help you find the areas of the triangles and the trapezoid.

Motivate

Review the parts of a triangle. Draw an acute triangle on the board. Define the base of the triangle as any side of the triangle, and label it. Draw the altitude that corresponds to the base. Explain that the altitude is the perpendicular segment from a vertex of the triangle to the opposite base. The height of the triangle is the length of the altitude.

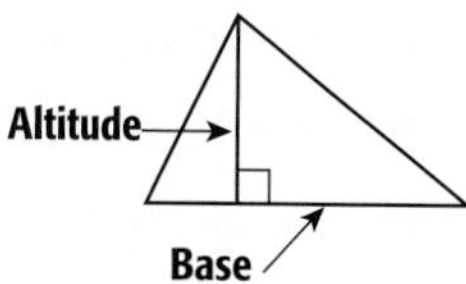

Exploration worksheet and answers on Chapter 8 Resource Book pp. 45 and 100

2 Teach

Lesson Presentation

Guided Instruction

In this lesson, students learn to find the area of triangles and trapezoids. Explain the importance of understanding how the formula for the area of each figure relates to a diagram of that figure. Encourage students to memorize the formulas, but it is more important that students be able to use diagrams and logical reasoning to derive the formulas on their own.

Teaching Tip Point out that you can use properties of multiplication to simplify a product. For example, to mentally compute $\frac{1}{2}(11 \cdot 14)$, rewrite the product: $\frac{1}{2}(11 \cdot 14) = (\frac{1}{2} \cdot 14) \cdot 11 = 7 \cdot 11 = 77$.

A parallelogram can be divided into two congruent trapezoids. The area of each trapezoid is one-half the area of the parallelogram.

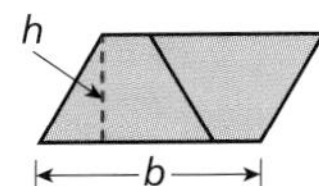

Area of trapezoid = $\frac{1}{2}$(base of parallelogram)(height)

The two parallel sides of a trapezoid are its bases. If we call the longer side b_1 and the shorter side b_2, then the base of the parallelogram is $b_1 + b_2$.

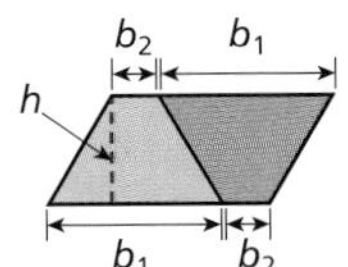

Area of trapezoid = $\frac{1}{2}$(base 1 + base 2)(height)

AREA OF A TRAPEZOID

The area of a trapezoid is half its height multiplied by the sum of the lengths of its two bases.	$A = \frac{1}{2}h(b_1 + b_2)$	(b_2, h, b_1)

EXAMPLE 2 Finding the Area of a Trapezoid

Find the area of each trapezoid.

A

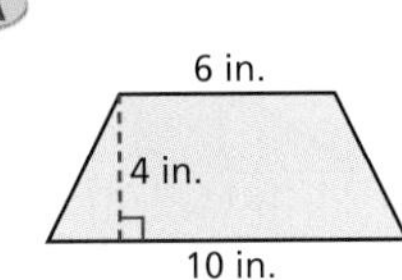

$A = \frac{1}{2}h(b_1 + b_2)$ *Use the formula.*

$A = \frac{1}{2} \cdot 4(10 + 6)$ *Substitute.*

$A = \frac{1}{2} \cdot 4(16)$ *Add.*

$A = 32$ *Multiply.*

The area of the trapezoid is 32 in^2.

B

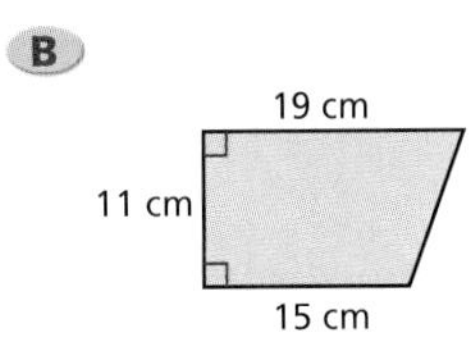

$A = \frac{1}{2}h(b_1 + b_2)$ *Use the formula.*

$A = \frac{1}{2} \cdot 11(15 + 19)$ *Substitute.*

$A = \frac{1}{2} \cdot 11(34)$ *Add.*

$A = 187$ *Multiply.*

The area of the trapezoid is 187 cm^2.

Think and Discuss

1. Tell how to use the sides of a right triangle to find its area.

2. Explain how to find the area of a trapezoid.

COMMON ERROR ALERT

Some students are often tempted to find the area of a triangle by mentally multiplying the base by the height, forgetting to multiply by $\frac{1}{2}$. Have students write the formula as a quick remedy for this common error.

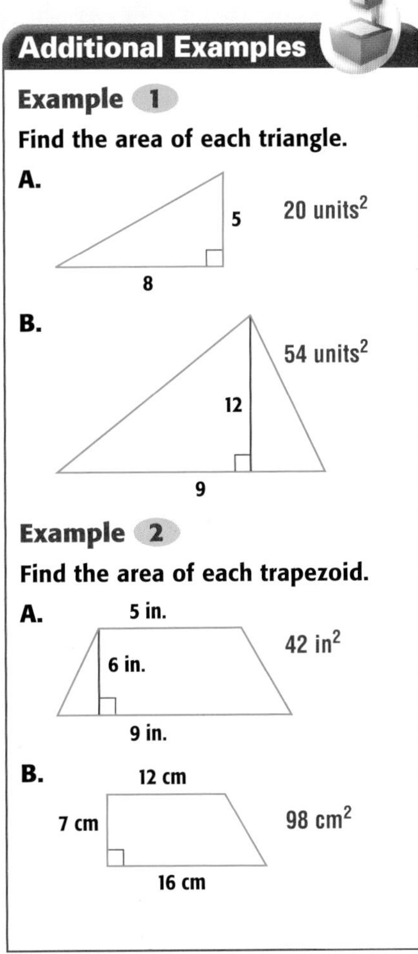

Additional Examples
Example 1
Find the area of each triangle.
A.
5
8
20 units²
B.
54 units²
12
9
Example 2
Find the area of each trapezoid.
A.
5 in.
42 in²
6 in.
9 in.
B.
12 cm
7 cm
98 cm²
16 cm

Example 2 note: Emphasize the importance of following the order of operations when using a formula to evaluate.

3 Close

Reaching All Learners
Through Grouping Strategies

Have students in small groups draw a triangle whose lengths have whole number measures that will fit onto a standard sheet of graph paper (e.g., a right triangle with side lengths 9, 12, and 15). Then let students cut out the triangle and use the formula to demonstrate that any of the three sides can serve as the base. Students can draw a rectangle around the cutout triangle on another sheet of graph paper to find the height of the triangle for each base.

Summarize

Have students write the formulas for the area of a triangle and a trapezoid and draw a variety of diagrams that demonstrate the variables in each formula.

Possible answers:

Triangle: $A = \frac{1}{2}bh$. Diagrams should show the base and the height on an acute triangle and on an obtuse triangle.

Trapezoid: $A = \frac{1}{2}h(b_1 + b_2)$. Diagrams should show the bases and the height on a right trapezoid and on another type of trapezoid.

Answers to Think and Discuss

1. Multiply the lengths of the perpendicular sides, and then divide by two.
2. Find the sum of the lengths of the two parallel sides, and then find $\frac{1}{2}$ of the height times that sum.

8-5 PRACTICE & ASSESS

Students may want to refer back to the lesson examples.

Assignment Guide

If you finished Example 1 assign:
Core 1–3, 7–9, 13, 17, 28–36
Enriched 1, 3, 7, 9, 13–15, 17, 19, 25, 28–36

If you finished Example 2 assign:
Core 1–12, 13, 15–17, 21–25 odd, 28–36
Enriched 1–11 odd, 13–36

Answers

16–19. Complete answers on p. A3

Notes

8-5 Exercises

FOR EXTRA PRACTICE see page 672

internet connect
Homework Help Online
go.hrw.com Keyword: MS4 8-5

GUIDED PRACTICE

See Example 1 Find the area of each triangle.

1. 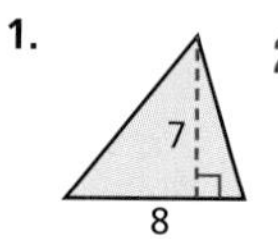

28 units^2

2. 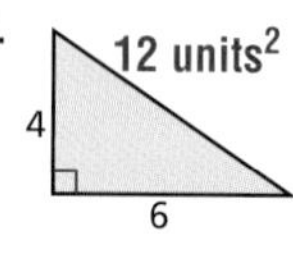

12 units^2

3. 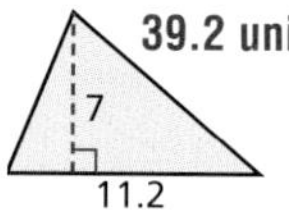 7, 11.2 **39.2 units^2**

See Example 2 Find the area of each trapezoid.

4. 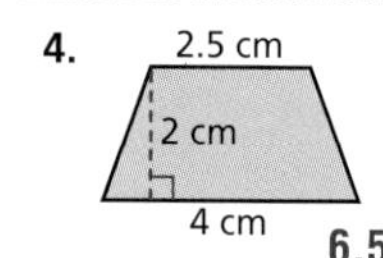

6.5 cm^2

5. 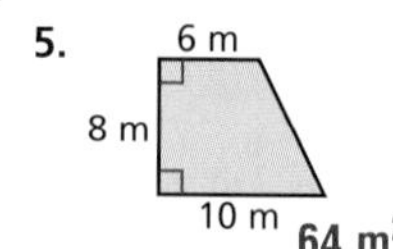

64 m^2

6. 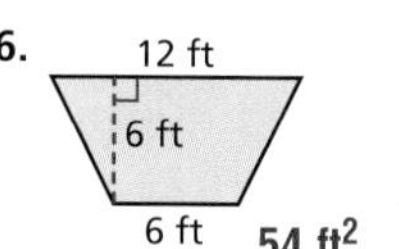

54 ft^2

INDEPENDENT PRACTICE

See Example 1 Find the area of each triangle.

7. 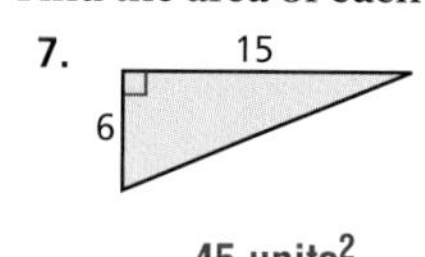

45 units^2

8. 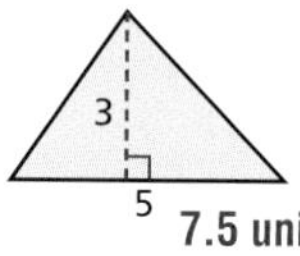 3, 5 **7.5 units^2**

9. 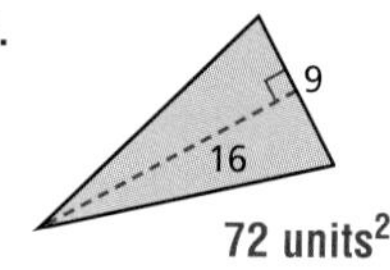

72 units^2

See Example 2 Find the area of each trapezoid.

10. 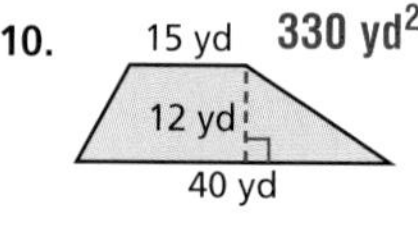

330 yd^2

11. 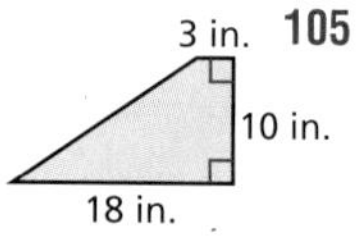 3 in., 10 in., 18 in. **105 in^2**

12. 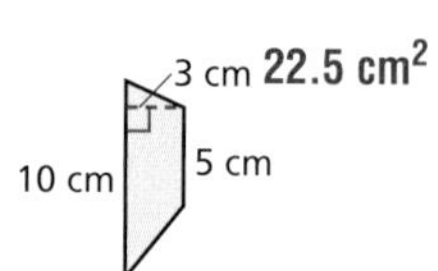

22.5 cm^2

PRACTICE AND PROBLEM SOLVING

Find the missing measurement of each triangle.

13. $b = 8$ cm
$h = ▒$ **4.5 cm**
$A = 18$ cm^2

14. $b = 16$ ft
$h = 0.7$ ft
$A = ▒$ **5.6 ft^2**

15. $b = ▒$ **22 in.**
$h = 95$ in.
$A = 1{,}045$ in^2

Graph the polygon with the given vertices. Then find the area of the polygon.

16. (1, 2), (4, 5), (8, 2), (8, 5) **16.5 units^2**

17. (1, −6), (5, −1), (7, −6) **15 units^2**

18. (2, 3), (2, 10), (7, 6), (7, 8) **22.5 units^2**

19. (3, 0), (3, 4), (−3, 0) **12 units^2**

20. When the Erie Canal opened, it was 42 ft wide at the top, 28 ft wide at the bottom, and 4 ft deep. Find the area of a trapezoidal cross section of the canal. **140 ft^2**

21. What is the height of a trapezoid with an area of 9 m^2 and bases that measure 2.4 m and 3.6 m? **3 m**

Math Background

Heron, a mathematician in ancient Alexandria, developed a formula for finding the area of a triangle from the length of its sides.

Heron's Formula (also known as Hero's Formula) is

$$A = \sqrt{s(s-a)(s-b)(s-c)},$$

where $s = \dfrac{a+b+c}{2}$.

In the formula, s stands for the semi-perimeter, or one-half the perimeter, of the triangle, and a, b, and c are the lengths of the sides.

RETEACH 8-5

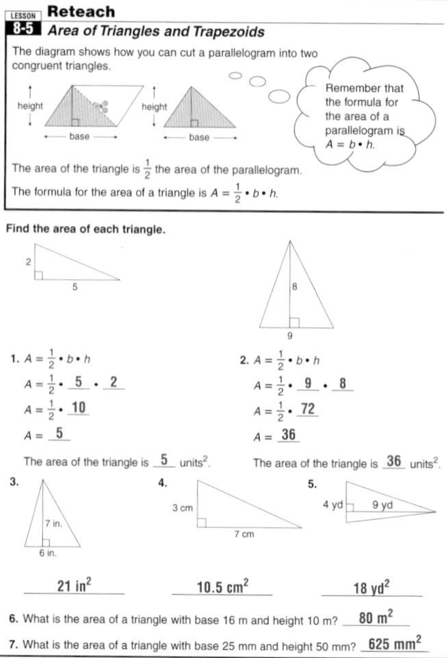

LESSON 8-5 **Reteach**
Area of Triangles and Trapezoids

The diagram shows how you can cut a parallelogram into two congruent triangles.

height, base — height, base

Remember that the formula for the area of a parallelogram is $A = b \cdot h$.

The area of the triangle is $\frac{1}{2}$ the area of the parallelogram.

The formula for the area of a triangle is $A = \frac{1}{2} \cdot b \cdot h$.

Find the area of each triangle.

1. $A = \frac{1}{2} \cdot b \cdot h$
$A = \frac{1}{2} \cdot$ 5 $\cdot$ 2
$A = \frac{1}{2} \cdot$ 10
$A =$ 5
The area of the triangle is 5 units^2.

2. $A = \frac{1}{2} \cdot b \cdot h$
$A = \frac{1}{2} \cdot$ 9 $\cdot$ 8
$A = \frac{1}{2} \cdot$ 72
$A =$ 36
The area of the triangle is 36 units^2.

3. 7 in., 6 in. — 21 in^2
4. 3 cm, 7 cm — 10.5 cm^2
5. 4 yd, 9 yd — 18 yd^2

6. What is the area of a triangle with base 16 m and height 10 m? 80 m^2
7. What is the area of a triangle with base 25 mm and height 50 mm? 625 mm^2

PRACTICE 8-5

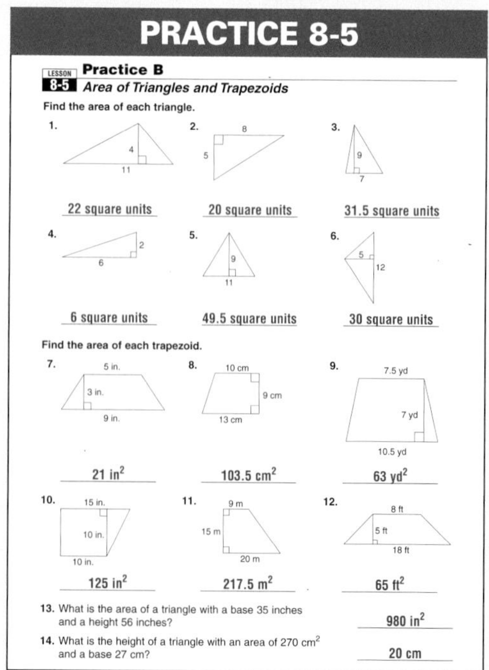
LESSON 8-5 **Practice B**
Area of Triangles and Trapezoids

Find the area of each triangle.

1. 22 square units
2. 20 square units
3. 31.5 square units
4. 6 square units
5. 49.5 square units
6. 30 square units

Find the area of each trapezoid.

7. 21 in^2
8. 103.5 cm^2
9. 63 yd^2
10. 125 in^2
11. 217.5 m^2
12. 65 ft^2

13. What is the area of a triangle with a base 35 inches and a height 56 inches? 980 in^2
14. What is the height of a triangle with an area of 270 cm^2 and a base 27 cm? 20 cm

Geography LINK

22. The state of Tennessee is shaped somewhat like a parallelogram. Find the approximate area of Tennessee. **50,830 mi²**

23. The state of Nevada is shaped somewhat like a trapezoid. What is the approximate area of Nevada? **108,000 mi²**

24. The state of Colorado is somewhat rectangular in shape. Estimate the perimeter and area of Colorado. **1,282 mi; 100,740 mi²**

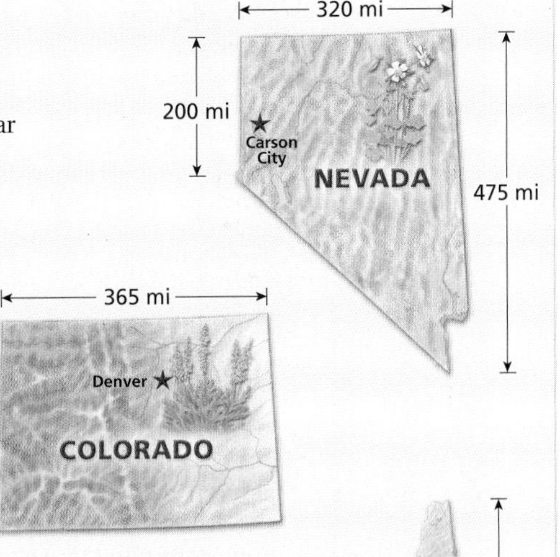

25. The shape of the state of New Hampshire is approximately a right triangle.
    a. Estimate the area of New Hampshire. **6,800 mi²**
    b. In 2000, the population of New Hampshire was 1,235,786. Estimate the population per square mile. **181.7**

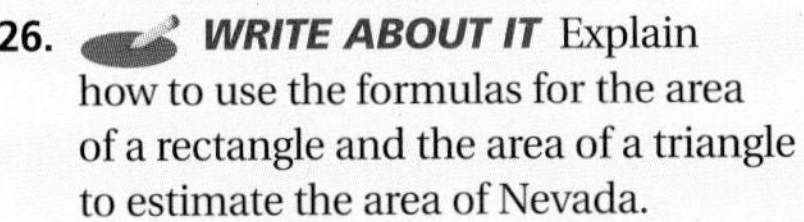

26. ***WRITE ABOUT IT*** Explain how to use the formulas for the area of a rectangle and the area of a triangle to estimate the area of Nevada.

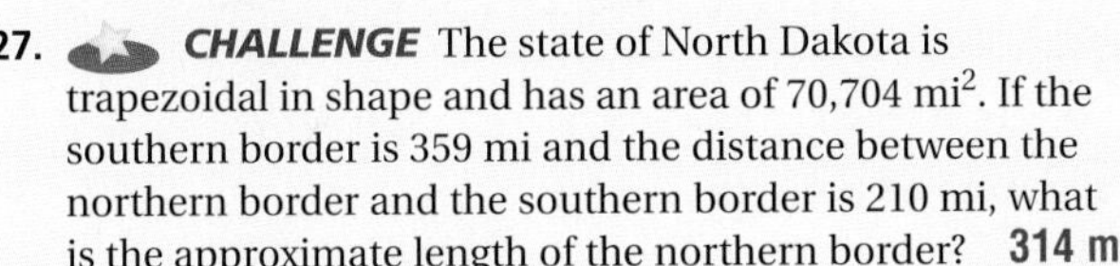

27. ***CHALLENGE*** The state of North Dakota is trapezoidal in shape and has an area of 70,704 mi². If the southern border is 359 mi and the distance between the northern border and the southern border is 210 mi, what is the approximate length of the northern border? **314 mi**

Spiral Review

Identify each number as prime or composite. (Lesson 2-4)

28. 16 **composite** **29.** 17 **prime** **30.** 111 **composite** **31.** 29 **prime**

Write each fraction as a decimal. (Lesson 3-9)

32. $\frac{1}{4}$ **0.25** **33.** $\frac{3}{5}$ **0.6** **34.** $\frac{5}{8}$ **0.625** **35.** $\frac{9}{6}$ **1.5**

36. TEST PREP What is the approximate radius of a circle with circumference 36? (Lesson 8-3) **B**

A 3.14 B 5.73 C 11.46 D 113.68

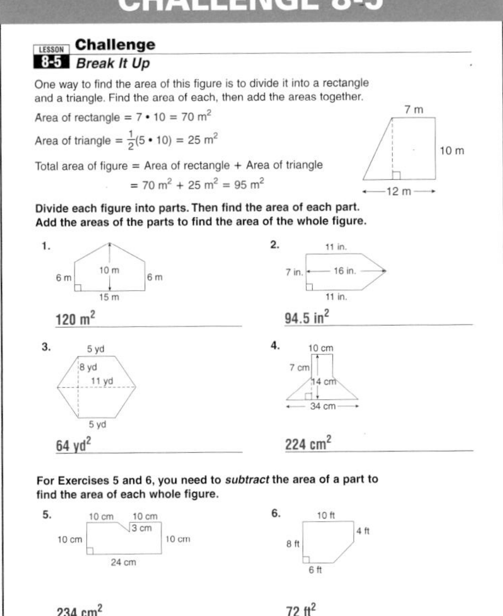

CHALLENGE 8-5

LESSON 8-5 **Challenge**
Break It Up

One way to find the area of this figure is to divide it into a rectangle and a triangle. Find the area of each, then add the areas together.

Area of rectangle = 7 • 10 = 70 m²

Area of triangle = $\frac{1}{2}$(5 • 10) = 25 m²

Total area of figure = Area of rectangle + Area of triangle
= 70 m² + 25 m² = 95 m²

Divide each figure into parts. Then find the area of each part. Add the areas of the parts to find the area of the whole figure.

1. (6 m, 10 m, 6 m, 15 m) **120 m²**
2. (11 in., 7 in., 16 in., 11 in.) **94.5 in²**
3. (5 yd, 8 yd, 11 yd, 5 yd) **64 yd²**
4. (10 cm, 7 cm, 14 cm, 34 cm) **224 cm²**

For Exercises 5 and 6, you need to *subtract* the area of a part to find the area of each whole figure.

5. (10 cm, 10 cm, 3 cm, 10 cm, 10 cm, 24 cm) **234 cm²**
6. (10 ft, 4 ft, 8 ft, 6 ft) **72 ft²**

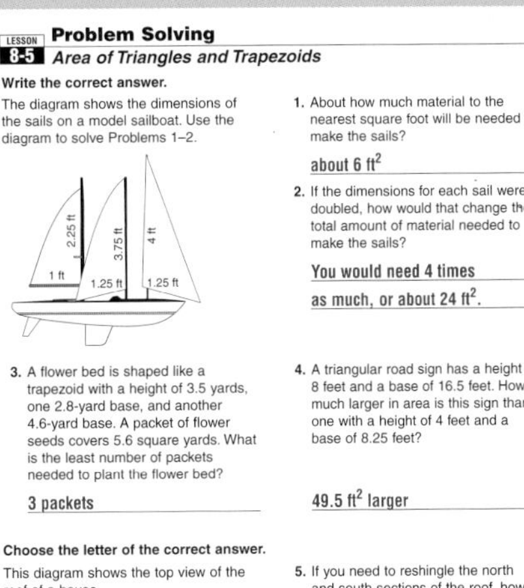

PROBLEM SOLVING 8-5

LESSON 8-5 **Problem Solving**
Area of Triangles and Trapezoids

Write the correct answer.

The diagram shows the dimensions of the sails on a model sailboat. Use the diagram to solve Problems 1–2.

1. About how much material to the nearest square foot will be needed to make the sails?
   about 6 ft²
2. If the dimensions for each sail were doubled, how would that change the total amount of material needed to make the sails?
   You would need 4 times as much, or about 24 ft².
3. A flower bed is shaped like a trapezoid with a height of 3.5 yards, one 2.8-yard base, and another 4.6-yard base. A packet of flower seeds covers 5.6 square yards. What is the least number of packets needed to plant the flower bed?
   3 packets
4. A triangular road sign has a height of 8 feet and a base of 16.5 feet. How much larger in area is this sign than one with a height of 4 feet and a base of 8.25 feet?
   49.5 ft² larger

Choose the letter of the correct answer.

This diagram shows the top view of the roof of a house.

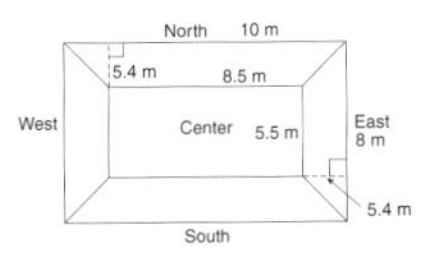

5. If you need to reshingle the north and south sections of the roof, how many square meters of shingles will you need?
   A 199.8 m² (B) 99.9 m² C 49.95 m² D 459 m²
6. If you need to reshingle the west section of the roof, how many square meters of shingles will you need?
   F 13.5 m² G 18.9 m² (H) 36.45 m² J 72.9 m²

Interdisciplinary LINK

Geography

In Exercises 22–27, students describe the shapes of some states in the United States. Students learn about the geography of the United States in middle school social studies programs, such as Holt, Rinehart and Winston's *People, Places, and Change.*

Answers

26. See p. A3.

Journal

Ask students to think of and write about a real-world situation in which it would be necessary to find the area of a triangle.

Test Prep Doctor

For Exercise 36, encourage students to write the formula for the circumference of a circle in terms of the radius: $C = 2\pi r$. Students can easily estimate the answer by substituting directly into the formula, letting $\pi = 3$. The only possible choice is the correct one, choice **B**.

Lesson Quiz

Find the area of each figure.

1. (9 ft, 10 ft) **45 ft²**

2. (3 in., 6 in.) **9 in²**

3.

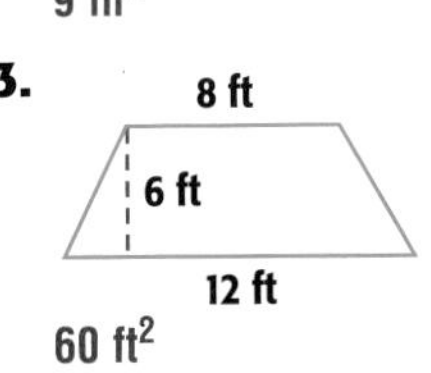

60 ft²

4.

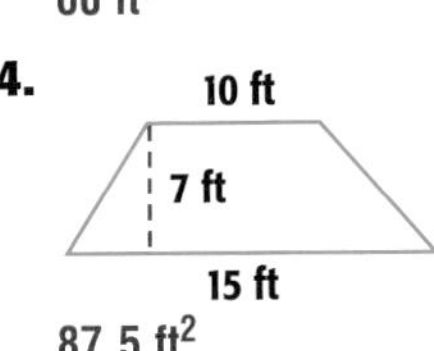

87.5 ft²

5. What is the height of a triangle with area 36 cm² and base 9 cm? **8 cm**

Available on Daily Transparency in CRB

8-6 Organizer

Pacing: Traditional 1 day
Block $\frac{1}{2}$ day

Objective: Students find the area of circles.

Warm Up

Simplify.

1. 8^2 **64**
2. 12^2 **144**
3. 6.2^2 **38.44**
4. 7.5^2 **56.25**

Problem of the Day

A 16 in. pizza sells for $11.99. A 10 in. pizza sells for $5.99. Which size gives you more pizza per penny? Explain.
The larger pizza; you get more than twice as much (64π in^2 instead of 25π in^2) for about twice the price.

Available on Daily Transparency in CRB

Teacher: What is the area of a circle?

First student: πr^2

Second student: Pie are not square. Pie are round.

8-6 Area of Circles

Learn to find the area of circles.

A circle can be cut into equal-sized sectors and arranged to resemble a parallelogram. The height h of the parallelogram is equal to the radius r of the circle, and the base b of the parallelogram is equal to one-half the circumference C of the circle. So the area of the parallelogram can be written as

$A = bh$, or $A = \frac{1}{2}Cr$.

Since $C = 2\pi r$, $A = \frac{1}{2}(2\pi r)r = \pi r^2$.

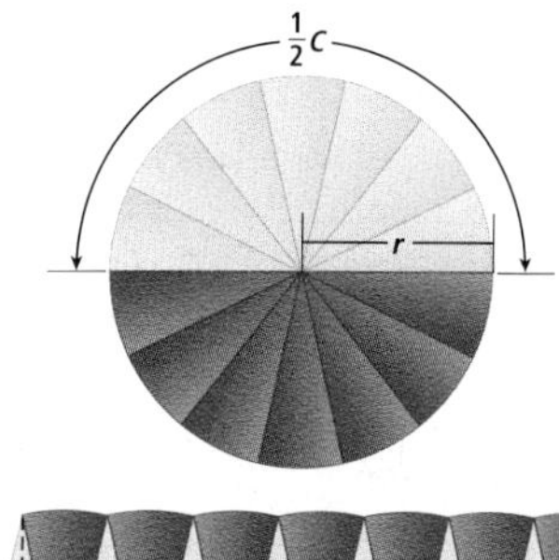

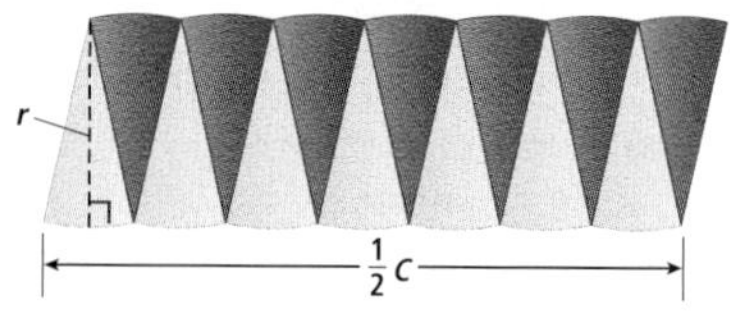

AREA OF A CIRCLE		
The area A of a circle is the product of π and the square of the circle's radius r.	$A = \pi r^2$	r

EXAMPLE 1 Finding the Area of a Circle

Find the area of each circle to the nearest tenth. Use 3.14 for π.

Remember!
The order of operations calls for evaluating the exponents before multiplying.

A

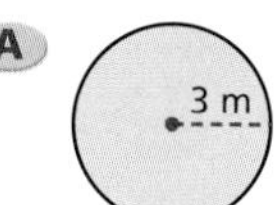

$A = \pi r^2$ *Use the formula.*
$A \approx 3.14 \cdot 3^2$ *Substitute. Use 3 for r.*
$A \approx 3.14 \cdot 9$ *Evaluate the power.*
$A \approx 28.26$ *Multiply.*

The area of the circle is about 28.3 m^2.

B

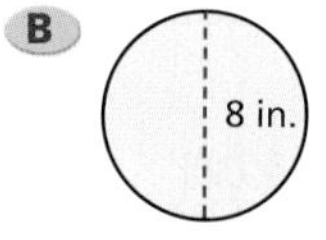

$A = \pi r^2$ *Use the formula.*
$A \approx 3.14 \cdot 4^2$ *Substitute. Use 4 for r.*
$A \approx 3.14 \cdot 16$ *Evaluate the power.*
$A \approx 50.24$ *Multiply.*

The area of the circle is about 50.2 in^2.

1 Introduce

Alternate Opener

EXPLORATION

8-6 Area of Circles

You can estimate the area of a circle by counting the number of squares inside the circle.

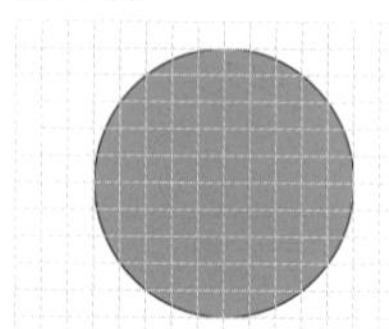

Use the circle and the grid to find the following.

1. Estimate the area of the circle.
2. Find the radius of the circle.
3. Square the radius.
4. Find the ratio of the area of the circle to the square of the radius.

Think and Discuss

5. **Explain** how you found the radius of the circle.
6. **Discuss** how you can find the area of a circle if you know the radius. (*Hint:* Use the ratio you found in number 4 in your discussion.)

Motivate

Ask students to describe what they would need to know to plan a pizza party for the class. Lead students to discuss how the size of the pizzas ordered affects the number of pizzas needed to feed the class. Discuss that you can find the best deal by comparing the unit costs per square inch of two differently sized pizzas if you can determine the area of each pizza, a circular figure.

Exploration worksheet and answers on Chapter 8 Resource Book pp. 55 and 102

2 Teach

Lesson Presentation

Guided Instruction

In this lesson, students learn to find the area of circles. Point out that although $A = \pi r^2$ is the more common formula for the area of a circle, you can also use $A = \frac{1}{2}Cr$. Stress the importance of following the order of operations while computing the area in each example.

Teaching Tip Remind students that the variable r in the formula works as a placeholder for the actual value of the radius. Since r is squared, you must also square the value. Introducing parentheses around r might help students better understand the substitution: $r^2 = (r)^2$, and $A = \pi r^2 = \pi(r)^2$.

EXAMPLE 2 *Social Studies Application*

Nomads in Mongolia carried their homes wherever they roamed. These homes, called *yurts*, were made of wood and felt.

A group of historians are building a yurt to display at a local multicultural fair. The yurt has a height of 8 feet 9 inches at its center, and it has a circular floor of radius 7 feet. What is the area of the floor of the yurt? Use $\frac{22}{7}$ for π.

$A = \pi r^2$ — *Use the formula for the area of a circle.*

$A \approx \frac{22}{7} \cdot 7^2$ — *Substitute. Use 7 for r.*

$A \approx \frac{22}{\cancel{7}_1} \cdot \cancel{49}^7$ — *Evaluate the power.*

$A \approx 22 \cdot 7$

$A \approx 154$ — *Multiply.*

The area of the floor of the yurt is about 154 ft^2.

EXAMPLE 3 *Agriculture Application*

These fields are located in the Wadi Rum Desert in Jordan. Here crops are grown on circular patches of irrigated land. If the radius of one irrigated field is 60 feet, what is the area of the field? Round your answer to the nearest whole number.

$A = \pi r^2$ — *Use the formula for the area of a circle.*

$A = \pi \cdot 60^2$ — *Substitute. Use 60 for r.*

$A \approx 11309.73355$ — *Use a calculator.* π × 60 x^2

$A \approx 11{,}310$ — *Round.*

The sprinkler covers about 11,310 ft^2.

Think and Discuss

1. **Compare** finding the area of a circle when given the radius with finding the area when given the diameter.
2. **Explain** how to find the area of a circle with a diameter of 3 feet.
3. **Give an example** of a circular object in your classroom. Tell how you could estimate the area of the object, and then estimate.

Additional Examples

Example 1

Find the area of each circle to the nearest tenth. Use 3.14 for π.

A. **153.9 cm^2**

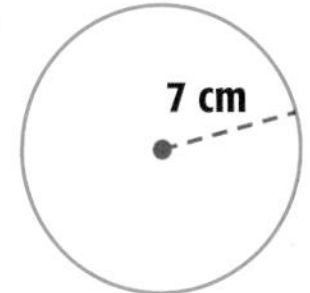

B. **254.3 ft^2**

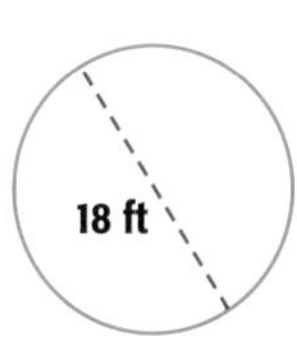

Example 2

Park employees are fitting a top over a circular drain in the park. If the radius of the drain is 14 inches, what is the area of the top that will cover the drain? Use $\frac{22}{7}$ for π. **616 in^2**

Example 3

A golf course is irrigated with sprinklers that spray in a circle. If a sprinkler waters a circular area with a radius of 25 feet, how many square feet does the sprinkler cover? Round your answer to the nearest whole number. **1,963 ft^2**

Example 3 note: Make sure that students are able to find and use the calculator keys for π and squaring. Also point out that when you use π on a calculator, you get a much more accurate answer than is asked for in the problem.

3 Close

Reaching All Learners
Through Curriculum Integration

Social Studies Have students use reference books to investigate values and sizes of different coins from around the world. Ask students to suggest reasons for the different values and sizes of coins. Discuss how the material from which the coin is made might also affect the value of the coin. Encourage volunteers to bring in foreign coins and share their research results.

Possible answers: Generally, the larger the coin, the greater the value of the coin. However, a more valuable coin made of a more valuable material might be smaller in size.

Summarize

Have students explain how to find the area of a circle with a radius of 12 inches and of a circle with a diameter of 16 feet.

Possible answers: Use the formula for the area of a circle, $A = \pi r^2$. For the first circle, substitute 12 for r in the formula, and evaluate. For the second circle, substitute 8 for r, and evaluate.

Answers to Think and Discuss

1. The formula for the area of a circle uses the radius of a circle. If the diameter is given, you must divide the diameter by 2 before you can use the formula.
2. Possible answer: Use $A = \pi r^2$, and use 3.14 for π. Since $d = 3$ and $r = 1.5$, $A \approx 3.14(1.5)^2 \approx 7.1$.
3. Possible answer: a clock; estimate the radius of the clock, square that number, and then multiply by 3.14; $(6 \text{ in.})^2 \cdot 3.14 = 113.04 \text{ in}^2$.

8-6 PRACTICE & ASSESS

Students may want to refer back to the lesson examples.

Assignment Guide

If you finished Example 1 assign:
Core 1–3, 6–11, 15–23 odd, 30–38
Enriched 1, 3, 7–11 odd, 15–23, 30–38

If you finished Example 2 assign:
Core 1–4, 6–12, 15–23 odd, 30–38
Enriched 1, 4, 7–11 odd, 12, 15–24, 30–38

If you finished Example 3 assign:
Core 1–14, 15–25 odd, 30–38
Enriched 1–13 odd, 15–38

Answers

15. 44.0 m; 153.9 m^2
16. 56.5 in.; 254.3 in^2
17. 75.4 ft; 452.2 ft^2
18. 69.1 m; 379.9 m^2
19. 40.2 cm; 128.6 cm^2
20. 59.7 in.; 283.4 in^2

8-6 Exercises

FOR EXTRA PRACTICE see page 672

internet connect
Homework Help Online
go.hrw.com Keyword: MS4 8-6

GUIDED PRACTICE

See Example 1 **Find the area of each circle to the nearest tenth. Use 3.14 for π.**

1. (5 in.) **78.5 in^2**
2. (16 cm) **201.0 cm^2**
3. (20 yd) **314 yd^2**

See Example 2
4. The most popular pizza at Sam's Pizza is the 14-inch pepperoni pizza. What is the area of a pizza with a diameter of 14 inches? Use $\frac{22}{7}$ for π. **154 in^2**

See Example 3
5. A radio station broadcasts a signal over an area with a 75-mile radius. What is the area of the region that receives the radio signal? **17,662.5 mi^2**

INDEPENDENT PRACTICE

See Example 1 **Find the area of each circle to the nearest tenth. Use 3.14 for π.**

6. (3 in.) **28.3 in^2**
7. (16 ft) **803.8 ft^2**
8. (6.4 yd) **32.2 yd^2**
9. (9 ft) **63.6 ft^2**
10. (15 cm) **176.6 cm^2**
11. (1.1 m) **3.8 m^2**

See Example 2
12. A circle has a radius of 14 centimeters. What is the area of the circle? Use $\frac{22}{7}$ for π. **616 cm^2**

See Example 3
13. A circular flower bed in Kay's backyard has a diameter of 8 feet. What is the area of the flower bed? Round your answer to the nearest tenth. **50.2 ft^2**

14. A company is manufacturing aluminum lids. If the radius of each lid is 3 centimeters, what is the area of one lid? Round your answer to the nearest tenth. **28.3 cm^2**

PRACTICE AND PROBLEM SOLVING

Given the radius or diameter, find the circumference and area of each circle to the nearest tenth. Use 3.14 for π.

15. $r = 7$ m
16. $d = 18$ in.
17. $d = 24$ ft
18. $r = 11$ m
19. $r = 6.4$ cm
20. $d = 19$ in.

Given the area, find the radius of each circle. Use 3.14 for π.

21. $A = 113.04$ cm^2 **$r = 6$ cm**
22. $A = 3.14$ ft^2 **$r = 1$ ft**
23. $A = 28.26$ in^2 **$r = 3$ in.**

Math Background

A **sector** of a circle is the region bound by two radii of the circle and their intercepted arc. In the figure below, sector AOB is bound by radii $\overline{OA}$ and $\overline{OB}$ and arc AB.

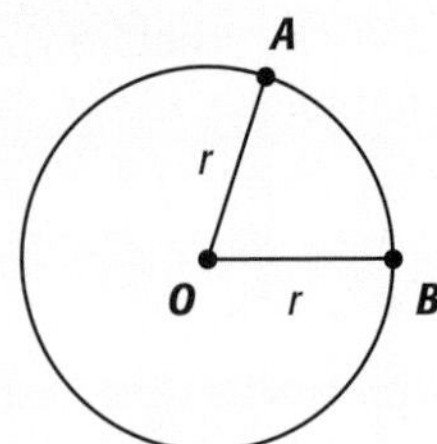

RETEACH 8-6

LESSON 8-6 **Reteach**
Area of Circles

The formula $A = \pi r^2$ is used to find the area of a circle. Since the value of π is about 3.14, you can use the formula $A \approx 3.14 \cdot r \cdot r$ to estimate the area of a circle. Remember that area is expressed in square units.

(4 in.)

The radius of the circle is 4 in.
$A \approx 3.14 \cdot r \cdot r$
$A \approx 3.14 \cdot 4 \cdot 4$
$A \approx 50.24$
The area of the circle is 50.2 in^2 to the nearest tenth.

Find the area of each circle to the nearest tenth. Use 3.14 for π.

1. (9 cm)
The radius is **9** cm.
$A = \pi r^2$
$A \approx 3.14 \cdot$ **9** $\cdot$ **9**
$A \approx$ **254.34**
The area is **254.3** cm^2 to the nearest tenth.

2. (10 mm)
The diameter is 10 mm.
The radius is **5** mm.
$A = \pi r^2$
$A \approx 3.14 \cdot$ **5** $\cdot$ **5**
$A \approx$ **78.5**
The area is **78.5** m^2 to the nearest tenth.

3. (11 yd) **379.9 yd^2**
4. (3 m) **28.3 m^2**
5. (12 ft) **113.0 ft^2**

6. What is the area of a circle with radius 13 yd? Round your answer to the nearest tenth. **530.7 yd^2**

PRACTICE 8-6

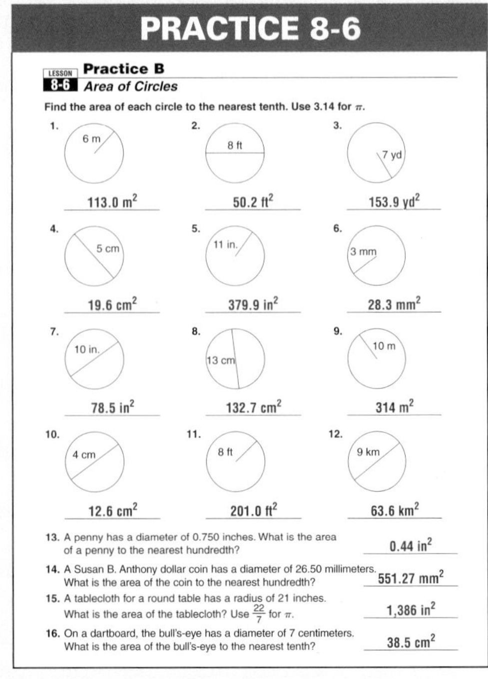

LESSON 8-6 **Practice B**
Area of Circles

Find the area of each circle to the nearest tenth. Use 3.14 for π.

1. (6 m) **113.0 m^2**
2. (8 ft) **50.2 ft^2**
3. (7 yd) **153.9 yd^2**
4. (5 cm) **19.6 cm^2**
5. (11 in.) **379.9 in^2**
6. (3 mm) **28.3 mm^2**
7. (10 in.) **78.5 in^2**
8. (13 cm) **132.7 cm^2**
9. (10 m) **314 m^2**
10. (4 cm) **12.6 cm^2**
11. (8 ft) **201.0 ft^2**
12. (9 km) **63.6 km^2**

13. A penny has a diameter of 0.750 inches. What is the area of a penny to the nearest hundredth? **0.44 in^2**
14. A Susan B. Anthony dollar coin has a diameter of 26.50 millimeters. What is the area of the coin to the nearest hundredth? **551.27 mm^2**
15. A tablecloth for a round table has a radius of 21 inches. What is the area of the tablecloth? Use $\frac{22}{7}$ for π. **1,386 in^2**
16. On a dartboard, the bull's-eye has a diameter of 7 centimeters. What is the area of the bull's-eye to the nearest tenth? **38.5 cm^2**

24. ***PHYSICAL SCIENCE*** The tower of a wind turbine is about the height of a 20-story building, and each turbine can produce 24 megawatt-hours of electricity in one day. Find the area covered by the turbine when it is rotating. Use 3.14 for π. Round your answer to the nearest tenth. **27,450.7 ft²**

25. A hiker was last seen near a fire tower in the Catalina Mountains. Searchers are dispatched to the surrounding area to find the missing hiker.

    a. Assume the hiker could walk in any direction at a rate of 3 miles per hour. How large an area would searchers have to cover if the hiker was last seen 2 hours ago? Use 3.14 for π. Round your answer to the nearest square mile. **113 mi²**

    b. How much additional area would the searchers have to cover if the hiker was last seen 3 hours ago? **141 mi²**

26. Two sprinklers are installed on opposite sides of a square lawn. Each sprinkler waters a semicircular area as shown. Find the area of the lawn not watered by the sprinklers. Use 3.14 for π. Round your answer to the nearest square yard. **14 yd²**

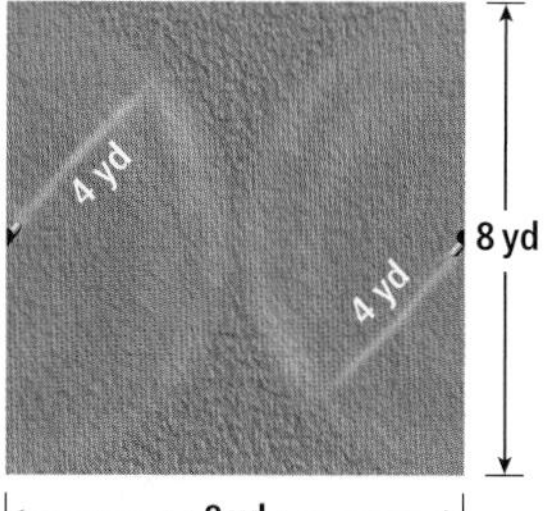

27. ***WHAT'S THE QUESTION?*** Chang painted half of a free-throw circle that had a diameter of 12 ft. The answer is 56.52 ft². What is the question?
Possible answer: What is the area that Chang painted?

28. ***WRITE ABOUT IT*** Two circles have the same radius. Is the combined area of the two circles the same as the area of one circle with twice the radius? Explain your answer.

29. ***CHALLENGE*** How does the area of a circle change if you multiply the radius by a factor of n, where n is a whole number?
The area is multiplied by a factor of n^2.

Spiral Review

Simplify. (Lesson 2-1)

30. 2^6 **64** 31. 5^3 **125** 32. 8^2 **64** 33. 3^5 **243**

Add or subtract. (Lessons 3-4, 3-5)

34. $9 + (-3)$ **6** 35. $-3 - 8$ **−11** 36. $-2 + (-9)$ **−11** 37. $-12 - 6$ **−18**

38. **TEST PREP** Identify the triangle by its angles. (Lesson 7-6) **B**

A Acute B Right C Scalene D Obtuse

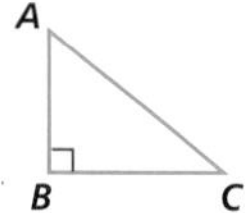

CHALLENGE 8-6

LESSON 8-6 Challenge
Part of the Picture

You can add or subtract to find the area of a shaded region.

Find the area of the rectangle. $A = \ell w = 10 \cdot 8 = 80$ m²

Find the area of the circle. $A = \pi r^2 = \pi \cdot 4^2 \approx 50.24$ m²

The shaded area ≈ 80 m² − 50.24 m² ≈ 29.76 m² ≈ 29.8 m².

Add or subtract to find the area of the shaded region. Round your answer to the nearest tenth.

1.
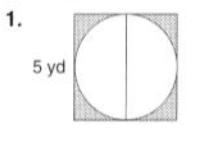

about 5.4 yd²

2.
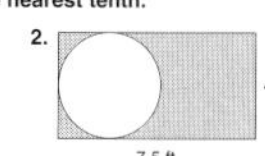

about 17.4 ft²

3.
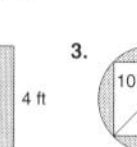
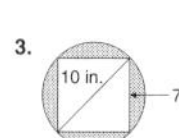
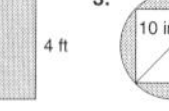
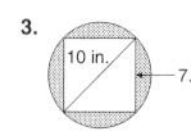

about 28.1 in²

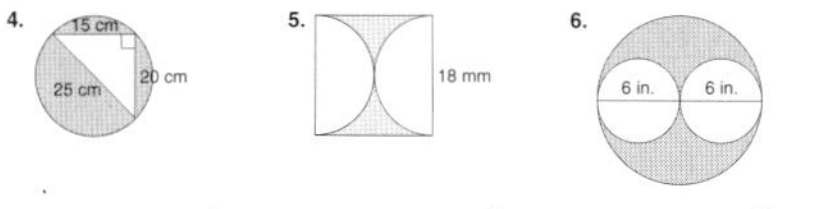

4.

about 340.6 cm²

5.
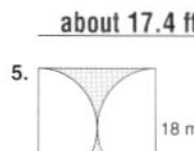
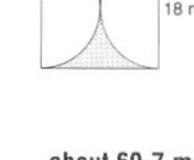

about 69.7 mm²

6.
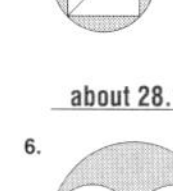
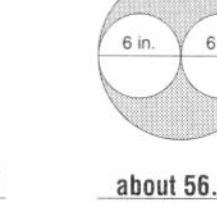

about 56.5 in²

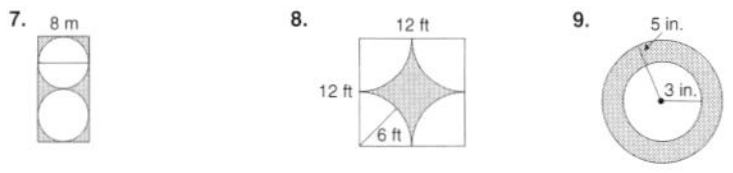

7.
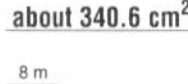

about 27.5 m²

8.
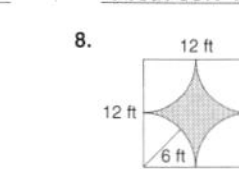

about 31.0 ft²

9.

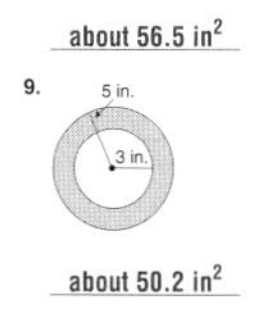

about 50.2 in²

PROBLEM SOLVING 8-6

LESSON 8-6 Problem Solving
Area of Circles

Write the correct answer.

1. According to the Royal Canadian Mint Act, a 50-cent Canadian coin must have a diameter of 27.13 millimeters. What is the area of this coin to the nearest tenth of a square millimeter?

   577.8 mm²

2. By regulation, the diameter of a 25-cent Canadian coin is 23.88 millimeters. What is the area of this coin to the nearest tenth of a square millimeter?

   447.6 mm²

3. There is a water reservoir beneath a circular garden to supply a fountain in the garden. The reservoir has a 26-inch diameter. The garden has a 12-foot diameter. How much of the garden does not contain the water reservoir?

   15,747.1 in²

4. A frying pan has a diameter of 11 inches. What is the area to the nearest square inch of the smallest cover that will fit on top of the frying pan?

   95 in²

Choose the letter of the correct answer.

5. In the state of Texas, Austin is about 80 miles northeast of San Antonio. What area is represented by all of the land within 80 miles of San Antonio?

   A 251.2 mi² C 5,024 mi²
   B 502.4 mi² (D) 20,096 mi²

6. A standard CD has a diameter of 12 centimeters. What is the area of a circular case that can be used to store a CD?

   (F) 130 cm² H 105 cm²
   G 112 cm² J 92 cm²

7. A round dining table has a diameter of 2.5 meters. A round tablecloth has a diameter of 3.5 meters. What is the area to the nearest tenth of a meter of the part of the tablecloth that will hang down the side of the table?

   A 18.8 m² (C) 4.7 m²
   B 6.3 m² D 1.0 m²

8. Justin just got his driver's license. His parents are giving him permission to drive within a 25-mile radius of his home. What is the area to which Justin is restricted when driving?

   F 7,850 mi² H 157 mi²
   (G) 1,962.5 mi² J 314 mi²

COMMON ERROR /// ALERT \\\

For Exercises 21–23, caution students that substitution into the formula for the area of the circle will leave r^2. Since students want to solve for r, they will have to ask themselves, "What number r when squared equals r^2?"

Answers

28. No; the combined area of two circles of the same radius is $2\pi r^2$, while the area of a circle with twice the radius is $\pi(2r)^2 = 4\pi r^2$.

Journal

Ask students to describe a real-world circular figure and have them explain what measurement they would need to find the area of the figure and how they might find that measurement.

Test Prep Doctor

For Exercise 38, point out that the triangle is named by its angles. This immediately eliminates **C.** Review the definition of each of the other triangles. As the given triangle has a right angle, the correct choice is **B.**

Lesson Quiz

Find the area of each circle to the nearest tenth. Use 3.14 for π.

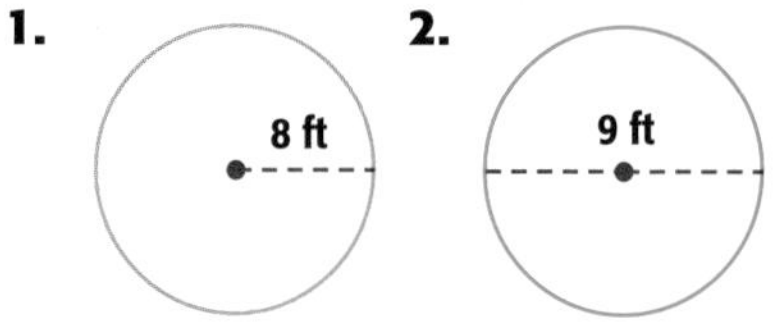

1. (circle, 8 ft radius) **201.0 ft²**

2. (circle, 9 ft diameter) **63.6 ft²**

3. The bull's-eye on a target has diameter 2 in. What is the area of the bull's-eye to the nearest tenth? Use 3.14 for π.
3.1 in²

4. A round tablecloth has a radius of 36 in. What is the area of the tablecloth? Use 3.14 for π. Round your answer to the nearest tenth.
4,069.4 in²

Available on Daily Transparency in CRB

Chapter 8

Mid-Chapter Quiz

***Purpose:** To assess students' mastery of concepts and skills in Lessons 8-1 through 8-6*

Assessment 
Resources

Section 8B Quiz

Assessment Resources . . . . p. 23

***Test and Practice Generator* CD-ROM**

Additional mid-chapter assessment items in both multiple-choice and free-response format may be generated for any objective in Lessons 8-1 through 8-6.

Chapter 8

Mid-Chapter Quiz

Mid-Chapter Quiz

LESSON 8-1 (pp. 414–417)

Convert.

1. 132 hr = ▢ days **5.5**
2. 748 m = ▢ km **0.748**
3. 12.5 gal = ▢ pt **100**

LESSON 8-2 (pp. 420–423)

Choose the more precise measurement in each pair.

4. 12 yd, 36 ft **36 ft**
5. 27 cm, 30.2 m **27 cm**
6. 150 g, 150.0 g **150.0 g**

Calculate. Use the correct number of significant digits in each answer.

7. 1.5 + 1.33 **2.8**
8. 4.9 · 2.70 **13**
9. 2.2 − 1.03 **1.2**

LESSON 8-3  (pp. 424–427)

10. Find the perimeter of the polygon at right. **45 cm**

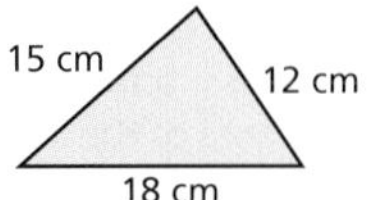

11. Find the circumference of a circle with a diameter of 3.75 cm. Use 3.14 for π. **11.775 cm**

LESSONS 8-4 AND 8-5  (pp. 430–437)

Find the area of each figure.

12. 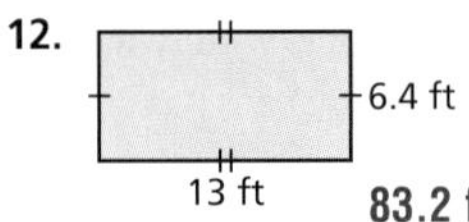

83.2 ft²

13. 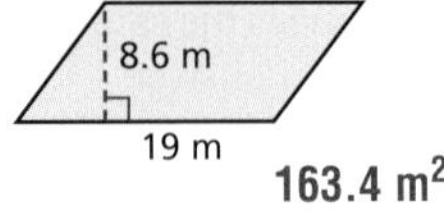

163.4 m²

14. 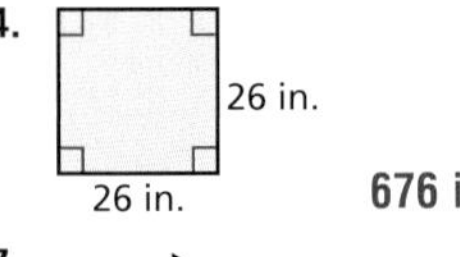

676 in²

15. 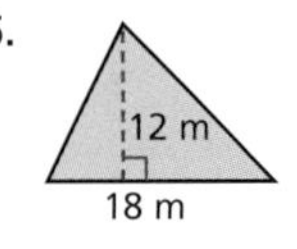

108 m²

16. 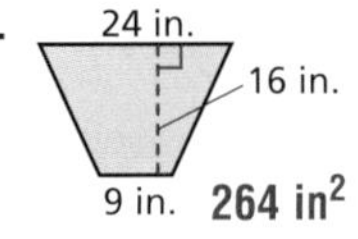

264 in²

17. 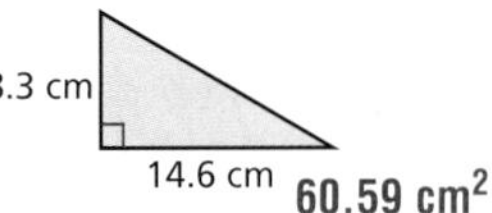

60.59 cm²

LESSON 8-6 (pp. 438–441)

Find the area of each circle to the nearest tenth. Use 3.14 for π.

18. 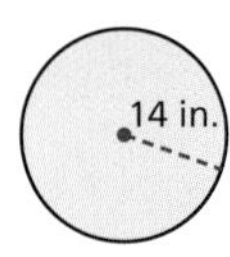

615.4 in²

19. 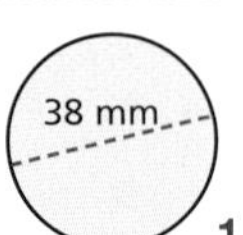

1,133.5 mm²

20. 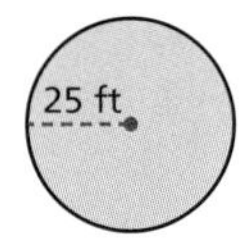

1,962.5 ft²

Focus on Problem Solving

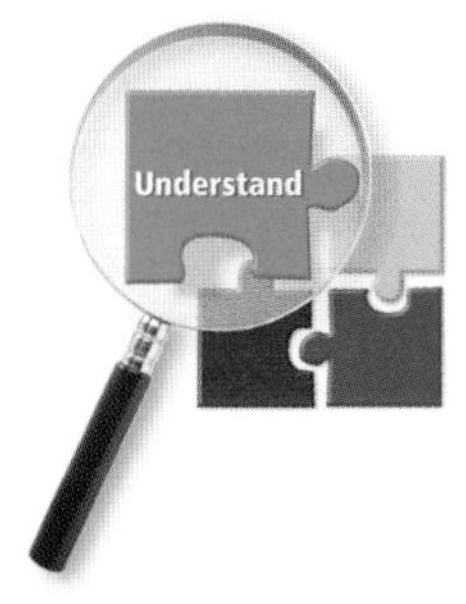

Understand the Problem

• Identify too much or too little information

Problems involving real-world situations sometimes give too much or too little information. Before solving these types of problems, you must decide what information is necessary and whether you have all the necessary information.

If the problem gives too much information, identify which of the facts are really needed to solve the problem. If the problem gives too little information, determine what additional information is required to solve the problem.

Copy each problem and underline the information you need to solve it. If necessary information is missing, write down what additional information is required.

1. Mrs. Wong wants to put a fence around her garden. One side of her garden measures 8 feet. Another side measures 5 feet. What length of fencing does Mrs. Wong need to enclose her garden?

2. Two sides of a triangle measure 17 inches and 13 inches. The perimeter of the triangle is 45 inches. What is the length in feet of the third side of the triangle? (There are 12 inches in 1 foot.)

3. During swim practice, Peggy swims 2 laps each of freestyle and backstroke. The dimensions of the pool are 25 meters by 50 meters. What is the area of the pool?

4. Each afternoon, Curtis walks his dog two times around the park. The park is a rectangle that is 315 yards long. How far does Curtis walk his dog each afternoon?

5. A trapezoid has bases that measure 12 meters and 18 meters and one side that measures 9 meters. The trapezoid has no right angles. What is the area of the trapezoid?

Answers

1. not enough information
2. 1.25 ft
3. 1,250 m^2
4. not enough information
5. not enough information

Focus on Problem Solving

Purpose: *To focus on understanding the problem*

Problem Solving Resources

Interactive Problem Solving . . pp. 68–75

Math: Reading and Writing in the Content Area . . . . pp. 68–75

Problem Solving Process

This page focuses on the first step of the problem-solving process: **Understand the Problem**

Discuss

Have students tell whether each problem has too much information, not enough information, or the correct amount of information. Then have them identify which information in the problem is necessary, and any additional information that they need to solve the problem.

Possible answers:

1. Not enough information; *One side of her garden measures 8 feet. Another side measures 5 feet;* need to know the shape of the garden; need the lengths of all of the garden's sides.
2. Correct amount of information; *Two sides of a triangle measure 17 inches and 13 inches. The perimeter of the triangle is 45 inches.*
3. Too much information; *The dimensions of the pool are 25 meters by 50 meters.*
4. Not enough information; *Each afternoon Curtis walks his dog two times around the park. The park is a rectangle that is 315 yards long;* need to know the width of the park.
5. Not enough information; *A trapezoid has bases that measure 12 meters and 18 meters and one side that measures 9 meters;* need to know the height of the trapezoid.

The Pythagorean Theorem

One-Minute Section Planner

Lesson	Materials	Resources
Lesson 8-7 Powers and Roots **NCTM:** Number and Operations, Communication **NAEP:** Number Properties 2d ☑ SAT-9 ☑ SAT-10 ☐ ITBS ☐ CTBS ☐ MAT ☑ CAT		• *Chapter 8 Resource Book,* pp. 64–72 • Daily Transparency T26, CRB • Additional Examples Transparencies T27–T29, CRB • *Alternate Openers: Explorations,* p. 74
Hands-On Lab 8B Explore the Pythagorean Theorem **NCTM:** Number and Operations, Geometry, Measurement, Connections, Representation **NAEP:** Geometry 2d ☐ SAT-9 ☐ SAT-10 ☐ ITBS ☐ CTBS ☐ MAT ☑ CAT	**Required** Scissors Graph paper *(CRB, p. 89)*	• *Hands-On Lab Activities,* pp. 71–74
Lesson 8-8 The Pythagorean Theorem **NCTM:** Number and Operations, Geometry, Measurement, Problem Solving, Communication, Connections **NAEP:** Geometry 3d ☐ SAT-9 ☐ SAT-10 ☐ ITBS ☐ CTBS ☐ MAT ☑ CAT	**Optional** Centimeter graph paper *(CRB, p. 91)* Teaching Transparency T31 *(CRB)*	• *Chapter 8 Resource Book,* pp. 73–81 • Daily Transparency T30, CRB • Additional Examples Transparencies T32–T35, CRB • *Alternate Openers: Explorations,* p. 75
Hands-On Lab 8C Graph Irrational Numbers **NCTM:** Number and Operations, Connections **NAEP:** Number Properties 1b ☐ SAT-9 ☐ SAT-10 ☐ ITBS ☐ CTBS ☐ MAT ☑ CAT	**Required** Calculators	• *Hands-On Lab Activities,* pp. 75–76
Extension Area of Irregular Figures **NCTM:** Reasoning and Proof, Connections **NAEP:** Measurement 1h ☑ SAT-9 ☑ SAT-10 ☑ ITBS ☑ CTBS ☐ MAT ☑ CAT	**Optional** Graph paper *(CRB, p. 89)*	• Additional Examples Transparencies T36–T37, CRB
Section 8C Assessment		• Section 8C Quiz AR p. 24 • *Test and Practice Generator* CD-ROM

SAT = *Stanford Achievement Tests* **ITBS** = *Iowa Test of Basic Skills* **CTBS** = *Comprehensive Test of Basic Skills/Terra Nova*
MAT = *Metropolitan Achievement Test* **CAT** = *California Achievement Test*

NCTM—Complete standards can be found on pages T27–T33. **NAEP**—Complete standards can be found on pages A35–A39.

SE = *Student Edition* **TE** = *Teacher's Edition* **AR** = *Assessment Resources* **CRB** = *Chapter Resource Book*
MK = *Manipulatives Kit*

Section Overview

Powers and Roots — *Lesson 8-7*

Why? Students already have some experience with powers. Now have them consider an operation that undoes squaring: finding the square root. Students must be able to evaluate powers and approximate square roots in order to use the Pythagorean Theorem.

$\sqrt{4} = 2$, $\sqrt{25} = 5$, $\sqrt{81} = 9$, $\sqrt{225} = 15$

The **square root** of a perfect square is a whole number.

To estimate the square root of a nonperfect square, such as $\sqrt{45}$, find the two closest perfect squares between which the nonperfect square lies.

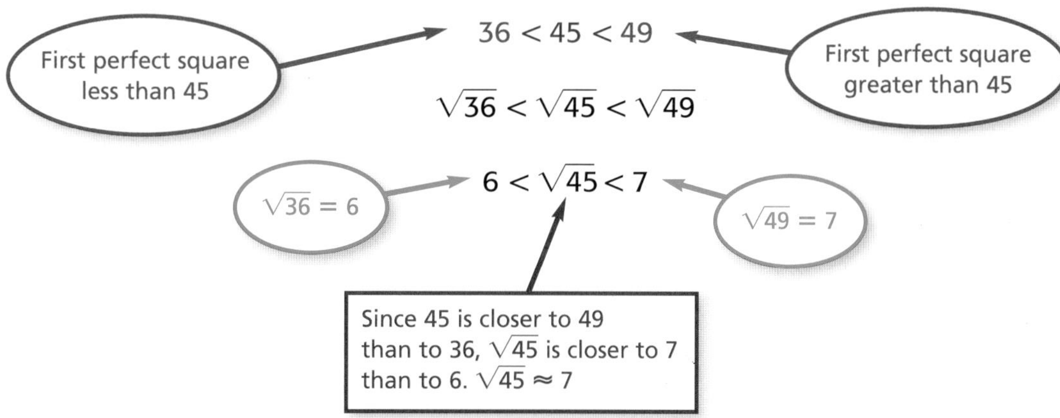

First perfect square less than 45
$36 < 45 < 49$
First perfect square greater than 45
$\sqrt{36} < \sqrt{45} < \sqrt{49}$
$\sqrt{36} = 6$
$6 < \sqrt{45} < 7$
$\sqrt{49} = 7$
Since 45 is closer to 49 than to 36, $\sqrt{45}$ is closer to 7 than to 6. $\sqrt{45} \approx 7$

The Pythagorean Theorem — *Hands-On Lab 8B, Lesson 8-8*

Why? The Pythagorean Theorem is used to solve problems involving the lengths of the sides of right triangles. Students will be able to use to the formula to solve problems that involve indirect measurement.

Find the missing value.

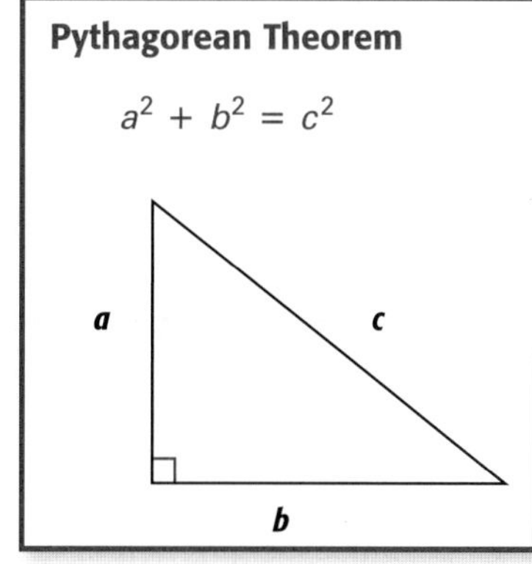

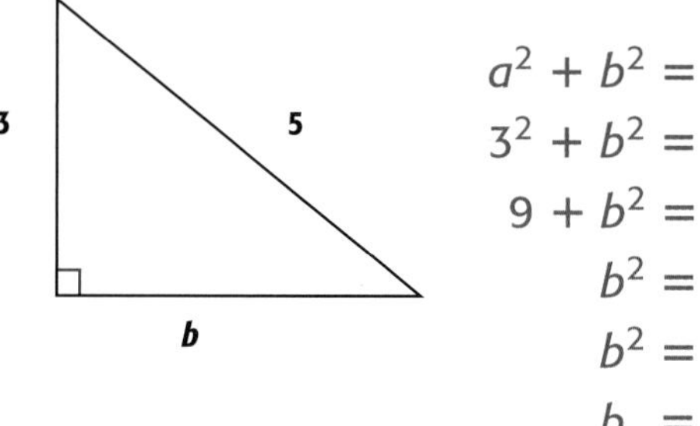

$$a^2 + b^2 = c^2$$
$$3^2 + b^2 = 5^2$$
$$9 + b^2 = 25$$
$$b^2 = 25 - 9$$
$$b^2 = 16$$
$$b = \sqrt{16}$$
$$b = 4$$

8-7 Organizer

Pacing: Traditional 1 day
Block $\frac{1}{2}$ day

Objective: Students express and evaluate numbers using powers and roots.

Warm Up

Simplify.

1. 6^2 36
2. 7^2 49
3. 11^2 121
4. 15^2 225

Problem of the Day

The squares of two whole numbers are 16 units apart on a number line. What are the two numbers? 3 and 5

Available on Daily Transparency in CRB

Math Fact !!

The square root of a negative number does not exist in the set of real numbers. However, the square root of a negative number does exist in the set of complex numbers, $a + bi$, where a and b are real and i is defined as $\sqrt{-1}$.

8-7 Powers and Roots

Learn to express and evaluate numbers using powers and roots.

Vocabulary
perfect square
square root
radical sign

Recall that a power is a number represented by a base and an exponent. The exponent tells you how many times to use the base as a repeated factor.

A square with sides that measure 3 units each has an area of $3 \cdot 3$, or 3^2. Notice that the area of the square is represented by a power in which the base is the side length and the exponent is 2. A power in which the exponent is 2 is called a *square.*

EXAMPLE 1 Finding Squares

Model each power using a square. Then evaluate the power.

A 7^2 **B** $(2.5)^2$

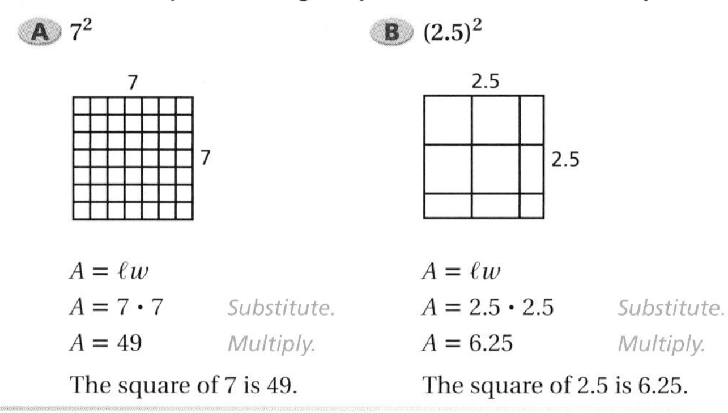

A		B	
$A = \ell w$		$A = \ell w$	
$A = 7 \cdot 7$	*Substitute.*	$A = 2.5 \cdot 2.5$	*Substitute.*
$A = 49$	*Multiply.*	$A = 6.25$	*Multiply.*
The square of 7 is 49.		The square of 2.5 is 6.25.	

A **perfect square** is the square of a whole number. The number 49 is a perfect square because $49 = 7^2$ and 7 is a whole number. The number 6.25 is not a perfect square.

Reading Math
$\sqrt{16} = 4$ is read as "The square root of 16 is 4."

The **square root** of a number is one of the two equal factors of the number. Four is a square root of 16 because $4 \cdot 4 = 16$. The symbol for a square root is $\sqrt{\ }$, which is called a **radical sign**.

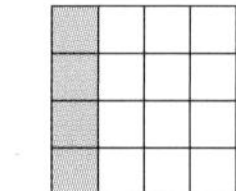

Most calculators have square-root keys that you can use to quickly find approximate square roots of nonperfect squares. You can also use perfect squares to estimate the square roots of nonperfect squares.

1 Introduce

Alternate Opener

EXPLORATION

8-7 Powers and Roots

You can use exponents to represent ***perfect squares.*** A perfect square is the square of a whole number.

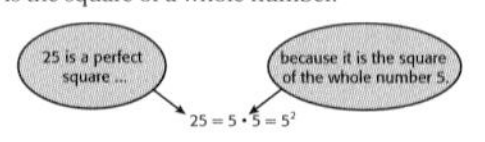

The ***square root*** of a perfect square is one of its two equal factors. For example, the square root of 25 is 5. Knowing the perfect squares can help you estimate square roots.

1. Complete the table of squares.

1^2	2^2	3^2	4^2	5^2	6^2	7^2	8^2	9^2	10^2
1									

2. Use the table of squares to help you estimate each square root to the nearest tenth. Use a calculator to check your estimates.

		Estimate	Actual
a.	$\sqrt{5}$		
b.	$\sqrt{30}$		
c.	$\sqrt{90}$		
d.	$\sqrt{45}$		

Think and Discuss

3. **Discuss** your strategy for estimating square roots.
4. **Explain** how you could estimate $\sqrt{120}$.

Motivate

Ask students to explain how addition and subtraction are related to each other. Then have students explain how multiplication and division are related to each other. In each case, they are inverses; one undoes the other. Remind students that when raising a number to an exponent, the exponent tells you how many times to use the base as a factor. To square a number means to raise the number to the second power. Just as you can square a number, you can use an inverse process to undo the square. This is known as finding the square root of the number.

Exploration worksheet and answers on Chapter 8 Resource Book pp. 65 and 104

2 Teach

Lesson Presentation

Guided Instruction

In this lesson, students learn to express and evaluate numbers using powers and roots. Point out that you can only estimate the square root of a nonperfect square whole number. The square root of a nonperfect square whole number is an irrational number. This means that you cannot express the number in the form $\frac{p}{q}$, where p and q are integers and $q \neq 0$.

Teaching Tip Have students make a list of the first 15 whole numbers and their respective squares. Tell students that they can refer to the list to find the two whole numbers the square root of a nonperfect square lies between.

EXAMPLE 2 Estimating Square Roots

Estimate each square root to the nearest whole number. Use a calculator to check your answer.

A $\sqrt{30}$

$25 < 30 < 36$ — *Find the perfect squares nearest 30.*

$\sqrt{25} < \sqrt{30} < \sqrt{36}$

$5 < \sqrt{30} < 6$ — *Find the square roots of 25 and 36.*

$\sqrt{30} \approx 5$ — *30 is nearer in value to 25 than to 36.*

Check

$\sqrt{30} \approx 5.477225575$ — *Use a calculator to approximate $\sqrt{30}$. 5 is a reasonable estimate.*

B $\sqrt{99}$

$81 < 99 < 100$ — *Find the perfect squares nearest 99.*

$\sqrt{81} < \sqrt{99} < \sqrt{100}$

$9 < \sqrt{99} < 10$ — *Find the square roots of 81 and 100.*

$\sqrt{99} \approx 10$ — *99 is nearer in value to 100 than to 81.*

Check

$\sqrt{99} \approx 9.949874371$ — *Use a calculator to approximate $\sqrt{99}$. 10 is a reasonable estimate.*

EXAMPLE 3 *Recreation Application*

While searching for a lost hiker, a helicopter pilot covers a square area of 150 mi^2. What is the approximate length of each side of the square area? Round your answer to the nearest mile.

The length of each side of the square is $\sqrt{150}$.

$144 < 150 < 169$ — *Find the perfect squares nearest 150.*

$\sqrt{144} < \sqrt{150} < \sqrt{169}$

$12 < \sqrt{150} < 13$ — *Find the square roots of 144 and 169.*

$\sqrt{150} \approx 12$ — *150 is nearer in value to 144 than to 169.*

Each side of the search area is about 12 miles long.

Think and Discuss

1. **Explain** how to estimate $\sqrt{75}$.
2. **Explain** how you might find the square root of 3^2.

Additional Examples

Example 1

Model each power using a square. Then evaluate the power.

A. 12^2

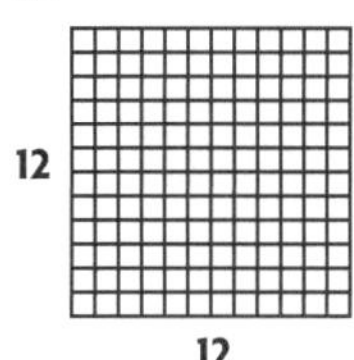

B. 3.5^2

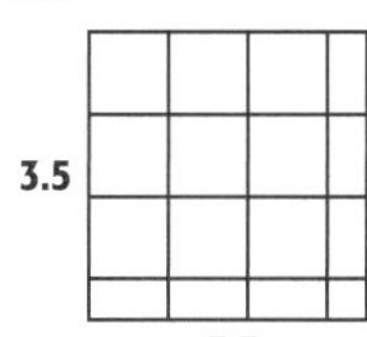

Example 2

Estimate each square root to the nearest whole number. Use a calculator to check the reasonableness of your answer.

A. $\sqrt{40}$ approximately 6

B. $\sqrt{79}$ approximately 9

Example 3

A Coast Guard boat searching for a lost sailboat covers a square area of 125 mi^2. What is the approximate length of each side of the square area? Round your answer to the nearest mile. about 11 miles long

3 Close

Reaching All Learners
Through Number Sense

Have students plot on a number line a series of nonperfect squares, such as $\sqrt{2}$, $\sqrt{7}$, $\sqrt{11}$, $\sqrt{15}$, and $\sqrt{19}$. Then have students use a number line to write the following numbers in order from least to greatest: $\sqrt{8}$, 3, 1, $\sqrt{12}$, $\sqrt{3}$, and 4.

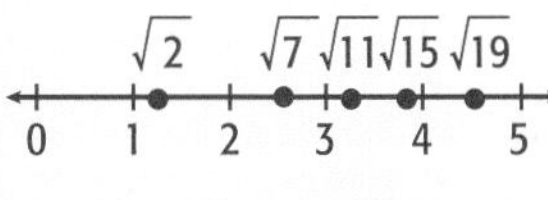

1, $\sqrt{3}$, $\sqrt{8}$, 3, $\sqrt{12}$, 4

Summarize

Have students explain how to use perfect squares to estimate $\sqrt{22}$.

Find the two perfect squares that 22 lies between. The square root of the perfect square closer to 22 is an estimate of $\sqrt{22}$. Since 22 lies between 16 and 25 and is closer to 25, you can estimate $\sqrt{22}$ as 5.

Answers to Think and Discuss

Possible answers:

1. 75 lies between the perfect squares 64 and 81. Since 75 is closer to 81 than to 64, $\sqrt{75}$ is closer to $\sqrt{81}$ than to $\sqrt{64}$. $\sqrt{81} = 9$, so $\sqrt{75} \approx 9$.
2. Since squaring and finding a square root are inverse operations, one undoes the other. Undoing 3^2 gives 3.

8-7 PRACTICE & ASSESS

Students may want to refer back to the lesson examples.

Assignment Guide

If you finished Example **1** assign:
- **Core** 1–4, 10–13, 25, 27, 48–55
- **Enriched** 1, 3, 11, 13, 24–27, 48–55

If you finished Example **2** assign:
- **Core** 1–8, 10–21, 25–37 odd, 48–55
- **Enriched** 1–7 odd, 11–21 odd, 24–37, 48–55

If you finished Example **3** assign:
- **Core** 1–23, 25–43 odd, 48–55
- **Enriched** 1–23 odd, 24–55

Notes

8-7 Exercises

FOR EXTRA PRACTICE see page 673

internet connect
Homework Help Online
go.hrw.com Keyword: MS4 8-7

GUIDED PRACTICE

See Example 1 Model each power using a square. Then evaluate the power.

1. 4^2 **16**
2. $(1.5)^2$ **2.25**
3. 9^2 **81**
4. 6^2 **36**

See Example 2 Estimate each square root to the nearest whole number. Use a calculator to check your answer.

5. $\sqrt{20}$ **4**
6. $\sqrt{45}$ **7**
7. $\sqrt{84}$ **9**
8. $\sqrt{58}$ **8**

See Example 3

9. A Coast Guard ship patrols an area of 125 square miles. If the area the ship patrols is a square, about how long is each side of the area? Round your answer to the nearest mile. **11 mi**

INDEPENDENT PRACTICE

See Example 1 Model each power using a square. Then evaluate the power.

10. 3^2 **9**
11. 8^2 **64**
12. 11^2 **121**
13. $(4.5)^2$ **20.25**

See Example 2 Estimate each square root to the nearest whole number. Use a calculator to check your answer.

14. $\sqrt{12}$ **3**
15. $\sqrt{39}$ **6**
16. $\sqrt{73}$ **9**
17. $\sqrt{109}$ **10**
18. $\sqrt{6}$ **2**
19. $\sqrt{180}$ **13**
20. $\sqrt{145}$ **12**
21. $\sqrt{216}$ **15**

See Example 3

22. The area of a square field is 200 ft^2. What is the approximate length of each side of the field? Round your answer to the nearest foot. **14 ft**
23. A square bandanna has an area of 1,000 cm^2. About how long is each edge of the bandanna? Round your answer to the nearest centimeter. **32 cm**

PRACTICE AND PROBLEM SOLVING

Evaluate each power.

24. 20^2 **400**
25. $\left(\frac{3}{8}\right)^2$ $\frac{9}{64}$
26. $(0.16)^2$ **0.0256**
27. $\left(\frac{1}{3}\right)^2$ $\frac{1}{9}$

Estimate each square root to the nearest whole number. Use a calculator to check your answer.

28. $\sqrt{300}$ **17**
29. $\sqrt{420}$ **20**
30. $\sqrt{700}$ **26**
31. $\sqrt{1{,}500}$ **39**

Estimate each sum or difference to the nearest whole number.

32. $\sqrt{18} + \sqrt{9}$ **7**
33. $\sqrt{34} + \sqrt{35}$ **12**
34. $\sqrt{50} - \sqrt{10}$ **4**
35. $\sqrt{98} - \sqrt{89}$ **1**
36. $\sqrt{8} + 8^2$ **67**
37. $14^2 - \sqrt{14}$ **192**

Math Background

Radicals are not restricted to square roots. The symbol $\sqrt[n]{a}$ is used to indicate the principal *n*th root of *a*, where *n* is a positive integer. This means you can have third (or cube) roots, fourth roots, fifth roots, and so on. In the special case $n = 2$, the root is the square root, and the root index, *n*, is omitted.

To find the *n*th root of a given number *a*, ask, "What number used as a factor *n* times is equal to *a*?"

Examples:

$\sqrt[3]{64} = 4$ since $4^3 = 64$

$\sqrt[3]{-8} = -2$ since $(-2)^3 = -8$

$\sqrt[4]{81} = 3$ since $3^4 = 81$

$\sqrt[5]{32} = 2$ since $2^5 = 32$

RETEACH 8-7

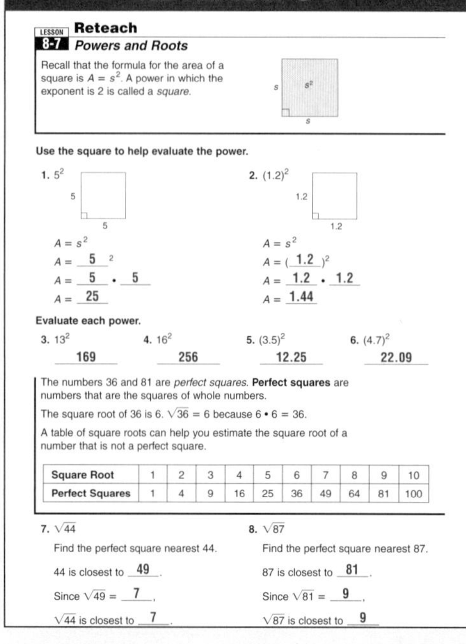

LESSON 8-7 **Reteach**
Powers and Roots

Recall that the formula for the area of a square is $A = s^2$. A power in which the exponent is 2 is called a *square*.

Use the square to help evaluate the power.

1. 5^2

$A = s^2$
$A = \underline{5}^2$
$A = \underline{5} \cdot \underline{5}$
$A = \underline{25}$

2. $(1.2)^2$

$A = s^2$
$A = (\underline{1.2})^2$
$A = \underline{1.2} \cdot \underline{1.2}$
$A = \underline{1.44}$

Evaluate each power.

3. 13^2 **169**
4. 16^2 **256**
5. $(3.5)^2$ **12.25**
6. $(4.7)^2$ **22.09**

The numbers 36 and 81 are *perfect squares*. **Perfect squares** are numbers that are the squares of whole numbers.

The square root of 36 is 6. $\sqrt{36} = 6$ because $6 \cdot 6 = 36$.

A table of square roots can help you estimate the square root of a number that is not a perfect square.

Square Root	1	2	3	4	5	6	7	8	9	10
Perfect Squares	1	4	9	16	25	36	49	64	81	100

7. $\sqrt{44}$

Find the perfect square nearest 44.
44 is closest to **49**.
Since $\sqrt{49} =$ **7**,
$\sqrt{44}$ is closest to **7**.

8. $\sqrt{87}$

Find the perfect square nearest 87.
87 is closest to **81**.
Since $\sqrt{81} =$ **9**,
$\sqrt{87}$ is closest to **9**

PRACTICE 8-7

LESSON 8-7 **Practice B**
Powers and Roots

Evaluate each power.

1. 6^2 **36**
2. $(1.4)^2$ **1.96**
3. 12^2 **144**
4. $(0.7)^2$ **0.49**
5. 15^2 **225**
6. $(3.5)^2$ **12.25**
7. 20^2 **400**
8. $(5.1)^2$ **26.01**

Estimate each square root to the nearest whole number. Use a calculator to check the reasonableness of your answers.

9. $\sqrt{45}$ **7**
10. $\sqrt{68}$ **8**
11. $\sqrt{21}$ **5**
12. $\sqrt{72}$ **8**
13. $\sqrt{17}$ **4**
14. $\sqrt{6}$ **2**
15. $\sqrt{60}$ **8**
16. $\sqrt{88}$ **9**
17. $\sqrt{11}$ **3**
18. $\sqrt{31}$ **6**
19. $\sqrt{98}$ **10**
20. $\sqrt{50}$ **7**
21. $\sqrt{152}$ **12**
22. $\sqrt{14}$ **4**
23. $\sqrt{70}$ **8**
24. $\sqrt{28}$ **5**
25. $\sqrt{39}$ **6**
26. $\sqrt{193}$ **14**
27. $\sqrt{119}$ **11**
28. $\sqrt{85}$ **9**
29. $\sqrt{5}$ **2**
30. $\sqrt{42}$ **6**
31. $\sqrt{75}$ **9**
32. $\sqrt{215}$ **15**

33. The area of a square vegetable garden is 75 ft^2. What is the approximate length of each side of the garden? Find your answer to the nearest foot. **9 ft**
34. The area of a computer screen is 138 in^2. What is the approximate length of each side of the screen? Find your answer to the nearest inch. **12 in.**
35. Tim broke a square picture window with his baseball. The area of the window is 52 ft^2. What is the approximate width of the window to be replaced? Find your answer to the nearest foot. **7 ft**
36. A square tile has an area of 413 cm^2. What is the approximate length of a side of the tile? Find your answer to the nearest centimeter. **20 cm**

To find the distance at which an object becomes visible, you can use your distance to the horizon and the object's distance to the horizon.

38. Order π, $\sqrt{15}$, 2.9, $\sqrt{20}$, and $\frac{25}{6}$ from greatest to least. **$\sqrt{20}$, $\frac{25}{6}$, $\sqrt{15}$, π, 2.9**

39. Find the perimeter of a square whose area is 49 square inches. **28 in.**

40. ***EARTH SCIENCE*** The formula $D = 3.56 \cdot \sqrt{A}$ gives the distance D in kilometers to the horizon from an airplane flying at an altitude A in meters. If a pilot is flying at an altitude of 1,800 m, about how far away is the horizon? Round your answer to the nearest kilometer. **151 km**

41. ***ART*** An artist is making two square stained-glass windows. One window has a perimeter of 48 inches. The other has an area of 110 square inches. Which window is bigger? Explain.

42. The Ricci family is building a new house on a square foundation. The floor area of the house is 1,316 ft^2. What is the length of one wall of the house, to the nearest foot? **36 ft**

43. Darien will need 154 ft^2 of wall-to-wall carpeting to cover the floor of his new square bedroom. What is the length of each wall of his room? Round your answer to the nearest foot. **12 ft**

44. For his new room, Darien's grandmother gave him a handmade quilt. The quilt is made up of 16 squares set in 4 rows of 4. If the area of each square is 324 in^2, what are the dimensions of the quilt in inches? **72 in. × 72 in.**

45. ***CHOOSE A STRATEGY*** The figure shows how two squares can be formed by drawing only seven lines. Show how two squares can be formed by drawing only six lines.

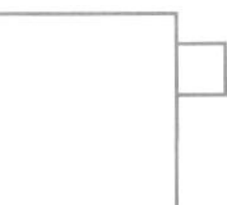

46. ***WRITE ABOUT IT*** Explain how to estimate the square root of a nonperfect square.

47. ***CHALLENGE*** Find the value of $\sqrt{5^2 + 12^2}$. **13**

46. Possible answer: Find the closest perfect square greater than the number, and the closest perfect square less than the number. The number's square root will be between the square roots of these perfect squares.

Spiral Review

Given the radius or diameter, find the circumference of each circle to the nearest tenth. Use 3.14 for π. (Lesson 8-3)

48. $d = 6$ ft **18.8 ft** **49.** $d = 9$ cm **28.3 cm** **50.** $r = 4$ in. **25.1 in.** **51.** $r = 5$ m **31.4 m**

Find the area of each parallelogram. (Lesson 8-4)

52. $b = 5$ cm; $h = 3$ cm **15 cm^2** **53.** $b = 12$ m; $h = 9$ m **108 m^2** **54.** $b = 4.8$ ft; $h = 2$ ft **9.6 ft^2**

55. TEST PREP What is the area of the trapezoid? (Lesson 8-5) **A**

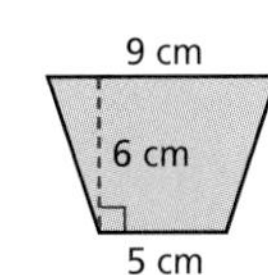

A 42 cm^2 C 135 cm^2

B 84 cm^2 D 270 cm^2

COMMON ERROR ALERT

For Exercises 32–37, some students may forget to estimate each square root before they add or subtract. For example, $\sqrt{18} + \sqrt{9} \neq \sqrt{18 + 9}$.

Answers

41. The window with the perimeter of 48 in. is larger because its sides are 12 in. long and its area is 144 in^2. The sides of the window with the area of 110 in^2 are about $10\frac{1}{2}$ in. long, and the perimeter is about 42 in.

45.

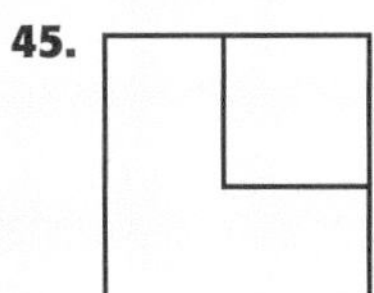

Journal

Have the students use a square diagram to write about the relationship between the square of a whole number and the square root of the area covered by the square.

Test Prep Doctor

The correct choice for Exercise 55, **A,** can be found using mental math as long as students remember the formula for the area of a trapezoid. Remind students to be careful to complete the entire calculation when using a formula. Often, partial calculations will be among the incorrect choices. In this case, if students forget to multiply by $\frac{1}{2}$, they will incorrectly choose **B.**

CHALLENGE 8-7

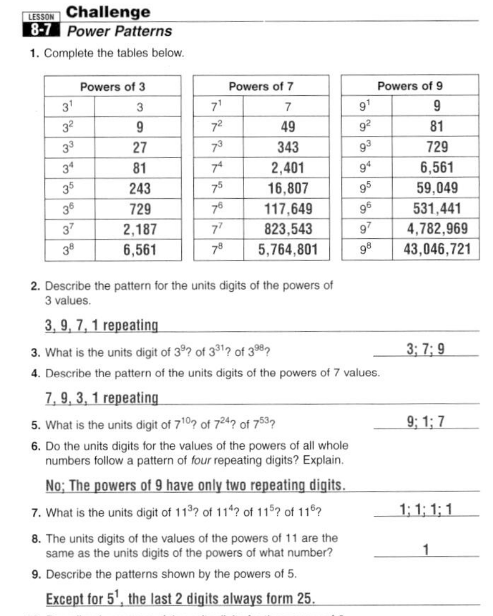

LESSON 8-7 **Challenge**
Power Patterns

1. Complete the tables below.

Powers of 3		Powers of 7		Powers of 9	
3^1	3	7^1	7	9^1	9
3^2	9	7^2	49	9^2	81
3^3	27	7^3	343	9^3	729
3^4	81	7^4	2,401	9^4	6,561
3^5	243	7^5	16,807	9^5	59,049
3^6	729	7^6	117,649	9^6	531,441
3^7	2,187	7^7	823,543	9^7	4,782,969
3^8	6,561	7^8	5,764,801	9^8	43,046,721

2. Describe the pattern for the units digits of the powers of 3 values.
   3, 9, 7, 1 repeating
3. What is the units digit of 3^9? of 3^{31}? of 3^{98}? 3; 7; 9
4. Describe the pattern of the units digits of the powers of 7 values.
   7, 9, 3, 1 repeating
5. What is the units digit of 7^{10}? of 7^{24}? of 7^{53}? 9; 1; 7
6. Do the units digits for the values of the powers of all whole numbers follow a pattern of *four* repeating digits? Explain.
   No; The powers of 9 have only two repeating digits.
7. What is the units digit of 11^3? of 11^4? of 11^5? of 11^6? 1; 1; 1; 1
8. The units digits of the values of the powers of 11 are the same as the units digits of the powers of what number? 1
9. Describe the patterns shown by the powers of 5.
   Except for 5^1, the last 2 digits always form 25.
10. Describe the pattern of the units digits for the powers of 6.
   They are all 6's.

PROBLEM SOLVING 8-7

LESSON 8-7 **Problem Solving**
Powers and Roots

Write the correct answer. For Problems 1 and 2, use the following formula to find the distance in meters a free-falling object falls from a place of rest: $d = 0.5 \cdot 9.8 \cdot t^2$ (t = time in seconds).

1. As part of a science experiment, Hsing drops a ball from the roof of the school. How far does the ball fall in 2 seconds?
   19.6 m
2. Mel drops a stone from the edge of a cliff overlooking the ocean. How far does the stone fall in 5 seconds?
   122.5 m
3. At the county fair, the apple pies are lined up side-by-side for judging on a 6-foot table. Each pie has an area of 50.24 in^2. How many pies are on the table?
   9 pies
4. The community swimming pool has an area of 1,024 square feet. The pool is in the shape of a square. What is the perimeter of the pool?
   128 ft

Choose the letter of the correct answer.

5. The Portuguese national flag is a rectangle. In the center of the flag is a coat of arms and shield on a circle. This circle has a diameter that is half the flag's height. If the flag's circle has an area of 3.14 square feet, what is the height of the flag?
   A 1 ft (C) 4 ft
   B 3 ft D 2 ft
6. A square picture has an area of 81 square inches. The perimeter of the frame for the picture is 8 inches longer than the perimeter of the picture itself. What is the length of each side of the square frame for this picture?
   F 8 in. H 9 in.
   G 10 in. (J) 11 in.
7. A basketball game starts with a jump ball. This occurs in the center of the basketball court within a circle that has an area of 113.04 square feet. What is the radius of this circle?
   A 3 ft C 9 ft
   (B) 6 ft D 36 ft
8. A square fence encloses a vegetable garden with an area of 169 square feet. What is the perimeter of the fence?
   (F) 52 ft H 13 ft
   G 26 ft J 56.25 ft

Lesson Quiz

Evaluate each power.

1. 16^2 **256** **2.** $(3.5)^2$ **12.25**

Estimate each square root to the nearest whole number. Use a calculator to check the reasonableness of your answers.

3. $\sqrt{15}$ **4** **4.** $\sqrt{52}$ **7**

5. A square dining room table has an area of 20 ft^2. What is the length of each side of the table, to the nearest tenth? **4.5 ft**

Available on Daily Transparency in CRB

8B
Explore the Pythagorean Theorem

Pacing: Traditional 1 day
Block $\frac{1}{2}$ day

Objective: To use paper and graph paper to explore the Pythagorean Theorem

Materials: Paper, scissors, graph paper

Lab Resources

Hands-On Lab Activities . . . . p. 71

Using the Pages

Draw a right triangle on the chalkboard. Discuss with students the parts of a right triangle: the legs, hypotenuse, and right angle. Mention that in an isosceles right triangle the legs have the same measure and the hypotenuse is always the longest side. Remind students that in a scalene right triangle the sides are all different lengths.

Find the area of the large square along the hypotenuse for each triangle.

1. a triangle with both legs equal to 4
32
2. a triangle with one leg equal to 6 and the other leg equal to 8
100

Answers

Activity 1

Think and Discuss

2. a. Squaring the side length of a square will give you the area of the square.
b. Possible answer: Squaring the length of each side of the triangle will give you the area of the square that shares that side with the triangle.
c. $a^2 + b^2 = c^2$

Explore the Pythagorean Theorem

Use with Lesson 8-8

An important and famous relationship in mathematics, known as the Pythagorean Theorem, involves the three sides of a right triangle. Recall that a right triangle is a triangle that has one right angle. If you know the lengths of two sides of a right triangle, you can find the length of the third side.

Activity 1

1. The drawing at right shows an isosceles right triangle and three squares. Make your own drawing similar to the one shown. (Recall that an isosceles right triangle has two congruent sides and a right angle.)

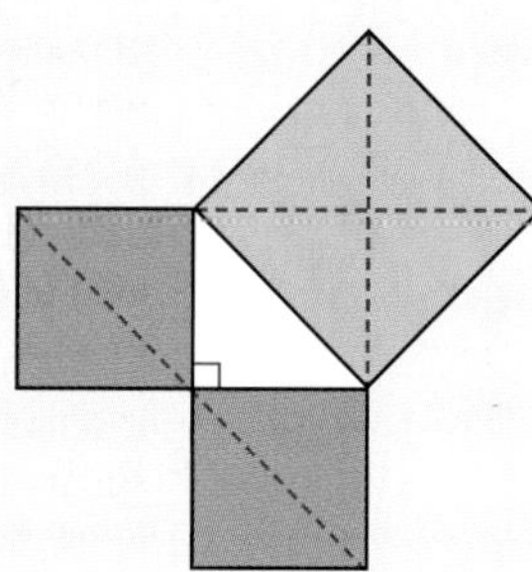

Cut out the two smaller squares of your drawing, then cut those squares in half along a diagonal. Fit the pieces of the smaller squares on top of the blue square.

Think and Discuss

1. What can you tell about the relationship between the areas of the squares?
The area of the two red squares added together is equal to the area of the blue square.
2. a. How does the side length of a square relate to the area of the square?
b. How do the side lengths of the triangle in your drawing relate to the areas of the squares around it?
c. Write an equation that shows the relationship between the lengths of the sides of the triangle in your drawing. Use the variables a and b to represent the lengths of the two shorter sides of your triangle, and c to represent the length of the longest side.

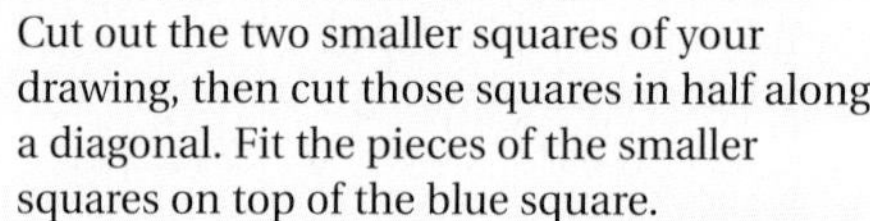

Try This

1. Repeat Activity 1 for other isosceles right triangles. Is the relationship that you found true for the areas of the squares around each triangle?
Yes, the relationship is true for each isosceles right triangle.

Kimberly Johnson-Green
Baltimore, Maryland

Teacher to Teacher

I introduce the Pythagorean Theorem by setting up a ramp (in the classroom you can use textbooks and a yardstick). I ask the students to consider riding a bicycle down the ramp. The students first walk along the base of the ramp and up the side of the ramp to get to the top. Then the students consider whether it would be shorter to walk up the front of the ramp (along the hypotenuse). After a discussion of the problem, I introduce the Pythagorean Theorem. We measure the base and the height of the ramp, and then use the formula to calculate the hypotenuse. The students are able to see that although the hypotenuse is the longest side of a right triangle, its length is shorter than the sum of the lengths of the two legs.

Activity 2

1. On graph paper, draw a segment that is 3 units long. At one end of this segment, draw a perpendicular segment that is 4 units long. Draw a third segment to form a triangle. Cut out the triangle.

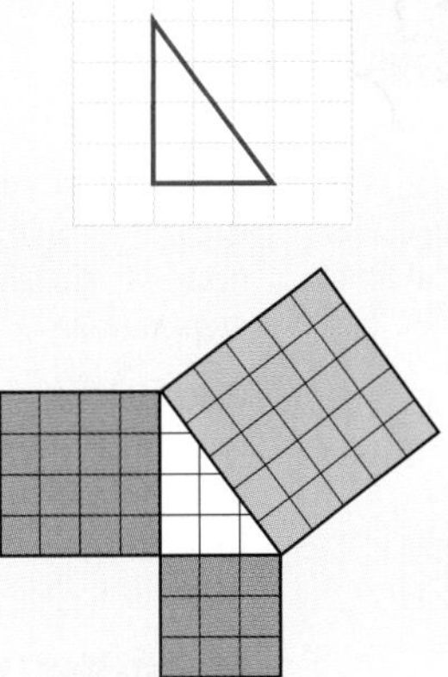

Cut out a 3-by-3 square and a 4-by-4 square from the same graph paper. Place the edges of the squares against the corresponding sides of the right triangle.

Cut the two squares into individual squares or strips. Arrange the squares into a large square along the third side of the triangle.

Think and Discuss

1. What is the area of each of the three squares? What relationship is there between the areas of the small squares and the area of the large square?
2. What is the length of the third side of the triangle?
3. Substitute the side lengths of your triangle into the equation you wrote in Think and Discuss problem **2c** in Activity 1. What do you find?
4. Do you think the relationship is true for triangles that are not right triangles?

Try This

1. Use graph paper to cut out three squares with sides that are 3 units, 4 units, and 6 units long. Fit the squares together to form a triangle as shown at right. Is the relationship between the areas of the red squares and the area of the blue square the same as the relationship shown in Activity 2? Explain.

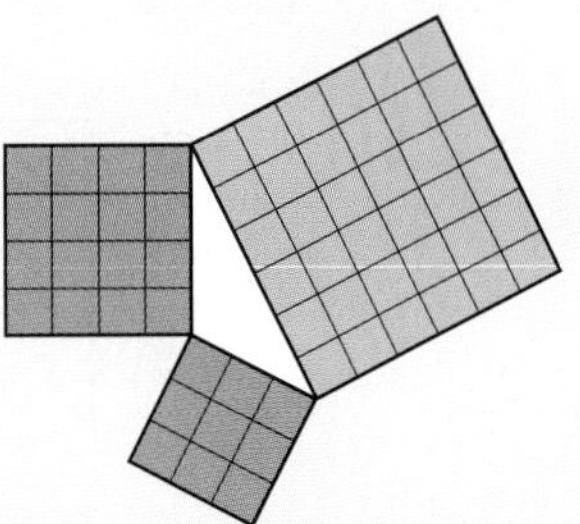

2. If you know the lengths of the two short sides of a right triangle are 9 and 12, can you find the length of the longest side? Show your work.
3. If you know the length of the longest side of a right triangle and the length of one of the shorter sides, how would you find the length of the third side?

Answers

Think and Discuss

Activity 2

Possible answers:

1. 9, 16, 25; if you add the areas of the two smaller squares, you get the area of the largest square.
2. 5 units
3. $3^2 + 4^2 = 5^2$; $9 + 16 = 25$; the equation seems to be true for right triangles other than just right isosceles triangles.
4. No; for example, the relationship is not true for an equilateral triangle with side length 1. $1^2 + 1^2 \neq 1^2$

Try This

1. No; the total area of the red squares is 25, but the area of the blue square is 36.
2. Yes; to find the length of the longest side, square each of the smaller sides and add them together: $9^2 + 12^2 = 81 + 144 = 225$. The length of the longest side is the square root of 225: $\sqrt{225} = 15$.
3. Square both numbers. Subtract the square of the shorter side from the square of the longest side.The length of the third side is the square root of the difference.

8-8 Organizer

Pacing: Traditional 1 day
Block $\frac{1}{2}$ day

Objective: Students use the Pythagorean Theorem to find the measure of a side of a right triangle.

Warm Up

Estimate each square root to the nearest whole number. Use a calculator to check the reasonableness of your answers.

1. $\sqrt{18}$ 4
2. $\sqrt{26}$ 5
3. $\sqrt{86}$ 9
4. $\sqrt{125}$ 11

Problem of the Day

A shipping carton measures 12 in. by 15 in. by 16 in. What is the longest rod that can be shipped in it? **25 in.**

Available on Daily Transparency in CRB

The Pythagorean Theorem was known to the Babylonians about 1,000 years before Pythagoras proved it.

8-8 The Pythagorean Theorem

Learn to use the Pythagorean Theorem to find the measure of a side of a right triangle.

Vocabulary
leg
hypotenuse
Pythagorean Theorem

In a right triangle, the two sides that form the right angle are called **legs**. The side opposite the right angle is called the **hypotenuse**.

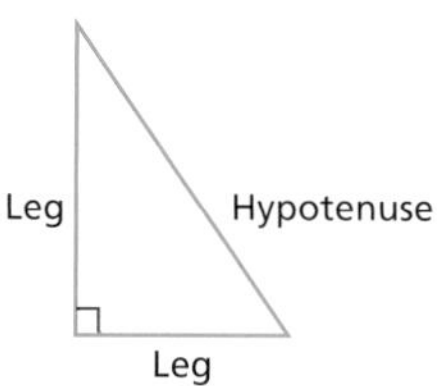

One of the first people to recognize the relationship between the sides of a right triangle was the Greek mathematician Pythagoras. This special relationship is called the *Pythagorean Theorem.*

PYTHAGOREAN THEOREM		
In a right triangle, the sum of the squares of the lengths of the legs is equal to the square of the length of the hypotenuse.	$a^2 + b^2 = c^2$	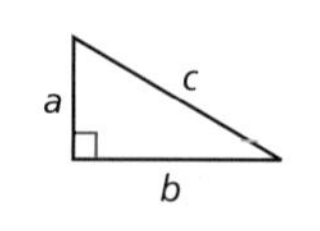

EXAMPLE 1 Calculating the Length of a Side of a Right Triangle

Use the Pythagorean Theorem to find each missing measure.

A

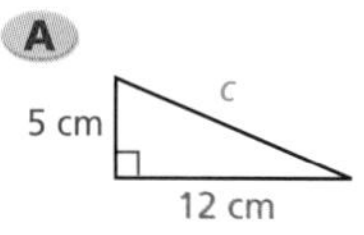

$a^2 + b^2 = c^2$ *Use the Pythagorean Theorem.*
$5^2 + 12^2 = c^2$ *Substitute for a and b.*
$25 + 144 = c^2$ *Evaluate the powers.*
$169 = c^2$ *Add.*
$\sqrt{169} = \sqrt{c^2}$ *Take the square root of both sides.*
$13 = c$
The length of the hypotenuse is 13 cm.

B

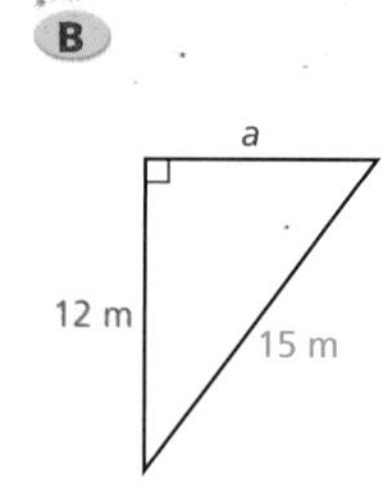

$a^2 + b^2 = c^2$ *Use the Pythagorean Theorem.*
$a^2 + 12^2 = 15^2$ *Substitute for b and c.*
$a^2 + 144 = 225$ *Evaluate the powers.*
$\underline{\quad - 144 \quad - 144}$
$a^2 = 81$ *Subtract 144 from both sides.*
$\sqrt{a^2} = \sqrt{81}$ *Take the square root of both sides.*
$a = 9$
The length of the missing leg is 9 m.

1 Introduce

Alternate Opener

EXPLORATION

8-8 The Pythagorean Theorem

Right triangles have one 90° angle. In the triangles below, each 90° angle is formed by the sides that have lengths a and b.

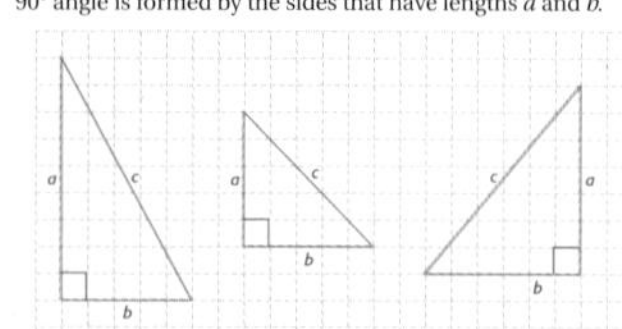

Use the grid to find the side lengths a and b on each triangle. Then square each length (a^2 and b^2) and add the squares ($a^2 + b^2$). Enter this sum in the column labeled c^2. Then use a calculator to find the square root of c^2, or c, the length of the longest side of the triangle. Round your answers to the nearest tenth.

	a	b	a^2	b^2	$a^2 + b^2$	c^2	c
1.							
2.							
3.							

Think and Discuss

4. **Discuss** whether only the longest side length of a right triangle can be found using $a^2 + b^2 = c^2$.

Motivate

Provide students with centimeter graph paper. Have students draw a rectangle with side lengths 10 cm and 24 cm. Then have them draw and measure the length of the diagonal to the nearest centimeter. **26 cm** Point out that the right triangle they constructed illustrates a special property of right triangles. Ask students to square the length of each side of the right triangle to see whether they can discover the property. **100, 576, 676; $10^2 + 24^2 = 26^2$**

Exploration worksheet and answers on Chapter 8 Resource Book pp. 74 and 106

2 Teach

Lesson Presentation

Guided Instruction

In this lesson, students learn to use the Pythagorean Theorem to find the measure of a side of a right triangle. Make sure students understand how the variables relate to the diagram and to the formula. The variables a and b represent the legs, and the variable c represents the hypotenuse of a right triangle. Stress that the longest side of a right triangle is always the hypotenuse.

Tell students that if the square of the length of one side of a triangle equals the sum of the squares of the lengths of the other two sides, then the triangle is a right triangle.

EXAMPLE 2 **PROBLEM SOLVING APPLICATION**

A regulation baseball diamond is a square with sides that measure 90 feet. About how far is it from home plate to second base? Round your answer to the nearest tenth.

1 Understand the Problem

Rewrite the question as a statement.

- Find the distance from home plate to second base.

List the **important information:**

- Drawing a segment between home plate and second base divides the diamond into two right triangles.
- The segment between home and second base is the hypotenuse.
- The base lines are legs, and they are each 90 feet long.

2 Make a Plan

You can use the Pythagorean Theorem to write an equation.

3 Solve

$a^2 + b^2 = c^2$	*Use the Pythagorean Theorem.*
$90^2 + 90^2 = c^2$	*Substitute for the known variables.*
$8{,}100 + 8{,}100 = c^2$	*Evaluate the powers.*
$16{,}200 = c^2$	*Add.*
$127.279 \approx c$	*Take the square root of both sides.*
$127.3 \approx c$	*Round.*

The distance from home plate to second base is about 127.3 ft.

4 Look Back

The hypotenuse is the longest side of a right triangle. Since the distance from home plate to second base is greater than the distance between the bases, the answer is reasonable.

Think and Discuss

1. **Explain** how to use the Pythagorean Theorem to determine whether a triangle with side lengths 3, 4, and 5 could be a right triangle.
2. **Demonstrate** whether a leg of a right triangle can be longer than the hypotenuse.

COMMON ERROR ALERT

Some students might confuse the legs and the hypotenuse of a right triangle when substituting values in the Pythagorean Theorem. Remind students to always write the formula and then identify the legs and the hypotenuse. Emphasize that the hypotenuse is always the longest side since it is opposite the greatest angle in the triangle, the right angle.

Additional Examples

Example 1

Use the Pythagorean Theorem to find each missing measure.

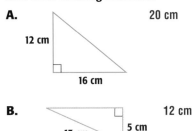

A. **20 cm**

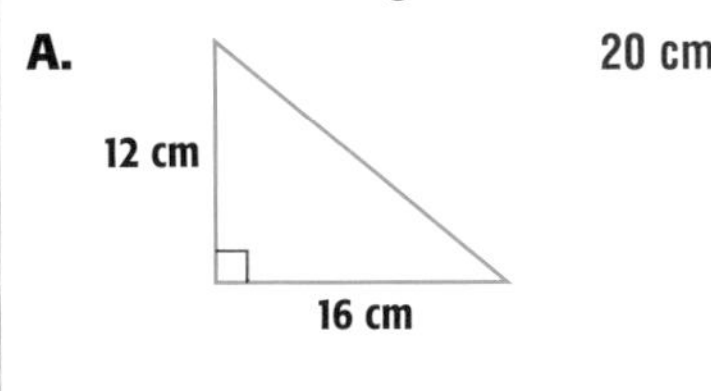

B. **12 cm**

13 cm
5 cm

Example 2

A square field has sides of 75 feet. About how far is it from one corner of the field to the opposite corner of the field? Round your answer to the nearest tenth. **106.1 ft**

Example 2 note: Point out that the figure of interest is a triangle, and in particular, it is a right triangle. This fact should suggest that the Pythagorean Theorem will have something to do with the solution.

3 Close

Reaching All Learners

Through World Math

Allow students to work in small groups to investigate other famous ancient Greek mathematicians and philosophers, such as Euclid, Archimedes, Heron, Socrates, and Aristotle. Have each group present an oral report on the person they chose and describe one of the person's important contributions.

Summarize

Have students draw and label a right triangle to illustrate the Pythagorean Theorem. Have them identify the legs and the hypotenuse and explain the relationship between these parts according to the theorem. Ask students to describe the cases in which they can use the Pythagorean Theorem.

The side opposite the right angle is the hypotenuse. The other two sides are the legs. If a and b represent the legs and c represents the hypotenuse, then $a^2 + b^2 = c^2$. Case 1: Find the hypotenuse when the legs are known. Case 2: Find the other leg when one leg and the hypotenuse are known.

Answers to Think and Discuss

Possible answers:

1. For the triangle to be a right triangle, $3^2 + 4^2$ must equal 5^2. Since $3^2 + 4^2 = 5^2$, a triangle with side lengths 3, 4, and 5 could be a right triangle.
2. A leg can never be greater than the hypotenuse. The hypotenuse of a right triangle is always the longest side since it is always opposite the greatest angle in the triangle, the right angle. Since the square of the hypotenuse is greater than the square of either leg, the hypotenuse must be longer than either leg.

8-8 PRACTICE & ASSESS

Students may want to refer back to the lesson examples.

Assignment Guide

If you finished Example 1 assign:
Core 1, 2, 4–7, 9–13 odd, 21–27
Enriched 1, 5, 7, 9–14, 21–27

If you finished Example 2 assign:
Core 1–8, 9–17 odd, 21–27
Enriched 1–7 odd, 9–27

Notes

8-8 Exercises

FOR EXTRA PRACTICE
see page 673

GUIDED PRACTICE

See Example 1 Use the Pythagorean Theorem to find each missing measure.

1. **20 m**

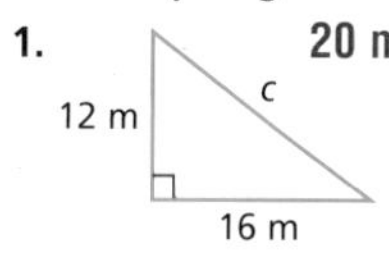

2. **8 ft**

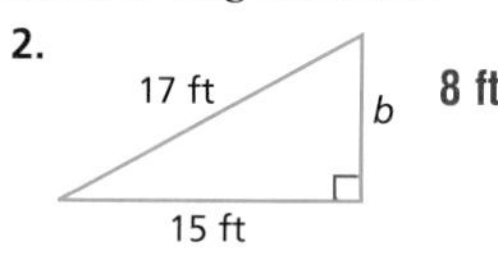

See Example 2 3. A 10 ft ladder is leaning against a wall. If the ladder is 5 ft from the base of the wall, how far above the ground does the ladder touch the wall? Round your answer to the nearest tenth. **about 8.7 ft**

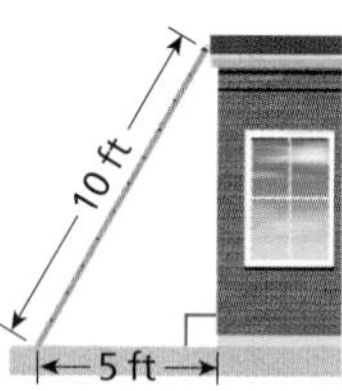

INDEPENDENT PRACTICE

See Example 1 Use the Pythagorean Theorem to find each missing measure.

4. **30 yd**

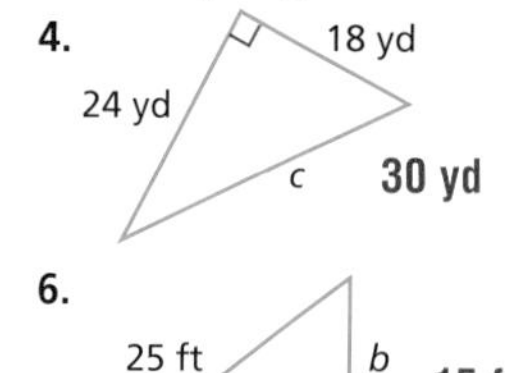

5. **24 cm**

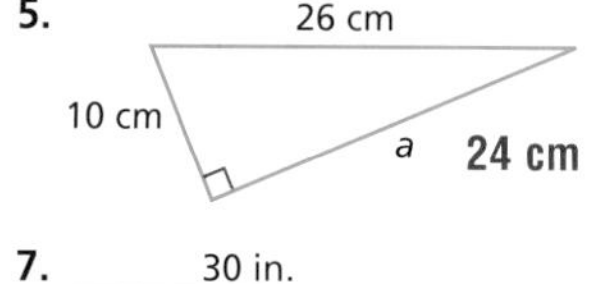

6. **15 ft**

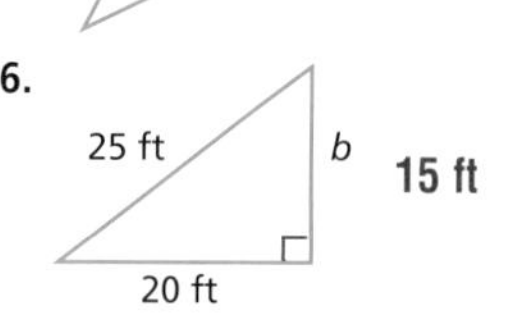

7. **16 in.**

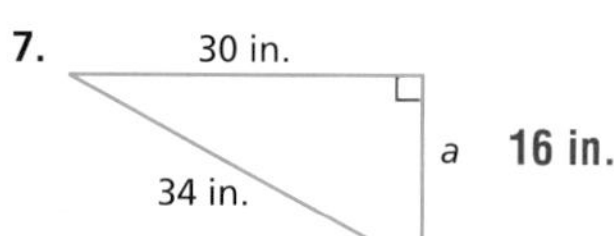

See Example 2 8. James rides his bike 15 miles west. Then he turns north and rides another 15 miles before he stops to rest. How far is James from his starting point when he stops to rest? Round your answer to the nearest tenth. **about 21.2 mi**

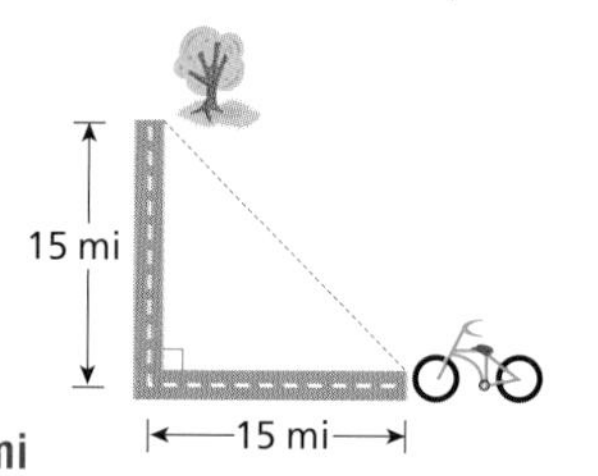

PRACTICE AND PROBLEM SOLVING

Find the missing length to the nearest tenth for each right triangle.

9. $a = 5$; $b = 8$; $c =$ ▒ **9.4**
10. $a = 10$; $b =$ ▒; $c = 15$ **11.2**
11. $a =$ ▒; $b = 13$; $c = 18$ **12.4**
12. $a = 21$; $b = 20$; $c =$ ▒ **29**

Determine whether each set of lengths forms a right triangle.

13. $a = 11$; $b = 60$; $c = 61$ **yes**
14. $a = 17$; $b = 20$; $c = 25$ **no**

Math Background

Every triangle must be either acute, right, or obtuse. You can derive three inequalities from the Pythagorean Theorem to find the type of a triangle, given its side lengths.

Pythagorean Inequalities

For $\triangle ABC$, with c being the length of the longest side:

- If $c^2 < a^2 + b^2$, then $\triangle ABC$ is an acute triangle.
- If $c^2 = a^2 + b^2$, then $\triangle ABC$ is a right triangle.
- If $c^2 > a^2 + b^2$, then $\triangle ABC$ is an obtuse triangle.

RETEACH 8-8

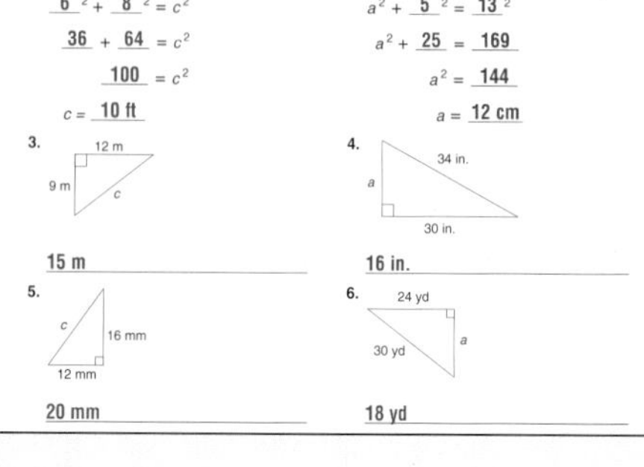

LESSON 8-8 **Reteach**
The Pythagorean Theorem

A triangle containing a right angle is called a *right triangle.* The sides adjacent to the right angle are the **legs,** represented by *a* and *b*. The side opposite the right angle is the **hypotenuse,** represented by *c*.

The **Pythagorean Theorem** states:

If *a* and *b* are the lengths of the legs of a right triangle and *c* is the length of the hypotenuse, then $a^2 + b^2 = c^2$.

Use the Pythagorean Theorem to find each missing length.

1. (6 ft, 8 ft, c)
$a^2 + b^2 = c^2$
$\underline{6}^2 + \underline{8}^2 = c^2$
$\underline{36} + \underline{64} = c^2$
$\underline{100} = c^2$
$c = \underline{10\text{ ft}}$

2. (5 cm, 13 cm, a)
$a^2 + b^2 = c^2$
$a^2 + \underline{5}^2 = \underline{13}^2$
$a^2 + \underline{25} = \underline{169}$
$a^2 = \underline{144}$
$a = \underline{12\text{ cm}}$

3. (12 m, 9 m, c) **15 m**
4. (34 in., a, 30 in.) **16 in.**
5. (c, 16 mm, 12 mm) **20 mm**
6. (24 yd, 30 yd, a) **18 yd**

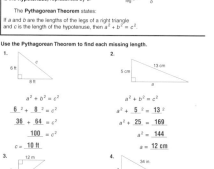

PRACTICE 8-8

LESSON 8-8 **Practice B**
The Pythagorean Theorem

Use the Pythagorean Theorem to find each missing length.

1. (9 in., 12 in.) **15 in.**
2. (17 cm, 15 cm) **8 cm**
3. (10 ft, 24 ft) **26 ft**
4. (7 m, 25 m) **24 m**
5. (12 yd, 13 yd) **5 yd**
6. (8 m, 6 m) **10 m**
7. (30 mm, 34 mm) **16 mm**
8. (18 in., 24 in.) **30 in.**
9. (20 yd, 25 yd) **15 yd**

10. A 20-ft ladder is leaning against a wall. If the ladder is 12 ft from the base of the wall, how high above the ground does the ladder touch the wall? **16 ft**

11. A checkerboard is 10 inches long on each side. What is the length of the diagonal from one corner to another? Round your answer to the nearest tenth. **14.1 in.**

12. Chang lives 8 miles east of the school. Deborah lives 12 miles south of the school. Approximately how far apart are Chang's and Deborah's homes? Round your answer to the nearest tenth. **14.4 mi**

13. A rectangle is 26 meters long and 18 meters wide. What is the length of the diagonal of the rectangle to the nearest meter? **32 m**

15. Ancient Egyptians built pyramids to serve as tombs for their kings. One pyramid, called Menkaure, has a square base with an area of about 12,100 m^2.
    a. What is the length of each side of the base? **110 m**
    b. What is the length of a diagonal of the base? Round your answer to the nearest tenth. **155.6 m**

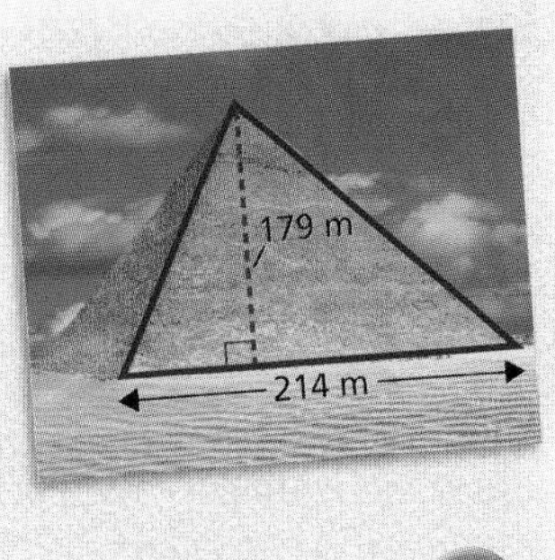

16. The photograph shows the Pyramid of Khafre in Egypt. Each side of its square base is about 214 meters long. Each triangular side is an isosceles triangle with a height of about 179 meters. What is the area of one side of the pyramid? **19,153 m^2**

17. Use the Pythagorean Theorem to find the distance from one corner of the Pyramid of Khafre to its peak. Round your answer to the nearest tenth. **208.5 m**

18. The pyramids were constructed using a unit of measurement called a cubit. There are about 21 inches in 1 cubit. If the height of a pyramid is 471 feet, what is its height in cubits? **269.1 cubits**

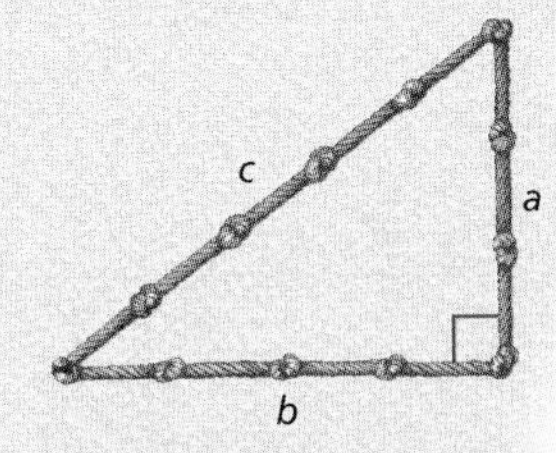

19. ***WRITE ABOUT IT*** To determine the boundaries of their fields after the Nile flooded each spring, ancient Egyptians used a loop of rope that was knotted at 12 equal intervals. They stretched the rope around three stakes to form a triangle so that the measures of the sides were 3, 4, and 5. Explain why the triangle formed by the knotted rope could be a right triangle.

20. ***CHALLENGE*** The pyramid at right has a square base. Find the height of the pyramid to the nearest tenth. **68.8 m**

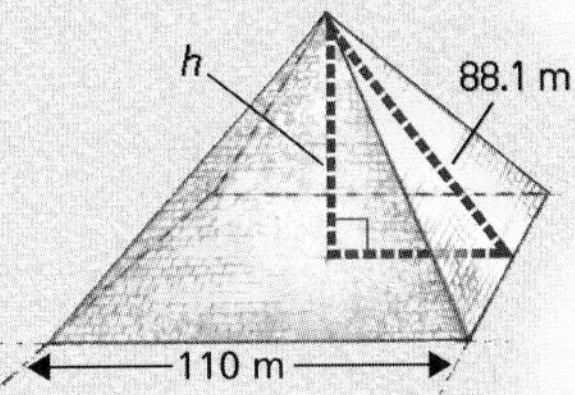

History

Exercises 15–20 involve finding measures of the ancient Egyptian pyramids. Students study Egyptian history and culture in middle school social studies programs, such as Holt, Rinehart and Winston's *People, Places, and Change.*

Answers

19. See p. A3.

Journal

Ask students to describe real-world situations in which the Pythagorean Theorem would be useful.

Test Prep Doctor

As long as students are able to remember the correct formula for the area of a circle, they can use estimation to select the correct answer for Exercise 27. Since $r = 6$, a rough estimate is $3(6^2) = 3(36) \approx 3(40) = 120$. The only choice close to 120 is **C,** the correct answer.

Spiral Review

Choose the more precise measurement in each pair. (Lesson 8-2)

21. 12 in., 1 ft **12 in.**
22. 5 m, 8 km **5 m**
23. 3.5 yd, 22 ft **22 ft**

Calculate. Use the correct number of significant digits in each answer. (Lesson 8-2)

24. $12.6 + 7.32$ **19.9**
25. $19 - 5.7$ **13**
26. $4.3 \cdot 2.5$ **11**

27. **TEST PREP** A circular mat has a radius of 6 inches. What is the area of the mat? (Lesson 8-6) **C**

    A 18.84 in^2 B 37.68 in^2 C 113.04 in^2 D 226.08 in^2

Lesson Quiz

Use the Pythagorean Theorem to find each missing length.

1. **40 m**

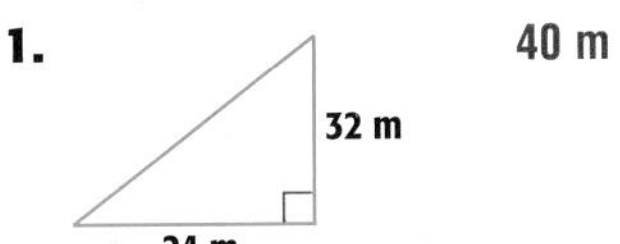

2. **21 in.**

28 in.
35 in.

Find the missing length of each right triangle.

3. $a = \square$, $b = 30$, $c = 34$ **16**
4. $a = 20$, $b = 21$, $c = \square$ **29**
5. Each rectangular section of a fence is braced by a board nailed on the diagonal of the section. The fence is 6 ft tall and the brace is 10 ft long. What is the length of the section? **8 ft**

Available on Daily Transparency in CRB

CHALLENGE 8-8

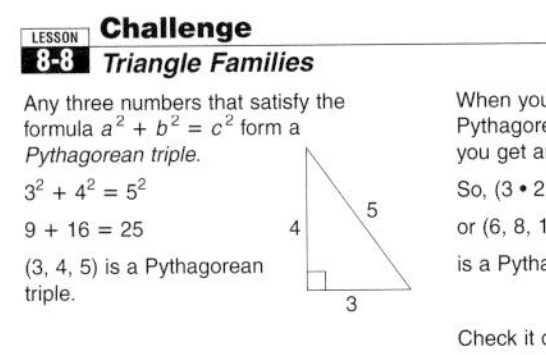

LESSON 8-8 **Challenge**
Triangle Families

Any three numbers that satisfy the formula $a^2 + b^2 = c^2$ form a *Pythagorean triple.*

$3^2 + 4^2 = 5^2$

$9 + 16 = 25$

(3, 4, 5) is a Pythagorean triple.

When you multiply or divide a Pythagorean triple by the same number, you get another Pythagorean triple.

So, $(3 \cdot 2, 4 \cdot 2, 5 \cdot 2)$, or (6, 8, 10), is a Pythagorean triple.

Check it out: $6^2 + 8^2 = 10^2$
$36 + 64 = 100$

Complete each table to find new Pythagorean triples. Then check some of your results.

1. **The (3, 4, 5) Family**

Multiply by 3.	(9, 12, 15)
Multiply by 5.	**(15, 20, 25)**
Multiply by 10.	**(30, 40, 50)**
Divide by 5.	$\left(\frac{3}{5}, \frac{4}{5}, 1\right)$

2. **The (5, 12, 13) Family**

Multiply by 2.	**(10, 24, 26)**
Multiply by 3.	**(15, 36, 39)**
Multiply by 8.	**(40, 96, 104)**
Divide by 10.	$\left(\frac{1}{2}, \frac{6}{5}, \frac{13}{10}\right)$

3. **The (7, 24, 25) Family**

Divide by 4.	$\left(\frac{7}{4}, 6, \frac{25}{4}\right)$
Multiply by 2.	**(14, 48, 50)**
Multiply by 4.	**(28, 96, 100)**
Multiply by 12.	**(84, 288, 300)**

4. **The (8, 15, 17) Family**

Divide by 2.	$\left(4, \frac{15}{2}, \frac{17}{2}\right)$
Multiply by 3.	**(24, 45, 51)**
Multiply by 4.	**(32, 60, 68)**
Multiply by 20.	**(160, 300, 340)**

5. Use the formula to check one triple of the (3, 4, 5) family.
   Possible answer: $15^2 + 20^2 = 25^2$; $225 + 400 = 625$
6. Use the formula to check one triple of the (5, 12, 13) family.
   Possible answer: $10^2 + 24^2 = 26^2$; $100 + 576 = 676$
7. Use the formula to check one triple of the (7, 24, 25) family.
   Possible answer: $28^2 + 96^2 = 100^2$; $784 + 9{,}216 = 10{,}000$

PROBLEM SOLVING 8-8

LESSON 8-8 **Problem Solving**
The Pythagorean Theorem

Write the correct answer.

1. During a storm, a tree falls toward a house. The top of the tree leans against the house 45 feet above the ground. The distance on the ground from the house to the base of the tree is 24 feet. What is the height of the tree?
   51 ft
2. During a training exercise, a firefighter leans a 40-foot ladder up to a window in a house. The bottom of the ladder is 24 feet from the bottom of the house. How high is the window from the ground?
   32 ft
3. A triangle has a hypotenuse of 25 centimeters and a base of 20 centimeters. What is the area of this right triangle?
   150 cm^2
4. The football field at the University of Texas at Arlington is 60 yards by 100 yards. Is the length of the diagonal across this field more or less than 200 yards? Explain.
   less, because $\sqrt{13{,}600}$ is less than 200

Choose the letter of the correct answer.

5. The minimum size of a soccer field for players under 8 years of age is 20 yards by 30 yards. About how far is the diagonal distance on a field with these dimensions?
   A about 12 yd (C) about 36 yd
   B about 25 yd D about 45 yd
6. The minimum size of a soccer field for international matches is 70 yards by 110 yards. If a player runs diagonally across this field, about how much farther does she run than if the field were 50 yards by 100 yards?
   F about 242 yd H about 112 yd
   G about 130 yd (J) about 19 yd
7. In the state of Virginia, Winchester is 21 miles north of Front Royal. Arlington is 58 miles east of Front Royal. What is the distance to the nearest mile from Winchester to Arlington?
   A 37 mi C 89 mi
   (B) 62 mi D 441 mi
8. On a child's slide, the distance from the bottom rung to the top of the ladder is 6 feet. The straight distance from the bottom rung of the ladder to the bottom of the slide is 36 inches. About how long is the slide?
   (F) about 6.7 ft H about 9.0 ft
   G about 8.4 ft J about 36.5 ft

8C
Graph Irrational Numbers

Pacing: Traditional 1 day
Block $\frac{1}{2}$ day

Objective: To use a number line to graph irrational numbers

Materials: Calculators

Lab Resources

Hands-On Lab Activities . . . . p. 75

Using the Pages

Discuss the difference between rational and irrational numbers. Ask students if it is possible to find the exact location of an irrational number on a number line.

Draw a number line from 1 to 2 that is marked in tenths. Locate each number on the number line.

1. 1.5

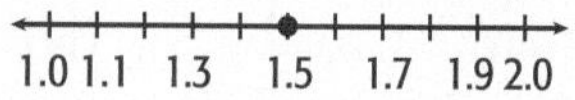

1.0 1.1 1.3 1.5 1.7 1.9 2.0

2. $1\frac{9}{10}$

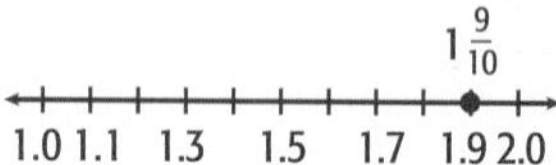

3. 1.15

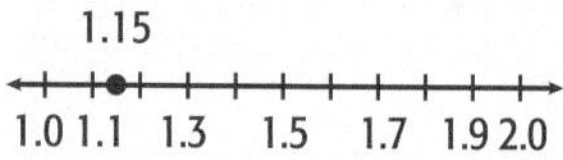

Graph Irrational Numbers

Use with Lesson 8-7

A rational number is a number that can be expressed as a ratio of two integers. All rational numbers can be written as either terminating or repeating decimals.
An irrational number is a number that cannot be expressed as a ratio of two integers or as a terminating or repeating decimal.

Every point on the number line corresponds to a real number, either a rational number or an irrational number. Between every two real numbers there is always another real number.

One way to find an approximate value of an irrational number is to locate it between two rational numbers on the number line. The number line below shows the location of several rational numbers.

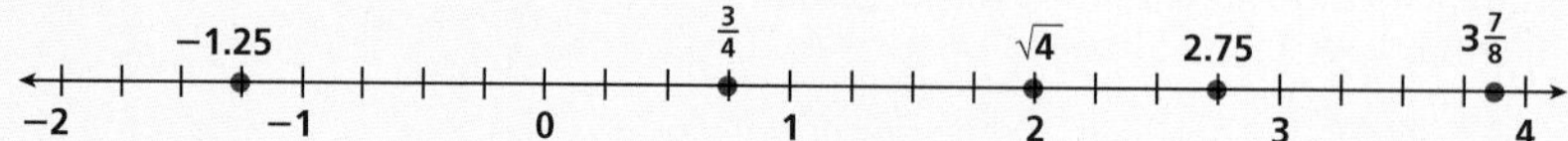

Activity

1 Copy the number line below. Locate $\sqrt{2}$ on the number line.

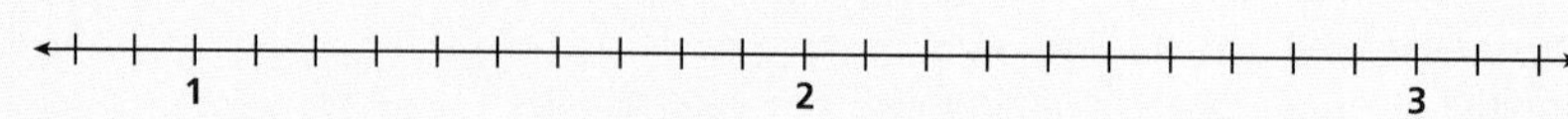

Since $\sqrt{2}$ is an irrational number, you must find an approximate value.

Think: 2 is between the perfect squares 1 and 4. Therefore, $\sqrt{2}$ is between $\sqrt{1}$ and $\sqrt{4}$, or between 1 and 2.

To find a closer approximation, you can use decimals rounded to the tenths place.

Think: $1.1^2 = 1.21$
$1.2^2 = 1.44$
$1.3^2 = 1.69$
$\mathbf{1.4^2 = 1.96}$
$\mathbf{1.5^2 = 2.25}$

Since $1.4^2 = 1.96$ and $1.5^2 = 2.25$, $\sqrt{2}$ is between 1.4 and 1.5.

To find an even closer approximation, you can use decimals rounded to the hundredths place or the thousandths place.

Think: $1.41^2 = 1.9881$
$1.42^2 = 2.0164$

Since $1.41^2 = 1.9881$ and $1.42^2 = 2.0164$, $\sqrt{2}$ is between 1.41 and 1.42.

Think: $1.411^2 = 1.990921$
$1.412^2 = 1.993744$
$1.413^2 = 1.996569$
$\mathbf{1.414^2 = 1.999396}$
$\mathbf{1.415^2 = 2.002225}$

So $\sqrt{2}$ is between 1.414 and 1.415.

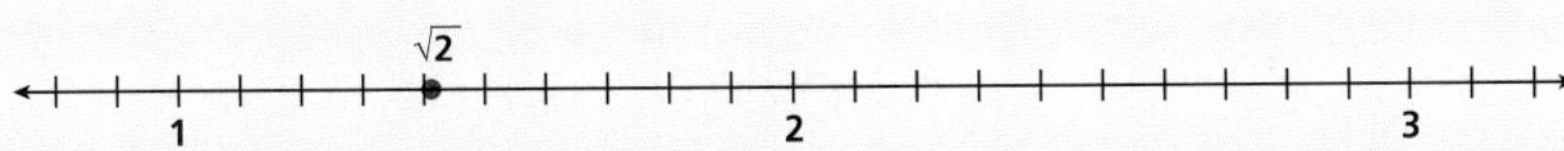

2 Locate $\sqrt{5}$ on a number line.

Think: 5 is between the perfect squares 4 and 9. Therefore, $\sqrt{5}$ is between $\sqrt{4}$ and $\sqrt{9}$, or between 2 and 3.

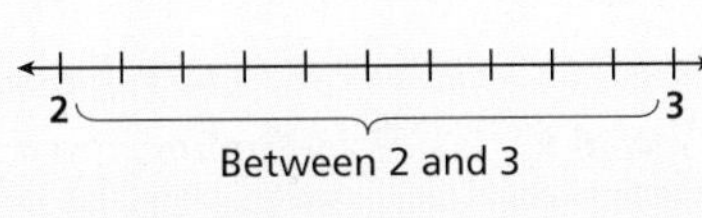

$2.1^2 = 4.41$
$\mathbf{2.2^2 = 4.84}$
$\mathbf{2.3^2 = 5.29}$

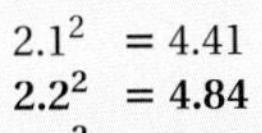

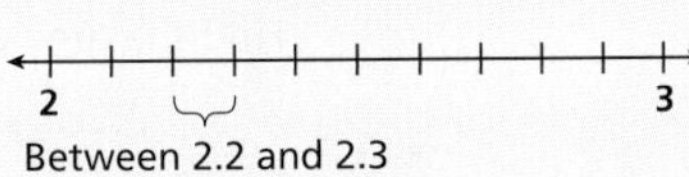

$2.21^2 = 4.8841$
$2.22^2 = 4.9284$
$\mathbf{2.23^2 = 4.9729}$
$\mathbf{2.24^2 = 5.0176}$

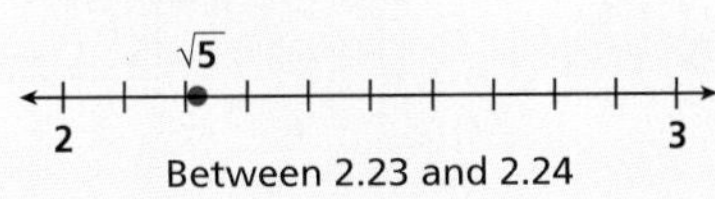

So $\sqrt{5}$ is between 2.23 and 2.24.

Think and Discuss

1. Use a calculator to find $\sqrt{5}$. How is this answer similar to the one you found? How is it different? Which is more precise? Why?
2. Is π a rational number or an irrational number? Explain.

Try This

Draw a number line from 2 to 4 that is marked in tenths. Locate each number on the number line.

1. $3\frac{3}{5}$
2. $\sqrt{8}$
3. 2.1
4. $\sqrt{10}$
5. $2\frac{1}{2}$
6. $\sqrt{11}$
7. $\sqrt{6}$
8. 2.25

Answers

Think and Discuss

1. Possible answer: $\sqrt{5} = 2.23606\ldots$; This answer is similar to the one found in the activity since it is between 2.23 and 2.24, but it has more decimal places, making it more precise.
2. Possible answer: π is an irrational number because it cannot be expressed as a terminating or repeating decimal.

Try This

1. $3\frac{3}{5}$ — 2.0 2.4 2.8 3.2 3.6 4.0
2. $\sqrt{8}$ — 2.0 2.4 2.8 3.2 3.6 4.0
3. 2.1 — 2.0 2.4 2.8 3.2 3.6 4.0
4. $\sqrt{10}$ — 2.0 2.4 2.8 3.2 3.6 4.0
5. $2\frac{1}{2}$ — 2.0 2.4 2.8 3.2 3.6 4.0
6. $\sqrt{11}$ — 2.0 2.4 2.8 3.2 3.6 4.0
7. $\sqrt{6}$ — 2.0 2.4 2.8 3.2 3.6 4.0
8. 2.25 — 2.0 2.4 2.8 3.2 3.6 4.0

Extension

Pacing: Traditional 1 day
Block $\frac{1}{2}$ day

Objective: Students find the areas of irregular shapes.

Using The Pages

In Lessons 8-4, 8-5, and 8-6, students found the areas of parallelograms, triangles, trapezoids, and circles. In this extension, students will find the areas of irregular shapes that are formed by combinations of familiar shapes.

EXTENSION Area of Irregular Figures

Learn to find the areas of irregular shapes.

A group of Eagle Scouts are constructing a new path through a local park. The section Martin and Carl are working on is irregularly shaped.

To find the area of an irregular shape, you can divide it into non-overlapping familiar shapes. The sum of these areas is the area of the irregular shape.

EXAMPLE 1 Finding the Area of an Irregular Figure

Find the area of each figure.

A

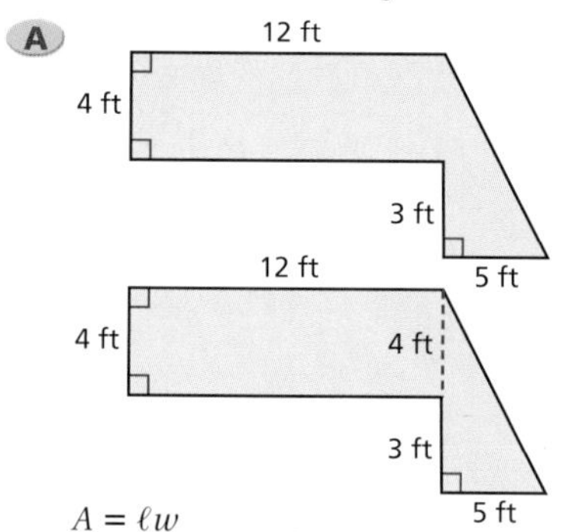

12 ft
4 ft
4 ft
3 ft
5 ft

Divide the figure into a rectangle and a triangle.

$A = \ell w$
$A = 12 \cdot 4$ *Find the area of the rectangle.*
$A = 48$

$A = \frac{1}{2}bh$
$A = \frac{1}{2}(5)(3 + 4)$ *Find the area of the triangle.*
$A = \frac{1}{2}(5)(7)$
$A = 17.5$

$A = 48 + 17.5$ *Total area = area of rectangle + area of triangle.*
$A = 65.5$ *Add the areas to find the total area.*

The area of the figure is 65.5 ft^2.

Introduce

Motivate

Tell students to draw a rectangle on a sheet of graph paper and label the length and width. Then have students use one side of the rectangle as a leg of a right triangle and draw the other two sides of the triangle outside the rectangle. Ask students to explain how to find the area of the figure formed by the rectangle and the triangle. Find the sum of the areas of the rectangle and the triangle.

Encourage volunteers to share their work with the class.

Teach

Lesson Presentation

Guided Instruction

In this extension, students learn to find the areas of irregular shapes. Emphasize that to find the area of an irregular shape, you need to break it into a combination of familiar shapes whose areas you know how to find.

Mention that sometimes one or more sides of an irregular figure are not labeled. Tell students that they can use the relationships indicated in the figure to find the missing measures.

Find the area of each figure. Use 3.14 for π.

B

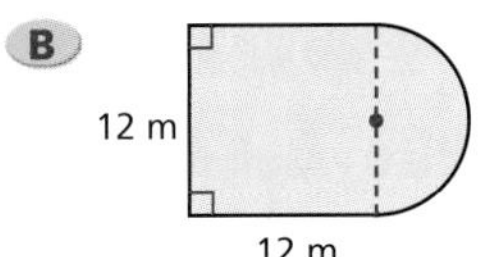

$A = s^2$	$A = \frac{1}{2}(\pi r^2)$	*Find the area of the square and the semicircle. The area of a semicircle is one-half the area of a circle.*
$A = 12^2$	$A \approx \frac{1}{2}(3.14 \cdot 6^2)$	
$A = 144$	$A \approx \frac{1}{2}(113.04)$	
	$A \approx 56.52$	

Total area = area of square + area of semicircle

$\approx 144 + 56.52$

≈ 200.52

Add the areas to find the total area.

The area of the figure is about 200.52 m^2.

EXTENSION Exercises

Find the area of each figure. Use 3.14 for π.

1. 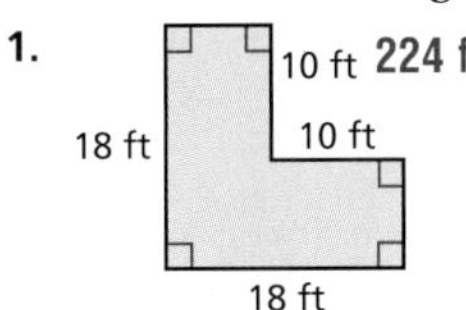

224 ft²

2. 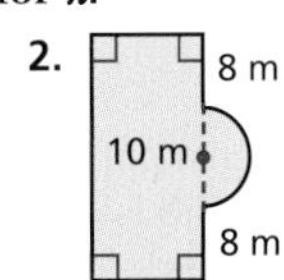

351.25 m²

3. 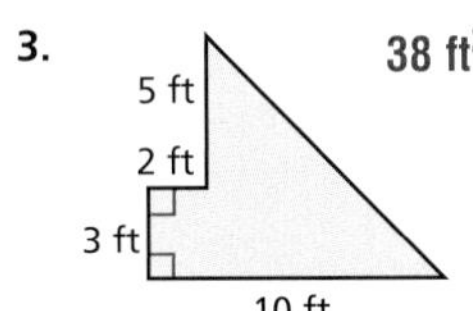

38 ft²

4. 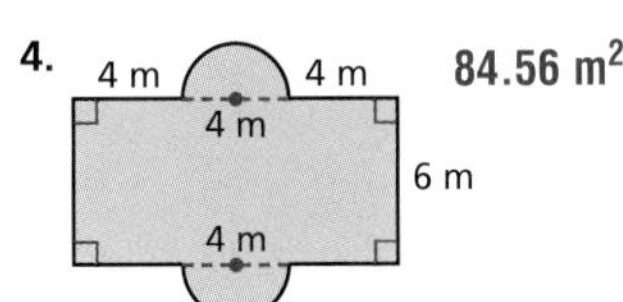

84.56 m²

5. 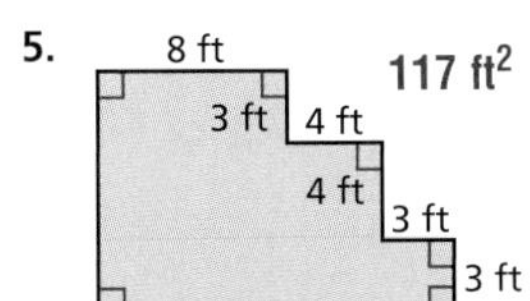

117 ft²

6. 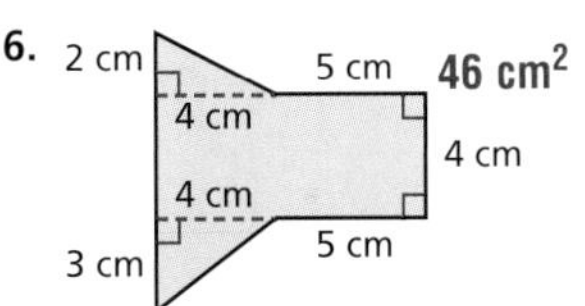

46 cm²

COMMON ERROR ALERT

Students might get confused by figures with circular sections. Remind students that they know how to find the area of a circle. Tell them that if the figure is a semicircle, they must find half the area of a circle. If the figure is a quarter circle, they must find one-fourth the area of a circle. Explain that if there are two semicircles with the same radius, the area of both semicircles is the area of a whole circle.

Additional Examples

Example 1

Find the area of each figure. Use 3.14 for π.

A.

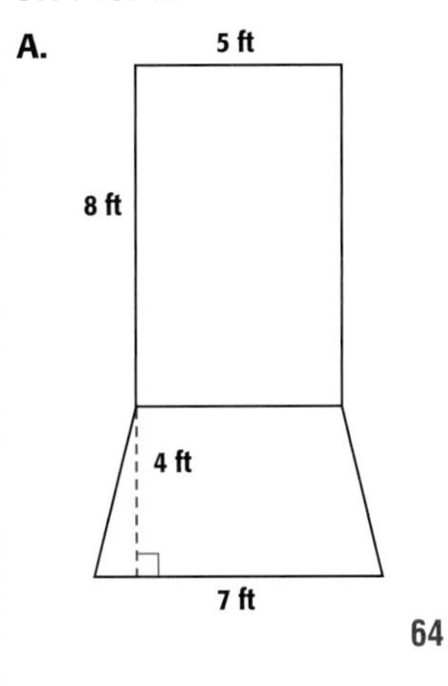

64 ft²

B.

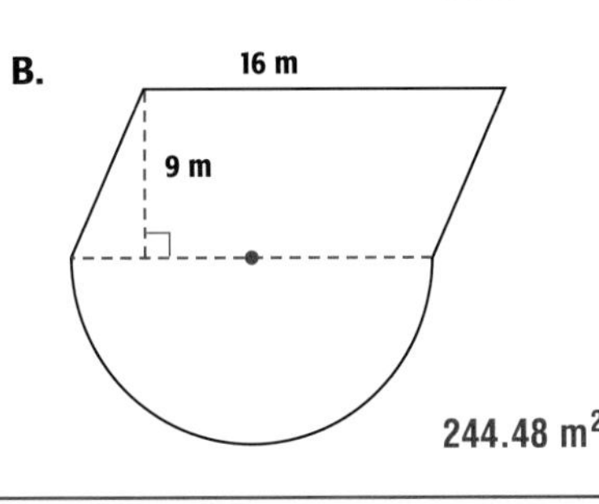

244.48 m²

3 Close

Summarize

Have volunteers draw several irregular figures that are composites of nonoverlapping triangles, squares, rectangles, parallelograms, trapezoids, circles, semicircles, and/or quarter circles. Discuss how to find the area of each irregular figure.

Divide each irregular figure into sections with recognizable areas. Find the area of each section. Add the areas to find the total area.

Teaching Tip

Stress the importance of naming each section as a separate area. The purpose of this is twofold. First, it will help students distinguish between the different sections of a figure and identify the appropriate formula to use for the section. Second, it will help students keep track of all the sections they need to find the total area of the irregular figure.

Problem Solving on Location

Missouri

Purpose: *To provide additional practice for problem-solving skills in Chapters 1–8*

Missouri Measures

- After problem 1, have students consider the following problem: The distance from Kansas City to Joplin is about 150 miles. The distance from Kansas City to St. Louis is about 260 miles. If the roads from Kansas City to Joplin and Kansas City to St. Louis form a right angle, what is the approximate distance from Joplin to St. Louis? about 300 miles
- After problem 4, have students find the number of yards in the length of the Mississippi River. 4,118,400 yd

Extension Have students measure the distances between Joplin and St. Louis, Kansas City and St. Louis, and Joplin and Kansas City on the map. Then have students use the scale to find the actual distances and check if their answers are close to those in the first activity.

Possible answers: Joplin and St. Louis: 282 miles; Kansas City and St. Louis: 257 miles; Joplin and Kansas City: 150 miles

Answers

1. You can think of the distance between Kansas City and Branson as the hypotenuse of a right triangle and have $167 = a$ and $75 = b$. You can then use the Pythagorean Theorem to find the distance: $167^2 + 75^2 = 33{,}514$; $c \approx 183$; The distance between Kansas City and Branson is about 183 miles.
3. Possible answer: The area of Missouri is about 68,000 mi^2. Divide the map into parallelograms and one right triangle. Find the area of each figure and add them to find the total area.
4. 40 yd by 11 yd by 2 yd; 1,440 in. by 396 in. by 72 in.; yards is a better measure to use than inches.

Problem Solving on Location

MISSOURI

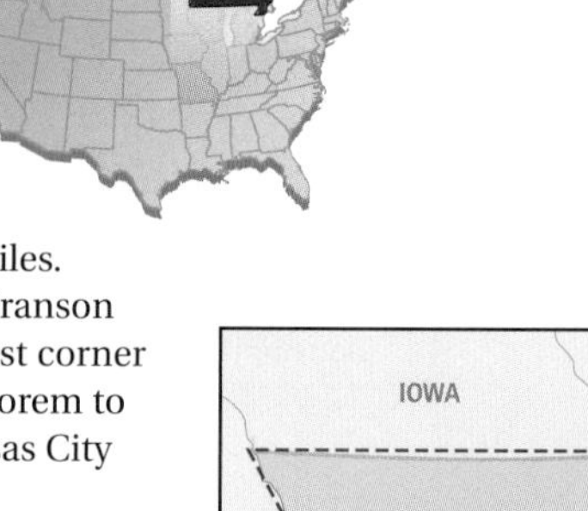

Missouri Measures

For 1–3, use the map of Missouri.

1. The distance from Kansas City to the southwest corner of Missouri is about 167 miles. The distance from the southwest corner to Branson is about 75 miles. If the angle of the southwest corner is 90°, how can you use the Pythagorean Theorem to find the approximate distance between Kansas City and Branson? Find the distance.
2. What is the approximate area of the triangular region formed by the line segment connecting Kansas City to Branson? **about 6,263 mi^2**
3. Use a ruler and what you know about the area of parallelograms to find the approximate area of the state of Missouri. (*Hint:* You will need to use information from problems 1 and 2.) Explain your method.
4. Riverboats have long been a popular mode of transportation along the Mississippi River. One riverboat, known as the *Mark Twain*, goes on excursions and dinner cruises from Hannibal, Missouri—the place where author Mark Twain (whose real name was Samuel Clemens) spent his boyhood. The *Mark Twain* is 120 feet by 33 feet by 6 feet and holds 400 passengers. Convert the dimensions of this riverboat into yards and then into inches. Which is the better measure to use, yards or inches?

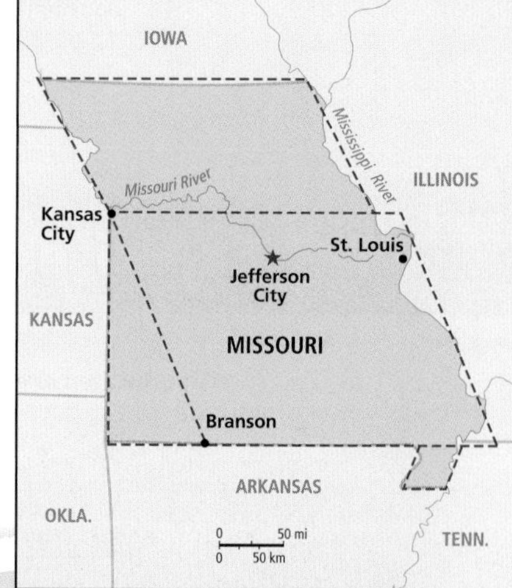

Points of Interest in St. Louis, Missouri

For 1–3, use the map of St. Louis.

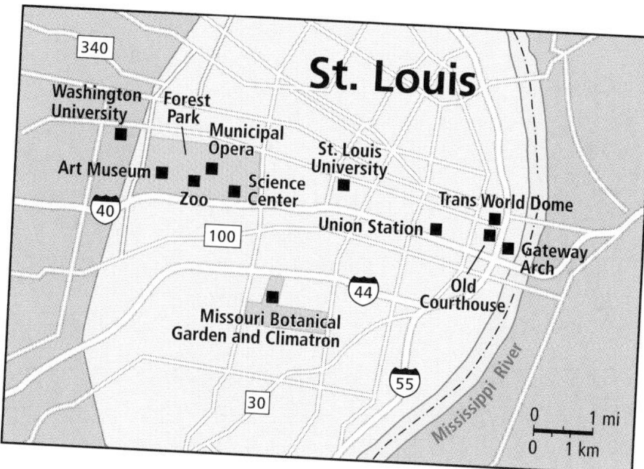

1. The Gateway Arch, located in a national park, is a 630-foot steel arch built in 1966 to honor Native Americans and settlers of the American West. Locate the Gateway Arch on the map in the eastern part of St. Louis. Suppose you walk from the Arch to the Trans World Dome, and then to Union Station and back to the Arch. About how many kilometers do you walk?
2. If you walk around the perimeter of Forest Park, about how many miles would you walk? About how many kilometers will you walk? **about 6 mi or 9.6 km**
3. What points of interest are within a 3-mile radius of the zoo?
4. The St. Louis Zoo houses about 3,500 animals on 38 acres. If 1 acre is about 43,560 square feet, about how many square feet of space per animal does the zoo have? **about 473 ft^2**
5. The Missouri Botanical Garden has Talipot palm trees with trunks 80 feet high and 3 feet in diameter. What is the circumference of the trunk of one of these Talipot palm trees? **about 9.42 ft**

Points of Interest in St. Louis, Missouri

- After problem 1, have students find the height of the Gateway Arch in yards and in inches. 210 yd; 7,560 in.
- After problem 4, have students consider the following problem: Grant's Farm, named after President Ulysses S. Grant, is a wildlife preserve and historical site near the city of St. Louis. Hundreds of exotic animals from around the world can be found there. The area of Grant's Farm is 12,240,360 ft^2. How many acres is Grant's Farm? 281 acres

Extension Have students look up and compare the heights of the Gateway Arch in St. Louis, the Washington Monument in Washington, D.C., the Statue of Liberty in New York, and the Sears Tower in Chicago. Ask students to list these famous structures in ascending order of their heights. Statue of Liberty: 302 ft; Washington Monument: 555 ft; Gateway Arch: 630 ft; Sears Tower: 1,450 ft

Answers

1. about 4.5 km

3. Possible answers: Forest Park, Washington University, Art Museum, Municipal Opera, Science Center, Missouri Botanical Garden and Climatron, St. Louis University

MATH-ABLES

Game Resources

Puzzles, Twisters & Teasers
Chapter 8 Resource Book

Shape-Up

Purpose: *To apply solving geometric problems to create fun puzzles*

Discuss: Ask students to explain how they found the area of the whole square.

Possible answer: I found the factors of 24 and 36. I used 8 and 3 for 24 and 9 and 4 for 36, since $8 + 4 = 9 + 3$. The length of each side of the square is 12, so the area of the square is 144.

Suggest that students make a table such as the following to find the maximum number of times that 6 circles can intersect.

Number of Circles	Number of Intersections
2	2
3	6
4	12
5	20
6	30

Extend: Challenge students to solve the following problem: A rectangle with a length of 8 cm and a width of 6 cm is inscribed in a circle. What is the area of the regions between the rectangle and the circle? Explain how you got your answer.

Possible answer: By the Pythagorean Theorem, the diagonal of the rectangle, which is also the diameter of the circle, is 10. The area of the circle is 78.5 cm^2. The area of the rectangle is 48 cm^2. The area of the regions between the circle and the rectangle is $78.5 - 48, = 30.5$ cm^2.

Circles and Squares

Purpose: *To play a game with circles and squares*

Discuss: Have students discuss the strategies they used to play the game.

Extend: Have students create their own sequences and play the game with a partner.

MATH-ABLES

Shape Up

Rectangles

The square below has been divided into four rectangles. The areas of two of the rectangles are given. If the length of each of the segments in the diagram is an integer, what is the area of the original square?

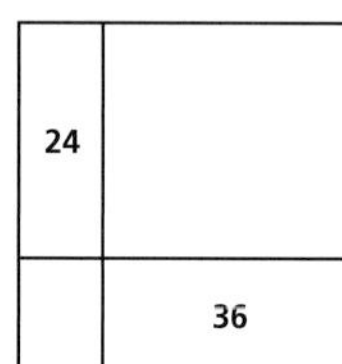

$a = 3$;
$b = 8$;
$c = 9$;
$d = 4$;
$A = 144$ units^2

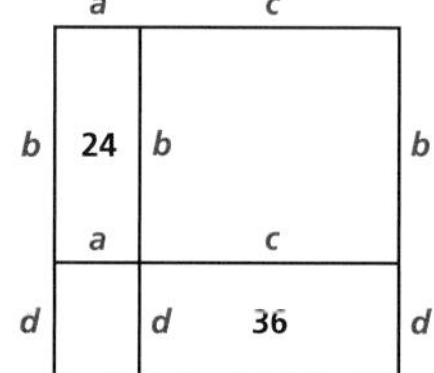

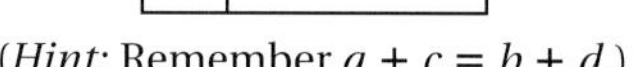

(*Hint:* Remember $a + c = b + d$.)

Use different lengths and a different answer to create your own version of this puzzle. **Check students' work.**

Circles

What is the maximum number of times that six circles of the same size can intersect? To find the answer, start by drawing two circles that are the same size. What is the greatest number of times they can intersect? Add another circle, and another, and so on. **30; 2; Check students' work.**

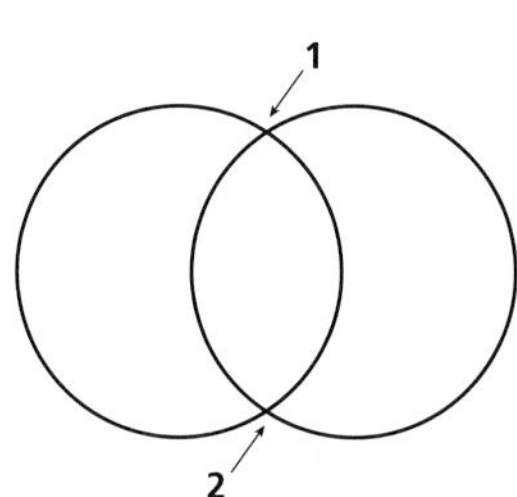

Circles and Squares

Two players start with a sequence of circles and squares. Before beginning the game, each player chooses whether to be a "circle" or a "square." The goal of the game is to have the final remaining shape be the shape you chose to be. Shapes are removed from the sequence according to the following rules: On each move, a player selects two shapes. If the shapes are identical, they are replaced with one square. If the shapes are different, they are replaced with one circle.

internet connect
Go to ***go.hrw.com*** for a complete set of rules and game pieces.
KEYWORD: MS4 Game8

Area and Perimeter

internet connect
Lab Resources Online
go.hrw.com
KEYWORD: MS4 TechLab8

You can use geometry software to explore the area and perimeter of geometric figures.

Activity

1 Construct and label a quadrilateral that resembles the one shown in the first window below. Then select the interior of the quadrilateral.

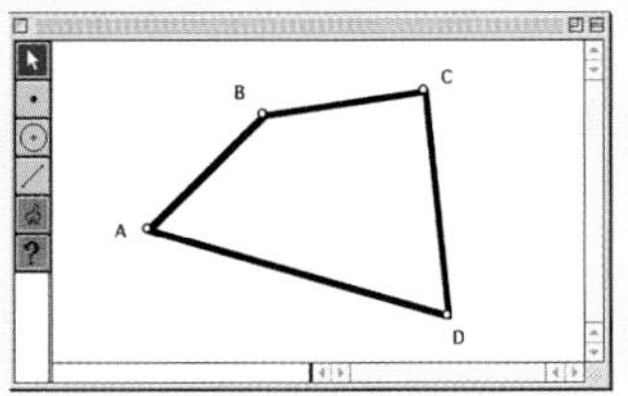

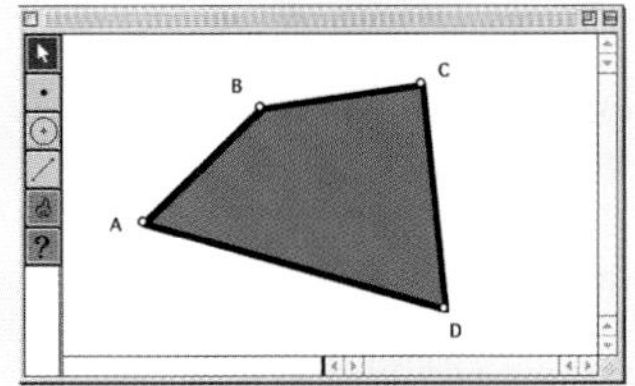

Use the software tools to measure the area and the perimeter of *ABCD*. Then select vertex *D* and drag it around. Notice that the measures of the area and the perimeter change as the shape of the quadrilateral changes.

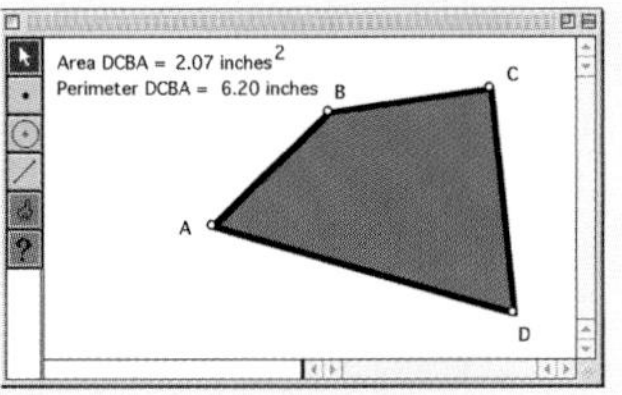

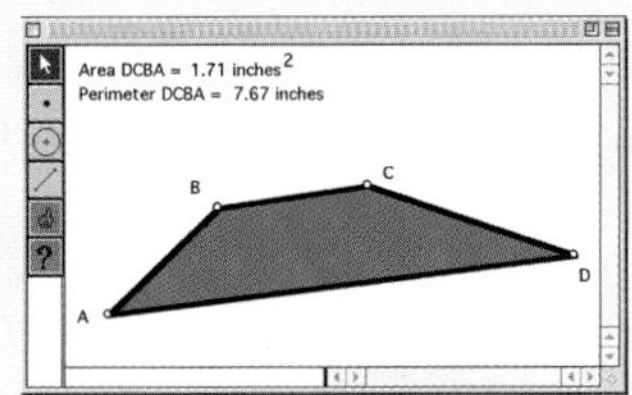

Think and Discuss

1. Will the area and perimeter of a translated polygon be the same as the area and perimeter of the original polygon? Explain.

Try This

1. Use geometry software to construct triangle *ABC*. Measure the area and perimeter of *ABC*. Then construct triangle *DEF* that has *twice the area* of *ABC*. Is the perimeter of *DEF* twice the perimeter of *ABC*? Explain.
2. Use geometry software to construct a 5-sided polygon *ABCDE*. Measure the area of *ABCDE*. Identify three triangles that make up polygon *ABCDE*. Measure the area of each triangle and find the sum of the areas. Compare this sum with the area of *ABCDE*.

Answers

Think and Discuss

1. Yes; A translated polygon is congruent to the original polygon. Therefore, the area and the perimeter will be the same for both.

Try This

1. Possible answer:

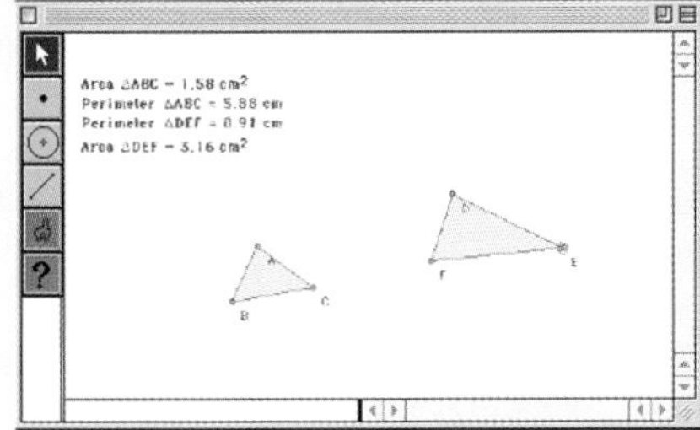

No, the perimeter of triangle *DEF* is not twice the perimeter of triangle *ABC*. Doubling the area does not double the perimeter.

2. Possible answer:

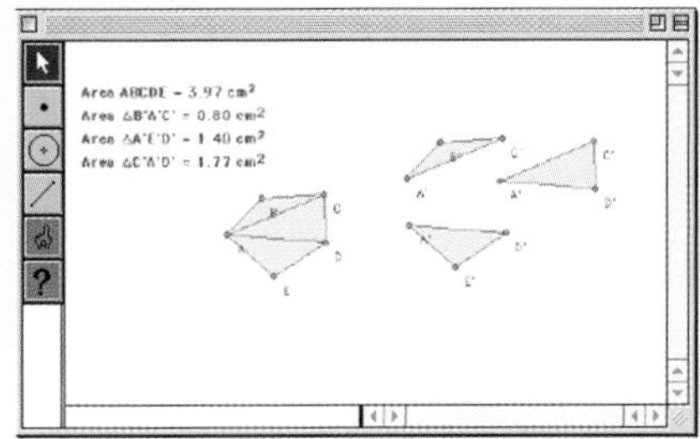

The sum of the areas of the three triangles is the same as the area of *ABCDE*.

Area and Perimeter

Objective: To use geometry software to explore the perimeter and area of geometric figures

Materials: Geometry software

Lab Resources

Technology Lab Activities . . . . p. 45

Using the Page

This technology activity shows students how to use geometry software to explore the perimeter and area of geometric figures.

The Think and Discuss problem can be used to assess students' understanding of whether translating a figure using geometry software will change its perimeter and area. While Try This problems 1 and 2 can be done without geometry software, they are meant to provide students with experiences that help them become familiar with how to use perimeter and area tools.

Assessment

Use geometry software to construct triangle *ABC*. Measure the area and perimeter of triangle *ABC*. Next, construct triangle *DEF* with sides that are twice as long as the sides of triangle *ABC*. Is the area of triangle *DEF* twice the area of triangle *ABC*? Possible answer: No, the area of triangle *DEF* is 4 times the area of triangle *ABC*.

Chapter 8

Study Guide and Review

Purpose: *To help students review and practice concepts and skills presented in Chapter 8*

Assessment Resources

Chapter Review

Chapter 8 Resource Book. . . . pp 82–83

***Test and Practice Generator* CD-ROM**

Additional review assessment items in both multiple-choice and free-response format may be generated for any objective in Chapter 8.

Answers

1. hypotenuse
2. circumference
3. precision
4. square root
5. 13
6. 3.4
7. 288
8. 458,000
9. 3 significant digits
10. 5 significant digits
11. 1 significant digit
12. 2 significant digits
13. 4 significant digits
14. 4 significant digits

Chapter 8

Study Guide and Review

Study Guide and Review

Vocabulary

accuracy	420	perimeter	424
area	430	precision	420
circumference	425	Pythagorean Theorem	450
hypotenuse	450	radical sign	444
leg	450	significant digits	420
perfect square	444	square root	444

Complete the sentences below with vocabulary words from the list above. Words may be used more than once.

1. The longest side of a right triangle is called the __?__.
2. The __?__ is the distance around a circle.
3. __?__ is the level of detail an instrument can measure.
4. A(n) __?__ is one of the two equal factors of a number.

8-1 Customary and Metric Measurements (pp. 414–417)

EXAMPLE

- **Convert 54 meters to centimeters.**

  There are 100 centimeters in 1 meter.

  $54 \text{ m} \cdot \frac{100 \text{ cm}}{1 \text{ m}} = 5{,}400 \text{ cm}$

  54 meters is equal to 5,400 centimeters.

EXERCISES

Convert.

5. 312 hr = ▒ days
6. 3,400 g = ▒ kg
7. 8 yd = ▒ in.
8. 458 km = ▒ m

8-2 Accuracy and Precision (pp. 420–423)

EXAMPLE

- **Determine the number of significant digits in 705.4 mL.**

  The digits 7, 5, and 4 are nonzero digits, and 0 is between two nonzero digits. So 705.4 mL has 4 significant digits.

EXERCISES

Determine the number of significant digits in each measurement.

9. 0.450 kg
10. 6,703.0 ft
11. 30,000 lb
12. 0.00078 g
13. 900.5 cm
14. 1,204 gal

8-3 Perimeter and Circumference (pp. 424–427)

EXAMPLE

- **Find the perimeter of the triangle.**

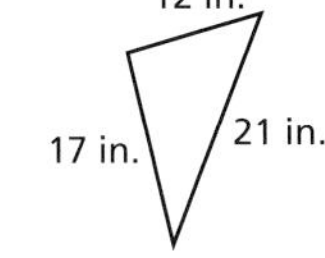

$P = 12 + 17 + 21$
$P = 50$
The perimeter of the triangle is 50 in.

- **Find the circumference of the circle. Use 3.14 for π.**

5 cm

$C = 2\pi r$
$C \approx 2 \cdot 3.14 \cdot 5$
$C \approx 31.4$
The circumference of the circle is about 31.4 cm.

EXERCISES

Find the perimeter of each polygon.

15. **16.**

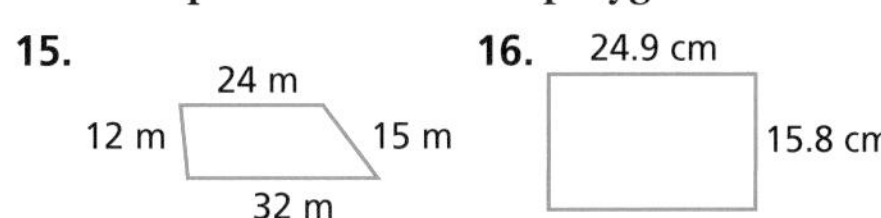

Find the circumference of each circle to the nearest tenth. Use 3.14 for π.

17.

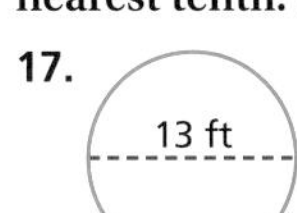

18.

8-4 Area of Parallelograms (pp. 430–433)

EXAMPLE

- **Find the area of the rectangle.**

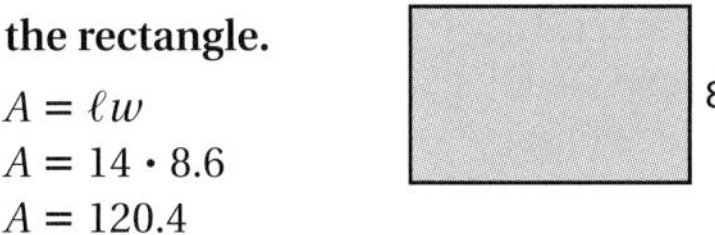

$A = \ell w$
$A = 14 \cdot 8.6$
$A = 120.4$
The area of the rectangle is 120.4 in^2.

EXERCISES

Find the area of each figure.

19. **20.**

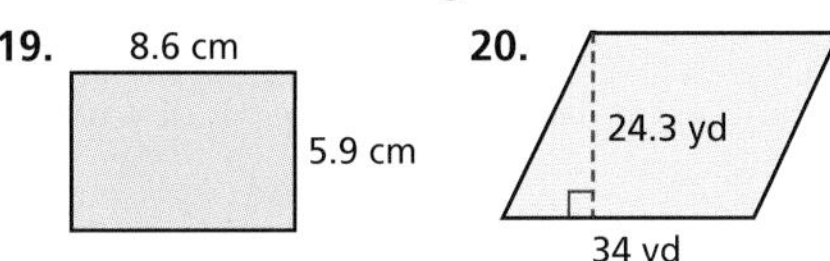

8-5 Area of Triangles and Trapezoids (pp. 434–437)

EXAMPLE

- **Find the area of the triangle.**

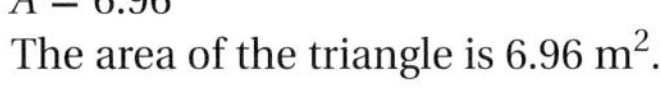

2.9 m
4.8 m

$A = \frac{1}{2}bh$
$A = \frac{1}{2}(4.8 \cdot 2.9)$
$A = \frac{1}{2}(13.92)$
$A = 6.96$
The area of the triangle is 6.96 m^2.

EXERCISES

Find the area of each polygon.

21.

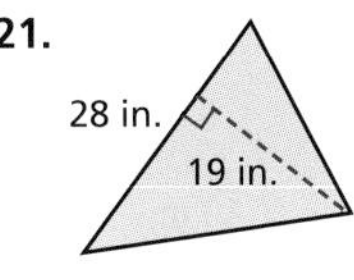

22.

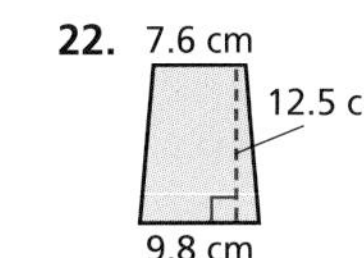

23.

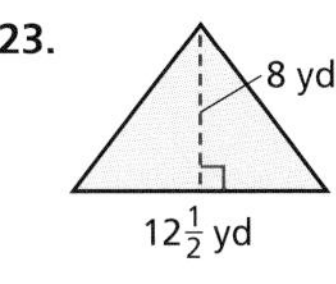

24.

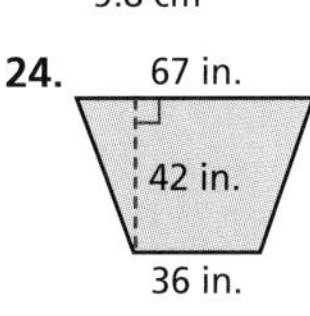

Answers

15. 83 m
16. 81.4 cm
17. 40.8 ft
18. 49.0 in.
19. 50.74 cm^2
20. 826.2 yd^2
21. 266 in^2
22. 108.75 cm^2
23. 50 yd^2
24. 2,163 in^2

Answers

25. 36.3 m^2
26. 226.9 ft^2
27. 5
28. 10
29. 10
30. 12
31. 16 ft
32. 34 cm
33. 60 ft
34. 2 m
35. 60 mm

Study Guide and Review

8-6 Area of Circles (pp. 438–441)

EXAMPLE

- **Find the area of the circle to the nearest tenth. Use 3.14 for π.**

5 in.

$A = \pi r^2$
$A \approx 3.14 \cdot 5^2$
$A \approx 3.14 \cdot 25$
$A \approx 78.5$
The area of the circle is about 78.5 in^2.

EXERCISES

Find the area of each circle to the nearest tenth. Use 3.14 for π.

25.
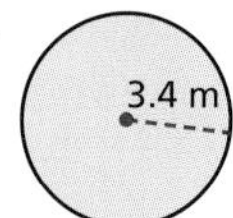

26.
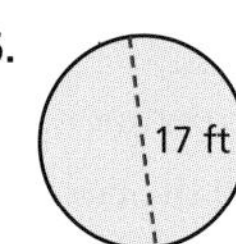

8-7 Powers and Roots (pp. 444–447)

EXAMPLE

- **Estimate $\sqrt{71}$ to the nearest whole number.**

$64 < \quad 71 < 81$ *Find the perfect squares nearest 71.*
$\sqrt{64} < \sqrt{71} < \sqrt{81}$
$8 < \sqrt{71} < 9$ *Find the square roots of 64 and 81.*

Since 71 is nearer in value to 64 than to 81, $\sqrt{71} \approx 8$.

EXERCISES

Estimate each square root to the nearest whole number.

27. $\sqrt{29}$ **28.** $\sqrt{92}$
29. $\sqrt{106}$ **30.** $\sqrt{150}$

31. The area of Rita's square vegetable garden is 265 ft^2. What is the length of each side of the garden to the nearest foot?

8-8 Pythagorean Theorem (pp. 450–453)

EXAMPLE

- **Use the Pythagorean Theorem to find the missing measure.**

$a^2 + b^2 = c^2$
$9^2 + 12^2 = c^2$
$81 + 144 = c^2$
$225 = c^2$
$\sqrt{225} = \sqrt{c^2}$
$15 = c$

9 in. 12 in.

The hypotenuse is 15 in.

EXERCISES

Use the Pythagorean Theorem to find each missing measure.

32. **33.**
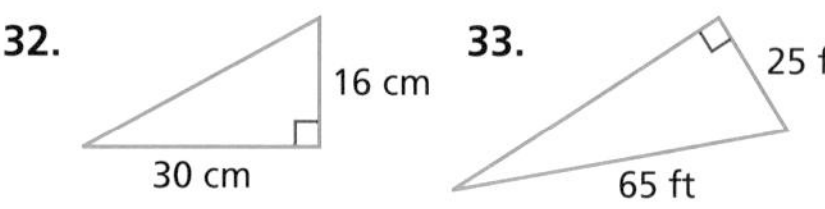

34.
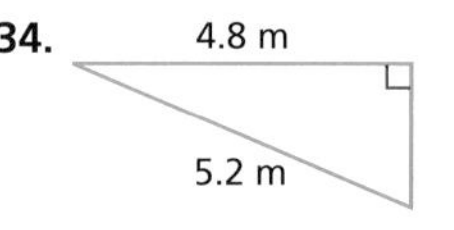

35.
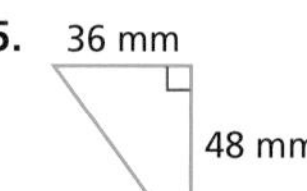

Chapter Test

Chapter 8

Convert.

1. 13 lb = ▢ oz **208** **2.** 450 m = ▢ km **0.45** **3.** 6 hr = ▢ s **21,600**

Choose the more precise measurement in each pair.

4. 80 m, 7.9 cm **7.9 cm** **5.** 18 yd, 5 mi **18 yd** **6.** 500 lb, 18 oz **18 oz**

Calculate. Use the correct number of significant digits in each answer.

7. 5.882 in. + 5.17 in. **11.05 in.** **8.** 5.6 g ÷ 2.59 **2.2 g** **9.** 3.14 · 125 cm **393 cm**

Find the perimeter of each polygon.

10.

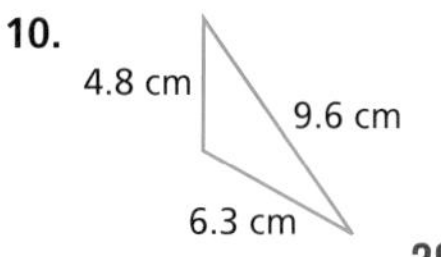

20.7 cm

11.

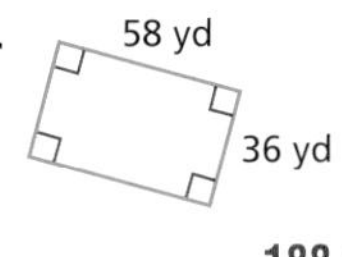

188 yd

12.

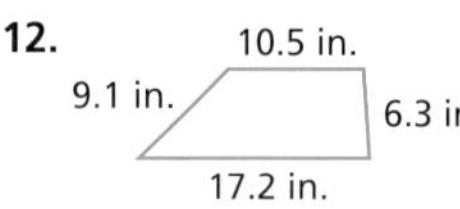

43.1 in.

Find the area of each figure.

13.

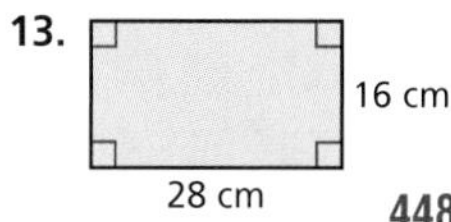

448 cm²

14.

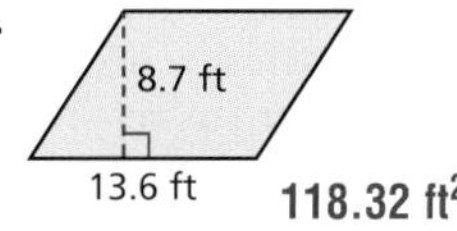

118.32 ft²

15.

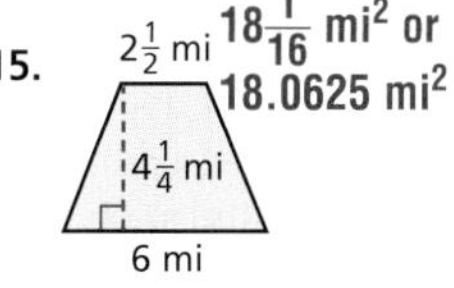

$18\frac{1}{16}$ mi² or 18.0625 mi²

Use the circle at right for items 16 and 17. Use 3.14 for π.

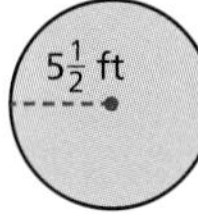

16. Find the circumference of the circle to the nearest tenth. **34.5 ft**

17. Find the area of the circle to the nearest tenth. **95.0 ft²**

18. What is the radius of a circle with circumference 51.496 in.? Use 3.14 for π. **8.2 in.**

Estimate each square root to the nearest whole number.

19. $\sqrt{42}$ **6** **20.** $\sqrt{78}$ **9** **21.** $\sqrt{115}$ **11**

22. The area of a square chessboard is 212 in². What is the length to the nearest inch of each side of the chessboard? **15 in.**

Use the triangle at right for items 23 and 24.

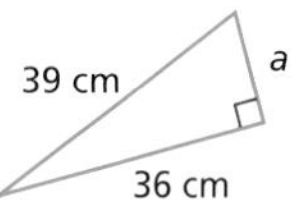

23. Use the Pythagorean Theorem to find the missing measure of the triangle. **15 cm**

24. Find the area of the triangle. **270 cm²**

25. A triangle has side lengths of 18 cm, 20 cm, and 29 cm. Could the triangle be a right triangle? Explain your answer.

Chapter Test

Chapter Test

Purpose: *To assess students' mastery of concepts and skills in Chapter 8*

Assessment Resources

Chapter 8 Tests (Levels A, B, C)
Assessment Resources. . . . . pp. 75–80

***Test and Practice Generator* CD-ROM**

Additional assessment items in both multiple-choice and free-response format may be generated for any objective in Chapter 8.

Answers

25. It could not be a right triangle because $18^2 + 20^2 \neq 29^2$.

Chapter 8 Performance Assessment

Purpose: To assess students' understanding of concepts in Chapter 8 and combined problem-solving skills

Assessment Resources

Performance Assessment
Assessment Resources .... p. 120

Performance Assessment Teacher Support
Assessment Resources .... p. 119

Answers

4. See Level 3 work sample below.

Scoring Rubric for Problem Solving Item 4

Level 3

Accomplishes the purpose of the task.

Student gives clear explanations, shows understanding of mathematical ideas and processes, and computes accurately.

Level 2

Purposes of the task not fully achieved.

Student demonstrates satisfactory but limited understanding of the mathematical ideas and processes.

Level 1

Purposes of the task not accomplished.

Student shows little evidence of understanding the mathematical ideas and processes and makes computational and/or procedural errors.

Chapter 8 Performance Assessment

Show What You Know

Create a portfolio of your work from this chapter. Complete this page and include it with your four best pieces of work from Chapter 8. Choose from your homework or lab assignments, mid-chapter quizzes, or any journal entries you have done. Put them together using any design you want. Make your portfolio represent what you consider your best work.

Short Response

1. $A = \frac{1}{2}(3.25)(6.4 + 8.2) = \frac{1}{2}(3.25)(14.6) = 23.725 \approx 24 \text{ m}^2$

1. The bases of a trapezoid are 6.4 m and 8.2 m, and the height is 3.25 m. Show the steps necessary to find the area of the trapezoid. Write the area using the rules for significant digits.
2. Jeanette wants to mount a circular photo onto a rectangular piece of cardboard. The area of the photo is 50.24 in^2. What are the smallest possible dimensions the piece of cardboard can have and still hold the entire photo? Use 3.14 for π and explain your answer.
3. Find the perimeter and area of a rectangle with length 12 m and width 7 m. Then find the length of each side of a square with the same area as the rectangle. Round your answers to the nearest meter, and show your work.

3. 12 m + 12 m + 7 m + 7 m = 38 m; (12 m)(7 m) = 84 m^2; $s^2 = 84$; $s \approx 9$ m

Extended Problem Solving

4. Washington, D.C., occupies about 68% of the area of the square shown in the center of the map. The length of each side of the square is 10 miles.
   a. Find the area of the square. Show your work.
   b. Explain how to use your answer from part **a** to calculate the area of Washington, D.C. Then find the area of the city.
   c. Explain how you could find the diagonal distance across the square. Find this distance to the nearest tenth. Show your work.

2. Since the area of the circular photo is 50.24 in^2, its radius is 4 in. and its diameter is 8 in. The dimensions of the piece of cardboard must be at least the diameter of the photo, so the smallest possible dimensions are 8 in. by 8 in.

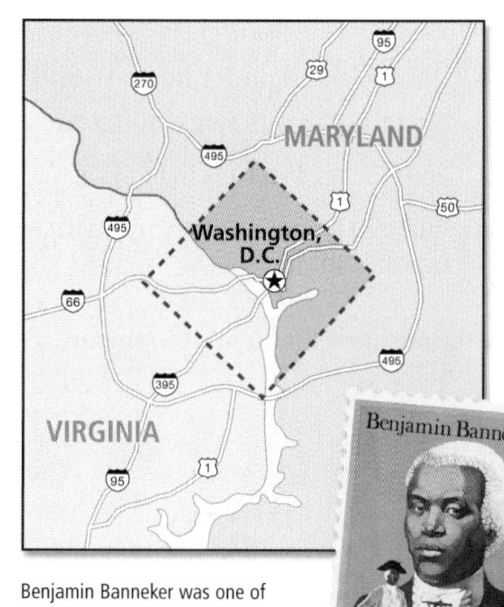

Benjamin Banneker was one of the first well-known African American scientists. In 1791, he helped to design the layout of Washington, D.C.

Performance Assessment

Student Work Samples for Item 4

Level 3

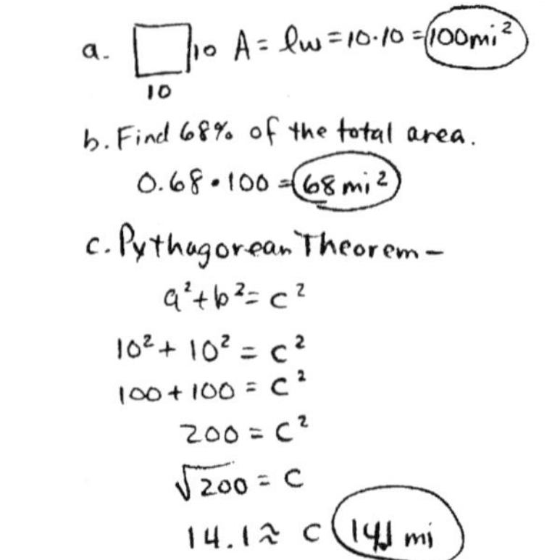

The student correctly answered each part with the appropriate units, showed the work, and explained the answers as necessary.

Level 2

a) 10×10 = 100
b) Multiply area by 0.68.
100 × 0.68 = 68
c. A triangle must add up to 180.
10+10 = 20
180 − 20 = 160

The student correctly answered parts **a** and **b**, but did not include units. The student did not identify or apply the Pythagorean Theorem in part **c.**

Level 1

a. .68 × 10 = 6.8 miles
b. half of 6.8 = 3.4 miles
c. 6.8 + 3.4 = 12.2 miles

The student performed operations on the numbers without demonstrating knowledge of the concepts necessary to solve the problems.

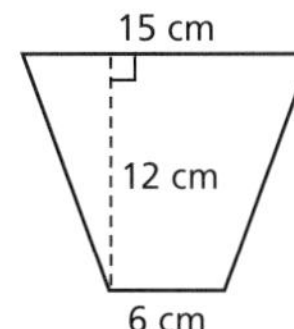

internet connect
State-Specific Test Practice Online
go.hrw.com Keyword: MS4 TestPrep

Standardized Test Prep

Chapter 8

Cumulative Assessment, Chapters 1–8

1. Solve the equation $78 = a + 49$. **A**
   Ⓐ $a = 29$ Ⓒ $a = 31$
   Ⓑ $a = 30$ Ⓓ $a = 127$

2. Which statement is false? **G**
   Ⓕ $\frac{85}{34}$ is equivalent to 2.5.
   Ⓖ $\frac{7}{80}$ is equivalent to 0.875.
   Ⓗ $\frac{3}{500}$ is equivalent to 0.006.
   Ⓙ $\frac{7}{35}$ is equivalent to 0.20.

3. What is the area of the trapezoid? **B**

   15 cm
   12 cm
   6 cm

   Ⓐ 81 cm^2 Ⓒ 135 cm^2
   Ⓑ 126 cm^2 Ⓓ 252 cm^2

4. The distance from Chattanooga to Nashville, Tennessee, is 128 mi. If a map scale is $\frac{1}{2}$ in. = 10 mi, what is the distance between the cities on the map? **F**
   Ⓕ 6.4 in. Ⓗ 12.8 in.
   Ⓖ 10.8 in. Ⓙ 25.6 in.

TEST TAKING TIP!
Eliminate choices by using 3 for π.

5. Find the circumference of a circle with diameter 18 m. Use 3.14 for π. **B**
   Ⓐ 28.26 m Ⓒ 113.03 m
   Ⓑ 56.52 m Ⓓ 254.34 m

6. A histogram looks most like which type of graph? **F**
   Ⓕ Bar graph
   Ⓖ Line graph
   Ⓗ Circle graph
   Ⓙ Box-and-whisker plot

7. The track team jogged 2.5 miles east from the school and then 1.7 miles north. At this point, about how far from the school was the team? **B**
   Ⓐ 4.2 miles Ⓒ 2.2 miles
   Ⓑ 3.0 miles Ⓓ 0.8 miles

8. Classify the triangle according to its sides and angles. **H**

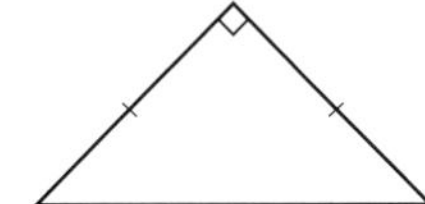

   Ⓕ Acute isosceles
   Ⓖ Obtuse scalene
   Ⓗ Right isosceles
   Ⓙ Acute scalene

9. ***SHORT RESPONSE*** 120 is 80% of what number? Show your work.

10. ***SHORT RESPONSE*** Libby bought 4.4 pounds of tomatoes for \$6.60. How much did she pay per pound? Explain how you determined your answer.

Standardized Test Prep

Answers

9. $120 = 80\% \cdot x$
   $120 = 0.8x$
   $\frac{120}{0.8} = \frac{0.8x}{0.8}$
   $150 = x$
   120 is 80% of 150.

10. Libby paid \$1.50 per pound for the tomatoes she purchased. To find this answer, divide \$6.60 by 4.4.

Standardized Test Prep

Chapter 8

Purpose: *To provide review and practice for Chapters 1–8 and standardized tests*

Assessment Resources

Cumulative Tests (Levels A, B, C)
Assessment Resources. . . . pp. 213–224

State-Specific Test Practice Online
KEYWORD: MS4 TestPrep

Test Prep Doctor

For item 5, since 3 and π are very close in value, 3 can be used as an estimate for π. Multiplying $3 \cdot 18$ m gives 54 m. The only answer choice that is close to 54 m is 56.52 m, or **B.**

Chapter 9

Volume and Surface Area

Section 9A

Three-Dimensional Figures and Volume

Hands-On Lab 9A
Draw Three-Dimensional Figures

Lesson 9-1
Introduction to Three-Dimensional Figures

Lesson 9-2
Volume of Prisms and Cylinders

Lesson 9-3
Volume of Pyramids, Cones, and Spheres

Section 9B

Surface Area

Lesson 9-4
Surface Area of Prisms, Cylinders, and Spheres

Lesson 9-5
Changing Dimensions

Hands-On Lab 9B
Build Polyhedrons, Cylinders, and Cones

Extension
Surface Area of Other Figures

Pacing Guide for 45-Minute Classes

Chapter 9

DAY 119	DAY 120	DAY 121	DAY 122	DAY 123
Hands-On Lab 9A	Lesson 9-1	Lesson 9-2	Lesson 9-3	Mid-Chapter Quiz Lesson 9-4
DAY 124	**DAY 125**	**DAY 126**	**DAY 127**	**DAY 128**
Lesson 9-4	Lesson 9-5	Lesson 9-5	Hands-On Lab 9B	Extension
DAY 129	**DAY 130**			
Chapter 9 Review	Chapter 9 Assessment			

Pacing Guide for 90-Minute Classes

Chapter 9

DAY 59	DAY 60	DAY 61	DAY 62	DAY 63
Chapter 8 Review Hands-On Lab 9A	Chapter 8 Assessment Lesson 9-1	Lesson 9-2 Lesson 9-3	Mid-Chapter Quiz Lesson 9-4	Lesson 9-5
DAY 64	**DAY 65**	**DAY 66**		
Hands-On Lab 4B Extension	Chapter 9 Review Lesson 10-1	Chapter 9 Assessment Lesson 10-2		

Across the Series

COURSE 1

- Draw, identify, and build three-dimensional figures.
- Find the volume of prisms and cylinders.
- Find the surface area of prisms, pyramids, and cylinders.

COURSE 2

- **Draw, identify, and build three-dimensional figures.**
- **Find the volume of prisms, cylinders, pyramids, cones, and spheres.**
- **Find the surface area of prisms, cylinders, and spheres.**
- **Find the surface area, volume, and weight of proportional three-dimensional figures.**
- **Find and compare the surface areas of three-dimensional figures built of cubes.**

COURSE 3

- Draw, identify, and build three-dimensional figures.
- Find the volume of prisms, cylinders, pyramids, cones, and spheres.
- Find the surface area of prisms, cylinders, and spheres.
- Identify symmetry in three dimensions.

Across the Curriculum

LANGUAGE ARTS 

Math: Reading and Writing in the Content Area .... pp. 76–80

Focus on Problem Solving

Solve .... p. 485

Journal .... TE, last page of each lesson

Write About It .... SE pp. 479, 483, 490

SOCIAL STUDIES 

History .... SE pp. 475, 495

SCIENCE 

Life Science .... SE p. 479

TE = *Teacher's Edition* **SE** = *Student Edition*

Interdisciplinary Bulletin Board

Social Studies

The most famous of Egypt's monuments are the huge stone pyramids at Giza, and the largest of these is the Great Pyramid. At its base, the pyramid's sides are each 230 m long, and the top of the pyramid rises 190 m along the center of each side. Find the area of one triangular face.

$\frac{1}{2}(230)(190) = 21{,}850 \text{ m}^2$

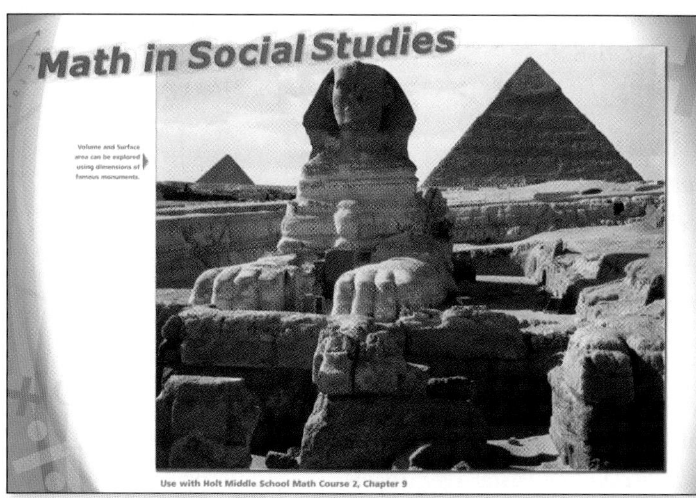

Math in Social Studies
Use with Holt Middle School Math Course 2, Chapter 9

Interdisciplinary posters and worksheets are provided in your resource material.

Chapter 9

Resource Options

Chapter 9 Resource Book

Student Resources

Teacher and Parent Resources

Reaching All Learners

English Language Learners

Individual Needs

Hands-On

Applications and Connections

Transparencies

Technology

Teacher Resources

Student Resources

Are You Ready? Intervention **CD-ROM**
Skills 11, 85, 86

internet connect

go.hrw.com

Homework Help Online	**KEYWORD:** MS4 HWHelp9
Math Tools Online	**KEYWORD:** MS4 Tools
Glossary Online	**KEYWORD:** MS4 Glossary
Chapter Project Online	**KEYWORD:** MS4 PSProject9
Chapter Opener Online	**KEYWORD:** MS4 Ch9

KEYWORD: MS4 CNN9

SE = *Student Edition* **TE** = *Teacher's Edition* **AR** = *Assessment Resources* **CRB** = *Chapter Resource Book* **MK** = *Manipulatives Kit*

Chapter 9

Assessment Options

Assessing Prior Knowledge

Determine whether students have the required prerequisite concepts and skills.

Are You Ready? . . . . SE p. 469

Inventory Test . . . . AR pp. 1–4

Test Preparation

Provide review and practice for chapter and standardized tests.

Standardized Test Prep . . . . SE p. 509

Spiral Review with Test Prep . . . . . SE, last page of each lesson

Study Guide and Review . . . . SE pp. 504–506

Test Prep Tool Kit

Technology 

 ***Test and Practice Generator* CD-ROM**

internet connect

State-Specific Test Practice Online KEYWORD: MS4 TestPrep

go.hrw.com

Performance Assessment

Assess students' understanding of chapter concepts and combined problem-solving skills.

Performance Assessment . . . . SE p. 508
Includes scoring rubric in TE

Performance Assessment . . . . AR p. 122

Performance Assessment Teacher Support . . . . AR p. 121

Portfolio

Portfolio opportunities appear throughout the Student and Teacher's Editions.

Suggested work samples:

Problem Solving Project . . . . TE p. 468

Performance Assessment . . . . SE p. 508

Portfolio Guide . . . . AR p. xxxv

Journal . . . . TE, last page of each lesson

Write About It . . . . SE pp. 479, 483, 490

Daily Assessment

Obtain daily feedback on students' understanding of concepts.

Spiral Review and Test Prep . . . . . . SE, last page of each lesson

Also Available on Transparency In Chapter 9 Resource Book

Warm Up . . . . TE, first page of each lesson

Problem of the Day . . . . TE, first page of each lesson

Lesson Quiz . . . . TE, last page of each lesson

Student Self-Assessment

Have students evaluate their own work.

Group Project Evaluation . . . . AR p. xxxii

Individual Group Member Evaluation . . . . AR p. xxxiii

Portfolio Guide . . . . AR p. xxxv

Journal . . . . TE, last page of each lesson

Formal Assessment

Assess students' mastery of concepts and skills.

Section Quizzes . . . . AR pp. 25–26

Mid-Chapter Quiz . . . . SE p. 484

Chapter Test . . . . SE p. 507

Chapter Tests (Levels A, B, C) . . . . AR pp. 81–86

Cumulative Tests (Levels A, B, C) . . . . AR pp. 225–236

Standardized Test Prep
Cumulative Assessment . . . . SE p. 509

End-of-Year Test . . . . AR pp. 273–276

Technology 

 ***Test and Practice Generator* CD-ROM**

Make tests electronically. This software includes:

- Dynamic practice for Chapter 9
- Customizable tests
- Multiple-choice items for each objective
- Free-response items for each objective
- Teacher management system

Chapter 9

Chapter 9 Tests

Three levels (A,B,C) of tests are available for each chapter in the *Assessment Resources.*

Level A

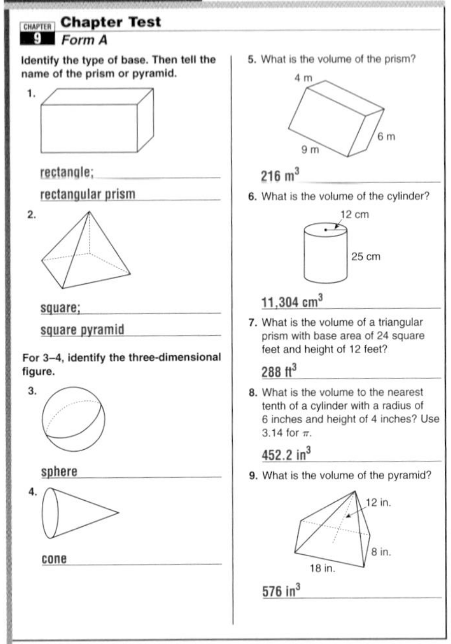

Chapter 9 Chapter Test *Form A*

Identify the type of base. Then tell the name of the prism or pyramid.

1. rectangle; rectangular prism
2. square; square pyramid

For 3–4, identify the three-dimensional figure.

3. sphere
4. cone
5. What is the volume of the prism? 216 m^3
6. What is the volume of the cylinder? $11{,}304 \text{ cm}^3$
7. What is the volume of a triangular prism with base area of 24 square feet and height of 12 feet? 288 ft^3
8. What is the volume to the nearest tenth of a cylinder with a radius of 6 inches and height of 4 inches? Use 3.14 for π. 452.2 in^3
9. What is the volume of the pyramid? 576 in^3

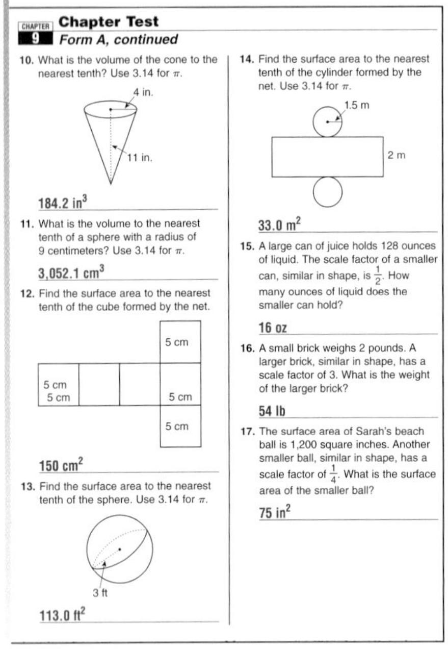

Chapter 9 Chapter Test *Form A, continued*

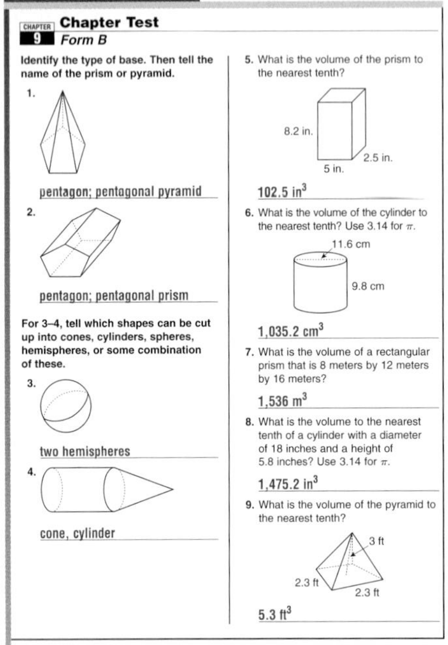

10. What is the volume of the cone to the nearest tenth? Use 3.14 for π. 184.2 in^3
11. What is the volume to the nearest tenth of a sphere with a radius of 9 centimeters? Use 3.14 for π. $3{,}052.1 \text{ cm}^3$
12. Find the surface area to the nearest tenth of the cube formed by the net. 150 cm^2
13. Find the surface area to the nearest tenth of the sphere. Use 3.14 for π. 113.0 ft^2
14. Find the surface area to the nearest tenth of the cylinder formed by the net. Use 3.14 for π. 33.0 m^2
15. A large can of juice holds 128 ounces of liquid. The scale factor of a smaller can, similar in shape, is $\frac{1}{2}$. How many ounces of liquid does the smaller can hold? 16 oz
16. A small brick weighs 2 pounds. A larger brick, similar in shape, has a scale factor of 3. What is the weight of the larger brick? 54 lb
17. The surface area of Sarah's beach ball is 1,200 square inches. Another smaller ball, similar in shape, has a scale factor of $\frac{1}{4}$. What is the surface area of the smaller ball? 75 in^2

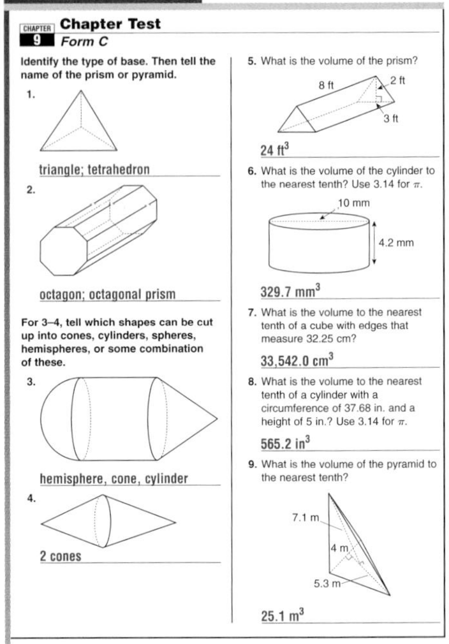

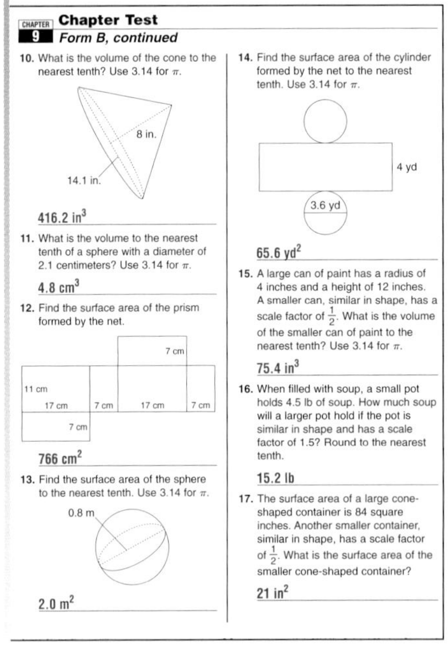

Level B

Chapter 9 Chapter Test *Form B*

Identify the type of base. Then tell the name of the prism or pyramid.

1. pentagon; pentagonal pyramid
2. pentagon; pentagonal prism

For 3–4, tell which shapes can be cut up into cones, cylinders, spheres, hemispheres, or some combination of these.

3. two hemispheres
4. cone, cylinder
5. What is the volume of the prism to the nearest tenth? 102.5 in^3
6. What is the volume of the cylinder to the nearest tenth? Use 3.14 for π. $1{,}035.2 \text{ cm}^3$
7. What is the volume of a rectangular prism that is 8 meters by 12 meters by 16 meters? $1{,}536 \text{ m}^3$
8. What is the volume to the nearest tenth of a cylinder with a diameter of 18 inches and a height of 5.8 inches? Use 3.14 for π. $1{,}475.2 \text{ in}^3$
9. What is the volume of the pyramid to the nearest tenth? 5.3 ft^3

Chapter 9 Chapter Test *Form B, continued*

10. What is the volume of the cone to the nearest tenth? Use 3.14 for π. 416.2 in^3
11. What is the volume to the nearest tenth of a sphere with a diameter of 2.1 centimeters? Use 3.14 for π. 4.8 cm^3
12. Find the surface area of the prism formed by the net. 766 cm^2
13. Find the surface area of the sphere to the nearest tenth. Use 3.14 for π. 2.0 m^2
14. Find the surface area of the cylinder formed by the net to the nearest tenth. Use 3.14 for π. 65.6 yd^2
15. A large can of paint has a radius of 4 inches and a height of 12 inches. A smaller can, similar in shape, has a scale factor of $\frac{1}{2}$. What is the volume of the smaller can of paint to the nearest tenth? Use 3.14 for π. 75.4 in^3
16. When filled with soup, a small pot holds 4.5 lb of soup. How much soup will a larger pot hold if the pot is similar in shape and has a scale factor of 1.5? Round to the nearest tenth. 15.2 lb
17. The surface area of a large cone-shaped container is 84 square inches. Another smaller container, similar in shape, has a scale factor of $\frac{1}{2}$. What is the surface area of the smaller cone-shaped container? 21 in^2

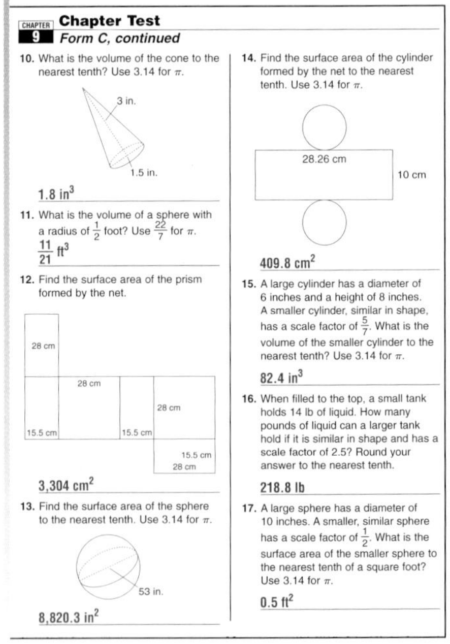

Level C

Chapter 9 Chapter Test *Form C*

Identify the type of base. Then tell the name of the prism or pyramid.

1. triangle; tetrahedron
2. octagon; octagonal prism

For 3–4, tell which shapes can be cut up into cones, cylinders, spheres, hemispheres, or some combination of these.

3. hemisphere, cone, cylinder
4. 2 cones
5. What is the volume of the prism? 24 ft^3
6. What is the volume of the cylinder to the nearest tenth? Use 3.14 for π. 329.7 mm^3
7. What is the volume to the nearest tenth of a cube with edges that measure 32.25 cm? $33{,}542.0 \text{ cm}^3$
8. What is the volume to the nearest tenth of a cylinder with a circumference of 37.68 in. and a height of 5 in.? Use 3.14 for π. 565.2 in^3
9. What is the volume of the pyramid to the nearest tenth? 25.1 m^3

Chapter 9 Chapter Test *Form C, continued*

10. What is the volume of the cone to the nearest tenth? Use 3.14 for π. 1.8 in^3
11. What is the volume of a sphere with a radius of $\frac{1}{2}$ foot? Use $\frac{22}{7}$ for π. $\frac{11}{21} \text{ ft}^3$
12. Find the surface area of the prism formed by the net. $3{,}304 \text{ cm}^2$
13. Find the surface area of the sphere to the nearest tenth. Use 3.14 for π. $8{,}820.3 \text{ in}^2$
14. Find the surface area of the cylinder formed by the net to the nearest tenth. Use 3.14 for π. 409.8 cm^2
15. A large cylinder has a diameter of 6 inches and a height of 8 inches. A smaller cylinder, similar in shape, has a scale factor of $\frac{5}{7}$. What is the volume of the smaller cylinder to the nearest tenth? Use 3.14 for π. 82.4 in^3
16. When filled to the top, a small tank holds 14 lb of liquid. How many pounds of liquid can a larger tank hold if it is similar in shape and has a scale factor of 2.5? Round your answer to the nearest tenth. 218.8 lb
17. A large sphere has a diameter of 10 inches. A smaller, similar sphere has a scale factor of $\frac{1}{2}$. What is the surface area of the smaller sphere to the nearest tenth of a square foot? Use 3.14 for π. 0.5 ft^2

Test and Practice Generator
CD-ROM

Create and customize multiple versions of the same tests with corresponding answers for any chosen chapter objectives.

Chapter 9 State and Standardized Test Preparation

Test Taking Skill Builder and Standardized Test Practice are provided for each chapter in the *Test Prep Tool Kit.*

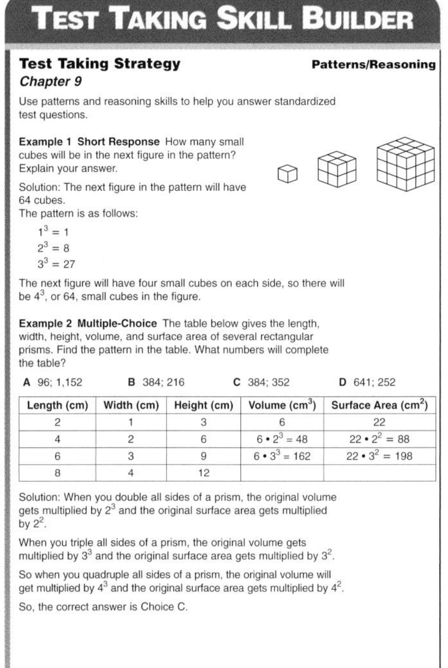

TEST TAKING SKILL BUILDER

Test Taking Strategy **Patterns/Reasoning**

Chapter 9

Use patterns and reasoning skills to help you answer standardized test questions.

Example 1 Short Response How many small cubes will be in the next figure in the pattern? Explain your answer.

Solution: The next figure in the pattern will have 64 cubes.
The pattern is as follows:

$1^3 = 1$
$2^3 = 8$
$3^3 = 27$

The next figure will have four small cubes on each side, so there will be 4^3, or 64, small cubes in the figure.

Example 2 Multiple-Choice The table below gives the length, width, height, volume, and surface area of several rectangular prisms. Find the pattern in the table. What numbers will complete the table?

A 96; 1,152 **B** 384; 216 **C** 384; 352 **D** 641; 252

Length (cm)	Width (cm)	Height (cm)	Volume (cm^3)	Surface Area (cm^2)
2	1	3	6	22
4	2	6	$6 \cdot 2^3 = 48$	$22 \cdot 2^2 = 88$
6	3	9	$6 \cdot 3^3 = 162$	$22 \cdot 3^2 = 198$
8	4	12		

Solution: When you double all sides of a prism, the original volume gets multiplied by 2^3 and the original surface area gets multiplied by 2^2.

When you triple all sides of a prism, the original volume gets multiplied by 3^3 and the original surface area gets multiplied by 3^2.

So when you quadruple all sides of a prism, the original volume will get multiplied by 4^3 and the original surface area gets multiplied by 4^2.

So, the correct answer is Choice C.

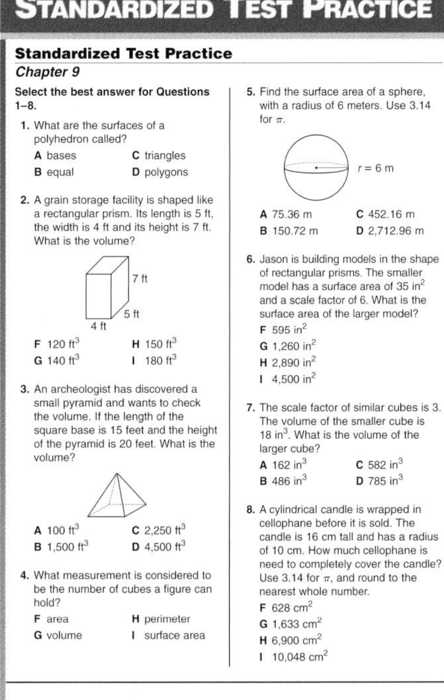

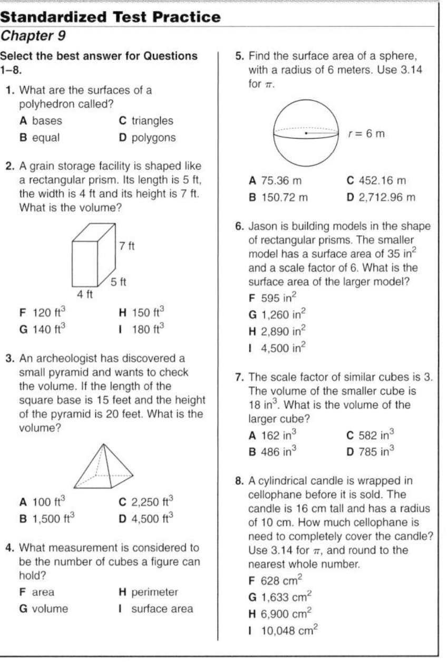

STANDARDIZED TEST PRACTICE

Standardized Test Practice

Chapter 9

Select the best answer for Questions 1–8.

1. What are the surfaces of a polyhedron called?
   A bases **C** triangles
   B equal **D** polygons

2. A grain storage facility is shaped like a rectangular prism. Its length is 5 ft, the width is 4 ft and its height is 7 ft. What is the volume?

   F 120 ft^3 **H** 150 ft^3
   G 140 ft^3 **I** 180 ft^3

3. An archeologist has discovered a small pyramid and wants to check the volume. If the length of the square base is 15 feet and the height of the pyramid is 20 feet. What is the volume?
   A 100 ft^3 **C** 2,250 ft^3
   B 1,500 ft^3 **D** 4,500 ft^3

4. What measurement is considered to be the number of cubes a figure can hold?
   F area **H** perimeter
   G volume **I** surface area

5. Find the surface area of a sphere, with a radius of 6 meters. Use 3.14 for π.

   A 75.36 m **C** 452.16 m
   B 150.72 m **D** 2,712.96 m

6. Jason is building models in the shape of rectangular prisms. The smaller model has a surface area of 35 in^2 and a scale factor of 6. What is the surface area of the larger model?
   F 595 in^2
   G 1,260 in^2
   H 2,890 in^2
   I 4,500 in^2

7. The scale factor of similar cubes is 3. The volume of the smaller cube is 18 in^3. What is the volume of the larger cube?
   A 162 in^3 **C** 582 in^3
   B 486 in^3 **D** 785 in^3

8. A cylindrical candle is wrapped in cellophane before it is sold. The candle is 16 cm tall and has a radius of 10 cm. How much cellophane is need to completely cover the candle? Use 3.14 for π, and round to the nearest whole number.
   F 628 cm^2
   G 1,633 cm^2
   H 6,900 cm^2
   I 10,048 cm^2

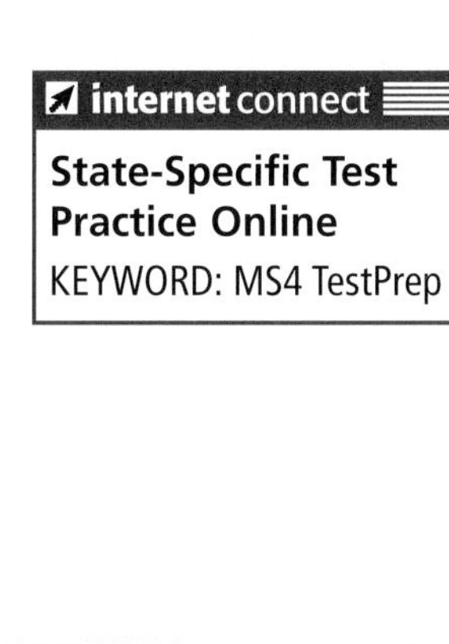

internet connect

State-Specific Test Practice Online

KEYWORD: MS4 TestPrep

Test Prep Tool Kit

- Standardized Test Prep Workbook
- Countdown to Testing transparencies
- State Test Prep CD-ROM
- Standardized Test Prep Video

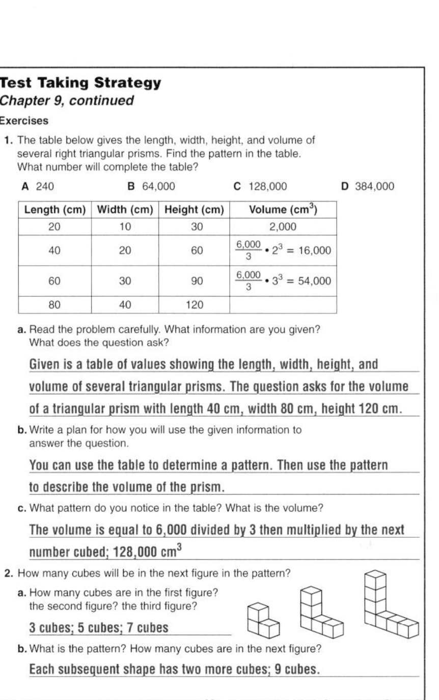

Test Taking Strategy

Chapter 9, continued

Exercises

1. The table below gives the length, width, height, and volume of several right triangular prisms. Find the pattern in the table. What number will complete the table?

   A 240 **B** 64,000 **C** 128,000 **D** 384,000

Length (cm)	Width (cm)	Height (cm)	Volume (cm^3)
20	10	30	2,000
40	20	60	$\frac{6,000}{3} \cdot 2^3 = 16,000$
60	30	90	$\frac{6,000}{3} \cdot 3^3 = 54,000$
80	40	120	

   a. Read the problem carefully. What information are you given? What does the question ask?

   Given is a table of values showing the length, width, height, and volume of several triangular prisms. The question asks for the volume of a triangular prism with length 40 cm, width 80 cm, height 120 cm.

   b. Write a plan for how you will use the given information to answer the question.

   You can use the table to determine a pattern. Then use the pattern to describe the volume of the prism.

   c. What pattern do you notice in the table? What is the volume?

   The volume is equal to 6,000 divided by 3 then multiplied by the next number cubed; 128,000 cm^3

2. How many cubes will be in the next figure in the pattern?

   a. How many cubes are in the first figure? the second figure? the third figure?

   3 cubes; 5 cubes; 7 cubes

   b. What is the pattern? How many cubes are in the next figure?

   Each subsequent shape has two more cubes; 9 cubes.

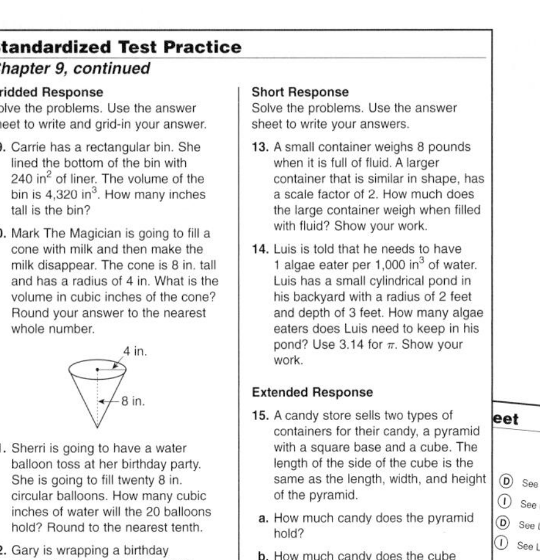

Standardized Test Practice

Chapter 9, continued

Gridded Response
Solve the problems. Use the answer sheet to write and grid-in your answer.

9. Carrie has a rectangular bin. She lined the bottom of the bin with 240 in^2 of liner. The volume of the bin is 4,320 in^3. How many inches tall is the bin?

10. Mark The Magician is going to fill a cone with milk and then make the milk disappear. The cone is 8 in. tall and has a radius of 4 in. What is the volume in cubic inches of the cone? Round your answer to the nearest whole number.

11. Sherri is going to have a water balloon toss at her birthday party. She is going to fill twenty 8 in. circular balloons. How many cubic inches of water will the 20 balloons hold? Round to the nearest tenth.

12. Gary is wrapping a birthday present for his mom. The box is 14 in. × 18 in. × 36 in. How many square feet of wrapping paper does Gary need to cover the box?

Short Response
Solve the problems. Use the answer sheet to write your answers.

13. A small container weighs 8 pounds when it is full of fluid. A larger container that is similar in shape, has a scale factor of 2. How much does the large container weigh when filled with fluid? Show your work.

14. Luis is told that he needs to have 1 algae eater per 1,000 in^3 of water. Luis has a small cylindrical pond in his backyard with a radius of 2 feet and depth of 3 feet. How many algae eaters does Luis need to keep in his pond? Use 3.14 for π. Show your work.

Extended Response

15. A candy store sells two types of containers for their candy, a pyramid with a square base and a cube. The length of the side of the cube is the same as the length, width, and height of the pyramid.

    a. How much candy does the pyramid hold?

    b. How much candy does the cube hold?

    c. Determine which container holds more candy. How many times more candy does the larger container hold than the smaller container?

eet

Ⓓ See Lesson 9-4.
Ⓘ See Lesson 9-5.
Ⓓ See Lesson 9-5.
Ⓘ See Lesson 9-4.

12. 19.5

See Lesson 9-4.

(scale factor)^3
$= 8 \times 2^3$
$= 8 \times 8$
$= 64$
The larger container will weigh 64 pounds when filled with fluid. (See Lesson 9-5.)

14. 3 feet = 36 inches; 2 feet = 24 inches;
$V = (36)(24)^2(3.14) \approx 65,111.04\ in^3$; $65,111.04 \div 1000 \approx 65$ algae eaters; Luis will need to keep 65 algae eaters in his pond.

Extended Response (See Lesson 9-3.)
Write your answers for Problem 15 on the back of this paper.

Customized answer sheets give students realistic practice for actual standardized tests.

Chapter 9

Volume and Surface Area

Why Learn This?

Pyramids are found mainly in Egypt, Guatemala, Honduras, Mexico, and Peru. Djoser's Step Pyramid, in Egypt, was the first large stone building in the world. Archaeological architects study how the pyramids were built. The pyramids each have a square base and four triangular faces. A pyramid's height is the distance from the center of its base to its top.

Using Data

To begin the study of this chapter, have students:

- Find the base area of each square pyramid in the table. El Castillo: 6,241 m^2, Tikal: 6,400 m^2, Pyramid of the Sun: 50,625 m^2
- Order the pyramids from least volume to greatest volume. Tikal, El Castillo, Pyramid of the Sun

TABLE OF CONTENTS

internet connect

Chapter Opener Online
go.hrw.com
KEYWORD: MS4 Ch9

Pyramid	Location	Height (m)	Base Length (m)
El Castillo	Chichén Itzá, Mexico	55.5	79.0
Tikal	Tikal, Guatemala	30.0	80.0
Pyramid of the Sun	Teotihuácan, Mexico	63.0	225.0

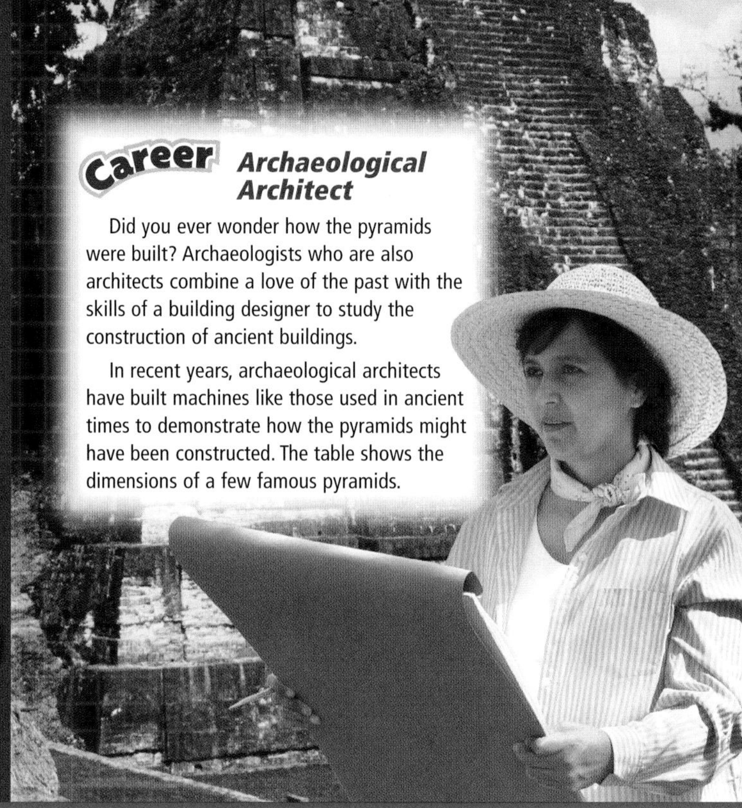

Career ***Archaeological Architect***

Did you ever wonder how the pyramids were built? Archaeologists who are also architects combine a love of the past with the skills of a building designer to study the construction of ancient buildings.

In recent years, archaeological architects have built machines like those used in ancient times to demonstrate how the pyramids might have been constructed. The table shows the dimensions of a few famous pyramids.

Problem Solving Project

Social Studies Connection

Purpose: To solve problems by using properties of volume and surface area

Materials: Pyramid Scheme worksheet, drawing and/or modeling materials

internet connect

Internet Activity: ***go.hrw.com***
KEYWORD: MS4 PSProject9

Understand, Plan, Solve, and Look Back

Have students:

- ✔ Examine the table. Ask students what they notice. Where is each of the pyramids in the table located? Which pyramid is the tallest? Which one has the greatest volume? How much larger is it than the smallest pyramid?
- ✔ Complete the Pyramid Scheme worksheet.
- ✔ Make a list of famous pyramids that are not listed in the table.
- ✔ Check students' work.

ARE YOU READY?

Choose the best term from the list to complete each sentence.

area
circumference
congruent
hexagon
pentagon
scale factor
similar

1. A polygon with six sides is called a(n) __?__. **hexagon**
2. __?__ figures are the same size and shape. **congruent**
3. A(n) __?__ is a ratio that relates the dimensions of two similar objects. **scale factor**
4. The formula for the __?__ of a circle can be written as πd or $2\pi r$. **circumference**
5. __?__ figures are the same shape but not necessarily the same size. **similar**
6. A polygon with five sides is called a(n) __?__. **pentagon**

Complete these exercises to review skills you will need for this chapter.

✓ Area of Rectangles and Triangles

Find the area of each figure.

7.

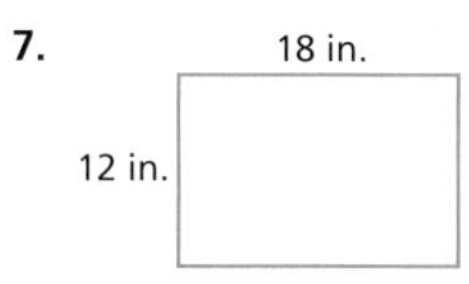

216 in^2

8.

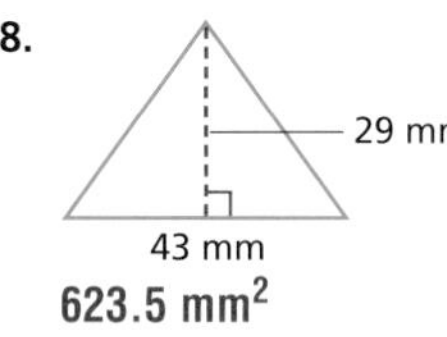

623.5 mm^2

9.

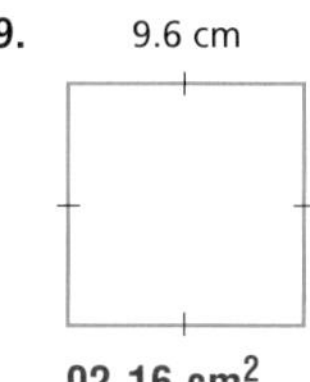

92.16 cm^2

✓ Area of Circles

Find the area of each circle to the nearest tenth. Use 3.14 for π.

10.

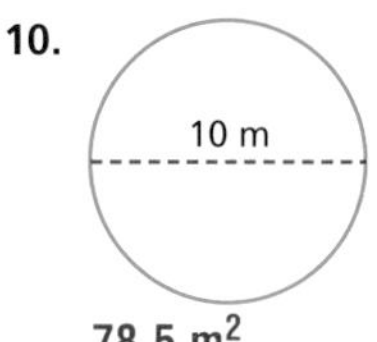

78.5 m^2

11.

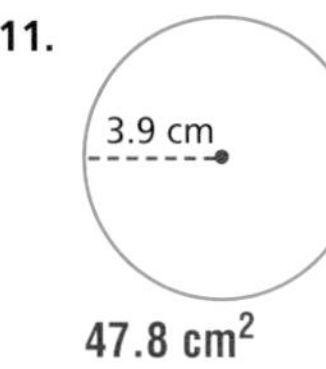

47.8 cm^2

12.

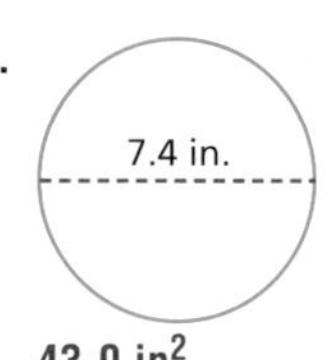

43.0 in^2

✓ Find the Cube of a Number

Find each value.

13. 3^3 **27**
14. 8^3 **512**
15. 2.5^3 **15.625**
16. 6.2^3 **238.328**
17. 10^3 **1,000**
18. 5.9^3 **205.379**
19. 800^3 **512,000,000**
20. 98^3 **941,192**

Assessing Prior Knowledge

INTERVENTION

Diagnose and Prescribe

Evaluate your students' performance on this page to determine whether intervention is necessary or whether enrichment is appropriate. Options that provide instruction, practice, and a check are listed below.

Resources for Are You Ready?

- ***Are You Ready? Intervention and Enrichment***
- **Recording Sheet for Are You Ready?**
  Chapter 9 Resource Book . . . . . . p. 3

Are You Ready? Intervention **CD-ROM**

internet connect

Are You Ready? Intervention
go.hrw.com
KEYWORD: MS4 AYR

ARE YOU READY?

Were students successful with Are You Ready?

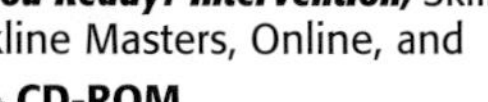

✓Area of Rectangles and Triangles
Are You Ready? Intervention, Skill 85
Blackline Masters, Online, and

CD-ROM
Intervention Activities

✓Area of Circles
Are You Ready? Intervention, Skill 86
Blackline Masters, Online, and

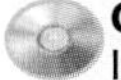

CD-ROM
Intervention Activities

✓Find the Cube of a Number
Are You Ready? Intervention, Skill 11
Blackline Masters, Online, and

CD-ROM
Intervention Activities

Are You Ready? Enrichment, pp. 423–424

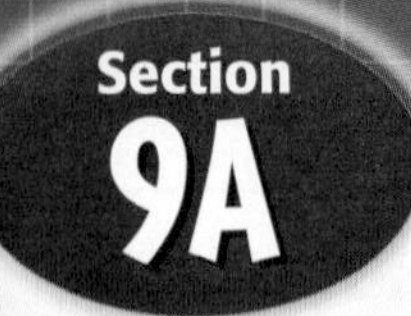

Section 9A

Volume

One-Minute Section Planner

Lesson	Materials	Resources
Hands-On Lab 9A Draw Three-Dimensional Figures **NCTM:** Geometry, Connections **NAEP:** Geometry 1f ☐ SAT-9 ☐ SAT-10 ☐ ITBS ☐ CTBS ☐ MAT ☐ CAT	**Required** Compasses *(MK)* Rulers *(MK)* Straightedges *(MK)*	• *Hands-On Lab Activities,* pp. 85–86, 127
Lesson 9-1 Introduction to Three-Dimensional Figures **NCTM:** Geometry, Communication **NAEP:** Geometry 1f ☑ SAT-9 ☑ SAT-10 ☑ ITBS ☐ CTBS ☑ MAT ☑ CAT	**Optional** Teaching Transparency T2 *(CRB)*	• *Chapter 9 Resource Book,* pp. 6–14 • Daily Transparency T1, CRB • Additional Examples Transparency T3, CRB • *Alternate Openers: Explorations,* p. 76
Lesson 9-2 Volume of Prisms and Cylinders **NCTM:** Geometry, Measurement, Reasoning and Proof, Communication, Connections **NAEP:** Measurement 1j ☑ SAT-9 ☑ SAT-10 ☐ ITBS ☐ CTBS ☑ MAT ☑ CAT	**Optional** Teaching Transparency T5 *(CRB)* Containers shaped like prisms and cylinders Rice Measuring cups	• *Chapter 9 Resource Book,* pp. 15–23 • Daily Transparency T4, CRB • Additional Examples Transparencies T6–T7 • *Alternate Openers: Explorations,* p. 77
Lesson 9-3 Volume of Pyramids, Cones, and Spheres **NCTM:** Geometry, Measurement, Communication, Connections **NAEP:** Measurement 1j ☐ SAT-9 ☑ SAT-10 ☐ ITBS ☐ CTBS ☐ MAT ☑ CAT	**Optional** Teaching Transparency T9 *(CRB)* Models of cones, pyramids, prisms, and cylinders Reference books	• *Chapter 9 Resource Book,* pp. 24–33 • Daily Transparency T8, CRB • Additional Examples Transparencies T10–T11, CRB • *Alternate Openers: Explorations,* p. 78
Section 9A Assessment		• Mid-Chapter Quiz, SE p. 484 • Section 9A Quiz, AR p. 25 • *Test and Practice Generator* CD-ROM

SAT = *Stanford Achievement Tests* **ITBS** = *Iowa Test of Basic Skills* **CTBS** = *Comprehensive Test of Basic Skills/Terra Nova*
MAT = *Metropolitan Achievement Test* **CAT** = *California Achievement Test*

NCTM—Complete standards can be found on pages T27–T33. **NAEP**—Complete standards can be found on pages A35–A39.

SE = *Student Edition* **TE** = *Teacher's Edition* **AR** = *Assessment Resources* **CRB** = *Chapter Resource Book*

MK = *Manipulatives Kit*

Section Overview

Three-Dimensional Figures

Hands-On Lab 9A, Lesson 9-1

Why? Identifying and distinguishing among three-dimensional figures is a prerequisite for finding the volume and surface area of these figures.

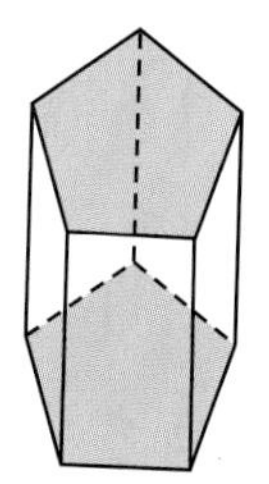

A **prism** has two parallel congruent faces; the remaining faces are parallelograms. This figure is a **pentagonal prism.**

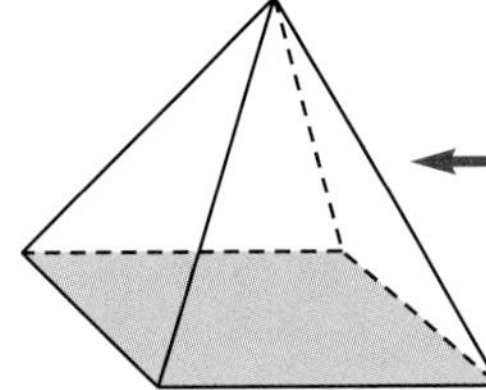

The faces of a pyramid are triangles. The base of the pyramid can be any polygon. This figure is a **square pyramid.**

Cylinder

Cone

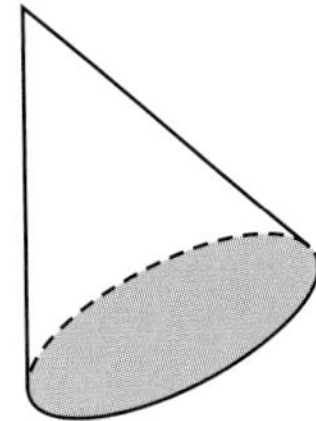

Sphere

Volume of Prisms and Cylinders

Lesson 9-2

Why? Volume is an important real-world concept. You need to be able to calculate volume to determine the amount of water needed to fill a swimming pool or to determine the size of a heating system for a home.

Volume Formulas

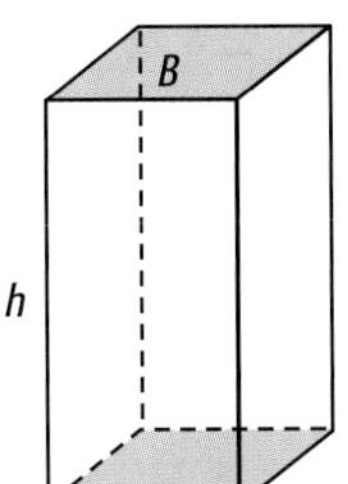

Prism

$V = Bh$

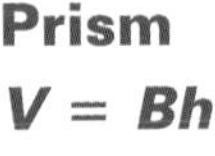

B represents the area of the base of the prism, and *h* represents the height.

Cylinder

$V = \pi r^2 h$

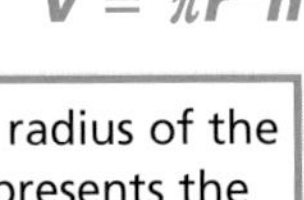

r represents the radius of the base, and *h* represents the height of the cylinder.

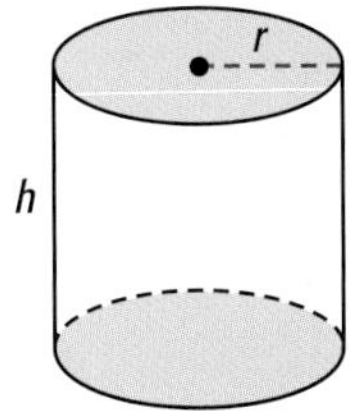

Volume of Pyramids, Cones, and Spheres

Lesson 9-3

Why? Finding the volume of more complex figures prepares students for later studies in geometry. Understanding how to use a formula to compute volume provides an early and accessible introduction to algebra.

More Volume Formulas

Pyramid

$V = \frac{1}{3}Bh$

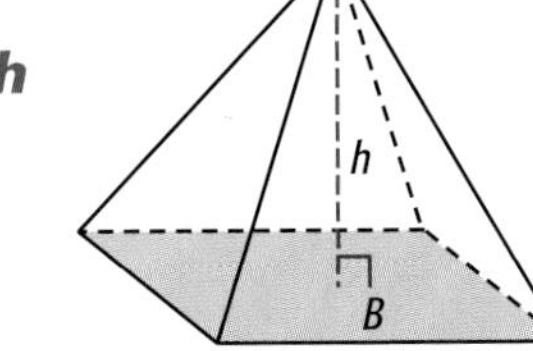

B represents the area of the base of the pyramid, and *h* represents the height.

Cone

$V = \frac{1}{3}\pi r^2 h$

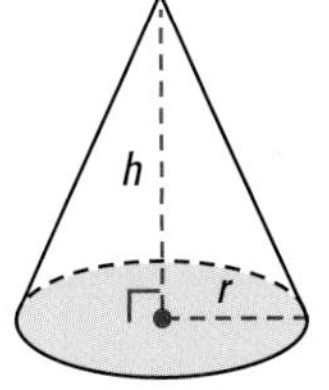

πr^2 corresponds to the area of the circular base, and *h* represents the height.

Sphere

$V = \frac{4}{3}\pi r^3$

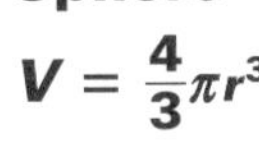

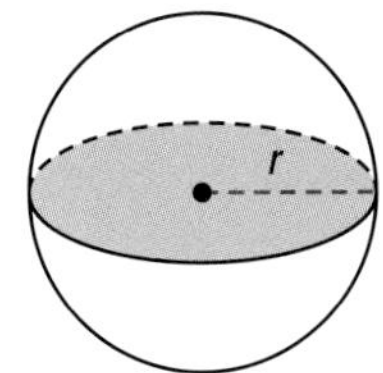

r represents the radius of the sphere.

9A Draw Three-Dimensional Figures

Pacing: Traditional 1 day
Block $\frac{1}{2}$ day

Objective: To draw three-dimensional figures

Materials: Straightedge, compass

Lab Resources

Hands-On Lab Activities pp. 85–86, 127

Using the Pages

Discuss with students the kinds of two-dimensional shapes they can use to make three-dimensional figures.

Tell which two-dimensional shapes could be used to draw each three-dimensional figure.

1. cylinder ovals and line segments
2. rectangular prism rectangles and parallelograms
3. sphere circle and oval

Draw Three-Dimensional Figures

Use with Lesson 9-1

internet connect
Lab Resources Online
go.hrw.com
KEYWORD: MS4 Lab9A

Three-dimensional figures have length, width, and height. To draw a three-dimensional figure, you first have to choose which view of the figure you will draw.

Activity

1. Draw the side view of a cone with a radius of 1.5 cm and a height of 2.5 cm.

   a. From the side, the circular base of a cone looks like an oval. Since the diameter of the cone is 3 cm, draw an oval with a length of 3 cm. Make the top half of the oval dashed.

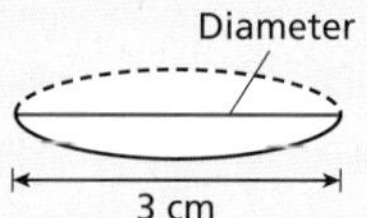

   b. Recall that a *perpendicular bisector* bisects a segment at 90° angles. Draw a perpendicular bisector of the diameter, so that one of its endpoints is on the diameter. The length of the bisector is 2.5 cm. This is the height of the cone.

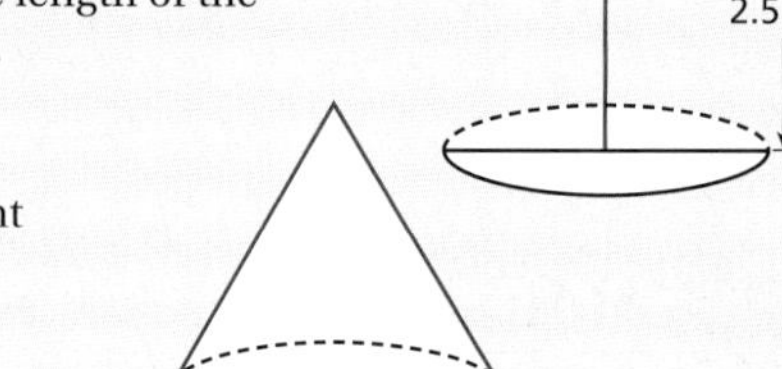

   c. Draw two line segments, one from each endpoint of the diameter to the *vertex* of the cone.

2. Draw the side view of a pyramid with a height of 2.5 cm and a square base that is 2 cm on each side.

   a. From the side, the square base looks like a parallelogram with no right angles. Draw a parallelogram like the one shown. The top and bottom are each 2 cm long. Make the top and one side dashed as shown.

   b. Find the midpoint of each side of the parallelogram. Draw two line segments to connect these points as shown.

c. From the point where the two segments meet, draw a 2.5 cm line segment perpendicular to the horizontal segment. The length of this vertical segment is the height of the pyramid.

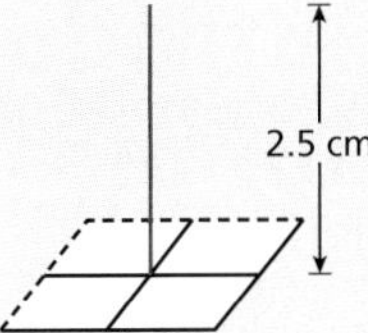

d. Draw four line segments, one from each vertex of the parallelogram to the *vertex* of the pyramid. The segment that meets the two dashed segments should also be dashed.

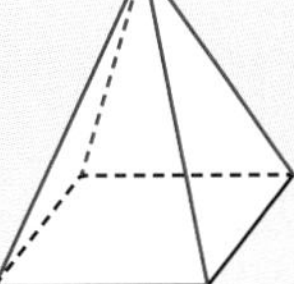

3 Draw the side view of a hemisphere and a sphere with a radius of 0.5 in.

a. From the side, the circular base of a hemisphere looks like an oval. Since the diameter of the hemisphere is 1 in., draw an oval with a length of 1 in. Make the top half of the oval dashed.

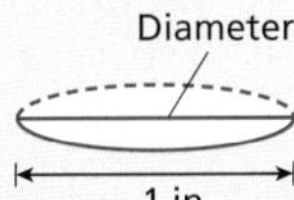

b. Draw a half of a circle, so that the endpoints of the arc meet with the endpoints of the diameter. This completes the drawing of the hemisphere.

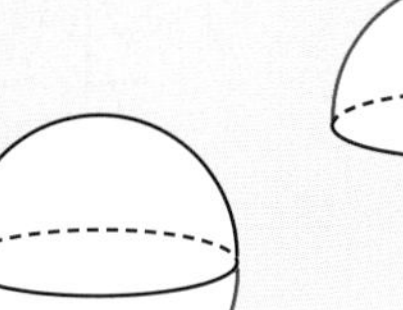

c. Now draw the other half of the circle. This completes the drawing of the sphere.

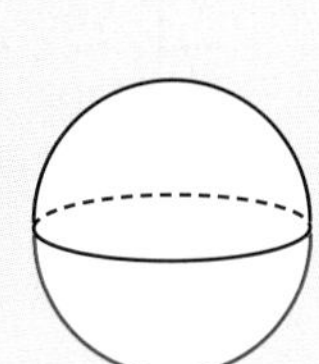

Think and Discuss

1. How is drawing a cone similar to drawing a pyramid? **You have to draw line segments from the base to a common point above the base.**
2. How is drawing a cone similar to drawing a hemisphere? **You draw an oval for the base of a cone and for the base of a hemisphere.**
3. How does drawing the side view of a cone or pyramid affect the appearance of the base? **When drawn from a side view, the circular base of a cone looks like an oval, and the rectangular base of a rectangular pyramid looks like a parallelogram.**

Try This

1. Draw the side view of a cone with a radius of 3 cm and a height of 3 cm.
2. Draw the side view of a pyramid with a height of 3.5 cm and a square base that is 2 cm on each side.
3. Draw the side view of a hemisphere and a sphere with a radius of 2 cm.

Answers

Try This

1.

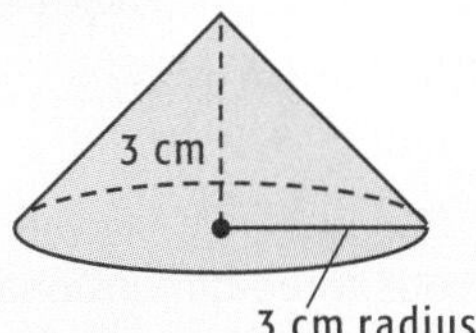

2.

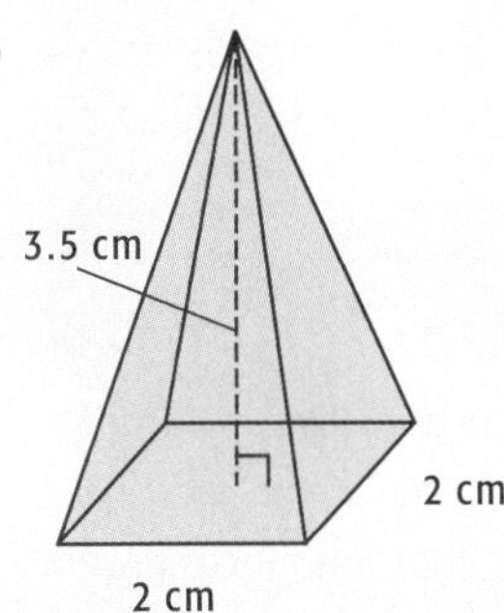

3.

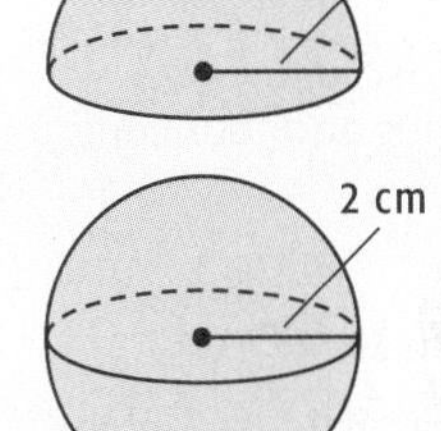

9-1 Organizer

Pacing: Traditional 1 day
Block $\frac{1}{2}$ day

Objective: Students identify various three-dimensional figures.

Warm Up

Identify each two-dimensional figure described.

1. four sides that are all congruent rhombus
2. six sides hexagon
3. four sides with parallel opposite sides parallelogram
4. four right angles and four congruent sides square

Problem of the Day

If the figure shown is folded into a cube so that 6 is on the top, what number would be on the bottom? 2

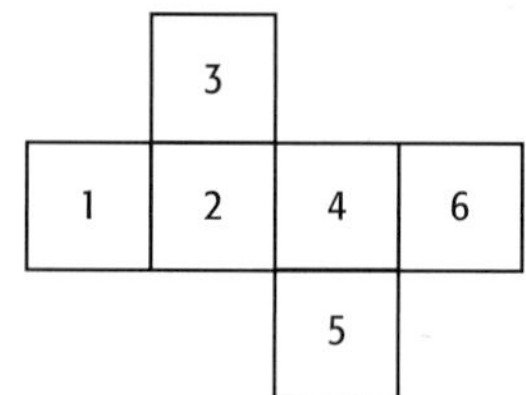

Available on Daily Transparency in CRB

9-1 Introduction to Three-Dimensional Figures

Learn to identify various three-dimensional figures.

Vocabulary
face
edge
vertex
base
polyhedron
prism
pyramid
lateral surface
cylinder
cone
sphere
hemisphere

Three-dimensional figures, or solids, have length, width, and height. A flat surface of a solid is a **face**. An **edge** is where two faces meet, and a **vertex** is where three or more edges meet. The face that is used to classify a solid is a **base**.

The surfaces of a three-dimensional figure determine the type of solid it is. A **polyhedron** is a three-dimensional figure whose surfaces, or faces, are all polygons. *Prisms* and *pyramids* are two types of polyhedrons.

Prisms	Pyramids
A **prism** is a polyhedron that has two parallel congruent bases. The bases can be any polygon. The other faces are parallelograms.	A **pyramid** is a polyhedron that has one base. The base can be any polygon. The other faces are triangles.
Vertex; 2 bases; Edge	Vertex; 1 base; Edge
A *cube* is a special prism whose faces are all congruent squares.	A *regular tetrahedron* is a special pyramid whose faces are all congruent equilateral triangles.

Prisms and pyramids are named by the shapes of their bases.

EXAMPLE 1 Naming Prisms and Pyramids

Identify the base or bases of each solid. Then name the solid.

A

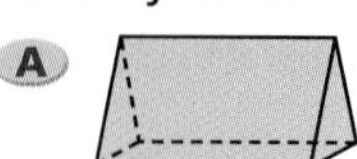

There are two bases, and they are both triangles.
The other faces are parallelograms.
The figure is a triangular prism.

B

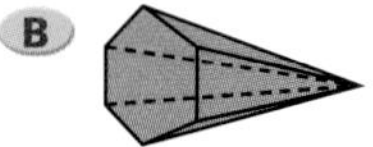

There is one base, and it is a hexagon.
The other faces are triangles.
The figure is a hexagonal pyramid.

Remember!
A polygon with six sides is called a hexagon.

1 Introduce

Alternate Opener

EXPLORATION

The figures below represent three-dimensional objects.

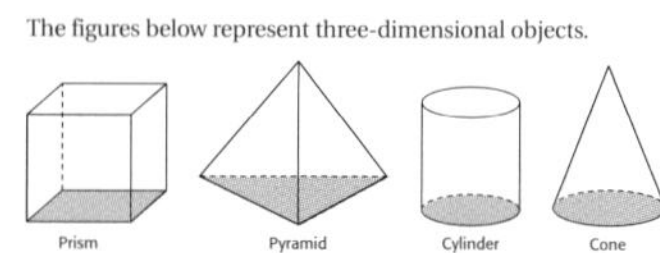

Write the name of the base (the shaded face) of each three-dimensional object shown above.

	Figure	Name of Base
1.	Prism	
2.	Pyramid	
3.	Cylinder	
4.	Cone	

Give a real-world example of each figure.

	Figure	Real-World Example
5.	Prism	
6.	Pyramid	
7.	Cylinder	
8.	Cone	

Think and Discuss

9. **Explain** what the third dimension of a three-dimensional figure is, given that the base is a two-dimensional figure.

Motivate

Review polygons by having students name types of polygons and give the number of sides for each. A triangle has three sides. A pentagon has five sides. To introduce three-dimensional figures, ask students to describe as many different kinds of three-dimensional figures as they can find in the classroom. For each three-dimensional figure, have students name the shapes of the sides and bases. The box has sides that are rectangles and bases that are squares.

Exploration worksheet and answers on Chapter 9 Resource Book pp. 7 and 60

2 Teach

Lesson Presentation

Guided Instruction

In this lesson, students learn to identify various three-dimensional figures. Prisms and pyramids are named according to the shapes of their bases (Teaching Transparency T2 in the Chapter 9 Resource Book). However, cylinders, cones, spheres, and hemispheres have basically only one shape and only one name. The cube and the tetrahedron are both examples of regular polyhedrons because all the faces of each figure are congruent.

Teaching Tip Point out that in a rectangular prism, any of the pairs of parallel faces can be considered to be bases, but in other types of prisms, the bases must be the pair of nonrectangular sides.

Other three-dimensional figures include *cylinders, cones,* and *spheres.* These figures are different from polyhedrons because they each have a curved surface and their bases are not polygons. The curved surface of a cylinder or a cone is called a **lateral surface**.

A **cylinder** has two parallel, congruent circular bases connected by a lateral surface.

A **cone** has one circular base and a lateral surface. The lateral surface of a cone comes to a point called its vertex.

A **sphere** has only one surface, which is curved, and has no base. All of the points on the surface are the same distance from the center of the sphere.

A plane that intersects a sphere through its center divides the sphere into two halves, or **hemispheres**.

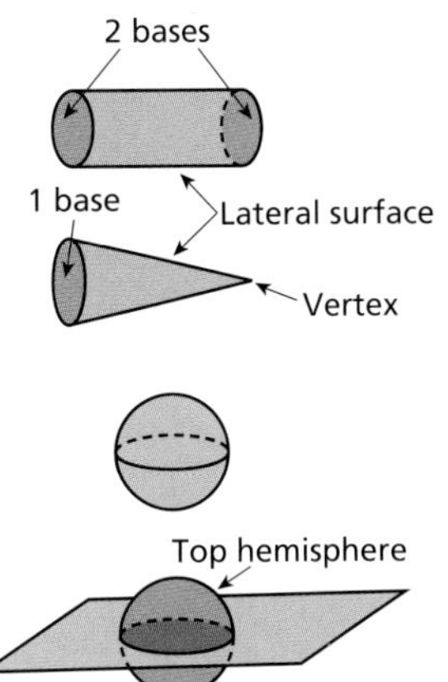

EXAMPLE 2 Identifying Combinations of Solids

Tell what solids make up each figure.

A

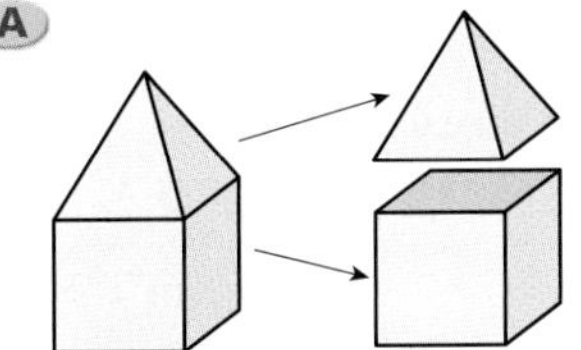

The figure is made up of a rectangular pyramid and a rectangular prism.

B

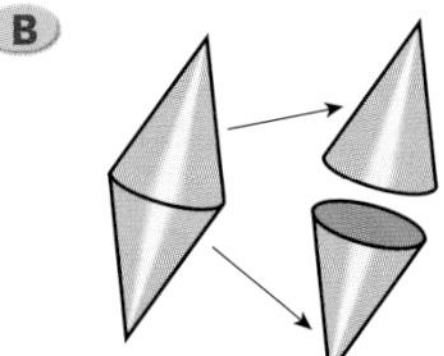

The figure is made up of two cones.

Think and Discuss

1. **Explain** how to identify the bases of a prism and the base of a pyramid. With what type of pyramid could any of the faces be considered the pyramid's base?
2. **Describe** what kinds of figures are made by cutting through a cylinder parallel to its bases.

Additional Examples

Example 1

Identify the base or bases of each solid. Then name each solid.

A.

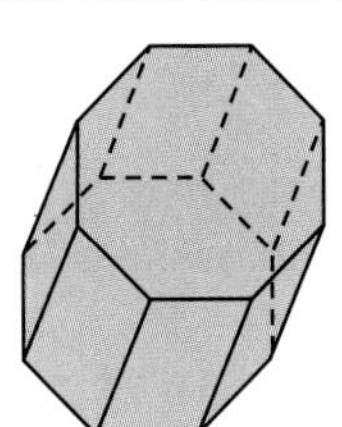

octagonal prism

B.

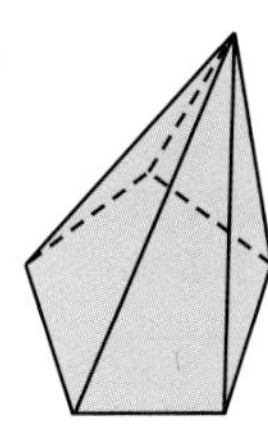

pentagonal pyramid

Example 2

Tell what solids make up each figure.

A.

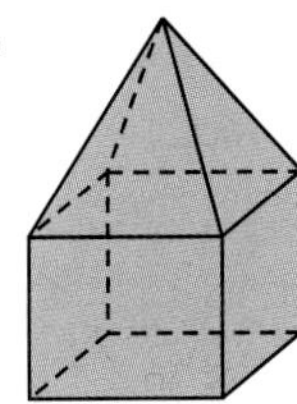

rectangular pyramid and rectangular prism

B.

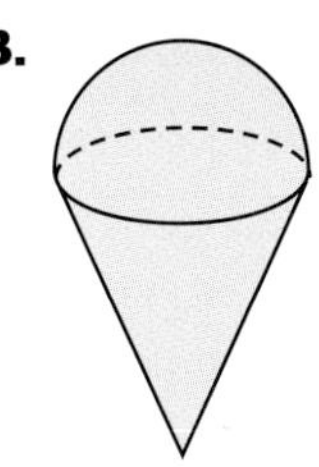

hemisphere and cone

3 Close

Reaching All Learners

Through Visual Organizers

Have students make a web that can be used to classify solid figures. Use these words in the web: *solid figures, spheres, prisms, cones, polyhedrons, pyramids,* and *cylinders.*

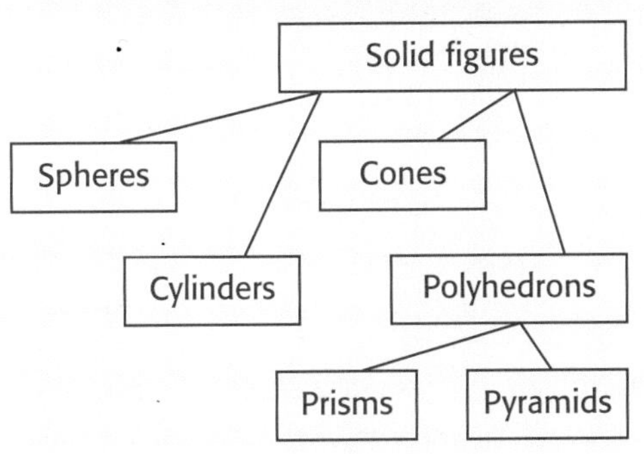

Summarize

Have students write brief definitions of each of the solids in this lesson.

Possible answers: A prism is a polyhedron with two parallel congruent faces and other faces that are parallelograms.

A pyramid is a polyhedron with a vertex and base at opposite ends and faces that are triangles.

A cylinder has two parallel congruent circular bases and a curved lateral surface.

A cone has a circular face, a vertex, and a curved lateral face.

A sphere is the set of points equidistant from a given point, and a hemisphere is created by plane running through the center of a sphere.

Answers to Think and Discuss

1. The bases of a prism are generally the ones that are not rectangular; although in a rectangular prism, the bases could be any pair of parallel bases. In a pyramid, the base is opposite a vertex. In a pyramid with a triangular base, any side could be considered the base.
2. cylinders

9-1 PRACTICE & ASSESS

Students may want to refer back to the lesson examples.

Assignment Guide

If you finished Example 1 assign:
Core 1–3, 7–9, 13, 17, 21–30
Enriched 1, 3, 7, 9, 13, 15, 17, 21–30

If you finished Example 2 assign:
Core 1–14, 17, 19, 21–30
Enriched 1–11 odd, 13–30

Answers

1. 1 rectangular base; rectangular pyramid
2. 2 octagonal bases; octagonal prism
3. 2 triangular bases; triangular prism
7. 1 triangular base; triangular pyramid
8. 2 rectangular bases; rectangular prism
9. 1 hexagonal base; hexagonal pyramid

9-1 Exercises

FOR EXTRA PRACTICE see page 674

GUIDED PRACTICE

See Example 1 Identify the base or bases of each solid. Then name the solid.

1. 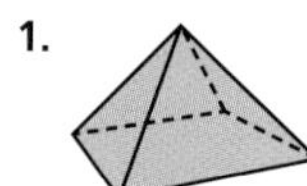
2. 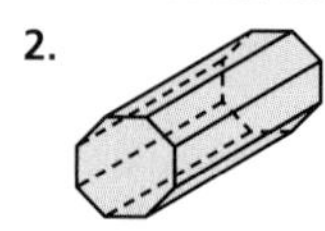
3. 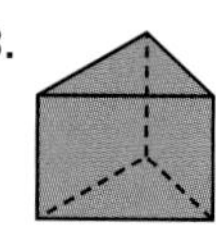

See Example 2 Tell what solids make up each figure.

4. 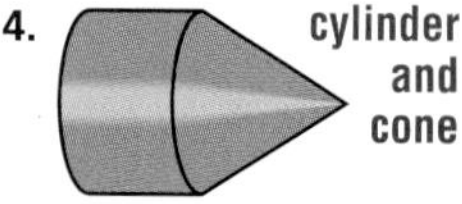 **cylinder and cone**
5.  **cube and triangular prism**
6. 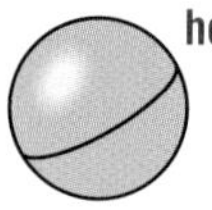 **hemispheres**

INDEPENDENT PRACTICE

See Example 1 Identify the base or bases of each solid. Then name the solid.

7. 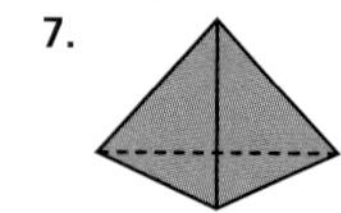
8. 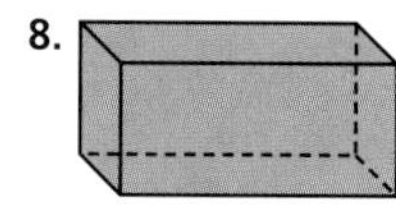
9. 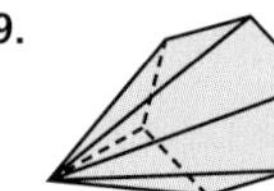

See Example 2 Tell what solids make up each figure.

10.  **cylinder, cone, and hemisphere**
11. 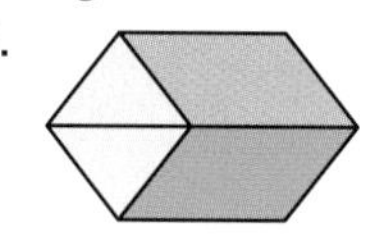 **2 triangular prisms**
12. 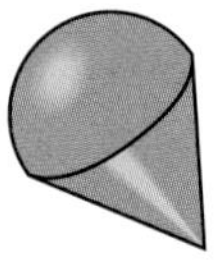  **cone and hemisphere**

PRACTICE AND PROBLEM SOLVING

Identify the three-dimensional figure described.

13. six congruent square faces **cube**
14. two circular bases, curved lateral surface **cylinder**
15. triangular base, three triangular lateral faces **triangular pyramid**
16. All points on the surface are the same distance from a given point. **sphere**

Math Background

As defined in this lesson, a polyhedron is a solid bounded by plane polygons. In particular, we consider only *convex polyhedrons.* In a convex polyhedron, the line segment that connects any two points lies entirely in the polyhedron. The intersection of two faces is called an *edge*, and the point where three or more edges intersect is called a *vertex*. According to the principle called Euler's Theorem, for any simple polyhedron, such as those considered in this lesson, $V - E + F = 2$, where V is the number of vertices, E is the number of edges, and F is the number of faces.

RETEACH 9-1

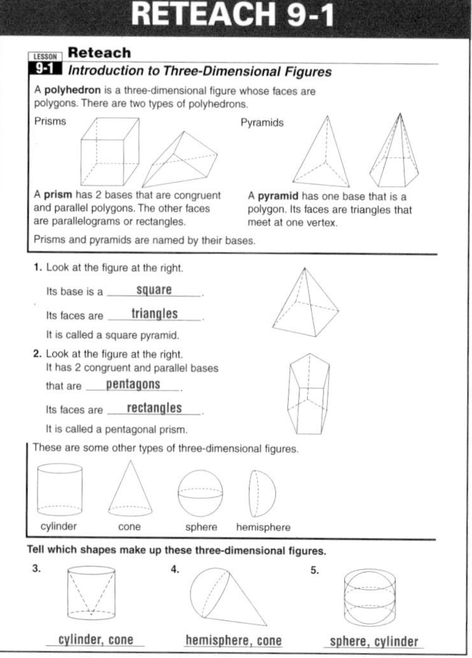

LESSON 9-1 **Reteach**
Introduction to Three-Dimensional Figures

A **polyhedron** is a three-dimensional figure whose faces are polygons. There are two types of polyhedrons.

Prisms | Pyramids

A **prism** has 2 bases that are congruent and parallel polygons. The other faces are parallelograms or rectangles.

A **pyramid** has one base that is a polygon. Its faces are triangles that meet at one vertex.

Prisms and pyramids are named by their bases.

1. Look at the figure at the right.
Its base is a **square**.
Its faces are **triangles**.
It is called a square pyramid.

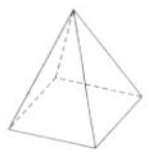

2. Look at the figure at the right.
It has 2 congruent and parallel bases that are **pentagons**.
Its faces are **rectangles**.
It is called a pentagonal prism.

These are some other types of three-dimensional figures.

cylinder cone sphere hemisphere

Tell which shapes make up these three-dimensional figures.

3. 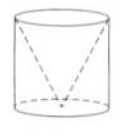 **cylinder, cone**
4. **hemisphere, cone**
5.  **sphere, cylinder**

PRACTICE 9-1

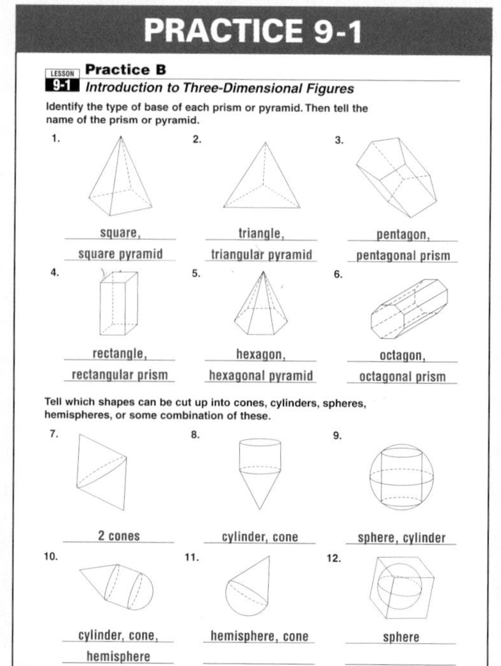

LESSON 9-1 **Practice B**
Introduction to Three-Dimensional Figures

Identify the type of base of each prism or pyramid. Then tell the name of the prism or pyramid.

1. **square, square pyramid**
2. **triangle, triangular pyramid**
3. **pentagon, pentagonal prism**
4. **rectangle, rectangular prism**
5. **hexagon, hexagonal pyramid**
6. **octagon, octagonal prism**

Tell which shapes can be cut up into cones, cylinders, spheres, hemispheres, or some combination of these.

7. **2 cones**
8. **cylinder, cone**
9. **sphere, cylinder**
10. **cylinder, cone, hemisphere**
11. **hemisphere, cone**
12. **sphere**

History LINK

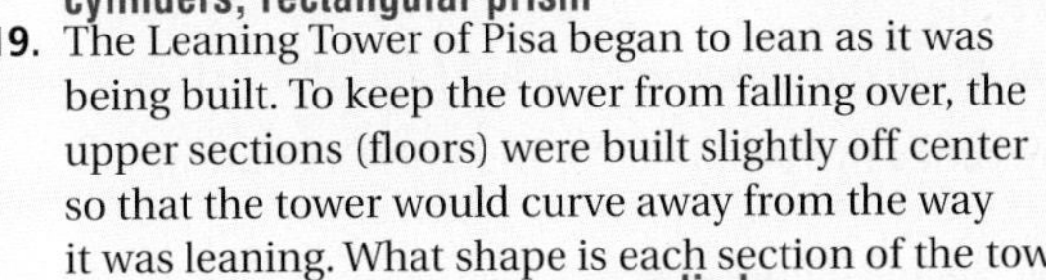

17. The structures in the photo at right are tombs of ancient Egyptian kings. No one knows exactly when the tombs were built, but some archaeologists think the first one might have been built around 2780 B.C. Name the shape of the ancient Egyptian structures. **rectangular pyramid**

18. The Parthenon was built around 440 B.C. by the ancient Greeks. Its purpose was to house a statue of Athena, the Greek goddess of wisdom. Describe the three-dimensional shapes you see in the structure. **Possible answer: cylinders, rectangular prism**

19. The Leaning Tower of Pisa began to lean as it was being built. To keep the tower from falling over, the upper sections (floors) were built slightly off center so that the tower would curve away from the way it was leaning. What shape is each section of the tower? **cylinder**

20. ***CHALLENGE*** The stainless steel structure at right, called the Unisphere, became the symbol of the New York World's Fair of 1964–1965. Explain why the structure is not a true representation of a sphere. **Possible answer: The Unisphere is not a true sphere because it has gaps in its surface.**

2600 B.C. Ancient Egyptian structures at Giza

440 B.C. Parthenon

1173 Leaning Tower of Pisa

1964 Unisphere

Spiral Review

Divide. (Lesson 4-4)

21. 4.24 ÷ 4 **1.06** **22.** 3.5 ÷ 5 **0.7** **23.** 28.53 ÷ 9 **3.17** **24.** 0.04 ÷ 8 **0.005**

Estimate each sum. (Lesson 4-9) **Possible answers:**

25. $\frac{2}{5} + \frac{3}{8}$ **1** **26.** $\frac{1}{16} + \frac{4}{9}$ $\frac{1}{2}$ **27.** $\frac{7}{9} + \frac{11}{12}$ **2** **28.** $\frac{1}{10} + \frac{1}{16}$ **0**

29. TEST PREP Which of the following is equivalent to 36 feet? (Lesson 8-1) **A**

A 432 inches **B** 108 yards **C** 0.06 miles **D** 3 yards

30. TEST PREP Which of the following could be the lengths of the sides of a right triangle? (Lesson 8-8) **J**

F 5, 11, 12 **G** 5, 7, 12 **H** 3, 4, 7 **J** 5, 12, 13

CHALLENGE 9-1

LESSON 9-1 Challenge
Platonic Solids

A three-dimensional figure in which all the faces are polygons is called a *polyhedron*. A polyhedron whose faces are all congruent regular polygons is called a *regular polyhedron*. Regular polyhedrons are called *Platonic solids*.

Below are patterns for four Platonic solids. Copy each pattern. You may enlarge the pattern if you like. Then cut out the pattern and fold it to build a model of the solid. Use your models to answer the questions.

Hexahedron Tetrahedron Octahedron Dodecahedron

1. How many faces does a hexahedron have? What is another name for a hexahedron?
6 faces; square prism or cube
2. How many faces does a tetrahedron have? What is another name for a tetrahedron?
4 faces; triangular pyramid
3. How many faces does an octahedron have?
8 faces
4. How many faces does a dodecahedron have?
12 faces

PROBLEM SOLVING 9-1

LESSON 9-1 Problem Solving
Introduction to Three-Dimensional Figures

Write the correct answer.

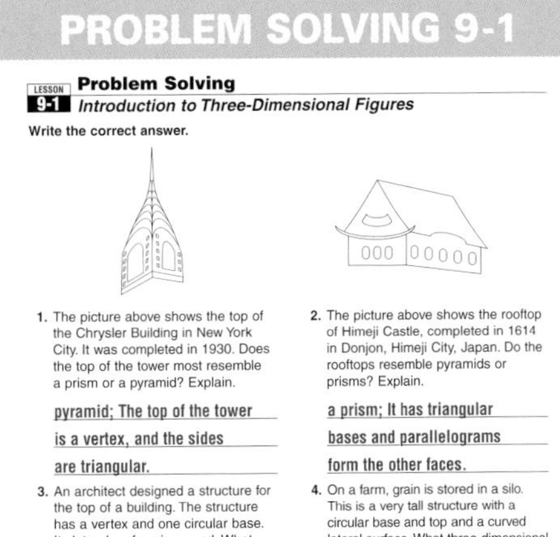

1. The picture above shows the top of the Chrysler Building in New York City. It was completed in 1930. Does the top of the tower most resemble a prism or a pyramid? Explain.
pyramid; The top of the tower is a vertex, and the sides are triangular.
2. The picture above shows the rooftop of Himeji Castle, completed in 1614 in Donjon, Himeji City, Japan. Do the rooftops resemble pyramids or prisms? Explain.
a prism; It has triangular bases and parallelograms form the other faces.
3. An architect designed a structure for the top of a building. The structure has a vertex and one circular base. Its lateral surface is curved. What three-dimensional figure is it?
a cone
4. On a farm, grain is stored in a silo. This is a very tall structure with a circular base and top and a curved lateral surface. What three-dimensional figure does it resemble?
a cylinder

Choose the letter of the correct answer.

5. James put two blocks together to build the figure shown. Identify the two figures he used.

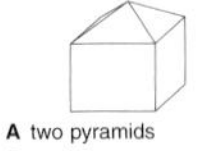

A two pyramids
(B) a pyramid and a prism
C a pyramid and a cone
D two prisms

6. Which of the following objects is an example of a hemisphere?
F a basketball
H a circle
(G) a dome
J a planet

7. The shape of Earth is most like which figure?
A hemisphere
C circle
B cylinder
(D) sphere

Interdisciplinary LINK

History

Exercises 17–20 involve applying students' knowledge of geometric shapes to their understanding of the architecture of historical structures.

Journal

Have students look in magazines or on the Internet to find buildings that are constructed from the figures shown in this lesson and describe them. Ask students to include buildings made from more than one figure and to name the figures involved.

Test Prep Doctor

For Exercise 29, students can eliminate **B** as too great. Remind students that since a yard is a greater unit than a foot, the number would need to be less. Students can use conversion factors to determine that the correct answer is **A.**

For Exercise 30, students can eliminate **G** and **H** because they do not form triangles. To find the correct answer, have students test the Pythagorean Theorem with the numbers in **F** and **J** to eliminate **F.**

Lesson Quiz

Identify the type of each prism or pyramid.

1.

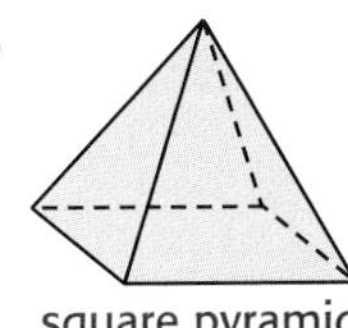

square pyramid

2.

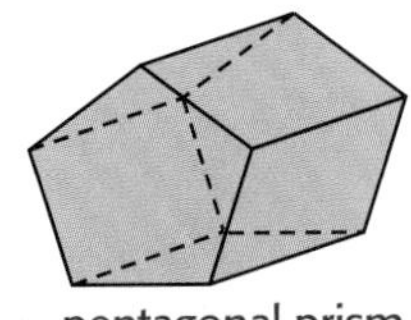

pentagonal prism

Identify the figure described.

3. two congruent circular faces connected by a curved surface
cylinder

4. one circular face and a curved lateral surface that comes to a point called the vertex cone

Available on Daily Transparency in CRB

9-2 Organizer

Pacing: Traditional 1 day
Block $\frac{1}{2}$ day

Objective: Students find the volume of prisms and cylinders.

Warm Up

Identify the figure described.

1. two triangular faces and the other faces in the shape of parallelograms
triangular prism
2. one hexagonal base and the other faces in the shape of triangles
hexagonal pyramid
3. one circular face and a curved lateral surface that forms a vertex
cone

Problem of the Day

How can you cut the rectangular prism into 8 pieces of equal volume by making only 3 straight cuts?

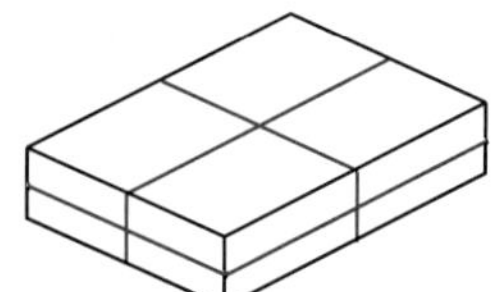

Available on Daily Transparency in CRB

9-2 Volume of Prisms and Cylinders

Learn to find the volume of prisms and cylinders.

Vocabulary
volume

Any solid figure can be filled completely with congruent cubes and parts of cubes. The **volume** of a solid is the number of cubes it can hold. Each cube represents a unit of measure called a cubic unit.

EXAMPLE 1 Using Cubes to Find the Volume of a Rectangular Prism

Find how many cubes the prism holds. Then give the prism's volume.

You can find the volume of this prism by counting how many cubes tall, long, and wide the prism is and then multiplying.

$2 \cdot 4 \cdot 2 = 16$

There are 16 cubes in the prism, so the volume is 16 cubic units.

Reading Math

Any unit of measurement with an exponent of 3 is a cubic unit. For example, cm^3 means "cubic centimeter" and in^3 means "cubic inch."

A cube that measures one centimeter on each side represents one cubic centimeter of volume. Suppose the cubes in the prism in Example 1 measure one centimeter on each side. The volume of the prism would be 16 cm^3.

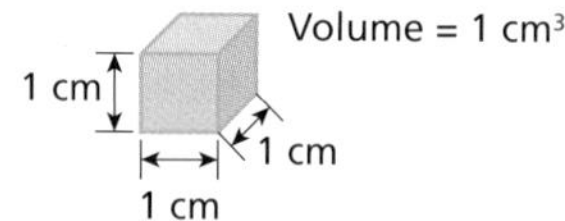

This volume is found by multiplying the prism's length times its width times its height.

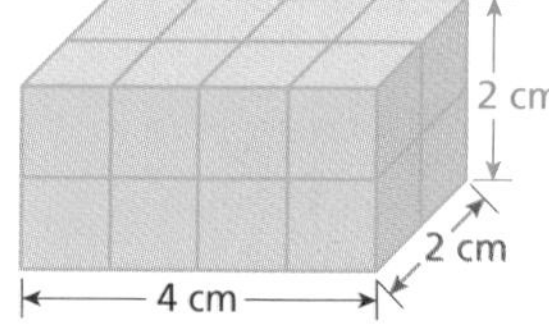

$4\text{ cm} \cdot 2\text{ cm} \cdot 2\text{ cm} = 16\text{ cm}^3$

length · width · height = volume

area of base · height = volume

Notice that for the rectangular prism, the volume is found by multiplying the area of its base times its height. This method can be used for finding the volume of any prism.

1 Introduce

Alternate Opener

EXPLORATION

9-2 Volume of Prisms and Cylinders

A box of sugar cubes contains 126 cubes. The box below is called a *rectangular prism* because its base is a rectangle.

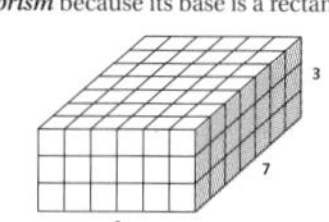

1. Sketch two different models that show how the same number of cubes (126) might be stacked in boxes with different dimensions. Label the dimensions of each box.
2. Use the formula *volume = length · width · height* to calculate the volume of each box you sketched in number 1.

Think and Discuss

3. **Explain** how you can determine the volume of a box if you know the dimensions.
4. **Explain** why the formula *volume = length · width · height* is equivalent to the formula *volume = area of base · height* when working with rectangular prisms.

Motivate

To introduce volume of prisms and cylinders, show students a variety of containers shaped like prisms and cylinders and ask them to speculate as to which container can hold more. As students discuss the containers, introduce the word *volume* to describe how much the container can hold.

You may want to test students' predictions by filling one container with rice or a similar substance and having students pour the contents into another container to compare sizes.

Exploration worksheet and answers on Chapter 9 Resource Book pp. 16 and 62

2 Teach

Lesson Presentation

Guided Instruction

In this lesson, students learn to find the volume of prisms and cylinders. Students use cubes to get an intuitive idea of what the volume of a prism is, and from that intuitive idea, you can lead them to formulas that can be used to find volumes of prisms and cylinders. To justify the formula for the volume of a cylinder, help students see the cylinder as a stack of circles with given area.

Teaching Tip Point out that although you can use unit cubes to measure the volumes of some prisms (e.g., when all the dimensions are whole numbers), most of the time you will need to use a formula to find the volume of a prism or cylinder.

VOLUME OF A PRISM

The volume V of a prism is the area of its base B times its height h.

$$V = Bh$$

EXAMPLE 2 Using a Formula to Find the Volume of a Prism

Find the volume of the prism to the nearest tenth.

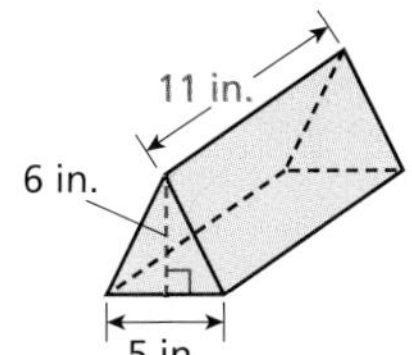

$V = Bh$ *Use the formula.*

The bases are triangles. The base of each triangle is 5 in., and the height is 6 in. The area of each triangular base is $\frac{1}{2}bh$, or $\frac{1}{2} \cdot 5 \cdot 6 = 15$.

$V = 15 \cdot 11$ *Substitute for B and h.*

$V = 165$ *Multiply.*

The volume is 165.0 in^3.

Finding the volume of a cylinder is similar to finding the volume of a prism.

VOLUME OF A CYLINDER

The volume V of a cylinder is the area of its base, πr^2, times its height h.

$$V = \pi r^2 h$$

EXAMPLE 3 Using a Formula to Find the Volume of a Cylinder

Find the volume of the cylinder to the nearest tenth. Use 3.14 for π.

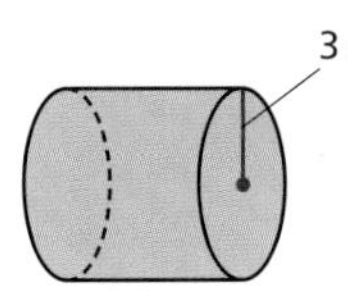

$V = \pi r^2 h$ *Use the formula.*

The radius of the cylinder is 3 cm, and the height is 6.1 cm.

$V \approx 3.14 \cdot 3^2 \cdot 6.1$ *Substitute for r and h.*

$V \approx 172.386$ *Multiply.*

$V \approx 172.4$ *Round.*

The volume is about 172.4 cm^3.

Think and Discuss

1. **Explain** what a cubic unit is.
2. **Tell** what units you would use to express the volume of a cylinder if the radius and the height are given in yards.

COMMON ERROR ALERT

Some students may use incorrect units to measure volume. Remind students that cubic units, not square units, are used to measure volume because solids have three dimensions, i.e., length × width × height.

Additional Examples

Example 1

Find how many cubes the prism holds. Then give the prism's volume.

12 cubes; 12 cubic units.

Example 2

Find the volume of the prism to the nearest tenth.

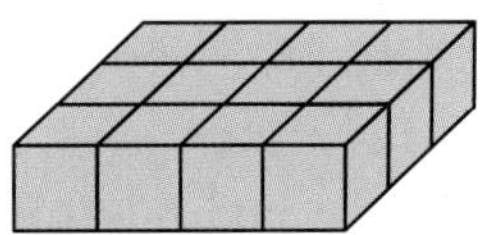

201.7 ft^3

Example 3

Find the volume of the cylinder to the nearest tenth. Use 3.14 for π.

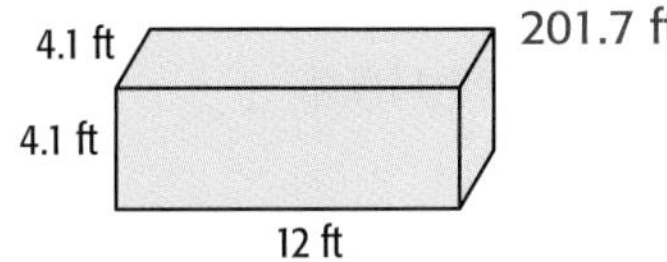

329.7 m^3

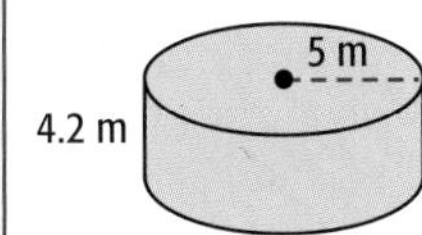

Example 3 note: Remind students that when they are finding the volume of a cylinder to the nearest tenth, they should complete the entire computation before rounding the answer.

3 Close

Reaching All Learners

Through Critical Thinking

Give each group one of the containers that you used in the Motivate section. Have each group calculate the volume of the container in cubic inches. Then tell each group to fill the container with rice or a similar substance and to measure its capacity in cups. Let each group share its results and then, as a class, determine the relationship between 1 cup and cubic inches.

One cup is about 17 cubic inches.

Summarize

You may wish to have students describe a general way to find the volume of a rectangular prism or a cylinder and then give the specific formulas for each.

Possible answers: To find volume, multiply the area of the base by the height. To find the volume of a rectangular prism, multiply length by width by height. To find the volume of a cylinder, multiply *pi* by the radius squared by the height.

Answers to Think and Discuss

1. Possible answer: A cubic unit is the unit used when finding volume.
2. cubic yards

9-2 PRACTICE & ASSESS

Students may want to refer back to the lesson examples.

Assignment Guide

If you finished Example 1 assign:
Core 1–3, 10–12, 30–36
Enriched 1–3, 10–12, 30–36

If you finished Example 2 assign:
Core 1–6, 10–15, 21, 23, 30–36
Enriched 1–5 odd, 11–15 odd, 20, 21, 23, 24, 26, 30–36

If you finished Example 3 assign:
Core 1–18, 19–25 odd, 30–36
Enriched 1–17 odd, 19–36

Notes

9-2 Exercises

FOR EXTRA PRACTICE
see page 674

internet connect
Homework Help Online
go.hrw.com Keyword: MS4 9-2

GUIDED PRACTICE

See Example 1 Find how many cubes each prism holds. Then give the prism's volume.

1. 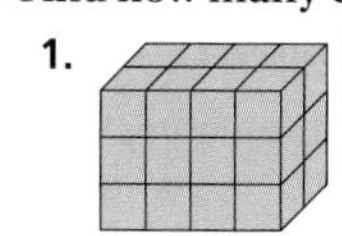 **24 cubes; 24 cubic units**

2. 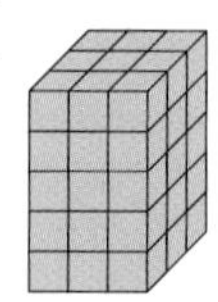 **45 cubes; 45 cubic units**

3. 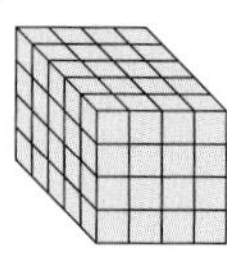 **80 cubes; 80 cubic units**

See Example 2 Find the volume of each prism to the nearest tenth.

4. 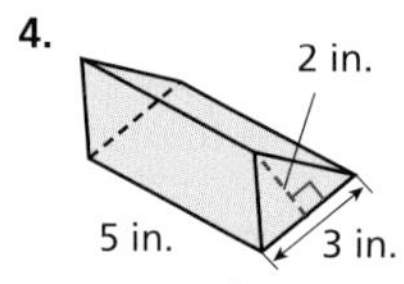

15.0 in³

5. 3.6 cm, 4 cm, 8.2 cm
118.1 cm³

6. 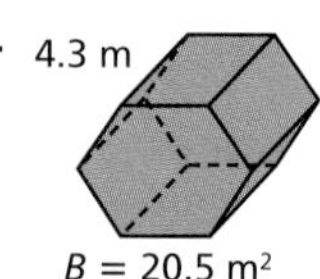

88.2 m³

See Example 3 Find the volume of each cylinder to the nearest tenth. Use 3.14 for π.

7. 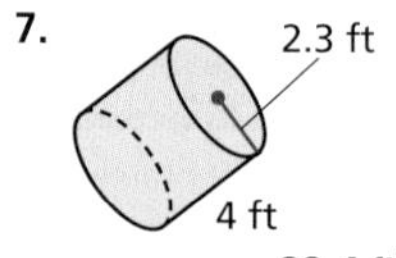

66.4 ft³

8. 5 ft, 9 ft
706.5 ft³

9. 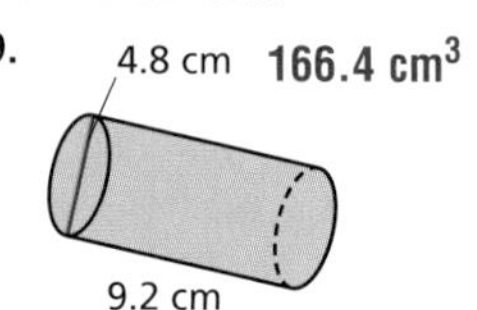

166.4 cm³

INDEPENDENT PRACTICE

See Example 1 Find how many cubes each prism holds. Then give the prism's volume.

10. 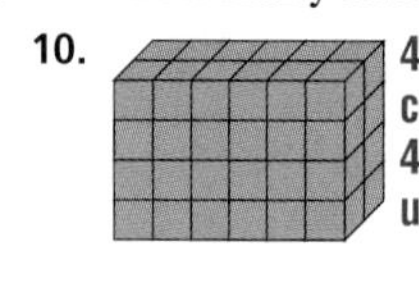 **48 cubes; 48 cubic units**

11. 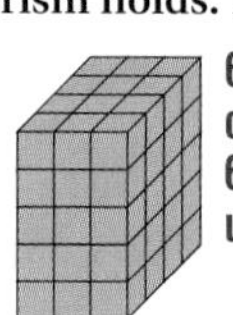 **60 cubes; 60 cubic units**

12. 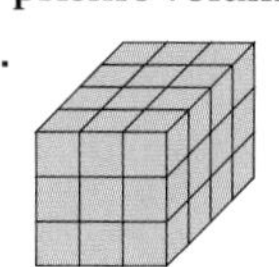 **36 cubes; 36 cubic units**

See Example 2 Find the volume of each prism to the nearest tenth.

13. 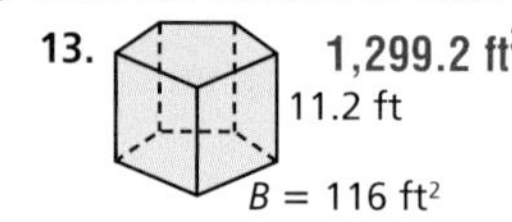

1,299.2 ft³

14. 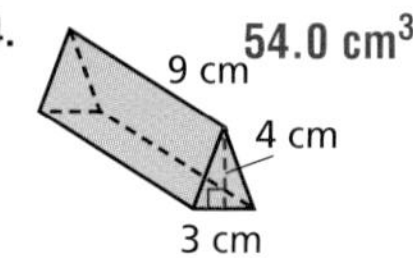

54.0 cm³

15. 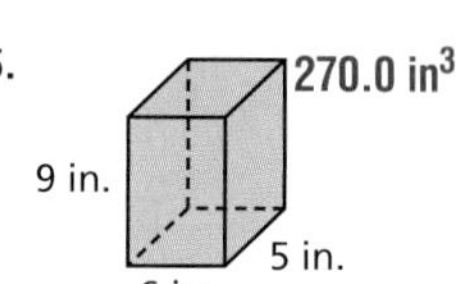

270.0 in³

See Example 3 Find the volume of each cylinder to the nearest tenth. Use 3.14 for π.

16. 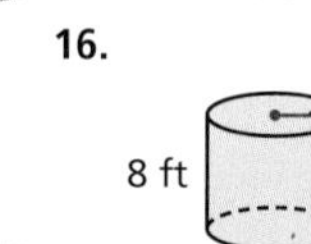

628.0 ft³

17. 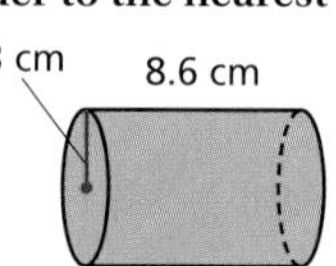

243.0 cm³

18. 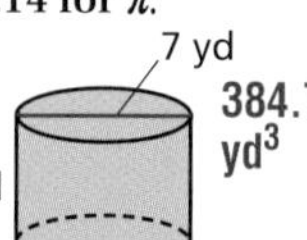

384.7 yd³

Math Background

To convert from one unit of volume to another, you can use conversion factors. For example, to convert from cubic yards to cubic feet, you can cube both sides of the conversion factor 1 yd = 3 ft to find that 1 yd³ = (3 ft)³ = 27 ft³. Thus, to find the number of cubic feet in a number of cubic yards, you must multiply by 27.

Similarly, to convert cubic centimeters to cubic millimeters, use 1 cm = 10 mm to determine that (1 cm)³ = (10 mm)³ = 1,000 mm³. So, to find the number of cubic millimeters in a volume given in cubic centimeters, multiply by 1,000. In general, to convert from one unit to another, multiply or divide by the cube of the conversion factor.

RETEACH 9-2

LESSON 9-2 **Reteach**
Volume of Prisms and Cylinders

The **volume** of a three-dimensional figure is the amount of space it takes up. Volume is measured in cubic units.

Find the volume of the prism.

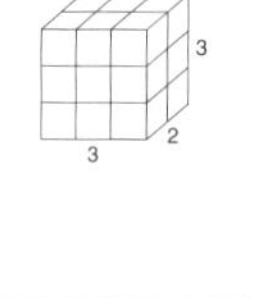

1. Think of the prism as layers of cubes. There are __6__ cubes in the bottom layer.
2. There are __3__ layers of cubes.
3. Multiply the number of cubes in the bottom layer by the number of layers. The volume of the prism is __18__ cubic units.

The volume of a prism or a cylinder is the area of its base times its height.
volume = base • height, or $V = B \cdot h$

Find the volume of the prism.

4. What is the shape of the base? __triangle__
5. The area of the base is $B = \frac{1}{2}bh$
$B = \frac{1}{2} \cdot$ __6__ $\cdot$ __3__ = __9__ in²
6. The height of the prism is __5__ in.
7. $V = B \cdot h =$ __9__ $\cdot$ __5__ = __45__ in³

(3 in., 5 in., 6 in.)

Find the volume of the cylinder to the nearest whole number.

8. What is the shape of the base? __circle__
9. The area of the base is $A = \pi r^2$.
$A = 3.14 \cdot$ __4__ ² = __50__ cm²
10. The height of the cylinder is __3__ cm.
11. $V = B \cdot h =$ __50__ $\cdot$ __3__ = __150__ cm³

(4 cm, 3 cm)

PRACTICE 9-2

LESSON 9-2 **Practice B**
Volume of Prisms and Cylinders

Find how many cubes the prism holds, and tell the volume of the prism.

1. 12 cubes, 12 cubic units
2. 24 cubes, 24 cubic units
3. 20 cubes, 20 cubic units

Calculate the volume of the prism to the nearest tenth.

4. (9 in., 4 in., 5 in.) 180 in³
5. (10 yd, 5 yd, 9 yd) 225 yd³
6. (7.4 in., 3.7 in., 2.1 in.) 57.5 in³
7. (8.3 mm, $B = 75.2$ mm²) 624.2 mm³
8. (5 cm, 11 cm, 13 cm) 357.5 cm³
9. (5.1 m, $B = 48.3$ m²) 246.3 m³

Calculate the volume of the cylinder to the nearest tenth.

10. (4 ft, 7 ft) 351.7 ft³
11. (8 in., 8 in.) 1,607.7 in³
12. (3 cm, 10 cm) 282.6 cm³

PRACTICE AND PROBLEM SOLVING

Find the volume of each solid to the nearest tenth. Use 3.14 for π.

19. cylinder: $r = 10$ m, $h = 7$ m **2,198.0 m³**
20. rectangular prism: $\ell = 8$ cm, $w = 7.3$ cm, $h = 10.7$ cm **624.9 cm³**
21. triangular prism: $B = 15\ \text{ft}^2$, $h = 8$ ft **120.0 ft³**
22. cylinder: $d = 10$ m, $h = 9.3$ m **730.1 m³**

Life Science LINK

Marine biologists insert tags containing tiny microchips into the bellies of salmon to study the migration patterns of these fish.

go.hrw.com KEYWORD: MS4 Tags

CNN Student News

23. The base of a triangular prism is a right triangle with hypotenuse 10 m long and one leg 6 m long. If the height of the prism is 12 m, what is the volume of the prism? **288 m³**
24. ***ENTERTAINMENT*** A compact-disc case, or jewel case, is 14 cm long, 12.5 cm wide, and 1 cm tall. What is the volume of the jewel case? **175 cm³**
25. An ID tag containing a microchip can be injected into a pet, such as a dog or cat. These microchips are cylindrical and can be as small as 12 mm in length and 2.1 mm in diameter. What is the volume, to the nearest tenth, of one of these microchips? Use 3.14 for π. **41.5 mm³**
26. ***RECREATION*** The tent shown is in the shape of a triangular prism. How many cubic feet of space are in the tent? **47.25 ft³**

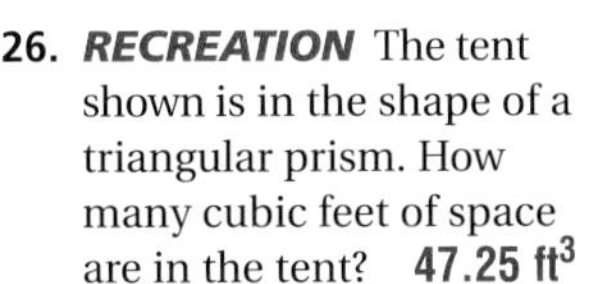
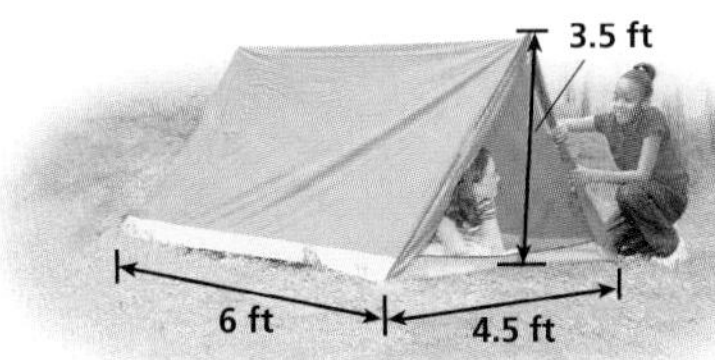

27. ***WHAT'S THE ERROR?*** A student said the volume of a cylinder with a 3-inch diameter is two times the volume of a cylinder with the same height and a 1.5-inch radius. What is the error?

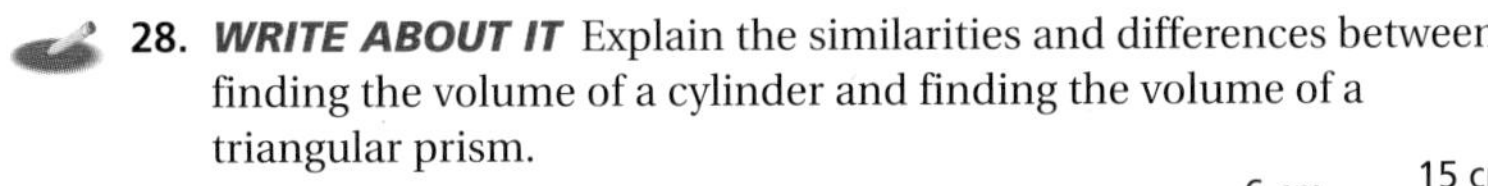

28. ***WRITE ABOUT IT*** Explain the similarities and differences between finding the volume of a cylinder and finding the volume of a triangular prism.

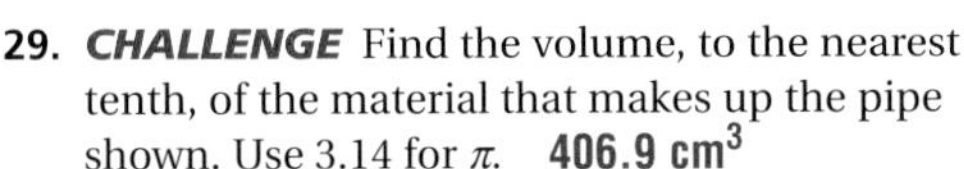

29. ***CHALLENGE*** Find the volume, to the nearest tenth, of the material that makes up the pipe shown. Use 3.14 for π. **406.9 cm³**

6 cm
15 cm
8.4 cm

Spiral Review

Write each fraction in decimal form. (Lesson 3-7)

30. $\frac{1}{2}$ **0.5**
31. $\frac{3}{5}$ **0.6**
32. $\frac{7}{8}$ **0.875**
33. $\frac{5}{16}$ **0.3125**

Find the simple interest. (Lesson 6-6)

34. $P = \$3,600$; $r = 5\%$; $t = 1.5$ years **$270**
35. $P = \$10,000$; $r = 3.2\%$; $t = 2$ years **$640**

36. **TEST PREP** Which is the equivalent in meters of 100.6 centimeters? (Lesson 8-1) **A**

A 1.006 **B** 10.06 **C** 1,006 **D** 10,060

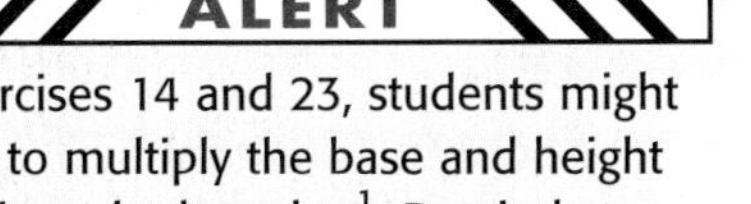

In Exercises 14 and 23, students might forget to multiply the base and height of a triangular base by $\frac{1}{2}$. Remind students of the derivation of the formula to help them remember to take half of the product of the triangular base and height.

Answers

27. Possible answer: The volumes are equal because a cylinder with a 3-inch diameter has a 1.5-inch radius.
28. For both, the volume is the area of the base times the height; the formulas for the base areas are different.

Journal

Ask students to think of at least two situations in which they might need to know the volume of a prism or cylinder and to describe each situation and how the volume would be used.

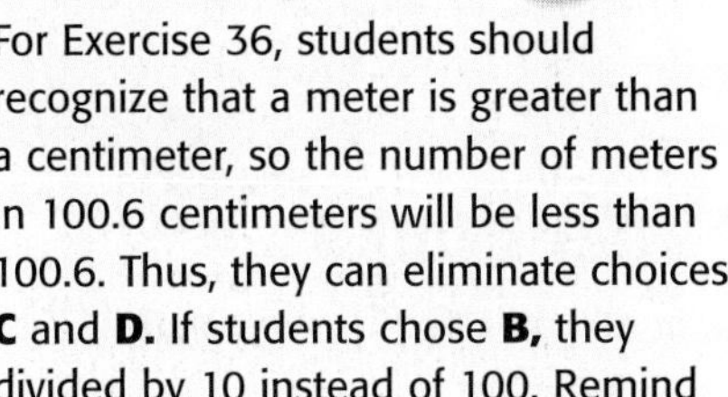

Test Prep Doctor

For Exercise 36, students should recognize that a meter is greater than a centimeter, so the number of meters in 100.6 centimeters will be less than 100.6. Thus, they can eliminate choices **C** and **D.** If students chose **B,** they divided by 10 instead of 100. Remind students that 1 m = 100 cm.

CHALLENGE 9-2

LESSON 9-2 **Challenge**
Painted Faces

A cube has six sides, or faces. Each of the six faces is a square.

This cube measures 2 units on each edge. The faces of the cube are painted.

1. How many small cubes make up the large cube? **8 cubes**
2. How many small cubes are painted on 3 faces? on 2 faces? on 1 face? not at all? **8 cubes; 0 cubes; 0 cubes; 0 cubes**

This cube measures 3 units on each edge.

3. How many small cubes make up the large cube? **27 cubes**
4. If the large cube is painted, how many small cubes will be painted on 3 faces? on 2 faces? on 1 face? not at all? **8 cubes; 12 cubes; 6 cubes; 1 cube**

This cube measures 4 units on each edge.

5. How many small cubes make up the large cube? **64 cubes**
6. If the large cube is painted, how many small cubes will be painted on 3 faces? on 2 faces? on 1 face? not at all? **8 cubes; 24 cubes; 24 cubes; 8 cubes**
7. Complete the table below by entering the number of small cubes that will be painted on the given number of faces.

Size of Large Cube	Painted on 3 Faces	Painted on 2 Faces	Painted on 1 Face	Painted on 0 Faces
2 × 2 × 2	8	0	0	0
3 × 3 × 3	8	12	6	1
4 × 4 × 4	8	24	24	8
5 × 5 × 5	8	36	54	27

8. Look at your table in Exercise 7. What is the rule for the number of cubes painted on 3 faces? **always 8**

PROBLEM SOLVING 9-2

LESSON 9-2 **Problem Solving**
Volume of Prisms and Cylinders

Write the correct answer.

1. The eight Corinthian columns at the National Building Museum in Washington, DC, are each 75 feet high and 8 feet in diameter. What is the volume of each column? **3,768 ft³**
2. A cubic centimeter holds 1 milliliter of liquid. How many liters of water to the nearest tenth are required to fill a fish tank that is 24 centimeters high, 28 centimeters long, and 36 centimeters wide? **24.2 L**
3. There are 231 cubic inches in a gallon. A large juice can has a diameter of 6 inches and a height of 10 inches. How many gallons of juice does the can hold? Round your answer to the nearest tenth. **1.2 gal**
4. A small gift box that holds a ring is shaped like a cube. The box measures 1.4 inches on each side. What is the volume of the gift box? Round your answer to the nearest tenth. **2.7 in³**

Choose the letter of the correct answer.

5. The Leaning Tower of Pisa in Italy appears to be cylindrical in shape. It's height is about 56 meters. If the volume of the tower is about 9,891 cubic meters, what is the diameter of the base?
   A about 3.5 m (**C**) about 15 m
   B about 7 m **D** about 20 m
6. A bricklayer is building a brick rectangular post to anchor a mailbox. The post is 3 feet tall, 2 feet deep, and 2 feet wide. Each brick is 3 inches by 6 inches by 3 inches. How many bricks does he need?
   F 12 bricks **H** 197 bricks
   G 54 bricks (**J**) 384 bricks
7. The average stone on the lowest level of the Great Pyramid in Egypt was a rectangular prism 5 feet long by 5 feet high by 6 feet deep and weighed 15 tons. What was the volume of the average casing stone?
   A 1,800 ft³ (**C**) 150 ft³
   B 1,800 ft² **D** 150 ft²
8. A cylindrical barrel is 2.8 feet in diameter and 8 feet high. If a cubic foot holds about 7.5 gallons of liquid, how many gallons of water will this barrel hold?
   F about 1,477 gal
   (**G**) about 369 gal
   H about 150 gal
   J about 470 gal

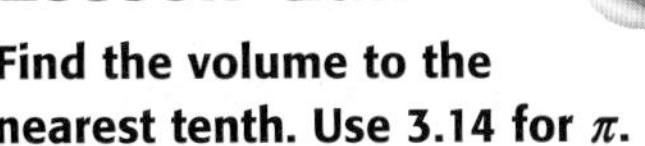

Lesson Quiz

Find the volume to the nearest tenth. Use 3.14 for π.

1.

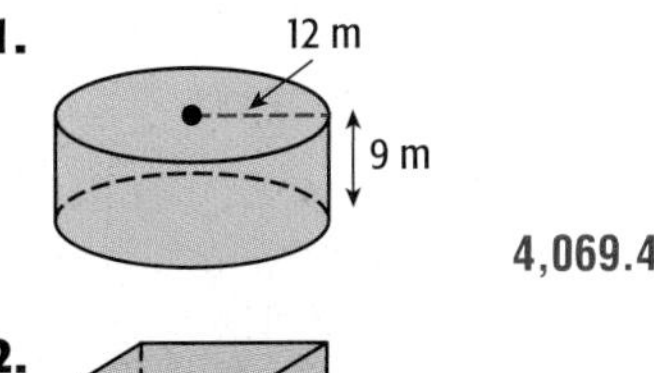

4,069.4 m³

2.

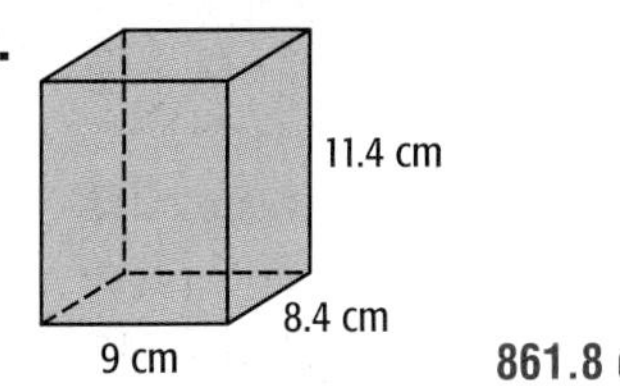

861.8 cm³

3. triangular prism: base area = 24 ft², height = 13 ft **312 ft³**

Available on Daily Transparency in CRB

9-3 Organizer

Pacing: Traditional 1 day
Block $\frac{1}{2}$ day

Objective: Students find the volume of pyramids, cones, and spheres.

Warm Up

Find each volume to the nearest tenth. Use 3.14 for π.

1. cylinder: radius = 6 m, height = 11 m **1,243.4 m^3**
2. rectangular prism: length = 10 cm, width = 8.64 cm, height = 12.9 cm **1,114.6 cm^3**
3. triangular prism: base area = 34 ft^2, height = 18 ft **612 ft^3**
4. cylinder: diameter = 8 m, height = 18 m **904.3 m^3**

Problem of the Day

The volume of a 10-meter-tall square pyramid is 120 m^3. What is the length of each side of the base? **6 m**

Available on Daily Transparency in CRB

What do you call a crushed angle?
A rect-angle

9-3 Volume of Pyramids, Cones, and Spheres

Learn to find the volume of pyramids, cones, and spheres.

If you pour sand from a pyramid-shaped container into a prism-shaped container with the same height, base shape, and base size, you will discover an interesting relationship. The prism-shaped container appears to hold three times as much sand as the pyramid-shaped container.

In fact, the volume of a pyramid is exactly one-third the volume of a prism that has the same height, base shape, and base size as the pyramid. The height of a pyramid is the perpendicular distance from the pyramid's base to its vertex.

VOLUME OF A PYRAMID

The volume V of a pyramid is one-third the area of its base B times its height h.

$$V = \frac{1}{3}Bh$$

EXAMPLE 1 Finding the Volume of a Pyramid

Find the volume of each pyramid.

A

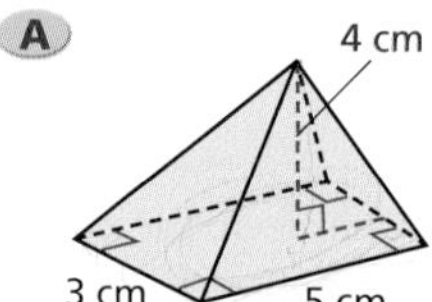

$V = \frac{1}{3}Bh$	*Use the formula.*
$B = 3 \cdot 5 = 15$	*Find the area of the rectangular base.*
$V = \frac{1}{3} \cdot 15 \cdot 4$	*Substitute for B and h.*
$V = 20$	*Multiply.*

The volume is 20 cm^3.

B

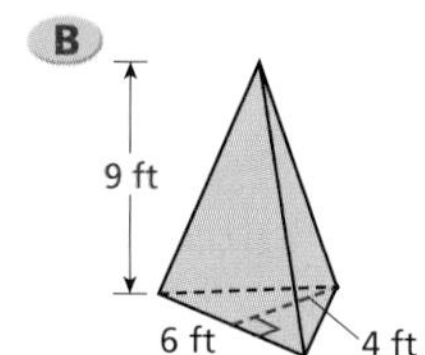

$V = \frac{1}{3}Bh$	*Use the formula.*
$B = \frac{1}{2} \cdot 6 \cdot 4 = 12$	*Find the area of the triangular base.*
$V = \frac{1}{3} \cdot 12 \cdot 9$	*Substitute for B and h.*
$V = 36$	*Multiply.*

The volume is 36 ft^3.

1 Introduce

Alternate Opener

9-3 Volume of Pyramids, Cones, and Spheres

The ***volume of a pyramid*** is one-third the volume of a prism with the same height and a congruent base.

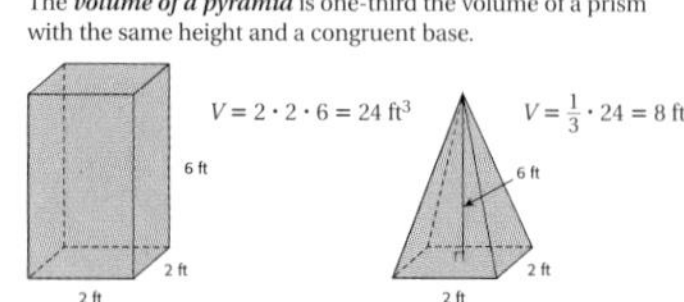

Use the example above as a guide to find the volume of each prism and the volume of each pyramid.

	Prism	Volume	Pyramid	Volume
1.	5 in., 3 in., 10 in.		5 in., 3 in., 10 in.	
2.	5 in., Area of base = 15 in^2		5 in., Area of base = 15 in^2	

Think and Discuss

3. **Explain** the relationship between the volume of a prism and the volume of a pyramid that has the same height and a congruent base.

Motivate

To introduce volume of cones and pyramids, show students models of cones, pyramids, prisms, and cylinders. Ask students to predict how the volumes of a cylinder and cone (or prism and pyramid) with the same base and height are related.

Exploration worksheet and answers on Chapter 9 Resource Book pp. 25 and 64

2 Teach

Lesson Presentation

Guided Instruction

In this lesson, students learn to find the volume of pyramids, cones, and spheres. It is somewhat difficult to prove that the volume of a pyramid or a cone is one-third that of a prism or cylinder with the same base and height. However, using models and rice or water to illustrate that you can fill the corresponding prism or cylinder three times from the original pyramid or cone helps illustrate the reasonableness of the formulas.

Teaching Tip Explain that the formula for the volume of a pyramid $v = \frac{1}{3}Bh$, is the same as the formula for a cone because $B = \pi r^2$.

The volume of a cone is one-third the volume of a cylinder with the same height and a congruent base. The height of a cone is the perpendicular distance from the cone's base to its vertex.

VOLUME OF A CONE

The volume V of a cone is one-third the area of its base, πr^2, times its height h.

$$V = \frac{1}{3}\pi r^2 h$$

EXAMPLE 2 Finding the Volume of a Cone

Find the volume of the cone to the nearest tenth. Use 3.14 for π.

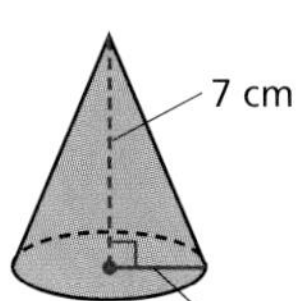

$V = \frac{1}{3}\pi r^2 h$ *Use the formula.*

$V \approx \frac{1}{3} \cdot 3.14 \cdot 3^2 \cdot 7$ *Substitute.*

$V \approx 65.94$ *Multiply.*

$V \approx 65.9$ *Round.*

The volume is about 65.9 cm^3.

VOLUME OF A SPHERE

The volume V of a sphere is $\frac{4}{3}$ times π times the radius r cubed.

$$V = \frac{4}{3}\pi r^3$$

EXAMPLE 3 Finding the Volume of a Sphere

Find the volume of the sphere to the nearest tenth. Use 3.14 for π.

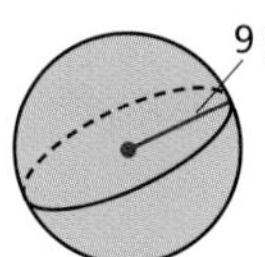

$V = \frac{4}{3}\pi r^3$ *Use the formula.*

$V \approx \frac{4}{3} \cdot 3.14 \cdot 9^3$ *Substitute.*

$V \approx 3{,}052.08$ *Multiply.*

$V \approx 3{,}052.1$ *Round.*

The volume is about 3,052.1 yd^3.

Think and Discuss

1. **Compare** the formulas for the volume of a pyramid and the volume of a prism.
2. **Describe** how to find the volume of a sphere with diameter 8 m.

Additional Examples

Example 1

Find the volume of the pyramid.

A. **30 ft^3**

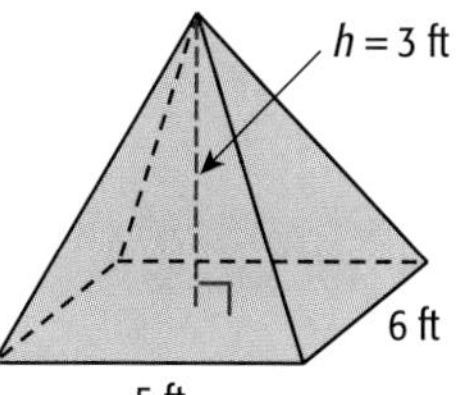

B. **The volume is 5 cm^3.**

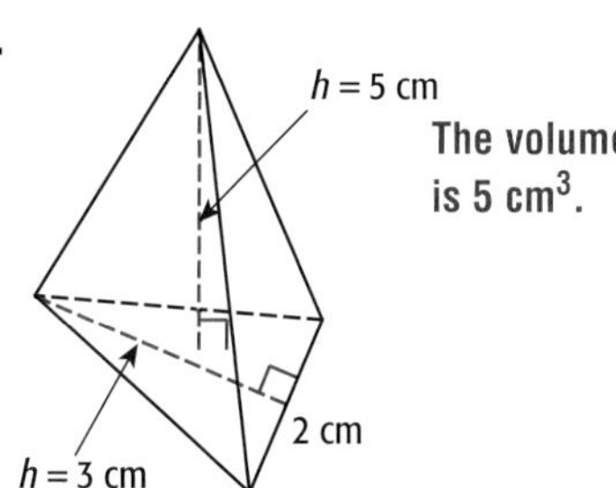

Example 2

Find the volume of the cone to the nearest tenth. Use 3.14 for π.

157.0 yd^3

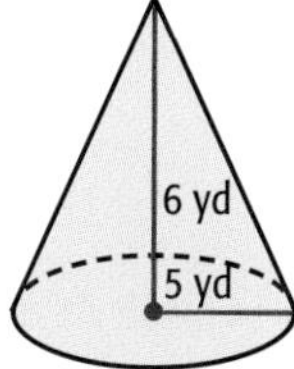

Example 3

Find the volume of the sphere to the nearest tenth. Use 3.14 for π.

1,436.0 in^3

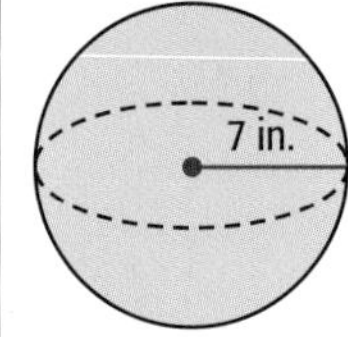

Reaching All Learners

Through World Math

Have students work with partners to research the Egyptian pyramids. Give students the approximate dimensions of the base and the height of the Great Pyramid of Giza (454 feet tall and 229 feet on each side of the base) and then calculate the volume of the pyramid.

3 Close

Summarize

Have students write descriptions of how to find the volume of a pyramid or cone and the volume of a sphere.

Possible answers: To find the volume of a cone or pyramid, multiply $\frac{1}{3}$ by the area of the base by the height.

To find the volume of a sphere, multiply $\frac{4}{3}$ by π by the radius cubed.

Answers to Think and Discuss

Possible answers:

1. The volume of a pyramid is one-third the volume of the corresponding prism with the same height and congruent base.
2. Multiply 8 by $\frac{1}{2}$ to get the radius of 4, and then find the product of $\frac{4}{3}$, π, and 4^3. The units are cubic meters.

9-3 PRACTICE & ASSESS

Students may want to refer back to the lesson examples.

Assignment Guide

If you finished Example 1 assign:
Core 1–3, 10–12, 19, 23, 27–33
Enriched 1–3, 10–12, 19, 23, 25, 27–33

If you finished Example 2 assign:
Core 1–6, 10–15, 19, 20, 22, 23, 27–33
Enriched 1–6, 10–15, 19, 20, 22, 23, 25, 27–33

If you finished Example 3 assign:
Core 1–18, 19–23 odd, 27–33
Enriched 1–17 odd, 19–33

Notes

Math Background

Archimedes (287–212 B.C.) deduced the formula for the volume of a sphere by observing that a sphere of radius r and a cone of radius and height $2r$ at 2 units from the fulcrum of a lever would balance a cylinder of radius and height $2r$ at 1 unit from the fulcrum. Thus, the sum of the volumes of the cone and the sphere is half the volume of the cylinder. Because the volume of the cone is one-third that of the cylinder, the volume of the sphere is one-sixth that of the cylinder. Simplifying $\frac{1}{6}(8\pi r^3)$ gives the formula for the volume of a sphere.

9-3 Exercises

FOR EXTRA PRACTICE
see page 674

internet connect
Homework Help Online
go.hrw.com Keyword: MS4 9-3

GUIDED PRACTICE

See Example 1 Find the volume of each pyramid.

1. 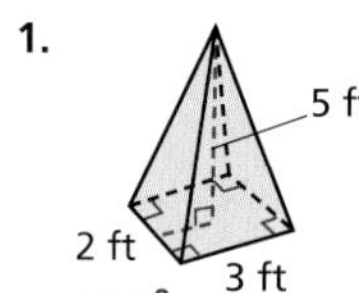

10 ft³

2. 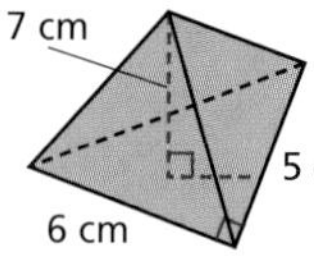 7 cm, 5 cm, 6 cm
35 cm³

3. 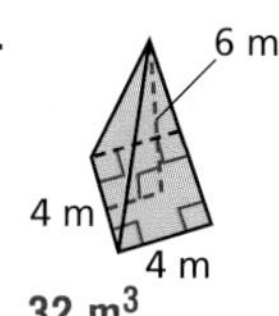

32 m³

See Example 2 Find the volume of each cone to the nearest tenth. Use 3.14 for π.

4. 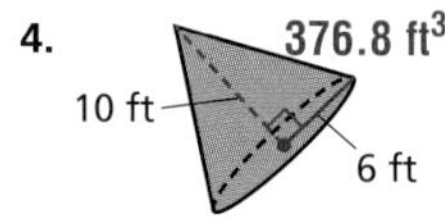

376.8 ft³

5. 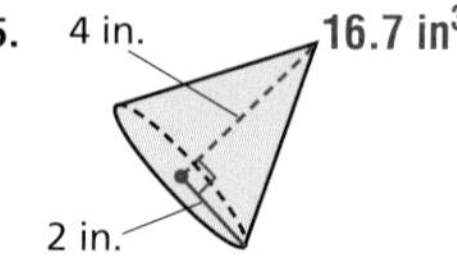

16.7 in³

6. 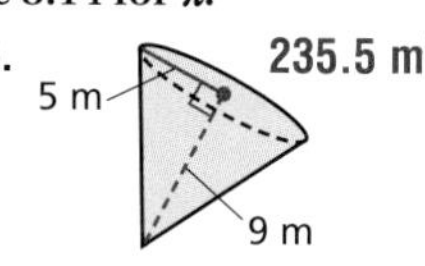

235.5 m³

See Example 3 Find the volume of each sphere to the nearest tenth. Use 3.14 for π.

7. 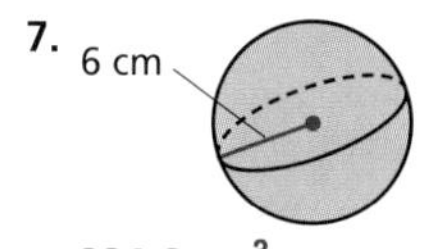

904.3 cm³

8. 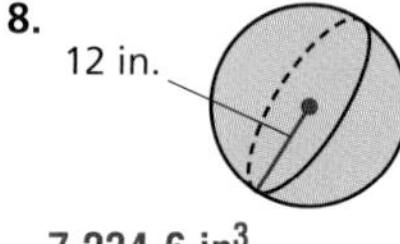

7,234.6 in³

9. 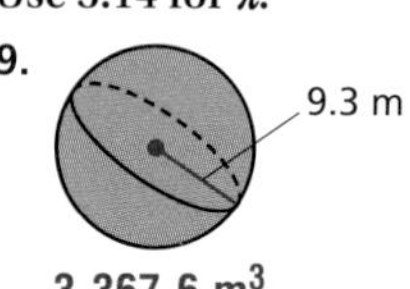

3,367.6 m³

INDEPENDENT PRACTICE

See Example 1 Find the volume of each pyramid.

10. 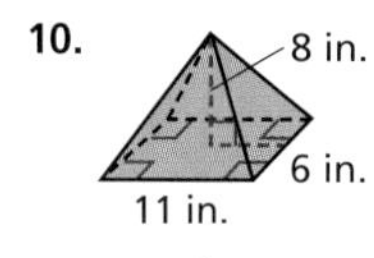

176 in³

11. 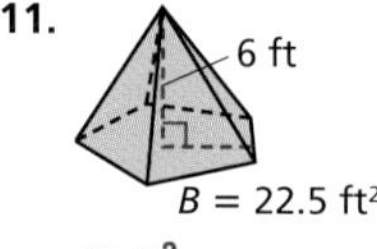

45 ft³

12. 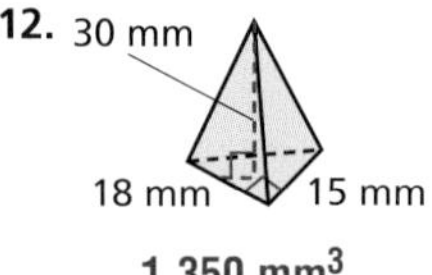

1,350 mm³

See Example 2 Find the volume of each cone to the nearest tenth. Use 3.14 for π.

13. 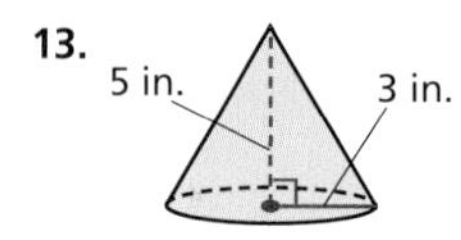

47.1 in³

14. 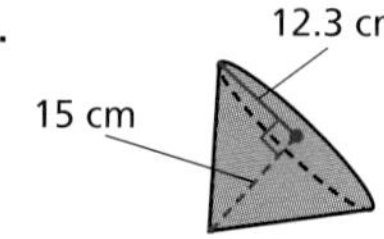

2,375.3 cm³

15. 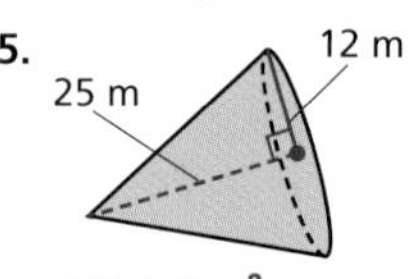

3,768.0 m³

See Example 3 Find the volume of each sphere to the nearest tenth. Use 3.14 for π.

16. 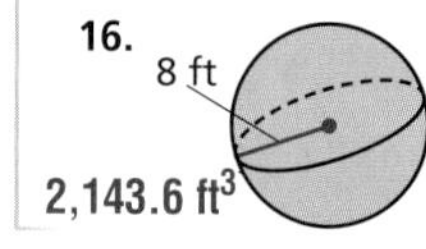

2,143.6 ft³

17. 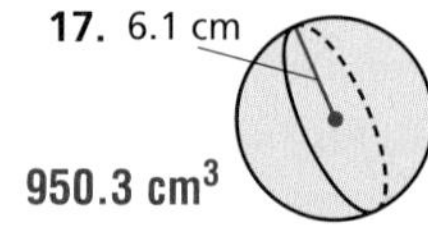

950.3 cm³

18. 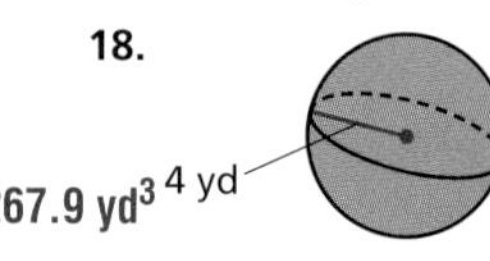

267.9 yd³

RETEACH 9-3

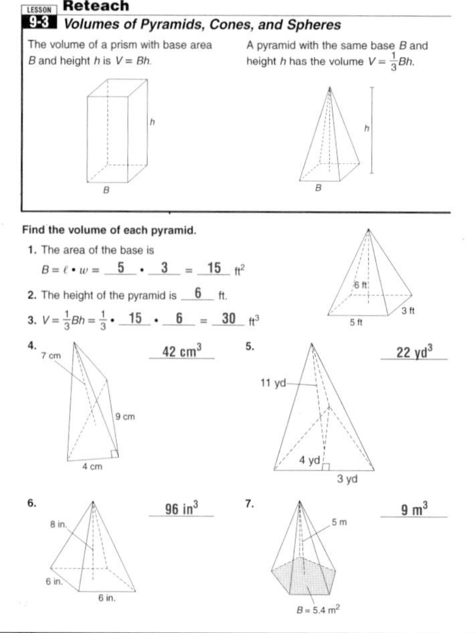

LESSON 9-3 Reteach
Volumes of Pyramids, Cones, and Spheres

The volume of a prism with base area B and height h is $V = Bh$.

A pyramid with the same base B and height h has the volume $V = \frac{1}{3}Bh$.

Find the volume of each pyramid.

1. The area of the base is $B = \ell \cdot w = 5 \cdot 3 = 15$ ft²
2. The height of the pyramid is 6 ft.
3. $V = \frac{1}{3}Bh = \frac{1}{3} \cdot 15 \cdot 6 = 30$ ft³
4. 42 cm³
5. 22 yd³
6. 96 in³
7. 9 m³

PRACTICE 9-3

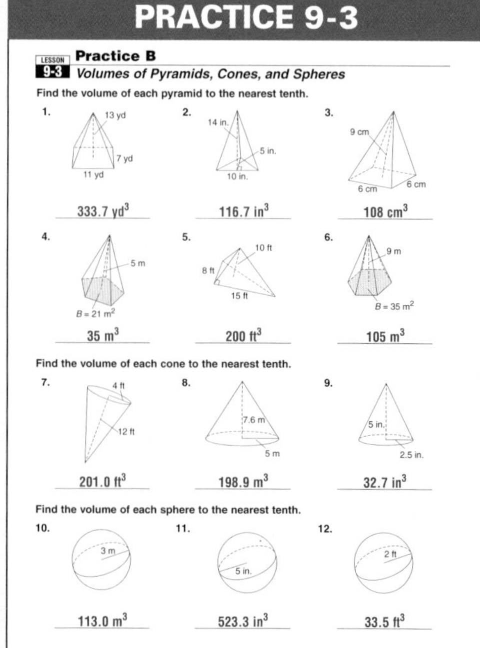

LESSON 9-3 Practice B
Volumes of Pyramids, Cones, and Spheres

Find the volume of each pyramid to the nearest tenth.

1. 333.7 yd³
2. 116.7 in³
3. 108 cm³
4. 35 m³
5. 200 ft³
6. 105 m³

Find the volume of each cone to the nearest tenth.

7. 201.0 ft³
8. 198.9 m³
9. 32.7 in³

Find the volume of each sphere to the nearest tenth.

10. 113.0 m³
11. 523.3 in³
12. 33.5 ft³

PRACTICE AND PROBLEM SOLVING

Find the volume of each solid to the nearest tenth. Use 3.14 for π.

19. a 7 ft tall rectangular pyramid with base 4 ft by 5 ft **46.7 ft³**
20. a cone with radius 8 yd and height 12 yd **803.8 yd³**
21. a sphere with diameter 5 m **65.4 m³**
22. ***BUSINESS*** A snack bar sells popcorn in the containers shown at right.
    a. How many cubic inches of popcorn, to the nearest tenth, does the cone-shaped container hold? Use 3.14 for π. **167.5 in³**
    b. How many cubic inches of popcorn does the cylinder-shaped container hold? Use 3.14 for π. **502.4 in³**
    c. About how many times as much popcorn does the larger container hold? **3**

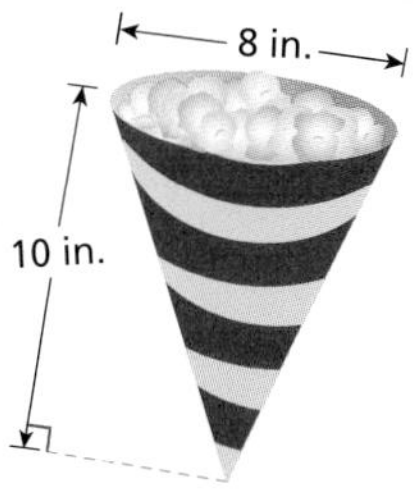

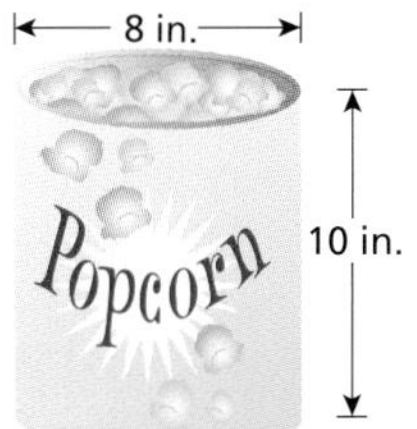

8 in.
10 in.
8 in.
Popcorn
10 in.

23. ***ARCHITECTURE*** The steeple on a building is a square pyramid with base area 12 square feet and height 15 feet. How many cubic feet of concrete was used to make the pyramid? **60 ft³**

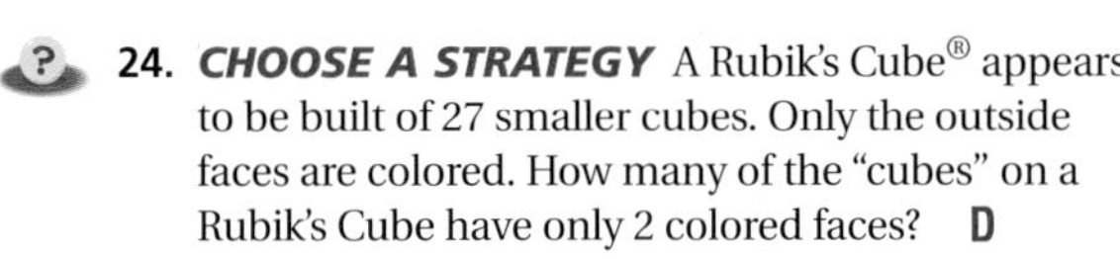

24. ***CHOOSE A STRATEGY*** A Rubik's Cube® appears to be built of 27 smaller cubes. Only the outside faces are colored. How many of the "cubes" on a Rubik's Cube have only 2 colored faces? **D**

A 3 **B** 8 **C** 9 **D** 12

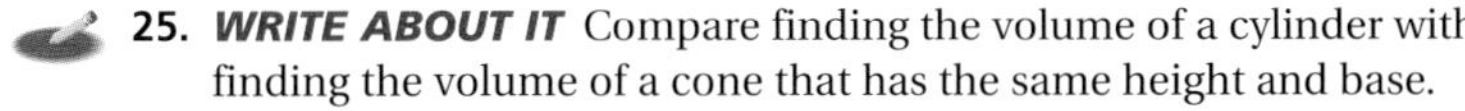

25. ***WRITE ABOUT IT*** Compare finding the volume of a cylinder with finding the volume of a cone that has the same height and base.

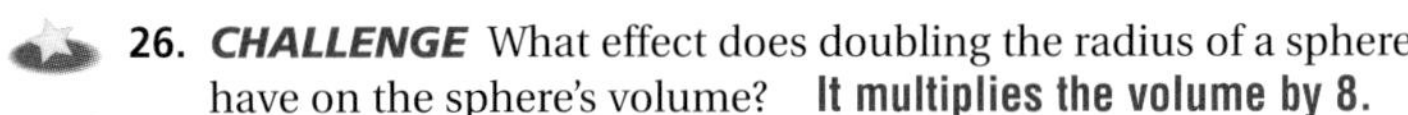

26. ***CHALLENGE*** What effect does doubling the radius of a sphere have on the sphere's volume? **It multiplies the volume by 8.**

Spiral Review

Solve by using cross products. (Lesson 5-3)

27. $\frac{5}{6} = \frac{a}{12}$ **$a = 10$**
28. $\frac{c}{16} = \frac{5}{8}$ **$c = 10$**
29. $\frac{b}{9} = \frac{21}{27}$ **$b = 7$**
30. $\frac{3}{5} = \frac{m}{25}$ **$m = 15$**

The two quadrilaterals are congruent. Give the measure of each angle. (Lesson 7-9)

31. $\angle GFE$ **115°**
32. $\angle FGH$ **75°**

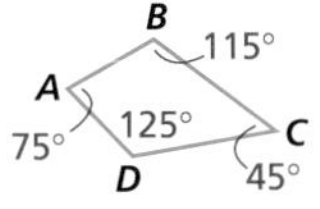

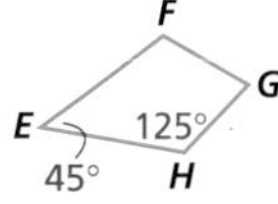

33. **TEST PREP** What is the volume of a cylinder with diameter 4 m and height 10 m? (Lesson 9-2) **B**

A 62.8 m³ **B** 125.6 m³ **C** 160 m³ **D** 502.4 m³

Answers

25. In both cases, you multiply the area of the base times the height. For the volume of the pyramid, divide the result by 3.

Journal

Ask students to find an example of a sphere used in the real world and then to describe how to find the volume of that sphere.

Test Prep Doctor

For Exercise 33, encourage students to estimate the answer before looking at the answer choices. Students who chose **D** used the diameter instead of the radius. If students calculate the radius first, they know that the volume will be about 3 · 2 · 2 · 10, or 120, so they can eliminate all choices but **B.**

Lesson Quiz

Find the volume of each solid to the nearest tenth. Use 3.14 for π.

1. **80 ft³**

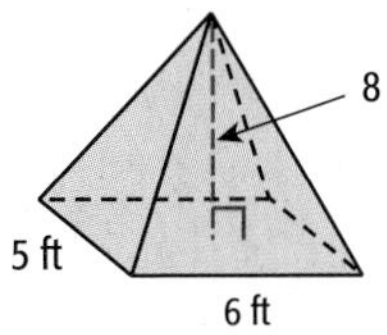

8 ft
5 ft
6 ft

2. **301.4 yd³**

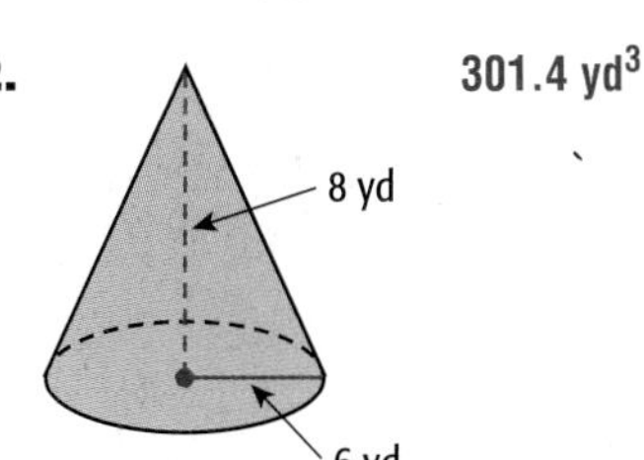

3. sphere with radius 3 ft **113.0 ft³**
4. 14 ft tall triangular pyramid whose base triangle has a 12 ft base and a height of 9 ft **252 ft³**

Available on Daily Transparency in CRB

CHALLENGE 9-3

LESSON 9-3 **Challenge**
Take It Out

Sometimes you can find the volume of an oddly shaped figure by first finding the volume of the entire solid and then subtracting a part that is missing.

Find the volume of each figure. Round to the nearest whole number.

1. 2 m, 2 m, 6 m, 6 m, 6 m

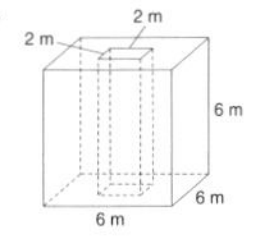

Cube with rectangular prism removed

V of cube: **216 m³**
V of missing part: **24 m³**
V of figure: **192 m³**

2.

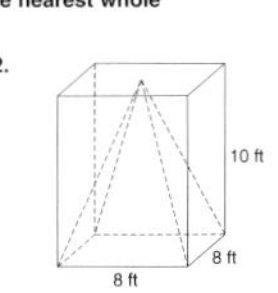

Rectangular prism with pyramid removed

V of prism: **640 ft³**
V of missing part: **213 ft³**
V of figure: **427 ft³**

3.

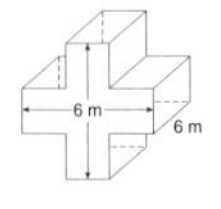

Cube with 2 m × 2 m × 6 m corners removed

V of cube: **216 m³**
V of missing part: **96 m³**
V of figure: **120 m³**

4.

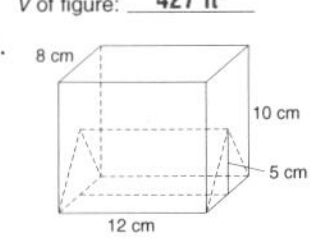

Rectangular prism with triangular prism removed

V of rectangular prism: **960 cm³**
V of missing part: **240 cm³**
V of figure: **720 cm³**

PROBLEM SOLVING 9-3

LESSON 9-3 **Problem Solving**
Volume of Pyramids, Cones, and Spheres

Write the correct answer.

1. Each of the cone-shaped cups near the water cooler has a radius of 3 centimeters and a height of 10 centimeters. If 1 cubic centimeter can hold 1 milliliter of liquid, how much water can each cup hold?

94.2 mL

2. The Great Pyramid in Egypt has a square base that measures 751 feet on each side. The pyramid is 481 feet high. What is the volume of the Great Pyramid? Round your answer to the nearest cubic foot.

90,428,160 ft³

3. A waffle cone that holds ice cream is 15 centimeters high and has a diameter of 10 centimeters. What volume of ice cream can it hold if it is filled to the top?

392.5 cm³

4. A basketball should be filled with air to reach a diameter of about 24 centimeters. About how many cubic centimeters of air is inside this basketball?

7,235 cm³

Choose the letter of the correct answer.

5. The 1933 rules for Women's Basketball require that the circumference of the ball be between $29\frac{1}{2}$ inches and $30\frac{1}{4}$ inches. What is the greatest volume the ball can have to the nearest cubic inch?
   A 926 in³ **C** 386 in³
   (**B**) 468 in³ **D** 97 in³

6. The top of a 44-story office building is shaped like a pyramid. The base of the pyramid is a right triangle with the two legs measuring 73 feet and 78 feet. The pyramid is 35 feet high. What is the volume of the pyramid?
   F 199,290 ft³ **H** 41,756 ft³
   G 66,430 ft³ (**J**) 33,215 ft³

7. The diameter of a cone-shaped container is 4 inches. Its height is 6 inches. How much greater is the volume of a cylinder-shaped container with the same diameter and height?
   (**A**) 50.24 in³ **C** 100.98 in³
   B 75.36 in³ **D** 200.96 in³

8. What is the difference in volume between a sphere with a radius of 12 centimeters and a sphere with a diameter of 12 centimeters?
   (**F**) 6,330.24 cm³ **H** 3,617.28 cm³
   G 5,994.36 cm³ **J** 904.32 cm³

Chapter 9 Mid-Chapter Quiz

Purpose: *To assess students' mastery of concepts and skills in Lessons 9-1 through 9-3*

Assessment Resources

Section 9A Quiz

Assessment Resources . . . . p. 25

***Test and Practice Generator* CD-ROM**

Additional mid-chapter assessment items in both multiple-choice and free-response format may be generated for any objective in Lessons 9–1 through 9–3.

Chapter 9 Mid-Chapter Quiz

Mid-Chapter Quiz

LESSON 9-1 (pp. 472–475)

Give the name of each prism or pyramid.

1. 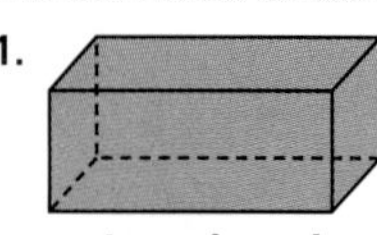
rectangular prism

2. 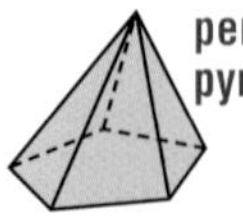 **pentagonal pyramid**

3. 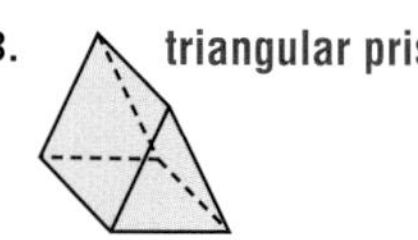
triangular prism

4. 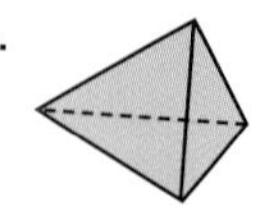
triangular pyramid

5. 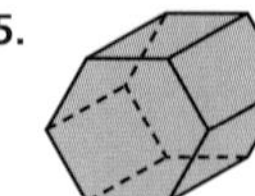
hexagonal prism

6. 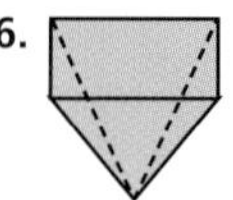
rectangular pyramid

LESSON 9-2 (pp. 476–479)

Find the volume of each figure to the nearest tenth. Use 3.14 for π.

7. 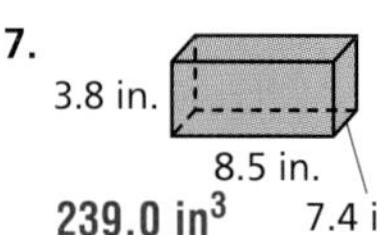

239.0 in^3

8. 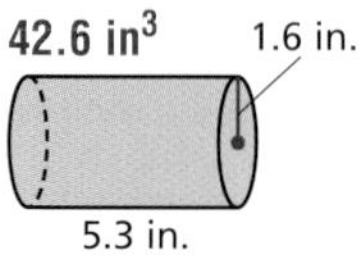 **42.6 in^3**
1.6 in.
5.3 in.

9. 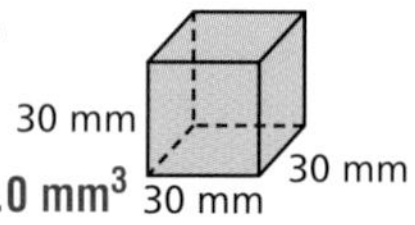 30 mm, 30 mm, 30 mm
27,000.0 mm^3

10. 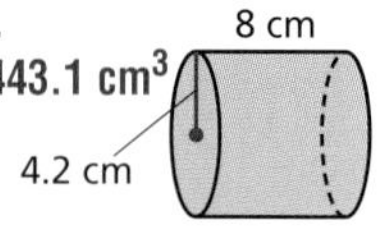 **443.1 cm^3**
8 cm
4.2 cm

11. 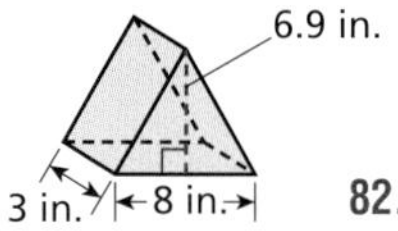 6.9 in.
3 in.
8 in.
82.8 in^3

12. 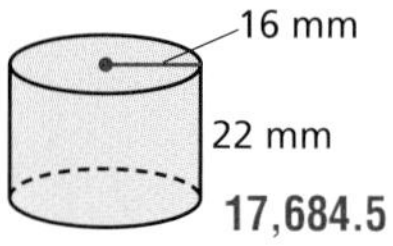 16 mm
22 mm
17,684.5 mm^3

LESSON 9-3 (pp. 480–483)

Find the volume of each figure to the nearest tenth. Use 3.14 for π.

13. 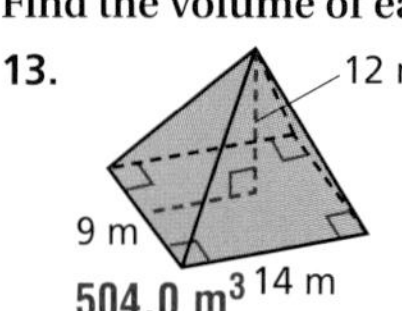

504.0 m^3

14. 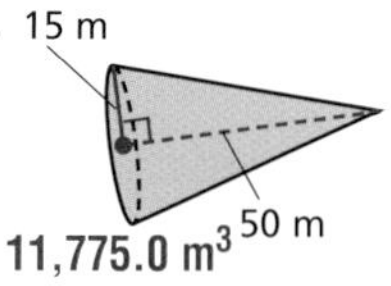 15 m
50 m
11,775.0 m^3

15. 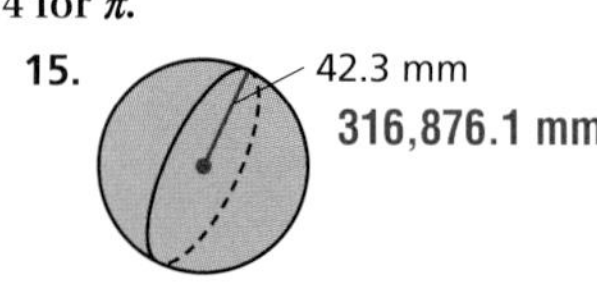

316,876.1 mm^3

16. 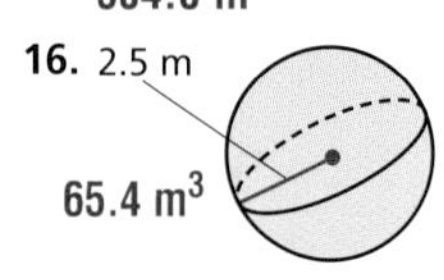

65.4 m^3

17. 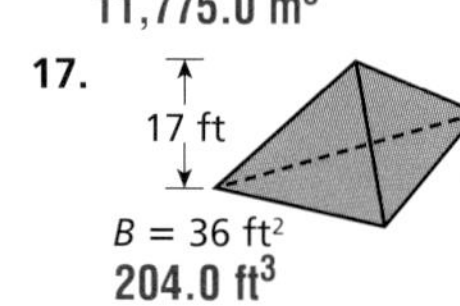

204.0 ft^3

18. 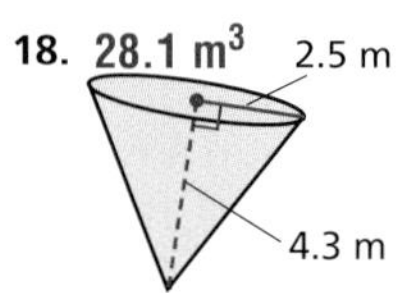

28.1 m^3

19. The diameter of a volleyball is about 21 cm. About how much air, to the nearest cubic centimeter, will fill the volleyball? Use 3.14 for π. **4,847 cm^3**

20. A cone has a radius of 2.5 cm and a height of 14 cm. What is the volume of the cone to the nearest hundredth? Use 3.14 for π. **91.58 cm^3**

Focus on Problem Solving

Solve

• Choose an operation

When choosing an operation to use when solving a problem, you need to decide which action the problem is asking you to take. If you are asked to combine numbers, then you need to add. If you are asked to take away numbers or to find the difference between two numbers, then you need to subtract. You need to use multiplication when you put equal parts together and division when you separate something into equal parts.

Determine the action in each problem. Then tell which operation should be used to solve the problem. Explain your choice.

1. Jeremy filled a sugar cone completely full of frozen yogurt and then put one scoop of frozen yogurt on top. The volume of Jeremy's cone is about 20.93 in^3, and the volume of the scoop that Jeremy used is about 16.75 in^3. About how much frozen yogurt, in cubic inches, did Jeremy use?

2. The volume of a cylinder equals the combined volumes of three cones that each have the same height and base size as the cylinder. What is the volume of a cylinder if a cone of the same height and base size has a volume of 45.2 cm^3?

3. The biology class at Jefferson High School takes care of a family of turtles that is kept in a glass tank with water, rocks, and plants. The volume of the tank is 2.75 cubic feet. At the end of the year, the baby turtles will have grown and will be moved into a tank that is 6.15 cubic feet. How much greater will the volume of the new tank be than that of the old tank?

4. Brianna is adding a second section to her hamster cage. The two sections will be connected by a tunnel that is made of 4 cylindrical parts, all the same size. If the volume of the tunnel is 56.52 cubic inches, what is the volume of each part of the tunnel?

Answers

1. 37.68 in^3
2. 135.6 cm^3
3. 3.4 ft^3
4. 14.13 in^3

Focus on Problem Solving

Purpose: *To focus on choosing an operation to solve a problem*

Problem Solving Resources

Interactive Problem Solving . . pp. 76–80

Math: Reading and Writing in the Content Area . . . . pp. 76–80

Problem Solving Process

This page focuses on the third step of the problem-solving process: **Solve**

Discuss

Have students tell which operation should be used to solve each problem. Have them explain which action the problem is asking them to perform and which words in the problem helped them determine the action.

Possible answers:

1. Addition; combine different volumes of yogurt; *how much.*
2. Multiplication; combine three equal volumes; *what is, combined volumes.*
3. Subtraction; take the original volume away from the new volume; *how much greater.*
4. Division; separate the total volume into 4 equal parts; *what is, each.*

Surface Area

One-Minute Section Planner

Lesson	Materials	Resources
Lesson 9-4 Surface Area of Prisms, Cylinders, and Spheres **NCTM:** Geometry, Measurement, Reasoning and Proof, Communication, Connections **NAEP:** Measurement 1j ☐ SAT-9 ☐ SAT-10 ☐ ITBS ☐ CTBS ☐ MAT ☑ CAT	**Optional** Teaching Transparency T13 *(CRB)* Empty food boxes Paper	• *Chapter 9 Resource Book,* pp. 35–44 • Daily Transparency T12, CRB • Additional Examples Transparencies T14–T15, CRB • *Alternate Openers: Explorations,* p. 79
Lesson 9-5 Changing Dimensions **NCTM:** Geometry, Measurement, Problem Solving, Communication, Connections **NAEP:** Geometry 3b ☐ SAT-9 ☐ SAT-10 ☐ ITBS ☐ CTBS ☐ MAT ☐ CAT	**Optional** Teaching Transparency T17 *(CRB)* Graph paper *(CRB, p. 59)* Drinking cups from fast-food restaurants or convenience stores	• *Chapter 9 Resource Book,* pp. 45–53 • Daily Transparency T16, CRB • Additional Examples Transparencies T18–T21, CRB • *Alternate Openers: Explorations,* p. 80
Hands-On Lab 9B Build Polyhedrons, Cylinders, and Cones **NCTM:** Geometry, Measurement **NAEP:** Geometry 1f ☐ SAT-9 ☐ SAT-10 ☐ ITBS ☐ CTBS ☐ MAT ☐ CAT	**Required** Compasses *(MK)* Rulers *(MK)* Straightedges *(MK)*	• *Hands-On Lab Activities,* pp. 93–94, 127
Extension Surface Area of Other Figures **NCTM:** Geometry, Measurement, Reasoning and Proof, Connections **NAEP:** Measurement 1j ☐ SAT-9 ☐ SAT-10 ☐ ITBS ☐ CTBS ☐ MAT ☐ CAT	**Optional** Unit cubes *(MK)*	• Additional Examples Transparencies T22–T24, CRB
Section 9B Assessment		• Section 9B Quiz, AR p. 26 • *Test and Practice Generator* CD-ROM

SAT = *Stanford Achievement Tests* **ITBS** = *Iowa Test of Basic Skills* **CTBS** = *Comprehensive Test of Basic Skills/Terra Nova*
MAT = *Metropolitan Achievement Test* **CAT** = *California Achievement Test*

NCTM—Complete standards can be found on pages T27–T33. **NAEP**—Complete standards can be found on pages A35–A39.

SE = *Student Edition* **TE** = *Teacher's Edition* **AR** = *Assessment Resources* **CRB** = *Chapter Resource Book* **MK** = *Manipulatives Kit*

Section Overview

Surface Area of Three-Dimensional Figures — *Lesson 9-4*

Why? You need to be able to find the surface area of three-dimensional figures for many real-world applications, such as finding the amount of paint needed to cover a cylindrical tank. You can find surface area using both nets and formulas.

Surface Area of a Rectangular Prism

$S = 2\ell w + 2\ell h + 2wh$

Surface Area of a Cylinder

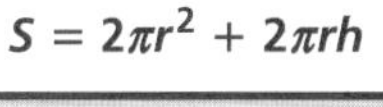

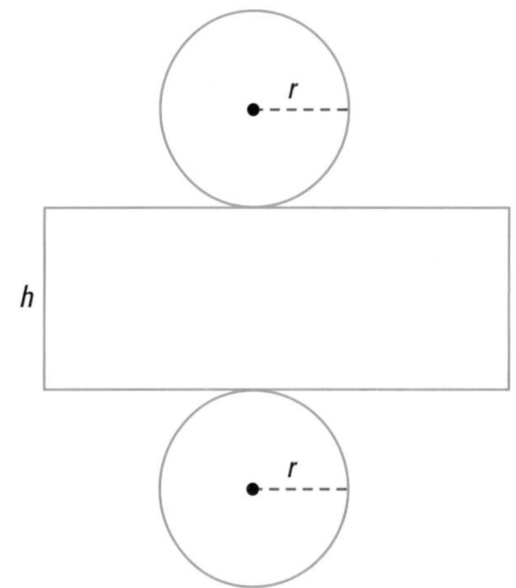

Changing Dimensions — *Lesson 9-5, Hands-On Lab 9B*

Why? Students need to understand how the surface area and volume of scale model figures relate to actual-size figures. Students learn how the scale factor of similar figures is used to find the surface area or volume of one figure, given the surface area or volume of the other figure.

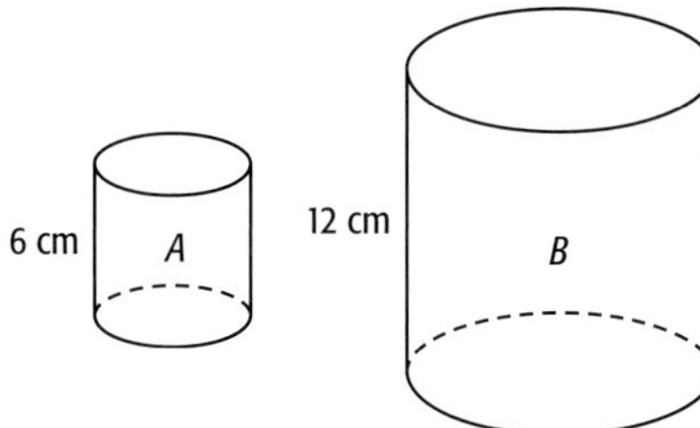

The **scale factor** of cylinder *A* to cylinder *B* is $\frac{1}{2}$.

$S_A = S_B \cdot \left(\frac{1}{2}\right)^2$

For any pair of similar figures, the ***surface area*** of the model figure equals the surface area of the original figure times the **scale factor squared.**

$V_A = V_B \cdot \left(\frac{1}{2}\right)^3$

For any pair of similar three-dimensional figures, the ***volume*** of the model figure equals the volume of the original figure times the **scale factor cubed.**

9-4 Organizer

Pacing: Traditional 2 days
Block 1 day

Objective: Students find the surface area of prisms, cylinders, and spheres.

Warm Up

Find the volume of each figure to the nearest tenth. Use 3.14 for π.

1. rectangular pyramid 7 ft by 8 ft by 10 ft tall **186.7 ft^3**
2. cone with radius 2 ft and height 3 ft **12.6 ft^3**
3. sphere with diameter 4 ft **33.5 ft^3**
4. triangular pyramid with base 54 ft^2 and height 9 ft **162 ft^3**

Problem of the Day

When my age is divided by 2, 3, 4, or 6 there is always a remainder of 1, but when it is divided by 7 there is no remainder. How old am I? **49**

Available on Daily Transparency in CRB

Math Fact

Earth is almost spherical, with a radius of about 3,960 miles. The surface area of Earth is about 62,726,400π square miles, or 196,960,896 square miles.

9-4 Surface Area of Prisms, Cylinders, and Spheres

Learn to find the surface area of prisms, cylinders, and spheres.

Vocabulary
net
surface area

If you remove the surface from a three-dimensional figure and lay it out flat, the pattern you make is called a **net**. You can construct nets to cover almost any geometric solid.

Since nets allow you to see all the surfaces of a solid at one time, you can use them to help find the *surface area* of a three-dimensional figure. **Surface area** is the sum of the areas of all of the surfaces of a figure.

SURFACE AREA OF A POLYHEDRON

The surface area of a polyhedron is found by adding the areas of each face of the polyhedron.

You can use nets to write formulas for the surface area of prisms. The surface area S is the sum of the areas of the faces of the prism. For the rectangular prism shown, $S = \ell w + \ell h + wh + \ell w + \ell h + wh$

$= 2\ell w + 2\ell h + 2wh.$

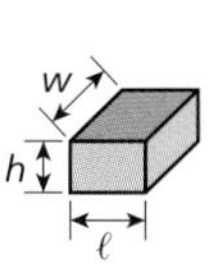

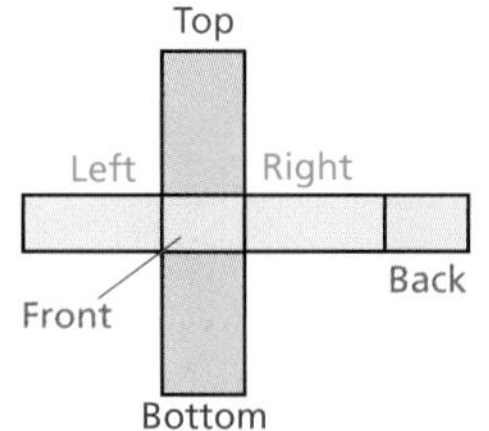

EXAMPLE 1 Finding the Surface Area of a Prism

Find the surface area of the prism formed by the net.

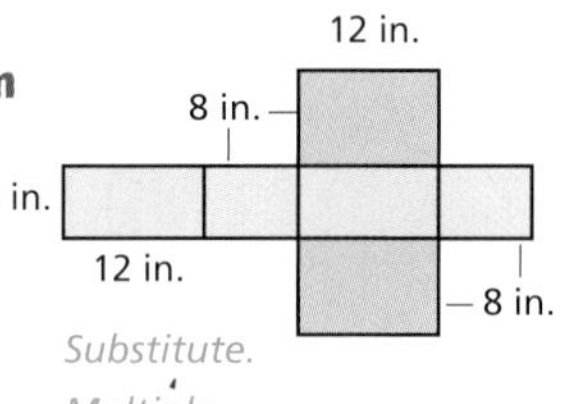

$S = 2\ell w + 2\ell h + 2wh$

$S = (2 \cdot 12 \cdot 8) + (2 \cdot 12 \cdot 6) + (2 \cdot 8 \cdot 6)$ *Substitute.*

$S = 192 + 144 + 96$ *Multiply.*

$S = 432$ *Add.*

The surface area of the prism is 432 in^2.

1 Introduce

Alternate Opener

Surface Area of Prisms, Cylinders, and Spheres

The figure below is called a *net*. A net is a flat two-dimensional shape that can be folded to form a three-dimensional figure.

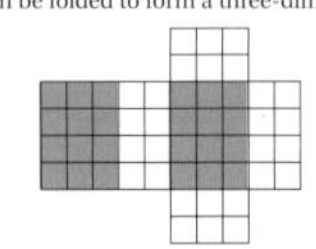

1. Suppose that you fold the net into a figure. What three-dimensional figure would be formed?
2. Find the area of each of the six faces of the three-dimensional figure.
3. Add the areas of the six faces. The total area is called the *surface area*.

Think and Discuss

4. **Explain** how you can find the surface area of a box.
5. **Describe** the net of a cylinder, such as a juice can.

Motivate

Give each student a rectangular sheet of paper. Discuss how to find the area of the sheet of paper (i.e., length times width). Point out that even if students have sheets of different sizes, the procedure for finding the area is the same. Then have students roll the paper to form a tube. Elicit from students that the area of the surface of this tube is the same as the area of the rectangle. Students may notice that the length or width of the rectangle corresponds to the circumference of the circular opening, depending on how they made the tube.

Exploration worksheet and answers on Chapter 9 Resource Book pp. 36 and 66

2 Teach

Lesson Presentation

Guided Instruction

In this lesson, students learn to find the surface area of prisms, cylinders, and spheres (Teaching Transparency T13, Chapter 9 Resource Book). Using a net makes it possible to find the surface area without referring to a formula, intuitively deriving the formula each time instead. Be sure students understand how circumference is used to find the surface area of a cylinder.

Point out that although the formulas for surface area of cylinders and spheres are exact, the computed values will not be exact since they involve using an approximation for π.

If you could remove the lateral surface from a cylinder, like peeling a label from a can, you would see that it has the shape of a rectangle when flattened out.

You can draw a net for a cylinder by drawing the circular bases (like the ends of a can) and the rectangular lateral surface as shown below. The length of the rectangle is the circumference, $2\pi r$, of the cylinder. So the area of the lateral surface is $2\pi rh$. The area of each base is πr^2.

SURFACE AREA OF A CYLINDER

The surface area S of a cylinder is the sum of the areas of its bases, $2\pi r^2$, plus the area of its lateral surface, $2\pi rh$.

$$S = 2\pi r^2 + 2\pi rh$$

EXAMPLE 2 Finding the Surface Area of a Cylinder

Find the surface area of the cylinder formed by the net to the nearest tenth. Use 3.14 for π.

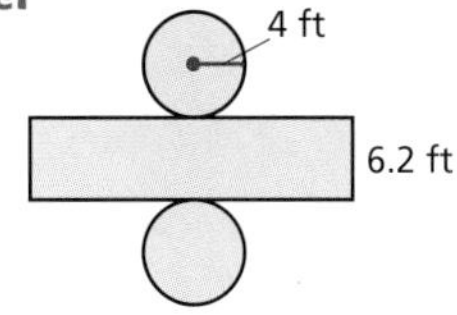

$S = 2\pi r^2 + 2\pi rh$	*Use the formula.*
$S \approx (2 \cdot 3.14 \cdot 4^2) + (2 \cdot 3.14 \cdot 4 \cdot 6.2)$	*Substitute.*
$S \approx 100.48 + 155.744$	*Multiply.*
$S \approx 256.224$	*Add.*
$S \approx 256.2$	*Round.*

The surface area of the cylinder is about 256.2 ft^2.

COMMON ERROR ALERT

Some students might try shortcuts when using the formulas for the surface area of rectangular prisms and cylinders. Stress the importance of following a logical series of steps when using a formula. First you substitute values into the formula; then you follow the order of operations to evaluate the surface area.

Additional Examples

Example 1

Find the surface area of the prism formed by the net.

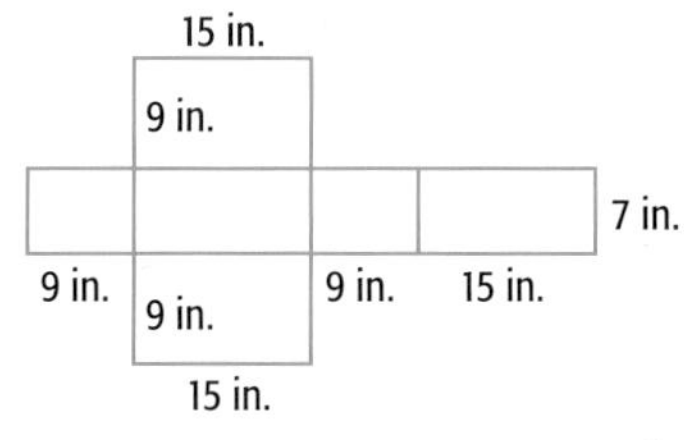

606 in^2

Example 2

Find the surface area of the cylinder formed by the net to the nearest tenth. Use 3.14 for π.

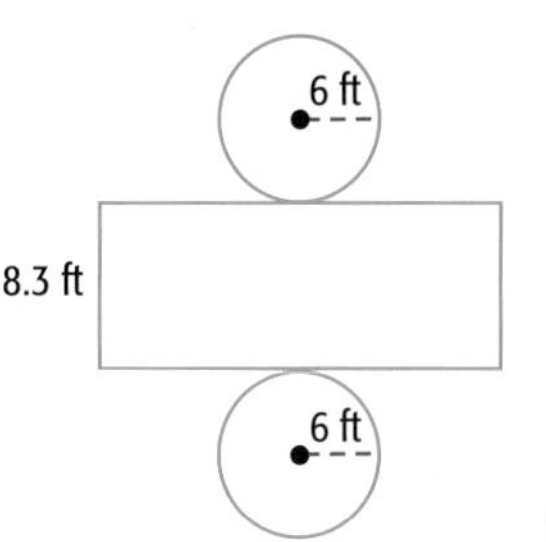

538.8 ft^2

Example 3

Find the surface area of the sphere to the nearest tenth. Use 3.14 for π.

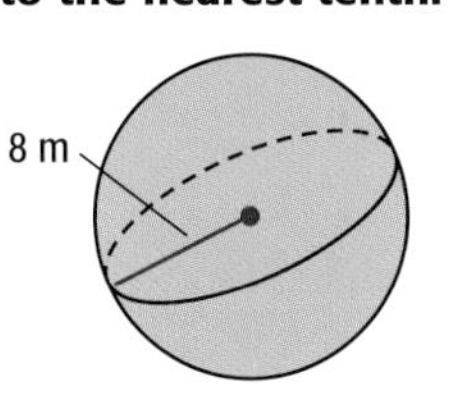

803.8 m^2

Example 2 note: Remind students that it is not necessary to memorize the formula for the surface area of a cylinder. Students should know the formulas for the circumference and area of a circle, and they can apply those formulas and multiply by the height to find the surface area of a cylinder.

Reaching All Learners

Through Hands-On Experience

If possible, bring in several empty food boxes, such as cereal or cracker boxes, which students can deconstruct to examine the actual nets of the figures.

Unlike the surface of a prism or a cylinder, the surface of a sphere cannot be flattened without stretching or shrinking. This is why it is not possible to draw a perfectly accurate flat map of Earth. In the *Mercator projection* of Earth, for example, Greenland appears much too large.

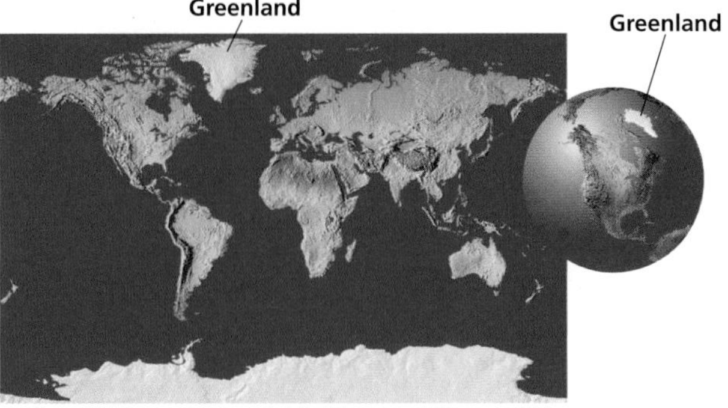

Because the surface of a sphere cannot be flattened out, it is impossible to make a net for a sphere. However, there is an exact formula for the area of a sphere.

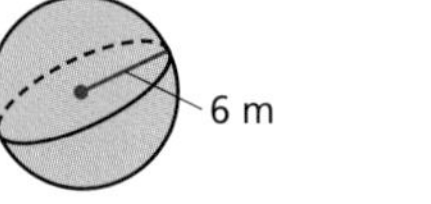

SURFACE AREA OF A SPHERE

The surface area S of a sphere is 4 times π times the radius r squared.

$$S = 4\pi r^2$$

EXAMPLE 3 Finding the Surface Area of a Sphere

Find the surface area of the sphere to the nearest tenth. Use 3.14 for π.

$S = 4\pi r^2$	*Use the formula.*
$S \approx 4 \cdot 3.14 \cdot 6^2$	*Substitute.*
$S \approx 452.16$	*Multiply.*
$S \approx 452.2$	*Round.*

The surface area of the sphere is about 452.2 m^2.

Think and Discuss

1. **Explain** how you would find the surface area of a rectangular prism.
2. **Describe** how to find the surface area of a cylinder 2 inches tall with a radius of 3 inches.
3. **Describe** the relationship between the area of a circle and the surface area of a sphere with the same radius.

3 Close

Summarize

Have students explain how to use a net to find the surface area of a rectangular prism and a cylinder.

Possible answers: The net of a rectangular prism shows each face of the prism. Find the area of each face. Then add the areas to find the total surface area.

The net of a cylinder divides the cylinder into a rectangle and two circles. The rectangular length is the circumference of the circular part of the cylinder, and the width is the height of the cylinder. The radius of each circle is the radius of each base of the cylinder. Find the area of each base and the area of the rectangle. Add to find the total surface area.

Answers to Think and Discuss

Possible answers:

1. The surface area of a prism is the sum of the areas of the faces of the prism. Since opposite faces are congruent, you can find the area of one face and then multiply by 2, as indicated in the formula. Then add the area for each set to find the total surface area.
2. Use the formula for the surface area of a cylinder. Substitute $r = 3$ and $h = 2$ into the formula $S = 2\pi r^2 + 2\pi rh$. Use an approximation for π, and then evaluate.
3. The surface area of the sphere is 4 times more than the area of a circle with the same radius.

9-4 Exercises

FOR EXTRA PRACTICE
see page 675

internet connect
Homework Help Online
go.hrw.com Keyword: MS4 9-4

GUIDED PRACTICE

See Example 1 Find the surface area of the prism formed by each net.

1. **286 ft²**

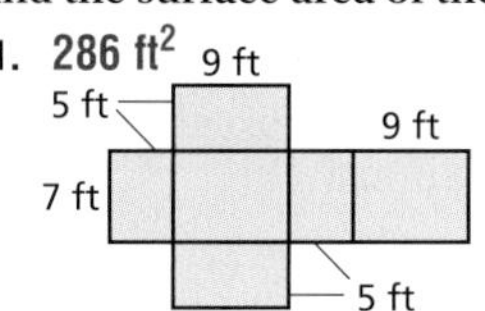

2. **856 cm²**

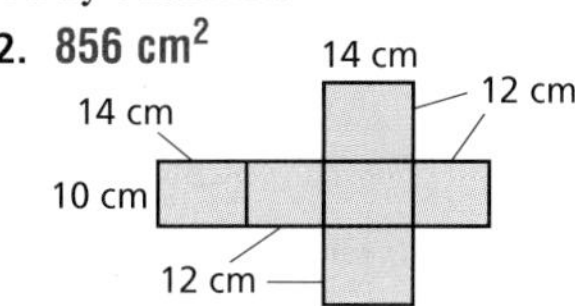

See Example 2 Find the surface area of the cylinder formed by each net to the nearest tenth. Use 3.14 for π.

3. **244.9 m²**

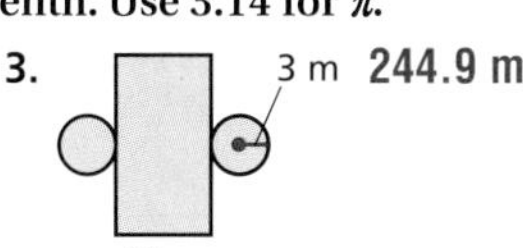

4. **1884.0 in²**

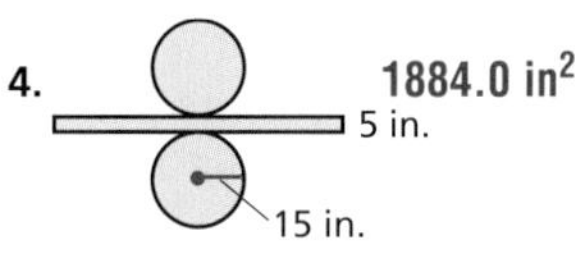

See Example 3 Find the surface area of each sphere to the nearest tenth. Use 3.14 for π.

5. **50.2 yd²**

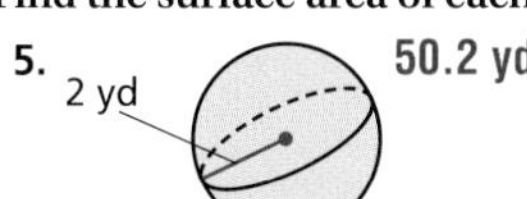

6. **1,017.4 ft²**

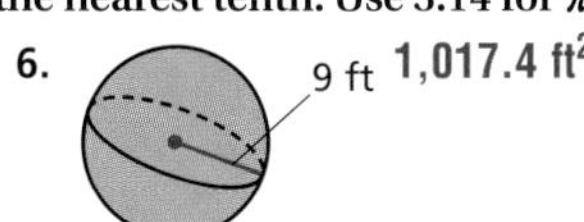

INDEPENDENT PRACTICE

See Example 1 Find the surface area of the prism formed by each net.

7. **928 in²**

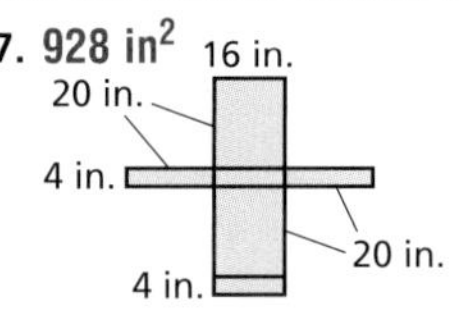

8. **1,160 ft²**

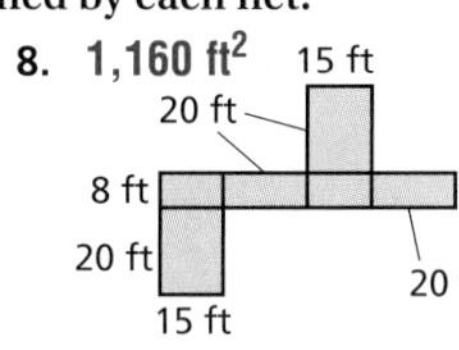

See Example 2 Find the surface area of the cylinder formed by each net to the nearest tenth. Use 3.14 for π.

9. **791.3 in²**

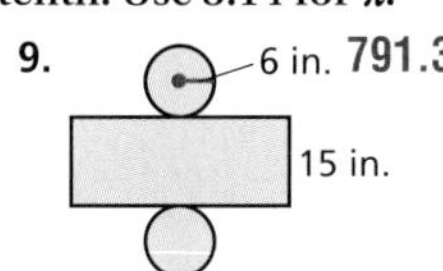

10. **188.4 cm²**

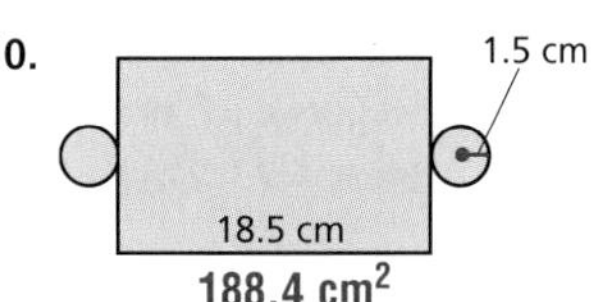

See Example 3 Find the surface area of each sphere to the nearest tenth. Use 3.14 for π.

11. **314 ft²**

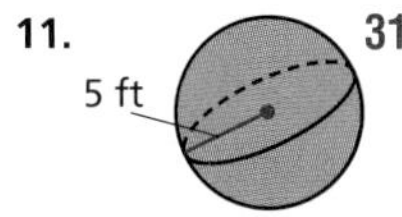

12. **1,808.6 m²**

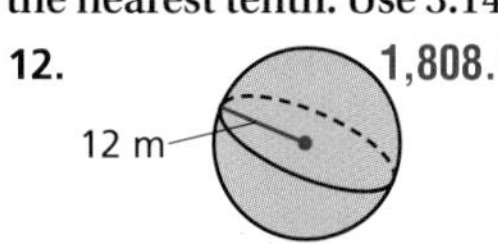

9-4 PRACTICE & ASSESS

Students may want to refer back to the lesson examples.

Assignment Guide

If you finished Example 1 assign:
Core 1, 2, 7, 8, 13, 20–28
Enriched 1, 2, 7, 8, 13, 20–28

If you finished Example 2 assign:
Core 1–4, 7–10, 13–15, 20–28
Enriched 1–4, 7–10, 13–15, 20–28

If you finished Example 3 assign:
Core 1–12, 13, 15, 20–28
Enriched 1–11 odd, 13–28

Notes

RETEACH 9-4

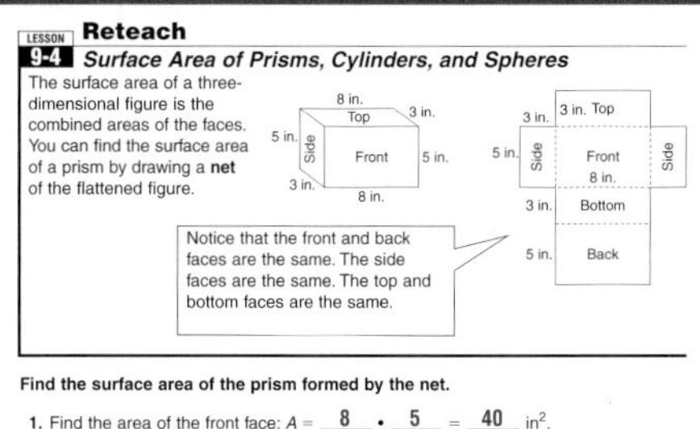
LESSON 9-4 **Reteach**
Surface Area of Prisms, Cylinders, and Spheres

The surface area of a three-dimensional figure is the combined areas of the faces. You can find the surface area of a prism by drawing a **net** of the flattened figure.

Notice that the front and back faces are the same. The side faces are the same. The top and bottom faces are the same.

Find the surface area of the prism formed by the net.

1. Find the area of the front face: A = 8 • 5 = 40 in².
The area of the front and back faces is 2 • 40 = 80 in².
2. Find the area of the side face: A = 5 • 3 = 15 in².
The area of the 2 side faces is 2 • 15 = 30 in².
3. Find the area of the top face: A = 8 • 3 = 24 in².
The area of the top and bottom faces is 2 • 24 = 48 in².
4. Combine the areas of the faces: 80 + 30 + 48 = 158 in².
The surface area of the prism is 158 in².

The surface area of a cylinder consists of a rectangle and 2 circular bases. The width of the rectangle is equal to the height of the cylinder. The length of the rectangle is equal to the circumference of the bases.

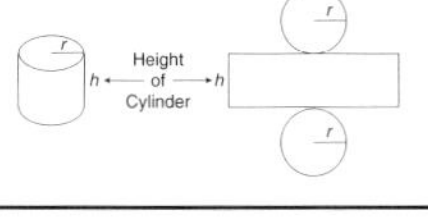

PRACTICE 9-4

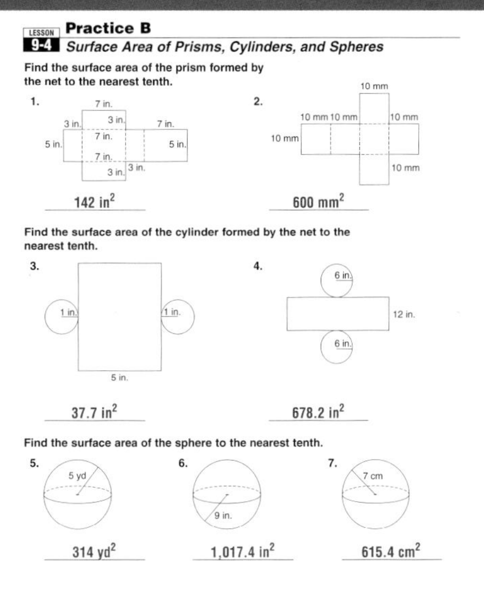
LESSON 9-4 **Practice B**
Surface Area of Prisms, Cylinders, and Spheres

Find the surface area of the prism formed by the net to the nearest tenth.

1. (7 in., 3 in., 5 in. net) 142 in²
2. (10 mm net) 600 mm²

Find the surface area of the cylinder formed by the net to the nearest tenth.

3. (1 in., 5 in.) 37.7 in²
4. (6 in., 12 in.) 678.2 in²

Find the surface area of the sphere to the nearest tenth.

5. (5 yd) 314 yd²
6. (9 in.) 1,017.4 in²
7. (7 cm) 615.4 cm²

Math Background

To find the surface area of a pyramid, add the area of the base and the area of each triangular face. The total area of the faces is called the lateral area, L.

$$S = B + L$$

In a regular pyramid, this formula converts to $S = B + \frac{1}{2}\ell p$, where ℓ represents the slant height (the height of one of the triangular faces), and p represents the perimeter of the base of the pyramid.

Answers

17. Possible answer: Find the surface area of a structure that is a cylinder topped with a hemisphere. The diameter of the structure is 10 feet, and the height of the cylinder part is 9 feet.

18. Possible answer: First find the surface area of the cylinder. Since the hemisphere covers one end of the cylinder, you need to include only the area of one of the circular bases: $3.14(5^2) + 3.14(10)(9) = 361.1 \text{ ft}^2$. Then find the surface area of the hemisphere: $\frac{1}{2}(4)(3.14)(5^2) = 157 \text{ ft}^2$. Finally, add the surface areas of the cylinder and the hemisphere: $361.1 \text{ ft}^2 + 157 \text{ ft}^2 = 518.1 \text{ ft}^2$.

Journal

Have students use diagrams to demonstrate how they would find the surface area of a classroom object shaped like a rectangular prism.

Test Prep Doctor

Students can use estimation to select the correct answer for Exercise 28. Since $r = 6$, a rough estimate is $\frac{4}{3}(3)(6^3) = 864$. The only choice close to 864 is **D,** the correct answer. Students who answered **A** or **C,** may have used the formula for surface area of a sphere.

Lesson Quiz

Find the surface area of each figure to the nearest tenth.

1. **352 ft²**

2. **100.5 ft²**

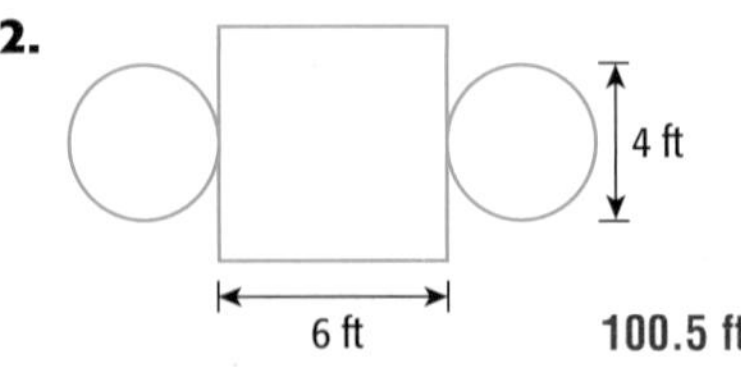

3. a sphere with radius 6 ft **452.2 ft²**

4. A drum is closed on the top and the bottom. The diameter of the drum is 18 in. The height is 32 in. Find the surface area. **2,317.3 in²**

Available on Daily Transparency in CRB

PRACTICE AND PROBLEM SOLVING

Find the surface area of each figure to the nearest tenth. Use 3.14 for π.

13. **38.4 ft²**

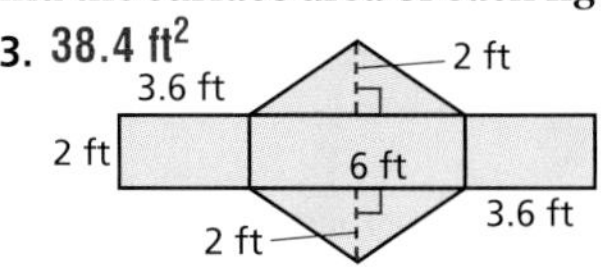

14. **3,215.4 ft²**

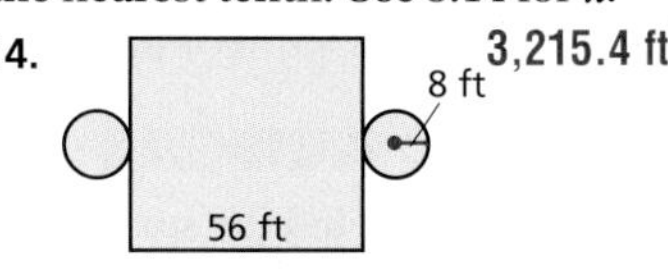

15a.

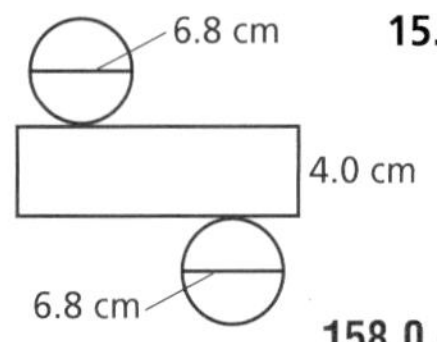

15. A cannery packs tuna into metal cans like the one shown. Round your answers to the nearest tenth, if necessary. Use 3.14 for π.

6.8 cm

4.0 cm

Tuna

a. Draw and label a net of the cylinder.

b. About how many square centimeters of metal are used to make each can? **158.0 cm²**

c. The label for each can goes all the way around the can. About how many square centimeters of paper are needed for each label? **85.4 cm²**

16a. 1519.8 cm²; 1345.5 cm²
b. 174.3 cm²

16. The table shows the approximate weight and diameter of size 4 and size 5 soccer balls.

Ball Size	Weight	Diameter
5	425 g	22 cm
4	370 g	20.7 cm

a. Find the surface area of each ball to the nearest tenth. Use 3.14 for π.

b. Find the difference between the surface areas.

Size 5

Size 4

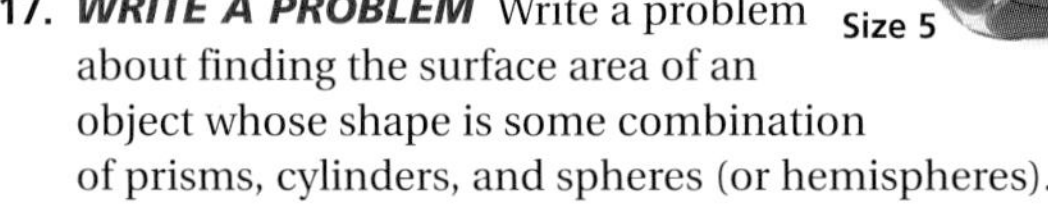

17. ***WRITE A PROBLEM*** Write a problem about finding the surface area of an object whose shape is some combination of prisms, cylinders, and spheres (or hemispheres).

18. ***WRITE ABOUT IT*** Explain how you would find the surface area of the figure you described in Exercise 17.

19. ***CHALLENGE*** Write a formula using r for radius and the symbol π to express the surface area of a hemisphere. Include in your formula the area of a base of the hemisphere. **$3\pi r^2$**

Spiral Review

State which integers each number lies between. (Lesson 3-7)

20. −6.4 **−6 and −7**
21. 5.3 **5 and 6**
22. −2.1 **−2 and −3**
23. −0.7 **0 and −1**

Divide. (Lesson 4-4)

24. 109.8 ÷ 6 **18.3**
25. −28.24 ÷ 4 **−7.06**
26. −27.6 ÷ 23 **−1.2**
27. 132.8 ÷ 16 **8.3**

28. **TEST PREP** A sphere has a radius of 6 inches. What is the volume of the sphere to the nearest tenth? Use 3.14 for π. (Lesson 9-3) **D**

A 75.4 in³ B 150.7 in³ C 452.2 in³ D 904.3 in³

CHALLENGE 9-4

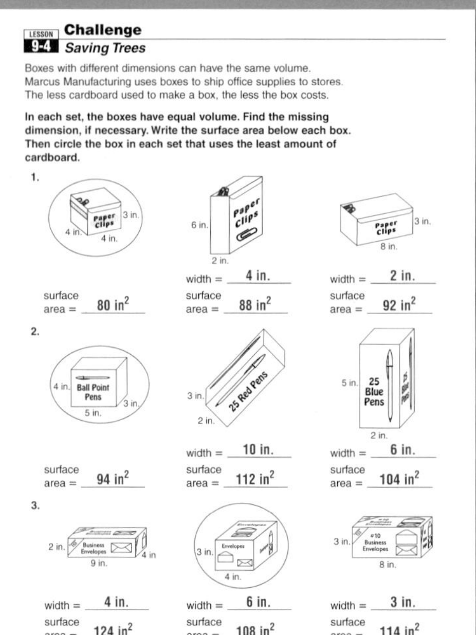

LESSON 9-4 **Challenge**
Saving Trees

Boxes with different dimensions can have the same volume. Marcus Manufacturing uses boxes to ship office supplies to stores. The less cardboard used to make a box, the less the box costs.

In each set, the boxes have equal volume. Find the missing dimension, if necessary. Write the surface area below each box. Then circle the box in each set that uses the least amount of cardboard.

1. (Paper Clips: 4 in., 4 in., 3 in.) surface area = **80 in²**
(Paper Clips: 6 in., 2 in.) width = **4 in.** surface area = **88 in²**
(Paper Clips: 8 in., 3 in.) width = **2 in.** surface area = **92 in²**

2. (Ball Point Pens: 4 in., 5 in., 3 in.) surface area = **94 in²**
(25 Red Pens: 3 in., 2 in.) width = **10 in.** surface area = **112 in²**
(25 Blue Pens: 5 in., 2 in.) width = **6 in.** surface area = **104 in²**

3. (Business Envelopes: 2 in., 9 in.) width = **4 in.** surface area = **124 in²**
(Envelopes: 3 in., 4 in.) width = **6 in.** surface area = **108 in²**
(Business Envelopes: 3 in., 8 in.) width = **3 in.** surface area = **114 in²**

PROBLEM SOLVING 9-4

LESSON 9-4 **Problem Solving**
Surface Area of Prisms, Cylinders, and Spheres

Write the correct answer.

1. Officially a baseball must not measure more than 8.5 inches in circumference and must be covered with leather. What is the most leather needed to cover the largest official baseball? Round your answer to the nearest square inch.
about 23 in²

2. The smallest circumference an official baseball can have is 6.5 inches. How many baseballs could be covered with 101 square inches of leather?
7 baseballs

3. A can of peas is 3 inches in diameter and 4.5 inches tall. What is the area of the label used around the can?
42.39 in²

4. How much wrapping paper do you need to completely cover a rectangular box that is 20 inches by 18 inches by 2 inches?
872 in²

Choose the letter of the correct answer.

5. The Sunsphere in Knoxville, Tennessee, is a 5-story reflective glass globe on top of a tall steel tower. The globe has a diameter of about 73 feet. What is the approximate surface area of the sphere?
(A) 16,733 ft² C 917 ft²
B 1,834 ft² D 66,969 ft²

6. The diameter of Earth is about 7,926 miles, and the diameter of Mars is about 4,194 miles. How much more surface area is there on Earth than on Mars to the nearest hundred million square miles?
(F) 142,000,000 mi²
G 14,000,000 mi²
H 284,000,000 mi²
J 197,000,000 mi²

7. A cylinder-shaped sculpture is 24 meters high with a diameter of 6.8 meters. An artist plans to spray-paint the entire surface with silver paint. If one can of spray paint covers 50 square meters, how many cans does the artist need to paint the sculpture?
A 51 cans (C) 12 cans
B 22 cans D 10 cans

8. A rectangular sofa cushion is 36 inches by 30 inches by 20 inches. How many cushions can be covered with 38,400 square inches of material?
F 6 cushions H 9 cushions
(G) 8 cushions J 10 cushions

9-5 Changing Dimensions

Learn to find the volume and surface area of similar three-dimensional figures.

Recall that similar figures are proportional. The surface areas of similar three-dimensional figures are also proportional. To see this relationship, you can compare the areas of corresponding faces of similar rectangular prisms.

Remember!
You can multiply numbers in any order. So $(3 \cdot 2) \cdot (5 \cdot 2)$ is the same as $(3 \cdot 5) \cdot (2 \cdot 2)$.

Area of front of smaller prism	Area of front of larger prism	
$3 \cdot 5$	$6 \cdot 10$	
15	$(3 \cdot 2) \cdot (5 \cdot 2)$	⟵ Each dimension has a scale factor of 2.
	$(3 \cdot 5) \cdot (2 \cdot 2)$	
	$15 \cdot 2^2$	

The area of the front face of the larger prism is 2^2 times the area of the front face of the smaller prism. This is true for all of the corresponding faces. Thus it is also true for the entire surface area of the prisms.

SURFACE AREA OF SIMILAR FIGURES

The surface area of a three-dimensional figure A is equal to the surface area of a similar figure B times the square of the scale factor of figure A.

$$\text{surface area of figure } A = \text{surface area of figure } B \cdot (\text{scale factor of figure } A)^2$$

EXAMPLE 1 Finding the Surface Area of a Similar Figure

A **The surface area of a box is 27 in^2. What is the surface area of a larger, similarly shaped box that has a scale factor of 5?**

$S = 27 \cdot 5^2$ *Use the surface area of the smaller box and the square of the scale factor.*

$S = 27 \cdot 25$ *Evaluate the power.*

$S = 675$ *Multiply.*

The surface area of the larger box is 675 in^2.

9-5 Organizer

Pacing: Traditional 2 days
Block 1 day

Objective: Students find the volume and surface area of similar three-dimensional figures.

Warm Up

Find the surface area of each figure to the nearest tenth. Use 3.14 for π.

1. a cylinder with radius 5 ft and height 11 ft **502.4 ft^2**
2. a sphere with diameter 6 ft **113.0 ft^2**
3. a rectangular prism 9 ft by 14 ft by 6 ft **528 ft^2**

Problem of the Day

If 6 cats can catch 6 mice in 6 minutes, how many cats are needed to catch 10 mice in 10 minutes? **6 cats**

Available on Daily Transparency in CRB

Because it was so heavy, the large scale model took a long time to build. But it was worth the weight.

1 Introduce

Alternate Opener

EXPLORATION

9-5 Changing Dimensions

The two nets below can be folded into boxes.

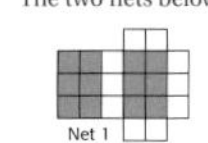

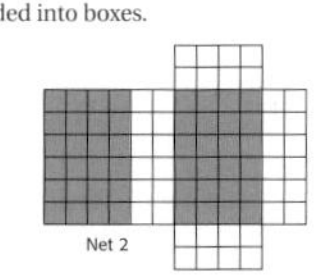

To complete the table, suppose that each net is folded into a box, and measure the length, width, and height.

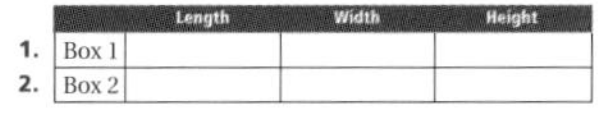

		Length	Width	Height
1.	Box 1			
2.	Box 2			

Count the number of squares in each net to find the surface area. Then use the dimensions of each box and the formula volume $= \ell \cdot w \cdot h$ to calculate the volume of each box.

		Surface Area	Volume $= \ell \cdot w \cdot h$
3.	Box 1		
4.	Box 2		

Think and Discuss

5. **Explain** how many times box 1 could fit into box 2.
6. **Predict** how many times box 1 would fit into box 2 if each dimension of box 2 were multiplied by 3.

Motivate

Provide students with graph paper. Tell them to draw squares with side lengths of 1, 3, 6, and 12 units. Have students find the area of each of the squares. **1, 9, 36, and 144 units^2** Then tell students to compare the areas of pairs of squares. Point out that all the squares are similar. Encourage students to compare the areas of the squares with the scale factors of the squares. For example, the square with side length 3 is similar to the square with side length 12. The scale factor is 4. The area of the larger square is 16 times more than the area of the smaller square.

Exploration worksheet and answers on Chapter 9 Resource Book pp. 46 and 68

2 Teach

Lesson Presentation

Guided Instruction

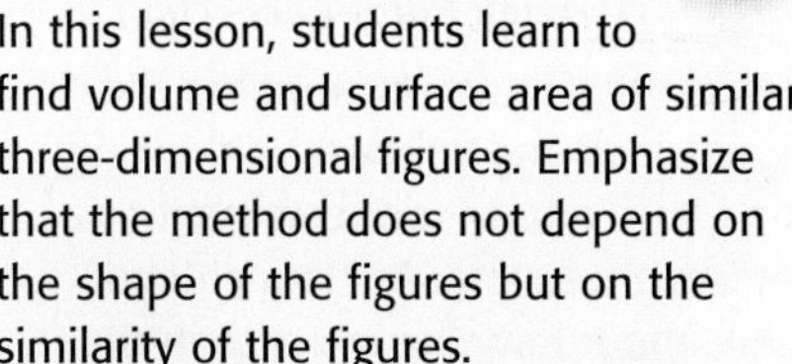

In this lesson, students learn to find volume and surface area of similar three-dimensional figures. Emphasize that the method does not depend on the shape of the figures but on the similarity of the figures.

Teaching Tip Point out that for any pair of similar figures, the greater surface area is equal to the lesser surface area multiplied by the scale factor of the greater figure squared. Likewise, the volume of the larger of two similar figures is equal to the lesser volume multiplied by the scale factor cubed.

Additional Examples 

Example 1

A. The surface area of a box is 35 in². What is the surface area of a larger, similarly shaped box that has a scale factor of 7?

1,715 in²

B. The surface area of a box is 1,300 in². Find the surface area of a smaller, similarly shaped box that has a scale factor of $\frac{1}{2}$.

325 in²

Example 2

The volume of a prism is 28 ft³. What is the volume of a larger, similarly shaped prism that has a scale factor of 4?

1,792 ft³

Example 3

Kevin's water tank weighs 80 pounds when full. He bought a larger tank with a similar shape that has a scale factor of 3. How much does the new tank weigh when full?

2,160 pounds

Example 1 note: Point out that in Example 1B, since the scale model is smaller, the scale factor is less than 1.

B **The surface area of the Great Pyramid was originally 1,160,280 ft². Find the surface area, to the nearest tenth, of a model of the pyramid that has a scale factor of $\frac{1}{500}$.**

$S = 1{,}160{,}280 \cdot \left(\frac{1}{500}\right)^2$ *Use the surface area of the actual pyramid and the square of the scale factor.*

$S = 1{,}160{,}280 \cdot \frac{1}{250{,}000}$ *Evaluate the power.*

$S = 4.64112$ *Multiply.*

The surface area of the model is about 4.6 ft².

The volumes of similar three-dimensional figures are also related.

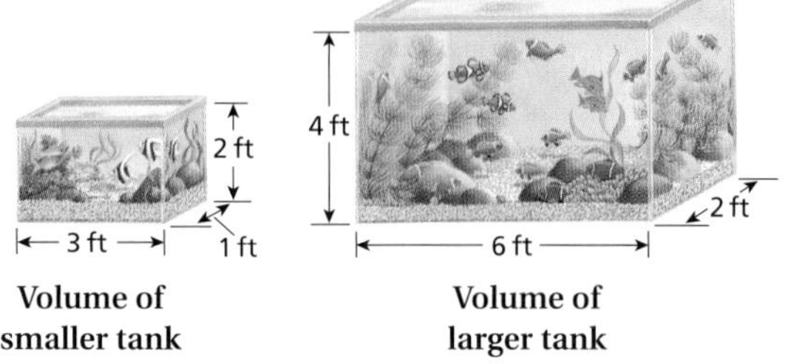

Remember!

$2 \cdot 2 \cdot 2 = 2^3$

Volume of smaller tank	Volume of larger tank
$2 \cdot 3 \cdot 1$	$4 \cdot 6 \cdot 2$
6	$(2 \cdot 2) \cdot (3 \cdot 2) \cdot (1 \cdot 2)$ ← Each dimension has a scale factor of 2.
	$(2 \cdot 3 \cdot 1) \cdot (2 \cdot 2 \cdot 2)$
	$6 \cdot 2^3$

The volume of the larger tank is 2^3 times the volume of the smaller tank.

VOLUME OF SIMILAR FIGURES

The volume of a three-dimensional figure *A* is equal to the volume of a similar figure *B* times the cube of the scale factor of figure *A*.

volume of figure *A* = volume of figure *B* · (scale factor of figure *A*)³

EXAMPLE 2 Finding Volume Using Similar Figures

The volume of a bucket is 231 in³. What is the volume of a larger, similarly shaped bucket that has a scale factor of 3?

$V = 231 \cdot 3^3$ *Use the volume of the smaller bucket and the cube of the scale factor.*

$V = 231 \cdot 27$ *Evaluate the power.*

$V = 6{,}237$ *Multiply.*

The volume of the larger bucket is 6,237 in³.

Teach

Reaching All Learners
Through Home Connection

Suggest that students compare the dimensions and volumes of drinking cups from a fast-food restaurant or a convenience store. Ask students to think about how the increase in the price of a soft drink or other beverage compares to the increase in volume for each type of cup. Encourage students to share their methods and conclusions.

When similar three-dimensional figures are made of the same material, their weights compare in the same way as their volumes. The weight of a three-dimensional figure is the weight of a similar three-dimensional figure multiplied by the cube of the scale factor of the original figure.

EXAMPLE  3 PROBLEM SOLVING APPLICATION

Elise's fish tank weighs 167 pounds when full. She bought a larger tank that has a similar shape with a scale factor of 2. How much does the new tank weigh when full?

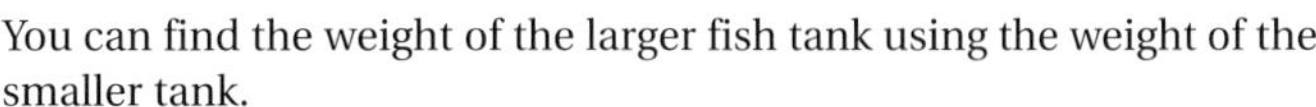

1 Understand the Problem

You can find the weight of the larger fish tank using the weight of the smaller tank.

List the **important information:**

- The smaller tank weighs 167 pounds when full.
- The scale factor of the larger tank is 2.

2 Make a Plan

You can write an equation that relates the weight of the smaller fish tank to the weight of the larger fish tank.

weight of large tank = weight of small tank · (scale factor)^3

3 Solve

weight of large tank = weight of small tank · (scale factor)^3

$= 167 \cdot 2^3$ *Substitute.*

$= 167 \cdot 8$ *Evaluate the power.*

$= 1{,}336$ *Multiply.*

The larger tank weighs 1,336 pounds when full.

4 Look Back

By estimation, the smaller tank weighs about 150 pounds when full, and 150 pounds · 8 = 1,200 pounds. So the answer is reasonable.

Think and Discuss

1. **Tell** whether an object's surface area has increased or decreased if the size of the object is changed by a factor of $\frac{1}{3}$. Explain.
2. **Compare** finding the volume of a similar figure with finding the weight of a similar figure.

COMMON ERROR ALERT

Stress the importance of distinguishing between surface area, volume, and weight. The scale factor is squared to find the new surface area but cubed to find the new volume or weight. Remind students that squaring a number is not the same as cubing the number.

3 Close

Summarize

Have students explain how to find the surface area and volume of the larger of two similar prisms. The smaller prism has a surface area of 54 cm^2 and a volume of 24 cm^3. The scale factor is 6.

Possible answer: To find the surface area of the larger prism, multiply the surface area of the smaller prism by 6^2, or 36. The surface area of the larger prism is 1,944 cm^2. To find the volume of the larger prism, multiply the volume of the smaller prism by 6^3, or 216. The volume of the larger prism is 5,184 cm^3.

Answers to Think and Discuss

1. The object's surface area has decreased because the scale factor is smaller than 1.
2. Possible answer: The process for finding the volumes of similar figures and the weights of similar figures is the same.

9-5 PRACTICE & ASSESS

Students may want to refer back to the lesson examples.

Assignment Guide

If you finished Example 1 assign:
Core 1, 2, 5, 6, 18–26
Enriched 1, 2, 5, 6, 18–26

If you finished Example 2 assign:
Core 1–3, 5–7, 10, 11, 18–26
Enriched 1–3, 5–7, 10, 11, 18–26

If you finished Example 3 assign:
Core 1–9, 11–15 odd, 18–26
Enriched 1–9 odd, 10–26

Notes

9-5 Exercises

FOR EXTRA PRACTICE see page 675

internet connect
Homework Help Online
go.hrw.com Keyword: MS4 9-5

GUIDED PRACTICE

See Example 1

1. The surface area of a box is 10.4 cm^2. What is the surface area of a larger, similarly shaped box that has a scale factor of 3? **93.6 cm^2**
2. The surface area of a ship's hull is about 11,000 m^2. Find the surface area, to the nearest tenth, of the hull of a model ship that has a scale factor of $\frac{1}{150}$. **0.5 m^2**

See Example 2

3. The volume of an ice chest is 2,160 in^3. What is the volume of a larger, similarly shaped ice chest that has a scale factor of 2.5? **33,750 in^3**

See Example 3

4. A fish tank weighs 18 pounds when it is full. A larger, similarly shaped fish tank has a scale factor of 3. How much does the larger tank weigh when full? **486 lb**

INDEPENDENT PRACTICE

See Example 1

5. The surface area of a triangular prism is 13.99 in^2. What is the surface area of a larger, similarly shaped prism that has a scale factor of 4? **223.84 in^2**
6. The surface area of a car frame is about 200 ft^2. Find the surface area, to the nearest tenth, of a square foot, of a model of the car that has a scale factor of $\frac{1}{12}$. **1.4 ft^2**

See Example 2

7. The volume of a sphere is about 523 cm^3. What is the volume, to the nearest tenth, of a smaller sphere that has a scale factor of $\frac{1}{4}$? **8.2 cm^3**

See Example 3

8. A small steel anchor weighs 17 pounds. A larger steel anchor that is similar in shape has a scale factor of 5. How much does the larger anchor weigh? **2,125 lb**

PRACTICE AND PROBLEM SOLVING

For each figure shown, find the surface area and volume of a similar figure with a scale factor of 25. Use 3.14 for π.

9. 5 ft, 4 ft, 3 ft
58,750 ft^2; 937,500 ft^3

10. 12 in., 13 in., 13 in., 10 in., 10 in.
300,000 in^2; 9,375,000 in^3

11. 12 cm
1,130,400 cm^2; 113,040,000 cm^3

12. The surface area of a cylinder is 1,620 m^2. Its volume is about 1,130 m^3. What are the surface area and volume of a similarly shaped cylinder that has a scale factor of $\frac{1}{9}$? Round to the nearest tenth, if necessary. **20 m^2; 1.6 m^3**

Math Background

If you know the ratio of the surface areas of any two similar figures, you can find the scale factor by taking the square root of the ratio.

For example, the ratio of the surface areas of the two similar figures in Example 1A is $\frac{675}{27}$. Therefore, the scale factor of the greater figure is 5 because $\frac{675}{27} = 25$, and $\sqrt{25} = 5$.

Similarly, if you know the ratio of the volumes of any two similar figures, you can find the scale factor by taking the cube root of the ratio.

RETEACH 9-5

LESSON 9-5 **Reteach**
Changing Dimensions

Changing the dimensions of a three-dimensional figure affects its surface area and its volume.

Cube A (1), Cube B (2), Cube C (3)

1. Complete the table for the cubes shown above.

Length of Side	Area of One Face	Surface Area	Volume
1	1 unit^2	6 units^2	1 unit^3
2	4 units^2	24 units^2	8 units^3
3	9 units^2	54 units^2	27 units^3

2. The length of one edge of B is __2__ times the length of one edge of A.
The area of one face of B is __4__ times the area of one face of A.
The surface area of B is __4__ times the surface area of A: $2^2 =$ __4__.
The volume of B is __8__ times the volume of A: $2^3 =$ __8__.

3. The length of one edge of C is __3__ times the length of one edge of A.
The area of one face of C is __9__ times the area of one face of A.
The surface area of C is __9__ times the surface area of A: $3^2 =$ __9__.
The volume of C is __27__ times the volume of A: $3^3 =$ __27__.

For any set of similar three-dimensional figures:
- The surface area of the larger figure equals the surface area of the smaller figure times the scale factor squared.
- The volume of the larger figure equals the volume of the smaller figure times the scale factor cubed.

The scale factor of two similar prisms is 4.

4. The surface area of the smaller prism is 9 in^2. Multiply by __4^2__, or __16__.
The surface area of the larger prism is __144__ in^2.

PRACTICE 9-5

LESSON 9-5 **Practice B**
Changing Dimensions

Given the scale factor, find the surface area of the similar prism.

1. The scale factor of two similar rectangular prisms is 3. The surface area of the smaller prism is 15 in^2. **135 in^2**
2. The scale factor of two similar triangular prisms is 2. The surface area of the smaller prism is 25 cm^2. **100 cm^2**
3. The scale factor of two similar rectangular prisms is 4. The surface area of the smaller prism is 20 ft^2. **320 ft^2**
4. The scale factor of two similar triangular prisms is 5. The surface area of the smaller prism is 10 m^2. **250 m^2**
5. The scale factor of two similar rectangular prisms is 3. The surface area of the smaller prism is 30 yd^2. **270 yd^2**
6. The scale factor of two similar pentagonal prisms is 4. The surface area of the smaller prism is 16 cm^2. **256 cm^2**

Given the scale factor, find the volume of the similar prism.

7. The scale factor of two similar triangular prisms is 3. The volume of the smaller prism is 8 in^3. **216 in^3**
8. The scale factor of two similar rectangular prisms is 2. The volume of the smaller prism is 25 m^3. **200 m^3**
9. The scale factor of two similar triangular prisms is 4. The volume of the smaller prism is 10 cm^3. **640 cm^3**
10. The scale factor of two similar rectangular prisms is 5. The volume of the smaller prism is 20 ft^3. **2,500 ft^3**
11. The scale factor of two similar triangular prisms is 2. The volume of the smaller prism is 72 yd^3. **576 yd^3**
12. A small tank weighs 24 pounds when it is full of water. A larger tank that is similar in shape has a scale factor of 3. How much does the larger tank weigh when filled with water? **648 lb**

History LINK

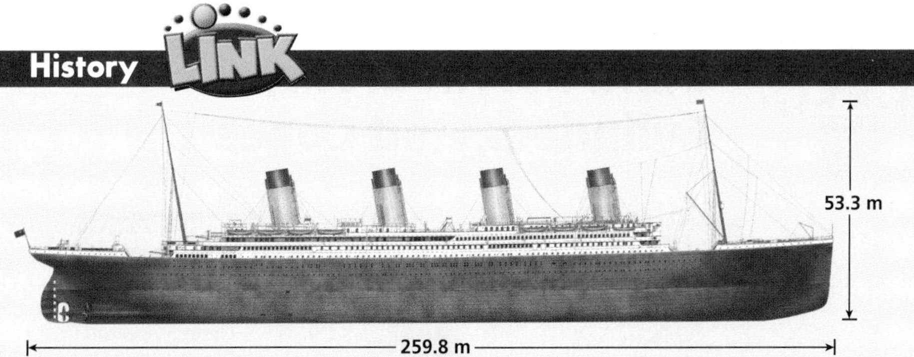

Natalie and Rebecca are making a scale model of the *Titanic* for a history class project. Their model has a scale factor of $\frac{1}{100}$. For Exercises 13–16, express your answers in both centimeters and meters. Use the conversion chart at right if needed.

METRIC CONVERSIONS	
1 m = 100 cm	1 cm = 0.01 m
$1\ m^2 = 10{,}000\ cm^2$	$1\ cm^2 = 0.0001\ m^2$
$1\ m^3 = 1{,}000{,}000\ cm^3$	$1\ cm^3 = 0.000001\ m^3$

13. The length and height of the *Titanic* are shown in the drawing above. What are the length and height of the students' scale model? **length: 259.8 cm or 2.598 m; height: 53.3 cm or 0.533 m**
14. On the students' model, the diameter of the outer propellers is 7.16 cm. What was the diameter of these propellers on the ship? **716 cm; 7.16 m**
15. The surface area of the deck of the students' model is $4{,}156.75\ cm^2$. What was the surface area of the deck of the ship? **$41{,}567{,}500\ cm^2$; $4{,}156.75\ m^2$**

These are propellers from the *Olympic*, the *Titanic's* sister ship. They are identical to those that were on the *Titanic.*

16. The volume of the students' model is about $127{,}426\ cm^3$. What was the volume of the ship? **$127{,}426{,}000{,}000\ cm^3$; $127{,}426\ m^3$**
17. **CHALLENGE** The weight of the *Titanic* was 38,760 tons. If the students could make a detailed model using the same materials as the ship, what would the model weigh in pounds? (*Hint:* 1 ton = 2,000 pounds.) **77.52 lb**

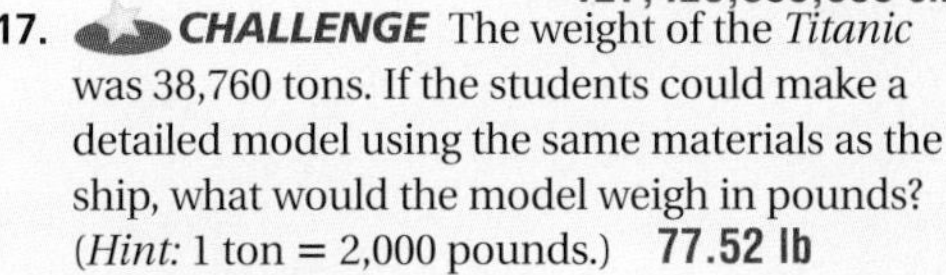

Some people have made very detailed models of the *Titanic.*

Spiral Review

Determine whether the ratios are proportional. (Lesson 5-2)

18. $\frac{7}{56}, \frac{35}{280}$ **yes**
19. $\frac{12}{20}, \frac{60}{140}$ **no**
20. $\frac{9}{45}, \frac{45}{225}$ **yes**
21. $\frac{5}{82}, \frac{65}{1{,}054}$ **no**

Write each percent as a fraction in simplest form. (Lesson 6-1)

22. 75% **$\frac{3}{4}$**
23. 60% **$\frac{3}{5}$**
24. 52% **$\frac{13}{25}$**
25. 18% **$\frac{9}{50}$**
26. **TEST PREP** Which polygon has ten angles and ten sides? (Lesson 7-5) **C**

A Pentagon B Octagon C Decagon D Dodecagon

CHALLENGE 9-5

LESSON 9-5 **Challenge**
Eggs-actly

The volumes of two similar-shaped figures are proportional to the cube of their lengths.

Suppose an extra-large egg is 2.5 inches long, compared to a smaller egg 1.25 inches long. What is the ratio of their volumes?

2.5 in. 1.25 in.

Cube the ratio of their lengths.

$\left(\frac{2.5}{1.25}\right)^3 = \left(\frac{2}{1}\right)^3 = \frac{8}{1}$

The ratio of their volumes is 8:1.

So, the larger egg has 8 times as much volume, 8 times as much weight, and 8 times as much food.

Solve. Show your work.

1. One egg is 2 inches long. Another is 2.75 inches long. How many times greater is the volume of the larger egg?
   $\left(\frac{2.75}{2}\right)^3 \approx \frac{20.8}{8} \approx 2.6$; about 2.6 times
2. One egg is 2.25 inches long. Another is 1.5 inches long. How many times greater is the weight of the larger egg?
   $\left(\frac{2.25}{1.5}\right)^3 \approx \left(\frac{3}{2}\right)^3$ about 3.4 times
3. The ratio of the lengths of two eggs is 5 to 2. The larger egg contains how many times the food of the smaller egg?
   $\left(\frac{5}{2}\right)^3 = \frac{125}{8} = 15.625$; about 15.6 times as much
4. An egg is 2 inches long. What is the approximate length of an egg with twice the volume?
   about 2.5 in.
5. An egg is 3 inches long. What is the approximate length of an egg with half the weight?
   about 2.4 in.
6. An egg is 1.75 inches long. What is the approximate length of an egg with twice the food?
   about 2.2 in.

PROBLEM SOLVING 9-5

LESSON 9-5 **Problem Solving**
Changing Dimensions

Write the correct answer.

1. In the late 1800s, wax cylinders were used to record sound. The lateral surface area of the cylinders was about 25 square inches. If a larger model of this cylinder is created using a scale factor of 3, what is the lateral surface area of the model?
   about $225\ in^2$
2. A 5-foot wide, 100-foot tall cylindrical water tower was built in St. Louis in the early 1800s. An architecture student wants to build a model using a scale factor of $\frac{1}{6}$. What will be the volume of the model to the nearest cubic foot?
   $9\ ft^3$
3. A cone-shaped plastic cup holds 24 ounces of water. A smaller cup has a scale factor of $\frac{1}{2}$. How much water does the smaller cup hold?
   3 oz
4. In the game of Ring Taw, players use a shooting marble that has a surface area of 1.77 square inches. What is the surface area of a large ball if the scale factor is 5?
   $44.25\ in^2$

Choose the letter of the correct answer.

5. The volume of a rectangular prism is 48 cubic centimeters. The volume of a similar rectangular prism is 6 cubic centimeters What is the scale factor for the rectangles?
   A 8 C 4
   B 6 (D) 2
6. A cooking pot used in the cafeteria weighs 64 pounds when it is filled with soup. How much would a similar pot with a scale factor of $\frac{1}{2}$ weigh when filled with the same soup?
   F 4 lb H 16 lb
   (G) 8 lb J 32 lb
7. For his science project, Marty is building a model of Pluto, which has a surface area of about 6,376,000 square miles. He plans to cover his model with red foil. If he uses a scale factor of 5,000, how much red foil will he need to the nearest hundredth of a square mile?
   A $1.26\ mi^2$ (C) $0.26\ mi^2$
   B $0.026\ mi^2$ D $0.126\ mi^2$
8. The scale factor of two similar triangular prisms is 5. What is the possible surface area of both prisms?
   (F) $2{,}000\ cm^2$ and $80\ cm^2$
   G $125\ cm^2$ and $25\ cm^2$
   H $5{,}000\ cm^2$ and $40\ cm^2$
   J $10{,}000\ cm^2$ and $60\ cm^2$

Interdisciplinary LINK

History

Exercises 13–17 involve using a scale factor to construct a model of a historical structure, a popular hobby of history buffs.

Journal

Ask students to describe how they would find the surface area of a real-world figure for which they have a scale model. Have students presume that they know both the surface area of the model and the scale factor of the original figure.

Test Prep Doctor

Students should be able to easily eliminate **A** and **B** for Exercise 26. If students remember that *deca* means "ten," they will quickly recognize that the correct answer is **C.** If not, suggest that they use logic and word clues to choose between **C** and **D.** Part of the prefix for **D** contains *do*, a prefix that may suggest two and not ten. This means **C** is the logical answer.

Lesson Quiz

Given the scale factor, find the surface area of the similar prism.

1. The scale factor of the larger of two similar triangular prisms is 8. The surface area of the smaller prism is $18\ ft^2$. **$1{,}152\ ft^2$**
2. The scale factor of the smaller of two similar rectangular prisms is $\frac{1}{3}$. The surface area of the larger prism is $630\ ft^2$. **$70\ ft^2$**

Given the scale factor, find the volume of the similar prism.

3. The scale factor of the larger of two similar rectangular prisms is 3. The volume of the smaller prism is $12\ cm^3$. **$324\ cm^3$**
4. The scale factor of the smaller of two similar triangular prisms is $\frac{1}{2}$. The volume of the larger prism is $120\ m^3$. **$15\ m^3$**

Available on Daily Transparency in CRB

9B Build Polyhedrons, Cylinders, and Cones

Pacing: Traditional 1 day
Block $\frac{1}{2}$ day

Objective: To use nets or cubes to build polyhedrons, cylinders, and cones

Materials: Paper, scissors, tape, ruler, compass, protractor, centimeter cubes

Lab Resources

Hands-On Lab Activities pp. 93–94, 127

Using the Pages

On the chalkboard, draw a net for a cube, a rectangular prism, a pyramid, a cylinder, and a cone. Ask students to identify the three-dimensional shapes that can be formed with each net.

Use a compass, ruler, or protractor to draw each of the following.

1. circle with radius of 2 inches

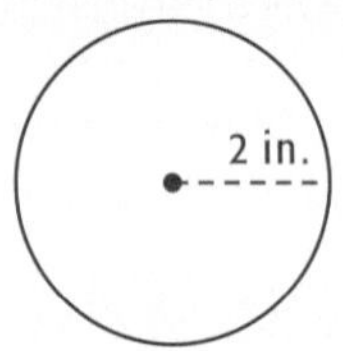

2. rectangle with a length of 3 inches and a width of 2 inches

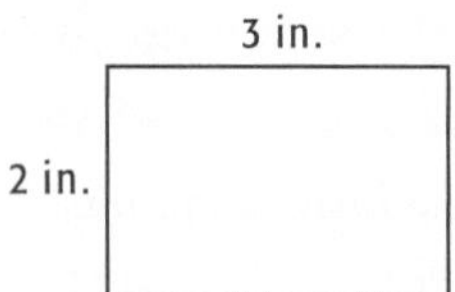

3. 120° angle

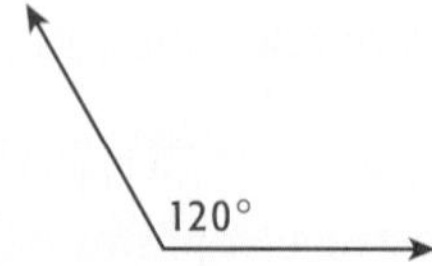

Build Polyhedrons, Cylinders, and Cones

Use with Lesson 9-4

internet connect
Lab Resources Online
go.hrw.com
KEYWORD: MS4 Lab9B

You can build geometric solids using nets or cubes.

Activity

1 Using a net, construct a cylinder with a radius of 1 inch and a height of 3.5 inches.

a. Draw a rectangle that is 6.28 inches by 3.5 inches. Then draw two circles as shown, one on each side of the rectangle. Each circle should have a radius of 1 inch. This is the net of a cylinder.

1 in.

6.28 in.

3.5 in.

b. Cut out the net. Fold the net as shown to make a cylinder. Tape the edges of the paper to hold them in place.

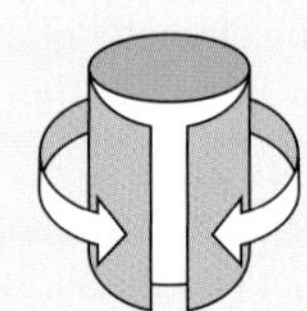

2 Using a net, construct a cone with a radius of 1 inch.

a. Draw a 115° angle. Make each side of the angle 3.13 inches long.

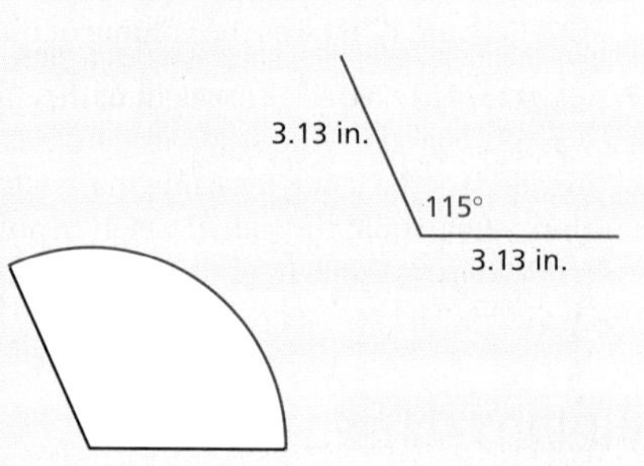

b. Place your compass on the vertex of the angle, and open it to the length of one side. Draw an arc to connect the two sides as shown.

c. Draw a circle with a 1-inch radius, touching the figure from part **b** as shown. This completes the net of a cone.

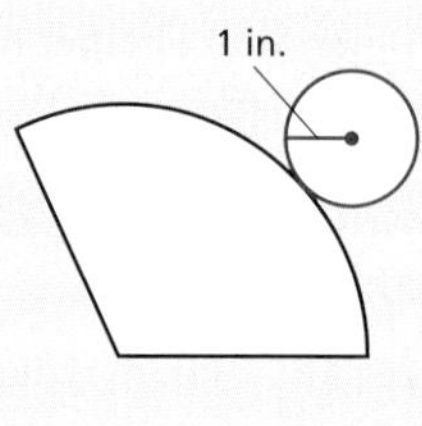

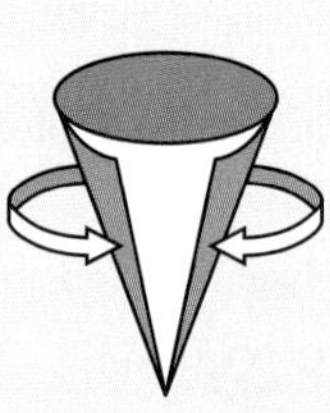

d. Cut out the net. Fold the net as shown to make a cone. Tape the edges of the paper to hold them in place.

Teacher to Teacher

Several of my students have trouble making their own nets, so I use polygon pieces that snap together. The students make a net using the shapes and then have to fold them and snap them together to make the solid figures. This makes a more tangible solid for them to examine while counting vertices, faces, and edges. After we make a tetrahedron and a cube, I have them experiment with the pieces to make an octahedron and a dodecahedron. It is like putting a puzzle together.

Lisa Stevenson
New Braunfels, Texas

❸ Construct a rectangular prism using a net.

a. Draw the net at right on a piece of graph paper. Each rectangle should be 10 squares by 4 squares. Each of the two large squares should be 4 small squares on each side.

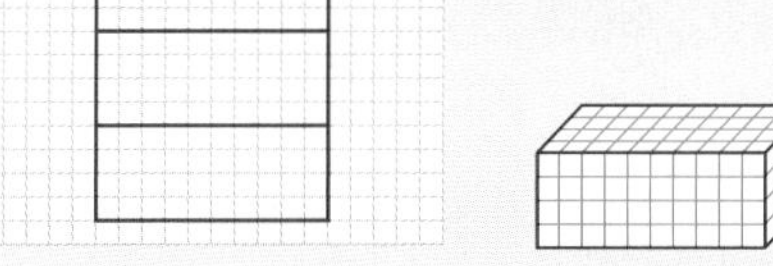

b. Cut out the net. Fold the net along the edges of each rectangle to make a rectangular prism. Tape the edges of the paper to hold them in place.

❹ Use centimeter cubes to build a rectangular prism.

a. Using the prism that you built in ❸, look at the graph paper squares on one of the large faces. Arrange centimeter cubes to match the view of the squares.

b. Now look at the graph paper squares on one of the smaller faces of the paper prism. Stack more cubes on top of the first layer of cubes until the stack's height matches the paper prism's height.

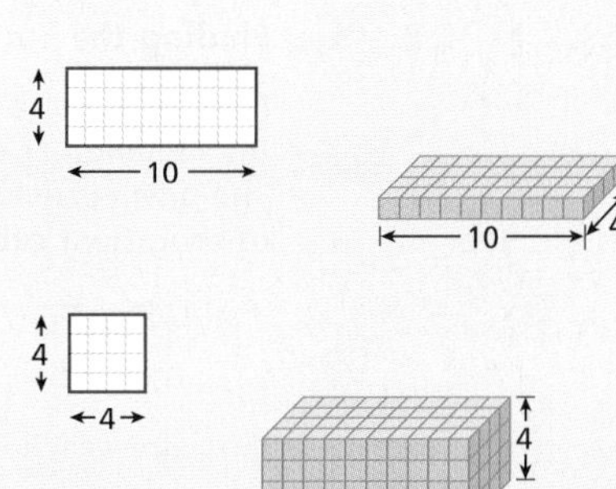

Think and Discuss

1. Find the volume in cubic units of the prism that you built in ❹. **160 cubic units**
2. Find the surface area of the prism that you built in ❹ by counting the exposed cube faces. Express your answer in square units. **192 square units**
3. On the net of the cone, describe the shape that forms the lateral surface of the cone. How is that shape related to the base of the cone?
4. In ❶, the width of the rectangle in the net is 6.28 inches. How does the width of the rectangle relate to the radius of the cylinder? **The width of the rectangle in the net is equal to $2\pi r$, where r is the radius of the cylinder.**

Try This

1. Use a net to construct a cylinder with a radius of 2 centimeters and a height of 4 centimeters.
2. Use a net to construct a cone whose base has a radius of 2 centimeters. To make the lateral surface, use an angle of 90° and side lengths of 8 centimeters.
3. Use a net to construct a rectangular prism that is 2 inches by 3 inches by 4 inches.
4. Use cubes to construct the rectangular prism in problem 3.

Answers

Think and Discuss

3. The lateral surface of the cone becomes a sector of a circle when flattened out. The arc of that sector is equal to the cirumference of the base of the cone.

Try This

1.

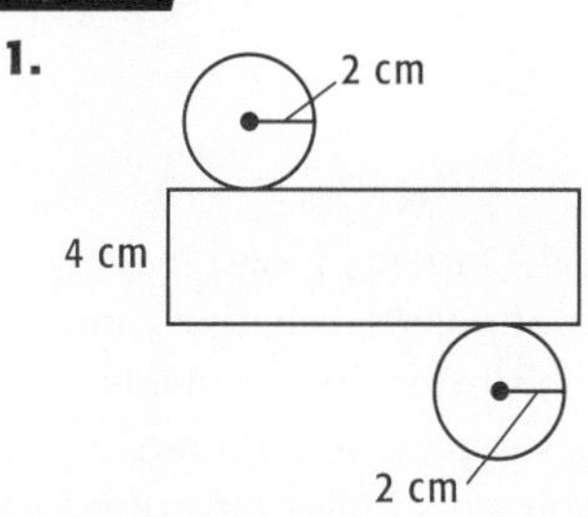

2.

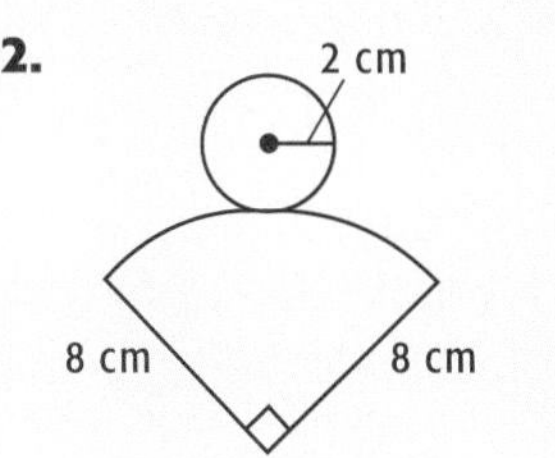

3.

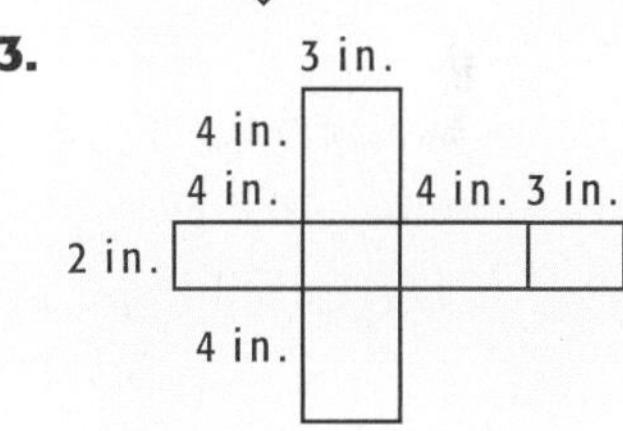

4.

Extension

Pacing: Traditional 1 day
Block $\frac{1}{2}$ day

Objective: Students find the surface area of three-dimensional figures built from cubes.

Using the Pages

In Lesson 9-4, students found the surface area of prisms, cylinders, and spheres. In this extension, students will find the surface area of three-dimensional figures built from cubes.

EXTENSION

Surface Area of Other Figures

Learn to find the surface area of three-dimensional figures built from cubes.

You can build a variety of figures with cubes. The surface area of a figure built of cubes can be found by adding the areas of the exposed cube faces.

EXAMPLE 1 **Finding the Surface Area of a Prism Built of Cubes**

Find the surface area of the rectangular prism. The prism is made up of congruent cubes.

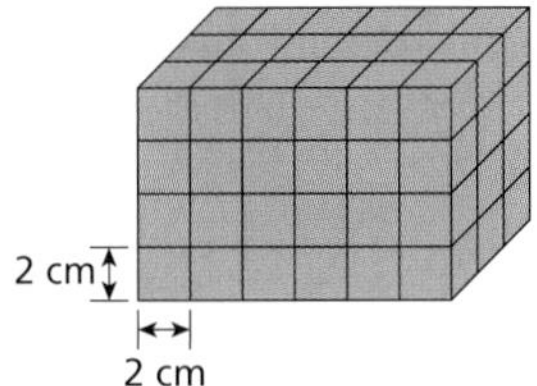

First, draw each view of the prism.

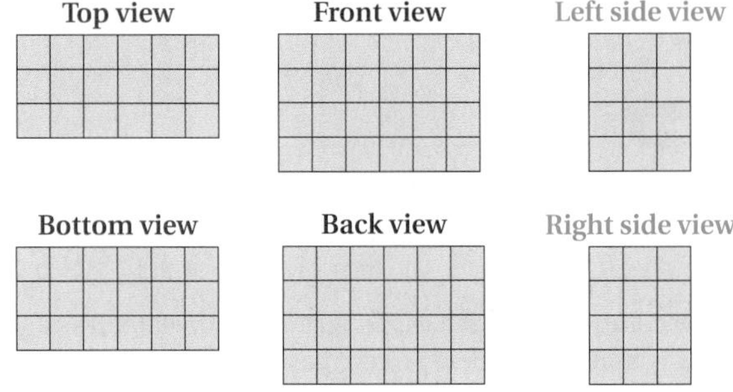

Since the cubes are congruent, you can count all of the cube faces that show and multiply this number by the area of one cube face. This will give you the total surface area of the prism.

Top view: 18 cube faces	**Front view:** 24 cube faces	**Left view:** 12 cube faces
Bottom view: 18 cube faces	**Back view:** 24 cube faces	**Right view:** 12 cube faces

$18 + 18 + 24 + 24 + 12 + 12 = 108$ *Find the total number of cube faces that show.*

Each edge of a cube is 2 cm, so the area of each face is 4 cm^2.

$108 \cdot 4 = 432$ *Multiply by the area of each face.*

The surface area of the prism is 432 cm^2.

1 Introduce

Motivate

If possible, provide small groups of students with unit cubes. Have each group build a tower by stacking the cubes. Have students suggest ways to find the surface area of their towers (e.g., count the faces of the cubes). If necessary, remind students that the bottom face of a tower should be included in the total surface area of the tower.

2 Teach

Lesson Presentation

Guided Instruction

In this lesson, students learn to find the surface area of three-dimensional figures built from cubes. Point out that while a three-dimensional figure may look complex, it can be simplified by breaking it up into its views of recognizable shapes with areas that can be easily found. The total surface area is the combined areas of the views.

Teaching Tip Remind students that they can use the formula for the area of a rectangle (multiply the length by the width) to find the area of rectangular views instead of counting the number of squares in these views.

EXAMPLE 2 Finding the Surface Area of a Complex Figure Built of Cubes

Find the surface area of the figure. The figure is made up of congruent cubes.

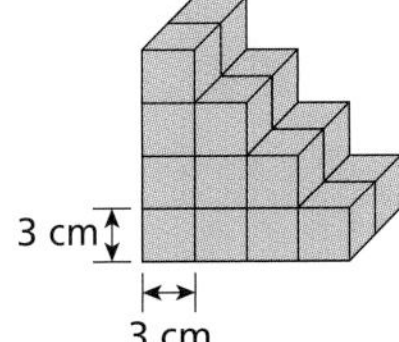

Draw each view.

Top view

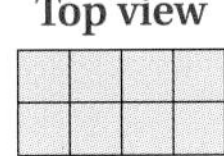

Front view

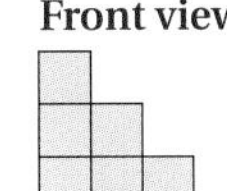

Left side view

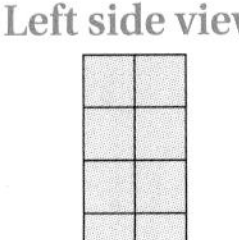

Bottom view

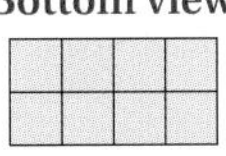

Back view

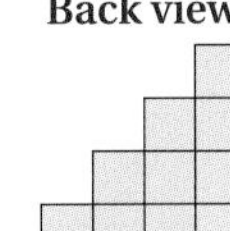

Right side view

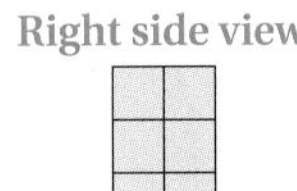

$8 + 8 + 10 + 10 + 8 + 8 = 52$ *Find the total number of cube faces that show.*

Each edge of a cube is 3 cm, so the area of each face is 9 cm^2.

$52 \cdot 9 = 468$ *Multiply by the area of each face.*

The surface area of the figure is 468 cm^2.

EXTENSION Exercises

Find the surface area of each figure. Each figure is made up of congruent cubes.

1. **448 cm^2**

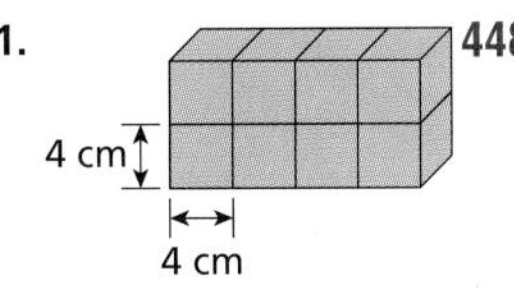

2. **306 cm^2**

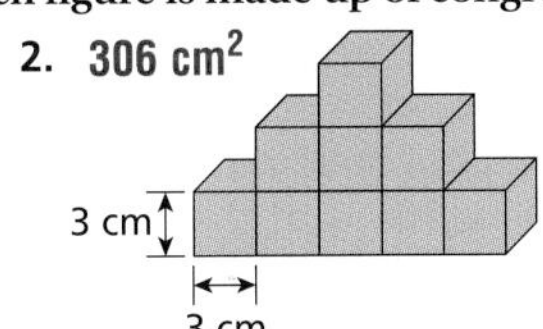

3. **208 cm^2**

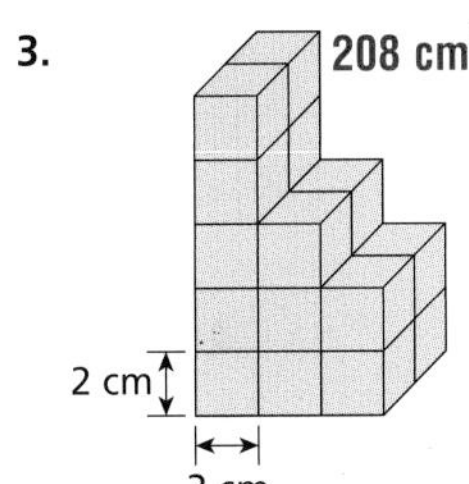

4. **1,450 cm^2**

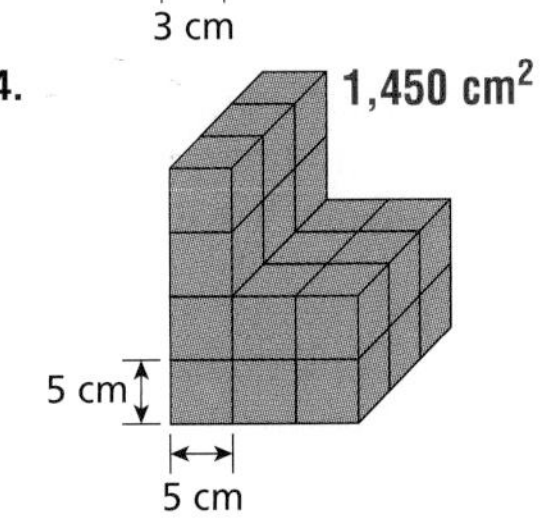

COMMON ERROR ALERT

Students might forget to check the size of each cube in the three-dimensional shapes. Remind students that the dimensions of the cubes are different: the cubes in the Examples and the Exercises are not unit cubes. It is essential that students recognize this fact to accurately compute the surface area of each figure.

Additional Examples

Example 1

Find the surface area of the rectangular prism. The prism is made up of congruent cubes.

1,300 cm^2

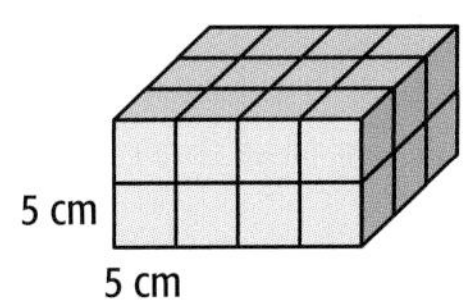

Example 2

Find the surface area of the figure. The figure is made up of congruent cubes.

1,584 cm^2

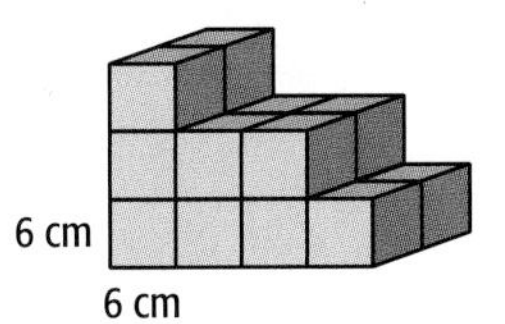

3 Close

Summarize

Have students explain how to find the surface area of the following figure:

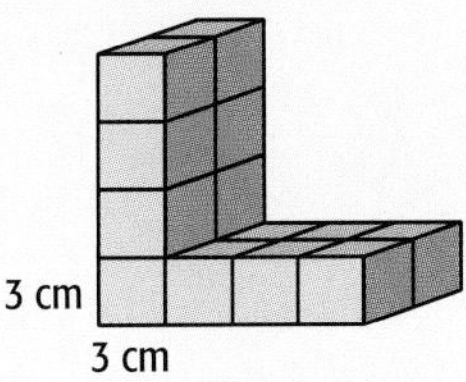

Possible answer: Find the area of each view, and then add to find the total surface area.
top and bottom view areas: $8 \cdot 9 = 72$
front and back view areas: $7 \cdot 9 = 63$
right and left view areas: $8 \cdot 9 = 72$
$S = 72 + 72 + 63 + 63 + 72 + 72 = 414$
The surface area of the figure is 414 cm^2.

Problem Solving on Location

Alabama

Purpose: *To provide additional practice for problem-solving skills in Chapters 1–9*

History of Alabama's State Capitol Building

- After problem 4, have students find the surface area of the rectangular-prism-shaped section of the actual building that the model represents. **13,500 ft^2**
- After problem 5, have students find the surface area of the cylindrical part of the actual building that the model represents. **≈2,198 ft^2**

Extension Have students use geometric solids to construct a model of a building. Then have students find the surface area of the outside walls of the model.

Problem Solving on Location

ALABAMA

History of Alabama's State Capitol Building

The photos below show the current and former capitol buildings of Alabama.

Cahaba, 1820

Tuscaloosa, 1826

Montgomery, 1851

1. Identify the geometric solids in the first capitol building of Alabama. **Possible answers: main building: rectangular prism; chimneys: rectangular prisms; roof: rectangular pyramid; cupola: cylinders, cone**
2. Explain how you would find the surface area of the outside walls of Alabama's second capitol building. **Find the dimensions of each side of the rectangular prisms that make up the main building. The surface area is the sum of the areas of each outside wall.**
3. The structure on the roof of the current capitol building is a *cupola.* Identify the geometric solids that make up the cupola. **Possible answer: cylinders, hemisphere**

For a school project, a student designed and built a model of a capitol building. The drawing at right shows the dimensions of the actual building. For 4 and 5, use the drawing.

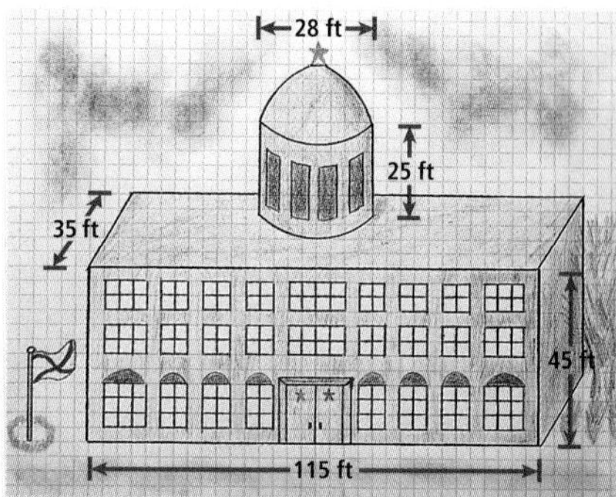

4. Every inch of the model equals 10 feet of the actual building. How many square inches of material did the student need to build the four walls of the part of the model shaped like a rectangular prism? **135 in^2**
5. About how many square inches of material did the student need to build the cylindrical part of the model's cupola? Use 3.14 for π. **≈21.98 in^2**

The U.S. Space & Rocket Center

The U.S. Space & Rocket Center is located in Huntsville, Alabama. The center has a museum and a space camp program.

1. One of the most popular attractions at the Space Center is the Mars Mission, a simulated trek across the Martian terrain. Approximate the surface area of Mars if its diameter is 4,194 miles. Use 3.14 for π. **55,231,457 mi^2**

2. In the Lunar Lander, younger children visiting the Space Center can experience a simulation of landing on the Moon. The mean radius of the Moon is 1,080 mi. What is the Moon's approximate surface area? Use 3.14 for π. **14,649,984 mi^2**

After visiting the Space Center, students in a science class built models of a simple rocket ship. For 3, use the table at right.

3. Each rocket ship was made using the shapes given in the table. Explain how to find the total volume of each model, and then find the volume. Use 3.14 for π.

Rocket Part	Shape	Height (in.)	Diameter (in.)	Base Area (in^2)
Top	1 cone	4	6	—
Body	1 cylinder	8	6	—
End wings	2 triangular prisms	2	—	1

The table at right shows the dimensions in kilometers of two lunar features. For 4 and 5, use the table.

Lunar Feature	Length (km)	Width (km)	Depth (km)	Diameter (km)
Crater Aristarchus	—	—	3.6	40
Hadley Rille	125	1.5	0.4	—

4. Use the formula for the volume of a cone to estimate the volume of Crater Aristarchus. Use 3.14 for π. **1,507.2 km^3**

5. Use the formula for the volume of a rectangular prism to estimate the volume of Hadley Rille. **75 km^3**

The U.S. Space & Rocket Center

- After problem 1, have students find the approximate circumference of Mars. about 13,169 mi
- After problem 2, have students find the approximate volume of the Moon. about 5,273,994,240 mi^3

Extension: Have students choose an object in space, such as a planet, and research to find its dimensions. Then have them choose a scale and construct a scale model of the object. Have students find the volume and surface area of their models.

Answers

3. Find the volumes of the cone, cylinder, and two triangular prisms, and add the volumes together; the total volume is $37.68 + 226.08 + 2 + 2 = 267.76$ in^3.

MATH-ABLES

Game Resources

Puzzles, Twisters & Teasers
Chapter 9 Resource Book

Blooming Minds

Purpose: *To find the volume of irregular shapes*

Discuss: Ask students to explain why they needed to find the volume of each flower bed. Possible answer: You would need to find the volume of each flower bed in order to determine the amount of peat moss that should be purchased to build the flower bed.

Extend: Challenge students to create a design for the flower bed that uses less peat moss.

Magic Cubes

Purpose: *To practice finding sums in a game format*

Discuss: When a student gets a sum of 10 on each side of the stack, have him or her demonstrate for the class how the winning solution was obtained.

Extend: Have students do this puzzle using magic cubes that have the numbers 3, 4, 5, and 6 written on the sides of the cubes. Ask students to identify the target sum for these cubes. 18

MATH-ABLES

Blooming Minds

Students in the Agriculture Club at Carter Middle School are designing a flower bed for the front of the school. The flower bed will be in the shape of the letter *C*. After considering the two designs shown below, the students decided to build the flower bed that required the least amount of peat moss. Which design did the students choose? (*Hint:* Find the volume of each flower bed.) **They chose the design on the left.**

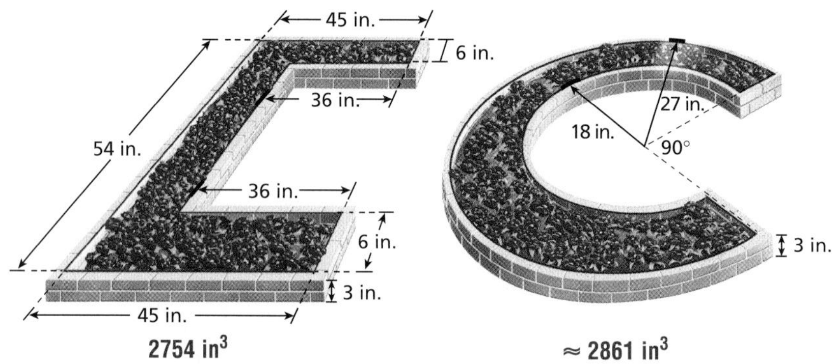

2754 in^3 **≈ 2861 in^3**

Magic Cubes

Four magic cubes are used in this fun puzzle. Each side of the four cubes has the number 1, 2, 3, or 4 written on it. The object of the game is to stack the cubes so that the numbers along each side of the stack add up to 10. No number can be repeated along any side of the stack.

internet connect
Go to ***go.hrw.com*** for a complete set of rules and to print out nets for the cubes.
KEYWORD: MS4 Game9

Explore Volume of Solids

internet connect
Lab Resources Online
go.hrw.com
KEYWORD: MS4 TechLab9

You can use a spreadsheet to explore how changing the dimensions of a rectangular pyramid affects the volume of the pyramid.

Activity

1. On a spreadsheet, enter the following headings:
   Base Length in cell A1,
   Base Width in cell B1,
   Height in cell C1, and
   Volume in cell D1.

   In row 2, enter the numbers 15, 7, and 22, as shown.

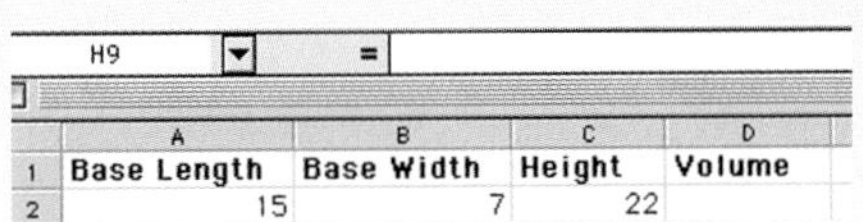

H9 =

	A	B	C	D
1	Base Length	Base Width	Height	Volume
2	15	7	22	

2. Then enter the formula for the volume of a pyramid in cell D2. To do this, enter **=(1/3)*A2*B2*C2.** Press **ENTER** and notice that the volume is 770.

3. Enter 30 in cell A2 and 11 in cell C2 to find out what happens to the volume when you double the base length and halve the height.

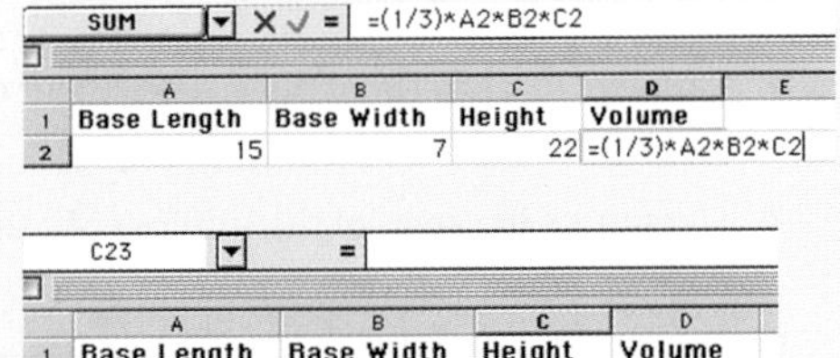

SUM =(1/3)*A2*B2*C2

	A	B	C	D	E
1	Base Length	Base Width	Height	Volume	
2	15	7	22	=(1/3)*A2*B2*C2	

C23 =

	A	B	C	D
1	Base Length	Base Width	Height	Volume
2	30	7	11	770

Think and Discuss

1. By doubling the length of the base, you are multiplying the volume by 2, and by halving the height, you are dividing the volume by 2. Multiplying and dividing by the same number leaves the value unchanged.

1. Explain why doubling the base length and halving the height does not change the volume of the pyramid.
2. What other ways could you change the dimensions of the pyramid without changing its volume? **Possible answer: You could multiply the length of the base by a number and divide the width of the base by that same number.**

Try This

1. Use a spreadsheet to compute the volume of each cone. Use 3.14 for π.
   a. radius = 2.75 inches; height = 8.5 inches **67.28 in^3**
   b. radius = 7.5 inches; height = 14.5 inches **853.69 in^3**
2. What would the volumes in problem 1 be if the radii were doubled? **269.12 in^3; 3,414.75 in^3**

Technology LAB

Explore Volume of Solids

Objective: To use spreadsheet software to explore the effects on volume when length, width, and height change

Materials: Spreadsheet software

Lab Resources

Technology Lab Activities . . . . pp. 50–51

Using the Page

The spreadsheet software used in this technology activity lets students see how the volume of a pyramid is affected when any of its dimensions are changed.

The Think and Discuss problems can be used to assess students' understanding of how changing more than one dimension may not affect the volume. While Try This problems 1 and 2 can be done without spreadsheet software, they are meant to help students become familiar with using spreadsheet software to find the volume of a cone.

Assessment

Use a spreadsheet to compute the volume V of a rectangular prism, which is given by the formula $V = \ell wh$. Use the following dimensions for the length, width, and height.

1. $\ell = 7.5$ in., $w = 4.2$ in., $h = 3.8$ in. **119.7 in^3**
2. $\ell = 15$ in., $w = 4.2$ in., $h = 1.9$ in. **119.7 in^3**

Study Guide and Review

Purpose: *To help students review and practice concepts and skills presented in Chapter 9*

Assessment Resources

Chapter Review

Chapter 9 Resource Book . . . pp. 54–55

***Test and Practice Generator* CD-ROM**

Additional review assessment items in both multiple-choice and free-response format may be generated for any objective in Chapter 9.

Answers

1. cylinder
2. surface area
3. bases
4. cone
5. triangular prism
6. rectangular pyramid

Chapter 9 Study Guide and Review

Study Guide and Review

Vocabulary

base	472	polyhedron	472
cone	473	prism	472
cylinder	473	pyramid	472
edge	472	sphere	473
face	472	surface area	486
hemisphere	473	vertex	472
lateral surface	473	volume	476
net	486		

Complete the sentences below with vocabulary words from the list above. Words may be used more than once.

1. A(n) __?__ has two parallel, congruent circular bases connected by a lateral surface.
2. The sum of the areas of the surfaces of a three-dimensional figure is called the __?__.
3. The two parallel congruent faces of a prism are the __?__, and they can be any polygon.
4. A(n) __?__ has one circular face and a curved lateral surface.

9-1 Introduction to Three-Dimensional Figures (pp. 472–475)

EXAMPLE

■ Give the name of the prism or pyramid.

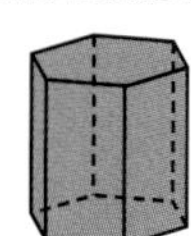

hexagonal prism

EXERCISES

Give the name of each prism or pyramid.

5. 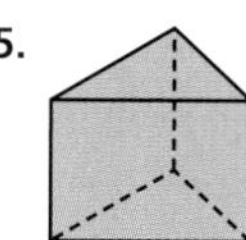

6. 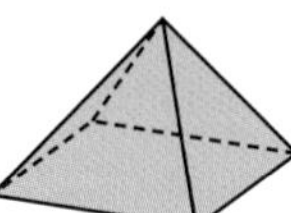

9-2 Volume of Prisms and Cylinders (pp. 476–479)

EXAMPLE

- **Find the volume of the prism.**

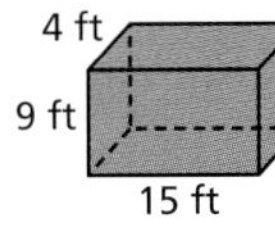

$V = Bh$

$V = (15 \cdot 4) \cdot 9$

$V = 540$

The volume of the prism is 540 ft^3.

- **Find the volume of the cylinder to the nearest tenth. Use 3.14 for π.**

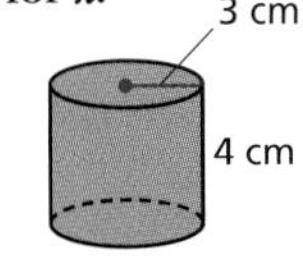

$V = \pi r^2 h$

$V \approx 3.14 \cdot 3^2 \cdot 4$

$V \approx 113.04$

The volume is about 113.0 cm^3.

EXERCISES

Find the volume of the prism.

7.

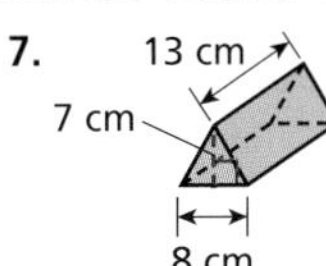

Find the volume of each cylinder to the nearest tenth. Use 3.14 for π.

8.

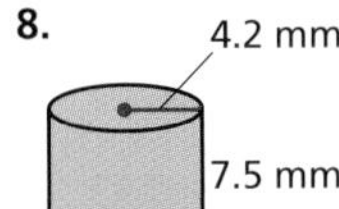

9.

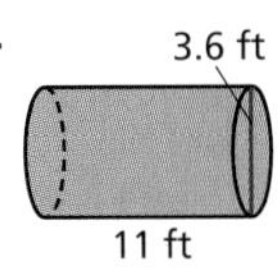

9-3 Volume of Pyramids, Cones, and Spheres (pp. 480–483)

EXAMPLE

- **Find the volume of the pyramid.**

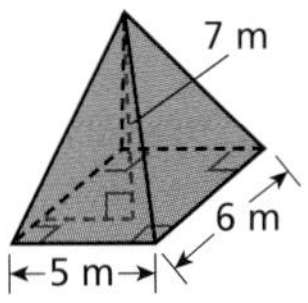

$V = \frac{1}{3} Bh$

$V = \frac{1}{3} \cdot (5 \cdot 6) \cdot 7$

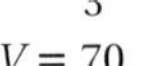

$V = 70$

The volume is 70 m^3.

- **Find the volume of the cone to the nearest tenth. Use 3.14 for π.**

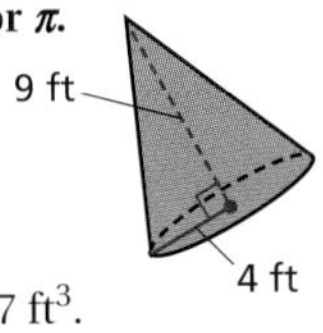

$V = \frac{1}{3} \pi r^2 h$

$V \approx \frac{1}{3} \cdot 3.14 \cdot 4^2 \cdot 9$

$V \approx 150.72$

The volume is about 150.7 ft^3.

- **Find the volume of the sphere to the nearest tenth. Use 3.14 for π.**

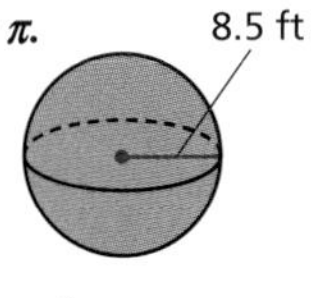

$V = \frac{4}{3} \pi r^3$

$V \approx \frac{4}{3} \cdot 3.14 \cdot 8.5^3$

$V \approx 2{,}571.13\overline{6}$

The volume is about 2,571.1 ft^3.

EXERCISES

Find the volume of the pyramid.

10.

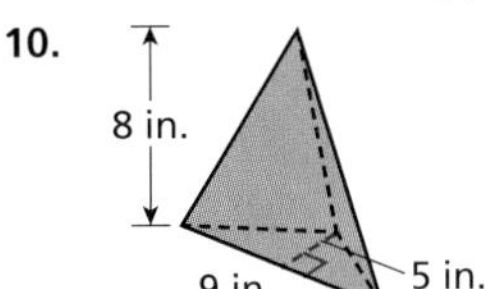

Find the volume of the cone to the nearest tenth. Use 3.14 for π.

11.

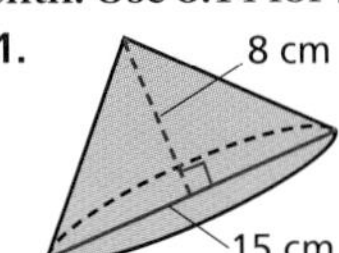

Find the volume of each sphere to the nearest tenth. Use 3.14 for π.

12.

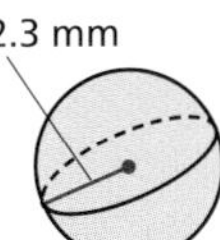

13.

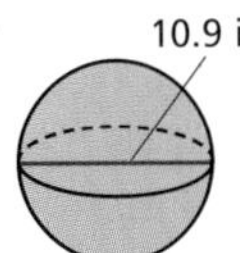

Answers

7. 364 cm^3
8. 415.4 mm^3
9. 111.9 ft^3
10. 60 in^3
11. 471 cm^3
12. 50.9 mm^3
13. 677.7 in^3

Answers

14. 250 m^2
15. 262.3 cm^2
16. 254.3 ft^2
17. 143,799.4 m^2
18. 2,970 in^2
19. 4.1 ft^3

9-4 Surface Area of Prisms, Cylinders, and Spheres (pp. 486–490)

EXAMPLE

- **Find the surface area of the rectangular prism formed by the net.**

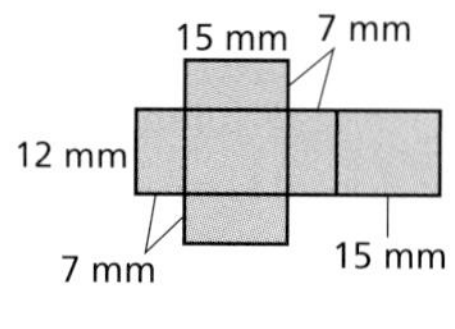

$S = 2\ell w + 2\ell h + 2wh$

$S = (2 \cdot 15 \cdot 7) + (2 \cdot 15 \cdot 12) + (2 \cdot 7 \cdot 12)$

$S = 738$

The surface area is 738 mm^2.

EXERCISES

Find the surface area of the rectangular prism formed by the net.

14. 5 m, 10 m, 5 m, 5 m, 10 m

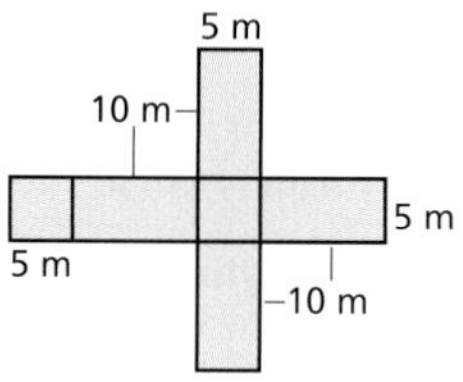

- **Find the surface area of the cylinder formed by the net to the nearest tenth. Use 3.14 for π.**

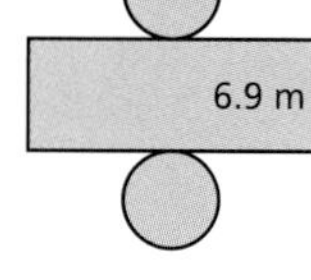

$S = 2\pi r^2 + 2\pi rh$

$S \approx (2 \cdot 3.14 \cdot 3^2) + (2 \cdot 3.14 \cdot 3 \cdot 6.9)$

$S \approx 186.516$

The surface area is about 186.5 m^2.

Find the surface area of the cylinder formed by the net to the nearest tenth. Use 3.14 for π.

15. 15 cm, 2.4 cm

- **Find the surface area of the sphere to the nearest tenth. Use 3.14 for π.**

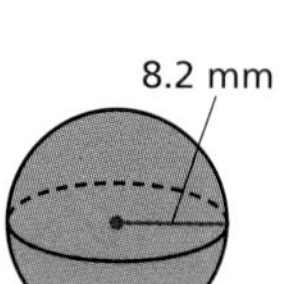

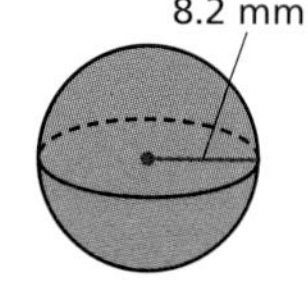

$S = 4\pi r^2$

$S \approx 4 \cdot 3.14 \cdot 8.2^2$

$S \approx 844.5344$

The surface area is about 844.5 mm^2.

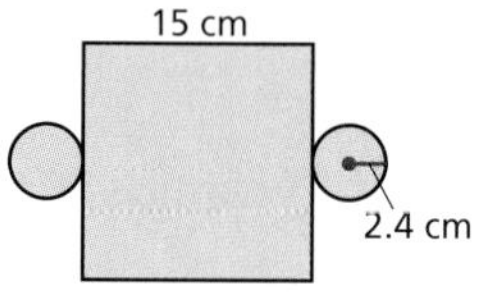

Find the surface area of each sphere to the nearest tenth. Use 3.14 for π.

16. 9 ft

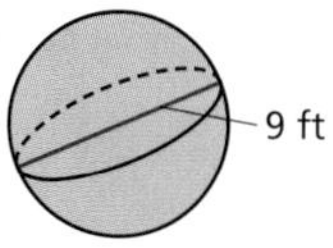

17.

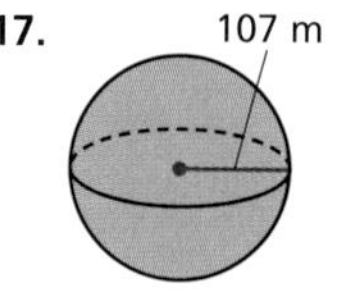

9-5 Changing Dimensions (pp. 491–495)

EXAMPLE

- **The surface area of a rectangular prism is 32 m^2, and its volume is 12 m^3. What are the surface area and volume of a similar rectangular prism with a scale factor of 6?**

$S = 32 \cdot 6^2$

$= 1{,}152$

$V = 12 \cdot 6^3$

$= 2{,}592$

The surface area of the larger prism is 1,152 m^2. Its volume is 2,592 m^3.

EXERCISES

18. A cylinder has a surface area of about 13.2 in^2. What is the surface area of a similar cylinder that has a scale factor of 15?

19. A refrigerator has a volume of 14 ft^3. What is the volume, to the nearest tenth, of a similarly shaped refrigerator that has a scale factor of $\frac{2}{3}$?

Chapter Test

Chapter 9

Give the name of each prism or pyramid.

1. 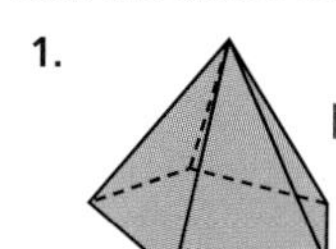 **pentagonal pyramid**

2. 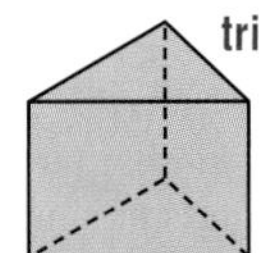 **triangular prism**

3. 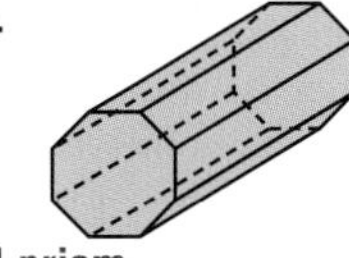 **octagonal prism**

4. 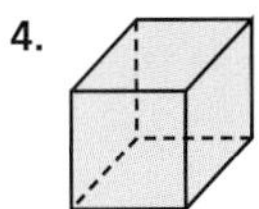 **rectangular prism**

5. 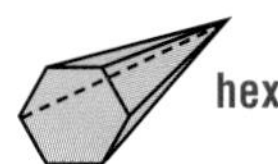 **hexagonal pyramid**

6. 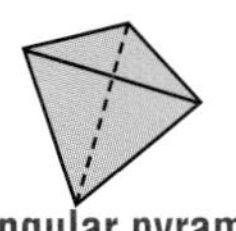 **triangular pyramid**

Find the volume of each figure to the nearest tenth. Use 3.14 for π.

7. 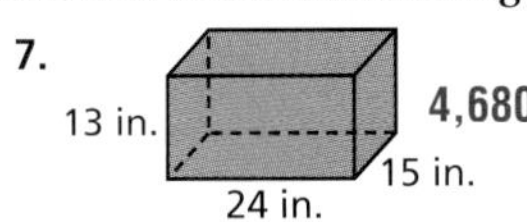

4,680.0 in³

8. 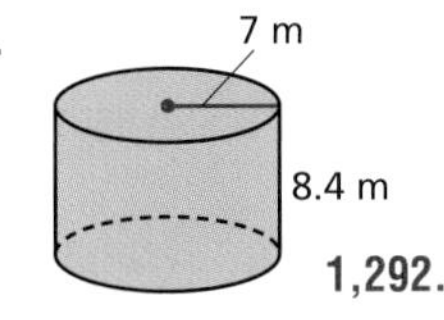

1,292.4 m³

9. 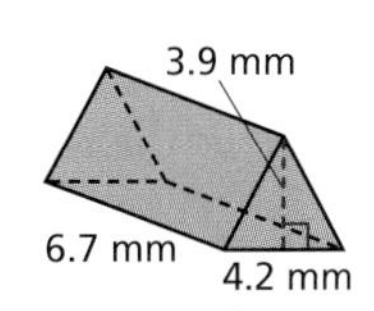

54.9 mm³

10. 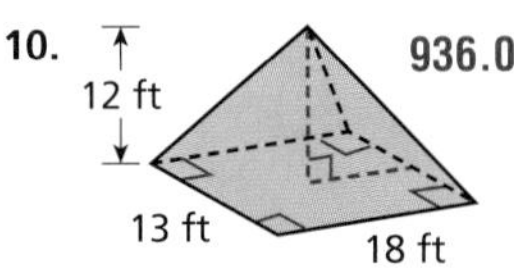

936.0 ft³

11. 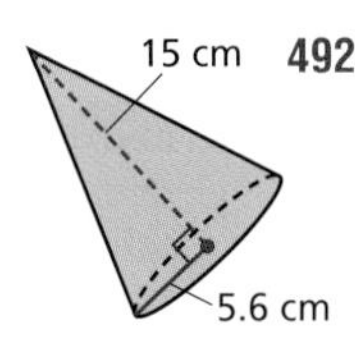

492.4 cm³

12. 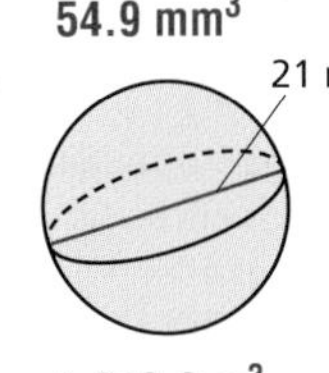

4,846.6 m³

Find the surface area of each figure to the nearest tenth. Use 3.14 for π.

13. 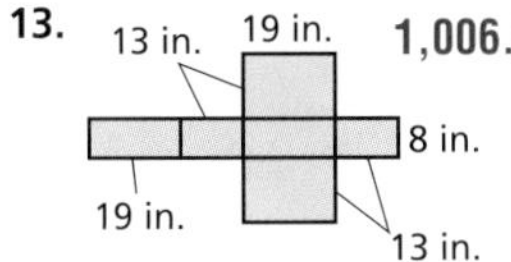

1,006.0 in²

14. 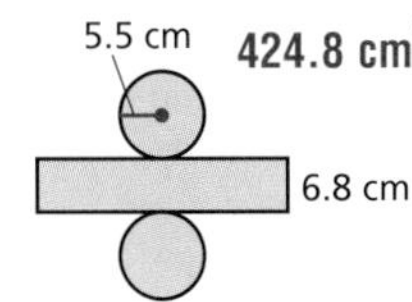

424.8 cm²

15. 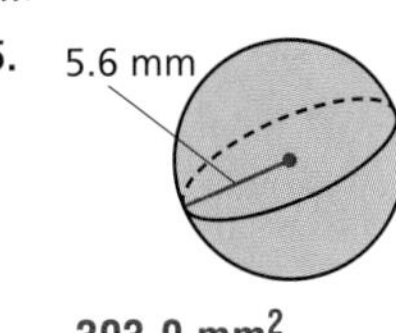

393.9 mm²

16. The surface area of a rectangular prism is 52 ft². What is the surface area of a similar prism that has a scale factor of 7? **2,548 ft²**

17. The surface area of a table is 8.4 m². What is the surface area to the nearest hundredth of a similarly shaped table that has a scale factor of $\frac{1}{8}$? **0.13 m²**

18. The volume of a cube is 35 mm³. What is the volume of a larger cube that has a scale factor of 9? **25,515 mm³**

19. The volume of a flowerpot is 7.5 cm³. What is the volume to the nearest hundredth of a similarly shaped flowerpot that has a scale factor of $\frac{1}{2}$? **0.94 cm³**

20. A round balloon has a volume of about 104.7 in³. If the balloon is inflated by a scale factor of 2, what is its new volume? **837.6 in³**

Chapter Test

Chapter 9

Purpose: *To assess students' mastery of concepts and skills in Chapter 9*

Assessment Resources

Chapter 9 Tests (Levels A, B, C)
Assessment Resources .... pp. 81–86

Test and Practice Generator CD-ROM

Additional assessment items in both multiple-choice and free-response format may be generated for any objective in Chapter 9.

Chapter 9 Performance Assessment

***Purpose:** To assess students' understanding of concepts in Chapter 9 and combined problem-solving skills*

Assessment Resources 

Performance Assessment
Assessment Resources. . . . . p. 122

Performance Assessment Teacher Support
Assessment Resources. . . . . p. 121

Answers

5. See Level 3 work sample below.

Scoring Rubric for Problem Solving Item 5

Level 3
Accomplishes the purposes of the task.
Student gives clear explanations, shows understanding of mathematical ideas and processes, and computes accurately.

Level 2
Purposes of the task not fully achieved.
Student demonstrates satisfactory but limited understanding of the mathematical ideas and processes.

Level 1
Purposes of the task not accomplished.
Student shows little evidence of understanding the mathematical ideas and processes and makes computational and/or procedural errors.

Chapter 9 Performance Assessment

2. $V = \frac{4}{3}\pi r^3 = \frac{4}{3} \cdot 3.14 \cdot 3^3 = 113.04$ ft^3; $S = 4\pi r^2 = 4 \cdot 3.14 \cdot 3^2 = 113.04$ ft^2

 Show What You Know

Create a portfolio of your work from this chapter. Complete this page and include it with your four best pieces of work from Chapter 9. Choose from your homework or lab assignments, mid-chapter quiz, or any journal entries you have done. Put them together using any design you want. Make your portfolio represent what you consider your best work.

3. The second prism is larger because the scale factor is greater than 1; $V = 60 \cdot \left(\frac{5}{3}\right)^3 \approx 277.8$ m^3.

Short Response

1. A polyhedron has two parallel square bases with edges 6 inches long. Its height is 12 inches. Identify the figure and find its volume. Show your work. **square prism; $V = Bh$; $V = (6 \cdot 6) \cdot 12 = 432$ in^3**
2. Find the volume and surface area of a sphere with radius 3 feet. Show your work.
3. The volume of a triangular prism is 60 m^3. A similar prism has a scale factor of $\frac{5}{3}$. Which prism is larger? Explain your answer. Then find the volume of the second prism, and show your work.
4. A three-dimensional figure has one vertex and a circular base. Tell whether the figure is a polyhedron. If it is, name the figure. If it is not, explain why not. **The figure is not a polyhedron because its surfaces are not all polygons. The figure is a cone.**

Performance Assessment

Extended Problem Solving

5. Use the diagram for the following problems. Round your answers to the nearest tenth, if necessary. Use 3.14 for π.
   a. What three-dimensional shapes make up the silo?
   b. What is the volume of the silo? Show your work.
   c. Approximate the surface area of the silo. Show your work.
   d. The bales of hay in the diagram are similarly shaped. The scale factor of the larger bale is 2, and it contains 60 cubic feet of hay. How much hay is in the smaller bale? Explain your answer.

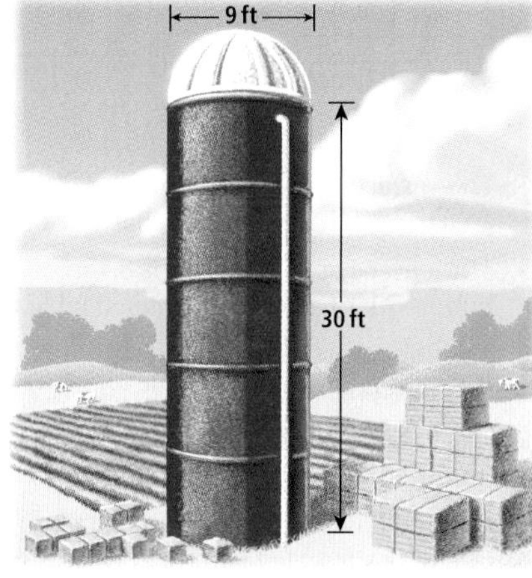

Student Work Samples for Item 5

Level 3

A. Hemisphere and Cylinder
B. $V = \pi r^2 h + (\frac{1}{2})\frac{4}{3}\pi r^3$
$= 3.14(4.5)^2 \cdot 30 + \frac{1}{2}(\frac{4}{3})3.14(4.5)^3$
$= 1907.55 + 190.755$
≈ 2098.3 ft^3
C. $S = 2\pi r h + 2\pi r^2$
$= 2 \cdot 3.14 \cdot 4.5 \cdot 30 + 2 \cdot 3.14 \cdot 4.5^2$
$= 847.8 + 127.17$
≈ 975.0 ft^2
D. $60 = V \cdot 2^3$
$60 = 8V$ ($V = 7.5$ ft^3)
$7.5 = V$

The student correctly answered each part with the appropriate units, showed the work, and explained the answers as necessary.

Level 2

a. cylinder and hemisphere
b. $V = \pi r^2 h + \frac{4}{3}\pi r^3$
$= 3.14 \cdot 4.5^2 \cdot 30 + \frac{4}{3} \cdot 3.14 \cdot 4.5^3$
$= 2289$ ft^3
c. $S = 2\pi r^2 + 2\pi r h + 4\pi r^2$
$= 2 \cdot 3.14 \cdot 4.5^2 + 2 \cdot 3.14 \cdot 4.5 \cdot 30 + 4 \cdot 3.14 \cdot 4.5^2$
$= 1229$ ft^2
d. $60 = V \cdot 2^3$
$60 = 8V$
7.5 ft$^3 = V$

The student correctly identified the shapes, but used incorrect formulas in parts **b** and **c**. The student also did not follow the directions for rounding.

Level 1

cylinder and cone
$\pi r^2 h = 3.14 \cdot 9^2 \cdot 30$
$= 7630.2$
$2\pi r h = 2 \cdot 3.14 \cdot 9 \cdot 30$
$= 1695.6$
$V = 60 \cdot 2^3$
$= 480$

The student identified one of the figures correctly, but used incomplete formulas to find answer parts **b** and **c**.

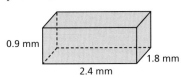

internet connect

State-Specific Test Practice Online
go.hrw.com Keyword: MS4 TestPrep

Standardized Test Prep

Chapter 9

Cumulative Assessment, Chapters 1–9

1. Find the measure of the unknown angle. **A**

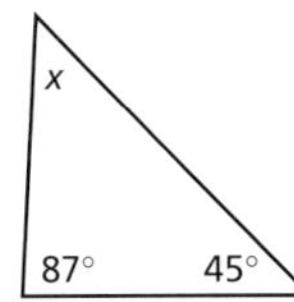

Ⓐ 48° Ⓒ 132°
Ⓑ 228° Ⓓ 52°

2. Find the mean of the data set 23, 15, 21, 23, 18, 20, 19, 13. **J**

Ⓕ 23 Ⓗ 10
Ⓖ 19.5 Ⓙ 19

3. Write −7, 0, −3, 4, 1 in order from least to greatest. **B**

Ⓐ −3, −7, 0, 1, 4 Ⓒ 4, 1, 0, −3, −7
Ⓑ −7, −3, 0, 1, 4 Ⓓ 4, 1, 0, −7, −3

4. Find the simple interest on $8,500 invested at 6% for 18 months. **G**

Ⓕ $9,180 Ⓗ $7,650
Ⓖ $765 Ⓙ $1,020

5. Find the volume of the cylinder to the nearest tenth. Use 3.14 for π. **D**

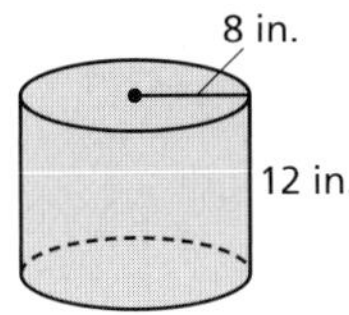

Ⓐ 602.9 in^3 Ⓒ 1,205.8 in^3
Ⓑ 3,215.4 in^3 Ⓓ 2,411.5 in^3

6. Find the surface area of the rectangular prism. **G**

0.9 mm, 2.4 mm, 1.8 mm

Ⓕ 8.1 mm^2 Ⓗ 15.84 mm^2
Ⓖ 16.2 mm^2 Ⓙ 3.888 mm^2

TIP!

TEST TAKING TIP!
When finding the prime factorization of a number, you can eliminate choices by looking for nonprime factors.

7. Find the prime factorization of 180. **C**

Ⓐ $4 \cdot 9 \cdot 5$ Ⓒ $2^2 \cdot 3^2 \cdot 5$
Ⓑ $10 \cdot 18$ Ⓓ $2^3 \cdot 3 \cdot 5$

8. Add $3\frac{2}{3} + 1\frac{3}{5}$. Write the answer in simplest form. **F**

Ⓕ $5\frac{4}{15}$ Ⓗ $4\frac{5}{8}$
Ⓖ $2\frac{1}{15}$ Ⓙ $3\frac{6}{15}$

9. ***SHORT RESPONSE*** The surface area of a sphere is about 86 ft^2.
   a. Find the surface area of a larger sphere that has a scale factor of 4.
   b. How does the surface area change when the dimensions are increased by a factor of 4?

10. ***SHORT RESPONSE*** What is the base length of a parallelogram with a height of 8 in. and an area of 56 in^2?

Standardized Test Prep

Answers

9. a. 1,376 ft^2
   b. The surface area is multiplied by 16, or 4^2.

10. 7 inches

Standardized Test Prep

Chapter 9

Purpose: *To provide review and practice for Chapters 1–9 and standardized tests*

Assessment Resources

Cumulative Tests (Levels A, B, C)
Assessment Resources . . . . . pp. 225–236

State-Specific Test Practice Online
KEYWORD: MS4 TestPrep

Test Prep Doctor

Expand on the Test Taking Tip given for item 7 by reminding students what prime numbers are. After students have eliminated **A** and **B,** have them multiply the numbers in **C** and **D** to find the correct answer, **C.**

Chapter 10

Probability

Section 10A

Introduction to Probability

Lesson 10-1
Probability

Lesson 10-2
Experimental Probability

Lesson 10-3
Make a List to Find Sample Spaces

Lesson 10-4
Theoretical Probability

Section 10B

Applications of Probability

Lesson 10-5
Probability of Independent and Dependent Events

Hands-On Lab 10A
Pascal's Triangle

Lesson 10-6
Combinations

Lesson 10-7
Permutations

Extension
Computing Odds

Pacing Guide for 45-Minute Classes

Chapter 10

DAY 131	DAY 132	DAY 133	DAY 134	DAY 135
Lesson 10-1	Lesson 10-2	Lesson 10-3	Lesson 10-4	Mid-Chapter Quiz Lesson 10-5
DAY 136	**DAY 137**	**DAY 138**	**DAY 139**	**DAY 140**
Hands-On Lab 10A	Lesson 10-6	Lesson 10-7	Extension	Chapter 10 Review
DAY 141				
Chapter 10 Assessment				

Pacing Guide for 90-Minute Classes

Chapter 10

DAY 65	DAY 66	DAY 67	DAY 68	DAY 69
Chapter 9 Review Lesson 10-1	Chapter 9 Assessment Lesson 10-2	Lesson 10-3 Lesson 10-4	Mid-Chapter Quiz Lesson 10-5 Hands-On Lab 10A	Lesson 10-6 Lesson 10-7
DAY 70	**DAY 71**			
Extension Chapter 10 Review	Chapter 10 Assessment Hands-On Lab 11A			

Across the Series

COURSE 1

- Find experimental and theoretical probabilities, including compound events.
- Use simulation to model experiments.
- Use an organized list, permutations, and combinations to find all possible outcomes of an experiment.
- Find the odds of a specified outcome.

COURSE 2

- **Find theoretical probabilities, including dependent and independent events.**
- **Use an organized list, permutations, and combinations to find all possible outcomes of an experiment.**
- **Use Pascal's Triangle, permutations, and combinations to find probabilities.**
- **Find the odds of a specified outcome.**

COURSE 3

- Find theoretical probabilities, including dependent and independent events.
- Use experiments and simulations to estimate probabilities.
- Use the Fundamental Counting Principle, permutations, and combinations to find probabilities.
- Convert between the probability and odds of a specified outcome.

Across the Curriculum

LANGUAGE ARTS LINK

Math: Reading and Writing in the Content Area .... pp. 81–87
Focus on Problem Solving
Understand the Problem. .... SE p. 529
Journal .... TE, last page of each lesson
Write About It. .... SE pp. 515, 523, 527, 533, 543
Literature .... SE p. 543

SCIENCE LINK

Life Science .... SE p. 515
Earth Science. .... SE pp. 515, 519
Health .... SE pp. 523, 543

TE = *Teacher's Edition* **SE** = *Student Edition*

Interdisciplinary Bulletin Board

Life Science

Follow the drawing to see how proteins are made. There are 4 bases, A, T, G, and C, that combine in groups of 3 to code for a specific amino acid. Any base can appear more than one time in a group of 3. How many combinations of bases are possible?
$4 \times 4 \times 4 = 64$ combinations

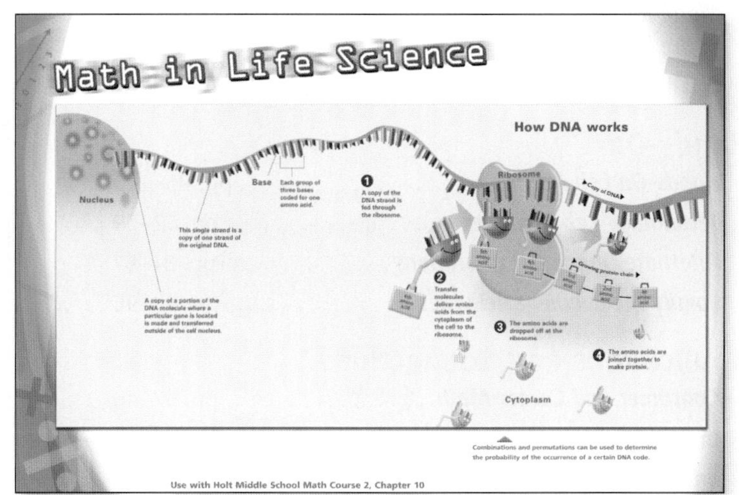

Interdisciplinary posters and worksheets are provided in your resource material.

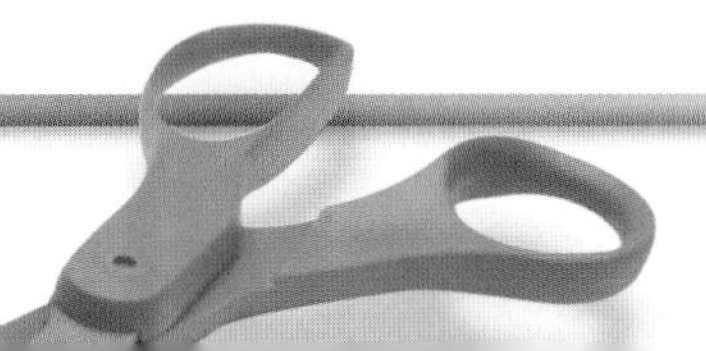

Chapter 10

Resource Options

Chapter 10 Resource Book

Student Resources

Practice (Levels A, B, C)..... pp. 8–10, 17–19, 26–28, 35–37, 45–47, 54–56, 63–65
Reteach .... pp. 11, 20, 29, 38, 48, 57, 66
Challenge .... pp. 12, 21, 30, 39, 49, 58, 67
Problem Solving .... pp. 13, 22, 31, 40, 50, 59, 68
Puzzles, Twisters & Teasers..... pp. 14, 23, 32, 41, 51, 60, 69
Recording Sheets .... pp. 3, 7, 16, 25, 34, 44, 53, 62, 72, 75
Chapter Review .... pp. 70–71

Teacher and Parent Resources

Chapter Planning and Pacing Guide.................... p. 4
Section Planning Guides .... pp. 5, 42
Parent Letter .... pp. 1–2
Teaching Tools .... p. 75
Teacher Support for Chapter Project .... p. 73
Transparencies .... pp. T1–T32
- Daily Transparencies
- Additional Examples Transparencies
- Teaching Transparencies

Reaching All Learners

English Language Learners

Success for English Language Learners ...... pp. 161–174
Math: Reading and Writing in the Content Area .... pp. 81–87
Spanish Homework and Practice .... pp. 81–87
Spanish Interactive Study Guide .... pp. 81–87
Spanish Family Involvement Activities .... pp. 89–96
Multilingual Glossary

Individual Needs

Are You Ready? Intervention and Enrichment .. pp. 85–88, 113–116, 129–132, 185–188, 423–424
Alternate Openers: Explorations .... pp. 81–87
Family Involvement Activities .... pp. 89–96
Interactive Problem Solving................. pp. 81–87
Interactive Study Guide .... pp. 81–87
Readiness Activities .... pp. 19–20
Math: Reading and Writing in the Content Area .... pp. 81–87
Challenge .... CRB pp. 12, 21, 30, 39, 49, 58, 67

Hands-On

Hands-On Lab Activities................... pp. 95–103
Technology Lab Activities.................... pp. 52–59
Alternate Openers: Explorations .... pp. 81–87
Family Involvement Activities............... pp. 89–96

Applications and Connections

Consumer and Career Math................. pp. 37–40
Interdisciplinary Posters .... Poster 10, TE p. 510B
Interdisciplinary Poster Worksheets.......... pp. 28–30

Transparencies

Alternate Openers: Explorations .... pp. 81–87
Exercise Answers Transparencies
Chapter 10 Resource Book.................... pp. T1–T32
- Daily Transparencies
- Additional Examples Transparencies
- Teaching Transparencies

Technology

Teacher Resources

***Lesson Presentations* CD-ROM**........... Chapter 10
***Test and Practice Generator* CD-ROM** ...... Chapter 10
***One-Stop Planner* CD-ROM** .... Chapter 10

Student Resources

***Are You Ready? Intervention* CD-ROM**
Skills 19, 26, 30, 44

Homework Help Online	**KEYWORD:** MS4 HWHelp10
Math Tools Online	**KEYWORD:** MS4 Tools
Glossary Online	**KEYWORD:** MS4 Glossary
Chapter Project Online	**KEYWORD:** MS4 PSProject10
Chapter Opener Online	**KEYWORD:** MS4 Ch10

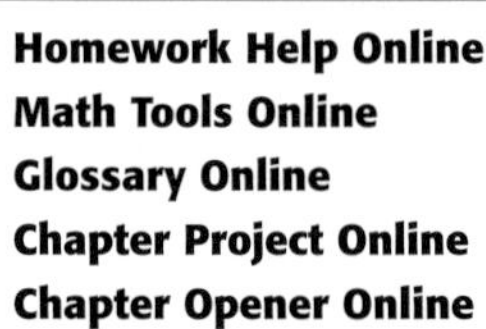

KEYWORD: MS4 CNN10

SE = *Student Edition* **TE** = *Teacher's Edition* **AR** = *Assessment Resources* **CRB** = *Chapter Resource Book* **MK** = *Manipulatives Kit*

Chapter 10

Assessment Options

Assessing Prior Knowledge

Determine whether students have the required prerequisite concepts and skills.

Are You Ready? . . . . SE p. 511

Inventory Test . . . . AR pp. 1–4

Test Preparation

Provide review and practice for chapter and standardized tests.

Standardized Test Prep . . . . SE p. 555

Spiral Review with Test Prep . . . . . SE, last page of each lesson

Study Guide and Review . . . . SE pp. 550–552

Test Prep Tool Kit

Technology 

 ***Test and Practice Generator*** **CD-ROM**

internet connect 

State-Specific Test Practice Online KEYWORD: MS4 TestPrep

Performance Assessment

Assess students' understanding of chapter concepts and combined problem-solving skills.

Performance Assessment . . . . SE p. 554
Includes scoring rubric in TE

Performance Assessment . . . . AR p. 124

Performance Assessment Teacher Support . . . . AR p. 123

Portfolio

Portfolio opportunities appear throughout the Student and Teacher's Editions.

Suggested work samples:

Problem Solving Project . . . . TE p. 510

Performance Assessment . . . . SE p. 554

Portfolio Guide . . . . AR p. xxxv

Journal . . . . TE, last page of each lesson

Write About It . . . . SE pp. 515, 523, 527, 533, 543

Daily Assessment

Obtain daily feedback on students' understanding of concepts.

Spiral Review and Test Prep . . . . . . SE, last page of each lesson

Also Available on Transparency In Chapter 10 Resource Book

Warm Up . . . . TE, first page of each lesson

Problem of the Day . . . . TE, first page of each lesson

Lesson Quiz . . . . TE, last page of each lesson

Student Self-Assessment

Have students evaluate their own work.

Group Project Evaluation . . . . AR p. xxxii

Individual Group Member Evaluation . . . . AR p. xxxiii

Portfolio Guide . . . . AR p. xxxv

Journal . . . . TE, last page of each lesson

Formal Assessment

Assess students' mastery of concepts and skills.

Section Quizzes . . . . AR pp. 27–28

Mid-Chapter Quiz . . . . SE p. 528

Chapter Test . . . . SE p. 553

Chapter Tests (Levels A, B, C) . . . . AR pp. 87–92

Cumulative Tests (Levels A, B, C) . . . . AR pp. 237–248

Standardized Test Prep
Cumulative Assessment . . . . SE p. 555

End-of-Year Test . . . . AR pp. 273–276

Technology 

 ***Test and Practice Generator*** **CD-ROM**

Make tests electronically. This software includes:

- Dynamic practice for Chapter 10
- Customizable tests
- Multiple-choice items for each objective
- Free-response items for each objective
- Teacher management system

SE = *Student Edition* **TE** = *Teacher's Edition* **AR** = *Assessment Resources* **CRB** = *Chapter Resource Book* **MK** = *Manipulatives Kit*

Chapter 10

Chapter 10 Tests

Three levels (A,B,C) of tests are available for each chapter in the *Assessment Resources.*

Level A

CHAPTER 10 **Chapter Test**
Form A

For 1–3, determine if each event is impossible, likely, or certain.

1. Everyone on the Scarlet Red basketball team is wearing red jerseys for the game. Tiffany is a guard on the Scarlet Reds. How likely is it that she is wearing a red jersey?
   certain
2. Mr. Wilson will take 5 of his 6 children to the zoo. Jamar is Mr. Wilson's son. How likely is it that he will go to the zoo?
   likely
3. There are 24 marbles in a bag. Half of them are green, the other half are blue. How likely is it that a red marble can be chosen from the bag?
   impossible
4. A basketball player made 7 of his last 10 free throws. What is the experimental probability he will make his next free throw?
   $\frac{7}{10}$
5. Cheryl rolls a 1–6 number cube 12 times. The cube lands on 3 twice. What is the experimental probability that it will land on 3 on the next roll?
   $\frac{1}{6}$
6. During the first week of summer, the temperature has been above 70° for 5 days out of 7. What is the experimental probability that the temperature will be above 70° on the eighth day of summer?
   $\frac{5}{7}$
7. Neil has 2 counters that are black on one side and white on the other side. He tosses them both in the air at the same time. What are the possible outcomes? How large is the sample space?
   BB, BW, WB, WW; 4
8. There are compact, mid-size, and luxury cars in the dealer's showroom. Each car is available in either gold, silver, red, blue, or white. How many different choices of cars does a customer have?
   15 choices

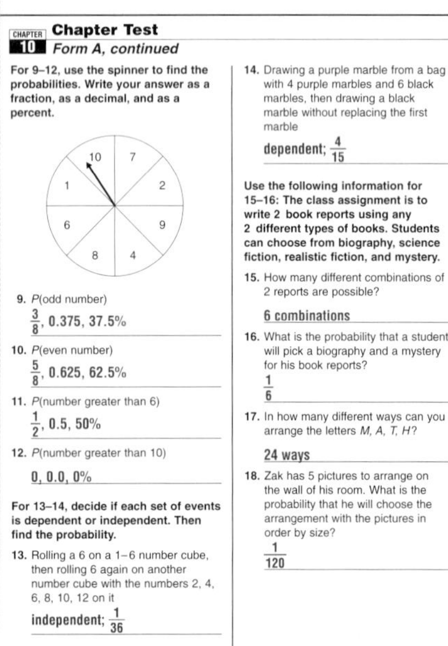

CHAPTER 10 **Chapter Test**
Form A, continued

For 9–12, use the spinner to find the probabilities. Write your answer as a fraction, as a decimal, and as a percent.

9. *P*(odd number)
   $\frac{3}{8}$, **0.375, 37.5%**
10. *P*(even number)
    $\frac{5}{8}$, **0.625, 62.5%**
11. *P*(number greater than 6)
    $\frac{1}{2}$, **0.5, 50%**
12. *P*(number greater than 10)
    0, 0.0, 0%

For 13–14, decide if each set of events is dependent or independent. Then find the probability.

13. Rolling a 6 on a 1–6 number cube, then rolling 6 again on another number cube with the numbers 2, 4, 6, 8, 10, 12 on it
    independent; $\frac{1}{36}$
14. Drawing a purple marble from a bag with 4 purple marbles and 6 black marbles, then drawing a black marble without replacing the first marble
    dependent; $\frac{4}{15}$

Use the following information for 15–16: The class assignment is to write 2 book reports using any 2 different types of books. Students can choose from biography, science fiction, realistic fiction, and mystery.

15. How many different combinations of 2 reports are possible?
    6 combinations
16. What is the probability that a student will pick a biography and a mystery for his book reports?
    $\frac{1}{6}$
17. In how many different ways can you arrange the letters *M, A, T, H*?
    24 ways
18. Zak has 5 pictures to arrange on the wall of his room. What is the probability that he will choose the arrangement with the pictures in order by size?
    $\frac{1}{120}$

Level B

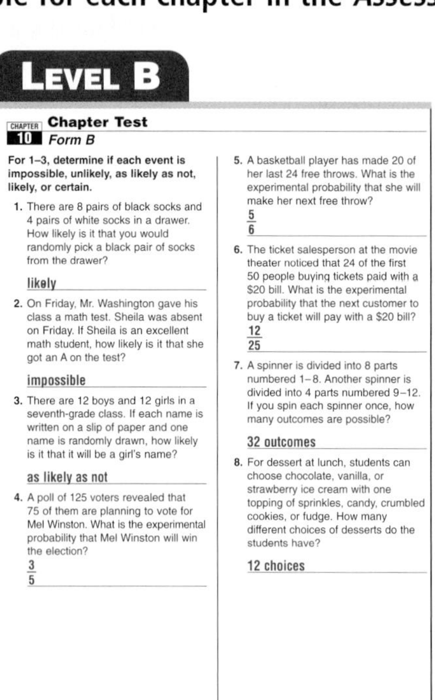

CHAPTER 10 **Chapter Test**
Form B

For 1–3, determine if each event is impossible, unlikely, as likely as not, likely, or certain.

1. There are 8 pairs of black socks and 4 pairs of white socks in a drawer. How likely is it that you would randomly pick a black pair of socks from the drawer?
   likely
2. On Friday, Mr. Washington gave his class a math test. Sheila was absent on Friday. If Sheila is an excellent math student, how likely is it that she got an A on the test?
   impossible
3. There are 12 boys and 12 girls in a seventh-grade class. If each name is written on a slip of paper and one name is randomly drawn, how likely is it that it will be a girl's name?
   as likely as not
4. A poll of 125 voters revealed that 75 of them are planning to vote for Mel Winston. What is the experimental probability that Mel Winston will win the election?
   $\frac{3}{5}$
5. A basketball player has made 20 of her last 24 free throws. What is the experimental probability that she will make her next free throw?
   $\frac{5}{6}$
6. The ticket salesperson at the movie theater noticed that 24 of the first 50 people buying tickets paid with a $20 bill. What is the experimental probability that the next customer to buy a ticket will pay with a $20 bill?
   $\frac{12}{25}$
7. A spinner is divided into 8 parts numbered 1–8. Another spinner is divided into 4 parts numbered 9–12. If you spin each spinner once, how many outcomes are possible?
   32 outcomes
8. For dessert at lunch, students can choose chocolate, vanilla, or strawberry ice cream with one topping of sprinkles, candy, crumbled cookies, or fudge. How many different choices of desserts do the students have?
   12 choices

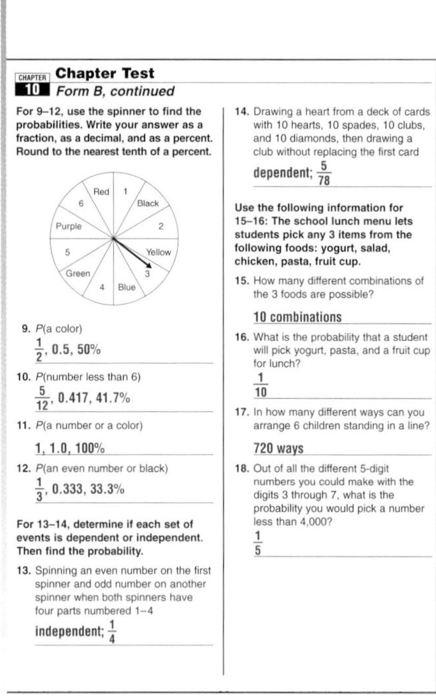

CHAPTER 10 **Chapter Test**
Form B, continued

For 9–12, use the spinner to find the probabilities. Write your answer as a fraction, as a decimal, and as a percent. Round to the nearest tenth of a percent.

9. *P*(a color)
   $\frac{1}{2}$, **0.5, 50%**
10. *P*(number less than 6)
    $\frac{5}{12}$, **0.417, 41.7%**
11. *P*(a number or a color)
    1, 1.0, 100%
12. *P*(an even number or black)
    $\frac{1}{3}$, **0.333, 33.3%**

For 13–14, determine if each set of events is dependent or independent. Then find the probability.

13. Spinning an even number on the first spinner and odd number on another spinner when both spinners have four parts numbered 1–4
    independent; $\frac{1}{4}$
14. Drawing a heart from a deck of cards with 10 hearts, 10 spades, 10 clubs, and 10 diamonds, then drawing a club without replacing the first card
    dependent; $\frac{5}{78}$

Use the following information for 15–16: The school lunch menu lets students pick any 3 items from the following foods: yogurt, salad, chicken, pasta, fruit cup.

15. How many different combinations of the 3 foods are possible?
    10 combinations
16. What is the probability that a student will pick yogurt, pasta, and a fruit cup for lunch?
    $\frac{1}{10}$
17. In how many different ways can you arrange 6 children standing in a line?
    720 ways
18. Out of all the different 5-digit numbers you could make with the digits 3 through 7, what is the probability you would pick a number less than 4,000?
    $\frac{1}{5}$

Level C

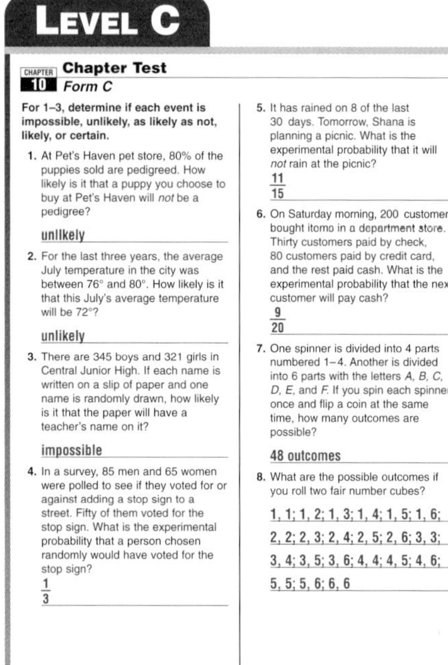

CHAPTER 10 **Chapter Test**
Form C

For 1–3, determine if each event is impossible, unlikely, as likely as not, likely, or certain.

1. At Pet's Haven pet store, 80% of the puppies sold are pedigreed. How likely is it that a puppy you choose to buy at Pet's Haven will *not* be a pedigree?
   unlikely
2. For the last three years, the average July temperature in the city was between 76° and 80°. How likely is it that this July's average temperature will be 72°?
   unlikely
3. There are 345 boys and 321 girls in Central Junior High. If each name is written on a slip of paper and one name is randomly drawn, how likely is it that the paper will have a teacher's name on it?
   impossible
4. In a survey, 85 men and 65 women were polled to see if they voted for or against adding a stop sign to a street. Fifty of them voted for the stop sign. What is the experimental probability that a person chosen randomly would have voted for the stop sign?
   $\frac{1}{3}$
5. It has rained on 8 of the last 30 days. Tomorrow, Shana is planning a picnic. What is the experimental probability that it will *not* rain at the picnic?
   $\frac{11}{15}$
6. On Saturday morning, 200 customers bought items in a department store. Thirty customers paid by check, 80 customers paid by credit card, and the rest paid cash. What is the experimental probability that the next customer will pay cash?
   $\frac{9}{20}$
7. One spinner is divided into 4 parts numbered 1–4. Another is divided into 6 parts with the letters *A, B, C, D, E,* and *F*. If you spin each spinner once and flip a coin at the same time, how many outcomes are possible?
   48 outcomes
8. What are the possible outcomes if you roll two fair number cubes?
   1, 1; 1, 2; 1, 3; 1, 4; 1, 5; 1, 6; 2, 2; 2, 3; 2, 4; 2, 5; 2, 6; 3, 3; 3, 4; 3, 5; 3, 6; 4, 4; 4, 5; 4, 6; 5, 5; 5, 6; 6, 6

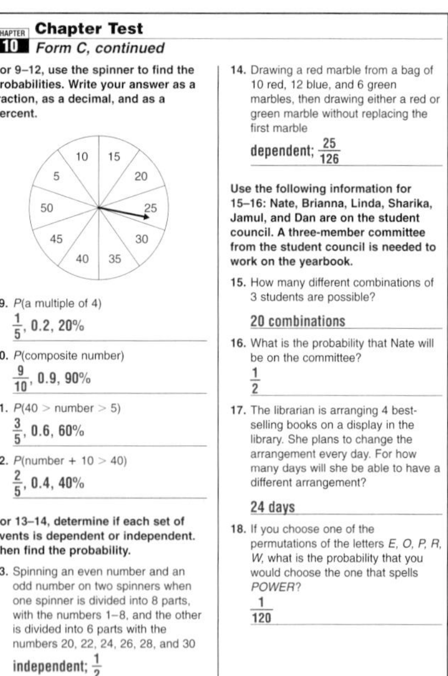

CHAPTER 10 **Chapter Test**
Form C, continued

For 9–12, use the spinner to find the probabilities. Write your answer as a fraction, as a decimal, and as a percent.

9. *P*(a multiple of 4)
   $\frac{1}{5}$, **0.2, 20%**
10. *P*(composite number)
    $\frac{9}{10}$, **0.9, 90%**
11. *P*(40 > number > 5)
    $\frac{3}{5}$, **0.6, 60%**
12. *P*(number + 10 > 40)
    $\frac{2}{5}$, **0.4, 40%**

For 13–14, determine if each set of events is dependent or independent. Then find the probability.

13. Spinning an even number and an odd number on two spinners when one spinner is divided into 8 parts, with the numbers 1–8, and the other is divided into 6 parts with the numbers 20, 22, 24, 26, 28, and 30
    independent; $\frac{1}{2}$
14. Drawing a red marble from a bag of 10 red, 12 blue, and 6 green marbles, then drawing either a red or green marble without replacing the first marble
    dependent; $\frac{25}{126}$

Use the following information for 15–16: Nate, Brianna, Linda, Sharika, Jamul, and Dan are on the student council. A three-member committee from the student council is needed to work on the yearbook.

15. How many different combinations of 3 students are possible?
    20 combinations
16. What is the probability that Nate will be on the committee?
    $\frac{1}{2}$
17. The librarian is arranging 4 best-selling books on a display in the library. She plans to change the arrangement every day. For how many days will she be able to have a different arrangement?
    24 days
18. If you choose one of the permutations of the letters *E, O, P, R, W*, what is the probability that you would choose the one that spells *POWER*?
    $\frac{1}{120}$

Test and Practice Generator CD-ROM

Create and customize multiple versions of the same tests with corresponding answers for any chosen chapter objectives.

Chapter 10 State and Standardized Test Preparation

Test Taking Skill Builder and Standardized Test Practice are provided for each chapter in the *Test Prep Tool Kit.*

TEST TAKING SKILL BUILDER

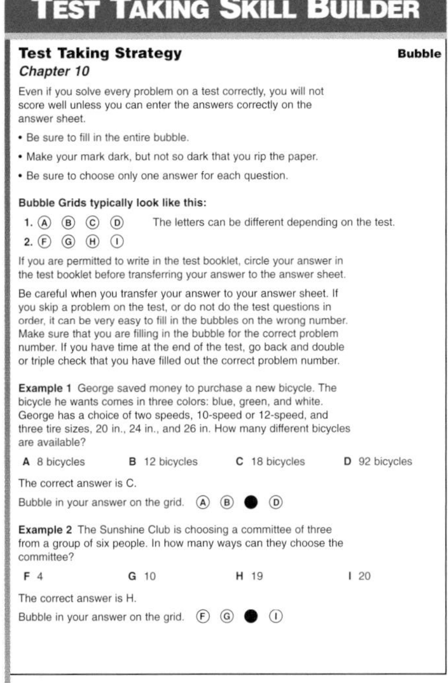

Test Taking Strategy — **Bubble**

Chapter 10

Even if you solve every problem on a test correctly, you will not score well unless you can enter the answers correctly on the answer sheet.

- Be sure to fill in the entire bubble.
- Make your mark dark, but not so dark that you rip the paper.
- Be sure to choose only one answer for each question.

Bubble Grids typically look like this:

1. Ⓐ Ⓑ Ⓒ Ⓓ The letters can be different depending on the test.
2. Ⓕ Ⓖ Ⓗ Ⓘ

If you are permitted to write in the test booklet, circle your answer in the test booklet before transferring your answer to the answer sheet.

Be careful when you transfer your answer to your answer sheet. If you skip a problem on the test, or do not do the test questions in order, it can be very easy to fill in the bubbles on the wrong number. Make sure that you are filling in the bubble for the correct problem number. If you have time at the end of the test, go back and double or triple check that you have filled out the correct problem number.

Example 1 George saved money to purchase a new bicycle. The bicycle he wants comes in three colors: blue, green, and white. George has a choice of two speeds, 10-speed or 12-speed, and three tire sizes, 20 in., 24 in., and 26 in. How many different bicycles are available?

A 8 bicycles B 12 bicycles C 18 bicycles D 92 bicycles

The correct answer is C.

Bubble in your answer on the grid. Ⓐ Ⓑ ● Ⓓ

Example 2 The Sunshine Club is choosing a committee of three from a group of six people. In how many ways can they choose the committee?

F 4 G 10 H 19 I 20

The correct answer is H.

Bubble in your answer on the grid. Ⓕ Ⓖ ● Ⓘ

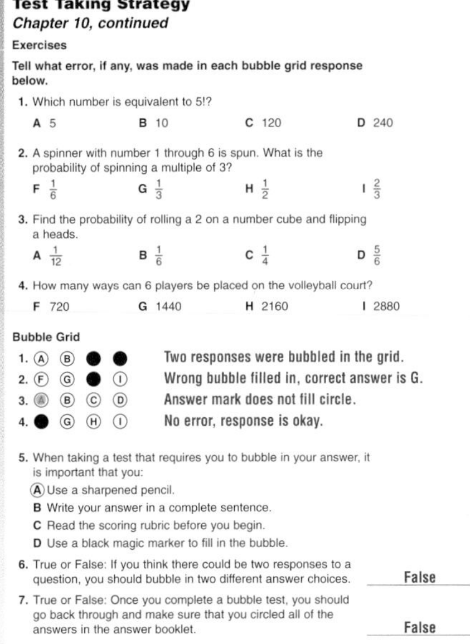

Test Taking Strategy

Chapter 10, continued

Exercises

Tell what error, if any, was made in each bubble grid response below.

1. Which number is equivalent to 5!?
   A 5 B 10 C 120 D 240
2. A spinner with number 1 through 6 is spun. What is the probability of spinning a multiple of 3?
   F $\frac{1}{6}$ G $\frac{1}{3}$ H $\frac{1}{2}$ I $\frac{2}{3}$
3. Find the probability of rolling a 2 on a number cube and flipping a heads.
   A $\frac{1}{12}$ B $\frac{1}{6}$ C $\frac{1}{4}$ D $\frac{5}{6}$
4. How many ways can 6 players be placed on the volleyball court?
   F 720 G 1440 H 2160 I 2880

Bubble Grid

1. Ⓐ Ⓑ ● ● Two responses were bubbled in the grid.
2. Ⓕ Ⓖ ● Ⓘ Wrong bubble filled in, correct answer is G.
3. Ⓐ Ⓑ Ⓒ Ⓓ Answer mark does not fill circle.
4. ● Ⓖ Ⓗ Ⓘ No error, response is okay.

5. When taking a test that requires you to bubble in your answer, it is important that you:
   Ⓐ Use a sharpened pencil.
   B Write your answer in a complete sentence.
   C Read the scoring rubric before you begin.
   D Use a black magic marker to fill in the bubble.
6. True or False: If you think there could be two responses to a question, you should bubble in two different answer choices. False
7. True or False: Once you complete a bubble test, you should go back through and make sure that you circled all of the answers in the answer booklet. False

STANDARDIZED TEST PRACTICE

Standardized Test Practice

Chapter 10

Select the best answer for Questions 1–6.

Use the information to answer Questions 1–3.

Nick has a bag of fruit that contains 8 apples, 4 oranges, and 3 pears.

1. Which fruit has the highest probability that it will be picked?
   A apple
   B pear
   C orange
   D cannot be determined
2. Which fruit has a $\frac{1}{5}$ probability of being picked?
   F apple
   G pear
   H orange
   I pears and oranges
3. Experimental probability is the ratio of the number of times an event occurs to the total number of what value?
   A trials
   B dice
   C numbers
   D outcomes

Use the information to answer Questions 4 and 5.

There are 2 pigs, 1 cat, 3 goats, and 4 cows at the state fair. As people enter the barn area they are randomly given one animal to pet.

4. What is the probability that a person will pet a dog?
   F 0%
   G 5%
   H 20%
   I 100%
5. What is the probability that a person will pet a cat?
   A 5%
   B 10%
   C 20%
   D 100%
6. A decorator needs to choose at least 2 colors from 4 standard paint colors for the walls of a kitchen. How many different combinations of colors can the decorator chose from?
   F 2
   G 5
   H 7
   I 11

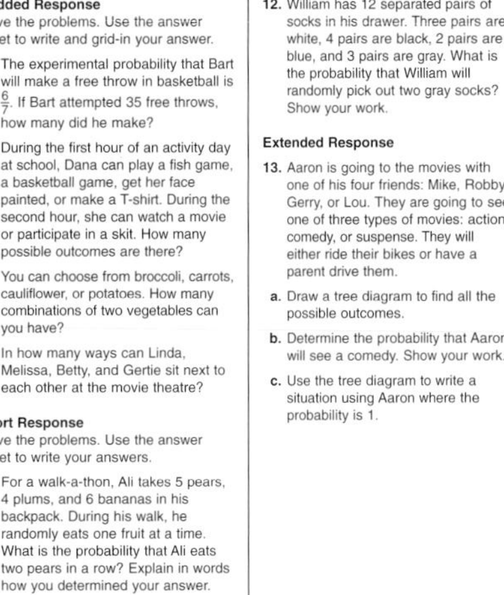

Standardized Test Practice

Chapter 10, continued

Gridded Response
Solve the problems. Use the answer sheet to write and grid-in your answer.

7. The experimental probability that Bart will make a free throw in basketball is $\frac{6}{7}$. If Bart attempted 35 free throws, how many did he make?
8. During the first hour of an activity day at school, Dana can play a fish game, a basketball game, get her face painted, or make a T-shirt. During the second hour, she can watch a movie or participate in a skit. How many possible outcomes are there?
9. You can choose from broccoli, carrots, cauliflower, or potatoes. How many combinations of two vegetables can you have?
10. In how many ways can Linda, Melissa, Betty, and Gertie sit next to each other at the movie theatre?

Short Response
Solve the problems. Use the answer sheet to write your answers.

11. For a walk-a-thon, Ali takes 5 pears, 4 plums, and 6 bananas in his backpack. During his walk, he randomly eats one fruit at a time. What is the probability that Ali eats two pears in a row? Explain in words how you determined your answer.
12. William has 12 separated pairs of socks in his drawer. Three pairs are white, 4 pairs are black, 2 pairs are blue, and 3 pairs are gray. What is the probability that William will randomly pick out two gray socks? Show your work.

Extended Response

13. Aaron is going to the movies with one of his four friends: Mike, Robby, Gerry, or Lou. They are going to see one of three types of movies: action, comedy, or suspense. They will either ride their bikes or have a parent drive them.
    a. Draw a tree diagram to find all the possible outcomes.
    b. Determine the probability that Aaron will see a comedy. Show your work.
    c. Use the tree diagram to write a situation using Aaron where the probability is 1.

...A) First, find ... first pear. Then find the probability of Ali eating a second pear. Then multiply the two probabilities together. P(Ali eating a pear): $\frac{5}{15} = \frac{1}{3}$. P(Ali eating a second pear): $\frac{4}{14}$. P(Ali eating two pears in a row) $= \frac{5}{15} \cdot \frac{4}{14} = \frac{20}{210} = \frac{2}{21}$. The probability of Ali eating two pears in a row is $\frac{2}{21}$. (See Lesson 10-5.)

12. For the first sock: P(choosing a gray sock) $= \frac{6}{24} = \frac{1}{4}$. For the second sock: P(choosing another gray sock) $= \frac{5}{23}$. P(choosing of 2 gray socks) $= \frac{1}{4} \cdot \frac{5}{23} = \frac{5}{92}$. The probability of William choosing two gray socks is $\frac{5}{92}$. (See Lesson 10-4.)

Extended Response
Write your answers for Problem 13 on the back of this paper. See Lesson 10-3.

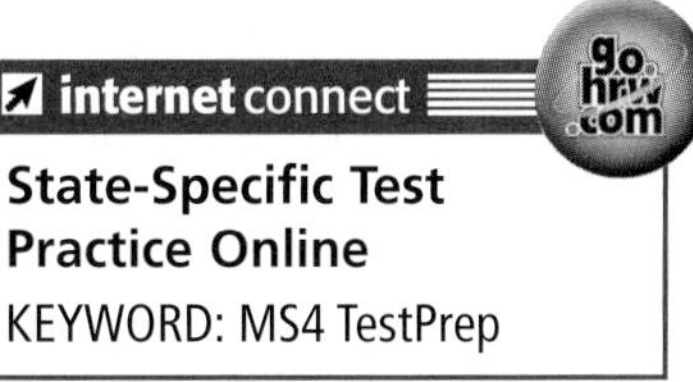

internet connect

State-Specific Test Practice Online

KEYWORD: MS4 TestPrep

Test Prep Tool Kit

- Standardized Test Prep Workbook
- Countdown to Testing transparencies
- State Test Prep CD-ROM
- Standardized Test Prep Video

Customized answer sheets give students realistic practice for actual standardized tests.

Chapter 10

Probability

Why Learn This?

You may have participated in a survey about a new product or answered questions about your family's favorite television shows. Demographers collect and use information to analyze consumer trends and even to determine ratings for television shows and radio stations. They often sort the information they collect based on characteristics, such as age, race, gender, and nationality, of the people being surveyed.

Using Data

To begin the study of this chapter, have students:

- Discuss who might use the information about mobile-phone use presented in the table. Possible answer: mobile-phone manufacturers
- Estimate the number of mobile phones used in each country in 2001, given the population of each country.
  Finland: 5,176,000
  3,509,328 mobile phones
  Norway: 4,503,000
  2,823,381 mobile phones
  Sweden: 8,875,000
  5,236,250 mobile phones
  Italy: 57,680,000
  30,108,960 mobile phones

Chapter 10

Probability

TABLE OF CONTENTS

internet connect
Chapter Opener Online
go.hrw.com
KEYWORD: MS4 Ch10

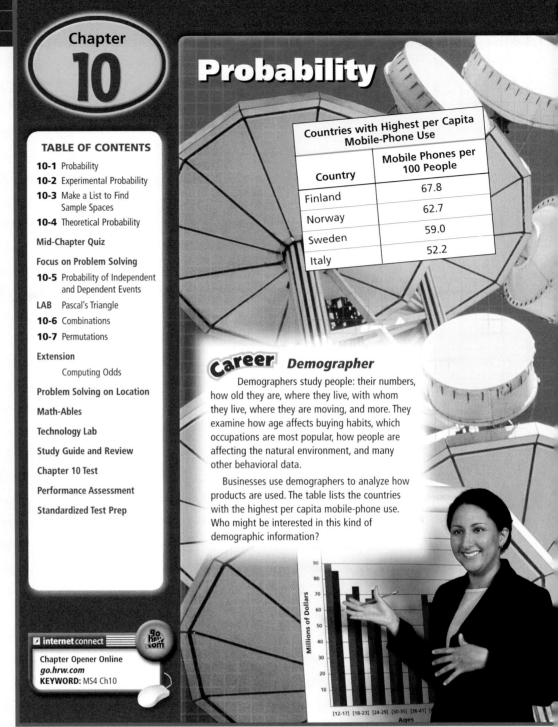

Countries with Highest per Capita Mobile-Phone Use

Country	Mobile Phones per 100 People
Finland	67.8
Norway	62.7
Sweden	59.0
Italy	52.2

Career ***Demographer***

Demographers study people: their numbers, how old they are, where they live, with whom they live, where they are moving, and more. They examine how age affects buying habits, which occupations are most popular, how people are affecting the natural environment, and many other behavioral data.

Businesses use demographers to analyze how products are used. The table lists the countries with the highest per capita mobile-phone use. Who might be interested in this kind of demographic information?

Problem Solving Project

Social Studies Connection

Purpose: To solve problems by using probability

Materials: What's the Chance? worksheet

internet connect
Chapter Project Online: ***go.hrw.com***
KEYWORD: MS4 PSProject10

Understand, Plan, Solve, and Look Back

Have students:

- ✔ Examine the table. Ask students which country from the table has the most mobile phones per capita.
- ✔ Complete the What's the Chance? worksheet.
- ✔ Research to find the necessary data to calculate the theoretical probability that a particular person in the United States has a mobile phone. Choose a sampling method and survey to find the experimental probability that a particular person in the United States has a mobile phone. How do the results compare?
- ✔ Check students' work.

ARE YOU READY?

Choose the best term from the list to complete each sentence.

1. A(n) __?__ is a comparison of two quantities by division. ratio
2. A(n) __?__ is an integer that is divisible by 2. even number
3. A(n) __?__ is a ratio that compares a number to 100. percent
4. A(n) __?__ is a number greater than 1 that has more than two whole number factors. composite number
5. A(n) __?__ is an integer that is not divisible by 2. odd number

composite number
even number
odd number
percent
prime number
ratio

Complete these exercises to review skills you will need for this chapter.

✔ Simplify Fractions

Simplify.

6. $\frac{6}{9}$ $\frac{2}{3}$ **7.** $\frac{12}{15}$ $\frac{4}{5}$ **8.** $\frac{8}{10}$ $\frac{4}{5}$ **9.** $\frac{20}{24}$ $\frac{5}{6}$

10. $\frac{2}{4}$ $\frac{1}{2}$ **11.** $\frac{7}{35}$ $\frac{1}{5}$ **12.** $\frac{12}{22}$ $\frac{6}{11}$ **13.** $\frac{72}{81}$ $\frac{8}{9}$

✔ Write Fractions as Decimals

Write each fraction as a decimal.

14. $\frac{3}{5}$ 0.6 **15.** $\frac{9}{20}$ 0.45 **16.** $\frac{57}{100}$ 0.57 **17.** $\frac{12}{25}$ 0.48

18. $\frac{3}{25}$ 0.12 **19.** $\frac{1}{2}$ 0.5 **20.** $\frac{7}{10}$ 0.7 **21.** $\frac{9}{5}$ 1.8

✔ Percents and Decimals

Write each decimal as a percent.

22. 0.14 14% **23.** 0.08 8% **24.** 0.75 75% **25.** 0.38 38%

26. 0.27 27% **27.** 1.89 189% **28.** 0.234 23.4% **29.** 0.0025 0.25%

✔ Multiply Fractions

Multiply. Write each answer in simplest form.

30. $\frac{1}{2} \cdot \frac{1}{4}$ $\frac{1}{8}$ **31.** $\frac{2}{3} \cdot \frac{3}{5}$ $\frac{2}{5}$ **32.** $\frac{3}{10} \cdot \frac{1}{2}$ $\frac{3}{20}$ **33.** $\frac{5}{6} \cdot \frac{3}{4}$ $\frac{5}{8}$

34. $\frac{5}{14} \cdot \frac{7}{17}$ $\frac{5}{34}$ **35.** $-\frac{1}{8} \cdot \frac{3}{8}$ $-\frac{3}{64}$ **36.** $-\frac{2}{15} \cdot \left(-\frac{2}{3}\right)$ $\frac{4}{45}$ **37.** $\frac{1}{4} \cdot \left(-\frac{1}{6}\right)$ $-\frac{1}{24}$

Assessing Prior Knowledge

INTERVENTION 

Diagnose and Prescribe

Evaluate your students' performance on this page to determine whether intervention is necessary or whether enrichment is appropriate. Options that provide instruction, practice, and a check are listed below.

Resources for Are You Ready?

- ***Are You Ready? Intervention and Enrichment***
- **Recording Sheet for Are You Ready?** *Chapter 10 Resource Book* . . . . . p. 3

 ***Are You Ready? Intervention* CD-ROM**

internet connect 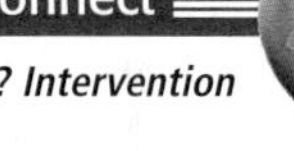

Are You Ready? Intervention
go.hrw.com
KEYWORD: MS4 AYR

ARE YOU READY?

Were students successful with Are You Ready?

NO INTERVENE 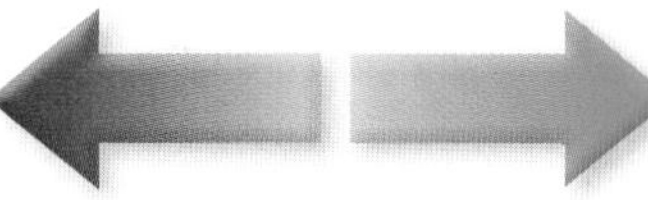 **YES ENRICH**

✔ Simplify Fractions
Are You Ready? Intervention, Skill 19
Blackline Masters, Online, and
 **CD-ROM** Intervention Activities

✔ Write Fractions as Decimals
Are You Ready? Intervention, Skill 26
Blackline Masters, Online, and
 **CD-ROM** Intervention Activities

✔ Percents and Decimals
Are You Ready? Intervention, Skill 30
Blackline Masters, Online, and
 **CD-ROM** Intervention Activities

✔ Multiply Fractions
Are You Ready? Intervention, Skill 44
Blackline Masters, Online, and
 **CD-ROM** Intervention Activities

Are You Ready? Enrichment, pp. 425–426

Introduction to Probability

One-Minute Section Planner

Lesson	Materials	Resources
Lesson 10-1 Probability **NCTM:** Data Analysis and Probability, Reasoning and Proof, Communication, Connections **NAEP:** Data Analysis and Probability 4a ☑ SAT-9 ☑ SAT-10 ☑ ITBS ☑ CTBS ☑ MAT ☑ CAT	**Optional** Recording Sheet for Reaching All Learners *(CRB p. 75)* Teaching Transparency T2 *(CRB)*	• *Chapter 10 Resource Book,* pp. 6–14 • Daily Transparency T1, CRB • Additional Examples Transparencies T3–T5, CRB • *Alternate Openers: Explorations,* p. 81
Lesson 10-2 Experimental Probability **NCTM:** Data Analysis and Probability, Reasoning and Proof, Communication, Connections **NAEP:** Data Analysis and Probability 4c ☑ SAT-9 ☑ SAT-10 ☑ ITBS ☑ CTBS ☑ MAT ☑ CAT	**Optional** Teaching Transparency T7 *(CRB)* Coins	• *Chapter 10 Resource Book,* pp. 15–23 • Daily Transparency T6, CRB • Additional Examples Transparencies T8–T9, CRB • *Alternate Openers: Explorations,* p. 82
Lesson 10-3 Make a List to Find Sample Spaces **NCTM:** Data Analysis and Probability, Problem Solving, Communication, Connections **NAEP:** Data Analysis and Probability 4e ☑ SAT-9 ☑ SAT-10 ☑ ITBS ☑ CTBS ☑ MAT ☑ CAT	**Optional** Teaching Transparency T11, *(CRB)* Colored paper Colored markers	• *Chapter 10 Resource Book,* pp. 24–32 • Daily Transparency T10, CRB • Additional Examples Transparencies T12–T13, CRB • *Alternate Openers: Explorations,* p. 83
Lesson 10-4 Theoretical Probability **NCTM:** Data Analysis and Probability, Reasoning and Proof, Communication, Connections **NAEP:** Data Analysis and Probability 4b ☑ SAT-9 ☑ SAT-10 ☑ ITBS ☑ CTBS ☑ MAT ☑ CAT	**Optional** Teaching Transparency T15 *(CRB)* Coins	• *Chapter 10 Resource Book,* pp. 33–41 • Daily Transparency T14, CRB • Additional Examples Transparencies T16–T18, CRB • *Alternate Openers: Explorations,* p. 84
Section 10A Assessment		• Mid-Chapter Quiz, SE p. 528 • Section 10A Quiz, AR p. 27 • *Test and Practice Generator* CD-ROM

SAT = *Stanford Achievement Tests* **ITBS** = *Iowa Test of Basic Skills* **CTBS** = *Comprehensive Test of Basic Skills/Terra Nova*
MAT = *Metropolitan Achievement Test* **CAT** = *California Achievement Test*

NCTM–Complete standards can be found on pages T27–T33. **NAEP**–Complete standards can be found on pages A35–A39.

SE = *Student Edition* **TE** = *Teacher's Edition* **AR** = *Assessment Resources* **CRB** = *Chapter Resource Book* **MK** = *Manipulatives Kit*

Section Overview

Probability Lesson 10-1

Why? The future is unknown, so every day you make decisions based on informal probabilities. A particular outcome is either certain, impossible, or somewhere in between.

Probability is the measure of how likely an event is to occur.

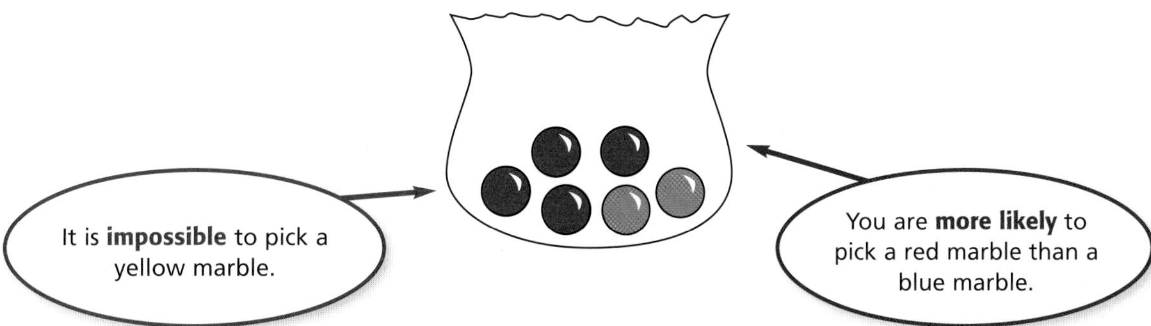

It is **impossible** to pick a yellow marble.
You are **more likely** to pick a red marble than a blue marble.

Experimental Probability — Lesson 10-2

Why? The probability of an event can be calculated based on previous experiences. When a store decides how much of a product to stock based on past sales, that is an example of a real-world application of experimental probability. Experimental probability is also a very useful tool for scientists.

$P(\text{certain event}) = 1$
$P(\text{impossible event}) = 0$
$0 \leq P(\text{event}) \leq 1$

Experimental Probability

$$\text{probability} \approx \frac{\text{number of times an event occurs}}{\text{total number of trials}}$$

Theoretical Probability — Lessons 10-3, 10-4

Why? You use **theoretical probability** to find the chance of something occurring, without directly measuring its occurrence. The set of all possible outcomes is called the **sample space.** You need to find the sample space and the number of favorable outcomes to determine a theoretical probability.

Theoretical Probability

$$\text{probability} = \frac{\text{number of favorable outcomes}}{\text{number of possible outcomes}}$$

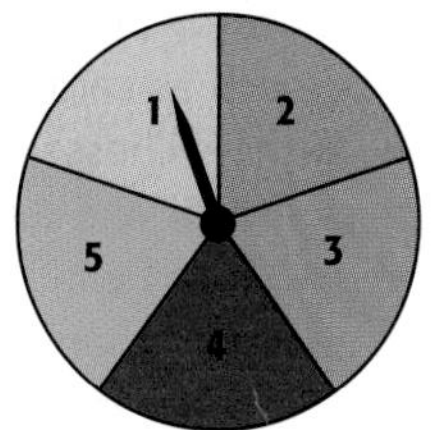

Sample Space

The sample space of outcomes for the spinner is 1, 2, 3, 4, and 5.

What is the probability of spinning an odd number on the spinner?

$$P(\text{odd}) = \frac{\text{favorable outcomes } \{1, 3, 5\}}{\text{possible outcomes } \{1, 2, 3, 4, 5\}} = \frac{3}{5}$$

10-1 Organizer

Pacing: Traditional 1 day
Block $\frac{1}{2}$ day

Objective: Students use informal measures of probability.

Warm Up

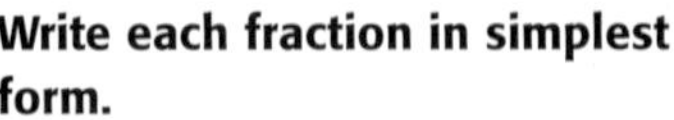

Write each fraction in simplest form.

1. $\frac{15}{21}$ $\frac{5}{7}$
2. $\frac{48}{64}$ $\frac{3}{4}$
3. $\frac{9}{81}$ $\frac{1}{9}$
4. $\frac{30}{45}$ $\frac{2}{3}$

Problem of the Day

You roll a regular pair of number cubes. How likely is it that the product of the two numbers you roll is odd and greater than 25? Explain.
Impossible; the only possible products greater than 25 (30 and 36) are even.

Available on Daily Transparency in CRB

Math Humor

The 50-50-90 rule: Whenever you have a 50-50 chance of getting something right, there's a 90% probability you'll get it wrong.

10-1 Probability

Learn to use informal measures of probability.

Vocabulary
- experiment
- outcome
- event
- probability
- equally likely
- impossible
- certain

Suppose you rolled one of these dice. The blue one is equally likely to land on any of the six numbers. The red one is more likely to land on one of the larger faces. So the likelihood is greater that you would roll a 5 with the red die than with the blue one.

Any activity involving chance, such as the roll of a die, is an **experiment**. The result of an experiment is an **outcome**. An **event** is a set of one or more outcomes.

Events that have the same probability are **equally likely**. **Probability** is the measure of how likely an event is to occur. The more likely an event is to occur, the higher its probability. The less likely an event is to occur, the lower its probability.

EXAMPLE 1 Determining the Likelihood of an Event

A bag contains 6 blue marbles, 6 red marbles, 3 green marbles, and 1 yellow marble. All of the marbles are the same size and weight.

A **Would you be more likely to pull a red marble or a green marble from the bag?**
Since there are more red marbles than green marbles, it is more likely that you would pull a red marble than a green marble.

B **Would you be more likely to pull a red marble or a blue marble from the bag?**
Since the number of red marbles equals the number of blue marbles, it is just as likely that you would pull a red marble as a blue marble. The events are equally likely.

Every event is either impossible, certain, or somewhere between these extremes. An event is mathematically **impossible** if it can never happen and mathematically **certain** if it will always happen. If an event is as likely as not, the probability that it will happen is the same as the probability that it will not happen.

Impossible	Unlikely	As likely as not	Likely	Certain

1 Introduce

Alternate Opener

EXPLORATION

10-1 Probability

The ***probability*** of an ***event*** happening can be expressed as a percent between 0% and 100%. The probability that an event is impossible is expressed as 0%. The probability that an event is certain to happen is expressed as 100%.

The table below shows a seven-day weather forecast, including the probability of precipitation (POP). The event in this case is rain, and the probability is a number expressed as a percent between 0% and 100%.

	Sun	Mon	Tue	Wed	Thu	Fri	Sat
POP	0%	0%	15%	50%	20%	30%	0%
High	75°	80°	72°	58°	68°	63°	70°
Low	47°	55°	45°	40°	42°	40°	45°

1. For which days does the forecast indicate no possibility of rain?
2. For which day does the forecast indicate that rain is as likely to happen as not?
3. On which day is it more likely to rain, Thursday or Friday?
4. On which day is it less likely to rain, Tuesday or Thursday?

Think and Discuss

5. **Discuss** whether the amount of rain on Tuesday (POP 15%) could be greater than the amount of rain on Thursday (POP 20%), assuming that it rains on both days.

Motivate

Invite students to name different types of games they enjoy playing (e.g., sports; games of chance, such as card games; games of strategy, such as chess). Discuss how the games are similar and different (e.g., you do not know who will win until the game is over; in games of chance, skill may not be as important as in sports). Encourage students to explain how they know whether a game is a game of chance.

Exploration worksheet and answers on Chapter 10 Resource Book pp. 7 and 76

2 Teach

Lesson Presentation

Guided Instruction

In this lesson, students learn to use informal measures of probability. You may want to mention that *probability* is another word for *chance*. Point out that although an event may be unlikely, it can still occur. Similarly, although an event may be likely, it is possible that it may *not* occur. Only certain events will always happen, and impossible events will never happen.

Teaching Tip Have students suggest events that are impossible, unlikely, as likely as not, likely, or certain. Do all students agree with the likelihoods of the suggested events? Discuss the reasons for any differences.

EXAMPLE 2 Classifying Likelihood

Determine whether each event is impossible, unlikely, as likely as not, likely, or certain.

A **All of the students in Ms. Caro's class are in school today. Jamie is in Ms. Caro's class. How likely is it that Jamie is in school today?**

It is certain that Jamie is in school today.

B **Karl has soccer practice on Monday afternoons. How likely is it that Karl is playing basketball on Monday afternoon?**

Soccer practice could have been canceled, and Karl could be playing basketball. However, it is unlikely that Karl is playing basketball.

C **There are four 2's and four 6's in a set of eight cards. If you draw a card, how likely is it that you will randomly draw a 6?**

Since the number of 2's equals the number of 6's, it is as likely as not that you will draw a 6.

D **Rita's family is visiting the Smithville Zoo. Her mother is out of town on a business trip. How likely is it that Rita's mother is at the Smithville Zoo?**

It is impossible that Rita's mother is at the Smithville Zoo.

EXAMPLE 3 *School Application*

Eric's math teacher almost always gives a pop quiz if the class did not ask many questions about the lesson on the previous class day. If it is Monday and no one asked questions during class on Friday, should Eric expect a pop quiz? Explain.

Since Eric's teacher often gives quizzes on days after few questions were asked, a quiz on this day is likely.

Think and Discuss

1. **Determine** whether you would be more likely to roll a 4 on the red die or on the blue die, as shown at the beginning of the lesson. Explain your answer.
2. **Give an example** of a certain event and of an impossible event.

Additional Examples

Example 1

A bag contains circular chips that are the same size and weight. There are 8 purple, 4 pink, 8 white, and 2 blue chips in the bag.

A. Would you be more likely to choose a purple chip or a blue chip from the bag? purple

B. Would you be more likely to choose a white chip or a purple chip from the bag? equally likely

Example 2

Determine whether each event is impossible, unlikely, as likely as not, likely, or certain.

A. Tina has a soccer game on Saturday. How likely is it that she is at home on Saturday? unlikely

B. Jason is canoeing on the river. How likely is it that he is shopping with Kevin? impossible

C. Maureen is running with her mother. Her mother is running in the park. How likely is it that Maureen is at the park? certain

Example 3

Mandy's science teacher almost always introduces a new chapter by conducting an experiment. Mandy's class finished a chapter on Friday. Should Mandy expect the teacher to conduct an experiment next week? Explain.

Since the class will be starting a new chapter, it is likely the teacher will conduct an experiment.

3 Close

Reaching All Learners

Through Home Connection

Encourage students to play a game at home with family members and then to write responses to the questions on the Recording Sheet for Reaching All Learners on Chapter 10 Resource Book p. 75.

Summarize

Discuss with students the following situation: A bag contains 5 black tiles. How likely is it that you will draw a black tile from the bag? certain a white tile? impossible If you add 2 white tiles to the bag, would you be more likely to draw a white tile or a black tile? black tile If you then add 3 more white tiles to the bag, would you be more likely to draw a white tile or a black tile? equally likely

Answers to Think and Discuss

Possible answers:

1. Blue die; the sides of the blue die are all the same size. On the red die, the side with the 4 on it is not the largest side, so it is less likely to land with 4 facing up.
2. Possible answers: It is certain that the sun will rise in the east. It is impossible that the sun will rise in the west.

10-1 PRACTICE & ASSESS

Students may want to refer back to the lesson examples.

Assignment Guide

If you finished Example 1 assign:
Core 1, 2, 6, 7, 11, 17–20
Enriched 1, 2, 6, 7, 11, 17–20

If you finished Example 2 assign:
Core 1–4, 6–9, 11, 17–20
Enriched 1, 3, 7, 9, 11–20

If you finished Example 3 assign:
Core 1–10, 13, 17–20
Enriched 1–9 odd, 11–20

Notes

10-1 Exercises

FOR EXTRA PRACTICE
see page 676

internet connect
Homework Help Online
go.hrw.com Keyword: MS4 10-1

GUIDED PRACTICE

See Example 1 **A bag contains 8 purple beads, 2 blue beads, and 2 pink beads. All of the beads are the same size and weight.**

1. Would you be more likely to pull a purple bead or a pink bead from the bag? **purple**
2. Would you be more likely to pull a blue bead or a pink bead from the bag? **The events are equally likely.**

See Example 2 **Determine whether each event is impossible, unlikely, as likely as not, likely, or certain.**

3. Natalie has dance lessons on Saturday morning. How likely is it that Natalie is attending dance class on Saturday morning? **likely**
4. There are three 2's, three 4's, and three 6's in a set of nine cards. If you draw a card, how likely is it that you will randomly draw a 3? **impossible**

See Example 3

5. Timothy went to a theater to see a movie that started at 3 P.M. and lasts for 2 hours 10 minutes. If it is now 5 P.M., would you expect Timothy to be in the theater? Explain. **Yes, it is likely, since the movie does not end for another 10 minutes.**

INDEPENDENT PRACTICE

See Example 1 **A bag contains 5 red markers, 4 blue markers, 4 black markers, and 2 yellow markers. All of the markers are the same size and weight.**

6. Would you be more likely to pull a blue marker or a black marker from the bag? **The events are equally likely.**
7. Would you be more likely to pull a black marker or a yellow marker from the bag? **black**

See Example 2 **Determine whether each event is impossible, unlikely, as likely as not, likely, or certain.**

8. A bag contains 12 red checkers and 12 black checkers. How likely is it that you will pull a white checker from the bag? **impossible**
9. Sixth-grade students have a 30 minute lunch break in the cafeteria at 11:30 A.M., and seventh-graders eat at noon. How likely is it that a sixth-grader is in the cafeteria at 12:15 P.M.? **unlikely**

See Example 3

10. The planetarium opens weekdays at noon. On Saturday, it is open from 10 A.M. until 10 P.M. Trisha wants to go to the planetarium on Wednesday morning. Should Trisha expect the planetarium to be open? Explain. **Since Wednesday is a weekday, it is not likely that the planetarium will be open before noon.**

Math Background

Probability did not develop as a branch of mathematics until the mid-seventeenth century. A French nobleman asked Blaise Pascal (1623–1662), a French mathematician and philosopher, to explain a difference the nobleman had noticed in the outcomes of a game of chance. This question led to a correspondence between Pascal and Pierre de Fermat (1601–1665), another French mathematician, that dealt with the nobleman's question and other questions related to probability. For this reason, Pascal and Fermat are credited with founding probability.

RETEACH 10-1

LESSON 10-1 **Reteach**
Probability

If you spin the spinner at right, you could land on any number from 1 to 5. There are five possible outcomes—1, 2, 3, 4, and 5. Each outcome is **equally likely.**

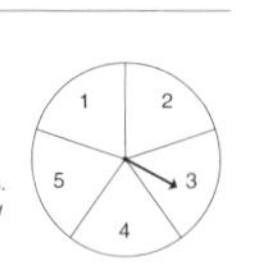

However, there are three odd numbers and two even numbers. So, when you spin this spinner, it is **more likely** that the arrow will land on an odd number than on an even number. The probability is greater that you will spin an odd number.

A bag contains 3 red cubes, 2 blue cubes, 2 yellow cubes, and 4 green cubes. All of the cubes are the same size. Write *more likely*, *equally likely*, or *less likely* to complete each statement.

1. There are 3 red cubes and 4 green cubes.
   You are __more likely__ to pick a green cube than a red cube.
2. There are 2 yellow cubes and 2 blue cubes.
   You are __equally likely__ to pick a yellow cube or a blue cube.
3. There are 4 green cubes and 2 blue cubes.
   You are __less likely__ to pick a blue cube than a green cube.

An event is **impossible** if it can never happen.
An event is **certain** if it will always happen.
An event can also be **unlikely, likely as not,** or **likely.**

Write *impossible*, *unlikely*, *likely as not*, *likely* or *certain* to complete each statement.

4. Rosa has a piano lesson on Thursday afternoon. It is __unlikely__ that Rosa goes ice skating on Thursday afternoon.
5. Sometimes Chris walks to school, and sometimes he rides his bike. It is __as likely as not__ that Chris rode his bike to school today.
6. Yoriko lives in Florida. She is visiting her grandparents in Virginia. Yoriko's class went on a field trip today. It is __certain__ that Yoriko did not go on the field trip.
7. There are 3 red marbles and 5 blue marbles in a bag. It is __impossible__ to draw a green marble.

PRACTICE 10-1

LESSON 10-1 **Practice B**
Probability

A bag contains five orange disks, five red disks, three green disks, and six yellow disks. All of the disks are the same size.

1. Would you be more likely to pull a red disk or a yellow disk from the bag? __yellow disk__
2. Would you be more likely to pull an orange disk or a green disk from the bag? __orange disk__
3. Would you be more likely to pull an orange disk or a red disk from the bag? __equally likely to pull either disk__

Determine if each event is impossible, unlikely, as likely as not, likely, or certain.

4. A number cube numbered 1–6 is rolled once. How likely is it that you would randomly roll a number less than 7? __certain__
5. A number cube numbered 1–6 is rolled once. How likely is it that you would randomly roll a number greater than 1? __likely__
6. There are 10 cards in a box numbered 1–10. A card is pulled at random from the box. How likely is it that a card with an even number is pulled from the box? __as likely as not__
7. Miranda's bowling average is 115. She bowls 122 and 119 in her first two games. How likely is it that she will bowl at least 100 in her next game? __likely__
8. A play starts at 8 P.M. and lasts for 2 hours 25 minutes. Yuko went to the play. If it is 11:35 P.M., how likely is it that Yuko is at the play? __unlikely__
9. A sporting goods store is open from 9 A.M. until 9 P.M. on weekdays and from 10 A.M. to 6 P.M. on weekends. How likely is it that Dustin can shop at the sporting goods store on Saturday night? __impossible__
10. The letters of the alphabet are written on cards in a box. A card is pulled at random from the box. Would you expect it to be a vowel or a consonant? __consonant__
11. Stan has 4 pairs of black socks and 4 pairs of brown socks. Assuming he picks a pair at random, how likely is it that he is wearing the black socks today? __as likely as not__

PRACTICE AND PROBLEM SOLVING

11. ***LIFE SCIENCE*** In a scientist's garden, there are 700 sweet pea plants with purple flowers and 200 with white flowers. If one plant from the garden were selected at random, would you expect the plant to have purple or white flowers? Explain.

12. ***LIFE SCIENCE*** Sharks belong to a class of fishes that have skeletons made of cartilage. Bony fishes, which account for 95% of all species of fish, have skeletons made of bone.

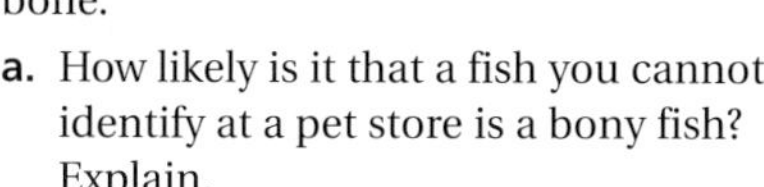

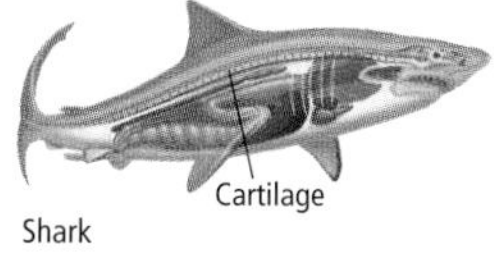

Shark

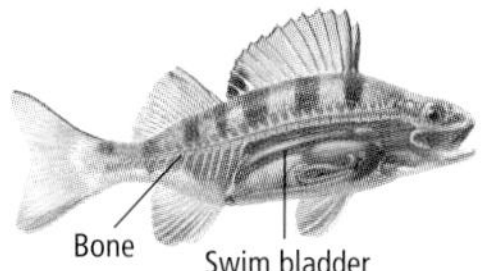

Bony fish

   a. How likely is it that a fish you cannot identify at a pet store is a bony fish? Explain.

   b. Only bony fishes have swim bladders, which keep them from sinking. How likely is it that a shark has a swim bladder?

13. ***EARTH SCIENCE*** The graph shows the carbon dioxide levels in the atmosphere from 1958 to 1994. How likely is it that the level of carbon dioxide fell from 1994 to 2000? Explain. **unlikely, since carbon dioxide levels increased steadily between 1958 and 1994**

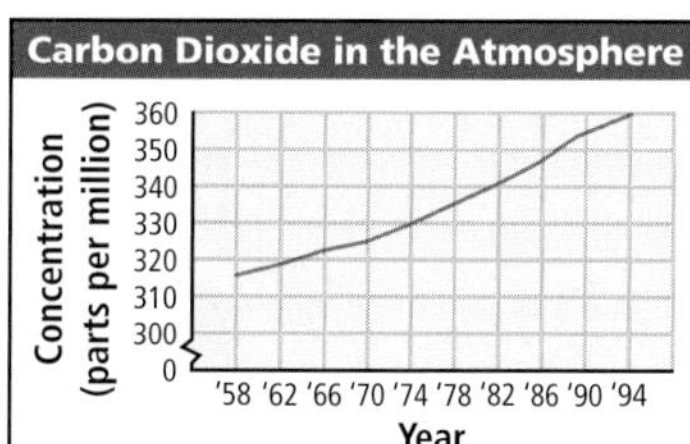

14. ***WRITE A PROBLEM*** Come up with an event that is mathematically certain, an event that is mathematically impossible, and an event that is as likely as not.

15. ***WRITE ABOUT IT*** Explain how to tell if an event is as likely as not.

16. ***CHALLENGE*** A bag contains 10 red marbles and 8 blue marbles, all the same size and weight. Keiko draws 2 red marbles from the bag and does not replace them. Will Keiko be more likely to draw a red marble than a blue marble on her next draw? Explain.

Spiral Review

Solve. (Lesson 6-4)

17. 27 is what percent of 54? **50%**

18. 13 is 40% of what number? **32.5**

19. **TEST PREP** What is the volume of the prism? (Lesson 9-2) **B**

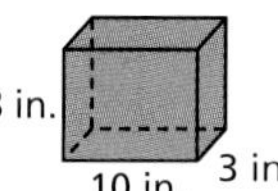

A 19 in^3 **B** 240 in^3 **C** 480 in^3 **D** 1,200 in^3

20. **TEST PREP** What is the surface area of the prism? (Lesson 9-4) **H**

F 70 in^2 **G** 118 in^2 **H** 268 in^2 **J** 240 in^2

CHALLENGE 10-1

LESSON 10-1 **Challenge**
A Likely Choice

There are 20 cards in a deck. One card is randomly selected. Provide additional information about the cards to describe each type of outcome.

Example: Describe a situation with a likely outcome.
There are 2 face cards and 18 number cards in the deck.
It is likely that you will select a number card. **Answers may vary. Possible answers are given.**

1. Describe a situation with an unlikely outcome.
   There are 3 red cards and 17 black cards. It is unlikely that you will select a red card.
2. Describe a situation with a certain outcome.
   There are 20 red cards. It is certain that you will select a red card.
3. Describe a situation with an outcome that is as likely as not.
   There are 10 red cards and 10 black cards. It is as likely as not that you will select a black card.
4. Describe a situation with an impossible outcome.
   There are 20 number cards. It is impossible that you will select a face card.
5. A 1–6 number cube is rolled. Describe a roll with a likely outcome.
   Roll a number less than 6.
6. A 1–6 number cube is rolled. Describe a roll with an outcome that is as likely as not.
   Roll an even number.
7. A 1–6 number cube is rolled. Describe a roll with an impossible outcome.
   Roll a 10.

PROBLEM SOLVING 10-1

LESSON 10-1 **Problem Solving**
Probability

Write the correct answer.

1. Of the original 56 signers of the Declaration of Independence, four of them represented North Carolina. If you selected one signer randomly, how likely is it that he represented North Carolina?
   unlikely
2. One question on a social studies multiple-choice test has four possible answers. Marianne is sure two of the choices are incorrect. How likely is she to choose the correct answer?
   as likely as not
3. There are 8 right-handed pitchers and 2 left-handed pitchers on the Tigers baseball team. How likely is it that their opponents will face a right-handed pitcher?
   likely
4. Every seventh-grade student is attending a presentation about recycling in the auditorium. Jaleel is a seventh-grade student. How likely is it that he is in the auditorium?
   certain

Choose the letter for the best answer.

The table shows the contents of Leticia's CD and DVD collection.

Leticia's CD and DVD Collection

Type of CD/DVD	Number
Rock CD	26
Pop CD	17
Comedy DVD	11
Drama DVD	2

5. How likely is it that a disk chosen randomly is a CD?
   A unlikely C certain
   B as likely as not (D) likely
6. How likely is it that a disk chosen randomly is a jazz CD?
   F unlikely H likely
   G as likely as not (J) impossible
7. Sally picks a disk at random from Leticia's collection. How likely is it that it is a comedy DVD?
   A as likely as not
   B likely
   C certain
   (D) unlikely
8. Leticia picks three disks from her collection at random. Which outcome is impossible?
   F They are all rock CDs.
   (G) They are all drama DVDs.
   H None of them are rock CDs.
   J They are all DVDs.

Answers

11. The plant would be more likely to have purple flowers because there are 500 more plants with purple flowers than plants with white flowers.
12. **a.** very likely, since most fish are bony fish
    b. impossible, since a shark is not a bony fish
14. Possible answer: You have a set of cards numbered 1–20. How likely are you to draw a number less than 100? How likely are you to draw a negative number? How likely are you to draw an even number?
15. Possible answer: There are just as many ways the event can happen as there are ways the event cannot happen.
16. Since there are now 8 red and 8 blue marbles, the events are equally likely.

Journal

Ask students to use their own experiences to describe a likely event and an unlikely event.

Test Prep Doctor

The correct answer to Exercise 19 is **B.** If students have difficulty with this question, it is likely that they have forgotten the formula for the volume of a prism.

Lesson Quiz

A bag holds 4 red marbles, 3 green marbles, 3 yellow marbles, and 2 blue marbles. You pull one out without looking.

1. Is it more likely to be red or blue? red
2. Is it more likely to be green or yellow? equally likely

Determine whether each event is impossible, unlikely, as likely as not, likely, or certain.

3. Bonnie's Spanish club meets on Tuesday afternoons. How likely is it that Bonnie is at the mall on Tuesday afternoon? unlikely
4. There are 12 SUVs and 12 vans in a parking lot. How likely is it that the next vehicle to move is a van? as likely as not

Available on Daily Transparency in CRB

10-2 Organizer

Pacing: Traditional 1 day
Block $\frac{1}{2}$ day

Objective: Students find experimental probability.

Warm Up

1. You have a jar containing 6 red, 8 blue, and 10 white marbles. Would you be more likely to pull out a red or blue marble? blue

Determine if the event is impossible, unlikely, as likely as not, likely, or certain.

2. Attendance at a city council meeting is at 100%. Mr. Lloyd is a council member. How likely is it that Mr. Lloyd is at the meeting? certain

Problem of the Day

Based on a series of free throws, Liana figured out that the probability of her making a free throw was $\frac{2}{3}$. If she made 24 of her free throws, how many did she miss? 12

Available on Daily Transparency in CRB

Math Fact

In a class with 25 students (or more), the probability that at least two students will have the same birthday is greater than 50%.

10-2 Experimental Probability

Learn to find experimental probability.

Vocabulary

experimental probability

trial

During hockey practice, Tanya made saves on 18 out of 25 shots. Based on these numbers, what is the probability that Tanya will make a save on the next shot?

Experimental probability is one way of estimating the probability of an event. It is based on actual experiments or observations. **Experimental probability** is found by comparing the number of times an event occurs to the total number of **trials**, the times that an experiment is carried out or an observation is made. The more trials you have, the more accurate the estimate is likely to be.

EXPERIMENTAL PROBABILITY

$$\text{probability} \approx \frac{\text{number of times an event occurs}}{\text{total number of trials}}$$

EXAMPLE 1 Sports Application

If Tanya made saves on 18 out of 25 shots, what is the experimental probability that she will make a save on the next shot?

$$P \approx \frac{\text{number of times an event occurs}}{\text{total number of trials}}$$

$$P(\text{save}) \approx \frac{\text{number of saves made}}{\text{number of shots attempted}}$$

$$\approx \frac{18}{25} \qquad \textit{Substitute.}$$

The experimental probability that Tanya will make a save on the next shot is approximately $\frac{18}{25}$.

Writing Math

"*P*(event)" represents the probability that an event will occur. For example, the probability of a flipped coin landing heads up could be written as "*P*(heads)."

Recall that an outcome of an experiment can be impossible, certain, or in between. If an event is impossible, it will never happen in any trial.

$$P(\text{impossible event}) = \frac{0}{\text{total number of trials}}$$

$$= 0 \qquad \textit{0 divided by any number except 0 equals 0.}$$

1 Introduce

Alternate Opener

EXPLORATION

10-2 Experimental Probability

You can flip a coin to demonstrate *experimental probability.*

experimental probability ≈ $\frac{\text{number of times an event occurs}}{\text{total number of trials}}$

1. Flip a coin 20 times, and record the results in the table.

Event	Number
Heads (H)	
Tails (T)	

2. Use the number of times each event occurred to calculate the probability of each event.

Event	Experimental Probability
Heads (H)	$\frac{H}{20} = \frac{\square}{20}$
Tails (T)	$\frac{T}{20} = \frac{\square}{20}$

Think and Discuss

3. **Discuss** what you think would happen to the experimental probability if you flipped a coin 100 times.
4. **Explain** what the sum of the two experimental probabilities in the table in number 2 equals.

Motivate

Ask students if they or their family members ever watch weather forecasts. Encourage students to describe the information that is given in a weather forecast (e.g., predicted temperatures, probabilities of precipitation). Ask students to consider when and why a forecast of a 60% chance of showers might cause a change in plans while a forecast of a 20% chance of showers might not (e.g., a picnic might be postponed in favor of an outing to the movies if there is a 60% chance of showers).

Exploration worksheet and answers on Chapter 10 Resource Book pp. 16 and 78

2 Teach

Lesson Presentation

Guided Instruction

In this lesson, students learn to find experimental probability. Point out that although likelihood is a useful concept, it is somewhat vague. With experimental probability, students use observations to make an educated guess about the outcome of an event. Therefore, you cannot determine experimental probability unless you are familiar with an event (i.e., observed it or have data about it).

Stress that probability is always 0, 1, or a number between 0 and 1. Probabilities may be expressed as fractions, decimals, or percents. So weather forecasts represent probabilities.

If an event is certain, it will always happen in every trial. This means that the number of times the event happens is equal to the total number of trials.

$$P(\text{certain event}) = \frac{\text{total number of trials}}{\text{total number of trials}}$$

$= 1$ *Any number except 0 divided by itself equals 1.*

All probabilities can be expressed numerically on a scale from 0 to 1.

Impossible	Unlikely	As likely as not	Likely	Certain
0		$\frac{1}{2}$		1

EXAMPLE 2 *Weather Application*

For the past three weeks, Karl has been recording the daily high temperatures for a science project. During that time, the high temperature was above 75°F for 14 out of 21 days.

A **What is the experimental probability that the high temperature will be above 75°F on the next day?**

$$P(\text{warmer than } 75°F) \approx \frac{\text{number of days warmer than } 75°F}{\text{total number of days}}$$

$\approx \frac{14}{21}$ *Substitute.*

$\approx \frac{2}{3}$ *Write in simplest form.*

The experimental probability that the temperature will be above 75°F on the next day is approximately $\frac{2}{3}$.

B **What is the experimental probability that the high temperature will be 75°F or below on the next day?**

$$P(75°F \text{ or cooler}) \approx \frac{\text{number of days } 75°F \text{ or cooler}}{\text{total number of days}}$$

$\approx \frac{7}{21}$ *Substitute.*

$\approx \frac{1}{3}$ *Write in simplest form.*

The experimental probability that the high temperature will be 75°F or below on the next day is approximately $\frac{1}{3}$.

Helpful Hint

The events "The temperature is above 75°F" and "The temperature is 75°F or below" are called complements.

Think and Discuss

1. **Find** the sum of the probabilities in Examples 2A and 2B. Why do you think adding the probabilities gives this sum?
2. **Tell** whether the experimental probability of an event is always the same. Explain.

COMMON ERROR ALERT

Students might not always use the total number of trials as the denominator when finding experimental probabilities. If students do not record the total number of trials, the experimental probability will be incorrect.

Additional Examples

Example 1

During skating practice, Sasha landed 7 out of 12 jumps. What is the experimental probability that she will land her next jump? $\frac{7}{12}$

Example 2

Students have checked out 55 books from the library. Of these, 32 books are fiction.

A. What is the experimental probability that the next book checked out will be fiction? $\frac{32}{55}$

B. What is the experimental probability that the next book checked out will be nonfiction? $\frac{23}{55}$

Example 1 note: Remind students that when a goalie makes a save, he or she stops the other team from making a goal.

3 Close

Reaching All Learners
Through Curriculum Integration

Science Students may be familiar with the scientific method from their science classes. In the scientific method, a hypothesis is formulated and then tested. Have students discuss observations and results from their science classes that are related to experimental probability. How are the results similar, and how are they different? How are the probability experiments in the lesson similar to, and different from, science experiments students have conducted?

Summarize

Ask students to answer the following question: As Casey watches the track team, he observes 7 girls and 9 boys running past him on the track. What is the experimental probability that the next student to run past Casey on the track will be a girl? $\frac{7}{16}$ a boy? $\frac{9}{16}$

Answers to Think and Discuss

1. The sum is 1. It is certain that one event or the other will occur, and the probability of an event that is certain is 1.
2. The experimental probability of an event is not always the same. It will only be the same if different experiments or observations yield the same results.

10-2 PRACTICE & ASSESS

Students may want to refer back to the lesson examples.

Assignment Guide

If you finished Example 1 assign:
Core 1, 3, 4, 6–8, 13–18
Enriched 1, 3, 4, 6–8, 13–18

If you finished Example 2 assign:
Core 1–5, 7–11 odd, 13–18
Enriched 1–5 odd, 6–18

Notes

10-2 Exercises

FOR EXTRA PRACTICE see page 676

internet connect
Homework Help Online
go.hrw.com Keyword: MS4 10-2

GUIDED PRACTICE

See Example 1

1. Terry's PE class is practicing archery. If Terry hit the target on 12 out of 20 tries, what is the experimental probability that she will hit the target on her next try? $\frac{3}{5}$

See Example 2

2. A reporter surveys 75 people to determine whether they plan to vote for or against a proposed bill. Of these people, 65 say they plan to vote for the bill.
   a. What is the experimental probability that the next person surveyed would say he or she plans to vote for it? $\frac{13}{15}$
   b. What is the experimental probability that the next person surveyed would say he or she plans to vote against it? $\frac{2}{15}$

INDEPENDENT PRACTICE

See Example 1

3. If Jack hit a baseball on 13 out of 30 tries during practice, what is the experimental probability that he will hit the ball on his next try? $\frac{13}{30}$
4. While playing darts, Cam hit the bull's-eye 8 times out of 15 throws. What is the experimental probability that Cam's next throw will hit the bull's-eye? $\frac{8}{15}$

See Example 2

5. For the past two weeks, Benita has been recording the number of people at Eastside Park at lunchtime. During that time, there were 50 or more people at the park 9 out of 14 days.
   a. What is the experimental probability that there will be 50 or more people at the park during lunchtime on the fifteenth day? $\frac{9}{14}$
   b. What is the experimental probability that there will be fewer than 50 people at the park during lunchtime on the fifteenth day? $\frac{5}{14}$

PRACTICE AND PROBLEM SOLVING

6. George is watching cars drive by. Of the first 46 cars he sees, 18 are red, and the rest are other colors. What is the experimental probability that the next car he sees will be red? $\frac{9}{23}$
7. While bowling with friends, Alexis rolls a strike in 4 out of the 10 frames. What is the experimental probability that Alexis will roll a strike in the first frame of the next game? $\frac{2}{5}$
8. Jeremiah is standing in line at a music store. Of the first 25 people he sees enter the store, 16 are wearing jackets and 9 are not. What is the experimental probability that the next person to enter the store will be wearing a jacket? $\frac{16}{25}$

Math Background

The Law of Large Numbers is an interesting theorem in probability theory. The theorem relates experimental probability and theoretical probability. The basic idea of the theorem is that as an experiment is repeated many times, the experimental probability of the event approaches the theoretical probability of the event. For example, consider flipping a coin ten times. The theoretical probability of heads is $\frac{1}{2}$. The individual flipping the coin ten times may not get 5 heads and 5 tails. However, after flipping the coin many more times, perhaps 100 times, the experimental probability will tend to get closer to $\frac{1}{2}$.

RETEACH 10-2

LESSON 10-2 **Reteach**
Experimental Probability

Experimental probability is an estimate of the probability of an event. It is called *experimental* because you make observations or experiments to find the number of times a certain event actually happened.

Experimental probability $\approx \frac{\text{number of times a certain event happened}}{\text{total number of trials}}$

Suppose you have 12 marbles. Without replacing any marbles, you pull a red marble 5 times. What is the experimental probability of getting another red marble the next time you pull a marble?

$P(\text{heads}) \approx \frac{\text{number of red marbles}}{\text{number of marbles}} = \frac{5}{12}$

The probability of getting red on the next pull is $\frac{5}{12}$.

At softball practice, Manny had 6 hits out of 15 times at bat.

1. What is the experimental probability that Manny will get a hit at his next time at bat?
   $P(\text{hit}) \approx \frac{\text{number of hits}}{\text{total number of times at bat}} = \frac{6}{15} = \frac{2}{5}$
2. What is the experimental probability that Manny will not get a hit at his next time at bat?
   $P(\text{no hit}) \approx 1 - \frac{\text{number of hits}}{\text{total number of times at bat}} = 1 - \frac{2}{5} = \frac{3}{5}$

Pam is playing darts. She hit the bull's eye 7 times out of 20 throws.

3. What is the experimental probability that Pam will hit the bull's eye on her next throw? $\frac{7}{20}$
4. What is the experimental probability that Pam will NOT hit the bull's eye on her next throw? $\frac{13}{20}$

So far this year Trisha's softball team has played 4 of their 20 games on Field A.

5. What is the experimental probability that they will play their next game on Field A? $\frac{1}{5}$
6. What is the experimental probability that they will play their next game on a field other than Field A? $\frac{4}{5}$

PRACTICE 10-2

LESSON 10-2 **Practice B**
Experimental Probability

Find the experimental probability.

1. Jaclyn is a soccer goalie. If she has 21 out of 23 saves in practice, what is the experimental probability that she will have a save on the next shot on goal? $\frac{21}{23}$
2. If Harris hit the bull's-eye 3 out of 8 times at archery practice, what is the experimental probability that he will hit the bull's-eye on his next try? $\frac{3}{8}$
3. After a movie premiere, 99 of the first 130 people surveyed said they liked the movie.
   a. What is the experimental probability that the next person surveyed will say he or she liked the movie? $\frac{99}{130}$
   b. What is the experimental probability that the next person surveyed will say he or she did not like the movie? $\frac{31}{130}$
4. For the past 30 days, Naomi has been recording the number of customers at her restaurant between 10 A.M. and 11 A.M. During that hour, there have been fewer than 20 customers on 25 out of 30 days.
   a. What is the experimental probability that there will be fewer than 20 customers on the thirty-first day? $\frac{5}{6}$
   b. What is the experimental probability that that there will be more than 20 customers on the thirty-first day? $\frac{1}{6}$
5. Nestor works at an ice cream stand. Of the first 27 sundaes that he made one day, 15 had chocolate ice cream. What is the experimental probability that the next sundae he made had chocolate ice cream? $\frac{5}{9}$
6. Nathan inspects new pants at a factory. Of the first 56 pairs of pants he inspected 48 were acceptible. What is the experimental probability that the next pairs of pants will be acceptible? $\frac{6}{7}$
7. Sara has gone to work for 62 days. On 36 of those days she has arrived at work before 8:30 A.M. On the rest of the days she has arrived after 8:30 A.M. What is the experimental probability that she will arrive at work after 8:30 A.M. the next day she goes to work? $\frac{13}{31}$

Earth Science LINK

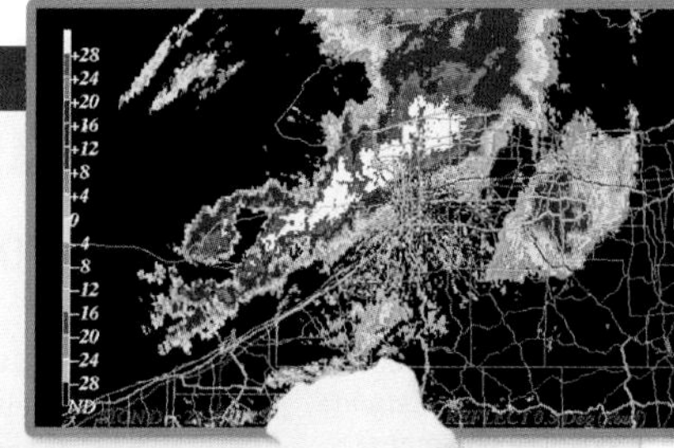

9. The stem-and-leaf plot shows the depth of snow in inches recorded in Buffalo, New York, over a 10-day period. **9.1 in.**

Stems	Leaves
7	9 9
8	
9	1 1 1 1 8 8
10	
11	8
12	
13	0

Key: 7|9 means 7.9

a. What is the median depth of snow for the 10-day period?

b. What is the experimental probability that the snow will be less than 6 in. deep on the eleventh day? **0**

c. What is the experimental probability that the snow will be more than 10 in. deep on the eleventh day? $\mathbf{\frac{1}{5}}$

10. Monty's class has been recording the daily low temperatures for 30 days. During that time, the low temperature was 48°F on 11 out of 30 days. What is the experimental probability that the low temperature will be 48°F on the next day? $\mathbf{\frac{11}{30}}$

11. The table shows the high temperatures recorded on July 4 in Orlando, Florida, over an eight-year period.

Year	Temp (°F)	Year	Temp (°F)
1994	86.0	1998	96.8
1995	95.0	1999	89.1
1996	78.8	2000	90.0
1997	98.6	2001	91.0

Source: Old Farmers' Almanac

a. What is the experimental probability that the high temperature on July 4, 2002 is below 90°F? $\mathbf{\frac{3}{8}}$

b. What is the experimental probability that the high temperature on July 4, 2002 is above 100°F? **0**

12. ***CHALLENGE*** A weather forecaster says that the probability of rain is 30%. What is the probability that it will not rain? $\mathbf{\frac{7}{10}}$

Spiral Review

Estimate each sum or difference. (Lesson 4-9)

13. $\frac{5}{9} + \frac{2}{5}$ **1**
14. $\frac{5}{6} - \frac{1}{8}$ **1**
15. $1\frac{4}{9} + 3\frac{7}{15}$ **5**
16. $6\frac{1}{6} - 2\frac{7}{8}$ **3**

17. TEST PREP How many days are equal to 360 hours? (Lesson 8-1) **B**

A 12 days **B** 15 days **C** 30 days **D** 4,320 days

18. TEST PREP Rita's dog is named Ally. How likely is it that Rita has a pet? (Lesson 10-1) **F**

F Certain **G** As likely as not **H** Unlikely **J** Impossible

Interdisciplinary LINK

Earth Science

Exercises 9–12 involve using probability to examine meteorology. Meteorology is studied in middle school Earth science programs, such as *Holt Science & Technology*.

Journal

Have students describe an event they would be interested in finding the experimental probability of. Have students outline how they could find the experimental probability.

Test Prep Doctor

In Exercise 17, students who selected incorrect choices **A** and **C** probably used a unit conversion factor but may have divided incorrectly. Have them check their division. Students who selected **D** probably do not understand how to use a unit conversion factor. The correct answer is **B.**

CHALLENGE 10-2

LESSON 10-2 Challenge
Pondering Probability

Materials needed: paper plate, construction paper, metal fastener

Use a paper plate, a construction paper arrow, and a metal fastener to construct a spinner. Your spinner should have 6 or 8 congruent sections. Draw a different design in each section.

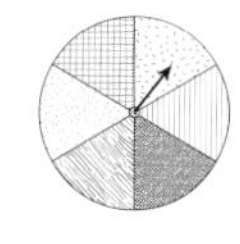

Spin the pointer 50 times and record your results in the table below.

Section								
Times Spun								

1. What is the mathematical probability that the pointer will stop on each section of the spinner?
   Possible answers: $\frac{1}{6}$ for 6 sections; $\frac{1}{8}$ for 8 sections
2. What is your experimental probability of landing on each section?
   Answers will vary depending on results recorded in the table.
3. Was your experimental probability of landing on any section close to the mathematical probability? Explain.
   Answers will vary; the experimental probability should be close to the mathematical probability.
4. Were any of your results surprising? Explain.
   Answers will vary.

PROBLEM SOLVING 10-2

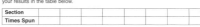

LESSON 10-2 Problem Solving
Experimental Probability

Write the correct answer in simplest form.

This table shows a breakdown by format of total music sales in the United States in 2001.

Total American Music Sales in 2001

Format	Total (%)
CD	90
Cassette	3
Single	2
Other	5

1. What is the experimental probability that any random music purchase in 2001 was a CD? $\mathbf{\frac{9}{10}}$
2. What is the experimental probability that any random music purchase in 2001 was not a cassette? $\mathbf{\frac{97}{100}}$
3. What is the experimental probability that any random music purchase in 2001 was a single? $\mathbf{\frac{1}{50}}$
4. Which combination of sales has an experimental probability of $\frac{1}{20}$? **cassettes and singles**

Choose the letter for the best answer.

5. Ethan hits 4 ringers in 10 attempts while pitching horseshoes. What does an experimental probability of $\frac{2}{5}$ describe?
   A P(horseshoes)
   B P(missed shots)
   C P(attempts)
   (D) P(ringers)
6. Jay beats Terry at table tennis 3 out of 5 games. What is the experimental probability that Terry will win their next game?
   F $\frac{1}{2}$ (H) $\frac{2}{5}$
   G $\frac{3}{5}$ J 1
7. Poonam counts 10 classmates out of 36 people in the library. What is the experimental probability that the next person will be a classmate?
   A $\frac{5}{36}$ C $\frac{1}{36}$
   (B) $\frac{5}{18}$ D $\frac{1}{10}$
8. Macy makes 15 of 20 free throws at basketball practice. What is the experimental probability that she will miss her next free throw?
   (F) $\frac{1}{4}$ H $\frac{2}{3}$
   G $\frac{1}{2}$ J $\frac{3}{4}$

Lesson Quiz

1. In a soccer shoot-out, Bryan made 4 out of 9 goals. What is the experimental probability that he will make the next shot? $\mathbf{\frac{4}{9}}$

2. It has rained on the last 2 out of 10 Fourth of July parades in Swanton. What is the experimental probability that it will rain this year? $\mathbf{\frac{1}{5}}$

3. There have been 15 or more birds eating at a feeder at noon on 12 of the last 15 days. What is the experimental probability that there will be 15 or more birds feeding at that same time on the 16th day? $\mathbf{\frac{4}{5}}$

Available on Daily Transparency in CRB

10-3 Organizer

Pacing: Traditional 1 day
Block $\frac{1}{2}$ day

Objective: Students use counting methods to determine possible outcomes.

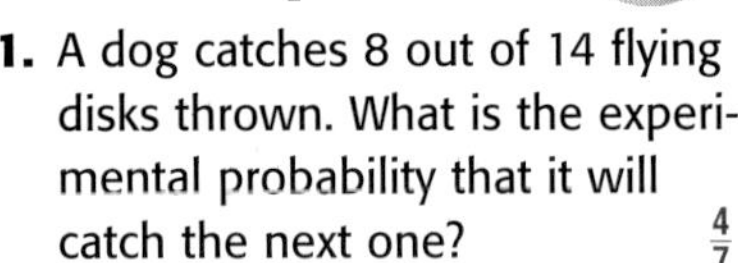

Warm Up

1. A dog catches 8 out of 14 flying disks thrown. What is the experimental probability that it will catch the next one? $\frac{4}{7}$
2. At a carnival, Ted threw darts to pop balloons. If he popped 8 balloons out of 12 tries, what is the experimental probability that he will pop the next balloon? $\frac{2}{3}$

Problem of the Day

How many different types of meat pizzas can be made if the choices of meat topping are pepperoni, sausage, ham, and meatball? (*Hint:* There can be 1, 2, 3, or 4 toppings on the pizza.)
15 (4 one-topping , 6 two-topping, 4 three-topping, and 1 four-topping)

Available on Daily Transparency in CRB

Math Humor

There was little chance of success for the inept thieves. After all, they had a low *rob-ability*.

10-3 Make a List to Find Sample Spaces

Problem Solving Skill

Learn to use counting methods to determine possible outcomes.

Vocabulary
sample space
Fundamental Counting Principle

Because you can roll the numbers 1, 2, 3, 4, 5, and 6 on a number cube, there are 6 possible outcomes. Together, all the possible outcomes of an experiment make up the **sample space**.

You can make an organized list to show all possible outcomes of an experiment.

EXAMPLE 1 PROBLEM SOLVING APPLICATION

Lucia flips two quarters at the same time. What are all the possible outcomes? How large is the sample space?

1 Understand the Problem

Rewrite the question as a statement.

- Find all the possible outcomes of flipping two quarters, and determine the size of the sample space.

List the **important information:**

- There are two quarters.
- Each quarter can land heads up or tails up.

2 Make a Plan

You can make an organized list to show all the possible outcomes.

3 Solve

Quarter 1	Quarter 2
H	H
H	T
T	H
T	T

Let H = heads and T = tails.

Record each possible outcome.

The possible outcomes are HH, HT, TH, and TT. There are four possible outcomes in the sample space.

4 Look Back

Each possible outcome that is recorded in the list is different.

When the number of possible outcomes of an experiment increases, it may be easier to track all the possible outcomes on a tree diagram.

1 Introduce

Alternate Opener

EXPLORATION

10-3 Make a List to Find Sample Spaces

When you flip a coin, the possible outcomes are heads (H) or tails (T). Together, all possible outcomes of an experiment make up a *sample space*.

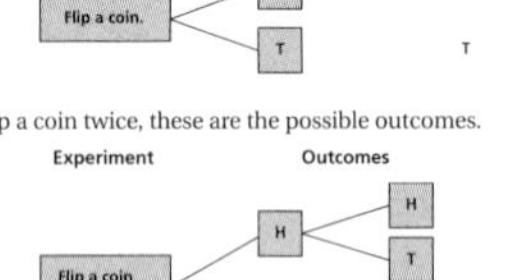

If you flip a coin twice, these are the possible outcomes.

1. List all the possible outcomes in the sample space.
2. Suppose you roll a 1–6 number cube. List all the possible outcomes in the sample space.
3. Suppose you roll a 1–6 number cube and then flip a coin. List all the possible outcomes in the sample space.

Think and Discuss

4. **Describe** how you organized the outcomes in number 3.

Motivate

Present the Simple Sandwich Shop menu on Teaching Transparency T11. Have students consider the number of different lunches that could be ordered from the menu if a lunch consists of a beverage, a sandwich, and a salad. Have students make guesses at the number of different lunches. Then ask each student to describe different lunch options until all eight options are listed.

Exploration worksheet and answers on Chapter 10 Resource Book pp. 25 and 80

2 Teach

Lesson Presentation

Guided Instruction

In this lesson, students learn to use counting methods to determine possible outcomes. Point out that the methods used in Examples 1 and 2 (making a table and making a tree diagram) will be difficult if there are many ways each task can occur. The Fundamental Counting Principle simplifies finding the total number of possible outcomes in a sample space. It replaces recording each outcome with using multiplication. However, while this method is accurate, it does not yield as much information because all of the possible outcomes are not recorded.

EXAMPLE 2 Using a Tree Diagram to Find a Sample Space

Claudia spins each of the spinners. What are all the possible outcomes? How large is the sample space?

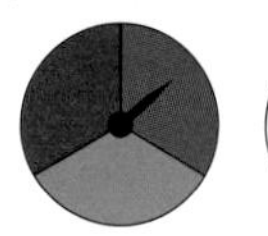

You can make a tree diagram to show the sample space.

List each color on spinner 1. Then list each number on spinner 2 for each color on spinner 1.

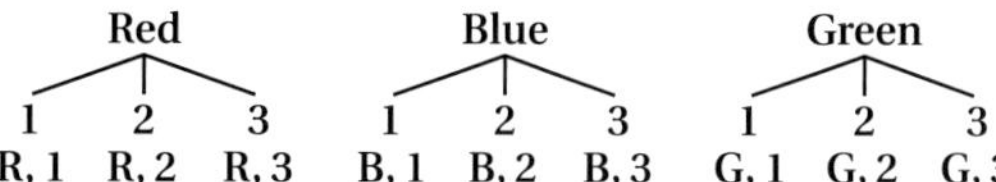

There are nine possible outcomes in the sample space.

In Example 1, there are two outcomes for each coin.

In Example 2, there are three outcomes for each spinner.

The **Fundamental Counting Principle** states that you can find the total number of ways that two or more separate tasks can happen by multiplying the number of ways each task can happen separately.

EXAMPLE  *Recreation Application*

In a game each player rolls a 1–6 number cube and spins a spinner. The spinner is divided into thirds, numbered 1, 2, and 3. How many outcomes are possible during one player's turn?

Use the Fundamental Counting Principle.
Number of ways the number cube can land: 6
Number of ways the spinner can land: 3
$6 \cdot 3 = 18$ *Multiply the number of ways each task can happen.*
There are 18 possible outcomes during one player's turn.

Think and Discuss

1. **Find** the size of the sample space for flipping 5 coins.
2. **Explain** how to use the Fundamental Counting Principle to find the number of possible outcomes in Example 1.

Additional Examples

Example 

One bag has a red tile, a blue tile, and a green tile. A second bag has a red tile and a blue tile. Vincent draws one tile from each bag. What are all the possible outcomes? How large is the sample space? RR, RB, BR, BB, GR, GB; 6

Example 2

There are 4 cards and 2 tiles in a board game. The cards are labeled N, S, E, and W. The tiles are numbered 1 and 2. A player randomly selects one card and one tile. What are all the possible outcomes? How large is the sample space? N1, N2, S1, S2, E1, E2, W1, W2; 8

Example 

Carrie rolls two 1–6 number cubes. How many outcomes are possible? 36

Example 1 note: Point out that although HT and TH both represent outcomes of one heads and one tails, a heads followed by tails is a different outcome than tails followed by heads.

 Close

Summarize

Present the following scenario: Ned has a 1–6 number cube and three cards: a jack, a queen, and a king. Ask the students to explain how many outcomes are possible if he rolls the number cube and selects one card at the same time.

Possible answer: Using the Fundamental Counting Principle reveals that there are $6 \cdot 3$, or 18, possible outcomes.

Reaching All Learners

Through Hands-On Experience

Provide groups of three students with three different colors of paper and four different-colored markers. Ask the groups to find how many different ways they can draw a circle on a piece of paper. Each circle should be a single color, and the interior should be shaded the same color as the circle. The size of the circles and their placement on the page do not matter. Have the groups make a list describing each combination of paper color and circle color. Discuss the strategies the groups used to avoid duplicating color combinations.

Answers to Think and Discuss

1. There are 32 possible outcomes in the sample space.
2. Possible answer: There are 2 possible ways each coin can land. Use the Fundamental Counting Principle, and multiply $2 \cdot 2 = 4$. There are 4 possible outcomes.

10-3 PRACTICE & ASSESS

Students may want to refer back to the lesson examples.

Assignment Guide

If you finished Example 1 assign:
Core 1, 4, 5, 9, 11, 16–21
Enriched 1, 4, 5, 9, 11, 16–21

If you finished Example 2 assign:
Core 1, 2, 4–7, 9, 12, 16–21
Enriched 1, 2, 5, 7, 9, 11, 12, 16–21

If you finished Example 3 assign:
Core 1–11, 16–21
Enriched 1–7 odd, 9–21

Answers

2. The possible outcomes are sugar–vanilla, sugar–chocolate, sugar–strawberry, sugar–pistachio, sugar–coffee, cake–vanilla, cake–chocolate, cake–strawberry, cake–pistachio, cake–coffee, waffle–vanilla, waffle–chocolate, waffle–strawberry, waffle–pistachio, waffle–coffee, cup–vanilla, cup–chocolate, cup–strawberry, cup–pistachio, and cup–coffee; 20.
4. football–football, football–movie, football–concert, basketball–football, basketball–movie, basketball–concert, documentary–football, documentary–movie, documentary–concert; 9
6. H1, H2, H3 H4, H5, T1, T2, T3, T4, T5; 10
7. See p. A3.

Math Background

Some experiments, such as rolling a 1–6 number cube, have outcomes that are numbers. Other experiments, such as tossing a coin, have outcomes that are not numbers. If each outcome of an experiment can be associated with a unique number, then a variable can be defined that is called a random variable. Assigning random variables to a probability experiment allows you to graph the probabilities in a histogram, which has numerical values rather than descriptive categories along the *x*-axis. This allows for other mathematical manipulation of the information.

10-3 Exercises

FOR EXTRA PRACTICE
see page 676

internet connect
Homework Help Online
go.hrw.com Keyword: MS4 10-3

GUIDED PRACTICE

See Example 1
1. Enrique flips a dime and spins the spinner at right. What are all the possible outcomes? How large is the sample space? **There are 4 possible outcomes in the sample space: H1, H2, T1, T2.**

See Example 2
2. An ice cream stand offers sugar cones, cake cones, waffle cones, or cups to hold ice cream. You can get vanilla, chocolate, strawberry, pistachio, or coffee flavored ice cream. If you order a single scoop, what are all the possible options you have? How large is the sample space?

See Example 3
3. A game includes a 1–6 number cube and a spinner divided into 4 equal sectors. Each player rolls the number cube and spins the spinner. How many outcomes are possible? **24 possible outcomes**

INDEPENDENT PRACTICE

See Example 1
4. At noon, Aretha can watch a football game, a basketball game, or a documentary about horses on TV. At 3:00, she can watch a second football game, a movie, or a concert. What are all the possible outcomes? How large is the sample space?
5. A spinner is divided into fourths and numbered 1 through 4. Jory spins the spinner and tosses a nickel. What are all the possible outcomes? How large is the sample space? **There are 8 possible outcomes in the sample space: 1H, 1T, 2H, 2T, 3H, 3T, 4H, 4T.**

See Example 2
6. Berto tosses a coin and spins the spinner at right. What are all the possible outcomes? How large is the sample space?
7. For breakfast, Clarissa can choose from oatmeal, corn flakes, or scrambled eggs. She can drink milk, orange juice, apple juice, or hot chocolate. What are all the possible outcomes? How large is the sample space?

See Example 3
8. A pizza shop offers thick crust, thin crust, or stuffed crust. The choices of toppings are pepperoni, cheese, hamburger, Italian sausage, Canadian bacon, onions, bell peppers, mushrooms, and pineapple. How many different one-topping pizzas could you order? **27 different one-topping pizzas can be ordered.**

PRACTICE AND PROBLEM SOLVING

9. Andie has a blue sweater, a red sweater, and a purple sweater. She has a white shirt and a tan shirt. How many different ways can she wear a sweater and a shirt together? **6 different ways**

RETEACH 10-3

LESSON 10-3 **Reteach**
Make a List to Find Sample Spaces

The set of all possible outcomes to an experiment is called the **sample space.**

A coin is tossed, and a number cube is rolled. What are all the possible outcomes? How large is the sample space? There are two ways to show the sample space for an experiment. You can make a list, or you can make a tree diagram.

Make a list.

1. The possible outcomes for tossing a coin are heads (H) and tails (T).
2. The possible outcomes for rolling a number cube are 1, 2, 3, 4, 5, and 6
3. The sample space is (H, 1), (H, 2), (H, 3), (H, 4), (H, 5), (H, 6), (T, 1), (T, 2), (T, 3), (T, 4), (T, 5), (T, 6). There are 12 possible outcomes in the sample space.

Make a tree diagram.

4. Heads: 1 → H1, 2 → H2, 3 → H3, 4 → H4, 5 → H5, 6 → H6
Tails: 1 → T1, 2 → T2, 3 → T3, 4 → T4, 5 → T5, 6 → T6

You can also find the number of possible outcomes by using the Fundamental Counting Principle.

Multiply the possible outcomes of each event.

5. flipping the coin: 2 outcomes; rolling the number cube: 6 outcomes
2 • 6 = 12 possible outcomes

PRACTICE 10-3

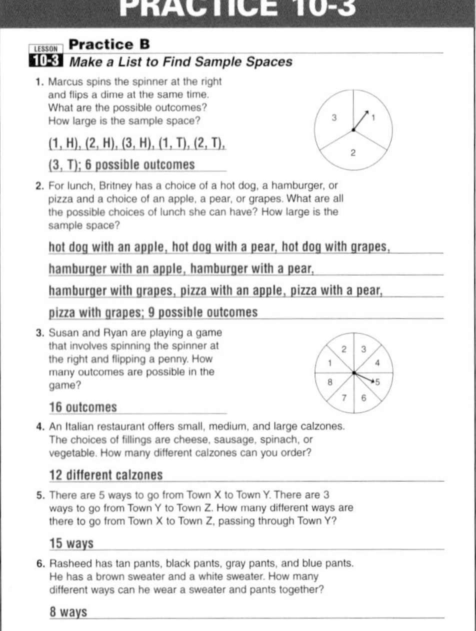
LESSON 10-3 **Practice B**
Make a List to Find Sample Spaces

1. Marcus spins the spinner at the right and flips a dime at the same time. What are the possible outcomes? How large is the sample space?
(1, H), (2, H), (3, H), (1, T), (2, T), (3, T); 6 possible outcomes
2. For lunch, Britney has a choice of a hot dog, a hamburger, or pizza and a choice of an apple, a pear, or grapes. What are all the possible choices of lunch she can have? How large is the sample space?
hot dog with an apple, hot dog with a pear, hot dog with grapes, hamburger with an apple, hamburger with a pear, hamburger with grapes, pizza with an apple, pizza with a pear, pizza with grapes; 9 possible outcomes
3. Susan and Ryan are playing a game that involves spinning the spinner at the right and flipping a penny. How many outcomes are possible in the game?
16 outcomes
4. An Italian restaurant offers small, medium, and large calzones. The choices of fillings are cheese, sausage, spinach, or vegetable. How many different calzones can you order?
12 different calzones
5. There are 5 ways to go from Town X to Town Y. There are 3 ways to go from Town Y to Town Z. How many different ways are there to go from Town X to Town Z, passing through Town Y?
15 ways
6. Rasheed has tan pants, black pants, gray pants, and blue pants. He has a brown sweater and a white sweater. How many different ways can he wear a sweater and pants together?
8 ways

Health LINK

The American Heart Association recommends that people exercise for 30–60 minutes three or four times a week to maintain healthy hearts.

10. ***HEALTH*** The graph shows the kinds of classes that health club members would like to see offered.
    a. If the health club offers the four most popular classes on one day, how many ways could they be arranged? **24 ways**
    b. If the health club offers each of the five classes on a different day of the week, how many ways could they be arranged? **120 ways**

New Class Survey Results

Class	Votes
Water aerobics	22
Swimming	15
Step class	40
Kickboxing	35
Circuit training	50

(Votes axis: 0, 20, 40, 60)

11. ***HEALTH*** For each pair of food groups to the right, give the number of possible outcomes if one item is chosen from each group.
    a. Group A and Group B
    b. Group B and Group D
    c. Group A and Group C

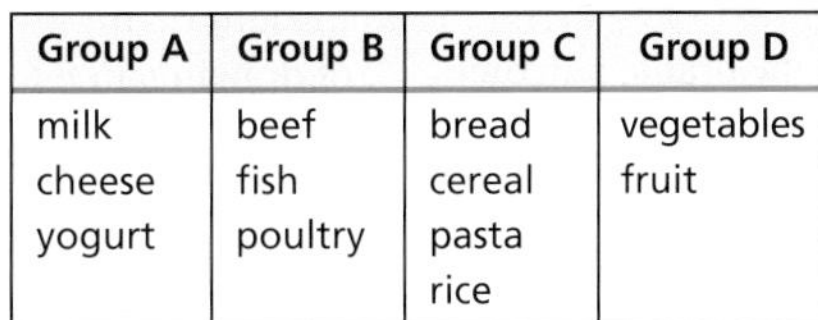

Group A	Group B	Group C	Group D
milk	beef	bread	vegetables
cheese	fish	cereal	fruit
yogurt	poultry	pasta	
		rice	

11.a. 9 outcomes
11.b. 6 outcomes
11.c. 12 outcomes

12. ***RECREATION*** There are 3 trails from the South Canyon trail head to Lake Solitude. There are 4 trails from Lake Solitude to Hidden Lake. How many possible routes could you take to hike from the South Canyon trail head to Hidden Lake that pass Lake Solitude? **12 possible trails**

13. ***WHAT'S THE QUESTION?*** Dan has 4 face cards and 5 number cards. He shuffles the cards separately and places each set in a separate pile. The answer is 20 possible outcomes. What is the question? **How many outcomes are possible if he draws one card from each pile?**

14. ***WRITE ABOUT IT*** Explain how to determine the size of the sample space when you toss two 1–6 number cubes at the same time.

15. ***CHALLENGE*** Suppose you flip a penny, a nickel, and a dime at the same time. What are all the possible outcomes? **HHH, HHT, HTH, HTT, THH, THT, TTH, TTT**

Spiral Review

Write each fraction as a percent. (Lesson 6-1)

16. $\frac{1}{8}$ **12.5%** 17. $\frac{3}{4}$ **75%** 18. $\frac{2}{5}$ **40%** 19. $\frac{3}{10}$ **30%**

20. **TEST PREP** What is the volume of a sphere with diameter 8 in.? Use 3.14 for π. (Lesson 9-3) **B**

    A 2143.6 in^3 B 267.9 in^3 C 50.24 in^3 D 200.96 in^3

21. **TEST PREP** During basketball practice, Owen made 15 out of 24 free throws. What is the experimental probability that he will make his next free throw? (Lesson 10-2) **H**

    F $\frac{3}{8}$ G $\frac{1}{2}$ H $\frac{5}{8}$ J $\frac{5}{6}$

CHALLENGE 10-3

LESSON 10-3 **Challenge**
Mutually Exclusive Cards?

Two events are *mutually exclusive* if they cannot occur at the same time.

Example: In a deck of 52 cards, there are 26 red and 26 black cards.

Event A: Draw a red card. *Event B*: Draw a black card. The events are mutually exclusive. They cannot occur at the same time because a card cannot be red and black.

Event A: Draw a red card. *Event B*: Draw a number card. The events are not mutually exclusive. They can occur at the same time since a number card may be red.

For each pair of events, tell whether the two events are mutually exclusive for a single experiment. If they are not, explain why.

1. In a deck of cards, there are 40 number cards and 12 face cards. *Event A*: Draw a number card. *Event B*: Draw a face card.
   yes
2. In a deck of cards, there are 26 black cards and 12 face cards. *Event A*: Draw a black card. *Event B*: Draw a face card.
   no; there are black face cards
3. In a deck of cards, there are 4 kings and 4 queens. *Event A*: Draw a king. *Event B*: draw a queen.
   yes
4. In a deck of cards, there are 12 diamonds and 12 hearts. *Event A*: Draw a diamond. *Event B*: Draw a heart.
   yes
5. In a deck of cards, there are 12 diamonds and 12 face cards. *Event A*: Draw a diamond. *Event B*: Draw a face card.
   no; you could draw the King of diamonds
6. In a deck of cards, there are 40 number cards and 4 jacks. *Event A*: Draw a number card. *Event B*: Draw a jack.
   yes
7. In a deck of cards, there are 4 tens and 13 clubs. *Event A*: Draw a ten. *Event B*: Draw a club.
   no; you could draw the ten of clubs

PROBLEM SOLVING 10-3

LESSON 10-3 **Problem Solving**
Make a List to Find Sample Spaces

Write the correct answer.

Benny's Bagels

Bagels	Toppings
Plain	Cream cheese
Poppy	Honey
Raisin	Butter
Sesame	Jam
Egg	

1. If you order one topping, how many different choices of bagel and toppings can you order?
   20 choices
2. Santana only likes cream cheese or jam on his bagel. How many choices does he have for a one-topping bagel?
   10 choices
3. Yesterday, Benny ran out of raisin bagels. How many choices of a bagel and one topping were there?
   16 choices
4. Today, Benny has all 5 types of bagels but runs out of honey. How many choices of a bagel with one topping can you order?
   15 choices

Choose the letter for the best answer.

5. The mall movie multiplex is showing 12 movies. Each movie is shown at five different times during the day. How many choices of movies and showtimes does Reggie have?
   A 5 C 17
   B 12 (D) 60
6. At Hi-Top Ski Resort, there are three chair lifts to the top of the mountain. There are six ski trails to the bottom of the mountain. How many possible choices of lifts and trails do the skiers have?
   F 9 H 81
   (G) 18 J 2
7. In a Little League game, Geri can bat first, second, or third. When at bat, she could strike out, walk, or get a hit. How large is the sample space for these events?
   A 3 (C) 9
   B 6 D 18
8. Ty is flipping a coin. He has decided that if he flips the same result twice in a row, he will do his homework. If he flips 2 different results, then he will go jogging. How likely is it that he will study?
   (F) as likely as not H unlikely
   G likely J certain

COMMON ERROR ALERT

Some students might try to find all the possible outcomes associated with the table in Exercise 11. Remind students that they are comparing only two food groups at a time.

Answers

14. Possible answer: Use the Fundamental Counting Principle. Each number cube can land 6 ways: 6 · 6 = 36 outcomes.

Journal

Have students draw two different spinners and describe all the possible outcomes associated with spinning each of the spinners once.

Test Prep Doctor

In Exercise 20, students who selected incorrect choices **C** and **D** either do not know the correct formula for the volume of a sphere or do not understand how to use the formula. Students who selected **A** cubed the diameter instead of the radius. Remind these students that the formula for the volume of a sphere calls for the radius to be cubed.

Lesson Quiz

Tell how large the sample space is for each situation. List the possible outcomes.

1. a three question true-false test 8 possible outcomes: TTT, TTF, TFT, TFF, FTT, FTF, FFT, FFF
2. tossing four coins 16 possible outcomes: HHHH, HHHT, HHTH, HTHH, THHH, HHTT, HTHT, HTTH, THHT, THTH, TTHH, HTTT, THTT, TTHT, TTTH, TTTT
3. choosing a pair of cocaptains from the following athletes: Anna, Ben, Carol, Dan, Ed, Fran 15 possible outcomes: AB, AC, AD, AE, AF, BC, BD, BE, BF, CD, CE, CF, DE, DF, EF

Available on Daily Transparency in CRB

10-4 Organizer

Pacing: Traditional 1 day
Block $\frac{1}{2}$ day

Objective: Students find the theoretical probability of an event.

Warm Up

1. What is the probability of getting two tails if two coins are tossed? $\frac{1}{4}$
2. Give the probability that the roll of a number cube will show 1 or 4. $\frac{1}{3}$
3. Give the expected number of rolls that will result in a 2 if a number cube is rolled 42 times. 7

Problem of the Day

The name of a U.S. state is spelled out with letter tiles. Then the tiles are placed in a bag, and one is picked at random. What state was spelled out if the probability of picking the letter *O* is $\frac{1}{2}$? $\frac{3}{8}$? $\frac{1}{3}$?
Ohio; Colorado; Oregon

Available on Daily Transparency in CRB

Math Fact !!

Game theory is a branch of mathematics that is used to study competitions.

10-4 Theoretical Probability

Learn to find the theoretical probability of an event.

Vocabulary
favorable outcome
theoretical probability
fair

In the game of Scrabble®, players use tiles bearing the letters of the alphabet to form words. Of the 100 tiles used in a Scrabble game, 12 have the letter *E* on them. What is the probability of drawing an *E* from a bag of 100 Scrabble tiles?

In this case, pulling an *E* from the bag is called a *favorable outcome*. A **favorable outcome** is an outcome that you are looking for when you conduct an experiment.

To find the probability of drawing an *E*, you can draw tiles from a bag and record your results, or you can find the *theoretical probability*. **Theoretical probability** is used to estimate the probability of an event when all outcomes are equally likely.

THEORETICAL PROBABILITY

$$\text{probability} = \frac{\text{number of favorable outcomes}}{\text{total number of possible outcomes}}$$

If each possible outcome of an experiment is equally likely, then the experiment is said to be **fair**. Experiments involving number cubes and coins are usually assumed to be fair.

You can write probability as a fraction, a decimal, or a percent.

EXAMPLE  **Finding Theoretical Probability**

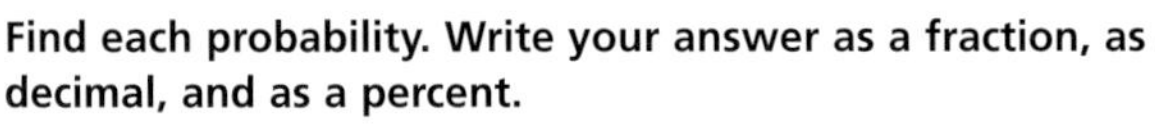

Find each probability. Write your answer as a fraction, as a decimal, and as a percent.

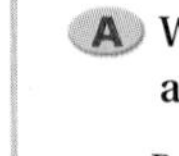

A **What is the probability of drawing one of the 12 *E*'s from a bag of 100 Scrabble tiles?**

$P = \frac{\text{number of favorable outcomes}}{\text{total number of possible outcomes}}$

$P(E) = \frac{\text{number of } E\text{'s}}{\text{total number of tiles}}$ *Write the ratio.*

$= \frac{12}{100}$ *Substitute.*

$= \frac{3}{25}$ *Write in simplest form.*

$= 0.12 = 12\%$ *Write as a decimal and as a percent.*

The theoretical probability of drawing an *E* is $\frac{3}{25}$, 0.12, or 12%.

1 Introduce

Alternate Opener

EXPLORATION

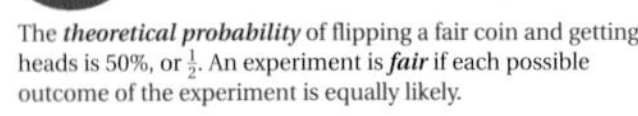

10-4 Theoretical Probability

The *theoretical probability* of flipping a fair coin and getting heads is 50%, or $\frac{1}{2}$. An experiment is *fair* if each possible outcome of the experiment is equally likely.

When you roll a fair number cube, there are 6 outcomes that are equally likely.

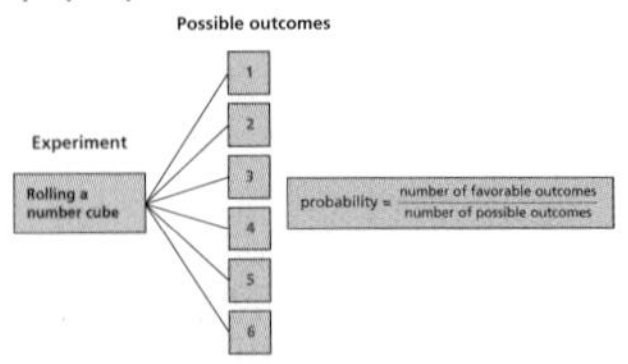

Use the formula for theoretical probability to answer each question.

1. What is the theoretical probability of rolling a 4?
2. What is the theoretical probability of rolling an even number?
3. What is the theoretical probability of rolling an odd number?

Think and Discuss

4. **Explain** how you determined each probability.

Motivate

Discuss how students start games. For example, in a team competition, how do students decide which team has the ball first? When playing a board game or a card game, how do they decide who goes first? Elicit what students think is important in deciding who goes first in a game or other competition (e.g., the decision should be fair).

Exploration worksheet and answers on Chapter 10 Resource Book pp. 34 and 82

2 Teach

Lesson Presentation

Guided Instruction

In this lesson, students learn to find the theoretical probability of an event. Remind students that the probability of an event does not guarantee that an event will occur. Emphasize the importance of understanding what is meant by *favorable*. A favorable event is one that is being looked for; it is not necessarily beneficial. Remind students of the difference between experimental and theoretical probability. Experimental probability compares the number of times an event occurs to the number of actual trials of an event. Theoretical probability compares the number of favorable outcomes to the number of possible outcomes.

Find each probability. Write your answer as a fraction, as a decimal, and as a percent.

B What is the probability of rolling a number greater than 2 on a fair number cube?

For a fair number cube, each of the six possible outcomes is equally likely. There are 4 ways to roll a number greater than 2: 3, 4, 5, or 6.

$$P = \frac{\text{number of favorable outcomes}}{\text{total number of possible outcomes}}$$

$$P = \frac{\text{4 numbers greater than 2}}{\text{6 possible outcomes}}$$

$$P = \frac{4}{6}$$

$$P = \frac{2}{3}$$

$$P \approx 0.667 \approx 66.7\%$$

EXAMPLE 2 *School Application*

Mr. Ashley has written the names of each of his students on a craft stick. He draws randomly from these sticks to choose a student to answer a question, and then replaces the stick in the pile.

A If there are 11 boys and 16 girls in Mr. Ashley's class, what is the theoretical probability that a boy's name will be drawn?

$$P(\text{boy}) = \frac{\text{number of boys in class}}{\text{number of students in class}} \quad \textit{Find the theoretical probability.}$$

$$= \frac{11}{27} \quad \textit{Substitute.}$$

B What is the theoretical probability that a girl's name will be drawn?

$$P(\text{girl}) = \frac{\text{number of girls in class}}{\text{number of students in class}} \quad \textit{Find the theoretical probability.}$$

$$= \frac{16}{27} \quad \textit{Substitute.}$$

Think and Discuss

1. **Give an example** of an experiment in which all of the outcomes are not equally likely. Explain.
2. **Find** the theoretical probability that a number cube will land with 6 up. If you roll a number cube 5 times without its landing 6 up, what is the theoretical probability that the cube will land 6 up on the sixth roll? Explain your answer.

COMMON ERROR ALERT

Some students might have difficulty converting between fractions, decimals, and percents. Recognizing that all probabilities lie between 0 and 1 may help them catch errors in their own work.

Additional Examples

Example 1

Andy has 20 marbles in a bag. Of these, 9 are clear. Find the probability of drawing a clear marble from the bag. Write your answer as a fraction, a decimal, and a percent.

$\frac{9}{20}$, **0.45, 45%**

Example 2

The coach has written the names of each of the track team members on an index card. She draws randomly from these cards to choose a student to run a sprint and then replaces the card in the stack.

A. If there are 13 boys and 10 girls on the team, what is the probability that a girl's name will be drawn? $\frac{10}{23}$

B. What is the theoretical probability that a boy's name will be drawn? $\frac{13}{23}$

Example 2 note: Explain that the probability in part A is $\frac{11}{27}$, not $\frac{11}{16}$, because the total number of outcomes is 27, not 16.

3 Close

Reaching All Learners

Through Number Sense

Have each student toss a coin ten times and record the results. Ask students to comment on how the experimental probability of getting tails compares with the theoretical probability of getting tails. Then combine class results and compute the experimental probability of tails. Again, compare the experimental and theoretical probabilities.

Students may notice more variation in the probabilities with 10 tosses than with the combined tosses. As the number of trials, or experiments, increases, the experimental probability gets closer to the theoretical probability.

Summarize

In a deck of 52 cards, there are 13 diamonds. What is the probability of drawing a diamond from a shuffled deck of cards?

$\frac{1}{4}$, **25%, 0.25**

Answers to Think and Discuss

1. Possible answer: If different Scrabble tiles had different weights, then the heavier tiles would fall to the bottom of the bag and would be less likely to be drawn.
2. $\frac{1}{6}$; the probability is still $\frac{1}{6}$; possible answer: for the theoretical probability, it does not matter what the previous outcomes were. There is still only 1 favorable outcome out of 6 possible outcomes.

10-4 PRACTICE & ASSESS

Students may want to refer back to the lesson examples.

Assignment Guide

If you finished Example 1 assign:
- **Core** 1, 2, 4–6, 13–17
- **Enriched** 1, 2, 4–6, 13–17

If you finished Example 2 assign:
- **Core** 1–7, 9, 13–17
- **Enriched** 1–7 odd, 8–17

Notes

Math Background

Normal distributions are symmetric probability distributions. In a graph of a normal distribution, the mean occurs at the peak of the curve. Normal distributions are often described as bell-shaped because scores are more concentrated in the middle than in the ends and the graph looks like a bell. Although some curves may be taller, and some may be wider, the area under each curve is the same: 1, representing the total population, or 100%.

10-4 Exercises

FOR EXTRA PRACTICE see page 676

internet connect go.hrw.com — Homework Help Online go.hrw.com Keyword: MS4 10-4

GUIDED PRACTICE

See Example 1 **Find each probability. Write your answer as a fraction, as a decimal, and as a percent.**

1. In Chinese checkers, 15 red marbles, 15 blue marbles, 15 green marbles, 15 yellow marbles, 15 black marbles, and 15 white marbles are used. What is the probability of randomly choosing a red marble from a bag of Chinese checkers marbles? **$\frac{1}{6}$, 0.17, 17%**
2. If you toss 2 fair pennies, what is the probability that both will land heads up? **$\frac{1}{4}$, 0.25, 25%**

See Example 2

3. A set of cards includes 15 yellow cards, 10 green cards, and 10 blue cards.
   a. What is the probability that the card chosen at random will be yellow? **$\frac{3}{7}$**
   b. What is the probability that the card chosen at random will be green? **$\frac{2}{7}$**
   c. What is the probability that the card chosen at random will not be yellow or green? **$\frac{2}{7}$**

INDEPENDENT PRACTICE

See Example 1 **Find each probability. Write your answer as a fraction, as a decimal, and as a percent.**

4. A standard deck of playing cards has 52 cards. These cards are divided into four 13-card suits: diamonds, hearts, clubs, and spades. Find the probability of drawing a heart or a club at random from a deck of shuffled cards. **$\frac{1}{2}$, 0.5, 50%**
5. A game requires 13 red disks, 13 purple disks, 13 orange disks, and 13 white disks. All of the disks are the same size and shape. What is the probability of randomly drawing a purple disk? **$\frac{1}{4}$, 0.25, 25%**
6. In Scrabble, 2 of the 100 tiles are blank. Find the probability of drawing a blank tile from an entire set of Scrabble tiles. **$\frac{1}{50}$, 0.02, 2%**

See Example 2

7. Sifu gives each student in his karate class a different-colored slip of paper. He puts corresponding slips of paper in a bag and randomly selects a slip. The student with the slip of paper that matches the slip drawn must demonstrate a self-defense technique.
   a. If there are 6 girls and 8 boys in the class, what is the probability that a girl will be selected? **$\frac{3}{7}$**
   b. What is the probability that a boy will be selected? **$\frac{4}{7}$**

RETEACH 10-4

LESSON 10-4 Reteach
Theoretical Probability

A **favorable outcome** is an outcome that you are looking for when you conduct an experiment. The **theoretical probability** of an event is found by comparing the number of favorable outcomes to the total number of possible outcomes.

$$\text{Theoretical probability} = \frac{\text{number of favorable outcomes}}{\text{number of possible outcomes}}$$

One of the games at a carnival is the Wheel of Letters. Find the probability that the wheel will stop on each letter.

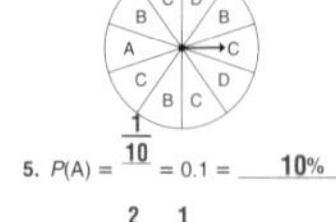

1. There are __10__ possible outcomes.
2. There are __3__ sections marked B.
3. There are __4__ sections marked C.
4. $P(B) = \frac{3}{10} = 0.3 =$ __30%__
5. $P(A) = \frac{1}{10} = 0.1 =$ __10%__
6. $P(C) = \frac{4}{10} = \frac{2}{5} = 0.4 =$ __40%__
7. $P(D) = \frac{2}{10} = \frac{1}{5} = 0.2 =$ __20%__

There are 11 pennies and 9 dimes in a bag. Find the probabilities.

8. Find the probability that a dime will be drawn from the bag.
   $P(\text{dime}) = \frac{9}{20} = 0.45 =$ __45%__
9. The first coin drawn from the bag was a dime. If the dime is not replaced, what is the probability that the next coin drawn from the bag is a dime? Round to the nearest percent.
   $\frac{8}{19} = 0.42 = 42\%$
10. The first four coins drawn from the bag were a dime and three pennies. If the coins were not replaced, find the probability that the fifth coin drawn from the bag is a dime.
    $P(\text{dime}) = \frac{1}{2} =$ __0.5__ $=$ __50%__

PRACTICE 10-4

LESSON 10-4 Practice B
Theoretical Probability

Find the probabilities. Write your answer as a fraction, as a decimal, and as a percent. Round to the nearest tenth of a percent.

1. In the first grade, each student has 12 red counters, 12 white counters, 12 green counters, and 12 blue counters. What is the probability of randomly drawing a white counter?
   $\frac{12}{48} = \frac{1}{4}$, 0.25, 25%
2. If you toss two fair nickels, what is the probability that one will land on tails and one will land on heads?
   $\frac{2}{4} = \frac{1}{2}$, 0.5, 50%
3. Maurice has a set of 24 cards. There are 18 orange cards and 6 black cards in the set. Maurice draws one card at random and then replaces it in the deck.
   a. What is the probability that the card he draws is orange?
      $\frac{18}{24} = \frac{3}{4}$, 0.75, 75%
   b. What is the probability that the next card he draws will NOT be orange?
      $\frac{6}{24} = \frac{1}{4}$, 0.25, 25%
4. A standard deck of playing cards has 52 cards. These cards are divided into four 13-card suits: hearts, clubs, spades, and diamonds. Find the probability of drawing a jack, queen, or king at random from a deck of shuffled cards.
   $\frac{12}{52} = \frac{3}{13}$, 0.231, 23.1%
5. A 1–6 number cube is rolled. Find the probability of rolling a number greater than 1.
   $\frac{5}{6}$, 0.833, 83.3%

PRACTICE AND PROBLEM SOLVING

8. ***RECREATION*** The table shows the approximate number of visitors to five different amusement parks in the United States.

   a. What is the probability that a randomly selected visitor to one of the amusement parks visited Disney World? Write your answer as a percent. **37%**

   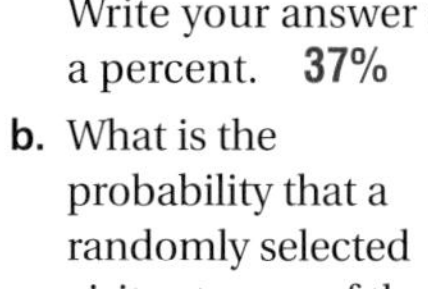

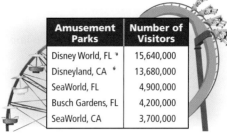

Amusement Parks	Number of Visitors
Disney World, FL	15,640,000
Disneyland, CA	13,680,000
SeaWorld, FL	4,900,000
Busch Gardens, FL	4,200,000
SeaWorld, CA	3,700,000

   Source: The Top 10 of Everything 2000

   b. What is the probability that a randomly selected visitor to one of the amusement parks visited a park in California? Write your answer as a decimal. **0.41**

9. ***GARDENING*** A package of mixed lettuce seeds contains seeds for green lettuce and red lettuce.

   a. Of the first 50 seeds planted, 18 are red lettuce seeds, and the rest are green lettuce seeds. Based on these results, what is the experimental probability that the next seed planted will be a green lettuce seed? Write your answer as a percent. **64%**

   b. If the package contains 150 green lettuce seeds and 50 red lettuce seeds, what is the probability that a randomly selected seed will be a red lettuce seed? Write your answer as a percent. **25%**

10. ***CHOOSE A STRATEGY*** Francis, Amanda, Raymond, and Albert wore different-colored T-shirts. The colors were tan, orange, purple, and aqua. Neither Raymond nor Amanda ever wears orange, and neither Francis nor Raymond ever wears aqua. Albert wore purple. What color was each person's T-shirt?

11. ***WRITE ABOUT IT*** Suppose the probability of an event happening is $\frac{3}{8}$. Explain what each number in the ratio represents.

12. ***CHALLENGE*** A spinner is divided into three sectors. Half of the spinner is red, $\frac{1}{3}$ is blue, and $\frac{1}{6}$ is green. What is the probability that the spinner will land on either red or green? $\frac{2}{3}$

Spiral Review

Solve. (Lesson 3-6)

13. $n + 12 = -9$ **$n = -21$**

14. $x - 25 = -6$ **$x = 19$**

15. $7 + s = -34$ **$s = -41$**

16. $y - 52 = -19$ **$y = 33$**

17. **TEST PREP** There are 3 red cards and 9 blue cards in a bag. If you draw a card, how likely is it that you will randomly draw a red card? (Lesson 10-1) **B**

    A Impossible   **B** Unlikely   **C** As likely as not   **D** Likely

Answers

10. Francis wore orange. Raymond wore tan. Albert wore purple. Amanda wore aqua.

11. The numerator means there are 3 favorable outcomes, and the denominator means there are 8 possible outcomes.

Journal

Have students find the probability of an event associated with a favorite game. Tell students to comment on how being able to find the probability might be useful to them.

Test Prep Doctor

In Exercise 17, students who selected incorrect choices **C** and **D** probably confused likelihoods. Discuss the differences between each type of likelihood. Students who selected **A** might not understand the concept of likelihood.

CHALLENGE 10-4

LESSON 10-4 **Challenge**
Number Cube Sums

1. Roll two number cubes 50 times. After each roll, find the sum of the values on the cubes. Put a tally mark in the table for each sum you roll.

Sum of Cubes	2	3	4	5	6	7	8	9	10	11	12
Tally of Number of Times Rolled											

Using your table, give the percents of getting each sum.
Answers will vary depending on tally. Possible answers are given.

2. sum of 4 = **8%**   3. sum of 8 = **14%**   4. sum < 6 = **28%**

5. Complete by filling in the sums if two number cubes are rolled.

Second Cube \ First Cube	1	2	3	4	5	6
1	2	3	4	5	6	7
2	**3**	**4**	**5**	**6**	**7**	**8**
3	**4**	**5**	**6**	**7**	**8**	**9**
4	**5**	**6**	**7**	**8**	**9**	**10**
5	**6**	**7**	**8**	**9**	**10**	**11**
6	**7**	**8**	**9**	**10**	**11**	**12**

6. Complete the table, using the chart of sums in Exercise 5.

Sum of Cubes	2	3	4	5	6	7	8	9	10	11	12
Number of Ways to Get the Sum	1	**2**	**3**	**4**	**5**	**6**	**5**	**4**	**3**	**2**	**1**

7. How many possible outcomes are there if you roll 2 number cubes? **36**

Using the table in Exercise 6, give the percents of getting each sum.

8. sum of 4 = **8%**   9. sum of 8 = **14%**   10. sum < 6 = **28%**

PROBLEM SOLVING 10-4

LESSON 10-4 **Problem Solving**
Theoretical Probability

Write the correct answer in simplest form.

The table lists the pieces used in the game of chess.

Chess Set

Type	White	Black
Pawn	8	8
Rook	2	2
Knight	2	2
Bishop	2	2
Queen	1	1
King	1	1

1. If you randomly choose a piece of the chess set, what is the probability that it is a pawn? Write your answer as a decimal.
   0.5

2. If you randomly choose a piece of the chess set, what is the probability that it is a white pawn? Write your answer as a decimal.
   0.25

3. If you randomly choose a piece of the chess set, what is the probability that it is a rook, knight, or bishop? Write your answer as a fraction.
   $\frac{3}{8}$

4. If you randomly choose a piece of the chess set, what is the probability that it is a queen? Write your answer as a fraction.
   $\frac{1}{16}$

Choose the letter for the best answer.

5. Mr. Rose draws names to see who will give the first book report. There are 10 boys and 14 girls in his class. What is the probability that he will draw a girl's name?
   A $\frac{2}{5}$ **(C)** $\frac{7}{12}$
   B $\frac{5}{12}$ D $\frac{5}{7}$

6. Eight students will give reports on novels, 9 will report on biographies, and 7 will report on history books. What is the probability that the first report will be a novel?
   F $\frac{3}{8}$ H $\frac{8}{17}$
   (G) $\frac{1}{3}$ J $\frac{1}{2}$

7. Stanley is reading a 224-page book. There are illustrations on 14 pages. If Stanley opens the book at random, what is the probability that the page will have an illustration?
   A 0.0004   C 0.0714
   (B) 0.0625   D 0.9375

8. In Congress, each of the 50 states is represented by 2 senators. If you choose a senator randomly, what is the probability that you will choose a senator that represents Virginia?
   F 25%   **(H)** 2%
   G 10%   J 1%

Lesson Quiz

Find the probabilities. Write your answer as a fraction, as a decimal to the nearest hundredth, and as a percent to the nearest whole percent. You have 11 cards, each with one of the letters from the word *mathematics.*

1. Find the probability of drawing an *m* from the pile of shuffled cards. **$\frac{2}{11}$, 0.18, 18%**

2. Find the probability of drawing a vowel. **$\frac{4}{11}$, 0.36, 36%**

3. Find the probability of drawing a consonant? **$\frac{7}{11}$, 0.64, 64%**

Available on Daily Transparency in CRB

Mid-Chapter Quiz

Purpose: *To assess students' mastery of concepts and skills in Lessons 10-1 through 10-4*

Assessment Resources

Section 10A Quiz

Assessment Resources .... p. 27

***Test and Practice Generator* CD-ROM**

Additional mid-chapter assessment items in both multiple-choice and free-response format may be generated for any objective in Lessons 10-1 through 10-4.

Chapter 10

Mid-Chapter Quiz

Mid-Chapter Quiz

LESSON **10-1** (pp. 512–515)

Determine whether each event is impossible, unlikely, as likely as not, likely, or certain.

1. Ramona went to school today. If her class went on a field trip, how likely is it that Ramona went on the field trip? **certain**
2. Neil has blue, black, tan, and gray pants. How likely is it that he will wear green pants to school today? **impossible**

LESSON **10-2** (pp. 516–519)

3. Carl is conducting a survey for the school paper. Of the 31 students he has interviewed, 10 have only a dog, 9 have only a cat, and 5 have both a dog and a cat. What is the experimental probability that the next person Carl surveys will not have a dog or a cat? $\frac{7}{31}$
4. During her ride home from school, Dana sees 15 cars driven by men and 34 cars driven by women. What is the experimental probability that the next car Dana sees will be driven by a man? $\frac{15}{49}$

5. The possible outcomes are H1, H2, H3, H4, H5, H6, T1, T2, T3, T4, T5, T6; there are 12 possible outcomes in the sample space.

LESSON **10-3** (pp. 520–523)

5. Shelly and Anthony are playing a game using a number cube numbered 1–6 and a nickel. Each player rolls the number cube and flips the coin. What are all the possible outcomes during one turn? How large is the sample space?

6. A yogurt shop offers 4 different flavors of yogurt and 3 different fruit toppings. How many different desserts can you have if you choose one flavor of yogurt and one topping? **12 desserts**

LESSON **10-4** (pp. 524–527)

A spinner with 10 equal sections numbered 1 through 10 is spun. Find each probability. Write your answer as a fraction, as a decimal, and as a percent.

7. $P(5)$ $\frac{1}{10}$, **0.1, 10%**
8. $P(\text{prime number})$ $\frac{2}{5}$, **0.4, 40%**
9. $P(\text{even number})$ $\frac{1}{2}$, **0.5, 50%**
10. $P(20)$ **0, 0.0, 0%**

Focus on Problem Solving

Understand the Problem

• Identify important details

When you are solving word problems, you need to identify information that is important to the problem. Read the problem several times to find all the important details. Sometimes it is helpful to read the problem aloud so that you can hear the words. Highlight the facts that are needed to solve the problem. Then list any other information that is necessary.

Highlight the important information in each problem, and then list any other important details.

1. A bag of bubble gum has 25 pink pieces, 20 blue pieces, and 15 green pieces. If Lauren selects 1 piece of bubble gum without looking, what is the probability that it is not blue?

2. Regina has a bag of marbles that contains 6 red marbles, 3 green marbles, and 4 blue marbles. Regina pulls 1 marble from the bag without looking. What is the probability that the marble is red?

3. Marco is counting the cars he sees on his ride home from school. Of 20 cars, 10 are white, 6 are red, 2 are blue, and 2 are green. What is the experimental probability that the next car Marco sees will be red?

4. Frederica has 8 red socks, 6 blue socks, 10 white socks, and 4 yellow socks in a drawer. What is the probability that she will randomly pull a brown sock from the drawer?

5. During the first 20 minutes of lunch, 5 male students, 7 female students, and 3 teachers went through the lunch line. What is the experimental probability that the next person through the line will be a teacher?

Answers

1. $\frac{2}{3}$
2. $\frac{6}{13}$
3. $\frac{3}{10}$
4. 0
5. $\frac{1}{5}$

Focus on Problem Solving

Purpose: *To focus on identifying important details to better understand the problem*

Problem Solving Resources

Problem Solving Process

This page focuses on the first step of the problem-solving process: **Understand the Problem**

Discuss

Have students give the important details they highlighted in each problem. Also have them give any other information that will help them solve the problem. Possible answers:

1. 25 pink pieces, 20 blue pieces, 15 green pieces; Lauren is selecting one piece of gum; the *not blue* pieces are pink and green.
2. 6 red marbles, 3 green marbles, 4 blue marbles; the probability that she drew a red marble; there are 13 marbles total.
3. 10 white cars, 6 red cars, 2 blue cars, 2 green cars; the experimental probability that the next car will be red; Marco has observed a total of 20 cars.
4. 8 red socks, 6 blue socks, 10 white socks, 4 yellow socks; the probability that she will pull a brown sock; there are no brown socks in the drawer.
5. 5 male students, 7 female students, 3 teachers; the probability that the next person through the line will be a teacher; 15 people have gone through the lunch line already.

Applications of Probability

One-Minute Section Planner

Lesson	Materials	Resources
Lesson 10-5 Probability of Independent and Dependent Events **NCTM:** Data Analysis and Probability, Reasoning and Proof, Communication, Connections **NAEP:** Data Analysis and Probability 4h ☐ SAT-9 ☑ SAT-10 ☐ ITBS ☐ CTBS ☑ MAT ☑ CAT	**Optional** Spinner *(MK)* Deck of cards Teaching Transparency T20 *(CRB)*	• *Chapter 10 Resource Book,* pp. 43–51 • Daily Transparency T19, CRB • Additional Examples Transparencies T21–T23, CRB • *Alternate Openers: Explorations,* p. 85
Hands-On Lab 10A Pascal's Triangle **NCTM:** Algebra, Data Analysis and Probability, Reasoning and Proof **NAEP:** Algebra 1a ☐ SAT-9 ☐ SAT-10 ☐ ITBS ☐ CTBS ☐ MAT ☐ CAT		• *Hands-On Lab Activities,* pp. 100–103
Lesson 10-6 Combinations **NCTM:** Data Analysis and Probability, Problem Solving, Reasoning and Proof, Communication **NAEP:** Algebra 4e ☐ SAT-9 ☑ SAT-10 ☐ ITBS ☐ CTBS ☐ MAT ☑ CAT		• *Chapter 10 Resource Book,* pp. 52–60 • Daily Transparency T24, CRB • Additional Examples Transparencies T25–T27, CRB • *Alternate Openers: Explorations,* p. 86
Lesson 10-7 Permutations **NCTM:** Data Analysis and Probability, Reasoning and Proof, Communication **NAEP:** Algebra 4e ☐ SAT-9 ☑ SAT-10 ☐ ITBS ☐ CTBS ☐ MAT ☑ CAT	**Optional** Index cards	• *Chapter 10 Resource Book,* pp. 61–69 • Daily Transparency T28, CRB • Additional Examples Transparencies T29–T30, CRB • *Alternate Openers: Explorations,* p. 87
Extension Computing Odds **NCTM:** Number and Operations, Data Analysis and Probability, Reasoning and Proof **NAEP:** Data Analysis and Probability 4j ☐ SAT-9 ☐ SAT-10 ☐ ITBS ☐ CTBS ☐ MAT ☐ CAT	**Optional** Teaching Transparency T31 *(CRB)*	• Additional Examples Transparency T32, CRB
Section 10B Assessment		

SAT = *Stanford Achievement Tests* **ITBS** = *Iowa Test of Basic Skills* **CTBS** = *Comprehensive Test of Basic Skills/Terra Nova*
MAT = *Metropolitan Achievement Test* **CAT** = *California Achievement Test*

NCTM–Complete standards can be found on pages T27–T33. **NAEP**–Complete standards can be found on pages A35–A39.

SE = *Student Edition* **TE** = *Teacher's Edition* **AR** = *Assessment Resources* **CRB** = *Chapter Resource Book* **MK** = *Manipulatives Kit*

Section Overview

Probability of Independent and Dependent Events — *Lesson 10-5*

Why? Some events are influenced by what has happened before. You must determine whether two events are independent or dependent in order to find the probability of both events occurring.

> **Independent Events**
> The occurrence of one event has no effect on the probability of the second event.

Probability of Independent Events

probability of both events = probability of first event · probability of second event

$P(A \text{ and } B) = P(A) \cdot P(B)$

> **Dependent Events**
> The occurrence of one event does have an effect on the probability of the second event.

Probability of Dependent Events

probability of both events = probability of first event · probability of second event after first event

$P(A \text{ then } B) = P(A) \cdot P(B \text{ after } A)$

Combinations and Permutations — *Hands-On Lab 10A, Lessons 10-6, 10-7*

To determine probabilities, it is necessary to determine all the possible outcomes. Sometimes the sample space for outcomes is a set of combinations, and sometimes it is a set of permutations.

> A **combination** is a grouping of objects or events in which the order does not matter.

In how many ways can Alison, Ben, and Carly pair off into groups of 2?

Find the number of combinations.

Make a List

Alison and Ben
Alison and Carly
Ben and Carly

or

Alison — Ben, Carly
Ben — ~~Alison~~, Carly
Carly — ~~Alison~~, ~~Ben~~

Cross out duplicates.

There are 3 possible groups: Alison and Ben, Alison and Carly, and Ben and Carly.

> A **permutation** is a grouping of objects or events in which the order is important.

In how many ways can Alison, Ben, and Carly stand in a line?

Find the number of permutations.

Make a List

Alison, Ben, Carly	Ben, Carly, Alison
Alison, Carly, Ben	Carly, Alison, Ben
Ben, Alison, Carly	Carly, Ben, Alison

> **Use the Fundamental Counting Principle**
> Multiply the number of choices for each place.
> $3 \cdot 2 \cdot 1 = 6$

There are 6 ways for Alison, Ben, and Carly to stand in line.

Factorials can also be used to find permutations. $3! = 3 \cdot 2 \cdot 1 = 6$

10-5 Organizer

Pacing: Traditional 1 day
Block $\frac{1}{2}$ day

Objective: Students find the probability of independent and dependent events.

Warm Up

Write each answer as a fraction, as a decimal, and as a percent.

A 1–6 number cube is rolled.

1. What is the probability that an even number will result? $\frac{1}{2}$, 0.5, 50%

2. What is the probability that the number will be prime? $\frac{1}{2}$, 0.5, 50%

Problem of the Day

I have two coins in my pocket that total 30 cents. One of the coins is not a nickel. What are the coins? a quarter and a nickel (One of the coins is not a nickel, but the other one is.)

Available on Daily Transparency in CRB

Math Fact !

On a die, every pair of opposite sides have a sum of 7.

10-5 Probability of Independent and Dependent Events

Learn to find the probability of independent and dependent events.

Vocabulary

independent events

dependent events

Raji and Kara must each choose a topic from a list of topics to research for their class. If Raji's choice has no effect on Kara's choice and vice versa, the events are *independent.* For **independent events**, the occurrence of one event has no effect on the probability that a second event will occur.

If once Raji chooses a topic, Kara must choose from the remaining topics, then the events are *dependent.* For **dependent events**, the occurrence of one event *does* have an effect on the probability that a second event will occur.

EXAMPLE 1 Determining Whether Events Are Independent or Dependent

Decide whether each set of events is independent or dependent. Explain your answer.

A **Erika rolls a 3 on one number cube and a 2 on another number cube.**

Since the outcome of rolling one number cube does not affect the outcome of rolling the second number cube, the events are independent.

B **Tomoko chooses a seventh-grader for her team from a group of seventh- and eighth-graders, and then Juan chooses a different seventh-grader from the remaining students.**

Since Juan cannot pick the same student that Tomoko picked, and since there are fewer students for Juan to choose from after Tomoko chooses, the events are dependent.

To find the probability that two independent events will happen, multiply the probabilities of the two events.

Probability of Two Independent Events

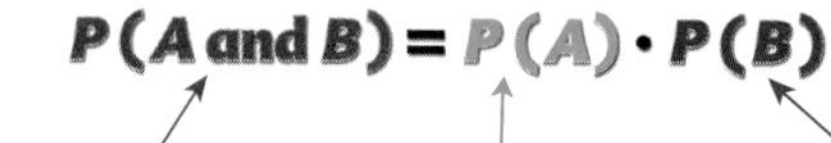

$$P(A \text{ and } B) = P(A) \cdot P(B)$$

Probability of both events — *Probability of first event* — *Probability of second event*

1 Introduce

Alternate Opener

EXPLORATION

10-5 Probability of Independent and Dependent Events

Each of four groups of students, A, B, C, and D, must choose one of the following types of music to write a report on: jazz, classical, rock, and blues. The types of music are written on four index cards, and once a card is chosen, it cannot be returned.

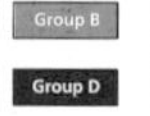

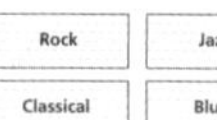

1. If group A chooses first, what is the probability that blues will be chosen?
2. Suppose group A chooses blues. When group B draws next, what is the probability that rock will be chosen?
3. Suppose group B chooses rock. When group C draws, what is the probability that jazz will be chosen?
4. Suppose group C chooses jazz. When group D draws, what is the probability that classical will be chosen?

Think and Discuss

5. **Discuss** why one group's draw is affected by what the previous group drew.
6. **Explain** why the probability that the last group will pick the last type of music must be 100%.

Motivate

Ask students to imagine that they have a bag with red and white marbles and that they get a dollar every time they pick a red marble from the bag. Discuss with students whether they would prefer to draw the marble from the bag after another student has already picked a marble from the bag or before anyone else has picked. Help students notice that if the marble is not replaced after the first student draws a red marble, then there may be fewer red marbles available for the next student.

Exploration worksheet and answers on Chapter 10 Resource Book pp. 44 and 84

2 Teach

Lesson Presentation

Guided Instruction

In this lesson, students learn to find the probability of independent and dependent events. Make sure students understand what these words mean. Students should also be able to determine whether events are dependent or independent. To strengthen their understanding, ask students to give other examples of both independent and dependent events.

Teaching Tip To help students distinguish between independent and dependent events, illustrate the examples with concrete objects, such as a spinner or a deck of cards.

EXAMPLE 2 Finding the Probability of Independent Events

Find the probability of flipping a coin and getting heads and then rolling a 6 on a number cube numbered 1 through 6.

The outcome of flipping the coin does not affect the outcome of rolling the number cube, so the events are independent.

$P(\text{heads and } 6) = P(\text{heads}) \cdot P(6)$

$= \frac{1}{2} \cdot \frac{1}{6}$ *There are 2 ways a coin can land and 6 ways a number cube can land.*

$= \frac{1}{12}$ *Multiply.*

The probability of getting heads and a 6 is $\frac{1}{12}$.

To find the probability of two dependent events, you must determine the effect that the first event has on the probability of the second event.

Probability of Two Dependent Events

Probability of both events — *Probability of first event* — *Probability of second event*

EXAMPLE 3 Finding the Probability of Dependent Events

Mica has five $1 bills, three $10 bills, and two $20 bills in her wallet. If she picks two bills at random, what is the probability of her picking the two $20 bills?

The first draw changes the number of bills left, and may change the number of $20 bills left, so the events are dependent.

$P(\text{first } \$20) = \frac{2}{10} = \frac{1}{5}$ *There are two $20 bills out of ten bills.*

$P(\text{second } \$20) = \frac{1}{9}$ *There is one $20 bill left out of nine bills.*

$P(\text{first } \$20\text{, then second } \$20) = P(A) \cdot P(B \text{ after } A)$

$= \frac{1}{5} \cdot \frac{1}{9}$

$= \frac{1}{45}$ *Multiply.*

The probability of Mica picking two $20 bills is $\frac{1}{45}$.

Think and Discuss

1. **Compare** probabilities of independent and dependent events.
2. **Explain** whether the probability of two events is greater or less than the probability of each individual event.

Additional Examples

Example 1

Decide whether each set of events is dependent or independent. Explain your answer.

A. Kathi draws a 4 from a set of cards numbered 1–10 and rolls a 2 on a number cube.

Since drawing the card does not affect the outcome of rolling the cube, the events are independent.

B. Yuki chooses a book from the shelf to read, and then Janette chooses a book from the books that remain.

They cannot pick the same book, and there are fewer books for Janette to choose from, so the events are dependent.

Example 2

Find the probability of choosing a green marble at random from a bag of 5 green and 10 white marbles and then flipping a coin and getting tails. $\frac{1}{6}$

Example 3

A reading list contains 5 historical books and 3 science-fiction books. What is the probability that Juan will randomly choose a historical book for his first report and a science-fiction book for his second? $\frac{15}{56}$

Example 3 note: Explain how the solution would change if the question were: "What is the probability that she will pick a $20 bill then a $10 bill?" (i.e., $P(\text{first } \$20 \text{ then } \$10) = \frac{2}{10} \cdot \frac{3}{9} = \frac{1}{5} \cdot \frac{1}{3} = \frac{1}{15}$).

3 Close

Reaching All Learners
Through Critical Thinking

Have students work with partners to solve this problem.

Suppose that the probability of germination for a seed from a seed packet is 20%. If you pick two of the seeds at random, what is the probability that they will both germinate? Write the probability as a percent. 4% If you pick three seeds at random, what is the probability that all three seeds will germinate? 0.8% Are the events dependent or independent? independent

Have students explain how they found their answers.

Summarize

Have students describe how to decide whether two events are dependent or independent.

Possible answer: If the second event is not affected by the first event, the events are independent. If the second event is affected by the first event, the events are dependent.

Answers to Think and Discuss

1. Possible answer: Both are products of individual probabilities, but for dependent events, you have to take into account the first event when calculating the probability of the second event.
2. The probability of two events is less than or equal to the probability of the individual events. If you find the product of two numbers between 0 and 1, the product will be less than either factor, and any number times 1 is equal to itself.

10-5 PRACTICE & ASSESS

Students may want to refer back to the lesson examples.

Assignment Guide

If you finished Example 1 assign:
Core 1, 2, 6, 7, 18–23
Enriched 1, 2, 6, 7, 18–23

If you finished Example 2 assign:
Core 1–4, 6–9, 11, 13, 18–23
Enriched 1–4, 6–9, 11, 13, 18–23

If you finished Example 3 assign:
Core 1–10, 11–13 odd, 18–23
Enriched 1–9 odd, 11–23

Notes

10-5 Exercises

FOR EXTRA PRACTICE see page 677

internet connect
Homework Help Online
go.hrw.com Keyword: MS4 10-5

GUIDED PRACTICE

See Example 1 **Decide whether each set of events is independent or dependent. Explain your answer.**

1. A student flips heads on one coin and tails on a second coin.
Independent; the outcome of one coin does not affect the outcome of the other.
2. A student chooses a red marble from a bag of marbles and then chooses another red marble without replacing the first.
Dependent; the outcome of the first draw affects the outcome of the second.

See Example 2 **Find the probability of each set of independent events.**

3. a flipped coin landing heads up and rolling a 5 or a 6 on a number cube numbered 1 through 6 $\frac{1}{6}$
4. drawing a 5 from 10 cards numbered 1 through 10 and rolling a 2 on a number cube numbered 1 through 6 $\frac{1}{60}$

See Example 3

5. Each day, Mr. Samms randomly chooses 2 students from his class to serve as helpers. If there are 15 boys and 10 girls in the class, what is the probability that Mr. Samms will choose 2 girls to be helpers? $\frac{3}{20}$

INDEPENDENT PRACTICE

See Example 1 **Decide whether each set of events is independent or dependent. Explain your answer.**

6. A student chooses a fiction book at random from a list of books and then chooses a second fiction book from those remaining.
Dependent; the choice of the first book affects the choice of the second.
7. A woman chooses a lily from one bunch of flowers and then chooses a tulip from a different bunch.
Independent; one event does not affect the other.

See Example 2 **Find the probability of each set of independent events.**

8. drawing a red marble from a bag of 6 red and 4 blue marbles, replacing it, and then drawing a blue marble $\frac{6}{25}$
9. rolling an even number on a number cube numbered 1 through 6 and rolling an odd number on a second roll of the same cube $\frac{1}{4}$

See Example 3

10. Francisco has 7 quarters in his pocket. Of these, 3 depict the state of Delaware, 2 depict Georgia, 1 depicts Connecticut, and 1 depicts Pennsylvania. Francisco removes 1 quarter from his pocket and then removes a second quarter without replacing the first. What is the probability that both will be Delaware quarters? $\frac{1}{7}$

Math Background

Sometimes when finding a probability, we already know the outcome of one event. For example, we might have flipped a coin and gotten heads, so we might ask, "What is the probability that a second flip will come up heads if the first one was heads?" This is called *conditional probability,* the probability of event *A* happening given that event *B* has happened. In the case of the coins, the sample space becomes {H, T} and {H, H}, so the probability of heads, given that heads has occurred, is $\frac{1}{2}$. Finding the probabilities of dependent and independent events is an application of conditional probability.

RETEACH 10-5

LESSON 10-5 **Reteach**
Probability of Independent and Dependent Events

Events are *independent* when the outcome of one event has no effect on the outcome of a second event. Rolling a number cube and flipping a coin are **independent events.**

Find the probability of rolling a 4 and flipping heads.

1. There are 6 outcomes for the number cube and 2 outcomes for the coin.
2. Using the Fundamental Counting Principle, there are 6 × 2, or 12, possible outcomes of rolling a number cube and flipping a coin.
3. Make a list of the possible outcomes:
(1, H), (2, H), (3, H), (4, H), (5, H), (6, H), (1, T), (2, T), (3, T), (4, T), (5, T), (6, T)
How many possible ways are there of rolling a 4 and flipping heads? 1
4. $P(4 \text{ and heads}) = \frac{\text{number of ways 4 and heads can occur}}{\text{number of possible outcomes}} = \frac{1}{12}$

Events are *dependent* when the outcome of one event does have an effect on the outcome of the next event. Drawing two marbles in a row from a bag without replacing the first marble are **dependent events.**

A bag contains 3 blue and 5 red marbles. Find the probability of drawing 2 blue marbles in a row without replacing the first marble.

5. The total number of marbles in the bag is 8. There are 3 blue marbles in the bag. $P(\text{blue marble on first draw}) = \frac{3}{8}$
6. There are now 7 marbles in the bag. If you drew a blue marble on the first draw, there are 2 blue marbles left in the bag.
$P(\text{blue marble on second draw}) = \frac{2}{7}$
7. $P(\text{blue, blue}) = P(\text{blue on 1st draw}) \times P(\text{blue on 2nd draw}) = \frac{3}{8} \times \frac{2}{7} = \frac{3}{28}$

PRACTICE 10-5

LESSON 10-5 **Practice B**
Probability of Independent and Dependent Events

Decide if each set of events is independent or dependent. Explain your answer.

1. spinning a spinner and choosing a Scrabble® tile
Independent; Spinning a spinner does not affect the outcome of choosing a Scrabble® tile.
2. choosing a sock from a drawer of socks, then choosing a second sock without replacing the first
Dependent; There are fewer socks in the drawer for the second sock picked.
3. picking a raffle ticket from a box, replacing the ticket, then picking a second raffle ticket
Independent; There are the same number of raffle tickets in the box for the second ticket picked.

Find the probability of each set of events.

4. drawing a red checker from a bag of 9 black checkers and 6 red checkers, replacing it, and drawing another red checker
$\frac{4}{25}$
5. drawing a black checker from a bag of 9 black checkers and 6 red checkers, replacing it, and drawing a red checker
$\frac{6}{25}$
6. rolling a 1, 2, or 3 on the first roll of a 1–6 number cube and rolling a 4, 5, or 6 on the second roll of the same cube
$\frac{1}{4}$
7. Randy has 4 pennies, 2 nickels, and 3 dimes in his pocket. If he randomly chooses 2 coins, what is the probability that both are dimes?
$\frac{1}{12}$

PRACTICE AND PROBLEM SOLVING

11. An even number is chosen randomly from a set of cards labeled with the numbers 1 through 8. A second even number is chosen without the first card's being replaced. Are these independent or dependent events? What is the probability of both events occurring? **dependent; $\frac{3}{14}$**

12. A school cafeteria has 3 containers of white milk, 5 containers of chocolate milk, and 2 containers of apple juice left. Ilana is first in line and Vishal is second. If the drinks are given out randomly, what is the probability that Ilana will get chocolate milk and Vishal will get apple juice? **$\frac{1}{9}$**

13. On a multiple-choice test, each question has five possible answers. A student does not know the answers to two questions, so he guesses. What is the probability that the student will get both answers wrong? **$\frac{16}{25}$**

14. ***BUSINESS*** The graph shows the dogs bathed at a dog-grooming business one day. What is the probability that the first two dogs bathed were large dogs? **$\frac{12}{145}$**

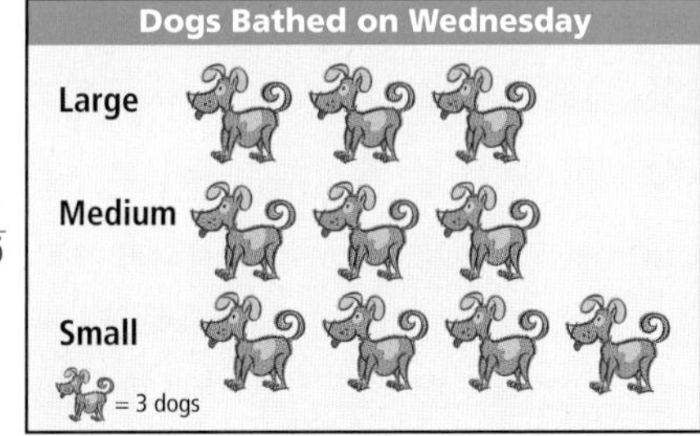

15. ***WRITE A PROBLEM*** Describe two events that are either independent or dependent, and make up a probability problem about them.

16. ***WRITE ABOUT IT*** At the beginning of a game of Scrabble, players take turns drawing 7 tiles. Is drawing an *A* on the first two tiles dependent or independent events? Explain.

17. ***CHALLENGE*** Weather forecasters have accurately predicted rain in one community $\frac{4}{5}$ of the time. What is the probability that they will accurately predict rain two days in a row? **$\frac{16}{25}$**

Spiral Review

Estimate each square root to the nearest whole number. (Lesson 8-7)

18. $\sqrt{134}$ **12** **19.** $\sqrt{11}$ **3** **20.** $\sqrt{175}$ **13** **21.** $\sqrt{217}$ **15**

22. TEST PREP Fritz jogged $1\frac{3}{4}$ mi on Monday, $2\frac{1}{2}$ mi on Wednesday, and 3 mi on Friday. How many miles did he jog altogether on these days? (Lesson 4-11) **B**

A $6\frac{3}{4}$ mi **B** $7\frac{1}{4}$ mi **C** $8\frac{1}{4}$ mi **D** $6\frac{2}{3}$ mi

23. TEST PREP There are 15 boys and 20 girls in a class. If you pick one student at random, what is the probability of choosing a girl? (Lesson 10-4) **F**

F $\frac{4}{7}$ **G** $\frac{3}{4}$ **H** $\frac{4}{3}$ **J** $\frac{3}{7}$

CHALLENGE 10-5

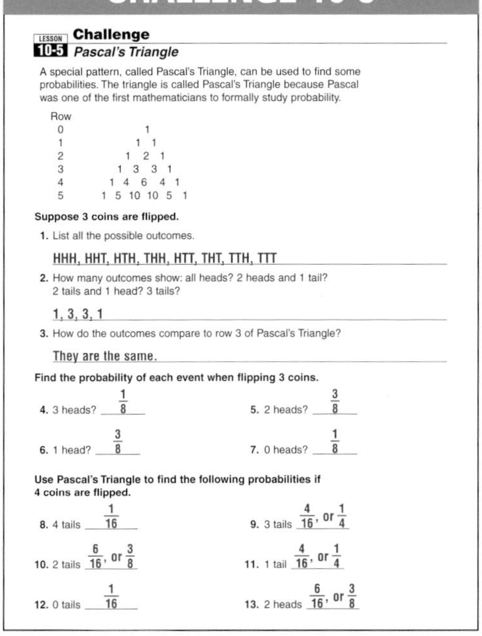

LESSON 10-5 **Challenge**
Pascal's Triangle

A special pattern, called Pascal's Triangle, can be used to find some probabilities. The triangle is called Pascal's Triangle because Pascal was one of the first mathematicians to formally study probability.

Row	
0	1
1	1 1
2	1 2 1
3	1 3 3 1
4	1 4 6 4 1
5	1 5 10 10 5 1

Suppose 3 coins are flipped.

1. List all the possible outcomes.
HHH, HHT, HTH, THH, HTT, THT, TTH, TTT

2. How many outcomes show: all heads? 2 heads and 1 tail? 2 tails and 1 head? 3 tails?
1, 3, 3, 1

3. How do the outcomes compare to row 3 of Pascal's Triangle?
They are the same.

Find the probability of each event when flipping 3 coins.

4. 3 heads? $\frac{1}{8}$
5. 2 heads? $\frac{3}{8}$
6. 1 head? $\frac{3}{8}$
7. 0 heads? $\frac{1}{8}$

Use Pascal's Triangle to find the following probabilities if 4 coins are flipped.

8. 4 tails $\frac{1}{16}$
9. 3 tails $\frac{4}{16}$, or $\frac{1}{4}$
10. 2 tails $\frac{6}{16}$, or $\frac{3}{8}$
11. 1 tail $\frac{4}{16}$, or $\frac{1}{4}$
12. 0 tails $\frac{1}{16}$
13. 2 heads $\frac{6}{16}$, or $\frac{3}{8}$

PROBLEM SOLVING 10-5

LESSON 10-5 **Problem Solving**
Probability of Independent and Dependent Events

Write the correct answer.

1. Li rolls a pair of number cubes twice. On both rolls, the sum is 7. Are the rolls dependent or independent events?
independent events

2. Nine boys and 12 girls want to play soccer. Teams are formed by selecting one player at a time. Is the probability of selecting a boy after a girl is selected a dependent or an independent event?
dependent event

3. Gregg has 12 cards. Half are black, and half are red. He picks two cards out of the deck. What is the probability that both cards are red?
$\frac{5}{22}$

4. In basketball, Alan makes 1 out of every 4 free throws he attempts. What is the probability that Alan will make his next 3 free throws?
$\frac{1}{64}$

Choose the letter for the best answer.

5. There are 8 blue marbles and 7 red marbles in a bag. Julie pulls two marbles at random from the bag first. What is the probability that she first pulls a blue marble and then a red marble?
A $\frac{8}{15}$ C $\frac{4}{7}$
(B) $\frac{4}{15}$ D $\frac{1}{2}$

6. You roll a 1–6 number cube twice. What is the probability that you roll a 3 on the first roll and a 6 on the second roll?
(F) $\frac{1}{36}$ H $\frac{1}{6}$
G $\frac{1}{9}$ J $\frac{1}{2}$

7. Andrew has $2.00 in quarters in his pocket, including three state quarters. He takes two quarters out of his pocket. What is the probability that they are **not** state quarters?
A $\frac{3}{8}$ C $\frac{3}{14}$
B $\frac{5}{8}$ (D) $\frac{5}{14}$

8. Jamie has 3 raffle tickets. One hundred tickets were sold. Her name was not drawn for the first prize. What is the probability that her name will be drawn for the second prize?
F $\frac{1}{3}$ (H) $\frac{1}{33}$
G $\frac{3}{100}$ J $\frac{2}{99}$

Answers

15. Possible answer: There are 15 boys and 17 girls in Mrs. Brown's class. She randomly chooses 2 students from the class to attend the student council meeting. What is the probability that both the students she chooses will be boys?

16. Dependent; with dependent events, the outcome of the first event influences the outcome of the second event.

Journal 

Have students consider their own lives and describe two events that are independent and then two events that are dependent.

Test Prep Doctor 

For Exercise 22, students can use estimation to eliminate **A** and **D.** If students recognize that the sum of the whole numbers is 6 and the sum of the fractions is slightly more than 1, they can also eliminate **C.** For Exercise 23, students can eliminate **H** because it is greater than 1. There are more girls than boys, so the probability will be greater than half, thus eliminating **J. G** is the ratio of boys to girls, so it is not correct either.

Lesson Quiz 

Decide whether each event is independent or dependent. Explain.

1. Mary chooses a game piece from a board game, and then Jason chooses a game piece from three remaining pieces. Dependent; Jason cannot pick the same piece that Mary already chose.

2. Sarah picks one item from a vending machine and then another item from a different machine. Independent; the choices do not affect one another.

3. Find the probability of spinning an evenly divided spinner numbered 1–8 and getting a composite number on one spin and getting an odd number on a second spin. $\frac{3}{16}$

Available on Daily Transparency in CRB

10A Pascal's Triangle

Pacing: Traditional 1 day
Block $\frac{1}{2}$ day

Objective: To use Pascal's Triangle to solve problems involving probability

Lab Resources

Hands-On Lab Activities. . . pp. 100–103

Using the Pages

Discuss with students how Pascal's Triangle is formed. Be sure students understand that every number in every row is the sum of the two numbers above it. It is important for students to know that the 1's on the left are in column 0 and that the row with a single 1 is row 0.

Find the number in the given row and column.

1. row 3 column 3 **1**
2. row 2 column 1 **2**
3. row 4 column 3 **4**
4. row 6 column 3 **20**

Pascal's Triangle

Use with Lesson 10-6

REMEMBER
- Probability is the likelihood of an event occurring.
- A combination is an arrangement of items or events in which order is not important.

Lab Resources Online
go.hrw.com
KEYWORD: MS4 Lab10A

The triangular arrangement of numbers below is called **Pascal's Triangle.** Each row starts and ends with 1. Each other number in the triangle is the sum of the two numbers above it.

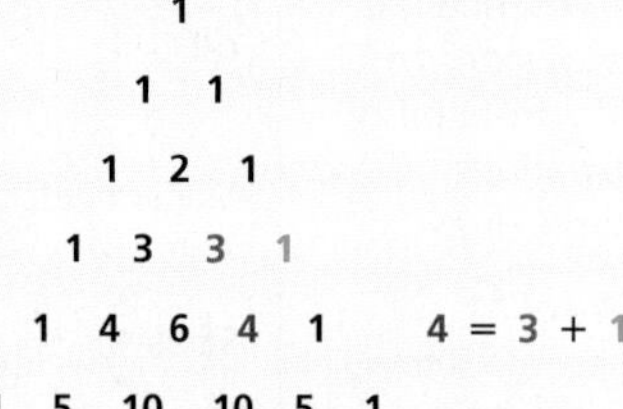

You can use Pascal's Triangle to solve problems involving probability.

Activity

1. Geri, Jan, Kathy, Annie, and Mia are on a women's bobsled team. Only two women can race at a time. How many pairings of bobsledders are possible?

   Write each name on a separate card. You will need four cards for each name. Show all of the possible pairings of bobsledders.

   Each pair of bobsledders shown is different. So there are 10 possible pairings of bobsledders.

Each pairing is a **combination,** because the order is not important. The number of possible combinations can be expressed using the following notation:

2 **Total number of people** ↘ $_5C_2$ ↙ Number of people in each combination

You can use Pascal's Triangle to find the value of $_5C_2$ or any other combination.

a. Copy Pascal's Triangle. Label the rows and columns as shown.

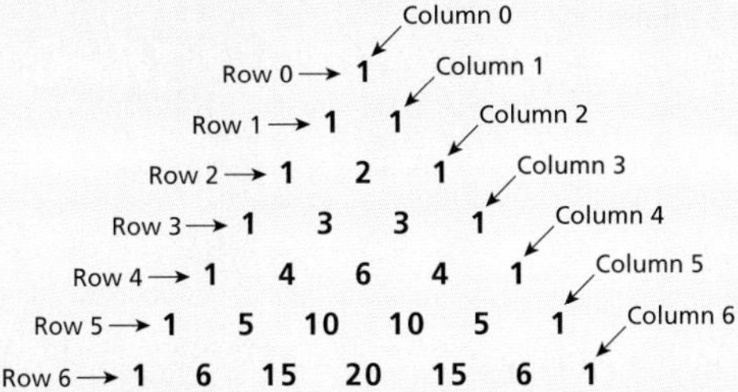

b. To find the value of $_5C_2$, look at where row 5 and column 2 intersect.

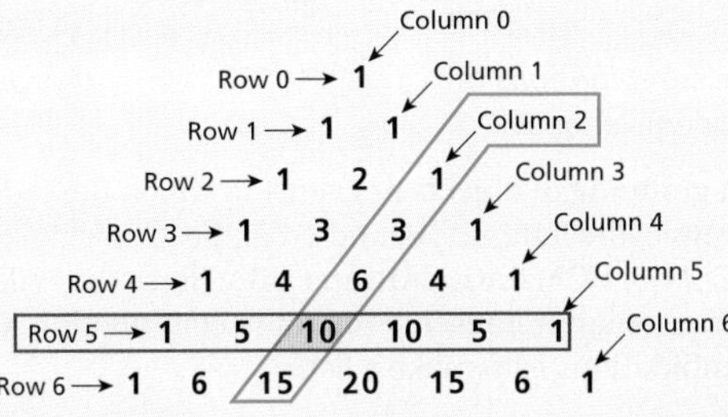

Therefore, $_5C_2 = 10$.

Think and Discuss

1. In **1**, why is the order of the bobsledders not important?
2. Complete rows 7 and 8 in Pascal's Triangle. **row 7: 1 7 21 35 35 21 7 1; row 8: 1 8 28 56 70 56 28 8 1**
3. What are some patterns that you see in Pascal's Triangle?
4. Find $_3C_3$, $_2C_2$, $_6C_6$, and $_4C_4$. What do you notice? Explain.
5. Ten students are on the basketball team, but only 5 can play at a time. Use Pascal's Triangle to find the number of possible combinations of players. **Look at row 10 column 5: 252.**

Try This

Use Pascal's Triangle to find the number of combinations.

1. $_3C_2$ **3**
2. $_3C_1$ **3**
3. $_6C_4$ **15**
4. $_5C_5$ **1**
5. $_7C_4$ **35**
6. $_6C_3$ **20**
7. $_6C_1$ **6**
8. $_4C_2$ **6**

Answers

Think and Discuss

1. Possible answer: The order is not important because the purpose of the combination is simply to determine who is on the team.
3. Possible answer: Every row starts and ends with 1. Every number in a row is the sum of the two numbers on either side of it and above it.
4. Possible answer: The answer is always 1. If the number of items in each combination is equal to the total number of items, there is only one possible combination.

10-6 Organizer

Pacing: Traditional 1 day
Block $\frac{1}{2}$ day

Objective: Students find the number of possible combinations.

Warm Up

Decide whether each event is independent or dependent. Explain your answer.

1. Bill picks a king from a pile of cards and keeps it. On his next turn he tries for a queen. Dependent; there are fewer cards from which to choose.
2. the chance of it raining on the third Tuesday of the month after it has rained on the first Tuesday. Independent; the rain on the first Tuesday has no effect on the weather two weeks later.

Problem of the Day

There are 7 players. Can more teams of 2 different people or 5 different people be formed? (*Hint:* Look for a shortcut.) The same number of both can be formed. For every 5-person team there is a 2-person team (the 2 players left out).

Available on Daily Transparency in CRB

10-6 Combinations

Learn to find the number of possible combinations.

Vocabulary

combination

Mrs. Logan's students have to read any two of the following books.

1. *The Adventures of Tom Sawyer,* by Mark Twain
2. *The Call of the Wild,* by Jack London
3. *A Christmas Carol,* by Charles Dickens
4. *Treasure Island,* by Robert Louis Stevenson
5. *Tuck Everlasting,* by Natalie Babbit

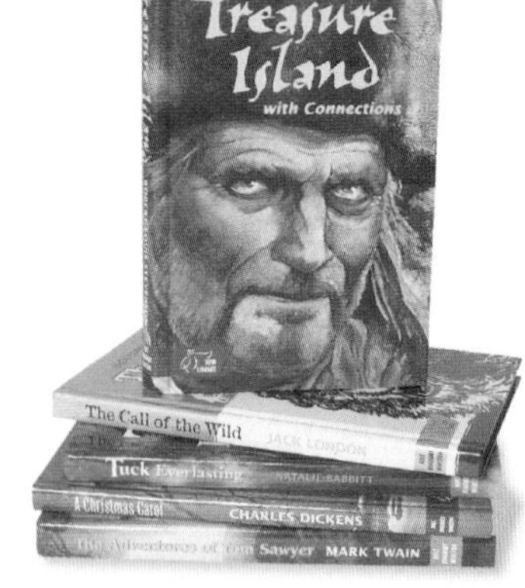

How many possible *combinations* of books could the students choose?

A **combination** is a grouping of objects or events in which the order does not matter. For example, the letters A, B, and C can be arranged in 6 different ways: ABC, ACB, BCA, BAC, CAB, and CBA. Since the order does not matter, each arrangement represents the same combination. One way to find possible combinations is to make a list.

EXAMPLE  1 **Using a List to Find Combinations**

How many different combinations of two books are possible from Mrs. Logan's list of five books?

Begin by listing all of the possible groupings of books taken two at a time.

1, 2	2, 1	3, 1	4, 1	5, 1
1, 3	2, 3	3, 2	4, 2	5, 2
1, 4	2, 4	3, 4	4, 3	5, 3
1, 5	2, 5	3, 5	4, 5	5, 4

Because order does not matter, you can eliminate repeated pairs. For example, 1, 2 is already listed, so 2, 1 can be eliminated.

1, 2	~~2, 1~~	~~3, 1~~	~~4, 1~~	~~5, 1~~
1, 3	2, 3	~~3, 2~~	~~4, 2~~	~~5, 2~~
1, 4	2, 4	3, 4	~~4, 3~~	~~5, 3~~
1, 5	2, 5	3, 5	4, 5	~~5, 4~~

There are 10 different combinations of two books on Mrs. Logan's list of five books.

1 Introduce

Alternate Opener

10-6 Combinations

Leticia has three different colors of jeans in her store: blue, white, and green. She wants to make a window display with some of the jeans. However, the window in her store has space for only two pairs of jeans. How many combinations of two colors can she make?

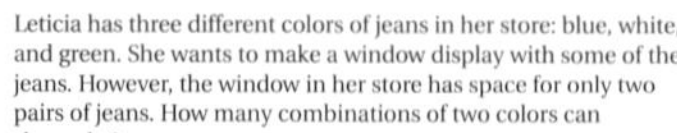

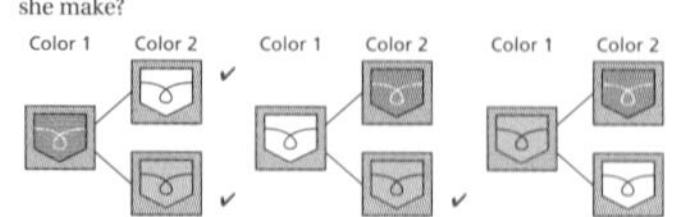

Since some combinations are repeated, Leticia has 3 different combinations of colors for her window display: blue and white, blue and green, and white and green.

1. How many combinations of two colors could she make if she had one more color, black, available?
2. How many combinations could she make with 4 colors available (blue, white, green, and black) and a bigger window that allows her to display 3 pairs of jeans?

Think and Discuss

3. **Explain** how you found the combinations in numbers 1 and 2.

Motivate

To introduce combinations, ask students to think of situations involving 4 students in which the order that the students are selected does not make any difference, such as 4 students being chosen to ride on a bus or play on a team.

Point out that sometimes the order does make a difference (e.g., 4 students chosen for different offices, such as president, vice-president, secretary, and treasurer).

Exploration worksheet and answers on Chapter 10 Resource Book pp. 53 and 86

2 Teach

Guided Instruction

In this lesson, students learn to find the number of possible combinations. Although there are formulas that can be used to find the number of combinations, in this lesson we rely on making an ordered list and making a tree diagram.

Talk about the importance of making an orderly list of the possibilities so that no possibility is inadvertently missed. In Example 1, point out that the numbers paired with 1 are listed in the first column, those paired with 2 are in the second column, and so on.

You can also use a tree diagram to find possible combinations.

EXAMPLE  PROBLEM SOLVING APPLICATION

As a caterer, Cuong offers four vegetable choices: potatoes, corn, peas, and carrots. Each person can choose two vegetables. How many different combinations of two vegetables can a person choose?

1 Understand the Problem

Rewrite the question as a statement.

- Find the number of possible combinations of two vegetables a person can choose.

List the **important information:**

- There are four vegetable choices in all.

2 Make a Plan

You can make a tree diagram to show the possible combinations.

 Solve

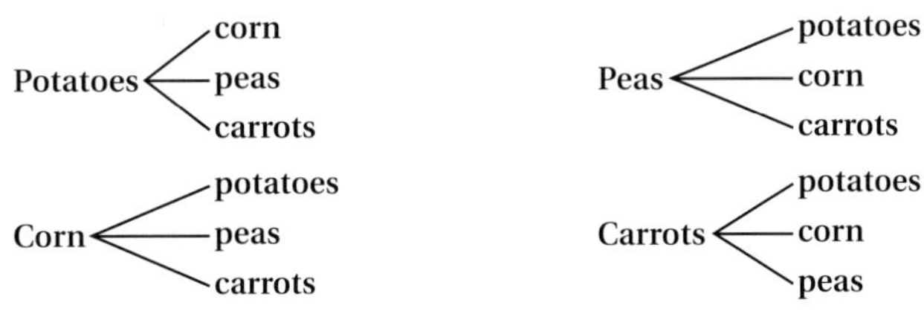

The tree diagram shows 12 possible ways to combine two vegetables, but each combination is listed twice. So there are $12 \div 2 = 6$ possible combinations.

 Look Back

You can also check by making a list. The potatoes can be paired with three other vegetables, corn with two, and peas with one. The total number of possible pairs is $3 + 2 + 1 = 6$.

Think and Discuss

1. **Find** the number of combinations there would be in Example 1 if the students had to choose three books.
2. **Describe** how you can use combinations to find the probability of an event.

COMMON ERROR ALERT

Remind students to eliminate duplicate listings before they count the number of combinations when using a tree diagram.

Additional Examples

Example 1

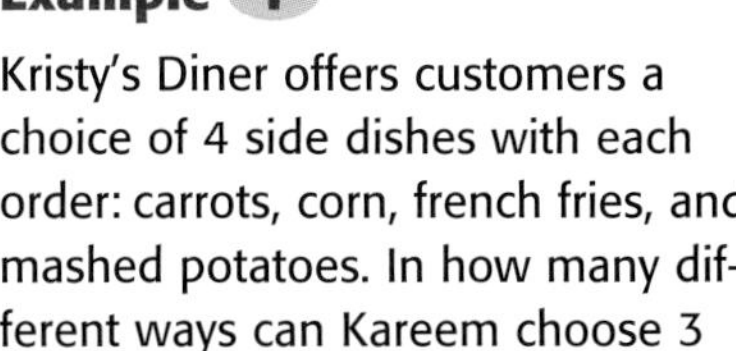

Kristy's Diner offers customers a choice of 4 side dishes with each order: carrots, corn, french fries, and mashed potatoes. In how many different ways can Kareem choose 3 side dishes with his order? **4**

Example 2

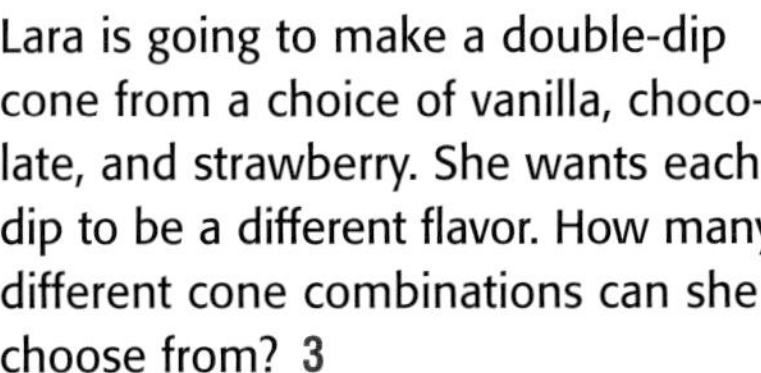

Lara is going to make a double-dip cone from a choice of vanilla, chocolate, and strawberry. She wants each dip to be a different flavor. How many different cone combinations can she choose from? **3**

Example 2 note: In Additional Example 2, point out that vanilla on top and chocolate on the bottom is the same as chocolate on top and vanilla on the bottom.

 Close

Reaching All Learners

Through Critical Thinking

Have students work in groups to find the number of combinations of 4 things taken 1, 2, and then 3 at a time and 5 things taken 1, 2, 3, and then 4 at a time. Encourage students to discuss any patterns they discover.

4 things taken 1 at a time = 4; 4 things taken 2 at a time = 6; 4 things taken 3 at a time = 4; 5 things taken 1 at a time = 5; 5 things taken 2 at a time = 10; 5 things taken 3 at a time = 10; 5 things taken 4 at a time = 5; students should discover that n things taken r at a time is the same as n things taken $n - r$ at a time.

Summarize

Have each student write a summary of how to find the number of combinations of 6 things taken 2 at a time.

Possible answer: Number or letter all the items. Then pair the first item with all the remaining items, the second item with all the items, and so on. Finally, eliminate all duplicates.

Answers to Think and Discuss

1. There would be 10 possible combinations of 3 books.
2. The number of combinations tells the number of ways an event can happen or the number of possible outcomes. To find the probability of an event, compare the number of favorable outcomes with the number of possible outcomes.

10-6 PRACTICE & ASSESS

Students may want to refer back to the lesson examples.

Assignment Guide

If you finished Example 1 assign:
Core 1, 2, 5, 6, 9, 11, 19–26
Enriched 1, 5, 9–12, 19–26

If you finished Example 2 assign:
Core 1–8, 13–17 odd, 19–26
Enriched 1–7 odd, 13–26

Notes

10-6 Exercises

FOR EXTRA PRACTICE
see page 677

internet connect
Homework Help Online
go.hrw.com Keyword: MS4 10-6

GUIDED PRACTICE

See Example 1

1. If you have an apple, a pear, an orange, and a plum, how many combinations of 2 fruits are possible? **6**
2. How many 3-letter combinations are possible from *A, E, I, O,* and *U*? **10**

See Example 2

3. Robin packages jam in boxes of 3 jars. She has 5 flavors: blueberry, apricot, grape, peach, and orange marmalade. How many packages with different combinations can she make? **10**
4. Eduardo has 6 colors of fabric: red, blue, green, yellow, orange, and white. He plans to make flags using 2 colors. How many possible combinations of 2 colors can he choose? **15**

INDEPENDENT PRACTICE

See Example 1

5. A restaurant allows you to "build your own burger" using a choice of any 2 toppings. The available toppings are bacon, grilled onions, sautéed mushrooms, Swiss cheese, and cheddar cheese. How many burgers with different toppings could you build? **10**
6. Jamil has to do reports on 3 cities. He can choose from Paris, New York, Moscow, and London. How many different combinations of cities are possible? **4**

See Example 2

7. A florist can choose from 6 different types of flowers to make a bouquet: carnations, roses, lilies, daisies, irises, and tulips. How many different combinations of 3 types of flowers can he choose from? **20**
8. How many different 2-member tennis teams can be made from 7 students? **21**

PRACTICE AND PROBLEM SOLVING

Find the number of combinations.

9. 7 things taken 2 at a time **21**
10. 8 items taken 3 at a time **56**
11. 6 things taken 5 at a time **6**
12. 6 things taken 1 at a time **6**
13. Rob, Caryn, and Sari are pairing up to play a series of chess matches.
    a. In how many different ways can they pair up? **3**
    b. What is the probability that Sari will play Rob in the first match? $\frac{1}{3}$
14. Gary has to write short biographies about 2 historical figures. He can choose from Winston Churchill, Martin Luther King, Jr., and Nelson Mandela. How many different combinations of biographies can Gary write? **3**

Math Background

A *combination* is simply a collection of objects in no particular order. In set language, a *combination* is a "subset of a set."

You can find the number of combinations of n objects taken r at a time, or $_nC_r$, using the following formula:

$$_nC_r = \frac{n!}{(n-r)! \cdot r!}$$

where $n!$ is the product of $n(n-1)(n-2)\ldots 3 \cdot 2 \cdot 1$.

Many calculators have a button for calculating the number of combinations of n things taken r at a time.

RETEACH 10-6

LESSON 10-6 **Reteach**
Combinations

A **combination** is a selection of objects in which the order is not important. You can make a list to find the number of combinations.

The school district is going to plant two types of trees around the playground. The landscaper has five kinds of trees to choose from.

Let the letters A, B, C, D, and E represent the different kinds of trees. You can make an organized list of all possible combinations.

Tree **A** with each other tree: AB AC AD AE
Tree **B** with each other tree: BA BC BD BE
Tree **C** with each other tree: CA CB CD CE
Tree **D** with each other tree: DA DB DC DE
Tree **E** with each other tree: EA EB EC ED

1. How many groups of 2 trees are in the list? **20**
2. AB is the same combination as **BA**. BD is the same combination as **DB**.
   AC is the same combination as **CA**. BE is the same combination as **EB**.
   AD is the same combination as **DA**. CD is the same combination as **DC**.
   AE is the same combination as **EA**. CE is the same combination as **EC**.
   BC is the same combination as **CB**. DE is the same combination as **ED**.
3. Cross out each of the duplications in the list above. How many are left? **10**
4. Make an organized list of all possible two-letter combinations using the letters U, V, W, X, Y, and Z. Cross out each duplication.
   UV, **UW**, **UX**, **UY**, **UZ** VU, **VW**, **VX**, **VY**, **VZ**
   WU, **WV**, **WX**, **WY**, **WZ** XU, **XV**, **XW**, **XY**, **XZ**
   YU, **YV**, **YW**, **YX**, **YZ** ZU, **ZV**, **ZW**, **ZX**, **ZY**
   There are **15** combinations of 6 letters taken 2 at a time.

PRACTICE 10-6

LESSON 10-6 **Practice B**
Combinations

1. A chef has some broccoli, cauliflower, carrots, and squash to make a vegetarian dish. List the possible combinations if he uses only 3 vegetables in the dish.
   broccoli, cauliflower, carrots; broccoli, cauliflower, squash; broccoli, carrots, squash; cauliflower, carrots, squash
2. Lauren, Manuel, Nick, Opal, and Pat are forming groups of two to work on a drama production. List the different combinations of students that are possible using the first initial of each name.
   LM, LN, LO, LP, MN, MO, MP, NO, NP, OP
3. Keiko has seven colors of lanyard. She uses three different colors to make a key chain. How many different combinations can she choose?
   35 combinations
4. On Sundays at Ice Cream Heaven, you can choose two free toppings for your sundae. The toppings are nuts, hot fudge, caramel, and sprinkles. How many different combinations of toppings can you order?
   6 combinations
5. How many different four-person relay teams can be chosen from eight students?
   70 teams
6. The students in Mrs. Mandel's class need to choose two class representatives from six nominated students. How many different combinations of class representatives are possible?
   15 combinations
7. There are nine varieties of muffins available at the Coffee Shop. How many different ways can you choose three different muffins?
   84 ways
8. How many five-person carpools are possible with seven people?
   21 carpools

15. Ms. Frennelle is teaching her class about famous impressionist painters. She asked her students to choose 2 artists from among Renoir, Monet, Manet, Degas, Pissarro, and Cassatt, and to find information about a painting made by each artist.
    a. How many possible pairs of artists can be chosen? **15**
    b. What is the probability that a student selecting a pair at random will select a pair including Renoir? $\frac{1}{3}$

The White Water Lilies, 1899, by Claude Monet

Woman with a Pearl Necklace in a Loge, 1879, by Mary Cassatt

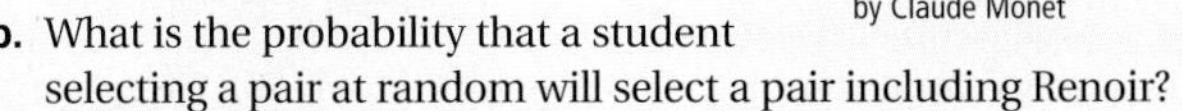

16. Trina wants to select 3 of Ansel Adams's 5 "surf sequence" photos to hang on her wall.
    a. How many combinations of 3 photos are possible? **10**
    b. What is the probability that the three photos she chooses will include surf sequence 1 and surf sequence 5? $\frac{3}{10}$

go.hrw.com
KEYWORD: MS4 Art
CNN Student News

17. The graph shows the number of paintings by artists of different nationalities that Matt found in an art history book. In how many ways can Matt select 4 paintings by Chinese artists? **5**

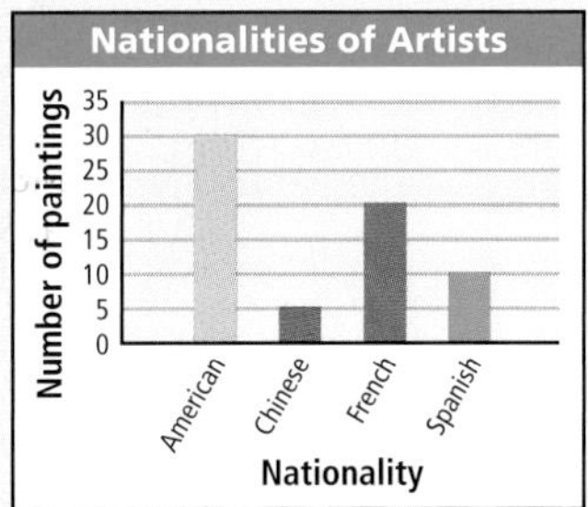

18. ***CHALLENGE*** A gallery is preparing a show by a new artist. The gallery has enough wall space to display 7 pieces of art. If the artist has prepared 4 paintings and 5 sculptures, how many distinct combinations of the artist's works are possible? **36**

Spiral Review

Find the area of each circle to the nearest tenth. Use 3.14 for π. (Lesson 8-6)

19. $r = 8$ cm **201.0 cm²** 20. $r = 2$ ft **12.6 ft²** 21. $d = 10$ in. **78.5 in²** 22. $d = 5$ m **19.6 m²**

Identify each figure. (Lesson 9-1)

23. 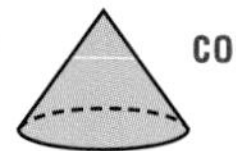 **cone**

24. 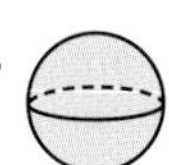 **sphere**

25. 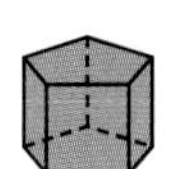 **pentagonal prism**

26. **TEST PREP** Which of the following describes the probability of selecting a red marble from a bag containing 4 blue marbles, 3 green marbles, and 3 white marbles? (Lesson 10-1) **C**

A Certain **B** Unlikely **C** Impossible **D** As likely as not

CHALLENGE 10-6

LESSON 10-6 **Challenge**
Compound Cards

An event that combines two or more simple events is called a *compound event.*

Example: Roll a 1–6 number cube.
Rolling a 6 is a simple event. Rolling a 1 is a simple event.
Rolling a 1 *or* a 6 is a compound event.

You can use the following addition rule to find the probability of a compound event.

$$P(A \text{ or } B) = P(A) + P(B) - P(A \text{ and } B)$$

Example: Roll a 1–6 number cube.

$$P(2 \text{ or an even number}) = P(2) + P(\text{even}) - P(2 \text{ and even}) = \frac{1}{6} + \frac{3}{6} - \frac{1}{6} = \frac{3}{6}, \text{ or } \frac{1}{2}$$

Use the following data about a deck of cards to find the probability of each compound event.

In a deck of 52 cards, there are 26 red cards and 26 black cards. There are 4 suits: diamonds and hearts (both red) and spades and clubs (both black). There are 40 number cards—half are red and half are black. There are 12 face cards—half are red and half are black. There are 4 of each type of number or face card.

1. P(red or king) $\frac{7}{13}$
2. P(red or number card) $\frac{23}{26}$
3. P(black or face card) $\frac{8}{13}$
4. P(red or 10) $\frac{7}{13}$
5. P(black or queen) $\frac{7}{13}$
6. P(red or diamond) $\frac{1}{2}$
7. P(heart or 4) $\frac{4}{13}$
8. P(club or face) $\frac{11}{26}$
9. P(spade or number) $\frac{43}{52}$

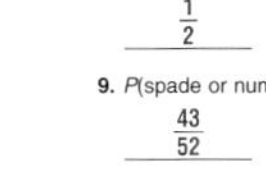

PROBLEM SOLVING 10-6

LESSON 10-6 **Problem Solving**
Combinations

Write the correct answer.

1. Six friends are going to play a ball game. Each team has 3 players. How many different team combinations are possible?
   20 combinations
2. Yung wants to visit one of the 5 Great Lakes this summer. He can go in June, July, or August. How many choices does he have?
   15 choices
3. A sandwich shop offers 4 types of cheese and 6 different meats. Customers may choose one type of cheese and one type of meat for their sandwiches. How many different combinations are possible?
   24 combinations
4. At summer camp, the campers pick two activities for the first day of camp. They can choose from among hiking, canoeing, rock climbing, and bird watching. How many different combinations of activities are there?
   6 combinations

Choose the letter for the best answer.

5. A soccer team is choosing a team uniform. They can choose red, green, yellow, or white shirts. They have to choose black, blue, or gray shorts. How many different uniforms are possible?
   A 8 uniforms
   (B) 12 uniforms
   C 20 uniforms
   D 32 uniforms
6. At Washington Middle School, a student takes 4 core classes a day. There are 6 different core classes offered. How many different combinations of classes are there?
   F 10 combinations
   G 12 combinations
   (H) 15 combinations
   J 24 combinations
7. The class is drawing maps of the 7 continents to display in the school lobby. The main wall in the lobby has room for 3 maps. How many combinations of maps are possible for that location?
   A 10 combinations
   B 21 combinations
   C 30 combinations
   (D) 35 combinations
8. Ms. Henrie's literature class is voting on the 2 most influential people of the eighteenth century. The choices are 5 famous people. How many different combinations are possible?
   F 7 combinations
   G 8 combinations
   (H) 10 combinations
   J 15 combinations

Art

Exercises 15–18 involve using combinations when considering artists and works of art.

Journal 

Have students write about two or three real-world situations in which combinations might be used. Then ask students to write a problem that would fit one of their situations.

Test Prep Doctor 

For Exercise 26, once students note that there are no red marbles in the bag, they can eliminate **A, B,** and **D.** If students chose **A, B,** or **D,** they may need to review the vocabulary of probability, or they did not read the question carefully enough to notice that no red marbles were included in the bag.

Lesson Quiz 

1. A pizzeria has on special a pizza with 2 toppings for $9.95. It offers pepperoni, olives, tomato, sausage, bacon, mushrooms, and ham as toppings. How many different specials could you build? **21**
2. Jamie has a red shirt and a blue shirt. She has a green scarf, a yellow scarf, and a purple scarf. How many different shirt-scarf combinations can she wear? **6**
3. Karl has to pick two reptiles to write a report on. If there are 8 possible reptiles to choose from, how many pairs are possible? **28**

Available on Daily Transparency in CRB

10-7 Organizer

Pacing: Traditional 1 day
Block $\frac{1}{2}$ day

Objective: Students find the number of possible permutations and the probability that a specific permutation will occur.

Warm Up

1. How many 2-side-dish meals can be made from 6 choices of side dishes? **15**
2. Kim has shorts in blue, black, and tan. She has shirts in blue, yellow, red, and green. How many different combinations can she make? **12**
3. If you go to the movies and are allowed to get 2 snacks and there are 9 snacks to choose from, how many combinations are there to pick from? **36**

Problem of the Day

Replace each ? with a different digit from 1 through 9 to make a proportion. (*Hint:* The digits are not being multiplied.) $\frac{??}{??} = \frac{??}{??}$

Possible answer: $\frac{27}{54} = \frac{19}{38}$

Available on Daily Transparency in CRB

10-7 Permutations

Learn to find the number of possible permutations and the probability that a specific permutation will occur.

Vocabulary
permutation
factorial

The conductor of a symphony orchestra is planning a concert titled "An Evening with the Killer B's." The concert will feature music by Bach, Beethoven, Brahms, and Bartok. In how many different ways can the conductor program each composer's music?

An arrangement of objects or events in which the order is important is called a **permutation**. You can use a list to find the number of permutations of a group of objects.

EXAMPLE 1 Using a List to Find Permutations

A **In how many different ways can the conductor order pieces composed by Bach, Beethoven, Brahms, and Bartok?**

Use a list to find the possible permutations.

Bach, Beethoven, Brahms, Bartok	Brahms, Bach, Beethoven, Bartok
Bach, Beethoven, Bartok, Brahms	Brahms, Bach, Bartok, Beethoven
Bach, Bartok, Beethoven, Brahms	Brahms, Beethoven, Bach, Bartok
Bach, Bartok, Brahms, Beethoven	Brahms, Beethoven, Bartok, Bach
Bach, Brahms, Beethoven, Bartok	Brahms, Bartok, Beethoven, Bach
Bach, Brahms, Bartok, Beethoven	Brahms, Bartok, Bach, Beethoven
Beethoven, Bach, Brahms, Bartok	Bartok, Bach, Beethoven, Brahms
Beethoven, Bach, Bartok, Brahms	Bartok, Bach, Brahms, Beethoven
Beethoven, Brahms, Bach, Bartok	Bartok, Beethoven, Bach, Brahms
Beethoven, Brahms, Bartok, Bach	Bartok, Beethoven, Brahms, Bach
Beethoven, Bartok, Brahms, Bach	Bartok, Brahms, Beethoven, Bach
Beethoven, Bartok, Bach, Brahms	Bartok, Brahms, Bach, Beethoven

There are 24 ways to order the music.

B **If the order is chosen randomly, what is the probability that the composers will be featured in alphabetical order?**

Of the 24 possible permutations, only 1 is in alphabetical order (Bach, Bartok, Beethoven, Brahms).

$$P(\text{alphabetical order}) = \frac{\text{number of alphabetical arrangements}}{\text{total number of arrangements}}$$

$$= \frac{1}{24}$$

The probability that the composers will be featured in alphabetical order is $\frac{1}{24}$.

Introduce

Alternate Opener

10-7 Permutations

Ms. Jones uses the four letters A, B, C, and D in different orders to assign computer log-in passwords to her 20 students. Each letter appears only once in a password, but the order of the letters can be different.

1. Complete the tables by forming four-letter passwords.

Password 1	ABCD
Password 2	ABDC
Password 3	
Password 4	
Password 5	
Password 6	
Password 7	
Password 8	
Password 9	
Password 10	
Password 11	
Password 12	

Password 13	
Password 14	
Password 15	
Password 16	
Password 17	
Password 18	
Password 19	
Password 20	

2. Are there enough possible passwords for 20 students?
3. What is the total number of passwords that Ms. Jones can create?

Think and Discuss

4. **Explain** how to find the number of passwords possible if there are 5 letters available, A, B, C, D, and E.

Motivate

To introduce permutations, ask students to describe situations in which order is important, such as putting on shoes and socks or standing in line with several friends.

Point out that when order is important, the arrangement 123 is different from the arrangement 321.

Exploration worksheet and answers on Chapter 10 Resource Book pp. 62 and 88

Teach

Lesson Presentation

Guided Instruction

In this lesson, students learn to find the number of possible permutations and the probability that a specific permutation will occur. Stress the difference between combinations and permutations by pointing out that with permutations, we do not eliminate groups with the same members that differ in order, such as 123, 321, and 132.

Teaching Tip You can also make a tree diagram to find the permutations of a group of objects, but both lists and tree diagrams become tedious. This is why we consider other ways to find the number of permutations.

By making an organized list, you can find the possible permutations as well as the number of permutations. You can use the Fundamental Counting Principle to find only the number of permutations.

EXAMPLE 2 **Using the Fundamental Counting Principle to Find the Number of Permutations**

Ed, Emily, and Lila have agreed to be president, vice president, and secretary of the Yearbook Club. In how many different ways can the students fill the positions? What is the probability that any two of the permutations will be chosen?

Once you fill a position, you have one less choice for the next position.

There are three choices for the first position.

There are two remaining choices for the second position.

There is one choice for the third position.

$3 \cdot 2 \cdot 1 = 6$ *Multiply.*

There are 6 different ways that the students can fill the positions. The probability that any two of the permutations will be chosen is $\frac{2}{6}$, or $\frac{1}{3}$.

Multiplying $3 \cdot 2 \cdot 1$ is called 3 *factorial* and is written as "3!" You can find the **factorial** of a whole number by multiplying all the whole numbers except zero that are less than or equal to the number.

$3! = 3 \cdot 2 \cdot 1 = 6$ $\qquad$ $6! = 6 \cdot 5 \cdot 4 \cdot 3 \cdot 2 \cdot 1 = 720$

You can use factorials to find the number of permutations in a given situation.

EXAMPLE 3 **Using Factorials to Find the Number of Permutations**

There are nine players in a baseball lineup. How many different batting orders are possible for these players?

Number of permutations $= 9!$

$= 9 \cdot 8 \cdot 7 \cdot 6 \cdot 5 \cdot 4 \cdot 3 \cdot 2 \cdot 1$

$= 362{,}880$

There are 362,880 different batting orders possible for 9 players.

Think and Discuss

1. **Give an example** that shows the difference between permutations and combinations.
2. **Explain** why 8! gives the number of permutations of 8 objects.

COMMON ERROR ALERT

It is easy to miss permutations when making a list to determine the number of possible permutations. Encourage students to use a systematic plan for listing possible permutations.

Additional Examples

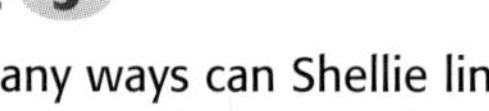

Example 1

A. In how many ways can you arrange the letters *A, B,* and *T*? **6**

B. What is the probability that an arrangement chosen at random will be a word? $\frac{1}{3}$

Example 2

Mary, Rob, Carla, and Eli are lining up for lunch. How many different permutations are there? What is the probability that any one of the permutations will be chosen at random? **24;** $\frac{1}{24}$

Example 3

In how many ways can Shellie line up 8 books on a shelf? **40,320**

3 Close

Reaching All Learners
Through Hands-On Experience

Put students in groups of four. Provide each group with four index cards, and have each student write his or her name on a separate card. Have the students work in their groups to find the number of permutations of the four names.

Summarize

Have students summarize the possible ways to find the number of permutations of a group of objects.

Possible answer: You can list the possibilities in an organized list, use the Fundamental Counting Principle, or use factorials.

Answers to Think and Discuss

1. Possible answer: If three students are to be chosen for a committee, it is a combination (order does not matter); but if three students are to be chosen for president, vice president, and secretary, it is a permutation (order matters).
2. There are 8 choices for the first position, 7 choices for the second, 6 for the third, and so on, and their product is 8!.

10-7 PRACTICE & ASSESS

Students may want to refer back to the lesson examples.

Assignment Guide

If you finished Example 1 assign:
Core 1, 5, 9, 10, 21–25
Enriched 1, 5, 9, 10, 21–25

If you finished Example 2 assign:
Core 1, 2, 5, 6, 9, 12, 16, 21–25
Enriched 1, 2, 9–11, 16, 19–25

If you finished Example 3 assign:
Core 1–8, 9–17 odd, 21–25
Enriched 1–3, 9–25

Notes

10-7 Exercises

FOR EXTRA PRACTICE
see page 677

internet connect
Homework Help Online
go.hrw.com Keyword: MS4 10-7

GUIDED PRACTICE

See Example 1

1. **a.** In how many ways can you arrange the numbers 1, 2, 3, and 4 to make a four-digit number? **24**
   b. If you choose one of the four-digit numbers at random, what is the probability that the number will be less than 2,000? $\frac{1}{4}$

See Example 2

2. **a.** Find the number of permutations of the letters in the word *quiet*. **120**
   b. What is the probability that any one of the permutations will be chosen? $\frac{1}{120}$

See Example 3

3. Sam wants to call 6 friends to invite them to a party. In how many possible orders can he make the calls? **720**
4. Seven people are waiting to audition for a play. In how many different orders can the auditions be done? **5,040**

INDEPENDENT PRACTICE

See Example 1

5. **a.** In how many ways can Eric, Meera, and Roger stand in line? **6**
   b. If you choose one of the orders at random, what is the probability that Meera will be first in line? $\frac{1}{3}$

See Example 2

6. **a.** Find the number of ways you can arrange the letters in the word *art*. **6**
   b. What is the probability that any one of the permutations will be chosen? $\frac{1}{6}$

See Example 3

7. How many permutations of the letters *A* through *I* are there? **362,880**
8. In how many different ways can 8 riders be matched up with 8 horses? **40,320**

PRACTICE AND PROBLEM SOLVING

Determine whether each problem involves combinations or permutations. Explain your answer.

9. Choose five books to read from a group of ten. **combinations**
10. Decide how many ways five people can be assigned to sit in five chairs. **permutations**
11. Choose a 4-digit code from the digits 3, 7, 1, and 8. **permutations**
12. Carl, Melba, Sean, and Ricki are going to present individual reports in their Spanish class. What is the probability that Melba will present her report first? $\frac{1}{4}$
13. Using the digits 1 through 7, Pima County is assigning new seven-digit numbers to all households. How many possible numbers can the county assign without repeating any of the digits in a number? **5,040**

Math Background

A *permutation* is an arrangement of objects in a definite order with no repetitions.

The Fundamental Counting Principle states that if event *A* can occur in *a* ways and, after event *A*, event *B* can occur in *b* ways, then event *A* followed by event *B* can occur in $a \cdot b$ ways. From this, we get the formula ${}_nP_r = \frac{n!}{(n-r)!}$.

In the cases we consider in the lesson, $r = n$ (that is, we consider permutations of *n* things taken *n* at a time), so the number of permutations is $\frac{n!}{0!}$. Because $0! = 1$, the number of permutations is $n!$.

RETEACH 10-7

LESSON 10-7 **Reteach**
Permutations

A **permutation** is a selection of objects in a particular order.

In how many ways can Allie, Bob, and Carl stand in a line?

You can draw a tree diagram to find the number of permutations.

1. Complete the tree diagram.

Allie — **Bob** — Carl; Allie — Carl — Bob
Bob — Allie — **Carl**; Bob — **Carl** — Allie
Carl — Allie — **Bob**; Carl — Bob — **Allie**

2. Complete the list of the outcomes.

Allie Bob Carl — Bob **Allie** Carl — Carl Allie **Bob**
Allie Carl **Bob** — Bob **Carl** Allie — **Carl** Bob Allie

You can also use multiplication to find the number of permutations.

3. Complete the multiplication.

3 × **2** × **1** = **6**
(Choices for first in line) (Choices for second in line) (Choices for third in line) (Number of permutations)

4. There are **6** permutations for 3 people standing in line.

You can find the probability that they will be standing in line alphabetically.

5. $P(\text{alphabetical order}) = \frac{\text{number of alphabetical arrangements}}{\text{total number of permutations}} = \frac{1}{6}$
6. Find the number of ways you can arrange the letters in the word MATH.
   4 • **3** • **2** • **1** = **24 ways**

PRACTICE 10-7

LESSON 10-7 **Practice B**
Permutations

1. **a.** Joe has homework assignments for math, Spanish, and history. In how many different ways can he do his homework? **6 ways**
   b. If you choose one of the permutations at random, what is the probability that it has math last? $\frac{1}{3}$
2. **a.** Find the number of permutations of the letters in the word SMART. **120**
   b. If you choose one of the permutations at random, what is the probability that it will start with a vowel? $\frac{1}{5}$
3. **a.** In how many ways can you arrange the numbers 6, 7, 8, and 9 to make a four-digit number? **24 ways**
   b. If you choose one of the four-digit numbers at random, what is the probability that the number will be greater than 8,000? $\frac{1}{2}$

Find the number of permutations for each situation.

4. Nine mountain bikers are on a bicycle trip. In how many possible ways can they follow each other? **362,880 ways**
5. Seven students are waiting in line at the cafeteria. In how many different orders can they be standing in line? **5,040 orders**
6. **a.** How many permutations of the letters A through F are there? **720**
   b. If you choose one of the permutations at random, what is the probability that the first letter is C? $\frac{1}{6}$
7. In how many different ways can a librarian arrange eight books on a shelf? **40,320 ways**
8. Melinda has 15 art trophies. Write an expression that shows how many different ways she can line up her trophies on a shelf. **15!**

Since its initial publication in 1868, *Little Women,* by Louisa May Alcott, has never been out of print. Over the years, the story has been translated into at least 27 languages.

go.hrw.com
KEYWORD: MS4 Alcott

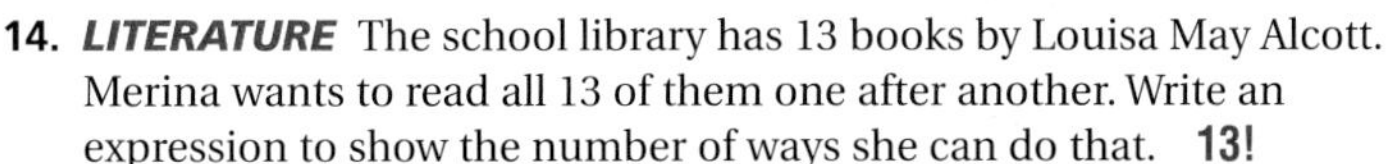

14. ***LITERATURE*** The school library has 13 books by Louisa May Alcott. Merina wants to read all 13 of them one after another. Write an expression to show the number of ways she can do that. **13!**

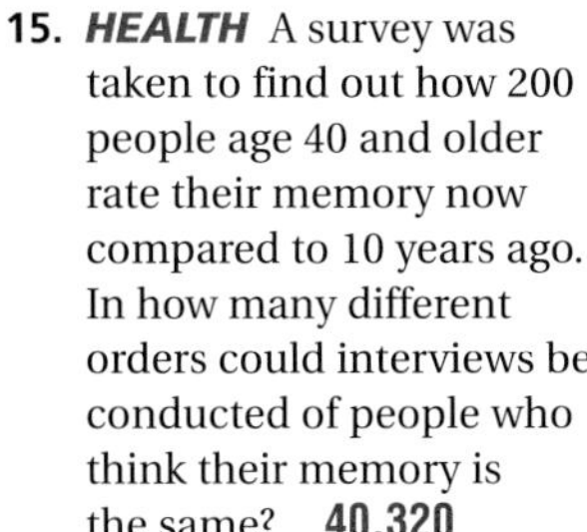

15. ***HEALTH*** A survey was taken to find out how 200 people age 40 and older rate their memory now compared to 10 years ago. In how many different orders could interviews be conducted of people who think their memory is the same? **40,320**

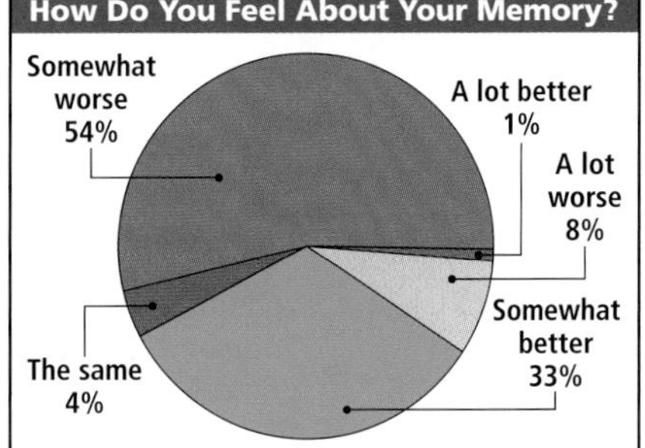

16. Use the letters *A, D, E, R.*
    a. How many permutations of the letters are there? **24**
    b. How many arrangements form English words? **3**
    c. What is the probability that a random arrangement of the letters shown will form an English word? $\frac{1}{8}$

17. ***SPORTS*** Ten golfers on a team are playing in a tournament. How many different lineups can the golf coach make? **3,628,800**

18. ***WHAT'S THE ERROR?*** A student was trying to find 5! and wrote the equation $5 + 4 + 3 + 2 + 1 = 15$. Why is this student incorrect?

19. ***WRITE ABOUT IT*** Explain the difference between combinations of objects and permutations of objects. Give examples of each.

20. ***CHALLENGE*** How many permutations are there of four objects taken two at a time? **12**

Spiral Review

Find each volume. (Lesson 9-2)

21. cylinder with $r = 3$ m and $h = 5$ m **141.3 m³**
22. rectangular prism with $\ell = 4$ ft, $w = 3$ ft, and $h = 9$ ft **108 ft³**
23. triangular prism with $B = 4.5\text{ cm}^2$ and $h = 13$ cm **58.5 cm³**

Determine the experimental probability. (Lesson 10-2)

24. Kaisia made 3 hits in 8 at bats. What is the probability that she will make a hit the next time at bat? $\frac{3}{8}$

25. **TEST PREP** Bertram has four \$1 bills, three \$5 bills, and three \$10 bills in his pocket. He draws a bill at random and then draws a second one without replacing the first. What is the probability that Bertram pulls out a \$5 bill and then a \$1 bill? (Lesson 10-5) **C**

A $\frac{7}{10}$ **B** 0.12 **C** $\frac{2}{15}$ **D** 0.1

Answers

18. The student added when he or she should have multiplied; $5! = 5 \cdot 4 \cdot 3 \cdot 2 \cdot 1 = 120$.
19. Possible answer: In combinations, order does not make a difference, as when choosing two students from five to go to a conference. With permutations, order does make a difference, as when deciding how many ways four students can line up.

Journal

Have students describe real-world situations in which permutations might be used.

Test Prep Doctor

For Exercise 25, if students selected **B,** they neglected to note that the problem does not include replacement, since $\frac{12}{100} = 0.12$. If students chose **A,** they may have added probabilities for independent events instead of multiplying, and they need to review the concept of dependent events. The computation $\frac{3}{10} \cdot \frac{4}{9}$ will verify that choice **C** is correct.

CHALLENGE 10-7

LESSON 10-7 Challenge
Factorial Fun

Sometimes you can use the definition of *factorial* to simplify computations with factorials.

Example: $\frac{8!}{5!2!} = \frac{8 \cdot 7 \cdot {}^{3}6 \cdot 5 \cdot 4 \cdot 3 \cdot 2 \cdot 1}{(5 \cdot 4 \cdot 3 \cdot 2 \cdot 1)(2 \cdot 1)} = \frac{8 \cdot 7 \cdot 3}{1} = 168$

Simplify. Remember to use the order of operations.

1. $(3 + 2)!$ **120**
2. $(4!)(2!)$ **48**
3. $(2 \cdot 3)!$ **720**
4. $5 + 4!$ **29**
5. $\frac{6!}{7!}$ $\frac{1}{7}$
6. $\frac{6!}{4!}$ **30**
7. $\frac{5!}{7!}$ $\frac{1}{42}$
8. $\frac{9!}{7!}$ **72**
9. $\frac{8!}{3!5!}$ **56**
10. $\frac{6!}{2!4!}$ **15**
11. $\frac{9!}{8!3!}$ $\frac{3}{2}$
12. $\frac{10!}{8!4!}$ $\frac{15}{4}$
13. $\frac{8!}{4!4!}$ **70**
14. $\frac{3!5!}{4!}$ **30**
15. $\frac{11!}{7!4!}$ **330**
16. $\frac{6!8!}{7!5!}$ **48**
17. $\frac{2! + 2!}{3!}$ $\frac{2}{3}$
18. $\frac{3!3! + 3}{3!}$ $\frac{13}{2}$
19. $\frac{4!}{3! + 4}$ $\frac{12}{5}$
20. $3(\frac{3!}{4!})$ $\frac{3}{4}$
21. $2!(3!)$ **12**
22. $4! - 3!$ **18**
23. $4!(3!)(2!)$ **288**
24. $5 + 4! + 3$ **32**

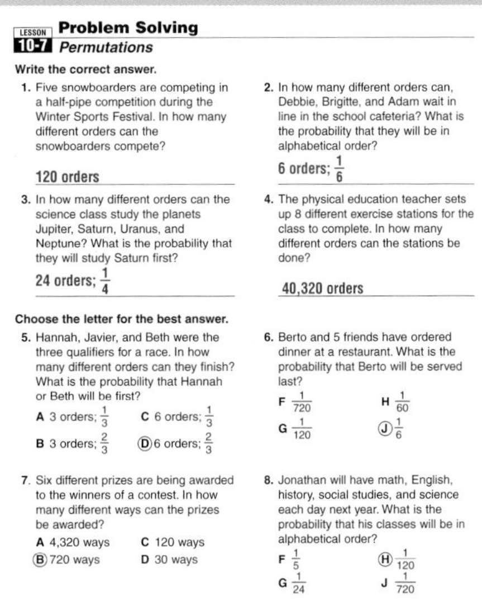

PROBLEM SOLVING 10-7

LESSON 10-7 Problem Solving
Permutations

Write the correct answer.

1. Five snowboarders are competing in a half-pipe competition during the Winter Sports Festival. In how many different orders can the snowboarders compete? **120 orders**
2. In how many different orders can, Debbie, Brigitte, and Adam wait in line in the school cafeteria? What is the probability that they will be in alphabetical order? **6 orders;** $\frac{1}{6}$
3. In how many different orders can the science class study the planets Jupiter, Saturn, Uranus, and Neptune? What is the probability that they will study Saturn first? **24 orders;** $\frac{1}{4}$
4. The physical education teacher sets up 8 different exercise stations for the class to complete. In how many different orders can the stations be done? **40,320 orders**

Choose the letter for the best answer.

5. Hannah, Javier, and Beth were the three qualifiers for a race. In how many different orders can they finish? What is the probability that Hannah or Beth will be first?
   A 3 orders; $\frac{1}{3}$ C 6 orders; $\frac{1}{3}$
   B 3 orders; $\frac{2}{3}$ (D) 6 orders; $\frac{2}{3}$
6. Berto and 5 friends have ordered dinner at a restaurant. What is the probability that Berto will be served last?
   F $\frac{1}{720}$ H $\frac{1}{60}$
   G $\frac{1}{120}$ (J) $\frac{1}{6}$
7. Six different prizes are being awarded to the winners of a contest. In how many different ways can the prizes be awarded?
   A 4,320 ways C 120 ways
   (B) 720 ways D 30 ways
8. Jonathan will have math, English, history, social studies, and science each day next year. What is the probability that his classes will be in alphabetical order?
   F $\frac{1}{5}$ (H) $\frac{1}{120}$
   G $\frac{1}{24}$ J $\frac{1}{720}$

Lesson Quiz

1. How many ways can Anna, Barbara, and Cara sit in a row? **6**
2. If you choose one of the orders at random, what is the probability that Anna will be in the front? $\frac{1}{3}$

Find the number of permutations of each situation.

3. How many different ways could 4 people enter a roller-coaster car? **24**
4. How many different ways could 6 basketball players sit on the bench while waiting to be announced at the beginning of a game? **720**

Available on Daily Transparency in CRB

CHAPTER 10 Extension

Pacing: Traditional 1 day
Block $\frac{1}{2}$ day

Objective: Students find the odds for and against events happening.

Using the Pages

In Lesson 10-4, students learned about finding simple probability. The odds of an event are related to its probability, but the odds of an event compare the favorable outcomes with the unfavorable outcomes instead of with the possible number of outcomes.

EXTENSION Computing Odds

Learn to find the odds for and against events happening.

Vocabulary
odds

What are the *odds* that the spinner will stop on the letter *e*? **Odds** are another way to express the likelihood that an event will occur. Odds compare the number of favorable outcomes for an event with the number of unfavorable outcomes.

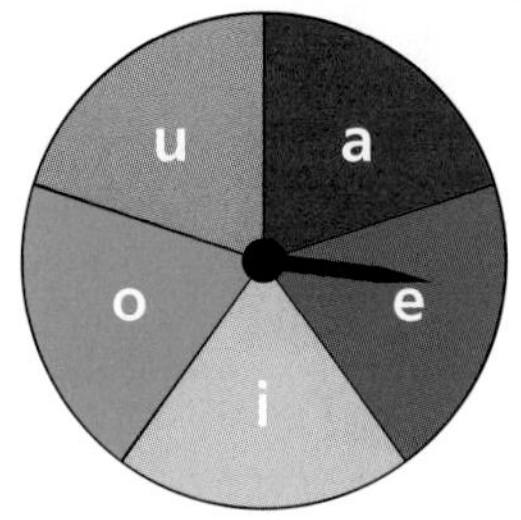

Reading Math

Odds are read as the number of favorable outcomes *to* the number of unfavorable outcomes. The odds of the spinner landing on e are 1 to 4, or 1:4.

ODDS OF AN EVENT

$$\text{odds} = \frac{\text{number of favorable outcomes}}{\text{number of unfavorable outcomes}}$$

There is only one way the spinner can land on *e*, but there are four equal ways for it not to land on *e*, so the odds of landing on *e* are $\frac{1}{4}$. In contrast, the probability that the spinner will land on *e* is $\frac{1}{5}$.

EXAMPLE 1 Computing the Odds of an Event

Suppose you choose a letter at random from the word *Indiana*.

A **What are the odds that the letter you choose will be a vowel?**

$$\text{odds of choosing a vowel} = \frac{\text{number of vowels}}{\text{number of consonants}} = \frac{4}{3}$$

The odds of choosing a vowel are 4:3.

B **What are the odds that the letter you choose will not be a vowel?**

$$\text{odds of not choosing a vowel} = \frac{\text{number of consonants}}{\text{number of vowels}} = \frac{3}{4}$$

The odds of not choosing a vowel are 3:4.

C **What are the odds that the letter you choose will be an *a*?**

$$\text{odds of choosing an } a = \frac{\text{number of } a\text{'s}}{\text{number of letters that are not } a} = \frac{2}{5}$$

The odds of choosing an *a* are 2:5.

1 Introduce

Motivate

As an introduction to odds, ask students to describe situations in which they have heard the term *odds* used. Talk about what they feel statements such as "the odds of rain are 2 to 1" or "the odds of winning are good" would mean.

You may want to point out that odds are related to probability but are not the same thing.

2 Teach

Lesson Presentation

Guided Instruction

In this lesson, students learn to find the odds for and against events happening. Odds for an event compare favorable outcomes with unfavorable outcomes, and odds against an event compare unfavorable outcomes with favorable outcomes. This is different from the probability of an event, which is the ratio of favorable outcomes to the total number of favorable and unfavorable outcomes. Use Examples 1A and 1B to point out that the odds for an event and the odds against an event are reciprocals.

EXTENSION

Exercises

Each card in a set of 7 cards has one letter from the word *Florida*.

1. What are the odds of choosing a card with a vowel? **3:4**
2. What are the odds of choosing a card that does not have a vowel? **4:3**
3. What are the odds of choosing a card with an *F*? **1:6**
4. What are the odds of choosing a card that does not have an *F*? **6:1**

A student is chosen at random from a class of 10 boys and 20 girls. Find the odds of each event.

5. A girl is chosen. **2:1**
6. A boy is chosen. **1:2**
7. A girl is not chosen. **1:2**
8. A boy is not chosen. **2:1**

Casey spins the spinner shown. Find the odds of each event.

9. The pointer lands on red. **5:3**
10. The pointer lands on blue. **1:3**
11. The pointer lands on yellow. **1:7**
12. The pointer lands on a color other than red. **3:5**
13. Find the odds of a coin landing heads up when you toss a coin. **1:1**
14. What are the odds against rolling a 1 on a 1–6 number cube? **5:1**
15. Each letter of the alphabet is written on one craft stick, for a total of 26 sticks. You choose one stick at random.
    a. What are the odds of choosing a stick with a vowel? **5:21**
    b. What are the odds against choosing a stick with a vowel? **21:5**
16. The letters in *Montgomery, Alabama* are written on slips of paper, one letter per slip.
    a. What are the odds of drawing an *A*? **4:13**
    b. What are the odds of drawing an *M*? **3:14**
17. The probability of choosing a red marble from a bag of marbles is $\frac{2}{5}$.
    a. What are the odds of choosing a red marble from the bag? **2:3**
    b. What are the odds against choosing a red marble from the bag? **3:2**

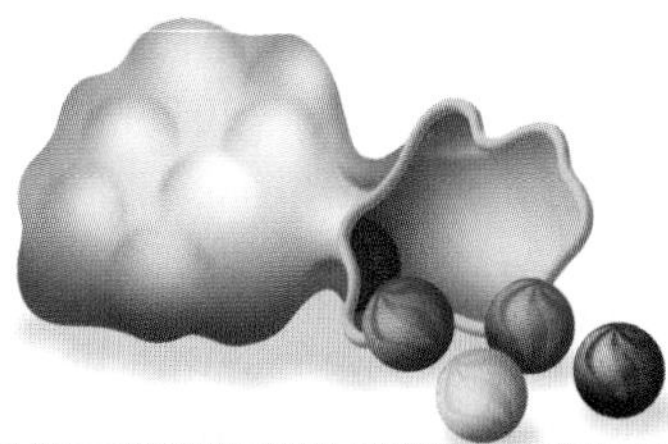

Additional Examples

Example 1

Suppose you choose a letter at random from the word *Mississippi*.

A. What are the odds that the letter you choose will be an *s*? $\frac{4}{7}$ or 4:7

B. What are the odds that the letter you choose will not be an *s*? $\frac{7}{4}$ or 7:4

C. What are the odds that the letter you choose will be a vowel? $\frac{4}{7}$ or 4:7

Teaching Tip In Example 1A, draw students' attention to the fact that the odds of choosing a vowel are greater than 1. Encourage students to explain why odds can be greater than 1, but the probability of an event can never be greater than 1.

The numerator can be greater than the denominator when finding the odds because the number of favorable outcomes may be greater than the number of unfavorable outcomes, or vice versa.

3 Close

Summarize

Have students compare calculating the odds of an event and the probability of an event.

Possible answer: Odds compare the number of favorable outcomes with the number of unfavorable outcomes and can be greater than or less than 1. Probability compares the number of favorable outcomes with the total number of outcomes and must always be less than or equal to 1.

Problem Solving on Location

Indiana

Purpose: *To provide additional practice for problem-solving skills in Chapters 1–10*

Hoosier Hills Bicycle Route

- After problem 3, have students consider the following problem: Which letters have the same chance as the letter *O* of being picked? *I, E, L*
- After problem 5, have students find the probability of selecting a trail not in northern Indiana if a trail is chosen at random. Have them each write their answer as a fraction, a decimal, and a percent. **$\frac{31}{40}$; 0.775; 77.5%**

Extension Have students find the probability of drawing each letter from the words *Hoosier Hills Bicycle Route.*

$P(H) = P(S) = P(R) = P(C) = \frac{1}{12}$;

$P(O) = P(I) = P(E) = P(L) = \frac{1}{8}$;

$P(B) = P(Y) = P(U) = P(T) = \frac{1}{24}$

Problem Solving on Location

INDIANA

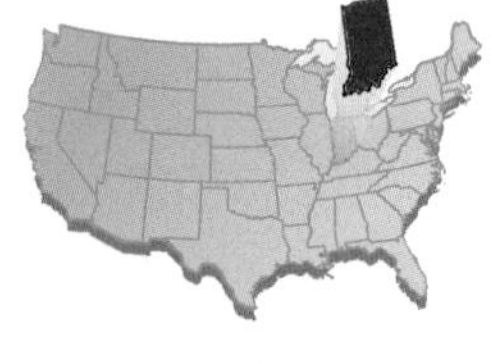

Hoosier Hills Bicycle Route

The Hoosier Hills Bicycle Route is about 27 miles long. It runs from Liberty Park to Versailles State Park. Motor vehicles can also use the bicycle route.

1. A group of friends plan to ride the entire bicycle route on Saturday if it doesn't rain. The weather forecast calls for a sunny day with a slight chance of showers. Is it impossible, unlikely, as likely as not, likely, or certain that it will
   a. rain on Saturday? **unlikely**
   b. be sunny on Saturday? **likely**
2. As Chen was taking a break from his ride along the Hoosier Hills Bicycle Route, he watched 52 cyclists ride by. Of the cyclists, 22 were female and 30 were male. What is the probability that the next person Chen sees ride by will be male? **$\frac{15}{26}$**
3. Latisha writes each letter from the words *Hoosier Hills Bicycle Route* on a separate slip of paper. The slips are all the same size. She places the slips in a bag, mixes them up, and then draws one slip from the bag without looking.
   a. What is the probability that she draws the letter *H*? **$\frac{1}{12}$**
   b. What is the probability that she draws the letter *I*? **$\frac{1}{8}$**
   c. What is the probability that she draws *H* or *I*? **$\frac{5}{24}$**

For 4 and 5, use the map of mountain-biking trails in Indiana at right.

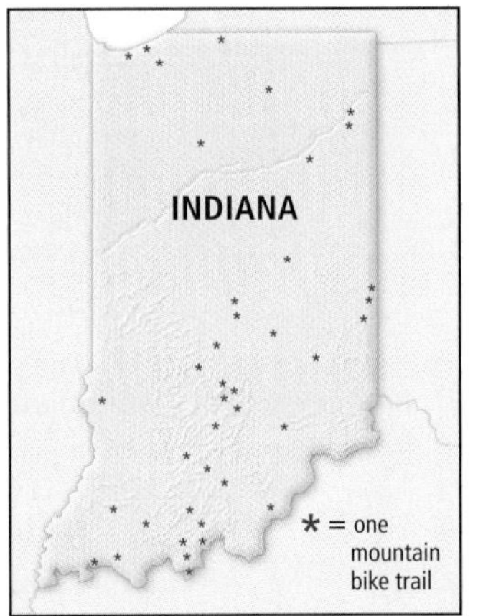

4. Would you be more likely to find a mountain-biking trail in northern Indiana or in southern Indiana? **southern Indiana**
5. Out of the 40 trails shown on the map, only 9 are in northern Indiana. What is the probability of selecting a trail in northern Indiana if you choose one of the trails on the map at random? Write your answer as a fraction, as a decimal, and as a percent.

Answers

5. **$\frac{9}{40}$; 0.225; 22.5%**

Turtle Days

In 1949, a giant turtle was spotted at Fulk Lake in Indiana. The turtle sighting brought reporters and thousands of other people to the small community of Churubusco after the owner of the lake decided that he would try to capture the turtle. The turtle, named Oscar, was never captured. However, his legend lives on in Churubusco, where Turtle Days are celebrated each year. In fact, Churubusco is now known as "Turtle Town, U.S.A."

Churubusco, "Turtle Town, U.S.A."

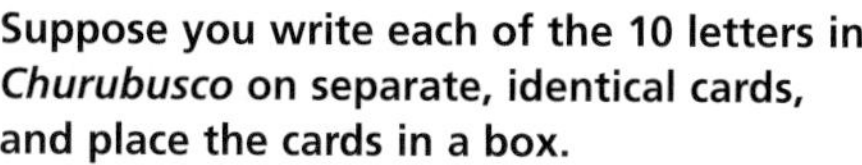

Suppose you write each of the 10 letters in *Churubusco* on separate, identical cards, and place the cards in a box.

1. You draw one letter and then draw a second letter without replacing the first. Are the two draws dependent or independent events? **dependent events**

2. You draw one letter and then draw a second letter without replacing the first. What is the probability of drawing the letter *C* both times? $\frac{1}{45}$

3. You draw one letter and then draw a second letter after replacing the first. What is the probability of drawing the letter *U* both times? $\frac{9}{100}$

For 4 and 5, use the table.

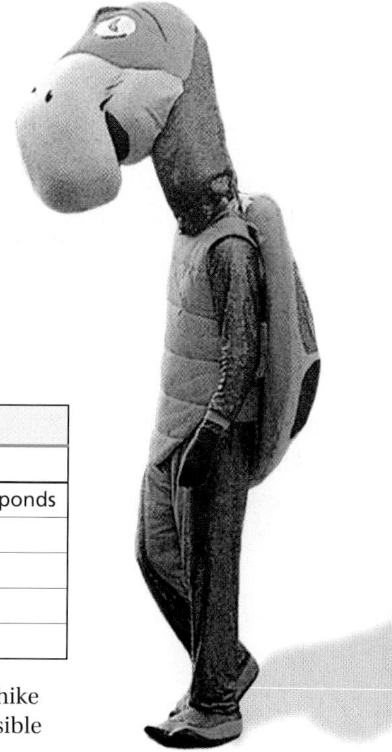

Indiana Dunes National Lakeshore Trails	
Trail	**Description**
West Beach	Dunes, woods, prairie, beach, Long Lake ponds
Bailly-Chellberg	Historical structures, woods, river
Little Calumet River	Woods, river, floodplain, old fields
Cowles Bog	Marsh, woods, dunes, ponds, beach
Mount Baldy	Dunes, woods, vistas, beach

4. A family visiting Indiana Dunes National Lakeshore wants to hike two different trails. How many combinations of hikes are possible from the above list? **10 possible combinations of hikes**

5. Cory wants to hike along the three trails in the park with dunes. In how many different ways can he plan these three hikes? Explain.

Turtle Days

- After problem 2, have students solve the following problem: You draw a card and replace it before drawing a second card. What is the probability of drawing the letter *C* both times? $\frac{1}{25}$
- After problem 4, have students consider the following: A family wants to hike 3 different trails. How many different combinations of trails are possible? 10 combinations

Extension: Have students find the total number of ways that the Indiana Dunes National Lakeshore trails can be hiked. 5! = 120 ways

Answers

5. He can plan 6, or 3!, hikes.

MATH-ABLES

Game Resources

Puzzles, Twisters & Teasers
Chapter 10 Resource Book

Buffon's Needle

Purpose: *To perform an experiment to re-create the first problem of geometric probability*

Discuss: Ask each student to check whether Buffon's formula holds for his or her experiment. Then combine the results of all the students and ask whether the combined results appear to be more accurate than the individual results.
Possible answer: The combined results are more accurate because they are the results of an experiment with more trials.

Extend: Encourage students to research other methods of estimating the value of π.
Possible answer: Measure the diameter of a circular object. Wrap a piece of string around the object to find its circumference. Measure the length of the string. Compare the length of the string to the diameter.

Pattern Match

Purpose: *To develop an understanding of the probability of accurately guessing the order of four items*

Discuss: Have students keep track of how many guesses they need in order to determine the correct arrangement of the pattern blocks.

Extend: Have students determine the probability of guessing, on the first guess, the correct order of the four pattern blocks.
The probability is $\frac{1}{24}$.

MATH-ABLES

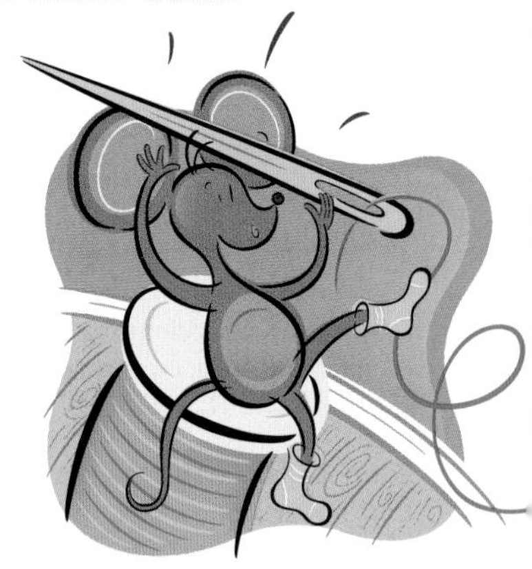

Buffon's Needle

If you drop a needle of a given length onto a wooden floor with evenly spaced cracks, what is the probability that it will land across a crack?

Compte de Buffon (1707–1788) asked this problem of geometric probability. To answer his question, Buffon developed a formula using ℓ to represent the length of the needle and d to represent the distance between the cracks.

$$\text{probability} = \frac{2\ell}{\pi d}$$

To re-create this experiment, you need a paper clip and several evenly spaced lines drawn on a piece of paper. Make sure that the distance between the lines is greater than the length of the paper clip. Toss the paper clip onto the piece of paper at least a dozen times. Divide the number of times the paper clip lands across a line by the number of times you toss the paper clip. Compare this quotient to the probability given by the formula.

The other interesting result of Buffon's discovery is that you can use the probability of the needle toss to estimate *pi*.

$$\pi = \frac{2\ell}{\text{probability} \cdot d}$$

Toss the paper clip 20 times to find the experimental probability. Use this probability in the formula above, and compare the result to 3.14.

Pattern Match

This game is for two players. Player A arranges four pattern blocks in a row out of the view of player B. Player B then tries to guess the arrangement. After each guess, player A reveals how many of the blocks are in the correct position without telling which blocks they are. The round ends when player B correctly guesses the arrangement.

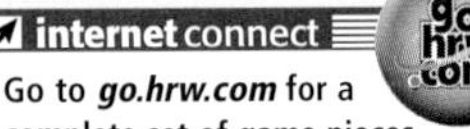

Go to *go.hrw.com* for a complete set of game pieces.
KEYWORD: MS4 Game10

Factorials and Permutations

You can use a graphing calculator to help compute factorials and permutations.

internet connect
Lab Resources Online
go.hrw.com
KEYWORD: MS4 TechLab10

Activity

1 To compute 7! you can do the computation 7 • 6 • 5 • 4 • 3 • 2 • 1 on a calculator as shown at right.

You can also use the factorial command, **!**, on a graphing calculator. This command is found in the **MATH** menu in the **PRB** submenu. It provides a faster method of computation.

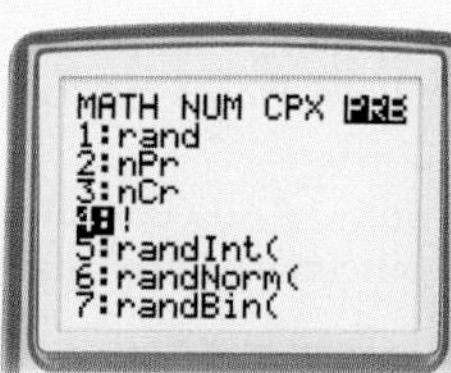

2 To compute 7! on a graphing calculator press

Think and Discuss

1. What is the greatest factorial you can compute on your calculator without getting an answer in scientific notation? **Check students' work. For the TI-83 the greatest factorial that does not give an answer in scientific notation is 13! = 6,227,020,800.**
2. Is $m! \cdot n! = (m \cdot n)!$ a true statement? Check by substituting values for the variables. **No; 3! · 2! = 6 · 2 = 12, while (3 · 2)! = 6! = 720.**

Try This

Compute each factorial by multiplication and by using the graphing calculator factorial command.

1. 5! **120**
2. 8! **40,320**
3. 10! **3,628,800**
4. 12! **479,001,600**
5. 11! ÷ 4! **1,663,200**
6. 15! ÷ 10! **360,360**

Factorials and Permutations

Objective: To use a graphing calculator to compute factorials and permutations

Materials: Graphing calculator

Lab Resources

Technology Lab Activities . . . . pp. 58–59

Using the Page

This technology activity shows students how to use the factorial command on a graphing calculator. Specific keystrokes may vary, depending on the make and model of the graphing calculator used. The keystrokes given are for a TI-83 model. For keystrokes to other models, visit go.hrw.com.

The Think and Discuss problems can be used to assess students' understanding of the technology activity. Try This problems 1–6 should be done first without a graphing calculator. Then have students do the exercises using the graphing calculator to show how much faster the calculator completes the problems.

Assessment

Use a graphing calculator to compute.

1. 6! **720**
2. 9! **362,880**

Chapter 10 Study Guide and Review

Purpose: *To help students review and practice concepts and skills presented in Chapter 10*

Assessment Resources

Chapter 10 Review

Chapter 10 Resource Book . . pp. 70–71

***Test and Practice Generator* CD-ROM**

Additional review assessment items in both multiple-choice and free-response format may be generated for any objective in Chapter 10.

Answers

1. independent events
2. combination
3. sample space
4. outcome
5. likely
6. unlikely
7. impossible

Chapter 10 Study Guide and Review

Study Guide and Review

Vocabulary

certain	512	Fundamental Counting Principle	521
combination	536	impossible	512
dependent events	530	independent events	530
equally likely	512	outcome	512
event	512	permutation	540
experiment	512	probability	512
experimental probability	516	sample space	520
factorial	541	theoretical probability	524
fair	524	trial	516
favorable outcome	524		

Complete the sentences below with vocabulary words from the list above. Words may be used more than once.

1. For __?__, the outcome of one event has no effect on the outcome of a second event.
2. A(n) __?__ is a grouping of objects or events in which order does not matter.
3. All the possible outcomes to an experiment make up the __?__.
4. A(n) __?__ is a result of an experiment.

10-1 Probability (pp. 512–515)

EXAMPLE

- **Sergio has math class during first period. Is it impossible, unlikely, as likely as not, likely, or certain that Sergio is in math class during second period?**

  It is unlikely that Sergio is in math class during second period because he has math during first period.

EXERCISES

Suppose you draw a card from a set of cards that is numbered 2–16. Determine whether each event is impossible, unlikely, as likely as not, likely, or certain.

5. How likely is it that you will draw a composite number?
6. How likely is it that you will draw a number less than 4?
7. How likely is it that you will draw a number greater than 20?

10-2 Experimental Probability (pp. 516–519)

EXAMPLE

- **Of the first 50 people surveyed, 21 said they liked mysteries better than comedies. What is the probability that the next person surveyed will favor mysteries?**

$P(\text{mysteries}) = \frac{\text{number who like mysteries}}{\text{total number surveyed}}$

$P(\text{mysteries}) = \frac{21}{50}$

The probability that the next person surveyed will favor mysteries is $\frac{21}{50}$.

EXERCISES

Sami has been keeping a record of her math grades. Of her first 15 grades, 10 have been above 82.

8. What is the probability that her next grade will be above 82?
9. What is the probability that her next grade will be 82 or below?

10-3 Make a List to Find Sample Spaces (pp. 520–523)

EXAMPLE

- **Anita tosses a coin and a 1–6 number cube. How many outcomes are possible?**

Use the Fundamental Counting Principle.
Number of ways the coin can land: 2
Number of ways the cube can land: 6
$2 \cdot 6 = 12$
There are 12 possible outcomes.

EXERCISES

Chen spins each of the spinners once.

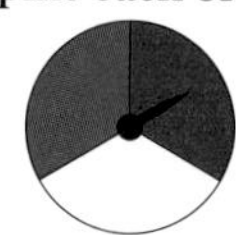

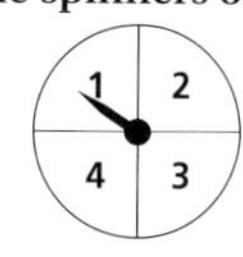

10. What are all the possible outcomes?
11. How large is the sample space?

10-4 Theoretical Probability (pp. 524–527)

EXAMPLE

- **Find the probability of drawing a 4 from a standard deck of 52 playing cards. Four cards in the deck are numbered 4. Write your answer as a fraction, as a decimal, and as a percent.**

$P(4) = \frac{\text{number of 4s in deck}}{\text{number of cards in deck}}$

$= \frac{4}{52}$

$= \frac{1}{13}$

$\approx 0.077 \approx 7.7\%$

EXERCISES

Find each probability. Write your answer as a fraction, as a decimal, and as a percent.

12. There are 9 girls and 12 boys on the student council. What is the probability that a girl will be chosen as president?
13. Anita tosses 3 coins. What is the probability that each coin will land tails up?

Answers

8. $\frac{2}{3}$
9. $\frac{1}{3}$
10. R1, R2, R3, R4, W1, W2, W3, W4, B1, B2, B3, B4
11. 12 possible outcomes
12. $\frac{3}{7}$, 0.43, 43%
13. $\frac{1}{8}$, 0.125, 12.5%

Answers

14. $\frac{4}{195}$

15. $\frac{16}{121}$

16. 10 ways

17. 35 committees

18. 84 combinations

19. 3,628,800 ways

20. 720 ways

21. 120 ways

Study Guide and Review

10-5 Probability of Independent and Dependent Events (pp. 530–533)

EXAMPLE

- **There are 4 red marbles, 3 green marbles, 6 blue marbles, and 2 black marbles in a bag. What is the probability that Angie will pick a green marble and then a black marble without replacing the first marble?**

$P(\text{green marble}) = \frac{3}{15} = \frac{1}{5}$

$P(\text{black marble}) = \frac{2}{14} = \frac{1}{7}$

$P(\text{green, then black}) = \frac{1}{5} \cdot \frac{1}{7} = \frac{1}{35}$

The probability of picking a green marble and then a black marble is $\frac{1}{35}$.

EXERCISES

14. There are 40 tags numbered 1 through 40 in a bag. What is the probability that Glenn will pick a multiple of 5 and then a multiple of 9 without replacing the first tag?
15. Each letter of the word *probability* is written on a card and put in a bag. What is the probability of picking a vowel on the first try and again on the second try if the first card is replaced?

10-6 Combinations (pp. 536–539)

EXAMPLE

- **Tina, Sam, and Jo are trying out for the 2 lead parts in a play. In how many ways can they be chosen for the parts?**

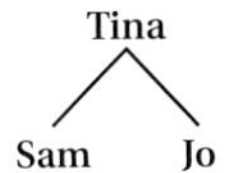

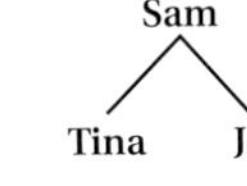

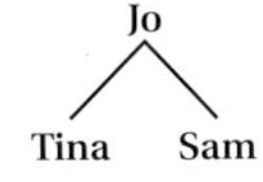

There are 3 possible ways the students can be chosen for the parts.

EXERCISES

16. How many ways can you select 3 pieces of fruit from a basket of 5 pieces?
17. How many 4-person committees can be chosen from 7 people?
18. How many combinations of 3 balloons can be chosen from 9 balloons?

10-7 Permutations (pp. 540–543)

EXAMPLE

- **How many different four-digit numbers can you make from the numbers 2, 4, 6, and 8 using each just once?**

There are 4 choices for the first digit, 3 choices for the second, 2 choices for the third, and 1 for the fourth.

$4 \cdot 3 \cdot 2 \cdot 1 = 24$

There are 24 different four-digit numbers possible.

EXERCISES

19. How many different batting orders are possible for 10 players on a softball team?
20. How many different ways can you arrange the letters in the word *number*?
21. In how many ways can Tanya, Rika, Andy, Evan, and Tanisha line up for lunch?

Chapter Test

Chapter 10

A box contains 3 orange cubes, 2 white cubes, 3 black cubes, and 4 blue cubes.

1. Would you be more likely to pick a white cube or a blue cube? **blue**
2. Would you be more likely to pick an orange cube or a black cube? **The events are equally likely.**
3. Simon tosses a coin 20 times. The coin lands heads up 7 times. Based on these results, how many times can Simon expect the coin to land heads up in the next 100 tosses? **35**
4. Emilio spins a 1–8 spinner 10 times. In his first three spins, the spinner lands on 8. What is the experimental probability that Emilio will spin a 10 on his fourth spin? **0**
5. A brand of jeans comes in 8 different waist sizes: 28, 30, 32, 34, 36, 38, 40, and 42. The jeans also come in three different colors: blue, black, and tan. How many different combinations of waist sizes and colors are possible? **24**
6. Greg is planning his vacation. He can choose from 3 ways to travel—train, bus, or plane—and four different activities—skiing, skating, snowboarding, or hiking. What are all the possible outcomes? How many different vacations could Greg plan?

Rachel spins a spinner that is divided into 10 equal sectors and numbered 1 through 10. Find each probability. Write your answer as a fraction, as a decimal, and as a percent.

7. *P*(odd number) $\frac{1}{2}$, **0.5, 50%**
8. *P*(composite number) $\frac{1}{2}$, **0.5, 50%**
9. *P*(number greater than 10) **0, 0.0, 0%**

Find the probability of each set of events.

10. spinning red on a spinner with equally sized red, blue, yellow, and green sections, and flipping a coin that lands tails up $\frac{1}{8}$
11. choosing a card labeled *vanilla* from a group of cards labeled *vanilla, chocolate, strawberry,* and *swirl,* and then choosing a card labeled *chocolate* without replacing the first card $\frac{1}{12}$
12. How many ways can 3 students be chosen from 10 students? **120 ways**
13. How many different 5-member basketball teams can be made from 7 students? **21 teams**
14. Timothy wants to arrange his 6 model cars on a shelf. How many ways could he arrange them? How many ways could he arrange 7 model cars? **720 ways; 5,040 ways**

Chapter Test

Chapter Test

Chapter 10

Purpose: *To assess students' mastery of concepts and skills in Chapter 10*

Assessment Resources

Chapter 10 Tests (Levels A, B, C)
Assessment Resources. . . . . . pp. 87–92

***Test and Practice Generator* CD-ROM**

Additional assessment items in both multiple-choice and free-response format may be generated for any objective in Chapter 10.

Answers

6. There are 12 different combinations: train–skiing, train–skating, train–snowboarding, train–hiking, bus–skiing, bus–skating, bus–snowboarding, bus–hiking, plane–skiing, plane–skating, plane–snowboarding, and plane–hiking.

Chapter 10 Performance Assessment

Purpose: To assess students' understanding of concepts in Chapter 10 and combined problem-solving skills

Assessment Resources 

Performance Assessment
Assessment Resources .... p. 124

Performance Assessment Teacher Support
Assessment Resources .... p. 123

Answers

1–4. See p. A3.

5. See Level 3 work sample below.

Scoring Rubric for Problem Solving Item 5

Level 3
Accomplishes the purpose of the task.
Student gives clear explanations, shows understanding of mathematical ideas and processes, and computes accurately.

Level 2
Purposes of the task not fully achieved.
Student demonstrates satisfactory but limited understanding of the mathematical ideas and processes.

Level 1
Purposes of the task not accomplished.
Student shows little evidence of understanding the mathematical ideas and processes and makes computational and/or procedural errors.

Chapter 10 Performance Assessment

Performance Assessment

Show What You Know

Create a portfolio of your work from this chapter. Complete this page and include it with your four best pieces of work from Chapter 10. Choose from your homework or lab assignments, mid-chapter quiz, or any journal entries you have done. Put them together using any design you want. Make your portfolio represent what you consider your best work.

Short Response

1. A coin is tossed 3 times. List the sample space. What is the probability that the outcomes of all 3 tosses are the same, either all heads or all tails? Explain how you found your answer.
2. Rhonda has 3 different-colored T-shirts—red, blue, and green—and a pair of blue jeans and a pair of white jeans. She randomly chooses a T-shirt and a pair of jeans. What is the probability that she will pair the red T-shirt with the white jeans? Show how you found your answer.
3. Chandra, Elias, Kenia, and Rob line up for lunch. In how many different orders can they line up? Are the orders permutations or combinations? Explain your answer.
4. The chart shows the results that Gregor Mendel obtained when he crossed two tall pea plants, each carrying a dominant (D) and a recessive (d) gene for tallness. What is the probability that an offspring will be a dwarf (dd) plant? Explain your answer.

	D	d
D	DD	Dd
d	Dd	dd

Gregor Mendel

 Extended Problem Solving

5. A bag contains 5 blue blocks, 3 red blocks, and 2 yellow blocks.
   a. What is the probability that Tip will draw a red block and then a blue block at random if the first block is replaced before the second is drawn? Show the steps necessary to find your answer.
   b. What is the probability that Tip will draw a red block and then a blue block at random if the first block is not replaced before the second is drawn? Show your work.
   c. Explain why replacing the first block affects the answers to parts **a** and **b.**

Student Work Samples for Item 5

Level 3

a. P(red) • P(blue) = P(red, blue)
$\frac{3}{10} \cdot \frac{5}{10} = \frac{15}{100} = \frac{3}{20}$

b. $\frac{3}{10} \cdot \frac{5}{9} = \frac{15}{90} = \frac{1}{6}$

c. Replacing the block makes the events independent. Not replacing it changes the sample space and makes them dependent events.

The student found both probabilities and correctly explained the difference between independent and dependent events.

Level 2

A. $\frac{3}{10} \times \frac{5}{10} = \frac{15}{100}$ or $\frac{3}{20}$

B. $\frac{3}{10} \times \frac{4}{9} = \frac{12}{90}$ or $\frac{2}{15}$

C. If you take the block out, you have 1 less block to choose from. So the probabilities are different.

The student correctly found the probability in part **a,** but had trouble with part **b.** The explanation in part **c** does not show that the student understands the concepts involved.

Level 1

a. $\frac{3+5}{20} = \frac{8}{20} = \frac{2}{5}$

b. $\frac{5-3}{20} = \frac{2}{20} = \frac{1}{10}$

c. Drawing red first is different from drawing blue first.

The student recognized that probability can be expressed as a ratio, but did not correctly answer any of the problems.

internet connect
State-Specific Test Practice Online
go.hrw.com Keyword: MS4 TestPrep

Standardized Test Prep

Chapter 10

Cumulative Assessment, Chapters 1–10

1. Convert 50 meters to kilometers. **B**

Ⓐ 50,000 km
Ⓑ 0.05 km
Ⓒ 500 km
Ⓓ 0.5 km

2. Find the perimeter of the rectangle. **H**

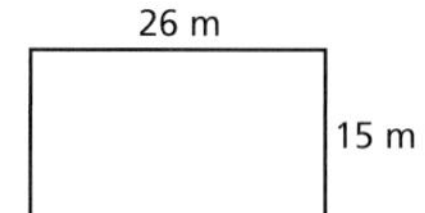

Ⓕ 41 m
Ⓖ 67 m
Ⓗ 82 m
Ⓙ 390 m

3. What is the probability that a phone number selected at random will end in a digit that is less than 5? **A**

Ⓐ As likely as not
Ⓑ Impossible
Ⓒ Unlikely
Ⓓ Likely

4. Marissa made 3 out of 10 foul shots. What is the probability that she will make the next foul shot? **F**

Ⓕ 30%
Ⓖ 70%
Ⓗ 3%
Ⓙ 7%

5. Manheim Middle School is ordering school caps. The caps come in 4 colors with 3 different designs. How many different caps could the school order? **B**

Ⓐ 7
Ⓑ 12
Ⓒ 24
Ⓓ 14

6. Rena, Nicole, Akira, and Rosa are going to the movies. In how many ways can they sit in four adjacent seats? **J**

Ⓕ 12
Ⓖ 16
Ⓗ 7
Ⓙ 24

7. Find the number of combinations of 8 things taken 3 at a time. **C**

Ⓐ 336
Ⓑ 24
Ⓒ 56
Ⓓ 28

8. The graph shows a town's high temperatures over a 5-day period. What was the average high temperature over these 5 days? **F**

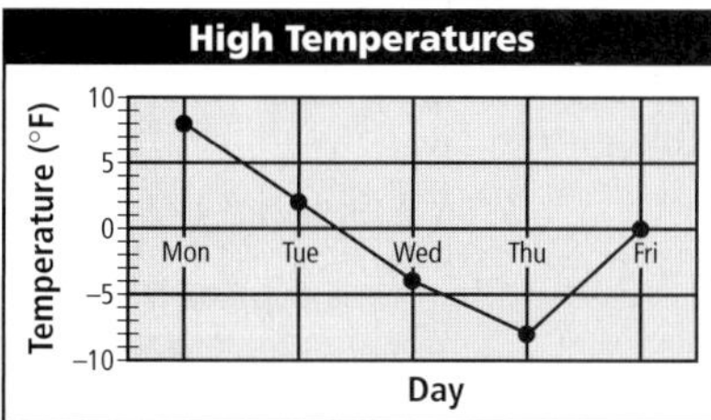

Ⓕ −0.4°F
Ⓖ 4.4°F
Ⓗ 0.4°F
Ⓙ −4.4°F

TEST TAKING TIP!
Eliminate choices by estimating the ratio of the two numbers.

9. 18 is what percent of 75? **C**

Ⓐ 76%
Ⓑ 42%
Ⓒ 24%
Ⓓ 416%

10. ***SHORT RESPONSE*** Find the measure of the third angle of a triangle whose other angles measure 59° and 22°. Explain your work.

11. ***SHORT RESPONSE*** Evaluate $72 \div 4 \cdot 3^2 - 13$. Explain how you got your answer, and show your steps.

Answers

10. Possible answer: The sum of the measures of the angles of any triangle is 180°. Add 59 and 22 and then subtract that number from 180 to get your answer. $180 - (59 + 22) = 99$. The third angle of this triangle measures 99°.

11. First, evaluate the exponent. Then divide and multiply from left to right, and then subtract.
$72 \div 4 \cdot 3^2 - 13$
$72 \div 4 \cdot 9 - 13$
$18 \cdot 9 - 13$
$162 - 13$
149

Standardized Test Prep

Chapter 10

Purpose: *To provide review and practice for Chapters 1–10 and standardized tests*

Assessment Resources

Cumulative Tests (Levels A, B, C)
Assessment Resources. . . . pp. 237–248

State-Specific Test Practice Online
KEYWORD: MS4 TestPrep

Test Prep Doctor

For item 9, students should first see that 18 is less than half of 75, so they can eliminate **A** and **D.** Students can use mental math to see that 20 is 25% of 80, so **C** is the correct answer. Students who chose **D** found what percent 75 is of 18.

Multistep Equations and Inequalities

Section 11A

Multistep Equations

Hands-On Lab 11A
Model Two-Step Equations

Lesson 11-1
Solving Two-Step Equations

Lesson 11-2
Solving Multistep Equations

Lesson 11-3
Solving Equations with Variables on Both Sides

Section 11B

Inequalities

Lesson 11-4
Inequalities

Lesson 11-5
Solving Inequalities by Adding or Subtracting

Lesson 11-6
Solving Inequalities by Multiplying or Dividing

Lesson 11-7
Solving Two-Step Inequalities

Extension
Solving for a Variable

Pacing Guide for 45-Minute Classes

Chapter 11

DAY 142	DAY 143	DAY 144	DAY 145	DAY 146
Hands-On Lab 11A	Lesson 11-1	Lesson 11-2	Lesson 11-3	Mid-Chapter Quiz Lesson 11-4
DAY 147	**DAY 148**	**DAY 149**	**DAY 150**	**DAY 151**
Lesson 11-5	Lesson 11-6	Lesson 11-7	Extension	Chapter 11 Review
DAY 152				
Chapter 11 Assessment				

Pacing Guide for 90-Minute Classes

Chapter 11

DAY 71	DAY 72	DAY 73	DAY 74	DAY 75
Chapter 10 Assessment Hands-On Lab 11A	Lesson 11-1 Lesson 11-2	Lesson 11-3 Lesson 11-4	Mid-Chapter Quiz Lesson 11-5 Lesson 11-6	Lesson 11-7 Extension
DAY 76	**DAY 77**			
Chapter 11 Review Lesson 12-1	Chapter 11 Assessment Lesson 12-2			

Across the Series

COURSE 1

- Solve one-step equations.
- Read, write, and graph inequalities on a number line.
- Solve one-step inequalities.

COURSE 2

- **Solve two-step and multistep equations, and equations with variables on both sides.**
- **Read, write, and graph inequalities on a number line.**
- **Solve one-step and two-step inequalities.**
- **Solve literal equations for one of the variables.**

COURSE 3

- Solve two-step and multistep equations, and equations with variables on both sides.
- Solve and graph one-step and two-step inequalities.
- Solve literal equations for one of the variables.
- Solve equations by graphing.
- Solve systems of equations.

Across the Curriculum

LANGUAGE ARTS LINK

SOCIAL STUDIES LINK

SCIENCE LINK

TE = *Teacher's Edition* **SE** = *Student Edition*

Interdisciplinary

Bulletin Board

Physical Science

Atmospheric pressure, measured in pascals (Pa), varies, depending on where you are in relation to sea level. If the boiling point of water decreases by approximately 1°C for every decrease of 2,230 Pa, you can use the formula $B = 100 - \frac{101{,}000 - \text{Pa}}{2{,}230}$ to find the boiling point B of water at any atmospheric pressure. Find the approximate boiling point of water at the top of Mount Everest.
(*Hint:* 101 kPa = 101,000 Pa)

$$B = 100 - \frac{101{,}000 - 33{,}000}{2{,}230} \approx 70°\text{C}$$

Interdisciplinary posters and worksheets are provided in your resource material.

Resource Options

Chapter 11 Resource Book

Student Resources

Practice (Levels A, B, C) . . . pp. 9–11, 18–20, 27–29, 37–39, 47–49, 56–58, 65–67
Reteach . . . pp. 12, 21, 30, 40–41, 50, 59, 68
Challenge . . . pp. 13, 22, 31, 42, 51, 60, 69
Problem Solving . . . pp. 14, 23, 32, 43, 52, 61, 70,
Puzzles, Twisters & Teasers . . . pp. 15, 24, 33, 44, 53, 62, 71
Recording Sheets . . . pp. 3–4, 8, 17, 26, 36, 46, 55, 64, 74, 77–79
Chapter Review . . . pp. 72–73

Teacher and Parent Resources

Chapter Planning and Pacing Guide . . . p. 5
Section Planning Guides . . . pp. 6, 34
Parent Letter . . . pp. 1–2
Teaching Tools . . . pp. 77–79
Teacher Support for Chapter Project . . . p. 75
Transparencies . . . pp. T1–T31
- Daily Transparencies
- Additional Examples Transparencies
- Teaching Transparencies

Reaching All Learners

English Language Learners

Success for English Language Learners . . . pp. 175–188
Math: Reading and Writing in the Content Area . . . pp. 88–94
Spanish Homework and Practice . . . pp. 88–94
Spanish Interactive Study Guide . . . pp. 88–94
Spanish Family Involvement Activities . . . pp. 97–104
Multilingual Glossary

Individual Needs

Are You Ready? Intervention and Enrichment . . pp. 145–148, 169–172, 177–180, 225–228, 245–248, 269–272, 425–426
Alternate Openers: Explorations . . . pp. 88–94
Family Involvement Activities . . . pp. 97–104
Interactive Problem Solving . . . pp. 88–94
Interactive Study Guide . . . pp. 88–94
Readiness Activities . . . pp. 21–22
Math: Reading and Writing in the Content Area . . . pp. 88–94
Challenge . . . CRB pp. 13, 22, 31, 42, 51, 60, 69

Hands-On

Hands-On Lab Activities . . . pp. 104–116
Technology Lab Activities . . . pp. 60–64
Alternate Openers: Explorations . . . pp. 88–94
Family Involvement Activities . . . pp. 97–104

Applications and Connections

Consumer and Career Math . . . pp. 41–44
Interdisciplinary Posters . . . Poster 11, TE p. 556B
Interdisciplinary Poster Worksheets . . . pp. 31–33

Transparencies

Alternate Openers: Explorations . . . pp. 88–94
Exercise Answers Transparencies
Chapter 11 Resource Book . . . pp. T1–T31
- Daily Transparencies
- Additional Examples Transparencies
- Teaching Transparencies

Technology

Teacher Resources

***Lesson Presentations* CD-ROM** . . . Chapter 11
***Test and Practice Generator* CD-ROM** . . . Chapter 11
***One-Stop Planner* CD-ROM** . . . Chapter 11

Student Resources

***Are You Ready? Intervention* CD-ROM**
Skills 34, 40, 42, 54, 59, 65

internet connect

Homework Help Online	**KEYWORD:** MS4 HWHelp11
Math Tools Online	**KEYWORD:** MS4 Tools
Glossary Online	**KEYWORD:** MS4 Glossary
Chapter Project Online	**KEYWORD:** MS4 PSProject11
Chapter Opener Online	**KEYWORD:** MS4 Ch11

KEYWORD: MRS4 CNN11

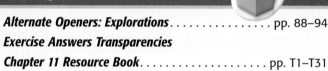

SE = *Student Edition* **TE** = *Teacher's Edition* **AR** = *Assessment Resources* **CRB** = *Chapter Resource Book* **MK** = *Manipulatives Kit*

Chapter 11

Assessment Options

Assessing Prior Knowledge

Determine whether students have the required prerequisite concepts and skills.

Are You Ready? . . . . SE p. 557
Inventory Test . . . . AR pp. 1–4

Test Preparation

Provide review and practice for chapter and standardized tests.

Standardized Test Prep . . . . SE p. 601
Spiral Review with Test Prep . . . . . SE, last page of each lesson
Study Guide and Review . . . . SE pp. 596–598
Test Prep Tool Kit

Technology

***Test and Practice Generator* CD-ROM**

internet connect

State-Specific Test Practice Online KEYWORD: MR4 TestPrep

Performance Assessment

Assess students' understanding of chapter concepts and combined problem-solving skills.

Performance Assessment . . . . SE p. 600
Includes scoring rubric in TE
Performance Assessment . . . . AR p. 126
Performance Assessment Teacher Support . . . . AR p. 125

Portfolio

Portfolio opportunities appear throughout the Student and Teacher's Editions.

Suggested work samples:

Problem Solving Project . . . . TE p. 556
Performance Assessment . . . . SE p. 600
Portfolio Guide . . . . AR p. xxxv
Journal . . . . TE, last page of each lesson
Write About It . . . . SE pp. 567, 571, 581, 585, 589

Daily Assessment

Obtain daily feedback on students' understanding of concepts.

Spiral Review and Test Prep . . . . . . SE, last page of each lesson

Also Available on Transparency In Chapter 11 Resource Book

Warm Up . . . . TE, first page of each lesson
Problem of the Day . . . . TE, first page of each lesson
Lesson Quiz . . . . TE, last page of each lesson

Student Self-Assessment

Have students evaluate their own work.

Group Project Evaluation . . . . AR p. xxxii
Individual Group Member Evaluation . . . . AR p. xxxiii
Portfolio Guide . . . . AR p. xxxv
Journal . . . . TE, last page of each lesson

Formal Assessment

Assess students' mastery of concepts and skills.

Section Quizzes . . . . AR pp. 29–30
Mid-Chapter Quiz . . . . SE p. 572
Chapter Test . . . . SE p. 599
Chapter Tests (Levels A, B, C) . . . . AR pp. 93–98
Cumulative Tests (Levels A, B, C) . . . . AR pp. 249–260
Standardized Test Prep
Cumulative Assessment . . . . SE p. 601
End-of-Year Test . . . . AR pp. 273–276

Technology

***Test and Practice Generator* CD-ROM**

Make tests electronically. This software includes:

- Dynamic practice for Chapter 11
- Customizable tests
- Multiple-choice items for each objective
- Free-response items for each objective
- Teacher management system

SE = *Student Edition* **TE** = *Teacher's Edition* **AR** = *Assessment Resources* **CRB** = *Chapter Resource Book* **MK** = *Manipulatives Kit*

Chapter 11 Tests

Three levels (A,B,C) of tests are available for each chapter in the *Assessment Resources.*

LEVEL A

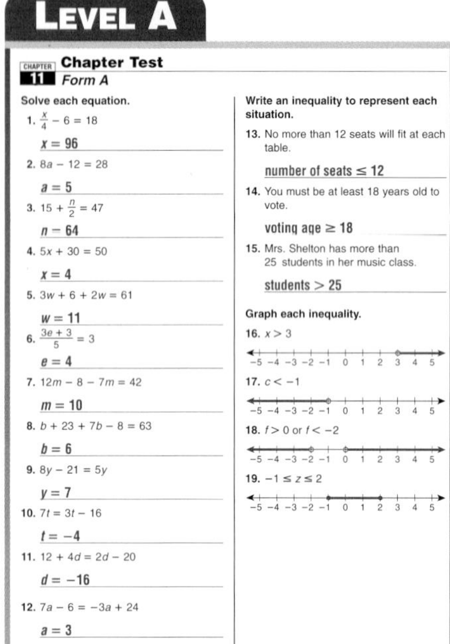

Chapter 11 Chapter Test
Form A

Solve each equation.

1. $\frac{x}{4} - 6 = 18$
   $x = 96$
2. $8a - 12 = 28$
   $a = 5$
3. $15 + \frac{n}{2} = 47$
   $n = 64$
4. $5x + 30 = 50$
   $x = 4$
5. $3w + 6 + 2w = 61$
   $w = 11$
6. $\frac{3e + 3}{5} = 3$
   $e = 4$
7. $12m - 8 - 7m = 42$
   $m = 10$
8. $b + 23 + 7b - 8 = 63$
   $b = 6$
9. $8y - 21 = 5y$
   $y = 7$
10. $7t = 3t - 16$
    $t = -4$
11. $12 + 4d = 2d - 20$
    $d = -16$
12. $7a - 6 = -3a + 24$
    $a = 3$

Write an inequality to represent each situation.

13. No more than 12 seats will fit at each table.
    number of seats $\leq$ 12
14. You must be at least 18 years old to vote.
    voting age $\geq$ 18
15. Mrs. Shelton has more than 25 students in her music class.
    students $>$ 25

Graph each inequality.

16. $x > 3$
17. $c < -1$
18. $f > 0$ or $f < -2$
19. $-1 \leq z \leq 2$

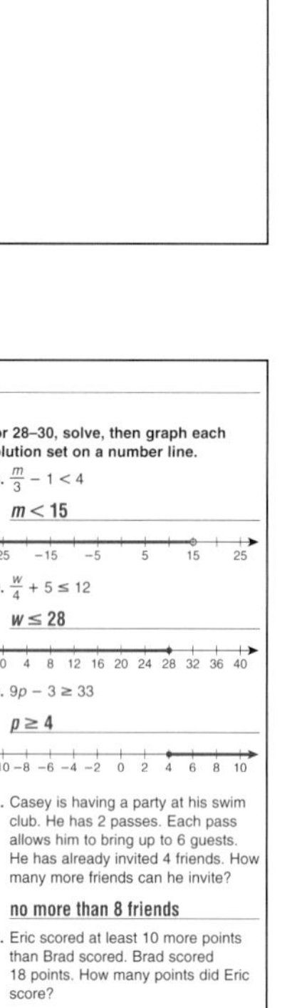

Chapter 11 Chapter Test
Form A, continued

Solve, then graph each solution set on a number line.

20 $y + 4 > 15$
   $y > 11$
21. $g - 3 < 4$
    $g < 7$
22. $k - 4 \leq 2$
    $k \leq 6$
23. $a + 12 < 10$
    $a < -2$

Solve each inequality.

24. $\frac{n}{4} < 12$
    $n < 48$
25. $\frac{s}{5} \leq 7$
    $s \leq 35$
26. $6h > 42$
    $h > 7$
27. $12c \geq 108$
    $c \geq 9$

For 28–30, solve, then graph each solution set on a number line.

28. $\frac{m}{3} - 1 < 4$
    $m < 15$
29. $\frac{w}{4} + 5 \leq 12$
    $w \leq 28$
30. $9p - 3 \geq 33$
    $p \geq 4$
31. Casey is having a party at his swim club. He has 2 passes. Each pass allows him to bring up to 6 guests. He has already invited 4 friends. How many more friends can he invite?
    no more than 8 friends
32. Eric scored at least 10 more points than Brad scored. Brad scored 18 points. How many points did Eric score?
    at least 28 points

LEVEL B

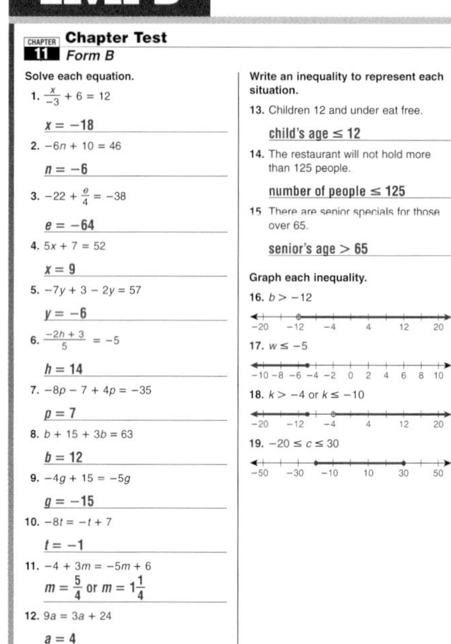

Chapter 11 Chapter Test
Form B

Solve each equation.

1. $\frac{x}{-3} + 6 = 12$
   $x = -18$
2. $-6n + 10 = 46$
   $n = -6$
3. $-22 + \frac{e}{4} = -38$
   $e = -64$
4. $5x + 7 = 52$
   $x = 9$
5. $-7y + 3 - 2y = 57$
   $y = -6$
6. $\frac{-2h + 3}{5} = -5$
   $h = 14$
7. $-8p - 7 + 4p = -35$
   $p = 7$
8. $b + 15 + 3b = 63$
   $b = 12$
9. $-4g + 15 = -5g$
   $g = -15$
10. $-8t = -t + 7$
    $t = -1$
11. $-4 + 3m = -5m + 6$
    $m = \frac{5}{4}$ or $m = 1\frac{1}{4}$
12. $9a = 3a + 24$
    $a = 4$

Write an inequality to represent each situation.

13. Children 12 and under eat free.
    child's age $\leq$ 12
14. The restaurant will not hold more than 125 people.
    number of people $\leq$ 125
15. There are senior specials for those over 65.
    senior's age $>$ 65

Graph each inequality.

16. $b > -12$
17. $w \leq -5$
18. $k > -4$ or $k \leq -10$
19. $-20 \leq c \leq 30$

Chapter 11 Chapter Test
Form B, continued

Solve, then graph each solution set on a number line.

20. $f - 4 > -13$
    $f > -9$
21. $a + 14 < -1$
    $a < -15$
22. $z - 40 \leq 0$
    $z \leq 40$
23. $d - 12 \geq -2$
    $d \geq 10$

Solve each inequality.

24. $\frac{x}{-5} < 15$
    $x > -75$
25. $\frac{w}{3} \leq -7$
    $w \leq -21$
26. $-4p > -124$
    $p < 31$
27. $24c \geq -168$
    $c \geq -7$

For 28–30, solve, then graph each solution set on a number line.

28. $\frac{n}{3} - 32 < -26$
    $n < 18$
29. $16h + 15 > -1$
    $h > -1$
30. $2y - 12 \geq -16$
    $y \geq -2$
31. Serena has $240 in her savings account. She wants to buy 4 matching wicker chairs for her front porch and still have at least $100 left in her account. How much can she spend on each chair?
    at most $35 each
32. Jordan washed at least 8 more cars than Julius. Julius washed 18 cars. How many cars did Jordan wash?
    at least 26 cars

LEVEL C

Chapter 11 Chapter Test
Form C

Solve each equation.

1. $\frac{s}{-5} + 12 = -2\frac{1}{2}$
   $s = 72\frac{1}{2}$
2. $-1.25z - 4.5 = -32$
   $z = 22$
3. $-6.4 - \frac{n}{4} = 12.75$
   $n = -76.6$
4. $\frac{1}{2} + \frac{x}{5} = \frac{7}{10}$
   $x = 1$
5. $-1.75t + 32 - 2t = -8.5$
   $t = 10.8$
6. $\frac{-0.5k + 1.4}{5} = -2.8$
   $k = 30.8$
7. $-3c - \frac{1}{4} + 5c = -3\frac{1}{8}$
   $c = -1\frac{7}{16}$
8. $\frac{2b + 1.5}{0.4} = -23$
   $b = -5.35$
9. $-\frac{3}{4}m + 3 = -1\frac{1}{2}m$
   $m = -4$
10. $-5x = -0.75x + 21.25$
    $x = -5$
11. $-(-6 + 13) + 0.8a = -1.2a - 5$
    $a = 1$
12. $0.9a + 6 = -0.3a + 3$
    $a = -2.5$

Write an inequality to represent each situation.

13. Medium fits sizes 6 through 8.
    6 $\leq$ medium $\leq$ 8
14. The snow was more than 2 feet deep, but at most 6 feet deep in the deepest spots.
    2 ft $<$ snow depth $\leq$ 6 ft
15. The salary is at least $5.75 per hour but less than $12 per hour.
    $5.75 $\leq$ salary $<$ $12

Graph each inequality.

16. $x > -2.5$
17. $n \leq \frac{1}{2}$
18. $y > -(3 \cdot -4)$ or $y \leq (-3 \cdot -2)$
19. $-(12 - 15.5) \leq z < 5.5$

Chapter 11 Chapter Test
Form C, continued

Solve, then graph each solution set on a number line.

20. $d - (-12) > (-21 + 15)$
    $d > -18$
21. $-55 + h < -4 \cdot 12$
    $h < 7$
22. $e - (12 - (-6)) \leq 32 + (-14)$
    $e \leq 36$
23. $g + 0.75 < -0.4 + 3.15$
    $g < 2$

Solve each inequality.

24. $\frac{w}{-4.6} < -1.05$
    $w > 4.83$
25. $-8m \leq 600$
    $m \geq -75$
26. $-\frac{5}{8}p > -75$
    $p < 120$
27. $6.5b \geq -16 + 42$
    $b \geq 4$

For 28–30, solve, then graph each solution set on a number line.

28. $\frac{k}{-2} - 5\frac{7}{8} < -2\frac{3}{8}$
    $k > -7$
29. $\frac{n}{-2} - (3 - (-12)) \leq -2 - 8$
    $n \geq -10$
30. $-3.5f - 4 \geq -(-6.5 + 3.5)$
    $f \leq -2$
31. Marissa saves 20% of her $8 weekly allowance. With the rest of it, she wants to buy some birthday cards that cost $1.50 each. At most, how many cards can she buy?
    at most 4 cards
32. Tina sold at least 23 more tickets than John. She sold 5 fewer tickets than April. John sold 41 tickets and April sold no more than 70 tickets. How many tickets did Tina sell?
    64 or 65 tickets

Test and Practice Generator CD-ROM

Create and customize multiple versions of the same tests with corresponding answers for any chosen chapter objectives.

Chapter 11 State and Standardized Test Preparation

Test Taking Skill Builder and Standardized Test Practice are provided for each chapter in the *Test Prep Tool Kit.*

TEST TAKING SKILL BUILDER

Test Taking Strategy **Know How the Test Is Scored**
Chapter 11

Different standardized tests are scored in different ways. Pay attention to the directions the test proctor reads aloud. It helps if you know ahead of time how the test is scored. You will experience the most success if you are prepared for the type of test you are taking.

- Some multiple choice sections have no penalty for guessing. In this case, be sure to answer every question, even if you are unsure of the answer.
- If the test has a penalty for guessing, eliminate as many answer choices as you can. If you cannot eliminate any answer choices, it is best to leave the question blank.
- Extended response and short response questions are graded using a scoring rubric. Never leave a response question blank. Always show each step of your calculations, and explain your thinking process in detail.
- Some tests allow the use of calculators. If so, use a calculator with which you are familiar. Make sure you have fresh batteries.
- Some tests include a list of formulas. Ask your teacher ahead of time if the test you are taking includes formulas.

Example Multiple Choice Solve for x. $8x + 3 = 6x - 7$

A $x = -5$ B $x = -2$ C $x = \frac{10}{14}$ D $x = 5$

Solution: If you have no idea how to solve an equation with variables on both sides of the equation, try using a problem solving strategy such as working backwards. If you are still unsure what to do, know how the test is scored. Leave the question blank if you are penalized for wrong answers. If there is no penalty for guessing, choose one of the answer choices.

Be careful of distracters. Distracters are answer choices that result when you make a simple error in the calculation. For instance, if you make a subtraction error, you might get the solution $x = 5$ rather than $x = -5$. Make sure you check your answer.

$$8x + 3 = 6x - 7$$
$$8x - 6x + 3 = 6x - 6x - 7$$
$$2x + 3 = -7$$
$$2x + 3 - 3 = -7 - 3$$
$$2x = -10$$
$$x = -5$$

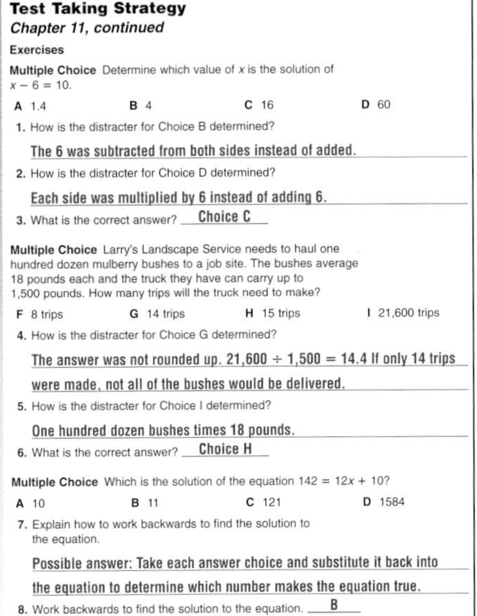

Test Taking Strategy
Chapter 11, continued

Exercises

Multiple Choice Determine which value of x is the solution of $x - 6 = 10$.

A 1.4 B 4 C 16 D 60

1. How is the distracter for Choice B determined?
   The 6 was subtracted from both sides instead of added.
2. How is the distracter for Choice D determined?
   Each side was multiplied by 6 instead of adding 6.
3. What is the correct answer? Choice C

Multiple Choice Larry's Landscape Service needs to haul one hundred dozen mulberry bushes to a job site. The bushes average 18 pounds each and the truck they have can carry up to 1,500 pounds. How many trips will the truck need to make?

F 8 trips G 14 trips H 15 trips I 21,600 trips

4. How is the distracter for Choice G determined?
   The answer was not rounded up. $21,600 \div 1,500 = 14.4$ If only 14 trips were made, not all of the bushes would be delivered.
5. How is the distracter for Choice I determined?
   One hundred dozen bushes times 18 pounds.
6. What is the correct answer? Choice H

Multiple Choice Which is the solution of the equation $142 = 12x + 10$?

A 10 B 11 C 121 D 1584

7. Explain how to work backwards to find the solution to the equation.
   Possible answer: Take each answer choice and substitute it back into the equation to determine which number makes the equation true.
8. Work backwards to find the solution to the equation. B

STANDARDIZED TEST PRACTICE

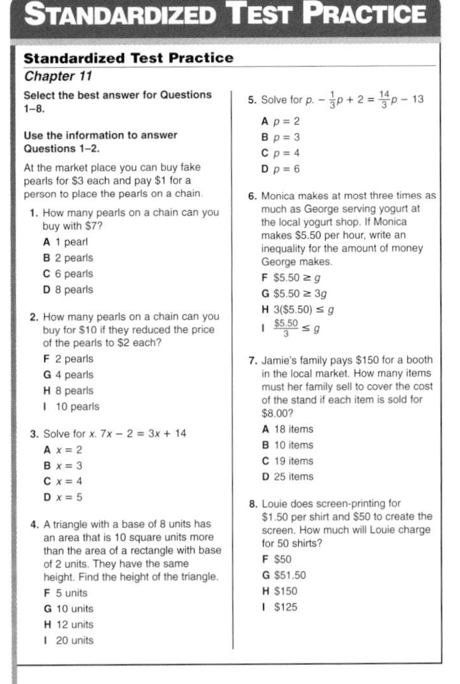

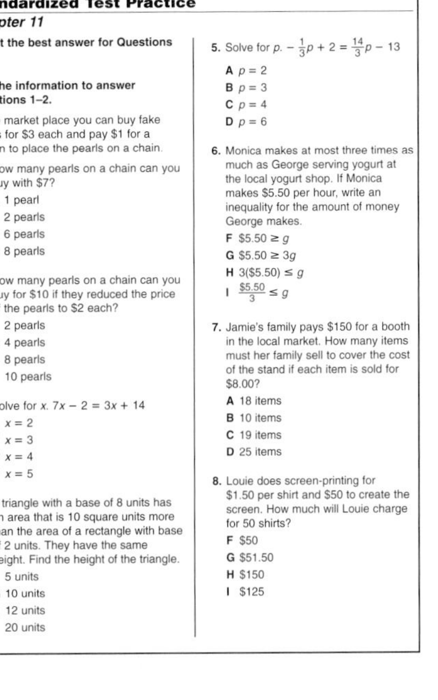

Standardized Test Practice
Chapter 11

Select the best answer for Questions 1–8.

Use the information to answer Questions 1–2.

At the market place you can buy fake pearls for $3 each and pay $1 for a person to place the pearls on a chain.

1. How many pearls on a chain can you buy with $7?
   A 1 pearl
   B 2 pearls
   C 6 pearls
   D 8 pearls
2. How many pearls on a chain can you buy for $10 if they reduced the price of the pearls to $2 each?
   F 2 pearls
   G 4 pearls
   H 8 pearls
   I 10 pearls
3. Solve for x. $7x - 2 = 3x + 14$
   A $x = 2$
   B $x = 3$
   C $x = 4$
   D $x = 5$
4. A triangle with a base of 8 units has an area that is 10 square units more than the area of a rectangle with base of 2 units. They have the same height. Find the height of the triangle.
   F 5 units
   G 10 units
   H 12 units
   I 20 units
5. Solve for p. $-\frac{1}{3}p + 2 = \frac{14}{3}p - 13$
   A $p = 2$
   B $p = 3$
   C $p = 4$
   D $p = 6$
6. Monica makes at most three times as much as George serving yogurt at the local yogurt shop. If Monica makes $5.50 per hour, write an inequality for the amount of money George makes.
   F $\$5.50 \geq g$
   G $\$5.50 \geq 3g$
   H $3(\$5.50) \leq g$
   I $\frac{\$5.50}{3} \leq g$
7. Jamie's family pays $150 for a booth in the local market. How many items must her family sell to cover the cost of the stand if each item is sold for $8.00?
   A 18 items
   B 10 items
   C 19 items
   D 25 items
8. Louie does screen-printing for $1.50 per shirt and $50 to create the screen. How much will Louie charge for 50 shirts?
   F $50
   G $51.50
   H $150
   I $125

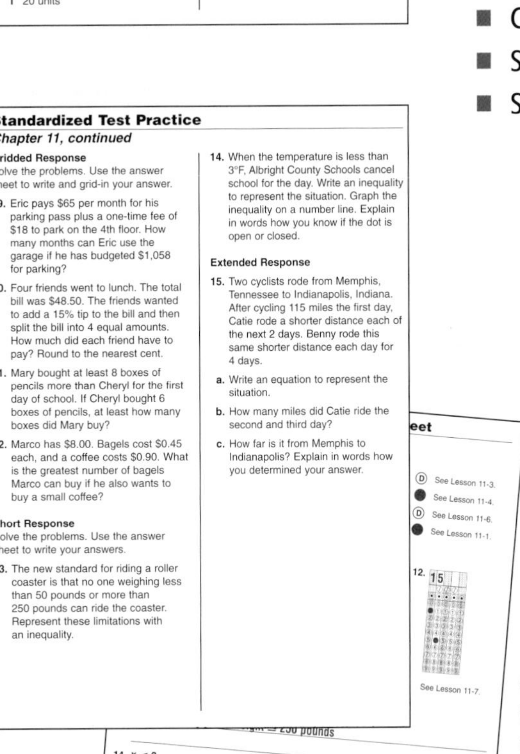

Standardized Test Practice
Chapter 11, continued

Gridded Response
Solve the problems. Use the answer sheet to write and grid-in your answer.

9. Eric pays $65 per month for his parking pass plus a one-time fee of $18 to park on the 4th floor. How many months can Eric use the garage if he has budgeted $1,058 for parking?
10. Four friends went to lunch. The total bill was $48.50. The friends wanted to add a 15% tip to the bill and then split the bill into 4 equal amounts. How much did each friend have to pay? Round to the nearest cent.
11. Mary bought at least 8 boxes of pencils more than Cheryl for the first day of school. If Cheryl bought 6 boxes of pencils, at least how many boxes did Mary buy?
12. Marco has $8.00. Bagels cost $0.45 each, and a coffee costs $0.90. What is the greatest number of bagels Marco can buy if he also wants to buy a small coffee?

Short Response
Solve the problems. Use the answer sheet to write your answers.

13. The new standard for riding a roller coaster is that no one weighing less than 50 pounds or more than 250 pounds can ride the coaster. Represent these limitations with an inequality.
14. When the temperature is less than 3°F, Albright County Schools cancel school for the day. Write an inequality to represent the situation. Graph the inequality on a number line. Explain in words how you know if the dot is open or closed.

Extended Response

15. Two cyclists rode from Memphis, Tennessee to Indianapolis, Indiana. After cycling 115 miles the first day, Catie rode a shorter distance each of the next 2 days. Benny rode this same shorter distance each day for 4 days.
    a. Write an equation to represent the situation.
    b. How many miles did Catie ride the second and third day?
    c. How far is it from Memphis to Indianapolis? Explain in words how you determined your answer.

...eet

Ⓓ See Lesson 11-3.
● See Lesson 11-4.
Ⓓ See Lesson 11-6.
● See Lesson 11-1.

12. 15

See Lesson 11-7.

... = 250 pounds

14. $x < 3$; (See Lesson 11-4.)

−5 −3 −1 1 3 5

Draw an open circle on 3 because 3 is not included as a solution. Draw an arrow from 3 going to the left of 3 because the numbers smaller than 3 are to the left of 3.

Extended Response (See Lesson 11-4.)
Write your answers for Problem 15 on the back of this paper.
See Lesson 11-3.

internet connect

State-Specific Test Practice Online
KEYWORD: MS4 TestPrep

Test Prep Tool Kit

- Standardized Test Prep Workbook
- Countdown to Testing transparencies
- State Test Prep CD-ROM
- Standardized Test Prep Video

Customized answer sheets give students realistic practice for actual standardized tests.

Multistep Equations and Inequalities

Why Learn This?

Tell students that satellite engineers use mathematics to program satellites to travel along a specific orbit and to figure out how to transmit the data that the satellites collect. Weather satellites track weather patterns to help meteorologists forecast the weather. Communication satellites connect phone calls and transmit television programs.

Using Data

To begin the study of this chapter, have students:

- Make a bar graph of the altitudes of the artificial satellites in the table.

Altitudes of Artificial Satellites

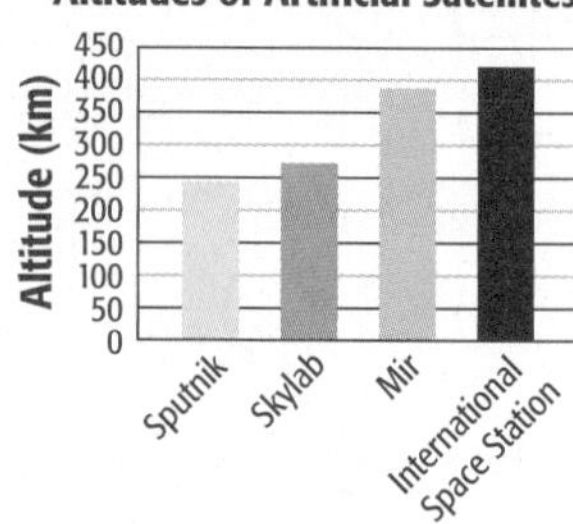

- Convert the altitudes in the table to the nearest mile. Use 1 mi = 1.6 km.
  245 km = 153 mi; 270 km = 169 mi
  390 km = 244 mi; 420 km = 263 mi

Chapter 11

TABLE OF CONTENTS

internet connect
Chapter Opener Online
go.hrw.com
KEYWORD: MS4 Ch11

Multistep Equations and Inequalities

Altitudes of Artificial Satellites	
Satellite	Altitude (km)
Sputnik	245
Skylab	270
Mir	390
International Space Station	420

Career ***Satellite Engineer***

Artificial satellites were born with the launch of *Sputnik* on October 4, 1957. The 84 kg ball with a 56 cm diameter circled Earth every 35 minutes and signified the beginning of changes in the way people live. Today, there are over 2,500 satellites orbiting Earth.

Satellite engineers work on satellite design, construction, orbit determination, launch, tracking, and orbit adjustment. Satellites can monitor weather, crop growth, and natural resources and communicate this information using television, radio, and other communication signals. Satellites can even directionally guide people who have GPS (Global Positioning System) devices.

Problem Solving Project

Physical Science Connection

Purpose: To solve problems using equations

Materials: Earth Orbit worksheet, drawing and/or modeling materials

internet connect
Chapter Project Online: ***go.hrw.com***
KEYWORD: MS4 PSProject11

Understand, Plan, Solve, and Look Back

Have students:

- ✓ Examine the table. Ask students which artificial satellite reached the highest altitude. How much higher did it reach than the others? Which countries launched these satellites?
- ✓ Complete the Earth Orbit worksheet.
- ✓ Create a model or drawing of the four artificial satellites, showing the distances that they would be from each other and from Earth if they were all still in orbit.
- ✓ Research to find out about the United States' first satellite.
- ✓ Check students' work.

ARE YOU READY?

Choose the best term from the list to complete each sentence.

isolate the variable
equation
proportion
inverse operations
expression

1. __?__ are mathematical operations that undo each other. **inverse operations**
2. To solve an equation you need to __?__. **isolate the variable**
3. A(n) __?__ is a mathematical statement that two expressions are equivalent. **equation**
4. A(n) __?__ is a mathematical statement that two ratios are equivalent. **proportion**

Complete these exercises to review skills you will need for this chapter.

✔ Add Whole Numbers, Decimals, Fractions, and Integers

Add.

5. $-24 + 16$ **−8**
6. $-34 + (-47)$ **−81**
7. $35 + (-61)$ **−26**
8. $-12 + (-29) + 53$ **12**
9. $2.7 + 3.5$ **6.2**
10. $\frac{2}{3} + \frac{1}{2}$ **$\frac{7}{6}$ or $1\frac{1}{6}$**
11. $-5.87 + 10.6$ **4.73**
12. $\frac{8}{9} + \left(-\frac{9}{11}\right)$ **$\frac{7}{99}$**

✔ Evaluate Expressions

Evaluate each expression for $a = 7$ and $b = -2$.

13. $a - b$ **9**
14. $b - a$ **−9**
15. $\frac{b}{a}$ **$-\frac{2}{7}$**
16. $2a + 3b$ **8**
17. $\frac{-4a}{b}$ **14**
18. $3a - \frac{8}{b}$ **25**
19. $1.2a + 2.3b$ **3.8**
20. $-5a - (-6b)$ **−47**

✔ Solve Multiplication Equations

Solve.

21. $8x = -72$ **$x = -9$**
22. $-12a = -60$ **$a = 5$**
23. $\frac{2}{3}y = 16$ **$y = 24$**
24. $-12b = 9$ **$b = -0.75$**
25. $12 = -4x$ **$x = -3$**
26. $13 = \frac{1}{2}c$ **$c = 26$**
27. $-2.4 = -0.8p$ **$p = 3$**
28. $\frac{3}{4} = 6x$ **$x = \frac{1}{8}$**

✔ Solve Proportions

Solve.

29. $\frac{3}{4} = \frac{x}{24}$ **$x = 18$**
30. $\frac{8}{9} = \frac{4}{a}$ **$a = 4.5$**
31. $-\frac{12}{5} = \frac{15}{c}$ **$c = -6.25$**
32. $\frac{y}{50} = \frac{35}{20}$ **$y = 87.5$**
33. $\frac{2}{3} = \frac{18}{w}$ **$w = 27$**
34. $\frac{35}{21} = \frac{d}{3}$ **$d = 5$**
35. $\frac{7}{13} = \frac{h}{195}$ **$h = 105$**
36. $\frac{9}{-15} = \frac{-27}{p}$ **$p = 45$**

Assessing Prior Knowledge

INTERVENTION

Diagnose and Prescribe

Evaluate your students' performance on this page to determine whether intervention is necessary or whether enrichment is appropriate. Options that provide instruction, practice, and a check are listed below.

Resources for Are You Ready?

- ***Are You Ready? Intervention and Enrichment***
- **Recording Sheet for Are You Ready?** *Chapter 11 Resource Book* ..... p. 3

***Are You Ready? Intervention* CD-ROM**

internet connect

Are You Ready? Intervention
go.hrw.com
KEYWORD: MS4 AYR

ARE YOU READY?

Were students successful with Are You Ready?

NO — INTERVENE

YES — ENRICH

✔ Add Whole Numbers, Decimals, Fractions, and Integers
Are You Ready? Intervention, Skill 34, 40, 42
Blackline Masters, Online, and

CD-ROM
Intervention Activities

✔ Evaluate Expressions
Are You Ready? Intervention, Skill 54
Blackline Masters, Online, and
CD-ROM
Intervention Activities

✔ Solve Multiplication Equations
Are You Ready? Intervention, Skill 59
Blackline Masters, Online, and

CD-ROM
Intervention Activities

✔ Solve Proportions
Are You Ready? Intervention, Skill 65
Blackline Masters, Online, and

CD-ROM
Intervention Activities

Are You Ready? Enrichment, pp. 427–428

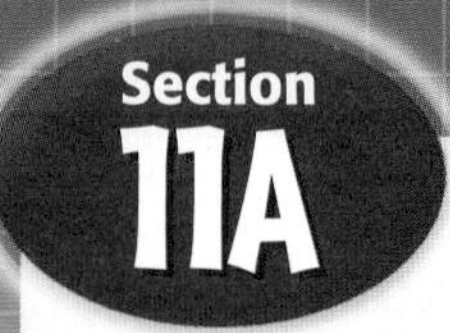

Multistep Equations

One-Minute Section Planner

Lesson	Materials	Resources
Hands-On Lab 11A Model Two-Step Equations **NCTM:** Algebra, Geometry, Reasoning and Proof, Representation **NAEP:** Algebra 2a ☐ SAT-9 ☐ SAT-10 ☐ ITBS ☐ CTBS ☐ MAT ☐ CAT	**Required** Algebra tiles (*MK*)	• *Hands-On Lab Activities,* pp. 104–107, 126
Lesson 11-1 Solving Two-Step Equations **NCTM:** Algebra, Communication **NAEP:** Algebra 4a ☐ SAT-9 ☐ SAT-10 ☐ ITBS ☐ CTBS ☐ MAT ☑ CAT	**Optional** Algebra tiles (*MK*)	• *Chapter 11 Resource Book,* pp. 7–15 • Daily Transparency T1, CRB • Additional Examples Transparencies T2–T5, CRB • *Alternate Openers: Explorations,* p. 88
Lesson 11-2 Solving Multistep Equations **NCTM:** Algebra, Problem Solving, Communication **NAEP:** Algebra 4a ☐ SAT-9 ☐ SAT-10 ☐ ITBS ☐ CTBS ☐ MAT ☑ CAT		• *Chapter 11 Resource Book,* pp. 16–24 • Daily Transparency T6, CRB • Additional Examples Transparencies T7–T9, CRB • *Alternate Openers: Explorations,* p. 89
Lesson 11-3 Solving Equations with Variables on Both Sides **NCTM:** Algebra, Communication **NAEP:** Algebra 4a ☐ SAT-9 ☐ SAT-10 ☐ ITBS ☐ CTBS ☐ MAT ☐ CAT	**Optional** Recording Sheet for Reaching All Learners (*CRB, p. 77*) Algebra tiles (*MK*)	• *Chapter 11 Resource Book,* pp. 25–33 • Daily Transparency T10, CRB • Additional Examples Transparencies T11–T14, CRB • *Alternate Openers: Explorations,* p. 90
Section 11A Assessment		• Mid-Chapter Quiz, SE p. 572 • Section 11A Quiz AR p. 29 • *Test and Practice Generator* CD-ROM

SAT = *Stanford Achievement Tests* **ITBS** = *Iowa Test of Basic Skills* **CTBS** = *Comprehensive Test of Basic Skills/Terra Nova*
MAT = *Metropolitan Achievement Test* **CAT** = *California Achievement Test*

NCTM—Complete standards can be found on pages T27–T33. **NAEP**—Complete standards can be found on pages A35–A39.

SE = *Student Edition* **TE** = *Teacher's Edition* **AR** = *Assessment Resources* **CRB** = *Chapter Resource Book* **MK** = *Manipulatives Kit*

Section Overview

Solve Two-Step Equations — *Hands-On Lab 11A, Lesson 11-1*

Why? To work effectively with formulas in science, students must be able to solve multistep equations. Solving two-step equations is a stepping stone to solving multistep equations and two-step inequalities.

To solve, reverse the order of operations and use inverse operations.

$$8x + 15 = 39$$
$$\underline{-\mathbf{15}} \quad \underline{-\mathbf{15}}$$
$$8x = 24$$
$$\frac{8x}{\mathbf{8}} = \frac{24}{\mathbf{8}}$$
$$x = 3$$

Subtract 15 from both sides of the equation.

Divide both sides of the equation by 8.

Solve Multistep Equations — *Lesson 11-2*

Why? Students will have to combine like terms when they solve equations with variables on both sides.

Combine like terms and clear the denominator. Then solve as a two-step equation.

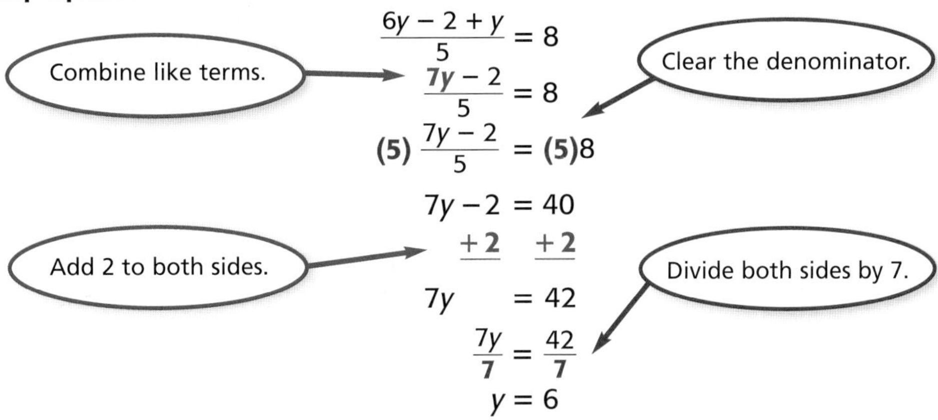

$\frac{6y - 2 + y}{5} = 8$
Combine like terms.
$\frac{\mathbf{7y} - 2}{5} = 8$
Clear the denominator.
$(\mathbf{5})\frac{7y - 2}{5} = (\mathbf{5})8$
$7y - 2 = 40$
Add 2 to both sides.
$\underline{+\mathbf{2}} \quad \underline{+\mathbf{2}}$
$7y = 42$
Divide both sides by 7.
$\frac{7y}{\mathbf{7}} = \frac{42}{\mathbf{7}}$
$y = 6$

Solve Equations with Variables on Both Sides — *Lesson 11-3*

Why? Students encounter more-complex equations as they study algebra and geometry. These more-complex equations are usually solved by extending the skills learned in this chapter.

To solve, the variables must be on one side of the equation.

$$3m + 15 = -5m - 9$$
$$\mathbf{5m} + 3m + 15 = -5m + \mathbf{5m} - 9$$
$$\mathbf{8m} + \mathbf{15} = -9$$
$$\underline{-\mathbf{15}} \quad \underline{-\mathbf{15}}$$
$$8m = -24$$
$$\frac{8m}{8} = \frac{-24}{8}$$
$$m = -3$$

Add 5*m* to both sides of the equation.

Combine like terms.

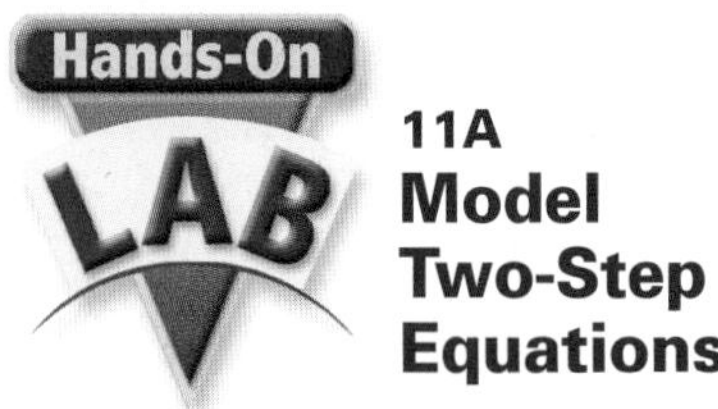

11A Model Two-Step Equations

Pacing: Traditional 1 day
Block $\frac{1}{2}$ day

Objective: To use algebra tiles to model two-step equations

Materials: Algebra tiles

Lab Resources

Hands-On Lab Activities. . . pp. 104–107, 126

Using the Pages

Discuss with students what each algebra tile represents and how to represent equations with algebra tiles.

Use algebra tiles to model each equation.

1. $x + 4 = 9$

2. $3n - 1 = 7$

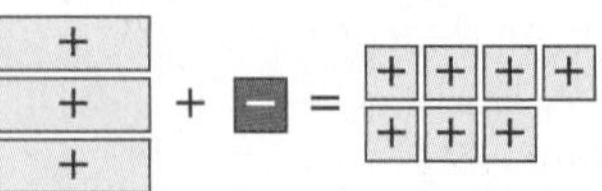

3. $2a - 3 = -5$

4. $-4y + 2 = -2$

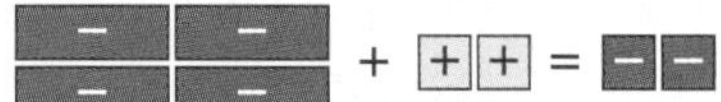

Model Two-Step Equations

Use with Lesson 11-1

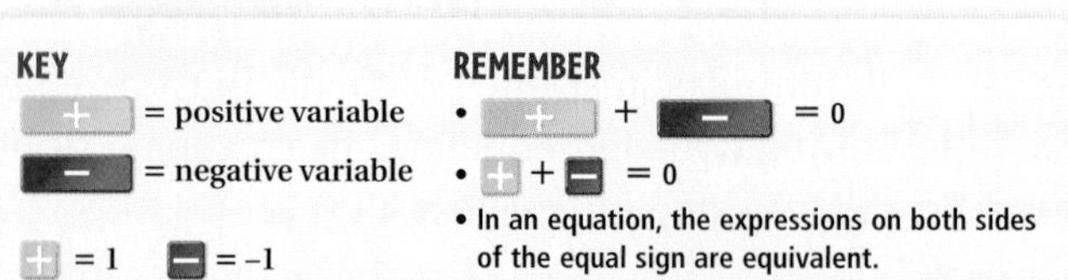

In Lab 3C, you learned how to solve one-step equations using algebra tiles. For example, to solve the equation $x + 2 = 6$, you need to isolate the variable by removing tiles.

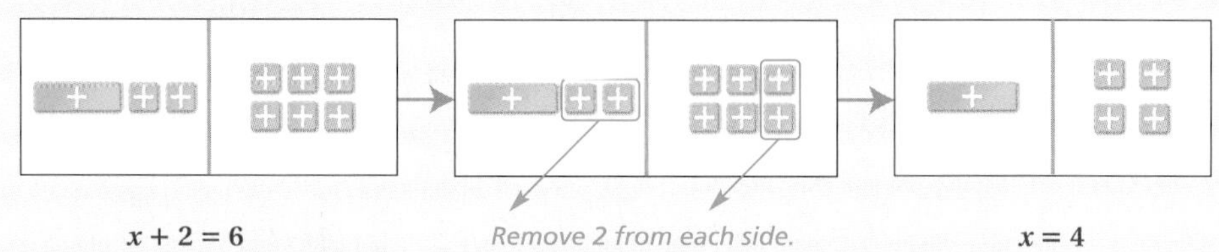

$x + 2 = 6$ — *Remove 2 from each side.* — $x = 4$

You can also use algebra tiles to solve two-step equations.

Activity

When solving a two-step equation, such as $2p + 2 = 10$, it is easiest to perform addition and subtraction before multiplication and division.

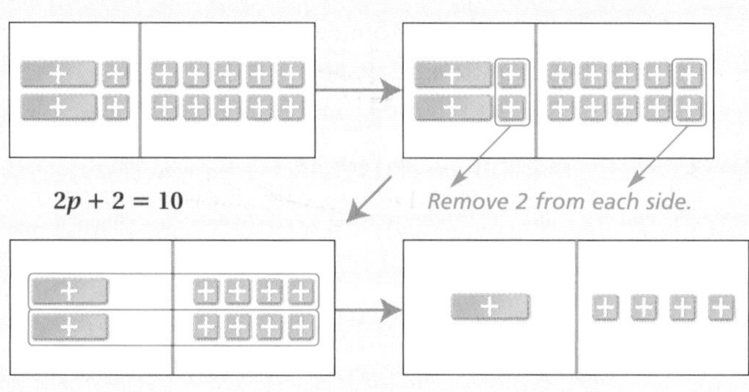

$2p + 2 = 10$ — *Remove 2 from each side.*

Divide each side into 2 equal groups. — $p = 4$

1 Use algebra tiles to model and solve each equation.

a. $3x + 5 = 14$ **$x = 3$** **b.** $2n - 1 = -5$ **$n = -2$** **c.** $4w + 3 = 7$ **$w = 1$** **d.** $3n - 6 = -18$ **$n = -4$**

To model solving the equation $3n + 6 = -15$, you must add neutral pairs to isolate the variable term.

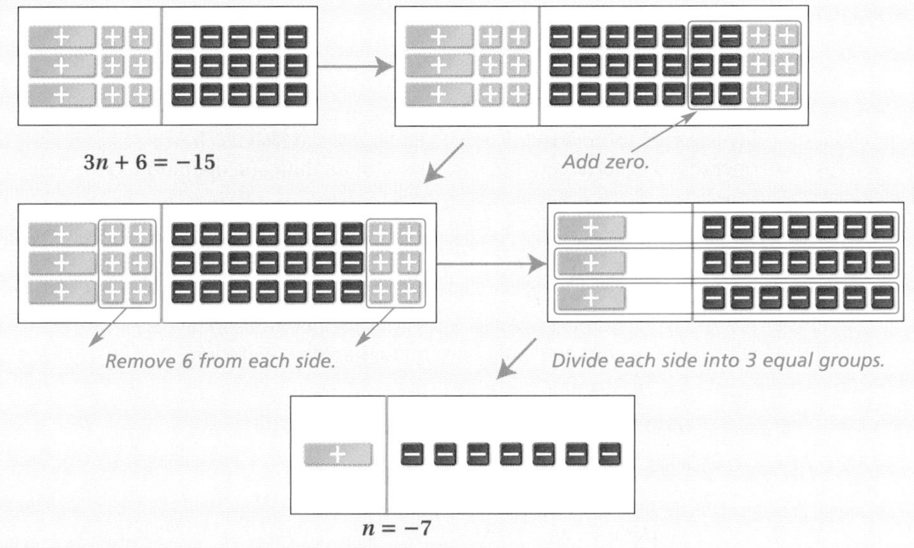

2 Use algebra tiles to model and solve each equation.

a. $2y - 4 = 10$ **$y = 7$** b. $3k + 3 = -12$ **$k = -5$** c. $-1 + 5m = 9$ **$m = 2$** d. $5 + 2k = -3$ **$k = -4$**

Think and Discuss

1. When you subtract a value from one side of an equation, why do you also have to subtract the same value from the other side?
2. When you solved $3n + 6 = -15$ in the activity, why didn't you have to add six yellow unit tiles and six red unit tiles to the left side of the equation when you added them to the right side? **Adding 6 yellow unit tiles and 6 red unit tiles is equivalent to adding 0.**
3. Model and solve $3x - 5 = 10$. Explain each step.
4. How would you check the solution to $3n + 6 = -15$ using algebra tiles? **Use the model for $3n + 6 = -15$, but substitute 7 red unit tiles for each yellow variable tile. Then check to see that both sides of the equation are equal.**

Try This

Use algebra tiles to model and solve each equation.

1. $4 + 2x = 20$ **$x = 8$**
2. $3r + 7 = -8$ **$r = -5$**
3. $-4m + 3 = -25$ **$m = 7$**
4. $-2n - 5 = 17$ **$n = -11$**
5. $10 = 2j - 4$ **$j = 7$**
6. $5 + r = 7$ **$r = 2$**
7. $4h + 2h + 3 = 15$ **$h = 2$**
8. $-3g = 9$ **$g = -3$**
9. $5k + (-7) = 13$ **$k = 4$**

Answers

Think and Discuss

1. The Subtraction Property of Equality states that you must subtract the same number from both sides of the equation for the statement to remain true.
3. To model $3x - 5 = 10$, use 3 yellow variable tiles and 5 red unit tiles on the left side. Use 10 yellow unit tiles on the right side. In order to remove 5 red unit tiles from the left side, you have to add 0 (5 yellow unit tiles and 5 red unit tiles) to the right side. After removing 5 red tiles from each side, you are left with the equation $3x = 15$. Separate the 15 yellow unit tiles on the right into 3 equal groups to solve for the variable. You find that $x = 5$.

11-1 Organizer

Pacing: Traditional 1 day
Block $\frac{1}{2}$ day

Objective: Students solve two-step equations.

Warm Up

Solve.

1. $n + 9 = 17$ $\quad n = 8$
2. $6x = 42$ $\quad x = 7$
3. $71 - z = 55$ $\quad z = 16$
4. $\frac{y}{8} = 9$ $\quad y = 72$

Problem of the Day

Rhombus *ABCD* has a perimeter of 19 cm. If you subtract 1.88 from the length of side *BC* and then divide the result by 7, you get 0.41. What is the length of side *BC*?
19 ÷ 4 = 4.75 cm (All sides of a rhombus are the same length.)

Available on Daily Transparency in CRB

Teacher: Now suppose the number of sheep is *x*...

Student: Yes, sir, but what happens if the number of sheep is not *x*?

11-1 Solving Two-Step Equations

Learn to solve two-step equations.

When you solve equations that have one operation, you use an inverse operation to isolate the variable. You can also use inverse operations to solve equations that have more than one operation.

$$\begin{array}{rcl} n + 7 &=& 15 \\ -7 && -7 \\ \hline n &=& 8 \end{array} \qquad \begin{array}{rcl} 2x + 3 &=& 23 \\ -3 && -3 \\ \hline \boxed{2x} &=& 20 \end{array}$$

You need to use another inverse operation to isolate x.

It is often a good plan to follow the order of operations in reverse when solving equations that have more than one operation.

EXAMPLE 1 Solving Two-Step Equations Using Division

Solve. Check each answer.

A $6n + 4 = 28$

$$\begin{array}{rcl} 6n + 4 &=& 28 \\ -4 && -4 \\ \hline 6n &=& 24 \end{array}$$
Subtract 4 from both sides.

$$\frac{6n}{6} = \frac{24}{6}$$
Divide both sides by 6.

$$n = 4$$

Check

$$6n + 4 = 28$$
$$6(4) + 4 \stackrel{?}{=} 28$$ *Substitute 4 for n.*
$$24 + 4 \stackrel{?}{=} 28$$
$$28 \stackrel{?}{=} 28 \checkmark$$ *4 is a solution.*

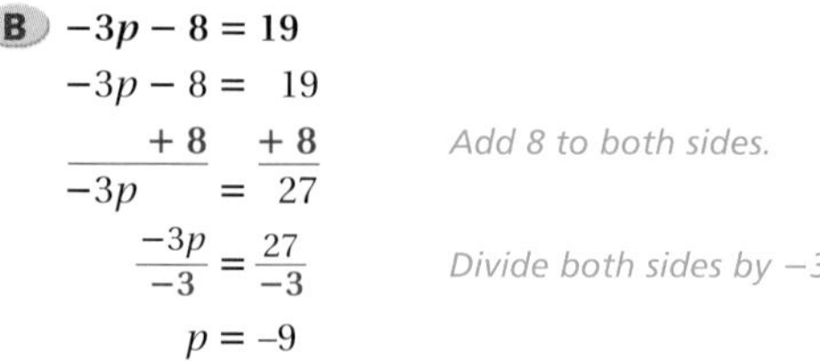

B $-3p - 8 = 19$

$$\begin{array}{rcl} -3p - 8 &=& 19 \\ +8 && +8 \\ \hline -3p &=& 27 \end{array}$$
Add 8 to both sides.

$$\frac{-3p}{-3} = \frac{27}{-3}$$
Divide both sides by −3.

$$p = -9$$

Check

$$-3p - 8 = 19$$
$$-3(-9) - 8 \stackrel{?}{=} 19$$ *Substitute −9 for p.*
$$27 - 8 \stackrel{?}{=} 19$$
$$19 \stackrel{?}{=} 19 \checkmark$$ *−9 is a solution.*

1 Introduce

Alternate Opener

11-1 Solving Two-Step Equations

You can use algebra tiles to solve two-step equations. The model below shows the equation $2x - 2 = 6$.

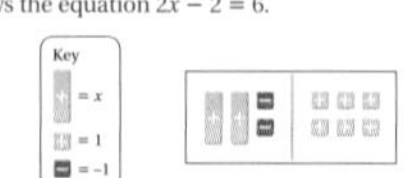

1. What can you do to remove the negative tiles and isolate the term $2x$?
2. What can you do to find the value of x?
3. Write an equation for the model below and find the solution.

Think and Discuss

4. **Explain** the relationship between the number of operations in an equation and the number of steps needed to solve the equation.
5. **Explain** what you did in number 3 to remove the positive tiles from the left side of the mat.

Motivate

Discuss how some activities must be performed in a certain order to yield a desired outcome. Have students name the steps involved for several such activities. Point out that with many activities, just as you can follow a series of steps to arrive at one point, you can "undo" the steps to return to the original starting point. For example, suppose you leave your house and walk two blocks north and one block east. You can return home undoing the order: walk one block west and two blocks south.

Exploration worksheet and answers on Chapter 11 Resource Book pp. 8 and 80

2 Teach

Guided Instruction

In this lesson, students learn to solve two-step equations. Use the concept of an equation as a balanced scale as you discuss solving two-step equations. The goal of solving a two-step equation is the same as the goal of solving a one-step equation: to isolate the variable.

Students may try to solve two-step equations by bringing every thing to one side of the equation to make the other side equal to zero. Demonstrate why this does not work. To solve an equation, the solution must take the form *variable* = *number*. Make sure students are writing each step of the solution process.

EXAMPLE 2 Solving Two-Step Equations Using Multiplication

Solve.

A $8 + \frac{j}{4} = 17$

$$\begin{aligned} 8 + \frac{j}{4} &= 17 \\ -8 \quad & \quad -8 \\ \frac{j}{4} &= 9 \\ (4)\frac{j}{4} &= (4)9 \\ j &= 36 \end{aligned}$$

Subtract 8 from both sides.

Multiply both sides by 4.

B $\frac{u}{6} - 12 = 3$

$$\begin{aligned} \frac{u}{6} - 12 &= 3 \\ +12 \quad & \quad +12 \\ \frac{u}{6} \quad &= 15 \\ (6)\frac{u}{6} &= (6)15 \\ u &= 90 \end{aligned}$$

Add 12 to both sides.

Multiply both sides by 6.

EXAMPLE 3 *Consumer Math Application*

A new one-year membership at Workout Nation costs \$630. A registration fee of \$150 is paid up front, and the rest is paid monthly. How much do new members pay each month?

Let m represent the monthly cost.

$$\begin{aligned} 12m + 150 &= 630 \\ -150 \quad & \quad -150 \\ 12m \quad &= 480 \\ \frac{12m}{12} &= \frac{480}{12} \\ m &= 40 \end{aligned}$$

Subtract 150 from both sides.

Divide both sides by 12.

New members pay \$40 per month for a one-year membership.

Think and Discuss

1. **Explain** how you decide which inverse operation to use first when solving a two-step equation.
2. **Tell** how each term in the equation in Example 3 relates to the word problem.

COMMON ERROR ALERT

Some students might get confused when two-step equations take the form $a + bx = c$. Have these students rewrite the equation as $bx + a = c$ before they attempt to solve the equation. Also, if an equation is written in the form $a - bx = c$, remind students that the subtraction symbol stays with the b making it negative: $-bx + a = c$.

Additional Examples

Example 1

Solve. Check each answer.

A. $9c + 3 = 39$ **$c = 4$**

B. $-4m - 6 = -34$ **$m = 7$**

Example 2

Solve.

A. $6 + \frac{y}{5} = 21$ **$y = 75$**

B. $\frac{x}{7} - 11 = 9$ **$x = 140$**

Example 3

Jamie rented a canoe while she was on vacation. She paid a flat rental fee of \$85.00 plus \$7.50 each day. Her total cost was \$130.00. For how many days did she rent the canoe?
6 days

Example 2 note: Because the solutions of two-step equations are not as obvious as the solutions of one-step equations, emphasize the importance of checking answers.

3 Close

Reaching All Learners
Through Critical Thinking

Let students work in pairs to create word problems that require two-step equations to solve. Students must be sure that their problems use two-step equations and have solutions. Ask each pair to write several problems. After the pairs have checked each problem, have them exchange problems and solve.

Summarize

Challenge students to solve and check each of the following equations and to explain each step in the solution:

$-8 + 3x = -14$ **$x = -2$**

$\frac{y}{4} - 15 = 7$ **$y = 88$**

Answers to Think and Discuss

Possible answers:

1. You do whichever inverse operation is easier. Often, it is easier to either add or subtract a number on both sides and then multiply or divide. Sometimes, though, as in the equation $3(x - 2) = 6$, it is easier to either multiply or divide first.
2. $12m$ represents the monthly fees for the whole year; 150 is the amount of the one-time registration fee; 630 is the total amount paid for the entire year.

11-1 PRACTICE & ASSESS

Students may want to refer back to the lesson examples.

Assignment Guide

If you finished Example 1 assign:
Core 1–3, 8–13, 25–29 odd, 39–41
Enriched 1, 3, 9–13 odd, 22, 25–31 odd, 39–41

If you finished Example 2 assign:
Core 1–6, 8–19, 22, 24–26, 39–41
Enriched 1–5 odd, 9–19 odd, 21–32, 39–41

If you finished Example 3 assign:
Core 1–26, 33–37 odd, 39–41
Enriched 1–19 odd, 21–41

Answers

21. 6 more than a number divided by 3 equals 18; $m = 36$

22. 15 more than 3 times a number equals 27; $x = 4$

23. 4 less than a number divided by 5 equals 2; $n = 30$

11-1 Exercises

FOR EXTRA PRACTICE see page 678

internet connect — Homework Help Online go.hrw.com Keyword: MS4 11-1

GUIDED PRACTICE

See Example 1 **Solve. Check each answer.**

1. $3n + 8 = 29$ **$n = 7$**
2. $-4m - 7 = 17$ **$m = -6$**
3. $-6x + 4 = 2$ **$x = \frac{1}{3}$**

See Example 2 **Solve.**

4. $12 + \frac{b}{6} = 16$ **$b = 24$**
5. $\frac{y}{8} - 15 = 2$ **$y = 136$**
6. $-8 + \frac{n}{4} = 10$ **$n = 72$**

See Example 3

7. A coffee shop offers a souvenir ceramic mug filled with coffee for $8.95. After that, refills cost $1.50. Sandra spent $26.95 on a mug and refills last month. How many refills did she buy? **12 refills**

INDEPENDENT PRACTICE

See Example 1 **Solve. Check each answer.**

8. $5x + 6 = 41$ **$x = 7$**
9. $-9p - 15 = 93$ **$p = -12$**
10. $-2m + 14 = 10$ **$m = 2$**
11. $7d - 8 = -7$ **$d = \frac{1}{7}$**
12. $-3c + 14 = -7$ **$c = 7$**
13. $12y - 11 = 49$ **$y = 5$**

See Example 2 **Solve.**

14. $24 + \frac{h}{4} = 10$ **$h = -56$**
15. $\frac{k}{5} - 13 = 4$ **$k = 85$**
16. $-17 + \frac{q}{8} = 13$ **$q = 240$**
17. $\frac{m}{10} + 32 = 24$ **$m = -80$**
18. $15 + \frac{v}{3} = -9$ **$v = -72$**
19. $\frac{m}{-7} - 14 = 2$ **$m = -112$**

See Example 3

20. Every Saturday, Workout Nation holds a 45-minute aerobics class. Weekday aerobics classes last 30 minutes. The number of weekday classes varies. Last week there were a total of 165 minutes of aerobics classes available. How many weekday aerobics classes were there? **4 weekday aerobics classes**

PRACTICE AND PROBLEM SOLVING

Translate each equation into words, and then solve the equation.

21. $6 + \frac{m}{3} = 18$
22. $3x + 15 = 27$
23. $\frac{n}{5} - 4 = 2$

Solve.

24. $18 + \frac{y}{4} = 12$ **$y = -24$**
25. $5x + 30 = 40$ **$x = 2$**
26. $\frac{s}{12} - 7 = 8$ **$s = 180$**
27. $-10 + 6g = 110$ **$g = 20$**
28. $\frac{z}{7} + 2 = -8$ **$z = -70$**
29. $-6w - 8 = 46$ **$w = -9$**
30. $-7 + \frac{r}{3} = 15$ **$r = 66$**
31. $-4p - 12 = -20$ **$p = 2$**
32. $\frac{1}{2} + \frac{r}{7} = \frac{5}{14}$ **$r = -1$**

33. A long-distance phone company charges $1.01 for the first 25 minutes of a call, and then $0.09 for each additional minute. If a call cost $9.56, how long did it last? **120 minutes**

Math Background

A *monomial* is an expression that consists of a single term. Examples include 12, $3y$, -7, $4x^2$, and ab. The numbers (-7 and 12) are called *constants.*

A *polynomial* can be a monomial or it can be the sum or difference of monomials. A *polynomial equation* is an equation with polynomials on both sides of the equation. The two-step equations introduced in this lesson are examples of polynomial equations.

RETEACH 11-1

LESSON 11-1 **Reteach**
Solving Two-Step Equations

You can solve two-step equations by undoing one operation at a time. First undo any addition or subtraction, then undo any multiplication or division.

Complete the steps to solve each equation.

1. $7x + 3 = 31$

$7x + 3 - \underline{3} = 31 - \underline{3}$ ← Subtract $\underline{3}$ from both sides to undo addition.

$7x = 28$

$\frac{7x}{7} = \frac{28}{7}$ ← Divide both sides by $\underline{7}$ to undo multiplication.

$x = 4$

Check

$7x + 3 = 31$

$(\underline{4}) + 3 \stackrel{?}{=} 31$ ← Substitute $\underline{4}$ for x.

$\underline{28} + 3 \stackrel{?}{=} 31$

$31 \stackrel{?}{=} 31$ ✓ ← 4 is a solution.

2. $\frac{n}{6} - 8 = 4$
$\frac{n}{6} - 8 + \underline{8} = 4 + \underline{8}$
$\frac{n}{6} = 12$
$6 \cdot \frac{n}{6} = \underline{6} \cdot 12$
$n = 72$

3. $8a - 5 = 11$
$8a - 5 + \underline{5} = 11 + \underline{5}$
$8a = \underline{16}$
$\frac{8a}{8} = \frac{16}{8}$
$a = \underline{2}$

4. $9 + \frac{w}{2} = 12$
$9 - \underline{9} + \frac{w}{2} = 12 - \underline{9}$
$\frac{w}{2} = \underline{3}$
$2 \cdot \frac{w}{2} = \underline{2} \cdot 3$
$w = \underline{6}$

Solve.

5. $4n + 11 = 27$ $\underline{n = 4}$
6. $\frac{z}{7} - 6 = 3$ $\underline{z = 63}$
7. $3 - 2k = -7$ $\underline{k = 5}$

PRACTICE 11-1

LESSON 11-1 **Practice B**
Solving Two-Step Equations

Solve. Check each answer.

1. $7x + 8 = 36$ $\underline{x = 4}$
2. $-3y - 7 = 2$ $\underline{y = -3}$
3. $4a - 13 = 19$ $\underline{a = 8}$
4. $6a - 4 = -2$ $\underline{a = \frac{1}{3}}$
5. $5k + 2 = 6$ $\underline{k = \frac{4}{5}}$
6. $9m - 14 = -8$ $\underline{m = \frac{2}{3}}$
7. $\frac{v}{4} - 3 = 5$ $\underline{v = 32}$
8. $\frac{u}{5} + 3 = 1$ $\underline{u = -10}$
9. $6 + \frac{z}{9} = 9$ $\underline{z = 27}$
10. $-7 + \frac{f}{2} = -1$ $\underline{f = 12}$
11. $9 + \frac{w}{4} = -5$ $\underline{w = -56}$
12. $\frac{e}{7} - 3 = -5$ $\underline{e = -14}$

Solve.

13. $-8 + \frac{d}{5} = 2$ $\underline{d = 50}$
14. $-8j - 1 = 1$ $\underline{j = -\frac{1}{4}}$
15. $\frac{f}{-3} + 5 = 8$ $\underline{f = -9}$

16. Two years of local Internet service costs $685, including the installation fee of $85. What is the monthly fee?
$25 per month

Health LINK

YOUR TOTAL COMES TO $76.41 AND 17,843 CALORIES.

As a service to health-conscious customers, many grocery stores have installed scanners that calculate the total number of calories purchased.

34. If you double the number of calories per day that the U.S. Department of Agriculture recommends for children who are 1 to 3 years old and then subtract 100, you get the number of calories per day recommended for teenage boys. If 2,500 calories are recommended for teenage boys, how many calories should children consume? **1,300 calories**

35. According to the U.S. Department of Agriculture, children who are 4 to 6 years old need about 1,800 calories per day. This is 700 calories more than half the recommended calories for teenage girls. How many calories does a teenage girl need per day? **2,200 calories**

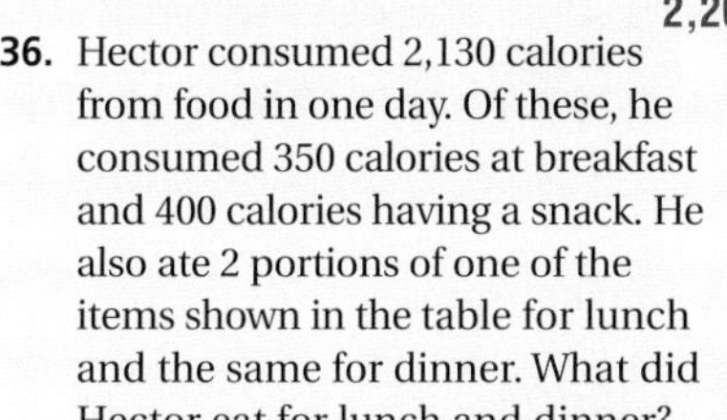

36. Hector consumed 2,130 calories from food in one day. Of these, he consumed 350 calories at breakfast and 400 calories having a snack. He also ate 2 portions of one of the items shown in the table for lunch and the same for dinner. What did Hector eat for lunch and dinner? **2 slices of pizza for lunch and again for dinner**

Calorie Counter

Food	Portion	Calories
Stir-fry	1 cup	250
Enchilada	1 whole	310
Pizza	1 slice	345
Tomato soup	1 cup	160

37. The U.S. Department of Agriculture recommends that the total amount of saturated fat in a diet not exceed 10% of calories. If a teenage girl consumes 2,200 calories per day, and a gram of fat has 9 calories, how many grams of fat can she consume without exceeding the recommended amounts? **24 grams**

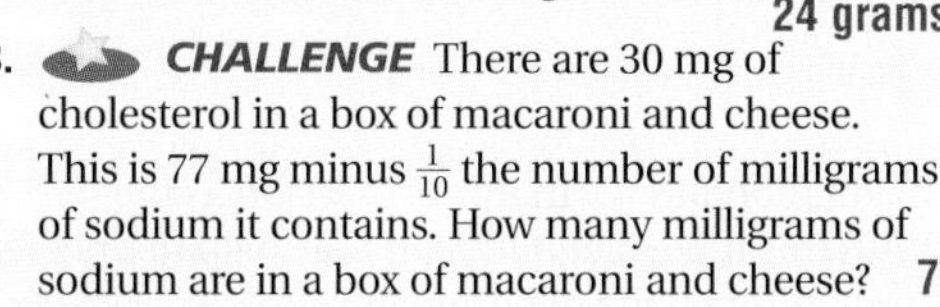

38. *CHALLENGE* There are 30 mg of cholesterol in a box of macaroni and cheese. This is 77 mg minus $\frac{1}{10}$ the number of milligrams of sodium it contains. How many milligrams of sodium are in a box of macaroni and cheese? **$77 - \frac{s}{10} = 30$; $s = 470$; it contains 470 mg of sodium.**

go.hrw.com
KEYWORD: MS4 Health
CNN Student News

Spiral Review

39. Caleb flips a dime and spins a spinner that is divided into fourths and numbered 1 through 4. How many outcomes are possible? (Lesson 10-3) **8**

40. **TEST PREP** The volume of a cylinder with height 6 inches and radius 2 inches is approximately __?__ cubic inches. (Lesson 9-2) **C**

A 18.84 B 37.68 C 75.36 D 226.08

41. **TEST PREP** The surface area of a cube with a side length of 4 cm is __?__ cm^2. (Lesson 9-4) **G**

F 256 G 96 H 64 J 24

Interdisciplinary LINK

Health

Exercises 34–38 involve using information about nutrition. Nutrition is studied in health courses as well as in middle school life science programs, such as *Holt Science & Technology*.

Journal

Ask students to write about a real-world situation that could be modeled as a two-step equation. Then have them write the equation.

Test Prep Doctor

In Exercise 40, if students chose **A, B,** or **D** they may be having difficulty using the formula. Students who chose **A** are forgetting to multiply by the radius squared. Students who selected **B** may not be squaring the radius in the formula for volume. Students who chose **D** are confusing the height and the radius.

CHALLENGE 11-1

LESSON 11-1 Challenge
Consecutive Number Search

Consecutive numbers are numbers that come one after the other.

For example, 3 and 4 are consecutive whole numbers.
6 and 8 are consecutive even numbers.
7 and 9 are consecutive odd numbers.

If n = a number, then $n + 1$ is the next consecutive whole number after n.

If n = an even number, then $n + 2$ is the next consecutive even number after n.

If n = an odd number, then $n + 2$ is the next consecutive odd number after n.

Solve. (*Hint:* Let n = the first number. Then write an equation for each sum.)

1. The sum of two consecutive numbers is 73. What are the numbers?
   $n + (n + 1) = 73$; 36 and 37
2. The sum of two consecutive numbers is 131. What are the numbers?
   $n + (n + 1) = 131$; 65 and 66
3. The sum of two consecutive even numbers is 70. What are the numbers?
   $n + (n + 2) = 70$; 34 and 36
4. The sum of two consecutive even numbers is 158. What are the numbers?
   $n + (n + 2) = 158$; 78 and 80
5. The sum of two consecutive odd numbers is 108. What are the numbers?
   $n + (n + 2) = 108$; 53 and 55
6. The sum of two consecutive odd numbers is 180. What are the numbers?
   $n + (n + 2) = 180$; 89 and 91

PROBLEM SOLVING 11-1

LESSON 11-1 Problem Solving
Solving Two-Step Equations

Write the correct answer.

1. Last week, Carlie had several rice cakes and 3 granola bars as snacks. The snacks contained a total of 800 calories. If each granola bar had 120 calories and each rice cake had 40 calories, how many rice cakes did she have?
   11 rice cakes
2. Jo eats 2,200 calories per day. She eats 450 calories at breakfast and twice as many at lunch. If she eats three meals with no snacks, which meal will contain the most calories?
   lunch
3. Erika is following a 2,200 calorie-per-day diet. She eats the recommended 9 servings of breads and cereals, averaging 120 calories per serving. She also eats 5 servings of vegetables. If the rest of her daily intake is 870 calories, what is the average number of calories in each serving of vegetables?
   50 calories
4. Brandon follows a 2,800 calorie-per-day diet. He has 11 servings of breads and cereals, which average 140 calories each. Yesterday, he had a combined 9 servings of fruits and vegetables, averaging 60 calories each. How many 180-calorie servings of meat and milk did he have to complete his diet?
   4 servings

Choose the letter for the best answer.

The table shows calories burned by a person performing different activities.

Calories Used in Activities

Activity	Calories (per min)
Basketball	7.5
Cycling (10 mi/h)	5.5
Jogging	9.3
Swimming	7.8

5. Kamisha swims for 0.25 hour. How many calories does she burn?
   A 30 calories C 1.95 calories
   B 195 calories (D) 117 calories
6. Stu jogs at a rate of 5 mi/h. How far must he jog to burn 418.5 calories?
   F 9 mi (H) 3.75 mi
   G 4.65 mi J 45 mi
7. Terry rides her bike for 40 minutes and plays basketball for an hour. How many calories does she burn?
   A 67 calories (C) 670 calories
   B 560 calories D 1,300 calories
8. How many hours would you have to ride your bike at 10 mi/h to burn 550 calories?
   (F) 1.67 hr H 1.0 hr
   G 1.5 hr J 0.75 hr

Lesson Quiz

Solve. Check your answer.

1. $6x + 8 = 44$ $x = 6$
2. $14y - 14 = 28$ $y = 3$
3. $\frac{m}{7} + 3 = 12$ $m = 63$
4. $\frac{v}{-8} - 6 = 8$ $v = -112$
5. Last Sunday, the Humane Society had a 3-hour adoption clinic. During the week the clinic is open for 2 hours on days when volunteers are available. If the Humane Society was open for a total of 9 hours last week, how many weekdays was the clinic open? 3 days

Available on Daily Transparency in CRB

11-2 Organizer

Pacing: Traditional 1 day
Block $\frac{1}{2}$ day

Objective: Students solve multistep equations.

Warm Up

Solve.

1. $-8p - 8 = 56$ $\quad p = -8$
2. $13d - 5 = 60$ $\quad d = 5$
3. $9x + 24 = 60$ $\quad x = 4$
4. $\frac{k}{7} + 4 = 11$ $\quad k = 49$
5. $19 + \frac{z}{4} = 24$ $\quad z = 20$

Problem of the Day

Without using a calculator, multiply 2.637455 by 6, add 12, divide the result by 3, subtract 4, and then multiply by 0.5. What number will you end with? (*Hint*: If you start with *x*, what do you end with?) 2.637455 (the number you started with)

Available on Daily Transparency in CRB

In 1637, René Descartes (1596–1650) began using the final letters of the alphabet to denote variables.

11-2 Solving Multistep Equations

Learn to solve multistep equations.

Levi has half as many comic books as Jamal has. If you add 6 to the number of comic books Jamal has and then divide by 7, you get the number of comic books Brooke has. If Brooke has 30 comic books, how many comic books does Levi have? To answer this question, you need to set up an equation that requires more than two steps to solve.

EXAMPLE 1 Solving Equations That Contain Like Terms

Solve $7n - 1 - 2n = 14$.

$$7n - 1 - 2n = 14$$
$$5n - 1 = 14 \qquad \text{Combine like terms.}$$
$$\underline{+1 \quad +1} \qquad \text{Add 1 to both sides.}$$
$$5n = 15$$
$$\frac{5n}{5} = \frac{15}{5} \qquad \text{Divide both sides by 5.}$$
$$n = 3$$

Sometimes one side of an equation has a variable expression as the numerator of a fraction. With this type of equation, it may help to first multiply both sides of the equation by the denominator.

EXAMPLE 2 Solving Equations That Contain Fractions

Solve $\frac{4x-8}{9} = 12$.

$$\frac{4x-8}{9} = 12$$
$$(9)\frac{4x-8}{9} = (9)12 \qquad \text{Multiply both sides by 9.}$$
$$4x - 8 = 108$$
$$\underline{+8 \quad +8} \qquad \text{Add 8 to both sides.}$$
$$4x = 116$$
$$\frac{4x}{4} = \frac{116}{4} \qquad \text{Divide both sides by 4.}$$
$$x = 29$$

1 Introduce

Alternate Opener

11-2 Solving Multistep Equations

To make milk-carton clocks for her gift shop, Marissa plans to order a number of clock movements online. Each clock movement costs \$4.50, and shipping is a flat rate of \$7.00.

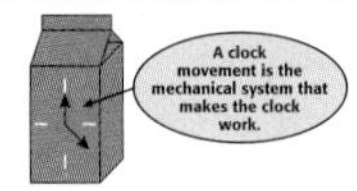

A clock movement is the mechanical system that makes the clock work.

1. Multiply the cost of a clock movement by *x*, the number of clock movements, and then add the shipping rate.
2. Set the expression in number 1 equal to *c*, the total cost of Marissa's online order.
3. Marissa wants the cost to be equal to \$70.00. Write the equation in number 2, using this amount.
4. Solve the equation for *x*. How many clock movements can Marissa order?

Think and Discuss

5. **Explain** why the shipping rate of \$7.00 was not multiplied by the number of clock movements *x*.
6. **Explain** what *x* represents in the equation you wrote.

Motivate

Ask volunteers to describe how they would attempt to solve equations such as the following: $x + 2 - 1 + 3 = 5$. Combine all the numbers on the left side of the equation, and then solve as you would any one-step equation. Have students find the solution. $x = 1$ Then ask students to make up and solve similar equations.

Exploration worksheet and answers on Chapter 11 Resource Book pp. 17 and 82

2 Teach

Guided Instruction

In this lesson, students learn to solve multistep equations. Explain that the goal is to transform each equation into a one-step or two-step equation, which students already know how to solve.

You may wish to liken solving multistep equations to solving puzzles. The key to the solution is in recognizing how to undo the operations and unlock the solution.

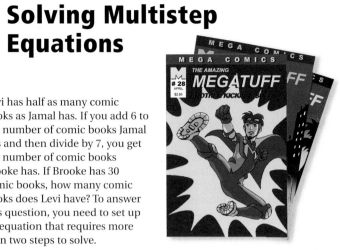

EXAMPLE 3 PROBLEM SOLVING APPLICATION

PROBLEM SOLVING

Jamal owns twice as many comic books as Levi owns. Adding 6 to the number of comic books Jamal owns and then dividing by 7 gives the number Brooke owns. If Brooke owns 30 comic books, how many does Levi own?

 **Understand the Problem**

Rewrite the question as a statement.

- Find the number of comic books that Levi owns.

List the **important information:**

- Jamal owns 2 times as many comic books as Levi owns.
- The number of comic books Jamal owns added to 6 and then divided by 7 equals the number Brooke owns.
- Brooke owns 30 comic books.

 **Make a Plan**

Let c represent the number of comic books Levi owns. Then $2c$ represents the number Jamal owns, and $\frac{2c+6}{7}$ represents the number Brooke owns, which equals 30. Solve the equation $\frac{2c+6}{7} = 30$ for c to find the number of comic books that Levi owns.

 **Solve**

$$\frac{2c+6}{7} = 30$$

$$(7)\frac{2c+6}{7} = (7)30 \quad \textit{Multiply both sides by 7.}$$

$$2c + 6 - 6 = 210 - 6 \quad \textit{Subtract 6 from both sides.}$$

$$2c = 204$$

$$\frac{2c}{2} = \frac{204}{2} \quad \textit{Divide both sides by 2.}$$

$$c = 102$$

Levi owns 102 comic books.

 **Look Back**

Check your answer by substituting 102 in the equation. $\frac{2(102)+6}{7} = 30$ ✓

Think and Discuss

1. **List** the steps required to solve $-n + 5n + 3 = 27$.
2. **Describe** how to solve the equations $\frac{2}{3}x + 7 = 4$ and $\frac{2x+7}{3} = 4$. Are the solutions the same or different? Explain.

COMMON ERROR ALERT

Some students may not understand how like terms are combined in equations. Confusion at this stage will make the next lesson especially difficult. You may wish to have these students group the like terms before combining them. For example: $7n - 1 - 2n = (7n - 2n) - 1 = 5n - 1$.

Additional Examples

Example 1

Solve $12 - 7b + 10b = 18$. $b = 2$

Example 2

Solve $\frac{3y-6}{7} = 3$. $y = 9$

Example 3

Troy has three times as many trading cards as Hillary. Subtracting 9 from the number of trading cards Troy has and then dividing by 6 gives the number of cards Sean has. If Sean owns 24 trading cards, how many cards does Hillary own? **51**

3 Close

Reaching All Learners

Through Home Connection

Suggest that students and family members use word phrases to make up number puzzles and that they solve them. You may wish to share with students this sample number puzzle and its solution:

> When a number is subtracted from the sum of twice the number and 3, the result is 10. What is the number?
>
> The solution to the puzzle: $2n + 3 - n = 10; n = 7$

Allow time for students to share their puzzles with the class.

Summarize

Challenge students to solve and check each of the following equations and to explain each step in the solution:

$-4y + 6 + y = 21$ **$y = -5$**

$\frac{6b-2}{4} = -5$ **$b = -3$**

Answers to Think and Discuss

1. First combine the like terms $-n$ and $5n$ to get $4n + 3 = 27$. Then, subtract 3 from both sides to get $4n = 24$. Finally, divide both sides by 4 to get $n = 6$.
2. Possible answer: For the first equation, subtract 7 from both sides, and then multiply by $\frac{3}{2}$. For the second equation, first multiply both sides by 3, and then subtract 7. Finally, divide by 2. The solutions are different because the left sides of the equations are different.

11-2 PRACTICE & ASSESS

Students may want to refer back to the lesson examples.

Assignment Guide

If you finished Example 1 assign:
Core 1–3, 8–13, 23, 26, 29, 38–45
Enriched 1–3, 8–13, 23, 26, 29, 38–45

If you finished Example 2 assign:
Core 1–6, 8–19, 21–26, 38–45
Enriched 1–5 odd, 8–19, 21–29, 38–45

If you finished Example 3 assign:
Core 1–26, 31, 38–45
Enriched 1–19 odd, 21–45

Notes

11-2 Exercises

FOR EXTRA PRACTICE see page 678

internet connect
Homework Help Online
go.hrw.com Keyword: MS4 11-2

GUIDED PRACTICE

See Example 1 Solve.

1. $14n + 2 - 7n = 37$ **$n = 5$**
2. $10x - 11 - 4x = 43$ **$x = 9$**
3. $-3 + 4p - 2p = 1$ **$p = 2$**

See Example 2

4. $\frac{3m + 6}{4} = 33$ **$m = 42$**
5. $\frac{5y - 6.6}{8} = 4.8$ **$y = 9$**
6. $\frac{4m - 6}{6} = -\frac{2}{3}$ **$m = \frac{1}{2}$**

See Example 3

7. Keisha read twice as many books this year as Ben read. Subtracting 4 from the number of books Keisha read and dividing by 2 gives the number of books Sheldon read. If Sheldon read 10 books this year, how many books did Ben read? **12 books**

INDEPENDENT PRACTICE

See Example 1 Solve.

8. $b + 18 + 3b = 74$ **$b = 14$**
9. $10x - 3 - 2x = 4$ **$x = \frac{7}{8}$**
10. $18w - 10 - 6w = 50$ **$w = 5$**
11. $5n + 7 - 3n = 19$ **$n = 6$**
12. $-3p + 15 - 3p = -27$ **$p = 7$**
13. $-x - 8 + 14x = -34$ **$x = -2$**

See Example 2

14. $\frac{2x + 4}{12} = \frac{5}{6}$ **$x = 3$**
15. $\frac{3n + 5}{8} = 4$ **$n = 9$**
16. $\frac{9p - 5.2}{4} = 9.95$ **$p = 5$**
17. $\frac{4r - 8}{10} = 48$ **$r = 122$**
18. $\frac{7k + 13}{-18} = \frac{4}{9}$ **$k = -3$**
19. $\frac{19 - 11t}{13} = 4$ **$t = -3$**

See Example 3

20. Abby ran 3 times as many laps as Karen. Adding 4 to the number of laps Abby ran and then dividing by 7 gives the number of laps Jill ran. If Jill ran 1 lap, how many laps did Karen run? **1 lap**

PRACTICE AND PROBLEM SOLVING

Solve.

21. $\frac{0.5x + 7}{8} = 5$ **$x = 66$**
22. $\frac{8t - 4}{5} = 6$ **$t = 4.25$**
23. $8w + 2.6 - 3.6 = 63$ **$w = 8$**
24. $\frac{3w + 0.5}{2} = 1$ **$w = 0.5$**
25. $\frac{\frac{1}{4}a - 12}{8} = 4$ **$a = 176$**
26. $1.8 + 6n - 3.2 = 7.6$ **$n = 1.5$**
27. $\frac{2b - 3.4}{0.6} = -29$ **$b = -7$**
28. $\frac{34.6 + 4h}{5} = 8.44$ **$h = 1.9$**
29. $-2.5x + 18 - 1.6x = 5.7$ **$x = 3$**
30. Three friends ate dinner at a restaurant. The total bill for their dinner was $27.00. The friends decided to add a 15% tip and then split the bill evenly. How much did each friend pay? **$10.35**
31. Ann earns 1.5 times her normal hourly pay for each hour that she works over 40 hours in a week. Last week she worked 51 hours and earned $378.55. What is her normal hourly pay? **$6.70**

Math Background

Polynomial equations can be named by the term of the highest degree. The degree of the polynomial is the highest power of the variable.

If $a \neq 0$, then $ax + b = 0$ is a first-degree polynomial equation. First-degree polynomial equations are called *linear equations*. The equations in Lessons 11-1, 11-2, and 11-3 are all linear equations.

If $a \neq 0$, then $ax^2 + bx + c = 0$ is a second-degree polynomial equation. Second-degree polynomial equations are called *quadratic equations*.

RETEACH 11-2

LESSON 11-2 **Reteach**
Solving Multistep Equations

Some equations require more than two steps to solve. To make these equations easier to solve, first combine any like terms. Also, clear any fractions.

Complete the steps to solve each equation.

1. $5a - 7 + 3a = 17$
   $\underline{8a} - 7 = 17$ ← Combine like terms: $5a + 3a = \underline{8a}$.
   $8a - 7 + \underline{7} = 17 + \underline{7}$ ← Add $\underline{7}$ to both sides of the equation.
   $8a = \underline{24}$
   $\frac{8a}{8} = \frac{24}{8}$ ← Divide both sides of the equation by $\underline{8}$.
   $a = \underline{3}$

2. $\frac{5x + 2}{4} = 8$
   $4 \cdot \frac{5x + 2}{4} = \underline{4} \cdot 8$ ← Multiply both sides of the equation by $\underline{4}$.
   $5x + 2 = \underline{32}$
   $5x + 2 - \underline{2} = 32 - \underline{2}$ ← Subtract $\underline{2}$ from both sides of the equation.
   $5x = \underline{30}$
   $\frac{5x}{5} = \frac{30}{5}$ ← Divide both sides of the equation by $\underline{5}$.
   $x = \underline{6}$

Solve.

3. $9b + 6 - 5b = 18$ **$b = 3$**
4. $2y - 7 + y = 8$ **$y = 5$**
5. $-5c - 12 - 5c = 8$ **$c = -2$**
6. $\frac{7r + 1}{5} = 10$ **$r = 7$**
7. $\frac{3s - 5}{8} = \frac{1}{2}$ **$s = 3$**
8. $\frac{4x + 11}{5} = -5$ **$x = -9$**

PRACTICE 11-2

LESSON 11-2 **Practice B**
Solving Multistep Equations

Solve.

1. $15x - 8 - 3x = 16$ **$x = 2$**
2. $5n + 3 + 4n = 30$ **$n = 3$**
3. $h - 6 + 7h = 42$ **$h = 6$**
4. $-3g + 6 + 2g = 15$ **$g = -9$**
5. $-2b + 7 - 3b = 2$ **$b = 1$**
6. $5y + 1 + 3y = -15$ **$y = -2$**
7. $4k - 14 + 3k = 21$ **$k = 5$**
8. $9m + 10 - 14m = -5$ **$m = 3$**
9. $-2d + 18 - 4d = 60$ **$d = -7$**
10. $\frac{4n - 2}{6} = 5$ **$n = 8$**
11. $\frac{7v + 1}{18} = \frac{5}{6}$ **$v = 2$**
12. $\frac{15 - 6t}{12} = \frac{3}{4}$ **$t = 1$**
13. $\frac{4m - 4.6}{5} = 6.2$ **$m = 8.9$**
14. $\frac{8s + 14}{4} = -\frac{1}{2}$ **$s = -2$**
15. $\frac{2c + 1.4}{2} = 4.5$ **$c = 3.8$**
16. Joel has twice as many CDs as Mariella has. Subtracting 7 from the number of CDs Joel has and dividing by 3 equals the number of CDs Blake has. If Blake has 25 CDs, how many CDs does Mariella have?

Mariella has 41 CDs.

32. ***CONSUMER MATH*** Patrice used a \$15 gift certificate when she purchased a pair of sandals. After 8% sales tax was applied to the price of the sandals, the \$15 was deducted. If Patrice had to pay an additional \$12, how much did the sandals cost before tax? **\$25**

33. ***PHYSICAL SCIENCE*** To convert temperatures between degrees Celsius and degrees Fahrenheit, you can use the formula $F = \frac{9}{5}C + 32$. The table shows the melting points of various elements.
    a. What is the melting point in degrees Celsius of gold?
    b. What is the melting point in degrees Celsius of hydrogen?

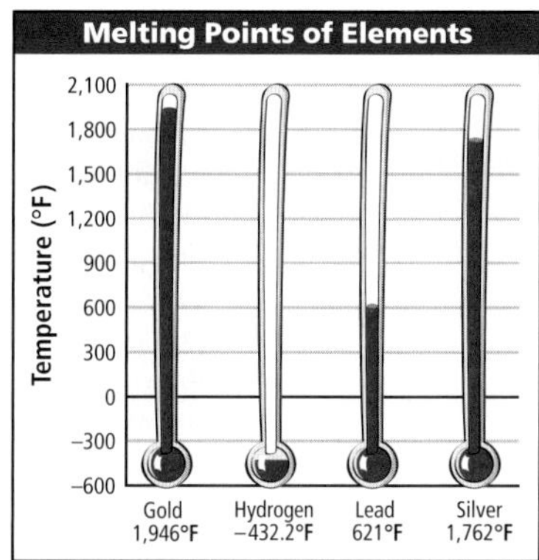

34. On his first two social studies tests, Billy made an 86 and a 93. What grade must Billy make on the third test to have an average of 90 for all three tests? **91**

35. ***WHAT'S THE QUESTION?*** Three friends shared a taxi ride from the airport to their hotel. After adding a \$7.00 tip, the friends divided the cost of the ride evenly. If solving the equation $\frac{c + \$7.00}{3} =$ \$11.25 gives the answer, what is the question?

36. ***WRITE ABOUT IT*** Explain why multiplying first in the equation $\frac{2x - 6}{5} = 2$ makes finding the solution easier than adding first does.

37. ***CHALLENGE*** Are the solutions to the following equations the same? Explain.

$$\frac{3y}{4} + 2 = 4 \text{ and } 3y + 8 = 16$$

Spiral Review

Solve. Write each answer in simplest form. (Lesson 4-12)

38. $\frac{3}{4}x = 9$ $x = 12$ 39. $y + \frac{7}{11} = \frac{2}{3}$ $y = \frac{1}{33}$ 40. $\frac{5}{6}k = \frac{5}{9}$ $k = \frac{2}{3}$ 41. $\frac{3}{8} + n = -\frac{11}{24}$ $n = -\frac{5}{6}$

Find the number of permutations for each situation. (Lesson 10-7)

42. There are 10 students lining up for lunch. **3,628,800**

43. Dan is putting 8 books on a shelf. **40,320**

44. **TEST PREP** Identify the ratios that are proportional. (Lesson 5-2) **D**

A $\frac{2}{6}, \frac{1}{12}$ B $\frac{15}{36}, \frac{18}{45}$ C $\frac{3}{12}, \frac{12}{36}$ D $\frac{12}{36}, \frac{60}{180}$

45. **TEST PREP** A spinner that is divided into tenths and numbered 1–10 is spun. Find P(prime number). (Lesson 10-2) **F**

F 40% G 0.1 H $\frac{1}{4}$ J 0.06

Answers

33. a. $1{,}063\frac{1}{3}$°C
b. −257.89°C

35. Possible answer: If the friends gave the driver a \$7.00 tip and then each friend paid \$11.25, what was the cost of the taxi ride before the tip?

36. Possible answer: Since $\frac{2x - 6}{5} = \frac{2x}{5} - \frac{6}{5}$, you would have to add $\frac{6}{5}$ to both sides and then multiply both sides by $\frac{5}{2}$ to solve for x. It is much easier to clear the denominator and then compute with integers.

37. Possible answer: The solutions are the same. In the second equation, each term from the first equation has been multiplied by 4. Since the same thing was done to both sides of the equation, the two statements are equivalent.

Journal

Have students describe situations similar to the Example 3 application. Then have them write equations that correspond to their problems.

Test Prep Doctor

For Exercise 45, students who chose **G, H,** or **J** might not understand how to find the probability of an event. Students who selected **H** might be confusing favorable outcomes with total outcomes. Students who selected **J** or **G** may need to review prime numbers as well as how to find probabilities. The correct answer is **F.**

CHALLENGE 11-2

LESSON 11-2 Challenge
Solve the System

When equations have two variables, you can sometimes find the point where two equations have the same solution—that is, where one value of x and one value of y solve both equations. This is called "solving a system of equations."
To solve a system of equations, you can substitute from one equation into the other.

Example: Solve $x + y = 6$ and $x - y = 2$.

Step 1: Solve one equation for y. $x + y = 6$
$y = 6 - x$

Step 2: Substitute that value of y into the second equation.
Solve for x. $x - y = 2$
$x - (6 - x) = 2$
$x - 6 + x = 2$
$2x - 6 = 2$
$2x = 8$
$x = 4$

Step 3: Substitute the solution for x from Step 2 into the other equation. $x + y = 6$
$4 + y = 6$
$y = 2$

Step 4: Write the solution as an ordered pair (x, y).
Solution: (4, 2)

Solve each system of equations.

1. $y = 3x$, $x + y = 20$ — (5, 15)
2. $m = 4n$, $m + n = 10$ — (8, 2)
3. $d = c - 2$, $c + d = 12$ — (7, 5)
4. $v - w = 2$, $3w + v = 14$ — (5, 3)
5. $j = k + 3$, $j + k = 7$ — (5, 2)
6. $b = a - 9$, $a + b = 3$ — (6, −3)
7. $r = 2 - s$, $2s + r = 9$ — (−5, 7)
8. $e + f = 2$, $3e + f = 8$ — (3, −1)

PROBLEM SOLVING 11-2

LESSON 11-2 Problem Solving
Solving Multistep Equations

Write the correct answer.
To convert a temperature from degrees Fahrenheit to degrees Celsius, you can use the formula $(°F - 32)\frac{5}{9} = °C$.

1. The record high temperature in North Carolina is 110°F. What is the record high in degrees Celsius?
   43.3°C
2. The record low temperature in Florida is −2°F. What is the record low in degrees Celsius?
   −18.9°C
3. The record high temperature in the United States is 134°F. This was recorded in Greenland Ranch, California, on July 10, 1913. What is that temperature in degrees Celsius?
   56.7°C
4. The record high in Texas is 120°F. The record low in Texas is −23°F. In degrees Celsius, what is the range between the record high and low temperatures in Texas?
   79.5°C
5. When the temperature is 4°C, you need to wear a heavy coat. Write 4°C as degrees Fahrenheit.
   39.2°F
6. When the temperature is 28°C, you might want to go to the beach. Write 28°C as degrees Fahrenheit.
   82.4°F

Choose the letter for the best answer.

7. Faith spent \$78 at Fashion Warehouse. She bought 2 shirts that each cost \$17.50 and a pair of shoes. How much did she spend for the shoes?
   A \$34.00 C \$60.50
   (B) \$43.00 D \$113.00
8. Three friends each pay \$4.15 to buy a pizza. A basic pizza costs \$9.45. Additional toppings cost \$1 each. How many toppings were on the pizza?
   F 2 toppings H 4 toppings
   (G) 3 toppings J 5 toppings
9. Todd buys 3 CDs at \$16.99 each and a DVD that costs \$24.99. He pays with a \$100 bill. How much change does he receive?
   (A) \$24.04 C \$49.03
   B \$8.04 D \$67.96
10. Marina bought 4 books. José bought half as many books as Ben bought. Together, the 3 friends bought 13 books. How many books did Ben buy?
   F 9 books H 3 books
   (G) 6 books J 2 books

Lesson Quiz

Solve.

1. $c + 21 + 5c = 63$ $c = 7$
2. $-x - 11 + 17x = 53$ $x = 4$
3. $w - 16 + 4w = 59$ $w = 15$
4. $\frac{4k + 6}{5} = 10$ $k = 11$
5. Kelly swam 4 times as many laps as Kathy. Adding 5 to the number of laps Kelly swam gives you the number of laps Julie swam. If Julie swam 9 laps, how many laps did Kathy swim? 1 lap

Available on Daily Transparency in CRB

11-3 Organizer

Pacing: Traditional 1 day
Block $\frac{1}{2}$ day

Objective: Students solve equations that have variables on both sides.

Warm Up

Solve.

1. $6n + 8 - 4n = 20$ $n = 6$
2. $-4w + 16 - 4w = -32$ $w = 6$
3. $25t - 17 - 13t = 67$ $t = 7$
4. $\frac{4k + 9}{-25} = \frac{3}{5}$ $k = -6$

Problem of the Day

You buy 1 cookie on the first day, 2 on the second day, 3 on the third day, and so on for 10 days. Your friend pays $10 for a cookie discount card and then buys 10 cookies at half price. You both pay the same total amount. What is the cost of one cookie? **$0.20**

Available on Daily Transparency in CRB

In chemistry, equations that model chemical reactions must balance. That is, there must be the same number of each type of atom on each side of the equation.

11-3 Solving Equations with Variables on Both Sides

Learn to solve equations that have variables on both sides.

Marilyn can rent a video game console for $2.20 per day or buy one for $74.80. The cost of renting a game is $1.99 per day. How many days would Marilyn have to rent both the game and the console to pay as much as she would if she had bought the console and rented the game instead?

Problems such as this require you to solve equations that have the same variable on both sides of the equal sign. To solve this kind of problem, you need to get the terms with variables on one side of the equal sign.

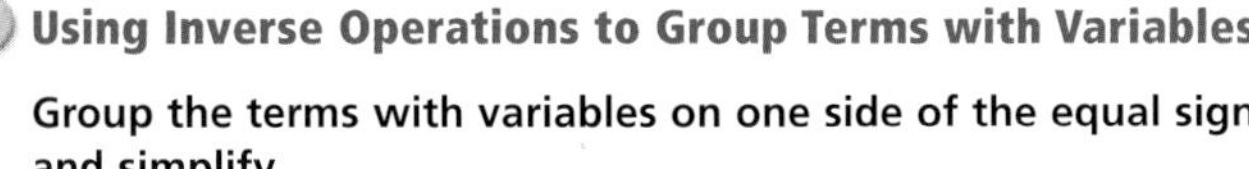

EXAMPLE 1 Using Inverse Operations to Group Terms with Variables

Group the terms with variables on one side of the equal sign, and simplify.

A $6m = 4m + 12$

$6m = 4m + 12$

$6m - 4m = 4m - 4m + 12$ *Subtract 4m from both sides.*

$2m = 12$ *Simplify.*

B $-7x - 198 = 5x$

$-7x - 198 = 5x$

$-7x + 7x - 198 = 5x + 7x$ *Add 7x to both sides.*

$-198 = 12x$ *Simplify.*

EXAMPLE 2 Solving Equations with Variables on Both Sides

Solve.

A $5n = 3n + 26$

$5n = 3n + 26$

$5n - 3n = 3n - 3n + 26$ *Subtract 3n from both sides.*

$2n = 26$ *Simplify.*

$\frac{2n}{2} = \frac{26}{2}$ *Divide both sides by 2.*

$n = 13$

1 Introduce

Alternate Opener

EXPLORATION

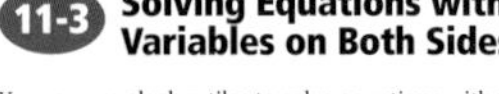

11-3 Solving Equations with Variables on Both Sides

You can use algebra tiles to solve equations with variables on both sides. The model below shows the equation $2x + 2 = x - 3$.

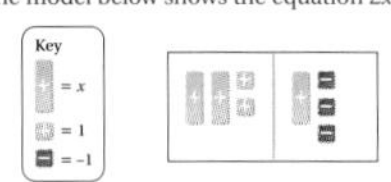

1. What will you do to remove the two positive tiles (+2) from the left side of the mat?
2. What will you do to remove the x tile from the right side of the mat?
3. What will you do to find the value of x?
4. Write an equation for the model below and find the solution.

Think and Discuss

5. **Explain** whether removing positive or negative tiles from the mat is different from removing x tiles.

Motivate

Pose the following problem: Eight times a number is 9 more than 5 times the number. What is the number?

Have students suggest how they would find the number. Encourage them to use word phrases to write an equation. If necessary, remind students that "is" corresponds to the equal sign in an equation.

Exploration worksheet and answers on Chapter 11 Resource Book pp. 26 and 84

2 Teach

Lesson Presentation

Guided Instruction

In this lesson, students learn to solve equations that have variables on both sides. Remind students that the equal sign is like the fulcrum of a balance scale. The lesson goal is the same as with the previous two lessons: to teach students to isolate the variable on one side of the equation.

Teaching Tip Point out that each equation can still be checked by substituting the solution into the original equation. You may wish to work through several checks with the class or to have volunteers demonstrate checks for the lesson examples.

Solve.

B $19 + 7n = -2n + 37$

$$19 + 7n = -2n + 37$$
$$19 + 7n + \mathbf{2n} = -2n + \mathbf{2n} + 37 \quad \text{Add 2n to both sides.}$$
$$19 + 9n = 37 \quad \text{Simplify.}$$
$$19 + 9n - \mathbf{19} = 37 - \mathbf{19} \quad \text{Subtract 19 from both sides.}$$
$$9n = 18 \quad \text{Simplify.}$$
$$\frac{9n}{9} = \frac{18}{9} \quad \text{Divide both sides by 9.}$$
$$n = 2$$

C $\frac{5}{9}x = \frac{4}{9}x + 9$

$$\frac{5}{9}x = \frac{4}{9}x + 9$$
$$\frac{5}{9}x - \frac{4}{9}x = \frac{4}{9}x - \frac{4}{9}x + 9 \quad \text{Subtract } \tfrac{4}{9}x \text{ from both sides.}$$
$$\frac{1}{9}x = 9 \quad \text{Simplify.}$$
$$(9)\frac{1}{9}x = (9)9 \quad \text{Multiply both sides by 9.}$$
$$x = 81$$

EXAMPLE 3 *Consumer Math Application*

Marilyn can buy a video game console for \$74.80 and rent a game for \$1.99 per day, or she can rent a console and the same game for a total of \$4.19 per day. How many days would Marilyn have to rent both the video game and the console to pay as much as she would if she had bought the console and rented the game instead?

Let d represent the number of days.

$$4.19d = 74.80 + 1.99d$$
$$4.19d - \mathbf{1.99d} = 74.80 + 1.99d - \mathbf{1.99d} \quad \text{Subtract 1.99d from both sides.}$$
$$2.20d = 74.80 \quad \text{Simplify.}$$
$$\frac{2.20d}{2.20} = \frac{74.80}{2.20} \quad \text{Divide both sides by 2.20.}$$
$$d = 34$$

Marilyn would need to rent both the video game and the console for 34 days to pay as much as she would have if she had bought the console.

Think and Discuss

1. **Explain** how you would solve $\frac{1}{2}x + 7 = \frac{2}{3}x - 2$.
2. **Describe** how you would decide which variable term to add or subtract on both sides of the equation $-3x + 7 = 4x - 9$.

COMMON ERROR ALERT

Some students might try to solve equations by writing all of the terms on one side of the equation. They then become confused and unable to solve the equation. Insist on the importance of showing each step in the solution.

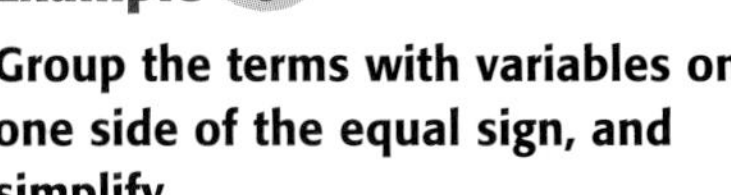

Additional Examples

Example 1

Group the terms with variables on one side of the equal sign, and simplify.

A. $60 - 4y = 8y$ **$60 = 12y$**

B. $-5b + 72 = -2b$ **$72 = 3b$**

Example 2

Solve.

A. $7c = 2c + 55$ **$c = 11$**

B. $49 - 3m = 4m + 14$ **$5 = m$**

C. $\frac{2}{5}x = \frac{1}{5}x - 12$ **$x = -60$**

Example 3

Christine can buy a new snowboard for \$136.50. She will still need to rent boots for \$8.50 a day. She can rent a snowboard and boots for \$18.25 a day. How many days would Christine need to rent both the snowboard and the boots to pay as much as she would if she buys the snowboard and rents only the boots for the season? 14 days

3 Close

Reaching All Learners

Through Cognitive Strategies

Review the techniques students have learned to solve equations by providing them with examples such as the following:

$x + 4 = 12$, $x - 4 = 12$, $4x = 12$, $\frac{x}{4} = 12$, $3x + x = 12$, $3x = 12 - x$, and $3x - 6 = 6 - x$.

Discuss the steps needed to find the solution to each equation.

A recording sheet and answers are on Chapter 11 Resource Book pp. 77 and 95.

Summarize

Challenge students to solve and check the following equations and to explain each step they used to find the solution:

$3a = 9a - 12$ **$a = 2$**

$5w - 6 = 8w + 6.$ **$w = -4$**

Answers to Think and Discuss

Possible answers:

1. $\frac{2}{3} > \frac{1}{2}$, so subtract $\frac{1}{2}x$ from both sides. Use a common denominator to subtract. Then add 2 to both sides of the equation. Finally, multiply both sides by 6 to solve; $x = 54$.
2. To keep the variables positive, add $3x$ to both sides of the equation to solve.

11-3 PRACTICE & ASSESS

Students may want to refer back to the lesson examples.

Assignment Guide

If you finished Example 1 assign:
Core 1–3, 8–13, 35–43
Enriched 1–3, 8–13, 35–43

If you finished Example 2 assign:
Core 1–6, 8–19, 21–25 odd, 35–43
Enriched 1–5 odd, 8–19, 21–26, 35–43

If you finished Example 3 assign:
Core 1–20, 21–31 odd, 35–43
Enriched 1–19 odd, 21–43

Notes

11-3 Exercises

FOR EXTRA PRACTICE see page 678

internet connect
Homework Help Online
go.hrw.com Keyword: MS4 11-3

GUIDED PRACTICE

See Example 1 Group the terms with variables on one side of the equal sign, and simplify.

1. $5n = 4n + 32$ **$n = 32$**
2. $-6x - 28 = 4x$ **$-28 = 10x$**
3. $8w = 32 - 4w$ **$12w = 32$**

See Example 2 Solve.

4. $4y = 2y + 40$ **$y = 20$**
5. $8 + 6a = -2a + 24$ **$a = 2$**
6. $\frac{3}{4}d + 4 = \frac{1}{4}d + 18$ **$d = 28$**

See Example 3
7. Members at the Star Theater pay $30.00 per month plus $1.95 for each movie. Nonmembers pay the regular $7.95 admission fee. How many movies would both a member and a nonmember have to see in a month to pay the same amount? **5 movies**

INDEPENDENT PRACTICE

See Example 1 Group the terms with variables on one side of the equal sign, and simplify.

8. $12h = 9h + 84$ **$3h = 84$**
9. $-10p - 8 = 2p$ **$-8 = 12p$**
10. $6q = 18 - 2q$ **$8q = 18$**
11. $-4c - 6 = -2c$ **$-6 = 2c$**
12. $-7s + 12 = -9s$ **$2s = -12$**
13. $6 + \frac{4}{5}a = \frac{9}{10}a$ **$6 = \frac{1}{10}a$**

See Example 2 Solve.

14. $9t = 4t + 120$ **$t = 24$**
15. $42 + 3b = -4b - 14$ **$b = -8$**
16. $\frac{6}{11}x + 4 = \frac{2}{11}x + 16$ **$x = 33$**
17. $1.5a + 6 = 9a + 12$ **$a = -0.8$**
18. $32 - \frac{3}{8}y = \frac{3}{4}y + 5$ **$y = 24$**
19. $-6 - 8c = 3c + 16$ **$c = -2$**

See Example 3
20. Members at a swim club pay $5 per lesson plus a one-time membership fee of $60. Nonmembers pay $11 per lesson. How many lessons would both a member and a nonmember have to take to pay the same amount? **10 lessons**

PRACTICE AND PROBLEM SOLVING

Solve. Check each answer.

21. $3y + 7 = -6y - 56$ **$y = -7$**
22. $-\frac{7}{8}x - 6 = -\frac{3}{8}x - 14$ **$x = 16$**
23. $5r + 6 - 2r = 7r - 10$ **$r = 4$**
24. $-10p + 8 = 7p + 12$ **$p = -\frac{4}{17}$**
25. $9 + 5r = -17 - 8r$ **$r = -2$**
26. $0.8k + 7 = -0.7k + 1$ **$k = -4$**

27. A choir is performing for the school fall festival. On the first night, 12 choir members were absent, so the choir stood in 5 equal rows. On the second night, only 1 choir member was absent, so the choir stood in 6 equal rows. How many members are in the choir? **67**

Math Background

Although all of the equations in this lesson have one solution, some linear equations may have no solution or an infinite number of solutions.

Equations that are *identities* have an infinite number of solutions. Identities state that a value is equal to itself. The equation $y + 4 = y + 4$ is true for all values of y.

An example of an equation with no solution is $x = x + 2$. Subtracting x from both sides leaves the false statement $0 = 2$. This equation has no real number solution.

RETEACH 11-3

CHAPTER 11-3 **Reteach**
Solving Equations with Variables on Both Sides

Some equations have like terms that are on opposite sides of the equal sign. To solve these equations, first identify the like term with the lesser coefficient.

$2x = 25 - 3x$ ← $2x$ and $-3x$ are like terms.

Since $-3 < 2$, $-3x$ is the term with the lesser coefficient. Move $-3x$ to the opposite side of the equation by adding $3x$ to each side of the equation.

$$2x = 25 - 3x$$
$$2x + \mathbf{3x} = 25 - 3x + \mathbf{3x}$$
$$5x = 25$$
$$\frac{5x}{5} = \frac{25}{5}$$
$$x = 5$$

Complete the steps to solve the equation.

1. $5x + 16 = 9x$
The like terms are **5x** and **9x**.
The like term with the lesser coefficient is **5x**.
$5x + 16 = 9x$
$5x - \mathbf{5x} + 16 = 9x - \mathbf{5x}$
$16 = \mathbf{4x}$
$\frac{16}{4} = \frac{4x}{4}$
$\mathbf{4} = x$

2. $3a + 1 = 15 - 4a$
The like terms are **3a** and **−4a**.
The like term with the lesser coefficient is **−4a**.
$3a + 1 = 15 - 4a$
$3a + \mathbf{4a} + 1 = 15 - 4a + \mathbf{4a}$
$\mathbf{7a} + 1 = 15$
$7a + 1 - \mathbf{1} = 15 - \mathbf{1}$
$7a = \mathbf{14}$
$\frac{7a}{7} = \frac{14}{7}$
$a = \mathbf{2}$

Solve.

3. $8d = 7d + 13$ **$d = 13$**
4. $-4p - 16 = 4p$ **$p = -2$**
5. $3n = 25 - 2n$ **$n = 5$**
6. $9c - 6 = 2c + 15$ **$c = 3$**
7. $16 - 6k = 20 - 2k$ **$k = -1$**
8. $2h + 8 = 2 - h$ **$h = -2$**

PRACTICE 11-3

LESSON 11-3 **Practice B**
Solving Equations with Variables on Both Sides

Group the terms with the variables on one side of the equal sign and simplify. Do not solve.

1. $10t = 6t + 24$ **$4t = 24$**
2. $-6x - 32 = 2x$ **$-32 = 8x$**
3. $j = 20 - 4j$ **$5j = 20$**
4. $-5d + 40 = 5d$ **$40 = 10d$**
5. $9m - 28 = 2m$ **$-28 = -7m$**
6. $\frac{8}{9}x = 8 + \frac{4}{9}x$ **$\frac{4}{9}x = 8$**

Solve.

7. $8k = 6k - 26$ **$k = -13$**
8. $7p + 25 = 12p$ **$p = 5$**
9. $-3r + 18 = 6r$ **$r = 2$**
10. $8w - 9 = 3w + 16$ **$w = 5$**
11. $32 - 5v = 3v + 8$ **$v = 3$**
12. $-12y - 10 = -6y + 14$ **$y = -4$**
13. $\frac{5}{8}a + 6 = \frac{3}{4}a$ **$a = 48$**
14. $\frac{1}{4}n + 10 = \frac{2}{3}n$ **$n = 24$**
15. $20 - \frac{1}{5}d = \frac{3}{10}d + 16$ **$d = 8$**

The figures in each pair have the same perimeter. Find the value of each variable.

28. $x = 6$ 29. $s = 11$

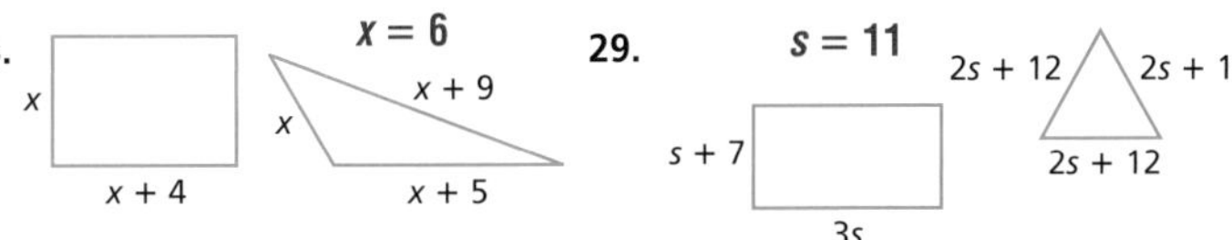

Recreation LINK

The first indoor rock-climbing gym was built in 1987. Today, hundreds of these kinds of gyms exist around the country.

30. ***RECREATION*** A rock-climbing gym charges nonmembers \$18 per day to use the wall plus \$7 per day for equipment rental. Members pay an annual fee of \$400 plus \$5 per day for equipment rental. How many days must both a member and a nonmember use the wall in one year so that both pay the same amount? **20 days**

31. ***SOCIAL STUDIES*** Two families drove from Denver to Cincinnati. After driving 582 miles the first day, the Smiths spread the rest of the trip equally over the next 3 days. The Chows spread their trip equally over 6 days. The distance the Chows drove each day was equal to the distance the Smiths drove each of the three days.
    a. How many miles did the Chows drive each day? **194 mi per day**
    b. How far is it from Denver to Cincinnati? **1,164 mi**

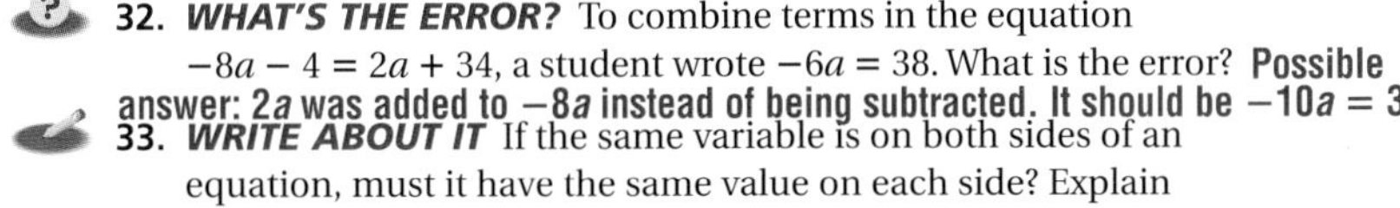

32. ***WHAT'S THE ERROR?*** To combine terms in the equation $-8a - 4 = 2a + 34$, a student wrote $-6a = 38$. What is the error? **Possible answer: $2a$ was added to $-8a$ instead of being subtracted. It should be $-10a = 38$.**

33. ***WRITE ABOUT IT*** If the same variable is on both sides of an equation, must it have the same value on each side? Explain your answer.

34. ***CHALLENGE*** Combine terms before solving the equation $12x - 4 - 12 = 4x + 8 + 8x - 24$. Do you think there is just one solution to the equation? Why or why not?
$12x - 16 = 12x - 16$; no, because the expressions are equal for any value of x.

Spiral Review

Estimate each percent. (Lesson 6-2) **Possible answers:**

35. 52% of 62 **30** 36. 31% of 47 **15** 37. 9% of 87 **9** 38. 23% of 79 **20**

Convert. (Lesson 8-1)

39. 24 feet to inches **288 in.** 40. 442 milliliters to liters **0.442 L** 41. 4 quarts to cups **16 c**

42. **TEST PREP** Which number is the solution to the equation $-13 = 14 + x$? (Lesson 2-10) **B**

A 1 B −27 C −1 D 27

43. **TEST PREP** For a circle with diameter 5 inches, what is the area to the nearest tenth? Use 3.14 for π. (Lesson 8-6) **H**

F 15.7 in^2 G 78.5 in^2 H 19.6 in^2 J 7.9 in^2

Answers

33. Possible answer: Yes, within an equation, each variable represents a single value, regardless of where in the equation the variable appears.

Journal

Ask students to work backward to create an equation similar to any of the equations in Example 2. Challenge them to solve their own equations.

Test Prep Doctor

For Exercise 43, the correct answer is **H.** This can be shown by estimating. Since the radius is 2.5 and the square of 2.5 is a bit more than 6, the area is somewhat more than $3 \cdot 6 = 18$ but less than $4 \cdot 7 = 28$. The only number that lies between these is choice **H.** Students who selected **F** may be confusing the formula for the circumference of a circle with the formula for the area of a circle. Students who selected **G** may not have noticed that the diameter is given, not the radius.

CHALLENGE 11-3

LESSON 11-3 **Challenge**
Use the Clues

You can write equations using clues to solve problems.

Example: The sum of two numbers is 36. The difference of the two numbers is 8. Find the numbers.

Let x = one number.

Let y = the other number.

The sum of the two numbers is 36. $x + y = 36$

The difference of the two numbers is 8. $x - y = 8$

Solve the system of equations. $x + y = 36$
$x - y = 8$

The solution is (22, 14), so the two numbers are 22 and 14.

Solve.

1. The sum of two numbers is 33. The difference of the two numbers is 5. Find the numbers.
   14 and 19
2. The sum of two numbers is 85. The difference of the two numbers is 13. Find the numbers.
   36 and 49
3. One number is 18 more than another number. The sum of the two numbers is 60. Find the numbers.
   21 and 39
4. The sum of two numbers is 99. The difference of the two numbers is 9. Find the numbers.
   45 and 54
5. The sum of two numbers is 42. One number is twice the other number. Find the numbers.
   14 and 28
6. The sum of two numbers is 43. One number is equal to 5 less than 3 times the other number. Find the numbers.
   12 and 31

PROBLEM SOLVING 11-3

LESSON 11-3 **Problem Solving**
Solving Equations with Variables on Both Sides

Write the correct answer.

1. Five added to twice Erik's age is the same as 3 times his age minus 2. How old is Erik?
   7 years old
2. Three times the perimeter of a triangle is the same as 75 decreased by twice the perimeter. What is the perimeter of the triangle?
   15 units
3. The area of a pentagon increased by 27 is the same as four times the area of the pentagon, minus 15. What is the area of the pentagon?
   14 square units
4. To repair body damage on a car, AutoBody charges \$125, plus \$18 per hour. CarCare charges \$200, plus \$12 per hour. Determine the number of hours for which the two body shops will cost the same.
   12.5 hours

Choose the letter for the best answer.

5. Sandy and Suzanne are planting flower pots around the school building. Sandy has planted 33 pots and is planting at the rate of 10 pots per hour. Suzanne has planted 25 pots and is planting at the rate of 14 pots per hour. In how many hours will they have planted the same number of flower pots?
   A 3 hr (C) 2 hr
   B 2.5 hr D 1 hr
6. The length of the sides of a square measure $2x - 5$. The length of a rectangle measures $2x$, and the width measures $x + 2$. For what value of x is the perimeter of the square the same as the perimeter of the rectangle?
   F $x = 2$ H $x = 10$
   G $x = 7$ (J) $x = 12$
7. Louisa used Downtown Taxi, which charges \$2 for the first mile and \$1.10 for each additional mile. Pietro used Uptown Cab, which charges \$5 for the first mile and \$0.95 for each additional mile. They paid the same amount and traveled the same distance. How far did they travel?
   A 25 mi C 20 mi
   (B) 21 mi D 15 mi
8. Toni bought some beach towels on sale for \$8 each. Theo bought the same number of beach towels at the full price of \$12. Toni's total was \$24 less than Theo's total. How many beach towels did they each buy?
   (F) 6 towels H 9 towels
   G 8 towels J 12 towels

Lesson Quiz

Group the terms with variables on one side of the equal sign, and simplify.

1. $14n = 11n + 81$ $3n = 81$

2. $-14k + 12 = -18k$ $4k = -12$

Solve.

3. $58 + 3y = -4y - 19$ $y = -11$

4. $-\frac{3}{4}x = \frac{1}{8}x - 14$ $x = 16$

Available on Daily Transparency in CRB

Mid-Chapter Quiz

Purpose: *To assess students' mastery of concepts and skills in Lessons 11-1 through 11-3*

Assessment Resources

Section 11A Quiz
Assessment Resources .... p. 29

***Test and Practice Generator* CD-ROM**

Additional mid-chapter assessment items in both multiple-choice and free-response format may be generated for any objective in Lessons 11-1 through 11-3.

Chapter **11**

Mid-Chapter Quiz

Mid-Chapter Quiz

LESSON **11-1** (pp. 560–563)

Solve.

1. $-4x + 6 = 54$ **$x = -12$**
2. $15 + \frac{y}{3} = 6$ **$y = -27$**
3. $\frac{z}{8} - 5 = -3$ **$z = 16$**
4. $-7a - 5 = -33$ **$a = 4$**
5. $\frac{r}{12} - 19 = -27$ **$r = -96$**
6. $11 - 2n = -13$ **$n = 12$**
7. $3x + 13 = 37$ **$x = 8$**
8. $\frac{p}{-8} - 7 = 12$ **$p = -152$**
9. $\frac{u}{7} + 45 = -60$ **$u = -735$**
10. A taxi service charges an initial fee of \$1.50 plus \$1.50 for every mile traveled. If a taxi ride costs \$21.00, how many miles did the taxi travel? **13**

LESSON **11-2** (pp. 564–567)

Solve.

11. $\frac{3x - 4}{5} = 7$ **$x = 13$**
12. $9b + 6 - 8 = -38$ **$b = -4$**
13. $\frac{15c + 3}{6} = -12$ **$c = -5$**
14. $\frac{24.6 + 3a}{4} = 9.54$ **$a = 4.52$**
15. $\frac{2b + 9}{11} = 18$ **$b = 94.5$**
16. $2c + 3 + 5c = 13$ **$c = \frac{10}{7}$**
17. $\frac{16w - 12}{4} = 17$ **$w = 5$**
18. $\frac{1.2s + 3.69}{0.3} = 47.9$ **$s = 8.9$**
19. $\frac{5p - 8}{12} = \frac{1}{2}$ **$p = \frac{14}{5}$ or $2\frac{4}{5}$**
20. Peter used a \$5.00 gift certificate to help pay for his lunch. After adding a 15% tip to the cost of his meal, Peter still had to pay \$2.36 in cash. How much did Peter's meal cost? **\$6.40**
21. A group of 10 friends had dinner together at a restaurant. The meal cost a total of \$99.50, including tax. After a 15% tip was added, they split the cost evenly. How much did each person pay? Round your answer to the nearest cent. **\$11.44**

LESSON **11-3** (pp. 568–571)

Solve.

22. $12m = 3m + 108$ **$m = 12$**
23. $\frac{7}{8}n - 3 = \frac{5}{8}n + 12$ **$n = 60$**
24. $1.2x + 3.7 = 2.2x - 4.5$ **$x = 8.2$**
25. $-7 - 7p = 3p + 23$ **$p = -3$**
26. $-2.3q + 16 = -5q - 38$ **$q = -20$**
27. $\frac{3}{5}k + \frac{7}{10} = \frac{11}{15}k - \frac{2}{5}$ **$k = \frac{33}{4}$ or $8\frac{1}{4}$**
28. $-19m + 12 = -14m - 8$ **$m = 4$**
29. $\frac{2}{3}v + \frac{1}{6} = \frac{7}{9}v - \frac{5}{6}$ **$v = 9$**
30. $8.9 - 3.3j = -2.2j + 2.3$ **$j = 6$**
31. $4a - 7 = -6a + 12$ **$a = 1.9$**
32. Nine more than 3 times a number is equal to 8 times the number decreased by 16. What is the number? **$9 + 3x = 8x - 16$; $x = 5$**

Focus on Problem Solving

Solve

• Write an equation

When you are asked to solve a problem, be sure to read the entire problem before you begin solving it. Sometimes you will need to perform several steps to solve the problem, and you will need to know all of the information in the problem before you decide which steps to take.

Read each problem and determine what steps are needed to solve it. Then write an equation that can be used to solve the problem.

1. Martin can buy a pair of inline skates and safety equipment for $49.50. At a roller rink, Martin can rent a pair of inline skates for $2.50 per day, but he still needs to buy safety equipment for $19.50. How many days would Martin have to skate to pay as much to rent skates and buy safety equipment as he would have to buy both?

2. Christopher draws caricatures at the local mall. He charges $5 for a simple sketch and $15 for a larger drawing. In one day, Christopher earned $175. If he drew 20 simple sketches that day, how many larger drawings did he make?

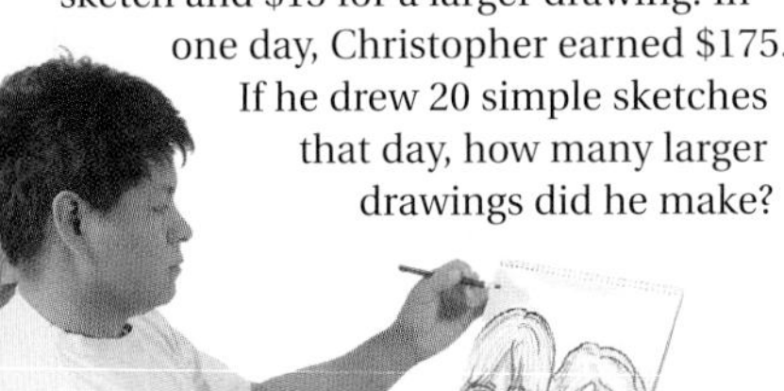

3. Coach Willis has won 150 games during his career as a baseball coach. This is 10 more than $\frac{1}{2}$ as many games as Coach Gentry has won. How many games has Coach Gentry won?

4. Book-club members are required to buy a minimum number of books each year. Leslee bought 3 times the minimum. Denise bought 7 more than the minimum. Together, they bought 23 books. What is the minimum number of books?

5. The perimeter of an isosceles triangle is 4 times the length of the shortest side. The longer sides are 4.5 ft longer than the shortest side. What is the length of each side of the triangle?

6. Miss Rankin's class is raising money for a class trip. The class has $100.00 so far and needs to collect a total of $225.00. How many $0.50 carnations must the class sell to reach its goal?

Answers

1. $d = 12$ days
2. $d = 5$ large drawings
3. $w = 280$ wins
4. $m = 4$ books
5. $x = 9$ ft; the lengths of the sides are 9 ft, 13.5 ft, and 13.5 ft.
6. $c = 250$ carnations

Focus on Problem Solving

Purpose: *To focus on writing an equation to solve a problem*

Problem Solving Resources

Problem Solving Process

This page focuses on the third step of the problem-solving process: **Solve**

Discuss

Have students discuss the steps involved in writing an equation to solve each problem. Then ask them to give the equation used.

Possible answers:

1. Multiply the cost to rent skates each day ($2.50) times the number of days he will rent the skates (d), and add the cost of the safety equipment ($19.50). This sum should equal $49.50; $2.50d + 19.50 = 49.50$.
2. The money earned for each type of sketch is the price of the sketch times the number sold. The sum of the money earned from simple sketches ($\$5 \cdot 20$) and the money earned from larger drawings ($\$15 \cdot d$) is equal to $175; $(5 \cdot 20) + 15d = 175$.
3. Multiply $\frac{1}{2}$ by Coach Gentry's wins (w) and add 10. The sum is equal to 150; $\frac{1}{2}w + 10 = 150$.
4. Multiply 3 times the minimum (m), and add that to 7 plus the minimum. The sum is equal to 23; $3m + (m + 7) = 23$.
5. Add the lengths of the shortest side (x) to the lengths of the two longer sides (each: $4.5 + x$). The sum of all three sides is equal to the perimeter of the triangle, which is 4 times the length of the shortest side; $x + (4.5 + x) + (4.5 + x) = 4x$.
6. Multiply the price of each carnation ($0.50) by the number of carnations (c) that the class must sell, and add the $100 that the class has already raised. This sum should equal $225; $0.50c + 100 = 225$.

Section 11B Inequalities

One-Minute Section Planner

Lesson	Materials	Resources
Lesson 11-4 Inequalities **NCTM:** Algebra, Communication, Representation **NAEP:** Number Properties 1b ☐ SAT-9 ☐ SAT-10 ☐ ITBS ☐ CTBS ☐ MAT ☑ CAT	**Optional** Teaching Transparency T16 *(CRB)*	• *Chapter 11 Resource Book,* pp. 35–44 • Daily Transparency T15, CRB • Additional Examples Transparencies T17–T18, CRB • *Alternate Openers: Explorations,* p. 91
Lesson 11-5 Solving Inequalities by Adding or Subtracting **NCTM:** Algebra, Communication **NAEP:** Algebra 4a ☐ SAT-9 ☐ SAT-10 ☐ ITBS ☐ CTBS ☐ MAT ☑ CAT	**Optional** Algebra tiles *(MK)*	• *Chapter 11 Resource Book,* pp. 45–53 • Daily Transparency T19, CRB • Additional Examples Transparencies T20–T22, CRB • *Alternate Openers: Explorations,* p. 92
Lesson 11-6 Solving Inequalities by Multiplying or Dividing **NCTM:** Algebra, Communication **NAEP:** Algebra 4a ☐ SAT-9 ☐ SAT-10 ☐ ITBS ☐ CTBS ☐ MAT ☑ CAT	**Optional** Recording Sheet for Reaching All Learners *(CRB, p. 78)*	• *Chapter 11 Resource Book,* pp. 54–62 • Daily Transparency T23, CRB • Additional Examples Transparencies T24–T26, CRB • *Alternate Openers: Explorations,* p. 93
Lesson 11-7 Solving Two-Step Inequalities **NCTM:** Algebra, Communication **NAEP:** Algebra 4a ☐ SAT-9 ☐ SAT-10 ☐ ITBS ☐ CTBS ☐ MAT ☐ CAT	**Optional** Recording sheet for Reaching All Learners *(CRB, p. 79)*	• *Chapter 11 Resource Book,* pp. 63–71 • Daily Transparency T27, CRB • Additional Examples Transparencies T28–T30, CRB • *Alternate Openers: Explorations,* p. 94
Extension Solving for a Variable **NCTM:** Algebra, Reasoning and Proof **NAEP:** Algebra 3b ☐ SAT-9 ☐ SAT-10 ☐ ITBS ☐ CTBS ☐ MAT ☐ CAT		• Additional Examples Transparency T31, CRB
Section 11B Assessment		• Section 11B Quiz, AR p. 30 • *Test and Practice Generator* CD-ROM

SAT = *Stanford Achievement Tests* **ITBS** = *Iowa Test of Basic Skills* **CTBS** = *Comprehensive Test of Basic Skills/Terra Nova*
MAT = *Metropolitan Achievement Test* **CAT** = *California Achievement Test*

NCTM—Complete standards can be found on pages T27–T33. **NAEP**—Complete standards can be found on pages A35–A39.

SE = *Student Edition* **TE** = *Teacher's Edition* **AR** = *Assessment Resources* **CRB** = *Chapter Resource Book* **MK** = *Manipulatives Kit*

Section Overview

Inequalities — Lesson 11-4

Why? Students must be able to recognize and interpret inequalities before they can solve them and understand how to apply them.

Inequality	Graph
$x > 1$	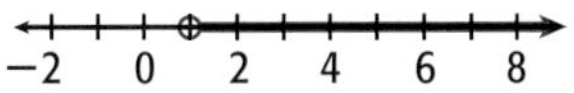 −2 0 2 4 6 8
$x \leq 1$	 −4 −2 0 2 4 6
$-1 < x < 1$	 −2 −1 0 1 2
$x \geq 1$ or $x \leq -1$	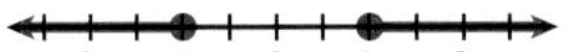 −2 −1 0 1 2

○ Use an open circle when the graph does not include the point.

● Use a closed circle when the graph includes the point.

Solve One-Step Inequalities — Lessons 11-5, 11-6

Why? Many real-world situations can be modeled by inequalities. Examples include describing the temperature needed to prevent a substance from deteriorating, or showing how tall a child must be to ride a specific carnival ride. Students must be able to solve one-step inequalities to apply their understanding to problem solving.

Solve the inequalities.

$$x + 5 \leq -9$$
$$\underline{-5} \quad \underline{-5}$$
$$x \quad \leq -14$$

Solve an addition or subtraction inequality as you would solve an equation.

$$-11y < -132$$
$$\frac{-11y}{-11} > \frac{-132}{-11}$$
$$y > 12$$

Reverse the direction of the inequality symbol when you multiply or divide by a negative number.

Solve Two-Step Inequalities — Lesson 11-7

Why? Solving two-step inequalities is the next logical step in solving inequalities. Students should be able to extend their problem-solving abilities to include problems with two-step inequalities.

Solve the inequality.

$$\frac{x}{-8} - 7 > 9$$
$$\underline{+7} \quad \underline{+7}$$
$$\frac{x}{-8} > 16$$
$$(-8)\frac{x}{-8} < (-8)16$$
$$x < -128$$

Add 7 to both sides of the inequality.

Reverse the direction of the inequality symbol when you multiply both sides of the inequality by −8.

11-4 Organizer

Pacing: Traditional 1 day
Block $\frac{1}{2}$ day

Objective: Students read and write inequalities and graph them on a number line.

Warm Up

Solve.

1. $-21z + 12 = -27z$ $\quad z = -2$

2. $-12n - 18 = -6n$ $\quad n = -3$

3. $12y - 56 = 8y$ $\quad y = 14$

4. $-36k + 9 = -18k$ $\quad k = \frac{1}{2}$

Problem of the Day

The dimensions of one rectangle are twice as large as the dimensions of another rectangle. The difference in the area is 42 cm^2. What is the area of each rectangle? 56 cm^2 and 14 cm^2

Available on Daily Transparency in CRB

What keeps a square from moving? Square roots, of course.

11-4 Inequalities

Learn to read and write inequalities and graph them on a number line.

Vocabulary
inequality
algebraic inequality
solution set
compound inequality

An **inequality** states that two quantities either are not equal or may not be equal. An inequality uses one of the following symbols:

Symbol	Meaning	Word Phrases
$<$	Is less than	Fewer than, below
$>$	Is greater than	More than, above
$\le$	Is less than or equal to	At most, no more than
$\ge$	Is greater than or equal to	At least, no less than

EXAMPLE 1 **Writing Inequalities**

Write an inequality for each situation.

A **There are at least 25 students in the auditorium.**

number of students ≥ 25 — *"At least" means greater than or equal to.*

B **No more than 150 people can occupy the room.**

room capacity ≤ 150 — *"No more than" means less than or equal to.*

An inequality that contains a variable is an **algebraic inequality** . A value of the variable that makes the inequality true is a solution of the inequality.

An inequality may have more than one solution. Together, all of the solutions are called the **solution set** .

You can graph the solutions of an inequality on a number line. If the variable is "greater than" or "less than" a number, then that number is indicated with an open circle.

This open circle shows that 5 is not a solution.

If the variable is "greater than or equal to" or "less than or equal to" a number, that number is indicated with a closed circle.

This closed circle shows that 3 is a solution.

1 Introduce

Alternate Opener

EXPLORATION

11-4 Inequalities

An inequality states that two values are not equal. When one of the values is expressed as a variable, there are four different inequality relationships possible.

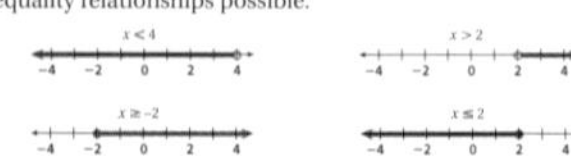

Graph each inequality on the number line.

1. $x > 2$
2. $x < -1$
3. $x \ge -3$
4. $x \le 0$

Think and Discuss

5. **Explain** how you determined which direction the arrow should point on your graphs in numbers 1–4.
6. **Explain** what an inequality is.

Motivate

Have students suggest inequality symbols that satisfy comparisons, such as the following: 1.8 ▢ 18, and -1 ▢ -3 $<$ or $\le$; $>$ or $\ge$. Then have students give examples of other numbers that satisfy similar inequalities: ▢ < 18, and ▢ > -3.

Possible answers: $-1, 0, 1; -2, 0, 5$

Exploration worksheet and answers on Chapter 11 Resource Book pp. 36 and 86

2 Teach

Lesson Presentation

Guided Instruction

In this lesson, students learn to read and write inequalities and to graph them on a number line. This lesson provides both a review of inequalities and an introduction to inequalities involving a variable. Students are now using a variable to generalize the inequalities to cover more than one pair of numbers. The inequalities compare a set of numbers to a single number.

Point out that you can check the graph of an inequality by selecting a point on the shaded portion of the graph. Any point selected should satisfy the inequality (i.e., make the inequality a true inequality).

EXAMPLE 2 Graphing Simple Inequalities

Graph each inequality.

A $x > -2$

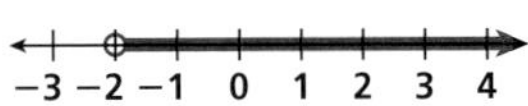

−2 is not a solution, so draw an open circle at −2. Shade the line to the right of −2.

B $y \le -1$

−1 is a solution, so draw a closed circle at −1. Shade the line to the left of −1.

Writing Math

The compound inequality $-2 < y$ and $y < 4$ can be written as $-2 < y < 4$.

A **compound inequality** is the result of combining two inequalities. The words *and* and *or* are used to describe how the two parts are related.

$x > 3$ or $x < -1$	$-2 < y$ and $y < 4$
x is either greater than 3 or less than −1.	*y is both greater than −2 and less than 4. y is between −2 and 4.*

EXAMPLE 3 Graphing Compound Inequalities

Graph each compound inequality.

A $s \ge 0$ or $s < -3$

First graph each inequality separately.

$s \ge 0$

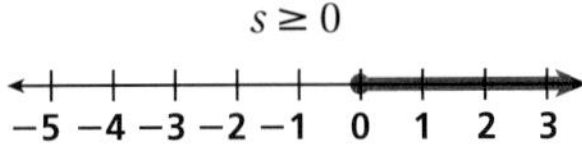

$s < -3$

Then combine the graphs.

The solutions of $s \ge 0$ or $s < -3$ are the combined solutions of $s \ge 0$ and $s < -3$.

B $1 < p \le 5$

$1 < p \le 5$ can be written as $1 < p$ and $p \le 5$. Graph each inequality.

$1 < p$

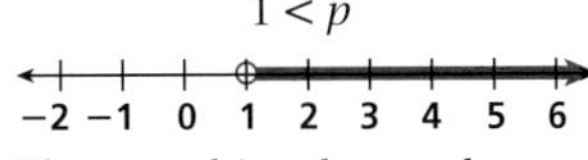

$p \le 5$

Then combine the graphs.

The solutions of $1 < p \le 5$ are the solutions common to $1 < p$ and $p \le 5$.

Think and Discuss

1. **Compare** the graphs of the inequalities $y > 2$ and $y \ge 2$.
2. **Explain** how to graph each type of compound inequality.

COMMON ERROR ALERT

When students are graphing compound inequalities, they might use two closed circles or two open circles without checking both of the inequalities. Remind students that they must check both inequalities to graph the compound inequality.

Additional Examples

Example 1

Write an inequality for each situation.

A. There are at least 15 people in the waiting room.

number of people ≥ 15

B. The tram attendant will allow no more than 60 people on the tram. number of people ≤ 60

Example 2

Graph each inequality.

A. $n < 3$

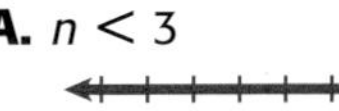

B. $a \ge -4$

Example 3

Graph each compound inequality.

A. $m \le -2$ or $m > 1$

B. $-3 < b \le 0$

3 Close

Reaching All Learners

Through Critical Thinking

Have students work together to consider absolute value inequalities, such as $|x| < 2$. First, have students find numbers that satisfy the inequality. Then have them use the numbers to sketch a graph of what they think the solution should be.

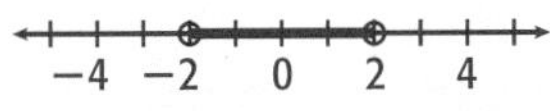

Summarize

Have students explain how to graph each of the following inequalities on a number line:

$x \le 0$ draw a closed circle at 0 and shade to the left

$x > 0$, draw an open circle at 0 and shade to the right

$0 \le x \le 1$ draw closed circles at 0 and 1 and shade between them

$x > 1$ or $x \le 0$ draw an open circle at 1 and shade to the right, and draw a closed circle at 0 and shade to the left

Answers to Think and Discuss

1. The graphs are the same, except that the circle is closed for $y \ge 2$ and open for $y > 2$.
2. Possible answer: If the variable is between the values, shade the line between the values. If the inequality is an "or" inequality, shade the lines at the ends of the number line.

11-4 PRACTICE & ASSESS

Students may want to refer back to the lesson examples.

Assignment Guide

If you finished Example **1** assign:
Core 1–3, 11–14, 31, 33, 36–41
Enriched 1, 3, 11, 13, 31, 33, 36–41

If you finished Example **2** assign:
Core 1–7, 11–20, 31, 33, 36–41
Enriched 1–7 odd, 11–20, 31, 33, 36–41

If you finished Example **3** assign:
Core 1–26, 27–33 odd, 36–41
Enriched 1–9 odd, 11–41

Answers

4.  −5 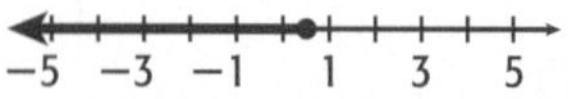 −3 −1 1 3 5

5. −5 −3 −1 1 3 5

6. 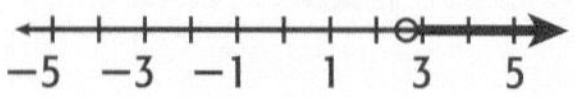 −5 −3 −1 1 3 5

7. 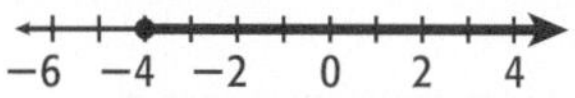 −6 −4 −2 0 2 4

8. 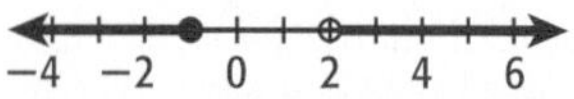 −4 −2 0 2 4 6

9. 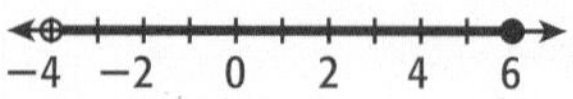 −4 −2 0 2 4 6

10. 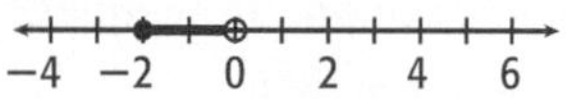 −4 −2 0 2 4 6

15–26. See pp. A3–A4.

11-4 Exercises

FOR EXTRA PRACTICE
see page 679

internet connect
Homework Help Online
go.hrw.com Keyword: MS4 11-4

GUIDED PRACTICE

See Example 1 **Write an inequality for each situation.**

1. No more than 18 people are allowed in the gallery at one time. **number of people ≤ 18**

2. There are fewer than 8 fish in the aquarium. **number of fish < 8**

3. The water level is above 45 inches. **water level > 45**

See Example 2 **Graph each inequality.**

4. $x < 3$ **5.** $r \leq \frac{1}{2}$ **6.** $w > 2.8$ **7.** $y \geq -4$

See Example 3 **Graph each compound inequality.**

8. $a > 2$ or $a \leq -1$ **9.** $-4 < p \leq 6$ **10.** $-2 \leq n < 0$

INDEPENDENT PRACTICE

See Example 1 **Write an inequality for each situation.**

11. The temperature is below 40°F. **temperature < 40**

12. There are at least 24 pictures on the roll of film. **number of pictures ≥ 24**

13. No more than 35 tables are in the cafeteria. **number of tables ≤ 35**

14. Fewer than 250 people attended the rally. **number of people < 250**

See Example 2 **Graph each inequality.**

15. $s \geq -1$ **16.** $y < 0$ **17.** $n \leq -3$

18. $x > 2$ **19.** $b \geq -6$ **20.** $m < -4$

See Example 3 **Graph each compound inequality.**

21. $p > 3$ or $p < 0$ **22.** $1 \leq x \leq 4$ **23.** $-3 < y < -1$

24. $k > 0$ or $k \leq -2$ **25.** $n \geq 1$ or $n \leq -1$ **26.** $-2 < w \leq 2$

PRACTICE AND PROBLEM SOLVING

Write each statement using inequality symbols.

27. The number c is between −2 and 3. **$-2 < c < 3$**

28. The number y is greater than −10. **$y > -10$**

Write an inequality shown by each graph.

29. −4 −3 −2 −1 0 1 2 3 4 **29. $-3 < x < 1$**

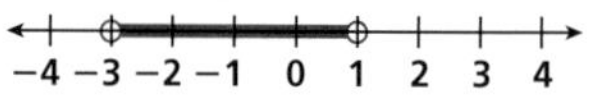

30. 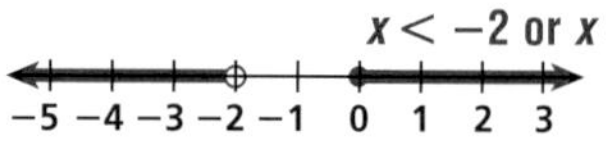 −5 −4 −3 −2 −1 0 1 2 3 **$x < -2$ or $x \geq 0$**

Math Background

Inequalities are based on the order of real numbers. The following definition of *greater than* ensures that a is located to the right of b on the number line. "If a and b are real numbers, then $a > b$ means that $a - b$ is positive." It is also true that $a > 0$ means that a is positive, and $a < 0$ means that a is negative.

The real numbers are ordered in the following sense. For any two real numbers a and b, only one of these statements is true: $a > b$, $a = b$, or $a < b$.

RETEACH 11-4

LESSON 11-4 **Reteach**
Inequalities

An equation is a statement that says two quantities are equal. An **inequality** is a statement that says two quantities are **not** equal.

The chart shows symbols and phrases that indicate inequalities.

<	>	≤	≥
Less than Fewer than Below	Greater than More than Above	Less than or equal to At most No more than	Greater than or equal to At least No less than

Complete the inequality for each situation.

1. No more than 200 people can be seated in the restaurant.
   number of people seated in restaurant ≤ 200
2. The waiting time for a table is at least 20 minutes.
   waiting time ≥ 20 minutes
3. The price of all special dinner entrees is below $10.
   special dinner entrees < $10
4. The Yoshida family spent more than $40 for dinner.
   Yoshida family spent > $40

An inequality can be shown on a graph.

The graph shows:	Inequality	Graph
All numbers greater than 3	$x > 3$	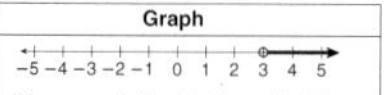 −5 −4 −3 −2 −1 0 1 2 3 4 5 The *open circle* at 3 shows that the value 3 is **not** included in the graph.
All numbers greater than or equal to 3	$x \geq 3$	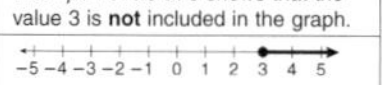 −5 −4 −3 −2 −1 0 1 2 3 4 5 The *closed circle* at 3 shows that the value 3 **is** included in the graph.
All numbers less than 3	$x < 3$	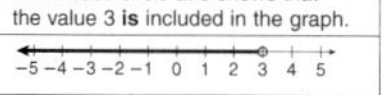 −5 −4 −3 −2 −1 0 1 2 3 4 5
All numbers less than or equal to 3	$x \leq 3$	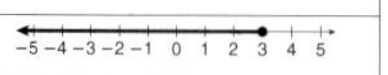 −5 −4 −3 −2 −1 0 1 2 3 4 5

PRACTICE 11-4

LESSON 11-4 **Practice B**
Inequalities

Write an inequality for each situation.

1. The temperature today will be at most 50°F. **$x \leq 50$**
2. The temperature tomorrow will be above 70°F. **$x > 70$**
3. Yesterday, there was less than 2 inches of rain. **$x < 2$**
4. Last Monday, there was at least 3 inches of rain. **$x \geq 3$**

Graph each inequality.

5. $t \leq -2$  −5 −4 −3 −2 −1 0 1 2 3 4 5
6. $j > -5$ −5 −4 −3 −2 −1 0 1 2 3 4 5 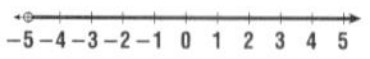
7. $y \leq 0$  −5 −4 −3 −2 −1 0 1 2 3 4 5
8. $b < \frac{1}{2}$ −5 −4 −3 −2 −1 0 1 2 3 4 5

Graph each compound inequality.

9. $f > 3$ or $f < -2$ −5 −4 −3 −2 −1 0 1 2 3 4 5
10. $-4 \leq w \leq 4$ 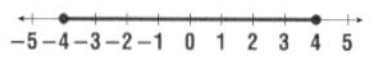 −5 −4 −3 −2 −1 0 1 2 3 4 5
11. $b < 0$ or $b \geq 5$ −5 −4 −3 −2 −1 0 1 2 3 4 5
12. $y \geq 3$ or $y \leq -1$  −5 −4 −3 −2 −1 0 1 2 3 4 5
13. $-4 < m < -2$ −5 −4 −3 −2 −1 0 1 2 3 4 5

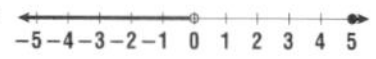

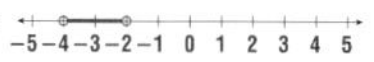

Earth Science LINK

A continental margin is divided into the continental shelf, the continental slope, and the continental rise.

31. The continental shelf begins at the shoreline and slopes toward the open ocean. The depth of the continental shelf can reach 200 meters. Write a compound inequality for the depth of the continental shelf. **−200 ≤ depth ≤ 0**

32. The continental slope begins at the edge of the continental shelf and continues down to the flattest part of the ocean floor. The depth of the continental slope ranges from about 200 meters to about 4,000 meters. Write a compound inequality for the depth of the continental slope. **−4,000 < depth < −200**

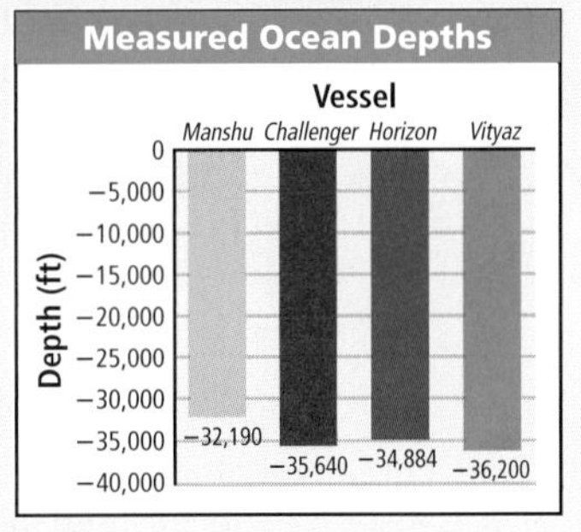

33. The bar graph shows the depth of the ocean in various locations as measured by different research vessels. Write a compound inequality that shows the ranges of depth measured by each vessel.

34. A submarine's *crush depth* is the depth at which water pressure will cause the submarine to collapse. A certain submarine has a crush depth of 2,250 feet. Write a compound inequality that shows at what depths this submarine can travel. **0 ft > submarine travel depth > −2,250 ft**

35. ***CHALLENGE*** Water freezes at 32°F and boils at 212°F. Write three inequalities to show the ranges of temperatures for which water is a solid, a liquid, and a gas.

Deep Flight is designed to explore the ocean in underwater flights.

Spiral Review

A 1–6 number cube is rolled. Find each probability. Write your answer as a fraction, as a decimal, and as a percent. (Lesson 10-4)

36. $P(3)$ **$\frac{1}{6}$, 0.17, 17%**
37. $P(\text{even number})$ **$\frac{1}{2}$, 0.5, 50%**
38. $P(12)$ **0, 0.0, 0%**
39. $P(2 \text{ or } 3)$ **$\frac{1}{3}$, 0.33, 33%**

40. **TEST PREP** What is the volume of a cylinder with radius 2 m and height 5 m? Use 3.14 for π. (Lesson 9-2) **A**

A 62.8 m^3 **B** 98.596 m^3 **C** 157 m^3 **D** 31.4 m^3

41. **TEST PREP** Solve $2x + 7 = 91$. (Lesson 11-1) **G**

F $x = 49$ **G** $x = 42$ **H** $x = 168$ **J** $x = 196$

Interdisciplinary LINK

Earth Science

Exercises 31–35 involve using inequalities in oceanography. Oceanography is studied in middle school Earth science programs, such as *Holt Science & Technology*

Answers

33. 0 ≥ *Manshu* depth measurement ≥ −32,190 ft; 0 ≥ *Challenger* depth measurement ≥ −35,640 ft; 0 ≥ *Horizon* depth measurement ≥ −34,884 ft; 0 ≥ *Vityaz* depth measurement ≥ −36,200 ft

35. 32°F < t < 212°F; t ≤ 32°F; t ≥ 212°F

Journal

Have students describe a real-world situation that can be translated into an inequality. Ask them to write an inequality to represent the situation.

Test Prep Doctor

For Exercise 40, students who selected **D** are forgetting to square the radius in the formula for the volume of a cylinder. Students who selected **B** or **C** do not understand how to find the volume of a cylinder. These students may need to review both the formula and how to use the formula to find the volume. The correct answer is **A.**

CHALLENGE 11-4

LESSON 11-4 Challenge
Square Equations

Some equations can be solved using square roots.

Example 1:
Solve $x^2 = 25$.
Think: $5^2 = 25$, and $(-5)^2 = 25$.
So, the equation has two solutions.
$x = -5, 5$

Example 2:
Solve $\frac{w}{2} = \frac{8}{w}$.
First, cross multiply: $w^2 = 16$.
Think: $4^2 = 16$, and $(-4)^2 = 16$.
So, the equation has two solutions.
$y = -4, 4$

Solve.

1. $x^2 = 64$ — $x = -8, 8$
2. $y^2 = 81$ — $y = -9, 9$
3. $n^2 = 121$ — $n = -11, 11$
4. $a^2 = 49$ — $a = -7, 7$
5. $m^2 = 100$ — $m = -10, 10$
6. $s^2 = 169$ — $s = -13, 13$
7. $\frac{c}{3} = \frac{3}{c}$ — $c = -3, 3$
8. $\frac{k}{4} = \frac{25}{k}$ — $k = -10, 10$
9. $\frac{e}{4} = \frac{16}{e}$ — $e = -8, 8$
10. $\frac{9}{t} = \frac{t}{4}$ — $t = -6, 6$
11. $\frac{16}{d} = \frac{d}{9}$ — $d = -12, 12$
12. $z^2 - 1 = 35$ — $z = -6, 6$
13. $p^2 - 5 = 20$ — $p = -5, 5$
14. $h^2 + 14 = 63$ — $h = -7, 7$
15. $29 + v^2 = 110$ — $v = -9, 9$

PROBLEM SOLVING 11-4

LESSON 11-4 Problem Solving
Inequalities

Write the correct answer.

The American College of Sports Medicine recommends exercising at an intensity of 60% to 90% of your maximum heart rate.

Heart Rates by Age

Age	Maximum Heart Rate	Target Range
20–24	200	120–180
25–29	195	117–176
30–34	190	114–171
35–39	185	111–167
40–44	180	108–162

1. Mara is 25 years old. Write a compound inequality to represent her target heart rate range while bike riding.
$117 \le x \le 176$

2. Leia is 38 years old. Write a compound inequality to represent the zone between her maximum heart rate and the upper end of her target range.
$167 < x \le 185$

3. Rudy is 42 years old. Write an inequality to represent at least 70% of his maximum heart rate.
$x \ge 0.7 \cdot 180$; $x \ge 126$

4. Write a compound inequality to represent 60% to 90% of your maximum heart rate in ten years.
Possible answer: $120 \le x \le 180$

Choose the letter for the graph that represents each statement.

5. Alena decided to pay not more than $25 to get her old bike repaired.
A I C III
B II (D) IV

6. It was so cold last week that the temperature never reached 25°F.
F I H III
(G) II J IV

7. There were at least 25 people ahead of Ivan in the cafeteria line.
A I (C) III
B II D IV

8. The garden yielded more than 25 pounds of potatoes.
(F) I H III
G II J IV

I. 0 5 10 15 20 25 30 35 40 45 50
II. 0 5 10 15 20 25 30 35 40 45 50
III. 0 5 10 15 20 25 30 35 40 45 50
IV. 0 5 10 15 20 25 30 35 40 45 50

Lesson Quiz

Write an inequality for each situation.

1. No more than 220 people are in the theater.
people in the theater ≤ 220

2. There are at least a dozen eggs left. number of eggs ≥ 12

3. Fewer than 14 people attended the meeting. people attending the meeting < 14

Graph the inequality.

4. $x > -1$

−3 −2 −1 0 1 2

5. $x \ge 4$ or $x < -1$

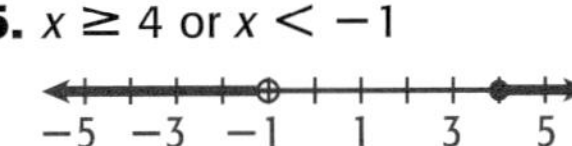

Available on Daily Transparency in CRB

11-5 Organizer

Pacing: Traditional 1 day
Block $\frac{1}{2}$ day

Objective: Students solve one-step inequalities by adding or subtracting.

11-5 Solving Inequalities by Adding or Subtracting

Learn to solve one-step inequalities by adding or subtracting.

Monday's high temperature was 32°F. The weather forecaster predicted a high of at least 71°F on Tuesday. At least how many degrees warmer is Tuesday's forecasted high temperature than Monday's high temperature? To find the answer, you can solve an inequality.

When you add or subtract the same number on both sides of an inequality, the resulting statement will still be true.

$$\begin{array}{rcr} -2 & < & 5 \\ \underline{+7} & & \underline{+7} \\ 5 & < & 12 \end{array}$$

You can find solution sets of inequalities the same way you find solutions of equations, by isolating the variable.

EXAMPLE 1 Solving Inequalities by Adding

Solve. Then graph each solution set on a number line.

A $x - 12 > 32$

$$\begin{array}{rcl} x - 12 & > & 32 \\ \underline{+12} & & \underline{+12} \\ x & > & 44 \end{array}$$

Add 12 to both sides.

0 11 22 33 44 55 66 77 88

44 is not a solution, so draw an open circle at 44. Then shade the line to include values greater than 44.

B $y - 8 \leq -14$

$$\begin{array}{rcl} y - 8 & \leq & -14 \\ \underline{+8} & & \underline{+8} \\ y & \leq & -6 \end{array}$$

Add 8 to both sides.

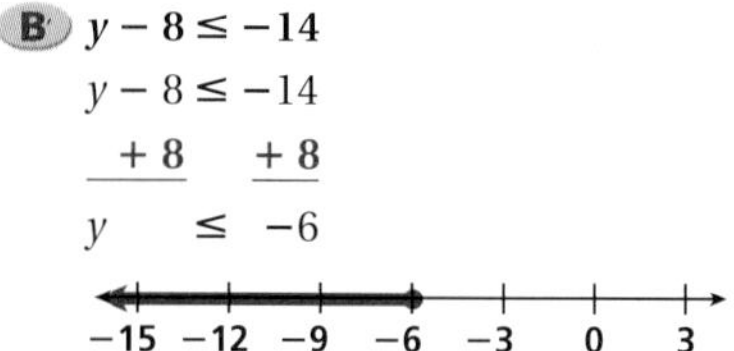

−15 −12 −9 −6 −3 0 3

−6 is a solution, so draw a closed circle at −6. Then shade the line to include values less than −6.

Warm Up

Write the inequality for each situation.

1. There are at least 28 days in a month. days in a month $\geq$ 28
2. The temperature is above 72°. temperature $>$ 72°
3. At most 9 passengers can ride in the van. passengers $\leq$ 9

Problem of the Day

Daryl gave the clerk less than \$20 for a CD and received change of at least \$5. He ended up with the CD and less money than he started with. Write a compound inequality to show what C, the cost in dollars of the CD, could have been. $0 < C < 15$

Available on Daily Transparency in CRB

Math Fact !

The negation of an equality corresponds to one or more inequalities. For example, $a \neq b$ is the same as the two inequalities $a < b$ or $a > b$.

1 Introduce

Alternate Opener

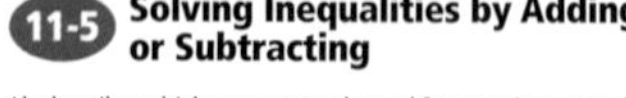

EXPLORATION

11-5 Solving Inequalities by Adding or Subtracting

Algebra tiles, which are commonly used for equations, can also be used to model adding or subtracting the same number from each side of an inequality. The model below shows the inequality $x + 4 > -1$.

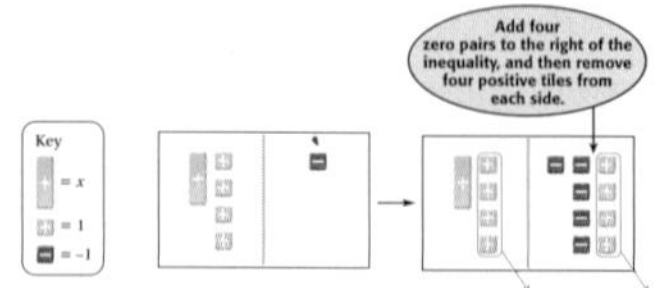

So the solution to $x + 4 > -1$ is $x > -5$. In other words, any number that is greater than −5 is a solution to the inequality.

Use a model to solve each inequality.

1. $x + 5 > -2$
2. $x - 5 < -4$
3. $8 + x < -1$
4. $4 - x < -4$

Think and Discuss

5. **Discuss** why inequalities have many solutions.
6. **Explain** how to solve the inequality $x + 4 < 10$ mentally.

Motivate

Discuss the differences in the following situations.

(1) Paolo has \$10. How much more money does he need to buy a shirt that costs \$16?

(2) Paula needs at least \$16 to buy a shirt. How much more money does she need if she already has \$10?

Lead students to notice that Paolo's situation corresponds to an equality while Paula's corresponds to an inequality.

Exploration worksheet and answers on Chapter 11 Resource Book pp. 46 and 88

2 Teach

Lesson Presentation

Guided Instruction

In this lesson, students learn to solve one-step inequalities by adding or subtracting. To "solve an inequality" means to find all of the numbers that are solutions of the inequality. These numbers make up the *solution set.*

Teaching Tip Have students solve the equations that correspond to the examples. Compare the solution sets of the equations with the solution sets of the inequalities.

You can see if the solution to an inequality is true by choosing any number in the solution set and substituting it into the original inequality.

EXAMPLE 2 Solving Inequalities by Subtracting

Solve. Check each answer.

A $c + 9 < 20$

$$\begin{aligned} c + 9 &< 20 \\ \underline{-9} \quad & \underline{-9} \\ c \quad &< 11 \end{aligned}$$

Subtract 9 from both sides.

Check

$c + 9 < 20$

$10 + 9 \overset{?}{<} 20$ — *10 is less than 11. Substitute 10 for c.*

$19 \overset{?}{<} 20$ ✔

B $x + 16 > -2$

$$\begin{aligned} x + 16 &> -2 \\ \underline{-16} \quad & \underline{-16} \\ x \quad &> -18 \end{aligned}$$

Subtract 16 from both sides.

Check

$x + 16 > -2$

$0 + 16 \overset{?}{>} -2$ — *0 is greater than −18. Substitute 0 for x.*

$16 \overset{?}{>} -2$ ✔

Helpful Hint

When checking your solution, choose a number in the solution set that is easy to work with.

EXAMPLE 3 *Meteorology Application*

Monday's high temperature was 32°F. The weather forecast for Tuesday includes a high temperature of at least 71°F. At least how many degrees warmer is the forecasted temperature for Tuesday than Monday's high temperature?

Let t represent the temperature increase from Monday to Tuesday.

$$\begin{aligned} 32 + t &\geq 71 \\ \underline{-32} \quad & \underline{-32} \\ t &\geq 39 \end{aligned}$$

Subtract 32 from both sides.

The temperature forecasted for Tuesday is at least 39°F warmer than the high temperature on Monday.

Think and Discuss

1. **Compare** solving addition and subtraction equations with solving addition and subtraction inequalities.
2. **Describe** how to check whether −36 is a solution of $s - 5 > 1$.

COMMON ERROR ALERT

Some students might have trouble identifying the correct inequality in application problems. Encourage students to review the meanings of the terms that correspond to each type of inequality.

Additional Examples

Example 1

Solve. Then graph each solution set on a number line.

A. $n - 7 \leq 15$ **$n \leq 22$**

−66 −44 −22 0 22 44

B. $a - 10 \geq -3$ **$a \geq 7$**

0 2 4 6 8 10

Example 2

Solve. Check each answer.

A. $d + 11 > 6$ **$d > -5$**

B. $b + 12 \leq 19$ **$b \leq 7$**

Example 3

Last year, the low temperature for March 1 was −2°F. This year the forecast calls for a low of at most 13°F on that day. At most, how many degrees warmer is the temperature forecast to be on March 1 this year than last year? **15°F**

Example 2 note: You may wish to point out that if zero is in the solution set, it is usually the easiest integer to use to check the solution of an inequality.

3 Close

Summarize

Challenge students to solve and check each of the following inequalities:

$-15 + y > 20$ **$y > 35$**

$6.5 + b \leq 1$ **$b \leq -5.5$**

Reaching All Learners

Through Curriculum Integration

Science Let students work in small groups to describe a situation from science that suggests inequalities. Topics may include comparing speeds, temperatures, weights, and so on. Have each group write an inequality for the situation and share results with the class.

Possible answers: The weight of sample A < 2.5 g; the weight of sample A > the weight of sample B.

Answers to Think and Discuss

1. The procedures are identical except for the symbols that distinguish equations and inequalities.
2. Possible answer: Substitute −36 for s in $s - 5 > 1$. If the inequality is a true inequality, then −36 is a solution. If the inequality is false, then −36 is not a solution. $-36 - 5 = -41$, so −36 is not a solution.

11-5 PRACTICE & ASSESS

Students may want to refer back to the lesson examples.

Assignment Guide

If you finished Example 1 assign:
Core 1–3, 8–13, 23, 24, 43–47
Enriched 1, 3, 9–13 odd, 23, 24, 28, 30, 33, 43–47

If you finished Example 2 assign:
Core 1–6, 8–19, 23–33 odd, 43–47
Enriched 1–5 odd, 9–19 odd, 22–33, 43–47

If you finished Example 3 assign:
Core 1–21, 23–39, 43–47
Enriched 1–21 odd, 22–47

Answers

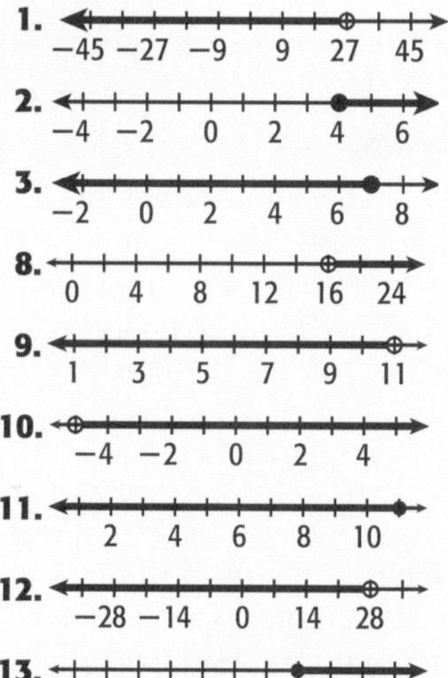

11-5 Exercises

FOR EXTRA PRACTICE
see page 679

internet connect
Homework Help Online
go.hrw.com Keyword: MS4 11-5

GUIDED PRACTICE

See Example 1 Solve. Then graph each solution set on a number line.

1. $x - 9 < 18$ **$x < 27$**
2. $y - 11 \geq -7$ **$y \geq 4$**
3. $p - 3 \leq 4$ **$p \leq 7$**

See Example 2 Solve. Check each answer.

4. $n + 5 > 26$ **$n > 21$**
5. $b + 21 \leq -3$ **$b \leq -24$**
6. $12 + k \geq 9$ **$k \geq -3$**

See Example 3

7. Yesterday's high temperature was 30°F. Tomorrow's weather forecast includes a high temperature of at most 42°F. At most, how many degrees warmer is the high-temperature forecast for tomorrow than yesterday's high temperature? **at most 12°F warmer**

INDEPENDENT PRACTICE

See Example 1 Solve. Then graph each solution set on a number line.

8. $s - 2 > 14$ **$s > 16$**
9. $m - 14 < -3$ **$m < 11$**
10. $b - 25 > -30$ **$b > -5$**
11. $c - 17 \leq -6$ **$c \leq 11$**
12. $y - 53 < -25$ **$y < 28$**
13. $x - 9 \geq 71$ **$x \geq 80$**

See Example 2 Solve. Check each answer.

14. $w + 16 < 4$ **$w < -12$**
15. $z + 9 > -3$ **$z > -12$**
16. $p + 21 \leq -4$ **$p \leq -25$**
17. $f + 32 > 26$ **$f > -6$**
18. $k + 54 < 65$ **$k < 11$**
19. $n + 29 \geq 25$ **$n \geq -4$**

See Example 3

20. Clark scored at least 12 points more than Josh scored. If Josh scored 15 points, at least how many points did Clark score? **at least 27 points**
21. Adriana counted 8 fewer birds on Tuesday than on Thursday. She counted at most 32 birds on Thursday. At most, how many birds did she count on Tuesday? **at most 24 birds**

PRACTICE AND PROBLEM SOLVING

Solve.

22. $k + 3.2 \geq 8$ **$k \geq 4.8$**
23. $a - 1.3 > -1$ **$a > 0.3$**
24. $c - 6\frac{1}{2} < -1\frac{1}{4}$ **$c < 5\frac{1}{4}$**
25. $18 + m \leq -20$ **$m \leq -38$**
26. $x + 7.02 > 4$ **$x > -3.02$**
27. $g + 3\frac{2}{3} < 10$ **$g < 6\frac{1}{3}$**
28. $r - 58 < -109$ **$r < -51$**
29. $5.9 + w \leq 21.6$ **$w \leq 15.7$**
30. $n - 21.6 > 26$ **$n > 47.6$**
31. $t + 92 \geq -150$ **$t \geq -242$**
32. $y + 4\frac{3}{4} \geq 1\frac{1}{8}$ **$y \geq -3\frac{5}{8}$**
33. $v - 0.9 \leq -1.5$ **$v \leq -0.6$**
34. ***CONSUMER MATH*** To get a group discount for baseball tickets, Marco's group must have at least 20 people. So far, 13 people have signed up for tickets. At least how many more people must sign up for the group to get a discount? **7 people**

Math Background

The following properties of inequalities indicate why solving inequalities is different from solving equations.

Let a, b, and c represent real numbers.

Property 1: If $a > b$, then $a + c > b + c$.

Property 2: If $a > b$ and $c > 0$, then $ac > bc$.

Property 3: If $a > b$ and $c < 0$, then $ac < bc$.

Although an inequality does not change if the same quantities are added to or subtracted from both sides of the inequality, it may change when both sides of the inequality are multiplied by or divided by the same quantity.

RETEACH 11-5

LESSON 11-5 **Reteach**
Solving Inequalities by Adding or Subtracting

Inequalities with variables may have more than one solution. All the solutions of an inequality are called the **solution set.**

You can solve an inequality involving addition or subtraction just as you would solve an equation.

Complete the steps to solve, graph, and check the inequality.

1. $n - 13 < 7$
$n - 13 +$ **13** $< 7 +$ **13**
$n <$ **20**
Graph the inequality.
−10 −5 0 5 10 15 20 25 30 35 40
Check:
Pick any number in the solution set of $n < 20$.
$19 < 20$
Substitute 19 into the inequality.
$n - 13 < 7$
19 $- 13 \overset{?}{<} 7$
6 $\overset{?}{<} 7$ ✓

2. $x + 18 \geq 2$
$x + 18 -$ **18** $\geq 2 -$ **18**
$x \geq$ **−16**
Graph the inequality.
−20 −16 −12 −8 −4 0 4 8 12 16 20
Check:
Pick any number in the solution set of $x \geq -16$.
$0 \geq -16$
Substitute 0 into the inequality.
$x + 18 \geq -2$
0 $+ 18 \overset{?}{\geq} -2$
18 $\overset{?}{\geq} -2$ ✓

Solve. Then graph each solution set.

3. $d + 3 > -5$ **$d > -8$**
−10 −8 −6 −4 −2 0 2 4 6 8 10
4. $s - 10 < -6$ **$s < 4$**
−10 −8 −6 −4 −2 0 2 4 6 8 10

Solve. Check each answer.

5. $y + 9 > 20$ **$y > 11$**
6. $h + 17 \leq -6$ **$h \leq -23$**
7. $a - 4 \geq -18$ **$a \geq -14$**

PRACTICE 11-5

LESSON 11-5 **Practice B**
Solving Inequalities by Adding or Subtracting

Solve. Then graph each solution set on a number line.

1. $y - 5 > -2$ **$y > 3$**
−5 −4 −3 −2 −1 0 1 2 3 4 5
2. $n + 5 \leq 11$ **$n \leq 6$**
−2 −1 0 1 2 3 4 5 6 7 8
3. $x + 4 < -1$ **$x < -5$**
−9 −8 −7 −6 −5 −4 −3 −2 −1 0 1
4. $h + 20 > 2$ **$h > -18$**
−20 −18 −16 −14 −12 −10
5. $p + 9 \geq -3$ **$p \geq -12$**
−18 −16 −14 −12 −10 −8
6. $s - 7 < -16$ **$s < -9$**
−10 −9 −8 −7 −6 −5 −4 −3 −2 −1 0

Solve. Check each answer.

7. $41 + g > 27$ **$g > -14$**
8. $w - 23 \geq -18$ **$w \geq 5$**
9. $a + 15 \leq 9$ **$a \leq -6$**
10. $z - 2.3 < 5$ **$z < 7.3$**
11. $t + 5.9 \geq 1.3$ **$t \geq -4.6$**
12. $4\frac{1}{2} + b \leq 5\frac{3}{4}$ **$b \leq 1\frac{1}{4}$**

Life Science LINK

One of the largest giant spider crabs on record weighed 41 lb and had a claw span of 12 ft 2 in.

go.hrw.com
KEYWORD: MS4 Crab

CNN Student News

35. ***LIFE SCIENCE*** The giant spider crab, the world's largest crab, lives off the southeastern coast of Japan. Giant spider crabs can grow to be more than 3.6 meters across. A scientist measures a giant spider crab that is 3.1 meters across. At least how many more meters might the crab grow? **at least 0.5 meters**

36. The *shinkansen*, or bullet train, of Japan travels at an average speed of 162.3 miles per hour. It has a top speed of 186 miles per hour. At most, how many more miles per hour can the train travel beyond its average speed before it reaches its maximum speed? **at most 23.7 mi/h**

37. The line graph shows the number of miles Amelia rode her bike in each of the last four months. She wants to ride at least 5 miles more in May than she did in April. At least how many miles does Amelia want to ride in May? **at least 22 miles**

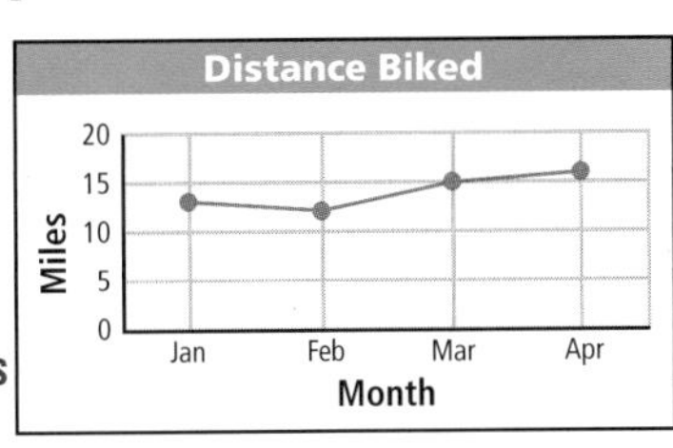

38. ***PHYSICAL SCIENCE*** The average human ear can detect sounds that have frequencies between 20 hertz and 20,000 hertz. The average dog ear can detect sounds with frequencies of up to 30,000 hertz greater than those a human ear can detect. Up to how many hertz can a dog hear? **up to 50,000 hertz**

39. ***LIFE SCIENCE*** Cheetahs have been known to run at speeds of more than 105 km/h for short bursts. A cheetah in a nature preserve is clocked running at 92.6 km/h. How many more kilometers per hour might an even faster cheetah run? **more than 12.4 km/h**

40. ***CHOOSE A STRATEGY*** If five days ago was the day after Saturday, what was the day before yesterday? **Wednesday**

41. ***WRITE ABOUT IT*** Explain how to solve and check the inequality $n - 9 < -15$.

42. ***CHALLENGE*** Solve the inequality $x + (4^2 - 2^3)^2 > -1$. **$x > -65$**

Spiral Review

The surface area of a prism is 16 in^2. Find the surface area of a larger, similarly shaped prism that has each scale factor. (Lesson 9-5)

43. scale factor = 3 **144 in^2**
44. scale factor = 8 **1,024 in^2**
45. scale factor = 10 **1,600 in^2**

46. **TEST PREP** Amber rolls two different-colored 1–6 number cubes at the same time. How many outcomes are possible? (Lesson 10-3) **D**

A 6 **B** 12 **C** 24 **D** 36

47. **TEST PREP** Which graph is a solution of $-3 < x \leq 1$? (Lesson 11-4) **J**

F −4 −2 0 2 **G** −4 −2 0 2 **H** −2 0 2 **J** −4 −2 0 2

Answers

41. Possible answer: Add 9 to both sides of the inequality: $n < -6$. Check by substituting a value less than −6 for n in $n - 9 < -15$.

Journal

Ask students to describe a real-world situation that could be represented by an addition or subtraction inequality. Have students tell how they would solve the inequality. You may wish to suggest that students describe a situation involving money.

Test Prep Doctor

Students who selected **A, B,** or **C** for Exercise 46 may need to review counting methods.

In Exercise 47, students who selected **F** and **G** are confusing the endpoints of the inequality. These students should review when the endpoints are inclusive (closed) and when they are not inclusive (open). Students who selected **H** are plotting an "or" graph. They need to distinguish between "and" and "or" inequalities. The correct answer is **J.**

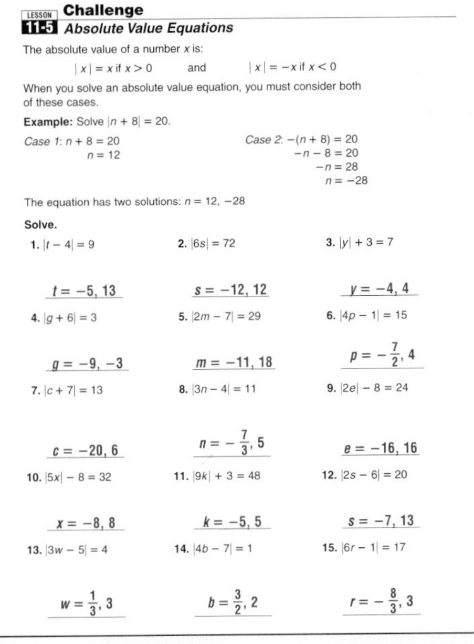

CHALLENGE 11-5

LESSON 11-5 **Challenge**
Absolute Value Equations

The absolute value of a number x is:

$|x| = x$ if $x > 0$ and $|x| = -x$ if $x < 0$

When you solve an absolute value equation, you must consider both of these cases.

Example: Solve $|n + 8| = 20$.

Case 1: $n + 8 = 20$
$n = 12$

Case 2: $-(n + 8) = 20$
$-n - 8 = 20$
$-n = 28$
$n = -28$

The equation has two solutions: $n = 12, -28$

Solve.

1. $|t - 4| = 9$ **$t = -5, 13$**
2. $|6s| = 72$ **$s = -12, 12$**
3. $|y| + 3 = 7$ **$y = -4, 4$**
4. $|g + 6| = 3$ **$g = -9, -3$**
5. $|2m - 7| = 29$ **$m = -11, 18$**
6. $|4p - 1| = 15$ **$p = -\frac{7}{2}, 4$**
7. $|c + 7| = 13$ **$c = -20, 6$**
8. $|3n - 4| = 11$ **$n = -\frac{7}{3}, 5$**
9. $|2e| - 8 = 24$ **$e = -16, 16$**
10. $|5x| - 8 = 32$ **$x = -8, 8$**
11. $|9k| + 3 = 48$ **$k = -5, 5$**
12. $|2s - 6| = 20$ **$s = -7, 13$**
13. $|3w - 5| = 4$ **$w = \frac{1}{3}, 3$**
14. $|4b - 7| = 1$ **$b = \frac{3}{2}, 2$**
15. $|6r - 1| = 17$ **$r = -\frac{8}{3}, 3$**

PROBLEM SOLVING 11-5

LESSON 11-5 **Problem Solving**
Solving Inequalities by Adding or Subtracting

Write the correct answer.

1. A small car averages up to 29 more miles per gallon of gas than an SUV. If a small car averages 44 miles per gallon, what is the average miles per gallon for an SUV?
at least 15 mi per gal

2. Carlos is taking a car trip that is more than 240 miles, depending on the route he chooses. He has already driven 135 miles. How much farther does he have to go?
more than 105 miles

3. Driving into the city usually takes 25 minutes. If there is a lot of traffic, the trip can take up to 45 minutes. How much additional time should you allow during a heavy traffic period?
no more than 20 min

4. To qualify for the heavyweight wrestling division, Kobe must weigh at least 180 pounds. If Kobe weighs 168 pounds now, how much weight should he gain?
at least 12 lb

Choose the letter for the best answer.

5. On one day, the range of temperatures in one state was at most 27°. If the lowest temperature in the state was 59°, what was the highest temperature?
A > 86°
(B) ≤ 86°
C 86°
D ≥ 86°

6. The highest possible score on the Scholastic Aptitude Test is 1,600. Rebecca scored 980. She needs a score of at least 1,150 to qualify for a scholarship. How much higher must her score be?
F ≤ 170
G ≤ 450
(H) ≥ 170
J ≥ 450

7. Kassie earns $5.85 an hour at the Burger Stand. She is the lowest-paid worker. The highest wage is $3.60 per hour higher than Kassie's wage. How much per hour do Kassie's co-workers earn?
A $x \geq \$5.85$ or $x \geq \$9.45$
B $x \leq \$5.85$ or $x \leq \$9.45$
C $\$5.85 \geq x \geq \$9.45$
(D) $\$5.85 \leq x \leq \$9.45$

8. The seating capacity of the school gym is 550. Generally, there are fewer than 210 fans attending each basketball game. How many more fans could attend each game?
F $210 \geq f \geq 550$
(G) $0 \leq f \leq 340$
H $f \geq 210$ or $f \geq 340$
J $f \geq 340$ or $f \leq 550$

Lesson Quiz

Solve. Then graph each solution set on a number line.

1. $x - 4 > 17$ **$x > 21$**

15 17 19 21 23 25

2. $z - 27 \leq 19$ **$z \leq 46$**

40 42 44 46 48 50

Solve.

3. $p + 18 \geq -6$ **$p \geq -24$**
4. $k + 47 > 65$ **$k > 18$**
5. There are at least 17 more bus riders than walkers in a class. If there are 7 walkers, how many bus riders are there?
bus riders ≥ 24

Available on Daily Transparency in CRB

11-6 Organizer

Pacing: Traditional 1 day
Block $\frac{1}{2}$ day

Objective: Students solve one-step inequalities by multiplying or dividing.

Warm Up

Solve.

1. $n + 42 > 27$ $n > -15$
2. $r + 15 < 39$ $r < 24$
3. $w - 52 > -17$ $w > 35$
4. $k - 34 > 26$ $k > 60$
5. $m - 19 > 34$ $m > 53$

Problem of the Day

Aracelli started riding her bike at 2 P.M. and returned home at 4 P.M. She rode less than 50 miles. What is the least her speed could have been at 3 P.M.? Explain. 0 mi/h (She could have been resting or stopped at a light, for example.)

Available on Daily Transparency in CRB

Math Fact !!

The graphs of such inequalities as $x > a$, where a is a real number, are known as *infinite intervals* because the graph continues indefinitely in one direction.

11-6 Solving Inequalities by Multiplying or Dividing

Learn to solve one-step inequalities by multiplying or dividing.

During the spring, the Schmidt family sells watermelons at a roadside stand for $5 apiece. Mr. Schmidt calculated that it cost $517 to plant, grow, and harvest the melons this year. At least how many melons must the Schmidts sell in order to make a profit for the year?

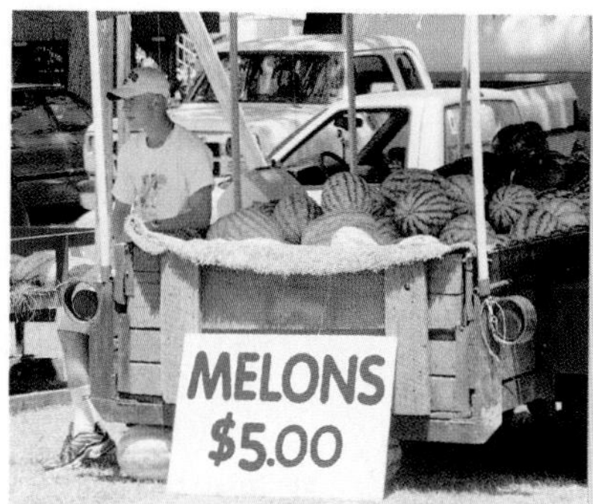

Problems like this require you to multiply or divide to solve an inequality.

When you multiply or divide both sides of an inequality by the same positive number, the statement will still be true. However, when you multiply or divide both sides by the same *negative* number, you need to reverse the direction of the inequality symbol for the statement to be true.

$$-4 < 2 \qquad\qquad -4 < 2$$
$$(3)(-4) < (3)(2) \qquad\qquad (-3)(-4) > (-3)(2)$$
$$-12 < 6 \qquad\qquad 12 > -6$$

EXAMPLE 1 Solving Inequalities by Multiplying

Solve.

A $\frac{x}{11} < 3$

$\frac{x}{11} < 3$

$(11)\frac{x}{11} < (11)3$ *Multiply both sides by 11.*

$x < 33$

B $\frac{r}{-6} \geq 4.8$

$\frac{r}{-6} \geq 4.8$

$(-6)\frac{r}{-6} \leq (-6)4.8$ *Multiply both sides by −6, and reverse the inequality symbol.*

$r \leq -28.8$

1 Introduce

Alternate Opener

EXPLORATION

11-6 Solving Inequalities by Multiplying or Dividing

Claire will start her own math-tutoring service in the summer. She will charge $32.00 an hour. She wants to know how much income she will make, depending on the number of hours she tutors.

1. Complete the table.

Number of Hours	Price per Hour	Income
1	$32.00	$1 \cdot 32 = \$32.00$
2	$32.00	
3	$32.00	
4	$32.00	
5	$32.00	
6	$32.00	
7	$32.00	

2. Use the table to find the number of hours that will give Claire an income that is
   a. equal to $128.00.
   b. less than $128.00.
   c. greater than $128.00.
3. Suppose Claire wants to make an income greater than $300.00. Write and solve an inequality to represent this.

Think and Discuss

4. **Explain** how you wrote the inequality in number 3.
5. **Explain** how you solved the inequality in number 3.

Motivate

Pose the following problem:

Heidi gets an allowance of $36 a month. How could she use the inequality $4x \leq \$36$ to plan a weekly budget?

Discuss how to solve the problem and what the solution means. $x \leq \$9$; she should spend at most $9 each week

Exploration worksheet and answers on Chapter 11 Resource Book pp. 55 and 90

2 Teach

Lesson Presentation

Guided Instruction

In this lesson, students learn to solve one-step inequalities by multiplying or dividing. Point out that the steps the students must follow to solve inequalities using multiplication and division are the same as those for solving equalities, except that multiplying or dividing by a negative number changes the direction of the inequality symbol.

Teaching Tip Provide additional examples of how multiplying and dividing both sides of an inequality by a negative number reverses the direction of the inequality symbol.

EXAMPLE 2 Solving Inequalities by Dividing

Solve. Check each answer.

A $4x > 9$

$4x > 9$

$\frac{4x}{4} > \frac{9}{4}$ *Divide both sides by 4.*

$x > \frac{9}{4}$, or $2\frac{1}{4}$

Check

$4x > 9$

$4(3) \overset{?}{>} 9$ *3 is greater than $2\frac{1}{4}$. Substitute 3 for x.*

$12 \overset{?}{>} 9$ ✔

B $-12y \le -60$

$-12y \le -60$

$\frac{-12y}{-12} \ge \frac{-60}{-12}$ *Divide both sides by −12, and reverse the inequality symbol.*

$y \ge 5$

Check

$-12y \le -60$

$-12(10) \overset{?}{\le} -60$ *10 is greater than 5. Substitute 10 for y.*

$-120 \overset{?}{\le} -60$ ✔

EXAMPLE 3 *Agriculture Application*

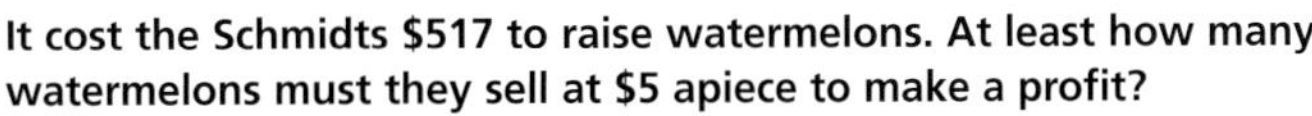

It cost the Schmidts $517 to raise watermelons. At least how many watermelons must they sell at $5 apiece to make a profit?

Since profit is the amount earned minus the amount spent, the Schmidts need to earn more than $517.

Let w represent the number of watermelons they must sell.

$5w > 517$ *Write an inequality.*

$\frac{5w}{5} > \frac{517}{5}$ *Divide both sides by 5.*

$w > 103.4$

The Schmidts cannot sell 0.4 watermelon, so they need to sell at least 104 watermelons to earn a profit.

Think and Discuss

1. **Compare** solving multiplication and division equations with solving multiplication and division inequalities.
2. **Explain** how you would solve the inequality $0.5y > 4.5$.

COMMON ERROR ALERT

Remind students that the inequality symbol does not change direction when adding or subtracting a negative number to both sides. This is done only when multiplying or dividing both sides by a negative number.

Additional Examples

Example 1

Solve.

A. $\frac{c}{4} \le -4$ $\quad c \le -16$

B. $\frac{t}{-4} > 0.3$ $\quad t < -1.2$

Example 2

Solve. Check each answer.

A. $5a \ge 23$ $\quad a \ge \frac{23}{5}$ or $4\frac{3}{5}$

B. $-24b < 192$ $\quad b > -8$

Example 3

It cost Josh $85 to make candles for the craft fair. How many candles must he sell at $4.00 each to make a profit? more than 21

Example 3 note: Ask students how the solution would change if the question had asked how many watermelons the Schmidt family would have to sell in order to break even or to make a profit. Guide students to recognize that the inequality symbol would be ≥ instead of >; however, the answer would be the same, since the family would still have to sell 104 whole watermelons.

3 Close

Summarize

Challenge students to solve and check each of the following inequalities:

$\frac{x}{1.5} \ge -3$ $\quad x \ge -4.5$

$-20y < 160$ $\quad y > -8$

Reaching All Learners

Through Grouping Strategies

Let students work together to decide which of the statements on the recording sheet provided on Chapter 11 Resource Book p. 78 are always true if a, b, and c are real numbers and $a > b$. If the statement is not always true, have students give an example to show that the statement is false.

Answers to Think and Discuss

Possible answers:

1. Although the procedures to solve inequalities and equalities are the same, the direction of the inequality symbol reverses when both sides of an inequality are multiplied or divided by a negative number.
2. Divide both sides of the inequality by 0.5; $y > 9$.

11-6 PRACTICE & ASSESS

Students may want to refer back to the lesson examples.

Assignment Guide

If you finished Example 1 assign:
Core 1–3, 8–13, 22, 26, 28, 41–46
Enriched 1, 3, 9–13 odd, 22, 24, 26–28, 32, 41–46

If you finished Example 2 assign:
Core 1–6, 8–19, 23–33 odd, 41–46
Enriched 1–5 odd, 9–19 odd, 22–33, 41–46

If you finished Example 3 assign:
Core 1–21, 23–37 odd, 41–46
Enriched 1–21 odd, 22–46

Notes

11-6 Exercises

FOR EXTRA PRACTICE see page 679

internet connect
Homework Help Online
go.hrw.com Keyword: MS4 11-6

GUIDED PRACTICE

See Example 1 Solve.

1. $\frac{w}{8} < -4$ **$w < -32$**
2. $\frac{z}{-6} \geq 7$ **$z \leq -42$**
3. $\frac{p}{-12} > -4$ **$p < 48$**

See Example 2 Solve. Check each answer.

4. $3m > -15$ **$m > -5$**
5. $-8y < 11$ **$y > -\frac{11}{8}$ or $-1\frac{3}{8}$**
6. $25c \leq 200$ **$c \leq 8$**

See Example 3

7. It cost Deirdre \$212 to make candles this month. At least how many candles must she sell at \$8 apiece to make a profit? **at least 27 candles**

INDEPENDENT PRACTICE

See Example 1 Solve.

8. $\frac{s}{5} > 1.4$ **$s > 7$**
9. $\frac{m}{-4} < -13$ **$m > 52$**
10. $\frac{b}{6} > -30$ **$b > -180$**
11. $\frac{c}{-10} \leq 12$ **$c \geq -120$**
12. $\frac{y}{9} < 2.5$ **$y < 22.5$**
13. $\frac{x}{1.1} \geq -1$ **$x \geq -1.1$**

See Example 2 Solve. Check each answer.

14. $6w < 4$ **$w < \frac{2}{3}$**
15. $-5z > -3$ **$z < \frac{3}{5}$**
16. $15p \leq -45$ **$p \leq -3$**
17. $-9f > 27$ **$f < -3$**
18. $20k < 30$ **$k < \frac{3}{2}$ or $1\frac{1}{2}$**
19. $-18n \geq 180$ **$n \leq -10$**

See Example 3

20. Attendance at a museum more than tripled from Monday to Saturday. On Monday, 186 people went to the museum. At least how many people went to the museum on Saturday? **more than 558 people**
21. It cost George \$678 to make wreaths. At least how many wreaths must he sell at \$15 apiece to make a profit? **at least 46 wreaths**

PRACTICE AND PROBLEM SOLVING

Solve.

22. $\frac{a}{65} \leq -10$ **$a \leq -650$**
23. $0.4p > 1.6$ **$p > 4$**
24. $-\frac{m}{5} < -20$ **$m > 100$**
25. $\frac{2}{3}y \geq 12$ **$y \geq 18$**
26. $\frac{x}{-9} \leq \frac{3}{5}$ **$x \geq -\frac{27}{5}$**
27. $\frac{g}{2.1} > 0.3$ **$g > 0.63$**
28. $\frac{r}{6} \geq \frac{2}{3}$ **$r \geq 4$**
29. $4w \leq 1\frac{1}{2}$ **$w \leq \frac{3}{8}$**
30. $-10n < 10^2$ **$n > -10$**
31. $-1\frac{3}{5}t > -4$ **$t < \frac{5}{2}$**
32. $-\frac{y}{12} < 3\frac{1}{2}$ **$y > -42$**
33. $5.6v \geq -14$ **$v \geq -2.5$**
34. A community theater group produced 8 plays over the last two years. The group's goal for the next two years is to produce at least $1\frac{1}{2}$ times as many plays as they did in the two previous years. At least how many plays does the group want to produce in the next two years? **at least 12 plays**

Math Background

The solution set can also be described using *interval notation.* In this notation, parentheses indicate that the endpoints are not included in the solution set. Brackets indicate that the endpoints are included in the solution set.

Suppose *a* and *b* are any real numbers.

Inequality	Interval notation
$a < x < b$	(a, b)
$a < x \leq b$	$(a, b]$
$a \leq x < b$	$[a, b)$
$a \leq x \leq b$	$[a, b]$

RETEACH 11-6

LESSON 11-6 **Reteach**
Solving Inequalities by Multiplying or Dividing

When you multiply or divide both sides of an inequality by the same *positive* number, the direction of the inequality symbol remains the same.

$3p < -18$
Divide both sides by *positive* 3.
$\frac{3p}{3} < \frac{-18}{3}$
$p < -6$

$\frac{x}{5} \geq -4$
Multiply both sides by *positive* 5.
$5 \cdot \frac{x}{5} \geq 5 \cdot -4$
$x \geq -20$

When you multiply or divide both sides of an inequality by the same *negative* number, the direction of the inequality symbol is reversed.

$-6y > -42$
Divide both sides by *negative* 6.
$\frac{-6y}{-6} < \frac{-42}{-6}$
$y < 7$

$\frac{m}{-2} \leq 15$
Multiply both sides by *negative* 2.
$-2 \cdot \frac{m}{-2} \geq -2 \cdot 15$
$m \geq -30$

Solve.

1. $\frac{a}{8} < -3$
   Multiply by **8**. The direction of the inequality symbol **remains the same**.
   $8 \cdot \frac{a}{8} < 8 \cdot -3$
   $a < -24$
2. $-4s \geq -36$
   Divide by **−4**. The direction of the inequality symbol **is reversed**.
   $\frac{-4s}{-4} \leq \frac{-36}{-4}$
   $s \leq 9$

Solve. Check each answer.

3. $\frac{r}{-7} \geq 2$ **$r \leq -14$**
4. $9b < -54$ **$b < -6$**
5. $-3n > -36$ **$n < 12$**
6. $\frac{c}{6} < -8$ **$c < -48$**

PRACTICE 11-6

LESSON 11-6 **Practice B**
Solving Inequalities by Multiplying or Dividing

Solve.

1. $7n \leq -28$ **$n \leq -4$**
2. $-8d > -56$ **$d < 7$**
3. $\frac{a}{3} \geq -9$ **$a \geq -27$**
4. $\frac{t}{-6} < -7$ **$t > 42$**
5. $-25y < 150$ **$y > -6$**
6. $\frac{r}{5.3} \leq 6$ **$r \leq 31.8$**

Solve. Check each answer.

7. $8c < -64$ **$c < -8$**
8. $-16a \geq -24$ **$a \leq 1\frac{1}{2}$**
9. $-12t > 9$ **$t < -\frac{3}{4}$**
10. $\frac{s}{-12} \leq -5$ **$s \geq 60$**
11. $\frac{b}{3} > -\frac{4}{9}$ **$b > -1\frac{1}{3}$**
12. $\frac{5}{6}m < 10$ **$m < 12$**
13. It cost Sophia \$530 to make wind chimes. How many wind chimes must she sell at \$12 apiece to make a profit?
    at least 45 wind chimes
14. It cost the Wilson children \$55 to make lemonade. How many glasses must they sell at 75¢ each to make a profit?
    at least 74 glasses
15. Jorge's soccer team is having its annual fund raiser. The team hopes to earn at least three times as much as it did last year. Last year the team earned \$87. What is the team's goal for this year?
    at least \$261

35. ***SOCIAL STUDIES*** Of the total U.S. population, about 874,000 people are Pacific Islanders. The graph shows where most of these Americans live.

a. According to the graph, more than 25% of Pacific Islanders do not live in the West. More than how many Pacific Islanders do not live in the West?

b. According to the graph, less than 75% of Pacific Islanders live in the West. Fewer than how many Pacific Islanders live in the West?

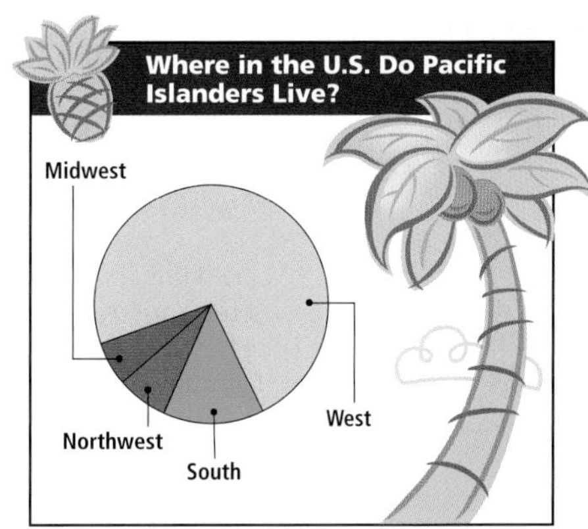

Source: USA Today

36. Seventh-graders at Mountain Middle School have sold 360 subscriptions to magazines. This is $\frac{3}{4}$ of the number of subscriptions that they need to sell to reach their goal and to beat the eighth grade's sales. At least how many total subscriptions must they sell to reach their goal? **at least 480 subscriptions**

37. ***RECREATION*** Malcolm has saved $362 to spend on his vacation. He wants to have at least $35 a day available to spend. How many days of vacation does Malcolm have enough money for? **10 days**

38. ***WRITE A PROBLEM*** Write a word problem that can be solved using the inequality $\frac{x}{2} \geq 7$. Solve the inequality.

39. ***WRITE ABOUT IT*** Explain how to solve the inequality $\frac{n}{-8} < -40$.

40. ***CHALLENGE*** Use what you have learned about solving multistep equations to solve the inequality $4x - 5 \leq 7x + 4$. $\mathbf{x \geq -3}$

Spiral Review

Solve. (Lesson 11-1)

41. $3x - 5 = 28$ $\mathbf{x = 11}$

42. $\frac{t}{2} + 8 = 9$ $\mathbf{t = 2}$

43. $5r - 12 = 18$ $\mathbf{r = 6}$

44. $\frac{y}{6} + 30 = 10$ $\mathbf{y = -120}$

45. **TEST PREP** Allana is painting a wall that is 11 feet tall and 23 feet long. What is the area of the wall? (Lesson 8-4) **B**

A 34 ft^2 B 253 ft^2 C 153 ft^2 D 353 ft^2

46. **TEST PREP** Which is the solution of the inequality $w + 8 < -5$? (Lesson 11-5) **F**

F $w < -13$ G $w > -3$ H $w < 3$ J $w > 13$

Answers

35. a. more than 218,500

b. fewer than 655,500

38. Possible answer: To be in the reading club, each member needs to read 7 books. Felicia read at least twice the minimum number of books required. How many books did she read? $x \geq 14$; Felicia read at least 14 books.

39. Possible answer: Multiply both sides of the inequality by -8 and reverse the inequality symbol to "is greater than." Check by substituting a value greater than 320 for n in the inequality $\frac{n}{-8} < -40$.

Journal

Have students create a memory aid to help them remember to reverse the inequality sign when multiplying or dividing by a negative number.

Test Prep Doctor

Students who chose **C** or **D** in Exercise 45 are probably making common errors in multiplication. However, students who chose **A** do not understand how to find the area of a rectangle. Instead of finding the product of the lengths of the sides, they are finding the sum.

In Exercise 46, students who chose **G** or **H** are not using the inverse operation to solve the inequality. Students who chose **J** might be confusing the rules for multiplying and dividing by a negative number with the rules for subtracting a negative number to solve an inequality.

CHALLENGE 11-6

LESSON 11-6 **Challenge**

Absolute Value Inequalities

Use the definition of absolute value to solve absolute value inequalities.

Remember: $|x| = x$ if $x > 0$ and $|x| = -x$ if $x < 0$

Example 1: $|10 - 2x| > 6$

Case 1: $10 - 2x > 6$
$-2x > -4$
$x < 2$

Case 2: $-(10 - 2x) > 6$
$-10 + 2x > 6$
$2x > 16$
$x > 8$

Solution: $x < 2$ or $x > 8$

Example 2: $|2y - 3| \leq 7$

Case 1: $2y - 3 \leq 7$
$2y \leq 10$
$y \leq 5$

Case 2: $-(2y - 3) \leq 7$
$-2y + 3 \leq 7$
$-2y \leq 4$
$y \geq -2$

Solution: $-2 \leq y \leq 5$

Solve.

1. $|m - 6| \leq 8$ $\mathbf{-2 \leq m \leq 14}$
2. $|x + 4| < 10$ $\mathbf{-14 < x < 6}$
3. $|6 - y| \leq 2$ $\mathbf{4 \leq y \leq 8}$
4. $|b + 5| > 8$ $\mathbf{b < -13 \text{ or } b > 3}$
5. $|4 - k| \geq 5$ $\mathbf{k \leq -1 \text{ or } k \geq 9}$
6. $|2 - p| - 3 < 1$ $\mathbf{-2 < p < 6}$
7. $4 - 3|e| < 1$ $\mathbf{e < -1 \text{ or } e > 1}$
8. $\left|\frac{h}{6}\right| \geq 1$ $\mathbf{h \leq -6 \text{ or } h \geq 6}$
9. $\left|\frac{n}{4}\right| \leq 2$ $\mathbf{-8 \leq n \leq 8}$
10. $|2a + 1| \geq 1$ $\mathbf{a \leq -1 \text{ or } a \geq 0}$
11. $|z - 2| < 5$ $\mathbf{-3 < z < 7}$
12. $\left|\frac{c}{2} - 3\right| \leq 2$ $\mathbf{2 \leq c \leq 10}$

PROBLEM SOLVING 11-6

LESSON 11-6 **Problem Solving**

Solving Inequalities by Multiplying or Dividing

Write the correct answer.

1. U.S. Postal Service regulations state that a package can be mailed using Parcel Post rates if it weighs no more than 70 pounds. What is the maximum number of books weighing 12 pounds each that can be mailed in one box using Parcel Post rates?

at most 5 books

2. Marc wants to buy a set of at least 6 antique chairs for his dining room. He has decided to spend no more than $390. What is the most he can spend per chair?

no more than $65

3. Alfonso earns $9.00 per hour working part-time as a lab technician. He wants to earn more than $144 this week. At least how many hours does Alfonso have to work?

more than 16 hours

4. Mrs. Menendez invited 8 children to her son's birthday party. She wants to make sure that each child gets at least 4 small prizes. At least how many prizes should she buy?

at least 32 prizes

Choose the letter for the best answer.

5. The Computer Club spent $2,565 on mouse pads. The members plan to sell the mouse pads during the book fair. If they charge $9.50 for each mouse pad, how many must they sell in order to make a profit?

A ≤ 271 (C) ≥ 271
B ≤ 270 D ≥ 270

6. The Parents Organization bought 1,000 bumper stickers at $1.25 each to sell at football games. They want to make at least $750 profit. What should be the selling price of the bumper stickers?

F $\geq \$1.25$ H $\geq \$1.75$
G $\geq \$1.50$ (J) $\geq \$2.00$

7. In 2000, the national ratio of students to computers with Internet access in public schools was 7:1. Winston School had 623 students. If the school had a lower ratio, how many computers with Internet access did Winston School have?

(A) ≥ 90 C ≥ 91
B ≤ 90 D ≤ 91

8. A new theme park averaged fewer than 2,000 visitors per week during the winter months. What was the average daily attendance?

F ≥ 290 H > 385
G ≤ 186 (J) < 286

Lesson Quiz

Solve.

1. $\frac{s}{9} > 12$ $s > 108$

2. $\frac{b}{-14} > 6$ $b < -84$

Solve. Check each answer.

3. $18w < 4$ $w < \frac{2}{9}$

4. $-4f > 36$ $f < -9$

5. It costs a candle company $51 to make a dozen candles. How many candles must it sell at $7 apiece to make a profit? more than 7 candles, or at least 8 candles

Available on Daily Transparency in CRB

11-7 Organizer

Pacing: Traditional 1 day
Block $\frac{1}{2}$ day

Objective: Students solve simple two-step inequalities.

Warm Up

Solve. Check each answer.

1. $7k < 42$ $\quad k < 6$

2. $-14n < 98$ $\quad n > -7$

3. $12t > 9$ $\quad t > \frac{3}{4}$

4. $21g < 3$ $\quad g < \frac{1}{7}$

Problem of the Day

It's 15 miles from Dixon to Elmont and 20 miles from Elmont to Fairlawn. Write an inequality for x, the distance in miles from Dixon to Fairlawn. $5 \le x \le 35$ (Dixon could be between Elmont and Fairlawn or Elmont could be between Dixon and Fairlawn.)

Available on Daily Transparency in CRB

The cosmetic surgeon specialized in bellybuttons. She changed innies to outies and outies to innies. She did a lot more of the second type of operation, thanks to the innie-quality of her work.

11-7 Solving Two-Step Inequalities

Learn to solve simple two-step inequalities.

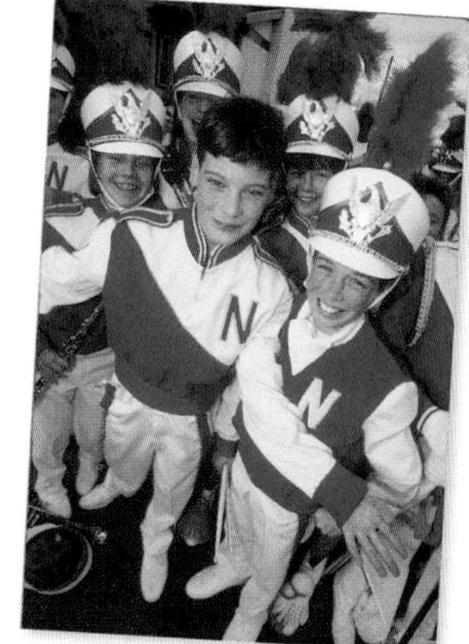

The band students at Newman Middle School are trying to raise at least \$5,000 to buy new percussion instruments. They already have raised \$850. How much should each of the 83 band students still raise, on average, to meet their goal?

When you solve two-step equations, you can use the order of operations in reverse to isolate the variable. You can use the same process when solving two-step inequalities.

EXAMPLE  Solving Two-Step Inequalities

Solve. Then graph each solution set on a number line.

> **Remember!**
> Draw a closed circle when the inequality includes the point and an open circle when it does not include the point.

A $\frac{x}{5} - 15 < 10$

$\frac{x}{5} - 15 < 10$

$\underline{+15 \quad +15}$ *Add 15 to both sides.*

$\frac{x}{5} < 25$

$(5)\frac{x}{5} < (5)25$ *Multiply both sides by 5.*

$x < 125$

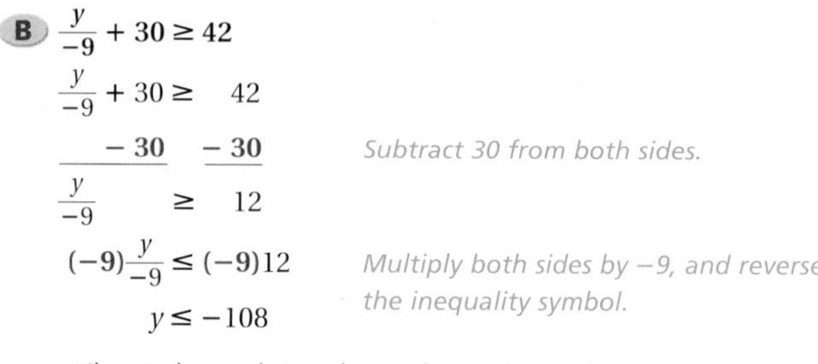

B $\frac{y}{-9} + 30 \ge 42$

$\frac{y}{-9} + 30 \ge 42$

$\underline{-30 \quad -30}$ *Subtract 30 from both sides.*

$\frac{y}{-9} \ge 12$

$(-9)\frac{y}{-9} \le (-9)12$ *Multiply both sides by −9, and reverse the inequality symbol.*

$y \le -108$

−124 −120 −116 −112 −108 −104 −100

1 Introduce

Alternate Opener

EXPLORATION

 **Solving Two-Step Inequalities**

Cecilia joins a CD club that offers its members early releases of new CDs. She pays \$16.00 per month plus \$12.00 for each CD she orders.

CD Club
\$16 per month plus
\$12 per newly released CD

1. Complete the table to show the monthly cost for each number of CDs.

CDs	0	1	2	3	4	5	6	7
Cost								

2. If Cecilia had \$50.00 to spend on CDs in one month, could she buy 3 CDs?
3. If Cecilia had \$90.00, could she buy 6 CDs?
4. Assume that Cecilia has \$100.00. Write and solve an inequality that shows how many CDs she could buy.

Think and Discuss

5. **Explain** how you wrote the inequality in number 4.
6. **Explain** how you solved the inequality in number 4.

Motivate

To introduce students to multistep inequalities, review how they solved multistep equations. Provide an example, such as $3x - 5 = 13$, and ask volunteers to describe the steps to solve it. Add 5 to each side of the equation, then divide each side by 3.

You may want to remind students of the goal in solving a two-step equation: first, get the term with the variable on one side of the equation and the constants on the other, and then solve for the variable.

Exploration worksheet and answers on Chapter 11 Resource Book pp. 64 and 92

2 Teach

Lesson Presentation

Guided Instruction

In this lesson, students learn to solve simple two-step inequalities. Remind students that when using the order of operations to evaluate an expression, they must multiply and divide first and then add and subtract; but in solving two-step equations and inequalities, students usually should follow the opposite order.

 Point out that the number lines used to graph solutions of inequalities need to show only the numbers near the point for which students must draw the open or closed circle on the graph.

Solve. Then graph each solution set on a number line.

C $3x - 12 \ge 9$

$$\begin{aligned} 3x - 12 &\ge 9 \\ +12 \quad &\quad +12 \\ 3x &\ge 21 \\ \frac{3x}{3} &\ge \frac{21}{3} \\ x &\ge 7 \end{aligned}$$

Add 12 to both sides.

Divide both sides by 3.

2 3 4 5 6 7 8 9 10 11 12

D $-4y + 6 < 10$

$$\begin{aligned} -4y + 6 &< 10 \\ -6 \quad &\quad -6 \\ -4y &< 4 \\ \frac{-4y}{-4} &> \frac{4}{-4} \\ y &> -1 \end{aligned}$$

Subtract 6 from both sides.

Divide both sides by −4, and reverse the inequality symbol.

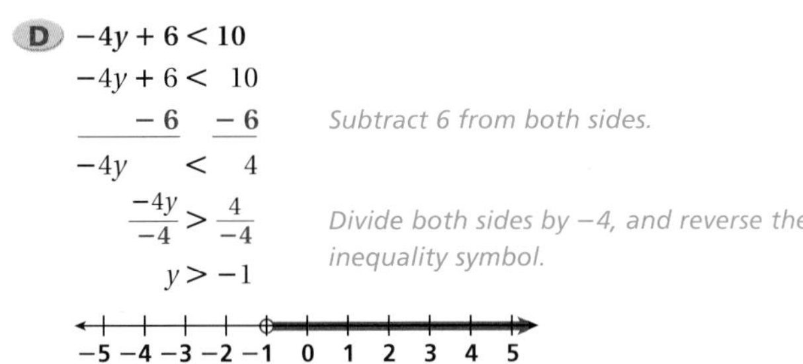

−5 −4 −3 −2 −1 0 1 2 3 4 5

EXAMPLE **2** ***School Application***

The 83 members of the Newman Middle School Band are trying to raise at least $5,000 to buy new percussion instruments. If they have already raised $850, how much should each student still raise, on average, to meet the goal?

Let d represent the average amount each student should still raise.

$$\begin{aligned} 83d + 850 &\ge 5{,}000 \\ -850 \quad &\quad -850 \\ 83d &\ge 4{,}150 \\ \frac{83d}{83} &\ge \frac{4{,}150}{83} \\ d &\ge 50 \end{aligned}$$

Write an inequality.

Subtract 850 from both sides.

Divide both sides by 83.

On average, each band member should raise at least $50.

Think and Discuss

1. **Tell** how you would solve the inequality $8x + 5 < 20$.
2. **Explain** why the *greater than or equal to* symbol was used in the inequality in Example 2.

COMMON ERROR ALERT

Caution students to remember to record the inequality symbol throughout the problem. Sometimes, students drop the inequality symbol and write an equal sign instead.

Additional Examples

Example 1

Solve. Then graph each solution set on a number line.

A. $\frac{y}{2} - 6 > 1$ $\quad y > 14$

−14 −7 0 7 14 28

B. $\frac{m}{-3} + 8 \le 5$ $\quad m \ge 9$

−3 0 3 6 9 12

C. $4y - 5 < 11$ $\quad y < 4$

−4 −2 0 2 4 6

D. $-3x + 5 \le -4$ $\quad x \ge 3$

−2 0 2 4 6 8

Example 2

Sun-Li has $30 to spend at the carnival. Admission is $5, and each ride costs $2. What is the greatest number of rides she can ride? **12**

Example 2 note: If students have difficulty seeing how to write the equation in this example, suggest that they test $50 per student to see if it is enough. Have students write a statement to show how they tested $50 and then have them use that statement to write the equation.

3 Close

Reaching All Learners

Through Critical Thinking

Have students work in pairs and give each pair the recording sheet for Reaching All Learners (Chapter 11 Resource Book p. 79). For each graph, ask each pair to construct an inequality that would take two steps to solve and that has the given graph as its solution. Have pairs exchange inequalities to solve and graph.

Summarize

Ask students to write a plan for solving a simple two-step inequality.

Possible answer: Begin by adding or subtracting constants to both sides of the inequality so that the variable term is on one side and the constant is on the other. Then multiply or divide both sides of the inequality by the same number. If that number is a negative number, reverse the inequality symbol.

Answers to Think and Discuss

1. Possible answer: Subtract 5 from both sides; then divide both sides of the inequality by 8; $x < \frac{15}{8}$ or $1\frac{7}{8}$.
2. Possible answer: The band members are trying to raise *at least* $5,000. *At least* means *greater than or equal to.*

11-7 PRACTICE & ASSESS

Students may want to refer back to the lesson examples.

Assignment Guide

If you finished Example 1 assign:
Core 1–6, 8–16, 19–29 odd, 39–44
Enriched 1–5 odd, 9–15 odd, 19–30, 39–44

If you finished Example 2 assign:
Core 1–18, 19–35 odd, 39–44
Enriched 1–17 odd, 19–44

Answers

1. 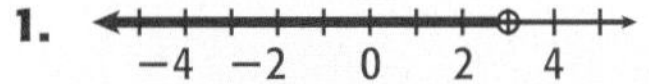

2. −294 0 294

3. −2 0 2 4 6 8

4. −4 −2 0 2 4

5. −8 −6 −4 −2 0 2

6. −30 −24 −18 −12 −6 0

8. −8 −6 −4 −2 0 2

9. −4 0 4 8 12

10. −10 −8 −6 −4 −2 0

11–16. See p. A4.

11-7 Exercises

FOR EXTRA PRACTICE see page 679

internet connect — Homework Help Online go.hrw.com Keyword: MS4 11-7

GUIDED PRACTICE

See Example 1 **Solve. Then graph each solution set on a number line.**

1. $5x + 3 < 18$ **$x < 3$**
2. $\frac{z}{7} + 23 \le -19$ **$z \le -294$**
3. $3y - 4 \ge 14$ **$y \ge 6$**
4. $\frac{m}{4} - 2 > -3$ **$m > -4$**
5. $-11p - 13 \ge 42$ **$p \le -5$**
6. $\frac{n}{-3} - 4 > 4$ **$n < -24$**

See Example 2

7. Three students collected more than $93 washing cars. They used $15 to reimburse their parents for cleaning supplies. Then they divided the remaining money equally. How much did each student earn? **more than $26 each**

INDEPENDENT PRACTICE

See Example 1 **Solve. Then graph each solution set on a number line.**

8. $5s - 7 > -42$ **$s > -7$**
9. $\frac{b}{2} + 3 < 9$ **$b < 12$**
10. $-2q + 5 \ge 19$ **$q \le -7$**
11. $-8c - 11 \le 13$ **$c \ge -3$**
12. $\frac{y}{-4} + 6 > 10$ **$y < -16$**
13. $\frac{x}{9} - 5 \le -8$ **$x \le -27$**
14. $\frac{r}{-2} - 9 > -14$ **$r < 10$**
15. $13j + 18 \le 44$ **$j \le 2$**
16. $\frac{d}{13} - 12 > 27$ **$d > 507$**

See Example 2

17. Rico has $5.00. Bagels cost $0.65 each, and a small container of cream cheese costs $1.00. What is the greatest number of bagels Rico can buy if he also buys one small container of cream cheese? **at most 6 bagels**
18. The 35 members of the Tigers drill team are trying to raise at least $1,200 to cover travel costs to a training camp. If they have already raised $500, at least how much should each member still raise, on average, to meet the goal? **at least $20**

PRACTICE AND PROBLEM SOLVING

Solve.

19. $9 - 2y < 15$ **$y > -3$**
20. $-3q + 10 < -2$ **$q > 4$**
21. $\frac{a}{-6} - 5 \ge 4$ **$a \le -54$**
22. $-4x + 8 \le 32$ **$x \ge -6$**
23. $0.5 + \frac{n}{5} > -0.5$ **$n > -5$**
24. $1.4 + \frac{c}{3} < 2$ **$c < 1.8$**
25. $-\frac{3}{4}b - 2.2 > -1$ **$b < -1.6$**
26. $12 + 2w - 8 \le 20$ **$w \le 8$**
27. $5k + 6 - k \ge -14$ **$k \ge -5$**
28. $\frac{s}{2} + 9 > 12 - 15$ **$s > -24$**
29. $4t - 3 - 10t < 15$ **$t > -3$**
30. $\frac{d}{2} + 1 + \frac{d}{2} \le 5$ **$d \le 4$**
31. Mr. Monroe keeps a bag of small prizes to distribute to his students. He likes to keep at least twice as many prizes in the bag as he has students. The bag currently has 79 prizes in it. If Mr. Monroe has 117 students, at least how many more prizes does he need to buy?

31. at least 155 prizes

Math Background

The graph of an inequality containing two variables, such as $y < x + 2$, is a part of the coordinate plane. If the inequality is strictly less than or greater than, the line is dotted. If the inequality includes an equal sign, the line is solid. Then the portion of the plane containing the solutions is shaded.

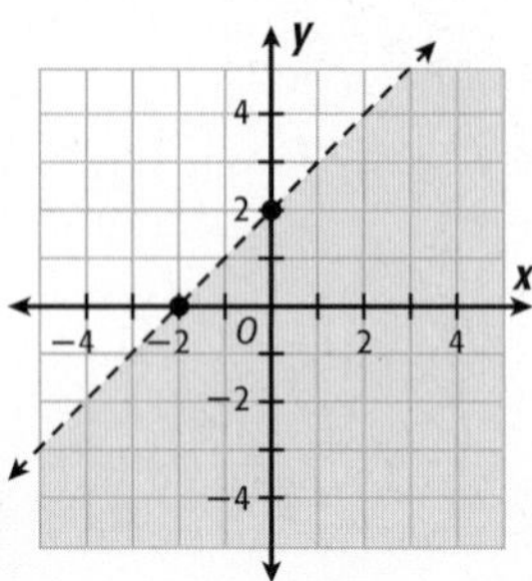

RETEACH 11-7

LESSON 11-7 **Reteach**
Solving Two-Step Inequalities

Two-step inequalities can be solved by first undoing addition or subtraction, then undoing multiplication or division.

Remember to reverse the inequality symbol if you multiply or divide by a negative number.

Complete the steps to solve the inequality. Then graph the solution set.

1. $-3x + 35 > -10$

$-3x + 35 \underline{- 35} > -10 \underline{- 35}$ ← First undo addition or subtraction.

$-3x > \underline{-45}$ ← Then undo multiplication or division.

$\frac{-3x}{-3} \boxed{<} \frac{-45}{-3}$ ← Divide by −3. The inequality symbol is reversed.

$x \boxed{<} \underline{15}$

Graph the inequality.

−10 −5 0 5 10 15 20 25 30 35 40

Solve. Then graph each solution set.

2. $7x + 32 < 18$ $\underline{x < -2}$ (−5 −4 −3 −2 −1 0 1 2 3 4 5)
3. $\frac{t}{4} - 8 \le -5$ $\underline{t \le 12}$ (0 2 4 6 8 10 12 14 16 18 20)
4. $6f - 6 > 48$ $\underline{f > 9}$ (2 3 4 5 6 7 8 9 10 11 12)
5. $-4w - 13 \ge 15$ $\underline{w \le -7}$ (−9 −8 −7 −6 −5 −4 −3 −2 −1 0 1)
6. $\frac{k}{-5} - 6 < -9$ $\underline{k > 15}$ (−10 −5 0 5 10 15 20 25 30 35 40)
7. $7 - 2p > -5$ $\underline{p < 6}$ (−10 −8 −6 −4 −2 0 2 4 6 8 10)

PRACTICE 11-7

LESSON 11-7 **Practice B**
Solving Two-Step Inequalities

Solve. Then graph each solution set on a number line.

1. $5x - 8 < 17$ $\underline{x < 5}$ (−3 −2 −1 0 1 2 3 4 5 6 7)
2. $\frac{r}{3} + 5 \ge 9$ $\underline{r \ge 12}$ (7 8 9 10 11 12 13 14 15 16 17)
3. $-4n + 8 < -4$ $\underline{n > 3}$ (−5 −4 −3 −2 −1 0 1 2 3 4 5)
4. $\frac{z}{7} - 6 \ge -5$ $\underline{z \ge 7}$ (0 1 2 3 4 5 6 7 8 9 10)
5. $\frac{w}{-5} + 4 < 9$ $\underline{w > -25}$ (−35 −25 −15 −5 0 5 15)
6. $\frac{u}{2} - 5 \le -9$ $\underline{u \le -8}$ (−10 −9 −8 −7 −6 −5 −4 −3 −2 −1 0)

Solve.

7. $-7d + 8 > 29$ $\underline{d < -3}$
8. $4g - 18 \le -2$ $\underline{g \le 4}$
9. $12 - 3b < 9$ $\underline{b > 1}$
10. $\frac{a}{-4} - 7 < -2$ $\underline{a > -20}$
11. $4.5 + \frac{c}{6} \le 6$ $\underline{c \le 9}$
12. $-\frac{2}{3}p - 8 \ge 4$ $\underline{p \le -18}$

32. The bar graph shows how many students from Warren Middle School participated in a reading challenge each of the past four years. This year, the goal is for at least 10 more students to participate than the average number of participants from the past four years. What is the goal for this year? **at least 225 students**

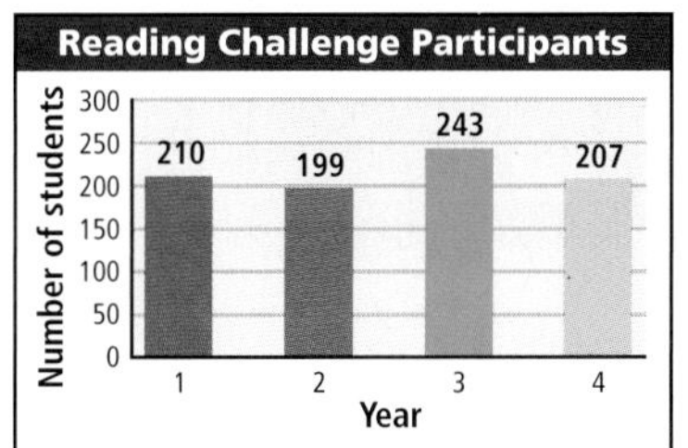

33. ***BUSINESS*** Darcy earns a salary of \$1,400 per month, plus a commission of 4% of her sales. If she wants to earn a total of at least \$1,600 this month, what is the least amount of sales she needs? **at least \$5,000**

34. ***CONSUMER MATH*** Michael wants to buy a belt that costs \$18. He also wants to buy some shirts that are on sale for \$14 each. He has \$70. At most, how many shirts can Michael buy together with the belt? **at most 3 shirts**

35. ***EARTH SCIENCE*** A granite rock contains the minerals feldspar, quartz, and biotite mica. The rock has $\frac{1}{3}$ as much biotite mica as quartz. If the rock is at least 30% quartz, what percent of the rock is feldspar? **at most 60%**

36. ***WHAT'S THE ERROR?*** A student's solution to the inequality $\frac{x}{-9} - 5 > 2$ was $x > 63$. What error did the student make in the solution?

37. ***WRITE ABOUT IT*** Explain how to solve the inequality $4y + 6 < -2$.

38. ***CHALLENGE*** A student scored 92, 87, 90, and 85 on four tests. She wants her average score for five tests to be at least 90. What is the lowest score the student can get on her fifth test? **96**

Spiral Review

39. Four friends are standing in line. In how many possible orders can they be standing? (Lesson 10-7) **24**

40. There are 6 jars lined up on a shelf. In how many possible orders can the jars be lined up? (Lesson 10-7) **720**

Solve. (Lesson 11-3)

41. $-8x - 210 = 6x$ **$x = -15$**
42. $50 + 9y = -3y + 14$ **$y = -3$**
43. $n + 27 = -n + 35$ **$n = 4$**

44. **TEST PREP** Which is the solution of the inequality $-6x > -54$? (Lesson 11-7) **C**

A $x < -9$ B $x > -9$ C $x < 9$ D $x > 9$

Answer

36. Possible answer: The student multiplied both sides of the inequality by 9 instead of by −9. The correct answer is $x < -63$.

37. Possible answer: Subtract 6 from both sides of the inequality: $4y < -8$. Then divide both sides by 4: $y < -2$.

Journal

Have students explain how they decide what numbers to use to check their solutions for inequalities.

Test Prep Doctor

For Exercise 44, have students think about the solution before they solve the inequality. Because both the constant and the coefficient of x are negative, the resulting constant will be positive, eliminating **A** and **B.** If students chose **D,** they have neglected to reverse the inequality symbol and may need additional help understanding when to reverse this symbol. The correct answer is **C.**

Lesson Quiz

Solve. Then graph each solution set on a number line.

1. $7s + 14 > -35$ $s > -7$

−10 −8 −6 −4 −2 0

2. $\frac{y}{-8} + 12 > 20$ $y < -64$

−68 −66 −64 −62 −60 −58

3. $18n - 22 \le 32$ $n \le 3$

−1 0 1 2 3 4

4. A cyclist has \$7.00. At the first stop on the tour, energy bars are \$1.15 each, and a sports drink is \$1.75. What is the greatest number of energy bars the cyclist can buy if he buys one sports drink? 4

Available on Daily Transparency in CRB

CHALLENGE 11-7

LESSON 11-7 **Challenge**
Inequalities With Two Variables

You can determine if an ordered pair is a solution of an inequality by substituting the values into the inequality.

- If the inequality is true, the ordered pair is a solution of the inequality.
- If the inequality is false, the ordered pair is not a solution of the inequality.

Example: Is (1, 1) or (2, −1) a solution of the inequality $y < 3x - 2$?

(1, 1)	$y < 3x - 2$ $1 < 3(1) - 2$ $1 < 1$ False (1, 1) is not a solution.	(2, −1)	$y < 3x - 2$ $-1 < 3(2) - 2$ $-1 < 4$ True (2, −1) is a solution.

Solve.

1. Which of the following ordered pairs are solutions of $y < 4x - 3$: $(-1, 1), (2, 5), (-\frac{1}{2}, -7), (0, -4)$?
$(-\frac{1}{2}, -7), (0, -4)$

2. Which of the following ordered pairs are solutions of $y \ge 6 - 2x$: $(0, 0), (1, 5), (3, 6), (\frac{1}{2}, 8)$?
$(1, 5), (3, 6), (\frac{1}{2}, 8)$

3. Which of the following ordered pairs are solutions of $4x + 2y \le 20$: $(3, 0), (0, 12), (5, 5), (2, -4)$?
$(3, 0), (2, -4)$

4. For the inequality $y < 5x - 2$, let $x = 0$. Solve for y.
$y < -2$

5. List 4 ordered pairs that are solutions to $y < 5x - 2$.
Possible answer: (−1, −9), (1, −3), (0, −5), (3, 0)

6. List 4 ordered pairs that are solutions of $3x + 2y > 4$.
Possible answer: (0, 3), (2, 0), (−1, 4), (5, 1)

PROBLEM SOLVING 11-7

LESSON 11-7 **Problem Solving**
Solving Two-Step Inequalities

Write the correct answer.

1. Grace earns \$7 for each car she washes. She always saves \$25 of her weekly earnings. This week, she wants to have at least \$65 in spending money. At least how many cars must she wash?
at least 13 cars

2. Monty has saved \$400 to spend on a video game player and games. The player he wants costs \$275. The games each cost \$39. At most, how many games can he buy along with the player?
at most 3 games

3. A video game club charges \$8 per month as a membership fee, plus \$2.75 for each game rental. Eugenie plans to join and rent no more than 5 games a month. What amount should she budget each month for video games?
at most \$21.75

4. Cooper Middle School has a goal of collecting more than 1,000 cans of food in a food drive. So far, 375 cans have been collected. During the last 13 days of the drive, at least how many cans must be collected each day in order to meet the goal?
more than 48 cans

Choose the letter for the best answer.

5. In January 2002, it cost \$0.34 to mail a letter weighing up to 1 ounce. Each additional ounce or part of an ounce cost \$0.23. At most, what is the weight of a letter with \$1.03 in postage?
A < 4 oz (C) ≤ 4 oz
B < 3 oz D ≤ 3 oz

6. Martin is planning a hedge along the back of his yard. The total length can be no more than 23 feet, and he will put a 4-foot-wide gate in the hedge. Each plant needs 2.5 feet of space to grow properly. How many plants should he buy?
(F) ≤ 7 H ≤ 9
G < 7 J < 9

7. The 12 members of the Middle School filmmaking club need to raise at least \$1,400 to make a short film. They already have raised \$650. How much more should each member raise?
(A) ≥ \$62.50 C < \$62.50
B ≤ \$62.50 D > \$62.50

8. The rule of thumb in filmmaking is that you must shoot at least 3 minutes of film for every minute in a movie's "final cut." A 30-minute roll of film costs \$250. How much will film cost to make a 90-minute movie?
F ≥ \$22,500 H ≤ \$67,500
G ≤ \$7,500 (J) ≥ \$2,250

Chapter 11 Extension

Pacing: Traditional 1 day
Block $\frac{1}{2}$ day

Objective: Students solve formulas with two or more variables for one of the variables.

Using the Pages

In this chapter, students have learned to solve multistep equations by adding or subtracting constants and then multiplying or dividing by constants. In this extension, students add, subtract, multiply, and divide with variable terms as well as with constants to solve a formula for a given variable.

EXTENSION Solving for a Variable

Learn to solve formulas with two or more variables for one of the variables.

The highest recorded speed of a magnetically elevated vehicle was achieved by the MLX01 on the Yamanashi Maglev Test Line in Japan. At its top speed, the MLX01 could travel the 229 miles from Tokyo to Kyoto in less than an hour.

The MLX01 attained the record speed of 343 miles per hour in January 1998.

The formula *distance* = *rate* · *time* ($d = rt$) tells how far an object travels at a certain rate over a certain time. In an equation or a formula that contains more than one variable, you can isolate one of the variables by using inverse operations. Recall that you cannot divide by a variable if it represents 0.

EXAMPLE 1 Solving for Variables in Formulas

Solve $d = rt$ for r.

$d = rt$

$\frac{d}{t} = \frac{rt}{t}$ *Divide both sides by t.*

$\frac{d}{t} = r$

EXAMPLE 2 *Physical Science Application*

How long would it take the MLX01 to travel 1,029 mi if it travels at a speed of 343 mi/h?

First solve the distance formula for t, since you want to find the time. Then use the given values to find t.

$d = rt$

$\frac{d}{r} = \frac{rt}{r}$ *Divide both sides by r.*

$\frac{d}{r} = t$

$\frac{1{,}029}{343} = t$ *Substitute 1,029 for d and 343 for r.*

$3 = t$

It would take the MLX01 3 hours to travel 1,029 miles.

1 Introduce

Motivate

To introduce students to the idea of solving a formula for a given variable, show them some formulas, such as the formula for converting from degrees Celsius to degrees Fahrenheit: $F = (\frac{9}{5} \cdot C) + 32$.

Ask students to compare and contrast formulas with equations that require more than one step to solve.

Mention that formulas can usually be solved for one of the variables just as equations can be solved for a single variable.

2 Teach

Lesson Presentation

Guided Instruction

In this lesson, students learn to solve formulas with two or more variables for one of the variables. Formulas can be solved in the same manner equations are solved. Remind students to add or subtract variables or constants and then multiply or divide to isolate the variable.

Teaching Tip To help students decide how to solve an equation for a specified variable, have them identify the operations done to the variable and then have them identify the inverse operations needed to undo those operations.

EXTENSION Exercises

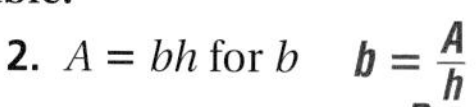

Solve each equation for the given variable.

1. $A = bh$ for h **$h = \frac{A}{b}$**
2. $A = bh$ for b **$b = \frac{A}{h}$**
3. $C = \pi d$ for d **$d = \frac{C}{\pi}$**
4. $P = 4s$ for s **$s = \frac{P}{4}$**
5. $V = Bh$ for B **$B = \frac{V}{h}$**
6. $d = 2r$ for r **$r = \frac{d}{2}$**
7. $xy = k$ for y **$y = \frac{k}{x}$**
8. $A = \ell w$ for w **$w = \frac{A}{\ell}$**
9. $W = Fd$ for F **$F = \frac{W}{d}$**
10. $I = Prt$ for P **$P = \frac{I}{rt}$**
11. $C = 2\pi r$ for r **$r = \frac{C}{2\pi}$**
12. $A = \frac{1}{2}bh$ for h **$h = \frac{2A}{b}$**
13. $V = \frac{1}{3}Bh$ for h **$h = \frac{3V}{B}$**
14. $K = C + 273$ for C **$C = K - 273$**
15. $E = Pt$ for t **$t = \frac{E}{P}$**
16. $D = \frac{m}{v}$ for v **$v = \frac{m}{D}$**
17. $F = ma$ for a **$a = \frac{F}{m}$**
18. $P = VI$ for I **$I = \frac{P}{V}$**
19. $r = \frac{V}{I}$ for V **$V = rI$**
20. $I = Prt$ for r **$r = \frac{I}{Pt}$**
21. $P = 2\ell + 2w$ for ℓ **$\ell = \frac{(P - 2w)}{2}$**
22. $V = \pi r^2 h$ for h **$h = \frac{V}{\pi r2}$**

23. ***PHYSICAL SCIENCE*** The formula $E = mc^2$ tells the amount of energy an object at rest has. In the equation, E stands for the amount of energy in joules, m stands for the rest mass in kilograms of the object, and c is the speed of light (approximately 300,000,000 meters per second). What is the rest mass of an object that has 90,000,000,000,000 joules of energy? **0.001 kg**

THE FAR SIDE® By GARY LARSON

"*Now* that desk looks better. Everything's squared away, yessir, squaaaaaared away."

24. ***PHYSICAL SCIENCE*** The Kelvin scale is a temperature scale. To convert between the Celsius temperature scale and the Kelvin temperature scale, use the formula $C = K - 273$, where C represents the temperature in degrees Celsius and K represents the temperature in kelvins. Use the formula to convert 38°C to an equivalent Kelvin temperature. **311 K**

25. ***PHYSICAL SCIENCE*** Density is mass per unit volume. The formula for density is $D = \frac{m}{v}$, where D represents density, m represents mass, and v represents volume. Find the mass of a gear with a density of 3.75 g/cm^3 and a volume of 20 cm^3. **75 g**

26. What is the height of the cone if its volume is 8,138.88 ft^3? Use 3.14 for π. **54 ft**

12 ft

COMMON ERROR ALERT

Students might be confused by using variables instead of constants. If students have difficulty working with variables, suggest that they substitute numbers for the variables not being solved for and determine how to solve with those numbers. Then, students can do the same steps with the variables in place.

Additional Examples

Example 1

Solve $y = mx + b$ for x.

$\frac{y - b}{m} = x$

Example 2

Maria has 28 feet of fencing to use around the perimeter of an animal pen. If she wants the pen to be 8 feet long, how wide will it be? **6 ft**

3 Close

Summarize

Have students describe how they would solve $Ax + By = c$ for x.

Possible answer: First, subtract By from both sides. Then divide all terms by A.

Problem Solving on Location

New York

Purpose: *To provide additional practice for problem-solving skills in Chapters 1–11*

New York Population Changes

- After problem 1, have students find the increase in the population of New York State between 1870 and 2000. about 14.6 million
- After problem 3, have students give the least number of people who could have lived in New York State in 1900. at least 7,200,000 people

Extension Have students research the lengths of two other suspension bridges in New York: the George Washington Bridge and the Verrazano-Narrows Bridge. Then have students use the information they find to write and solve an inequality problem.

Possible answer:

George Washington Bridge: 3,500 ft; Verrazano-Narrows Bridge: 4,260 ft; The 3,500 ft long George Washington Bridge is at least 82.2% as long as the Verrazano-Narrows Bridge. Write and solve an inequality to show at least how long, to the nearest foot, the Verrazano-Narrows Bridge is; $0.822 \cdot x \geq 3{,}500$; $x \geq 4{,}258$ ft.

Problem Solving on Location

NEW YORK

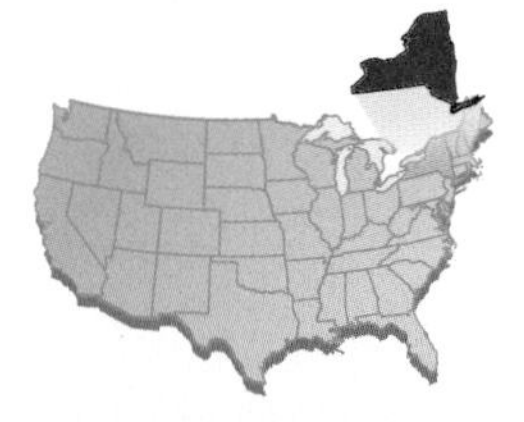

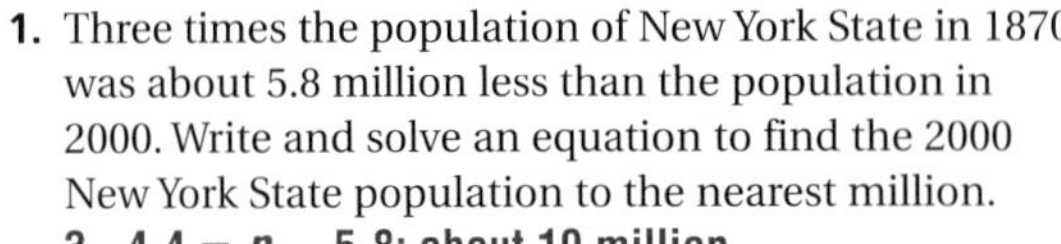

New York Population Changes

For 1 and 2, use the graph.

1. Three times the population of New York State in 1870 was about 5.8 million less than the population in 2000. Write and solve an equation to find the 2000 New York State population to the nearest million.
   $3 \cdot 4.4 = p - 5.8$; about 19 million
2. In 1870, the population of New York State was at most three times the population of New York City. At least how many people lived in New York City in 1870?
   at least 1.47 million people
3. There were about 1.9 million more people in New York State in 1910 than in 1900. The sum of the 1900 and 1910 populations was at least 16.3 million. Write and solve an inequality to find at least how many people lived in New York State in 1910.

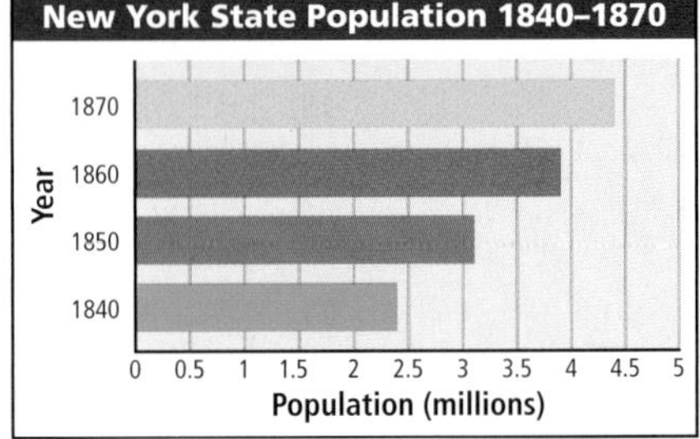

Source: New York State Dept. of Economic Development, State Data Center

For 4 and 5, use the article.

> **John A. Roebling's Legacy**
>
> John A. Roebling's two major contributions to New York State were the Niagara Falls Suspension Bridge and the Brooklyn Bridge. Completed in 1855, the Niagara Falls Suspension Bridge was the first large suspension bridge in the world. The bridge is 821 feet long. John Roebling was appointed chief engineer for the Brooklyn Bridge in 1867, but he died before the actual work had begun.

4. The Niagra Falls Suspension bridge is at least 700 feet shorter than the Brooklyn Bridge. Write and solve an inequality to show at least how long the Brooklyn Bridge is.
5. The Brooklyn Bridge was not completed until more than 10 years after John Roebling's death. Roebling died 2 years after he was appointed chief engineer. What is the earliest year that the Brooklyn Bridge could have been completed? **no earlier than 1879**

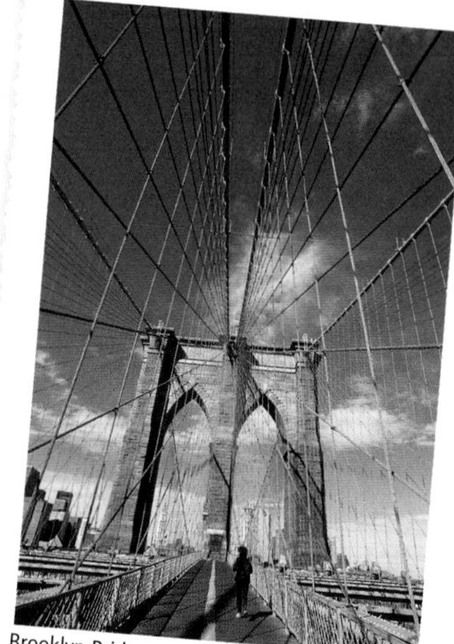

Brooklyn Bridge

Answers

3. $p_{1900} + p_{1910} \geq 16.3$;
$p_{1910} = p_{1900} + 1.9$;
$2p_{1900} + 1.9 \geq 16.3$;
$p_{1900} \geq 7.2$;
$p_{1910} \geq 9.1$; at least 9.1 million people lived in New York State in 1910.

4. $821 \leq x - 700$; $1{,}521 \leq x$; the Brooklyn Bridge is longer than 1,521 feet.

New York Waterways

1. If you double the length of the Mohawk River and then add 10 miles, you get the length of the Hudson River, which is 306 miles. Write an equation to find the length of the Mohawk River, and solve it.
   $2x + 10 = 306$; $x = 148$; The Mohawk River is 148 miles long.

For 2–4, use the graph at right.

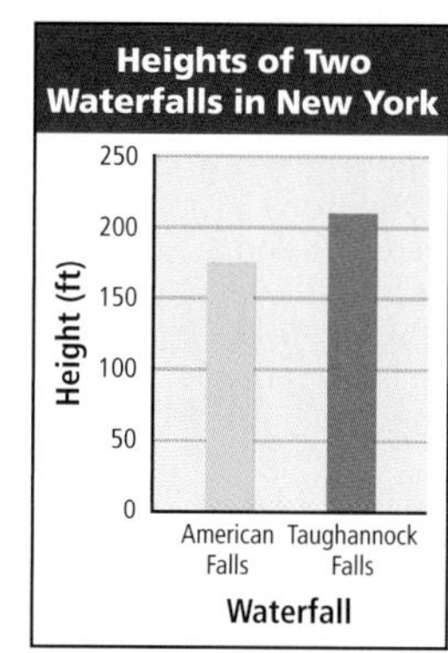

2. Niagara Falls lies on the U.S.–Canadian border. A part of Niagara Falls that is on the American side of the border is called American Falls. Write an inequality to show at least how big the drop of American Falls is. **Possible answer: $d > 150$**

3. Write an inequality to show the greatest drop that Taughannock Falls might have. **Possible answer: $d < 250$**

4. The actual drop of Taughannock Falls is 215 ft. Use the equation $\frac{2x}{4} + 127 = 215$, where x is the height of American Falls, to find a more accurate measure of American Falls. **176 ft**

For 5–7, use the graph at right.

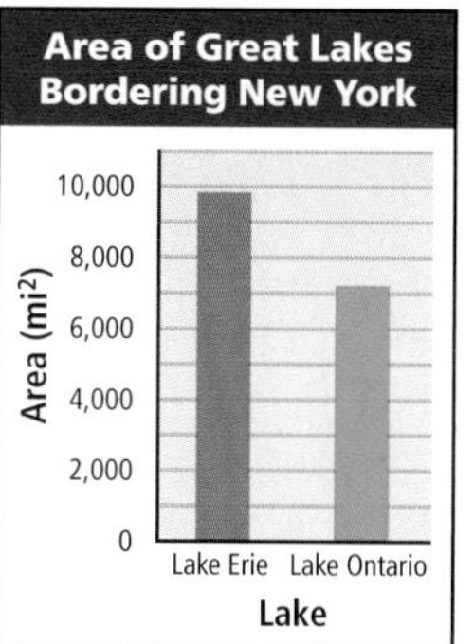

5. Write compound inequalities to show the greatest and least possible areas of Lake Erie and Lake Ontario.
   Lake Erie: $9{,}000 < a < 10{,}000$; Lake Ontario: $7{,}000 < a < 7{,}500$
6. The actual area of Lake Ontario is 7,320 square miles. Use the equation $2x - 1{,}000 = x + 8{,}910$ to find a more accurate measure of the area of Lake Erie than the measure shown on the graph. Let x be the area of Lake Erie in square miles. **$x = 9{,}910$; the area of Lake Erie is 9,910 square miles.**
7. The area of Lake Ontario is at most $\frac{1}{4}$ the area of Lake Superior, the largest of the Great Lakes. Write and solve an inequality to find the area of Lake Superior.

Answers

7. $\frac{1}{4}x \geq 7{,}320$; $x \geq 29{,}280$; the area of Lake Superior is at least 29,280 square miles.

New York Waterways

- After problem 4, have students find the difference between the drops of the American Falls and the Taughannock Falls. **39 ft**
- After problem 6, have students find the difference in the areas of Lake Erie and Lake Ontario. **2,590 mi^2**

Extension Encourage students to use the data on the page to write a problem about a waterfall, lake, or river in New York. Then have students exchange problems and solve. Possible answer: How much longer is the Hudson River than the Mohawk River? 158 ft

MATH-ABLES

Game Resources

Puzzles, Twisters & Teasers
Chapter 11 Resource Book

Flapjacks

Purpose: *To relate an algebraic expression to the problem-solving skill of modeling a problem*

Discuss: Ask students to explain what the variable n represents in the expression $3n - 2$. Ask: What is the maximum number of flips if 6 disks are used? The variable n represents the number of disks. The maximum number of flips with 6 disks is $3(6) - 2$, or 16.

Extend: Have students work in pairs. Have each pair set up 5 disks in the same order and see which partner can arrange them from largest to smallest in the least number of flips.

Leaping Counters

Purpose: *To develop a strategy for eliminating as many counters as possible from the board*

Discuss: Encourage students to discuss any strategies that they discovered for winning the game.

Extend: Have students use counters and a board to create a game. Encourage students to present their game rules to the class and invite other students to play the game.

MATH-ABLES

Flapjacks

Five pancakes of different sizes are stacked in a random order. How can you get the pancakes in order from largest to smallest by flipping portions of the stack?

To find the answer, stack five disks of different sizes in no particular order. Arrange the disks from largest to smallest in the fewest number of moves possible. Move disks by choosing a disk and flipping the whole stack over from that disk up.

Start with a stack of five.

Flip the stack from the second disk up.

Now flip the stack from the third disk up.

Finally, flip the stack from the second disk up.

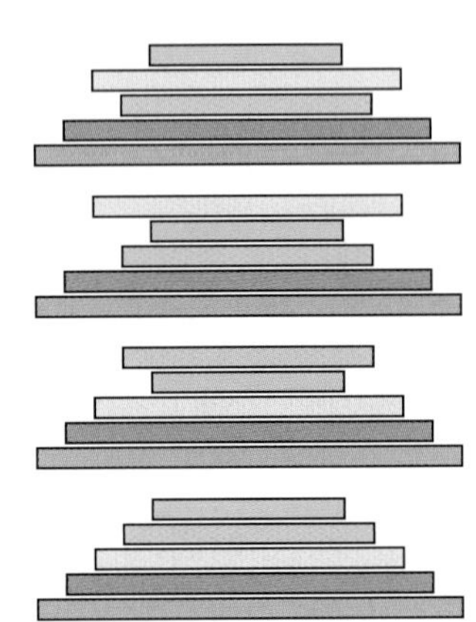

At most, it should take $3n - 2$ turns, where n is the number of disks, to arrange the disks from largest to smallest. The five disks above were arranged in three turns, which is less than $3(5) - 2 = 13$. Try it on your own.

Leaping Counters

Remove all but one of the counters from the board by jumping over each counter with another and removing the jumped counter. The game is over when you can no longer jump a counter. A perfect game would result in one counter being left in the center of the board.

internet connect
Go to ***go.hrw.com*** for a complete set of rules and a game board.
KEYWORD: MS4 Game11

Solve Multistep Equations

You can use the graph function on your graphing calculator to find the solutions to multistep equations.

internet connect
Lab Resources Online
go.hrw.com
KEYWORD: MS4 TechLab11

Activity

1 Use a graphing calculator to solve the equation $3x - 7 = 26$.

On your calculator, enter the expressions that are from each side of the equation separately. Set the size of the window as shown.

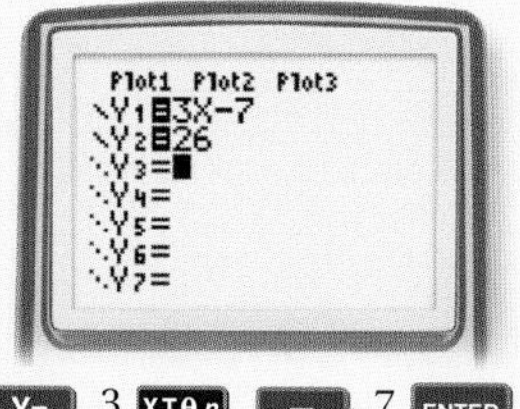

Y= 3 X,T,θ,n − 7 ENTER 26

WINDOW (−) 20 ENTER 20 ENTER 2 ENTER (−) 50 ENTER 50 ENTER 5 ENTER

To see the graph, press GRAPH.

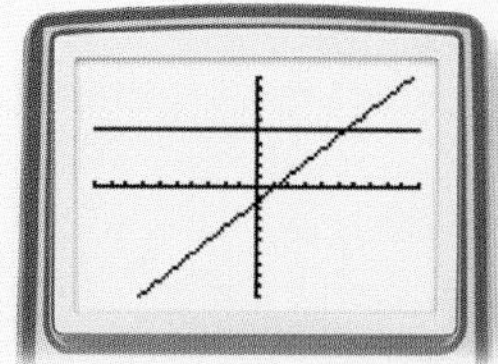

Use the **CALC** function to find the intersection.

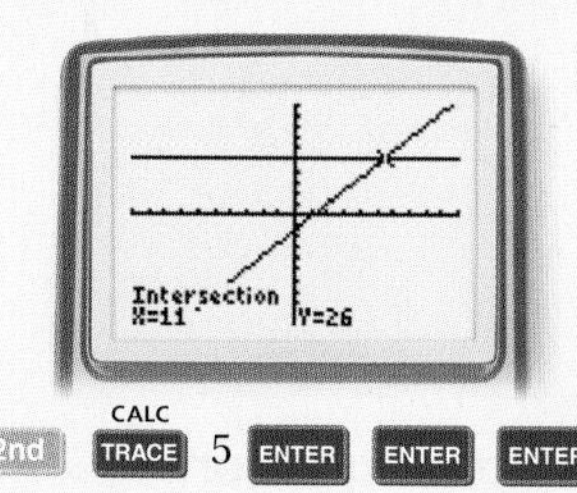

CALC
2nd TRACE 5 ENTER ENTER ENTER

The solution to the equation is the value shown for x. For $3x - 7 = 26$, $x = 11$.

Think and Discuss

1. Why does the intersection of the two lines give the solution to the equation? **The point of intersection for the two lines is the point where the x-value and y-value is the same for both equations.**
2. How would you enter the expression $\frac{2x+6}{3}$ into the calculator? **(2 X,T,θ,n + 6) ÷ 3**

Try This

Use a graphing calculator to solve each equation.

1. $4x + 9 = 17$ **$x = 2$**
2. $\frac{x-8}{5} = 3$ **$x = 23$**
3. $-3x - 2 = -14$ **$x = 4$**
4. $\frac{2x+1}{7} = 3$ **$x = 10$**

Solve Multistep Equations

Objective: To use a graphing calculator to solve multistep equations

Materials: Graphing calculator

Lab Resources

Using the Page

This technology activity shows students how to solve multistep equations on a graphing calculator by graphing each side of the equation separately. Specific keystrokes may vary, depending on the make and model of the graphing calculator used. The keystrokes given are for a TI-83 model.

The Think and Discuss problems can be used to assess students' understanding of the technology activity. While Try This problems 1–4 can be done without a graphing calculator, they are meant to help students become familiar with solving multistep equations on a graphing calculator.

Assessment

Use a graphing calculator to solve each equation.

1. $7x + 8 = 43$ **$x = 5$**
2. $\frac{x-6}{4} = 3$ **$x = 18$**

Chapter 11 Study Guide and Review

Purpose: *To help students review and practice concepts and skills presented in Chapter 11*

Assessment Resources

Chapter 11 Review

Chapter 11 Resource Book . . pp. 72–73

***Test and Practice Generator* CD-ROM**

Additional review assessment items in both multiple-choice and free-response format may be generated for any objective in Chapter 11.

Answers

1. inequality
2. compound inequality
3. solution set
4. $y = 8$
5. $z = 30$
6. $w = 147$
7. $a = -7$
8. $b = 4$
9. $j = 9$
10. $y = 5$
11. $x = 12$

Chapter 11 Study Guide and Review

Vocabulary

Complete the sentences below with vocabulary words from the list above.

1. A(n) ___?___ states that two quantities either are not equal or may not be equal.
2. A(n) ___?___ is a combination of more than one inequality.
3. Together, the solutions of an inequality are called the ___?___.

Study Guide and Review

11-1 Solving Two-Step Equations (pp. 560–563)

EXAMPLE

■ Solve $6a - 3 = 15$.

$$6a - 3 = 15$$
$$6a - 3 + 3 = 15 + 3$$
$$6a = 18$$
$$\frac{6a}{6} = \frac{18}{6}$$
$$a = 3$$

EXERCISES

Solve.

4. $-5y + 6 = -34$
5. $9 + \frac{z}{6} = 14$
6. $\frac{w}{-7} + 13 = -8$

11-2 Solving Multistep Equations (pp. 564–567)

EXAMPLE

■ Solve $\frac{4x - 3}{7} = 3$.

$$\frac{4x - 3}{7} = 3$$
$$(7)\frac{4x - 3}{7} = (7)3$$
$$4x - 3 = 21$$
$$4x - 3 + 3 = 21 + 3$$
$$4x = 24$$
$$\frac{4x}{4} = \frac{24}{4}$$
$$x = 6$$

EXERCISES

Solve.

7. $7a + 4 - 13a = 46$
8. $\frac{8b - 5}{3} = 9$
9. $\frac{6j - 18}{4} = 9$
10. $-9 + 16y - 19 = 52$
11. $\frac{12x + 15}{3} = 53$

11-3 Solving Equations with Variables on Both Sides (pp. 568–571)

EXAMPLE

- **Solve $8a = 3a + 25$.**

$$8a = 3a + 25$$
$$8a - 3a = 3a - 3a + 25$$
$$5a = 25$$
$$\frac{5a}{5} = \frac{25}{5}$$
$$a = 5$$

EXERCISES

Solve.

12. $-6b + 9 = 12b$
13. $5 - 7c = -3c - 19$
14. $18m - 14 = 12m + 2$
15. $4 - \frac{2}{5}x = \frac{1}{5}x - 8$

11-4 Inequalities (pp. 574–577)

EXAMPLE

Write an inequality for each situation.

- **You have to be at least 17 years old to drive a car in New Jersey.**
  age of driver ≥ 17
- **There can be at most 60 people on the bus.**
  number of people ≤ 60

EXERCISES

Write an inequality for each situation.

16. You must have an average of at least 65 to pass math class.
17. A bridge's load limit is at most 9 tons.
18. The large tree in the park is more than 200 years old.
19. It is less than 2 miles from home to the grocery store.

11-5 Solving Inequalities by Adding or Subtracting (pp. 578–581)

EXAMPLE

Solve. Graph each solution set.

- $\mathbf{b + 6 > -10}$

$$b + 6 > -10$$
$$b + 6 - 6 > -10 - 6$$
$$b > -16$$

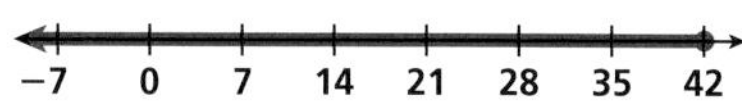

- $\mathbf{p - 17 \leq 25}$

$$p - 17 \leq 25$$
$$p - 17 + 17 \leq 25 + 17$$
$$p \leq 42$$

−7 0 7 14 21 28 35 42

EXERCISES

Solve. Graph each solution set.

20. $r - 16 > 9$
21. $s + 7 \geq 21$
22. $12 + x \leq -14$
23. $\frac{3}{4} + g < 8\frac{3}{4}$
24. $\frac{2}{3} + t \leq \frac{5}{6}$
25. $7.46 > r - 1.54$
26. $z + 17 < -13$
27. $u - 57.7 \geq -123.7$

Study Guide and Review

Answers

12. $b = \frac{1}{2}$
13. $c = 6$
14. $m = \frac{8}{3}$ or $2\frac{2}{3}$
15. $x = 20$
16. average ≥ 65
17. weight limit ≤ 9 tons
18. age > 200
19. distance < 2 mi
20. $r > 25$;
    −5 5 15 25 35 45
21. $s \geq 14$;
    −2 2 6 10 14 18
22. $x \leq -26$;
    −78 −52 −26 0 26 52
23. $g < 8$;
    −4 0 4 8 12 16
24. $t \leq \frac{1}{6}$;
    $-\frac{1}{2}$ $-\frac{1}{6}$ $\frac{1}{6}$ $\frac{1}{2}$ $\frac{5}{6}$
25. $9 > r$;
    −15 −9 −3 3 9 15
26. $z < -30$;
    −90 −30 0
27. $u \geq -66$;
    −66 0 66 132 198

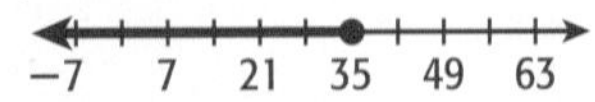

11-6 Solving Inequalities by Multiplying or Dividing (pp. 582–585)

EXAMPLE

Solve.

■ $\frac{m}{-4} \ge 3.8$

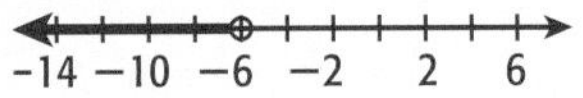

$$\frac{m}{-4} \ge 3.8$$
$$(-4)\frac{m}{-4} \le (-4)3.8$$
$$m \le -15.2$$

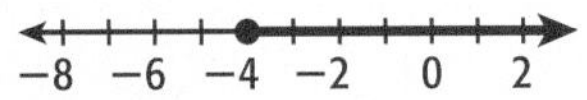

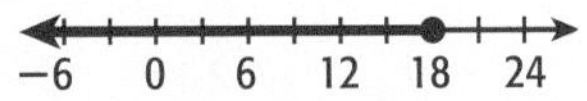

■ $8b < -48$

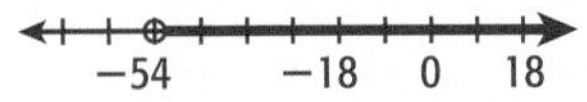

$$8b < -48$$
$$\frac{8b}{8} < \frac{-48}{8}$$
$$b < -6$$

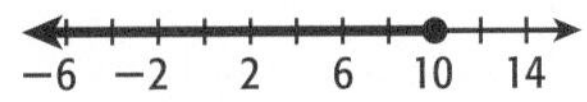

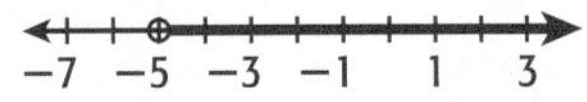

EXERCISES

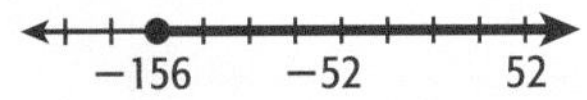

Solve.

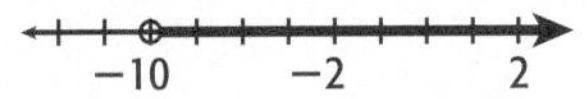

28. $\frac{n}{-8} > 6.9$
29. $4x \le 24$
30. $-3p \ge -18$
31. $\frac{k}{13} < -10$
32. $-5p > -25$
33. $\frac{v}{1.2} \ge 2.3$
34. $\frac{c}{-11} < -3$
35. $1.3y \le 3.51$

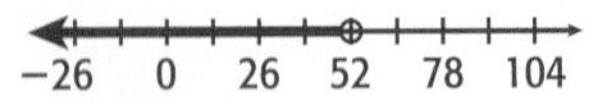

11-7 Solving Two-Step Inequalities (pp. 586–589)

EXAMPLE

Solve. Graph each solution set.

■ $\frac{k}{3} - 18 > 24$

$$\frac{k}{3} - 18 > 24$$
$$\frac{k}{3} - 18 + 18 > 24 + 18$$
$$\frac{k}{3} > 42$$
$$(3)\frac{k}{3} > (3)42$$
$$k > 126$$

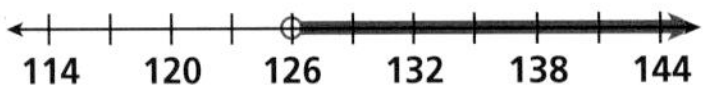

114 120 126 132 138 144

■ $-5b + 11 \le -4$

$$-5b + 11 \le -4$$
$$-5b + 11 - 11 \le -4 - 11$$
$$-5b \le -15$$
$$\frac{-5b}{-5} \ge \frac{-15}{-5}$$
$$b \ge 3$$

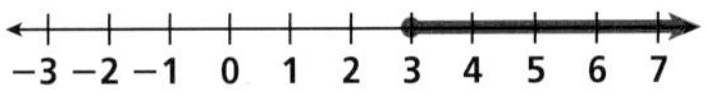

−3 −2 −1 0 1 2 3 4 5 6 7

EXERCISES

Solve. Graph each solution set.

36. $-7b - 16 > -2$
37. $3.8 + \frac{d}{5} < 2.6$
38. $15 - 4n + 9 \le 40$
39. $\frac{y}{-3} + 18 \ge 12$
40. $\frac{c}{3} + 7 > -11$
41. $4x - 8 \le 32$
42. $12 - 7m < 47$
43. $18 + \frac{h}{6} \ge -8$
44. $14 > -2t - 6$
45. $-3 < \frac{w}{-4} + 10$
46. $\frac{y}{7} + 3.9 \le 8.9$

Study Guide and Review

Answers

28. $n < -55.2$
29. $x \le 6$
30. $p \le 6$
31. $k < -130$
32. $p < 5$
33. $v \ge 2.76$
34. $c > 33$
35. $y \le 2.7$
36. $b < -2$; −4 −2 0 2 4 6
37. $d < -6$; −14 −10 −6 −2 2 6
38. $n \ge -4$; −8 −6 −4 −2 0 2
39. $y \le 18$; −6 0 6 12 18 24
40. $c > -54$; −54 −18 0 18
41. $x \le 10$; −6 −2 2 6 10 14
42. $m > -5$; −7 −5 −3 −1 1 3
43. $h \ge -156$; −156 −52 52
44. $-10 < t$; −10 −2 2
45. $52 > w$; −26 0 26 52 78 104
46. $y \le 35$; −7 7 21 35 49 63

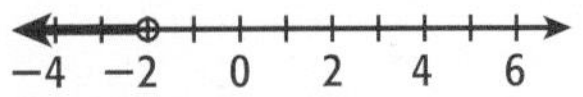

Chapter Test
Chapter 11

Solve.

1. $3y - 8 = 16$ **$y = 8$**
2. $\frac{x}{3} + 12 = -4$ **$x = -48$**
3. $\frac{a}{6} - 7 = -4$ **$a = 18$**
4. $-7b + 5 = -51$ **$b = 8$**
5. $\frac{5y - 4}{3} = 7$ **$y = 5$**
6. $8r + 7 - 13 = 58$ **$r = 8$**
7. $\frac{12s - 6}{5} = 6$ **$s = 3$**
8. $\frac{19.8 - 4t}{3} = 8.7$ **$t = -1.575$**
9. $-14q = 4q - 126$ **$q = 7$**
10. $\frac{5}{6}p + 4 = \frac{1}{6}p - 16$ **$p = -30$**
11. $9 - 6k = 3k - 54$ **$k = 7$**
12. $-3.6l = -7l + 34$ **$l = 10$**
13. The bill for the repair of a computer was \$179. The cost of the parts was \$44, and the labor charge was \$45 per hour. How many hours did it take to repair the computer? **3 hr**
14. Members of the choir are baking cookies for a fund-raiser. It costs \$2.25 to make a dozen cookies, and the choir's initial expenses were \$15.75. If they sell the cookies for \$4.50 a dozen, how many dozen do they have to sell to cover their costs? **7 dozen**

Write an inequality for each situation.

15. You must be more than 4 ft tall to go on the ride. **height > 4 ft**
16. You cannot go more than 65 miles per hour on Route 18. **speed ≤ 65 mi/h**

Graph each inequality.

17. $a < -2$
18. $b \geq 3$
19. $c > -1$ or $c < -5$
20. $-5 < d \leq 2$

Solve. Then graph each solution on a number line.

21. $n + 8 < -9$
22. $n - 124 > -59$
23. $\frac{x}{32} < -40$
24. $-\frac{3}{4}y \leq -12$
25. Rosa wants to save at least \$125 to buy a new skateboard. She has already saved \$46. How much more does Rosa need to save? **at least \$79**
26. Gasoline costs \$1.25 a gallon. At most, how many gallons can be bought for \$15.00? **at most 12 gal**

Solve.

27. $m - 7.8 \leq 23.7$ **$m \leq 31.5$**
28. $6z > -2\frac{2}{3}$ **$z > -\frac{4}{9}$**
29. $\frac{w}{-4.9} \leq 3.4$ **$w \geq -16.66$**
30. $4a + 9 > -15$ **$a > -6$**
31. $2.8 - \frac{c}{4} \geq 7.4$ **$c \leq -18.4$**
32. $\frac{d}{5} - 8 > -4$ **$d > 20$**
33. The seventh-grade students at Fulmore Middle School are trying to raise at least \$7,500 for the local public library. So far, each of the 198 students has raised an average of \$20. At least how much more money must the seventh-graders collect to reach their goal? **at least \$3,540.00**

Chapter Test

Chapter Test
Chapter 11

Purpose: *To assess students' mastery of concepts and skills in Chapter 11*

Assessment Resources

Chapter 11 Tests (Levels A, B, C)
Assessment Resources. . . . . . pp. 93–98

***Test and Practice Generator* CD-ROM**

Additional assessment items in both multiple-choice and free-response format may be generated for any objective in Chapter 11.

Answers

17.
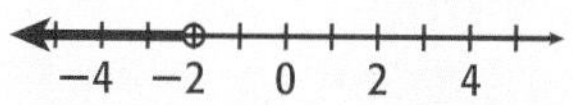

18.
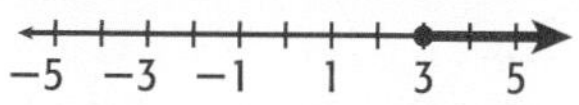

19.
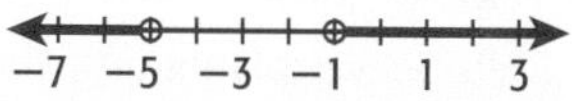

20.
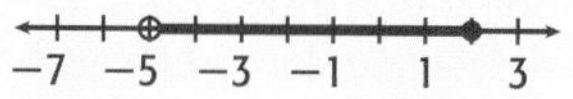

21. $n < -17$;
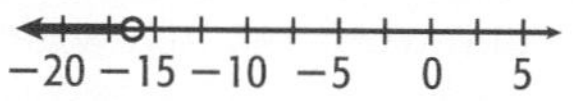

22. $n > 65$;
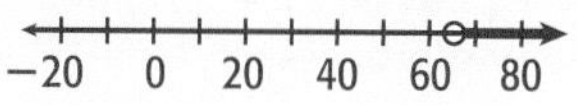

23. $x < -1{,}280$;
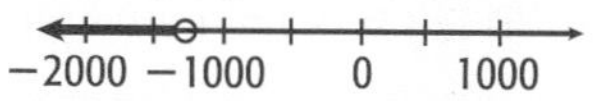

24. $y \geq 16$;
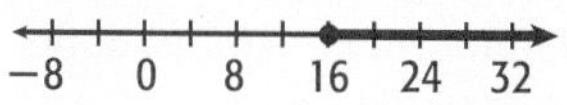

Chapter 11 Performance Assessment

Purpose: *To assess students' understanding of concepts in Chapter 11 and combined problem solving skills*

Assessment Resources

Performance Assessment

Assessment Resources .... p. 126

Performance Assessment Teacher Support

Assessment Resources .... p. 125

Answers

5. See Level 3 work sample below.

Scoring Rubric for Problem Solving Item 5

Level 3

Accomplishes the purpose of the task.

Student gives clear explanations, shows understanding of mathematical ideas and processes, and computes accurately.

Level 2

Purposes of the task not fully achieved.

Student demonstrates satisfactory but limited understanding of the mathematical ideas and processes.

Level 1

Purposes of the task not accomplished.

Student shows little evidence of understanding the mathematical ideas and processes and makes computional and/or procedural errors.

Performance Assessment

Chapter 11 Performance Assessment

3. Let m represent the number of months. $50m = 100 + 40m$; $10m = 100$; $m = 10$ months

Show What You Know

Create a portfolio of your work from this chapter. Complete this page and include it with your four best pieces of work from Chapter 11. Choose from your homework or lab assignments, mid-chapter quiz, or any journal entries you have done. Put them together using any design you want. Make your portfolio represent what you consider your best work.

Short Response

1. Write an equation for the sentence "Two more than three times a number is seventeen." Then solve the equation and show your work. $3n + 2 = 17$; $3n = 15$; $n = 5$

2. Solve the inequality $-5y < 25$, and then graph the solution set on a number line. $y > -5$; [number line: −6 −4 −2 0 2]

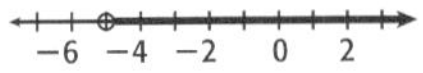

3. Jumping Jack's Fitness Facility charges members $50 per month to work out. Sweat Dog Fitness Center charges members $100 to join and $40 per month. After how many months of being a member of one place would you have paid as much as if you were a member of the other? Show how you found your answer.

4. The maximum weight that the school elevator can carry is 1,500 pounds. If a group of 35 seventh-graders, with an average weight of 90 pounds each, wants to use the elevator, how many trips will be needed to take the students to the fourth floor? Explain your answer. **The total weight of the students is 3,150 pounds. Since the elevator can carry only 1,500 pounds per trip, 3 trips are needed.**

Extended Problem Solving

5. Tim and his crew trim trees. They charge a service fee of $40 for each job, plus an hourly rate.

a. Use the graph to determine the crew's hourly rate. Explain how you found your answer.

b. Write an equation to find y, their income for x hours of work.

c. How many hours did Tim's crew work if they earned $490? Show your work.

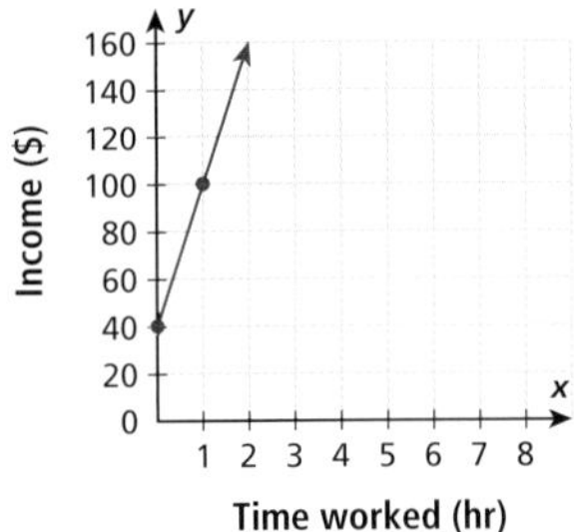

Student Work Samples for Item 5

Level 3

a. $60 per hour
After 1 hour, they make $100.
so 100 − 40 = 60.
b. y = 60x + 40
c. 490 = 60x + 40
−40   −40
450 = 60x
60   60
7.5 = x (7.5 hours)

The student identified the hourly rate, wrote the correct equation, and solved the equation to find the correct number of hours worked.

Level 2

a) $60, 100 − 40 = 60
b) y = 60 + 40x
c) y = 60 + 40(490)
y = 19,660

The student answered part **a** correctly, but made an error writing the equation. The student also substituted incorrectly in part **c.**

Level 1

A. $100. Graph shows 1 hour is equal to $100.
B. Y = 100x
C. 5 hrs.

The student did not account for the $40 fee when answering parts **a** and **b.** The student gave an incorrect answer without explanation in part **c.**

internet connect
State-Specific Test Practice Online
go.hrw.com Keyword: MS4 TestPrep

Standardized Test Prep

Chapter 11

Cumulative Assessment, Chapters 1–11

1. What is $\sqrt{55}$ to the nearest whole number? **B**

Ⓐ 8 Ⓑ 7 Ⓒ 7.4 Ⓓ 3,025

2. Calculate 26 m − 0.42 m, and give the answer with the correct number of significant digits. **J**

Ⓕ 25.58 m Ⓖ 30 m Ⓗ 26.6 m Ⓙ 26 m

3. Meera has 5 yards of beaded ribbon with which to make necklaces. How many 15-inch necklaces can she make? **A**

Ⓐ 12 Ⓑ 4 Ⓒ 75 Ⓓ 3

4. Of 4,500 books, $\frac{3}{5}$ are fiction. Of the remaining books, $\frac{1}{2}$ are nonfiction. The rest are children's books. How many of the books are children's books? **G**

Ⓕ 500 Ⓖ 900 Ⓗ 1,800 Ⓙ 2,700

5. Solve the inequality $\frac{y}{8} > -12$. **D**

Ⓐ $y < -96$ Ⓑ $y < 96$ Ⓒ $y < -1.5$ Ⓓ $y > -96$

6. If 6 is added to 3 times a number and then that result is divided by 2, the answer is 12. What is the number? **H**

Ⓕ 2 Ⓖ 10 Ⓗ 6 Ⓙ 18

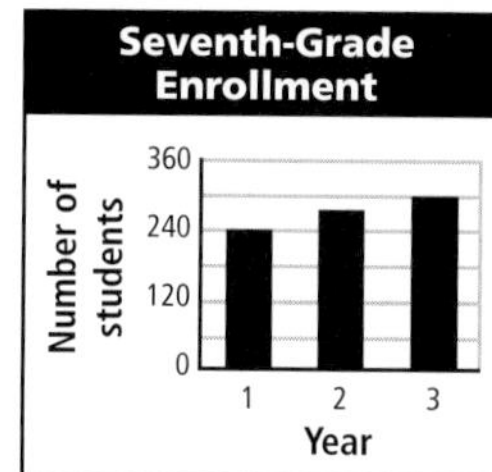

TEST TAKING TIP!
Eliminate choices by considering the meanings of words such as *increase* and *decrease.*

7. If the number of students in seventh grade at Madison Middle School is going to increase by 15% from year three to year four, what will enrollment be? **C**

Seventh-Grade Enrollment

Ⓐ 42 Ⓑ 295 Ⓒ 345 Ⓓ 238

8. Solve the equation $x + -9 = -20$. **J**

Ⓕ $x = -29$ Ⓖ $x = 29$ Ⓗ $x = 11$ Ⓙ $x = -11$

9. ***SHORT RESPONSE*** A spinner is divided into ten equal sectors and numbered 1–10. Monica spins the spinner. List all of the outcomes that are a multiple of 3. What is the probability that the spinner will land on a multiple of 3?

10. ***SHORT RESPONSE*** Nine less than four times a number is the same as twice the number increased by 11. What is the number?
 a. Write the above statement as an equation.
 b. Solve the equation.

Standardized Test Prep

Answers

9. {3, 6, 9}; $\frac{3}{10}$

10. a. Possible answer: $4n - 9 = 2n + 11$

b. $4n - 9 = 2n + 11$
$2n = 20$
$n = 10$

Standardized Test Prep

Chapter 11

Purpose: *To provide review and practice for Chapters 1–11 and standardized tests*

Assessment Resources 

Cumulative Tests (Levels A, B, C)
Assessment Resources. . . . pp. 249–260

State-Specific Test Practice Online
KEYWORD: MS4 TestPrep

Test Prep Doctor 

Expand on the test-taking tip for item 7 by reminding students that they can eliminate all answers that are less than 300.

Chapter 12

Graphs and Functions

Section 12A

Introducing Functions

Lesson 12-1
Introduction to Functions

Lesson 12-2
Find a Pattern in Sequences

Lesson 12-3
Interpreting Graphs

Lesson 12-4
Linear Functions

Lesson 12-5
Slope

Section 12B

Nonlinear Functions and Set Theory

Hands-On Lab 12A
Explore Nonlinear Functions

Lesson 12-6
Nonlinear Functions

Lesson 12-7
Rates of Change

Lesson 12-8
Set Theory

Extension
Venn Diagrams

Pacing Guide for 45-Minute Classes

Chapter 12

DAY 153	DAY 154	DAY 155	DAY 156	DAY 157
Lesson 12-1	Lesson 12-2	Lesson 12-3	Lesson 12-4	Lesson 12-5
DAY 158	**DAY 159**	**DAY 160**	**DAY 161**	**DAY 162**
Mid-Chapter Quiz Hands-On Lab 12A	Lesson 12-6	Lesson 12-7	Lesson 12-8	Extension
DAY 163	**DAY 164**			
Chapter 12 Review	Chapter 12 Assessment			

Pacing Guide for 90-Minute Classes

Chapter 12

DAY 76	DAY 77	DAY 78	DAY 79	DAY 80
Chapter 11 Review Lesson 12-1	Chapter 11 Assessment Lesson 12-2	Lesson 12-3 Lesson 12-4	Lesson 12-5 Hands-On Lab 12A	Mid-Chapter Quiz Lesson 12-6 Lesson 12-7
DAY 81	**DAY 82**	**DAY 83**		
Lesson 12-8 Extension	Chapter 12 Review	Chapter 12 Assessment		

Across the Series

COURSE 1

- Explore linear and nonlinear relationships.
- Represent linear functions with ordered pairs and graphs.

COURSE 2

- **Use tables to generate and graph ordered pairs.**
- **Find patterns to complete sequences in tables.**
- **Interpret graphs and graph linear functions.**
- **Determine the slope of a line from its graph; draw a line, given one point and the slope.**
- **Explore graphs of nonlinear functions.**
- **Recognize constant and variable rates of change.**
- **Use set notation, and identify relationships between sets and subsets.**

COURSE 3

- Use slopes, intercepts, and points to write and graph linear equations, including direct-variation equations.
- Graph inequalities in two variables.
- Identify and graph nonlinear functions.

Across the Curriculum

LANGUAGE ARTS 

Math: Reading and Writing in the Content Area . . . . pp. 95–102

Focus on Problem Solving
Understand the Problem . . . . SE p. 625

Journal . . . . TE, last page of each lesson

Write About It . . . . SE pp. 607, 615, 619, 623, 631, 635, 639

SOCIAL STUDIES LINK

Social Studies . . . . SE p. 639

Geography . . . . SE p. 639

SCIENCE LINK

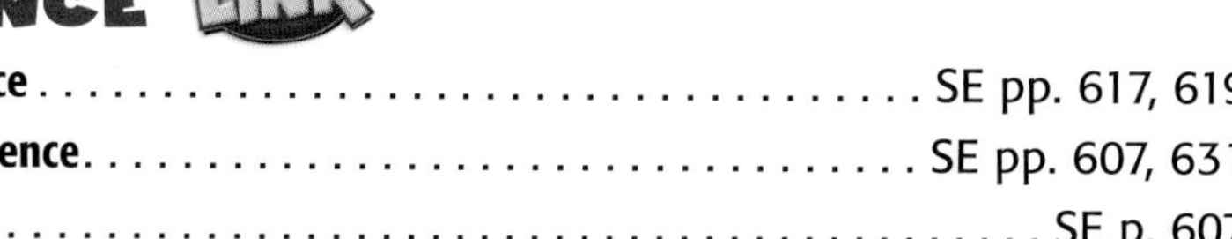

Earth Science . . . . SE pp. 617, 619

Physical Science . . . . SE pp. 607, 631

Health . . . . SE p. 607

Nutrition . . . . SE p. 615

TE = *Teacher's Edition* **SE** = *Student Edition*

Interdisciplinary Bulletin Board

Social Studies

The world population in mid 2001 was about 6.14 billion and growing at a rate of 1.8%. This is modeled by the function $P(t) = 6.14(1.018)^{t-1}$, where t represents time in years and $t = 0$ represents the year 2000. How does this rate of growth differ from a linear growth rate? It keeps increasing faster and faster, whereas a linear growth rate increases at a constant speed.

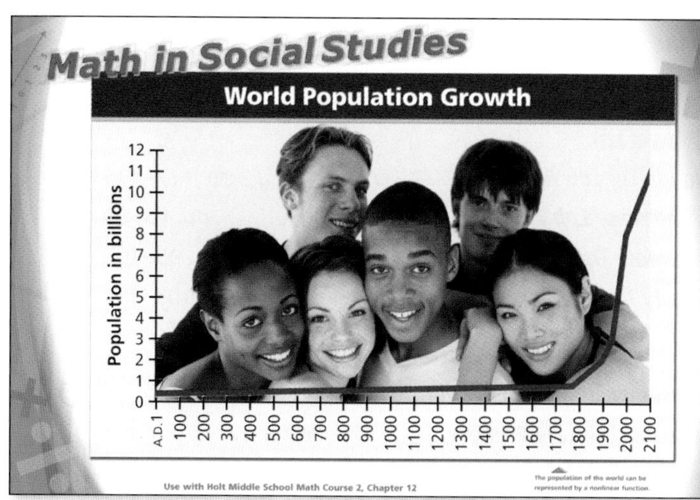

Interdisciplinary posters and worksheets are provided in your resource material.

Chapter 12

Resource Options

Chapter 12 Resource Book

Student Resources

Practice (Levels A, B, C) . . . . pp. 9–11, 18–20, 27–29, 36–38, 45–47, 56–58, 65–67, 74–76
Reteach . . . . pp. 12, 21, 30, 39, 48–49, 59, 68, 77
Challenge . . . . pp. 13, 22, 31, 40, 50, 60, 69, 78
Problem Solving . . . . pp. 14, 23, 32, 41, 51, 61, 70, 79
Puzzles, Twisters & Teasers . . . . pp. 15, 24, 33, 42, 52, 62, 71, 80
Recording Sheets . . . pp. 3–4, 8, 17, 26, 35, 44, 55, 64, 73, 84
Chapter Review . . . . pp. 81–83

Teacher and Parent Resources

Chapter Planning and Pacing Guide . . . . p. 5
Section Planning Guides . . . . pp. 6, 53
Parent Letter . . . . pp. 1–2
Teaching Tools . . . . p. 87
Teacher Support for Chapter Project . . . . p. 85
Transparencies . . . . pp. T1–T37

- Daily Transparencies
- Additional Examples Transparencies
- Teaching Transparencies

Reaching All Learners

English Language Learners

Success for English Language Learners . . . . . . pp. 189–204
Math: Reading and Writing in the Content Area . . . . pp. 95–102
Spanish Homework and Practice . . . . pp. 95–102
Spanish Interactive Study Guide . . . . pp. 95–102
Spanish Family Involvement Activities . . . . pp. 105–112
Multilingual Glossary

Individual Needs

Are You Ready? Intervention and Enrichment . . pp. 225–228, 241–244, 249–252, 281–284, 427–428
Alternate Openers: Explorations . . . . pp. 95–102
Family Involvement Activities . . . . pp. 105–112
Interactive Problem Solving . . . . pp. 95–102
Interactive Study Guide . . . . pp. 95–102
Readiness Activities . . . . pp. 23–24
Math: Reading and Writing in the Content Area . . . . pp. 95–102
Challenge . . . . CRB pp. 13, 22, 31, 40, 50, 60, 69, 78

Hands-On

Hands-On Lab Activities . . . . pp. 117–125
Technology Lab Activities . . . . pp. 65–69
Alternate Openers: Explorations . . . . pp. 95–102
Family Involvement Activities . . . . pp. 105–112

Applications and Connections

Consumer and Career Math . . . . pp. 45–48
Interdisciplinary Posters . . . . Poster 12, TE p. 602B
Interdisciplinary Poster Worksheets . . . . pp. 34–36

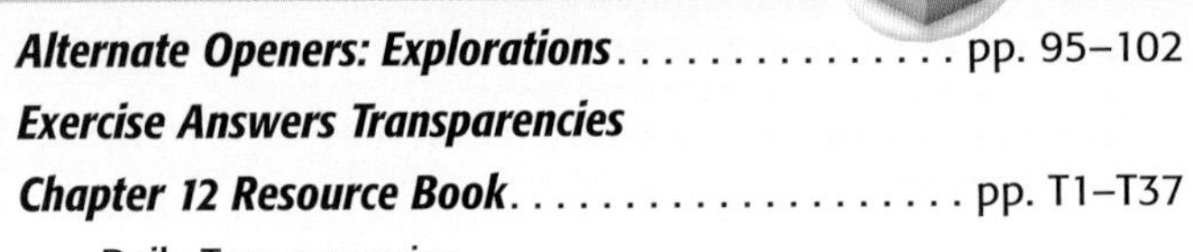

Transparencies

Alternate Openers: Explorations . . . . pp. 95–102
Exercise Answers Transparencies
Chapter 12 Resource Book . . . . pp. T1–T37

- Daily Transparencies
- Additional Examples Transparencies
- Teaching Transparencies

Technology

Teacher Resources

***Lesson Presentations* CD-ROM** . . . . Chapter 12
***Test and Practice Generator* CD-ROM** . . . . . . Chapter 12
***One-Stop Planner* CD-ROM** . . . . Chapter 12

Student Resources

***Are You Ready? Intervention* CD-ROM**
Skills 54, 58, 60, 68

internet connect go.hrw.com

Homework Help Online	**KEYWORD:** MS4 HWHelp12
Math Tools Online	**KEYWORD:** MS4 Tools
Glossary Online	**KEYWORD:** MS4 Glossary
Chapter Project Online	**KEYWORD:** MS4 PSProject12
Chapter Opener Online	**KEYWORD:** MS4 Ch12

KEYWORD: MS4 CNN12

SE = *Student Edition* **TE** = *Teacher's Edition* **AR** = *Assessment Resources* **CRB** = *Chapter Resource Book* **MK** = *Manipulatives Kit*

Chapter 12

Assessment Options

Assessing Prior Knowledge

Determine whether students have the required prerequisite concepts and skills.

Are You Ready? . . . . SE p. 603
Inventory Test . . . . AR pp. 1–4

Test Preparation

Provide review and practice for chapter and standardized tests.

Standardized Test Prep . . . . SE p. 651
Spiral Review with Test Prep . . . . . SE, last page of each lesson
Study Guide and Review . . . . SE pp. 646–648
Test Prep Tool Kit

Technology 

 ***Test and Practice Generator* CD-ROM**

internet connect 
State-Specific Test Practice Online KEYWORD: MS4 TestPrep

Performance Assessment

Assess students' understanding of chapter concepts and combined problem-solving skills.

Performance Assessment . . . . SE p. 650
Includes scoring rubric in TE
Performance Assessment . . . . AR p. 128
Performance Assessment Teacher Support . . . . AR p. 127

Portfolio

Portfolio opportunities appear throughout the Student and Teacher's Editions.

Suggested work samples:

Problem Solving Project . . . . TE p. 602
Performance Assessment . . . . SE p. 650
Portfolio Guide . . . . AR p. xxxv
Journal . . . . TE, last page of each lesson
Write About It . . . . . . SE pp. 607, 615, 619, 623, 631, 635, 639

Daily Assessment

Obtain daily feedback on students' understanding of concepts.

Spiral Review and Test Prep . . . . . . SE, last page of each lesson

Also Available on Transparency In Chapter 12 Resource Book 

Warm Up . . . . TE, first page of each lesson
Problem of the Day . . . . . . TE, first page of each lesson
Lesson Quiz . . . . TE, last page of each lesson

Student Self-Assessment

Have students evaluate their own work.

Group Project Evaluation . . . . AR p. xxxii
Individual Group Member Evaluation . . . . AR p. xxxiii
Portfolio Guide . . . . AR p. xxxv
Journal . . . . TE, last page of each lesson

Formal Assessment

Assess students' mastery of concepts and skills.

Section Quizzes . . . . AR pp. 31–32
Mid-Chapter Quizzes . . . . SE p. 624
Chapter Test . . . . SE p. 649
Chapter Tests (Levels A, B, C) . . . . . . AR pp. 99–104
Cumulative Tests (Levels A, B, C) . . . . . AR pp. 261–272
Standardized Test Prep
Cumulative Assessment . . . . SE p. 651
End-of-Year Test . . . . AR pp. 273–276

Technology 

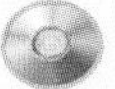 ***Test and Practice Generator* CD-ROM**

Make tests electronically. This software includes:

- Dynamic practice for Chapter 12
- Customizable tests
- Multiple-choice items for each objective
- Free-response items for each objective
- Teacher management system

SE = *Student Edition* **TE** = *Teacher's Edition* **AR** = *Assessment Resources* **CRB** = *Chapter Resource Book* **MK** = *Manipulatives Kit*

Chapter 12 Tests

Three levels (A,B,C) of tests are available for each chapter in the *Assessment Resources.*

Level A

Chapter 12 Chapter Test
Form A

1. Find the output for each input value for $y = x + 7$.

Input	Rule	Output
x	$x + 7$	y
-5	$-5 + 7$	2
-1	$-1 + 7$	6
2	$2 + 7$	9

2. Make an input/output table. Graph the ordered pairs for $y = 2x$.

Input	Rule	Output	Ordered Pair
x	$2x$	y	(x, y)
-2	$2(-2)$	-4	$(-2, -4)$
0	$2(0)$	0	$(0, 0)$
1	$2(1)$	2	$(1, 2)$

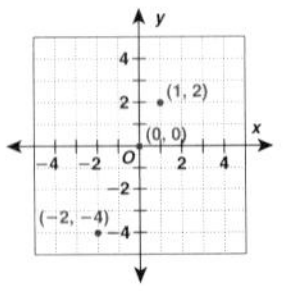

For 3–4, find a rule that describes each sequence. Use the function to find the next three terms in the sequence.

3. 2, 4, 6

$y = 2n$; 8, 10, 12

4. 2, 3, 4

$y = n + 1$; 5, 6, 7

5. Josie spends $3 each hour she plays video games. Draw a graph to show how much she might spend.

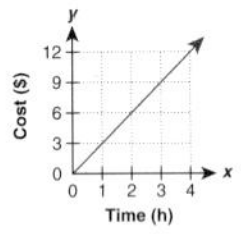

6. Find the domain and range of the graph.

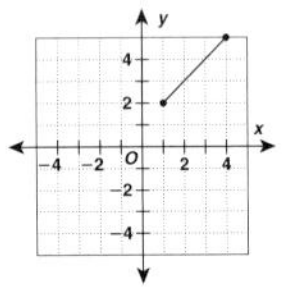

domain: $1 \leq x \leq 4$;

range: $2 \leq y \leq 5$

Chapter 12 Chapter Test
Form A, continued

7. Complete the table and graph the linear function $y = x - 1$.

Input	Rule	Output	Ordered Pair
x	$y = x - 1$	y	(x, y)
-3	$-3 - 1$	-4	$(-3, -4)$
0	$0 - 1$	-1	$(0, -1)$
4	$4 - 1$	3	$(4, 3)$

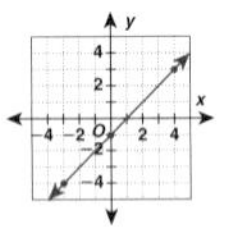

8. Solve $y + x = 5$ for y. $y = -x + 5$

Give the slope and y-intercept.

9. $y = x + 2$ 1, 2

10. $y = 2x + 3$ 2, 3

11. Tell whether the graph is linear or nonlinear.

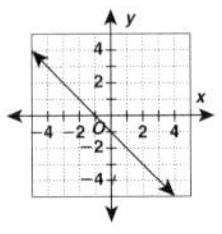

linear

12. Tell whether the function in the table could be linear or is nonlinear.

x	1	2	3
y	1	4	9

nonlinear

13. Tell for which intervals of x the graph shows constant rates of change.

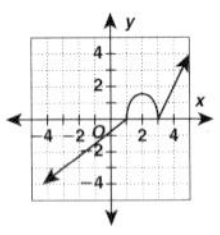

$x \leq 1$ and $x \geq 3$

14. Tell whether the graph above shows a constant or variable rate of change.

variable

15. $A = \{10, 20, 30\}$ and $B = \{5, 10, 15\}$. Find $A \cap B$ and $A \cup B$, and tell whether A or B is a subset of the other.

$A \cap B = \{10\}$,

$A \cup B = \{5, 10, 15, 20, 30\}$; no

16. If A = {the oceans in the world}, give a set B such that B is a subset of A.

Possible answer:

B = {Atlantic, Pacific}

Level B

Chapter 12 Chapter Test
Form B

1. Find the output for each input value for $y = 2x + 6$.

Input	Rule	Output
x	$2x + 6$	y
-5	$2(-5) + 6$	-4
0	$2(0) + 6$	6
3	$2(3) + 6$	12

2. Make an input/output table, and graph the resulting ordered pairs for $y = -3x$.

Input	Rule	Output	Ordered Pair
x	$-3x$	y	(x, y)
-1	$-3(-1)$	3	$(-1, 3)$
0	$-3(0)$	0	$(0, 0)$
1	$-3(1)$	-3	$(1, -3)$

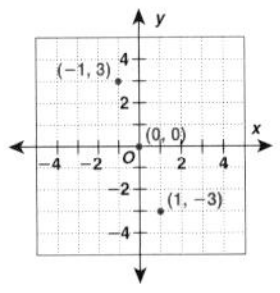

For 3–4, find a rule that describes each sequence and use the function to find the next three terms in the sequence.

3. 3, 6, 9

$y = 3n$; 12, 15, 18

4. $-3, -2, -1$

$y = n - 4$; 0, 1, 2

5. Tim earns $4 an hour mowing lawns. Draw a graph to show how much he might earn.

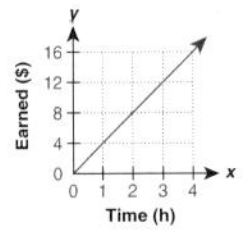

6. Find the domain and range of the graph.

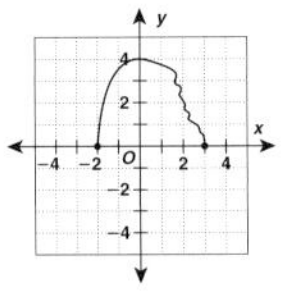

domain: $-2 \leq x \leq 3$;

range: $0 \leq y \leq 4$

Chapter 12 Chapter Test
Form B, continued

7. Complete the table and graph the linear function $y = x + 1$.

Input	Rule	Output	Ordered Pair
x	$y = x + 1$	y	(x, y)
-4	$-4 + 1$	-3	$(-4, -3)$
-2	$-2 + 1$	-1	$(-2, -1)$
3	$3 + 1$	4	$(3, 4)$

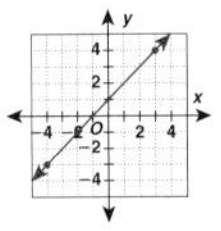

8. Solve $\frac{y}{3} - x = 0$ for y. $y = 3x$

Give the slope and y-intercept.

9. $y = 4x - 2$ 4, −2

10. $y = -2x + 1$ −2, 1

11. Tell whether the graph is linear or nonlinear.

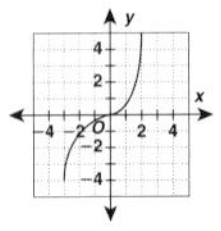

nonlinear

12. Tell whether the function in the table could be linear or is nonlinear.

x	6	10	14
y	15	23	31

linear

13. Tell for which intervals of x the graph shows constant rates of change.

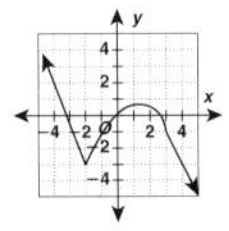

$x \leq -2$ and $x \geq 3$

14. Tell whether the graph above shows a constant or variable rate of change.

variable

15. $A = \{2, 4, 6, 8\}$ and $B = \{1, 2, 3, 4\}$. Find $A \cap B$ and $A \cup B$, and tell whether A or B is a subset of the other.

$A \cap B = \{2, 4\}$,

$A \cup B = \{1, 2, 3, 4, 6, 8\}$; no

16. If A = {all states | the name has two words}, give a set B such that B is a subset of A.

Possible answer:

B = {New York, South Dakota}

Level C

Chapter 12 Chapter Test
Form C

1. Find the output for each input value for $y = -5x + 2$.

Input	Rule	Output
x	$-5x + 2$	y
-1	$-5(-1) + 2$	7
0	$-5(0) + 2$	2
1	$-5(1) + 2$	-3

2. Make an input/output table, and graph the resulting ordered pairs for $y = 4 - x$.

Input	Rule	Output	Ordered Pair
x	$4 - x$	y	(x, y)
-1	$4 - (-1)$	5	$(-1, 5)$
0	$4 - 0$	4	$(0, 4)$
1	$4 - 1$	3	$(1, 3)$

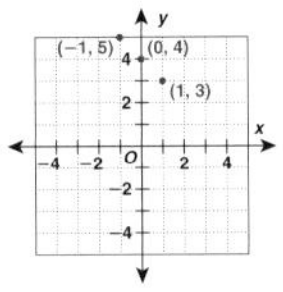

For 3–4, find a rule that describes each sequence and use the function to find the next three terms in the sequence.

3. 2, 5, 8

$y = 3n - 1$; 11, 14, 17

4. 1, 8, 27

$y = n^3$; 64, 125, 216

5. Kim earns $6 per hour for the first 3 hours he works and $8 per hour after that. Draw a graph to show how much he might earn.

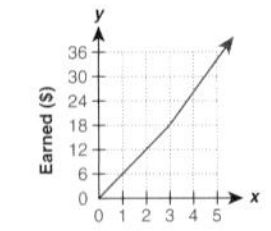

6. Find the domain and range of the graph.

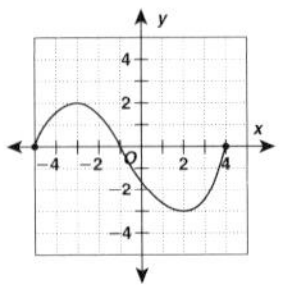

domain: $-5 \leq x \leq 4$;

range: $-3 \leq y \leq 2$

Chapter 12 Chapter Test
Form C, continued

7. Complete the table and graph the linear function $y = -x - 1$.

Input	Rule	Output	Ordered Pair
x	$y = -x - 1$	y	(x, y)
-1	$-(-1) - 1$	0	$(-1, 0)$
0	$0 - 1$	-1	$(0, -1)$
1	$-1 - 1$	-2	$(1, -2)$

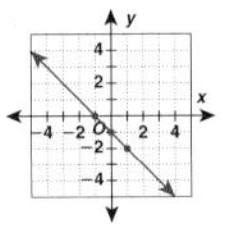

8. Solve $5y - 3x = 10$ for y.

$y = \frac{3}{5}x + 2$

Give the slope and y = intercept.

9. $3x = 6 - y$ −3, 6

10. $y = \frac{x}{3} - \frac{3}{2}$ $\frac{1}{3}, -\frac{3}{2}$

11. Tell whether the graph is linear or nonlinear.

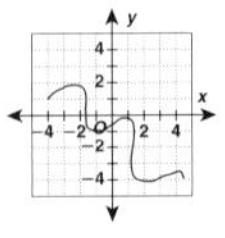

nonlinear

12. Tell whether the function in the table could be linear or is nonlinear.

x	6	8	10
y	12	16	−20

nonlinear

13. Tell for which intervals of x the graph shows constant rates of change.

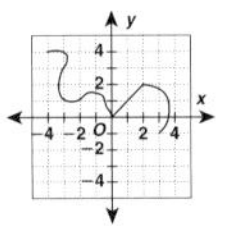

$0 \leq x \leq 2$

14. Tell whether the graph above shows a constant or variable rate of change.

variable

15. $A = \{x|x \text{ is an odd number}\}$ and $B = \{x|x \text{ is a multiple of 2}\}$. Find $A \cap B$ and $A \cup B$, and tell whether A or B is a subset of the other.

$A \cap B = \phi$, $A \cup B =$

$\{x|x \text{ is an integer}\}$; no

16. If $A = \{x|x \text{ is an irrational number}\}$, give a set B such that B is a subset of A.

possible answer: $B = \{\pi, \sqrt{2}\}$

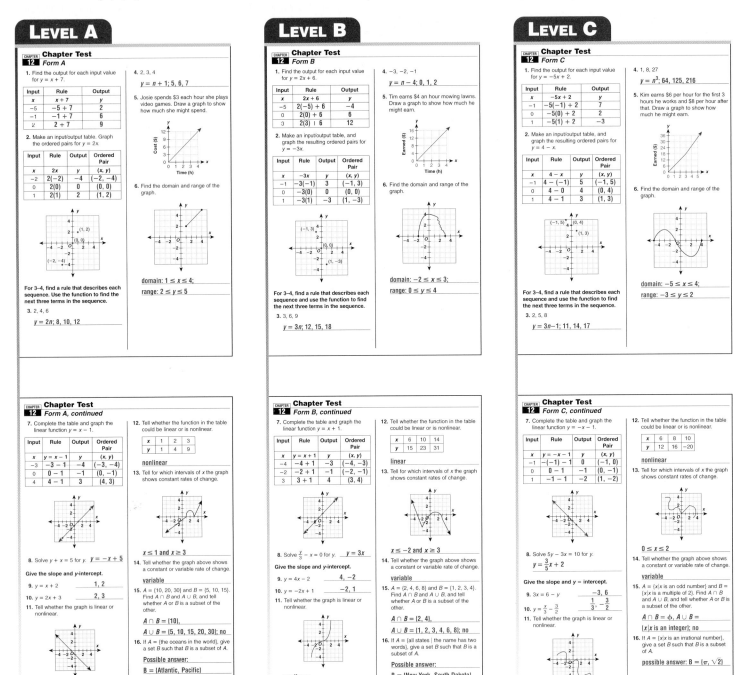

Test and Practice Generator CD-ROM

Create and customize multiple versions of the same tests with corresponding answers for any chosen chapter objectives.

Chapter 12 State and Standardized Test Preparation

Test Taking Skill Builder and Standardized Test Practice are provided for each chapter in the *Test Prep Tool Kit.*

TEST TAKING SKILL BUILDER

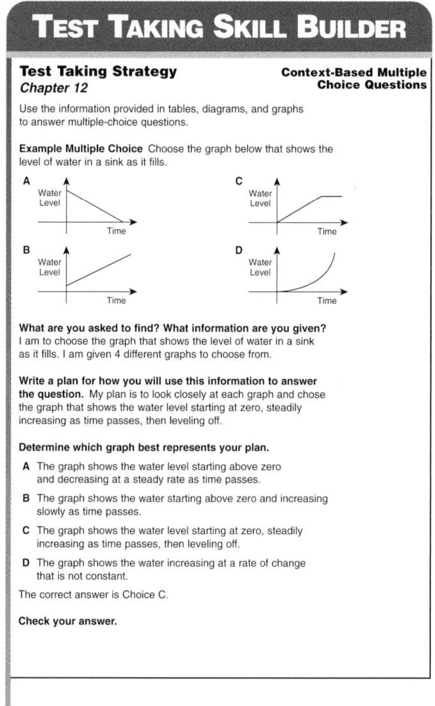

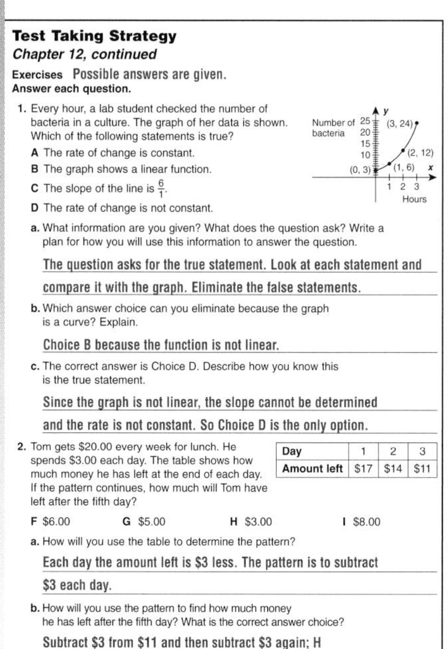

STANDARDIZED TEST PRACTICE

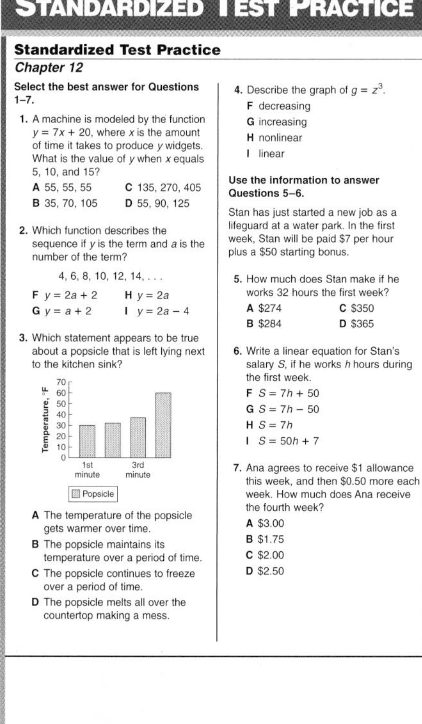

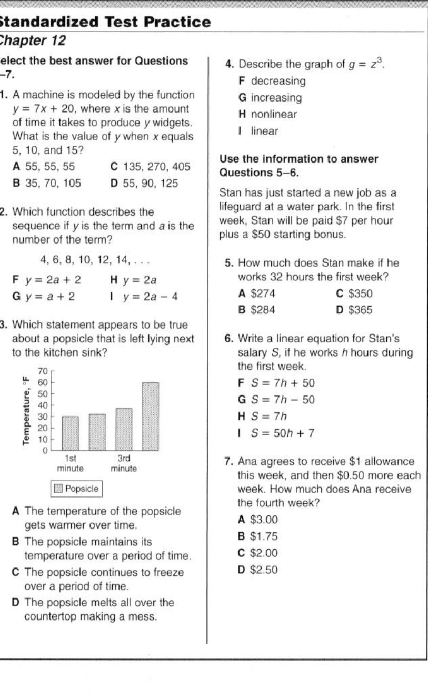

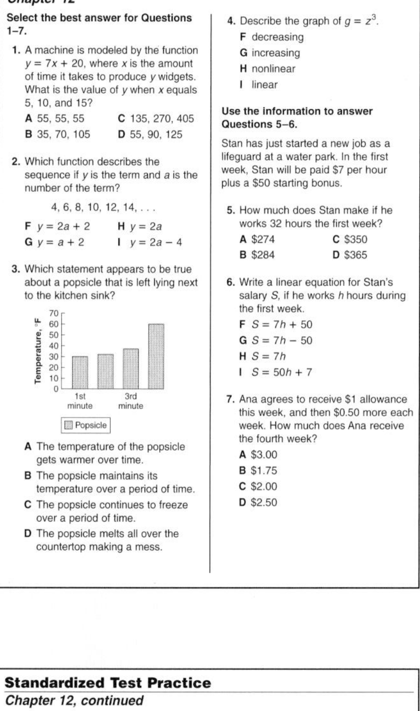

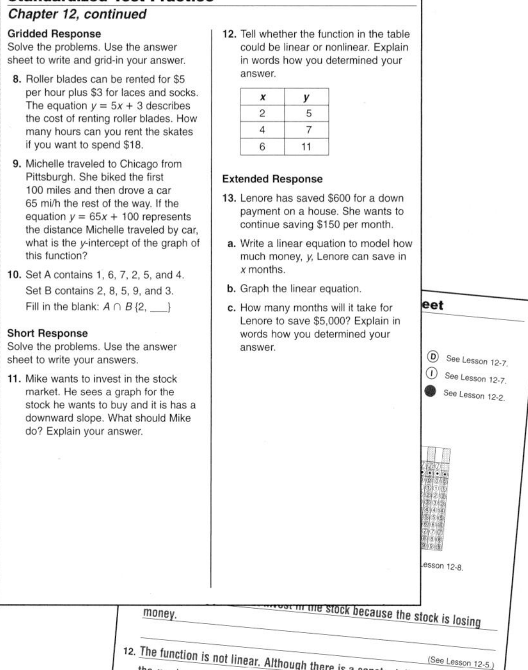

Test Prep Tool Kit

- Standardized Test Prep Workbook
- Countdown to Testing transparencies
- State Test Prep CD-ROM
- Standardized Test Prep Video

Customized answer sheets give students realistic practice for actual standardized tests.

Chapter 12

Graphs and Functions

Why Learn This?

Tell students that roller coaster designers use mathematics to make roller coasters safe and fun to ride. The teardrop shape used in many roller coasters is called a *clothoid* (pronounced "klockoid") loop.

The Clothoid Loop

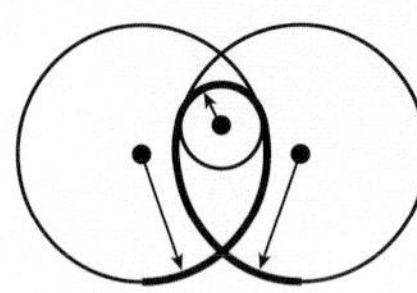

The radius at the bottom of a clothoid loop is much larger than the radius at the top.

Using Data

To begin the study of this chapter, have students:

- Make a bar graph showing the speeds of the four fastest U.S. roller coasters.

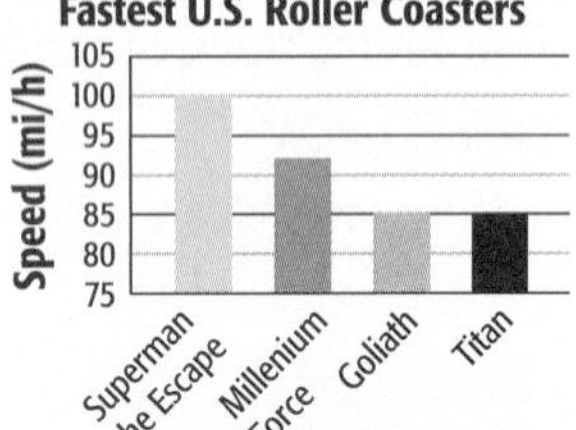

Chapter 12

Graphs and Functions

TABLE OF CONTENTS

Fastest U.S. Roller Coasters

Roller Coaster	Speed (mi/h)
Superman the Escape	100
Millennium Force	92
Goliath	85
Titan	85

Career ***Roller Coaster Designer***

Traditional roller-coaster designs rely on gravity for a coaster to gain speed. Some of these designs include loops and turns to make rides more exciting.

Jim Seay is a roller-coaster designer who uses high-tech methods to create exhilarating rides. His designs include a system that can propel a coaster from 0 to 70 miles per hour in less than four seconds!

internet connect
Chapter Opener Online
go.hrw.com
KEYWORD: MS4 Ch12

Problem Solving Project

Physical Science Connection

Purpose: To solve problems by using properties and graphs of functions

Materials: Ups and Downs worksheet, roller coaster building materials, marbles, stop watches

Understand, Plan, Solve, and Look Back

Have students:

- ✓ Complete the Ups and Downs worksheet.
- ✓ Research to find out why roller coasters have clothoid loops instead of totally round circles.
- ✓ Ask classmates about their experiences with roller coasters. What characteristics seem to make roller coasters fun? Display results in a table or graph.
- ✓ Check students' work.

internet connect
Chapter Project Online: go.hrw.com
KEYWORD: MS4 PSProject12

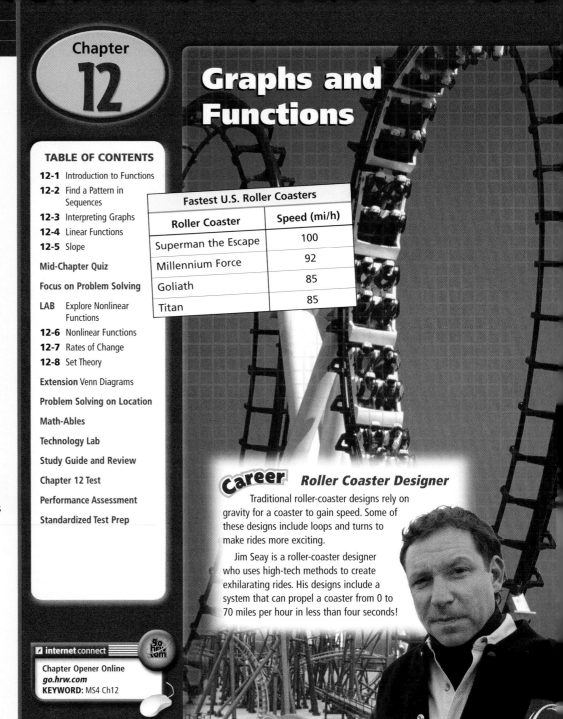

ARE YOU READY?

Choose the best term from the list to complete each sentence.

1. A(n) __?__ states that two expressions are equivalent. **equation**
2. To __?__ an expression is to substitute a number for the variable. **evaluate**
3. The __?__ is the horizontal number line on a coordinate plane. **x-axis**
4. A(n) __?__ is a number that can be written as a ratio of two integers. **rational number**

equation
evaluate
irrational number
rational number
x-axis
y-axis

Complete these exercises to review skills you will need for this chapter.

✓ Evaluate Expressions

Evaluate each expression.

5. $x + 5$ for $x = -18$ **−13**
6. $-9y$ for $y = 13$ **−117**
7. $\frac{z}{-6}$ for $z = 96$ **−16**
8. $w - 9$ for $w = -13$ **−22**
9. $-3z + 1$ for $z = 4$ **−11**
10. $3w + 9$ for $w = 7$ **30**
11. $5 - \frac{y}{3}$ for $y = -3$ **6**
12. $x^2 + 1$ for $x = -2$ **5**

✓ Solve Equations

Solve each equation.

13. $13 + y = -3$ **$y = -16$**
14. $-4y = -56$ **$y = 14$**
15. $3y = -12$ **$y = -4$**
16. $25 - y = 7$ **$y = 18$**
17. $3y + 8 = 3$ **$y = -\frac{5}{3}$**
18. $5 - 3y = 7$ **$y = -\frac{2}{3}$**
19. $5y - 4 = 16$ **$y = 4$**
20. $\frac{y}{3} = -9$ **$y = -27$**

✓ Write Ordered Pairs

Write the ordered pair for each point.

21. point A **(5, 4)**
22. point B **(−2, −3)**
23. point C **(0, 1)**
24. point D **(−5, 4)**
25. point E **(5, −4)**
26. point F **(−6, 0)**

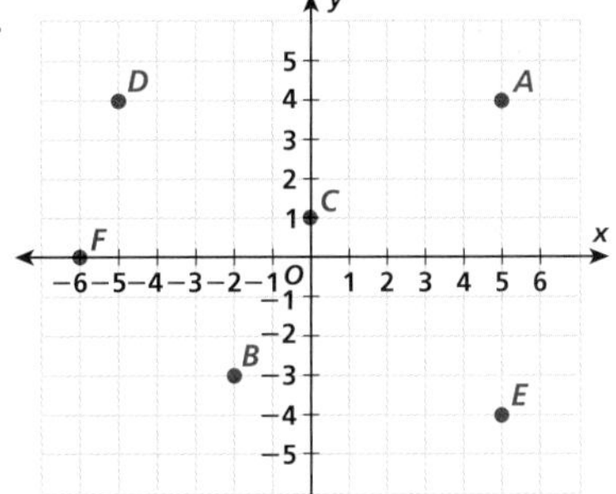

Assessing Prior Knowledge

INTERVENTION 

Diagnose and Prescribe

Evaluate your students' performance on this page to determine whether intervention is necessary or whether enrichment is appropriate. Options that provide instruction, practice, and a check are listed below.

Resources for Are You Ready?

- ***Are You Ready? Intervention and Enrichment***
- **Recording Sheet for Are You Ready?** *Chapter 12 Resource Book* ..... p. 3

 ***Are You Ready? Intervention* CD-ROM**

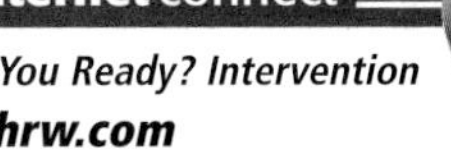

internet connect
Are You Ready? Intervention
go.hrw.com
KEYWORD: MS4 AYR

ARE YOU READY?

Were students successful with Are You Ready?

NO INTERVENE

✓Evaluate Expressions
Are You Ready? Intervention, Skill 54
Blackline Masters, Online, and

 **CD-ROM** Intervention Activities

✓Solve Equations
Are You Ready? Intervention, Skill 58, 60
Blackline Masters, Online, and

CD-ROM Intervention Activities

✓Write Ordered Pairs
Are You Ready? Intervention, Skill 68
Blackline Masters, Online, and

 **CD-ROM** Intervention Activities

YES ENRICH

Are You Ready? Enrichment, pp. 429–430

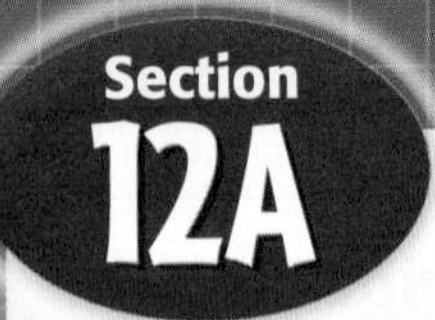

Introducing Functions

One-Minute Section Planner

Lesson	Materials	Resources
Lesson 12-1 Introduction to Functions **NCTM:** Algebra, Communication, Connections **NAEP:** Algebra 1c ☐ SAT-9 ☑ SAT-10 ☐ ITBS ☑ CTBS ☑ MAT ☑ CAT		• *Chapter 12 Resource Book,* pp. 7–15 • Daily Transparency T1, CRB • Additional Examples Transparencies T2–T3, CRB • *Alternate Openers: Explorations,* p. 95
Lesson 12-2 Find a Pattern in Sequences **NCTM:** Algebra, Problem Solving, Communication, Connections **NAEP:** Algebra 1a ☑ SAT-9 ☑ SAT-10 ☑ ITBS ☑ CTBS ☑ MAT ☑ CAT		• *Chapter 12 Resource Book,* pp. 16–24 • Daily Transparency T4, CRB • Additional Examples Transparencies T5–T7, CRB • *Alternate Openers: Explorations,* p. 96
Lesson 12-3 Interpreting Graphs **NCTM:** Algebra, Data Analysis and Probability, Reasoning and Proof, Communication, Connections, Representation **NAEP:** Algebra 1b ☑ SAT-9 ☑ SAT-10 ☑ ITBS ☑ CTBS ☑ MAT ☑ CAT	Optional Sale advertisements	• *Chapter 12 Resource Book,* pp. 25–33 • Daily Transparency T8, CRB • Additional Examples Transparencies T9–T11, CRB • *Alternate Openers: Explorations,* p. 97
Lesson 12-4 Linear Functions **NCTM:** Algebra, Communication, Connections **NAEP:** Algebra 2e ☐ SAT-9 ☐ SAT-10 ☐ ITBS ☑ CTBS ☐ MAT ☑ CAT	Optional Graph paper *(CRB, p. 87)* Straightedges *(MK)* Science textbooks	• *Chapter 12 Resource Book,* pp. 34–42 • Daily Transparency T12, CRB • Additional Examples Transparencies T13–T15, CRB • *Alternate Openers: Explorations,* p. 98
Lesson 12-5 Slope **NCTM:** Algebra, Geometry, Communication, Connections **NAEP:** Algebra 1f ☐ SAT-9 ☐ SAT-10 ☐ ITBS ☑ CTBS ☐ MAT ☑ CAT	Optional Graph paper *(CRB, p. 87)* Teaching Transparency T17 *(CRB)*	• *Chapter 12 Resource Book,* pp. 43–52 • Daily Transparency T16, CRB • Additional Examples Transparencies T18–T20, CRB • *Alternate Openers: Explorations,* p. 99
Section 12A Assessment		• Mid-Chapter Quiz, SE p. 624 • Section 12A Quiz, AR p. 31 • *Test and Practice Generator* CD-ROM

SAT = *Stanford Achievement Tests* **ITBS** = *Iowa Test of Basic Skills* **CTBS** = *Comprehensive Test of Basic Skills/Terra Nova*
MAT = *Metropolitan Achievement Test* **CAT** = *California Achievement Test*

NCTM—Complete standards can be found on pages T27–T33. **NAEP**—Complete standards can be found on pages A35–A39.

SE = *Student Edition* **TE** = *Teacher's Edition* **AR** = *Assessment Resources* **CRB** = *Chapter Resource Book*
MK = *Manipulatives Kit*

Section Overview

Input/Output Tables and Functions **Lesson 12-1**

Why? Students must understand how to use an input/output table to be able to graph a function.

A **function** is a relation, or rule, that assigns a unique y-value to every x-value.

Function: $y = x^2$

Input: x	Output: y
-2	$(-2)^2 = 4$
-1	$(-1)^2 = 1$
0	$(0)^2 = 0$
1	$(1)^2 = 1$
2	$(2)^2 = 4$

Graph of $y = x^2$

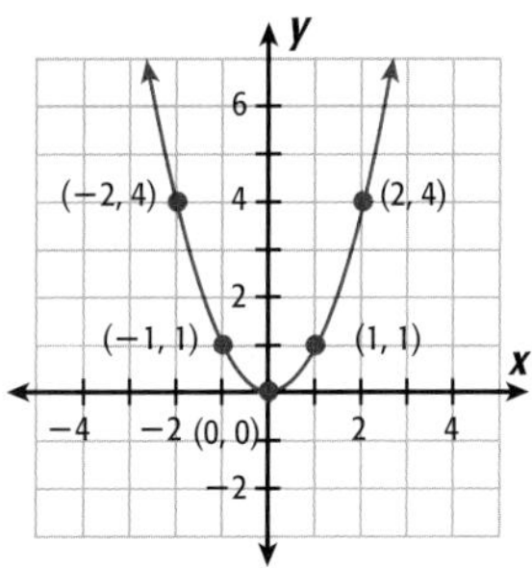

Patterns and Graphs **Lessons 12-2, 12-3**

Why? Students should recognize that the rule that describes a number pattern also describes the corresponding function. Students will continue to study functions and their graphs in algebra and geometry.

A **sequence** is an ordered list of numbers. The variable n represents a number's place in a sequence.

Find the next term in the sequence: **3, 6, 9, 12, . . .**
The function $y = 3n$ can be used to describe the sequence.
The next, or fifth, term in the sequence is **3(5)**, or **15**.

The graph of $y = 3x$ is a straight line.

The **range** is all possible values y can assume. The range of $y = 3x$ is the set of real numbers.

The **domain** is all possible values x can assume. The domain of $y = 3x$ is the set of real numbers.

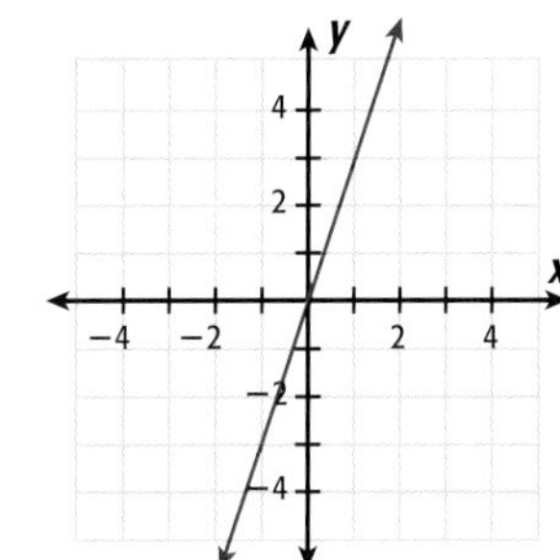

Linear Equations **Lessons 12-4, 12-5**

Why? Students are introduced to linear equations, their slopes, and their y-intercepts. All of these concepts will be explored in greater detail in future studies in algebra.

The graphs of linear equations are straight lines.
The slope-intercept form of a linear equation is $y = mx + b$.

The **slope** tells how steep a line is. It is the ratio of the rise over the run. $m = \frac{\text{rise}}{\text{run}}$

The **y-intercept** is the y-value at which the graph crosses the y-axis, $(0, b)$.

$y = 2x + 1$

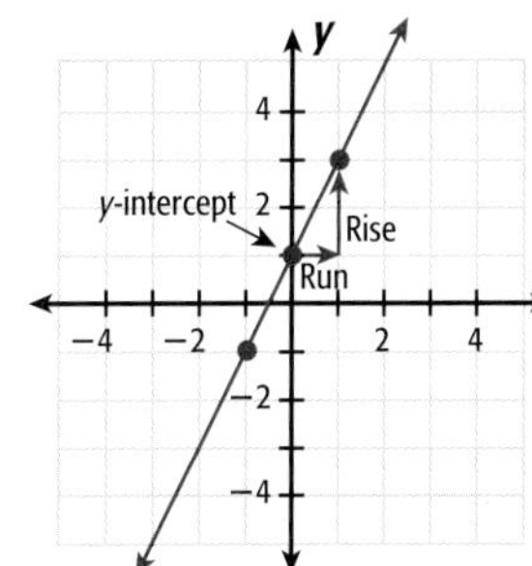

12-1 Organizer

Pacing: Traditional 1 day
Block $\frac{1}{2}$ day

Objective: Students use function tables to generate and graph ordered pairs.

Warm Up

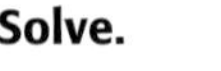

Solve.

1. $x + 4 = 19$ — $x = 15$
2. $y - 2.3 = 7.8$ — $y = 10.1$
3. $4z = 120$ — $z = 30$
4. $\frac{w}{9} = 8$ — $w = 72$

Problem of the Day

Substitute the numbers 1, 2, and 3 for the letters a, b, and c in such a way that the number sentence is correct.

$$\frac{1}{a^a} + \frac{1}{a^b} = \frac{1}{a^c} - \frac{1}{a^b}$$

$a = 2,\ b = 3,\ c = 1$

Available on Daily Transparency in CRB

Math Humor

Teacher: Why did the cube cross over from the second dimension to the third dimension?

Student: Because the second dimension was too square

12-1 Introduction to Functions

Learn to use function tables to generate and graph ordered pairs.

Vocabulary
function

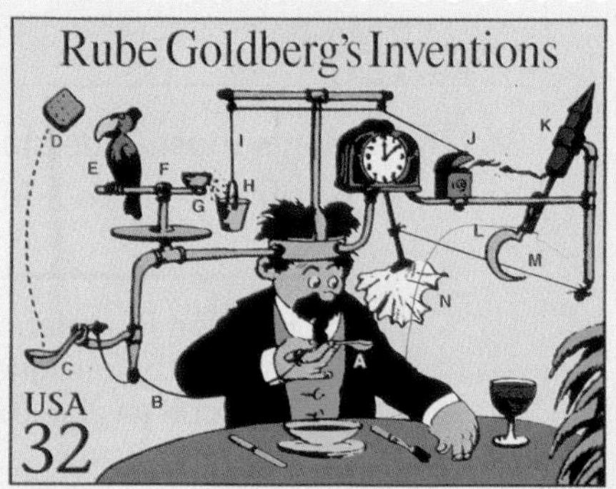

As you raise spoon of soup (A) to your mouth, it pulls string (B), thereby jerking ladle (C), which throws cracker (D) past parrot (E). Parrot jumps after cracker, and perch (F) tilts, upsetting seeds (G) into pail (H). Extra weight in pail pulls cord (I), which opens and lights automatic cigar lighter (J), setting off sky rocket (K), which causes sickle (L) to cut string (M) and allow pendulum with attached napkin to swing back and forth, thereby wiping off your chin.

Rube Goldberg, a famous cartoonist, invented machines that perform ordinary tasks in extraordinary ways. Each machine operates according to a rule, or a set of steps, to produce a particular output.

In mathematics, a **function** operates according to a rule to produce a single output value for each input value.

A function can be represented as a rule written in words, such as "double the number and then add nine to the result."

A function can also be represented by an equation with two variables. One variable represents the input, and the other represents the output.

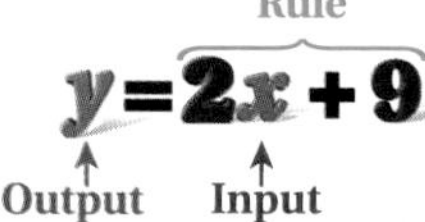

You can use a table to organize the input and output values of a function. Your table may show as many possible input and output values as you choose.

EXAMPLE  **Completing a Function Table**

Find the output for each input.

A $y = 4x - 2$

Input	Rule	Output	
x	$4x - 2$	y	
-1	$4(-1) - 2$	-6	*Substitute −1 for x and simplify.*
0	$4(0) - 2$	-2	*Substitute 0 for x and simplify.*
3	$4(3) - 2$	10	*Substitute 3 for x and simplify.*

1 Introduce

Alternate Opener

 **Introduction to Functions**

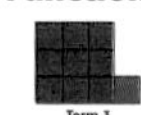

1. Use the model to show that the first term is $1^2 + 1$, the second term is $2^2 + 1$, and the third term is $3^2 + 1$.
2. Complete the input/output table. Then use the input values (x) and the output values (y) to complete the graph.

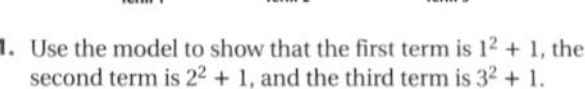

Input x	Rule $x^2 + 1$	Output y	(x, y)
1	$1^2 + 1$	2	(1, 2)
2			
3			
4			
5			

Think and Discuss

3. **Name** the output for an input value of 6 by using the rule in the table.
4. **Explain** how to graph the input and output values.

Motivate

Discuss how to plan the time it would take to have a class program. Consider situations such as the following: How long would it take for each student to make a 1-minute presentation? a 2-minute presentation? How long would it take groups of three students to make 5-minute presentations?

Exploration worksheet and answers on Chapter 12 Resource Book pp. 8 and 88

2 Teach

Guided Instruction

In this lesson, students learn to use function tables to generate and graph ordered pairs. You may wish to emphasize that a table can help students organize the input/output data of a function. Point out that although integers are chosen for all of the inputs in the examples, any real numbers could be substituted for the inputs. Integers are just easier to work with.

Discuss why Examples 1B and 2B are functions. Tell students that in a function two different inputs can give the same output, but each output must come from a different input.

Find the output for each input.

B $y = 6x^2$

Input	Rule	Output
x	$6x^2$	y
−5	$6(-5)^2$	150
0	$6(0)^2$	0
5	$6(5)^2$	150

Substitute −5 for x and simplify.
Substitute 0 for x and simplify.
Substitute 5 for x and simplify.

Remember!

An ordered pair is a pair of numbers that represents a point on a graph.

You can also use a graph to represent a function. The corresponding input and output values together form unique ordered pairs.

EXAMPLE 2 Graphing Functions Using Ordered Pairs

Make a function table, and graph the resulting ordered pairs.

A $y = 2x$

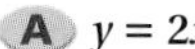

Helpful Hint

When writing an ordered pair, write the input value first and then the output value.

Input	Rule	Output	Ordered Pair
x	$2x$	y	(x, y)
−2	2(−2)	−4	(−2, −4)
−1	2(−1)	−2	(−1, −2)
0	2(0)	0	(0, 0)
1	2(1)	2	(1, 2)
2	2(2)	4	(2, 4)

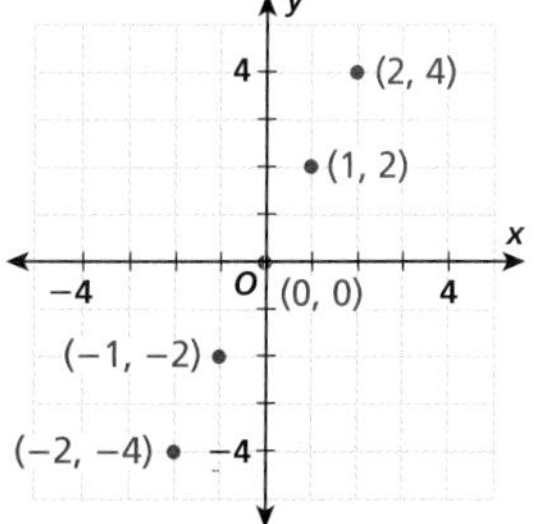

B $y = x^2$

Input	Rule	Output	Ordered Pair
x	x^2	y	(x, y)
−2	$(-2)^2$	4	(−2, 4)
−1	$(-1)^2$	1	(−1, 1)
0	$(0)^2$	0	(0, 0)
1	$(1)^2$	1	(1, 1)
2	$(2)^2$	4	(2, 4)

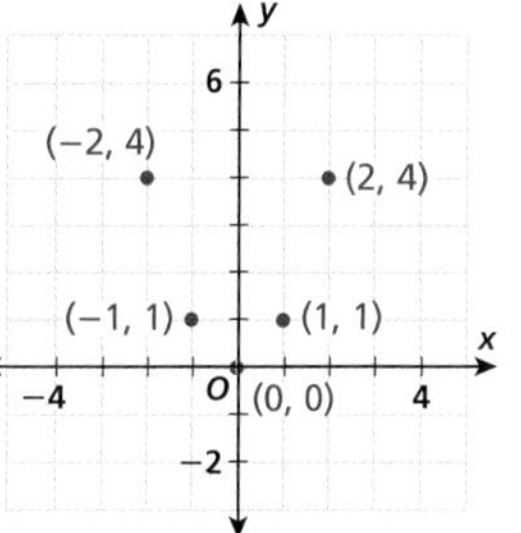

Think and Discuss

1. **Describe** how a function works like a machine.
2. **Give an example** of a rule that takes an input value of 4 and produces an output value of 10.

Additional Examples

Example 1

Find the output for each input.

$y = 8x + 5$

Input	Rule	Output
x	$8x + 5$	y
−4	8(−4) + 5	−27
−2	8(−2) + 5	−11
1	8(1) + 5	13

Example 2

Make a function table, and graph the resulting ordered pairs.

$y = 3x - 4$

Input	Rule	Ordered Pair
x	$3x - 4$	(x, y)
−2	3(−2) − 4	(−2, −10)
−1	3(−1) − 4	(−1, −7)
0	3(0) − 4	(0, −4)
1	3(1) − 4	(1, −1)
2	3(2) − 4	(2, 2)

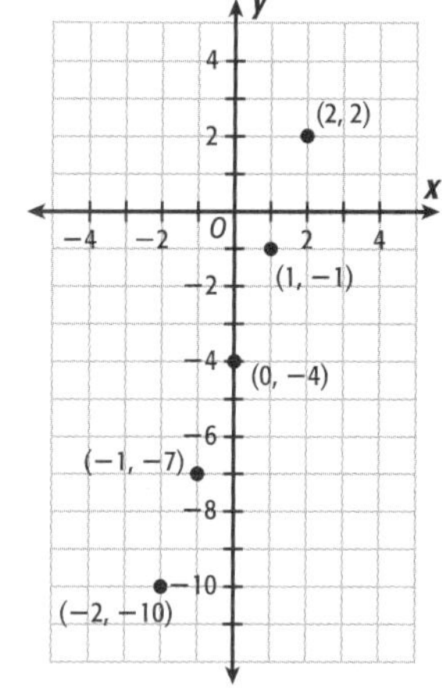

3 Close

Reaching All Learners

Through Home Connection

Have students discuss how and why some common household bills vary from month to month or season to season. For example, heating use may increase in the winter, and water consumption may increase in the summer. How are these changes reflected in the bills? Let students share observations and generalizations with the class. For example, the heating bill is a function of the temperature, and the water bill is a function of the time of year—more water is used during the growing season.

Summarize

Have students find the output of $y = x^2 + 1$ for each of the following inputs: $x = -2$, $x = -1$, $x = 0$, $x = 1$, and $x = 2$.

5, 2, 1, 2, 5

Answers to Think and Discuss

1. Possible answer: A machine always performs the same task. When you input a value in a function, the same thing is always done to yield an output.
2. Possible answer: $y = 2x + 2$

12-1 PRACTICE & ASSESS

Students may want to refer back to the lesson examples.

Assignment Guide

If you finished Example 1 assign:
Core 1–3, 6–8, 18–24
Enriched 1–3, 6–8, 18–24

If you finished Example 2 assign:
Core 1–11, 13, 18–24
Enriched 1–9 odd, 11–24

Answers

1.

Input	Rule	Output
x	$2x + 1$	y
−3	2(−3) + 1	−5
0	2(0) + 1	1
1	2(1) + 1	3

2.

Input	Rule	Output
x	$-x + 3$	y
−2	−(−2) + 3	5
0	−(0) + 3	3
2	−(2) + 3	1

4.–5, 7–10. See p. A4.

12-1 Exercises

FOR EXTRA PRACTICE
see page 680

internet connect
Homework Help Online
go.hrw.com Keyword: MS4 12-1

GUIDED PRACTICE

See Example 1 Find the output for each input.

1. $y = 2x + 1$

Input	Rule	Output
x	$2x + 1$	y
−3		
0		
1		

2. $y = -x + 3$

Input	Rule	Output
x	$-x + 3$	y
−2		
0		
2		

3. $y = 2x^2$

Input	Rule	Output
x	$2x^2$	y
−5	$2(-5)^2$	50
1	$2(1)^2$	2
3	$2(3)^2$	18

See Example 2 Make a function table, and graph the resulting ordered pairs.

4. $y = 3x - 2$

Input	Rule	Output	Ordered Pair
x	$3x - 2$	y	(x, y)
−1			
0			
1			
2			

5. $y = x^2 + 2$

Input	Rule	Output	Ordered Pair
x	$x^2 + 2$	y	(x, y)
−1			
0			
1			
2			

INDEPENDENT PRACTICE

See Example 1 Find the output for each input.

6. $y = -2x$

Input	Rule	Output
x	$-2x$	y
−2	−2(−2)	4
0	−2(0)	0
4	−2(4)	−8

7. $y = 3x + 2$

Input	Rule	Output
x	$3x + 2$	y
−3		
−1		
2		

8. $y = 3x^2$

Input	Rule	Output
x	$3x^2$	y
−10		
−6		
−2		

See Example 2 Make a function table, and graph the resulting ordered pairs.

9. $y = x \div 2$

Input	Rule	Output	Ordered Pair
x	$x \div 2$	y	(x, y)
−1			
0			
1			
2			

10. $y = x^2 - 4$

Input	Rule	Output	Ordered Pair
x	$x^2 - 4$	y	(x, y)
−1			
0			
1			
2			

Math Background

The *domain* of a function is the set of all possible values for which the function is defined. The values obtained by applying a function to members of the domain are called *images.*

Function notation is often used to denote functions. It allows you to record both the value from the domain (the input) and its image (the output). In function notation, if x represents a member of the domain, then $f(x)$ represents the image of x. In the following notation, $f(x)$ represents the output: $y = f(x)$.

RETEACH 12-1

LESSON 12-1 **Reteach**
Introduction to Functions

A **function** is a relationship in which the value of one quantity depends on the value of another quantity. A function can be represented by a rule or an equation. An *input/output table* can help you find the ordered pair values for a function.

Complete the missing values in the table.

	Input	Rule	Output	Ordered Pair
	x	$3x + 2$	y	(x, y)
1.	−2	3(−2) + 2 = −6 + 2	−4	(−2, −4)
2.	−1	3(−1) + 2 = −3 + 2	−1	(−1, −1)
3.	0	3(0) + 2 = 0 + 2	2	(0, 2)
4.	1	3(1) + 2 = 3 + 2	5	(1, 5)

You can graph the resulting ordered pairs from the input/output table.

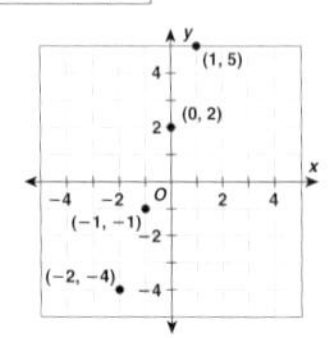

Find the output for each input value, and graph the resulting ordered pairs.

5. $y = 2x - 1$

Input	Rule	Output	Ordered Pair
x	$2x - 1$	y	(x, y)
−2	2(−2) − 1	−5	(−2, −5)
−1	2(−1) − 1	−3	(−1, −3)
0	2(0) − 1	−1	(0, −1)
1	2(1) − 1	1	(1, 1)
2	2(2) − 1	3	(2, 3)

PRACTICE 12-1

LESSON 12-1 **Practice B**
Introduction to Functions

Find the output for each input value.

1. $y = 5x - 1$

Input	Rule	Output
x	$5x - 1$	y
−2	5(−2) − 1	−11
0	5(0) − 1	−1
3	5(3) − 1	14
6	5(6) − 1	29

2. $y = -2x^2$

Input	Rule	Output
x	$-2x^2$	y
−2	$-2(-2)^2$	−8
2	$-2(2)^2$	−8
3	$-2(3)^2$	−18
4	$-2(4)^2$	−32

Make an input/output table, and graph the resulting ordered pairs.

3. $y = x \div 4$

Input	Rule	Output	Ordered Pair
x	$x \div 4$	y	(x, y)
−4	−4 ÷ 4	−1	(−4, −1)
0	0 ÷ 4	0	(0, 0)
2	2 ÷ 4	$\frac{1}{2}$	$(2, \frac{1}{2})$
4	4 ÷ 4	1	(4, 1)

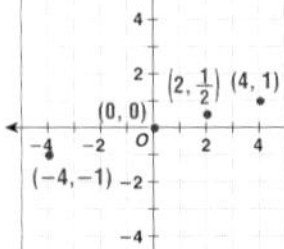

4. $y = x^2 - 5$

Input	Rule	Output	Ordered Pair
x	$x^2 - 5$	y	(x, y)
−2	$(-2)^2 - 5$	−1	(−2, −1)
−1	$(-1)^2 - 5$	−4	(−1, −4)
0	$(0)^2 - 5$	−5	(0, −5)
1	$(1)^2 - 5$	−4	(1, −4)

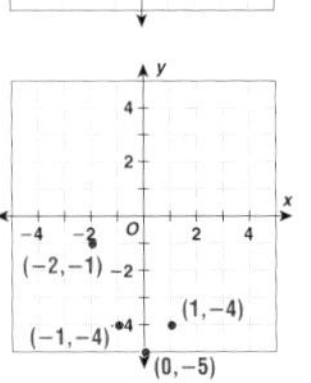

PRACTICE AND PROBLEM SOLVING

11. ***PHYSICAL SCIENCE*** The equation $F = \frac{9}{5}C + 32$ gives the Fahrenheit temperature F for a given Celsius temperature C. Make a function table for the values $C = -20°, -5°, 0°, 20°$, and $100°$.

12. ***HEALTH*** You burn about 3 calories a minute paddling a canoe. The equation $y = 3x$, where y is the number of calories burned and x is the number of minutes, describes your calorie use. Make a function table using the values $x = 1, 2, 3, 4$, and 5. Then graph the ordered pairs.

13. ***CONSUMER MATH*** Sharlyn pays $15 annually for a pool membership and $2 each time she swims. The equation $y = 2x + 15$ gives her cost y to swim x times per year. Make a function table using $x = 0, 1, 5$, and 10. Then graph the ordered pairs.

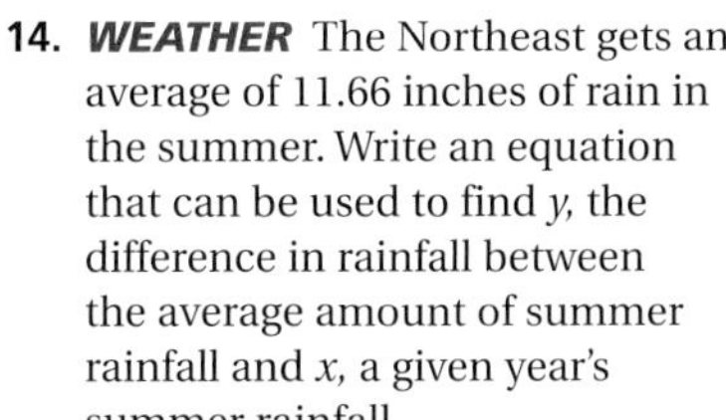

14. ***WEATHER*** The Northeast gets an average of 11.66 inches of rain in the summer. Write an equation that can be used to find y, the difference in rainfall between the average amount of summer rainfall and x, a given year's summer rainfall.

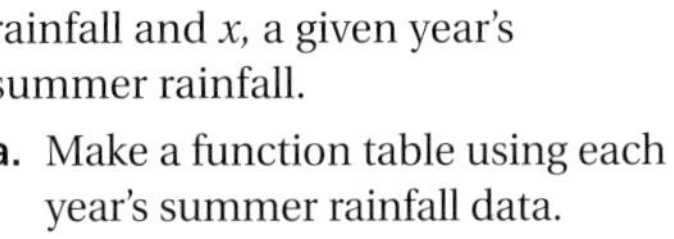

a. Make a function table using each year's summer rainfall data.

b. What do the values of y in the table tell you?

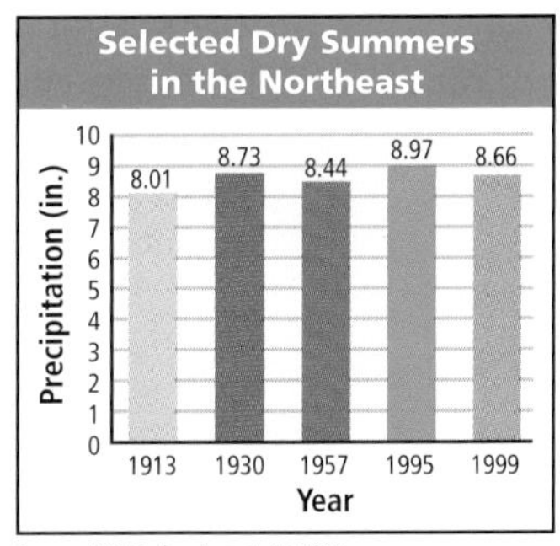

Source: USA Today, August 17, 2001

Weather LINK

Most of Jordan is desert, but parts of the country have a rainy season. The heavy rains in Jordan flooded the steps where this photo was taken.

go.hrw.com
KEYWORD: MS4 Weather

CNN Student News

15. ***WHAT'S THE ERROR?*** What is the error in the function table at right?

x	$y = x^3$	y
−2	$y = (-2)^3$	8
−1	$y = (-1)^3$	1
0	$y = 0^3$	0
1	$y = 1^3$	1

16. ***WRITE ABOUT IT*** Explain how to make a function table for $y = 2x + 11$. **Possible answer: Substitute each value for x into the expression $2x + 11$.**

17. ***CHALLENGE*** Mountain Rental charges a $25 deposit plus $10 per hour to rent a bicycle. Write an equation that gives the cost y to rent a bike for x hours, and then write the ordered pairs for $x = \frac{1}{2}$, 5, and $8\frac{1}{2}$.
$y = 10x + 25$; $\left(\frac{1}{2}, 30\right)$, $(5, 75)$, $\left(8\frac{1}{2}, 110\right)$

Spiral Review

Find each probability if you roll a number cube labeled 1–6. (Lesson 10-4)

18. $P(1)$ **$\frac{1}{6}$**
19. $P(2 \text{ or } 3)$ **$\frac{1}{3}$**
20. $P(\text{even number})$ **$\frac{1}{2}$**

Solve each equation. (Lesson 11-1)

21. $3x + 5 = 14$ **$x = 3$**
22. $\frac{y}{2} - 7 = 5$ **$y = 24$**
23. $5x - 3x = 11$ **$x = 5.5$**

24. **TEST PREP** Which of the following is the solution to $4x + 3 < 11$? (Lesson 11-7) **C**

A $x > 3.5$ B $x > -3.5$ C $x < 2$ D $x > -2$

COMMON ERROR ALERT

In Exercise 2, students might disregard the negative sign before the coefficient of x. Remind students to keep in mind as they find each output that $-x = -1(x)$.

Answers

11–15. See p. A4.

Journal

Ask students to write about a real-world situation that could be modeled by a mathematical function. For students who have difficulty thinking up a situation, you may wish to suggest that they consider situations involving money.

Test Prep Doctor

In Exercise 24, students who are unable to identify the correct answer, **C**, may need to review how to solve both two-step equations and two-step inequalities.

Lesson Quiz

1. Find the output for each input value.

Input	Rule	Output
x	$4x - 1$	y
−2		**−9**
0		**−1**
4		**15**

2. Make a function table with three input values for $y = x^2 - 1$, and graph the resulting ordered pairs.

Possible answer:

x	y
−2	3
0	−1
2	3

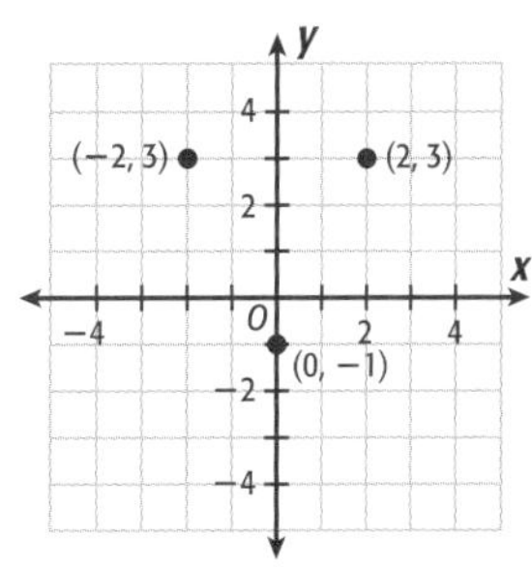

Available on Daily Transparency in CRB

CHALLENGE 12-1

LESSON 12-1 **Challenge**
Function Notation

You can use the equation of a function to find values for y that satisfy the equation for any value of x.

For example, if $y = 3x + 1$, then for input $x = 2$, the output is $y = 7$.

Function notation allows you to keep track of both input and output. In function notation, the variable y is written as $f(x)$. This reminds you that the value of the function, $f(x)$, depends on the value of x.

Suppose $f(x) = 3x + 1$.

To find $f(2)$, substitute 2 for x in the equation.

$f(2) = 3(2) + 1$
$f(2) = 7$

Find $g(-3)$ if $g(x) = x^2 + 1$
$g(-3) = (-3)^2 + 1 = 9 + 1$
$g(-3) = 10$

Find $h(7)$ if $h(x) = (x - 5)^2$
$h(7) = (7 - 5)^2 = (2)^2$
$h(7) = 4$

Evaluate using function notation.

1. Let $f(x) = 3x + 1$. Find $f(0)$, $f(-1)$, and $f(1)$.
$f(0) = 1$, $f(-1) = -2$, $f(1) = 4$
2. Let $g(x) = x^2 + 1$. Find $g(0)$, $g(1)$, and $g(5)$.
$g(0) = 1$, $g(1) = 2$, $g(5) = 26$
3. Let $f(x) = (x - 5)^2$. Find $f(0)$, $f(1)$, and $f(-1)$.
$f(0) = 25$, $f(1) = 16$, $f(-1) = 36$
4. Let $h(x) = 2x^2$. Find $h(0)$, $h(-1)$, and $h(2)$.
$h(0) = 0$, $h(-1) = 2$, $h(2) = 8$
5. Let $f(x) = 8x - 11$. Find $f(0)$, $f(-3)$, and $f(5)$.
$f(0) = -11$, $f(-3) = -35$, $f(5) = 29$
6. Let $g(x) = x^2 - 1$. Find $g(0)$, $g(1)$, and $g(-4)$.
$g(0) = -1$, $g(1) = 0$, $g(-4) = 15$
7. Let $h(x) = (x + 1)^2$. Find $h(0)$, $h(1)$, and $h(-1)$.
$h(0) = 1$, $h(1) = 4$, $h(-1) = 0$

PROBLEM SOLVING 12-1

LESSON 12-1 **Problem Solving**
Introduction to Functions

Write the correct answer.

1. Film passes through a projector at the rate of 24 frames per second. The equation $y = 24x$ describes the number of frames, y, that have passed over any number of seconds, x. Complete the input/output table.

Input	Rule	Output
x	$24x$	y
2	**24 • 2**	48
3	**24 • 3**	72
4	**24 • 4**	96
5	**24 • 5**	120
6	**24 • 6**	144

2. Anne pays $40 a month for cable TV, plus $4 for each movie she watches on pay-per-view channels. Complete the input/output table, where x is the number of pay-per-view movies she watches each month and y is her monthly cable bill.

Input	Rule	Output
x	**$4x + 40$**	y
3	**4(3) + 40**	52
5	**4(5) + 40**	60
7	**4(7) + 40**	68
9	**4(9) + 40**	76
11	**4(11) + 40**	84

Choose the letter of the best answer.

Madeline has a discount coupon for $5 off her next purchase of tennis balls. Tennis balls are on sale for $3 per can. The equation $y = 3x - 5$ gives her final cost, y, to purchase x cans of tennis balls.

3. If $x = 3$, what is the value of y?
A 15 C 9
B 14 (D) 4

4. If $x = 5$, what is the value of y?
F 25 (H) 10
G 15 J 5

5. If $x = 10$, what is the value of y?
(A) 25 C 35
B 30 D 50

6. If $x = 4$, what is the value of y?
F 5 H 12
(G) 7 J 17

7. If $x = 9$, what is the ordered pair (x, y)?
A (5, 9) (C) (9, 22)
B (9, 5) D (9, 10)

8. If $x = 6$, what is the ordered pair (x, y)?
F (6, 18) H (12, 31)
G (6, 30) (J) (6, 13)

12-2 Organizer

Pacing: Traditional 1 day
Block $\frac{1}{2}$ day

Objective: Students find patterns to complete sequences using function tables.

Warm Up

Find the output for each input value.

Input	Rule	Output
x	$-3x+2$	y
-4		14
0		2
4		-10

Problem of the Day

Function Rule A: Square the input. Divide by 2. Subtract 3.

Function Rule B: Square the input. Subtract 6. Divide by 2.

If the input value for each rule is 222, what is the difference of the two output values? Why? 0; they are equivalent rules.

Available on Daily Transparency in CRB

12-2 Find a Pattern in Sequences

Problem Solving Skill

Learn to find patterns to complete sequences using function tables.

Vocabulary
sequence

A **sequence** is an ordered list of numbers. One of the most well-known sequences is the Fibonacci sequence. In this sequence, each term after the second term is the sum of the two terms before it.

$$1, 1, 2, 3, 5, 8, 13, \ldots$$

When the list follows a pattern, the numbers in the sequence are the output values of a function, and the value of each number depends on the number's place in the list.

Many natural things, such as the arrangement of seeds in the head of a sunflower, follow the pattern of the Fibonacci sequence.

You can use a variable to represent a number's place in a sequence.

n (place in list):	1	2	3	4
	↓ 1st number ↓	↓ 2nd number ↓	↓ 3rd number ↓	↓ 4th number ↓
Number in sequence:	2	4	6	8

You can use a function table to help identify the pattern in a sequence.

EXAMPLE 1 Identifying Functions in Sequences

Find a function that describes each sequence. Use y for the term in the sequence and n for its place in the list. Then use the function to find the next three terms in the sequence.

A 2, 4, 6, 8, . . .

n	Rule	y
1	$1 \cdot 2$	2
2	$2 \cdot 2$	4
3	$3 \cdot 2$	6
4	$4 \cdot 2$	8

Multiply n by 2.

$y = 2n$ *Write the function.*
$y = 2(5) = 10$ *Substitute for n*
$y = 2(6) = 12$ *to find the next*
$y = 2(7) = 14$ *three terms.*

B 4, 5, 6, 7, . . .

n	Rule	y
1	$1+3$	4
2	$2+3$	5
3	$3+3$	6
4	$4+3$	7

Add 3 to n.

$y = n + 3$ *Write the function.*
$y = 5 + 3 = 8$ *Substitute for n*
$y = 6 + 3 = 9$ *to find the next*
$y = 7 + 3 = 10$ *three terms.*

1 Introduce

Alternate Opener

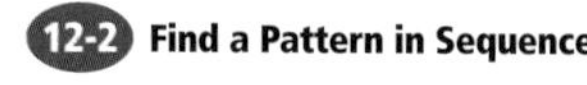

EXPLORATION

12-2 Find a Pattern in Sequences

Find the next three terms in each sequence.

	Term 1	Term 2	Term 3	Term 4	Term 5	Term 6
1.	1	4	9	___	___	___
2.	4	8	12	___	___	___
3.	7	11	15	___	___	___
4.	3	6	9	___	___	___

Find the first three terms in each sequence.

	Term 1	Term 2	Term 3	Term 4	Term 5	Term 6
5.	___	___	___	20	25	30
6.	___	___	___	20	10	5

Think and Discuss

7. **Discuss** how the first three terms in numbers 1–4 are used to find the next three terms.
8. **Explain** how the last three terms in numbers 5 and 6 are used to find the first three terms.

Motivate

Discuss patterns with which students are familiar, such as skip counting. Ask students to describe what they think of when they hear the word *patterns.* Have them explain what they think a pattern is and the purpose of a pattern. Compare and contrast different suggested patterns by having students find similarities and differences between the patterns. Patterns may include number patterns and geometric patterns.

Exploration worksheet and answers on Chapter 12 Resource Book pp. 17 and 90

2 Teach

Lesson Presentation

Guided Instruction

In this lesson, students learn to find patterns to complete sequences using function tables. Explain that a sequence of numbers may be finite or infinite. The Fibonacci sequence is an infinite sequence.

Stress that the variable n represents a number's place in the list of terms of a sequence. Because of this convention, it is easy to find any term of interest in a sequence without listing all of the preceding terms.

Teaching Tip Encourage students to compare pairs of terms to come up with a rule to describe a sequence.

EXAMPLE 2 PROBLEM SOLVING APPLICATION

Kevin has \$20.00. Every day, he spends \$1.80 on bus fare. Write a sequence to show how much money Kevin will have left after 1, 2, 3, and 4 days.

1 Understand the Problem

List the **important information:**

- Kevin has \$20.00.
- He spends \$1.80 each day.

The **answer** will be the amount of money he has left after 1, 2, 3, and 4 days.

2 Make a Plan

You can find a pattern, then write a rule that can be used to find a sequence.

After the first day, Kevin will have \$20.00 − \$1.80.

After the second day, Kevin will have \$20.00 − 2 · \$1.80.

The rule \$20.00 − n · \$1.80 can be used to find the terms in the sequence.

3 Solve

n	Rule	y
1	20 − 1 · 1.80	18.20
2	20 − 2 · 1.80	16.40
3	20 − 3 · 1.80	14.60
4	20 − 4 · 1.80	12.80

After 1, 2, 3, and 4 days, Kevin will have \$18.20, \$16.40, \$14.60, and \$12.80 left, respectively.

4 Look Back

If Kevin spends about \$2 per day, he will have about \$18, \$16, \$14, and \$12 left after each of the 4 days, respectively. The answer is reasonable.

Think and Discuss

1. **Give an example** of a sequence involving addition, and give the rule you used.
2. **Describe** how to find a pattern in the sequence 1, 4, 16, 64, ...

COMMON ERROR ALERT

In sequences that do not start with 1 as the initial term, such as in Example 1B, students might forget that n needs to be 1 in order for them to write the rule and determine the first term.

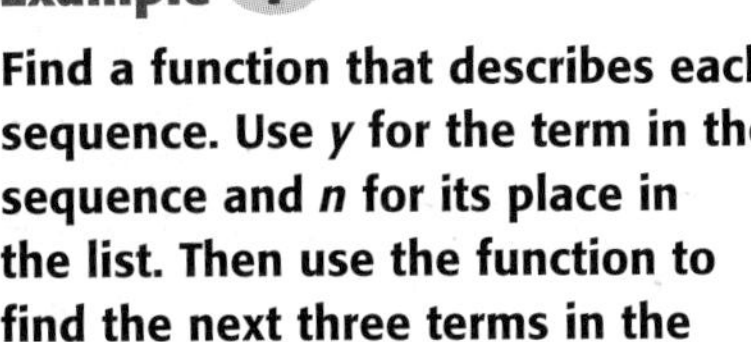

Additional Examples

Example 1

Find a function that describes each sequence. Use y for the term in the sequence and n for its place in the list. Then use the function to find the next three terms in the sequence.

A. 4, 8, 12, 16 $y = 4n$; **20, 24, 28**

B. −4, −3, −2, −1 $y = n - 5$; **0, 1, 2**

Example 2

Holli earned \$3.50 a day pet sitting for her neighbor's fish. Holli pet sat for 5 days. Her neighbor also paid her \$8 for picking up the mail each day. Write a sequence showing how much money Holli earned after 1, 2, 3, 4, and 5 days.

\$11.50, \$15.00, \$18.50, \$22.00, \$25.50

3 Close

Reaching All Learners

Through Number Sense

Let students work in pairs to investigate sequences similar to the Fibonacci sequence. Tell students to generate their own sequences of numbers by starting with two whole numbers that are not both 1 (e.g., 2, 2, 4, 6, ... or 3, 2, 5, 7, ...). Then have students investigate ratios $\left(\frac{\text{greater term}}{\text{lesser term}}\right)$ of consecutive terms in their sequences. Students may be surprised to find that the ratio of the terms will get closer and closer to the golden mean, or ratio, which is about 1.618.

Summarize

Ask students to find a function that describes each of the following sequences: 3, 6, 9, ... $y = 3n$ and 10, 11, 12, ... $y = n + 9$ What is the next term in each sequence? 12; 13

Answers to Think and Discuss

1. Possible answer: 6, 7, 8, 9, ...; $y = n + 5$
2. Possible answer: Compare how pairs of terms change. One possible rule is to multiply each term by 4 to find the next term.

12-2 PRACTICE & ASSESS

Students may want to refer back to the lesson examples.

Assignment Guide

If you finished Example 1 assign:
Core 1–4, 6–13, 17–27 odd, 32–34
Enriched 1, 3, 7–13 odd, 16–27, 32–34

If you finished Example 2 assign:
Core 1–15, 17–29 odd, 32–34
Enriched 1–15 odd, 16–34

16. multiply 35 by n; 175, 210, 245
17. subtract 0.3 from n; 4.7, 5.7, 6.7
18. add $\frac{1}{2}$ to n; $\frac{11}{2}$, $\frac{13}{2}$, $\frac{15}{2}$
19. subtract 2 from n; 3, 4, 5
20. divide n by 3; $\frac{5}{3}$, 2, $\frac{7}{3}$
21. multiply n by 5 and add 1; 26, 31, 36
28. Friday; 2 hours 40 minutes

12-2 Exercises

FOR EXTRA PRACTICE see page 680

GUIDED PRACTICE

See Example 1

Find a function that describes each sequence. Use y for the term in the sequence and n for its place in the list. Then use the function to find the next three terms in the sequence. **$y = n - 1$; 4, 5, 6**

1. 3, 6, 9, 12, . . . **$y = 3n$; 15, 18, 21**
2. 3, 4, 5, 6, . . . **$y = n + 2$; 7, 8, 9**
3. 0, 1, 2, 3, . . .
4. 5, 10, 15, 20, . . . **$y = 5n$; 25, 30, 35**

See Example 2

5. Sara ran 20 miles last week. This week, she ran 3 miles each day for five days. Write a sequence to show the total distance, including the first 20 miles, that Sara had run after each of the last 5 days. **23 mi, 26 mi, 29 mi, 32 mi, 35 mi**

INDEPENDENT PRACTICE

See Example 1

Find a function that describes each sequence. Use y for the term in the sequence and n for its place in the list. Then use the function to find the next three terms in the sequence.

6. 1.5, 2.5, 3.5, 4.5, . . . **$y = n + 0.5$; 5.5, 6.5, 7.5**
7. $\frac{1}{2}, 1, \frac{3}{2}, 2, \ldots$ **$y = \frac{n}{2}$; $\frac{5}{2}$, 3, $\frac{7}{2}$**
8. 7, 14, 21, 28, . . . **$y = 7n$; 35, 42, 49**
9. −2, −1, 0, 1, . . . **$y = n - 3$; 2, 3, 4**
10. 20, 40, 60, 80, . . . **$y = 20n$; 100, 120, 140**
11. 3, 5, 7, 9, . . . **$y = 2n + 1$; 11, 13, 15**
12. 5, 6, 7, 8, . . . **$y = n + 4$; 9, 10, 11**
13. 1, 4, 9, 16, . . . **$y = n^2$; 25, 36, 49**

See Example 2

14. Macy purchased a box of cereal that contained 567 grams of cereal. Each day, he ate 52 grams for breakfast. Write a sequence to show how much cereal he had left after each of the 4 days. **515g, 463g, 411g, 359g**
15. Shaundra opened a savings account with $50.00. Every week, she added $2.50. Write a sequence to show how much money she had in her account after 1, 2, 3, 4, 5, and 6 weeks. **$52.50, $55.00, $57.50, $60.00, $62.50, $65.00**

PRACTICE AND PROBLEM SOLVING

Write the rule for each sequence in words. Then find the next three terms.

16. 35, 70, 105, 140, . . .
17. 0.7, 1.7, 2.7, 3.7, . . .
18. $\frac{3}{2}, \frac{5}{2}, \frac{7}{2}, \frac{9}{2}, \ldots$
19. −1, 0, 1, 2, . . .
20. $\frac{1}{3}, \frac{2}{3}, 1, \frac{4}{3}, \ldots$
21. 6, 11, 16, 21, . . .

Find a function that describes each sequence. Use the function to find the tenth term in the sequence.

22. 0.5, 1.5, 2.5, 3.5, . . . **$y = n - 0.5$; 9.5**
23. 0, 2, 4, 6, . . . **$y = 2n - 2$; 18**
24. 5, 8, 11, 14, . . . **$y = 3n + 2$; 32**
25. 3, 8, 13, 18, . . . **$y = 5n - 2$; 48**
26. 1, 3, 5, 7, . . . **$y = 2n - 1$; 19**
27. 6, 10, 14, 18, . . . **$y = 4n + 2$; 42**
28. Dominique ran 40 minutes on Saturday, 1 hour 20 minutes on Monday, and 2 hours on Wednesday. Use the sequence to predict the next day that Dominique ran and how long he ran on that day.

Math Background

The ratios of consecutive terms in the Fibonacci sequence approach the golden ratio. The golden ratio, φ (*phi*), is $\varphi = \frac{1 + \sqrt{5}}{2} \approx 1.618$.

The first seven ratios of consecutive terms in the Fibonacci sequence are as follows:

$\frac{1}{1} = 1$; $\frac{2}{1} = 2$; $\frac{3}{2} = 1.5$; $\frac{5}{3} = 1.\overline{6}$; $\frac{8}{5} = 1.6$; $\frac{13}{8} = 1.625$; $\frac{21}{13} = 1.61538$

RETEACH 12-2

LESSON 12-2 **Reteach**
Find a Pattern in Sequences

Making a table is helpful for finding a function rule for a sequence of numbers.

Complete the tables for each sequence.

1. 4, 8, 12, 16

Term n	1	2	3	4	5	6	7
Value y	4	8	12	16	**20**	**24**	**28**

Rule: Add **4** to each term to find the value of the next term.

Notice that the value of each term is 4 times the term number.

Term n	1	2	3	4	5	6	7
Rule	4 • 1	4 • 2	4 • 3	4 • 4	**4 • 5**	**4 • 6**	**4 • 7**
Value y	4	8	12	16	20	24	28

Write a function to describe this sequence.

Multiply the term number by **4**, or $y =$ **4** n.

2. 6, 7, 8, 9

Term n	1	2	3	4	5	6	7
Value y	6	7	8	9	**10**	**11**	**12**

Rule: Add **5** to each term to find the value of the next term.

Notice that the value of each term is 5 more than the term number.

Term n	1	2	3	4	5	6	7
Rule	1 + 5	2 + 5	3 + 5	4 + 5	**5 + 5**	**6 + 5**	**7 + 5**
Value y	6	7	8	9	**10**	**11**	**12**

Write a function to describe this sequence.

Add **5** to the term number, or $y = n +$ **5**

Find a function that describes each sequence. Use the function to find the next three terms in the sequence.

3. 6, 12, 18, 24
$y = 6n$; 30, 36, 42
4. 8, 7, 6, 5
$y = 9 - n$; 4, 3, 2

PRACTICE 12-2

LESSON 12-2 **Practice B**
Find a Pattern in Sequences

Find a function that describes each sequence. Use the function to find the next three terms in the sequence.

1. 6, 12, 18, 24
$y = 6x$
30, 36, 42
2. 0.2, 1.2, 2.2, 3.2
$y = x - 0.8$
4.2, 5.2, 6.2
3. 2, 6, 10, 14
$y = 4x - 2$
18, 22, 26
4. −5, 0, 5, 10
$y = 5x - 10$
15, 20, 25
5. 10, 12, 14, 16
$y = 2x + 8$
18, 20, 22
6. 6, 11, 16, 21
$y = 5x + 1$
26, 31, 26
7. −1, 1, 3, 5
$y = 2x - 3$
7, 9, 11
8. 2, 5, 10, 17
$y = x^2 + 1$
26, 37, 50
9. −5, −4, −3, −2
$y = x - 6$
−1, 0, 1
10. 8, 16, 24, 32
$y = 8x$
40, 48, 56
11. 1.1, 2.1, 3.1, 4.1
$y = x + 0.1$
5.1, 6.1, 7.1
12. 0.25, 0.5, 0.75, 1
$y = x \div 4$
1.25, 1.5, 1.75
13. Mike did 25 push-ups on Monday. For each of the next 5 days, he did 4 more push-ups than the previous day. Write a sequence to find how many push-ups Mike did on Saturday of that week.
25, 29, 33, 37, 41, 45; 45 push-ups

Computer Science 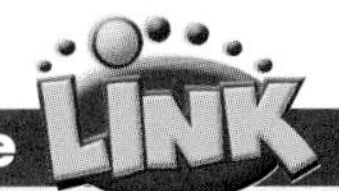

Computer programmers use functions to create beautiful designs known as *fractals.* A fractal is a *self-similar* pattern, which means that each part of the pattern is similar to the whole pattern. Fractals are created by repeating a set of steps, called *iterations.* Use this information for Exercises 29–31.

29. Below is part of a famous fractal called Cantor dust. In each iteration, part of a line segment is removed, resulting in twice as many segments as before. The table lists the number of line segments that result from the iterations shown. Find a function that describes the sequence. $y = 2^n$

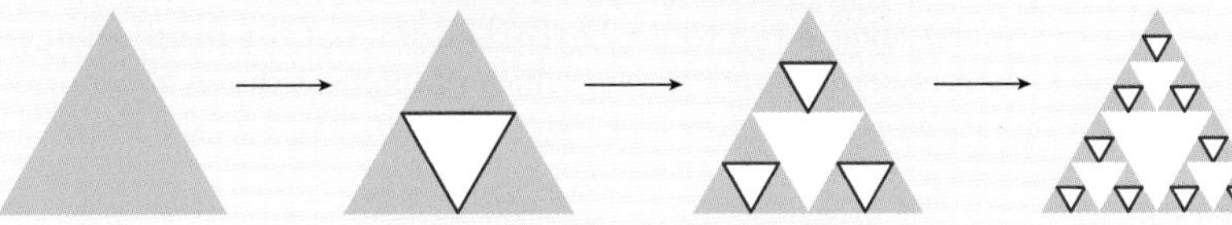

Iteration (n)	Number of Segments (y)
1	2
2	4
3	8

30. These are the first three iterations of another famous fractal called the Sierpinski triangle. In each iteration, a certain number of smaller triangles are cut out of the larger triangle in the pattern shown.

Iteration 1
1 triangle removed

Iteration 2
3 more triangles removed

Iteration 3
9 more triangles removed

Create a table to list the total number of yellow triangles that exist after each iteration. Then find a function that describes the sequence.

31. ***CHALLENGE*** Find a function that describes the number of triangles removed in each iteration of the Sierpinski triangle. $y = 3^{n-1}$

go.hrw.com
KEYWORD: MS4 Fractals
CNN Student News

Spiral Review

Determine the number of combinations. (Lesson 10-6)

32. 6 objects taken 2 at a time **15**

33. 8 objects taken 7 at a time **8**

34. TEST PREP Martin spent $26 for 4 equally priced CDs. Which equation could be used to find how much each CD cost? (Lesson 2-12) **C**

A $4 \cdot 26 = n$ B $n = 26 - 4$ C $4 \cdot n = 26$ D $n \cdot 26 = 4$

CHALLENGE 12-2

LESSON 12-2 **Challenge**
Find the Term

You can use the pattern in a sequence to write an expression for the nth term of the sequence. Then you can use this expression to find any term in the sequence.

Find the fiftieth term of the following sequence: $\frac{1}{1}, \frac{1}{2}, \frac{1}{3}, \frac{1}{4}, \ldots$

- The first term in this sequence is $\frac{1}{1}$. The numerator and the denominator of the fraction are both the same number as the location of the term in the sequence.
- The second term in this sequence is $\frac{1}{2}$. The numerator is 1, and the denominator is 2, the same number as the location of the term in the sequence.
- The third term in this sequence is $\frac{1}{3}$. The numerator is 1 and the denominator is 3, the same number as the location of the term in the sequence.

From the pattern, the nth term is $\frac{1}{n}$. So, the fiftieth term is $\frac{1}{50}$.

Solve.

1. Find the nth term and the twentieth term of the following sequence: −2, −1, 0, 1, …
   $n - 3$, 17
2. Find the nth term and the fortieth term of the following sequence: 9, 10, 11, 12, …
   $n + 8$, 48
3. Find the nth term and the fifteenth term of the following sequence: 5, 10, 15, 20, …
   $5n$, 75
4. Find the nth term and the twenty-fifth term of the following sequence: −2, −4, −6, −8, …
   $-2n$; −50
5. Find the nth term and the twentieth term of the following sequence: $\frac{1}{2}, \frac{2}{3}, \frac{3}{4}, \frac{4}{5}, \ldots$
   $\frac{n}{n+1}$, $\frac{20}{21}$
6. Find the nth term and the fiftieth term of the following sequence: $\frac{1}{2}, \frac{1}{4}, \frac{1}{6}, \frac{1}{8}, \ldots$
   $\frac{1}{2n}$, $\frac{1}{100}$

PROBLEM SOLVING 12-2

LESSON 12-2 **Problem Solving**
Find a Pattern in Sequences

Write the correct answer.

1. Rodney collects baseball cards. He started his collection with 113 cards. Every week, he bought a new pack of 20 cards. Write a sequence to show how many cards he had after 5 weeks.
   113, 133, 153, 173, 193, 213; 213 cards
2. For English class, Jen is reading a novel that is 463 pages long. Each night, she reads 40 pages. Write a sequence showing how many pages she has left to read after 4 nights.
   423, 383, 343, 303; 303 pages left
3. In 2000, the operating costs for a Boeing 747 aircraft were about $7,000 per hour. Write a sequence to show the cost to operate a Boeing 747 aircraft for flights lasting 2, 4, and 6 hours.
   $14,000, $28,000, $42,000
4. A Boeing 747 aircraft consumes about 3,257 gallons of fuel per hour. Write a sequence to show the amount of fuel the aircraft consumes in flights lasting 3, 4, and 5 hours.
   9,771, 13,028, 16,285 gal

Choose the letter of the best answer.

Use the sequence 3, 6, 9, 12 for the following exercises.

5. What is the rule for this sequence?
   A Add 3 to n.
   B Subtract 3 from n.
   (C) Multiply n by 3.
   D Divide n by 3.
6. What is the function that describes this sequence?
   (F) $y = 3n$
   G $y = \frac{n}{3}$
   H $y = n + 3$
   J $y = n - 3$
7. What are the next 3 terms in the sequence?
   A 9, 6, 3
   (B) 15, 18, 21
   C 15, 19, 24
   D 36, 432, 5,184
8. What is the ninth term in the sequence?
   F 24
   (G) 27
   H 30
   J 33

Interdisciplinary 

Computer Science

Exercises 29–31 involve relating sequences to computer-generated designs.

Answer

30.

n	Number of Yellow Triangles
1	3
2	9
3	27

$y = 3^n$

Journal 

Have students create a sequence and write a description of the sequence.

Test Prep Doctor 

In Exercise 34, if students answered **A** or **D,** they may be confusing inverse operations in multiplication and division equations. Those students should review how to state and solve equations involving multiplication and division. Students who chose **B** are confusing subtraction and division. Those students need to work on distinguishing between these two operations.

Lesson Quiz 

Find a function that describes each sequence. Use the function to find the next three terms in the sequence.

1. 6, 12, 18, 24 **$y = 6n$; 30, 36, 42**

2. −3, −2, −1, 0 **$y = n - 4$; 1, 2, 3**

3. 24, 21, 18, 15 **$y = 27 - 3n$; 12, 9, 6**

4. 7, 14, 21, 28 **$y = 7n$; 35, 42, 49**

5. Arisha bought a 5-pound bag of chocolate chips. She adds 0.5 lb of chips to each batch of cookies she makes. Find a function that describes this relationship. How many pounds of chips remain after she makes 5 batches of cookies? $y = 5 - 0.5x$; 2.5 lb remain.

Available on Daily Transparency in CRB

12-3 Organizer

Pacing: Traditional 1 day
Block $\frac{1}{2}$ day

Objective: Students relate graphs to situations.

Warm Up

Find a function that describes each sequence. Use the function to find the next two terms in the sequence.

1. 5, 10, 15, 20 — $y = 5n$; 25, 30

2. −7, −5, −3, −1 — $y = -9 + 2n$; 1, 3

3. −3, −6, −9, −12 — $y = -3n$; −15, −18

Problem of the Day

$y = |x|$

What letter is formed by the graph of this function? V

Available on Daily Transparency in CRB

Why is a spoof of a coordinate grid just like the start of a flight? It's a take-off on a plane.

12-3 Interpreting Graphs

Learn to relate graphs to situations.

Vocabulary
domain
range

You can use a graph to show the relationship between speed and time, time and distance, or speed and distance.

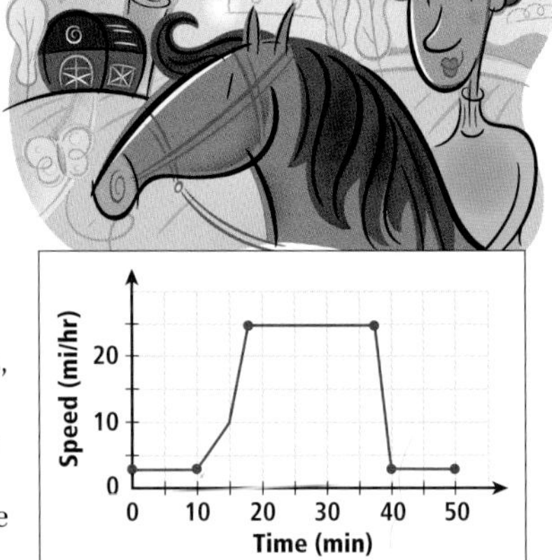

The graph at right shows the varying speeds at which Emma exercises her horse. The horse walks at a constant speed for the first 10 minutes. Its speed increases over the next 7 minutes, and then it gallops at a constant rate for 20 minutes. Then it slows down over the next 3 minutes and then walks at a constant pace for 10 minutes.

Speed (mi/hr): 0, 10, 20
Time (min): 0, 10, 20, 30, 40, 50

EXAMPLE 1 Relating Graphs to Stories

Jenny takes a trip to the beach. She stays at the beach all day before driving back home. Which graph best shows the story?

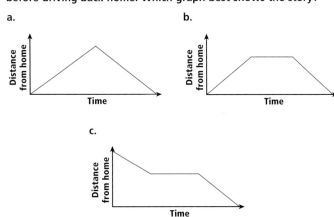

a.

Distance from home / Time

b.

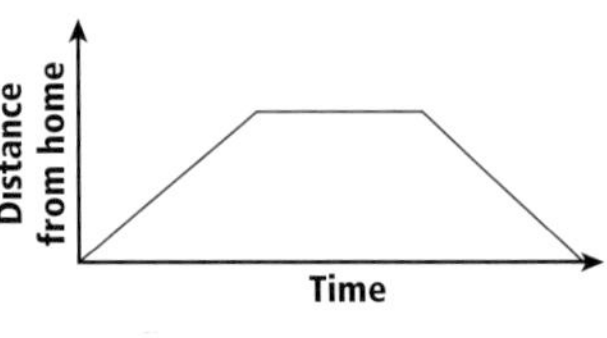

c.

Distance from home / Time

As Jenny drives to the beach, her distance from home *increases.* While she is at the beach, her distance from home is *constant.* As she returns home, her distance from home *decreases.* The answer is graph b.

1 Introduce

Alternate Opener

An inventor is testing a new motion detector that graphs the distance traveled by a person in motion. She walked in front of the motion detector to create the graph shown.

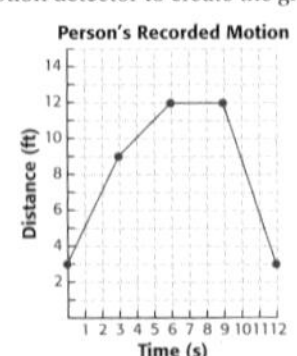

1. How many feet did the inventor walk during
   a. the first three seconds (0–3 s)?
   b. the next three seconds (3–6 s)?
   c. the next three seconds (6–9 s)?
   d. the final three seconds (9–12 s)?
2. During which interval did she walk fastest? slowest?

Think and Discuss

3. **Discuss** what it means in terms of the inventor's speed when the line is very steep.
4. **Explain** what happened between the sixth second and the ninth second.

Motivate

Have students describe some of the characteristics of different graphs they have encountered and studied this year. Encourage them to include graphs from areas of study other than math (e.g., social studies and science). Discuss why graphs are used to represent data (e.g., graphs are used to summarize a data set and to show how data change).

Exploration worksheet and answers on Chapter 12 Resource Book pp. 26 and 92

2 Teach

Lesson Presentation

Guided Instruction

In this lesson, students learn to relate graphs to situations. Tell students that a graph is a pictorial representation of a numerical relationship. A graph conveys how data change and relate to each other. Point out that the straight lines of the graphs in Examples 1–2 show that the rate of change is constant, while the curve of the graph in Example 3 shows that the rate of change is not constant.

EXAMPLE 2 Using a Graph to Tell a Story

Draw a graph for each situation.

Helpful Hint

Some graphs are curves or lines that show continuous data. Other graphs may show only points.

A Maria is selling boxes of greeting cards for $5 a box. Draw a graph to show her possible income from sales.

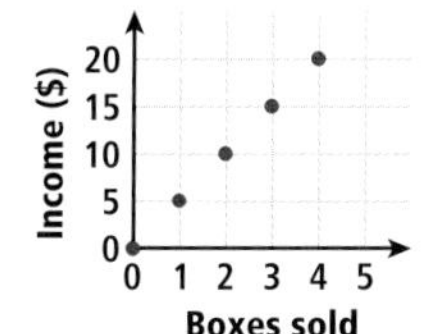

Each box is $5, so the amount of money she can make is a multiple of $5. This graph is only points.

B Pecans cost $3 per pound, and they can be sold in fractions of a pound. Draw a graph to show how much the pecans can cost.

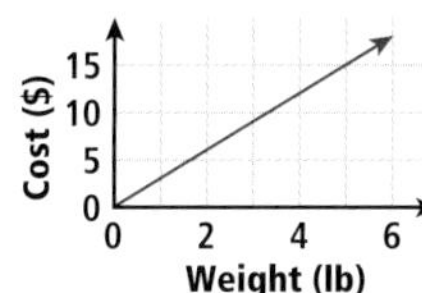

One pound costs $3, two pounds cost $6, and so on. However, you can buy any weight of pecans. This graph is continuous.

The set of input values of a function is the **domain**, and the set of resulting output values is the **range**. In the graph of boxes sold, the domain is the possible number of boxes sold, or the set of whole numbers. The range in this graph is Maria's possible income, or all nonnegative multiples of $5.

EXAMPLE 3 Finding Domain and Range

Find the domain and range of the graph.

Helpful Hint

When a graph is continuous, its domain and range contain all real numbers or those within a certain interval.

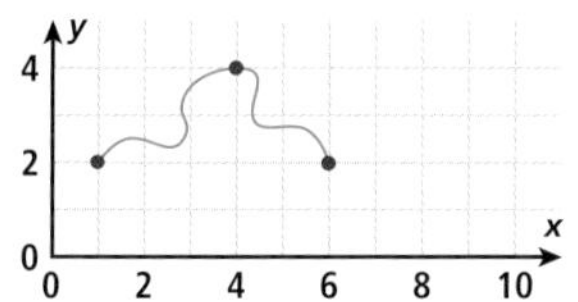

The graph goes from 1 to 6 on the x-axis and from 2 to 4 on the y-axis.

Domain: all real numbers from 1 through 6; $1 \le x \le 6$
Range: all real numbers from 2 through 4; $2 \le y \le 4$

Think and Discuss

1. **Give an example** of a situation that could be represented by a graph that shows the range increasing as the domain increases.
2. **Compare** domain and range of a function.

Additional Examples

Example 1

The height of a tree increases over time, but not at a constant rate. Which graph best shows this? b

a.

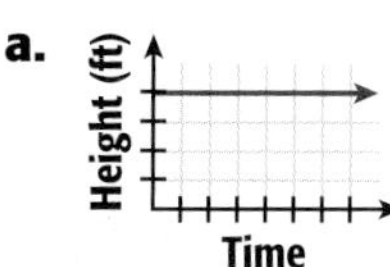

b.

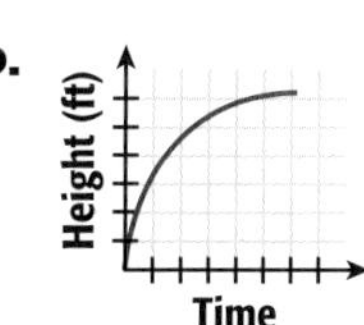

Example 2

For every packet of 10 business flyers Joel delivers, he is paid $3.00. He is not paid for delivering partial packets. Draw a graph to show how much money Joel can earn.

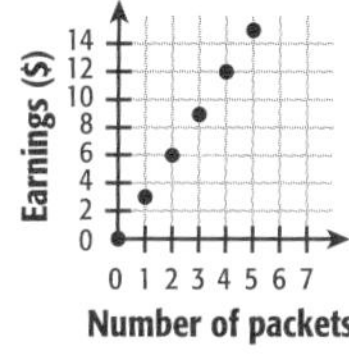

Example 3

Find the domain and range of the graph.

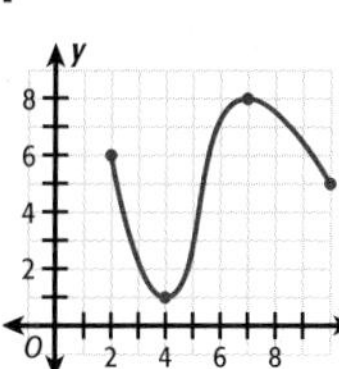

Domain: $2 \le x \le 10$
Range: $1 \le y \le 8$

3 Close

Reaching All Learners
Through Grouping Strategies

To reinforce the concepts of continuous functions and functions that show only points, have students work in small groups to analyze the data in sale advertisements. Encourage them to find examples of sale items whose graphs would be continuous for different purchase amounts, such as pounds of meat. Then ask students to find other examples of sale items whose graphs would consist of points for different purchases, such as boxes of cereal. You may also want to have students draw graphs for selected domains.

Summarize

Ask students to describe the relationship shown in the graph below.

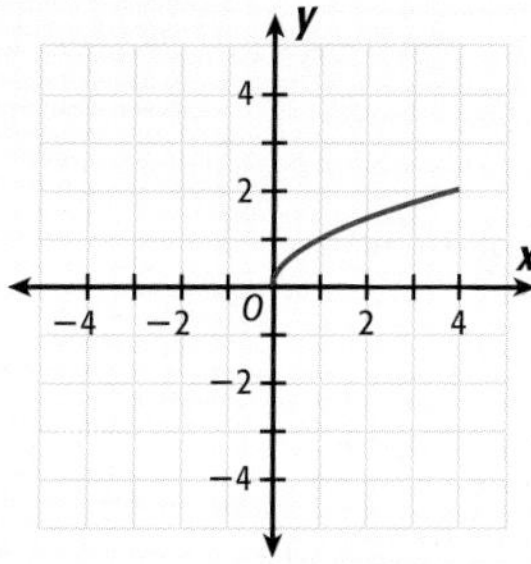

As x increases, y increases; however, the rate of increase is not constant.

Answers to Think and Discuss

1. Possible answer: the cost of purchasing CDs: the more CDs purchased, the greater the cost
2. The input values, or x-values, of a function are the domain. The output values, or y-values, of a function are the range.

12-3 PRACTICE & ASSESS

Students may want to refer back to the lesson examples.

Assignment Guide

If you finished Example 1 assign:
Core 1, 6, 11, 14, 19–25
Enriched 1, 6, 11, 14, 19–25

If you finished Example 2 assign:
Core 1, 2, 6, 7, 11–13, 14, 19–25
Enriched 1, 2, 6, 7, 11–13, 14, 19–25

If you finished Example 3 assign:
Core 1–10 odd, 11–15 odd, 19–25
Enriched 1–9 odd, 11–25

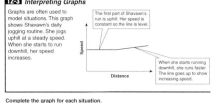

Answers

2.

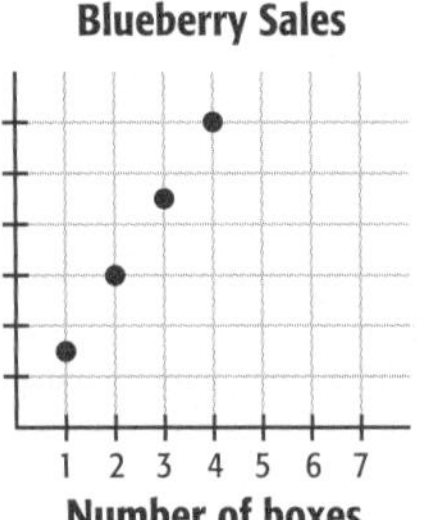

3. D: $-1 \le x \le 3$; R: $0 \le y \le 2$
4. D: $-4 \le x \le -1$; R: $-3 \le y \le -1$
5. D: $1 \le x \le 5$; R: $0 \le y \le 3$
8. D: $1 \le x \le 6$; R: $-3.5 < y \le -1$
9. D: $-4 \le x \le 1$; R: $-1 \le y \le 1$
7 and 10. See pp. A4–A5.

Math Background

A function is said to be *increasing* if its graph rises steadily from left to right. For every increasing function, when $a < b$, $f(a) < f(b)$. For example, $y = x$ and $y = x^3$ are both increasing functions.

A function is said to be *decreasing* if its graph falls steadily from left to right. For every decreasing function, when $a > b$, $f(a) < f(b)$. For example, $y = -x$ and $y = -x^3$ are both decreasing functions.

The graph of a *constant* function, such as $y = a$ or $f(x) = a$, where a is a real number, is a horizontal line. Such functions are said to be neither increasing nor decreasing.

12-3 Exercises

FOR EXTRA PRACTICE see page 680

internet connect
Homework Help Online
go.hrw.com Keyword: MS4 12-3

GUIDED PRACTICE

See Example 1

1. The temperature of an ice cube increases until it starts to melt. While it melts, its temperature stays constant. Which graph best shows the story? **a**

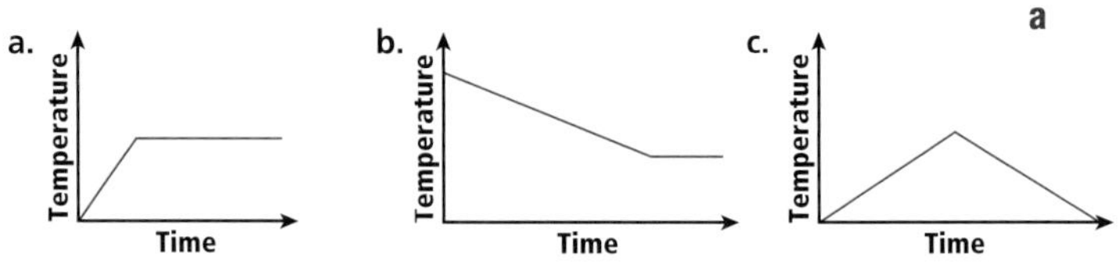

a. Temperature / Time

b.

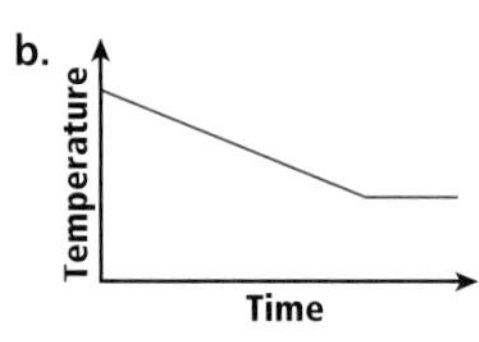

c.

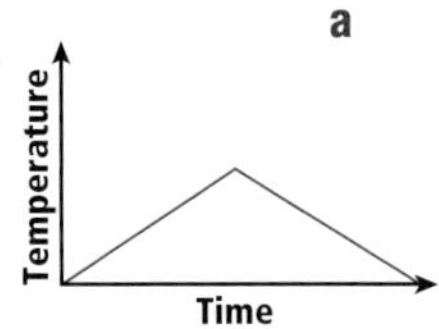

See Example 2

2. Kim sells blueberries for $3 a box. Draw a graph to show how much he can make.

See Example 3

Find the domain and range of each graph.

3.

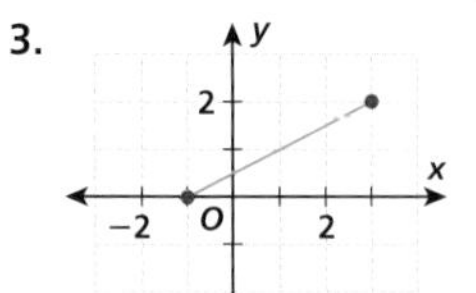

4.

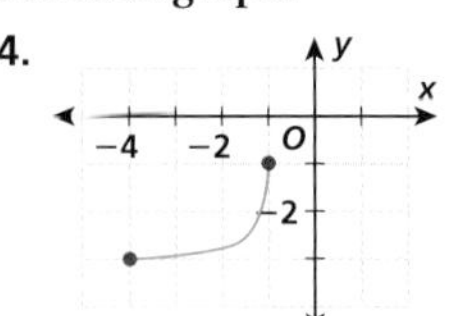

5.

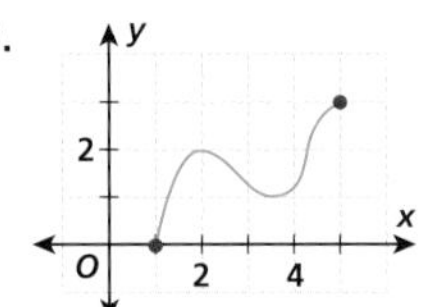

INDEPENDENT PRACTICE

See Example 1

6. The ink in a printer is used until the ink cartridge is empty. The cartridge is refilled, and the ink is used up again. Which graph best shows the story? **b**

a. b.

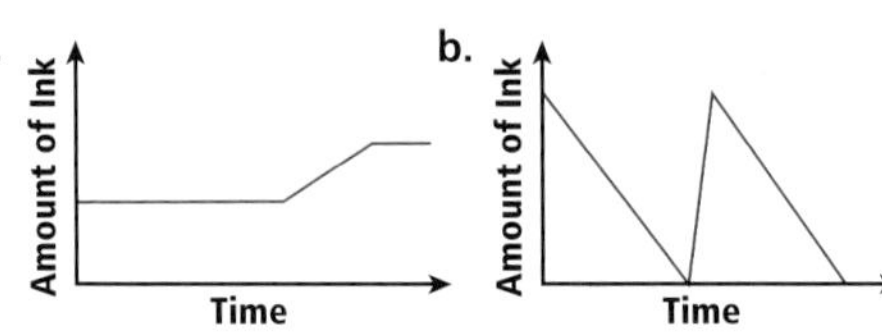

c.

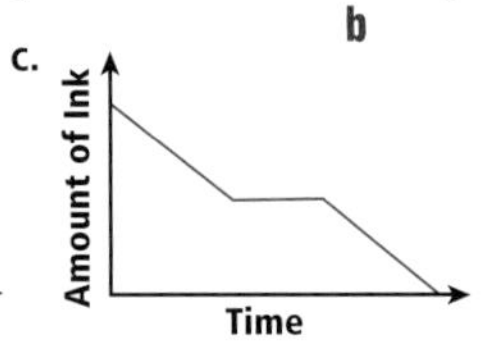

See Example 2

7. Elena uses 4 gallons of water per minute to fill plastic bottles. Draw a graph to show how much water she uses.

See Example 3

Find the domain and range of each graph.

8.

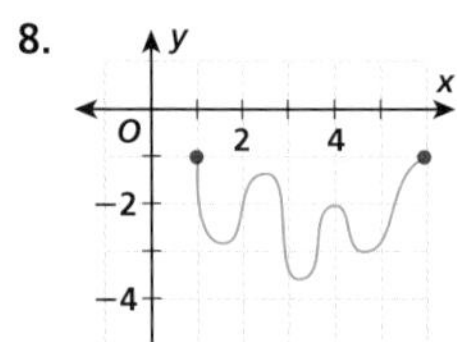

9.

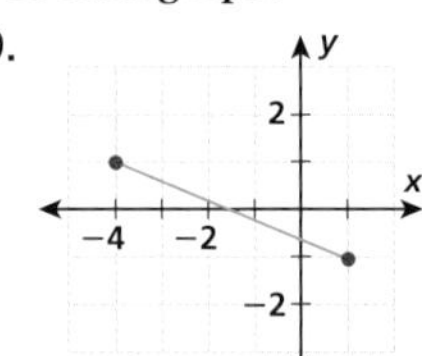

10.

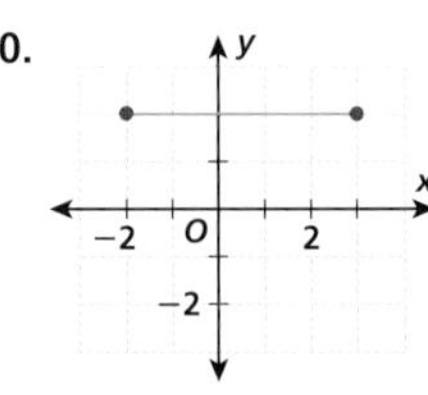

RETEACH 12-3

LESSON 12-3 **Reteach**
Interpreting Graphs

Graphs are often used to model situations. This graph shows Shavawn's daily jogging routine. She jogs uphill at a steady speed. When she starts to run downhill, her speed increases.

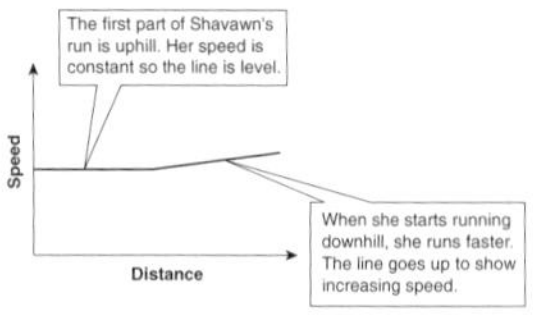

The first part of Shavawn's run is uphill. Her speed is constant so the line is level.

When she starts running downhill, she runs faster. The line goes up to show increasing speed.

Speed / Distance

Complete the graph for each situation.

1. You pour your warm tea into a glass, then add ice cubes.
2. You are watching TV and lower the volume during a commercial.

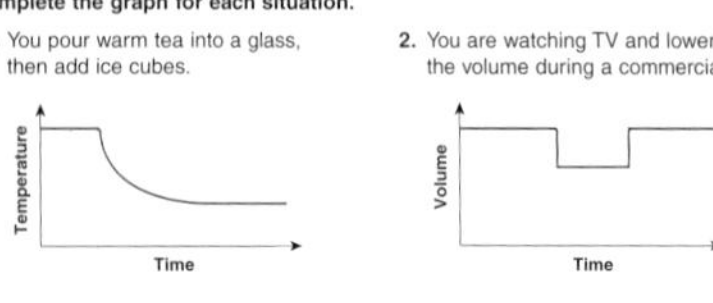

On a continuous graph, the *x*-values of the graph are called the **domain**. The *y*-values of the graph are called the **range**.

Complete the statements about the graph.

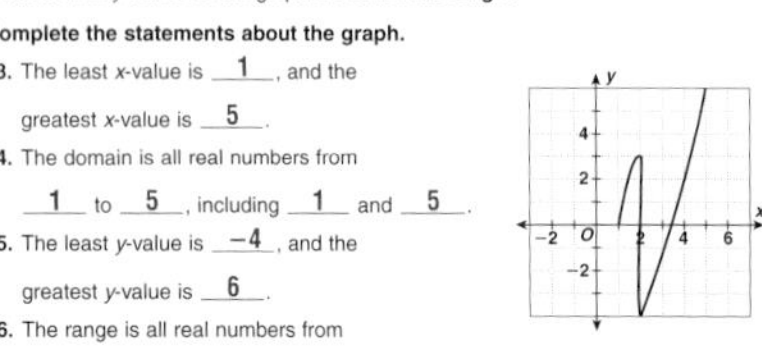

3. The least *x*-value is 1, and the greatest *x*-value is 5.
4. The domain is all real numbers from 1 to 5, including 1 and 5.
5. The least *y*-value is −4, and the greatest *y*-value is 6.
6. The range is all real numbers from −4 to 6, including −4 and 6.

PRACTICE 12-3

LESSON 12-3 **Practice B**
Interpreting Graphs

Tell what relationship each graph shows.

1. Rollerblading

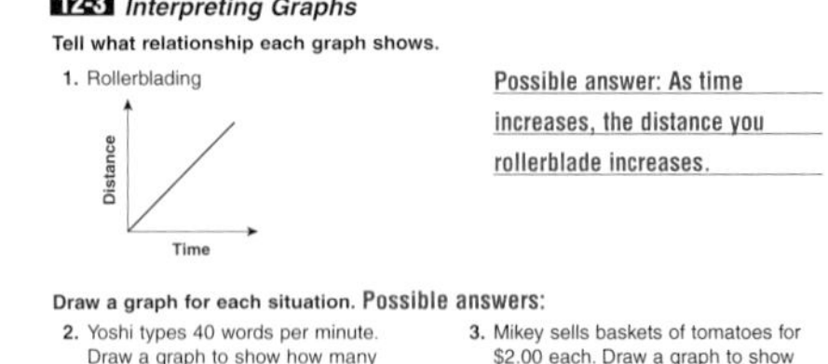

Possible answer: As time increases, the distance you rollerblade increases.

Draw a graph for each situation. Possible answers:

2. Yoshi types 40 words per minute. Draw a graph to show how many words she can type.

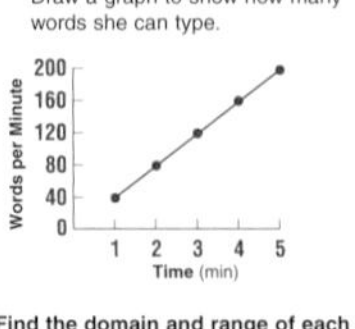

3. Mikey sells baskets of tomatoes for $2.00 each. Draw a graph to show how much money he can make.

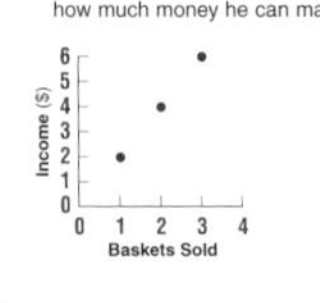

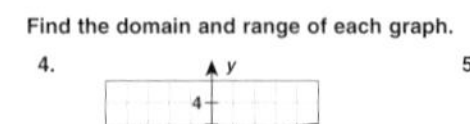

Find the domain and range of each graph.

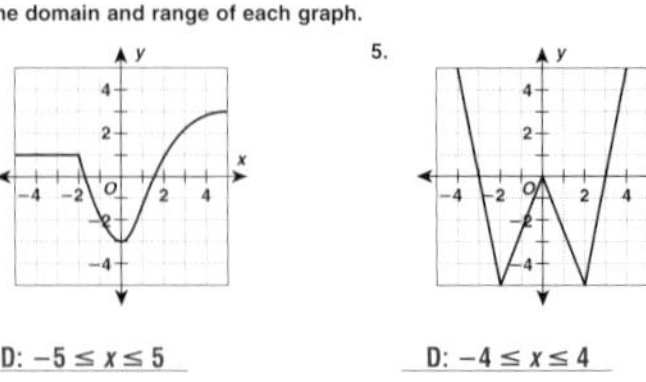

4. D: $-5 \le x \le 5$; R: $-3 \le y \le 3$
5. D: $-4 \le x \le 4$; R: $-5 \le y \le 5$

PRACTICE AND PROBLEM SOLVING

11. Tell a story that fits the graph at right.

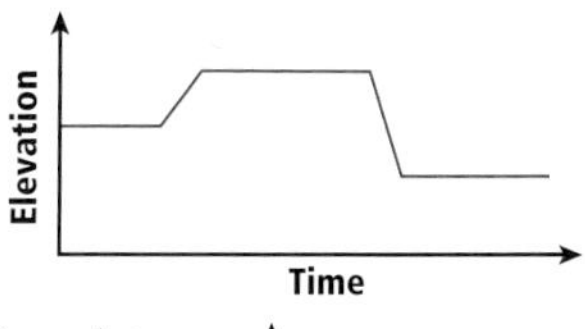

12. ***SPORTS*** A basketball team plays 2 games a week. Make a graph showing the total number of games the team can play in a 12-week season.

13. ***NUTRITION*** There are 60 calories in each chocolate-crunch rice cake. Make a graph to show how many calories you can consume eating these rice cakes.

14. The graph at right shows sound being recorded in a studio. Interpret the graph.
The sound stays at the same level.

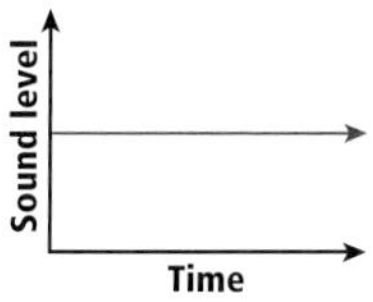

Sound level
Time

15. a. 1990, 1995, 2000, 2005, 2010
b. Possible answer: 15.5, 17, 18, 18.5,19

15. The graph at right shows high school enrollment, including future projections.
    a. Give the domain of the graph.
    b. Give the range of the graph.

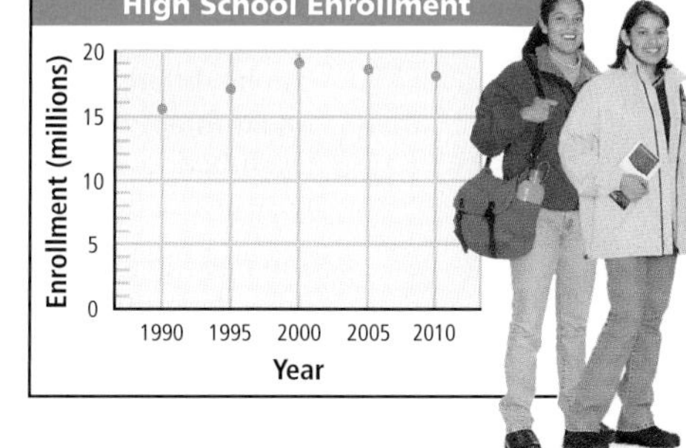

16. ***CHOOSE A STRATEGY*** Three bananas were given to two mothers who were with their daughters. Each person had a banana to eat. How is that possible? **One of the mothers is the daughter of the other mother.**

17. ***WRITE ABOUT IT*** Explain the difference between a graph made up of single points and a continuous graph.

18. ***CHALLENGE*** The graph of a line segment represents the function $y = 3x$, where the domain is all real numbers from -2 to 4, including -2 and 4. What is the range of the graph?
all real numbers from −6 to 12, including −6 and 12

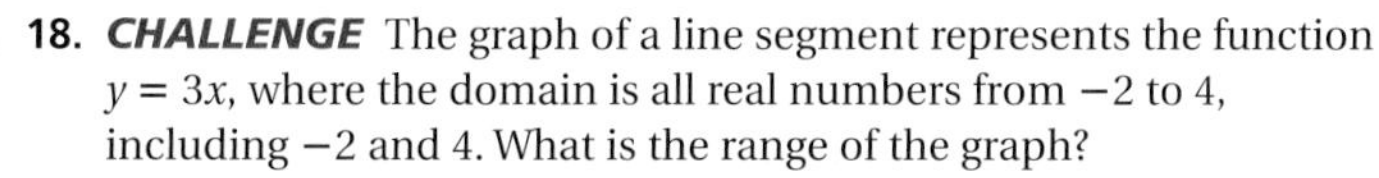

Spiral Review

Estimate each value. (Lesson 6-2) **Possible answers:**

19. 18% of 21 **4**
20. 35% of 88 **30**
21. 51% of 39 **20**

Determine the number of lines of symmetry in each figure. (Lesson 7-11)

22.
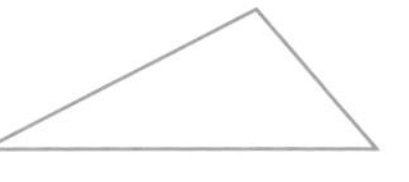
none

23.
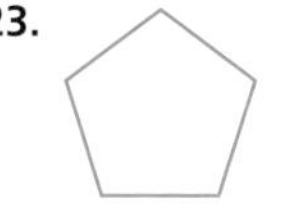
five

24.

two

25. **TEST PREP** By what will the volume of a rectangular prism be multiplied if you double each dimension? (Lesson 9-5) **A**

A 8 B 4 C 2 D 1

CHALLENGE 12-3

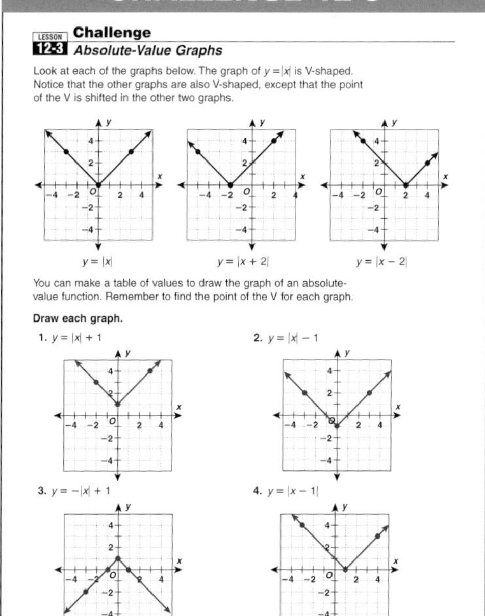
LESSON 12-3 **Challenge**
Absolute-Value Graphs

Look at each of the graphs below. The graph of $y = |x|$ is V-shaped. Notice that the other graphs are also V-shaped, except that the point of the V is shifted in the other two graphs.

$y = |x|$ $y = |x + 2|$ $y = |x - 2|$

You can make a table of values to draw the graph of an absolute-value function. Remember to find the point of the V for each graph.

Draw each graph.

1. $y = |x| + 1$
2. $y = |x| - 1$
3. $y = -|x| + 1$
4. $y = |x - 1|$

PROBLEM SOLVING 12-3

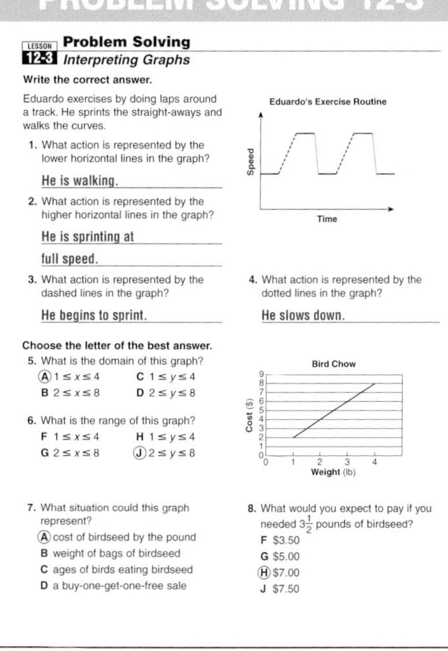
LESSON 12-3 **Problem Solving**
Interpreting Graphs

Write the correct answer.

Eduardo exercises by doing laps around a track. He sprints the straight-aways and walks the curves.

Eduardo's Exercise Routine (Speed, Time)

1. What action is represented by the lower horizontal lines in the graph?
He is walking.
2. What action is represented by the higher horizontal lines in the graph?
He is sprinting at full speed.
3. What action is represented by the dashed lines in the graph?
He begins to sprint.
4. What action is represented by the dotted lines in the graph?
He slows down.

Choose the letter of the best answer.

Bird Chow (Cost ($), Weight (lb))

5. What is the domain of this graph?
   Ⓐ $1 \le x \le 4$ C $1 \le y \le 4$
   B $2 \le x \le 8$ D $2 \le y \le 8$
6. What is the range of this graph?
   F $1 \le x \le 4$ H $1 \le y \le 4$
   G $2 \le x \le 8$ Ⓙ $2 \le y \le 8$
7. What situation could this graph represent?
   Ⓐ cost of birdseed by the pound
   B weight of bags of birdseed
   C ages of birds eating birdseed
   D a buy-one-get-one-free sale
8. What would you expect to pay if you needed $3\frac{1}{2}$ pounds of birdseed?
   F \$3.50
   G \$5.00
   Ⓗ \$7.00
   J \$7.50

Answers

11. Possible answer: Mary walked along a flat trail for some time and then walked up a hill. She walked along the top of the hill for a while and then walked down the hill.

12–13, 17. See p. A5.

Journal 

Ask students to contrast real-world situations represented by continuous graphs with real-world situations represented by graphs consisting of points.

Test Prep Doctor 

In Exercise 25, students who selected **B** may be confusing the rules for how surface area and volume change as dimensions change. If students chose **C** or **D,** they do not understand how changes in dimensions affect changes in volume. These students should review this relationship.

Lesson Quiz 

1. A ball is tossed into the air. Interpret the graph.

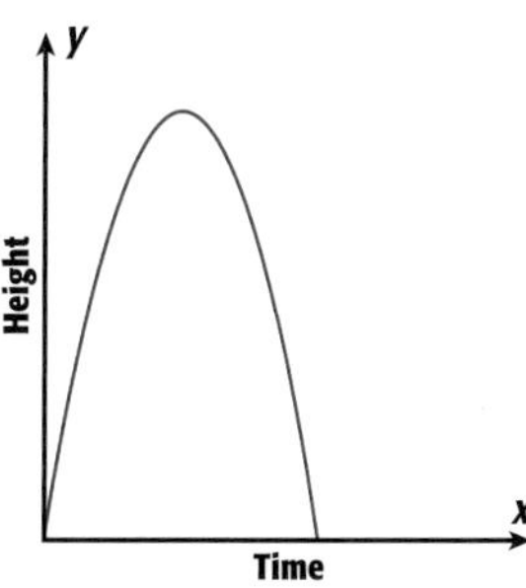

The ball's height increases until gravity gradually stops the ball; then its height decreases in a mirror image of the ascent.

2. Samantha sells decorated ornamental balls for \$4 each. Draw a graph to show how much she can make if she can sell up to 7 balls.

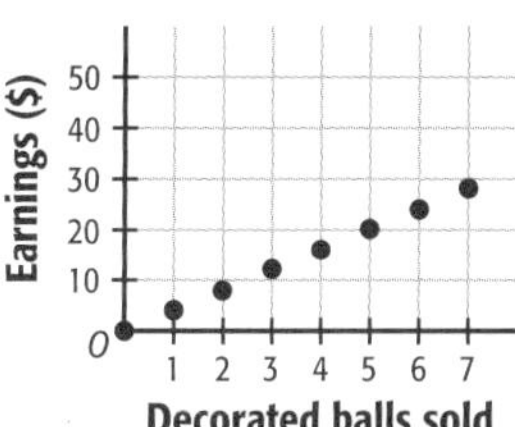

3. Name the domain and range of the graph in problem 2. Domain is 0 to 7; range is 0 to 28.

Available on Daily Transparency in CRB

12-4 Organizer

Pacing: Traditional 1 day
Block $\frac{1}{2}$ day

Objective: Students identify and graph linear equations.

Warm Up

Interpret the graph.

A rocket is fired into the air.

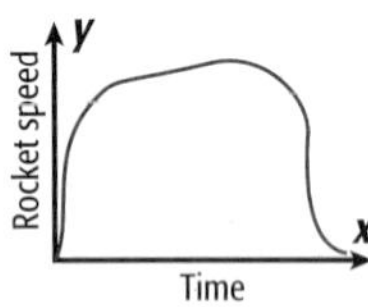

The rocket's speed increases until gravity gradually slows the rocket and causes it to fall to the ground.

Problem of the Day

The mean of a, 31, 42, 65, and b is 51. The greatest number is 67 more than the least number. What are the missing numbers? 25 and 92

Available on Daily Transparency in CRB

Why is an equation whose graph is a straight line sillier than an equation whose graph is not straight? It's a *loonier* equation.

12-4 Linear Functions

Learn to identify and graph linear equations.

Vocabulary
linear equation
linear function

The graph below shows how far an inner tube travels down a river if the current flows 2 miles per hour. The graph is linear because all of the points fall on a line. It is part of the graph of a *linear equation.*

A **linear equation** is an equation whose graph is a line. The solutions of a linear equation are the points that make up its graph. Linear equations and linear graphs can be different representations of *linear functions.* A **linear function** is a function whose graph is a nonvertical line.

You need to know only two points to draw the graph of a linear function. However, graphing a third point serves as a check. You can use a function table to find each ordered pair.

EXAMPLE 1 Graphing Linear Functions

Graph each linear function.

A $y = 2x + 1$

Input	Rule	Output	Ordered Pair
x	$2x + 1$	y	(x, y)
0	$2(0) + 1$	1	(0, 1)
2	$2(2) + 1$	5	(2, 5)
−2	$2(-2) + 1$	−3	(−2, −3)

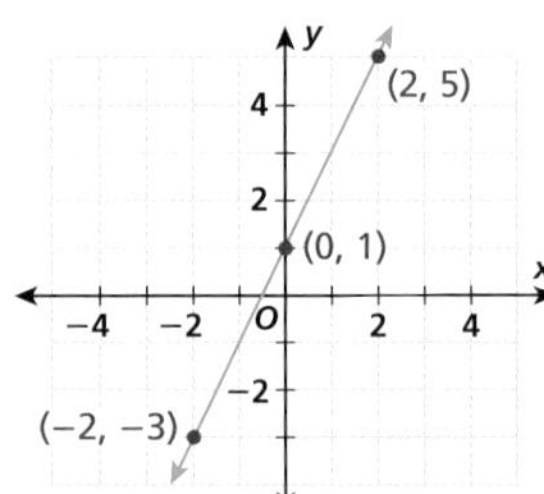

Place each ordered pair on the coordinate grid, and then connect the points with a line.

1 Introduce

Alternate Opener

EXPLORATION

12-4 Linear Functions

The graph of a ***linear function*** is a nonvertical straight line. Linear functions can be represented by a ***linear equation*** or by a graph.

1. Complete the table of values for the linear equation $y = 2x + 2$.

x	$y = 2x + 2$	(x, y)	Graph
−4	$2(-4) + 2 = -6$	(−4, −6)	
−3			
−2			
−1			
0			
1			
2			

2. Plot points on the graph using the x- and y-values generated in the table. Then draw a line through the points.

Think and Discuss

3. **Discuss** how you can recognize a linear function by its equation.
4. **Discuss** how you can recognize a linear function by its graph.

Motivate

Ask students to demonstrate different paths connecting two points. Discuss the type of path that represents the shortest distance between the two points (a straight line).

Exploration worksheet and answers on Chapter 12 Resource Book pp. 35 and 94

2 Teach

Lesson Presentation

Guided Instruction

In this lesson, students learn to identify and graph linear equations. You may wish to remind students that they are already familiar with the main concepts of the lesson. Students already know how to use input/output tables, and they know how to plot points on the plane. They also know how to solve equations. Students will now apply these concepts together and relate them to linear equations and their graphs.

Teaching Tip Have students use graph paper to sketch the graphs. Some students have trouble making clean graphs on standard notebook paper because the lines are too close together.

Graph each linear function.

B $y = 4$

The equation $y = 4$ is the same equation as $y = 0x + 4$.

Input	Rule	Output	Ordered Pair
x	$0x + 4$	y	(x, y)
0	$0(0) + 4$	4	(0, 4)
3	$0(3) + 4$	4	(3, 4)
−1	$0(-1) + 4$	4	(−1, 4)

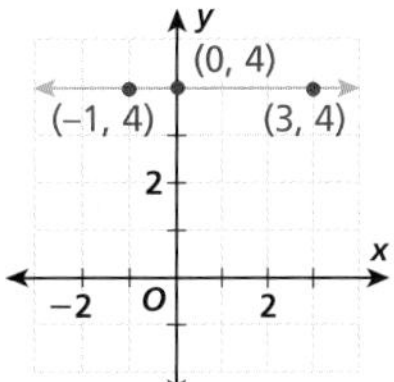

EXAMPLE  ***Earth Science Application***

The Atlantic Ocean floor is spreading by 4 cm each year. Scientists began studying two parts of the ocean floor when they were 10 cm apart. Write a linear function that describes the spread of the ocean floor over time. Then make a graph to show how far the ocean floor will spread over the next 10 years.

The function is $y = 4x + 10$, where x is the number of years and y is the spread in centimeters.

The dark red region in the center of the map is the midocean ridge, where the ocean floor is spreading.

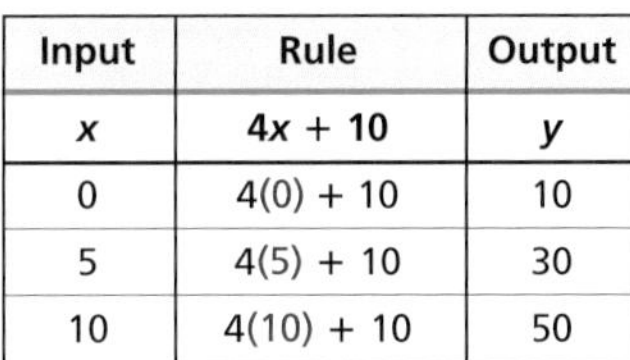

Input	Rule	Output
x	$4x + 10$	y
0	$4(0) + 10$	10
5	$4(5) + 10$	30
10	$4(10) + 10$	50

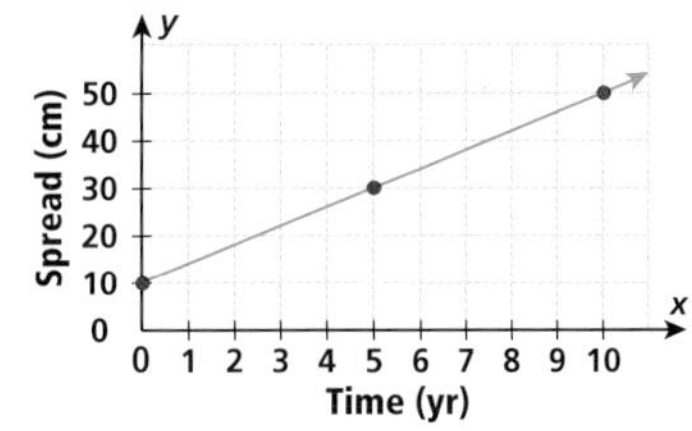

Since each output y depends on the input x, y is called the *dependent variable* and x is called the *independent variable.*

Think and Discuss

1. **Describe** how a linear equation is related to a linear graph.
2. **Explain** what $x = -1$ would mean in Example 2.

Additional Examples

Example 

Graph each linear function.

A. $y = 4x - 1$

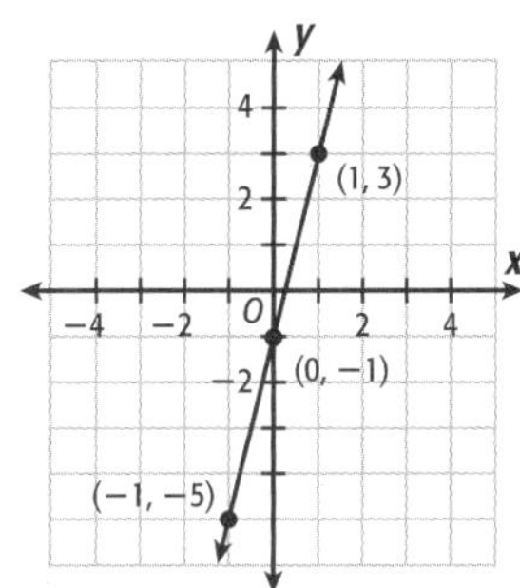

B. $y = -1$

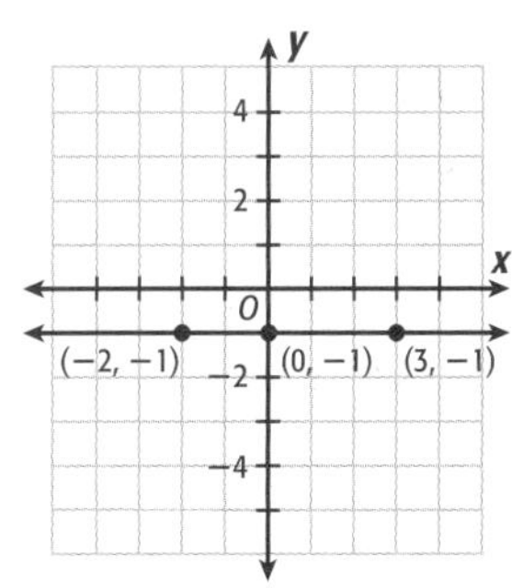

Example 2

The fastest-moving tectonic plates on Earth move apart at a rate of 15 centimeters per year. Scientists began studying two parts of these plates when they were 30 centimeters apart. How far apart will the two parts be after 4 years? **90 cm**

3 Close

Summarize

Have students graph the equation $y = 3x + 1$ for $x = -1, 0,$ and 1.

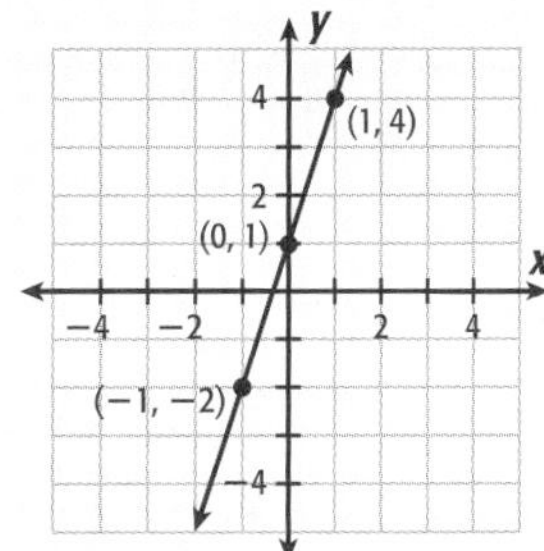

Reaching All Learners

Through Curriculum Integration

Science Have students look through science textbooks for examples of formulas and graphs of linear equations. Ask students to explain how they can recognize a formula of a linear equation.

Possible answer: In a formula of a linear equation, the variable in the formula is not raised to a power.

Answers to Think and Discuss

1. Possible answer: A linear equation and a linear graph are different representations that describe the same relationship between an independent variable x and a dependent variable y.
2. Possible answer: A value of −1 for x would be one year before scientists began the study.

12-4 PRACTICE & ASSESS

Students may want to refer back to the lesson examples.

Assignment Guide

If you finished Example 1 assign:
Core 1, 2, 4–7, 9–13 odd, 20–27
Enriched 1, 5, 7, 9–14, 20–27

If you finished Example 2 assign:
Core 1–8, 9–15 odd, 20–27
Enriched 1–7 odd, 9–27

Answers

1.

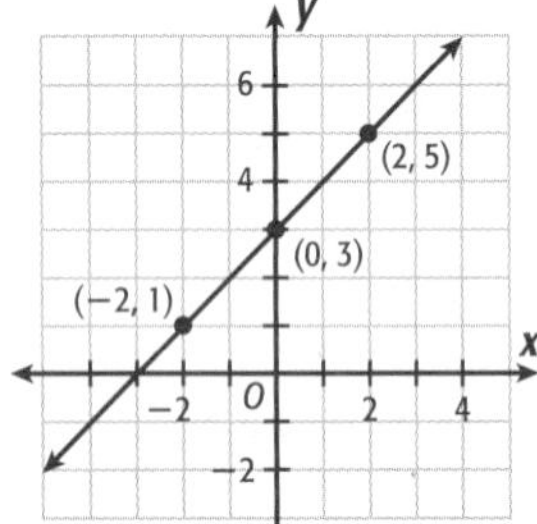

2.

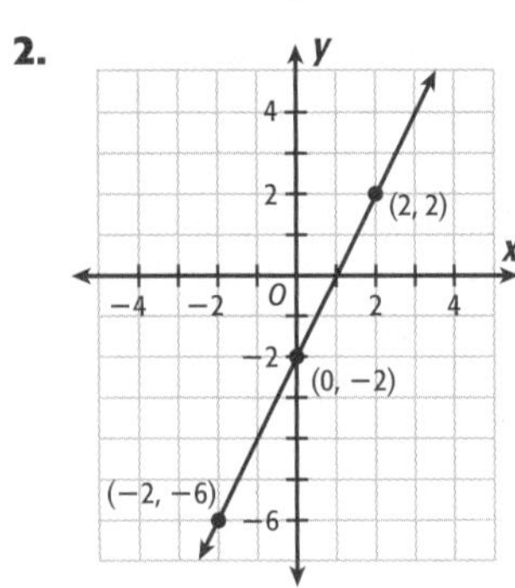

3–8. Complete answers on p. A5

12-4 Exercises

FOR EXTRA PRACTICE see page 680

internet connect
Homework Help Online
go.hrw.com Keyword: MS4 12-4

GUIDED PRACTICE

See Example 1 **Graph each linear function.**

1. $y = x + 3$

Input	Rule	Output	Ordered Pair
x	$x + 3$	y	(x, y)
−2			(−2, 1)
0			(0, 3)
2			(2, 5)

2. $y = 2x - 2$

Input	Rule	Output	Ordered Pair
x	$2x - 2$	y	(x, y)
−2			(−2, −6)
0			(0, −2)
2			(2, 2)

See Example 2

3. A water tanker is used to fill a community pool. The tanker pumps 750 gallons of water per hour. Write a linear function that describes the amount of water in the pool over time. Then make a graph to show the amount of water in the pool over the first 6 hours. $y = 750x$

INDEPENDENT PRACTICE

See Example 1 **Graph each linear function.**

4. $y = -x + 2$

Input	Rule	Output	Ordered Pair
x	$-x + 2$	y	(x, y)
−2			(−2, 4)
0			(0, 2)
2			(2, 0)

5. $y = \frac{x}{2} + 1$

Input	Rule	Output	Ordered Pair
x	$\frac{x}{2} + 1$	y	(x, y)
−2			(−2, 0)
0			(0, 1)
2			(2, 2)

6. $y = 1$

Input	Rule	Output	Ordered Pair
x	$0x + 1$	y	(x, y)
−2			(−2, 1)
0			(0, 1)
2			(2, 1)

7. $y = 2x + 3$

Input	Rule	Output	Ordered Pair
x	$2x + 3$	y	(x, y)
−2			(−2, −1)
0			(0, 3)
2			(2, 7)

See Example 2

8. The temperature of a liquid is increasing at the rate of 3°C per hour. When Joe begins measuring the temperature, it is 40°C. Write a linear function that describes the temperature of the liquid over time. Then make a graph to show the temperature over the first 12 hours. $y = 3x + 40$

Math Background

Graphs of linear equations of the form $y = a$, where a is a real number, are horizontal lines. The line $y = a$ intersects the y-axis at the point $(0, a)$. All horizontal lines are parallel to the x-axis and have a slope of 0. In particular, the equation of the x-axis is $y = 0$.

Graphs of linear equations of the form $x = a$, where a is a real number, are vertical lines. The line $x = a$ intersects the x-axis at the point $(a, 0)$. All vertical lines are parallel to the y-axis and have no slope. That is, the slope of a vertical line does not exist. In particular, the equation of the y-axis is $x = 0$.

RETEACH 12-4

LESSON 12-4 **Reteach**
Linear Functions

The graph of a linear equation is a straight line. A **linear function** is a function whose graph is a straight line that is not vertical. To graph a linear equation, first make an input/output table.

Complete the input/output table for $y = 2x - 3$.

	Input	Linear Equation	Output	Ordered Pair
	x	$y = 2x - 3$	y	(x, y)
1.	0	$y = 2(0) - 3 = 0 - 3$	−3	(0, −3)
2.	1	$y = 2(1) - 3 = 2 - 3$	−1	(1, −1)
3.	2	$y = 2(2) - 3 = 4 - 3$	1	(2, 1)

To graph the equation, graph ordered pairs. Then draw a line through the points.

Complete the input/output table and graph the equation.

4. $y = -x + 1$

Input	Linear Equation	Output	Ordered Pair
x	$y = -x + 1$	y	(x, y)
0	$y = -0 + 1$	1	(0, 1)
1	$y = -1 + 1$	0	(1, 0)
2	$y = -2 + 1$	−1	(2, −1)

PRACTICE 12-4

LESSON 12-4 **Practice B**
Linear Functions

Graph each linear function.

1. $y = -x - 5$

Input	Linear Equation	Output	Ordered Pair
x	$y = -x - 5$	y	(x, y)
−4	$y = -(-4) - 5$	−1	(−4, −1)
−2	$y = -(-2) - 5$	−3	(−2, −3)
0	$y = -0 - 5$	−5	(0, −5)

2. $y = 2x - 1$

Input	Linear Equation	Output	Ordered Pair
x	$y = 2x - 1$	y	(x, y)
−2	$y = 2(-2) - 1$	−5	(−2, −5)
0	$y = 2(0) - 1$	−1	(0, −1)
1	$y = 2(1) - 1$	1	(1, 1)

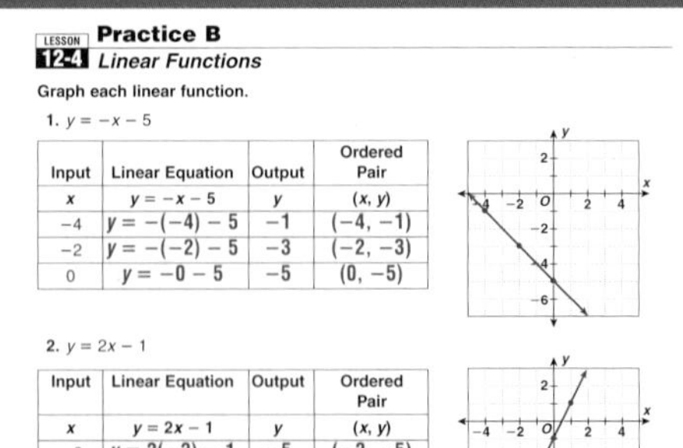

3. The temperature of a swimming pool is 75°F. When the pool heater is turned on, the temperature rises 2°F every hour. What will the temperature be after 3 hours? Make an input/output table to answer the question.

81°F

Input	Equation	Output
x	$y = 2x + 75$	y
1	$y = 2(1) + 75$	77
2	$y = 2(2) + 75$	79
3	$y = 2(3) + 75$	81

4. Mel's Pizza Place charges $15.00 for a large cheese pizza plus $1.25 for each additional topping. What will be the cost of a large pizza with 3 additional toppings? Make an input/output table to answer the question.

$18.75

Input	Equation	Output
x	$y = 1.25x + 15$	y
1	$y = 1.25(1) + 15$	16.25
2	$y = 1.25(2) + 15$	17.50
3	$y = 1.25(3) + 15$	18.75

PRACTICE AND PROBLEM SOLVING

About 15% of the methane gas in the atmosphere comes from farm animals such as cows and sheep.

Solve each equation for y. Then graph the function.

9. $y - x = 0$ $y = x$
10. $2x + y = 1$ $y = -2x + 1$
11. $6y = -12$ $y = -2$
12. $2y - 5x + 2 = 0$
13. $\frac{y}{2} - 3 = 0$ $y = 6$
14. $2y + x + 6 = 0$

15. ***ENVIRONMENT*** The graph shows the concentration of carbon dioxide in the atmosphere from 1958 to 1994.

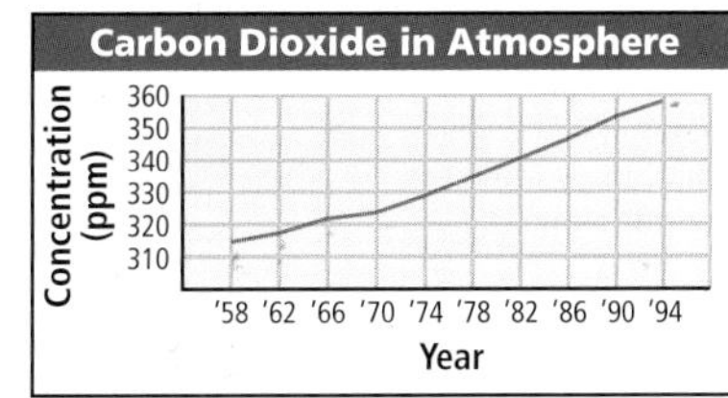

  a. The graph is approximately linear. About how many parts per million (ppm) were added each 4-year period? **5 ppm**

  b. Given the parts per million in 1994 shown on the graph, about how many parts per million do you predict there will be after four more 4-year periods, or in 2010? **about 378 ppm**

16. ***EARTH SCIENCE*** Water is seeping into an underground water supply at a rate of 10 centimeters per year. It is being pumped out at a rate of 2 meters per year. If the depth of the water in the water supply is 100 meters deep, how deep will it be in 10 years? **8,100 cm, or 81 m**

17. ***WHAT'S THE QUESTION?*** Tron used the equation $y = 100 + 25x$ to track his savings y after x months. If the answer is \$250, what is the question? **Possible answer: How much money does Tron have after 6 months?**

18. ***WRITE ABOUT IT*** Explain how to graph $y = 2x - 5$.

19. ***CHALLENGE*** Bacteria of a certain species divide every 30 minutes. To find how many bacteria there are after each half-hour period, starting with one bacterium, you can use the function $y = 2^x$, where x is the number of half-hour periods. Make a table of values for $x = 1, 2, 3, 4$, and 5. Graph the points. How does the graph differ from those you have seen so far in this lesson? **It is not linear.**

Spiral Review

Name the polygon with the given number of sides. (Lesson 7-5)

20. five **pentagon**
21. eight **octagon**
22. six **hexagon**
23. three **triangle**

Find the area of each parallelogram. (Lesson 8-4)

24. 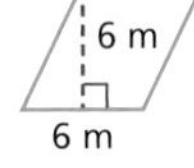

36 m²

25. 

96 in²

26. 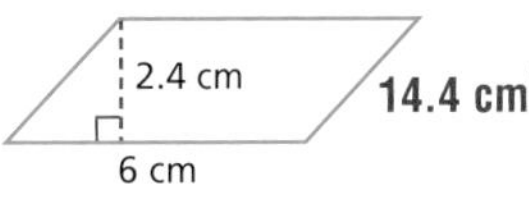

14.4 cm²

27. **TEST PREP** Use the pattern in the sequence 3, 2, 0, −3, . . . , to find the next integer in the sequence. (Lesson 12-2) **B**

A 0 B −7 C −6 D −2

CHALLENGE 12-4

LESSON 12-4 Challenge
Linear Functions

A linear equation is referred to as a "first-degree polynomial equation." The *standard form* of a first-degree equation is $ax + by + c = 0$. In standard form, a, b, and c are integers.

The *slope-intercept form* of a linear equation is $y = mx + b$. In slope-intercept form, m and b are both real numbers.

You can write a linear equation in either of these forms.

Example 1: Write $y = \frac{2}{3}x - 2$ in standard form.

$$y = \frac{2}{3}x - 2$$
$$y + 2 = \frac{2}{3}x \quad \leftarrow \text{Add 2 to both sides.}$$
$$3(y + 2) = 3\left(\frac{2}{3}x\right) \quad \leftarrow \text{Multiply both sides by 3.}$$
$$3y + 6 = 2x \quad \leftarrow \text{Simplify.}$$
$$-2x + 3y + 6 = 0 \quad \leftarrow \text{Subtract } 2x \text{ from both sides.}$$

Example 2: Write $3x + 5y + 1 = 0$ in slope-intercept form.

$$3x + 5y + 1 = 0$$
$$5y = -3x - 1 \quad \leftarrow \text{Subtract } 3x + 1 \text{ from both sides.}$$
$$\frac{5y}{5} = \frac{-3x - 1}{5} \quad \leftarrow \text{Divide both sides by 5.}$$
$$y = -\frac{3}{5}x - \frac{1}{5} \quad \leftarrow \text{Simplify.}$$

Write each equation in standard form.

1. $y = \frac{5}{6}x - 4$ **$-5x + 6y + 24 = 0$ or $5x - 6y - 24 = 0$**
2. $y = 2x - \frac{1}{2}$ **$-4x + 2y + 1 = 0$ or $4x - 2y - 1 = 0$**
3. $y = -\frac{1}{3}x + 8$ **$x + 3y - 24 = 0$ or $-x - 3y + 24 = 0$**

Write each equation in slope-intercept form.

4. $x - 4y + 1 = 0$ **$y = \frac{1}{4}x + \frac{1}{4}$**
5. $2x - 4y + 8 = 0$ **$y = \frac{1}{2}x + 2$**
6. $6x - 3y - 2 = 0$ **$y = 2x - \frac{2}{3}$**

PROBLEM SOLVING 12-4

LESSON 12-4 Problem Solving
Linear Functions

Write the correct answer.

This graph shows the approximate population density (people per square mile) in the United States from 1950 to 2000.

U.S. Population Density

Density (per mi²): 0–85; Year: 1950 1960 1970 1980 1990 2000

1. Based on this graph, do you think the population of the United States is growing, shrinking, or staying about the same? **growing**
2. How do you know that this is the graph of a linear function? **because the graph is a straight line**
3. On average, by about how many people did the density increase every ten years? **about 7 people**
4. Estimate the population density in 2010. **about 87 per mi²**
5. Estimate the population density in 2050. **about 115 per mi²**

Choose the letter of the best answer.

6. Given the linear equation $y = 4x + 1$ and the input $x = 3$, what is the resulting ordered pair?
   A (15, 3) C (12, 3)
   (B) (3, 13) D (12, 11)
7. Given the linear equation $y = \frac{1}{3}x - 4$ and the input $x = 6$, what is the resulting ordered pair?
   (F) (6, −2) H (−3, 6)
   G (6, 2) J $\left(\frac{1}{3}, 6\right)$
8. A technician is adding chemicals to a 210-liter tank. She is adding the liquid at a rate of 2.5 liters per minute. How long will it take to fill the tank half full?
   (A) 42 min C 168 min
   B 84 min D 525 min
9. A basic set of 4 golf lessons costs \$95.00. Additional lessons can be purchased at the discounted rate of \$15.00 each. What will Veronica pay for a series of 10 lessons?
   F \$150 **(H)** \$185
   G \$155 J \$245

COMMON ERROR ALERT

Some students might disregard the negative sign associated with the variable x in Exercises 4 and 9. Remind students that the negative sign is meaningful and changes a number to its opposite. Suggest that students use parentheses in the substitution-and-evaluation process.

Answers

12. $y = \frac{5}{2}x - 1$

14. $y = -\frac{1}{2}x - 3$

9–14, 19. Complete answers on p. A5

18. Possible answer: Find y for three values of x, graph the three points, and connect them with a straight line.

Journal

Ask students to describe how to sketch the graph of a linear equation.

Test Prep Doctor

In Exercise 27, students who selected **C** may be comparing only the last two terms in the sequence. Students who selected **A** or **D** are probably identifying an alternating pattern in the sequence. Remind students that all pairs of terms in the sequence must be compared to find the pattern.

Lesson Quiz

Graph the linear functions.

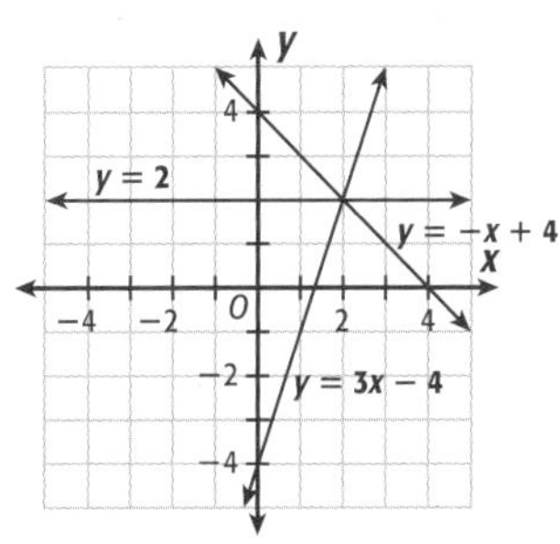

1. $y = 3x - 4$

2. $y = -x + 4$

3. $y = 2$

4. The temperature of a liquid is decreasing at a rate of 12°F per hour. Susan begins measuring the liquid at 200°F. What will the temperature be after 5 hours? **140°F**

Available on Daily Transparency in CRB

12-5 Organizer

Pacing: Traditional 1 day
Block $\frac{1}{2}$ day

Objective: Students determine the slope of a line and graph a line, given one point, the y-intercept, and the slope.

Warm Up

Graph the linear function $y = 2x + 4$.

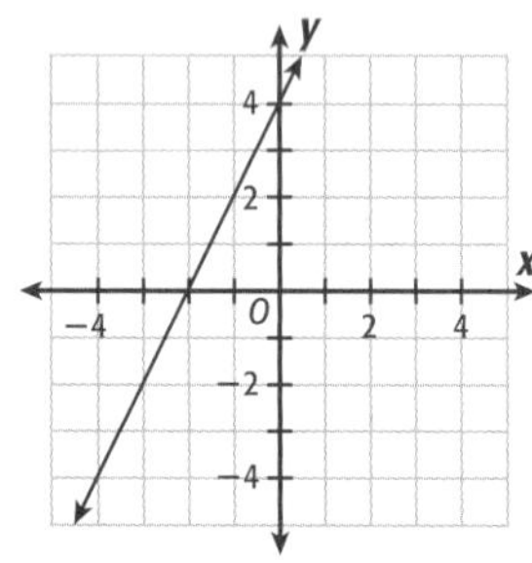

Problem of the Day

One vertex of a triangle is at the origin. The other two vertices are at the x- and y-intercepts of $y = 2x + 10$. What is the area of the triangle?
25 square units

Available on Daily Transparency in CRB

12-5 Slope

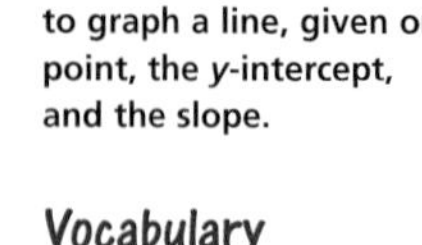

Learn to determine the slope of a line and to graph a line, given one point, the y-intercept, and the slope.

Vocabulary
slope
y-intercept
slope-intercept form

The steepness of the pyramid steps is measured by dividing the height of each step by its depth. Another way to express the height and depth is with the words *rise* and *run*.

In Chitchén Itzá, Mexico, during the spring and fall equinoxes, shadows fall on the pyramid El Castillo, giving the illusion of a snake crawling down the steps.

The **slope** of a line is a measure of its steepness and is the ratio of rise to run:

$$\textbf{slope} = \frac{\textbf{rise}}{\textbf{run}}$$

The y-coordinate of the point where a line crosses the y-axis is called the **y-intercept**.

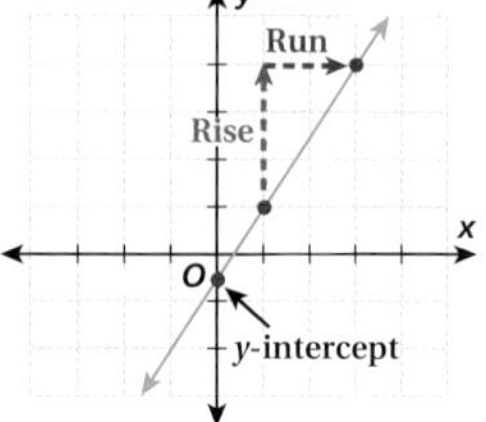

EXAMPLE 1 Identifying Slope and y-intercept of a Line

Give the slope and y-intercept of each line.

A

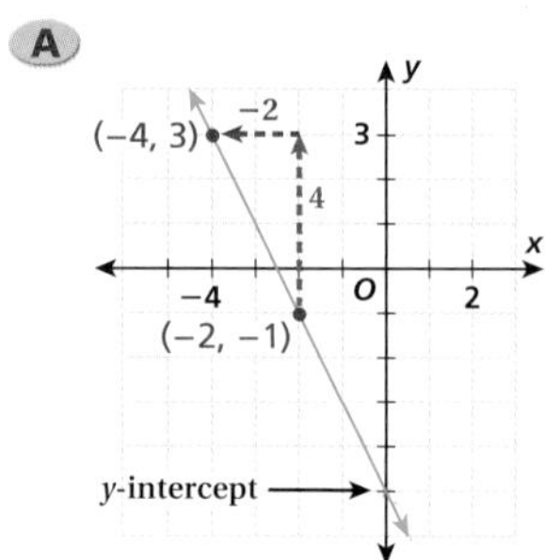

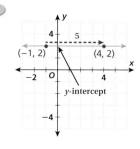

The rise is 4.
The run is −2.
$\text{slope} = \frac{\text{rise}}{\text{run}} = \frac{4}{-2} = -2$
The y-intercept is -5.

B

The rise is 0.
The run is 5.
$\text{slope} = \frac{\text{rise}}{\text{run}} = \frac{0}{5} = 0$
The y-intercept is 2.

1 Introduce

Alternate Opener

12-5 Slope

Catherine used a motion detector to gather data about the distance a toy car traveled as it moved away from the motion detector at a constant rate.

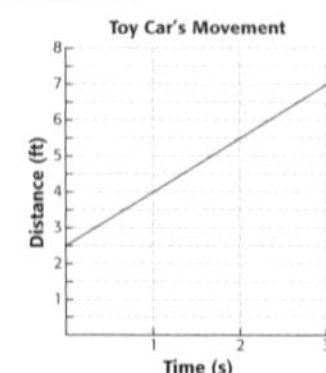

1. How far away from the detector was the toy car when the car started moving?
2. How many feet did the car travel in 3 seconds?
3. Use the graph to determine the speed of the car.

Think and Discuss

4. **Explain** how you determined the speed of the toy car.
5. **Discuss** how the graph represents a constant rate of motion. What feature of the graph shows that the rate was constant?

Motivate

Ask students what "steepness" suggests to them. Have them give real-world examples of things with varying degrees of steepness (e.g., roads, ramps, mountain trails, the ascent of an airplane during take-off).

Exploration worksheet and answers on Chapter 12 Resource Book pp. 44 and 96

2 Teach

Lesson Presentation

Guided Instruction

In this lesson, students learn to determine the slope of a line and to graph a line, given one point, the y-intercept, and the slope. Stress that the slope of a line describes the steepness, or tilt, of the line. Point out that in the slope ratio $\left(\frac{\text{rise}}{\text{run}}\right)$, the rise is recorded before the run. This is the opposite of students' understanding from working in the coordinate plane. Everything up until now has been x (or horizontal) first and then y (or vertical) second. Direct students' attention to this difference.

You may wish to mention that there can be only one line with a given slope through any point.

A linear equation with the variable y isolated on the left-hand side of the equation is in **slope-intercept form**.

$y = mx + b$
Slope (m) y-intercept (b)

EXAMPLE 2 **Identifying Slope and y-intercept in a Linear Equation**

Give the slope and y-intercept of each line, given the equation.

A $y = 12x - 9$

$y = 12x - 9$

The slope is 12.

The y-intercept is -9.

B $y = \frac{4}{5}x$

$y = \frac{4}{5}x + 0$

The slope is $\frac{4}{5}$.

The y-intercept is 0.

When you know the slope and any one point on a line, you can graph the line.

EXAMPLE 3 **Graphing Linear Equations Using Slope and y-intercept**

Graph each line, given the equation.

A $y = -\frac{1}{3}x + 2$

$y = -\frac{1}{3}x + 2$

The slope is $-\frac{1}{3}$ or $\frac{1}{-3}$. The y-intercept is 2. From point (0, 2), move 1 unit up (rise) and 3 units left (run) to find another point on the line. Draw a line to connect the points.

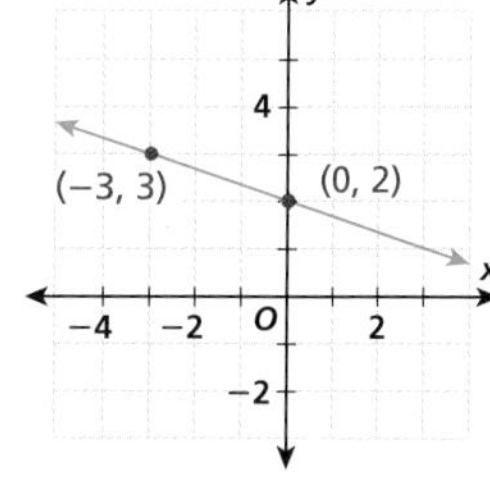

B $y = -1$

$y = 0x - 1$

The slope is 0. The y-intercept is -1. Locate the point $(0, -1)$. When the slope is zero, the line is horizontal. Draw a horizontal line through point $(0, -1)$.

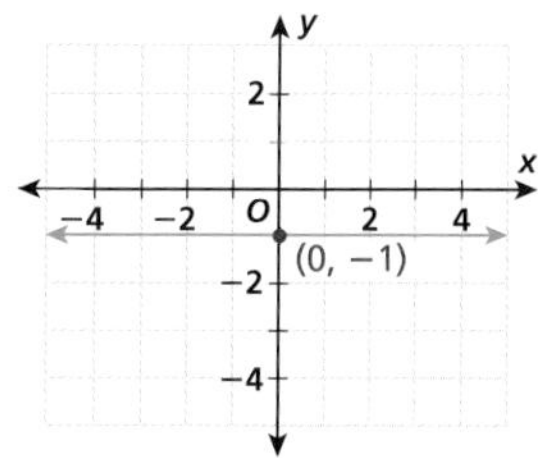

Think and Discuss

1. **Explain** why a horizontal line has a slope of 0.
2. **Describe** a line with a negative value for slope.
3. **Explain** how to write $-x + 2y = 8$ in slope-intercept form.

Additional Examples

Example 1

Tell the slope and y-intercept of the line. 1; -4

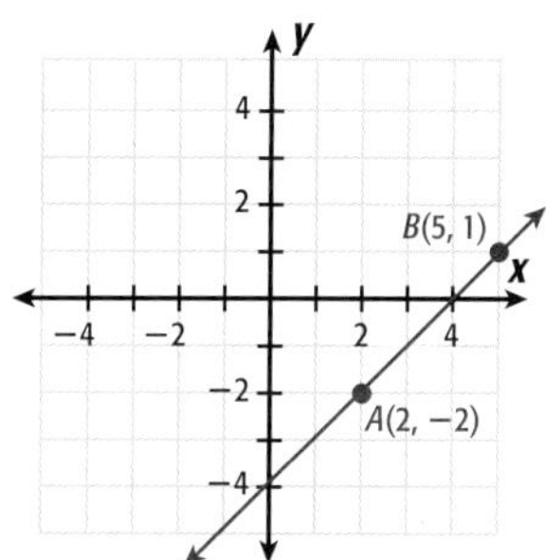

Example 2

Tell the slope and y-intercept of each line, given the equation.

A. $y = 3x - 1$ 3; -1

B. $y = \frac{1}{2}x + 2$ $\frac{1}{2}$; 2

Example 3

Graph the line, given the equation $y = -2x + 1$.

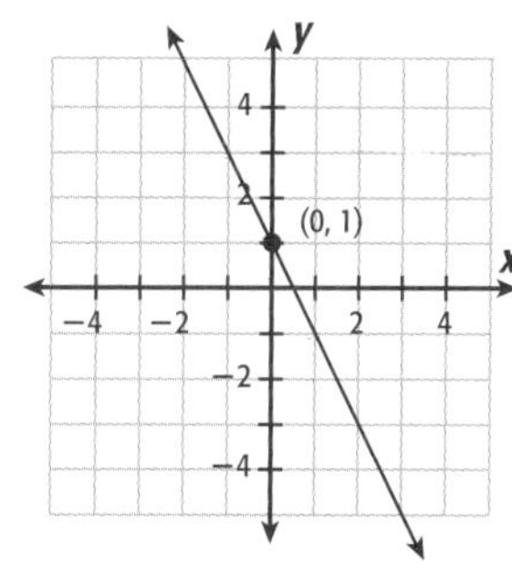

Example 2 note: Point out that graphs of equations of the form $y = mx$ always pass through the origin.

3 Close

Reaching All Learners

Through Critical Thinking

Supply students with graph paper (provided on Chapter 12 Resource Book p. 87). Have students work in pairs to create their own linear graphs and corresponding equations. You may wish to provide a suggestion, such as: "Draw a graph with a negative slope and a negative y-intercept. What is the equation of your line?" Remind students to use the rise and run to record the slope of their lines. Encourage students to share their examples and explanations with the class.

Summarize

Have students tell the slope and y-intercept of the line $y = \frac{1}{2}x - 1$. Then have them draw the graph of the line. $\frac{1}{2}$; -1

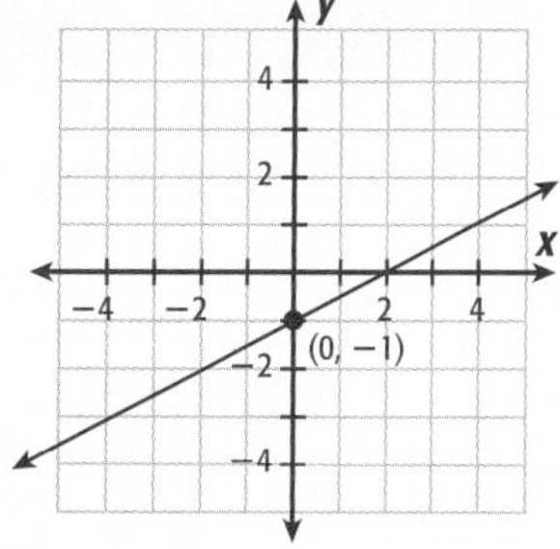

Answers to Think and Discuss

1. The change in the rise is 0, so we are dividing 0 by the change in the run.
2. Possible answer: A line with a negative value for a slope will fall from the left to the right.
3. First add x to both sides, and then divide both sides by 2. The slope-intercept form is $y = \frac{1}{2}x + 4$.

12-5 PRACTICE & ASSESS

Students may want to refer back to the lesson examples.

Assignment Guide

If you finished Example 1 assign:
Core 1, 2, 9, 10, 37–42
Enriched 1, 2, 9, 10, 37–42

If you finished Example 2 assign:
Core 1–5, 9–13, 17–19, 37–42
Enriched 1–5, 9–13, 17–19, 37–42

If you finished Example 3 assign:
Core 1–16, 17–33 odd, 37–42
Enriched 1–15 odd, 17–42

Answers

6.

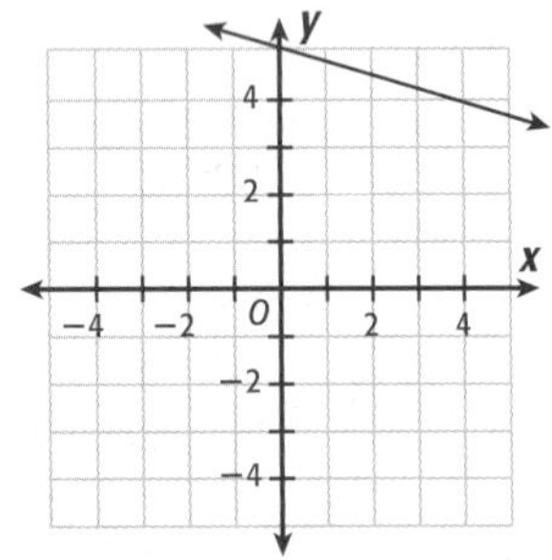

7–8, 14–16. See pp. A5–A6.

17. $y = 3x + 8$; positive

18. $y = \frac{7}{8}x - 3$; positive

19. $y = -5x + 1$; negative

12-5 Exercises

FOR EXTRA PRACTICE see page 680

GUIDED PRACTICE

See Example 1 — Give the slope and *y*-intercept of each line.

1. **1; 0**

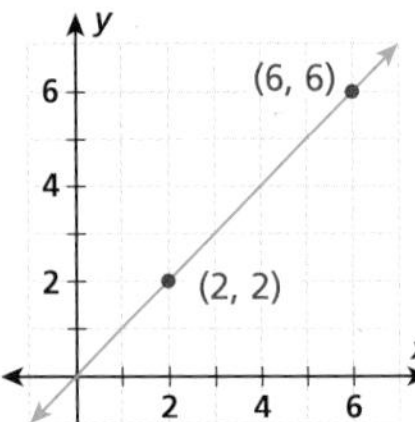

2. **$-\frac{1}{2}$; 3**

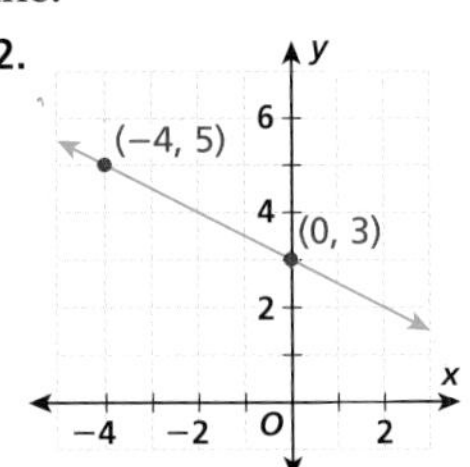

See Example 2 — Give the slope and *y*-intercept of each line, given the equation.

3. $y = 3x - 4$ **3; −4** **4.** $y = \frac{1}{3}x$ **$\frac{1}{3}$; 0** **5.** $y = -3x + 8$ **−3; 8**

See Example 3 — Graph each line, given the equation.

6. $y = -\frac{1}{4}x + 5$ **7.** $y = -5$ **8.** $y = \frac{2}{5}x - 2$

INDEPENDENT PRACTICE

See Example 1 — Give the slope and *y*-intercept of each line.

9. **−3; −4**

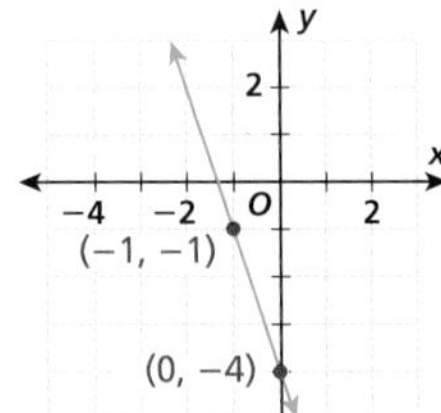

10. **0; 2**

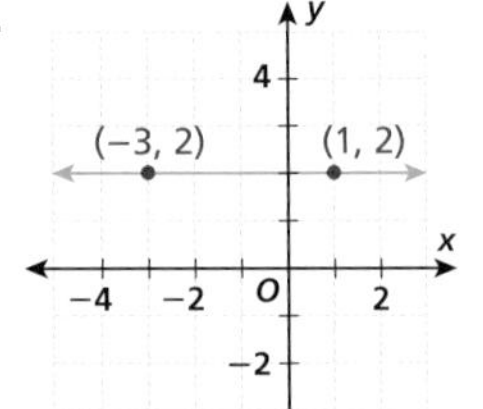

See Example 2 — Give the slope and *y*-intercept of each line, given the equation.

11. $y = x - 2$ **1; −2** **12.** $y = \frac{2}{5}x$ **$\frac{2}{5}$; 0** **13.** $y = 4x + 2$ **4; 2**

See Example 3 — Graph each line, given the equation.

14. $y = -\frac{5}{6}x + 4$ **15.** $y = 3$ **16.** $y = \frac{1}{5}x - 1$

PRACTICE AND PROBLEM SOLVING

Write each equation in slope-intercept form. Then tell whether its graph has a positive or a negative slope.

17. $-3x + y = 8$ **18.** $3 + y = \frac{7}{8}x$ **19.** $y + 5x = 1$

Math Background

The slope intercept form for the equation of a line, $y = mx + b$, is one of several ways to write a linear equation.

The point-slope form of a line uses a point, (x_1, y_1), that lies on the line, together with the slope, *m*, to characterize the line. The point-slope form of a line is $(y - y_1) = m(x - x_1)$.

The standard form for a linear equation is $Ax + By + C = 0$, where *A*, *B*, and *C* are integers and $A > 0$. All three forms of the linear equations are equivalent.

RETEACH 12-5

LESSON 12-5 **Reteach**
Slope

The **slope** of a line is a ratio that measures the steepness of that line. The sign of the slope tells whether the line is rising or falling.

You can find the slope of a line by comparing any two points on that line. Find the slope of the line between (2, 1) and (4, 4).

$\text{slope} = \frac{\text{rise}}{\text{run}} = \frac{\text{up (+) or down (−)}}{\text{right (+) or left (−)}}$

$= \frac{4-1}{4-2} = \frac{3}{2}$

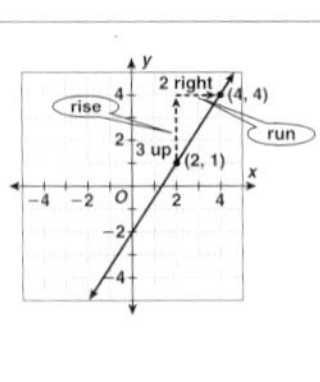

Use the graph to complete the statements.

1. You have to move up __3__ and right __2__ to go from one point to the other.

$\text{slope} = \frac{\text{rise}}{\text{run}} = \frac{\text{up (+) or down (−)}}{\text{right (+) or left (−)}} = \frac{3}{2}$

2. The slope of the line is __$\frac{3}{2}$__.

You can find the *y*-intercept of a line by locating the point where it crosses the *y*-axis. The *y*-intercept is the *y*-coordinate of that point.

3. The line crosses the *y*-axis at the point (__0, −2__). The *y*-intercept is __−2__.

Tell the slope and *y*-intercept of each line given its graph.

4. (0, 1) (1, −2)

slope $= \frac{\text{up or down}}{\text{right or left}} = \frac{-3}{1} = -3$

y-intercept = __1__

5. (−2, −2) (2, −2)

slope $= \frac{\text{up or down}}{\text{right or left}} = \frac{0}{4} = 0$

y-intercept = __−2__

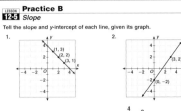

PRACTICE 12-5

LESSON 12-5 **Practice B**
Slope

Tell the slope and *y*-intercept of each line, given its graph.

1. (1, 3) (2, 2) (3, 1) — __−1, 4__

2. (3, 2) (0, −2) — __$\frac{4}{3}$, −2__

Tell the slope and *y*-intercept, given the equation.

3. $y = 2x + 3$ __2, 3__
4. $y = \frac{1}{3}x - 5$ __$\frac{1}{3}$, −5__
5. $y = 4x$ __4, 0__
6. $y = -4x + 1$ __−4, 1__
7. $y = x - 4$ __1, −4__
8. $y = -2x - 8$ __−2, −8__

Graph each line, given the equation.

9. $y = -\frac{1}{2}x + 5$

10. $y = -4$

Graph each line, given the equation. Solve for y when necessary.

20. $2x + y = -1$ **$y = -2x - 1$**
21. $2x + 5y = 0$ **$y = -\frac{2}{5}x$**
22. $3y - 2x = 3$ **$y = \frac{2}{3}x + 1$**

Graph each pair of points. Find the slope and y-intercept of each line that connects the points in each pair.

23. $(3, 2), (-2, -3)$ **1; −1**
24. $(-4, -3), (0, -4)$ **$-\frac{1}{4}$; −4**
25. $(-3, 3), (3, 5)$ **$\frac{1}{3}$; 4**

Graph each pair of points. Find the slope and y-intercept of the line containing each pair of points. Then write an equation for the line in slope-intercept form.

26. $(3, 2), (4, 2)$ **0; 2; $y = 2$**
27. $(-2, -6), (2, 2)$ **2; −2; $y = 2x - 2$**
28. $(-2, 13), (1, 4)$ **−3; 7; $y = -3x + 7$**
29. $(-2, -3), (2, 3)$ **29. $\frac{3}{2}$; 0; $y = \frac{3}{2}x$**
30. $(2, -3), (3, -5)$ **−2; 1; $y = -2x + 1$**
31. $(-5, -3), (4, -3)$ **0; −3; $y = -3$**
32. A carpenter is building a staircase leading up to a loft. The slope of the staircase is $\frac{1}{2}$. If the staircase has 30 steps and the depth of each step is 8 inches (from its edge to the bottom of the next step), how high up is the loft? **120 inches**

33. ***CONSUMER MATH*** The table shows the value of a used car over time.

a. Draw a line showing the change in value from a one-year-old car to a three-year-old car.

b. Find the slope of the line. **−1,000**

c. Tell whether the slope is positive or negative. **negative**

d. What does the slope show about the value of the car? **The older the car is, the lower the value.**

Value of a Used Ford Mustang to the Nearest Thousand Dollars

Age	Value
1 year	\$14,000
2 years	\$13,000
3 years	\$12,000

Source: Kelley Blue Book

34. ***WHAT'S THE QUESTION?*** A line has point A at $(3, 2)$ and point B at $(4, 3)$. What question could you answer about this line? **Possible answer: What is the slope of the line?**

35. ***WRITE ABOUT IT*** Explain how you can tell whether the slope of a linear graph is positive or negative.

36. ***CHALLENGE*** Describe the slope of a line that contains points $(3, 4)$ and $(3, 6)$. **Possible answer: The rise is 2 and the run is 0, which means $\frac{\text{rise}}{\text{run}} = \frac{2}{0}$. Since you cannot divide by 0, the slope cannot be defined.**

Spiral Review

Solve. (Lesson 11-6)

37. $\frac{b}{4} < 8$ **$b < 32$**
38. $\frac{s}{-8} \geq 1.6$ **$s \leq -12.8$**
39. $5m > 1.5$ **$m > 0.3$**
40. $-9y \leq 108$ **$y \geq -12$**

41. **TEST PREP** Use the pattern in the sequence −2, ▢, 0, 1, 2, . . . to find the missing integer. (Lesson 12-2) **C**

A 3 B −3 C −1 D 1

42. **TEST PREP** Evaluate the expression $x - y$ for $x = 6$ and $y = -4$. (Lesson 2-7) **J**

F −10 G −2 H 2 J 10

Answers

20–31, 33, 35. Complete answers on p. A6

Journal

Have students describe places where they can see examples of positive and negative slopes in the real world (e.g., roofs, mountains).

Test Prep Doctor

In Exercise 42, students who selected **H** may be rushing in their computation. Students who selected **F** or **G** may be confusing negative signs when substituting to evaluate the expression. Have all these students write out the expression they must evaluate and then substitute the values into the expression before they compute. Discourage using mental math to quickly evaluate the expression.

CHALLENGE 12-5

LESSON 12-5 **Challenge**
Find the x-Intercept

The y-intercept of a nonvertical line is the point where the line intersects the y-axis. To find the y-intercept, set $x = 0$ in the equation of a line and solve for y. The coordinates of the y-intercept are $(0, y)$.

Similarly, a nonhorizontal line has an x-intercept. This is the point where the line intersects the x-axis. To find the x-intercept, set $y = 0$ in the equation of a line and solve for x. The coordinates of the x-intercept are $(x, 0)$.

Example: Find the x-intercept for $y = 5x + 10$.

$$0 = 5x + 10$$
$$-10 = 5x$$
$$-2 = x$$

The coordinates of the x-intercept for $y = 5x + 10$ are $(-2, 0)$.

Find the coordinates of the x-intercept for each equation.

1. $y = 8x + 16$ **(−2, 0)**
2. $y = 3x - 6$ **(2, 0)**
3. $y = 4x + 12$ **(−3, 0)**
4. $y = 6x - 24$ **(4, 0)**
5. $y = \frac{1}{2}x + 4$ **(−8, 0)**
6. $y = \frac{1}{3}x - 9$ **(27, 0)**

Find the coordinates of the x-intercept and the y-intercept for each equation.

7. $y = 4x + 4$ **(−1, 0), (0, 4)**
8. $y = 6x - 18$ **(3, 0), (0, −18)**
9. $y = 4x + 2$ **$\left(-\frac{1}{2}, 0\right), (0, 2)$**
10. $y = \frac{1}{3}x + 1$ **(−3, 0), (0, 1)**
11. $y = \frac{3}{4}x - 9$ **(12, 0), (0, −9)**
12. $y = \frac{1}{2}x - \frac{1}{2}$ **$(1, 0), \left(0, -\frac{1}{2}\right)$**
13. $y = \frac{x}{2} + 2$ **(−4, 0), (0, 2)**
14. $y - 1 = 3x - 7$ **(2, 0), (0, −6)**
15. $y = 3x - \frac{1}{2}$ **$\left(\frac{1}{6}, 0\right), \left(0, -\frac{1}{2}\right)$**

PROBLEM SOLVING 12-5

LESSON 12-5 **Problem Solving**
Slope

Write the correct answer.

This graph shows the salary paid each year to a major-league athlete over the period of a 4-year contract.

Athlete's Salary
Salary (\$ millions): 0–7
Contract Year: 1, 2, 3, 4

1. In which year will the athlete receive the most money? **the last year**
2. What is the slope of the line? **slope = 1**
3. What conclusion about this contract can you draw from the graph? **Possible answer: The longer the contract lasts, the more money the athlete earns.**

Choose the letter of the best answer.

4. At the Indianapolis 500, racecars can go as fast as 170 mi/h. If you were to draw a graph to show the racecar accelerating from 0 to 170 mi/h, what might the slope of the line be? Assume the y-axis is mi/h.

A −1 C 1
B $\frac{1}{10}$ **(D)** 10

5. If you were to draw a graph relating your age in months to your height in inches, what might the slope of the line be?

F −1 H 1
(G) $\frac{1}{10}$ J 10

6. It is getting very cold outside—the temperature is dropping about a degree every hour. If you were to draw a graph relating the temperature in degrees to time in hours, what might the slope of the line be?

(A) −1 C 1
B $\frac{1}{10}$ D 10

7. You forgot to return your library books, and now they are overdue. If you were to draw a graph relating the overdue fines to time in months, what might the slope of the line be?

F −1 **(H)** 1
G $\frac{1}{10}$ J 10

Lesson Quiz

Tell the slope and y-intercept of each line, given the equation.

1. $y = x - 5$ 1; −5
2. $y = \frac{3}{4}x$ $\frac{3}{4}$; 0
3. $y = -2x + 7$ −2; 7
4. Graph the line, given the equation $y = \frac{1}{2}x - 2$.

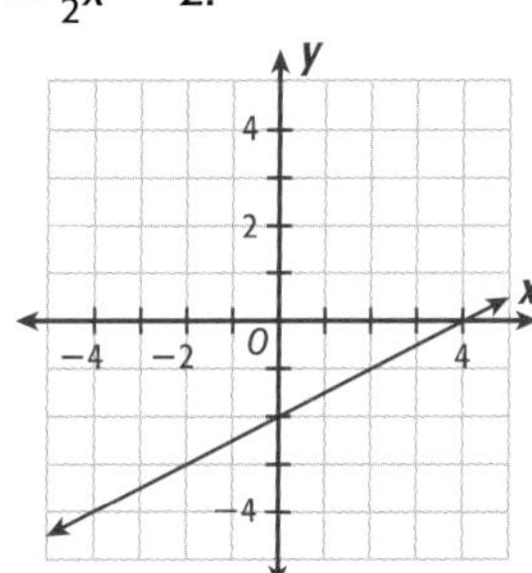

Available on Daily Transparency in CRB

Chapter 12 Mid-Chapter Quiz

Purpose: *To assess students' mastery of concepts and skills in Lessons 12-1 through 12-5*

Assessment Resources 

Section 12A Quiz

Assessment Resources .... p. 31

 ***Test and Practice Generator* CD-ROM**

Additional mid-chapter assessment items in both multiple-choice and free-response format may be generated for any objective in Lessons 12-1 through 12-5.

Answers

1.

Input	Rule	Output
x	$3x - 1$	y
−3	3(−3) − 1	−10
−2	3(−2) − 1	−7
−1	3(−1) − 1	−4

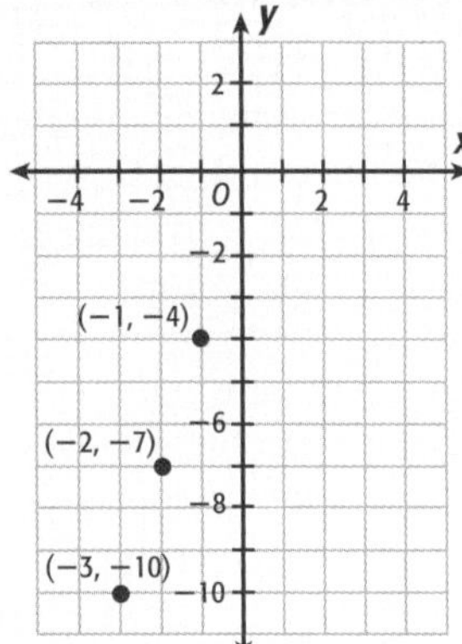

2.

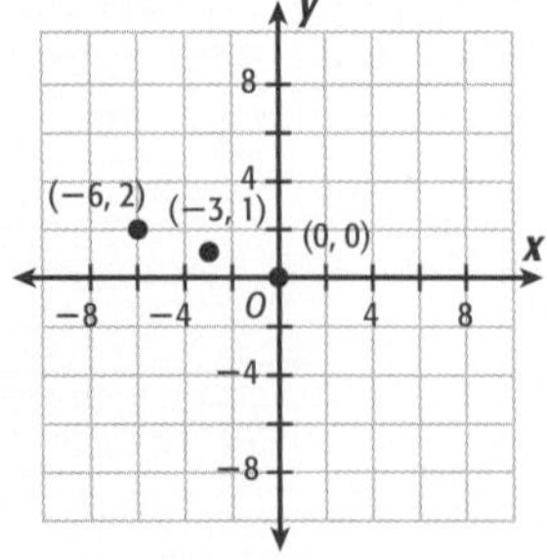

Chapter 12 Mid-Chapter Quiz

Mid-Chapter Quiz

LESSON 12-1 (pp. 604–607)

Make a function table, and graph the resulting ordered pairs.

1. $y = 3x - 1$

Input	Rule	Output
x	$3x - 1$	y
−3		
−2		
−1		

2. $y = x \div (-3)$

Input	Rule	Output
x	$x \div (-3)$	y
−6	$-6 \div (-3)$	2
−3	$-3 \div (-3)$	1
0	$0 \div (-3)$	0

3. $y = x^2 + 2$

Input	Rule	Output
x	$x^2 + 2$	y
−2	$(-2)^2 + 2$	6
0	$0^2 + 2$	2
2	$2^2 + 2$	6

LESSON 12-2 (pp. 608–611)

Find a function that describes each sequence. Use the function to find the next three terms in the sequence.

4. 99, 199, 299, 399, . . . **$y = 100n - 1$; 499, 599, 699**

5. 12, 13, 14, 15, . . . **$y = n + 11$; 16, 17, 18**

6. 21, 41, 61, 81, . . . **$y = 20n + 1$; 101, 121, 141**

7. Jamie put 15 cents in a jar on Sunday. Each day that week, he put double the amount that he had put in the jar the day before. Write a sequence to find how much money Jamie put in the jar on Friday.
15, 30, 60, 120, 240, 480, 480 cents

LESSON 12-3 (pp. 612–615)

Find the domain and range of each graph.

8.

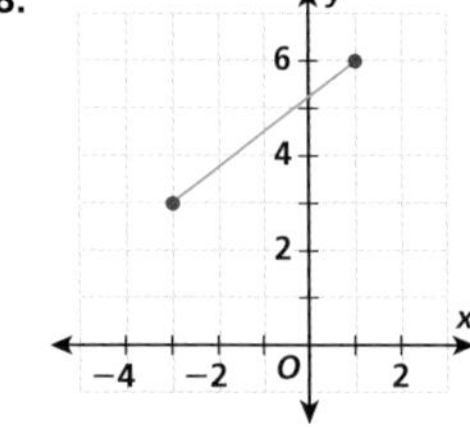

D: $-3 \le x \le 1$; R: $3 \le y \le 6$

9.

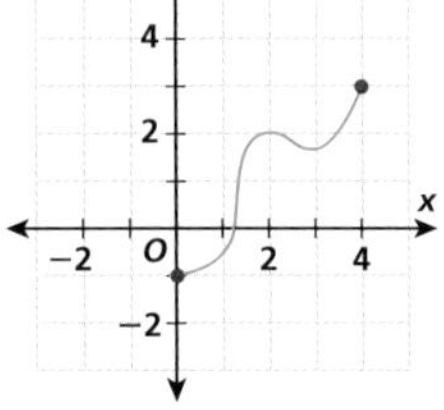

D: $0 \le x \le 4$; R: $-1 \le y \le 3$

10.

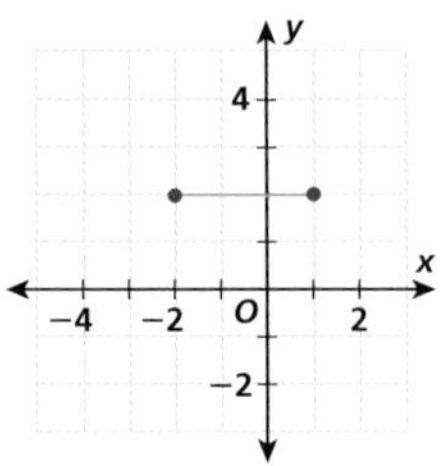

D: $-2 \le x \le 1$; R: $y = 2$

LESSON 12-4 (pp. 616–619)

Solve each equation for *y*. Then graph the linear function.

11. $3x + y = 2$ **$y = -3x + 2$**

12. $4y = -20x$ **$y = -5x$**

13. $3y - 4x + 6 = 0$ **$y = \frac{4}{3}x - 2$**

LESSON 12-5 (pp. 620–623)

Give the slope and *y*-intercept of each line, given the equation.

14. $y = 4x + 1$ **4, 1**

15. $y = \frac{3}{4}x$ **$\frac{3}{4}$, 0**

16. $y + 2x = 6$ **−2, 6**

3.

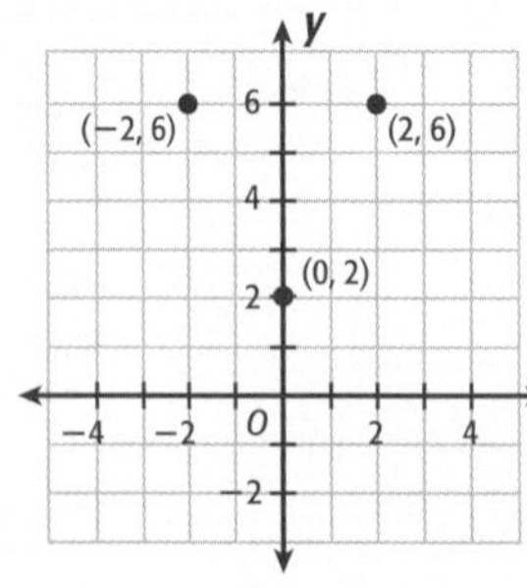

12.

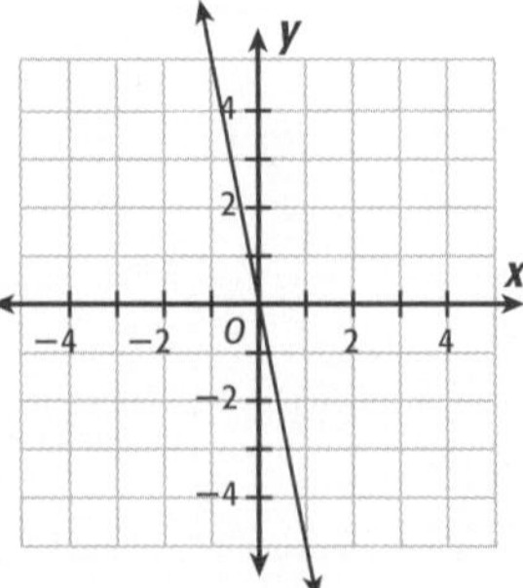

11.

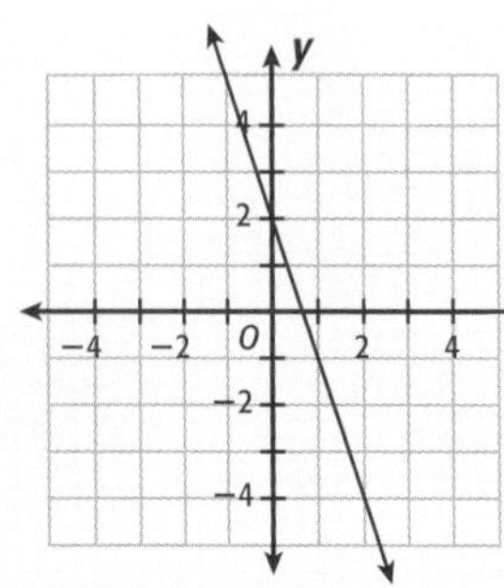

13.

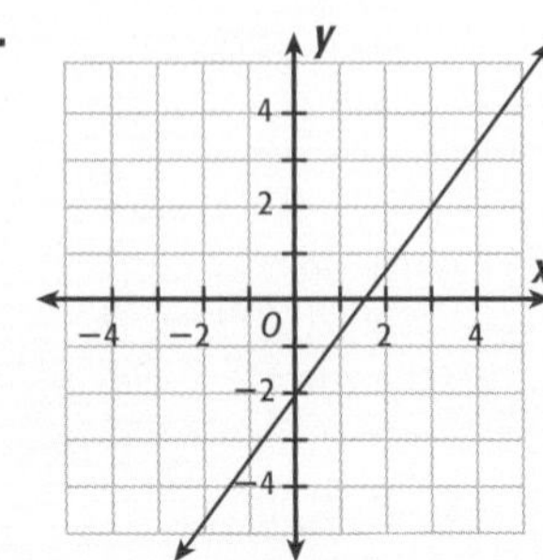

Focus on Problem Solving

Understand the Problem

• Sequence and prioritize information

When you are reading a math problem, putting events in order, or in *sequence,* can help you understand the problem better. It helps to *prioritize* the information when you put it in sequence. To prioritize, you decide which of the information in your list is most important. The most important information has highest priority.

Use the information in the list or table to answer each question.

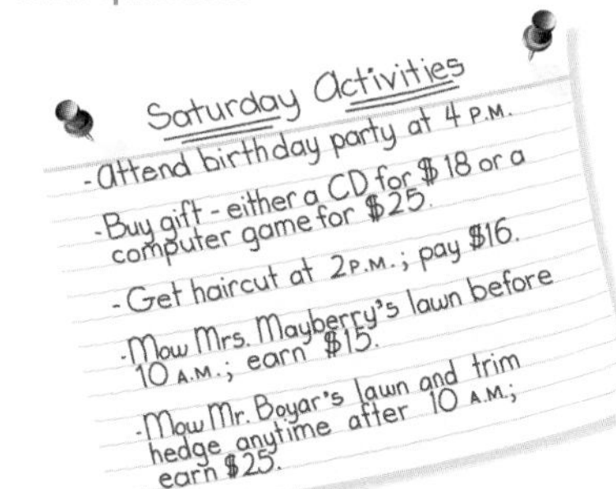

Saturday Activities
- Attend birthday party at 4 P.M.
- Buy gift - either a CD for $18 or a computer game for $25.
- Get haircut at 2 P.M.; pay $16.
- Mow Mrs. Mayberry's lawn before 10 A.M.; earn $15.
- Mow Mr. Boyar's lawn and trim hedge anytime after 10 A.M.; earn $25.

1. The list at right shows all of the things that Roderick has to do on Saturday. He starts the day without any money.
   - **a.** Which two activities on Roderick's list must be done before any of the other activities? Do these two activities have higher or lower priority?
   - **b.** Is there more than one way that he can order his activities? Explain.
   - **c.** List the order in which Roderick's activities could occur on Saturday.

2. Tara and her family will visit Ocean World Park from 9:30 to 4:00. They want to see the waterskiing show at 10:00. Each show in the park is 50 minutes long. The time they choose to eat lunch will depend on the schedule they choose for seeing the shows.
   - **a.** Which of the information given in the paragraph above has the highest priority? Which has the lowest priority?
   - **b.** List the order in which they can see all of the shows, including the time they will see each.
   - **c.** At what time should they plan to have lunch?

Show Times at Ocean World Park

9:00, 12:00	Underwater acrobats
9:00, 3:00	Whale acts
10:00, 2:00	Dolphin acts
10:00, 1:00	Waterskiing
11:00, 4:00	Aquarium tour

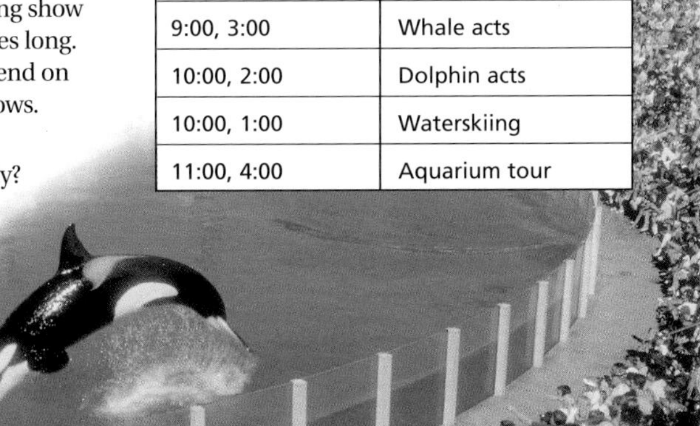

Focus on Problem Solving

Purpose: *To focus on better understanding the problem by sequencing and prioritizing information*

Problem Solving Resources

Problem Solving Process

This page focuses on the first step of the problem-solving process: **Understand the Problem**

Discuss

Have students discuss how they sequenced and prioritized the information in the problems.

Possible answers:

1. by the time of day of each activity
2. by the time of each show, based on seeing the waterskiing show at 10:00

Answers

1. a. Mow Mrs. Mayberry's lawn; mow Mr. Boyar's lawn and trim hedge; higher priority.

b. Only the activities *get haircut* and *buy gift* can be switched. The rest of the order is predetermined by time and money restrictions.

c. Possible answer: Mow Mrs. Mayberry's lawn, mow Mr. Boyar's lawn and trim hedge, buy gift, get haircut, and attend birthday party.

2. a. They want to see the waterskiing show at 10:00. They will eat lunch whenever it is convenient.

b. waterskiing at 10:00, aquarium tour at 11:00, underwater acrobats at 12:00, dolphin acts at 2:00, and whale acts at 3:00

c. 1:00

Section 12B

Nonlinear Functions and Set Theory

One-Minute Section Planner

Lesson	Materials	Resources
Hands-On Lab 12A Explore Nonlinear Functions **NCTM:** Algebra, Geometry, Reasoning and Proof, Representation **NAEP:** Algebra 1a ☐ SAT-9 ☐ SAT-10 ☐ ITBS ☑ CTBS ☐ MAT ☑ CAT		• *Hands-On Lab Activities,* pp. 117–120
Lesson 12-6 Nonlinear Functions **NCTM:** Algebra, Reasoning and Proof, Communication, Connections **NAEP:** Algebra 1e ☐ SAT-9 ☐ SAT-10 ☐ ITBS ☑ CTBS ☐ MAT ☑ CAT	Optional Graph paper *(CRB, p. 87)* Teaching Transparency T22 *(CRB)* Teaching Transparency for Close T23 *(CRB)*	• *Chapter 12 Resource Book,* pp. 54–62 • Daily Transparency T21, CRB • Additional Examples Transparencies T24–T26, CRB • *Alternate Openers: Explorations,* p. 100
Lesson 12-7 Rates of Change **NCTM:** Algebra, Reasoning and Proof, Communication **NAEP:** Algebra 4d ☐ SAT-9 ☐ SAT-10 ☐ ITBS ☑ CTBS ☐ MAT ☑ CAT	Optional Graph paper *(CRB, p. 87)* String Glue or tape	• *Chapter 12 Resource Book,* pp. 63–71 • Daily Transparency T27, CRB • Additional Examples Transparencies T28–T30, CRB • *Alternate Openers: Explorations,* p. 101
Lesson 12-8 Set Theory **NCTM:** Algebra, Reasoning and Proof, Communication, Connections **NAEP:** Data Analysis and Probability 1a ☐ SAT-9 ☐ SAT-10 ☐ ITBS ☐ CTBS ☐ MAT ☐ CAT	Optional Maps of Europe, Asia, Africa, South America Teaching Transparency T32 *(CRB)*	• *Chapter 12 Resource Book,* pp. 72–80 • Daily Transparency T31, CRB • Additional Examples Transparencies T33–T34, CRB • *Alternate Openers: Explorations,* p. 102
Extension Venn Diagrams **NCTM:** Algebra, Reasoning and Proof, Connections **NAEP:** Data Analysis and Probability 1b ☐ SAT-9 ☐ SAT-10 ☐ ITBS ☐ CTBS ☐ MAT ☐ CAT	Optional Teaching Transparency T35 *(CRB)*	• Additional Examples Transparencies T36–T37, CRB
Section 12B Assessment		• Section 12B Quiz, AR p. 32 • *Test and Practice Generator* CD-ROM

SAT = *Stanford Achievement Tests* **ITBS** = *Iowa Test of Basic Skills* **CTBS** = *Comprehensive Test of Basic Skills/Terra Nova*
MAT = *Metropolitan Achievement Test* **CAT** = *California Achievement Test*

NCTM—Complete standards can be found on pages T27–T33. **NAEP**—Complete standards can be found on pages A35–A39.

SE = *Student Edition* **TE** = *Teacher's Edition* **AR** = *Assessment Resources* **CRB** = *Chapter Resource Book* **MK** = *Manipulatives Kit*

Section Overview

Nonlinear Functions — *Hands-On Lab 12A, Lesson 12-6*

Why? Students should be able to differentiate between linear and nonlinear functions because both types of graphs will be encountered as students continue their studies in mathematics and science.

A **nonlinear** function is a function whose graph is not a straight line.

$y = -x^2$

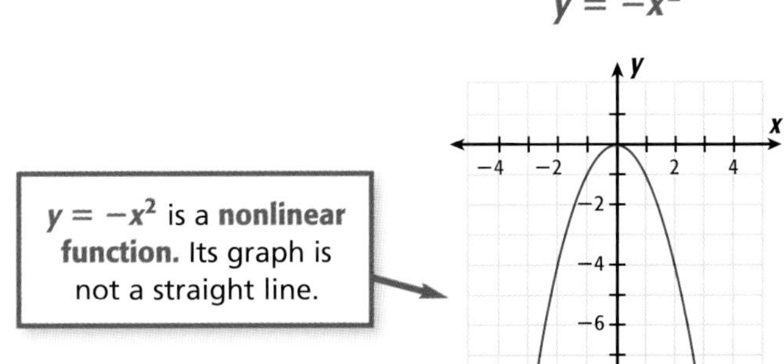

Rates of Change — *Lesson 12-7*

Why? Scientists use mathematical models, such as equations and functions, to describe such real-world phenomena as biological and economic systems. *Rate of change* is an important consideration in developing a mathematical model.

The slope reflects the constant rate of change for each interval on the graph.

Linear Function	Nonlinear Function
The graph of a linear function shows a **constant rate of change.**	The graph of a nonlinear function shows a nonlinear, or **variable, rate of change.**

The rate of change varies for each interval on the graph.

Set Theory — *Lesson 12-8*

Why? Students will need a basic understanding of set notation and its uses when they are introduced to more formal definitions and descriptions of sets in algebra.

A **set** is a collection of distinct objects, or elements.

Roster Notation

$S = \{-2, -1, 0, 1, 2\}$

lists all elements

Set-Builder Notation

$S = \{x|x$ is an integer greater than -3 and less than $3\}$

All of the members in set T are in set S.

If $T = \{-2, -1\}$, then $T \subset S$, or T is a **subset** of S.

12A
Explore Nonlinear Functions

Pacing: Traditional 1 day
Block $\frac{1}{2}$ day

Objective: To use square tiles to model linear and nonlinear functions

Materials: Square tiles

Lab Resources

Hands-On Lab Activities. . . pp. 117–120

Using the Pages

Discuss with students how to use the square tiles to model linear and nonlinear functions.

1. Model the next two figures in the pattern, and make a table of the perimeter and area for each step modeled.

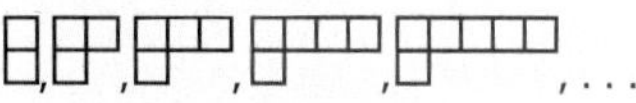

Perimeter	Area (number of tiles)
6	2
8	3
10	4
12	5
14	6

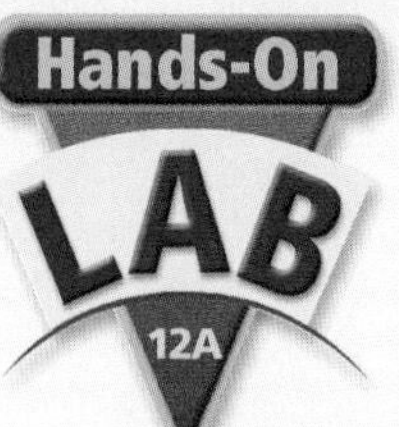

Explore Nonlinear Functions

Use with Lesson 12-6

REMEMBER
- Linear functions can be represented by straight lines on a coordinate plane.
- The graphs of nonlinear functions are not straight lines.

You can use patterns involving squares and rectangles to explore the difference between linear and nonlinear functions.

Activity

1 The perimeter of a 1-inch-long square tile is 4 inches. Place 2 tiles together side by side. The perimeter of this figure is 6 inches.

1 in. 1 in. 1 in. 1 in. — 2 in. 1 in. 1 in. 2 in.

a. Complete the table at right by adding tiles side by side and finding the perimeter of each new figure.

b. If x equals the number of tiles, what is the difference between consecutive x-values? If y equals the perimeter, what is the difference between consecutive y-values? How do these differences compare?

c. Graph the ordered pairs from your table on a coordinate plane. Is the graph linear or nonlinear? What does the table indicate about this type of function?

Number of Tiles	Perimeter (in.)
1	4
2	6
3	8
4	10
5	12

2 Draw the pattern at right and complete the next two sets of dots in the pattern.

a. Complete the table at right. Let x equal the number of dots in the top row of each set, and let y equal the total number of dots in the set.

b. What is the difference between consecutive x-values? What is the difference between consecutive y-values? How do these differences compare?

c. Graph the ordered pairs on a coordinate plane. Is the graph linear or nonlinear? What does the table indicate about this type of function?

x	y
2	3
3	8
4	15
5	24
6	35

Answers

Activity

1. b. There is a constant difference of 1 between consecutive x-values and a constant difference of 2 between consecutive y-values. Both variables are changing at a constant rate.

c.

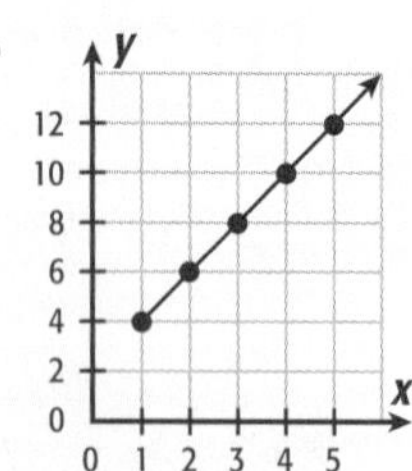

Linear; the table indicates that, for a linear function, a constant change in one variable indicates a constant change in the other variable.

2. b. There is a constant difference of 1 between consecutive x-values and a varying difference between consecutive y-values. One variable is changing at a constant rate, and the other is not.

c.

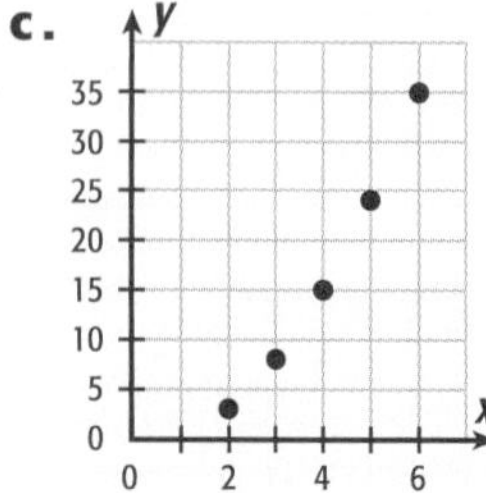

Nonlinear; the table indicates that, for a nonlinear function, while the difference between consecutive x-values is constant, the difference between consecutive y-values varies.

3. b. There is a constant difference of 4 between consecutive x-values and a varying difference between consecutive y-values. One variable is changing at a constant rate, and the other is not.

c. Nonlinear, because while the difference between consecutive x-values is constant, the difference between consecutive y-values varies.

d.

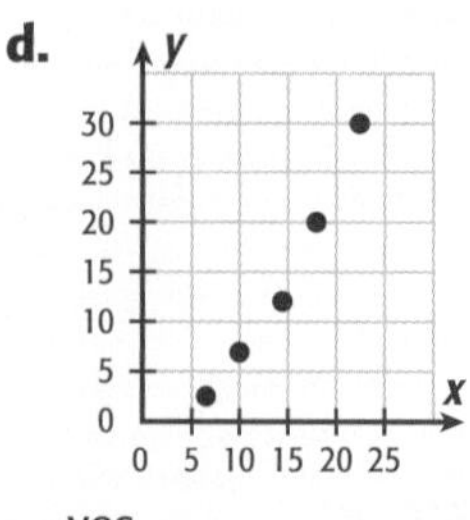

yes

3 Use square tiles to model rectangles of the following sizes: 1 × 2, 2 × 3, 3 × 4, 4 × 5, and 5 × 6. An example of the first three rectangles is shown.

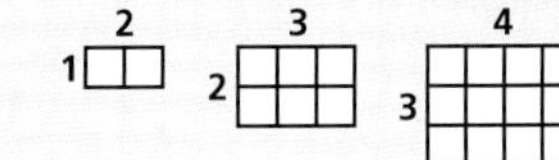

a. Find the perimeter and area of each rectangle. Complete the table at right. Let x = perimeter and y = area.

b. What is the difference between consecutive x-values? What is the difference between consecutive y-values? How do these differences compare?

c. Using what you have observed in **1** and **2**, tell whether the relationship between x and y in the table is linear or nonlinear.

d. Graph the ordered pairs from your table on a coordinate plane. Does the shape of your graph agree with the type of function you gave in **c**?

Rectangle	x	y
1 × 2	6	2
2 × 3	10	6
3 × 4	14	12
4 × 5	18	20
5 × 6	22	30

Think and Discuss

1. Refer to **1** and **2** to explain how linear and nonlinear functions compare.
2. Is $y = x^2$ linear or nonlinear? Explain your answer.
3. If $x = 1$ and keeps increasing by 1, are $y = x^2$ and $x = y^2$ the same graph? Does $x = y^2$ represent a linear or nonlinear function? Explain your answer.

Try This

1. Use square tiles to model each pattern.
2. Model the next two sets in each pattern using square tiles.
3. Complete each table.
4. Explain whether each function is linear or nonlinear.

Pattern 1

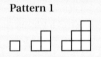

Perimeter	Area
4	1
8	3
12	6
16	10
20	15

Pattern 2

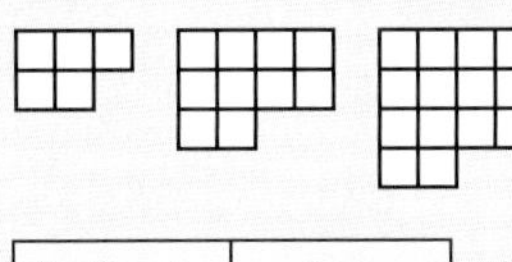

Perimeter	Area
10	5
14	10
18	17
22	26
26	37

Pattern 3

Perimeter	Area
4	1
6	2
8	3
10	4
12	5

Answers

Think and Discuss

1. For a linear function, both variables change at a constant rate. For a non-linear function, one variable changes at a constant rate, but the other does not.
2. Nonlinear; the difference between each consecutive x-value is constant, but the difference between each consecutive y-value varies.
3. No; the equation $x = y^2$ is a nonlinear function because the difference between each consecutive x-value is constant, but the difference between each consecutive y-value varies.

Try This

2. **Pattern 1:**

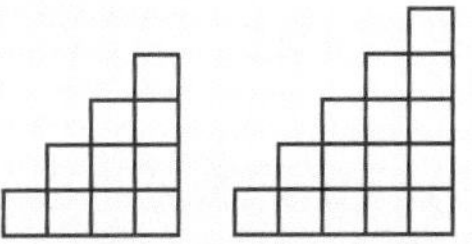

Pattern 2:

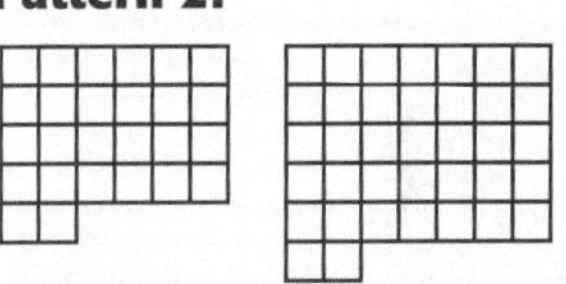

Pattern 3:

4. **Pattern 1:** nonlinear; there is not a constant change between consecutive y-values.
Pattern 2: nonlinear; there is not a constant change between consecutive y-values.
Pattern 3: linear; there is a constant change of 1 between consecutive y-values.

12-6 Organizer

Pacing: Traditional 1 day
Block $\frac{1}{2}$ day

Objective: Students identify nonlinear functions.

Warm Up

Tell the slope and y-intercept of each line, given the equation.

1. $y = -8x + 7$ $-8; 7$

2. $y = \frac{1}{7}x - 1$ $\frac{1}{7}; -1$

3. $y = 9x$ $9; 0$

4. $y = -\frac{2}{3}x + 5$ $-\frac{2}{3}; 5$

Problem of the Day

Name a value of x for which $y = 5x$ is less than $y = x^2$, for which $y = 5x$ equals $y = x^2$, and for which $y = 5x$ is greater than $y = x^2$. any x less than 0 and greater than 5; $x = 0$ or 5; any x between 0 and 5

Available on Daily Transparency in CRB

Math Fact !

A linear function does not have a maximum or a minimum value. Nonlinear functions, however, may have a maximum or minimum value.

12-6 Nonlinear Functions

Learn to identify nonlinear functions.

Vocabulary
nonlinear function

As you inflate a balloon, its volume increases. The table at right shows the increase in volume of a round balloon as its radius changes. Do you think a graph of the data would or would not be a straight line? You can make a graph to find out.

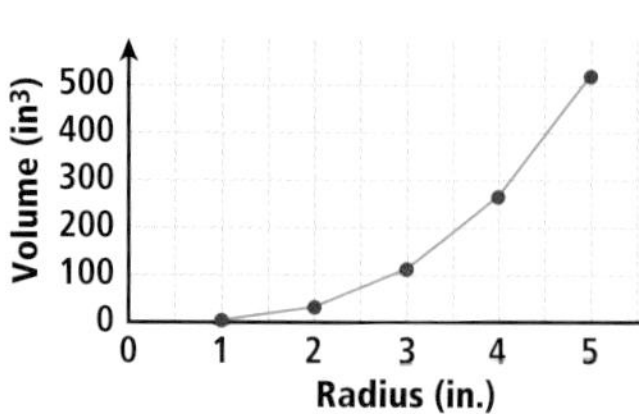

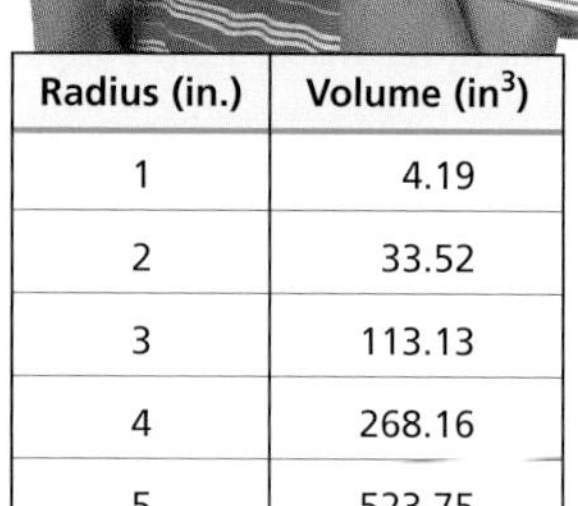

Radius (in.)	Volume (in^3)
1	4.19
2	33.52
3	113.13
4	268.16
5	523.75

A **nonlinear function** is a function whose graph is not a straight line.

EXAMPLE 1 Identifying Graphs of Nonlinear Functions

Tell whether the graph is linear or nonlinear.

A

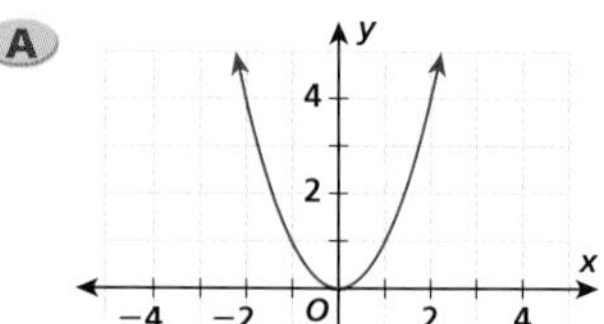

The graph is not a straight line, so it is nonlinear.

B

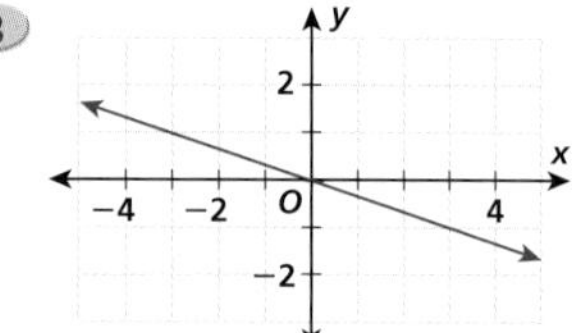

The graph is a straight line, so it is linear.

C

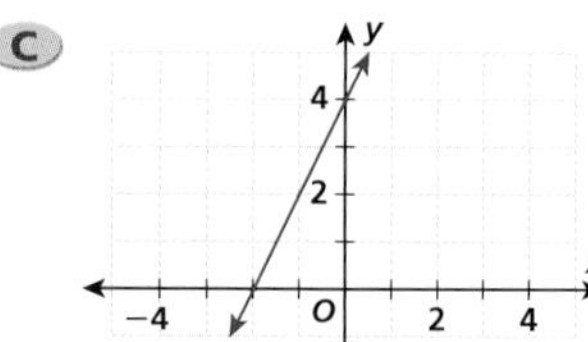

The graph is a straight line, so it is linear.

D

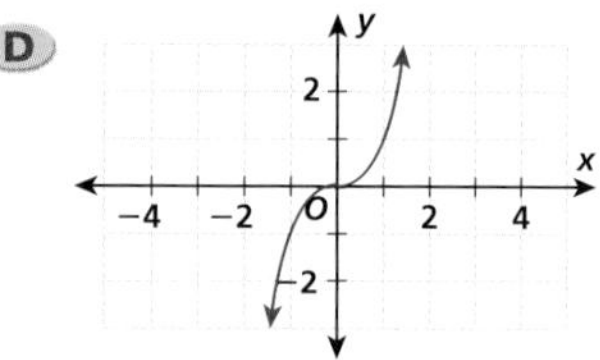

The graph is not a straight line, so it is nonlinear.

1 Introduce

Alternate Opener

EXPLORATION

12-6 Nonlinear Functions

The graph below shows the value of a computer each year it is used for the first three years.

1. Use the points on the graph to complete the table.

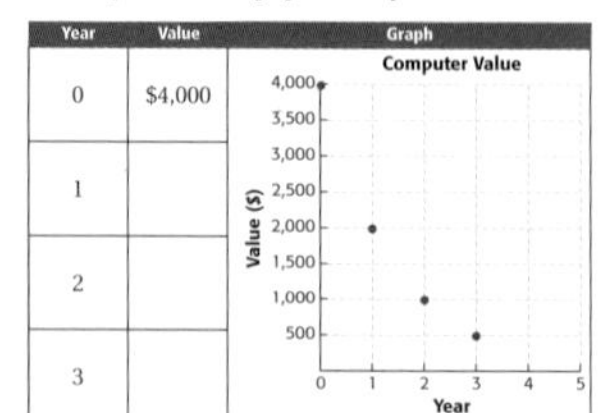

Year	Value
0	$4,000
1	
2	
3	

2. Compare the loss of value between each consecutive year. Is the computer losing the same amount of value from year to year?

3. Use the graph to predict the value of the computer in year 4.

Think and Discuss

4. Discuss why you think computers lose value so quickly.
5. Explain why the graph is nonlinear.

Motivate

Discuss the rate at which living things grow. Ask such questions as: "Does a tree grow at the same rate throughout its life? Does a child?" Have students describe how they think different living things grow. You may wish to direct this discussion to a single aspect of growth, such as height. Ask students to consider what the graph of a tree's height throughout its lifetime might look like. The graph might look like a line with a positive slope at first and then change into a horizontal line.

Exploration worksheet and answers on Chapter 12 Resource Book pp. 55 and 98

2 Teach

Lesson Presentation

Guided Instruction

In this lesson, students learn to identify nonlinear functions. Point out that nonlinear functions are similar to linear functions in that they both have an independent variable, x, and a dependent variable, y. Likewise, you can find the domain and range of nonlinear functions. However, the graphs of nonlinear functions are not straight lines.

Teaching Tip You may wish to mention that the points on the graphs of most nonlinear functions are connected by a smooth curve, not by a single line or separate line segments.

You can use a function table to determine whether ordered pairs describe a linear or a nonlinear relationship.

For a function that has a linear relationship, when the difference between each successive input value is constant, the difference between each corresponding output value is *constant*.

For a function that has a nonlinear relationship, when the difference between each successive input value is constant, the difference between each corresponding output value *varies*.

EXAMPLE 2 Identifying Nonlinear Relationships in Function Tables

Tell whether the function represented in each table has a linear or nonlinear relationship.

A

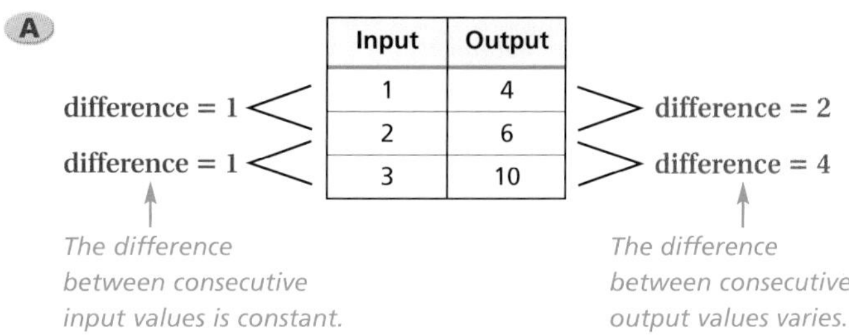

Input	Output
1	4
2	6
3	10

The function represented in the table has a nonlinear relationship.

B

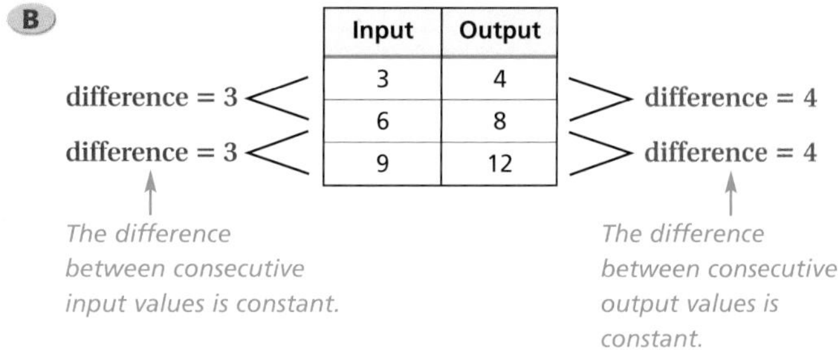

Input	Output
3	4
6	8
9	12

The function represented in the table has a linear relationship.

Think and Discuss

1. **Tell** whether the relationship between the area of a square and the length of its sides is linear or nonlinear. Explain your answer.
2. **Give an example** of a nonlinear relationship between two sets of data and a linear relationship between two sets of data.

Additional Examples

Example  1

Tell whether the graph is linear or nonlinear.

A.

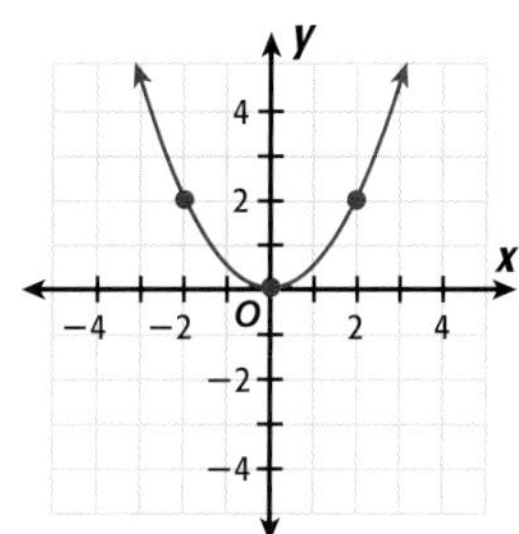

It is not a straight line, so the graph is nonlinear.

B.

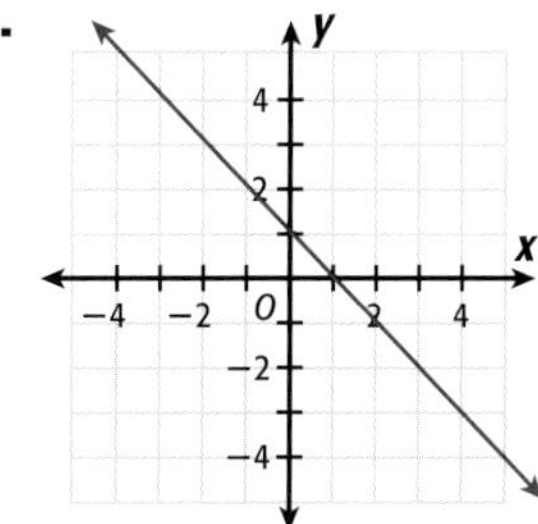

It is a straight line, so the graph is linear.

Example 2

Tell whether the function represented in the table has a linear or nonlinear relationship.

x	y
1	2
2	5
3	11

The function represented in the table is nonlinear.

3 Close

Reaching All Learners

Through Graphic Cues

Have students sketch the graphs of $y = x$ and $y = x^2$ on the same set of axes, using the integer values of x between -4 and 4. Have students use the graphs to compare how y changes as x changes. You may wish to point out that the graphs intersect at (0, 0) and (1, 1). Remind students to use a smooth curve to connect the points in their graph of $y = x^2$.

Possible answer: As x gets larger, y increases much faster in $y = x^2$ than in $y = x$; In $y = x^2$, y takes on only nonnegative values, while it takes on all values in $y = x$.

Summarize

Have students compare linear and nonlinear functions that are

- represented by a graph. Possible answer: The graph of a linear function is a straight line, while the graph of a nonlinear function is not straight.
- represented by a table. Possible answer: The differences between the y-values in a linear function will be equal, while the differences in the y-values in a nonlinear function will either increase or decrease.

Answers to Think and Discuss

1. Since the area of a square increases at a greater rate than the side lengths, the relationship is nonlinear.
2. Possible answers: a person's height and weight over time; the number of tickets sold for a football game and the amount of money earned

12-6 PRACTICE & ASSESS

Students may want to refer back to the lesson examples.

Assignment Guide

If you finished Example 1 assign:

Core 1–3, 7–9, 13, 17–25
Enriched 1–3, 7–9, 13, 17–25

If you finished Example 2 assign:

Core 1–12, 17–25
Enriched 1–11 odd, 13–25

Answers

10. nonlinear
11. nonlinear
12. linear

12-6 Exercises

FOR EXTRA PRACTICE see page 681

internet connect
Homework Help Online
go.hrw.com Keyword: MS4 12-6

GUIDED PRACTICE

See Example 1 Tell whether the graph is linear or nonlinear.

1.
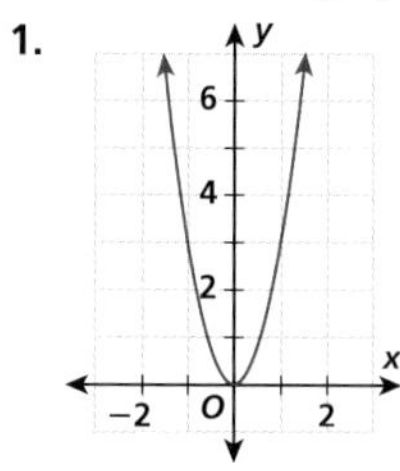
nonlinear

2.
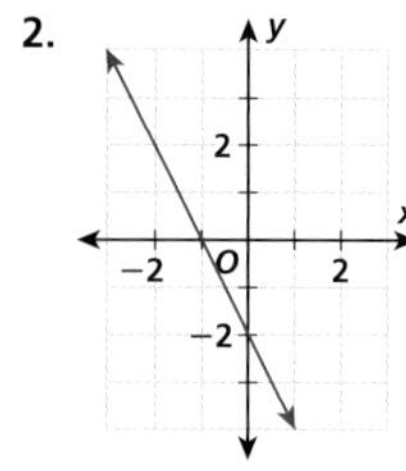
linear

3.
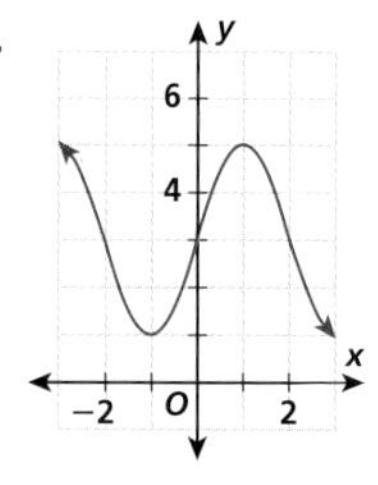
nonlinear

See Example 2 Tell whether the function represented in each table has a linear or nonlinear relationship.

4.

x	y
2	5
4	7
6	9

linear

5.

x	y
10	100
20	400
30	900

nonlinear

6.

x	y
1	6
2	9
3	14

nonlinear

INDEPENDENT PRACTICE

See Example 1 Tell whether the graph is linear or nonlinear.

7.
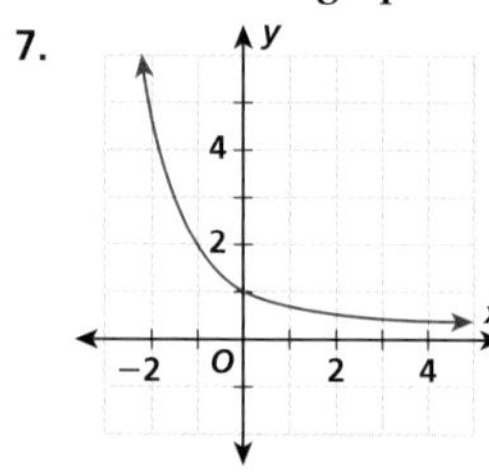
nonlinear

8.
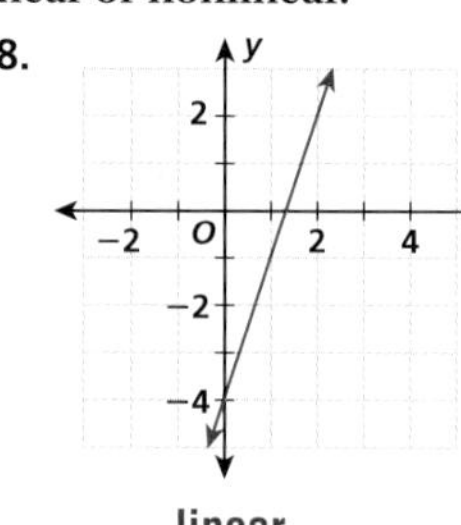
linear

9.
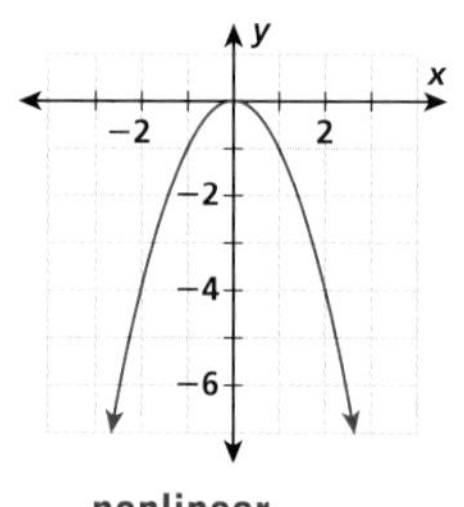
nonlinear

See Example 2 Tell whether the function represented in each table has a linear or nonlinear relationship.

10.

x	y
4	25
8	36
12	49

11.

x	y
25	125
50	2,000
75	5,125

12.

x	y
1	822
2	824
3	826

Math Background

Recall that you can use another notation, called *function notation*, to represent a function. In this notation, $y = f(x)$.

An *even* function is a function with the following property: $f(-x) = f(x)$ for all x in the domain of the function. The function $y = x^2$, graphed in Example 1A, is an example of an even function. An even function is symmetrical with respect to the y-axis.

An *odd* function is a function with the following property: $f(-x) = -f(x)$ for all x in the domain of the function. The function $v = s^3$ is an example of an odd function. An odd function is symmetrical with respect to the origin.

RETEACH 12-6

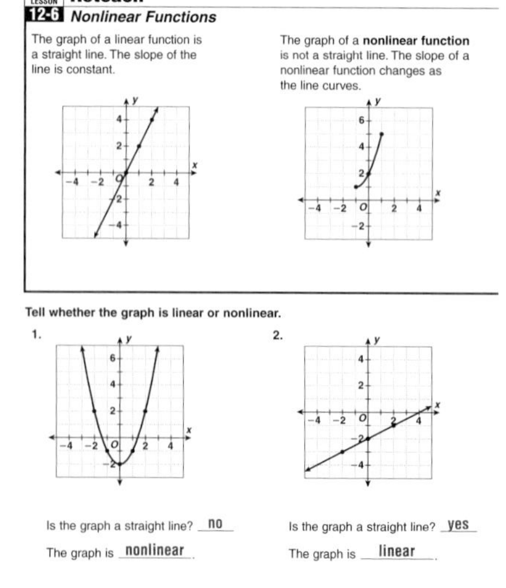

LESSON 12-6 **Reteach**
Nonlinear Functions

The graph of a linear function is a straight line. The slope of the line is constant.

The graph of a **nonlinear function** is not a straight line. The slope of a nonlinear function changes as the line curves.

Tell whether the graph is linear or nonlinear.

1. Is the graph a straight line? no
The graph is nonlinear

2. Is the graph a straight line? yes
The graph is linear

PRACTICE 12-6

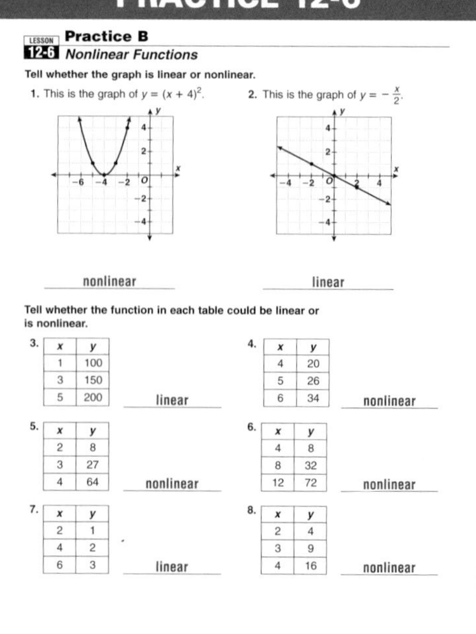

LESSON 12-6 **Practice B**
Nonlinear Functions

Tell whether the graph is linear or nonlinear.

1. This is the graph of $y = (x + 4)^2$. nonlinear

2. This is the graph of $y = -\frac{x}{2}$. linear

Tell whether the function in each table could be linear or is nonlinear.

3.

x	y
1	100
3	150
5	200

linear

4.

x	y
4	20
5	26
6	34

nonlinear

5.

x	y
2	8
3	27
4	64

nonlinear

6.

x	y
4	8
8	32
12	72

nonlinear

7.

x	y
2	1
4	2
6	3

linear

8.

x	y
2	4
3	9
4	16

nonlinear

Physical Science 

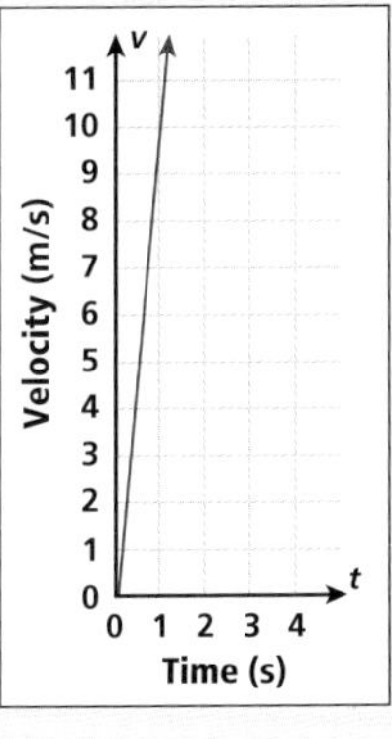

13. Galileo showed that falling objects increase their speed by about 9.8 meters per second for each second they fall. The speed of an object falling from rest is represented by the function $v = g \cdot t$, where v stands for velocity or speed, g stands for the acceleration due to gravity, or 9.8 m/s^2, and t stands for time.

a. Explain what the graph shows about time and speed.

b. Is the graph linear or nonlinear?

c. What speed would an object have after falling for 10 seconds?

14. Galileo also developed the following rule to calculate the distance an object falls from rest in a given amount of time, on Earth.

$$d = \frac{1}{2} \cdot \frac{32 \text{ ft}}{\text{s}^2} \cdot t^2$$

The graph shows the distance in feet that an object fell from 0 to 4 seconds. Make a table to show the data on the graph. Is the graph linear or nonlinear?

(Graph: d; Distance (ft): 0, 50, 100, 150, 200, 250, 300; t; Time (s): 0, 1, 2, 3, 4)

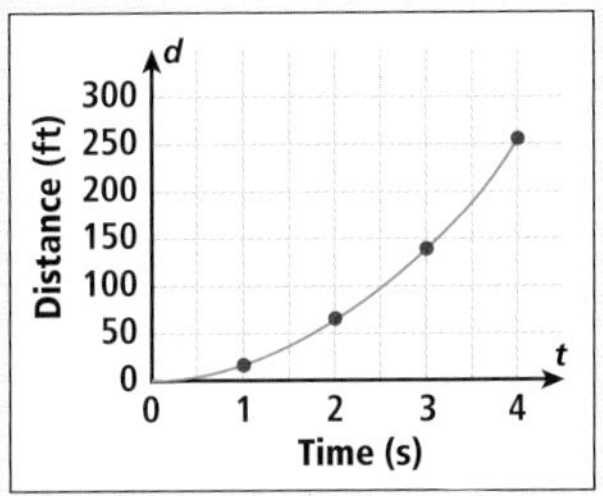

15. ***WRITE ABOUT IT*** Explain what the graph in Exercise 14 shows about the relationship between distance and time for falling objects.

16. ***CHALLENGE*** Pretend you have discovered a new planet. Create a rule for the distance that an object falls in a given amount of time on your planet. Use the rule to write a function that has a nonlinear relationship. Show a table for your rule.

Spiral Review

Solve each proportion using cross products. (Lesson 5-3)

17. $\frac{1}{p} = \frac{3}{12}$ **p = 4** **18.** $\frac{4}{7} = \frac{x}{14}$ **x = 8** **19.** $\frac{m}{5} = \frac{16}{20}$ **m = 4** **20.** $\frac{7}{9} = \frac{35}{s}$ **s = 45** **21.** $\frac{6}{7} = \frac{24}{a}$ **a = 28**

Solve. (Lesson 11-3)

22. $5x + 2 = 2x - 1$ **x = −1** **23.** $4m + 14 = 11m$ **m = 2** **24.** $3y - 2 = 2 - y$ **y = 1**

25. TEST PREP Find a ratio equivalent to $\frac{10}{15}$. (Lesson 5-2) **D**

A $\frac{2}{5}$ B $\frac{20}{45}$ C $\frac{5}{30}$ D $\frac{20}{30}$

Interdisciplinary 

Physical Science

Exercises 13–16 involve examining functions that are related to gravity. Gravity is studied in middle school Earth science programs, such as *Holt Science & Technology*.

Answers

13. a. Possible answer: The graph shows that the longer an object falls, the faster it falls.

b. The graph is linear.

c. 98 m/s

14–16. See Additional Answers p. A6.

Journal 

Ask students to describe two different real-world situations: one that could be modeled by a linear equation and one that could be modeled by a nonlinear equation.

Test Prep Doctor 

In Exercise 25, students who selected **A** or **B** might be rushing their computations. Remind these students to make sure that they multiply or divide *both* the numerator and denominator by the *same* number. Students who selected **C** may have forgotten how to find equivalent ratios and may need to review this concept.

Lesson Quiz 

1. Tell whether the graph is linear or nonlinear. nonlinear

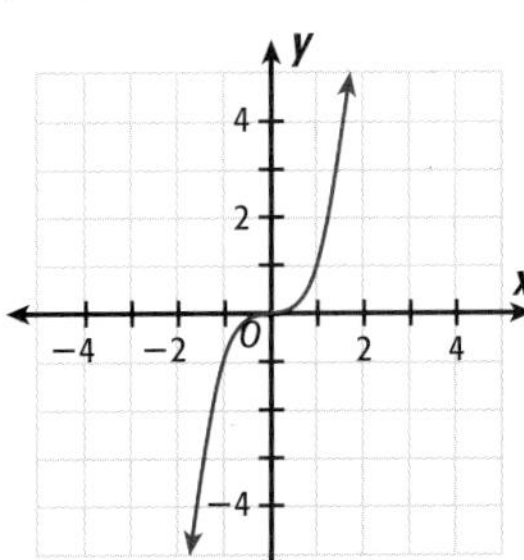

2. Tell whether the function in the table could be linear or is nonlinear. could be linear

x	y
2	7
4	13
6	19

Available on Daily Transparency in CRB

CHALLENGE 12-6

LESSON 12-6 **Challenge**
Point-Slope Form

You can write the equation of a line if you know its slope, m, and one point, (x_1, y_1), on the line. The *point-slope form* of the equation of a line is:

$$y - y_1 = m(x - x_1)$$

In the point-slope form, m, x_1, and y_1 are replaced with the corresponding values for the slope and the coordinates of a point.

Example: What is the equation of a line with a slope of 2 that passes through the point (−1, 1)?

- $m = 2$ and $(x_1, y_1) = (-1, 1)$
- Substitute these values into $y - y_1 = m(x - x_1)$.

$y - 1 = 2(x - (-1))$
$y - 1 = 2(x + 1)$

You can also write the equation in slope-intercept form.

Slope-intercept form is $y = mx + b$.

Example: Write $y - 1 = 2(x + 1)$ in slope-intercept form.

$y - 1 = 2x + 2$
$y = 2x + 3$

Use the slope and the coordinates of a point to write the equation of each line in point-slope form.

1. $m = 3$; (2, 5) $y - 5 = 3(x - 2)$
2. $m = -1$; (1, −2) $y + 2 = -(x - 1)$
3. $m = -2$; (−3, 4) $y - 4 = -2(x + 3)$
4. $m = 4$; (−1, −2) $y + 2 = 4(x + 1)$
5. $m = \frac{1}{2}$; (1, 1) $y - 1 = \frac{1}{2}(x - 1)$
6. $m = \frac{2}{3}$; (−2, −3) $y + 3 = \frac{2}{3}(x + 2)$

Write the equation of each line in point-slope form and in slope-intercept form.

7. $m = -3$; (0, −2) $y + 2 = -3x$; $y = -3x - 2$
8. $m = -1$; (1, 0) $y = -(x - 1)$; $y = -x + 1$
9. $m = 2$; (4, 2) $y - 2 = 2(x - 4)$; $y = 2x - 6$

PROBLEM SOLVING 12-6

LESSON 12-6 **Problem Solving**
Nonlinear Functions

Write the correct answer.

1. The graph of an equation contains the following 3 points: (4, 13), (8, 20), and (12, 27). Is the graph linear or nonlinear?
linear

2. The graph of an equation contains the following 3 points: (11, 64), (22, 72), and (33, 81). Is the graph linear or nonlinear?
nonlinear

3. The volume of a sphere can be found using the equation $V = \frac{4}{3}\pi r^3$. If you draw a graph relating volume to the radius of the sphere, will the graph be linear or nonlinear?
nonlinear

4. The surface area of a cylinder can be found using the equation $SA = 2\pi r^2 + 2\pi rh$. If you draw a graph relating surface area to the height of a cylinder, will the graph be linear or nonlinear?
linear

Choose the letter of the best answer.

This graph shows the population of bacteria in a test tube, starting with a single bacterium.

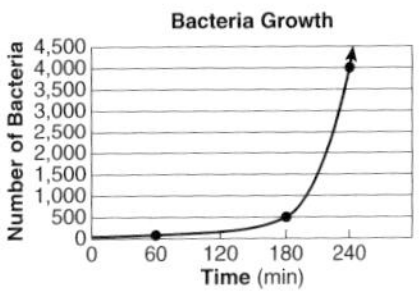

(Graph: Bacteria Growth; Number of Bacteria: 0, 500, 1,000, 1,500, 2,000, 2,500, 3,000, 3,500, 4,000, 4,500; Time (min): 0, 60, 120, 180, 240)

5. Estimate how often the bacteria population doubles.
A every hour
B every minute
Ⓒ every 20 minutes
D every 2 hours

6. Which statement about the graph is true?
Ⓕ This is a nonlinear graph.
G The slope of the line does not change.
H This is a linear graph.
J The y-intercept is 5,000.

7. What does this graph show about the bacteria's population growth?
A The growth is slow and steady.
Ⓑ The growth is very rapid.
C The growth levels off at 3,000.
D There is little growth.

8. At 300 minutes, estimate the number of bacteria.
F 5,000
G 8,000
H 16,000
Ⓙ 32,000

12-7 Organizer

Pacing: Traditional 1 day
Block $\frac{1}{2}$ day

Objective: Students recognize constant and variable rates of change.

Warm Up

Tell whether the function in each table could be linear or is nonlinear.

1.

x	y
2	4
8	64
4	196

nonlinear

2.

x	y
16	192
32	384
48	576

could be linear

Problem of the Day

What two 3-digit numbers have a product of 19,019? **133 and 143**

Available on Daily Transparency in CRB

Math Fact !

All things fall with the same constant acceleration only if they are in a vacuum. In reality, because of air resistance, the size and shape of an object affect how fast the object falls.

12-7 Rates of Change

Learn to recognize constant and variable rates of change.

If you dropped a bowling ball and a baseball from the same height at the same time, which do you think would hit the ground first? Without air resistance, both would hit the ground at the same time. Gravity pulls all objects to the ground at the same rate, no matter what their sizes or weights.

As each ball drops, it falls faster and faster due to gravity. The *rate of change*, the change in the ball's speed as it falls, is a change that can be measured.

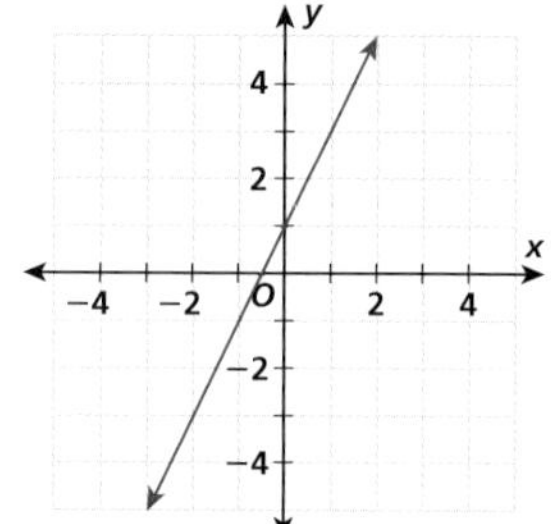

A *constant rate of change* means that something changes by the same amount during equal intervals. A graph that has a constant rate of change is a line, and the *rate of change* is the same as the *slope* of the line.

EXAMPLE 1 Identifying Constant Rates of Change

Tell in which intervals of x the graph shows constant rates of change.

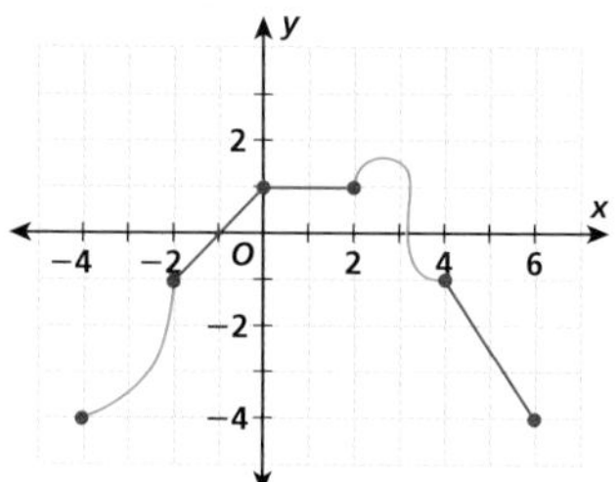

Look for parts of the graph that are line segments.

Identify the intervals of x for each line segment.

The graph shows constant rates of change in the intervals from $x = -2$ to $x = 0$, $x = 0$ to $x = 2$, and $x = 4$ to $x = 6$.

A *variable rate of change* means that something changes by a different amount during equal intervals. Variable rates of change are also called nonlinear rates of change, because a graph that represents a variable rate of change is not a line.

1 Introduce

Alternate Opener

EXPLORATION

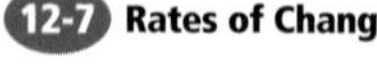

12-7 Rates of Change

Speed is a *rate of change* that occurs in many real-world situations.

The graph shows the speed of a cheetah (in red) and of a lion (in blue) while chasing prey in the wild for five seconds.

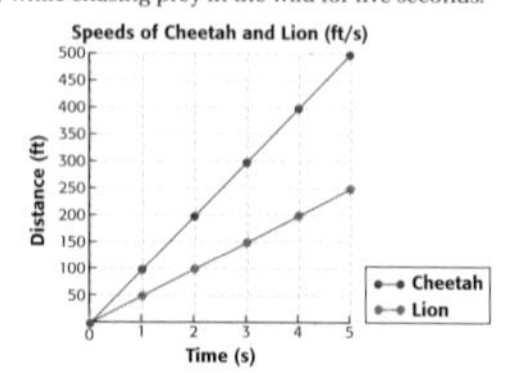

1. How can you tell which cat is faster from the graph?
2. Find the speed in feet per second of each cat.

Think and Discuss

3. **Discuss** what a constant rate of change is.
4. **Explain** what feature of the graph represents that the speed of each cat was constant.

Motivate

To introduce constant and variable rates of change, ask students to describe how they would run 100 yards as compared with 1 mile. Introduce the idea that although they might run a short distance at a constant speed, while running a long distance, they might vary their speed quite a bit.

Exploration worksheet and answers on Chapter 12 Resource Book pp. 64 and 100

2 Teach

Lesson Presentation

Guided Instruction

In this lesson, students learn to recognize constant and variable rates of change. Mention that students can gather information about rate of change both from a graph and from an equation. If the equation is linear, the rate of change is constant. If the equation is not linear, the rate of change is variable.

Teaching Tip Talk about how students can decide by looking at a graph whether the graph represents a constant or a variable rate of change. Encourage students to draw examples of each to share with others in the class.

EXAMPLE 2 Identifying Variable Rates of Change

Tell whether each graph shows a constant or variable rate of change.

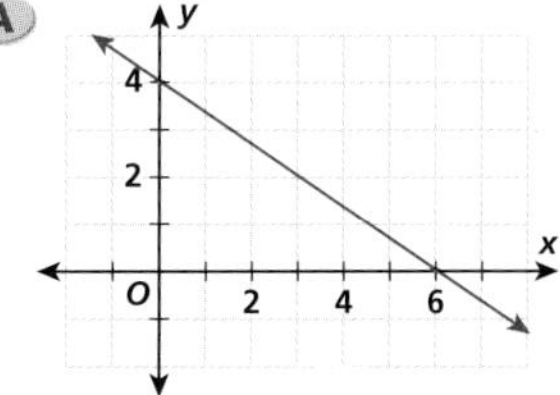

The graph is linear, so the rate of change is constant.

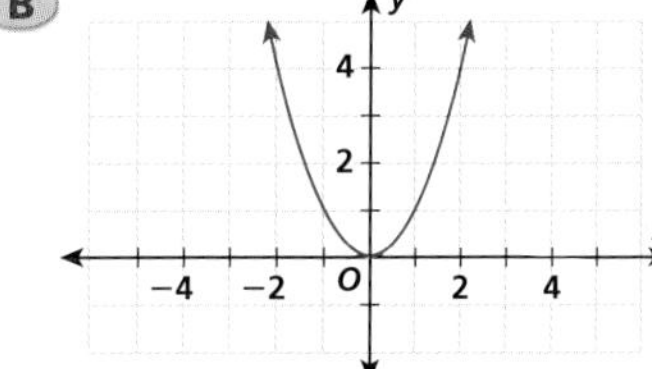

The graph is nonlinear, so the rate of change is variable.

EXAMPLE 3 Using Rate of Change to Solve Problems

Remember!

slope = $\frac{\text{rise}}{\text{run}}$

The graph shows the distance a bicyclist travels over time. Does the bicyclist travel at a constant or variable speed? How fast does the bicyclist travel?

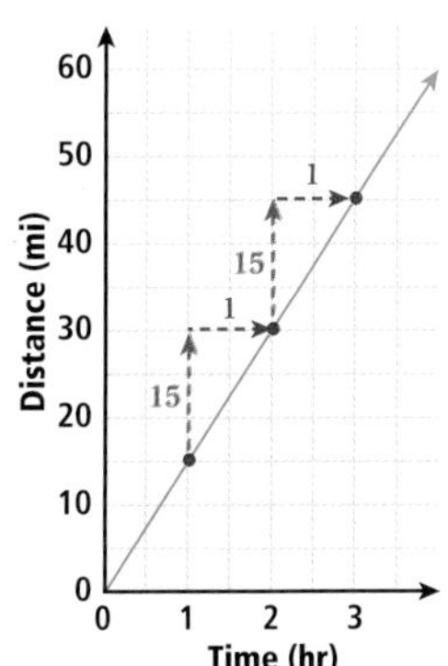

Use two points on the line, such as (1, 15) and (2, 30), to find the slope.

The graph is linear. You can see that the same amount of distance (rise) is traveled during equal time intervals (run), so the bicyclist is traveling at a constant speed.

The slope of the graph is rise ÷ run, or distance ÷ time.

Since speed = distance ÷ time, you can find the speed by finding the slope.

slope = $\frac{\text{rise}}{\text{run}} = \frac{15 \text{ mi}}{1 \text{ hr}}$

The bicyclist travels at 15 miles per hour.

Think and Discuss

1. **Compare** constant and variable rates of change.
2. **Explain** how you can use the appearance of a graph to decide whether the rate of change is constant or variable.
3. **Give an example** of a real-world situation that would involve more than one constant rate of change.

Additional Examples

Example 1

Tell in which intervals of x the graph shows constant rates of change. between $x = 0$ and $x = 3$.

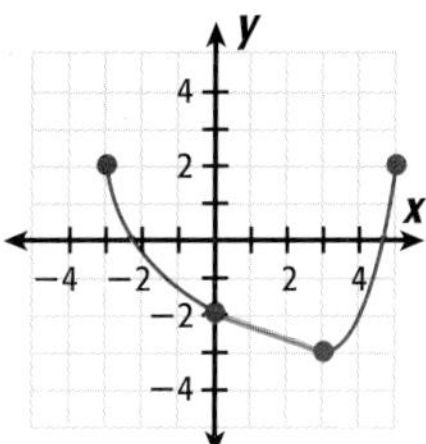

Example 2

Tell whether the graph shows a constant or variable rate of change.

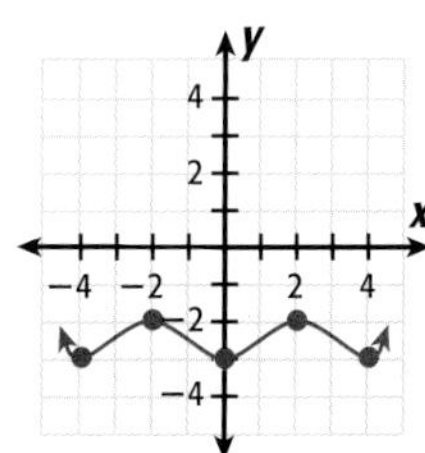

The rate of change is variable.

Example 3

The graph shows the distance a monarch butterfly travels at a constant rate of speed. How fast is the butterfly traveling? 20 mi/h

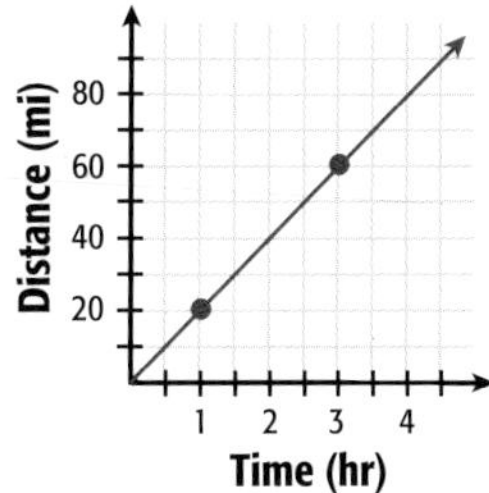

3 Close

Reaching All Learners

Through Hands-On Experience

Provide pairs of students with graph paper, string, and tape or glue. Tell each pair to first draw a large coordinate grid and then tape or glue the string to the paper. The graph should meet the following conditions:

- For $x < -2$, the graph shows a constant rate of change.
- For $-2 \leq x \leq 5$, the graph shows a variable rate of change.
- For $x > 5$, the graph shows a constant rate of change.

When the pairs have completed the graphs, have them share their graphs with the class.

Summarize

Have students explain how to decide if a graph shows a constant or variable rate of change.

Possible answer: If the graph is a straight line, the rate of change is constant. If the graph is a curve, the rate of change is variable.

Answers to Think and Discuss

1. Possible answers: A constant rate of change is one that is always the same. A variable rate of change is different at least some of the time.
2. If a graph is linear, the rate of change is constant. If a graph is nonlinear, the rate of change is variable.
3. Possible answer: The price of fire wood is low during the summer and high during the winter.

12-7 PRACTICE & ASSESS

Students may want to refer back to the lesson examples.

Assignment Guide

If you finished Example 1 assign:
Core 1–3, 8–10, 16, 21–29
Enriched 1–3, 8–10, 16, 21–29

If you finished Example 2 assign:
Core 1–6, 8–13, 16, 17, 21–29
Enriched 1–6, 8–13, 16, 17, 21–29

If you finished Example 3 assign:
Core 1–14, 21–29
Enriched 1–13 odd, 15–29

Answers

2. from $x = -1$ to $x = 0$ and $x = 0$ to $x = 1$

9. from $x = -3$ to $x = -1$ and $x = -1$ to $x = 0$

Math Background

When two objects fall through air, they fall at the same rate, but the drag force due to air resistance on each object depends upon the object's speed. The faster an object goes, the greater the drag. As an object falls, the drag on it increases until the object cannot go any faster. This maximum speed is called the *terminal speed* of an object. The terminal speed of a person in free fall is about 120 miles per hour; with a parachute, it is about 14 miles per hour.

12-7 Exercises

FOR EXTRA PRACTICE see page 681

internet connect
Homework Help Online
go.hrw.com Keyword: MS4 12-7

GUIDED PRACTICE

See Example 1 Tell in which intervals of x each graph shows constant rates of change.

1.
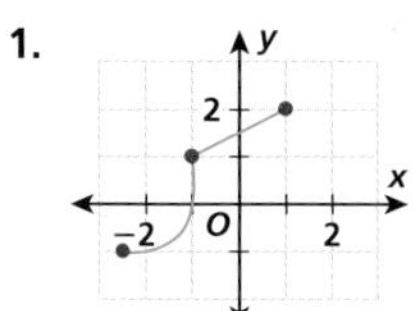
from $x = -1$ to $x = 1$

2.
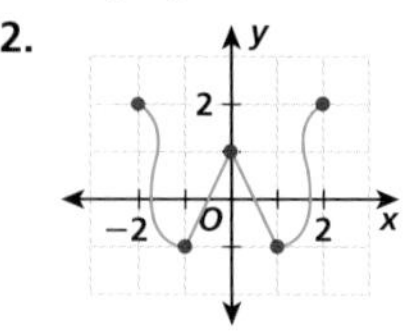

3.
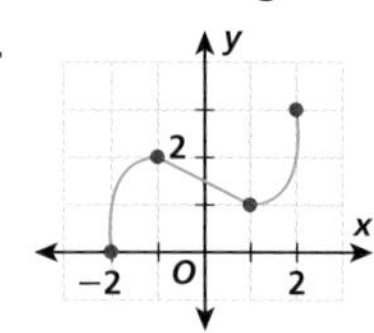
from $x = -1$ to $x = 1$

See Example 2 Tell whether each graph shows a constant or variable rate of change.

4.
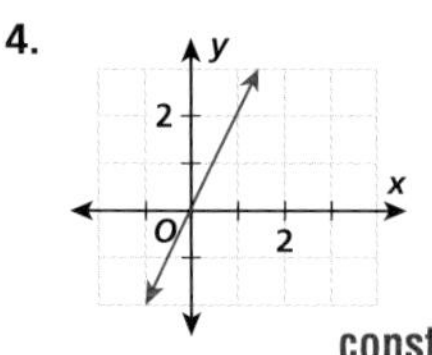
constant

5.
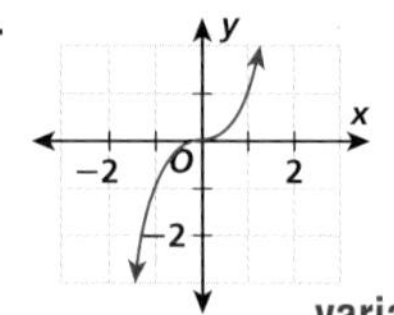
variable

6.
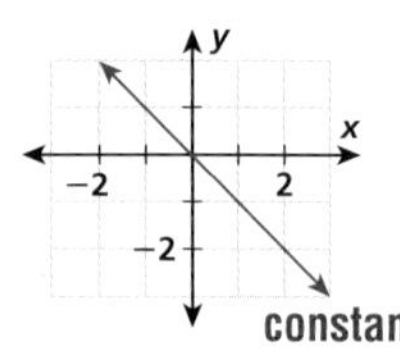
constant

See Example 3 **7.** The graph shows the distance a trout swims over time. Does the trout swim at a constant or variable speed? How fast does the trout swim? **constant; 15 mi/h**

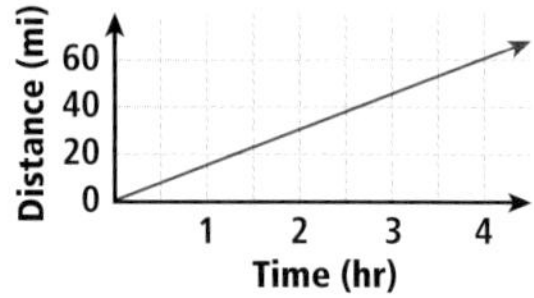

INDEPENDENT PRACTICE

See Example 1 Tell in which intervals of x each graph shows constant rates of change.

8.
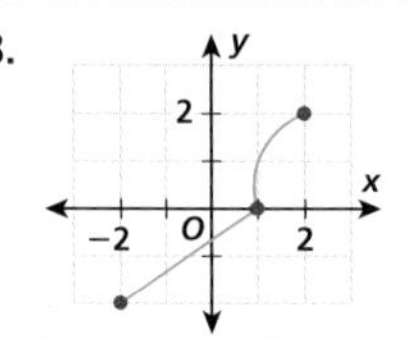
from $x = -2$ to $x = 1$

9.
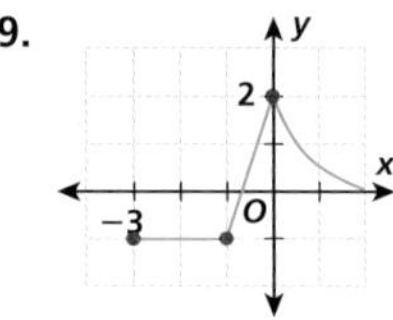

10.
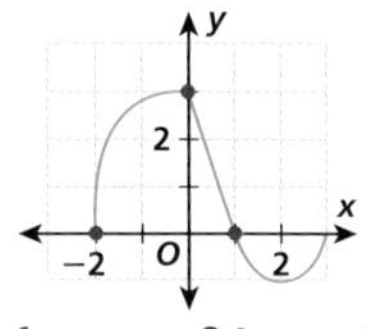
from $x = 0$ to $x = 1$

See Example 2 Tell whether each graph shows a constant or variable rate of change.

11.
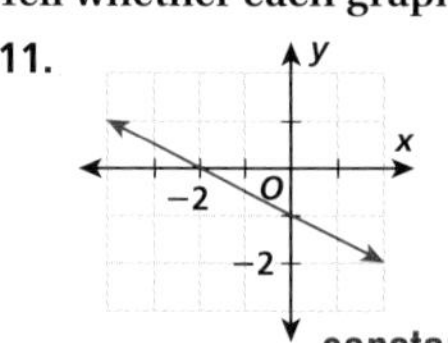
constant

12.
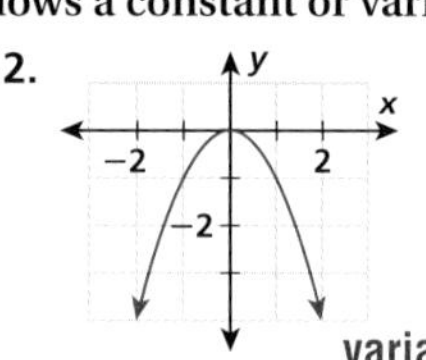
variable

13.
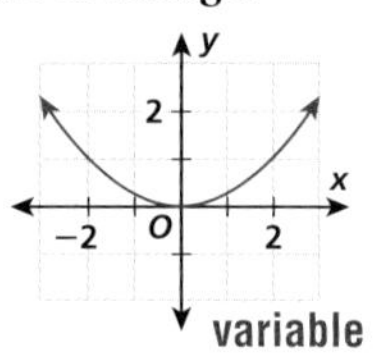
variable

See Example 3 **14.** The graph shows an amount of rain that falls over time. Does the rain fall at a constant or variable rate? How much rain falls per hour? **constant; 1 in./h**

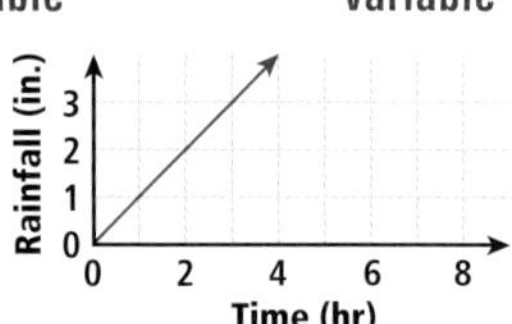

RETEACH 12-7

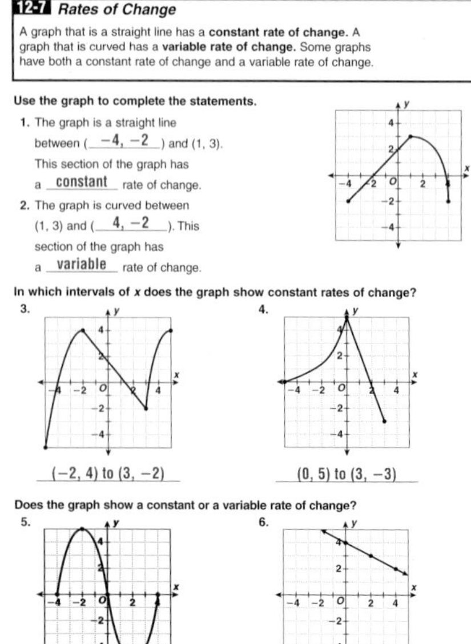

LESSON 12-7 **Reteach**

Rates of Change

A graph that is a straight line has a **constant rate of change.** A graph that is curved has a **variable rate of change.** Some graphs have both a constant rate of change and a variable rate of change.

Use the graph to complete the statements.

1. The graph is a straight line between (−4, −2) and (1, 3). This section of the graph has a constant rate of change.
2. The graph is curved between (1, 3) and (4, −2). This section of the graph has a variable rate of change.

In which intervals of *x* does the graph show constant rates of change?

3. (−2, 4) to (3, −2)
4. (0, 5) to (3, −3)

Does the graph show a constant or a variable rate of change?

5. variable
6. constant

PRACTICE 12-7

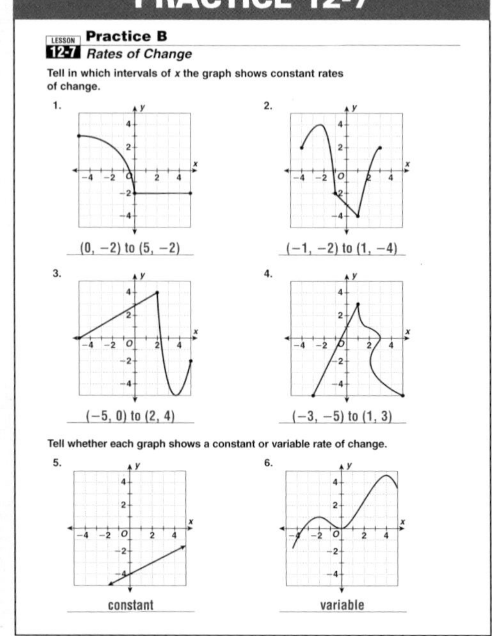

LESSON 12-7 **Practice B**

Rates of Change

Tell in which intervals of *x* the graph shows constant rates of change.

1. (0, −2) to (5, −2)
2. (−1, −2) to (1, −4)
3. (−5, 0) to (2, 4)
4. (−3, −5) to (1, 3)

Tell whether each graph shows a constant or variable rate of change.

5. constant
6. variable

PRACTICE AND PROBLEM SOLVING

This water tower can be seen in Gaffney, South Carolina, where the South Carolina Peach Festival is held every year.

15. ***AGRICULTURE*** The graph at right shows the cost of buying peaches when the cost is the same per pound no matter how much you buy.
    a. How much does a pound of peaches cost? **$1.50 per pound**
    b. Write an equation that represents the cost of the peaches. **$y = 1.5x$**

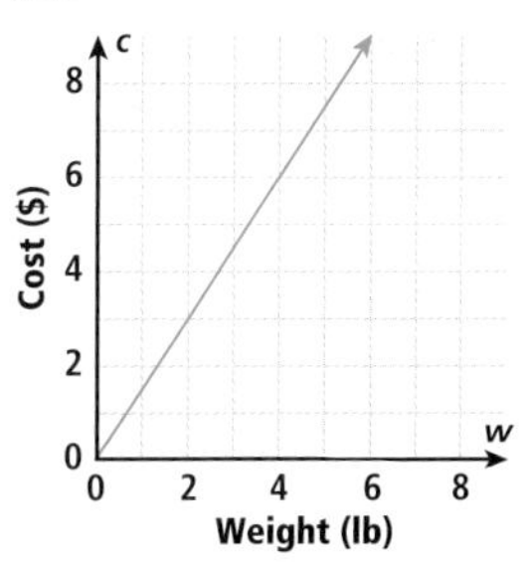

16. ***SPORTS*** The graph at right shows a runner's progress during a race.
    a. During which interval was the runner going at a constant speed?
    b. During which interval was the runner's speed changing at a constant rate?

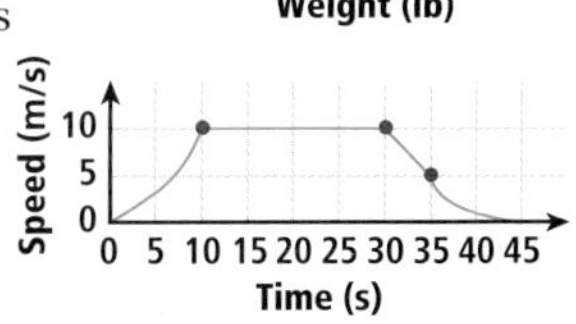

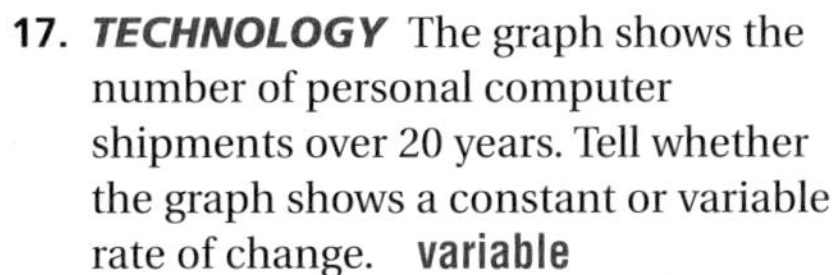

17. ***TECHNOLOGY*** The graph shows the number of personal computer shipments over 20 years. Tell whether the graph shows a constant or variable rate of change. **variable**

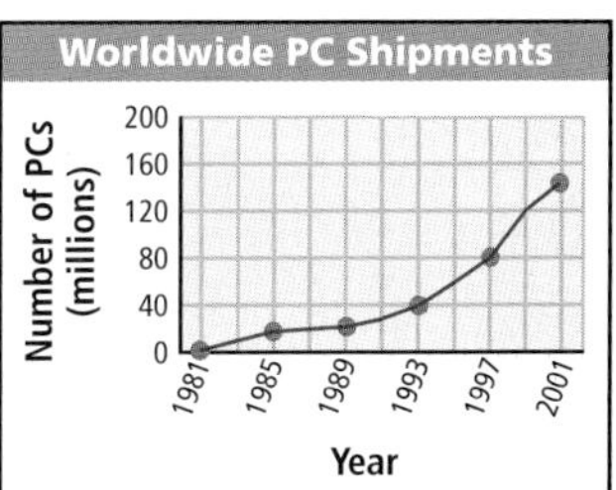

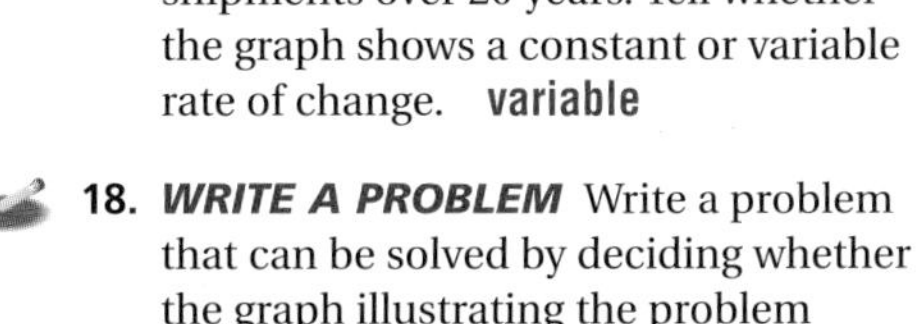

18. ***WRITE A PROBLEM*** Write a problem that can be solved by deciding whether the graph illustrating the problem shows a constant or variable rate of change.

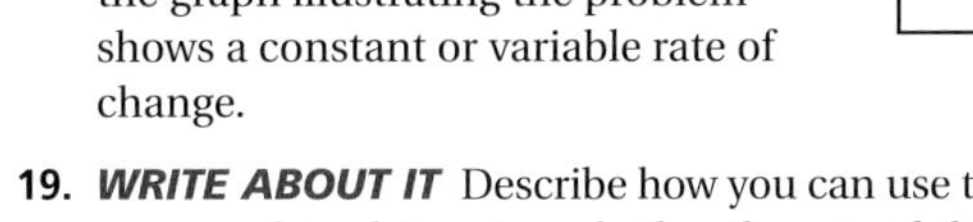

19. ***WRITE ABOUT IT*** Describe how you can use three points shown on a graph to determine whether the rate of change is constant or variable.

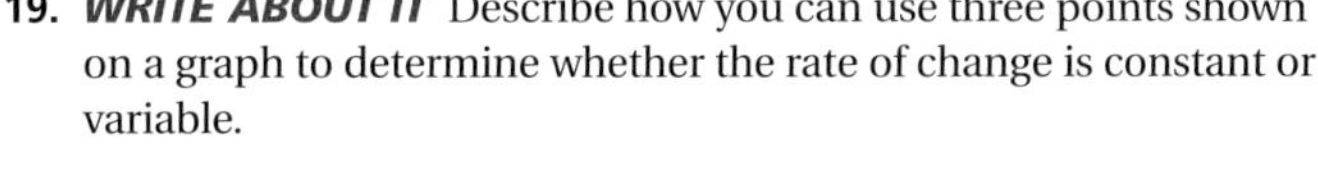

20. ***CHALLENGE*** The population of prairie dogs in a park doubles every year. Does this population show a constant or variable rate of change? Explain. **Variable; if you graph the population, the graph will not be a straight line.**

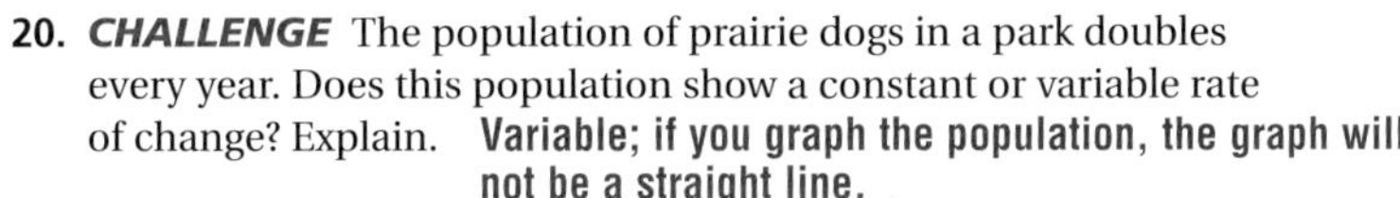

Spiral Review

Solve each inequality. (Lesson 11-6)

21. $x + 9 < 12$ **$x < 3$**
22. $x - 3 > -2$ **$x > 1$**
23. $-11 < 4 + x$ **$-15 < x$**
24. $x + 8 > -5$ **$x > -13$**

Graph each linear function. (Lesson 12-4)

25. $y = x - 3$
26. $y = 2x + 1$
27. $y = 4$
28. $y = -x + 1$

29. **TEST PREP** Which of the following points is not on the graph of $y = -x^2 + 1$? (Lesson 12-5) **C**

A $(1, 0)$ B $(-1, 0)$ C $(0, 0)$ D $(0, 1)$

Answers

16. a. from time = 10 s to time = 30 s
    b. from time = 30 s to time = 35 s
18. Possible answer: The graph shows the number of gallons of water flowing past a point in a river over time. Does the water flow at a constant rate or a variable rate?
19. Possible answer: Find the slope between two points and then between two different points. If the slope is the same, the rate of change is constant, and the graph is linear. The rate of change is called the *slope*.

25–28. See pp. A6–A7.

Journal

Ask students to compare and contrast real-world situations that involve constant rates of speed with those that involve variable rates.

Test Prep Doctor

For Exercise 29, students should recognize that x^2 must be 1 for y to be 0, so both **A** and **B** are points on the graph. Quick substitution will show that **D** is on the graph, whereas **C** is not.

CHALLENGE 12-7

LESSON 12-7 **Challenge**
Another Distance Formula

The formula $h = vt - 16t^2$ approximates the height, in feet, of an object t seconds after it is propelled upward with an initial speed of v feet per second. If you know the initial speed and the time, you can approximate the height of the object.

Use the formula $h = vt - 16t^2$ to solve.

1. Approximate the height of a rocket fired upward with an initial speed of 200 feet per second after 3 seconds. **456 ft**
2. Approximate the height of a rocket fired upward with an initial speed of 200 feet per second after 6 seconds. **624 ft**
3. Approximate the height of a rocket fired upward with an initial speed of 200 feet per second after 9 seconds. **504 ft**
4. Approximate the height of a rocket fired upward with an initial speed of 200 feet per second after 12 seconds. **96 ft**
5. Compare the height at each time in Exercises 1–4. Describe what happens as time increases. Why?
   Possible answers: The height increases and then decreases; The rocket goes up and then comes down.

The formula $h = vt - 4.9t^2$ approximates the height, in meters, of an object t seconds after it is propelled upward with an initial speed of v meters per second. Use this formula to solve.

6. Approximate the height of a ball thrown upward with an initial speed of 35 meters per second after 1 second. **30.1 m**
7. Approximate the height of a ball thrown upward with an initial speed of 35 meters per second after 4 seconds. **61.6 m**
8. Approximate the height of a ball thrown upward with an initial speed of 35 meters per second after 6 seconds. **33.6 m**
9. What happens to the height of the ball over time? Explain.
   Possible answer: The ball goes up and then comes down, so the height increases and then decreases.

PROBLEM SOLVING 12-7

LESSON 12-7 **Problem Solving**
Rates of Change

Write the correct answer.

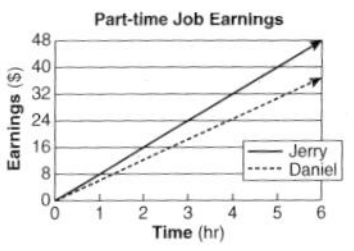

Part-time Job Earnings (graph: Earnings ($) 0–48 vs. Time (hr) 0–6; Jerry, Daniel)

1. How much does Jerry earn per hour?
   $8
2. What is the slope of the graph that represents Daniel's rate of pay? How much does Daniel earn per hour?
   6; $6
3. Jerry and Daniel each worked 10 hours this week. How much more than Daniel did Jerry earn?
   $20
4. For more than 10 hours of work, the rate of pay is 1.5 times that shown in the graph. How much would Jerry earn by working 14 hours?
   $128

Choose the letter of the best answer.

The graph shows the changing height of two rockets over time.

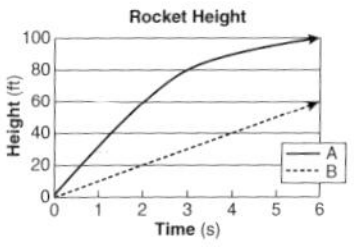

Rocket Height (graph: Height (ft) 0–100 vs. Time (s) 0–6; A, B)

5. The graph shows that the rate of change in the height of rocket A is not constant. During which time interval was the rocket's height increasing at the fastest rate?
   A between 2 seconds and 4 seconds
   B between 3 seconds and 5 seconds
   (C) between 0 seconds and 2 seconds
   D between 4 seconds and 6 seconds
6. The graph shows that the rate of change in the height of rocket B is constant. How fast is the height of rocket B increasing?
   F 5 feet per second
   (G) 10 feet per second
   H 20 feet per second
   J 40 feet per second
7. What is an equation that could represent the height of rocket B at any time t?
   (A) $h = 10t$
   B $h = 10t^2$
   C $h = 10t + 30$
   D $h = \frac{t^2}{10}$

Lesson Quiz

1. Tell whether the graph shows a constant or variable rate of change. variable rate of change

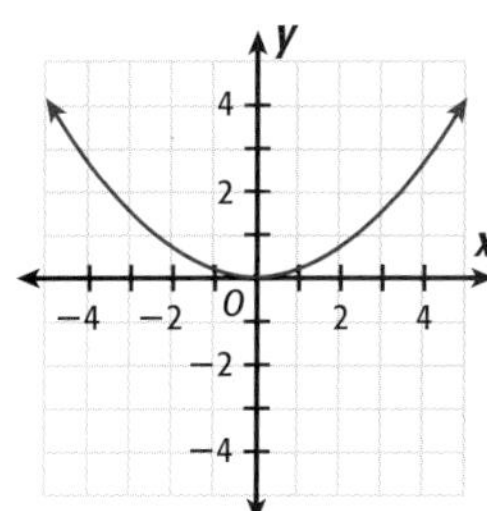

2. During a flood, a river rose 0.5 inch per minute. In another flood, the river rose 2 feet per hour. Which rate of change was faster? 0.5 inch/minute

Available on Daily Transparency in CRB

12-8 Organizer

Pacing: Traditional 1 day
Block $\frac{1}{2}$ day

Objective: Students use set notation and identify relationships between sets.

Warm Up

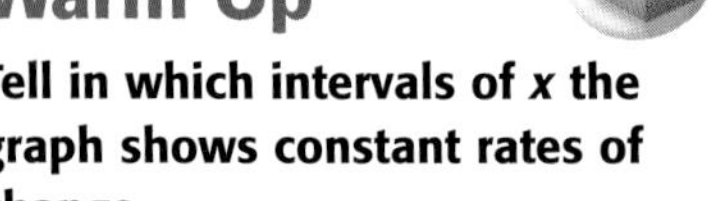

Tell in which intervals of x the graph shows constant rates of change.

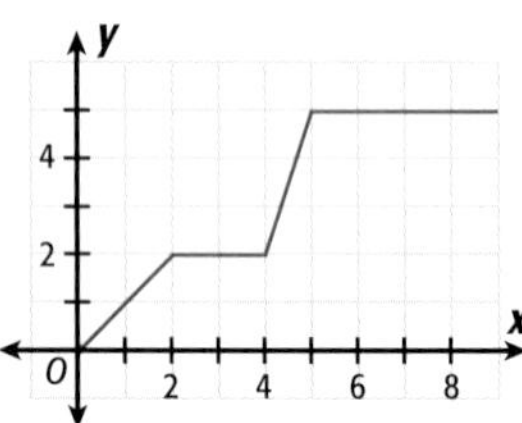

from $x = 0$ to $x = 2$, $x = 2$ to $x = 4$, $x = 4$ to $x = 5$, and $x = 5$ to $x = 9$

Problem of the Day

What is the intersection of the set of all prime numbers and the set of all even numbers? 2

Available on Daily Transparency in CRB

Math Humor

What is the definition of *subset?*

It is what happens 12 hours after subrise.

12-8 Set Theory

Learn to use set notation and to identify relationships between sets.

Vocabulary
set
element

The states that are bordered by the Pacific Ocean form a *set*. The *set* of states in the United States that are bordered by the Pacific Ocean includes California, Oregon, Washington, Alaska, and Hawaii.

A **set** is a collection of objects. Each object in a set is an **element** of the set. The special set that contains no elements is the *null set*, or *empty set*. When describing sets using symbols, you can use either *roster notation* or *set-builder notation*.

Reading Math

Read the notation $\{x|x$ is a real number$\}$ as "the set of all x such that x is a real number."

{CA, OR, WA, AK, HI} — *Roster notation lists all of the elements.*

$\{x|x$ is a state that is bordered by the Pacific Ocean$\}$ — *Set-builder notation gives a rule.*

EXAMPLE 1 Writing in Set Notation

Write each set using roster notation or set-builder notation.

A the set of all even numbers from 1 to 10, including 10

{2, 4, 6, 8, 10} *The numbers can be listed conveniently. Use roster notation.*

B the set of all integers greater than zero

$\{x|x$ is a counting number$\}$ *The numbers follow a rule but cannot all be listed conveniently. Use set-builder notation.*

The following notations show how different sets can relate to each other.

Subset		
Words	**Notation**	**Example**
A is a *subset* of B if all the elements of set A are in set B.	$A \subset B$	A = {Mary, Bill} B = {Mary, Bill, Chim, Selena} $A \subset B$ All of the elements of A are in B.

1 Introduce

Alternate Opener

EXPLORATION

12-8 Set Theory

A *set* is a collection of objects. There are various ways to denote sets. A convenient way is to use braces, especially if the number of *elements* in the set is relatively small. For example, {1, 2, 3} is a set that contains three elements: 1, 2, and 3.

Use braces to represent each set.

1. List the prime numbers between 1 and 30.
2. List the even numbers between 1 and 30.
3. List the odd numbers between 1 and 30.
4. List the odd numbers between 1 and 30 that are prime.
5. List the even numbers between 1 and 30 that are prime.

Think and Discuss

6. **Discuss** whether some sets in numbers 1–5 are subsets of the others. (*Hint:* The elements of a subset are also elements of another set.)
7. **Give an example** of a set that has no elements (an empty set).

Motivate

To introduce sets, ask students to describe collections of common things, such as sets of dishes or silverware. When you have listed the collections, ask students if there is anything the collections have in common that you could use to describe them.

Exploration worksheet and answers on Chapter 12 Resource Book pp. 73 and 102

2 Teach

Lesson Presentation

Guided Instruction

In this lesson, students learn to use set notation and to identify relationships between sets. Once students have learned about sets and subsets, they can then find intersections and unions of sets. Point out that the concepts of union and intersection of sets are somewhat parallel to the concepts of addition and subtraction of numbers. For example, to find the union of the set, you add all the unique elements of the sets. To find the intersection, you identify only those elements that are members of each set, eliminating all of the others.

Intersection		
Words	**Notation**	**Example**
The *intersection* of sets *A* and *B* is the set of all elements that are in both sets *A* and *B*.	$A \cap B$	A = {Des Moines, Kent, Seattle} B = {Seattle, Portland, San Francisco} $A \cap B$ = {Seattle} Seattle is the only city in both sets.

Union		
Words	**Notation**	**Example**
The *union* of sets *A* and *B* is the set of all elements that are in either set *A* or set *B*.	$A \cup B$	$A = \{1, 2, 4, 7\}$; $B = \{5, 6, 7\}$ $A \cup B = \{1, 2, 4, 5, 6, 7\}$ All of the numbers in either set are included.

EXAMPLE 2 Identifying Relationships Between Sets

Find $A \cap B$ and $A \cup B$. Tell whether $A \subset B$, $B \subset A$, or neither.

A $A = \{2, 4, 6, 8\}$; $B = \{2, 4, 8\}$

$A \cap B = \{2, 4, 8\}$ — *2, 4, and 8 are in both A and B.*

$A \cup B = \{2, 4, 6, 8\}$ — *List the elements of both sets.*

$B \subset A$ — *All of the elements of B are in A.*

B $A = \{0, 3, 6\}$; $B = \{0, 2, 3, 5, 6\}$

$A \cap B = \{0, 3, 6\}$ — *0, 3, and 6 are in both A and B.*

$A \cup B = \{0, 2, 3, 5, 6\}$ — *List the elements of both sets.*

$A \subset B$ — *All the elements of A are in B.*

C $A = \{x|x$ is a rational number$\}$; $B = \{x|x$ is an irrational number$\}$

$A \cap B = \{\ \} = \varnothing$ — *No number is both rational and irrational.*

$A \cup B = \{x|x$ is a real number$\}$ — *Together, the set of rational numbers and the set of irrational numbers make up the set of real numbers.*

Neither set is a subset of the other.

Writing Math

The null, or empty, set is written as { } or $\varnothing$.

Think and Discuss

1. **Give an example** of two sets whose intersection is the null set.
2. **Tell** what is true if the intersection of sets *A* and *B* is set *A*.

COMMON ERROR ALERT

Students often confuse the symbols for union and intersection and consequently give wrong answers. Introduce the visual idea of pouring both sets into the union symbol to help students distinguish between the operations.

Additional Examples

Example 1

Write each set using roster notation or set-builder notation.

A. the set of all positive multiples of 3 less than or equal to 15
{3, 6, 9, 12, 15}

B. the set of all multiples of 3
$\{x|x$ is a multiple of 3$\}$

Example 2

Find $A \cap B$ and $A \cup B$. Tell if $A \subset B$, $B \subset A$, or neither.

A. $A = \{0, 5, 10\}$; $B = \{1, 2, 3, 4, 5\}$
$A \cap B = \{5\}$
$A \cup B = \{0, 1, 2, 3, 4, 5, 10\}$
Neither set is a subset of the other.

B. $A = \{1, 2, 3\}$; $B = \{1, 2, 3, 4, 5\}$
$A \cap B = \{1, 2, 3\}$
$A \cup B = \{1, 2, 3, 4, 5\}$
$A \subset B$

C. $A = \{x|x$ is an even integer$\}$;
$B = \{x|x$ is an odd integer$\}$
$A \cap B = \varnothing$
$A \cup B = \{x|x$ is an integer$\}$
Neither set is a subset of the other.

3 Close

Reaching All Learners
Through Curriculum Integration

Geography Have students work in pairs. Tell each partner to refer to a map of Europe, Asia, Africa, or South America and to choose a set of cities, countries, or other geographic features with something in common. Partners should then write a description of their sets in set-builder notation. After they have finished their descriptions, ask partners to exchange their sets and use the roster method to list the sets.

Summarize

Have students write definitions of *set, subset, union of two sets,* and *intersection of two sets.*

Possible answers: A set is a collection of objects, and one set is a subset of another if every member of the first set is also a member of the second set. The union of two sets is the set of all elements in either the first set or the second set, and the intersection of two sets is the set of all elements that are common to both sets.

Answers to Think and Discuss

1. Possible answer: the set of cats and the set of dogs
2. Set *A* must be a subset of set *B*.

12-8 PRACTICE & ASSESS

Students may want to refer back to the lesson examples.

Assignment Guide

If you finished Example 1 assign:

Core 1–4, 9–12, 28–35

Enriched 1–4, 9–12, 28–35

If you finished Example 2 assign:

Core 1–18, 19–23 odd, 28–35

Enriched 1–17 odd, 19–35

12-8 Exercises

FOR EXTRA PRACTICE
see page 681

internet connect
Homework Help Online
go.hrw.com Keyword: MS4 12-8

GUIDED PRACTICE

See Example 1 **Write each set using roster notation or set-builder notation.**

1. the set of all odd numbers from 1 through 11 **{1, 3, 5, 7, 9, 11}**
2. the set of all negative integers **$\{x|x$ is an integer less than 0}**
3. the set of all integers from -4 through -6 **$\{-6, -5, -4\}$**
4. the set of all even numbers greater than 10 **$\{x|x > 10$ and x is even}**

See Example 2 **Find $A \cap B$ and $A \cup B$. Tell whether $A \subset B$, $B \subset A$, or neither.**

5. $A = \{11, 13, 15, 19\}$; $B = \{5, 10, 15, 20\}$
$A \cap B = \{15\}$; $A \cup B = \{5, 10, 11, 13, 15, 19, 20\}$; neither is a subset of the other.
6. $A = \{100, 200, 300\}$; $B = \{100, 200, 300, 400\}$
$A \cap B = \{100, 200, 300\}$; $A \cup B = \{100, 200, 300, 400\}$; $A \subset B$.
7. $A = \{x|x$ is an even integer}; $B = \{x|x$ is an odd integer}
$A \cap B = \varnothing$; $A \cup B = \{x|x$ is an integer}; neither is a subset of the other.
8. $A = \{x|x$ is a real number}; $B = \{x|x = 0\}$
$A \cap B = \{0\}$; $A \cup B = \{x|x$ is a real number}; $B \subset A$.

INDEPENDENT PRACTICE

See Example 1 **Write each set using roster notation or set-builder notation.**

9. the set of positive multiples of 3, less than 20 **{3, 6, 9, 12, 15, 18}**
10. the set of even multiples of 5 from 10 through 20 **{10, 20}**
11. the set of even numbers **$\{x|x$ is even}**
12. the set of all two-word states in the United States
{NH, NJ, NM, NY, NC, SC, ND, SD, RI, WV}

See Example 2 **Find $A \cap B$ and $A \cup B$. Tell whether $A \subset B$, $B \subset A$, or neither.**

13. $A = \{-6, -4, -2, 0\}$; $B = \{-2, 0, 4, 6\}$
$A \cap B = \{-2, 0\}$; $A \cup B = \{-6, -4, -2, 0, 4, 6\}$; neither is a subset of the other.
14. $A = \{x|x$ is a vowel}; $B = \{x|x$ is a consonant}
$A \cap B = \varnothing$; $A \cup B = \{x|x$ is a letter of the alphabet}; neither is a subset of the other.
15. $A = \{1, 2, 3, 4, 5\}$; $B = \{1, 2, 3\}$
$A \cap B = \{1, 2, 3\}$; $A \cup B = \{1, 2, 3, 4, 5\}$; $B \subset A$
16. $A = \{1, 3, 12, 15\}$; $B = \{1, 3\}$
$A \cap B = \{1, 3\}$; $A \cup B = \{1, 3, 12, 15\}$; $B \subset A$
17. $A = \{x|x$ is a European country}; B = {Germany, France}
$A \cap B$ = {Germany, France}; $A \cup B = \{x|x$ is a European Country}; $B \subset A$
18. $A = \{x|x$ is a multiple of 3}; $B = \{x|x$ is a multiple of 2}
$A \cap B = \{x|x$ is a multiple of 6}; $A \cup B = \{x|x$ is a multiple of 2 or 3}; neither is a subset of the other.

PRACTICE AND PROBLEM SOLVING

Find the missing set of values.

19. $A = \{1, 2, 3\}$; $B =$ ▢
$A \cup B = \{1, 2, 3, 4, 5\}$
$A \cap B = \varnothing$ **$B = \{4, 5\}$**

20. $A =$ ▢; $B = \{0, 5, 10, 15\}$
$A \subset B$
$A \cap B = \{0, 5, 10\}$ **$A = \{0, 5, 10\}$**

Math Background

The set operations of union and intersection have many of the same properties as addition and multiplication.

Commutative Properties: For all sets A and B, $A \cap B = B \cap A$, and $A \cup B = B \cup A$.

Associative Properties: For all sets A, B, and C, $(A \cup B) \cup C = A \cup (B \cup C)$, and $(A \cap B) \cap C = A \cap (B \cap C)$.

Union distributes over intersection, and intersection distributes over union.

Distributive Properties: For all sets A, B, and C, $A \cap (B \cup C) = (A \cap B) \cup (A \cap C)$, and $A \cup (B \cap C) = (A \cup B) \cap (A \cup C)$.

RETEACH 12-8

LESSON 12-8 **Reteach**
Set Theory

A **set** is a collection of objects or things. A set can be described using different notations.

Roster notation: a list of all the **elements** in the set
{0, 1, 2, 3, 4, 5}

Set-builder notation: a description in words using a variable
$\{x|x$ is a whole number less than 6}

Sometimes a set will have no elements. This is called the *null set*, or *empty set*, and is designated by the symbol ∅ or { }.

Complete the set descriptions.

1. the set of all integers between −3 and 3
Roster notation: {−2, __−1__, __0__, __1__, 2}
Set-builder notation: $x|x$ is an __integer__ between −3 and 3}
2. the set of all the days of the week that start with the letter *T*
Roster notation: {Tuesday, __Thursday__}
Set-builder notation: $\{T|T$ is a __day of the week__ that starts with the letter *T*}

Certain relationships exist between sets.
- *Subset:* $A \subset B$ means that all the members of set *A* are also members of set *B*.
- *Intersection:* $A \cap B$ is the set of all elements that are in both sets.
- *Union:* $A \cup B$ is the set of all elements that are in either set.

Complete the statements about sets *A*, *B*, and *C*.

$A = \{1, 2, 3, 4, 5, 6\}$; $B = \{1, 2, 3, 4\}$; $C = \{7, 8, 9\}$

3. All the elements in set __*B*__ are in set __*A*__. Therefore, *B* __⊂__ *A*.
4. The elements __1__, __2__, __3__, and __4__ are in both sets *A* and *B*.
$A \cap B$ = {__1, 2, 3, 4__}
5. The elements in sets *B* and *C* put together are 1, 2, 3, 4, 7, 8, 9.
B __∪__ $C = \{1, 2, 3, 4, 7, 8, 9\}$
6. The intersection of sets __*A* or *B*__ and __*C*__ is the null set.

PRACTICE 12-8

LESSON 12-8 **Practice B**
Set Theory

Write each set using roster notation or set-builder notation.

1. The set of all odd numbers from 2 to 17, including 17
{3, 5, 7, 9, 11, 13, 15, 17}
2. The set of all even integers greater than 4
$\{x|x$ is an even integer greater than 4}
3. The set of all integers between −9 and −6, inclusive
{−9, −8, −7, −6}
4. The set of all positive multiples of 3 less than 20
{3, 6, 9, 12, 15, 18}
5. The set of all states that start with *New*
{New York, New Hampshire, New Mexico, New Jersey}
6. The set of all integers between −4 and 4
{−3, −2, −1, 0, 1, 2, 3}

Find $A \cap B$ and $A \cup B$, and tell whether one of the sets is a subset of the other.

7. $A = \{5, 6, 7, 8\}$ and $B = \{6, 8, 10, 12\}$
$A \cap B = \{6, 8\}$; $A \cup B = \{5, 6, 7, 8, 10, 12\}$;
Neither is a subset of the other.
8. $A = \{20, 30, 40\}$ and $B = \{20, 25, 30, 35, 40\}$
$A \cap B = \{20, 30, 40\}$; $A \cup B = \{20, 25, 30, 35, 40\}$;
$A \subset B$.
9. $A = \{7, 14\}$ and $B = \{8, 9, 10, 11, 12, 13\}$
$A \cap B = \varnothing$; $A \cup B = \{7, 8, 9, 10, 11, 12, 13, 14\}$;
Neither is a subset of the other.
10. $A = \{x|x$ is an odd number less than 20} and
$B = \{x|x$ is a multiple of 5 less than 25}
$A \cap B = \{5, 15\}$; $A \cup B = \{1, 3, 5, 7, 9, 10, 11,13, 15, 17, 19, 20\}$;
Neither is a subset of the other.

21. The graph shows the number of branches of several libraries serving 1,000,000 or more people.

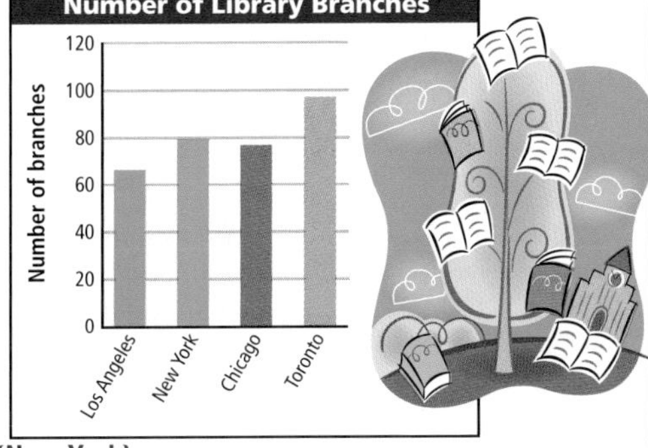

21a. A = {New York, Chicago, Toronto}

a. Give the set A of libraries with 70 or more branches.

b. Give the set B of all libraries with a number of branches that is a multiple of 20. **B = {New York}**

c. Find $A \cap B$. **$A \cap B$ = {New York}**

22. ***GEOGRAPHY*** Find $A \cap B$ if A = {all U.S. states|the state name starts with W} and B = {all U.S. states|the state borders Oregon}. **{Washington}**

23. ***SPORTS*** Given that A = {all basketball players} and B = {all people who are more than 80 inches tall}, describe the members of the intersection of A and B. **basketball players who are taller than 80 in.**

24. ***SOCIAL STUDIES*** Let $M = \{x|x$ is a person who lives in Illinois$\}$ and $N = \{x|x$ is a person who lives in Chicago$\}$.

a. Determine $M \cup N$ and $M \cap N$.

b. Is either set a subset of the other?

25. ***WHAT'S THE ERROR?*** If $A = \{1, 2, 3, 4\}$ and $B = \{2, 4\}$, what is the error if you write $A \cup B = B$? **Possible answer: Because $B \subset A$, it should be $A \cap B = B$ (or $A \cup B = A$).**

26. ***WRITE ABOUT IT*** Explain how you can determine the members of the intersection of two sets A and B. **Possible answer: Find the members that are in both sets and list them.**

27. ***CHALLENGE*** If a is in $A \cap B$, is a in $A \cup B$? Explain. If a is in $A \cup B$, is a in $A \cap B$? Explain. **Yes; if it is in either set, it is in their union. Not necessarily; it could be only in A or only in B and hence not in the intersection.**

Spiral Review

Determine the number of permutations in each case. (Lesson 10-7)

28. the numbers 1–5 **120**

29. the letters A, B, C, and D **24**

30. the number of ways six people can line up to go into the auditorium **720**

Solve each equation. (Lesson 11-3)

31. $2x + 5 = 3x$ **$x = 5$**
32. $4 - x = x$ **$x = 2$**
33. $3n + 16 = 7n$ **$n = 4$**
34. $11x + 1 = 8x + 10$ **$x = 3$**

35. **TEST PREP** What is the slope of the line that passes through (3, 5) and (6, 10)? (Lesson 12-5) **A**

A $\frac{5}{3}$ B $\frac{3}{5}$ C $-\frac{5}{3}$ D $-\frac{3}{5}$

COMMON ERROR ALERT

For Exercises 5–8 and 13–18, remind students that they do not have to list elements twice when they are finding the union of two sets containing the same elements.

24. a. $M \cup N = \{x|x$ is a person who lives in Illinois$\}$; $M \cap N = \{x|x$ is a person who lives in Chicago$\}$.

b. $N \subset M$

Journal

Suggest that students describe several school situations where set notation can be used. Students' descriptions should also include set unions and set intersections.

Test Prep Doctor

For Exercise 35, if students chose **B** or **D**, they need to review the definition of slope as "rise over run." Encourage students to note that if they start at (3, 5) and move to (6, 10), the line they draw will rise, so they can eliminate **C** and **D.** Because they go up more than they move to the right, the slope should be greater than 1, so students can eliminate **B**, leaving **A** as the correct answer.

Lesson Quiz

Write each set using roster notation or set-builder notation.

1. the set of positive multiples of 4 less than 24 **{4, 8, 12, 16, 20}**

2. the set of all state capitals $\{x|x$ is the capital of a state$\}$

Find $A \cup B$ and $A \cap B$, and tell whether one of the sets is a subset of the other.

3. $A = \{-8, -10, -12, -14\}$ and $B = \{-8, -12, -16\}$ $A \cup B = \{-8, -10, -12, -14, -16\}$

$A \cap B = \{-8, -12\}$; neither is a subset of the other.

4. A = {whole numbers} and $B = \{3, 5, 7, 9, 12\}$

$A \cup B$ = {whole numbers}

$A \cap B = \{3, 5, 7, 9, 12\}$; $B \subset A$.

Available on Daily Transparency in CRB

CHALLENGE 12-8

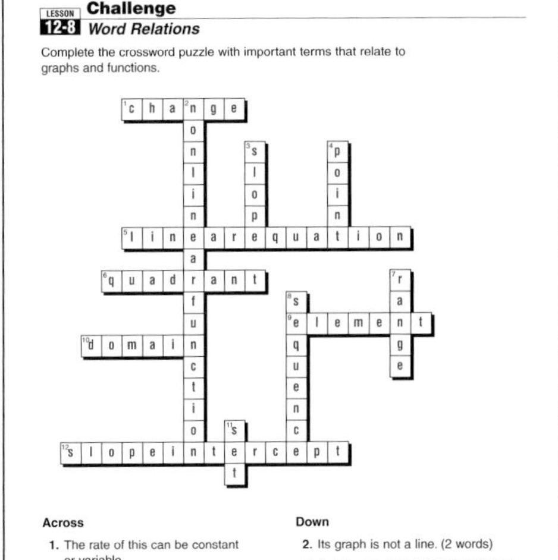

LESSON 12-8 **Challenge**
Word Relations

Complete the crossword puzzle with important terms that relate to graphs and functions.

Across

1. The rate of this can be constant or variable.
5. Its graph is a line. (2 words)
6. One of the four regions that make up a coordinate plane
9. A member of a set
10. Input values of a rule
12. Its equation is $y = mx + b$. (2 words)

Down

2. Its graph is not a line. (2 words)
3. A ratio measuring the steepness of a line
4. An ordered pair names its position on a plane.
7. Output values of a rule
8. An ordered list of numbers
11. A collection of objects or things

PROBLEM SOLVING 12-8

LESSON 12-8 **Problem Solving**
Set Theory

Write the correct answer.

1. List all the members of the set: $\{x|x$ is a state with at least 20,000,000 visitors to its national parks in 1999$\}$.

{CA, NC, VA}

2. List all members of the set: $\{x|x$ is a state in which the number of visitors in 1999 was $\leq 9{,}000{,}000\}$.

{AK, CO, FL, IN}

1999 Total National Park Visitors in Selected States	
Alaska (AK)	2,055,152
Arizona (AZ)	10,988,475
California (CA)	32,554,774
Colorado (CO)	5,597,641
Florida (FL)	8,923,251
Indiana (IN)	2,010,602
North Carolina (NC)	21,333,633
Virginia (VA)	24,605,608

Use these sets for the following problems.

A = {all states|the states in which the national parks had more than 10,000,000 visitors in 1999}
B = {all states|the states in the table that border the Atlantic Ocean}
W = {all states|the states in the table west of the Mississippi River}
Z = {all states|the states in the table south of Canada}
E = {all states|the states in the table that border the Pacific Ocean}
C = {all states|the states whose national parks had more than 15,000,000 visitors in 1999}

3. Find $A \cap B$. {NC, VA}

4. Find $A \cup B$. {AZ, CA, FL, NC, VA}

Choose the letter of the best answer.

5. Which states are in $W \cup Z$?
Ⓐ {AK, AZ, CA, CO, FL, IN, NC, VA}
B {AZ, CA, CO}
C {AK, AZ, CA, CO}
D {FL, IN, NC, VA}

6. Which states are in $W \cap Z$?
F {AK, AZ, CA, CO}
G {AZ, CA, CO, FL}
Ⓗ {AZ, CA, CO}
J {FL, IN, NC, VA}

7. Which set describes states that are members of $C \cup E$ but *not* of $C \cap E$?
A {AK, CA}
Ⓑ {AK, NC, VA}
C {CA, NC, VA}
D { }

8. Which set describes states that are members of C but *not* of $C \cup E$?
Ⓕ { }
G {AK}
H {AK, IN}
J {NC, VA}

CHAPTER 12 Extension

Pacing: Traditional 1 day
Block $\frac{1}{2}$ day

Objective: Students create and analyze Venn diagrams.

Using the Pages

In Lesson 12-8, students learned about set operations. In this lesson, students learn how to show set operations using Venn diagrams. Students also use Venn diagrams to determine the members of intersections and unions of sets.

EXTENSION Venn Diagrams

Learn to create and analyze Venn diagrams.

Vocabulary
Venn diagram

How are spaghetti and earthworms alike? In more ways than you might think. You can organize their similarities and differences in a *Venn diagram.*

A **Venn diagram** is a drawing that shows the relationships between two or more sets.

Characteristics that are shared are in the overlapping region. This is the intersection. Characteristics that appear in any region are part of the union.

Since all of the characteristics of a subset are shared by the larger set, the subset is drawn completely inside the larger set.

EXAMPLE 1 Drawing Venn Diagrams

Draw a Venn diagram to show the relationships between the sets.

A

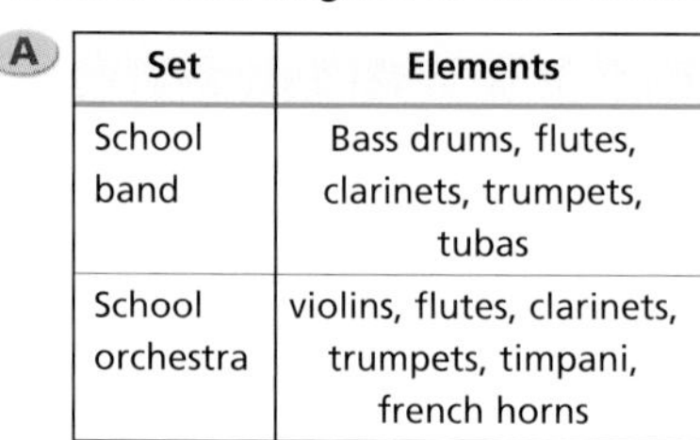

Set	Elements
School band	Bass drums, flutes, clarinets, trumpets, tubas
School orchestra	violins, flutes, clarinets, trumpets, timpani, french horns

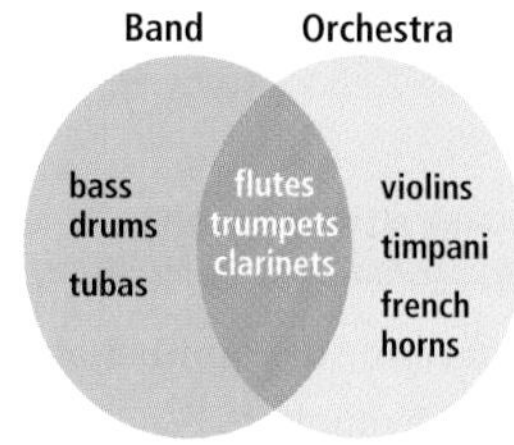

The two sets have an intersection of flutes, clarinets, and trumpets.

B

Set	Elements
Multiples of 4	4, 8, 12, 16, 20, 24, 28, 32, 36, 40
Multiples of 8	8, 16, 24, 32, 40

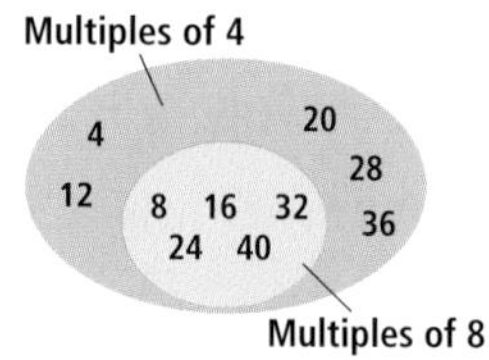

The set "Multiples of 8" is a subset of the set "Multiples of 4."

1 Introduce

Motivate

Draw two separate circles on the chalkboard. Label one "multiples of 2" and the other "multiples of 3." Ask students to name at least six numbers that would go in each circle Possible answers: multiples of 2: 2, 4, 6, 8, 10, 12; multiples of 3: 3, 6, 9, 12, 15, 18. Write the numbers in the appropriate circle. Ask students to identify the numbers that are common to both circles and to underline the numbers (i.e., 6, 12, 18). Then have students determine what those numbers have in common (i.e., the numbers are multiples of 6).

2 Teach

Lesson Presentation

Guided Instruction

In this lesson, students learn to create and analyze Venn diagrams. You may wish to point out that Venn diagrams often include a rectangle to represent the universe, or whole, and circles to represent sets within the universe. The circles do not have to be any particular size, but their position is significant. If they overlap, they have members in common.

Teaching Tip Discuss how to decide what a particular Venn diagram might look like. If the sets have some members in common, the circles will overlap. If one is a subset of another, one circle will be inside the other.

EXAMPLE  **Analyzing Venn Diagrams**

Use the Venn diagrams to identify intersections, unions, and subsets.

A

Intersection: 6, 12, 18, 24

Union: 2, 3, 4, 6, 8, 9, 10, 12, 14, 15, 16, 18, 20, 21, 22, 24

B

Fruit
strawberries
apples
bananas
grapes
pears
oranges
lemons
Citrus fruit

Intersection: oranges, lemons

Union: apples, pears, bananas, grapes, strawberries, oranges, lemons

Subset: citrus fruit

EXTENSION Exercises

Draw a Venn diagram to show the relationships between the sets.

1.

Set	Elements
Math club members	Harry, Jason, Juan, Doris, Keisha, Elden
Band members	Tyrone, Cara, Harry, Megan, Doris, Ricky

2.

Set	Elements
Multiples of 7 between 0 and 50	7, 14, 21, 28, 35, 42, 49
Odd numbers between 0 and 50	1, 3, 5, 7, 9, 11, 13, 15, 17, 19, 21, 23, 25, 27, 29, 31, 33, 35, 37, 39, 41, 43, 45, 47, 49

Use the Venn diagrams to identify intersections, unions, and subsets.

3. 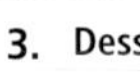

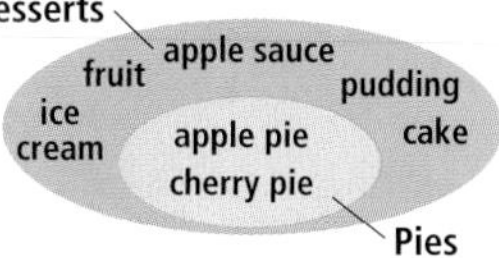

4.

 **5.** ***CHALLENGE*** Draw a Venn diagram to show the relationships between different kinds of quadrilaterals.

3 Close

Summarize

Have students write a description of how they would draw a Venn diagram to show two sets of numbers.

Possible answer: Draw a rectangle. If the sets have some numbers in common, draw overlapping circles. If one is a subset of the other, draw one circle inside the other. Then label each circle with its members.

Answers

1.

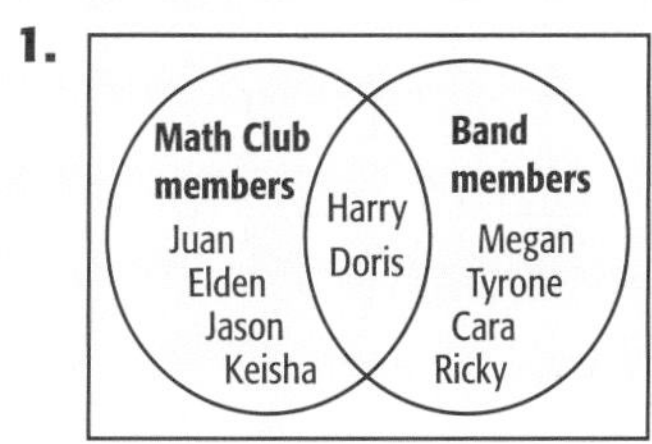

2.

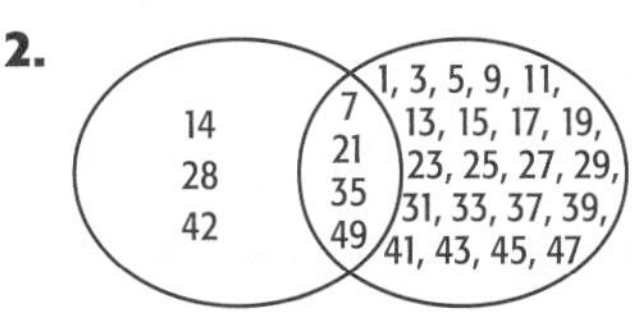

3. intersection: apple pie, cherry pie; union: pudding, cake, fruit, applesauce, ice cream, apple pie, cherry pie; subset of desserts: pies

4. intersection: tail, fur, four legs; union: barks, canine, tail, fur, four legs, purrs, feline

5.

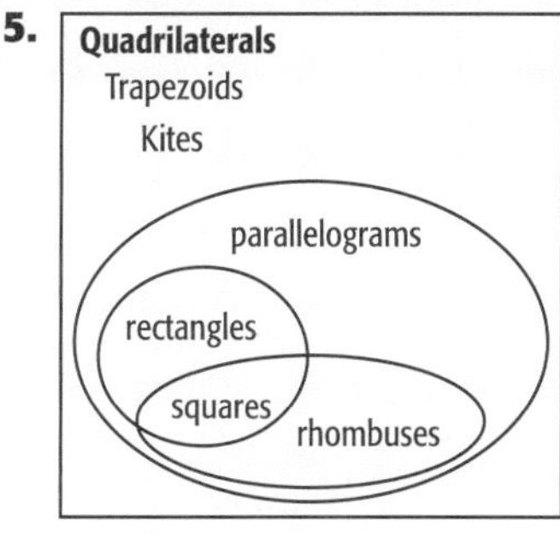

Additional Examples

Example 

Draw a Venn diagram to show the relationships between the sets.

Sets	Elements
Mary's favorite foods	pizza, hamburgers, tacos, seafood
Sean's favorite foods	hamburgers, spaghetti, seafood, sandwiches

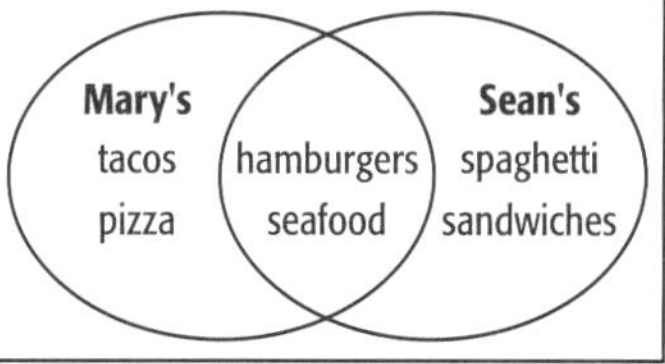

The sets have an intersection of hamburgers and seafood.

Example 2

Use the Venn diagram to identify intersections, unions, and subsets.

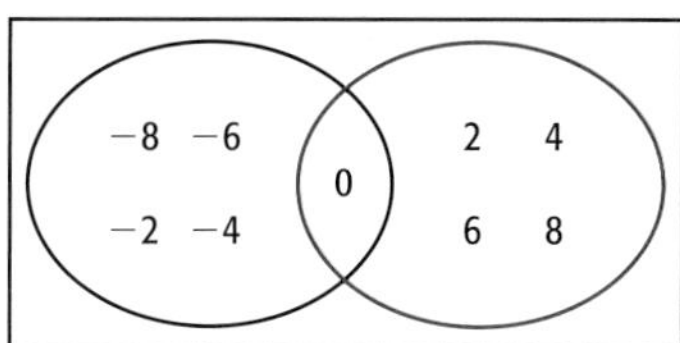

intersection: 0

union: −8, −6, −4, −2, 0, 2, 4, 6, 8

Problem Solving on Location

Tennessee

Purpose: *To provide additional practice for problem-solving skills in Chapters 1–12*

Traveling Tennessee Roadways

- After problem 1, ask students whether the function appears to be linear or nonlinear. nonlinear
- After problem 2, have students find the total time for Becky's round-trip from Chattanooga to Athens if her average speed was 45, 50, or 60 mi/h. Presume that she stayed in Athens for 2 hours. 45 mi/h: 4.44 hours; 50 mi/h: 4.2 hours; 60 mi/h: 3.83 hours

Extension Have students solve the following problem: How much time would it take you to drive from Memphis to Cookeville if you drove the first 100 miles at 50 mi/h and the remaining miles at 55 mi/h? 5.67 hours

Problem Solving on Location

TENNESSEE

Traveling Tennessee Roadways

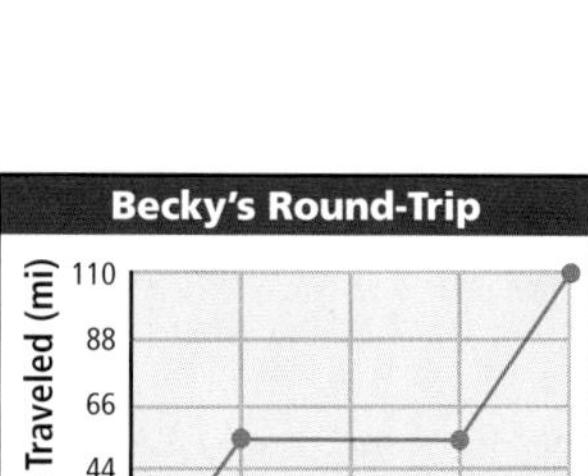

1. The distance from Memphis to Cookeville along Highway 40 is 302 miles. The equation $y = \frac{302}{x}$ describes the time y in hours that it takes to drive that distance at an average speed of x miles per hour.

a. Create a function table using $x = 45, 50, 55$, and 60.

b. How much more time does it take to get from Memphis to Cookeville driving 50 mi/h than it takes driving 60 mi/h?

c. Use the information in the table to make a graph.

d. Use your graph to tell how long the trip would take averaging a speed of 70 miles per hour.

For 2, use the graph.

2. The graph shows the time and distance Becky traveled round-trip from Chattanooga to Athens. She left Chattanooga at 9:00 A.M.

a. About how far is it from Chattanooga to Athens?

b. What does the horizontal portion of the graph indicate?

c. What time did Becky leave Athens?

d. Find the slope of each section of the graph.

e. Did Becky drive at the same speed going to Athens as she did driving back to Chattanooga? Explain.

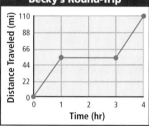

Becky's Round-Trip
Distance Traveled (mi): 0, 22, 44, 66, 88, 110
Time (hr): 0, 1, 2, 3, 4

Answers

1. a.

Input	Rule	Output
x	$\frac{302}{x}$	y
45	$\frac{302}{45}$	6.71
50	$\frac{302}{50}$	6.04
55	$\frac{302}{55}$	5.49
60	$\frac{302}{60}$	5.03

b. about 1.01 hours

c.

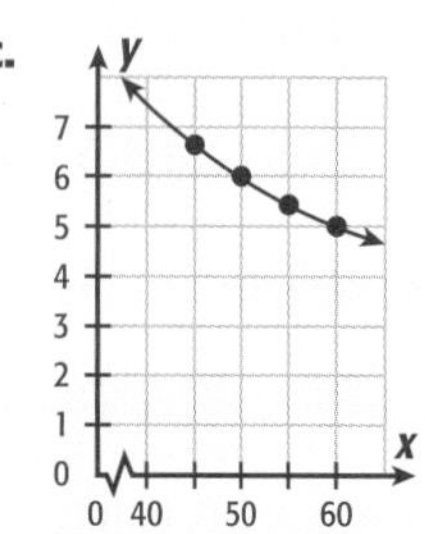

d. about 4.3 hours, which is about 4 hours and 20 minutes

2. a. about 55 miles

b. Becky stayed in Athens for 2 hours before returning to Chatanooga

c. noon

d. The slope is 55 for the first section, 0 for the second section, and 55 for the third section.

e. Yes; for each direction of the trip, Becky traveled the same distance in the same amount of time, so her rate (speed) must have been the same

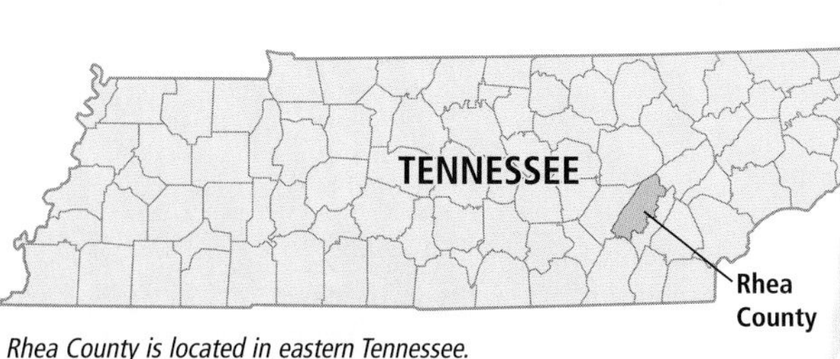

Rhea County is located in eastern Tennessee.

Rhea County Courthouse

Rhea County, Tennessee

The U.S. Census Bureau statistics show that the population of Rhea County, Tennessee, in the year 2000 was 28,400. It is predicted that the population of Rhea County will grow by an average of 660 people per year for the next 10 years. Use this data for 1–5.

1. Complete the table at right to find a pattern in the predicted populations of Rhea County for the next ten years. Let x equal the number of years. Let y equal the total increase in population after x years.

Input	Rule	Output
x	$x \cdot 660$	y
1	$1 \cdot 660$	660
2	$2 \cdot 660$	1,320
3	$3 \cdot 660$	1,980
4	$4 \cdot 660$	2,640
5	$5 \cdot 660$	3,300
6	$6 \cdot 660$	3,960
7	$7 \cdot 660$	4,620
8	$8 \cdot 660$	5,280
9	$9 \cdot 660$	5,940
10	$10 \cdot 660$	6,600

2. What is Rhea County's population projected to be in the year 2010? **35,000**

3. Write the function that describes the sequence of y-values. $y = 660x$

4. Is the function linear or nonlinear? How can you tell?
Linear; each successive input and output has a constant change.

5. Find the slope and y-intercept of the graph of the function.
slope: 660; y-intercept: 0

Rhea County has a land area of 316 square miles. In 2000, the county had a population density of about 90:1. This means that for each square mile of land area there were about 90 people.

6. If the land area stays the same, what would be the population density each year from 2000 to 2004, to the nearest whole number? Make a function table for $y = \frac{x}{316}$ to find out. Let x equal the number of people in the county each year from 2000 to 2004.

7. Is the function you used in problem 6 linear or nonlinear? How can you tell? Graph the function to help explain your answer. **Linear; each successive input and output has a constant change.**

Rhea County, Tennessee

- After problem 2, ask students to project what the population of Rhea County will be in the year 2020 if the current population trend continues. 41,600 people
- After problem 6, have students project the population density for the year 2020 to the nearest whole number. 132 people per square mile

Extension: Have students use an almanac to find the population and the number of square miles of the county in which they live. Using this data, have students find the population density where they live and compare it with the population density of Rhea County.

Possible answer: In the year 2000, the population density of Alachua County in Florida was 249 people per square mile. This is more than twice the population density of Rhea County in the year 2000.

Answers

6. The outputs in this table have been rounded up to the nearest whole number.

Year	Input	Rule	Output
	x	$\frac{x}{316}$	y
2000	28,400	$\frac{28,400}{316}$	90
2001	29,060	$\frac{29,060}{316}$	92
2002	29,720	$\frac{29,720}{316}$	94
2003	30,380	$\frac{30,380}{316}$	96
2004	31,040	$\frac{31,040}{316}$	98

7.

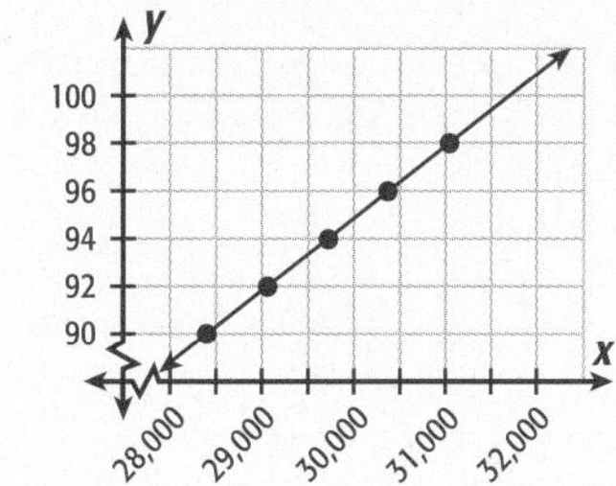

MATH-ABLES

Game Resources

Puzzles, Twisters & Teasers
Chapter 12 Resource Book

Clothes Encounters

Purpose: *To apply the problem-solving skill of logical thinking*

Discuss: Ask students to explain the various methods that they could have used to solve this problem. Possible answers: make a table, predict and check Then have students explain how they used the clues to find the person seated in seat 1 and what shirt and shoes that person was wearing. Possible answer: From clue 7, Robin is in seat 1. From clue 2, Robin is wearing a blue shirt. From clue 1, the girls' shoes were sandals, flip-flops, and boots. From clue 5, April is wearing flip-flops. From clue 3, Lila is not wearing sandals, so Lila must be wearing boots; therefore, Robin must be wearing sandals.

Extend: Have students work in pairs to create a logic problem with at least 5 clues. Have pairs exchange problems and solve.

MATH-ABLES

Clothes Encounters

Five students from the same math class met to study for an upcoming test. They sat around a circular table with seat 1 and seat 5 next to each other. No two students were wearing the same color of shirt or the same type of shoes. From the clues provided, determine where each student sat, each student's shirt color, and what type of shoes each student was wearing.

1. The girls' shoes were sandals, flip-flops, and boots.
2. Robin, wearing a blue shirt, was sitting next to the person wearing the green shirt. She was not sitting next to the person wearing the orange shirt.
3. Lila was sitting between the person wearing sandals and the person in the yellow shirt.
4. The boy who was wearing the tennis shoes was wearing the orange shirt.
5. April had on flip-flops and was sitting between Lila and Charles.
6. Glenn was wearing loafers, but his shirt was not brown.
7. Robin sat in seat 1.

You can use a chart like the one below to organize the information given. Put *X*'s in the spaces where the information is false and *O*'s in the spaces where the information is true. Some of the information from the first two clues has been included on the chart already. You will need to read through the clues several times and use logic to complete the chart.

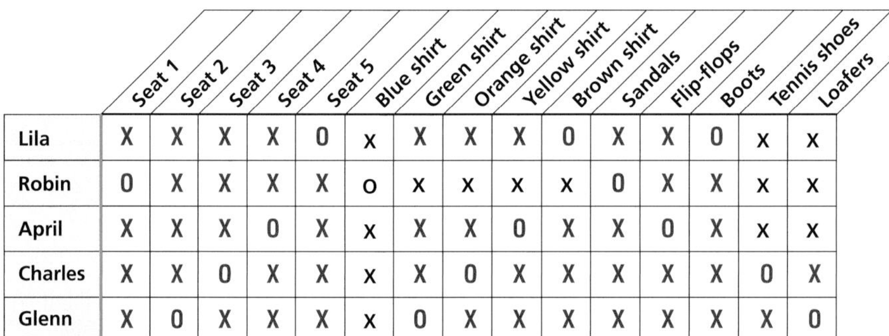

	Seat 1	Seat 2	Seat 3	Seat 4	Seat 5	Blue shirt	Green shirt	Orange shirt	Yellow shirt	Brown shirt	Sandals	Flip-flops	Boots	Tennis shoes	Loafers
Lila	X	X	X	X	0	x	X	X	X	0	X	X	0	x	x
Robin	0	X	X	X	X	o	x	x	x	x	0	X	X	x	x
April	X	X	X	0	X	x	X	X	0	X	X	0	X	x	x
Charles	X	X	0	X	X	x	X	0	X	X	X	X	X	0	X
Glenn	X	0	X	X	X	x	0	X	X	X	X	X	X	X	0

Answers

Seat	Student	Shirt Color	Shoe Type
1	Robin	Blue	Sandals
2	Lila	Brown	Boots
3	April	Yellow	Flip-flops
4	Charles	Orange	Tennis shoes
5	Glenn	Green	Loafers

Graph Linear Equations

A graphing calculator can be used to graph linear equations.

Activity

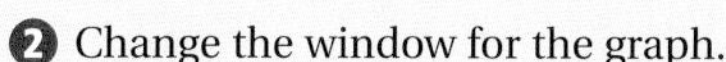

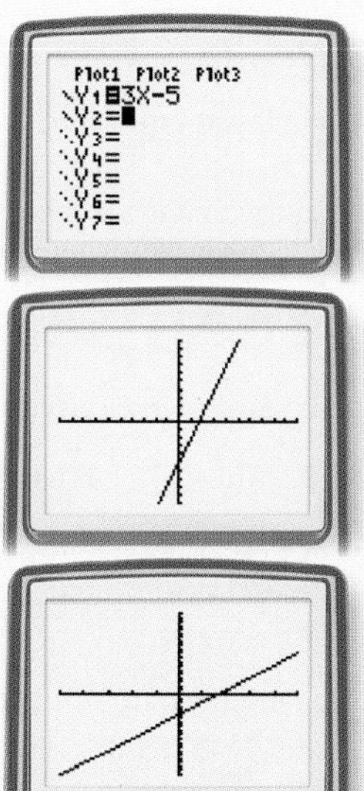

1 Graph the equation $y = 3x - 5$.

a. Start by pressing [Y=] 3 [X,T,θ,n] [−] 5 [ENTER]. You will get the screen shown at right.

b. Now select the standard viewing window by pressing [ZOOM] 6. The graph will immediately be displayed as shown.

You can check the graph by finding its slope and y-intercept. The graph crosses the y-axis at $(0, -5)$, so the y-intercept is -5. The graph also crosses the x-axis at $(2, 0)$, which gives a slope of 3. This agrees with the equation $y = 3x - 5$, which is in slope-intercept form.

2 Change the window for the graph.

Change the window for the graphed equation by pressing [WINDOW], and edit the entries by pressing [(−)] 5 [ENTER] 5 [ENTER] [ENTER] [(−)] 20 [ENTER] 20. Then press [GRAPH].

The slope of the graph looks like it has changed, but the mathematical slope is still 3.

Think and Discuss

1. Explain why the slope appears to have changed in **2**. Is the graph incorrect? Does the graph still represent the original equation? Explain.

Try This

Use a graphing calculator to graph each equation. Specify an appropriate viewing window. Check the graph by finding the slope and y-intercept of the equation to see whether they agree with the graph.

1. $y = x + 3$
slope = 1; y-intercept = 3

2. $y = 4 - x$
slope = −1; y-intercept = 4

3. $y = 4 - 2x$
slope = −2; y-intercept = 4

4. $y = 4x + 8$
slope = 4; y-intercept = 8

5. $y = 10x + 15$
slope = 10; y-intercept = 15

6. $x - y = 2$
slope = 1; y-intercept = −2

Answers

Think and Discuss

1. When you use a graphing calculator to graph a linear equation, the slope may *appear* to be different than the mathematical slope because the axes are scaled differently. The graph still accurately represents the equation; it just looks different.

Try This

1–6. Complete answers on p. A7

1. Use standard viewing window.

2. Use standard viewing window.

3. Use standard viewing window.

4. $-10 \leq x \leq 10$; $-6 \leq y \leq 14$

5. $-5 \leq x \leq 5$; $-5 \leq y \leq 20$

6. Use standard viewing window.

Graph Linear Equations

Objective: To use a graphing calculator to graph linear equations

Materials: Graphing calculator

Lab Resources

Technology Lab Activities . . . . p. 66

Using the Page

This technology activity shows students how to graph linear equations on a graphing calculator. Specific keystrokes may vary, depending on the make and model of the graphing calculator used. The keystrokes given are for a TI-83 model.

The Think and Discuss problem can be used to assess students' understanding of why mathematical slope and "visual" slope may differ. While Try This problems 1–6 can be done without a graphing calculator, they are meant to help students become familiar with using a graphing calculator to graph linear equations.

Assessment

Use a graphing calculator to graph each equation. Specify an appropriate viewing window.

1. $y = 2x + 4$

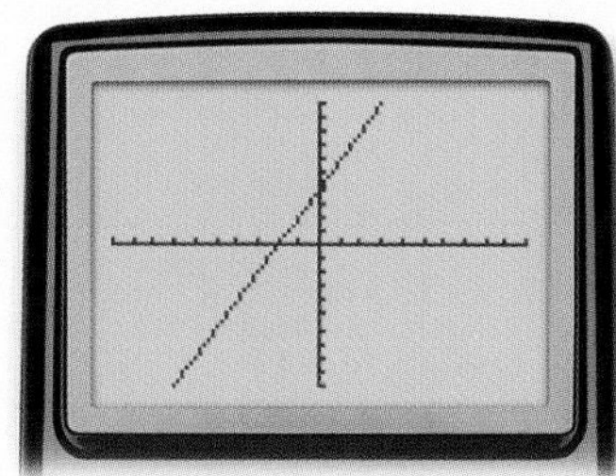

Use standard viewing window.

2. $y = 15 - x$

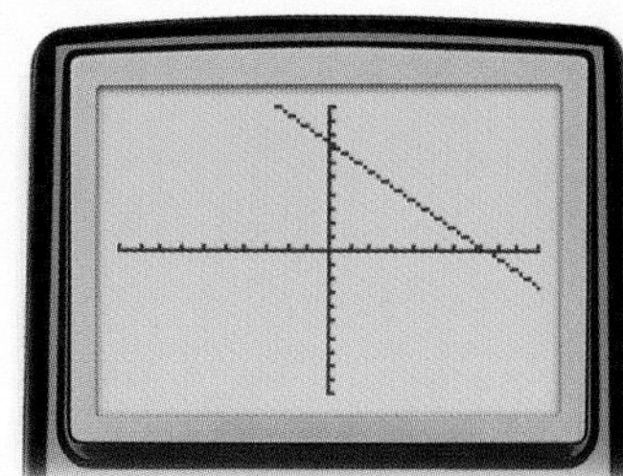

Use viewing window with **x min** = −20, **x max** = 20, **y min** = −20, and **y max** = 20.

Chapter 12 **Study Guide and Review**

Purpose: *To help students review and practice concepts and skills presented in Chapter 12*

Assessment Resources

Chapter Review

Chapter 12 Resource Book . . pp. 81–83

***Test and Practice Generator* CD-ROM**

Additional review assessment items in both multiple-choice and free-response format may be generated for any objective in Chapter 12.

Answers

1. sequence

2. function

3. linear function

4.

Input	Rule	Output
x	$x^2 - 1$	y
-2	$(-2)^2 - 1$	3
3	$(3)^2 - 1$	8
5	$(5)^2 - 1$	24

5. $y = 25n$; 125, 150, 175

6. $y = n - 4$; 1, 2, 3

7. $y = 3n - 7$; 8, 11, 14

8. $y = 2n + 2$; 12, 14, 16

Chapter 12 Study Guide and Review

Study Guide and Review

Vocabulary

domain	613	range	613
element	636	sequence	608
function	604	set	636
linear equation	616	slope	620
linear function	616	slope-intercept form	621
nonlinear function	628	*y*-intercept	620

Complete the sentences below with vocabulary words from the list above. Words may be used more than once.

1. A(n) __?__ is an ordered list of numbers.

2. A(n) __?__ gives exactly one output for every input.

3. A(n) __?__ is a function whose graph is a nonvertical line.

12-1 Introduction to Functions (pp. 604–607)

EXAMPLE

■ **Find the output for each input.**

Input	Rule	Output
x	$3x + 4$	y
-1	$3(-1) + 4$	1
0	$3(0) + 4$	4
2	$3(2) + 4$	10

EXERCISES

Find the output for each input.

4.

Input	Rule	Output
x	$x^2 - 1$	y
-2		
3		
5		

12-2 Find a Pattern in Sequences (pp. 608–611)

EXAMPLE

■ **Find a function that describes the sequence. Then use it to find the next three terms in the sequence.**

3, 6, 9, 12, . . .

Function: $y = 3n$

The next three terms are 15, 18, and 21.

n	Rule	y
1	$1 \cdot 3$	3
2	$2 \cdot 3$	6
3	$3 \cdot 3$	9
4	$4 \cdot 3$	12

EXERCISES

Find a function that describes each sequence. Then use it to find the next three terms in the sequence.

5. 25, 50, 75, 100, . . .

6. $-3, -2, -1, 0, \ldots$

7. $-4, -1, 2, 5, \ldots$

8. 4, 6, 8, 10, . . .

12-3 Interpreting Graphs (pp. 612–615)

EXAMPLE

■ Find the domain and range of the graph.

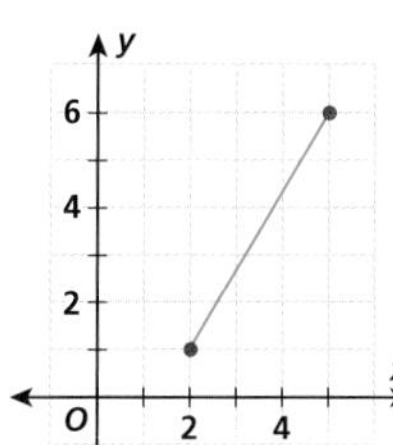

Domain: $2 \le x \le 5$

Range: $1 \le y \le 6$

EXERCISES

Find the domain and range of the graph.

9.

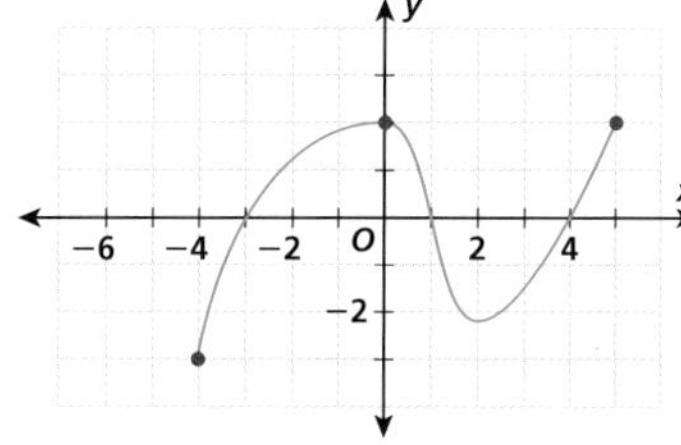

12-4 Linear Functions (pp. 616–619)

EXAMPLE

■ Graph $y = -x + 2$.

Input	Rule	Output	Ordered Pair
x	$-x + 2$	y	(x, y)
0	$-(0) + 2$	2	(0, 2)
2	$-(2) + 2$	0	(2, 0)
−1	$-(-1) + 2$	3	(−1, 3)

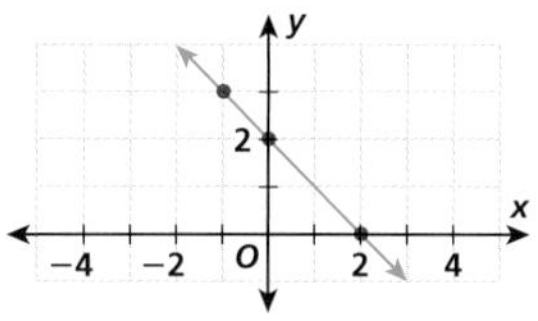

EXERCISES

Graph each linear function.

10. $y = 2x - 1$

11. $y = -3x$

12. $x + y = -3$

13. $y - 2x = 4$

14. $2y = x - 6$

15. $x - 3y = -9$

12-5 Slope (pp. 620–623)

EXAMPLE

■ Graph $y = x - 2$.

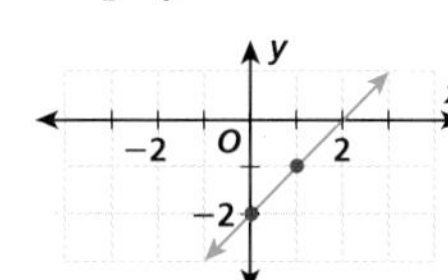

The slope is 1. The y-intercept is –2.

EXERCISES

Graph each line, given the equation.

16. $y = \frac{1}{3}x + 1$

17. $y = -x + 4$

18. $y = -1$

Answers

9. D: $-4 \le x \le 5$; R: $-3 \le y \le 2$

10.

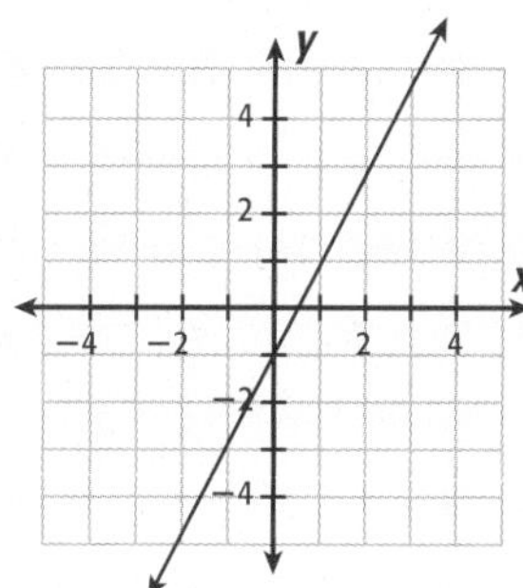

11.

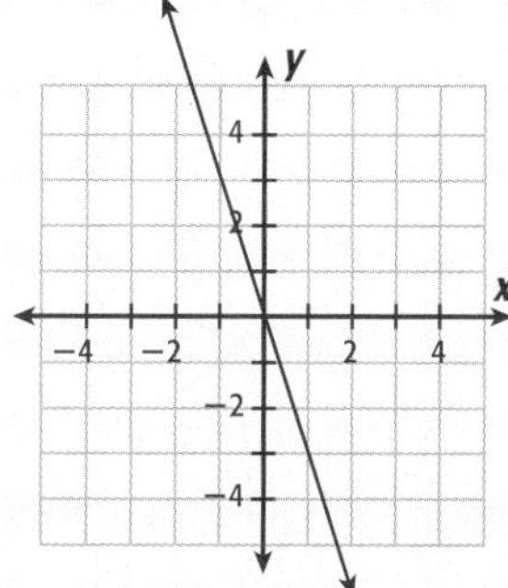

12.

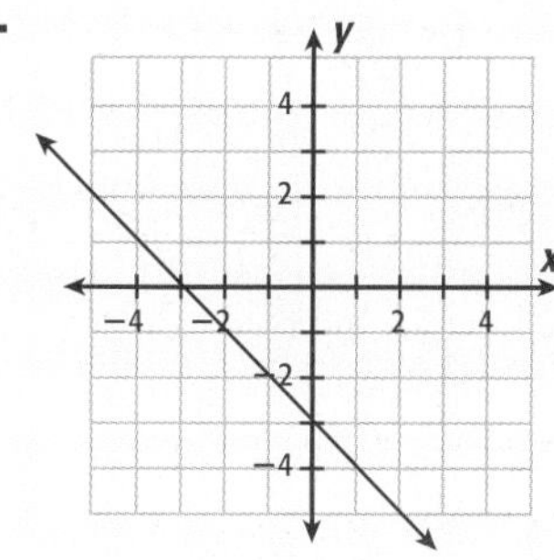

13.

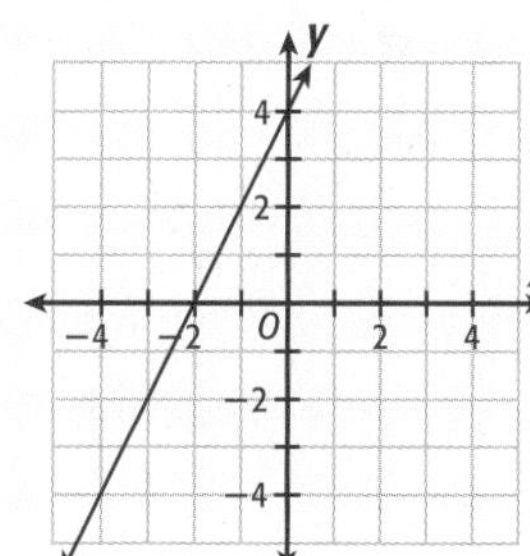

14.

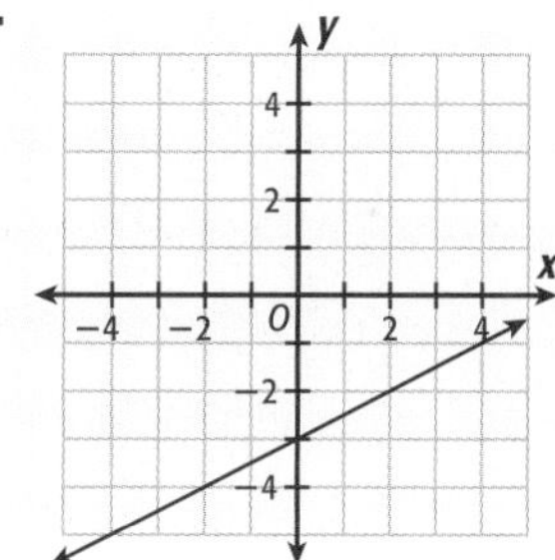

15.

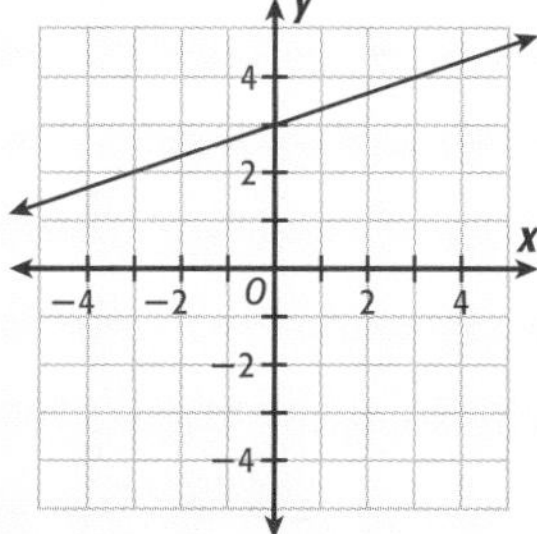

16.

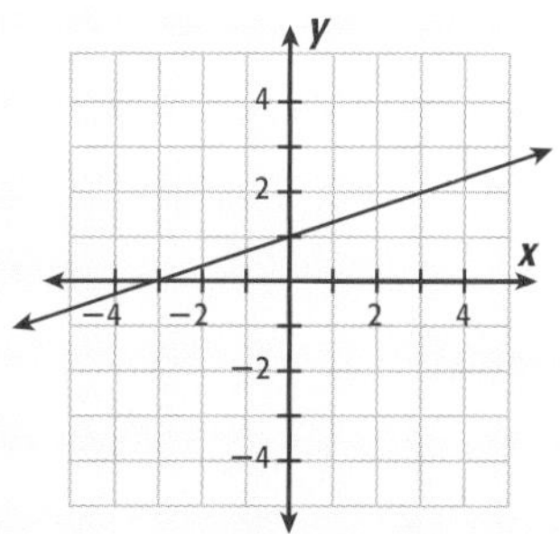

17.

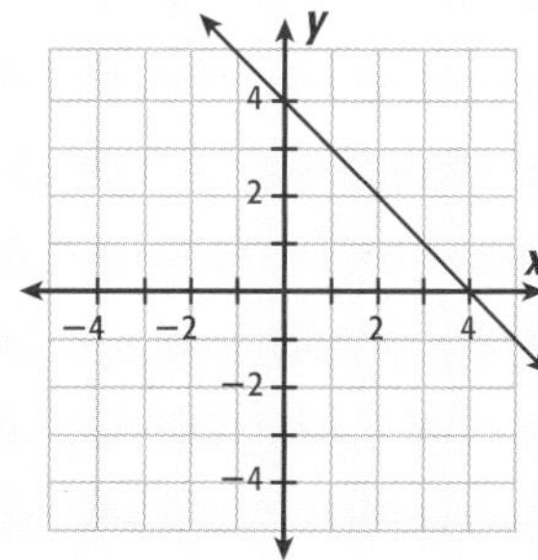

18.

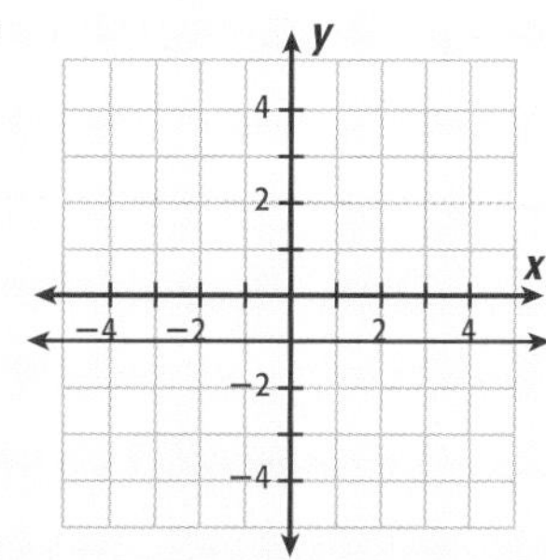

Answers

19. nonlinear

20. linear

21. variable

22. $A \cap B = \{3, 5, 7\}$; $A \cup B = \{1, 2, 3, 5, 7, 9\}$; neither is a subset of the other.

23. $A \cap B = \{x|x$ is divisible by $8\}$; $A \cup B = \{x|x$ is divisible by $2\}$; $B \subset A$

24. $A \cap B =$ {New Hampshire, New Jersey, New Mexico, New York}; $A \cup B = \{x|x$ is a state in the United States$\}$; $A \subset B$

12-6 Nonlinear Functions (pp. 628–631)

EXAMPLE

- **Tell whether the function represented in the table has a linear or nonlinear relationship.**

Difference is constant.

Difference in x	x	y	Difference in y
	2	5	
1			5
	3	10	
1			7
	4	17	

Difference varies.

The function has a nonlinear relationship.

EXERCISES

Tell whether the function represented in each table has a linear or nonlinear relationship.

19.

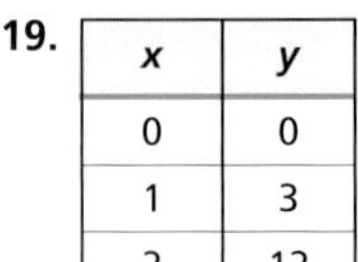

x	y
0	0
1	3
2	12

20.

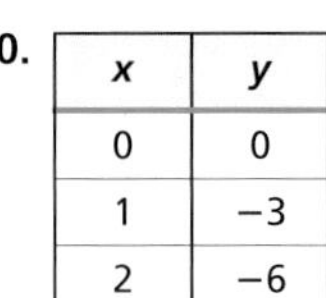

x	y
0	0
1	−3
2	−6

12-7 Rates of Change (pp. 632–635)

EXAMPLE

- **Tell whether the graph shows a constant or variable rate of change.**

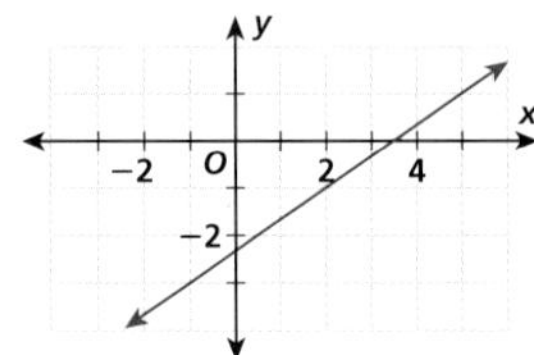

The rate of change is constant.

EXERCISES

Tell whether the graph shows a constant or variable rate of change.

21.

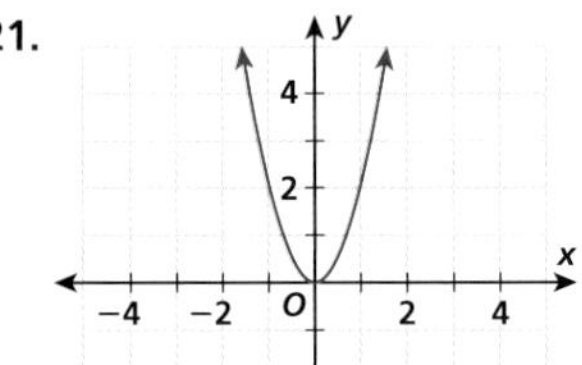

12-8 Set Theory (pp. 636–639)

EXAMPLE

- **Find $A \cap B$ and $A \cup B$, and tell whether one of the sets is a subset of the other.**

$A = \{1, 3, 5, 7\}$; $B = \{3, 5\}$

$A \cap B = \{3, 5\}$
$A \cup B = \{1, 3, 5, 7\}$
$B \subset A$

EXERCISES

Find $A \cap B$ and $A \cup B$, and tell whether one of the sets is a subset of the other.

22. $A = \{x|x$ is a prime number less than $10\}$;
$B = \{x|x$ is an odd number less than $10\}$

23. $A = \{x|x$ is divisible by $2\}$;
$B = \{x|x$ is divisible by $8\}$

24. $A = \{x|x$ is a U.S. state beginning with the word *New*$\}$;
$B = \{x|x$ is a state in the United States$\}$

Chapter Test

Chapter 12

Find the output for each input.

1.

Input	Rule	Output
x	$-2x + 5$	y
-1		
0		
1		

2.

Input	Rule	Output
x	$x \div 4$	y
-8	$-8 \div 4$	-2
0	$0 \div 4$	0
4	$4 \div 4$	1

Find a function that describes each sequence. Use the function to find the next three terms in the sequence.

3. 4, 6, 8, 10, . . . $y = 2n + 2$; 12, 14, 16

4. 11, 21, 31, 41, . . . $y = 10n + 1$; 51, 61, 71

5. $-2, -1, 0, 1, \ldots$ $y = n - 3$; 2, 3, 4

6. 15, 30, 45, 60, . . . $y = 15n$; 75, 90, 105

Find the domain and range of each graph.

7. 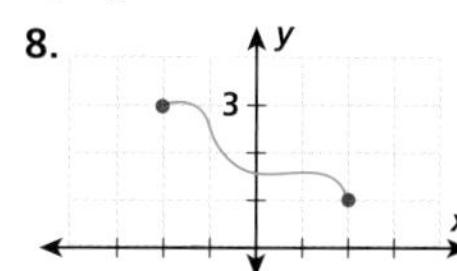

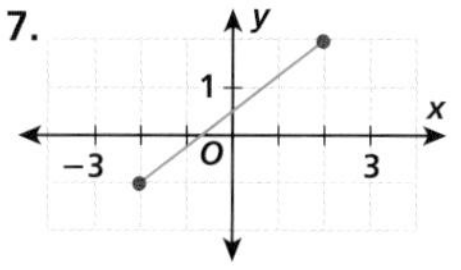

D: $-2 \leq x \leq 2$; R: $-1 \leq y \leq 2$

8. 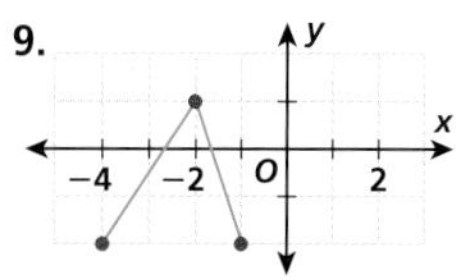

D: $-2 \leq x \leq 2$; R: $1 \leq y \leq 3$

9. D: $-4 \leq x \leq -1$; R: $-2 \leq y \leq 1$

10. June deposited \$1,500 into a savings account. Because of the interest earned, the amount will double every 10 years. Write a sequence to show how much money will be in the account at the end of 40 years. **\$24,000**

Use the slope and y-intercept to graph each linear function.

11. $y = 2x - 5$ **12.** $y = 4$ **13.** $2y - 5x - 4 = 0$ **14.** $-x + 2y = 10$

Tell whether the function represented in each table has a linear or nonlinear relationship.

15.

x	y
1	-3
2	-12
3	-27

nonlinear

16.

x	y
1	4
2	1
3	0

nonlinear

17.

x	y
1	6
2	10
3	14

linear

18. Tell whether the graph shows a constant or variable rate of change. **constant**

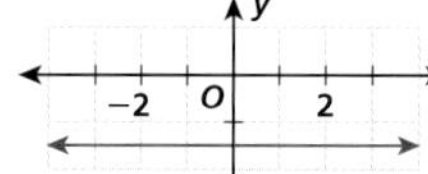

Find $A \cap B$ and $A \cup B$, and tell whether one of the sets is a subset of the other.

19. $A = \{-5, -3, -1, 1\}$; $B = \{-3, -1\}$

20. $A = \{x | x \text{ is a cat}\}$; $B = \{x | x \text{ is a dog}\}$

14. $\frac{1}{2}$; 5

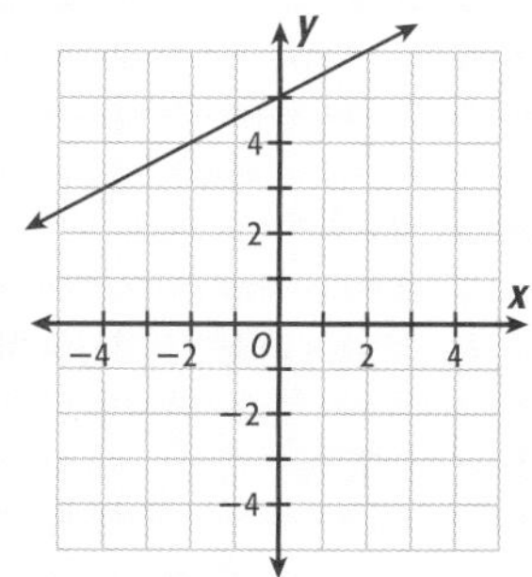

19. $A \cap B = \{-3, -1\}$; $A \cup B = \{-5, -3, -1, 1\}$; $B \subset A$

20. $A \cap B = \varnothing$, $A \cup B = \{x | x \text{ is a cat or a dog}\}$; neither is a subset of the other.

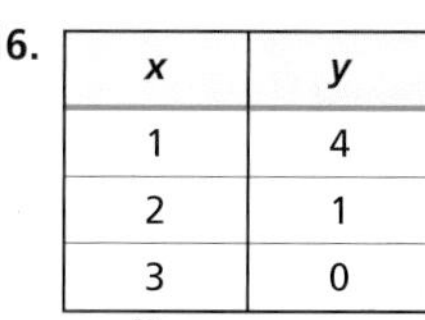

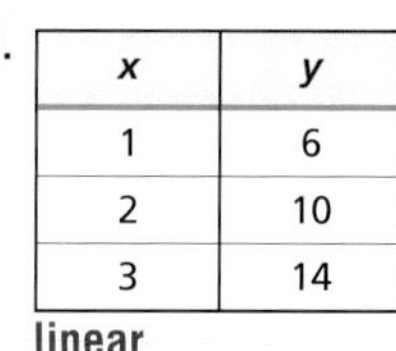

Chapter Test

Chapter 12

Purpose: *To assess students' mastery of concepts and skills in Chapter 12*

Assessment Resources

Chapter 12 Tests (Levels A, B, C)
Assessment Resources . . . . pp. 99–104

***Test and Practice Generator* CD-ROM**

Additional assessment items in both multiple-choice and free-response format may be generated for any objective in Chapter 12.

Answers

1.

Input	Rule	Output
x	$-2x + 5$	y
-1	$-2(-1) + 5$	7
0	$-2 \cdot 0 + 5$	5
1	$-2 \cdot 1 + 5$	3

11. 2; -5

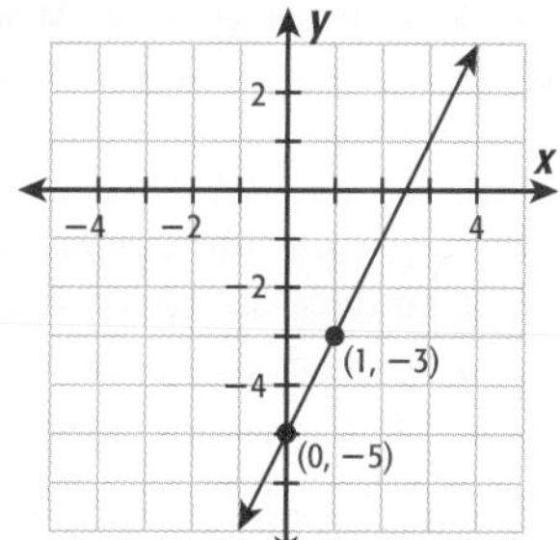

12. 0; 4

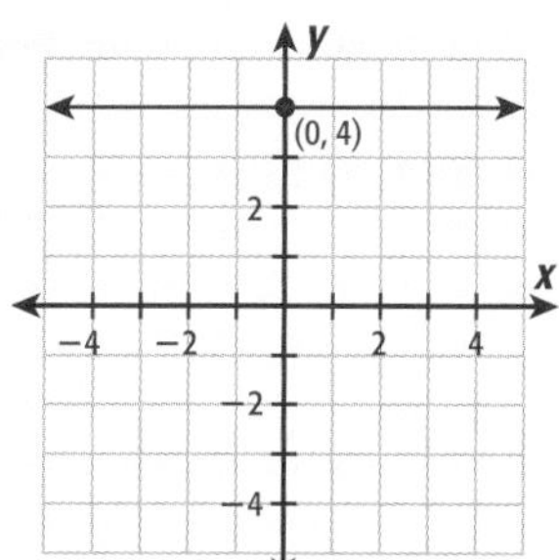

13. $\frac{5}{2}$; 2

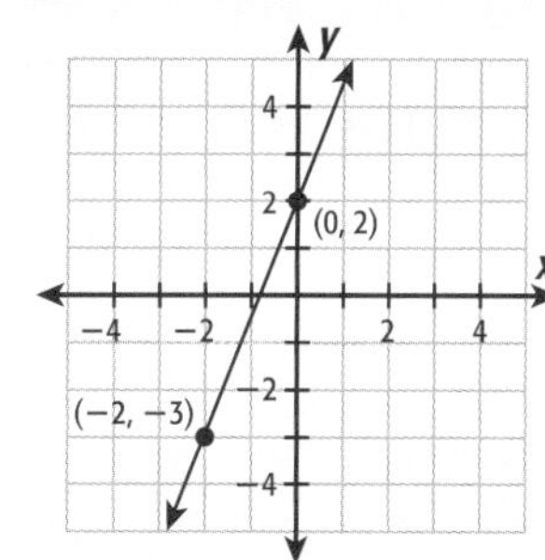

Chapter 12 Performance Assessment

Purpose: To assess students' understanding of concepts in Chapter 12 and combined problem-solving skills

Assessment Resources 

Performance Assessment
Assessment Resources .... p. 128

Performance Assessment Teacher Support
Assessment Resources .... p. 127

Answers

2, 4, 5. See p. A7.

6. See Level 3 work sample below.

Scoring Rubric for Problem Solving Item 6

Level 3
Accomplishes the purposes of the task.
Student gives clear explanations, shows understanding of mathematical ideas and processes, and computes accurately.

Level 2
Purposes of the task not fully achieved.
Student demonstrates satisfactory but limited understanding of the mathematical ideas and processes.

Level 1
Purposes of the task not accomplished.
Student shows little evidence of understanding the mathematical ideas and processes and makes computational and/or procedural errors.

Chapter 12 Performance Assessment

Performance Assessment

Show What You Know

Create a portfolio of your work from this chapter. Complete this page and include it with your four best pieces of work from Chapter 12. Choose from your homework or lab assignments, mid-chapter quiz, or any journal entries you have done. Put them together using any design you want. Make your portfolio represent what you consider your best work.

Short Response

1. The graph shows the population growth of a species of paramecium, a microscopic organism, in a test tube. Describe the growth. Is it linear or variable? Explain your answer.
   It increases at first and then levels off; variable.
2. Make a function table for $y = 2x - 3$. Is the function linear or nonlinear? Explain your answer.
3. Find a pattern in the sequence 17, 34, 51, 68, ... Write a function for the sequence, and give the next three terms. **$y = 17n$; 85, 102, 119**
4. Graph the function $y = x^2 - 1$. Give the domain and range of the function.
5. Find the slope and y-intercept of the line that represents the equation $y = 3x + 1$. Explain in words how you found your answer. Then use the slope and intercept to graph the line.

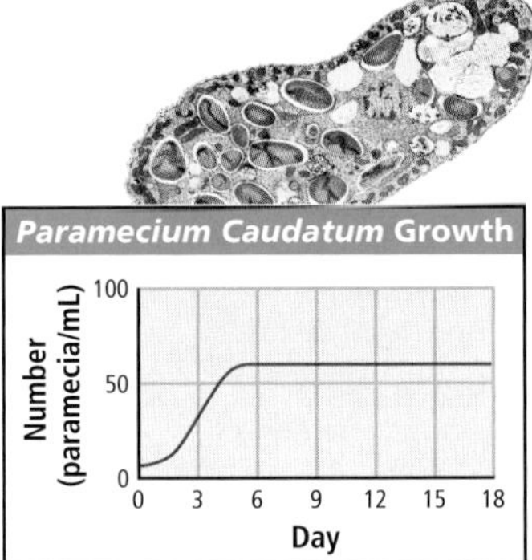

 Extended Problem Solving

6. The graph shows speed limits on rural interstates in six states.
   a. List the members of set A, the set of all states with a speed limit of 70 mi/h.
   b. List the members of set B, the set of all states with a speed limit greater than 65 mi/h.
   c. Find $A \cap B$ and $A \cup B$.
   d. Explain how sets A and B are related.

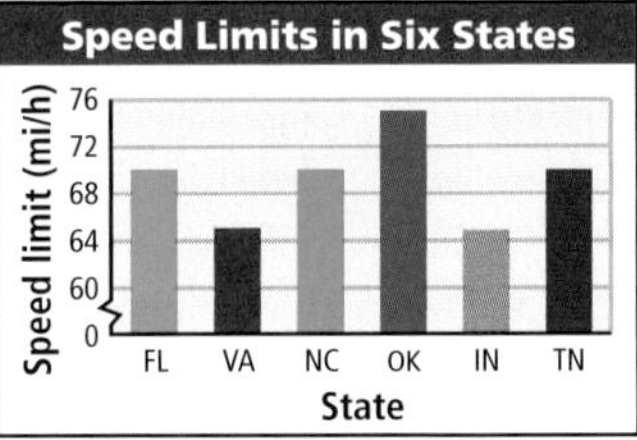

Student Work Samples for Item 6

Level 3

a) A = {FL, NC, TN}
b) B = {FL, NC, OK, TN}
c) A ∩ B = A or {FL, NC, TN}
A ∪ B = B or {FL, NC, OK, TN}
d) A is a subset of B.

The student correctly identified the sets and their relationships and used the correct notation.

Level 2

A. FL, NC, TN
B. FL, NC, OK, TN
C. ∩ = FL, NC, OK, TN
U = FL, NC, TN
D. They have the same states except one has Oklahoma.

The student identified the sets, but did not use set notation. The student confused the union and intersection and did not recognize that one set is a subset of the other.

Level 1

a. FL, NC, TN
b. FL, VA, NC, OK, IN, TN
c. FL, NC, TN
d. They have states.

The student did not use set notation and did not list the elements of the second set correctly. The answers to parts **c** and **d** are incomplete.

internet connect
State-Specific Test Practice Online
go.hrw.com Keyword: MS4 TestPrep

Standardized Test Prep

Chapter 12

Cumulative Assessment, Chapters 1–12

1. Estimate the sum $\sqrt{21} + \sqrt{68}$ to the nearest whole number. **C**

Ⓐ 11　Ⓑ 40　Ⓒ 13　Ⓓ 14

2. Find the range of the data set.
13, 22, 21, 18, 12, 21, 20, 25 **G**

Ⓕ 21　Ⓖ 13　Ⓗ 12　Ⓙ 19

3. Find the least common multiple of 18, 24, and 30. **A**

Ⓐ 360　Ⓑ 240　Ⓒ 12,960　Ⓓ 6,480

4. Evaluate the expression $3a - b$ for $a = -5$ and $b = 9$. **J**

Ⓕ −6　Ⓖ 21　Ⓗ −21　Ⓙ −24

5. Find the area of the circle to the nearest tenth. Use 3.14 for π. **B**

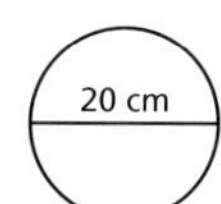

Ⓐ 1,256 cm^2　Ⓑ 314 cm^2　Ⓒ 62.8 cm^2　Ⓓ 125.6 cm^2

6. Stewart spent $12.86 at a restaurant. About how much should he leave for a 15% tip? **F**

Ⓕ $1.95　Ⓖ $3.00　Ⓗ $6.00　Ⓙ $2.50

7. Tell which rule can describe the sequence 5, 7, 9, 11, ... **D**

Ⓐ $n + 2$　Ⓑ $2n - 3$　Ⓒ $n - 2$　Ⓓ $2n + 3$

TEST TAKING TIP!

When finding the percent of a number, you can eliminate choices by deciding whether the answer should be greater or less than the original number.

8. A seventh-grade class is going to increase in size by 15% next year. There are 280 seventh graders now. What will be the enrollment next year? **H**

Ⓕ 42　Ⓖ 295　Ⓗ 322　Ⓙ 238

9. This is a graph of which linear equation? **A**

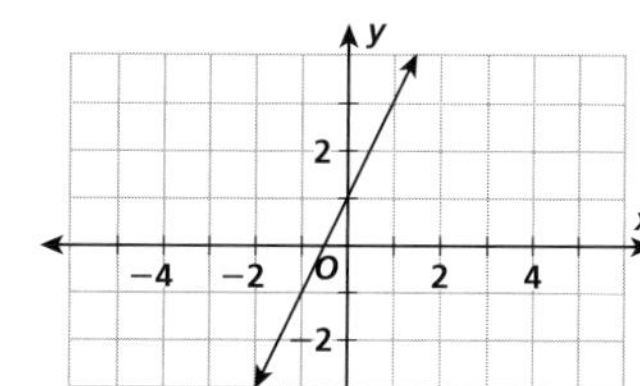

Ⓐ $y = 2x + 1$　Ⓑ $y = -2x - 1$　Ⓒ $y = 2x$　Ⓓ $y = 2x - 1$

10. ***SHORT RESPONSE*** A right triangle has side lengths of 7 inches and 24 inches. Use the Pythagorean Theorem to find the length of the hypotenuse. Show your work.

11. ***SHORT RESPONSE*** Identify the sample space for tossing three coins, and give the probability that when three coins are tossed, all three would land on heads.

Standardized Test Prep

Standardized Test Prep

Chapter 12

Purpose: *To provide review and practice for Chapters 1–12 and standardized tests*

Assessment Resources

Cumulative Tests (Levels A, B, C)
Assessment Resources . . . . . pp. 261–272

State-Specific Test Practice Online
KEYWORD: MS4 TestPrep

Test Prep Doctor

Expand on the test taking tip for item 8 by reminding the students that they can eliminate all answers that are less than 280. Students who chose **G** are adding 15 students to the current enrollment, not 15%.

Answers

10.
$$a^2 + b^2 = c^2$$
$$7^2 + 24^2 = c^2$$
$$49 + 576 = c^2$$
$$625 = c^2$$
$$\sqrt{625} = c$$
$$25 = c$$

The length of the hypotenuse of a right triangle with side lengths 7 inches and 24 inches is 25 inches.

11. {HHH, HHT, HTH, HTT, TTT, THT, THH, TTH}; $\frac{1}{8}$

Student Handbook

Student Handbook

Student Handbook

Extra Practice

Extra Practice ■ Chapter 1

1A Organizing Data

LESSON 1-1

Identify the population and sample in each situation.

1. Researchers poll 2,000 middle school students to find out about the kinds of music middle school students like most. **population: all middle school students; sample: the 2,000 students who are polled**
2. Scientists tag the ears of 85 deer to get information on the migratory patterns of deer in the wild. **population: all wild deer; sample: the 85 deer that are tagged**

A reporter is gathering responses from local families. Tell whether each sampling method is random. Explain your answer.

3. The reporter surveys families by choosing all families whose last names begin with the letters *A–G*. **The sampling method is not random. Families with last names that do not start with letters *A–G* have no chance of being chosen.**
4. The reporter selects families by programming a computer to select names randomly. **The sampling method is random. The reporter has no chance of knowing which names will be chosen.**

LESSON 1-2

Find the mean, median, mode, and range of each data set.

5.

Daily High Temperatures							
Day	Sun	Mon	Tue	Wed	Thu	Fri	Sat
Temperature (°F)	37	53	56	55	59	52	45

51; 53; no mode; 22

6. 13, 8, 40, 19, 5, 8 **15.5; 10.5; 8; 35**
7. 21, 19, 23, 26, 15, 25, 25 **22; 23; 25; 11**
8. 61, 89, 93, 102, 47, 93, 61 **78; 89; 61 and 93; 55**
9. 65, 82, 207, 185, 45, 149, 127, 136 **124.5; 131.5; no mode; 162**

Identify the outlier in each data set. Then determine how the outlier affects the mean, median, and mode of the data. **10–13. See p. A7.**

10. 23, 27, 31, 19, 56, 22, 25, 21
11. 66, 78, 57, 87, 66, 59, 239, 84
12. 36, 37, 35, 39, 35, 39, 10, 31
13. 152, 155, 153, 148, 143, 47, 159, 147

LESSON 1-3 **14–15. See p. A7.**

The table shows the number of points a player scored during the last ten games of the season.

Game Date	Points	Game Date	Points
Feb 7	36	Feb 25	18
Feb 14	34	Feb 27	31
Feb 18	27	Mar 1	43
Feb 20	46	Mar 3	42
Feb 23	32	Mar 4	28

14. Make a cumulative frequency table of the data.
15. Make a stem-and-leaf plot of the data.
16. Find the mean, median, mode, and range of the data set. Round to the nearest tenth, if necessary. **33.7; 33; no mode; 28**

Extra Practice ■ Chapter 1

1B Displaying Data

LESSON 1-4 **1–2. See p. A8.**

1. The table shows the populations of four countries. Make a double-bar graph of the data.
2. The list below shows the scores on a history quiz. Make a histogram of the data.

   87, 92, 75, 79, 64, 88, 96, 99, 69, 77, 78, 78, 88, 83, 93, 76

Country	1998 Population (millions)	2001 Population (millions)
Tunisia	9.3	9.7
Syria	15.3	16.7
Turkey	64.5	66.5
Algeria	30.1	31.7

LESSON 1-5

The circle graph shows the results of a survey of 100 people from Iran who were asked about their ethnic backgrounds. Use the graph for Exercises 3–5.

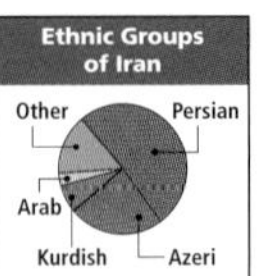

3. Which ethnic group is the second largest? **Azeri**
4. Approximately what percent of the people are Persian? **50%**
5. According to the survey, 3% of the people are Arab. How many of the people surveyed are Arab? **3 people**

Decide whether a bar graph or a circle graph would best display the information. Explain your answer.

6. the number of guitars sold compared with the number of drum sets sold for the year 2002 **A bar graph would show the data best because you can easily compare the two pieces of data on a bar graph.**
7. the average temperature for each day of one week **A bar graph would show the data best because you can easily see how the numbers relate with the heights of the bars on a bar graph.**

LESSON 1-6

Use the box-and-whisker plot for Exercises 8–10.

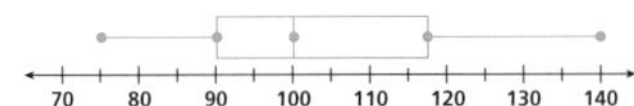

8. What is the first quartile? **90**
9. What is the range of the data? **65**
10. About what fraction of the data are less than 90? $\frac{1}{4}$
11. Use the data below to make a box-and-whisker plot. 22, 41, 39, 27, 29, 30, 40, 61, 25, 28, 32 **See p. A8.**

Extra Practice ■ Chapter 1

1C Trends and Relations in Graphs

LESSON 1-7

The table at right shows the number of students Karen tutored during certain months of the year. Use the table for Exercises 1–3.

Month	Number of Students
Jan	5
Mar	8
May	9
Jul	12
Sep	14
Nov	18

1. Make a line graph of the data in the table. Use the graph to determine during which months the number of students increased the most. **1. See p. A8.**
2. When did the number of students increase the least? **from March to May**
3. Use the graph to estimate the number of students Karen tutored during the month of October. **about 16 students**

LESSON 1-8

4. The table shows the average number of points per game that Michael Jordan scored during each season with the Chicago Bulls. Use the data to make a scatter plot. Describe the relationship between the data sets. **4. See p. A8.**

Year	Points	Year	Points
1988	35.0	1993	32.6
1989	32.5	1994	26.9
1990	33.6	1995	30.4
1991	31.5	1996	29.6
1992	30.1	1997	28.7

Write *positive correlation, negative correlation,* or *no correlation* to describe each relationship. Explain.

5. the number of students at a school and the number of teachers at a school **positive correlation**
6. the length of a person's hair and the size of the person's shoes **no correlation**
7. the number of people in a movie theater and the number of empty seats in a movie theater. **negative correlation**

LESSON 1-9

Explain why each graph could be misleading. **8–9. See p. A8.**

8. Populations of Australia and Iran

9.

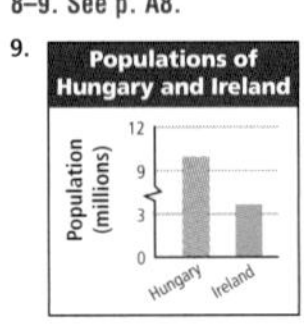

Extra Practice ■ Chapter 2

2A Exponents

LESSON 2-1

Find each value.

1. 5^3 **125**
2. 7^3 **343**
3. 5^5 **3,125**
4. 6^5 **7,776**
5. 4^0 **1**
6. 8^2 **64**
7. 12^2 **144**
8. 100^3 **1,000,000**
9. 2^7 **128**
10. 4^5 **1,024**
11. 9^3 **729**
12. 10^6 **1,000,000**

Write each number using an exponent and the given base.

13. 121, base 11 $\mathbf{11^2}$
14. 4,096, base 4 $\mathbf{4^6}$
15. 216, base 6 $\mathbf{6^3}$
16. 1,296, base 6 $\mathbf{6^4}$
17. 256, base 2 $\mathbf{2^8}$
18. 8,000, base 20 $\mathbf{20^3}$
19. 225, base 15 $\mathbf{15^2}$
20. 27,000, base 30 $\mathbf{30^3}$
21. 1,728, base 12 $\mathbf{12^3}$

LESSON 2-2

Multiply.

22. $24 \cdot 10^3$ **24,000**
23. $22 \cdot 10^2$ **2,200**
24. $20 \cdot 10^5$ **2,000,000**
25. $32 \cdot 10^2$ **3,200**
26. $15 \cdot 10^4$ **150,000**
27. $17 \cdot 10^2$ **1,700**
28. $26 \cdot 10^3$ **26,000**
29. $50 \cdot 10^2$ **5,000**
30. $318 \cdot 10^3$ **318,000**
31. $281 \cdot 10^5$ **28,100,000**
32. $124 \cdot 10^0$ **124**
33. $525 \cdot 10^5$ **52,500,000**
34. $2{,}180 \cdot 10^4$ **21,800,000**
35. $2{,}508 \cdot 10^5$ **250,800,000**
36. $5.555 \cdot 10^6$ **5,555,000**

Write each number in scientific notation.

37. 387,000 $\mathbf{3.87 \times 10^5}$
38. 2,056,000 $\mathbf{2.056 \times 10^6}$
39. 65,400,000 $\mathbf{6.54 \times 10^7}$
40. 1,560 $\mathbf{1.56 \times 10^3}$
41. 7,000,000,000 $\mathbf{7.0 \times 10^9}$
42. $206.7 \cdot 10^3$ $\mathbf{2.067 \times 10^5}$
43. 6,800,000 $\mathbf{6.8 \times 10^6}$
44. $841.3 \cdot 10^6$ $\mathbf{8.413 \times 10^8}$
45. 123,000,000,000 $\mathbf{1.23 \times 10^{11}}$

LESSON 2-3

Evaluate.

46. $9 \div 3 + 6 \cdot 5$ **33**
47. $6 \cdot 7 - 8 \div 2$ **38**
48. $16 + (20 \div 5) - 3^2$ **11**
49. $5^3 - (7 \cdot 6 + 8)$ **75**
50. $(6 - 3)^3 \div 9 + 7$ **10**
51. $(4 \cdot 9) - (9 - 3)^2$ **0**
52. $5^3 \div 25 + 3 \cdot 5$ **20**
53. $(4 \cdot 4 - 6)^2 - (5 \cdot 7)$ **65**
54. $(6 - 5)^7 \cdot 3^2$ **9**
55. $5 + 9 \cdot 2^2 \div 6$ **11**
56. $(4 \cdot 2)^2 - 5^2$ **39**
57. $6{,}842 - (5^3 \cdot 5 \cdot 10)$ **592**
58. Charlotte bought 4 shirts and 3 pairs of pants. She got the pants at a discount. Evaluate the expression $4 \cdot 32 + 3 \cdot 25 - (3 \cdot 25) \div 5$ to find out how much she paid for the clothes. **$188**

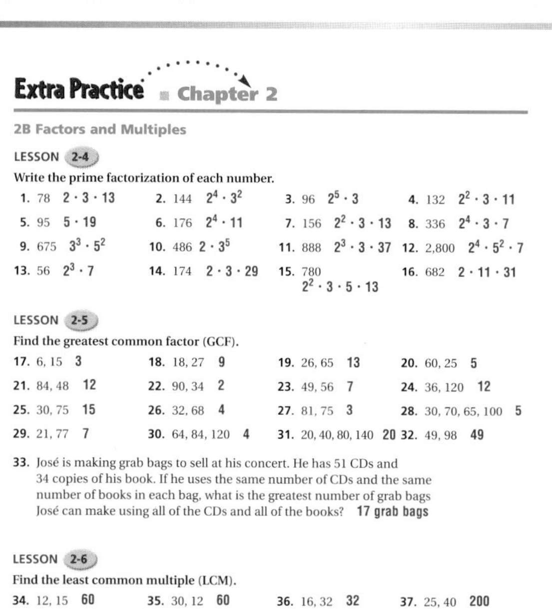

Extra Practice ■ Chapter 2

2B Factors and Multiples

LESSON 2-4

Write the prime factorization of each number.

1. 78 $2 \cdot 3 \cdot 13$ 2. 144 $2^4 \cdot 3^2$ 3. 96 $2^5 \cdot 3$ 4. 132 $2^2 \cdot 3 \cdot 11$
5. 95 $5 \cdot 19$ 6. 176 $2^4 \cdot 11$ 7. 156 $2^2 \cdot 3 \cdot 13$ 8. 336 $2^4 \cdot 3 \cdot 7$
9. 675 $3^3 \cdot 5^2$ 10. 486 $2 \cdot 3^5$ 11. 888 $2^3 \cdot 3 \cdot 37$ 12. 2,800 $2^4 \cdot 5^2 \cdot 7$
13. 56 $2^3 \cdot 7$ 14. 174 $2 \cdot 3 \cdot 29$ 15. 780 $2^2 \cdot 3 \cdot 5 \cdot 13$ 16. 682 $2 \cdot 11 \cdot 31$

LESSON 2-5

Find the greatest common factor (GCF).

17. 6, 15 **3** 18. 18, 27 **9** 19. 26, 65 **13** 20. 60, 25 **5**
21. 84, 48 **12** 22. 90, 34 **2** 23. 49, 56 **7** 24. 36, 120 **12**
25. 30, 75 **15** 26. 32, 68 **4** 27. 81, 75 **3** 28. 30, 70, 65, 100 **5**
29. 21, 77 **7** 30. 64, 84, 120 **4** 31. 20, 40, 80, 140 **20** 32. 49, 98 **49**

33. José is making grab bags to sell at his concert. He has 51 CDs and 34 copies of his book. If he uses the same number of CDs and the same number of books in each bag, what is the greatest number of grab bags José can make using all of the CDs and all of the books? **17 grab bags**

LESSON 2-6

Find the least common multiple (LCM).

34. 12, 15 **60** 35. 30, 12 **60** 36. 16, 32 **32** 37. 25, 40 **200**
38. 36, 48 **144** 39. 60, 24 **120** 40. 32, 18 **288** 41. 20, 110 **220**
42. 30, 75 **150** 43. 12, 64 **192** 44. 15, 50 **150** 45. 15, 30, 50, 100 **300**
46. 21, 28 **84** 47. 15, 22, 30 **330** 48. 20, 40, 80, 120 **240** 49. 42, 90 **630**

50. Marita completes a lap around the track in 5 minutes. Joselle completes a lap around the track in 7 minutes. They start running at the same time. How many minutes will have passed when they start another lap at the same time? **35 minutes**
51. Ahmad can paint a sign in 4 minutes. Hoang can paint a sign in 6 minutes. They start painting at the same time. How many minutes will have passed when they first finish a sign at the same time? **12 minutes**
52. Kanisha shoots a basket every 7 seconds. Thomas shoots a basket every 12 seconds. They start out together. How many seconds will have passed when they next shoot a basket at the same time? **84 seconds**

658 *Extra Practice*

Extra Practice ■ Chapter 2

2C Beginning Algebra

LESSON 2-7

Evaluate each expression for the given value of the variable.

1. $8k - 7$ for $k = 4$ **25** 2. $9n + 12$ for $n = 6$ **66** 3. $12t - 15$ for $t = 4$ **33**
4. $v \div 5 + v$ for $v = 20$ **24** 5. $3r - 20 \div r$ for $r = 5$ **11** 6. $5x^2 + 3x$ for $x = 3$ **54**

LESSON 2-8

Write each phrase as an algebraic expression.

7. 12 less than a number $n - 12$ 8. the quotient of a number and 8 $n \div 8$
9. add 7 to 8 times a number $8n + 7$ 10. 6 times the sum of 13 and a number $6(13 + n)$
11. A music store sells packages of guitar strings. David bought s strings for $24. Write an algebraic expression for the cost of one string. $24 \div s$

LESSON 2-9

Identify like terms in each list.

12. $2d$ $5d^2$ x $4x^2$ d^2 $6x$ **$5d^2$ and d^2; x and $6x$** 13. 9 $5y$ $\frac{y}{2}$ $4g^2$ y^2 y **$5y$, $\frac{y}{2}$, and y**

Combine like terms.

14. $5b + 3t + b$ $6b + 3t$ 15. $t + 3b + 3t + 3b + x$ $6b + 4t + x$ 16. $8g + 3g + 12$ $11g + 12$
17. $3u + 6 + 5k + u$ $4u + 5k + 6$ 18. $11 + 5t^2 + t + 6t$ $5t^2 + 7t + 11$ 19. $y^3 + 3y + 6y^3$ $7y^3 + 3y$

LESSON 2-10

Determine whether each number is a solution of $17 = 45 - j$.

20. 31 **no** 21. 28 **yes** 22. 14 **no** 23. 22 **no**

Determine whether each number is a solution of $x + 23 = 51$.

24. 42 **no** 25. 31 **no** 26. 19 **no** 27. 28 **yes**

28. Dano has 87 CDs. This is 12 more than Megan has. The equation $87 = c + 12$ can be used to represent the number of CDs that Megan has. Does Megan have 99, 85, or 75 CDs? **75 CDs**

LESSON 2-11

Solve each equation. Check your answer.

29. $n - 22 = 16$ $n = 38$ 30. $y + 27 = 42$ $y = 15$ 31. $x - 81 = 14$ $x = 95$
32. $t - 32 = 64$ $t = 96$ 33. $z + 39 = 72$ $z = 33$ 34. $a + 43 = 61$ $a = 18$

LESSON 2-12

Solve each equation. Check your answer.

35. $20 = s \div 3$ $s = 60$ 36. $12y = 84$ $y = 7$ 37. $15 = \frac{n}{9}$ $n = 135$
38. $\frac{m}{36} = 12$ $m = 432$ 39. $144 = 3p$ $p = 48$ 40. $72j = 360$ $j = 5$

Extra Practice 659

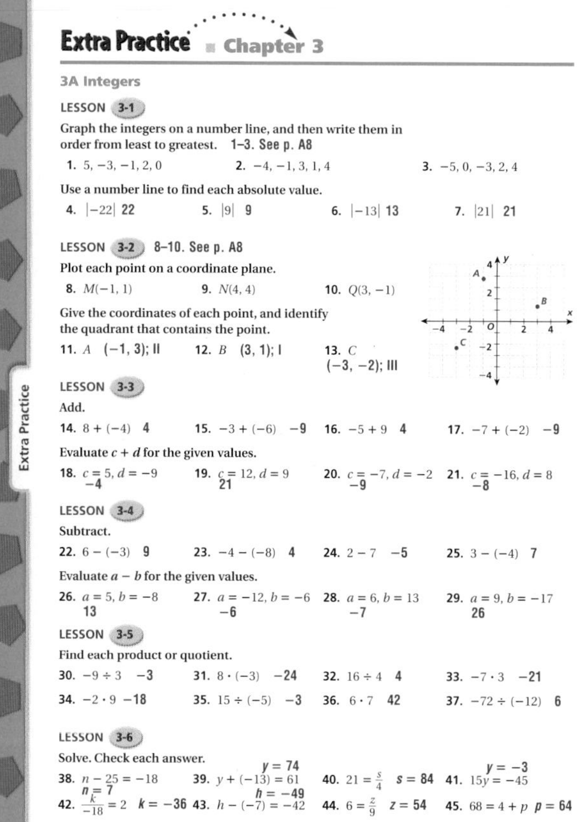

Extra Practice ■ Chapter 3

3A Integers

LESSON 3-1

Graph the integers on a number line, and then write them in order from least to greatest. **1–3. See p. A8**

1. 5, −3, −1, 2, 0 2. −4, −1, 3, 1, 4 3. −5, 0, −3, 2, 4

Use a number line to find each absolute value.

4. $|-22|$ **22** 5. $|9|$ **9** 6. $|-13|$ **13** 7. $|21|$ **21**

LESSON 3-2 **8–10. See p. A8**

Plot each point on a coordinate plane.

8. $M(-1, 1)$ 9. $N(4, 4)$ 10. $Q(3, -1)$

Give the coordinates of each point, and identify the quadrant that contains the point.

11. A **(−1, 3); II** 12. B **(3, 1); I** 13. C **(−3, −2); III**

LESSON 3-3

Add.

14. $8 + (-4)$ **4** 15. $-3 + (-6)$ **−9** 16. $-5 + 9$ **4** 17. $-7 + (-2)$ **−9**

Evaluate $c + d$ for the given values.

18. $c = 5, d = -9$ **−4** 19. $c = 12, d = 9$ **21** 20. $c = -7, d = -2$ **−9** 21. $c = -16, d = 8$ **−8**

LESSON 3-4

Subtract.

22. $6 - (-3)$ **9** 23. $-4 - (-8)$ **4** 24. $2 - 7$ **−5** 25. $3 - (-4)$ **7**

Evaluate $a - b$ for the given values.

26. $a = 5, b = -8$ **13** 27. $a = -12, b = -6$ **−6** 28. $a = 6, b = 13$ **−7** 29. $a = 9, b = -17$ **26**

LESSON 3-5

Find each product or quotient.

30. $-9 \div 3$ **−3** 31. $8 \cdot (-3)$ **−24** 32. $16 \div 4$ **4** 33. $-7 \cdot 3$ **−21**
34. $-2 \cdot 9$ **−18** 35. $15 \div (-5)$ **−3** 36. $6 \cdot 7$ **42** 37. $-72 \div (-12)$ **6**

LESSON 3-6

Solve. Check each answer.

38. $n - 25 = -18$ $n = 7$ 39. $y + (-13) = 61$ $y = 74$ 40. $21 = \frac{s}{4}$ $s = 84$ 41. $15y = -45$ $y = -3$
42. $\frac{k}{-18} = 2$ $k = -36$ 43. $h - (-7) = -42$ $h = -49$ 44. $6 = \frac{z}{9}$ $z = 54$ 45. $68 = 4 + p$ $p = 64$

660 *Extra Practice*

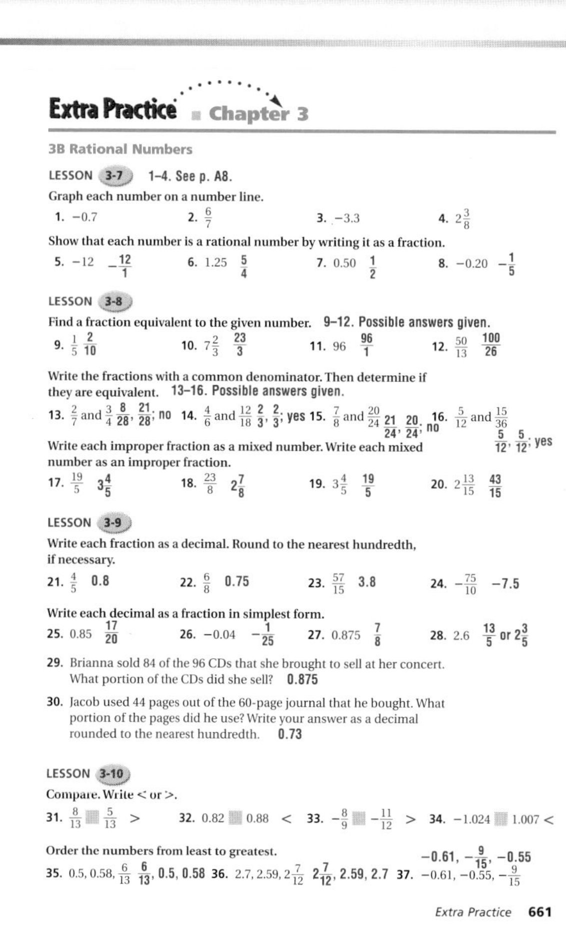

Extra Practice ■ Chapter 3

3B Rational Numbers

LESSON 3-7 **1–4. See p. A8.**

Graph each number on a number line.

1. -0.7 2. $\frac{6}{7}$ 3. -3.3 4. $2\frac{3}{8}$

Show that each number is a rational number by writing it as a fraction.

5. -12 $-\frac{12}{1}$ 6. 1.25 $\frac{5}{4}$ 7. 0.50 $\frac{1}{2}$ 8. -0.20 $-\frac{1}{5}$

LESSON 3-8

Find a fraction equivalent to the given number. **9–12. Possible answers given.**

9. $\frac{1}{5}$ $\frac{2}{10}$ 10. $7\frac{2}{3}$ $\frac{23}{3}$ 11. 96 $\frac{96}{1}$ 12. $\frac{50}{13}$ $\frac{100}{26}$

Write the fractions with a common denominator. Then determine if they are equivalent. **13–16. Possible answers given.**

13. $\frac{2}{7}$ and $\frac{3}{4}$ $\frac{8}{28}, \frac{21}{28}$; **no** 14. $\frac{4}{6}$ and $\frac{12}{18}$ $\frac{2}{3}, \frac{2}{3}$; **yes** 15. $\frac{7}{8}$ and $\frac{20}{24}$ $\frac{21}{24}, \frac{20}{24}$; **no** 16. $\frac{5}{12}$ and $\frac{15}{36}$ $\frac{5}{12}, \frac{5}{12}$; **yes**

Write each improper fraction as a mixed number. Write each mixed number as an improper fraction.

17. $\frac{19}{5}$ $3\frac{4}{5}$ 18. $\frac{23}{8}$ $2\frac{7}{8}$ 19. $3\frac{4}{5}$ $\frac{19}{5}$ 20. $2\frac{13}{15}$ $\frac{43}{15}$

LESSON 3-9

Write each fraction as a decimal. Round to the nearest hundredth, if necessary.

21. $\frac{4}{5}$ **0.8** 22. $\frac{6}{8}$ **0.75** 23. $\frac{57}{15}$ **3.8** 24. $-\frac{75}{10}$ **−7.5**

Write each decimal as a fraction in simplest form.

25. 0.85 $\frac{17}{20}$ 26. −0.04 $-\frac{1}{25}$ 27. 0.875 $\frac{7}{8}$ 28. 2.6 $\frac{13}{5}$ or $2\frac{3}{5}$

29. Brianna sold 84 of the 96 CDs that she brought to sell at her concert. What portion of the CDs did she sell? **0.875**
30. Jacob used 44 pages out of the 60-page journal that he bought. What portion of the pages did he use? Write your answer as a decimal rounded to the nearest hundredth. **0.73**

LESSON 3-10

Compare. Write < or >.

31. $\frac{8}{13}$ ▒ $\frac{5}{13}$ **>** 32. 0.82 ▒ 0.88 **<** 33. $-\frac{8}{9}$ ▒ $-\frac{11}{12}$ **>** 34. −1.024 ▒ 1.007 **<**

Order the numbers from least to greatest.

35. $0.5, 0.58, \frac{6}{13}$ **$\frac{6}{13}$, 0.5, 0.58** 36. $2.7, 2.59, 2\frac{7}{12}$ **$2\frac{7}{12}$, 2.59, 2.7** 37. $-0.61, -0.55, -\frac{9}{15}$ **−0.61, $-\frac{9}{15}$, −0.55**

Extra Practice 661

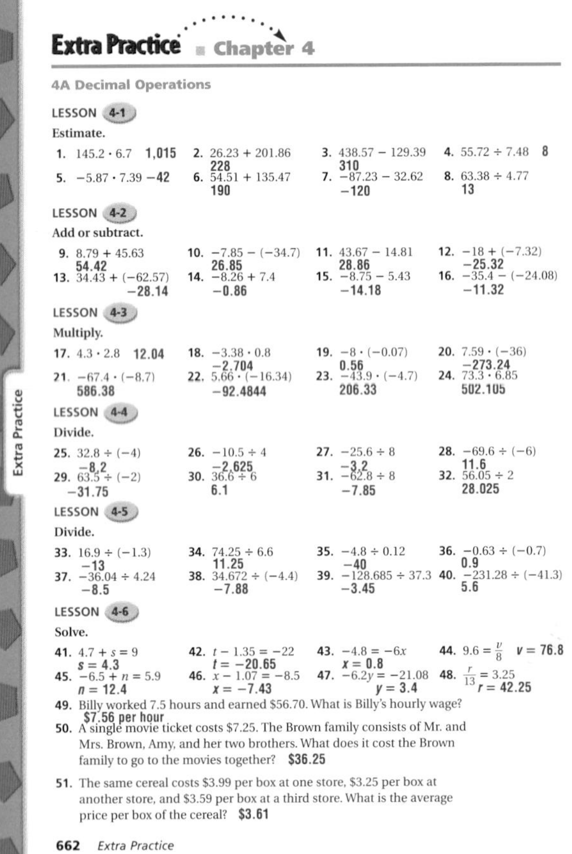

Extra Practice ■ Chapter 4

4A Decimal Operations

LESSON 4-1

Estimate.

1. $145.2 \cdot 6.7$ **1,015**
2. $26.23 + 201.86$ **228**
3. $438.57 - 129.39$ **310**
4. $55.72 \div 7.48$ **8**
5. $-5.87 \cdot 7.39$ **−42**
6. $54.51 + 135.47$ **190**
7. $-87.23 - 32.62$ **−120**
8. $63.38 \div 4.77$ **13**

LESSON 4-2

Add or subtract.

9. $8.79 + 45.63$ **54.42**
10. $-7.85 - (-34.7)$ **26.85**
11. $43.67 - 14.81$ **28.86**
12. $-18 + (-7.32)$ **−25.32**
13. $34.43 + (-62.57)$ **−28.14**
14. $-8.26 + 7.4$ **−0.86**
15. $-8.75 - 5.43$ **−14.18**
16. $-35.4 - (-24.08)$ **−11.32**

LESSON 4-3

Multiply.

17. $4.3 \cdot 2.8$ **12.04**
18. $-3.38 \cdot 0.8$ **−2.704**
19. $-8 \cdot (-0.07)$ **0.56**
20. $7.59 \cdot (-36)$ **−273.24**
21. $-67.4 \cdot (-8.7)$ **586.38**
22. $5.66 \cdot (-16.34)$ **−92.4844**
23. $-43.9 \cdot (-4.7)$ **206.33**
24. $73.3 \cdot 6.85$ **502.105**

LESSON 4-4

Divide.

25. $32.8 \div (-4)$ **−8.2**
26. $-10.5 \div 4$ **−2.625**
27. $-25.6 \div 8$ **−3.2**
28. $-69.6 \div (-6)$ **11.6**
29. $63.5 \div (-2)$ **−31.75**
30. $36.6 \div 6$ **6.1**
31. $-62.8 \div 8$ **−7.85**
32. $56.05 \div 2$ **28.025**

LESSON 4-5

Divide.

33. $16.9 \div (-1.3)$ **−13**
34. $74.25 \div 6.6$ **11.25**
35. $-4.8 \div 0.12$ **−40**
36. $-0.63 \div (-0.7)$ **0.9**
37. $-36.04 \div 4.24$ **−8.5**
38. $34.672 \div (-4.4)$ **−7.88**
39. $-128.685 \div 37.3$ **−3.45**
40. $-231.28 \div (-41.3)$ **5.6**

LESSON 4-6

Solve.

41. $4.7 + s = 9$ **$s = 4.3$**
42. $t - 1.35 = -22$ **$t = -20.65$**
43. $-4.8 = -6x$ **$x = 0.8$**
44. $9.6 = \frac{v}{8}$ **$v = 76.8$**
45. $-6.5 + n = 5.9$ **$n = 12.4$**
46. $x - 1.07 = -8.5$ **$x = -7.43$**
47. $-6.2y = -21.08$ **$y = 3.4$**
48. $\frac{r}{13} = 3.25$ **$r = 42.25$**
49. Billy worked 7.5 hours and earned $56.70. What is Billy's hourly wage? **$7.56 per hour**
50. A single movie ticket costs $7.25. The Brown family consists of Mr. and Mrs. Brown, Amy, and her two brothers. What does it cost the Brown family to go to the movies together? **$36.25**
51. The same cereal costs $3.99 per box at one store, $3.25 per box at another store, and $3.59 per box at a third store. What is the average price per box of the cereal? **$3.61**

662 *Extra Practice*

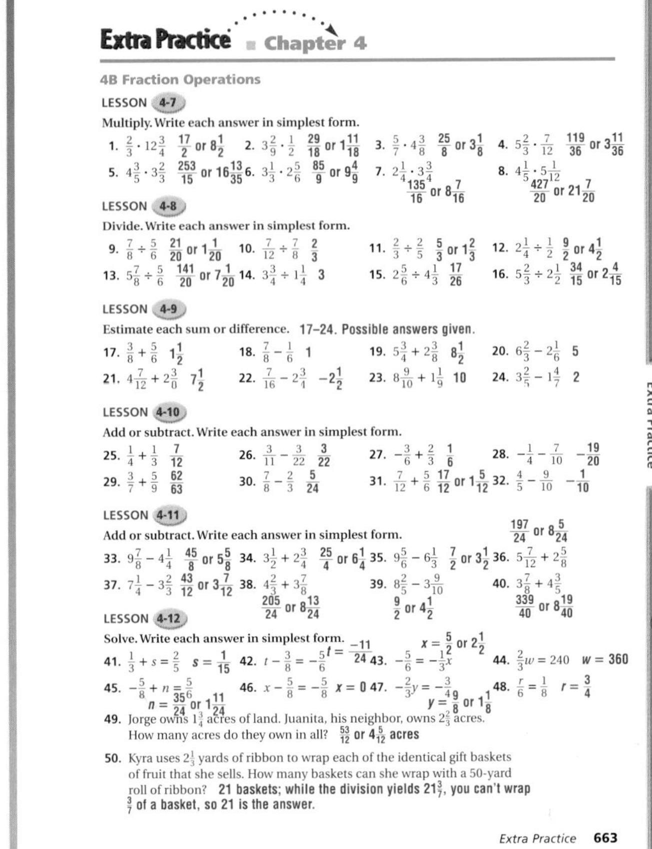

Extra Practice ■ Chapter 4

4B Fraction Operations

LESSON 4-7

Multiply. Write each answer in simplest form.

1. $\frac{2}{3} \cdot 12\frac{3}{4}$ **$\frac{17}{2}$ or $8\frac{1}{2}$**
2. $3\frac{2}{9} \cdot \frac{1}{2}$ **$\frac{29}{18}$ or $1\frac{11}{18}$**
3. $\frac{5}{7} \cdot 4\frac{3}{8}$ **$\frac{25}{8}$ or $3\frac{1}{8}$**
4. $5\frac{2}{3} \cdot \frac{7}{12}$ **$\frac{119}{36}$ or $3\frac{11}{36}$**
5. $4\frac{3}{5} \cdot 3\frac{2}{3}$ **$\frac{253}{15}$ or $16\frac{13}{35}$**
6. $3\frac{1}{3} \cdot 2\frac{5}{6}$ **$\frac{85}{9}$ or $9\frac{4}{9}$**
7. $2\frac{1}{4} \cdot 3\frac{3}{4}$ **$\frac{135}{16}$ or $8\frac{7}{16}$**
8. $4\frac{1}{5} \cdot 5\frac{1}{12}$ **$\frac{427}{20}$ or $21\frac{7}{20}$**

LESSON 4-8

Divide. Write each answer in simplest form.

9. $\frac{7}{8} \div \frac{5}{6}$ **$\frac{21}{20}$ or $1\frac{1}{20}$**
10. $\frac{7}{12} \div \frac{7}{8}$ **$\frac{2}{3}$**
11. $\frac{2}{3} \div \frac{2}{5}$ **$\frac{5}{3}$ or $1\frac{2}{3}$**
12. $2\frac{1}{4} \div \frac{1}{2}$ **$\frac{9}{2}$ or $4\frac{1}{2}$**
13. $5\frac{7}{8} \div \frac{5}{6}$ **$\frac{141}{20}$ or $7\frac{1}{20}$**
14. $3\frac{3}{4} \div 1\frac{1}{4}$ **3**
15. $2\frac{5}{6} \div 4\frac{1}{3}$ **$\frac{17}{26}$**
16. $5\frac{2}{3} \div 2\frac{1}{2}$ **$\frac{34}{15}$ or $2\frac{4}{15}$**

LESSON 4-9

Estimate each sum or difference. **17–24. Possible answers given.**

17. $\frac{3}{8} + \frac{5}{6}$ **$1\frac{1}{2}$**
18. $\frac{7}{8} - \frac{1}{6}$ **1**
19. $5\frac{3}{4} + 2\frac{3}{8}$ **$8\frac{1}{2}$**
20. $6\frac{2}{3} - 2\frac{1}{6}$ **5**
21. $4\frac{7}{12} + 2\frac{3}{8}$ **$7\frac{1}{2}$**
22. $\frac{7}{16} - 2\frac{3}{4}$ **$-2\frac{1}{2}$**
23. $8\frac{9}{10} + 1\frac{1}{9}$ **10**
24. $3\frac{2}{5} - 1\frac{4}{7}$ **2**

LESSON 4-10

Add or subtract. Write each answer in simplest form.

25. $\frac{1}{4} + \frac{1}{3}$ **$\frac{7}{12}$**
26. $\frac{3}{11} - \frac{3}{22}$ **$\frac{3}{22}$**
27. $-\frac{3}{6} + \frac{2}{3}$ **$\frac{1}{6}$**
28. $-\frac{1}{4} - \frac{7}{10}$ **$-\frac{19}{20}$**
29. $\frac{3}{7} + \frac{5}{9}$ **$\frac{62}{63}$**
30. $\frac{7}{8} - \frac{2}{3}$ **$\frac{5}{24}$**
31. $\frac{7}{12} + \frac{5}{6}$ **$\frac{17}{12}$ or $1\frac{5}{12}$**
32. $\frac{4}{5} - \frac{9}{10}$ **$-\frac{1}{10}$**

LESSON 4-11

Add or subtract. Write each answer in simplest form.

33. $9\frac{7}{8} - 4\frac{1}{4}$ **$\frac{45}{8}$ or $5\frac{5}{8}$**
34. $3\frac{1}{2} + 2\frac{3}{4}$ **$\frac{25}{4}$ or $6\frac{1}{4}$**
35. $9\frac{5}{6} - 6\frac{1}{3}$ **$\frac{7}{2}$ or $3\frac{1}{2}$**
36. $5\frac{7}{12} + 2\frac{5}{8}$ **$\frac{197}{24}$ or $8\frac{5}{24}$**
37. $7\frac{1}{4} - 3\frac{2}{3}$ **$\frac{43}{12}$ or $3\frac{7}{12}$**
38. $4\frac{2}{3} + 3\frac{7}{8}$ **$\frac{205}{24}$ or $8\frac{13}{24}$**
39. $8\frac{2}{5} - 3\frac{9}{10}$ **$\frac{9}{2}$ or $4\frac{1}{2}$**
40. $3\frac{7}{8} + 4\frac{3}{5}$ **$\frac{339}{40}$ or $8\frac{19}{40}$**

LESSON 4-12

Solve. Write each answer in simplest form.

41. $\frac{1}{3} + s = \frac{2}{5}$ **$s = \frac{1}{15}$**
42. $t - \frac{3}{8} = -\frac{5}{6}$ **$t = \frac{-11}{24}$**
43. $-\frac{5}{6} = -\frac{1}{3}x$ **$x = \frac{5}{2}$ or $2\frac{1}{2}$**
44. $\frac{2}{3}w = 240$ **$w = 360$**
45. $-\frac{5}{8} + n = \frac{5}{6}$ **$n = \frac{35}{24}$ or $1\frac{11}{24}$**
46. $x - \frac{5}{8} = -\frac{5}{8}$ **$x = 0$**
47. $-\frac{2}{3}y = -\frac{3}{4}$ **$y = \frac{9}{8}$ or $1\frac{1}{8}$**
48. $\frac{r}{6} = \frac{1}{8}$ **$r = \frac{3}{4}$**
49. Jorge owns $1\frac{3}{4}$ acres of land. Juanita, his neighbor, owns $2\frac{2}{3}$ acres. How many acres do they own in all? **$\frac{53}{12}$ or $4\frac{5}{12}$ acres**
50. Kyra uses $2\frac{1}{3}$ yards of ribbon to wrap each of the identical gift baskets of fruit that she sells. How many baskets can she wrap with a 50-yard roll of ribbon? **21 baskets; while the division yields $21\frac{3}{7}$, you can't wrap $\frac{3}{7}$ of a basket, so 21 is the answer.**

Extra Practice 663

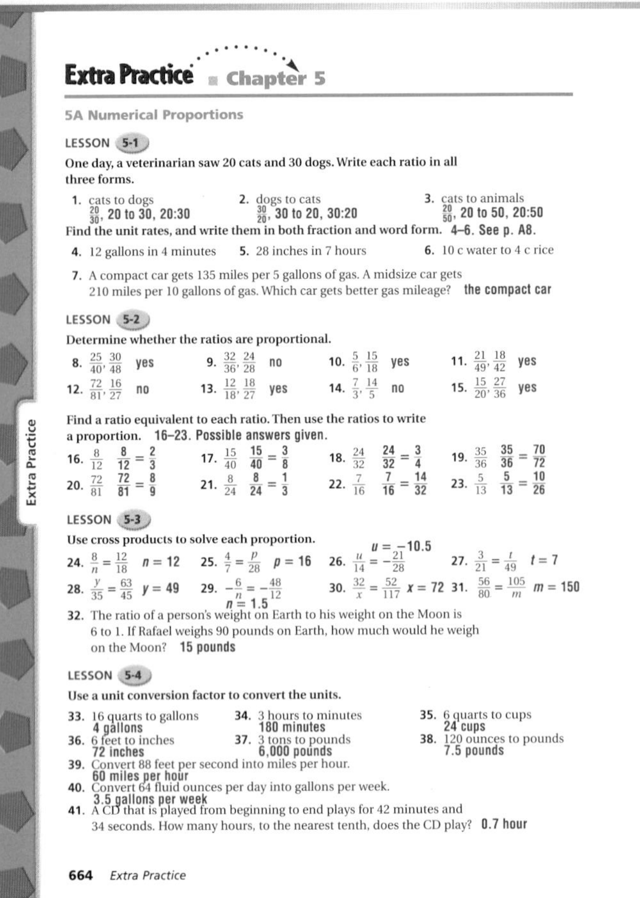

Extra Practice ■ Chapter 5

5A Numerical Proportions

LESSON 5-1

One day, a veterinarian saw 20 cats and 30 dogs. Write each ratio in all three forms.

1. cats to dogs **$\frac{20}{30}$, 20 to 30, 20:30**
2. dogs to cats **$\frac{30}{20}$, 30 to 20, 30:20**
3. cats to animals **$\frac{20}{50}$, 20 to 50, 20:50**

Find the unit rates, and write them in both fraction and word form. **4–6. See p. A8.**

4. 12 gallons in 4 minutes
5. 28 inches in 7 hours
6. 10 c water to 4 c rice
7. A compact car gets 135 miles per 5 gallons of gas. A midsize car gets 210 miles per 10 gallons of gas. Which car gets better gas mileage? **the compact car**

LESSON 5-2

Determine whether the ratios are proportional.

8. $\frac{25}{40}, \frac{30}{48}$ **yes**
9. $\frac{32}{36}, \frac{24}{28}$ **no**
10. $\frac{5}{6}, \frac{15}{18}$ **yes**
11. $\frac{21}{49}, \frac{18}{42}$ **yes**
12. $\frac{72}{81}, \frac{16}{27}$ **no**
13. $\frac{12}{18}, \frac{18}{27}$ **yes**
14. $\frac{7}{3}, \frac{14}{5}$ **no**
15. $\frac{15}{20}, \frac{27}{36}$ **yes**

Find a ratio equivalent to each ratio. Then use the ratios to write a proportion. **16–23. Possible answers given.**

16. $\frac{8}{12}$ **$\frac{8}{12} = \frac{2}{3}$**
17. $\frac{15}{40}$ **$\frac{15}{40} = \frac{3}{8}$**
18. $\frac{24}{32}$ **$\frac{24}{32} = \frac{3}{4}$**
19. $\frac{35}{36}$ **$\frac{35}{36} = \frac{70}{72}$**
20. $\frac{72}{81}$ **$\frac{72}{81} = \frac{8}{9}$**
21. $\frac{8}{24}$ **$\frac{8}{24} = \frac{1}{3}$**
22. $\frac{7}{16}$ **$\frac{7}{16} = \frac{14}{32}$**
23. $\frac{5}{13}$ **$\frac{5}{13} = \frac{10}{26}$**

LESSON 5-3

Use cross products to solve each proportion.

24. $\frac{8}{n} = \frac{12}{18}$ **$n = 12$**
25. $\frac{4}{7} = \frac{p}{28}$ **$p = 16$**
26. $\frac{u}{14} = -\frac{21}{28}$ **$u = -10.5$**
27. $\frac{3}{21} = \frac{t}{49}$ **$t = 7$**
28. $\frac{y}{35} = \frac{63}{45}$ **$y = 49$**
29. $-\frac{6}{n} = -\frac{48}{12}$ **$n = 1.5$**
30. $\frac{32}{x} = \frac{52}{117}$ **$x = 72$**
31. $\frac{56}{80} = \frac{105}{m}$ **$m = 150$**
32. The ratio of a person's weight on Earth to his weight on the Moon is 6 to 1. If Rafael weighs 90 pounds on Earth, how much would he weigh on the Moon? **15 pounds**

LESSON 5-4

Use a unit conversion factor to convert the units.

33. 16 quarts to gallons **4 gallons**
34. 3 hours to minutes **180 minutes**
35. 6 quarts to cups **24 cups**
36. 6 feet to inches **72 inches**
37. 3 tons to pounds **6,000 pounds**
38. 120 ounces to pounds **7.5 pounds**
39. Convert 88 feet per second into miles per hour. **60 miles per hour**
40. Convert 64 fluid ounces per day into gallons per week. **3.5 gallons per week**
41. A CD that is played from beginning to end plays for 42 minutes and 34 seconds. How many hours, to the nearest tenth, does the CD play? **0.7 hour**

664 *Extra Practice*

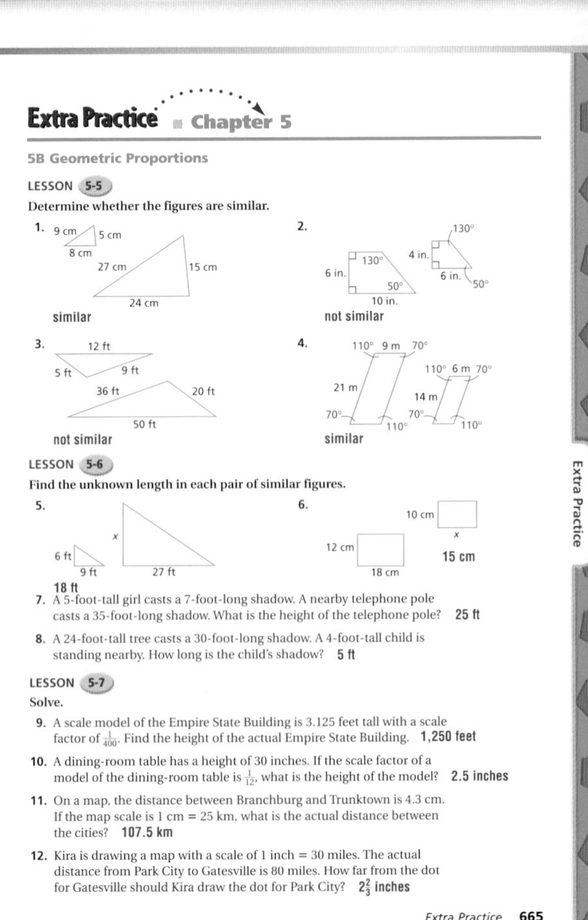

Extra Practice ■ Chapter 5

5B Geometric Proportions

LESSON 5-5

Determine whether the figures are similar.

1.
similar

2.
not similar

3.
not similar

4.
similar

LESSON 5-6

Find the unknown length in each pair of similar figures.

5.
18 ft

6.
15 cm

7. A 5-foot-tall girl casts a 7-foot-long shadow. A nearby telephone pole casts a 35-foot-long shadow. What is the height of the telephone pole? **25 ft**
8. A 24-foot-tall tree casts a 30-foot-long shadow. A 4-foot-tall child is standing nearby. How long is the child's shadow? **5 ft**

LESSON 5-7

Solve.

9. A scale model of the Empire State Building is 3.125 feet tall with a scale factor of $\frac{1}{400}$. Find the height of the actual Empire State Building. **1,250 feet**
10. A dining-room table has a height of 30 inches. If the scale factor of a model of the dining-room table is $\frac{1}{12}$, what is the height of the model? **2.5 inches**
11. On a map, the distance between Branchburg and Trunktown is 4.3 cm. If the map scale is 1 cm = 25 km, what is the actual distance between the cities? **107.5 km**
12. Kira is drawing a map with a scale of 1 inch = 30 miles. The actual distance from Park City to Gatesville is 80 miles. How far from the dot for Gatesville should Kira draw the dot for Park City? **$2\frac{2}{3}$ inches**

Extra Practice 665

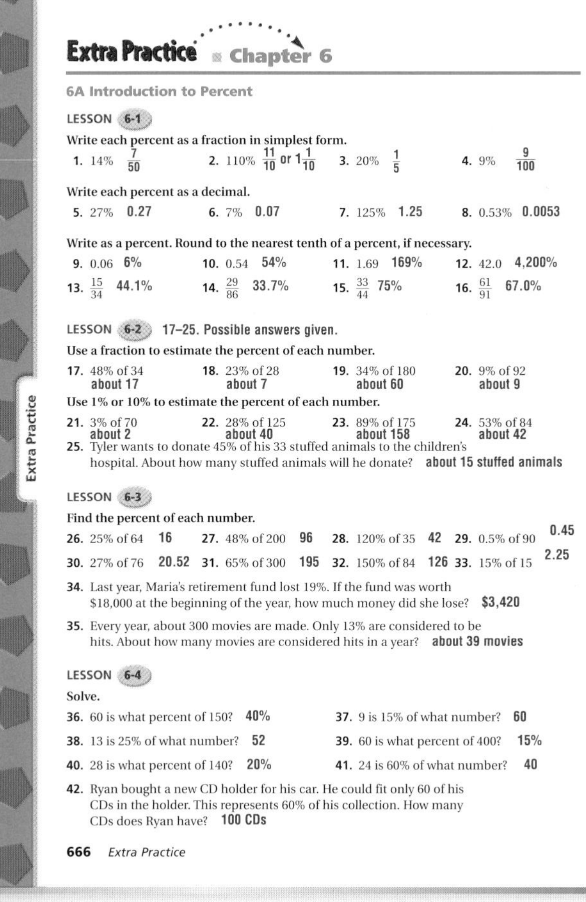

Extra Practice ■ Chapter 6

6A Introduction to Percent

LESSON 6-1

Write each percent as a fraction in simplest form.

1. 14% $\frac{7}{50}$ 2. 110% $\frac{11}{10}$ or $1\frac{1}{10}$ 3. 20% $\frac{1}{5}$ 4. 9% $\frac{9}{100}$

Write each percent as a decimal.

5. 27% **0.27** 6. 7% **0.07** 7. 125% **1.25** 8. 0.53% **0.0053**

Write as a percent. Round to the nearest tenth of a percent, if necessary.

9. 0.06 **6%** 10. 0.54 **54%** 11. 1.69 **169%** 12. 42.0 **4,200%**

13. $\frac{15}{34}$ **44.1%** 14. $\frac{29}{86}$ **33.7%** 15. $\frac{33}{44}$ **75%** 16. $\frac{61}{91}$ **67.0%**

LESSON 6-2 **17–25. Possible answers given.**

Use a fraction to estimate the percent of each number.

17. 48% of 34 **about 17** 18. 23% of 28 **about 7** 19. 34% of 180 **about 60** 20. 9% of 92 **about 9**

Use 1% or 10% to estimate the percent of each number.

21. 3% of 70 **about 2** 22. 28% of 125 **about 40** 23. 89% of 175 **about 158** 24. 53% of 84 **about 42**

25. Tyler wants to donate 45% of his 33 stuffed animals to the children's hospital. About how many stuffed animals will he donate? **about 15 stuffed animals**

LESSON 6-3

Find the percent of each number.

26. 25% of 64 **16** 27. 48% of 200 **96** 28. 120% of 35 **42** 29. 0.5% of 90 **0.45**

30. 27% of 76 **20.52** 31. 65% of 300 **195** 32. 150% of 84 **126** 33. 15% of 15 **2.25**

34. Last year, Maria's retirement fund lost 19%. If the fund was worth $18,000 at the beginning of the year, how much money did she lose? **$3,420**

35. Every year, about 300 movies are made. Only 13% are considered to be hits. About how many movies are considered hits in a year? **about 39 movies**

LESSON 6-4

Solve.

36. 60 is what percent of 150? **40%** 37. 9 is 15% of what number? **60**

38. 13 is 25% of what number? **52** 39. 60 is what percent of 400? **15%**

40. 28 is what percent of 140? **20%** 41. 24 is 60% of what number? **40**

42. Ryan bought a new CD holder for his car. He could fit only 60 of his CDs in the holder. This represents 60% of his collection. How many CDs does Ryan have? **100 CDs**

666 *Extra Practice*

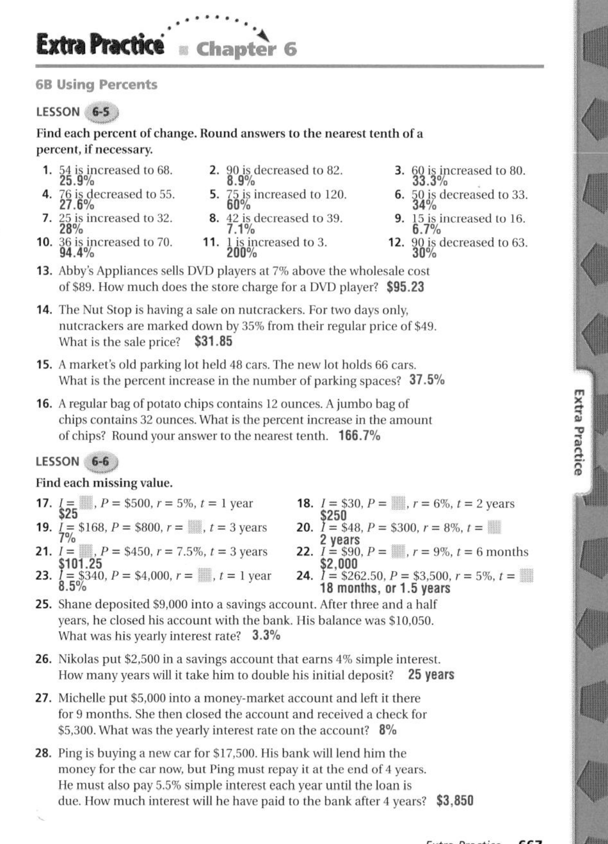

Extra Practice ■ Chapter 6

6B Using Percents

LESSON 6-5

Find each percent of change. Round answers to the nearest tenth of a percent, if necessary.

1. 54 is increased to 68. **25.9%** 2. 90 is decreased to 82. **8.9%** 3. 60 is increased to 80. **33.3%**
4. 76 is decreased to 55. **27.6%** 5. 75 is increased to 120. **60%** 6. 50 is decreased to 33. **34%**
7. 25 is increased to 32. **28%** 8. 42 is decreased to 39. **7.1%** 9. 15 is increased to 16. **6.7%**
10. 36 is increased to 70. **94.4%** 11. 1 is increased to 3. **200%** 12. 90 is decreased to 63. **30%**

13. Abby's Appliances sells DVD players at 7% above the wholesale cost of $89. How much does the store charge for a DVD player? **$95.23**

14. The Nut Stop is having a sale on nutcrackers. For two days only, nutcrackers are marked down by 35% from their regular price of $49. What is the sale price? **$31.85**

15. A market's old parking lot held 48 cars. The new lot holds 66 cars. What is the percent increase in the number of parking spaces? **37.5%**

16. A regular bag of potato chips contains 12 ounces. A jumbo bag of chips contains 32 ounces. What is the percent increase in the amount of chips? Round your answer to the nearest tenth. **166.7%**

LESSON 6-6

Find each missing value.

17. I = ■, P = $500, r = 5%, t = 1 year **$25**
18. I = $30, P = ■, r = 6%, t = 2 years **$250**
19. I = $168, P = $800, r = ■, t = 3 years **7%**
20. I = $48, P = $300, r = 8%, t = ■ **2 years**
21. I = ■, P = $450, r = 7.5%, t = 3 years **$101.25**
22. I = $90, P = ■, r = 9%, t = 6 months **$2,000**
23. I = $340, P = $4,000, r = ■, t = 1 year **8.5%**
24. I = $262.50, P = $3,500, r = 5%, t = ■ **18 months, or 1.5 years**

25. Shane deposited $9,000 into a savings account. After three and a half years, he closed his account with the bank. His balance was $10,050. What was his yearly interest rate? **3.3%**

26. Nikolas put $2,500 in a savings account that earns 4% simple interest. How many years will it take him to double his initial deposit? **25 years**

27. Michelle put $5,000 into a money-market account and left it there for 9 months. She then closed the account and received a check for $5,300. What was the yearly interest rate on the account? **8%**

28. Ping is buying a new car for $17,500. His bank will lend him the money for the car now, but Ping must repay it at the end of 4 years. He must also pay 5.5% simple interest each year until the loan is due. How much interest will he have paid to the bank after 4 years? **$3,850**

Extra Practice 667

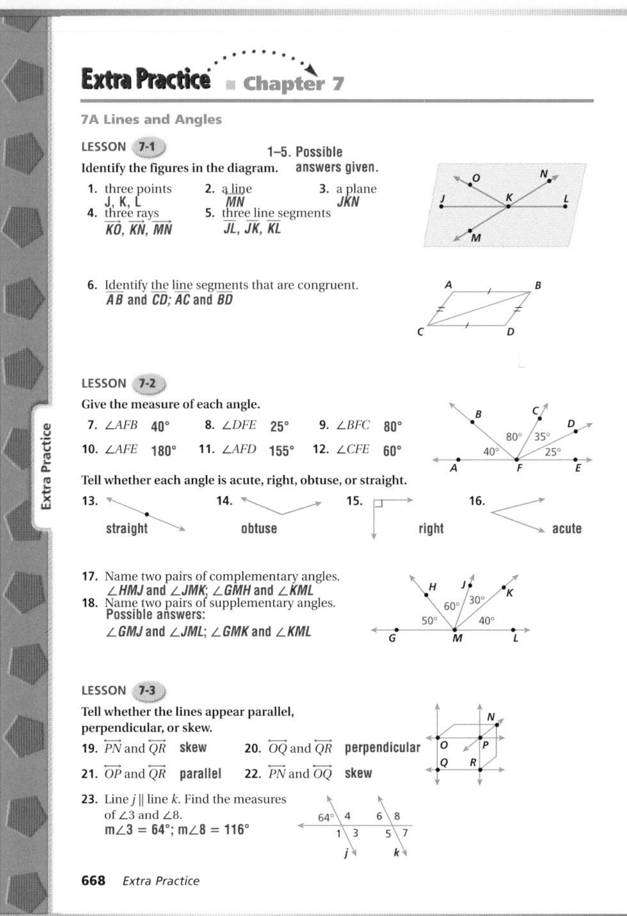

Extra Practice ■ Chapter 7

7A Lines and Angles

LESSON 7-1 **1–5. Possible answers given.**

Identify the figures in the diagram.

1. three points **J, K, L** 2. a line **$\overleftrightarrow{MN}$** 3. a plane **JKN**
4. three rays **$\overrightarrow{KO}$, $\overrightarrow{KN}$, $\overrightarrow{MN}$** 5. three line segments **$\overline{JL}$, $\overline{JK}$, $\overline{KL}$**

6. Identify the line segments that are congruent. **$\overline{AB}$ and $\overline{CD}$; $\overline{AC}$ and $\overline{BD}$**

LESSON 7-2

Give the measure of each angle.

7. ∠AFB **40°** 8. ∠DFE **25°** 9. ∠BFC **80°**
10. ∠AFE **180°** 11. ∠AFD **155°** 12. ∠CFE **60°**

Tell whether each angle is acute, right, obtuse, or straight.

13. **straight** 14. **obtuse** 15. **right** 16. **acute**

17. Name two pairs of complementary angles. **∠HMJ and ∠JMK; ∠GMH and ∠KML**
18. Name two pairs of supplementary angles. **Possible answers: ∠GMJ and ∠JML; ∠GMK and ∠KML**

LESSON 7-3

Tell whether the lines appear parallel, perpendicular, or skew.

19. $\overleftrightarrow{PN}$ and $\overleftrightarrow{QR}$ **skew** 20. $\overleftrightarrow{OQ}$ and $\overleftrightarrow{QR}$ **perpendicular**
21. $\overleftrightarrow{OP}$ and $\overleftrightarrow{QR}$ **parallel** 22. $\overleftrightarrow{PN}$ and $\overleftrightarrow{OQ}$ **skew**

23. Line $j \parallel$ line k. Find the measures of ∠3 and ∠8. **m∠3 = 64°; m∠8 = 116°**

668 *Extra Practice*

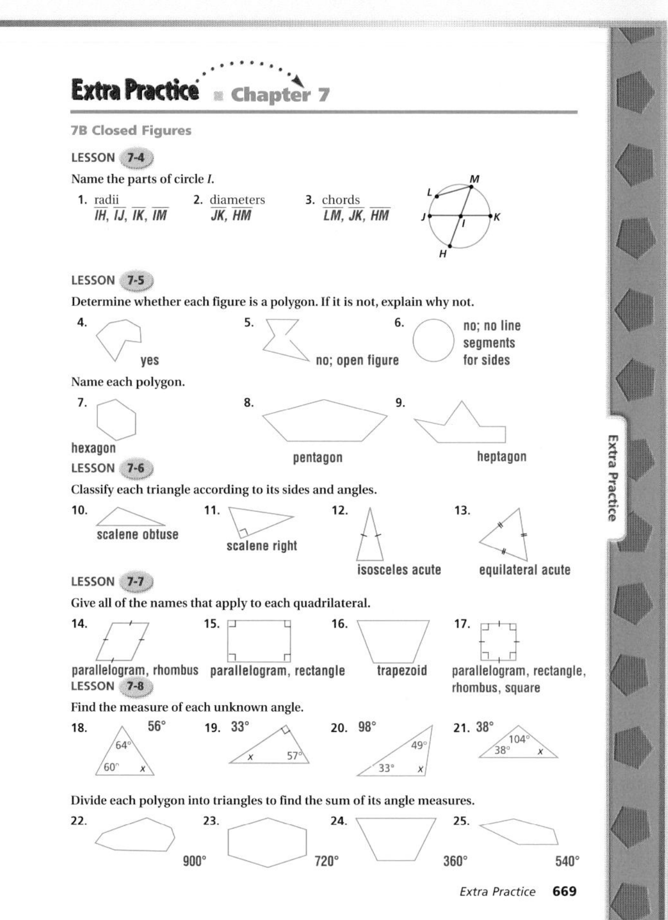

Extra Practice ■ Chapter 7

7B Closed Figures

LESSON 7-4

Name the parts of circle I.

1. radii **$\overline{IH}$, $\overline{IJ}$, $\overline{IK}$, $\overline{IM}$** 2. diameters **$\overline{JK}$, $\overline{HM}$** 3. chords **$\overline{LM}$, $\overline{JK}$, $\overline{HM}$**

LESSON 7-5

Determine whether each figure is a polygon. If it is not, explain why not.

4. **yes** 5. **no; open figure** 6. **no; no line segments for sides**

Name each polygon.

7. **hexagon** 8. **pentagon** 9. **heptagon**

LESSON 7-6

Classify each triangle according to its sides and angles.

10. **scalene obtuse** 11. **scalene right** 12. **isosceles acute** 13. **equilateral acute**

LESSON 7-7

Give all of the names that apply to each quadrilateral.

14. **parallelogram, rhombus** 15. **parallelogram, rectangle** 16. **trapezoid** 17. **parallelogram, rectangle, rhombus, square**

LESSON 7-8

Find the measure of each unknown angle.

18. **56°** 19. **33°** 20. **98°** 21. **38°**

Divide each polygon into triangles to find the sum of its angle measures.

22. **900°** 23. **720°** 24. **360°** 25. **540°**

Extra Practice 669

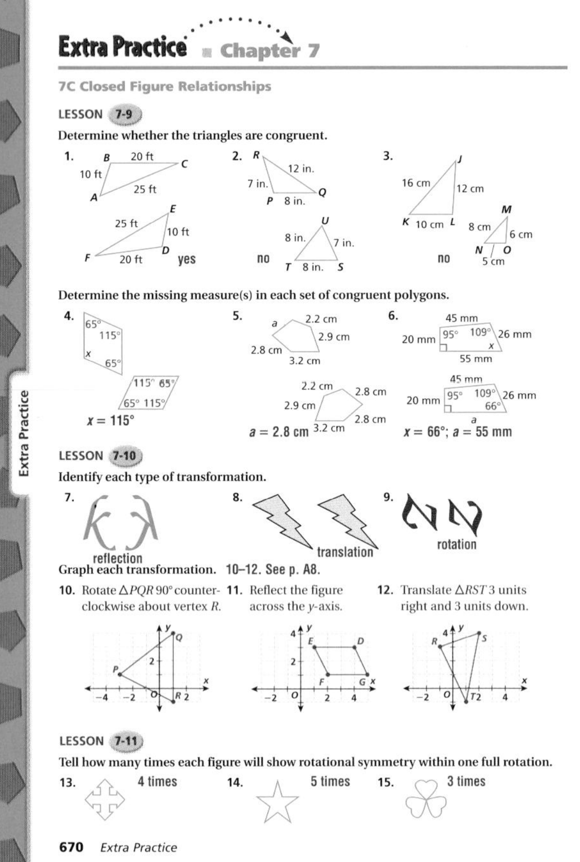

Extra Practice ■ Chapter 7

7C Closed Figure Relationships

LESSON 7-9

Determine whether the triangles are congruent.

1. yes 2. no 3. no

Determine the missing measure(s) in each set of congruent polygons.

4. $x = 115°$ 5. $a = 2.8$ cm 6. $x = 66°$; $a = 55$ mm

LESSON 7-10

Identify each type of transformation.

7. reflection 8. translation 9. rotation

Graph each transformation. 10–12. See p. A8.

10. Rotate $\triangle PQR$ 90° counterclockwise about vertex R.
11. Reflect the figure across the y-axis.
12. Translate $\triangle RST$ 3 units right and 3 units down.

LESSON 7-11

Tell how many times each figure will show rotational symmetry within one full rotation.

13. 4 times 14. 5 times 15. 3 times

670 *Extra Practice*

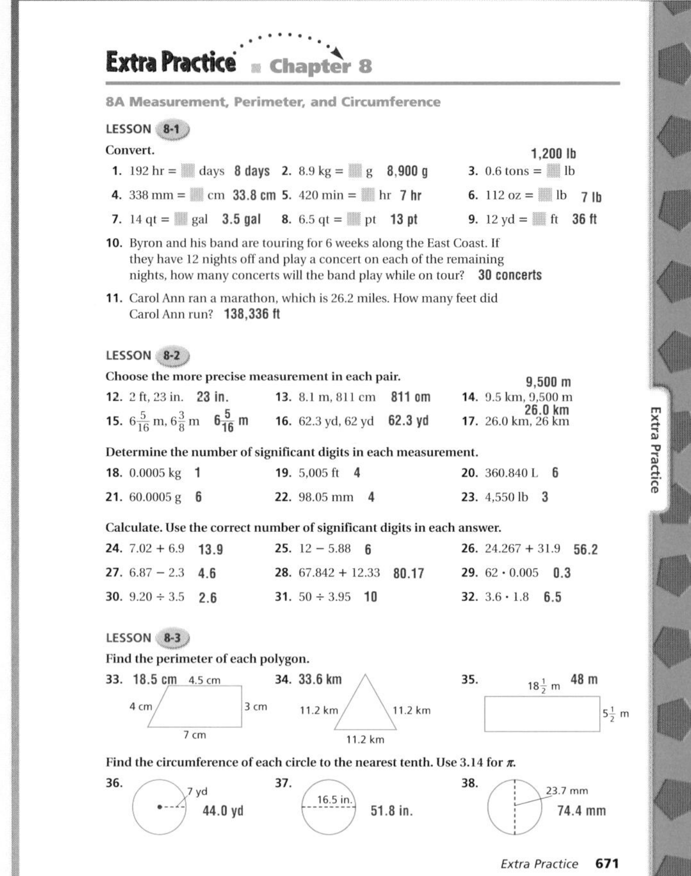

Extra Practice ■ Chapter 8

8A Measurement, Perimeter, and Circumference

LESSON 8-1

Convert.

1. 192 hr = ▒ days **8 days**
2. 8.9 kg = ▒ g **8,900 g**
3. 0.6 tons = ▒ lb **1,200 lb**
4. 338 mm = ▒ cm **33.8 cm**
5. 420 min = ▒ hr **7 hr**
6. 112 oz = ▒ lb **7 lb**
7. 14 qt = ▒ gal **3.5 gal**
8. 6.5 qt = ▒ pt **13 pt**
9. 12 yd = ▒ ft **36 ft**
10. Byron and his band are touring for 6 weeks along the East Coast. If they have 12 nights off and play a concert on each of the remaining nights, how many concerts will the band play while on tour? **30 concerts**
11. Carol Ann ran a marathon, which is 26.2 miles. How many feet did Carol Ann run? **138,336 ft**

LESSON 8-2

Choose the more precise measurement in each pair.

12. 2 ft, 23 in. **23 in.**
13. 8.1 m, 811 cm **811 cm**
14. 9.5 km, 9,500 m **9,500 m**
15. $6\frac{5}{16}$ m, $6\frac{3}{8}$ m **$6\frac{5}{16}$ m**
16. 62.3 yd, 62 yd **62.3 yd**
17. 26.0 km, 26 km **26.0 km**

Determine the number of significant digits in each measurement.

18. 0.0005 kg **1**
19. 5,005 ft **4**
20. 360.840 L **6**
21. 60.0005 g **6**
22. 98.05 mm **4**
23. 4,550 lb **3**

Calculate. Use the correct number of significant digits in each answer.

24. 7.02 + 6.9 **13.9**
25. 12 − 5.88 **6**
26. 24.267 + 31.9 **56.2**
27. 6.87 − 2.3 **4.6**
28. 67.842 + 12.33 **80.17**
29. 62 · 0.005 **0.3**
30. 9.20 ÷ 3.5 **2.6**
31. 50 ÷ 3.95 **10**
32. 3.6 · 1.8 **6.5**

LESSON 8-3

Find the perimeter of each polygon.

33. **18.5 cm** 34. **33.6 km** 35. **48 m**

Find the circumference of each circle to the nearest tenth. Use 3.14 for π.

36. **44.0 yd** 37. **51.8 in.** 38. **74.4 mm**

Extra Practice 671

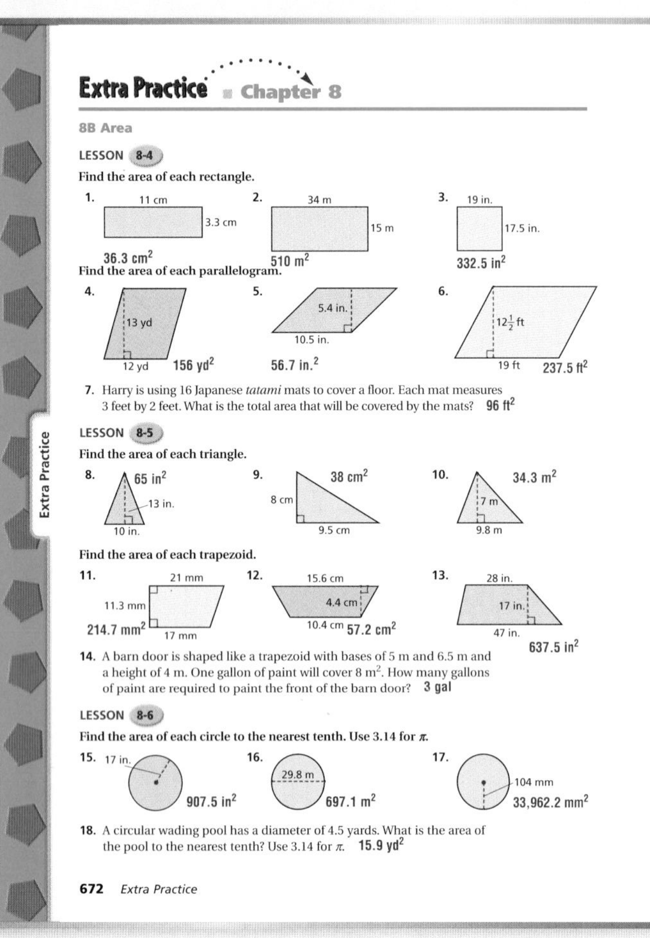

Extra Practice ■ Chapter 8

8B Area

LESSON 8-4

Find the area of each rectangle.

1. **36.3 cm²** 2. **510 m²** 3. **332.5 in²**

Find the area of each parallelogram.

4. **156 yd²** 5. **56.7 in.²** 6. **237.5 ft²**

7. Harry is using 16 Japanese *tatami* mats to cover a floor. Each mat measures 3 feet by 2 feet. What is the total area that will be covered by the mats? **96 ft²**

LESSON 8-5

Find the area of each triangle.

8. **65 in²** 9. **38 cm²** 10. **34.3 m²**

Find the area of each trapezoid.

11. **214.7 mm²** 12. **57.2 cm²** 13. **637.5 in²**

14. A barn door is shaped like a trapezoid with bases of 5 m and 6.5 m and a height of 4 m. One gallon of paint will cover 8 m². How many gallons of paint are required to paint the front of the barn door? **3 gal**

LESSON 8-6

Find the area of each circle to the nearest tenth. Use 3.14 for π.

15. **907.5 in²** 16. **697.1 m²** 17. **33,962.2 mm²**

18. A circular wading pool has a diameter of 4.5 yards. What is the area of the pool to the nearest tenth? Use 3.14 for π. **15.9 yd²**

672 *Extra Practice*

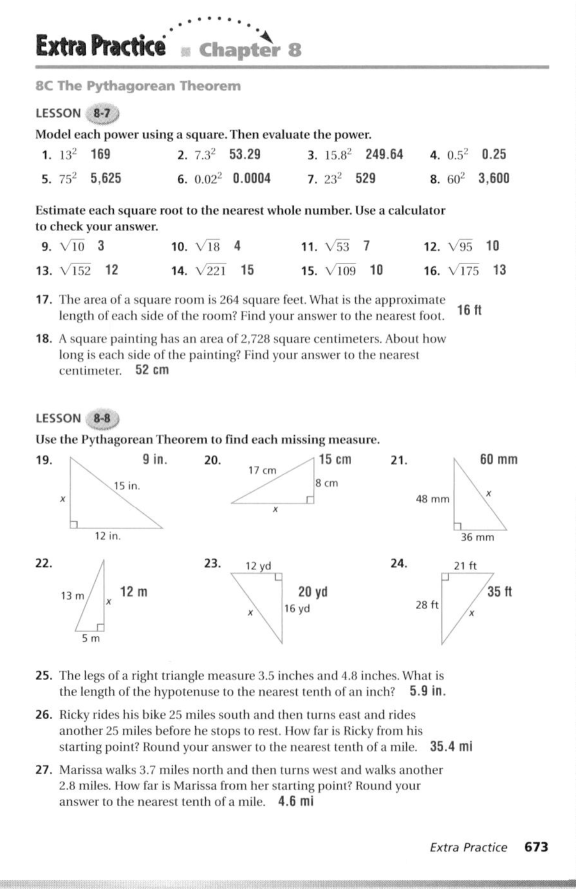

Extra Practice ■ Chapter 8

8C The Pythagorean Theorem

LESSON 8-7

Model each power using a square. Then evaluate the power.

1. 13^2 **169**
2. 7.3^2 **53.29**
3. 15.8^2 **249.64**
4. 0.5^2 **0.25**
5. 75^2 **5,625**
6. 0.02^2 **0.0004**
7. 23^2 **529**
8. 60^2 **3,600**

Estimate each square root to the nearest whole number. Use a calculator to check your answer.

9. $\sqrt{10}$ **3**
10. $\sqrt{18}$ **4**
11. $\sqrt{53}$ **7**
12. $\sqrt{95}$ **10**
13. $\sqrt{152}$ **12**
14. $\sqrt{221}$ **15**
15. $\sqrt{109}$ **10**
16. $\sqrt{175}$ **13**
17. The area of a square room is 264 square feet. What is the approximate length of each side of the room? Find your answer to the nearest foot. **16 ft**
18. A square painting has an area of 2,728 square centimeters. About how long is each side of the painting? Find your answer to the nearest centimeter. **52 cm**

LESSON 8-8

Use the Pythagorean Theorem to find each missing measure.

19. **9 in.** 20. **15 cm** 21. **60 mm**
22. **12 m** 23. **20 yd** 24. **35 ft**

25. The legs of a right triangle measure 3.5 inches and 4.8 inches. What is the length of the hypotenuse to the nearest tenth of an inch? **5.9 in.**
26. Ricky rides his bike 25 miles south and then turns east and rides another 25 miles before he stops to rest. How far is Ricky from his starting point? Round your answer to the nearest tenth of a mile. **35.4 mi**
27. Marissa walks 3.7 miles north and then turns west and walks another 2.8 miles. How far is Marissa from her starting point? Round your answer to the nearest tenth of a mile. **4.6 mi**

Extra Practice 673

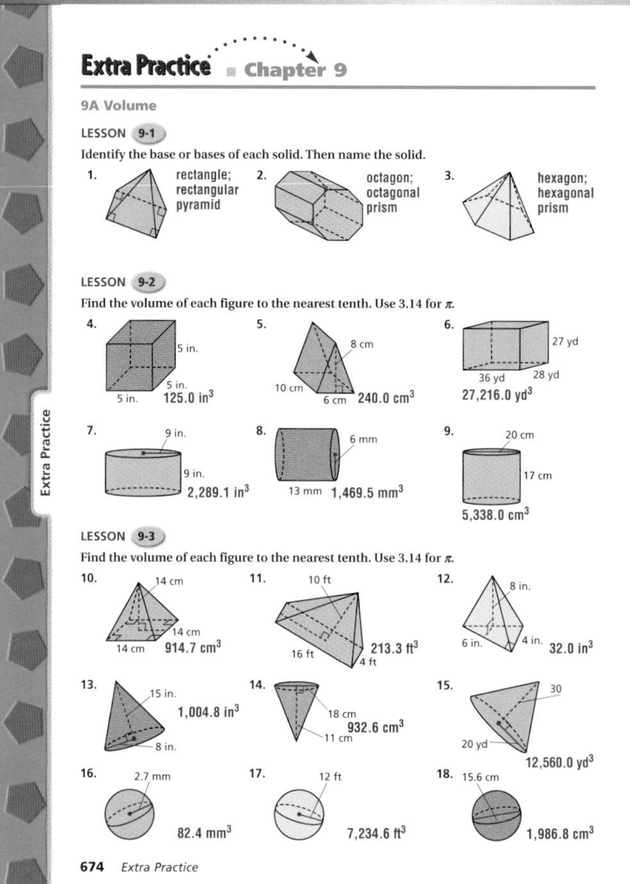

Extra Practice ■ Chapter 9

9A Volume

LESSON 9-1

Identify the base or bases of each solid. Then name the solid.

1. **rectangle; rectangular pyramid**
2. **octagon; octagonal prism**
3. **hexagon; hexagonal prism**

LESSON 9-2

Find the volume of each figure to the nearest tenth. Use 3.14 for π.

4. 5 in., 5 in., 5 in. **125.0 in³**
5. 8 cm, 10 cm, 6 cm **240.0 cm³**
6. 27 yd, 36 yd, 28 yd **27,216.0 yd³**
7. 9 in., 9 in. **2,289.1 in³**
8. 6 mm, 13 mm **1,469.5 mm³**
9. 20 cm, 17 cm **5,338.0 cm³**

LESSON 9-3

Find the volume of each figure to the nearest tenth. Use 3.14 for π.

10. 14 cm, 14 cm, 14 cm **914.7 cm³**
11. 10 ft, 16 ft, 4 ft **213.3 ft³**
12. 8 in., 6 in., 4 in. **32.0 in³**
13. 15 in., 8 in. **1,004.8 in³**
14. 18 cm, 11 cm **932.6 cm³**
15. 30, 20 yd **12,560.0 yd³**
16. 2.7 mm **82.4 mm³**
17. 12 ft **7,234.6 ft³**
18. 15.6 cm **1,986.8 cm³**

674 *Extra Practice*

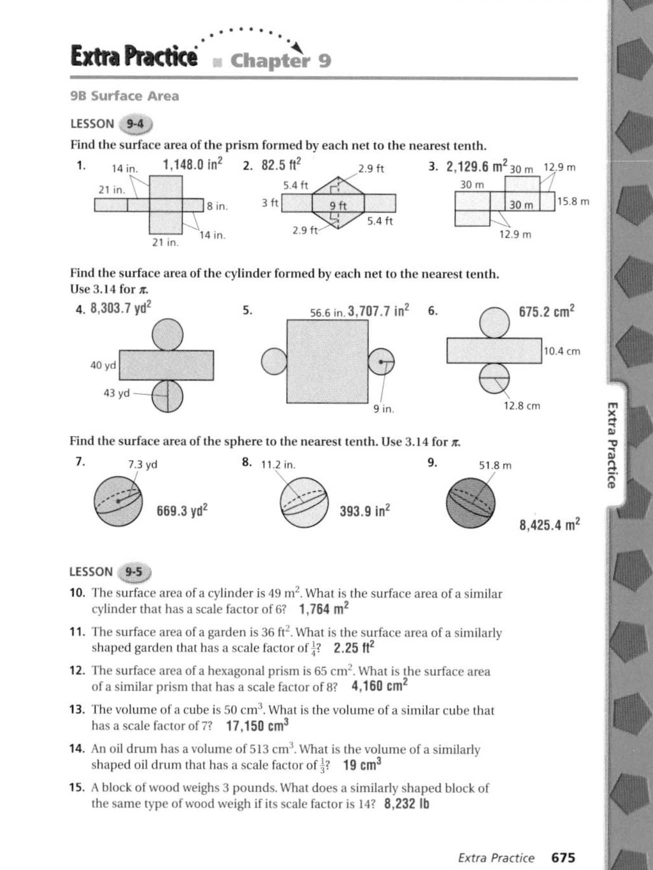

Extra Practice ■ Chapter 9

9B Surface Area

LESSON 9-4

Find the surface area of the prism formed by each net to the nearest tenth.

1. 14 in., 21 in., 8 in., 14 in., 21 in. **1,148.0 in²**
2. 2.9 ft, 5.4 ft, 3 ft, 9 ft, 5.4 ft, 2.9 ft **82.5 ft²**
3. 30 m, 12.9 m, 30 m, 15.8 m, 12.9 m **2,129.6 m²**

Find the surface area of the cylinder formed by each net to the nearest tenth. Use 3.14 for π.

4. 40 yd, 43 yd **8,303.7 yd²**
5. 56.6 in., 9 in. **3,707.7 in²**
6. 10.4 cm, 12.8 cm **675.2 cm²**

Find the surface area of the sphere to the nearest tenth. Use 3.14 for π.

7. 7.3 yd **669.3 yd²**
8. 11.2 in. **393.9 in²**
9. 51.8 m **8,425.4 m²**

LESSON 9-5

10. The surface area of a cylinder is 49 m². What is the surface area of a similar cylinder that has a scale factor of 6? **1,764 m²**
11. The surface area of a garden is 36 ft². What is the surface area of a similarly shaped garden that has a scale factor of $\frac{1}{4}$? **2.25 ft²**
12. The surface area of a hexagonal prism is 65 cm². What is the surface area of a similar prism that has a scale factor of 8? **4,160 cm²**
13. The volume of a cube is 50 cm³. What is the volume of a similar cube that has a scale factor of 7? **17,150 cm³**
14. An oil drum has a volume of 513 cm³. What is the volume of a similarly shaped oil drum that has a scale factor of $\frac{1}{3}$? **19 cm³**
15. A block of wood weighs 3 pounds. What does a similarly shaped block of the same type of wood weigh if its scale factor is 14? **8,232 lb**

Extra Practice 675

Extra Practice ■ Chapter 10

10A Introduction to Probability

LESSON 10-1

Determine whether each event is impossible, unlikely, as likely as not, likely, or certain. 1–2. See p. A8.

1. Ian's soccer team has a game every evening in April and May. If it is a Monday evening in May, what is the likelihood that Ian is playing soccer?
2. A pouch contains 9 purple marbles and 6 black marbles. If you pull out a marble without looking, what is the likelihood that it will be blue?

LESSON 10-2

3. Drivers for a courier service made 24 trips last week. Eighteen of those trips were across the Delaware River. What is the experimental probability that the next trip will be across the Delaware River? $\frac{3}{4}$
4. Out of the last 100 games Bo bowled, he scored 200 points or better in 85 of them. What is the experimental probability that Bo will score *less* than 200 the next time he bowls? $\frac{3}{20}$
5. A quarterback completed 16 of 24 passes during the first half of a football game. What is the experimental probability that he will complete the first pass he throws in the second half of the game? $\frac{2}{3}$

LESSON 10-3

6. The Heavenly Dairy makes 23 flavors of ice cream. You can get each flavor in a waffle cone, a sugar cone, a cake cone, or a cup. How large is the sample space? **92**
7. Between New Jersey and New York City there are 3 bridges and 2 tunnels. There are 3 highways between New York City and Connecticut. How many possible routes are there by bridge or tunnel and by highway between New Jersey and Connecticut that go through New York City? **15**
8. For her new car, Mrs. Chen has a choice of black, white, tan, silver, blue, or red. She also must choose the interior color. The choices are black or ivory leather or gray or tan fabric. How large is the sample space? **24**

LESSON 10-4

A spinner with 12 equal sections numbered 1–12 is spun. Find each probability. Write your answer as a fraction, as a decimal, and as a percent.

9. *P*(odd number) $\frac{1}{2}$, 0.5, 50%
10. *P*(prime number) $\frac{5}{12}$, 0.42, 42%
11. *P*(number divisible by 3) $\frac{1}{3}$, 0.33, 33%

676 *Extra Practice*

Extra Practice ■ Chapter 10

10B Applications of Probability

LESSON 10-5

Decide whether each set of events is independent or dependent. Explain your answer.

1. Mr. Fernandez's class contains 14 boys and 16 girls. Mr. Fernandez randomly picks a boy and a girl to represent the class at the school spelling bee. **Independent; the sample space of boys is different from the sample space of girls.**
2. Mrs. Rogers' class received new math books. Mrs. Rogers selects a student to hand out the new books. She also picks a second student to collect the old books. **Dependent; the sample space changes after the first student is selected.**
3. There are 52 playing cards in a standard deck of playing cards. Alex draws a card and holds onto it while Suzi draws a card. **Dependent; the outcome of the first draw affects the outcome of the second draw.**

Find the probability of each set of independent events.

4. flipping 2 coins at the same time and both landing heads up $\frac{1}{4}$, or 0.25, or 25%
5. drawing a 3 from 5 cards numbered 1 through 5 and rolling an even number on a number cube numbered from 1 through 6 $\frac{1}{10}$, or 0.10, or 10%

LESSON 10-6

6. Venus has decided to have a 2-color paint job done on her car. There are 6 paint colors from which to choose. How many combinations are possible? **15 combinations**
7. Philip has 5 different coins. How many combinations of 3 coins can he make from those? **10 combinations**
8. A juice bar offers 8 different juice blends. You and a friend want to each try a different blend. How many combinations are possible? **28 combinations**
9. Wagger's hot-dog stand offers the following choices of toppings: mustard, ketchup, sauerkraut, relish, onions, sour pickles, and chili. If you can choose 3 toppings, how many combinations are possible? **35 combinations**

LESSON 10-7

10. In how many different ways can Ralph, Randy, and Robert stand in line at the movie theater? **6 ways**
11. Roseanne and Rita join Ralph, Randy, and Robert at the movie theater. In how many different ways could they all stand in line? **120 ways**
12. a. Doris has a \$1 bill, a \$2 bill, a \$5 bill, a \$10 bill, a \$20 bill, and a \$50 bill. In how many different ways can she arrange them in a stack? **720 ways**
    b. If one arrangement was picked at random, what is the probability that the \$50 bill would be on top? $\frac{1}{6}$

Extra Practice 677

Extra Practice ■ Chapter 11

11A Multistep Equations

LESSON 11-1

Solve.

1. $4c - 13 = 15$ **$c = 7$**
2. $3h + 14 = 23$ **$h = 3$**
3. $-5j - 13 = 22$ **$j = -7$**
4. $\frac{e}{7} + 2 = 5$ **$e = 21$**
5. $\frac{m}{6} - 3 = 1$ **$m = 24$**
6. $\frac{x}{3} + 5 = -13$ **$x = -54$**
7. If you multiply the number of DVDs Sarah has by 6 and then add 5, you get 41. How many DVDs does Sarah have? **6**

LESSON 11-2

Solve.

8. $2w - 11 + 4w = 7$ **$w = 3$**
9. $7v + 5 - v = 11$ **$v = 1$**
10. $-7z + 4 - z = -12$ **$z = 2$**
11. $\frac{5x - 7}{3} = 15$ **$x = \frac{52}{5}$, or $10\frac{2}{5}$**
12. $2t - 7 - 5t = 11$ **$t = -6$**
13. $\frac{6t + 8}{5} = 2$ **$t = \frac{1}{3}$**
14. $12a - 3 - 8a = -1$ **$a = \frac{1}{2}$**
15. $\frac{2.9h - 5.1}{2} = 4.7$ **$h = 8$**
16. $\frac{3s - 14}{4} = 4$ **$s = 10$**
17. $\frac{10 - 4t}{8} = -12$ **$t = \frac{106}{4}$, or $26\frac{1}{2}$**
18. Erika has received scores of 82, 87, 93, 95, 88, and 90 on math quizzes. What score must Erika get on her next quiz to have an average of 90? **95**

LESSON 11-3

Solve.

19. $6a = 4a - 8$ **$a = -4$**
20. $3d - 5 = 7d - 9$ **$d = 1$**
21. $-2j + 6 = j - 3$ **$j = 3$**
22. $7 + 5m = 2 - m$ **$m = -\frac{5}{6}$**

Solve.

23. $7y - 9 = -2y$ **$y = 1$**
24. $2c - 13 = 5c + 11$ **$c = -8$**
25. $\frac{2}{5}g + 9 = -6 - \frac{6}{10}g$ **$g = -15$**
26. $7d + 4 = 8 - d$ **$d = \frac{1}{2}$**
27. $-3p + 8 = -7p - 12$ **$p = -5$**
28. $1.2k + 2.3 = -0.5k + 7.4$ **$k = 3$**
29. Roberta and Stanley are collecting signatures for a petition. So far, Roberta has twice as many signatures as Stanley. If she collects 30 more signatures, she will have 4 times as many signatures as Stanley currently has. How many signatures has Stanley collected? **15**

Extra Practice ■ Chapter 11

11B Inequalities

LESSON 11-4

Write an inequality for each situation.

1. The cafeteria could hold no more than 50 people. **number of people $\le$ 50**
2. There were fewer than 20 boats in the marina. **number of boats $<$ 20**

Graph each inequality. **3–6. See p. A8.**

3. $y < -2$
4. $f \ge 3$
5. $n \le -1.5$
6. $x > 4$

Graph each compound inequality. **7–10. See p. A8.**

7. $1 < s < 4$
8. $-1 \le v < 2$
9. $w < 0$ or $w \ge 5$
10. $-3.5 \le y < -2$

LESSON 11-5

Solve. Then graph each solution set on a number line. **11–14. See p. A8.**

11. $c - 6 > -5$
12. $v - 3 \ge 1$
13. $w - 6 \le -7$
14. $a - 2 \le 5$

Solve. Check each answer.

15. $q + 3 \le 5$ **$q \le 2$**
16. $m + 1 > 0$ **$m > -1$**
17. $p + 7 \le 4$ **$p \le -3$**
18. $z + 2 \ge -3$ **$z \ge -5$**
19. By Saturday night, 3 inches of rain had fallen in Happy Valley. The weekend forecast predicted at least 8 inches of rain. How much more rain must fall on Sunday for this forecast to be correct? **at least 5 in.**

LESSON 11-6

Solve.

20. $\frac{a}{5} \le 4.5$ **$a \le 22.5$**
21. $-\frac{v}{2} > 2$ **$v < -4$**
22. $\frac{x}{3.9} \ge -2$ **$x \ge -7.8$**
23. $-\frac{c}{4} < 2.3$ **$c > -9.2$**
24. $13y < 39$ **$y < 3$**
25. $2t \le 5$ **$t \le \frac{5}{2}$, or $2\frac{1}{2}$**
26. $-7r > 56$ **$r < -8$**
27. $3s \ge -4.5$ **$s \ge -1.5$**
28. The local candy store buys candy in bulk and then sells it by the pound. If the store owner spends $135 on peppermints and then sells them for $3.50 per pound, how many pounds must he sell to make a profit? **at least 39 lb**

LESSON 11-7 **29–37. See p. A8.**

Solve. Then graph each solution set on a number line.

29. $\frac{m}{3} - 1 \le 2$
30. $7.2x - 4.8 > 24$
31. $-5.5h + 2 < 13$
32. $-1 - \frac{s}{3.5} \ge 1$
33. $-\frac{w}{1.5} - 8 \le -10$
34. $4j - 6 > 16$
35. $5 - 2u < 15$
36. $\frac{r}{7} - 1 \ge 0$
37. $5 - \frac{m}{9} \le 17$
38. Jill, Serena, and Erin are trying to earn enough money to rent a beach house for a week. They estimate that it will cost at least $1,650. If Jill has already earned $600, how much must each of the others earn? **at least $525 each**

Extra Practice ■ Chapter 12

12A Introducing Functions

LESSON 12-1 **1–2. Complete answers on p. A9.**

Make a function table, and graph the resulting ordered pairs.

1. $y = 2x - 5$

Input	Rule	Output	Ordered Pair
x	$2x - 5$	y	(x, y)
0	**2(0) − 5**	**−5**	**(0, −5)**
1	**2(1) − 5**	**−3**	**(1, −3)**
2	**2(2) − 5**	**−1**	**(2, −1)**

2. $y = x^2 - 1$

Input	Rule	Output	Ordered Pair
x	$x^2 - 1$	y	(x, y)
0	**$(0)^2 - 1$**	**−1**	**(0, −1)**
1	**$(1)^2 - 1$**	**0**	**(1, 0)**
2	**$(2)^2 - 1$**	**3**	**(2, 3)**

LESSON 12-2

Find a function that describes each sequence. Use y for the term in the sequence and n for its place in the list. Then use the function to find the next three terms in the sequence.

3. 5, 6, 7, 8, . . . **$y = n + 4$; 9, 10, 11**
4. −4, −3, −2, −1, . . . **$y = n - 5$; 0, 1, 2**
5. 1, 8, 27, 64, . . . **$y = n^3$; 125, 216, 343**
6. 2, 5, 10, 17, . . . **$y = n^2 + 1$; 26, 37, 50**

LESSON 12-3

7. A marathon runner runs the same distance every day. Draw a graph to show how many miles the marathon runner runs. **7. See p. A9.**

Find the domain and range for each graph.

8.
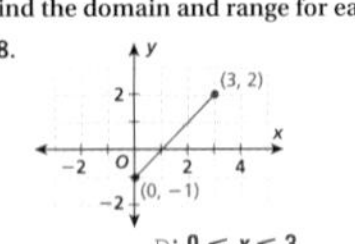

D: $0 \le x \le 3$

9.
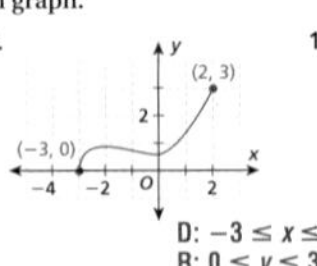

D: $-3 \le x \le 2$; R: $0 \le y \le 3$

10.
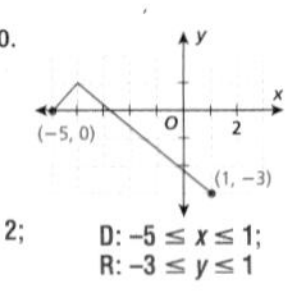

D: $-5 \le x \le 1$; R: $-3 \le y \le 1$

LESSON 12-4

Graph each linear function. **11–12. See p. A9.**

11. $y = 2x + 3$
12. $y = x \div 3$

LESSON 12-5

Give the slope and y-intercept of each line, given the equation.

13. $y = 9x - 4$ **slope: 9; y-intercept: −4**
14. $y = \frac{x}{3} + 1$ **slope: $\frac{1}{3}$; y-intercept: 1**
15. $y = -2.5x - 3$ **slope: −2.5; y-intercept: −3**
16. $y = -x - \frac{1}{2}$ **slope: −1; y-intercept: $-\frac{1}{2}$**

Extra Practice ■ Chapter 12

12B Nonlinear Functions and Set Theory

LESSON 12-6

Tell whether the graph is linear or nonlinear.

1. 2. 3.

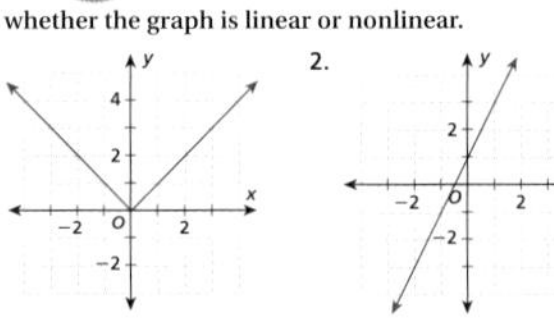
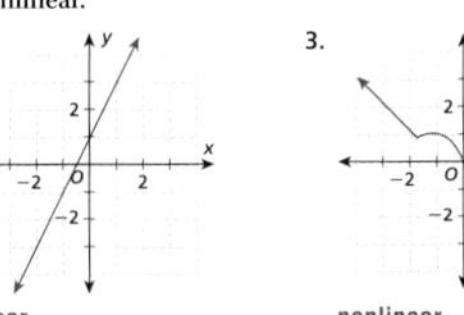

1. **nonlinear** 2. **linear** 3. **nonlinear**

Tell whether the function represented in each table is linear or nonlinear.

4.

x	y
1	3
4	7
7	11

linear

5.

x	y
4	0
3	5
2	7

nonlinear

6.

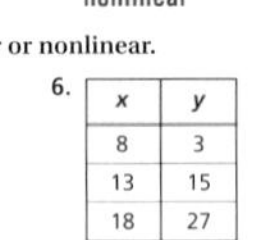

x	y
8	3
13	15
18	27

linear

LESSON 12-7

Give the intervals of x in which the graph shows constant rates of change.

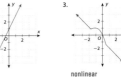

7. 8. 9.

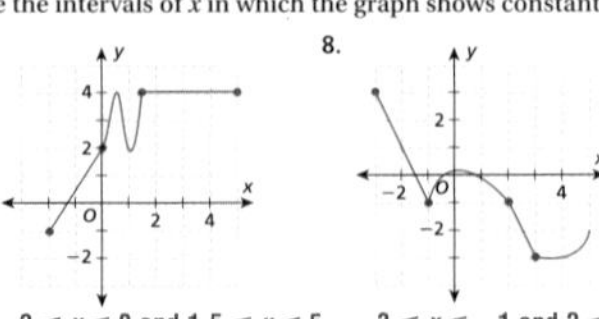
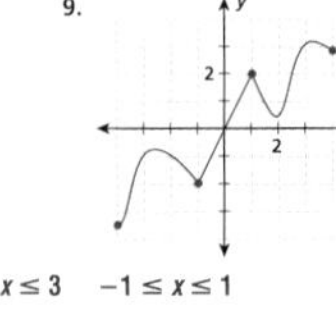

7. **$-2 \le x \le 0$ and $1.5 \le x \le 5$** 8. **$-3 \le x \le -1$ and $2 \le x \le 3$** 9. **$-1 \le x \le 1$**

LESSON 12-8

Write each set using roster notation or set-builder notation.

10. the set of all integers from −2 to 3, including −2 and 3 **{−2, −1, 0, 1, 2, 3}**
11. the set of all rational numbers greater than 5 **{x|x is all rational numbers greater than 5}**

Find $A \cap B$ and $A \cup B$, and tell whether $A \subset B$, $B \subset A$, or neither.

12. A = {4, 8, 12, 16}; B = {8, 16, 24, 32} **$A \cap B$ = {8, 16}; $A \cup B$ = {4, 8, 12, 16, 24, 32}; neither is a subset of the other.**
13. A = {all even numbers between 1 and 11}; B = {all multiples of 4 between 1 and 10} **$A \cap B$ = {4, 8}; $A \cup B$ = {2, 4, 6, 8, 10}; $B \subset A$**

Skills Bank

Skills Bank Review Skills

Place Value

You can use a place-value chart to help you read and write numbers.
The number 213,867 is shown.

Hundred Thousands	Ten Thousands	Thousands	Hundreds	Tens	Ones
2	1	3	8	6	7

EXAMPLE

Use the chart to determine the place value of each digit.

A 2
The 2 is in the hundred thousands place.

B 8
The 8 is in the hundreds place.

PRACTICE

Determine the place value of each underlined digit.

1. 543,201 **tens**
2. 239,487 **thousands**
3. 730,432 **ten thousands**
4. 4,382,121 **millions**

Compare and Order Whole Numbers

You can use place values from left to right to compare and order numbers.

EXAMPLE

Compare and order from least to greatest: 42,810; 142,997; 42,729; 42,638.

Start at the leftmost place value.
There is one number with a digit in the greatest place. It is the greatest of the four numbers.

Compare the remaining three numbers. All values in the next two places, the ten thousands and thousands, are the same.

In the hundreds place, the values are different. Use this digit to order the remaining numbers.

42,810
142,997
42,729
42,638

42,638; 42,729; 42,810; 142,997

PRACTICE

Compare and order the numbers in each set from least to greatest.

1. 2,564; 2,546; 2,465; 2,654 **2,465; 2,546; 2,564; 2,654**
2. 6,237; 6,372; 6,273; 6,327 **6,237; 6,273; 6,327; 6,372**
3. 132,957; 232,795; 32,975; 31,999 **31,999; 32,975; 132,957; 232,795**
4. 9,614; 29,461; 129,164; 129,146 **9,614; 29,461; 129,146; 129,164**

Read and Write Decimals

When reading and writing a decimal, you need to know the place value of the digit in the last decimal place. Also, when writing a decimal in word form remember the following:

- "and" goes in place of the decimal for numbers greater than one.
- a hyphen is used in two-digit numbers, such as twenty-five.
- a hyphen is used in two-word place values, such as ten-thousandths.

EXAMPLE

Write 728.34 in words.

The 4 is in the hundredths place, so 728.34 is written as "seven hundred twenty-eight and thirty-four hundredths."

PRACTICE

Write each decimal in words. **1–5. See p. A9.**

1. 17.238
2. 9.0023
3. 534.01972
4. 33.00084
5. 4,356.67

Rules for Rounding

To round a number to a certain place value, locate the digit with that place value, and look at the digit to the right of it.

- If the digit to the right is 5 or greater, increase the number you are rounding by 1.
- If the digit to the right is 4 or less, leave the number you are rounding as it is.

EXAMPLE

A **Round 765.48201 to the nearest hundredth.**

765.48201 *Locate the hundredths place.*
The digit to the right is less than 5, so the digit in the rounding place stays the same.
765.48

B **Round 765.48201 to the nearest tenth.**

765.48201 *Locate the tenths place.*
The digit to the right is greater than 5, so the digit in the rounding place increases by 1.
765.5

PRACTICE

Round 203.94587 to the place indicated.

1. hundreds place **200**
2. hundredths place **203.95**
3. thousandths place **203.946**
4. tens place **200**
5. ones place **204**
6. tenths place **203.9**

Properties

Addition and multiplication follow certain rules. The tables show basic properties of addition and multiplication.

Addition Properties	
Commutative:	$a + b = b + a$
Associative:	$(a + b) + c = a + (b + c)$
Identity Property of Zero:	$a + 0 = a$
Inverse Property:	$a + (-a) = 0$
Closure Property:	The sum of two real numbers is a real number.

Multiplication Properties	
Commutative:	$a \times b = b \times a$
Associative:	$(a \times b) \times c = a \times (b \times c)$
Identity Property of One:	$a \times 1 = a$
Inverse Property:	$a \times \frac{1}{a} = 1$ if $a \neq 0$
Property of Zero:	$a \times 0 = 0$
Closure Property:	The product of two real numbers is a real number.
Distributive:	$a(b + c) = a \times b + a \times c$

The following properties are true when a, b, and c are real numbers.

Substitution Property: If $a = b$, then a can be substituted for b in any expression.

Transitive Property: If $a = b$ and $b = c$, then $a = c$.

PRACTICE

Name the property represented by each equation.

1. $8 + 0 = 8$ **Identity Property of Zero**
2. $(9 \times 3) \times 7 = 9 \times (3 \times 7)$ **Associative Property of Multiplication**
3. 3×5 is a real number **Closure Property of Multiplication**
4. $7 \times 345 = 345 \times 7$ **Commutative Property of Multiplication**
5. $2(3 + 5) = 2 \times 3 + 2 \times 5$ **Distributive Property**
6. $15 \times \frac{1}{15} = 1$ **Inverse Property of Multiplication**
7. $3.6 + 4.4 = 4.4 + 3.6$ **Commutative Property of Addition**
8. $\frac{3}{4} \times \frac{4}{4} = \frac{3}{4}$ **Identity Property of One**
9. $18 + (-18) = 0$ **Inverse Property of Addition**
10. $(5 + 17) + 23 = 5 + (17 + 23)$ **Associative Property**

Overestimates and Underestimates

An **overestimate** is an estimate that is greater than the actual answer.
An **underestimate** is an estimate that is less than the actual answer.

EXAMPLE 1

Give an overestimate for each expression.

A 124 + 371
$124 + 371 \approx 130 + 380$
≈ 510

B 316 ÷ 12
$316 \div 12 \approx 320 \div 10$
≈ 32

EXAMPLE 2

Give an underestimate for each expression.

A 64 − 12
$64 - 12 \approx 60 - 15$
≈ 45

B 28 · 8
$28 \cdot 8 \approx 25 \cdot 8$
≈ 200

PRACTICE

Give an overestimate and underestimate for each expression. **Possible answers are given.**

1. 224 + 545 **780; 760**
2. 756 + 142 **910; 890**
3. 643 − 104 **550; 530**
4. 2,456 − 435 **2,100; 1,900**
5. 13 × 17 **300; 170**
6. 7 × 85 **630; 560**
7. 261 ÷ 9 **30; 26**
8. 85 ÷ 34 **3; 2**

Compatible Numbers

You can use compatible numbers to estimate products and quotients. Compatible numbers are close to the numbers in the problem and can help you do math mentally.

EXAMPLES

Estimate each product or quotient.

A 327 · 28
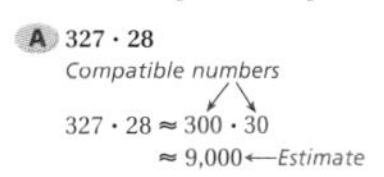
Compatible numbers
$327 \cdot 28 \approx 300 \cdot 30$
$\approx 9{,}000$ ← *Estimate*

B 637 ÷ 8
Compatible numbers
$637 \div 8 \approx 640 \div 8$
≈ 80 ← *Estimate*

PRACTICE

Use compatible numbers to estimate each product or quotient. **Possible answers are given.**

1. 42 · 7 **280**
2. 3,957 ÷ 23 **200**
3. 5,169 · 21 **100,000**
4. 813 ÷ 8 **100**
5. 78 · 42 **3,200**
6. 1,443 ÷ 7 **200**
7. 98 · 48 **5,000**
8. 3,372 ÷ 415 **8**
9. 58 · 9 **540**
10. 27,657 ÷ 67 **400**

Multiply and Divide by Powers of Ten

When you *multiply* by powers of ten, move the decimal point one place to the right for each zero in the power of ten. When you *divide* by powers of ten, move the decimal point one place to the left for each zero in the power of ten.

EXAMPLE

Find each product or quotient.

A $0.37 \cdot 100$

$0.37 \cdot 100 = 0.37$
$= 37$

B $43 \cdot 1{,}000$

$43 \cdot 1{,}000 = 43.000$
$= 43{,}000$

C $0.24 \div 10$

$0.24 \div 10 = 0.24$
$= 0.024$

D $1{,}467 \div 100$

$1{,}467 \div 100 = 1467.$
$= 14.67$

PRACTICE

Find each product or quotient.

1. 10×8.53 **85.3**
2. 0.55×10^4 **5,500**
3. $48.6 \times 1{,}000$ **48,600**
4. $2.487 \div 1{,}000$ **0.002487**
5. $6.03 \div 10^3$ **0.00603**

Multiply Whole Numbers

When you multiply two whole numbers, think of the second number's expanded form, and multiply by each value.

EXAMPLE

Find the product of 621 · 485.

Step 1: Think of 485 as 4 hundreds, 8 tens, and 5 ones. Multiply 621 by 5 ones.	**Step 2:** Multiply 621 by 8 tens.	**Step 3:** Multiply 621 by 4 hundreds.	**Step 4:** Add the partial products.
621 × 485 3,105 ← 5 × 621	621 × 485 3,105 49,680 ← 80 × 621	621 × 485 3,105 49,680 248,400 ← 400 × 621	621 × 485 3,105 49,680 + 248,400 **301,185**

621 · 485 = 301,185

PRACTICE

Multiply.

1. 493 × 37 **18,241**
2. 539 × 82 **44,198**
3. 134 × 145 **19,430**
4. 857 × 662 **567,334**
5. 1,872 × 43 **80,496**
6. 5,849 × 67 **391,883**
7. 36,735 × 28 **1,028,580**
8. 121,614 × 58 **7,053,612**

Divide Whole Numbers

EXAMPLE

Find the quotient of 5,712 ÷ 28.

Step 1: Write the first number inside the long division symbol, and write the second number to the left of the symbol. Divide by the number outside the symbol.	**Step 2:** Multiply 28 by 2, and place the product under 57. Subtract and bring down the next digit of the dividend.	**Step 3:** Divide 112 by 28. Multiply 28 by 4 and place the product under 112. Subtract.
2 28)5712 *28 cannot go into 5, so try 57.*	20 28)5712 −56 11 −0 112 *28 cannot go into 11, so put a 0 in the quotient, and bring down the 2.*	204 28)5712 − 56 11 −0 112 −112 0

PRACTICE

Divide.

1. 23,148 ÷ 18 **1,286**
2. 5,772 ÷ 37 **156**
3. 56,088 ÷ 41 **1,368**
4. 34,540 ÷ 55 **628**
5. 68,894 ÷ 74 **931**
6. 143,296 ÷ 32 **4,478**
7. 398,736 ÷ 72 **5,538**
8. 566,746 ÷ 79 **7,174**

Divisibility Rules

A number is divisible by another number if the quotient is a whole number with no remainder.

A number is divisible by . . .	Divisible	Not Divisible
2 if the last digit is an even number.	13,776	4,221
3 if the sum of the digits is divisible by 3.	327	97
4 if the last two digits form a number divisible by 4.	3,128	526
5 if the last digit is 0 or 5.	9,415	50,501
6 if the number is divisible by 2 and 3.	762	62
9 if the sum of the digits is divisible by 9.	21,222	96
10 if the last digit is 0.	1,680	8,255

PRACTICE

Determine whether each number is divisible by 2, 3, 4, 5, 6, 9, or 10.

1. 324 **2, 3, 4, 6, 9**
2. 501 **3**
3. 200 **2, 4, 5, 10**
4. 812 **2, 4**
5. 60 **2, 3, 4, 5, 6, 10**
6. 784 **2, 4**
7. 351 **3, 9**
8. 3,009 **3**
9. 2,345 **5**
10. 555,555 **3, 5**

Factors

A **factor** of a number is any number that divides into it without leaving a remainder.

EXAMPLE

List all the factors of 28.

The possible factors are whole numbers from 1 to 28.

1 · 28 = 28 *The numbers 1 and 28 are factors of 28.*
2 · 14 = 28 *The numbers 2 and 14 are factors of 28.*
3 · ? = 28 *No whole number multiplied by 3 equals 28, so 3 is not a factor of 28.*
4 · 7 = 28 *The numbers 4 and 7 are factors of 28.*
5 · ? = 28 *No whole number multiplied by 5 equals 28, so 5 is not a factor of 28.*
6 · ? = 28 *No whole number multiplied by 6 equals 28, so 6 is not a factor of 28.*

The factors of 28 are 1, 2, 4, 7, 14, and 28.

PRACTICE

List all the factors of each number.

1. 10 **1, 2, 5, 10**
2. 8 **1, 2, 4, 8**
3. 18 **1, 2, 3, 6, 9, 18**
4. 54 **1, 2, 3, 6, 9, 18, 27, 54**
5. 27 **1, 3, 9, 27**
6. 36 **1, 2, 3, 4, 6, 9, 12, 18, 36**
7. 19 **1, 19**
8. 24 **1, 2, 3, 4, 6, 8, 12, 24**
9. 50 **1, 2, 5, 10, 25, 50**
10. 32 **1, 2, 4, 8, 16, 32**
11. 49 **1, 7, 49**
12. 39 **1, 3, 13, 39**

Prime and Composite Numbers

A **prime number** has exactly two factors, 1 and itself.
A **composite number** has more than two factors.

EXAMPLE

Determine whether each number is prime or composite.

A 19
Factors: 1, 19
So 19 is prime.

B 20
Factors: 1, 2, 4, 5, 10, 20
So 20 is composite.

PRACTICE

Determine whether each number is prime or composite.

1. 7 **P**
2. 15 **C**
3. 18 **C**
4. 8 **C**
5. 113 **P**
6. 31 **P**
7. 12 **C**
8. 49 **C**
9. 77 **C**
10. 67 **P**
11. 9 **C**
12. 79 **P**

Simplest Form of Fractions

A fraction is in simplest form when the only common factor of the numerator and denominator is 1.

EXAMPLE

Simplify.

A $\frac{24}{30}$

24: 1, 2, 3, 4, 6, 8, 12, 24
30: 1, 2, 3, 5, 6, 10, 15, 30 *Find the greatest common factor of 24 and 30.*

$\frac{24 \div 6}{30 \div 6} = \frac{4}{5}$ *Divide both the numerator and the denominator by 6.*

B $\frac{18}{28}$

18: 1, 2, 3, 6, 9, 18
28: 1, 2, 4, 7, 14, 28 *Find the greatest common factor of 18 and 28.*

$\frac{18 \div 2}{28 \div 2} = \frac{9}{14}$ *Divide both the numerator and the denominator by 2.*

PRACTICE

Simplify.

1. $\frac{15}{20}$ $\mathbf{\frac{3}{4}}$
2. $\frac{32}{40}$ $\mathbf{\frac{4}{5}}$
3. $\frac{14}{35}$ $\mathbf{\frac{2}{5}}$
4. $\frac{30}{75}$ $\mathbf{\frac{2}{5}}$
5. $\frac{17}{51}$ $\mathbf{\frac{1}{3}}$
6. $\frac{18}{42}$ $\mathbf{\frac{3}{7}}$
7. $\frac{19}{38}$ $\mathbf{\frac{1}{2}}$
8. $\frac{22}{121}$ $\mathbf{\frac{2}{11}}$
9. $\frac{10}{32}$ $\mathbf{\frac{5}{16}}$
10. $\frac{39}{91}$ $\mathbf{\frac{3}{7}}$

Roman Numerals

In the Roman numeral system, numbers do not have place values to show what they represent. Instead, numbers are represented by letters.

I = 1 V = 5 X = 10 L = 50 C = 100 D = 500 M = 1,000

The values of the letters do not change based on their place in a number.

If a numeral is to the right of an equal or greater numeral, add the two numerals' values. If a numeral is immediately to the left of a greater numeral, subtract the numeral's value from the greater numeral.

EXAMPLE

A Write CLIV as a decimal number.

CLIV = C + L + (V − I)
= 100 + 50 + (5 − 1)
= 154

B Write 1,109 as a Roman numeral.

1,109 = 1,000 + 100 + 9
= M + C + (X − I)
= MCIX

PRACTICE

Write each decimal number as a Roman numeral and each Roman numeral as a decimal number.

1. XXVI **26**
2. 29 **XXIX**
3. MCMLII **1,952**
4. 224 **CCXXIV**
5. DCCCVI **806**
6. 8 **VIII**
7. XLIV **44**
8. 1,557 **MDLVII**
9. XCIX **99**
10. 2,004 **MMIV**

Binary Numbers

Computers use the **binary number system.** In the binary, or base-2, system of numbers, numbers are formed using the digits 0 and 1. Each place in a binary number is associated with a power of 2. Binary numbers are written with the subscript *two* so that they are not confused with numbers in the decimal system.

The binary number 1101_{two} can be thought of as $(1 \cdot 2^3) + (1 \cdot 2^2) + (0 \cdot 2^1) + (1 \cdot 2^0)$.

Binary Place Value

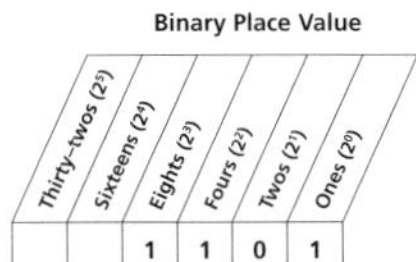

You can use the expanded form of 1101_{two} to find the value of the number as a decimal, or base-10, number.

$$\begin{aligned}(1 \cdot 2^3) + (1 \cdot 2^2) + (0 \cdot 2^1) + (1 \cdot 2^0) &= (1 \cdot 8) + (1 \cdot 4) + (0 \cdot 2) + (1 \cdot 1)\\ &= 8 + 4 + 0 + 1\\ &= 13\end{aligned}$$

So $1101_{two} = 13_{ten}$.

EXAMPLE

Write each binary number as a decimal number.

A 101110_{two}

$$\begin{aligned}101110_{two} &= (1 \cdot 2^5) + (0 \cdot 2^4) + (1 \cdot 2^3) + (1 \cdot 2^2) + (1 \cdot 2^1) + (0 \cdot 1)\\ &= 32 + 0 + 8 + 4 + 2 + 0\\ &= 46\end{aligned}$$

B 10001_{two}

$$\begin{aligned}10001_{two} &= (1 \cdot 2^4) + (0 \cdot 2^3) + (0 \cdot 2^2) + (0 \cdot 2^1) + (1 \cdot 1)\\ &= 16 + 0 + 0 + 0 + 1\\ &= 17\end{aligned}$$

PRACTICE

Write each binary number as a decimal number.

1. 100_{two} **4**
2. 110_{two} **6**
3. 101_{two} **5**
4. 1100_{two} **12**
5. 1011_{two} **11**
6. 11011_{two} **27**
7. 11110_{two} **30**
8. 101010_{two} **42**
9. 111111_{two} **63**
10. 100111_{two} **39**

Estimate Measurements

You can use benchmarks to estimate with metric and customary units.

1 meter (m)	Width of a doorway	**1 centimeter (cm)**	Width of a large paper clip
1 liter (L)	Water in a 1-quart bottle	**1 milliliter (mL)**	Water in an eyedropper
1 gram (g)	Mass of a dollar bill	**1 kilogram (kg)**	Mass of 8 rolls of pennies
30°C (Celsius)	Temperature on a hot day	**0°C (Celsius)**	Temperature on a freezing day

EXAMPLE 1

Choose the most reasonable estimate of the height of the ceiling in your classroom.

A 30 cm B 3 m C 30 m D 30,000 cm

The most reasonable estimate is 3 m.

Length	Temperature	Capacity
1 inch (in.)—about the length of a small paper clip **1 foot (ft)**—about the length of a standard sheet of paper **1 yard (yd)**—about the width of a doorway	**32°F** (Fahrenheit)—water freezes **70°F**—air on a comfortably warm day **90°F**—air on a hot day **212°F**—boiling water	**1 fluid ounce (fl oz)**—amount of water in two tablespoons **1 cup (c)**—amount of water held in a standard measuring cup **1 pint (pt), 1 quart (qt), 1 gallon (gal)**—Think about containers of water at a store.

EXAMPLE 2

Choose the most appropriate estimate.

A **the length of a classroom**

A 30 in. B 30 ft C 30 yd

The most appropriate estimate is 30 ft.

B **a temperature for wearing a T-shirt**

A 20°F B 40°F C 80°F

The most appropriate estimate is 80°F.

PRACTICE

Choose the most reasonable estimate.

1. the temperature on a warm day

   A −22°C B 22°C C 68°C **B**

2. the capacity of a kitchen sink

   A 12 mL B 1,200 mL C 12 L **C**

Choose the most appropriate estimate.

3. the capacity of a tall drinking glass

   A 1 pt B 4 qt C $\frac{1}{2}$ gal **A**

4. a temperature for wearing a warm coat

   A 20°F B 60°F C 80°F **A**

5. the temperature of a cup of hot cocoa

   A 32°F B 120°F C 250°F **B**

6. the width of a pizza box

   A 18 in. B 8 ft C 2 yd **A**

Relate Metric Units of Length, Mass, and Capacity

Within the metric system, measures of length, mass, and capacity are related. A cube that has a volume of 1 cm^3 has a capacity of 1 mL. If the cube were filled with water, the mass of the water would be 1 g.

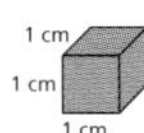

EXAMPLE

Find the capacity of a 50 cm × 60 cm × 30 cm rectangular box. Then find the mass of the water that would fill the box.

Volume: 50 cm × 60 cm × 30 cm = 90,000 cm^3

Capacity: 1 cm^3 = 1 mL, so 90,000 cm^3 = 90,000 mL, or 90 L.

Mass: 1 mL of water has a mass of 1 g, so 90,000 mL of water has a mass of 90,000 g, or 90 kg.

PRACTICE

Find the capacity of each rectangular box. Then find the mass of the water that would fill the box.

1. 2 cm × 5 cm × 8 cm **80 mL; 80 g**
2. 10 cm × 18 cm × 4 cm **720 mL; 720 g**
3. 8 cm × 8 cm × 8 cm **512 mL; 512 g**
4. 10 cm × 10 cm × 10 cm **1,000 mL, or 1 L; 1,000 g, or 1 kg**
5. 15 cm × 18 cm × 16 cm **4,320 mL, or 4.32 L; 4,320 g, or 4.32kg**
6. 23 cm × 19 cm × 11 cm **4,807 mL, or 4.807 L; 4,807 g, or 4.807 kg**

Negative Exponents

A positive exponent tells how many times the base of a power is used as a factor. The table below shows one way you can determine the values of powers with negative exponents.

Power	8^3	8^2	8^1	8^0	8^{-1}	8^{-2}
Value	512	64	8	1	$\frac{1}{8}$	$\frac{1}{64}$

÷ 8 ÷ 8 ÷ 8 ÷ 8 ÷ 8

Each time the exponent is decreased by 1, the value of the power is divided by the base. There is another pattern in the table.

$8^{-1} = \frac{1}{8^1} = \frac{1}{8}$ $8^{-2} = \frac{1}{8^2} = \frac{1}{64}$ $8^{-3} = \frac{1}{8^3} = \frac{1}{512}$

A number raised to a negative exponent equals 1 divided by that number raised to the opposite (positive) exponent. You can write the general rule for this property as $a^{-b} = \frac{1}{a^b}$.

PRACTICE

Evaluate.

1. 2^{-3} **$\frac{1}{8}$**
2. 7^{-2} **$\frac{1}{49}$**
3. 10^{-4} **$\frac{1}{10,000}$**
4. 8^{-4} **$\frac{1}{4,096}$**
5. 1^{-20} **1**
6. 5^{-1} **$\frac{1}{5}$**

Preview Skills

Probability of Two Disjoint Events

In probability, two events are considered to be **disjoint** if they cannot happen at the same time. Examples of disjoint events are getting a 5 or a 6 on a single roll of a 1–6 number cube. To find the probability that either one or the other of two disjoint events will occur, add the probabilities of each event occurring separately.

EXAMPLE

Find the probability of each set of disjoint events.

A **rolling either a 5 or a 6 on a 1–6 number cube**

$P(5 \text{ or } 6) = P(5) + P(6)$

$= \frac{1}{6} + \frac{1}{6}$

$= \frac{2}{6}$

$= \frac{1}{3}$

The probability of rolling a 5 or a 6 on a 1–6 number cube is $\frac{1}{3}$.

B **choosing either an *A* or an *E* from the letters in the word *mathematics***

$P(A \text{ or } E) = P(A) + P(E)$

$= \frac{2}{11} + \frac{1}{11}$

$= \frac{3}{11}$

The probability of choosing an *A* or an *E* is $\frac{3}{11}$.

PRACTICE

Find the probability of each set of disjoint events.

1. tossing a coin and getting heads or tails **1**
2. spinning red or green on a spinner that has four equal sectors colored red, green, blue, and yellow **$\frac{1}{2}$**
3. drawing a black marble or a red marble from a bag that contains 4 white marbles, 3 black marbles, and 2 red marbles **$\frac{5}{9}$**
4. choosing either a boy or a girl from a class of 13 boys and 17 girls **1**
5. choosing either *A* or *E* from a list of the five vowels **$\frac{2}{5}$**
6. choosing either a number less than 3 or a number greater than 12 from a set of 20 cards numbered 1–20 **$\frac{1}{2}$**

Inductive and Deductive Reasoning

You use **inductive reasoning** when you look for a pattern in individual cases to draw conclusions. Conclusions drawn using inductive reasoning are sometimes like predictions. They may be proven false.

You use **deductive reasoning** when you use given facts to draw conclusions. A conclusion based on facts must be true.

EXAMPLE

Identify the type of reasoning used. Explain your answers.

A ***Statement:* A number pattern begins with 2, 5, 8, 11, . . .**
***Conclusion:* The next number in the pattern will be 14.**

This is inductive reasoning. The conclusion is based on the pattern established by the first four terms in the sequence.

B ***Statement:* It has rained for the past three days.**
***Conclusion:* It will rain tomorrow.**

This is inductive reasoning. The conclusion is based on the weather pattern over the past three days.

C ***Statement:* The measures of two angles of a triangle are 30° and 70°.**
***Conclusion:* The measure of the third angle is 80°.**

This is deductive reasoning. Since you know that the measures of the angles of a triangle have a sum of 180°, the third angle of this triangle must measure 80° (30° + 70° + 80° = 180°).

PRACTICE

Identify the type of reasoning used. Explain your answers.

1. *Statement:* Shawna has received a score of 100 on the last five math tests.
Conclusion: Shawna will receive a score of 100 on the next math test.
This is inductive reasoning. The conclusion is based on Shawna's previous performance on tests.
2. *Statement:* The mail has arrived late every Monday for the past 4 weeks.
Conclusion: The mail will arrive late next Monday.
This is inductive reasoning. The conclusion is based on the pattern over the past 4 Mondays.
3. *Statement:* Three angles of a quadrilateral measure 100°, 90°, and 70°.
Conclusion: The measure of the fourth angle is 100°. **See answer below.**
4. *Statement:* Perpendicular lines *AB* and *CD* intersect at point *E*.
Conclusion: Angle *AED* is a right angle. **This is deductive reasoning. The definition of perpendicular lines is that they intersect to form right angles.**
5. *Statement:* A pattern of numbers begins 1, 2, 4, . . .
Conclusion: The next number in the pattern is 8. **This is inductive reasoning. The conclusion is based on the pattern established by the first three terms in the sequence.**
6. *Statement:* Ten of the first ten seventh-grade students surveyed listed soccer as their favorite sport.
Conclusion: Soccer is the favorite sport of all seventh-graders.
This is inductive reasoning. The conclusion is based on the responses of ten students.

3. This is deductive reasoning. The sum of the measures of the four angles of a quadrilateral is 360°, so the fourth angle of this quadrilateral must measure 100°.

Make Conjectures

Conjecture is another word for conclusion. Conjectures in math are based on observations and in some cases have not yet been proven to be true. To prove that a conjecture is false, you need to find just one case, or *counterexample*, for which the conclusion does not hold true.

EXAMPLE 1

Test each conjecture to decide whether it is true or false. If the conjecture is false, give a counterexample.

A **The sum of two even numbers is always an even number.**

An even number is divisible by 2. The sum of two even numbers can be written as $2m + 2n = 2(m + n)$, which is divisible by 2, so it is even. The conjecture is true.

B **All prime numbers are odd.**

The first prime number is 2, which is an even number. The conjecture is false.

EXAMPLE 2

Formulate a conjecture based on the given information. Then test your conjecture.

$1 \cdot 3 = 3$ $3 \cdot 5 = 15$ $5 \cdot 7 = 35$ $7 \cdot 9 = 63$

Conjecture: The product of two odd numbers is always an odd number.

An odd number does not have 2 as a factor, so the product of two odd numbers also does not have 2 as a factor. The conjecture is true.

PRACTICE

Test each conjecture to decide whether it is true or false. If the conjecture is false, give a counterexample.

1. The sum of two odd numbers is always an odd number. **false; 3 + 5 = 8**
2. The product of two even numbers is always an even number. **true**
3. The sum of twice a whole number and 1 is always an odd number. **true**
4. If you subtract a whole number from another whole number, the result will always be a whole number. **false; 3 − 5 = −2**
5. If you multiply two fractions, the product will always be greater than either fraction. **false; $\frac{1}{2} \cdot \frac{3}{4} = \frac{3}{8}$**

Formulate a conjecture based on the given information. Then test your conjecture. **Check students' work.**

6. 12 + 21 = 33 13 + 31 = 44 23 + 32 = 55 17 + 71 = 88
7. 15 × 15 = 225 25 × 25 = 625 35 × 35 = 1,225

Trigonometric Ratios

You can use ratios to find information about the sides and angles of a right triangle. These ratios are called *trigonometric ratios*, and they have names, such as **sine** (abbreviated *sin*), **cosine** (abbreviated *cos*), and **tangent** (abbreviated *tan*).

The **sine** of $\angle 1 = \sin \angle 1 = \frac{\text{length of side opposite } \angle 1}{\text{length of hypotenuse}} = \frac{a}{c}$.

The **cosine** of $\angle 1 = \cos \angle 1 = \frac{\text{length of side adjacent to } \angle 1}{\text{length of hypotenuse}} = \frac{b}{c}$.

The **tangent** of $\angle 1 = \tan \angle 1 = \frac{\text{length of side opposite } \angle 1}{\text{length of side adjacent to } \angle 1} = \frac{a}{b}$.

EXAMPLE 1

Find the sine, cosine, and tangent of $\angle J$.

$\sin \angle J = \frac{LK}{JK} = \frac{3}{5}$

$\cos \angle J = \frac{JL}{JK} = \frac{4}{5}$

$\tan \angle J = \frac{LK}{JL} = \frac{3}{4}$

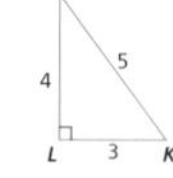

EXAMPLE 2

Use your calculator to find the measure of side $\overline{MN}$ to the nearest tenth.

Side $\overline{MN}$ is adjacent to the 58° angle. The length of the hypotenuse is given. The ratio that uses the lengths of the adjacent side and the hypotenuse is cosine.

$\cos(58°) = \frac{MN}{9}$ *Write the ratio that is equal to the cosine of 58°.*

$9 \cdot \cos(58°) = MN$ *Multiply both sides by 9.*

9 × COS 58 ENTER *Use your calculator.*

$MN = 4.8$

PRACTICE

Find the sine, cosine, and tangent of each angle.

1. $\angle D$
2. $\angle F$

1. $\sin \angle D = \frac{8}{10}$, or $\frac{4}{5}$; $\cos \angle D = \frac{6}{10}$, or $\frac{3}{5}$; $\tan \angle D = \frac{8}{6}$, or $\frac{4}{3}$

2. $\sin \angle F = \frac{6}{10}$, or $\frac{3}{5}$; $\cos \angle F = \frac{8}{10}$, or $\frac{4}{5}$; $\tan \angle F = \frac{6}{8}$, or $\frac{3}{4}$

Use your calculator to find the measure of each side, to the nearest tenth.

3. $\overline{QR}$ **10.6**
4. $\overline{PR}$ **22.7**

Half-life

Some atoms give off energy by emitting particles from their centers, or nuclei. The ability of these atoms to release nuclear radiation is called *radioactivity*, and the process is called *radioactive decay*.

Half-life is the amount of time it takes for one-half of the nuclei of a radioactive sample to decay. The half-life of an element can range from less than a second to millions of years.

EXAMPLE 1

The half-life of sodium-24 is 15 hours. If a sample of sodium-24 contains $\frac{1}{8}$ of its original amount, how old is the sample?

Every 15 hours, $\frac{1}{2}$ the sample decays.

Fraction of Sample	1	$\frac{1}{2}$	$\frac{1}{4}$	$\frac{1}{8}$
Time	0 hours	15 hours	30 hours	45 hours

The sample is 45 hours old.

EXAMPLE 2

The half-life of phosphorous-24 is 14.3 days. How much of a 6-gram sample will remain after 42.9 days?

Time	0 days	14.3 days	28.6 days	42.9 days
Amount of Sample (g)	6	3	1.5	0.75

After 42.9 days, 0.75 g of phosphorous-24 will remain.

PRACTICE

1. The half-life of cobalt-60 is 5.26 years. If a sample of cobalt-60 contains $\frac{1}{4}$ of its original amount, how old is the sample? **10.52 years**
2. The half-life of sodium-24 is 15 hours. How much of a 9.6-gram sample will remain after 60 hours? **0.6 grams**
3. Iodine-131 has a half-life of 8.07 days. How much of a 4.4 g sample will there be after 40.35 days? **0.1375 grams**
4. A sample of bismuth-212 decayed from 18 g to 1.125 g in 242 minutes. What is the half-life of bismuth-212? **60.5 minutes**

Skills Bank

pH Scale

An acid is a compound that produces hydrogen ions in solution. A base is a compound that produces hydroxide ions in solution. Chemists use the **pH scale** to measure how acidic or basic a solution is.

The range of the pH scale for a solution is 0 to 14. A solution with a pH below 7 is acidic. A solution with a pH above 7 is basic. A solution with a pH of 7 is neutral—that is, it has an equal number of hydrogen and hydroxide ions.

The pH numbers are related by powers of 10.

A pH of 6 is 10 times more acidic than a pH of 7.

A pH of 8 is 10 times more basic than a pH of 7.

0 Strong acids   Weak acids 7 Weak bases   Strong bases 14

EXAMPLE 1

Solution A and solution B have the same volume. Solution A has a pH of 2, and solution B has a pH of 4. How much more acidic is solution A than solution B?

Since $4 - 2 = 2$ and $10^2 = 100$ solution A is 100 times more acidic than solution B.

EXAMPLE 2

Solution C and solution D have the same volume. Solution C has a pH of 13, and solution D has a pH of 8. How much more basic is solution C than solution D?

Since $13 - 8 = 5$ and $10^5 = 100{,}000$ solution C is 100,000 times more basic than solution D.

PRACTICE

1. Solution E and solution F have the same volume. Solution E has a pH of 5, and solution F has a pH of 1. How much more basic is solution E than solution F? **10,000 times**
2. Solution G and solution H have the same volume. Solution G has a pH of 9, and solution H has a pH of 8. How much more basic is solution G than solution H? **10 times**
3. Solution K and solution J have the same volume. Solution J has a pH of 7, and solution K has a pH of 5. How much more acidic is solution K than solution J? **100 times**
4. Solution M and solution L have the same volume. Solution L has a pH of 14, and solution M has a pH of 7. How much more basic is solution L than solution M? **10,000,000 times**

Richter Scale

The magnitude of an earthquake is a measure of the amount of energy the earthquake releases. The **Richter scale** is used to express the magnitude of earthquakes. This scale uses the counting numbers. Each number represents a magnitude that is 10 times stronger than the magnitude represented by the previous number.

You can relate Richter scale numbers to the exponents in powers of 10.

$10^1 = 10$ $10^2 = 100$ $10^3 = 1{,}000$ $10^4 = 10{,}000$ $10^5 = 100{,}000$

Just as 10^2 is 10 times 10^1, an earthquake with a magnitude of 2 on the Richter scale is 10 times stronger than an earthquake with a magnitude of 1.

EXAMPLE 1

An earthquake has a magnitude of 5 on the Richter scale. How much stronger is it than an earthquake with a magnitude of 2?

$10^5 = 100{,}000$ and $10^2 = 100$

Since 100,000 is 1,000 times 100, 10^5 is 1,000 times 10^2.

An earthquake with a magnitude of 5 is 1,000 times stronger than an earthquake with a magnitude of 2.

EXAMPLE 2

An earthquake had a magnitude of 3. If the earthquake had been 10,000 times stronger, what would its magnitude have been?

$10^3 = 1{,}000$

$1{,}000 \cdot 10{,}000 = 10{,}000{,}000 = 10^7$

The earthquake would have had a magnitude of 7.

PRACTICE

1. How many times stronger is an earthquake with a magnitude of 3 than an earthquake with a magnitude of 1? **100 times**
2. How many times stronger is an earthquake with a magnitude of 6 than an earthquake with a magnitude of 3? **1,000 times**
3. An earthquake has a magnitude of 2. How many times stronger would the earthquake have to be to have a magnitude of 6? **10,000 times**
4. An earthquake has a magnitude of 3. How many times stronger would the earthquake have to be to have a magnitude of 9? **1,000,000 times**
5. An earthquake had a magnitude of 5. If the earthquake had been 1,000 times stronger, what would its magnitude have been? **8**
6. An earthquake had a magnitude of 4. If the earthquake had been 100,000 times stronger, what would its magnitude have been? **9**

Surface Area to Volume Ratios

A surface area to volume ratio is a ratio that compares the surface area and volume of a solid. You can use the surface area to volume ratio of a solid to find the surface area of the solid if you know its volume, or to find the volume of the solid if you know its surface area.

EXAMPLE 1

Find the surface area to volume ratio of the cube.

5 ft, 5 ft, 5 ft

surface area $= 2\ell w + 2\ell h + 2wh$

$= (2 \cdot 5 \cdot 5) + (2 \cdot 5 \cdot 5) + (2 \cdot 5 \cdot 5)$

$= 150$

volume $= \ell wh$

$= 5 \cdot 5 \cdot 5$

$= 125$

$\frac{\text{surface area}}{\text{volume}} = \frac{150}{125}$

$= \frac{6}{5}$ *Simplify.*

The surface area to volume ratio is $\frac{6}{5}$.

EXAMPLE 2

Find the surface area of a cube that has a volume of 64 cubic units and a surface area to volume ratio of $\frac{3}{2}$.

$\frac{3}{2} = \frac{\text{surface area}}{64}$ *Write a proportion.*

$2 \cdot \text{surface area} = 3 \cdot 64$ *Find the cross products.*

$2(\text{surface area}) = 192$ *Multiply.*

surface area $= 96$ *Divide both sides by 2.*

The surface area of the cube is 96 square units.

PRACTICE

Find the surface area to volume ratio of each solid.

1. 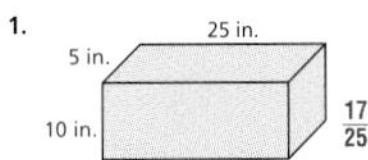

$\frac{17}{25}$

2. 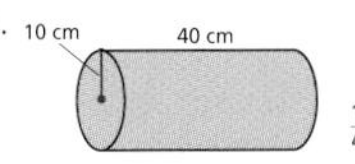

$\frac{1}{4}$

3. Find the surface area of a cylinder that has a volume of 5,001 cubic meters and a surface area to volume ratio of $\frac{1}{3}$. **1,667 m²**
4. Find the volume of a cylinder that has a surface area of 11,781 square feet and a surface area to volume ratio of $\frac{231}{500}$. **25,500 ft³**

Quadratic Relationships

Quadratic relationships involve one squared value related to another value. An example of a quadratic relationship is shown in the equation $a = x^2 + 5$. If you know the value of one variable, you can substitute for it in the equation and then solve to find the second variable.

EXAMPLE

The distance d in feet that an object falls is related to the amount of time t in seconds that it falls. This relationship is given by the equation $d = 16t^2$.

What distance will an object fall in 3 seconds?

$d = 16t^2$ *Write the equation.*
$d = 16 \cdot (3)^2$ *Substitute 3 for t.*
$= 144$ *Simplify.*

The object will fall 144 feet in 3 seconds.

PRACTICE

A small rocket is shot vertically upward from the ground. The distance d in feet between the rocket and the ground as the rocket goes up can be found by using the equation $d = 128t - 16t^2$, where t is the amount of time in seconds that the rocket has been flying upward.

1. How far above the ground is the rocket at 1 second and at 2 seconds? **112 ft, 192 ft**
2. Did the rocket's distance change by the same amount in each of the first 2 seconds? Explain. **No; between 0 and 1 second, the rocket flew 112 feet. Between 1 and 2 seconds, the rocket flew 80 feet.**
3. When the rocket is returning to the ground, the distance that the rocket falls is given by the equation $d = 16t^2$. If the rocket hits the ground 4 seconds after it starts to return, how far up did it go? **256 ft**
4. As the rocket falls to the ground, does it fall the same distance each second? Explain. **No; between 0 and 1 second, the rocket falls 16 feet. Between 1 and 2 seconds, the rocket falls 48 feet.**

The graph for $y = x^2$ is shown at right. Use the graph for problems 5–7.

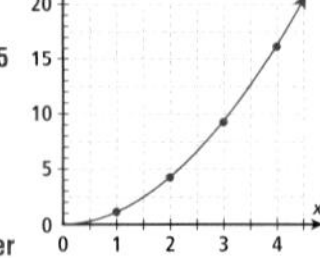

5. Find the value of y for $x = 1, 2, 3, 4$, and 5. **1, 4, 9, 16, 25**
6. Does y increase by the same amount for each value of x? Explain. **No; as x changes by 1, y changes by the square of x.**
7. How would the part of the graph from $x = 5$ to $x = 6$ compare to the part of the graph from $x = 4$ to $x = 5$? **The curve from $x = 5$ to $x = 6$ would be longer and steeper than the curve from $x = 4$ to $x = 5$.**

Skills Bank

Skills Bank 701

Selected Answers

Selected Answers

Chapter 1

1-1 Exercises

1. population: all humpback whales; sample: the pod of humpback whales being studied **2.** population: all seventh-grade students; sample: the 25 students who are asked their ideas **3.** not random **4.** random **5.** population: all wild moose; sample: the 50 moose that are tagged **7.** population: all voters, sample: the voters who are polled **9.** not random **11.** use a sample **13.** survey the population **17. a.** students in grade 7 at your school who watch TV or who use a computer **19.** not random **23.** 88 **25.** 63 **27.** 11 **29.** 7 **31.** B

1-2 Exercises

1. 20; 20; 5 and 20; 30 **2.** 55; 54; 48; 24 **3.** 12; Adding the outlier increases the mean by 1. The median and the mode did not change. **5.** 14; 11; 11; 14 **7.** 151; Adding the outlier increased the mean by 10 and the median by 7.5. The mode did not change because there was no mode. **9.** $791; $1,822; $1,793 **11.** 9; 8; 12 **17.** 100 **19.** 820 **21.** 1,000 **23.** 6,100

1-3 Exercises

1.

Ages of American Presidents		
Age	Frequency	Cumulative Frequency
40–49	3	3
50–59	10	13
60–69	5	18

2. Ages of American Presidents

Stems	Leaves
4	6 8 9
5	0 1 2 4 6 7 7 7 7 8
6	1 1 4 5 8

Key: 5|2 means 52

3.

States with Drive-ins in 2000		
Age	Frequency	Cumulative Frequency
20–29	6	6
30–39	1	7
40–49	1	8
50–59	3	11

5. 4; 31; 27 **7.** b **9.** Chile and Surinam; Brazil

11. 6

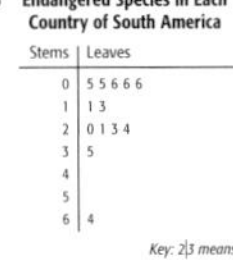

Endangered Species in Each Country of South America

Stems	Leaves
0	5 5 6 6 6
1	1 3
2	0 1 3 4
3	5
4	
5	
6	4

Key: 2|3 means 23

13. 64; Adding the outlier increases the mean by approximately 3.8. **17.** no **19.** yes **21.** J

1-4 Exercises

1. grapes **2.** about 15 pounds

3.

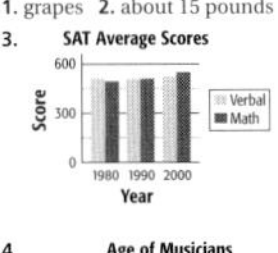

4. Age of Musicians

5. Florida

7.

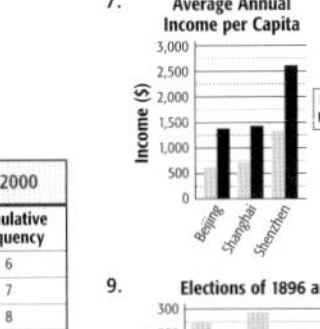

9. Elections of 1896 and 1900

11. about 100

13. President's Years in Office

17. < **19.** 398, 402, 410, 417 **21.** 7°F, 8°F, 14°F, 41°F, 78°F

1-5 Exercises

1. outdoor **2.** 25% **3.** $50,000 **4.** bar graph **5.** circle graph **7.** 30% **9.** circle graph **11.** Asia, Africa, North America, South America, Antarctica, Europe, Australia **13.** about 25% **19.** 62 **21.** 4 **23.** 423

1-6 Exercises

1. 175 in. **2.** 45 in. **3.** $\frac{1}{4}$

4.

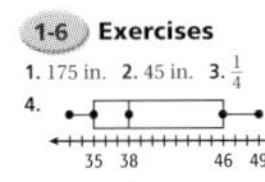

5. $475 **7.** $\frac{1}{2}$

702 Selected Answers

9. a.

b.

11. a. 60 in.

b.

15. 730 **17.** 378 **19.** C

1-7 Exercises

1. 1990–1995 **2.** about $4.90

3.

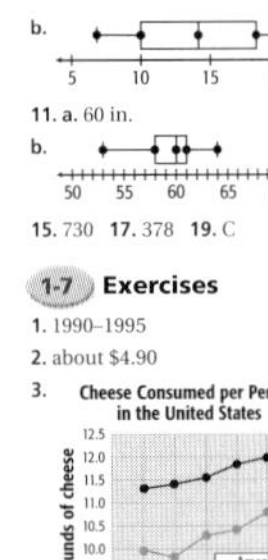

5. 1990–1995

7. Normal Daily Temperature

9. a. 0.9 million **13.** 168 **15.** 44,062 **17.** 5,000 + 40 + 7 **19.** 100,000 + 9,000 + 200 + 40 + 4

1-8 Exercises

1. The heart rate tends to decrease as the size increases. **2.** no correlation **3.** positive correlation **4.** negative correlation **5.** The scatter plot shows that the capacity increases with time, a positive correlation. **7.** negative correlation **9.** negative correlation **11.** positive correlation **13.** As latitude increases, temperature decreases. **17.** 3 **19.** 3 **21.** F

1-9 Exercises

1. graph A **2.** The vertical axis is broken, so differences in weight appear greater. **3.** The vertical axis does not begin with zero, so differences in scale appear greater. **5.** The scale of the graph is not divided into equal intervals, so differences in sales appear less than they actually are.

7. a.

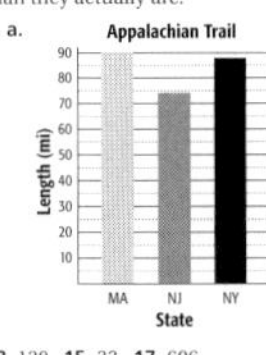

13. 120 **15.** 33 **17.** 606

Chapter 1 Study Guide and Review

1. population; sample **2.** mean **3.** histogram; bar graph **4.** negative correlation **5.** population: the students in the school; sample: the first 5 students **6.** 4; 4; 2 and 5; 8 **7.** 302; 311.5; 233 and 324; 166 **8.** 43; 46; none; 25

9.

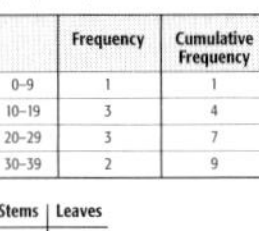

	Frequency	Cumulative Frequency
0–9	1	1
10–19	3	4
20–29	3	7
30–39	2	9

10.

Stems	Leaves
0	8
1	4 6 9
2	5 7 9
3	2 5

Key: 1|4 means 14

11. Favorite Pet

12. yellow **13.** 35 people

14.

15.

16. U.S. Open Winning Scores

17. positive correlation **18.** The temperature did not change that much, though the graph makes the changes look significant.

Chapter 2

2-1 Exercises

1. 32 **2.** 27 **3.** 36 **4.** 1 **5.** 5^2 **6.** 4^2 **7.** 3^3 **8.** 10^2 **9.** 100 times stronger **11.** 243 **13.** 1 **15.** 81 **17.** 5 **19.** 125 **21.** 10,000 **23.** 4^1 **25.** 7^0 **27.** 2^7 **29.** 50^2 **31.** 3^4 = 81 points **33.** 2^4 or 4^2 **35.** 9^3 or 3^6 **37.** 25 **39.** 108 **41.** 126 **43.** 3 **45.** 216 cubic inches **47.** Yuma: 484,152; Phoenix: 9,272,112 **49.** 4, 16, and 64 **53.** a **55.** 4.3 **57.** F

2-2 Exercises

1. 1,500 **2.** 18,000 **3.** 11 **4.** 120,000 **5.** 208,000 **6.** 1,130,000,000 **7.** 472,000 **8.** 362.2 **9.** 3.6×10^6 **10.** 2.14×10^5 **11.** 8.0×10^9 **12.** 4.2×10^4 **13.** 2,000,000,000,000,000,000,000 **15.** 80,000 **17.** 400,000 **19.** 19,000 **21.** 140 **23.** 105 **25.** 216.4 **27.** 1,020 **29.** 700,300 **31.** 1.61×10^6 **33.** 6.01×10^4 **35.** 2.98×10^8 **37.** 5×10^5 **39.** 9.8×10^8 feet per second **41.** 1.68 **43.** 5 **45.** 6.0; 7

Selected Answers 703

47. 2.44; 8 **49.** 1.83×10^8 years

53.

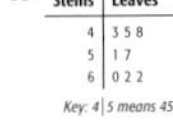

Stems	Leaves
4	3 5 8
5	1 7
6	0 2 2

Key: 4|5 means 45

55. C

2-3 Exercises

1. 47 **2.** 30 **3.** 23 **4.** 7 **5.** 4 **6.** 40 **7.** $280 **9.** 42 **11.** 15 **13.** 73 **15.** 588 **17.** $139 **19.** > **21.** > **23.** = **25.** $4 \cdot (8 - 3) = 20$ **27.** $(12 - 2)^2 \div 5 = 20$ **29.** $(4 + 6 - 3) \div 7 = 1$ **31.** $82 **33. a.** $4 \cdot 15$ **b.** $2 \cdot 30$ **c.** $126 **39.** H

2-4 Exercises

1. 2^4 **2.** $2 \cdot 3^3$ **3.** 3^4 **4.** $3 \cdot 5 \cdot 7$ **5.** $2 \cdot 3^2$ **6.** $2 \cdot 13$ **7.** $3^2 \cdot 5$ **8.** $2^4 \cdot 5$ **9.** $2 \cdot 5^2$ **10.** $2 \cdot 3^2 \cdot 5$ **11.** $2^2 \cdot 5^2$ **12.** $2^2 \cdot 3 \cdot 5$ **13.** $3^2 \cdot 7$ **14.** $2 \cdot 7$ **15.** $2^3 \cdot 5^3$ **16.** $2^2 \cdot 5 \cdot 7$ **17.** $2^2 \cdot 17$ **19.** $2^3 \cdot 3 \cdot 5$ **21.** $3^3 \cdot 5$ **23.** $2 \cdot 7 \cdot 11$ **25.** $2^5 \cdot 5^2$ **27.** 5^4 **29.** $3^2 \cdot 5 \cdot 7$ **31.** $3^3 \cdot 7$ **33.** $2 \cdot 11^2$ **35.** $11 \cdot 17$ **37.** $5^2 \cdot 7^2$ **39.** $2^3 \cdot 3^2 \cdot 5$ **41.** $2^4 \cdot 3^2$ **43.** $2^3 \cdot 5^2$ **45.** $2 \cdot 32$, $4 \cdot 16$, $8 \cdot 8$ **47.** 180 **49.** 448 **51.** 462 **53.** 117 **55.** 210 **57.** the chicken coop and the sheep pen **63.** 5.5 **65.** 23 **67.** 343 **69.** H

2-5 Exercises

1. 6 **2.** 9 **3.** 12 **4.** 3 **5.** 4 **6.** 10 **7.** 12 kits **9.** 12 **11.** 11 **13.** 38 **15.** 2 **17.** 26 **19.** 3 **21.** 1 **23.** 2 **25.** 22 **27.** 40 **29.** 1 **31.** 7 **33.** 3 **35.** 13 **37.** $2^2 \cdot 3 \cdot 11$ **39.** 4 sections

45.

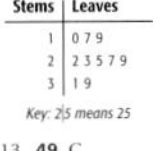

Stems	Leaves
1	0 7 9
2	2 3 5 7 9
3	1 9

Key: 2|5 means 25

47. 13 **49.** C

2-6 Exercises

1. 28 **2.** 84 **3.** 48 **4.** 240 **5.** 45 **6.** 200 **7.** 24 minutes **9.** 24 **11.** 42 **13.** 120 **15.** 80 **17.** 180 **19.** 360 **21.** 60 minutes **23.** 10 **25.** 36 **27.** 108 **29.** 90 **31.** 12 **33.** 144 **35.** 60 **37.** 42 days **39.** no **43.** 1 **45.** 1,000 **47.** $1.0245 \cdot 10^2$ **49.** 769 **51.** D

2-7 Exercises

1. 12 **2.** 11 **3.** 20 **4.** 5 **5.** 8 **6.** 26 **7.** 19 **8.** 16 **9.** 22 **11.** 5 **13.** 11 **15.** 24 **17.** 12 **19.** 41 **21.** 10 **23.** 22 **25.** 24 **27.** 13 **29.** $2 \cdot 5 \cdot c \cdot c \cdot c \cdot d \cdot d$ **31.** $4.50 **33.** 86°F **39.** $3^2 \cdot 11$ **41.** $2^3 \cdot 7$ **43.** C

2-8 Exercises

1. $7p$ **2.** $n - 3$ **3.** $3(n + 5)$ **4.** $5 \div n$ or $\frac{5}{n}$ **5.** $46 + 21m$ **7.** $y - 2$ **9.** $9n$ **11.** $45 \div v$ **13.** $m + 6n$ **15.** $6k - 14$ **17.** $100 \div (6 + w)$ **19–23.** Possible answers given. **19.** h plus 3 **21.** s minus 405 **23.** the difference between 4 times p and 10 **25. a.** $17n$ **b.** $17 \cdot 24d$ **27.** $8m$ **33.** 93 **35.** Possible answer: 8^4 **37.** 43,800,000 **39.** B

2-9 Exercises

1. $6b$ and $\frac{b}{2}$, $5x^2$ and x^2 **2.** $12a^2$ and $4a^2$, $4x^3$ and $3.5x^3$, b and $\frac{5}{6}b$ **3.** $8x$ **4.** $5a^2 + 16$ **5.** There are no like terms. **6.** $10n + 12b$ **7.** b^6 and $3b^6$, $2b$ and b **9.** m and $2m$, 3^3 and 2 **11.** $8a + 2b$ **13.** $12b + 10$ **15.** $18 + 2d^3 + 4d$ **17.** $11a + 4n$ **19.** $27y$ **21.** $2d^2 + d$ **23.** no like terms **25.** no like terms **29.** $4n + 5n + 6n = 15n$; 15, 30, 45, 60, 75 **31. a.** $21.5d + 23d + 15.5d + 19d$; $79d$ **b.** $750.50 **c.** the amount Brad earned in June **37.** 3^5 **39.** 5^3 **41.** 9 **43.** 44

2-10 Exercises

1. no **2.** no **3.** yes **4.** no **5.** 88 cards **6.** $34 **7.** no **9.** no **11.** no **13.** no **15.** 53 video games **17.** no **19.** yes **21.** yes **23.** no **25.** no **27.** Possible answer: $6 - j = 3$ **29.** 318 mi/h **33.** 4 **35.** 142 **37.** $2^3 \cdot 7$ **39.** $2^2 \cdot 3^3$ **41.** C

2-11 Exercises

1. $r = 176$ **2.** $v = 168$ **3.** $x = 88$ **4.** $d = 9$ **5.** $f = 9$ **6.** $m = 971$ **7.** 14 yd **9.** $t = 82$ **11.** $m = 74$ **13.** $w = 43$ **15.** $x = 35$ **17.** $q = 99$ **19.** 2 books **21.** $n = 81$ **23.** $a = 45$ **25.** $f = 1{,}000$ **27.** $s = 159$ **29.** $z = 766$ **31.** $f = 14$ **33.** $m = \$39$ **37.** 262,144 **39.** 1,024 **41.** 14,700 **43.** C

2-12 Exercises

1. $s = 847$ **2.** $b = 100$ **3.** $y = 40$ **4.** $x = 9$ **5.** $c = 32$ **6.** $x = 1$ **7.** 9 people **9.** $k = 1{,}296$ **11.** $c = 175$ **13.** $n = 306$ **15.** $p = 21$ **17.** $a = 2$ **19.** $d = 45$ **21.** $g = 27$ **23.** $r = 12$ **25.** $b = 62$ **27.** $c = 716$ **29.** $d = 42$ **31.** $d = 12$ **33.** $x = \$20$ **35.** 12 toys **37.** $13,300 **41.** 10 **43.** $7x^2 + 6$ **45.** D

Chapter 2 Study Guide and Review

1. exponent; base **2.** numerical expression **3.** composite number **4.** algebraic expression **5.** 81 **6.** 10 **7.** 128 **8.** 1 **9.** 121 **10.** 14,400 **11.** 1,320 **12.** 220,000,000 **13.** 340 **14.** 560,000 **15.** 780 **16.** 3 **17.** 103 **18.** $2 \cdot 2 \cdot 2 \cdot 11$ **19.** $3 \cdot 3 \cdot 3$ **20.** $2 \cdot 3 \cdot 3 \cdot 3 \cdot 3$ **21.** $2 \cdot 2 \cdot 2 \cdot 2 \cdot 2 \cdot 3$ **22.** 30 **23.** 3 **24.** 12 **25.** 220 **26.** 60 **27.** 32 **28.** 27 **29.** 90 **30.** 12 **31.** 315 **32.** 19 **33.** 524 **34.** $4 \div (n + 12)$ **35.** $2(t - 11)$

704 Selected Answers

36. $10b^2 + 8$ **37.** $15a^2 + 2$ **38.** $x^4 + x^3 + 6x^2$ **39.** yes **40.** no **41.** no **42.** $b = 8$ **43.** $n = 32$ **44.** $c = 18$ **45.** $t = 112$ **46.** $n = 72$ **47.** $p = 9$ **48.** $d = 98$ **49.** $x = 13$

Chapter 3

3-1 Exercises

1. **2.** **3.** **4.**

5. −5, −3, −1, 4, 6 **6.** −8, −2, 1, 7, 8 **7.** −6, −4, 0, 1, 3 **8.** 2 **9.** 8 **10.** 7 **11.** 10

13. **15.**

17. −9, −7, −5, −2, 0 **19.** 16 **21.** 20 **23.** < **25.** = **27.** = **29.** > **31.** > **33.** < **35.** 294 **37.** 45 **39.** −32 **41.** −282 **43. a.** baseball **b.** decreased by about 9% **c.** increased by about 27% **45.** second quarter **49.** 64 **51.** 1 **53.** 64 **55.** 256 **57.** 75 **59.** 4 **61.** 585 **63.** 0 **65.** C

3-2 Exercises

1. II **2.** IV **3.** III **4.** I

5–8.

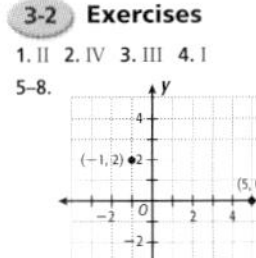

9. (6, −3) **10.** (−3, 2) **11.** (−4, 0) **12.** (5, 0) **13.** I **15.** IV **21.** (−4, 4) **23.** (−5, −4) **25.** (5, 6)

27.

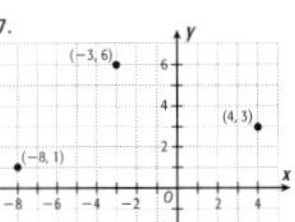

29. triangle; Quadrants I and II **31.** III **33.** II **35. a.** (−68°, 26°) **b.** (−80°, 26°) **c.** (−91°, 32°) **39.** 15 **41.** 87 **43.** C

3-3 Exercises

1. 12 **2.** −6 **3.** −2 **4.** 3 **5.** 15 **6.** −13 **7.** −15 **8.** 11 **9.** −12 **10.** 0 **11.** −20 **12.** −5 yards **13.** −9 **15.** 13 **17.** 7 **19.** −17 **21.** −19 **23.** −16 **25.** −88 **27.** −55 **29.** −14 **31.** −13 **33.** −13 **35.** −15 **37.** 27 **39.** −18 **41.** −29 **43.** = **45.** < **47.** = **49.** 7 **51.** 3 **53.** −9 **55.** 4,150 ft **57.** $4 **61.** 8.39×10^5 **63.** 4.023×10^9 **65.** F

3-4 Exercises

1. −3 **2.** −11 **3.** 6 **4.** −6 **5.** −4 **6.** 5 **7.** −10 **8.** −10 **9.** 7 **10.** −14 **11.** −14 **12.** 47°F **13.** −5 **15.** 8 **17.** 12 **19.** 16 **21.** −17 **23.** 8 **25.** 50 **27.** 18 **29.** 16 **31.** −5 **33.** −20 **35.** 83°F **37.** −14 **39.** −2 **41.** 2 **43.** 16 **45.** 0 **47.** 16 **49.** −27 **51.** −17 **53.** 1,266°F **55.** 531°F **57.** 16,500 ft **59.** 8 **61.** 22 **63.** 0 **65.** B

3-5 Exercises

1. −15 **2.** −10 **3.** −15 **4.** 15 **5.** 10 **6.** 15 **7.** −8 **8.** −6 **9.** 4 **10.** −7 **11.** 3 ft **13.** −10 **15.** 24 **17.** 32 **19.** 7 **21.** −8 **23.** −40 **25.** −3 **27.** 50 **29.** −120 **31.** 90 **33.** 16 **35.** −1 **37.** −24 **39.** 5 **41.** −26 **43.** 10 **45.** −60 ft **47.** The average change was $55 per day. **51.** $2x + 2y$ **53.** $8a^2$ **55.** $2y + 6$ **57.** D

3-6 Exercises

1. $w = 4$ **2.** $x = -12$ **3.** $k = -7$ **4.** $n = -8$ **5.** $y = -30$ **6.** $a = -60$ **7.** This year's loss is $57 million. **9.** $k = -3$ **11.** $v = -4$ **13.** $a = 20$ **15.** $t = -32$ **17.** $n = 150$ **19.** $l = -144$ **21.** $y = 100$ **23.** $j = -63$ **25.** $c = 17$ **27.** $y = -11$ **29.** $w = -41$ **31.** $x = -58$ **33.** $x = 4$ **35.** $t = 9$ **37.** $h = 20$ **39.** 60° **41. a.** $280 **b.** $240 **c.** $15 **43.** oceans or beaches **45.** C **49.** −10, −8, −3, 0, 7 **51.** −3, −1, 0, 2, 4 **53.** −9, −2, −1, 7, 10 **55.** G

3-7 Exercises

1. $-2\frac{1}{4}$ **2.** 3.25 **3.** −1.5 **4.** $\frac{1}{2}$

5. $-\frac{1}{4}$ **6.** $\frac{3}{4}$ **7.** $-\frac{1}{2}$ **8. a.** $-\frac{1}{2}$ in. **b.** 1.75 in.

9.

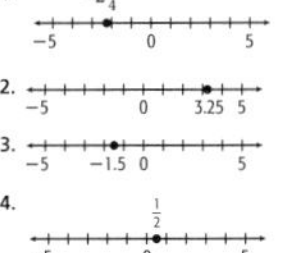

11. −1.1 **13.** **15.** $-\frac{3}{4}$

17. $\frac{5}{4}$ **19.** $-\frac{1}{1}$ **21.** $\frac{0}{1}$ **23. a.** about $\frac{3}{2}$°C **b.** about −3.5°C

25. $-2\frac{1}{2}$, $2\frac{3}{4}$

27–31. Possible answers given. **27.** $-\frac{1}{4}$ **29.** $\frac{3}{4}$ **31.** $\frac{1}{2}$ **37.** 4.5 **39.** 71 **41.** J

Selected Answers 705

3-8 Exercises

1–25. Possible answers given. **1.** $\frac{2}{4}$ **2.** $\frac{12}{20}$ **3.** $\frac{30}{36}$ **4.** $\frac{45}{120}$ **5.** $\frac{24}{72}, \frac{54}{72}$; no **6.** $\frac{5}{6}, \frac{5}{6}$; yes **7.** $\frac{4}{3}, \frac{4}{3}$; yes **8.** $\frac{45}{24}, \frac{38}{24}$; no **9.** $3\frac{3}{4}$ **10.** $4\frac{2}{5}$ **11.** $1\frac{4}{13}$ **12.** $4\frac{2}{3}$ **13.** $\frac{31}{5}$ **14.** $\frac{23}{12}$ **15.** $\frac{38}{5}$ **16.** $\frac{39}{16}$ **17.** $\frac{3}{9}$ **19.** $\frac{9}{10}$ **21.** $\frac{9}{12}$ **23.** $\frac{18}{30}$ **25.** $\frac{1}{2}, \frac{1}{2}$; yes **27–31.** Possible answers given. **27.** $\frac{5}{4}, \frac{5}{4}$; yes **29.** $\frac{2}{3}, \frac{2}{3}$; yes **31.** $\frac{6}{11}, \frac{7}{11}$; no **33.** $6\frac{1}{3}$ **35.** $7\frac{4}{11}$ **37.** $\frac{128}{5}$ **39.** $\frac{29}{3}$ **41–51.** Possible answers given. **41.** $\frac{10}{2}$ **43.** $\frac{52}{8}$ **45.** $\frac{32}{84}$ **47.** $\frac{11}{2}$ **49.** $\frac{202}{2}$ **51.** $\frac{19}{3}$ **53.** $\frac{21}{35}, \frac{3}{5}$ **55.** $\frac{2}{3}, \frac{20}{30}$ **57.** $2\frac{1}{12}$ ft **59.** $30\frac{2}{12}$ or $30\frac{1}{6}$ ft **61.** $80\frac{5}{12}$ ft **63.** $\frac{150}{4}$ **69.** 36 **71.** 100,000 **73.** 4.75×10^5 **75.** 8.8×10^1 **77.** J

3-9 Exercises

1. 0.6 **2.** 2.63 **3.** 1.83 **4.** 0.78 **5.** $\frac{1}{125}$ **6.** $-\frac{3}{5}$ **7.** $-2\frac{1}{20}$ **8.** $3\frac{3}{4}$ **9.** 0.720 **11.** 6.4 **13.** 0.88 **15.** 1 **17.** 1.92 **19.** $\frac{1}{100}$ **21.** $-\frac{2}{25}$ **23.** $\frac{61}{4}$, $15\frac{1}{4}$ **25.** $\frac{67}{8}$, $8\frac{3}{8}$ **27–33.** Possible answers given. **27.** 8.75, $8\frac{6}{8}$ **29.** $5\frac{1}{20}$, $5\frac{5}{100}$ **31.** $15\frac{7}{20}$, $\frac{307}{20}$ **33.** 4.003, $\frac{4{,}003}{1{,}000}$ **35.** yes **37.** no **39.** yes **41.** no **43.** $17\frac{9}{10}$, $18\frac{1}{20}$, $18\frac{1}{25}$, $18\frac{11}{20}$ **47.** 32 **49.** 36 **51.** 9 **53.** 8 **55.** B

3-10 Exercises

1. < **2.** > **3.** < **4.** > **5.** < **6.** > **7.** < **8.** > **9.** 0.505, 0.55, $\frac{3}{4}$ **10.** 2.05, 2.5, $\frac{13}{5}$ **11.** −0.875, $\frac{5}{8}$, 0.877 **13.** > **15.** > **17.** < **19.** < **21.** < **23.** < **25.** < **27.** 1.6, $1\frac{4}{5}$, 1.82 **29.** −3.02, −3, $1\frac{1}{2}$ **31.** $\frac{4}{5}$, 0.82, $\frac{5}{6}$ **33.** $-1\frac{2}{5}$, −1.20, −1.02 **35.** $\frac{3}{4}$ **37.** $\frac{7}{8}$ **39.** 0.32 **41.** $-\frac{7}{8}$ **43.** $\frac{22}{24}$, 0.917 **45.** Saturn, Jupiter and Uranus, Neptune, Pluto, Mars, Venus, Mercury, Earth **51.** 1.08×10^2 **53.** 1×10^7 **55.** $a = 28.4$ **57.** $c = 320$

Chapter 3 Extension

1. terminates **3.** terminates **5.** repeats, $0.\overline{1}$ **7.** repeats, $0.\overline{01}$ **9.** repeats, $0.\overline{142857}$ **11.** repeats, no visible pattern **13.** rational **15.** irrational **17.** rational **19.** rational **21.** irrational **23.** irrational

Chapter 3 Study Guide and Review

1. rational number; integer; terminating decimal **2.** ordered pair; x-axis **3.** −6, −2, 0, 4, 5 **4.** 0 **5.** 17 **6.** 6 **7.** I **8.** III **9.** II **10.** IV **7–10.**

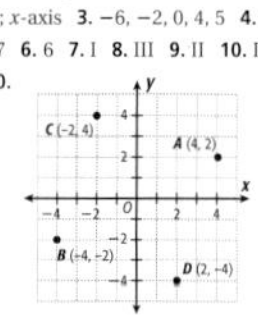

11. −3 **12.** 1 **13.** −56 **14.** 9 **15.** 14 **16.** −6 **17.** 6 **18.** −9 **19.** −1 **20.** −9 **21.** −50 **22.** 3 **23.** 16 **24.** −2 **25.** −12 **26.** −3 **27.** $y = 10$ **28.** $d = 14$ **29.** $j = -26$ **30.** $n = 72$ **31.** $c = 13$ **32.** $m = -4$ **33–35.**

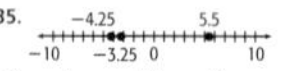

36. $\frac{12}{1}$ **37.** $\frac{1}{4}$ **38.** $-\frac{37}{10}$ **39.** $\frac{21}{5}$ **40.** $\frac{19}{6}$ **41.** $\frac{43}{4}$ **42.** $3\frac{1}{3}$ **43.** $2\frac{1}{2}$ **44.** $2\frac{3}{7}$ **45.** $\frac{1}{4}$ **46.** $-\frac{1}{250}$ **47.** $\frac{1}{20}$ **48.** 3.5 **49.** −0.6 **50.** 0.667 **51.** < **52.** > **53.** >

Chapter 4

4-1 Exercises

1–6. Possible answers given. **1.** 63 **2.** 12 **3.** 2 **4.** 240 **5.** −225 **6.** 7 **7.** no, 36 · 10 = 360 **9.** 92 **11.** 8 **13.** 55 **15–35.** Possible answers given. **15.** 5 **17.** −120 **19.** 9 **21.** −7 **23.** −59 **25.** −90 **27.** −36 **29.** 11 **31.** −98 **33.** 225 **35.** 13 **37.** about 8 weeks **39. a.** English **b.** 36% **41.** yes **45.** −17, −12, −3, 6, 9 **47.** −5, −3, −1, 2, 4 **49.** 10 **51.** −35 **53.** F

4-2 Exercises

1. 21.82 **2.** −18.52 **3.** 12.826 **4.** 1.98 **5.** 9.65 **6.** 1.77 **7.** $37.2 billion **9.** 18.97 **11.** 15.33 **13.** −25.52 **15.** 9.01 **17.** 4.47 **19.** 31.15 **21.** 77.13 g **23.** −4.883 **25.** −125.55 **27.** 30.12 **29.** 661.902 **31.** −3.457 **33.** 0.9 g/mL **39.** 7 **41.** −6 **43.** $w = 19$ **45.** $p = -66$ **47.** F

4-3 Exercises

1. −3.6 **2.** 0.6 **3.** 0.18 **4.** 2.04 **5.** 1.04 **6.** −0.315 **7.** 334.7379 miles **9.** 0.35 **11.** 29.4 **13.** 90.73 **15.** 4.48 **17.** −0.1542 **19.** −40.945 **21.** 5.445 mi **23.** 0.0021 **25.** −0.0876 **27.** 1.911 **29.** −0.7728 **31.** 21.5124 **33.** −83.538 **35.** −6,692.985 **37. a.** about 47 million people **b.** about 60 million people **43.** 35 **45.** −25 **47.** −24 **49.** H

4-4 Exercises

1. 6.14 **2.** 3.06 **3.** −3.09 **4.** −2.56 **5.** 0.017 **6.** 0.234 **7.** $5.54 **9.** −8.9 **11.** −8.92 **13.** −4.8 **15.** 2.04 **17.** 1.13 **19.** −3.07 **21.** $9.75 **23.** 1.56 **25.** 4.19 **27.** −2.8 **29.** −1.91 **31.** −0.019 **33.** 6.49 **35.** 1.44 **37.** −262.113 **39.** 93.295 **41.** 14.53 million people **43.** $72.33 **47.** −5 **49.** 38 **51.** −23 **53.** 31 **55.** A

4-5 Exercises

1. 0.9 **2.** −35 **3.** 4.6 **4.** 5.3 **5.** −3.2 **6.** −12.24 **7.** 2.5 **8.** 35 **9.** −16 **10.** −20 **11.** −4.8 **12.** 22.5 **13.** 28 mi/gal **15.** −0.12 **17.** −14 **19.** 4.2 **21.** 47.5 **23.** 4 **25.** −48.75 **27.** 2.4 min **29.** 22.5

31. −0.4 **33.** 25 **35.** 5.9 **37.** 16 **39.** −5.8 **41.** 253.2 **43.** −27 **45.** 240 days **47.** 202.228 m **51.** $2^3 \cdot 11$ **53.** $3^2 \cdot 5^2$ **55.** −3.328 **57.** 0.4806 **59.** J

4-6 Exercises

1. $w = 7$ **2.** $x = 7.85$ **3.** $k = 24.09$ **4.** $n = 21.25$ **5.** $b = 5.04$ **6.** $x = 5.76$ **7.** $t = 9$ **8.** $y = 1.5$ **9.** $4.25 **11.** $c = 44.56$ **13.** $a = 5.08$ **15.** $p = -53.21$ **17.** $z = 16$ **19.** $w = 11.76$ **21.** $a = -74.305$ **23.** $7.50 **25.** $n = -4.92$ **27.** $r = 0.72$ **29.** $m = -0.15$ **31.** $k = 0.9$ **33.** $t = 0.936$ **35.** $v = -2$ **37.** $n = 12.254$ **39. a.** 148.1 million **b.** between Italian and English **41.** 7.14 g/cm³ **45.** 6 **47.** 141 **49.** −3, $\frac{3}{5}$, 3.5 **51.** −2, $-1\frac{1}{4}$, 1.4 **53.** F

4-7 Exercises

1. $2\frac{1}{2}$ hr **2.** −6 **3.** $\frac{2}{5}$ **4.** $-\frac{1}{6}$ **5.** 14 **6.** $\frac{12}{5}$ or $2\frac{2}{5}$ **7.** $\frac{7}{3}$ or $2\frac{1}{3}$ **9.** $1\frac{2}{3}$ tsp **11.** $\frac{1}{2}$ **13.** 4 **15.** $\frac{1}{4}$ **17.** $-\frac{5}{9}$ **19.** $\frac{222}{5}$ or $44\frac{2}{5}$ **21.** $\frac{35}{2}$ or $17\frac{1}{2}$ **23.** $\frac{7}{3}$ or $2\frac{1}{3}$ **25.** $\frac{33}{4}$ or $8\frac{1}{4}$ **27.** $\frac{155}{42}$ or $3\frac{29}{42}$ **29.** $\frac{1}{3}$ **31.** $-\frac{1}{6}$ **33.** $\frac{1}{12}$ **35.** $\frac{1}{5}$ **37.** $\frac{7}{10}$ **39.** $\frac{1}{5}$ **41.** 1 **43.** 5 **45.** $2\frac{1}{12}$ lb **47.** $11\frac{1}{3}$ mi **53.** 3.43×10^6 **55.** −27 **57.** 60

4-8 Exercises

1. 18 **2.** $\frac{4}{5}$ **3.** $\frac{3}{32}$ **4.** $\frac{1}{4}$ **5.** $\frac{5}{4}$ or $1\frac{1}{4}$ **6.** 2 **7.** 3 capes **9.** 18 **11.** $\frac{32}{9}$ or $3\frac{5}{9}$ **13.** $\frac{3}{20}$ **15.** $\frac{5}{14}$ **17.** $\frac{13}{32}$ **19.** $\frac{77}{24}$ or $3\frac{5}{24}$ **21.** 6 pieces **23.** $\frac{3}{4}$ **25.** $\frac{60}{7}$ or $8\frac{4}{7}$ **27.** $\frac{8}{147}$ **29.** $\frac{16}{25}$ **31.** $\frac{18}{25}$ **33.** $\frac{21}{2}$ or $10\frac{1}{2}$ **35.** $-\frac{4}{9}$ **37.** $34\frac{1}{4}$ mi **39.** 42 side pieces **41.** $11\frac{3}{4}$ hours **45.** $2^6 \cdot 5$ **47.** B

4-9 Exercises

1. about 4 feet **2.** $1\frac{1}{2}$ **3.** 0 **4.** $5\frac{1}{2}$ **5.** exact **6.** estimate **7.** 3 feet **9.** $4\frac{1}{2}$ **11.** $\frac{1}{2}$ **13.** $11\frac{1}{2}$ **15.** exact **17.** $1\frac{1}{2}$ **19.** 4 **21.** 1 **23.** $18\frac{1}{2}$ **25.** 10 **27.** 5 **29.** $10\frac{1}{2}$ miles **35.** $5b + 2a$ **37.** $6z - 5y$ **39.** G

4-10 Exercises

1. $\frac{1}{3}$ **2.** $\frac{1}{6}$ **3.** $\frac{3}{7}$ **4.** $\frac{1}{2}$ **5.** $\frac{3}{20}$ **6.** $\frac{19}{24}$ **7.** $\frac{1}{12}$ **9.** $\frac{1}{2}$ **11.** $\frac{1}{6}$ **13.** $\frac{1}{3}$ **15.** $\frac{1}{4}$ **17.** $\frac{3}{8}$ **19.** $\frac{3}{14}$ **21.** $\frac{1}{6}$ mi **23.** $\frac{13}{18}$ **25.** $\frac{22}{21}$ or $1\frac{1}{21}$ **27.** $\frac{23}{20}$ or $1\frac{3}{20}$ **29.** $-\frac{1}{20}$ **31.** $\frac{9}{56}$ **33.** 0 **35.** 0 **37.** $\frac{3}{8}$ cup **39.** $\frac{3}{8}$ measure **41. a.** $\frac{1}{16}$ lb **b.** 1 oz **47.** 8 **49.** $y = 7$

4-11 Exercises

1. $5\frac{1}{6}$ ft **2.** $7\frac{3}{5}$ **3.** $6\frac{5}{8}$ **4.** $6\frac{1}{3}$ **5.** $1\frac{1}{3}$ **6.** $5\frac{1}{3}$ **7.** $\frac{11}{12}$ **9.** 15 **11.** $5\frac{2}{3}$ **13.** $15\frac{1}{40}$ **15.** $\frac{6}{7}$ **17.** $5\frac{1}{4}$ **19.** $\frac{17}{24}$ **21.** $15\frac{8}{15}$ **23.** $13\frac{5}{6}$ **25.** $29\frac{1}{6}$ **27.** $8\frac{3}{4}$ **29.** $4\frac{1}{6}$ **31.** $4\frac{1}{3}$ **33.** < **35.** > **37.** $\frac{97}{100}$ **39.** the waterfall trail; $\frac{1}{6}$ mi **43.** 5 **45.** −4 **47.** 0.625 **49.** $0.\overline{2}$ **51.** G

4-12 Exercises

1. $a = \frac{3}{4}$ **2.** $m = \frac{2}{3}$ **3.** $p = \frac{3}{2}$ or $1\frac{1}{2}$ **4.** $x = 40$ **5.** $r = \frac{9}{10}$ **6.** $w = \frac{1}{7}$ **7.** $\frac{9}{8}$ c or $1\frac{1}{8}$ c **9.** $t = \frac{5}{8}$ **11.** $x = \frac{53}{24}$ or $2\frac{5}{24}$ **13.** $y = \frac{7}{60}$ **15.** $w = \frac{1}{2}$ **17.** $z = \frac{1}{12}$ **19.** $n = \frac{48}{25}$ or $1\frac{23}{25}$ **21.** $t = \frac{1}{4}$ **23.** $w = 6$ **25.** $x = \frac{3}{5}$ **27.** $n = \frac{12}{5}$ or $2\frac{2}{5}$ **29.** $y = \frac{1}{2}$ **31.** $r = \frac{1}{77}$ **33.** $h = -\frac{1}{12}$ **35.** $v = \frac{3}{4}$ **37.** $d = \frac{577}{40}$ or $14\frac{17}{40}$ **39.** $11\frac{3}{16}$ lb **41.** 15 million species **43.** 48 stories **49.** $2\frac{1}{5}$ **51.** $4\frac{1}{3}$ **53.** $1\frac{4}{7}$

Chapter 4 Study Guide and Review

1. compatible numbers **2.** reciprocals **3.** 110 **4.** 5 **5.** 75 **6.** 4 **7.** 27.88 **8.** −51.2 **9.** 6.22 **10.** 52.902 **11.** 14.095 **12.** 35.88 **13.** 3.5 **14.** −38.7 **15.** 40.495 **16.** 60.282 **17.** 77.348 **18.** −18.81 **19.** 2.3 **20.** −4.9 **21.** 0.08 **22.** −5.8 **23.** −1.65 **24.** 3.4 **25.** 4.5 **26.** −1.09 **27.** −15.4 **28.** −500 **29.** 2 **30.** 4 **31.** $x = -10.44$ **32.** $s = 107$ **33.** $n = 0.007$ **34.** $k = 8.64$ **35.** $7\frac{1}{2}$ **36.** $1\frac{21}{25}$ **37.** $17\frac{17}{63}$ **38.** $6\frac{1}{4}$ **39.** $\frac{4}{75}$ **40.** $\frac{2}{15}$ **41.** 1 **42.** $1\frac{11}{12}$ **43.** 24 **44.** $2\frac{1}{2}$ **45.** −8 **46.** $22\frac{1}{2}$ **47.** 3 **48.** 1 **49.** $\frac{5}{12}$ **50.** $\frac{17}{20}$ **51.** $\frac{5}{11}$ **52.** $\frac{1}{9}$ **53.** $6\frac{5}{24}$ **54.** $3\frac{1}{3}$ **55.** $6\frac{1}{4}$ **56.** $1\frac{5}{12}$ **57.** $1\frac{2}{3}$ **58.** $\frac{1}{15}$ **59.** $1\frac{5}{7}$ **60.** $\frac{13}{28}$

Chapter 5

5-1 Exercises

1. $\frac{10}{3}$, 10 to 3, 10:3 **2.** Possible answer: $\frac{3}{30}$, 3 to 30, 3:30 **3.** $\frac{5 \text{ mi}}{1 \text{ h}}$; 5 miles per hour **4.** $\frac{12 \text{ points}}{1 \text{ game}}$; 12 points per game **5.** the 10-lb box **7.** $\frac{25}{70}$, 25 to 70, 25:70 **9.** $\frac{45}{25}$, 45 to 25, 45:25 **11.** $\frac{\$7}{1 \text{ CD}}$; $7 per CD **13.** Andre **15.** 2:1, $\frac{2}{1}$, 2 to 1; 3:1, $\frac{3}{1}$, 3 to 1; 4:1, $\frac{4}{1}$, 4 to 1; 3:2, $\frac{3}{2}$, 3 to 2; 4:3, $\frac{4}{3}$, 4 to 3 **19.** $c = 15$ **21.** $m = 5$ **23.** Possible answer: $\frac{6}{10}, \frac{9}{15}, \frac{12}{20}$ **25.** Possible answer: $\frac{8}{14}, \frac{12}{21}, \frac{16}{28}$ **27.** $\frac{5}{6}$ **29.** $\frac{1}{2}$

5-2 Exercises

1. yes **2.** no **3.** yes **4.** no **5.** yes **6.** yes **7.** no **8.** yes **9–12.** Possible answers given. **9.** $\frac{1}{3} = \frac{2}{6}$ **10.** $\frac{9}{21} = \frac{3}{7}$ **11.** $\frac{8}{3} = \frac{16}{6}$ **12.** $\frac{10}{4} = \frac{5}{2}$ **13.** no **15.** no **17.** no **19.** no **21–27.** Possible answers given. **21.** $\frac{5}{9} = \frac{10}{18}$ **23.** $\frac{6}{15} = \frac{2}{5}$ **25.** $\frac{11}{13} = \frac{55}{65}$ **27.** $\frac{78}{104} = \frac{39}{52}$ **29.** 3, 8, 24, 15 **31–37.** Possible answers given. **31.** 6 to 14, 9 to 21 **33.** $\frac{10}{24}, \frac{15}{36}$ **35.** 2 to 3, 12 to 18 **37.** 5:2, 20:8 **39. a.** $\frac{1 \text{ can}}{4 \text{ hours}}$ **b.** no **41.** 176 students **47.** $2^3 \cdot 3 \cdot 5$ **49.** $2^4 \cdot 3$ **51.** 2 **53.** 33 **55.** −6 **57.** 5

5-3 Exercises

1. $x = 60$ **2.** $p = 8.75$ **3.** $m = 16.4$ **4.** $t = 21$ **5.** 3 lb **7.** $h = 144$ **9.** $y = 336$ **11.** $t = 36$ **13.** $n = 22.4$ **15.** 227 grams **17–33.** Possible answers given. **17.** $x = 2$; $\frac{4}{30}$ **19.** $w = 18$; $\frac{11}{12}$ **21.** $x = 90$; $\frac{2}{10}$ **23.** $q = 17.4$; $\frac{26.1}{6}$ **25.** $k = 324$; $\frac{1}{4}$ **27.** $j = 16.5$; $\frac{10}{33}$ **29.** $\frac{4}{10} = \frac{6}{15}$ **31.** $\frac{3}{75} = \frac{4}{100}$ **33.** $\frac{5}{6} = \frac{90}{108}$ **35.** 3 hours **37.** 105 oxygen atoms **39.** 3 km **43.** $y = 3$ **45.** $x = 13$ **47.** 15.03 **49.** D

5-4 Exercises

1. 4 lb **2.** 2,000 mL **3.** $\frac{384 \text{ in.}}{1 \text{ s}}$ **4.** $\frac{\$5.25}{1 \text{ yd}}$ **5.** 2,291,030 m **7.** 4 ft **9.** $\frac{\$0.15}{1 \text{ min}}$ **11.** $\frac{1 \text{ ft}}{12 \text{ in.}}$ **13.** $\frac{1 \text{ h}}{60 \text{ min}}$ **15.** 3.5 ft **17.** 2,000 m **19.** 4.5 gallons **21.** 6 minutes faster **23.** 6.8 stone **29.** Possible answer: −540 **31.** $\frac{7}{3}$ or $2\frac{1}{3}$ **33.** $\frac{13}{27}$ **35.** D

5-5 Exercises

1. similar **2.** not similar **3.** similar **4.** not similar **5.** not similar **7.** similar **9.** 4 in. × 6 in., 16 in. × 24 in., 20 in. × 30 in. **11.** not similar **13. a.** similar **b.** not similar **c.** similar **15.** no **21.** 9.13 **23.** $\frac{8 \text{ min}}{1 \text{ mi}}$; 8 minutes per mile **25.** $\frac{2 \text{ c}}{1 \text{ serving}}$; 2 cups per serving

5-6 Exercises

1. $a = 22.5$ cm **2.** $y = 56$ m **3.** 28 ft **4.** 25 ft **5.** $x = 13.5$ in. **7.** 3.9 ft **9.** 36 m **15.** $y = 11$ **17.** $a = 0$ **19.** −30.72 **21.** 0.1035

5-7 Exercises

1. $\frac{1}{14}$ **2.** 67.2 cm tall, 40 cm wide **3.** 129 mi **5.** 135 in. **7.** 16 in. **9.** height: $2\frac{2}{3}$ in., length: $5\frac{3}{4}$ in. **11.** $4\frac{7}{24}$ in. **13.** 0.81 in., or about $\frac{13}{16}$ in. **17.** −1.2, 0.2, $\frac{1}{4}$ **19.** 0.064 **21.** 2.7 **23.** C

Chapter 5 Study Guide and Review

1. similar **2.** ratio; rate or unit rate **3.** scale factor **4.** indirect measurement **5.** $\frac{6}{10}$, 6 to 10, 6:10 **6.** $\frac{10}{16}$, 10 to 16, 10:16 **7.** $\frac{2 \text{ gal}}{1 \text{ min}}$; 2 gallons per minute **8.** $\frac{3.5 \text{ mi}}{1 \text{ min}}$; 3.5 miles per minute **9.** no **10.** no **11.** yes **12.** no **13.** no **14.** yes **15–17.** Possible answers given. **15.** $\frac{10}{12} = \frac{5}{6}$ **16.** $\frac{45}{50} = \frac{9}{10}$ **17.** $\frac{9}{15} = \frac{3}{5}$ **18.** $n = 2$ **19.** $a = 6$ **20.** $b = 4$ **21.** $x = 66$ **22.** $y = 22$ **23.** $k = 100$ **24.** 40 qt **25.** 1.5 gal **26.** 2.2 mi **27.** 45 ft **28.** similar **29.** not similar **30.** $x = 100$ ft **31.** 12.1 in. **32.** 148 mi

Chapter 6

6-1 Exercises

1. $\frac{1}{10}$ **2.** $\frac{9}{20}$ **3.** $\frac{3}{5}$ **4.** $\frac{7}{25}$ **5.** 0.85 **6.** 0.3 **7.** 0.09 **8.** 1.0 **9.** 18% **10.** 40% **11.** 75% **12.** 3% **13.** 40% **14.** 25% **15.** 14% **16.** 12.5% **17.** $\frac{3}{10}$ **19.** $\frac{22}{25}$ **21.** 0.16 **23.** 1.05 **25.** 21% **27.** 8% **29.** 30% **31.** 27.5% **33.** $\frac{2}{25}$, 0.08 **35.** $\frac{1}{40}$, 0.025 **37.** $\frac{3}{400}$, 0.0075 **39.** $\frac{703}{1{,}000}$, 0.703 **41.** 90% **43.** 33.3% **45.** 0.1% **47.** 270% **49.** > **51.** < **53.** $\frac{3}{50}$, 0.06, 6% **55.** 6.8% > 6.2% **59.** 144 **61.** 512 **63.** H

6-2 Exercises

1–4. Possible answers given. **1.** 30 **2.** 40 **3.** 5 **4.** 15 **5.** Yes **6–17.** Possible answers given. **6.** 4 **7.** 8 **8.** 14 **9.** 7.7 **10.** $3.45 **11.** 26 **13.** 70 **15.** 216 **17.** 13 **19.** Betty's Boutique **21–35.** Possible answers given. **21.** 24 **23.** 12 **25.** 12 **27.** 24 **29.** 60 **31.** 3 **33.** 72 **35.** 15 **37.** about 26 oz **39.** about 16 hits **41.** Possible answer: 600 people **47.** 1.2 **49.** 0.375 **51.** H

6-3 Exercises

1. 24 **2.** 152 **3.** 20 **4.** 162 **5.** 8 **6.** 14 **7.** 423 **8.** 30 **9.** 171 students **11.** 11.2 **13.** 3,540 **15.** 0.04 **17.** 18 **19.** 13 **21.** 1.74 **23.** 39.6 **25.** 12.4 **27.** 6 **29.** 4.5 **31.** 11.75 **33.** 5,125 **35.** 80 **37.** 120 **39.** 0.61 **41.** 4.21 **43.** 2.25 grams **45.** 0.98 **51.** $x = 40$ **53.** $b = 1.1$ **55.** $\frac{\$1.75}{1 \text{ card}}$; $1.75 per card **57.** B

6-4 Exercises

1. 25% **2.** 40 **3.** 18% **4.** 200 **5.** 60 **6.** 80% **7.** 50 **8.** 90% **9.** 40% **11.** $33\frac{1}{3}$% **13.** 30 **15.** 100% **17.** 225 **19.** 300% **21.** 22 **23.** $235.00 **25.** 17.6 **27.** 63.2% **29.** 644.4 **31.** 62.5% **33.** 45 pieces **35.** about 700 words **39.** 25 **41.** $5\frac{5}{7}$ **43.** B

6-5 Exercises

1. 28% **2.** 133.3% **3.** 16.1% **4.** 242.9% **5.** $8.60; $34.39 **6.** $24.75 **7.** 37.5% **9.** 366.7% **11.** 22.2% **13.** $9.75, $55.25 **15.** $199.75 **17.** 100% **19.** 43.6% **21.** 30 **23. a.** $41,500 **b.** $17,845 **c.** 80.7% **25. a.** about 22,134 trillion Btu **b.** about 8,506 trillion Btu **27.** 64 pt **29.** 40 yd **31.** $\frac{1}{50}$ **33.** $\frac{12}{25}$

6-6 Exercises

1. $I = \$24$ **2.** $I = \$10$ **3.** $P = \$400$ **4.** $r = 3\%$ **5.** just over 4 years **7.** $I = \$3{,}240$ **9.** $P = \$2{,}200$ **11.** $r = 11\%$ **13.** almost 9 years **15.** $5,200 **17.** $212.75 **19.** 20 years **21.** $416.16 **25.** 5% **27.** 14% **29.** A

Chapter 6 Study Guide and Review

1. interest; simple interest; principal **2.** percent of increase **3.** percent of decrease **4.** percent **5.** 0.78 **6.** 0.4 **7.** 0.05 **8.** 1.19 **9.** 60% **10.** 16.7% **11.** 66.7% **12.** 8% **13–18.** Possible answers given. **13.** 8 **14.** 24 **15.** 40 **16.** 90 **17.** 32 **18.** 3 **19.** 68 **20.** 24 **21.** 4.41 **22.** 120 **23.** 27.3 **24.** 54 **25.** 125 **26.** 8% **27.** 12 **28.** 37.5% **29.** 8 **30.** 27.8% **31.** 50% **32.** 14.3% **33.** 30% **34.** 83.1% **35.** 23.1% **36.** 75% **37.** discount: $36.75; sale price: $208.25 **38.** $I = \$15$ **39.** $t = 3$ years **40.** $I = \$243$ **41.** $r = 3.9\%$ **42.** $P = \$2{,}300$ **43.** 7 years

Chapter 7

7-1 Exercises

1–5. Possible answers given: **1.** Q, R, S **2.** $\overrightarrow{QS}, \overrightarrow{RT}$ **3.** QRS **4.** $\overrightarrow{UQ}, \overrightarrow{UT}, \overrightarrow{US}$ **5.** $\overline{QU}, \overline{RU}, \overline{SU}$ **6.** $\overline{BA}$ and $\overline{BC}$, $\overline{AE}$ and $\overline{CE}$, $\overline{AD}$ and $\overline{CD}$ **7.** D, E, F **9.** DEF **11.** $\overline{DE}, \overline{EF}, \overline{DF}$ **21.** $\frac{7}{100}$ **23.** $\frac{31}{50}$ **25.** 4.5 **27.** C

7-2 Exercises

1. 60° **2.** 30° **3.** 120° **4.** 180° **5.** right angle **6.** acute angle **7.** straight angle **8.** ∠MNL and ∠ONP, ∠ONP and ∠PNQ **9.** Possible answer: ∠PNQ and ∠MNP, ∠LNQ and ∠PNQ **11.** 70° **13.** 120° **15.** right angle **17.** ∠BAC and ∠GAF; ∠EAF and ∠GAF **19.** supplementary; 152° **21.** supplementary; 46° **23. a.** right angles **b.** about 39°N, 77°W **27.** 70% **29.** 145% **31.** 57.1% **33.** 46.7%

7-3 Exercises

1. parallel **2.** skew **3.** perpendicular **4.** 115° **5.** 115° **6.** 65° **7.** skew **9.** parallel **11.** 150° **13.** parallel **15.** perpendicular **17.** 45° **19. a.** parallel **b.** skew **c.** perpendicular **d.** none **23.** $33 **25.** $45

7-4 Exercises

1. $\overline{OQ}, \overline{OR}, \overline{OS}, \overline{OT}$ **2.** $\overline{RT}$ **3.** $\overline{RT}, \overline{RS}, \overline{ST}, \overline{TQ}$ **4.** 36° **5.** $\overline{CA}, \overline{CB}, \overline{CD}, \overline{CE}, \overline{CF}$ **7.** $\overline{GB}, \overline{BF}, \overline{DE}, \overline{FE}, \overline{AE}$ **9.** 10 cm **11.** 72° **13. a.** 133.2° **b.** 122.4° **17.** $w = 19.3$ **19.** $y = 1.96$ **21.** acute **23.** straight **25.** A

7-5 Exercises

1. no **2.** yes **3.** no **4.** octagon **5.** quadrilateral **6.** nonagon **7.** square; yes **8.** rectangle; no **9.** triangle; no **11.** no **13.** pentagon **15.** heptagon **17.** pentagon; no **21.** 16-gon **25.** 65° **27.** 24° **29.** 45° **31.** B

7-6 Exercises

1. isosceles right **2.** scalene obtuse **3.** isosceles acute **4.** 2 isosceles right; 1 isosceles acute; 2 scalene obtuse **5.** scalene right **7.** equilateral acute **9.** isosceles **11.** equilateral **13.** equilateral **15.** acute **17.** right **19.** right **21.** 8 in., isosceles **23.** scalene **29.** 384 **31.** 0.56 **33.** $h = 6$ **35.** $m = 10$

7-7 Exercises

1. parallelogram **2.** parallelogram, rectangle **3.** parallelogram, rhombus **4.** False **5.** True **7.** parallelogram **9.** parallelogram; rhombus **11.** parallelogram; rectangle **13.** False **15.** False **17.** parallelogram, rectangle, rhombus, square **19.** parallelogram, rhombus, rectangle, square **21.** 1 triangle, 1 pentagon, 2 trapezoids **23.** parallelogram, rhombus, square, rectangle, trapezoid, right triangle **27.** 16 **29.** 5 **31.** −3 **33.** −5 **35.** A

7-8 Exercises

1. 77° **2.** 110° **3.** 55° **4.** 720° **5.** 540° **6.** 360° **7.** 60° **9.** 32° **11.** 1,080° **13.** 23° **15.** 60° **17.** no **19. a.** 540° **b.** 108° **21.** 51° and 102° **27.** about 5 lb **29.** 7.88 **31.** 445.885

7-9 Exercises

1. The triangles on the gameboard are congruent; the holes on the gameboard are congruent. **2.** no congruent figures **3.** bowling pins are congruent **4.** yes **5.** no **6.** 90° **7.** 2.5 **9.** The triangles on the kite design are congruent. **11.** no **13.** 80°; 8 cm **15.** the lengths of all the sides **17.** the length of adjacent sides in each rectangle **21.** the squares and triangles **25.** 8.0 **27.** 1.2 **29.** 70% **31.** 50

7-10 Exercises

1. reflection **2.** translation **3.**

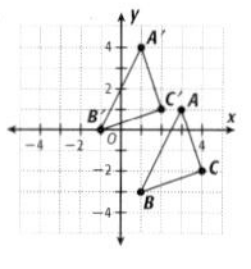

4.

5.

7. rotation

9.

11. Rotation is shown, but not translation or reflection. 15. none 17. $y = 24$ 19. A

7-11 Exercises

1. 5 lines 2. 2 lines 3. 4 lines 4. horizontal line through center of flag 5. none 6. vertical line through center of flag 7. 6 times 8. 2 times 9. 3 times 11. 6 lines 13. none 15. horizontal and vertical lines through center of flag 17. 8 times 21. 1 line 23. a. 4 times b. none 27. $\frac{3}{4}$ 29. 1 31. $x = 18$ 33. $m = \frac{1}{9}$

Chapter 7 Study Guide and Review

1. acute isosceles 2. parallel lines 3. D, E, F 4. $\overrightarrow{DF}$ 5. plane DEF 6. $\overrightarrow{ED}, \overrightarrow{FD}, \overrightarrow{DF}$ 7. $\overline{DE}, \overline{DF}, \overline{EF}$ 8. acute 9. straight 10. skew

11. $\overline{HF}, \overline{FI}, \overline{FG}$ 12. $\overline{GI}$ 13. $\overline{HI}, \overline{GI}, \overline{GJ}, \overline{JI}$ 14. a regular polygon (square) 15. not a regular polygon 16. equilateral acute 17. scalene right 18. parallelogram; rhombus 19. parallelogram; rectangle 20. 53° 21. 133° 22.

23. 1 line of symmetry

Chapter 8

8-1 Exercises

1. 576 hr 2. 7.5 min 3. 20 qt 4. 10 hr 5. 3.7 g 6. 10,000 cm 7. 42,240 ft 8. 4.5 lb 9. 6 gallon containers 11. 2,700 s 13. 498 min 15. 1,000 lb 17. 2.17 m 19. 2.5 gal 21. 25 ft 23. 2,880 tributes 25. 4 lb 27. 3,520 yd 29. 1,600 mm 31. > 33. = 35. > 37. 2.4 mi 39. 2,200 mL 41. about 69,000 mi 47. 1.82 49. 18.15 51. H

8-2 Exercises

1. 4 ft 2. 21 mm 3. $5\frac{1}{4}$ in. 4. 4 5. 1 6. 2 7. 12 8. 4.2 9. 7 10. 180 11. 25 12. 6.3 13. 11 in. 15. 14.2 km 17. 2.8 m 19. 1 21. 6 23. 3 25. 15.1 27. 1 29. 18.0 31. 1,800 33. 2.3 35. 300 37. foot 39. milliliter 41. 180,000 43. 280 45. 21.8 47. 2 49. 2,400 mg 53. $\frac{31}{4}$ 55. $\frac{52}{5}$ 57. $m = 3.2$ 59. $n = 24.21$ 61. H

8-3 Exercises

1. 18 m 2. 24 in. 3. 32 ft 4. 36 in. 5. 20 m 6. 12 ft 7. 37.7 m 8. 9.4 ft 9. 50.2 in. 10. 440 ft 11. 48 cm 13. 44 m 15. 8 ft 17. 25.1 cm 19. 32.0 in. 21. 2.8 m; 5.7 m 23. 5.3 in.; 33.3 in. 25. 1.98 m 27. 141 mi 29. 96 ft 33. −12 35. 54 37. 24.5 39. 12

8-4 Exercises

1. 33.6 ft² 2. 21 m² 3. 147.6 cm² 4. 48 in² 5. $11\frac{1}{5}$ cm² 6. 28.6 m² 7. 40 tiles 9. $131\frac{3}{4}$ in² 11. 6 m² 13. 31.98 cm² 15. 72 yd² 17. 192 cm² 19. 14 units² 21. 18 units² 23. 6 in. 25. a. 713 in² b. 108 in. c. 1,073 in² 31. $d = 8$ 33. $b = -4$ 35. 43.2 37. 34.5

8-5 Exercises

1. 28 units² 2. 12 units² 3. 39.2 units² 4. 6.5 cm² 5. 64 m² 6. 54 ft² 7. 45 units² 9. 72 units² 11. 105 in² 13. 4.5 cm 15. 22 in. 17. 15 units² 19. 12 units² 21. 3 m 23. 108,000 mi² 25. a. 6,800 mi² b. 181.7 29. prime 31. prime 33. 0.6 35. 1.5

8-6 Exercises

1. 78.5 in² 2. 201.0 cm² 3. 314 yd² 4. 154 in² 5. 17,662.5 mi² 7. 803.8 ft² 9. 63.6 ft² 11. 3.8 m² 13. 50.2 ft² 15. 44.0 m; 153.9 m² 17. 75.4 ft; 452.2 ft² 19. 40.2 cm; 128.6 cm² 21. $r = 6$ cm 23. $r = 3$ in. 25. a. 113 mi² b. 141 mi² 31. 125 33. 243 35. −11 37. −18

8-7 Exercises

1. 16 2. 2.25 3. 81 4. 36 5. 4 6. 7 7. 9 8. 8 9. 11 mi 11. 64 13. 20.25 15. 6 17. 10 19. 13 21. 15 23. 32 cm 25. $\frac{9}{64}$ 27. $\frac{1}{9}$ 29. 20 31. 39 33. 12 35. 1

37. 192 39. 28 in. 41. The window with the perimeter of 48 in. is larger. 43. 12 ft 49. 28.3 cm 51. 31.4 m 53. 108 m² 55. A

8-8 Exercises

1. 20 m 2. 8 ft 3. about 8.7 ft 5. 24 cm 7. 16 in. 9. 9.4 11. 12.4 13. yes 15. a. 110 m b. 155.6 m 17. 208.5 m 21. 12 in. 23. 22 ft 25. 13 27. C

Chapter 8 Extension

1. 224 ft² 3. 38 ft² 5. 117 ft²

Chapter 8 Study Guide and Review

1. hypotenuse 2. circumference 3. precision 4. square root 5. 13 6. 3.4 7. 288 8. 458,000 9. 3 significant digits 10. 5 significant digits 11. 1 significant digit 12. 2 significant digits 13. 4 significant digits 14. 4 significant digits 15. 83 m 16. 81.4 cm 17. 40.8 ft 18. 49.0 in. 19. 50.74 cm² 20. 826.2 yd² 21. 266 in² 22. 108.75 cm² 23. 50 yd² 24. 2,163 in² 25. 36.3 m² 26. 226.9 ft² 27. 5 28. 10 29. 10 30. 12 31. 16 ft 32. 34 cm 33. 60 ft 34. 2 m 35. 60 mm

Chapter 9

9-1 Exercises

1. 1 rectangular base; rectangular pyramid 2. 2 octagonal bases; octagonal prism 3. 2 triangular bases; triangular prism 4. cylinder and cone 5. cube and triangular prism 6. hemispheres 7. 1 triangular base; triangular pyramid 9. 1 hexagonal base; hexagonal pyramid 11. 2 triangular prisms 13. cube 15. triangular pyramid 17. rectangular pyramid 19. cylinder 21. 1.06 23. 3.17 25. 1 27. 2 29. A

9-2 Exercises

1. 24 cubes; 24 cubic units 2. 45 cubes; 45 cubic units 3. 80 cubes; 80 cubic units 4. 15 in³ 5. 118.1 cm³ 6. 88.2 m³ 7. 66.4 ft³ 8. 706.5 ft³ 9. 166.4 cm³ 11. 60 cubes; 60 cubic units 13. 1,299.2 ft³ 15. 270 in³ 17. 243.0 cm³ 19. 2,198 m³ 21. 120 ft³ 23. 288 m³ 25. 41.5 m³ 31. 0.6 33. 0.3125 35. $640

9-3 Exercises

1. 10 ft³ 2. 35 cm³ 3. 32 m³ 4. 376.8 ft³ 5. 16.7 in³ 6. 235.5 m³ 7. 904.3 cm³ 8. 7,234.6 in³ 9. 3,367.6 m³ 11. 45 ft³ 13. 47.1 in³ 15. 3,768.0 m³ 17. 950.3 cm³ 19. 46.7 ft³ 21. 65.4 m³ 23. 60 ft³ 27. $a = 10$ 29. $b = 7$ 31. 115° 33. B

9-4 Exercises

1. 286 ft² 2. 856 cm² 3. 244.9 m² 4. 1,884.0 in² 5. 50.2 yd² 6. 1,017.4 ft² 7. 928 in² 9. 791.3 in² 11. 314.0 ft² 13. 38.4 ft² 15. b. 158.0 cm² c. 85.4 cm² 21. 5 and 6 23. 0 and −1 25. −7.06

9-5 Exercises

1. 93.6 cm² 2. 0.5 m² 3. 33,750 in³ 4. 486 lb 5. 223.84 in² 7. 8.2 cm³ 9. 58,750 ft²; 937,500 ft³ 11. 1,130,400 cm²; 113,040,000 cm³ 13. 259.8 cm or 2.598 m; 53.3 cm or 0.533 m 15. 41,567,500 cm²; 4,156.75 m² 19. no 21. no 23. $\frac{3}{5}$ 25. $\frac{9}{50}$

Chapter 9 Extension

1. 448 cm² 3. 208 cm²

Chapter 9 Study Guide and Review

1. cylinder 2. surface area 3. bases of a prism 4. cone 5. triangular prism 6. rectangular pyramid 7. 364 cm³ 8. 415.4 mm³ 9. 111.9 ft³ 10. 60 in³ 11. 471 cm³ 12. 50.9 mm³ 13. 677.7 in³ 14. 250 m² 15. 262.3 cm² 16. 254.3 ft² 17. 143,799.4 m² 18. 2,970 in² 19. 4.1 ft²

Chapter 10

10-1 Exercises

1. purple 2. equally likely 3. likely 4. impossible 5. Tim will likely be at the theater. 7. black 9. unlikely 11. purple 13. unlikely 17. 50% 19. B

10-2 Exercises

1. $\frac{3}{5}$ 2. a. $\frac{13}{15}$ b. $\frac{2}{15}$ 3. $\frac{13}{30}$ 5. a. $\frac{9}{14}$ b. $\frac{5}{14}$ 7. $\frac{2}{5}$ 9. a. 9.1 in. b. 0 c. $\frac{1}{5}$ 11. a. $\frac{3}{8}$ b. 0 13. 1 15. 5 17. B

10-3 Exercises

1. There are 4 possible outcomes in the sample space. 2. There are 20 possible outcomes in the sample space. 3. 24 possible outcomes 5. There are 8 possible outcomes in the sample space. 7. There are 12 possible outcomes in the sample space. 9. 6 different ways 11. a. 9 outcomes b. 6 outcomes c. 12 outcomes 17. 75% 19. 30% 21. H

10-4 Exercises

1. $\frac{1}{6}$, 0.17, 17% 2. $\frac{1}{4}$, 0.25, 25% 3. a. $\frac{3}{7}$ b. $\frac{2}{7}$ c. $\frac{2}{7}$ 5. $\frac{1}{4}$, 0.25, 25% 7. a. $\frac{3}{7}$ b. $\frac{4}{7}$ 9. a. 64% b. 25% 13. $n = -21$ 15. $s = -41$ 17. B

10-5 Exercises

1. independent 2. dependent 3. $\frac{1}{6}$ 4. $\frac{1}{60}$ 5. $\frac{3}{20}$ 7. independent 9. $\frac{1}{4}$ 11. dependent; $\frac{3}{14}$ 13. $\frac{16}{25}$ 19. 3 21. 15

10-6 Exercises

1. 6 2. 10 3. 10 4. 15 5. 10 7. 20 9. 21 11. 6 13. a. 3 b. $\frac{1}{3}$ 15. a. 15 b. $\frac{1}{3}$ 17. 5 19. 201.0 cm² 21. 78.5 in² 23. cone 25. pentagonal prism

10-7 Exercises

1. a. 24 b. $\frac{1}{4}$ 2. a. 120 b. $\frac{1}{120}$ 3. 720 4. 5,040 5. a. 6 b. $\frac{1}{3}$ 7. 362,880 9. combinations 11. permutations 13. 5,040 15. 40,320 different orders 17. 3,628,800 21. 141.3 m³ 23. 58.5 cm³ 25. C

Chapter 10 Extension

1. 3:4 3. 1:6 5. 2:1 7. 1:2 9. 5:3 11. 1:7 13. 1:1 15. a. 5:21 b. 21:5 17. a. 2:3 b. 3:2

Chapter 10 Study Guide and Review

1. independent events 2. combination 3. sample space 4. outcome 5. likely 6. unlikely 7. impossible 8. $\frac{2}{3}$ 9. $\frac{1}{3}$ 10. R1, R2, R3, R4, W1, W2, W3, W4, B1, B2, B3, B4 11. 12 possible outcomes 12. $\frac{3}{7}$, 0.43, 43% 13. $\frac{1}{8}$, 0.125, 12.5% 14. $\frac{4}{195}$ 15. $\frac{16}{121}$ 16. 10 ways 17. 35 committees 18. 84 combinations 19. 3,628,800 ways 20. 720 ways 21. 120 ways

Chapter 11

11-1 Exercises

1. $n = 7$ 2. $m = -6$ 3. $x = \frac{1}{3}$ 4. $b = 24$ 5. $y = 136$ 6. $n = 72$ 7. 12 refills 9. $p = -12$ 11. $d = \frac{1}{7}$ 13. $y = 5$ 15. $k = 85$ 17. $m = -80$ 19. $m = -112$ 21. 6 more than a number divided by 3 equals 18; $m = 36$ 23. 4 less than a number divided by 5 equals 2; $n = 30$ 25. $x = 2$ 27. $g = 20$ 29. $w = -9$ 31. $p = 2$ 33. 120 minutes 35. 2,200 calories 37. 24 grams 39. 8 41. G

11-2 Exercises

1. $n = 5$ 2. $x = 9$ 3. $p = 2$ 4. $m = 42$ 5. $y = 9$ 6. $m = \frac{1}{2}$ 7. 12 books 9. $x = \frac{7}{8}$ 11. $n = 6$ 13. $x = -2$ 15. $n = 9$ 17. $r = 122$ 19. $t = -3$ 21. $x = 66$ 23. $w = 8$ 25. $a = 176$ 27. $b = -7$ 29. $x = 3$ 31. $6.70 33. a. 1,063.$\bar{3}$°C b. −257.$\bar{8}$°C 39. $y = \frac{1}{33}$ 41. $n = -\frac{5}{6}$ 43. 40,320 45. F

11-3 Exercises

1. $n = 32$ 2. $-28 = 10x$ 3. $12w = 32$ 4. $y = 20$ 5. $a = 2$ 6. $d = 28$ 7. 5 movies 9. $-8 = 12p$ 11. $-6 = 2c$ 13. $6 = \frac{1}{10}a$ 15. $b = -8$ 17. $a = -0.8$ 19. $c = -2$ 21. $y = -7$ 23. $r = 4$ 25. $r = -2$ 27. 67 29. $s = 11$ 31. a. 194 mi per day b. 1,164 mi 35. Possible answer: 30 37. Possible answer: 9 39. 288 in. 41. 16 c 43. H

11-4 Exercises

1. number of people ≤18 2. number of fish < 8 3. water level > 45 4. 5. 6. 7. 8. 9. 10. 11. temperature < 40 13. number of tables ≤ 35 15. 17. 19. 21. 23. 25. 27. $-2 < c < 3$ 29. $-3 < x < 1$ 31. 0 ≤ depth ≤ −200 33. 0 ≥ *Manshu* depth measurement ≥ −32,190 ft; 0 ≥ *Challenger* depth measurement ≥ −35,640 ft; 0 ≥ *Horizon* depth measurement ≥ −34,884 ft; 0 ≥ *Vityaz* depth measurement ≥ −36,200 ft 37. $\frac{1}{2}$, 0.5, 50% 39. $\frac{1}{3}$, 0.33, 33% 41. G

11-5 Exercises

1. $x < 27$ 2. $y \geq 4$ 3. $p \leq 7$ 4. $n > 21$ 5. $b \leq -24$ 6. $k \geq -3$ 7. at most 12°F warmer 9. $m < 11$ 11. $c \leq 11$ 13. $x \geq 80$ 15. $z > -12$ 17. $f > -6$ 19. $n \geq -4$ 21. at most 24 birds 23. $a > 0.3$ 25. $m \leq -38$ 27. $g < 6\frac{1}{3}$ 29. $w \leq 15.7$ 31. $t \geq -242$ 33. $v \leq -0.6$ 35. at least 0.5 meters 37. at least 22 miles 39. more than 12.4 km/h 43. 144 in² 45. 1,600 in² 47. J

11-6 Exercises

1. $w < -32$ 2. $z \leq -42$ 3. $p < 48$ 4. $m > -5$ 5. $y > -\frac{11}{8}$ or $-1\frac{3}{8}$ 6. $c \leq 8$ 7. at least 27 candles 9. $m > 52$ 11. $c \geq -120$ 13. $x \geq -1.1$ 15. $z < \frac{3}{5}$ 17. $f < -3$ 19. $n \leq -10$ 21. at least 46 wreaths 23. $p > 4$ 25. $y \geq 18$ 27. $g > 0.63$ 29. $w \leq \frac{3}{8}$ 31. $t < \frac{5}{2}$ 33. $v \geq -2.5$ 35. a. more than 218,500 b. fewer than 655,500 37. 10 days 41. $x = 11$ 43. $r = 6$ 45. B

11-7 Exercises

1. $x < 3$ 2. $z \leq -294$ 3. $y \geq 6$ 4. $m > -4$ 5. $p \leq -5$ 6. $n < -24$ 7. more than $26 each 9. $b < 12$ 11. $c \geq -3$ 13. $x \leq -27$ 15. $j \leq 2$ 17. at most 6 bagels 19. $y > -3$ 21. $a \leq -54$ 23. $n > -5$ 25. $b < -1.6$ 27. $k \geq -5$ 29. $t > -3$ 31. at least 155 prizes 33. at least $5,000 35. at most 60% 39. 24 41. $x = -15$ 43. $n = 4$

Chapter 11 Study Guide and Review

1. inequality 2. compound inequality 3. solution set 4. $y = 8$ 5. $z = 30$ 6. $w = 147$ 7. $a = -7$ 8. $b = 4$ 9. $j = 9$ 10. $y = 5$ 11. $x = 12$ 12. $b = \frac{1}{2}$ 13. $c = 6$ 14. $m = \frac{8}{3}$ or $2\frac{2}{3}$ 15. $x = 20$ 16. average ≥ 65 17. weight limit ≤ 9 tons 18. age > 200 19. distance < 2 mi 20. $r > 25$ 21. $s \geq 14$ 22. $x \leq -26$ 23. $g < 8$ 24. $t \leq \frac{1}{6}$ 25. $9 > r$ 26. $z < -30$ 27. $u \geq -66$ 28. $n < -55.2$ 29. $x \leq 6$ 30. $p \leq 6$ 31. $k < -130$ 32. $p < 5$ 33. $v \geq 2.76$ 34. $c > 33$ 35. $y \leq 2.7$ 36. $b < -2$ 37. $d < -6$ 38. $n \geq -4$ 39. $y \leq 18$ 40. $c > -54$ 41. $x \leq 10$ 42. $m > -5$ 43. $h \geq -156$ 44. $-10 < t$ 45. $52 < w$ 46. $y \leq 35$

Chapter 12

12-1 Exercises

1. −5, 1, 3 2. 5, 3, 1 3. 50, 2, 18

4.

5.

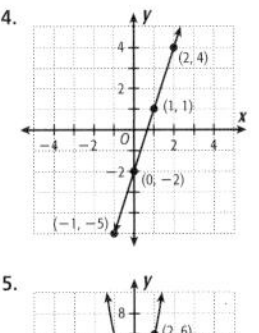

7. −7, −1, 8

9.

11.

Input	Rule	Output
C	$\frac{9}{5}C + 32$	F
−20°	$\frac{9}{5}(-20) + 32$	−4°
−5°	$\frac{9}{5}(-5) + 32$	23°
0°	$\frac{9}{5}(0) + 32$	32°
20°	$\frac{9}{5}(20) + 32$	68°
100°	$\frac{9}{5}(100) + 32$	212°

13.

19. $\frac{1}{3}$ 21. $x = 3$ 23. $x = 5.5$

12-2 Exercises

1. $y = 3n$; 15, 18, 21 2. $y = n + 2$; 7, 8, 9 3. $y = n - 1$; 4, 5, 6 4. $y = 5n$; 25, 30, 35 5. 23 mi, 26 mi, 29 mi, 32 mi, 35 mi 7. $y = \frac{n}{2}$; $\frac{5}{2}$, 3, $\frac{7}{2}$ 9. $y = n - 3$; 2, 3, 4 11. $y = 2n + 1$; 11, 13, 15 13. $y = n^2$; 25, 36, 49 15. $52.50, $55.00, $57.50, $60.00, $62.50, $65.00 17. 4.7, 5.7, 6.7 19. 3, 4, 5 21. 26, 31, 36 23. $y = 2n - 2$; 18 25. $y = 5n - 2$; 48 27. $y = 4n + 2$; 42 29. $y = 2^n$ 33. 8

12-3 Exercises

1. a

2.

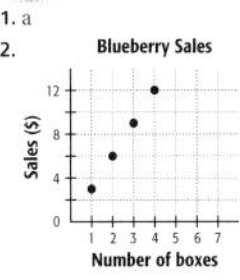

3. D: $-1 \leq x \leq 3$; R: $0 \leq y \leq 2$ 4. D: $-4 \leq x \leq -1$; R: $-3 \leq y \leq -1$ 5. D: $1 \leq x \leq 5$; R: $0 \leq y \leq 3$

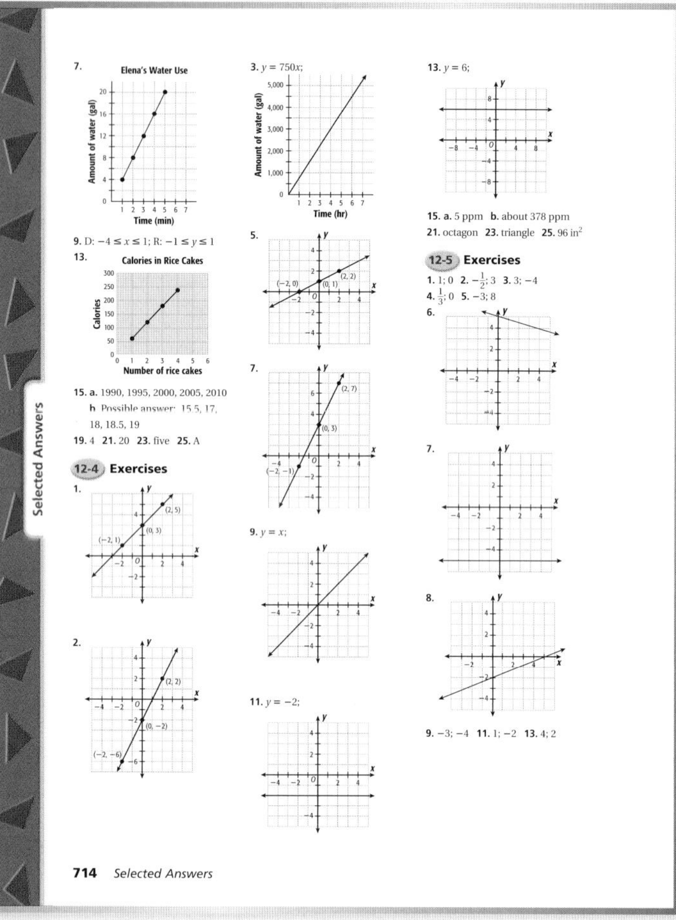

7. Elena's Water Use

9. D: $-4 \le x \le 1$; R: $-1 \le y \le 1$

13. Calories in Rice Cakes

15. a. 1990, 1995, 2000, 2005, 2010 b. Possible answer: 15.5, 17, 18, 18.5, 19

19. 4 21. 20 23. five 25. A

12-4 Exercises

1. 2.

3. $y = 750x$;

5. 7.

9. $y = x$;

11. $y = -2$;

13. $y = 6$;

15. a. 5 ppm b. about 378 ppm

21. octagon 23. triangle 25. 96 in^2

12-5 Exercises

1. 1; 0 2. $-\frac{1}{2}$; 3 3. 3; −4 4. $\frac{1}{3}$; 0 5. −3; 8

6. 7. 8.

9. −3; −4 11. 1; −2 13. 4; 2

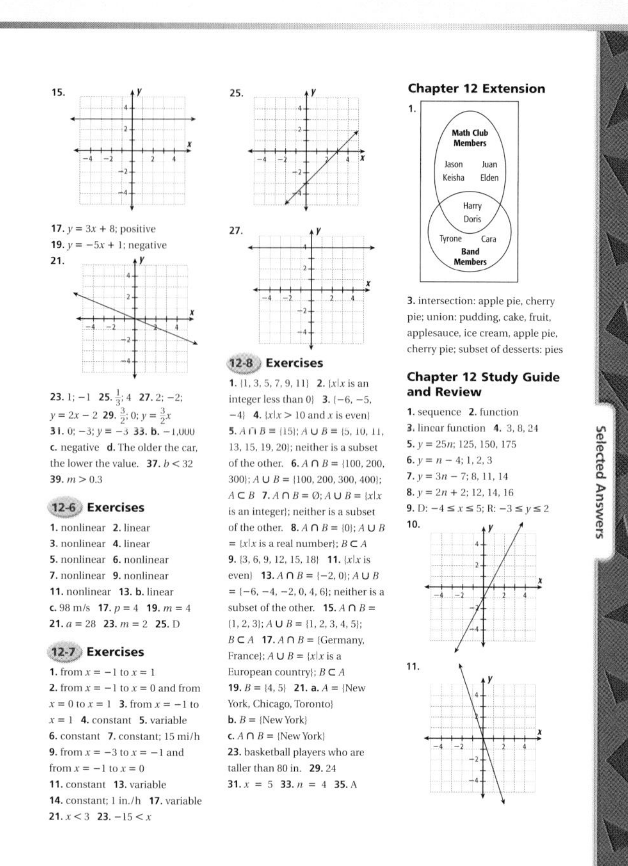

15.

17. $y = 3x + 8$; positive

19. $y = -5x + 1$; negative

21.

23. 1; −1 25. $\frac{1}{3}$; 4 27. 2; −2; $y = 2x - 2$ 29. $\frac{3}{2}$; 0; $y = \frac{3}{2}x$ 31. 0; −3; $y = -3$ 33. b. −1,000 c. negative d. The older the car, the lower the value. 37. $b < 32$ 39. $m > 0.3$

12-6 Exercises

1. nonlinear 2. linear 3. nonlinear 4. linear 5. nonlinear 6. nonlinear 7. nonlinear 9. nonlinear 11. nonlinear 13. b. linear c. 98 m/s 17. $p = 4$ 19. $m = 4$ 21. $a = 28$ 23. $m = 2$ 25. D

12-7 Exercises

1. from $x = -1$ to $x = 1$ 2. from $x = -1$ to $x = 0$ and from $x = 0$ to $x = 1$ 3. from $x = -1$ to $x = 1$ 4. constant 5. variable 6. constant 7. constant; 15 mi/h 9. from $x = -3$ to $x = -1$ and from $x = -1$ to $x = 0$ 11. constant 13. variable 14. constant; 1 in./h 17. variable 21. $x < 3$ 23. $-15 < x$

25. 27.

12-8 Exercises

1. {1, 3, 5, 7, 9, 11} 2. {x|x is an integer less than 0} 3. {−6, −5, −4} 4. {x|x > 10 and x is even} 5. $A \cap B$ = {15}; $A \cup B$ = {5, 10, 11, 13, 15, 19, 20}; neither is a subset of the other. 6. $A \cap B$ = {100, 200, 300}; $A \cup B$ = {100, 200, 300, 400}; $A \subset B$ 7. $A \cap B = \emptyset$; $A \cup B$ = {x|x is an integer}; neither is a subset of the other. 8. $A \cap B$ = {0}; $A \cup B$ = {x|x is a real number}; $B \subset A$ 9. {3, 6, 9, 12, 15, 18} 11. {x|x is even} 13. $A \cap B$ = {−2, 0}; $A \cup B$ = {−6, −4, −2, 0, 4, 6}; neither is a subset of the other. 15. $A \cap B$ = {1, 2, 3}; $A \cup B$ = {1, 2, 3, 4, 5}; $B \subset A$ 17. $A \cap B$ = {Germany, France}; $A \cup B$ = {x|x is a European country}; $B \subset A$ 19. B = {4, 5} 21. a. A = {New York, Chicago, Toronto} b. B = {New York} c. $A \cap B$ = {New York} 23. basketball players who are taller than 80 in. 29. 24 31. $x = 5$ 33. $n = 4$ 35. A

Chapter 12 Extension

1.

3. intersection: apple pie, cherry pie; union: pudding, cake, fruit, applesauce, ice cream, apple pie, cherry pie; subset of desserts: pies

Chapter 12 Study Guide and Review

1. sequence 2. function 3. linear function 4. 3, 8, 24 5. $y = 25n$; 125, 150, 175 6. $y = n - 4$; 1, 2, 3 7. $y = 3n - 7$; 8, 11, 14 8. $y = 2n + 2$; 12, 14, 16 9. D: $-4 \le x \le 5$; R: $-3 \le y \le 2$

10. 11.

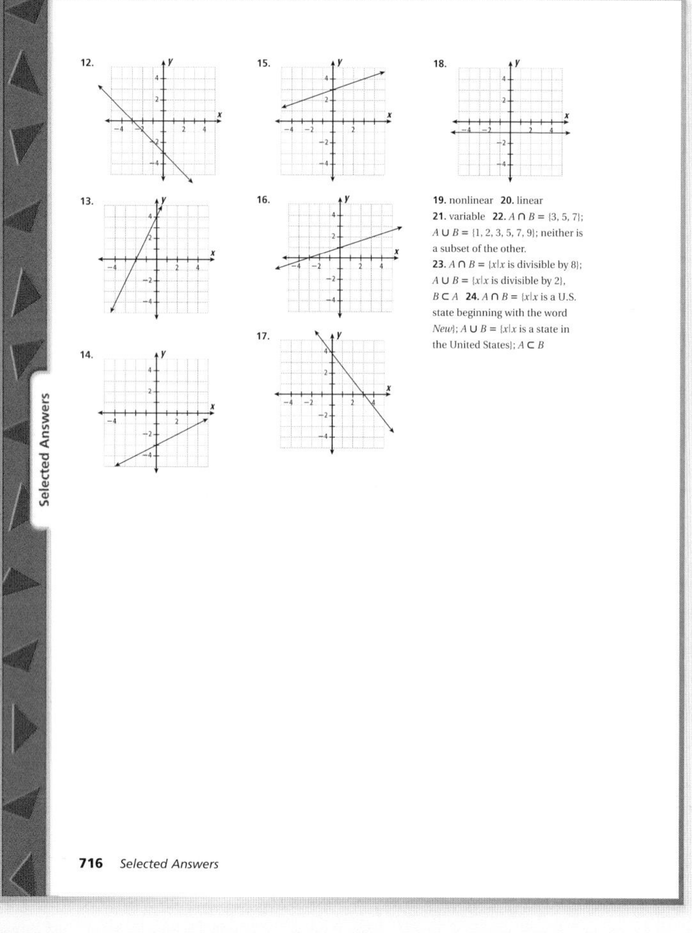

12. 13. 14. 15. 16. 17. 18.

19. nonlinear 20. linear 21. variable 22. $A \cap B$ = {3, 5, 7}; $A \cup B$ = {1, 2, 3, 5, 7, 9}; neither is a subset of the other. 23. $A \cap B$ = {x|x is divisible by 8}; $A \cup B$ = {x|x is divisible by 2}, $B \subset A$ 24. $A \cap B$ = {x|x is a U.S. state beginning with the word *New*}; $A \cup B$ = {x|x is a state in the United States}; $A \subset B$

Additional Answers

Chapter 1

Lesson 1-3

10. 7

Endangered Species in Each Country of South America		
Species	Frequency	Cumulative Frequency
0–9	5	5
10–19	2	7
20–29	4	11
30–39	1	12
40–49	0	12
50–59	0	12
60–69	1	13

11. 6

Endangered Species in Each Country of South America

Stems	Leaves
0	5 5 6 6 6
1	1 3
2	0 1 3 4
3	5
4	
5	
6	4

Key: 2|3 means 23

13. 64; adding the outlier increases the mean by approximately 3.8.

14. Possible answer: By making the intervals in the table smaller, I might be able to see better where the numbers are grouped.

Lesson 1-8

9. Negative correlation; the higher the elevation of a city, the lower the temperature would be expected to be.

13. As latitude increases, temperature decreases.

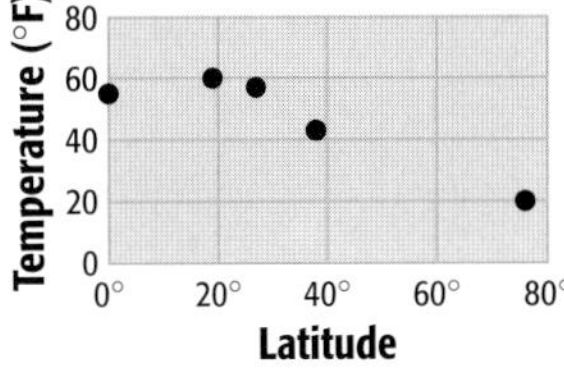

14. As altitude increases, pressure decreases.

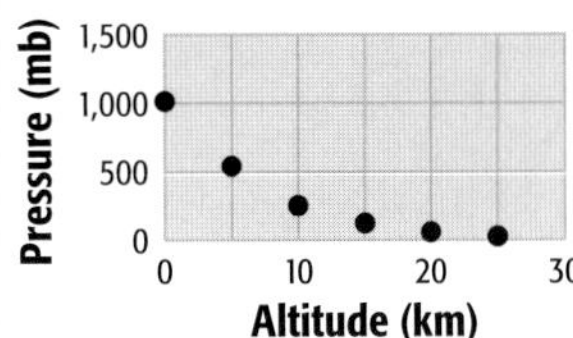

Chapter 2

Lesson 2-4

41. $2^4 \cdot 3^2$

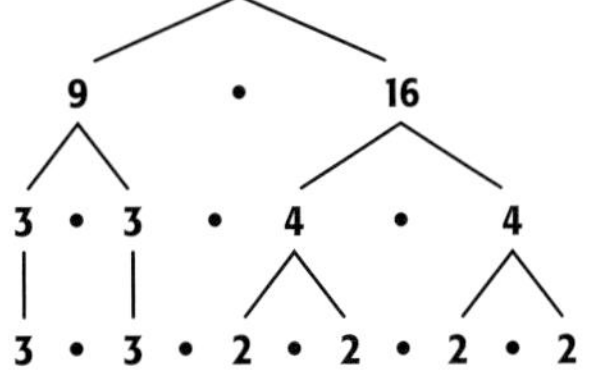

42. $2^4 \cdot 3^2$

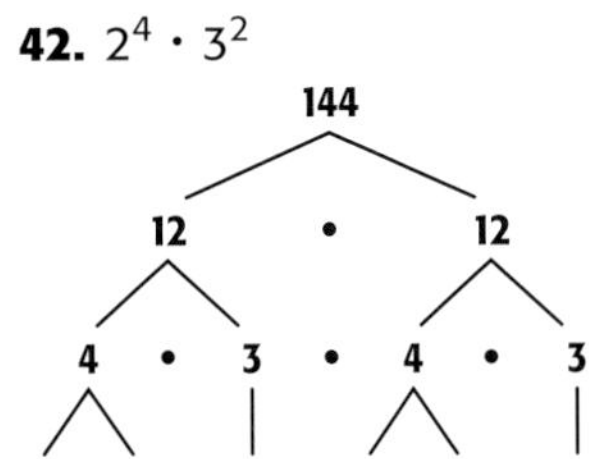

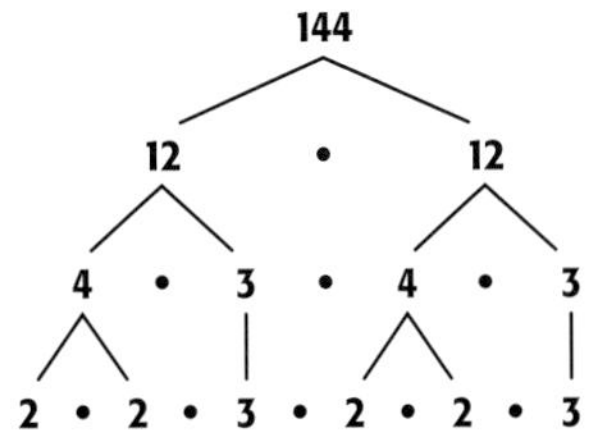

43. $2^3 \cdot 5^2$

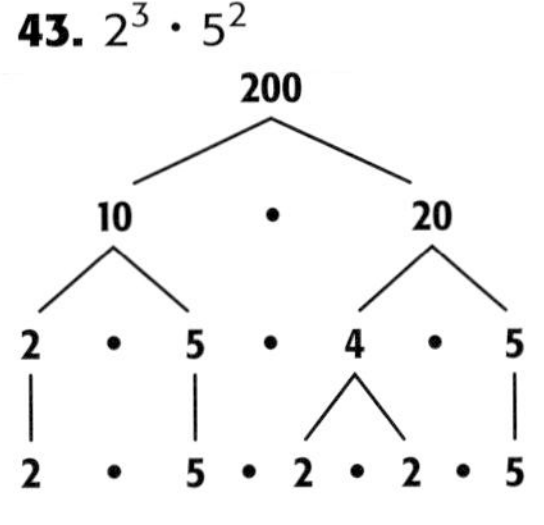

44. $2^3 \cdot 5^2$

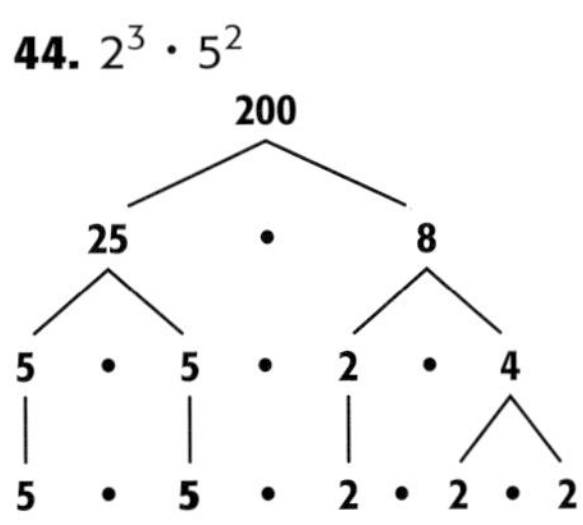

Chapter 3

Lesson 3-1

1.

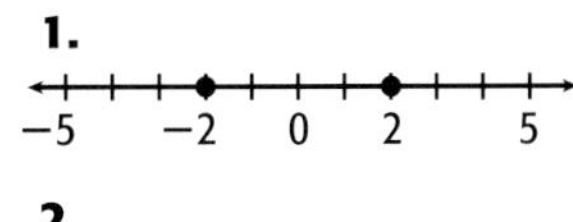

2.

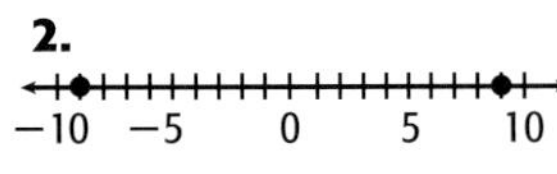

3.

4.

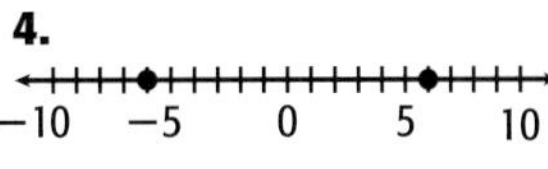

5. −5, −3, −1, 4, 6

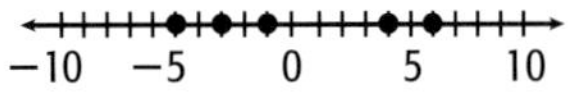

−10 −5 0 5 10

6. −8, −2, 1, 7, 8

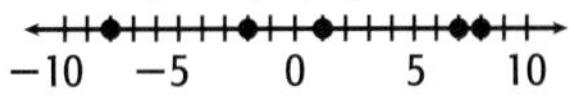

−10 −5 0 5 10

7. −6, −4, 0, 1, 3

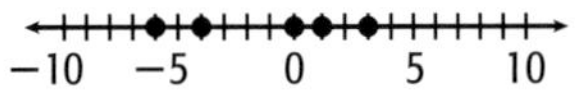

−10 −5 0 5 10

8. 2

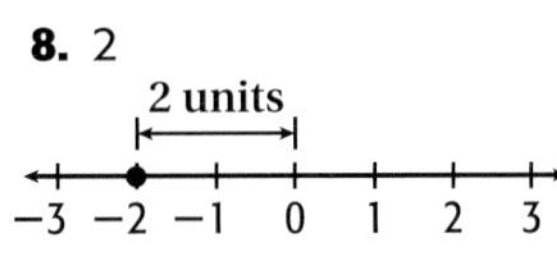

9. 8

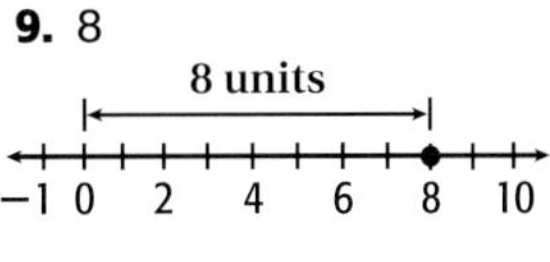

10. 7

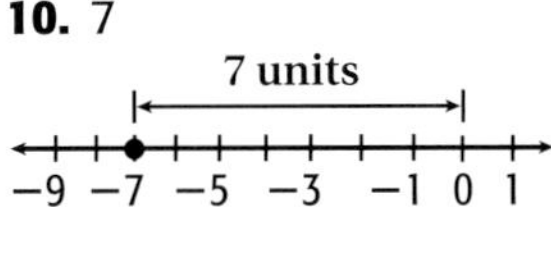

11. 10

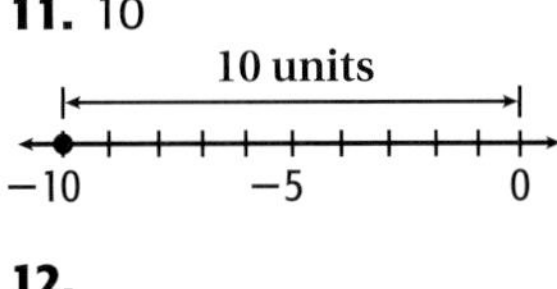

12.

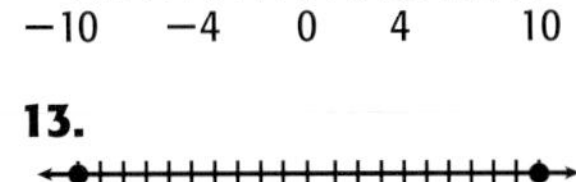

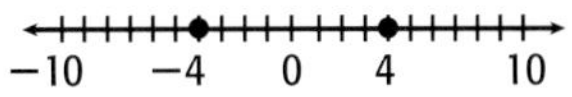

13.

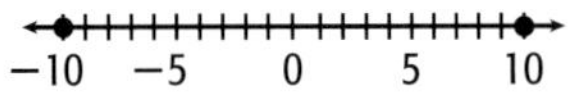

−10 −5 0 5 10

14.

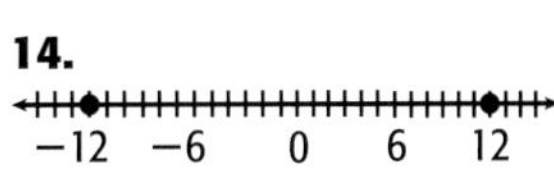

15.

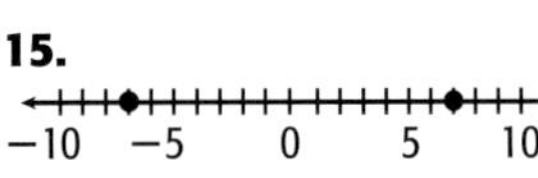

16. −6, −5, −3, 2, 5

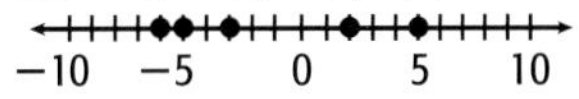

−10 −5 0 5 10

17. −9, −7, −5, −2, 0

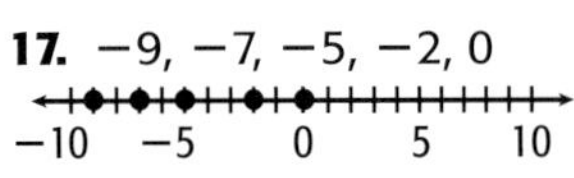

18. −6, −2, −1, 3, 9

−10 −5 0 5 10

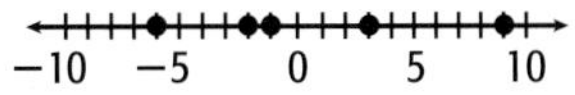

19. 16

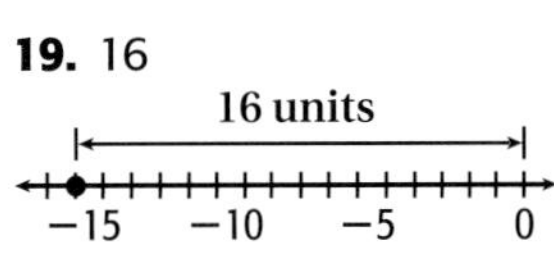

20. 12

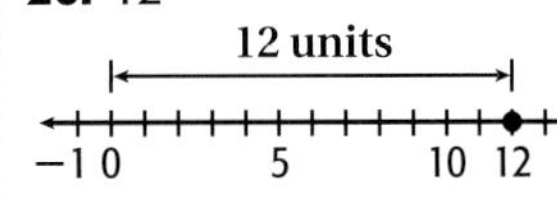

21. 20

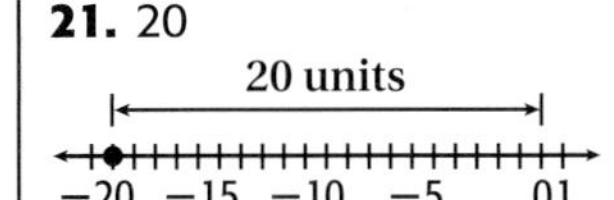

22. 15

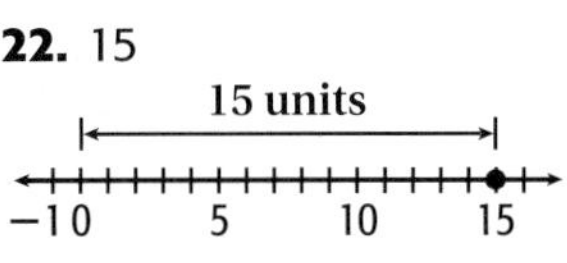

Lesson 3-2

17–20.

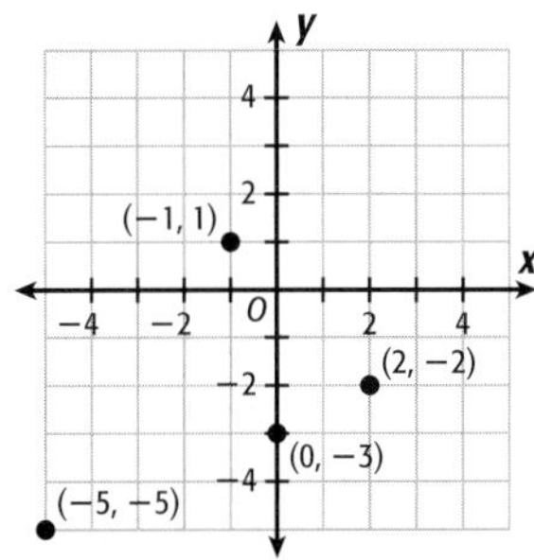

27.

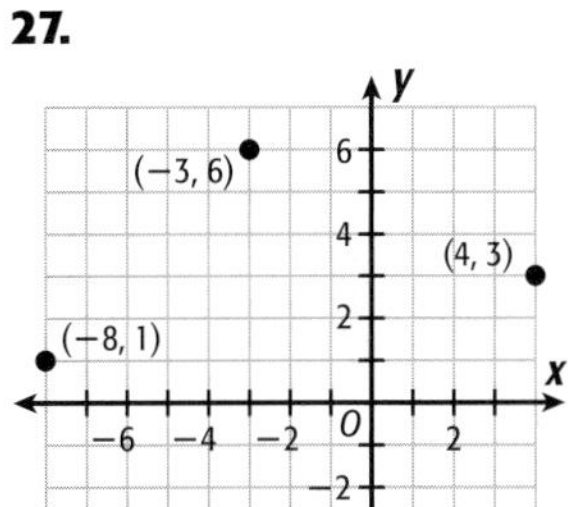

28.

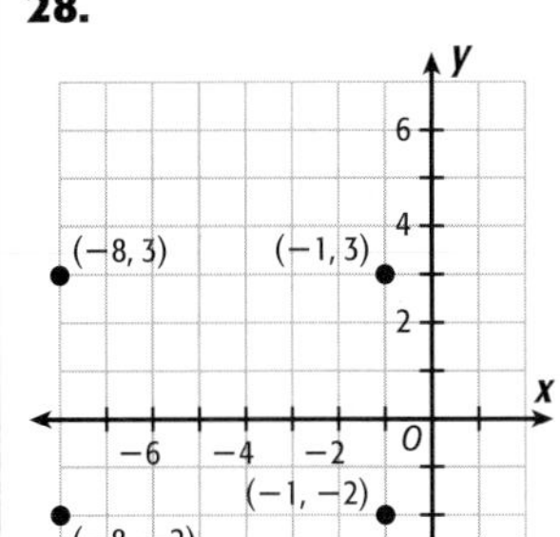
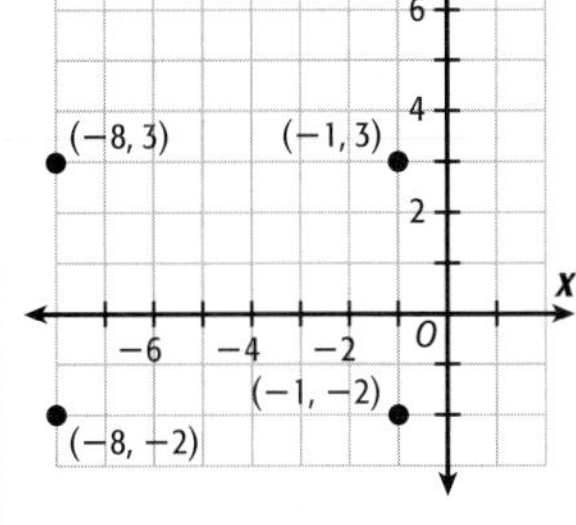

Lesson 3-4

1. −3

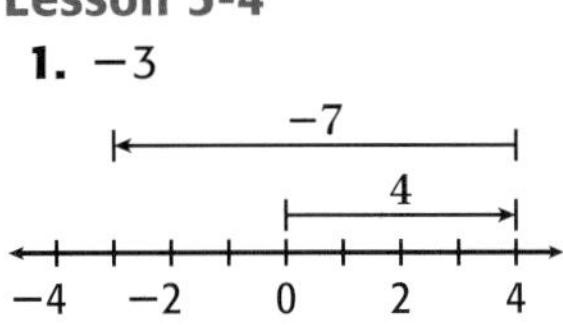

2. −11

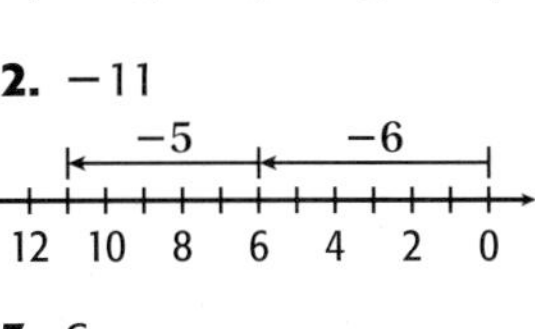

3. 6

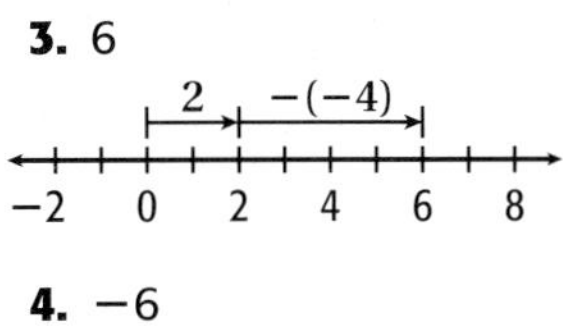

4. −6

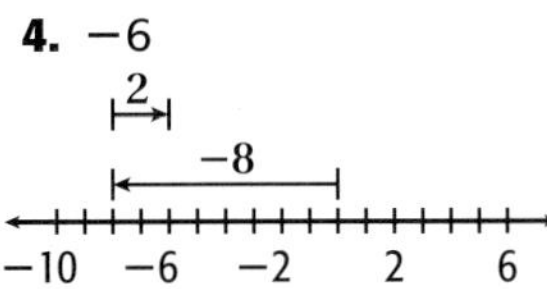

13. −5

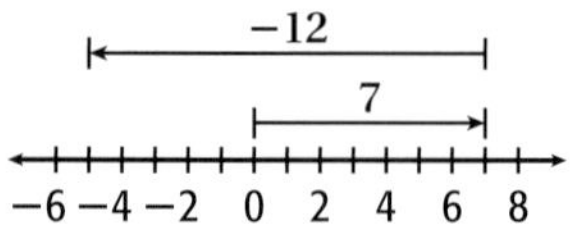

−12
7
−6 −4 −2 0 2 4 6 8

14. 4

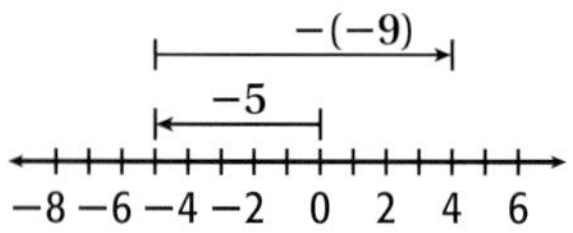

−(−9)
−5
−8 −6 −4 −2 0 2 4 6

15. 8

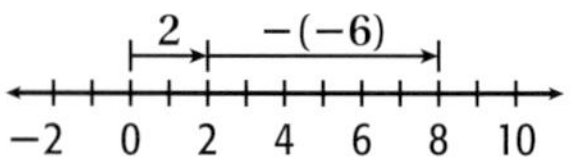

2 −(−6)
−2 0 2 4 6 8 10

16. 15

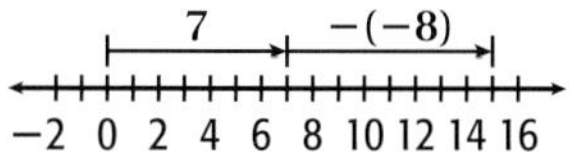

7 −(−8)
−2 0 2 4 6 8 10 12 14 16

17. 12

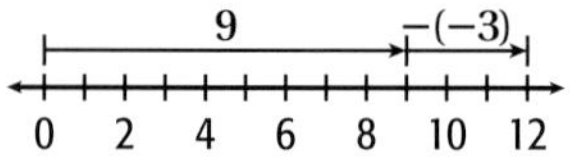

9 −(−3)
0 2 4 6 8 10 12

18. −14

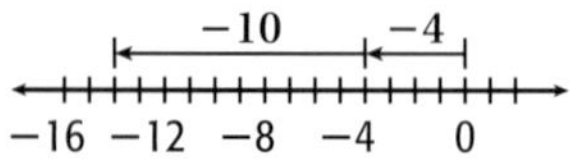

−10 −4
−16 −12 −8 −4 0

19. 16

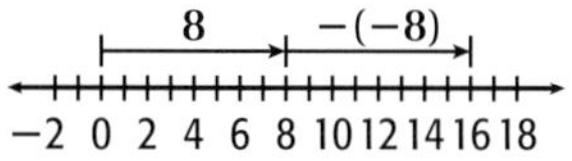

8 −(−8)
−2 0 2 4 6 8 10 12 14 16 18

20. 0

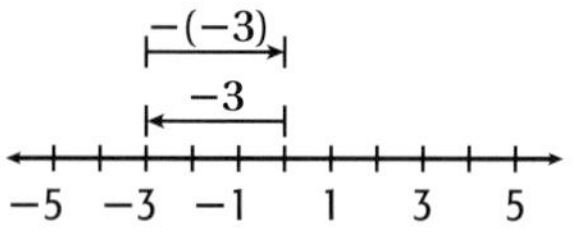

−(−3)
−3
−5 −3 −1 1 3 5

Lesson 3-7

1.

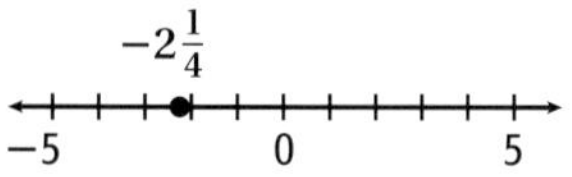

$-2\frac{1}{4}$
−5 0 5

2.

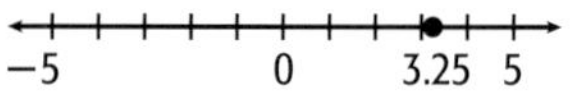

−5 0 3.25 5

3.

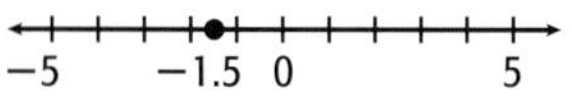

−5 −1.5 0 5

4.

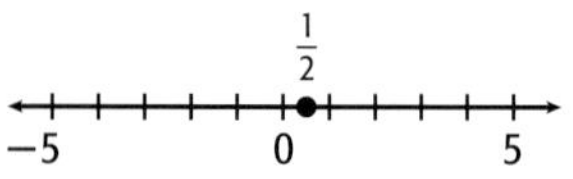

$\frac{1}{2}$
−5 0 5

9.

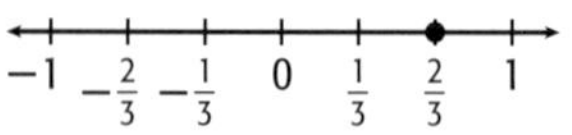

-1 $-\frac{2}{3}$ $-\frac{1}{3}$ 0 $\frac{1}{3}$ $\frac{2}{3}$ 1

10.

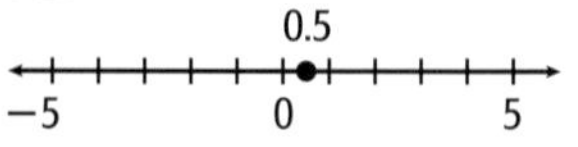

0.5
−5 0 5

11.

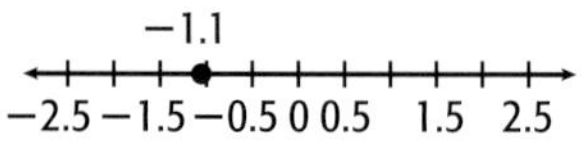

−1.1
−2.5 −1.5 −0.5 0 0.5 1.5 2.5

12.

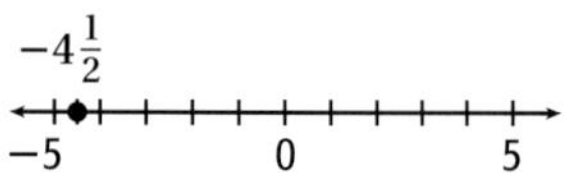

$-4\frac{1}{2}$
−5 0 5

13.

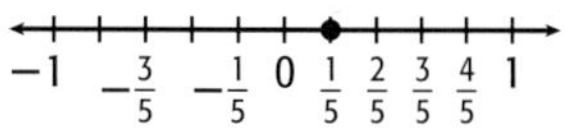

-1 $-\frac{3}{5}$ $-\frac{1}{5}$ 0 $\frac{1}{5}$ $\frac{2}{5}$ $\frac{3}{5}$ $\frac{4}{5}$ 1

14.

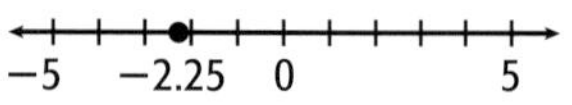

−5 −2.25 0 5

15.

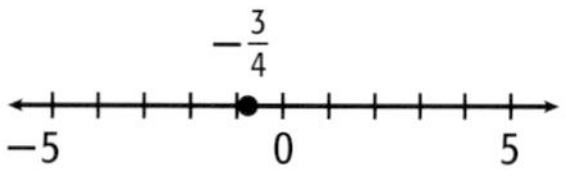

$-\frac{3}{4}$
−5 0 5

16.

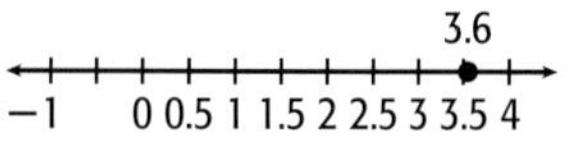

3.6
−1 0 0.5 1 1.5 2 2.5 3 3.5 4

24.

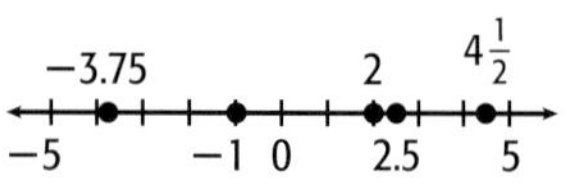

−3.75 2 $4\frac{1}{2}$
−5 −1 0 2.5 5

25.

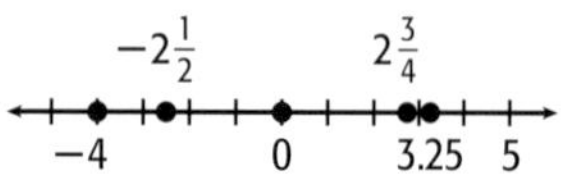

$-2\frac{1}{2}$ $2\frac{3}{4}$
−4 0 3.25 5

Chapter 4

Performance Assessment

1. \$18.41 · 40 · 52
= \$38,292.80
\$12.07 · 40 · 52
= \$25,105.60
The difference is \$13,187.20.

Chapter 5

Performance Assessment

1. Draw and label two similar triangles; then write and solve a proportion; $\frac{x}{5} = \frac{20}{4}$; the tree is 25 feet tall.

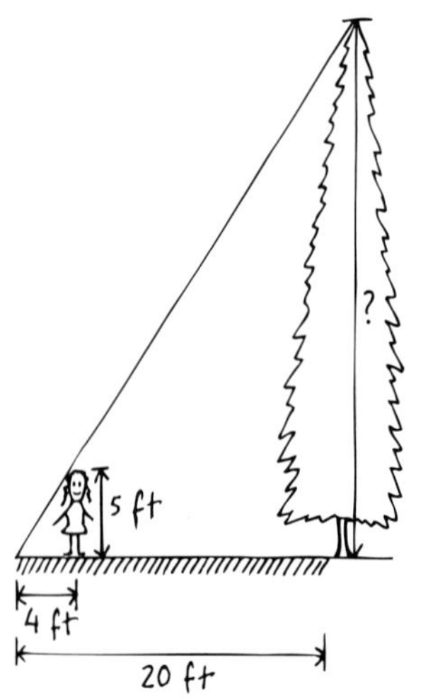

Chapter 7

Lesson 7-1

14. a–b.

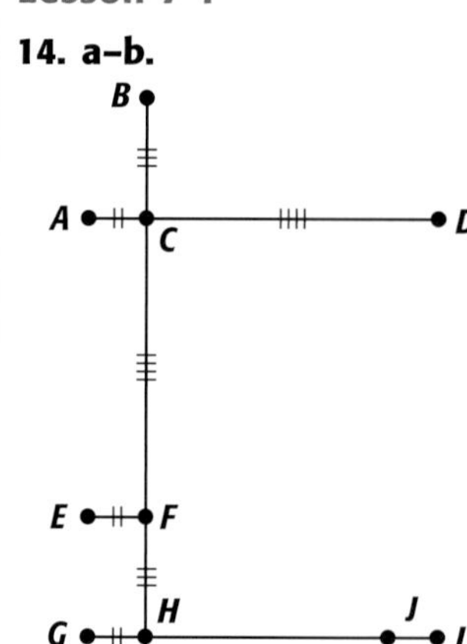

c. Possible answer: $\overline{AC} \cong \overline{EF}$, $\overline{CD} \cong \overline{CF}$, $\overline{BC} \cong \overline{FH}$, $\overline{HI} \cong \overline{JK}$, $\overline{EF} \cong \overline{GH}$

15. a.

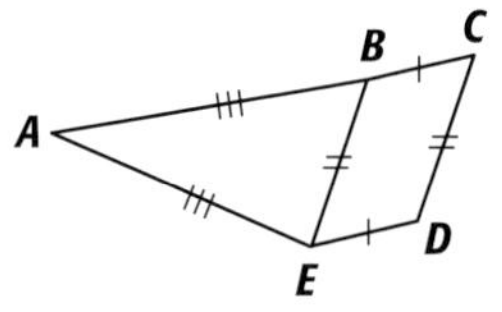

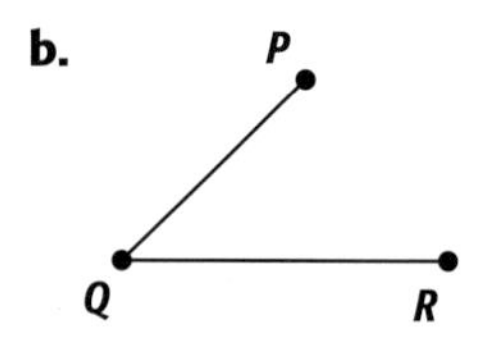

b.

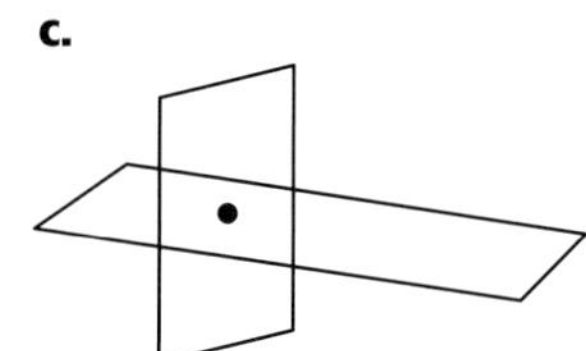

c.

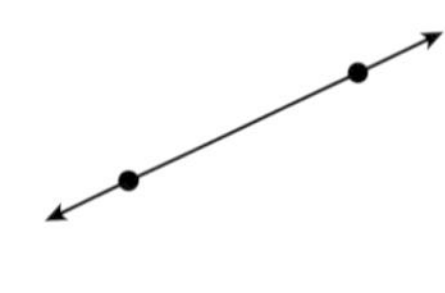

16. No; two points cannot be shared by two different line segments. If two line segments share two points in common, then the lines are the same.

17.

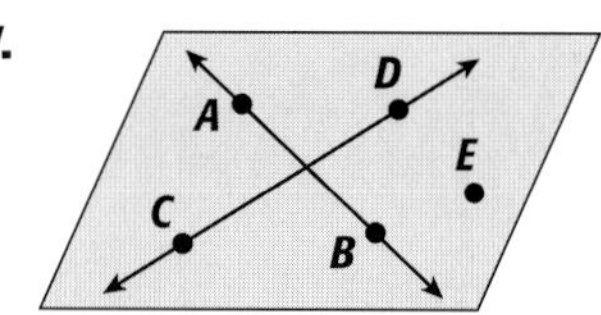

Possible answer: plane *ABC;* points *A, B, C, D, E;* lines $\overleftrightarrow{AB}$, $\overleftrightarrow{CD}$; and rays $\overrightarrow{AB}$, $\overrightarrow{BA}$, $\overrightarrow{CD}$, $\overrightarrow{DC}$

18. A line is a straight path that extends forever in two directions; a ray is a straight path that extends forever in one direction from an endpoint; and a segment is a straight path from one endpoint to another. It is possible to estimate the length of a segment, because it does not extend forever in any direction.

19. Yes; since a plane extends forever, it is possible that two faces could be on the same plane and still not touch.

Lesson 7-10

3.

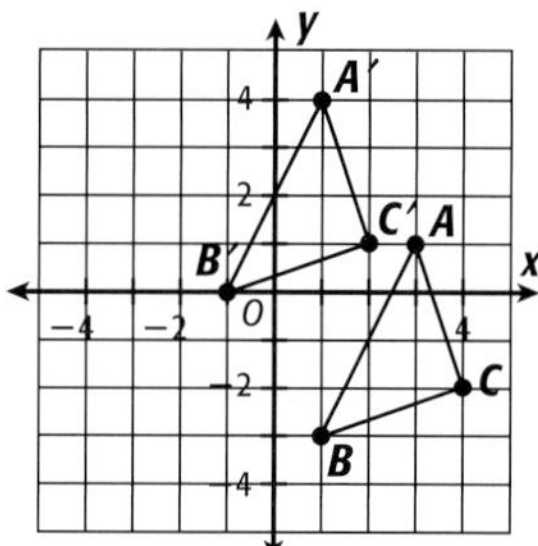

4.

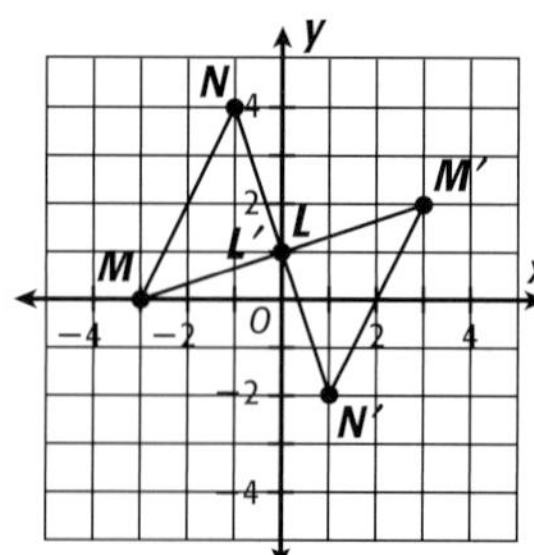

5.

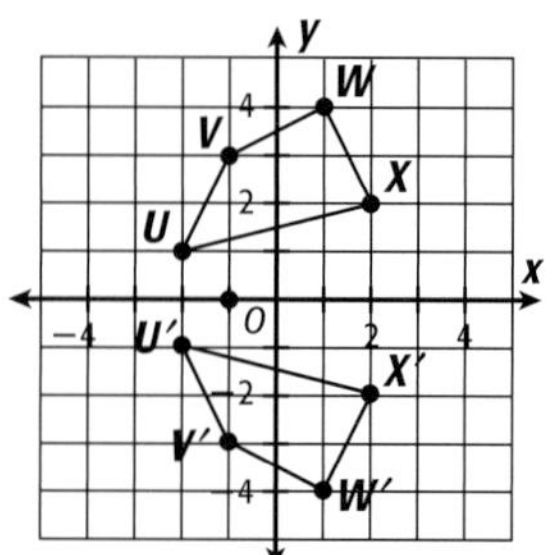

8.

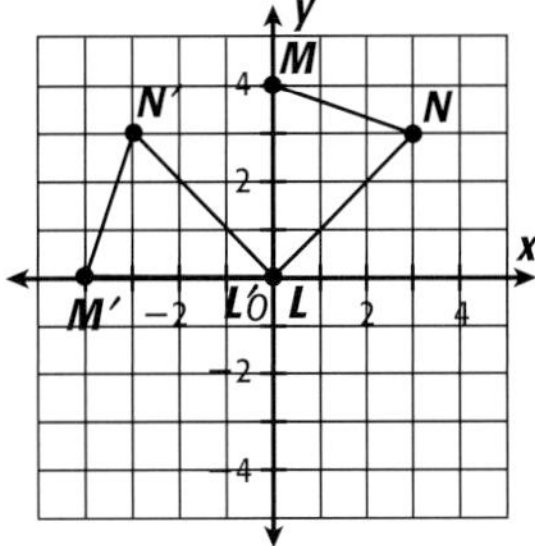

9.

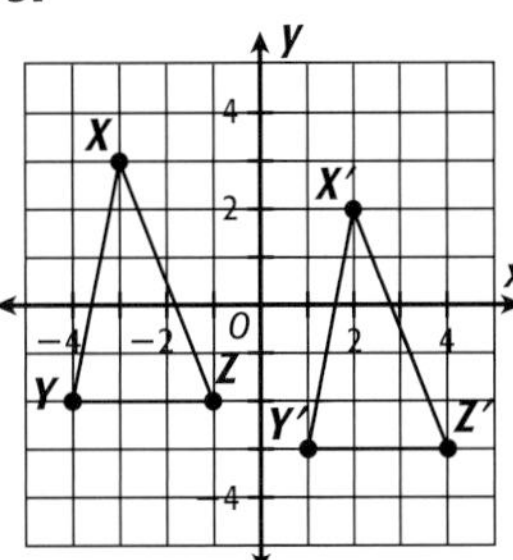

10.

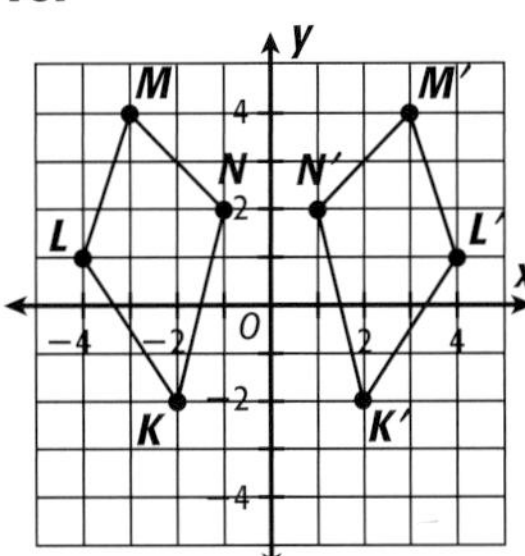

Chapter 8

Lesson 8-4

19. 14 units^2

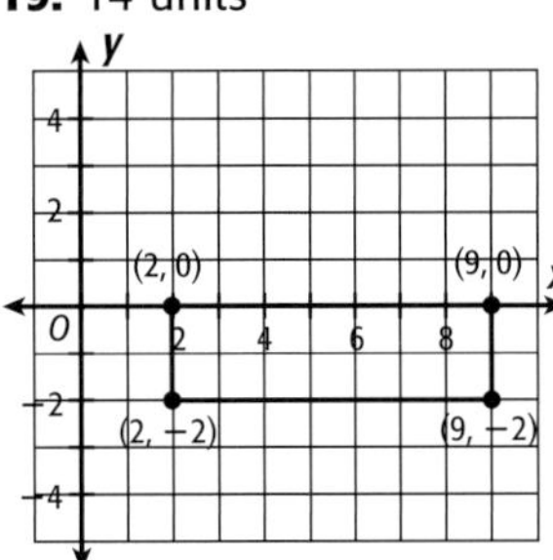

20. 20 units^2

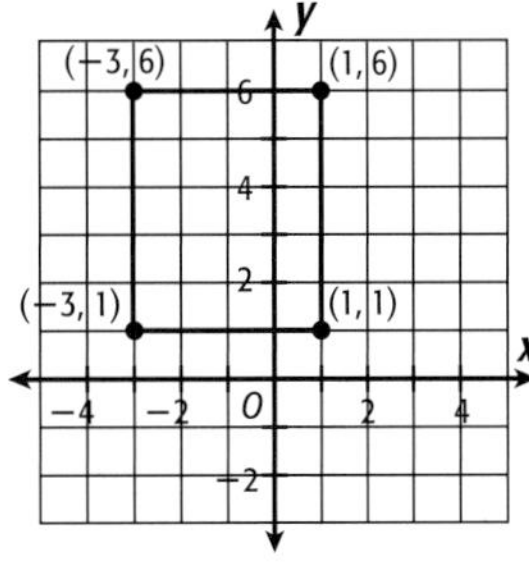

21. 18 units^2

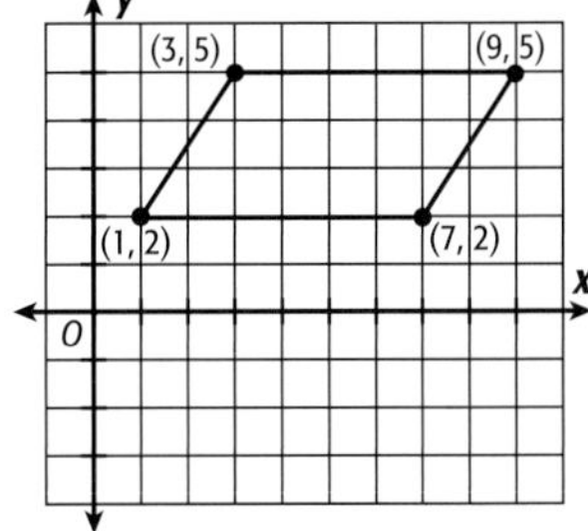

22. 18 units^2

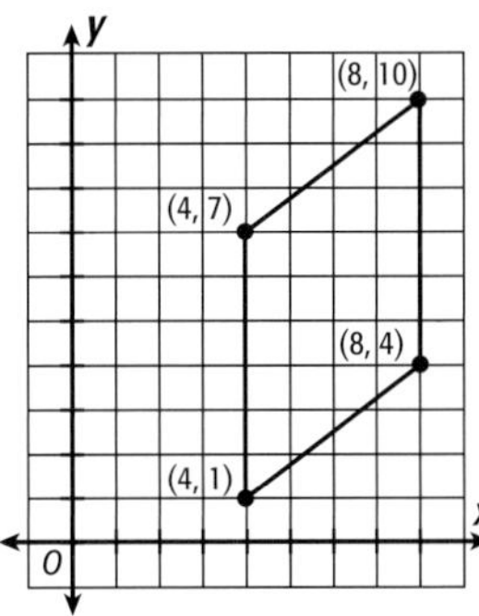

Lesson 8-5

16. 16.5 units^2

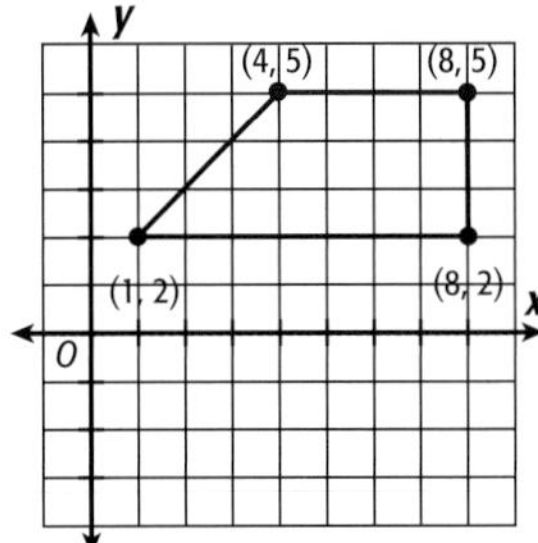

17. 15 units^2

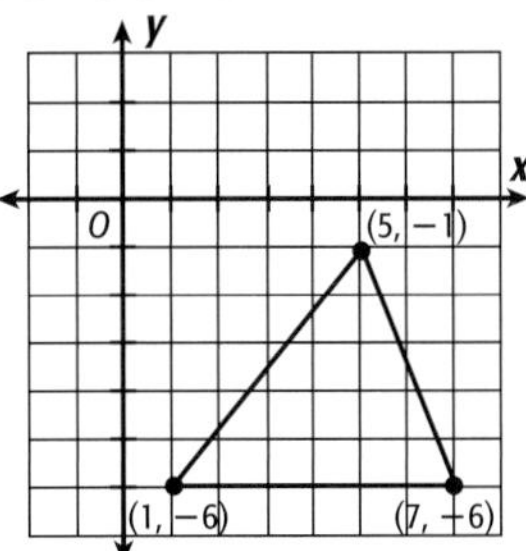

18. 22.5 units^2

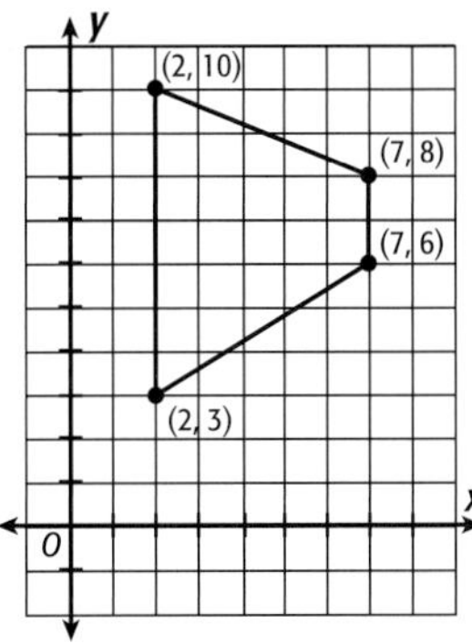

19. 12 units^2

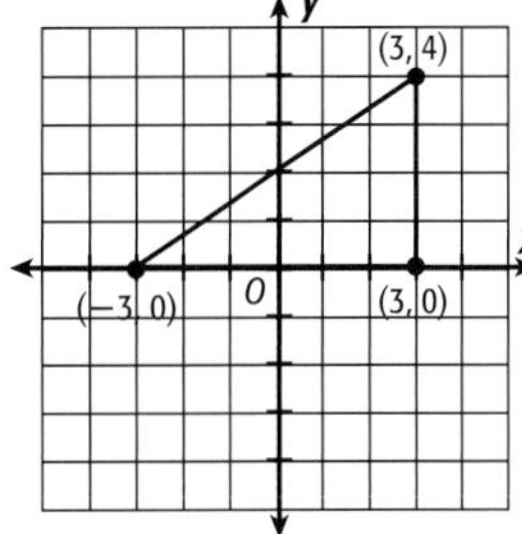

26. Think of the state as a rectangle 200 mi by 320 mi and a triangle with height 320 mi and base 275 mi (475 − 200 = 275); area of the rectangle part: 200 · 320 = 64,000; area of the triangle part: $\frac{1}{2}(320)\ 275 =$ 44,000; area of the whole state: 63,000 + 44,000 = 108,000 mi^2.

Lesson 8-8

19. If you use the Pythagorean Theorem, you find that $3^2 + 4^2 = 5^2$, so the triangle could be a right triangle.

Chapter 10

Lesson 10-3

7. oatmeal–milk, oatmeal–orange juice, oatmeal–apple juice, oatmeal–hot chocolate, corn flakes–milk, corn flakes–orange juice, corn flakes–apple juice, corn flakes–hot chocolate, scrambled eggs–milk, scrambled eggs–orange juice, scrambled eggs–apple juice, scrambled eggs–hot chocolate; 12

Performance Assessment

1. The possible outcomes are HHH, HHT, HTT, HTH, TTT, TTH, THH, and THT. There are 8 possible outcomes in the sample space and 2 outcomes in which all three tosses are the same; $\frac{2}{8} = \frac{1}{4}$.

2. The Fundamental Counting Principle shows that there are 6 possible outcomes, so the probability of 1 outcome occurring is $\frac{1}{6}$.

3. 24 ways; they are permutations because order is important.

4. The chart shows that one out of four offspring will carry two recessive genes, so the probability that an offspring will be a dwarf is $\frac{1}{4}$.

Chapter 11

Lesson 11-4

15.

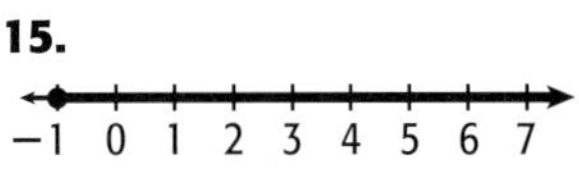

16.

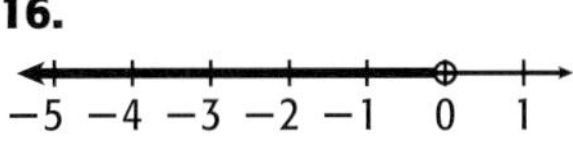

17.

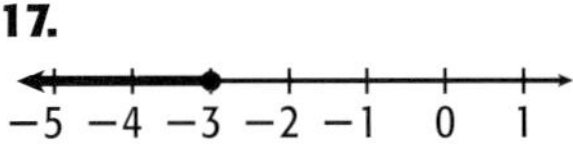

18.

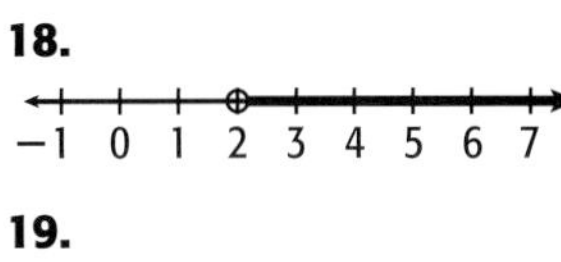

19.

20.

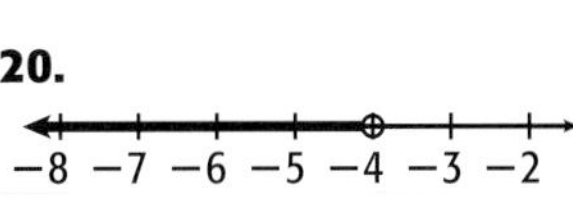

21.

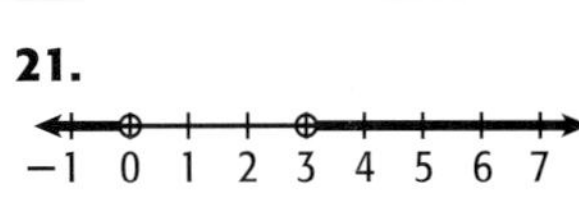

22.

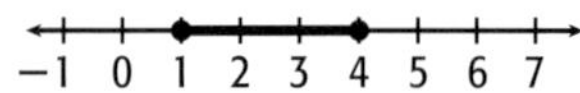

23.

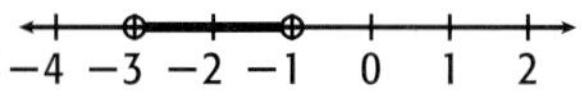

24.

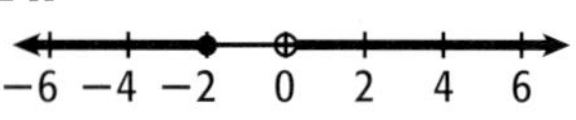

25.

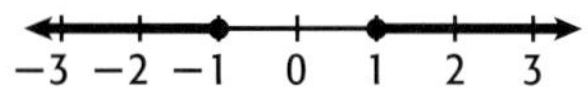

−3 −2 −1 0 1 2 3

26.

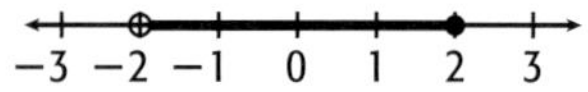

−3 −2 −1 0 1 2 3

Lesson 11-7

11. 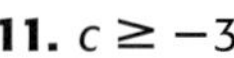 $c \geq -3$

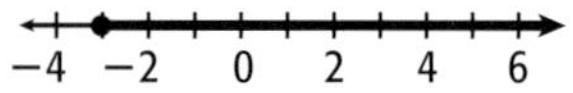

−4 −2 0 2 4 6

12. $y < -16$

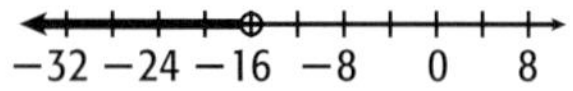

−32 −24 −16 −8 0 8

13. $x \leq -27$

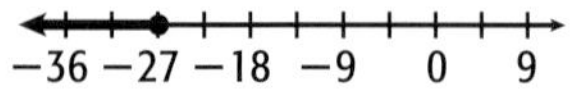

−36 −27 −18 −9 0 9

14. $r < 10$

−10 −6 −2 2 6 10

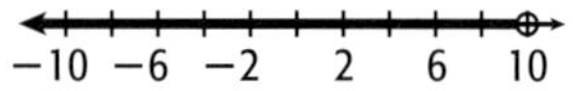

15. $j \leq 2$

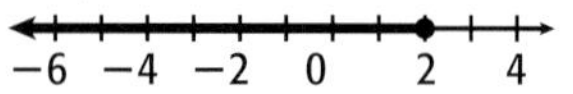

−6 −4 −2 0 2 4

16. $d > 507$

0 200 400 600 800 1000

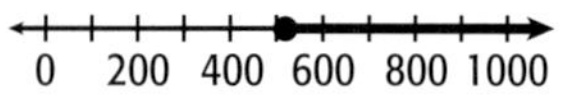

Chapter 12

Lesson 12-1

4.

Input	Rule	Output	Ordered Pair
x	$3x - 2$	y	(x, y)
−1	$3(-1) - 2$	−5	(−1, −5)
0	$3(0) - 2$	−2	(0, −2)
1	$3(1) - 2$	1	(1, 1)
2	$3(2) - 2$	4	(2, 4)

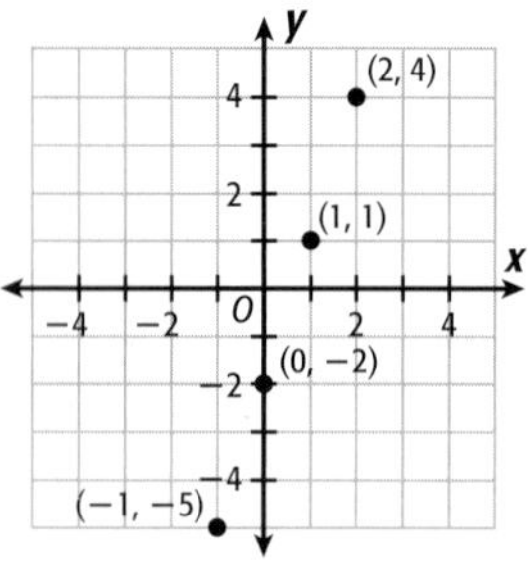

5.

Input	Rule	Output	Ordered Pair
x	$x^2 + 2$	y	(x, y)
−1	$(-1)^2 + 2$	3	(−1, 3)
0	$(0)^2 + 2$	2	(0, 2)
1	$(1)^2 + 2$	3	(1, 3)
2	$(2)^2 + 2$	6	(2, 6)

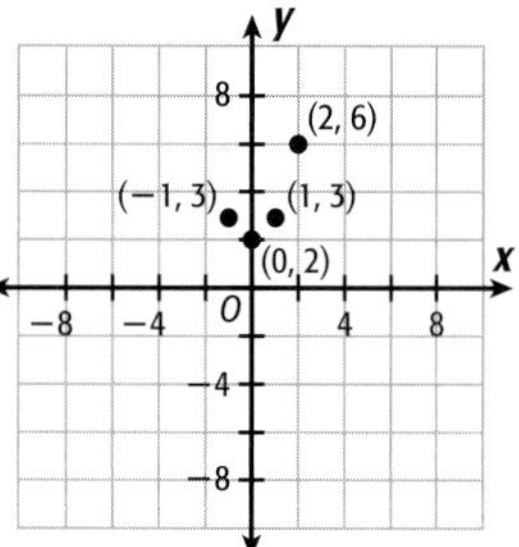

7.

Input	Rule	Output
x	$3x + 2$	y
−3	$3(-3) + 2$	−7
−1	$3(-1) + 2$	−1
2	$3(2) + 2$	8

8.

Input	Rule	Output
x	$3x^2$	y
−10	$3(-10)^2$	300
−6	$3(-6)^2$	108
−2	$3(-2)^2$	12

9.

Input	Rule	Output	Ordered Pair
x	$x \div 2$	y	(x, y)
−1	$-1 \div 2$	$-\frac{1}{2}$	$(-1, -\frac{1}{2})$
0	$0 \div 2$	0	(0, 0)
1	$1 \div 2$	$\frac{1}{2}$	$(1, \frac{1}{2})$
2	$2 \div 2$	1	(2, 1)

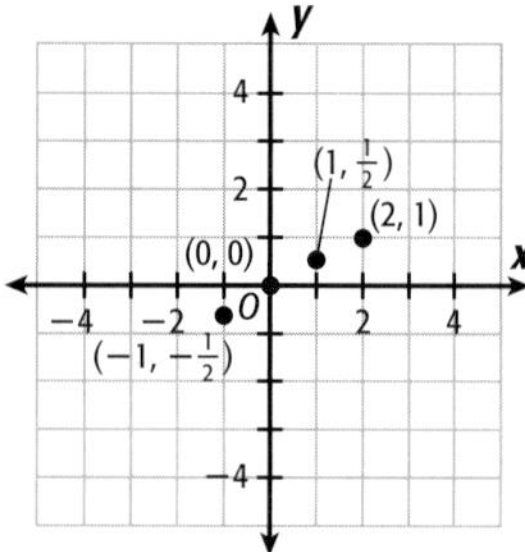

10.

Input	Rule	Output	Ordered Pair
x	$x^2 - 4$	y	(x, y)
−1	$(-1)^2 - 4$	−3	(−1, −3)
0	$(0)^2 - 4$	−4	(0, −4)
1	$(1)^2 - 4$	−3	(1, −3)
2	$(2)^2 - 4$	0	(2, 0)

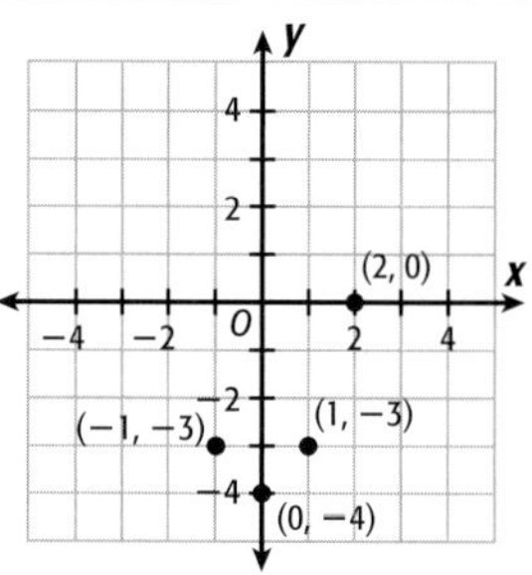

11.

Input	Rule	Output
C	$\frac{9}{5}C + 32$	F
−20°	$\frac{9}{5}(-20) + 32$	−4°
−5°	$\frac{9}{5}(-5) + 32$	23°
0°	$\frac{9}{5}(0) + 32$	32°
20°	$\frac{9}{5}(20) + 32$	68°
100°	$\frac{9}{5}(100) + 32$	212°

12.

Input	Rule	Output	Ordered Pair
x	$3x$	y	(x, y)
1	$3(1)$	3	(1, 3)
2	$3(2)$	6	(2, 6)
3	$3(3)$	9	(3, 9)
4	$3(4)$	12	(4, 12)
5	$3(5)$	15	(5, 15)

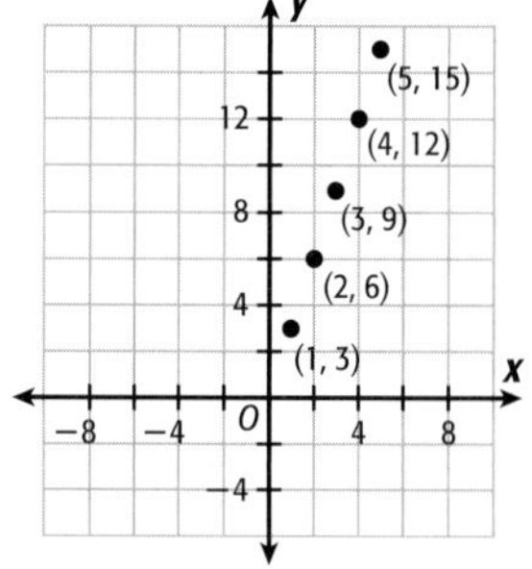

13.

Input	Rule	Output	Ordered Pair
x	$2x + 15$	y	(x, y)
0	$2(0) + 15$	15	(0, 15)
1	$2(1) + 15$	17	(1, 17)
5	$2(5) + 15$	25	(5, 25)
10	$2(10) + 15$	35	(10, 35)

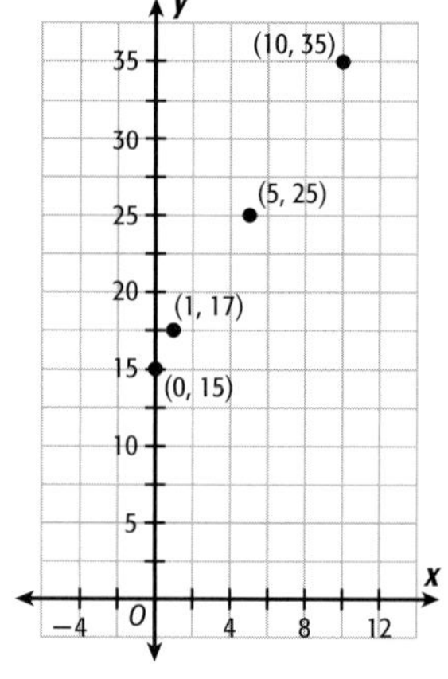

14. a.

Input	Rule	Output	Ordered Pair
x	$11.66 - x$	y	(x, y)
8.01	11.66 − 8.01	3.65	(8.01, 3.65)
8.73	11.66 − 8.73	2.93	(8.73, 2.93)
8.44	11.66 − 8.44	3.22	(8.44, 3.22)
8.97	11.66 − 8.97	2.69	(8.97, 2.69)
8.66	11.66 − 8.66	3	(8.66, 3)

b. Possible answer: There has been less rainfall than average in the years shown in the graph.

15. Possible answer: The signs are wrong for the negative values of x. When a negative number is cubed, the result is a negative number.

Lesson 12-3

7.

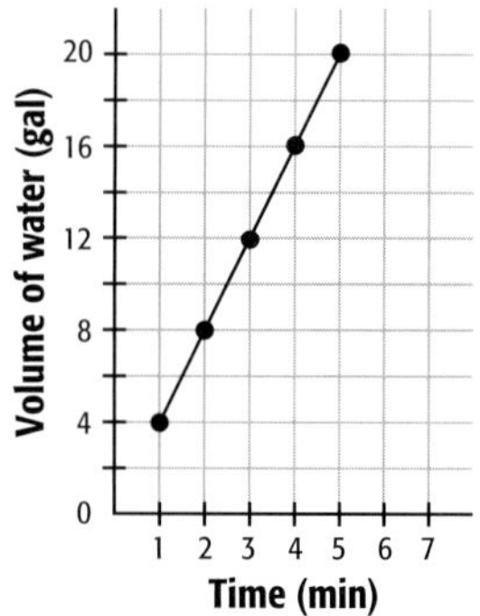

10. D: $-2 \le x \le 3$; R: $y = 2$

12.

Basketball Games

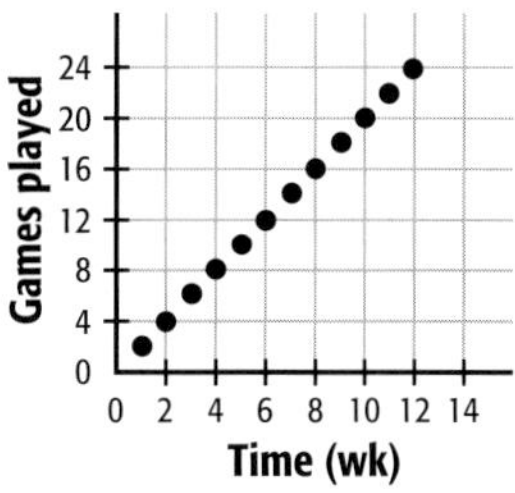

13.

Calories in Rice Cakes

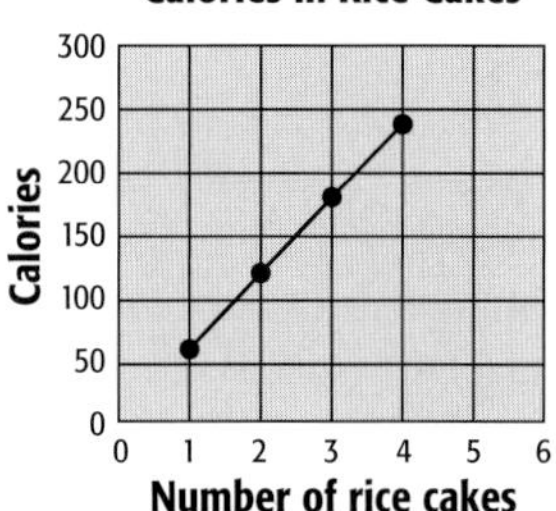

17. Possible answer: In the graph made up of points, only those points are included. In a graph that is continuous, all points on the line connecting the points are included.

Lesson 12-4

3. $y = 750x$

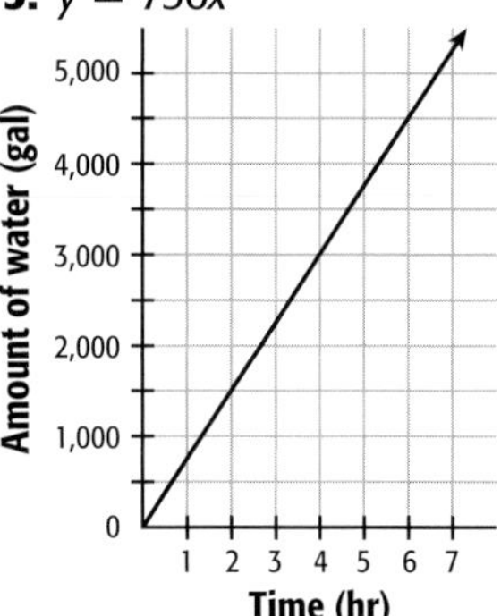

4.

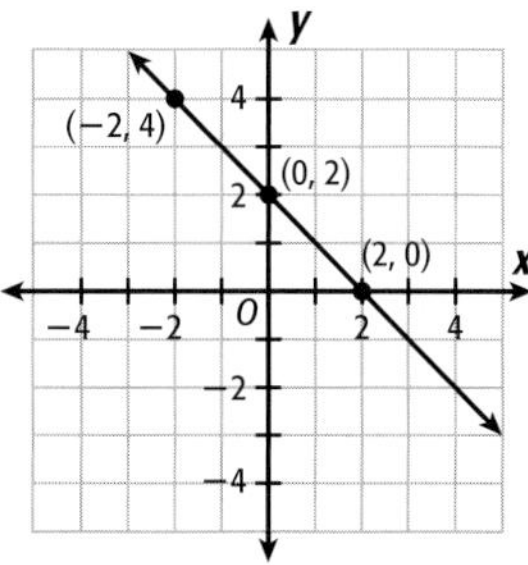

Input	Rule	Output	Ordered Pair
x	$-x + 2$	y	(x, y)
−2	$-(-2) + 2$	4	(−2, 4)
0	$-(0) + 2$	2	(0, 2)
2	$-(2) + 2$	0	(2, 0)

5.

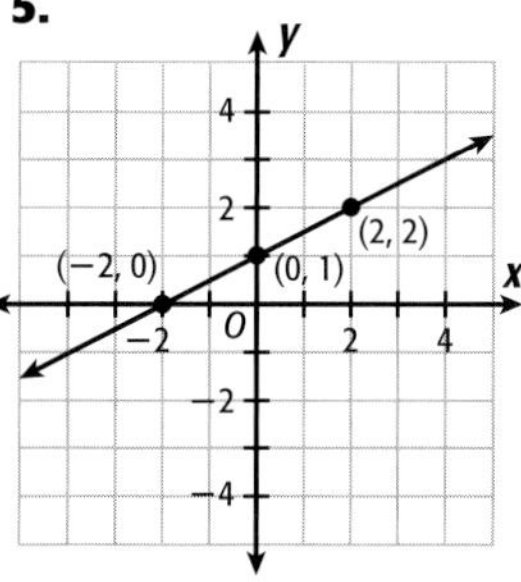

Input	Rule	Output	Ordered Pair
x	$\frac{x}{2} + 1$	y	(x, y)
−2	$\frac{-2}{2} + 1$	0	(−2, 0)
0	$\frac{0}{2} + 1$	1	(0, 1)
2	$\frac{2}{2} + 1$	2	(2, 2)

6.

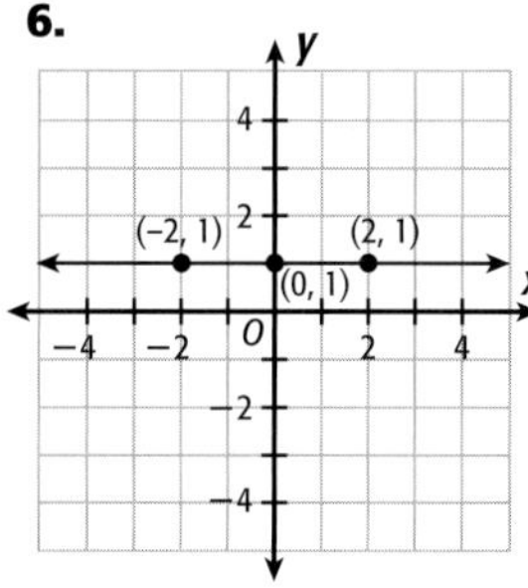

Input	Rule	Output	Ordered Pair
x	$0x + 1$	y	(x, y)
−2	$0(-2) + 1$	1	(−2, 1)
0	$0(0) + 1$	1	(0, 1)
2	$0(2) + 1$	1	(2, 1)

7.

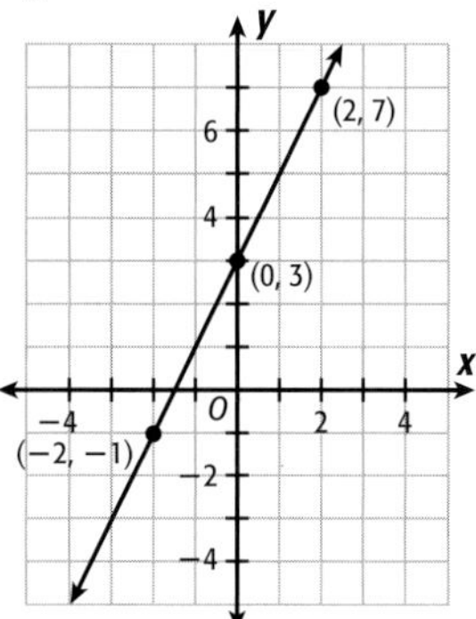

Input	Rule	Output	Ordered Pair
x	$2x + 3$	y	(x, y)
−2	$2(-2) + 3$	−1	(−2, −1)
0	$2(0) + 3$	3	(0, 3)
2	$2(2) + 3$	7	(2, 7)

8. $y = 3x + 40$

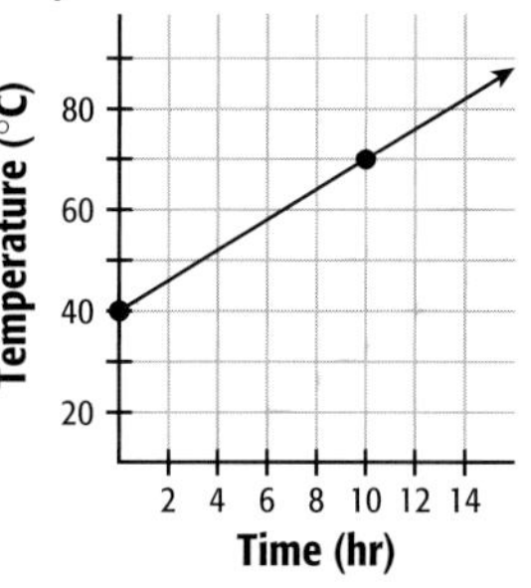

9. $y = x$

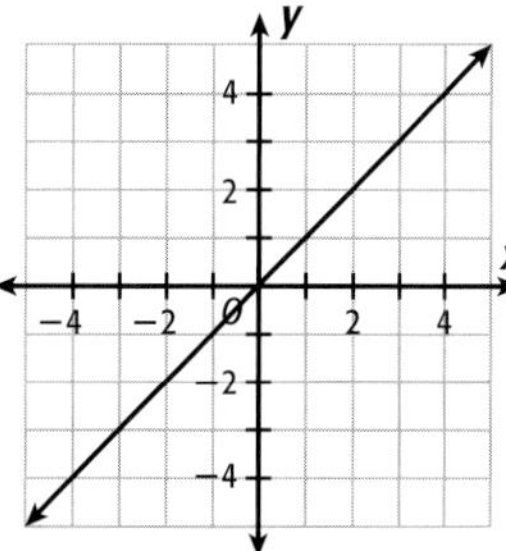

10. $y = -2x + 1$

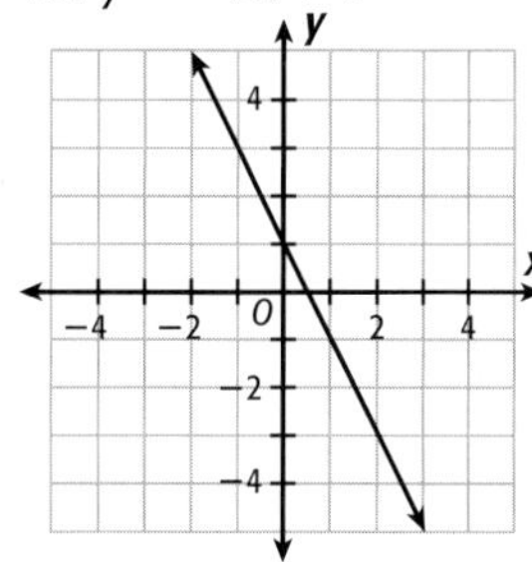

11. $y = -2$

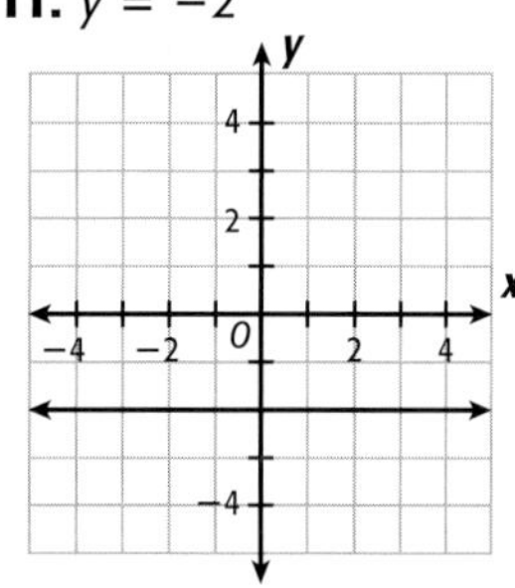

12. $y = \frac{5}{2}x - 1$

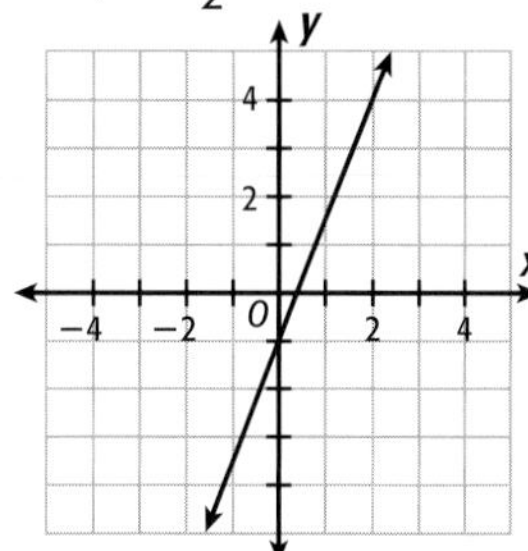

13. $y = 6$

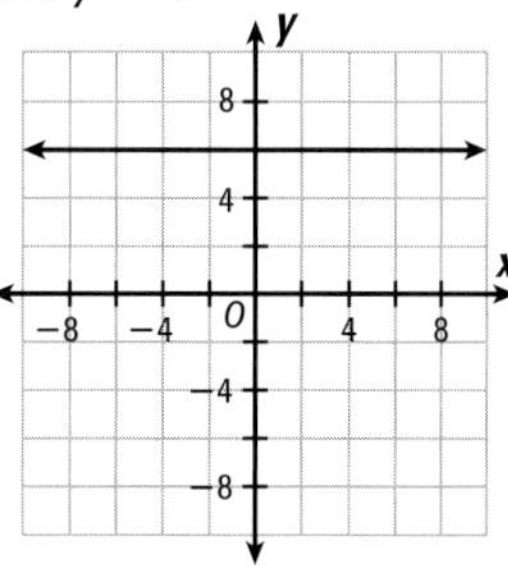

14. $y = -\frac{1}{2}x - 3$

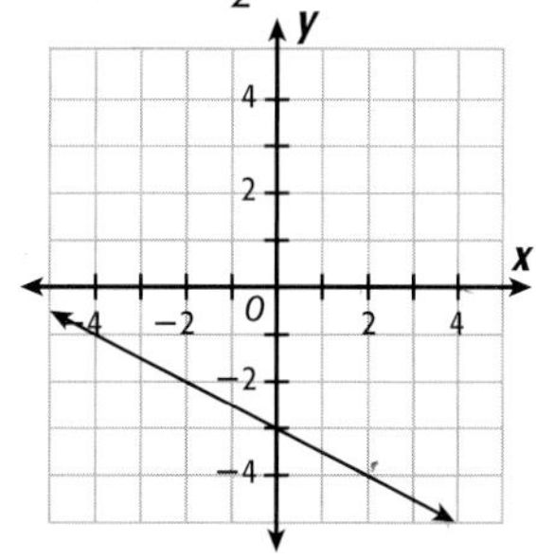

19. It is not linear.

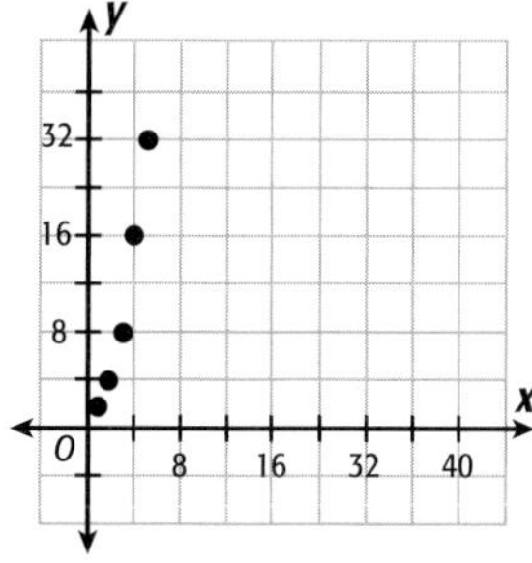

Input	Rule	Output	Ordered Pair
x	2^x	y	(x, y)
1	2^1	2	(1, 2)
2	2^2	4	(2, 4)
3	2^3	8	(3, 8)
4	2^4	16	(4, 16)
5	2^5	32	(5, 32)

Lesson 12-5

7.

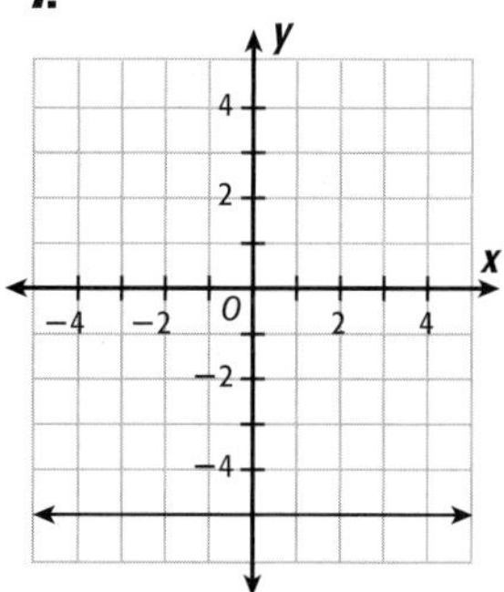

8.

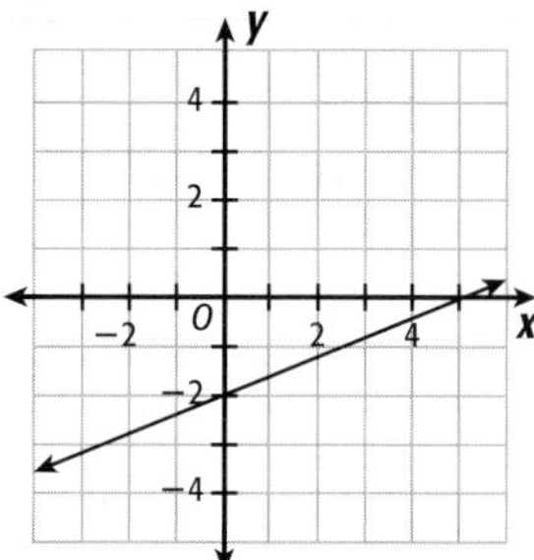

14.

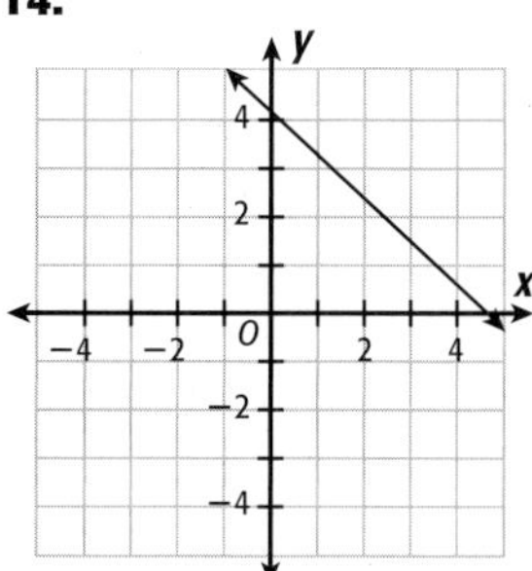

15.

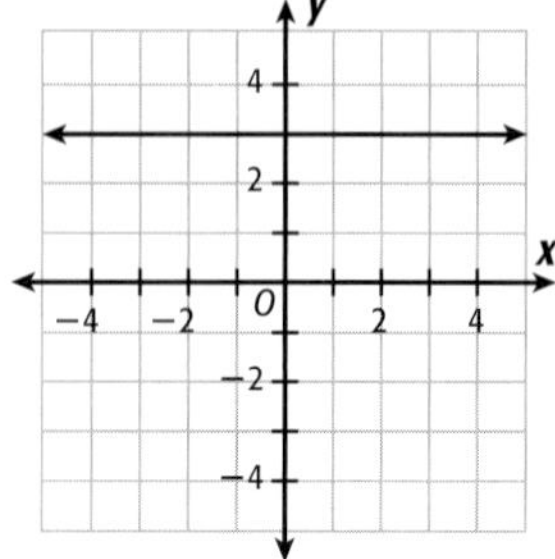

16.

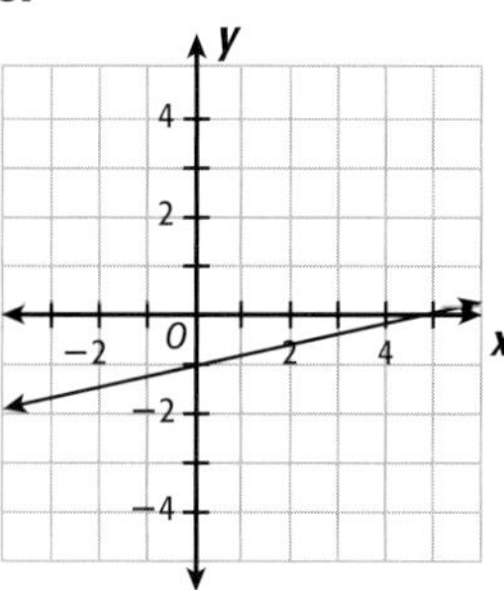

20. $y = -2x - 1$

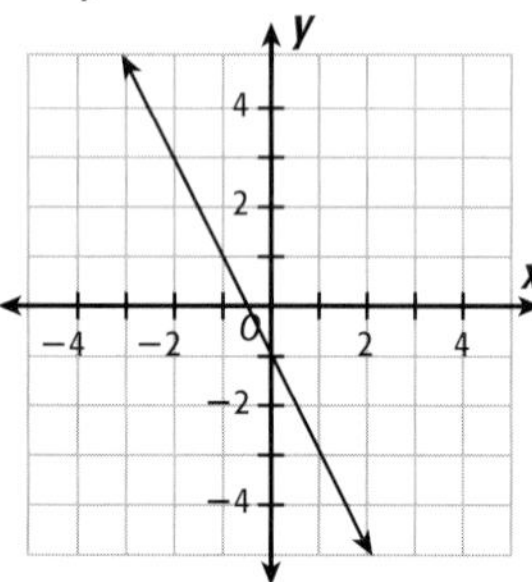

21. $y = -\frac{2}{5}x$

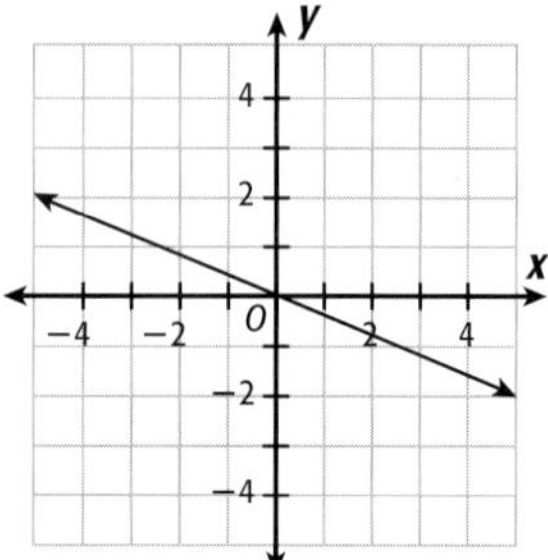

22. $y = \frac{2}{3}x + 1$

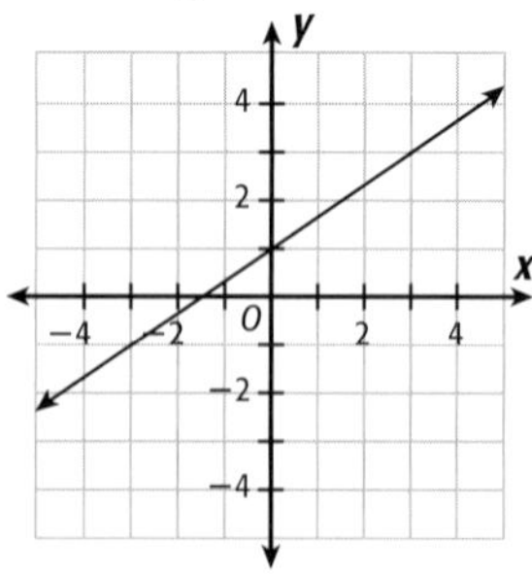

23.

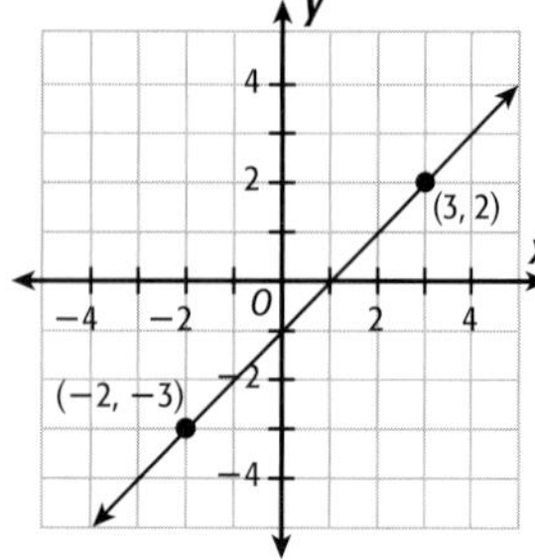

1; −1

24.

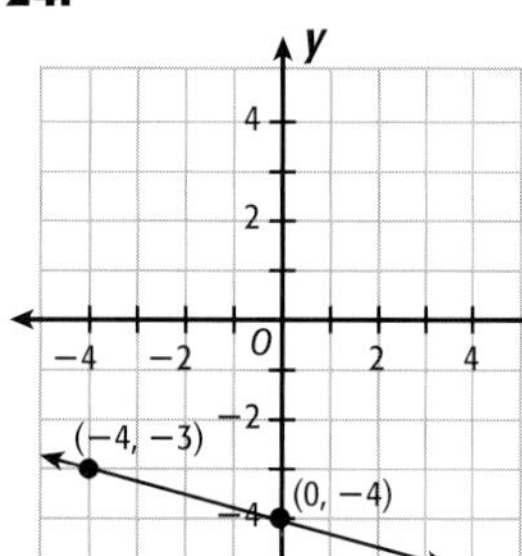

$-\frac{1}{4}$; −4

25.

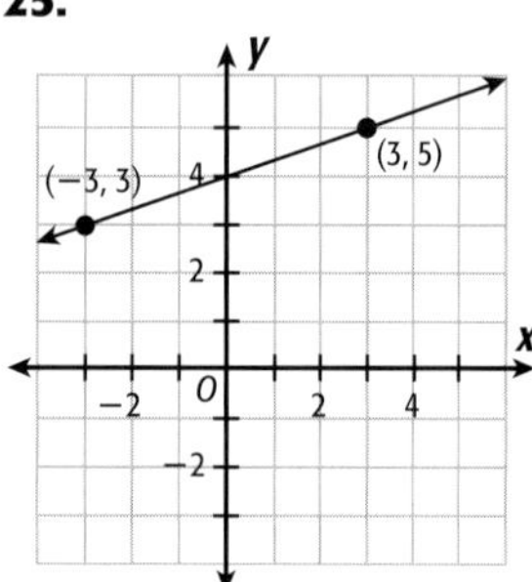

$\frac{1}{3}$; 4

26. 0; 2; $y = 2$

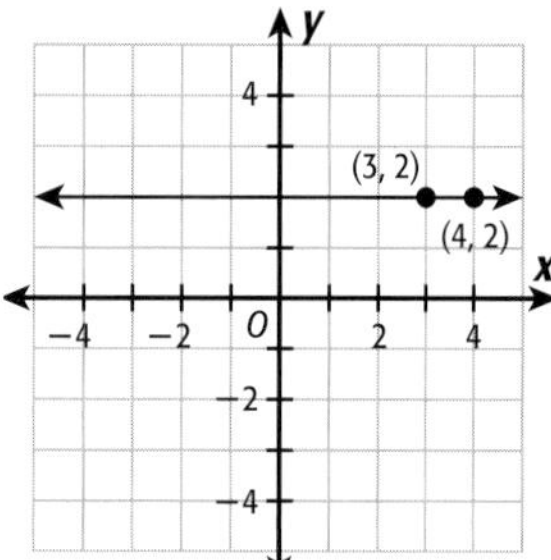

27. 2; −2; $y = 2x - 2$

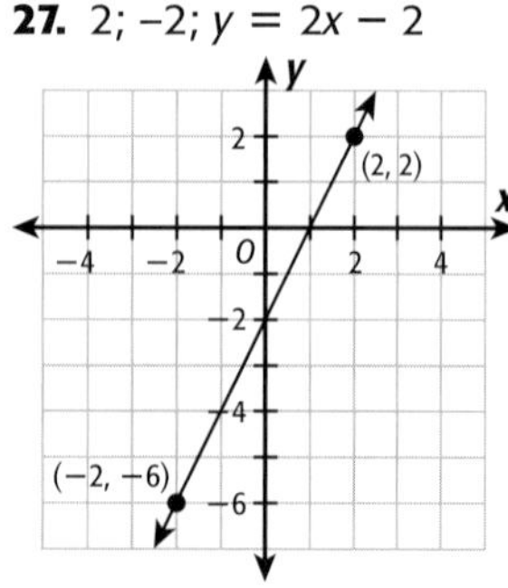

28. −3; 7; $y = -3x + 7$

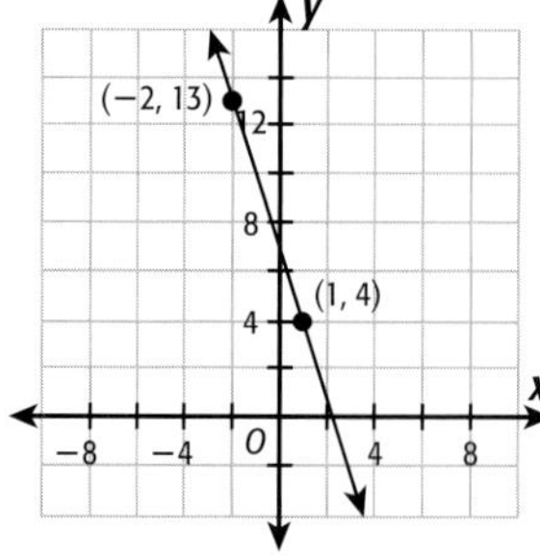

29. $\frac{3}{2}$; 0; $y = \frac{3}{2}x$

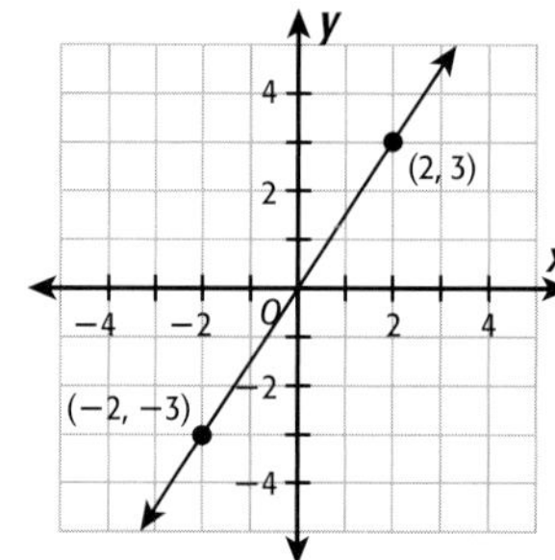

30. −2; 1; $y = -2x + 1$

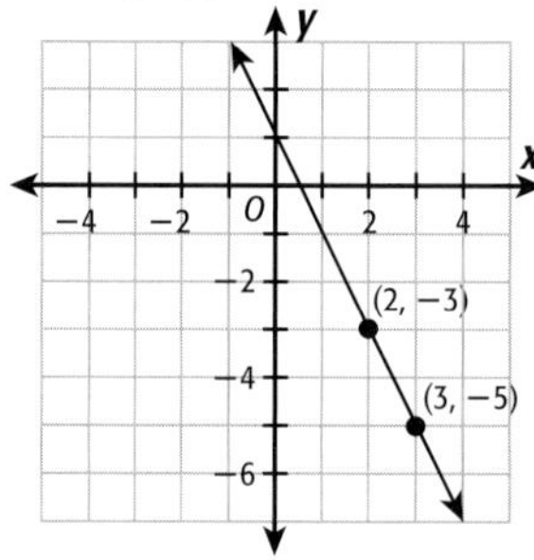

31. 0, −3; $y = -3$

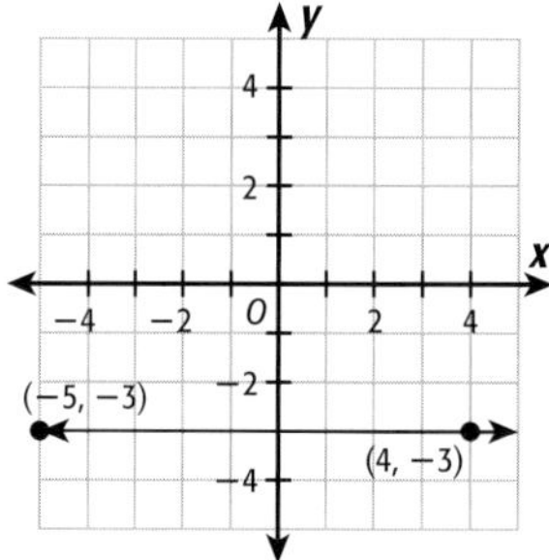

33. a.

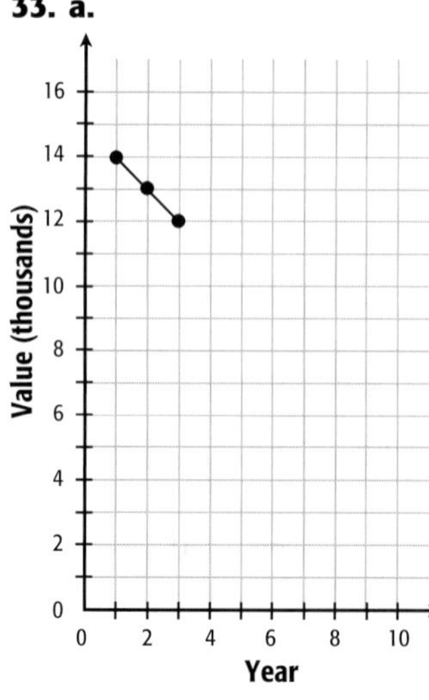

35. Possible answer: A line with a positive slope goes upward from left to right, and a line with a negative slope goes downward from left to right.

Lesson 12-6

14.

Time (s)	Distance (ft)
1	16
2	64
3	144
4	256

nonlinear

15. Possible answer: It shows that the longer an object falls, the more the distance increases, but not at a constant rate.

16. Possible answer: rule: $d = 2 \cdot 10 \text{ ft/s} \cdot t^2$

Time (s)	Distance (ft)
1	20
2	80
3	180
4	320

Lesson 12-7

25.

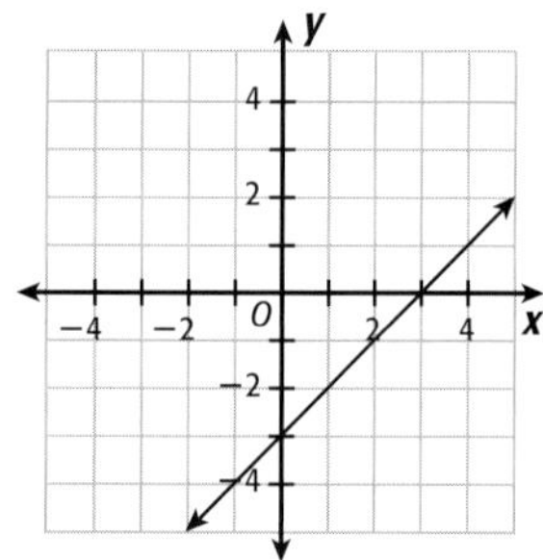

26.

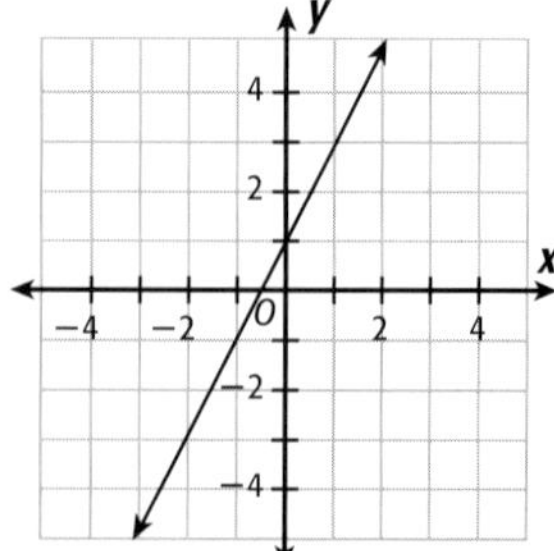

27.

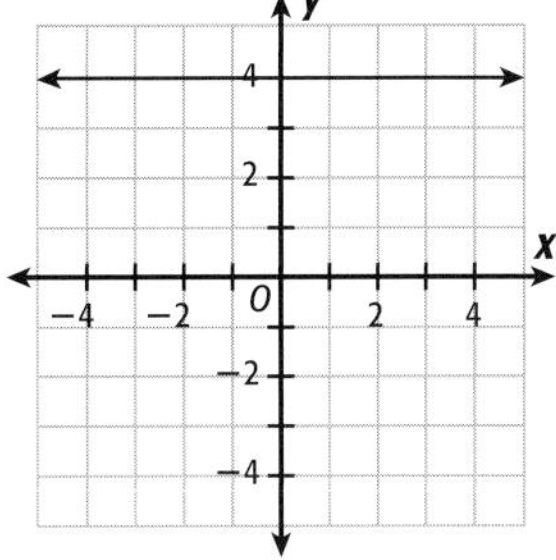

28.

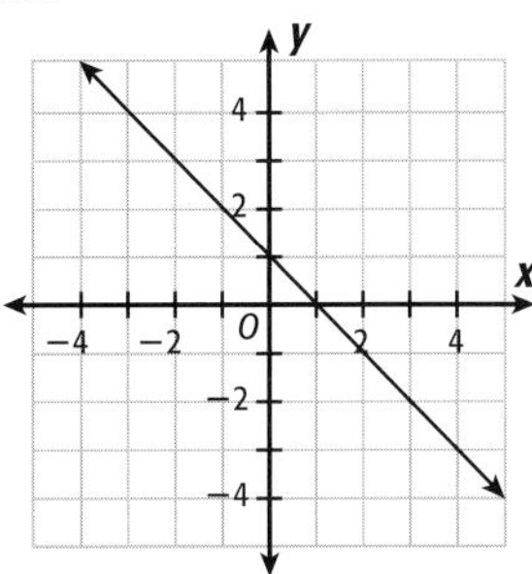

Technology Lab: Graph Linear Equations

1.

WINDOW
Xmin=-10
Xmax=10
Xscl=1
Ymin=-10
Ymax=10
Yscl=1
Xres=1

slope = 1; y-intercept = 3

2.

WINDOW
Xmin=-10
Xmax=10
Xscl=1
Ymin=-10
Ymax=10
Yscl=1
Xres=1

slope = −1; y-intercept = 4

3.

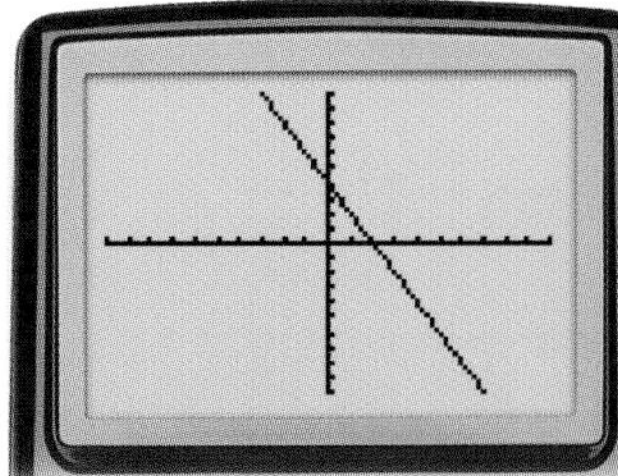

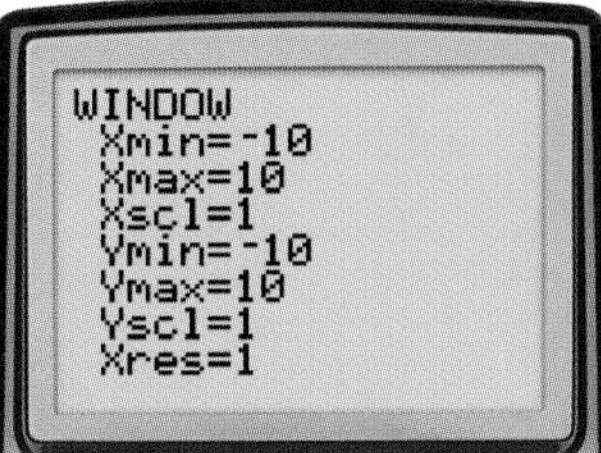

slope = −2;
y-intercept = 4

4.

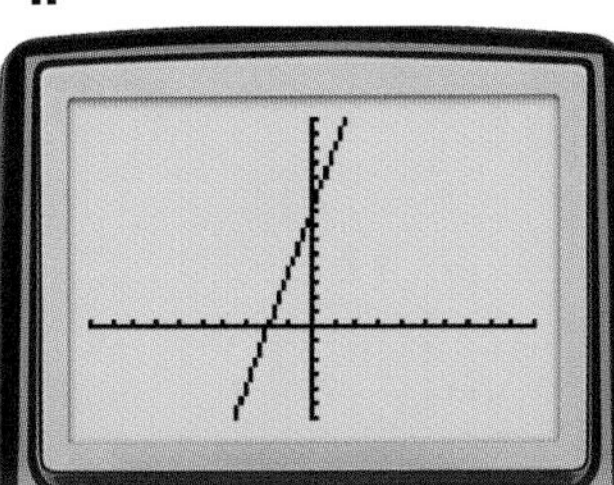

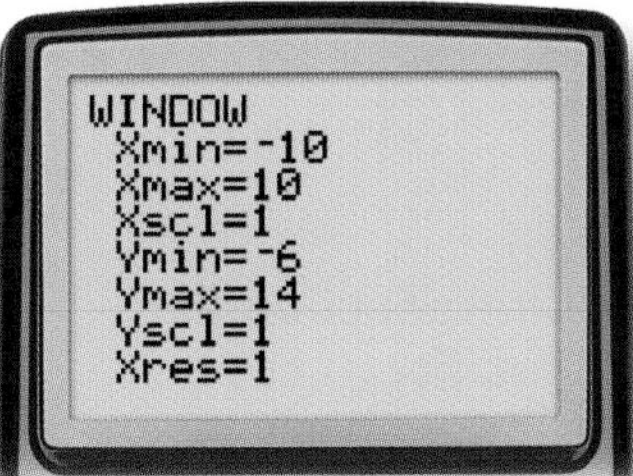

slope = 4; y-intercept = 8

5.

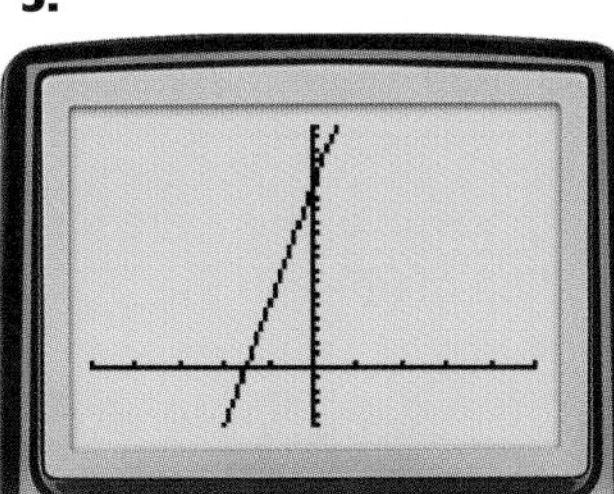

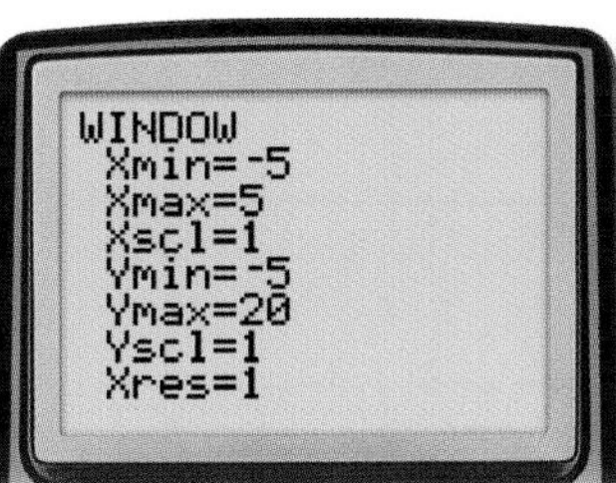

slope = 10;
y-intercept = 15

6.

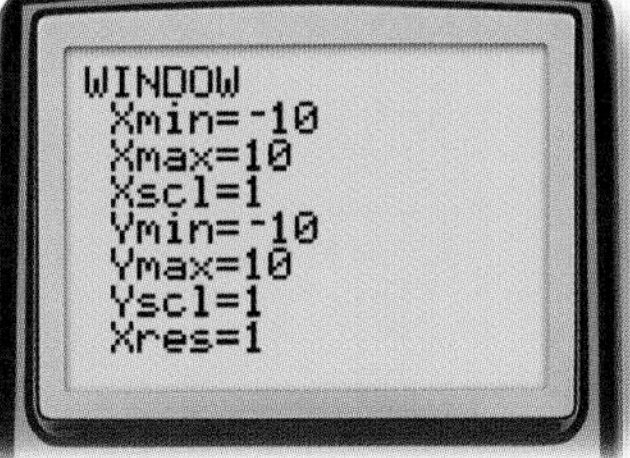

slope = 1;
y-intercept = −2

Performance Assessment

2.

x	y
0	−3
2	1
4	5
6	9

It is linear, because the differences between consecutive input and consecutive output terms are the same.

4.

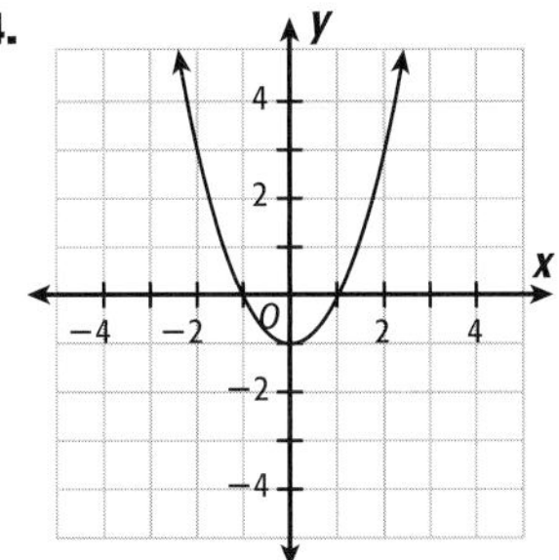

D: all real numbers; R: all real numbers greater than or equal to −1

5. The slope is the numerical coefficient of x, or 3, and the y-intercept is the number added to the x-term, or 1.

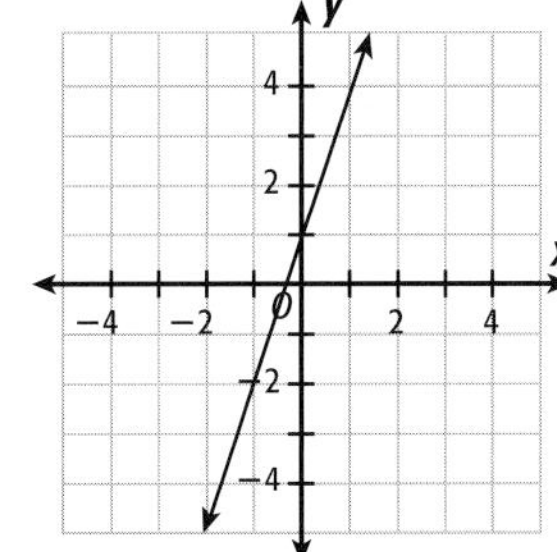

Extra Practice

1A Organizing Data

10. Outlier is 56. Without the outlier the mean is 24, and with the outlier the mean is 28. Without the outlier the median is 23, and with the outlier the median is 24. There is no mode in either situation.

11. Outlier is 239. Without the outlier the mean is 71, and with the outlier the mean is 92. Without the outlier the median is 66, and with the outlier the median is 72. The mode is 66 in either situation.

12. Outlier is 10. Without the outlier the mean is 36, and with the outlier the mean is 32.75. Without the outlier the median is 36, and with the outlier the median is 35.5. The modes are 35 and 39 in either situation.

13. Outlier is 47. Without the outlier the mean is 151, and with the outlier the mean is 138. Without the outlier the median is 152, and with the outlier the median is 150. There is no mode in either situation.

14.

Points Scored During the Last Ten Games of the Season

Points Scored	Frequency	Cumulative Frequency
10–20	1	1
21–30	2	3
31–40	4	7
41–50	3	10

15.

Number of Points Scored

Stems	Leaves
1	8
2	7 8
3	1 2 4 6
4	2 3 6

Key: 1|8 means 18

1B Displaying Data

1.

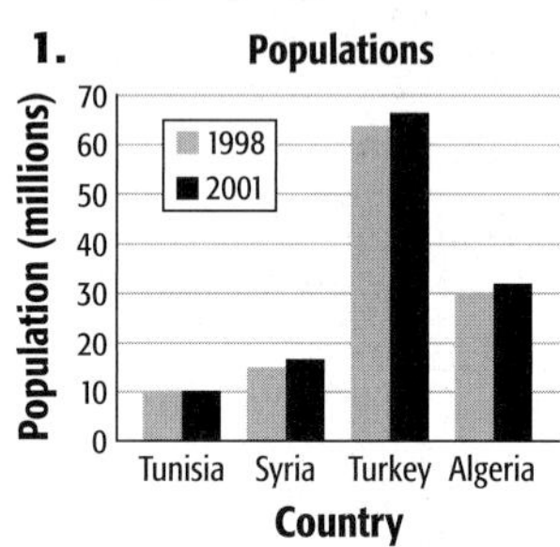

2.

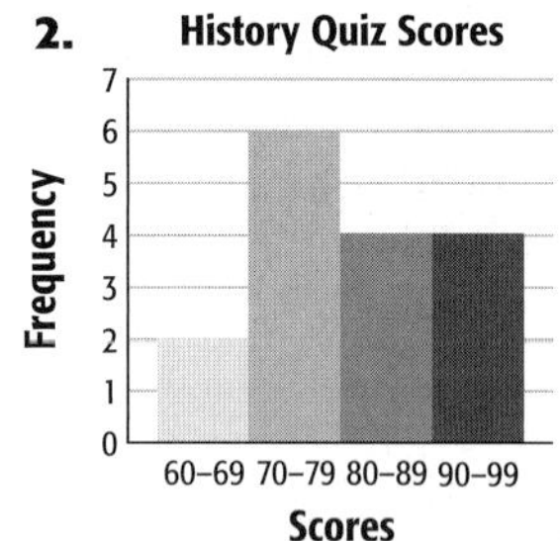

11.

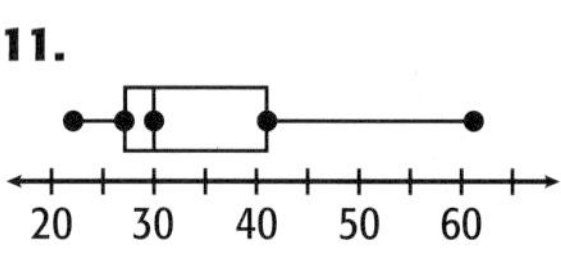

1C Trends and Relations in Graphs

1.

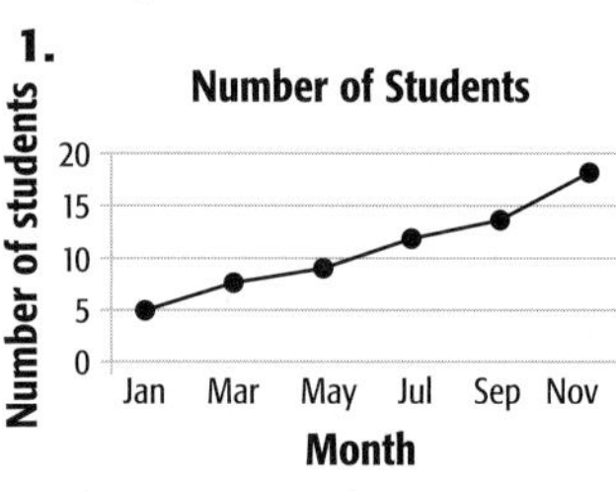

from September to November

4.

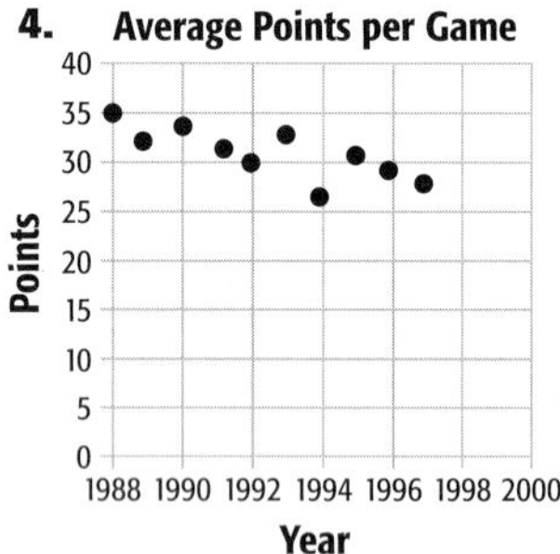

no correlation

8. The scale on the *y*-axis does not start at zero, so it looks as though Iran's population is less than 2 times greater than Australia's when it is actually more than 2 times greater.

9. The *y*-axis is broken, so it looks as if Hungary's population is less than twice as large as Ireland's when it is almost 3 times greater.

3A Integers

1.

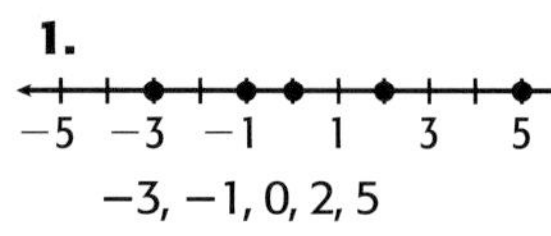

$-3, -1, 0, 2, 5$

2.

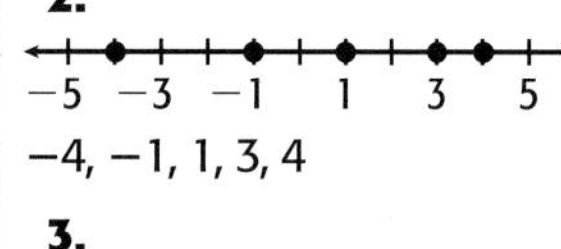

$-4, -1, 1, 3, 4$

3.

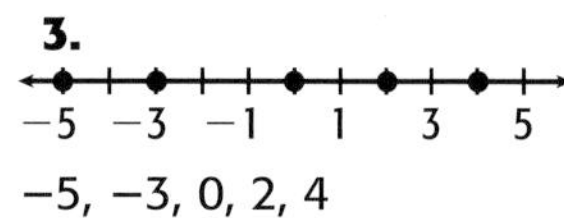

$-5, -3, 0, 2, 4$

8.

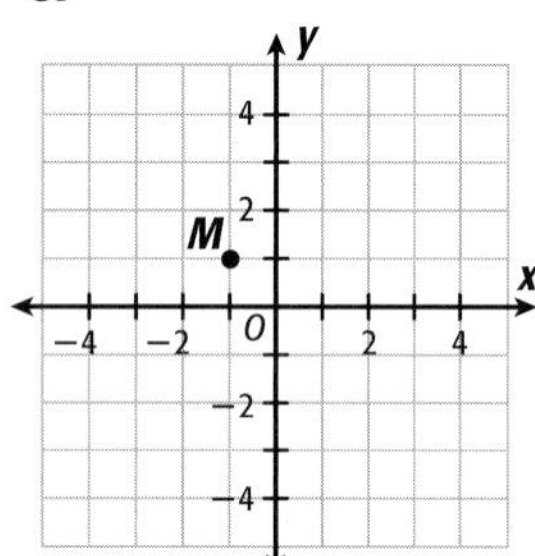

9.

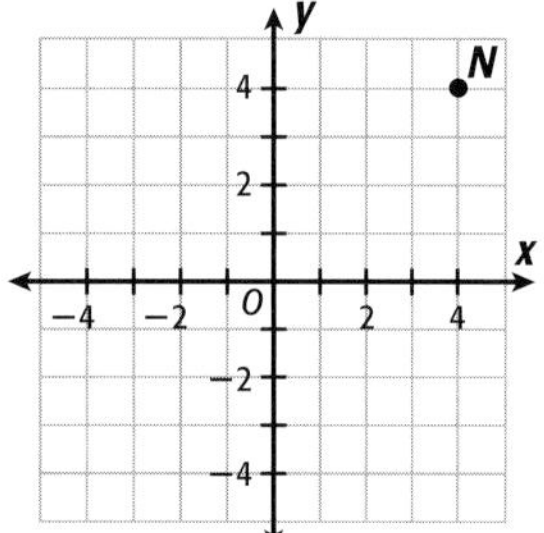

10.

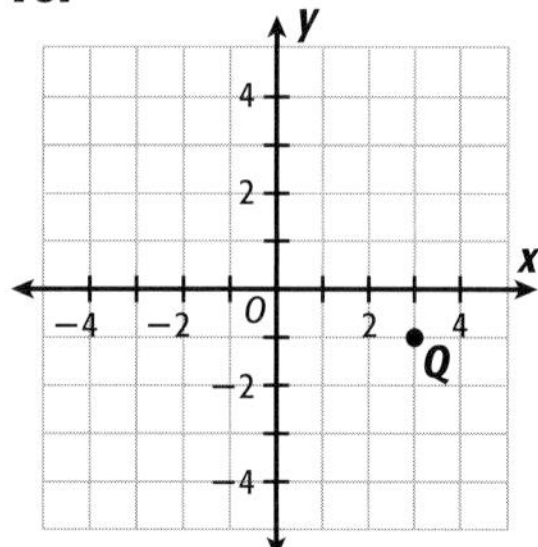

3B Rational Numbers

1.

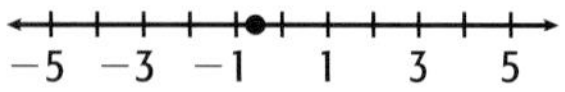

2.

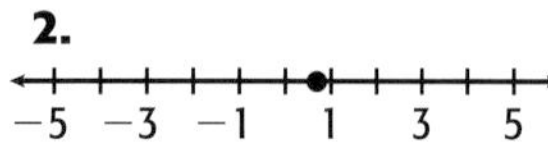

3.

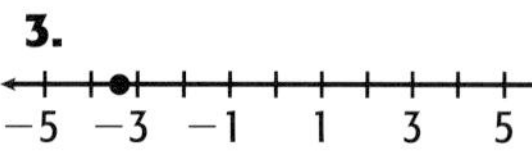

4.

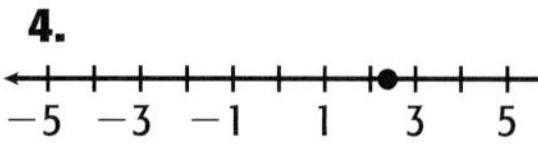

5A Numerical Proportions

4. $\frac{3 \text{ gal}}{1 \text{ min}}$, 3 gal per minute

5. $\frac{4 \text{ in}}{1 \text{ h}}$, 4 in. per hour

6. $\frac{2.5 \text{ c water}}{1 \text{ c rice}}$, 2.5 c water per 1 c rice

7C Closed Figure Relationships

10.

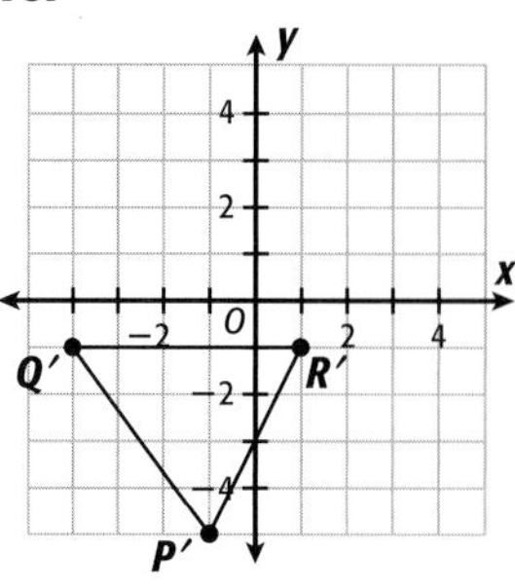

11.

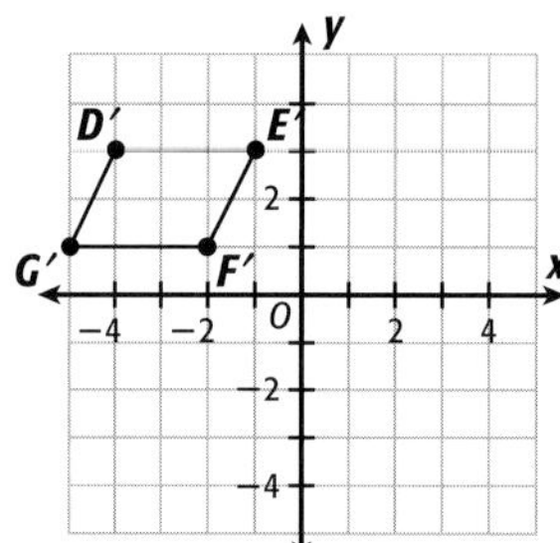

12.

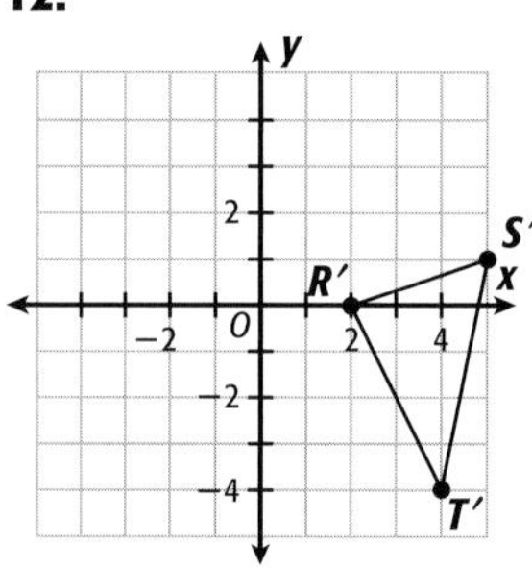

10A Introduction to Probability

1. Likely; since Ian may not be playing tonight, or the game may have been canceled or postponed, it is not certain that Ian is playing soccer.

2. Impossible; there are no blue marbles in the pouch.

11B Inequalities

3.

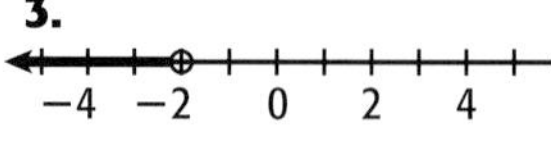

4.

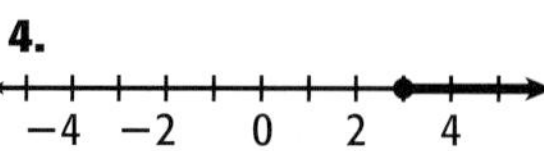

5.

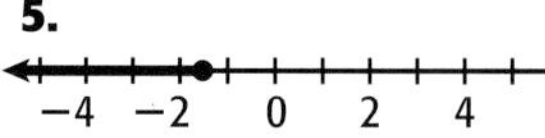

6.

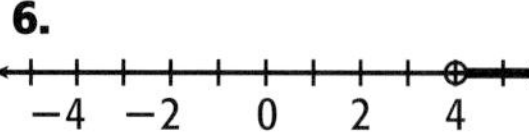

7.

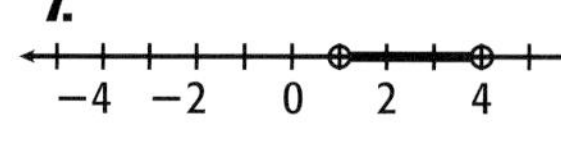

8.

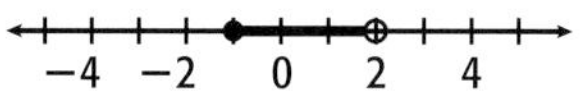

9.

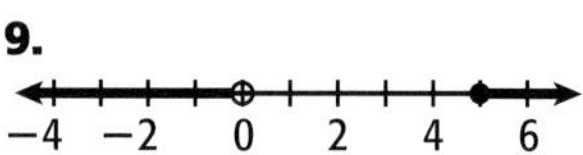

10.

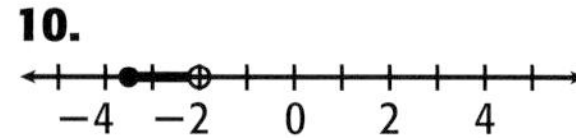

11. $c > 1$

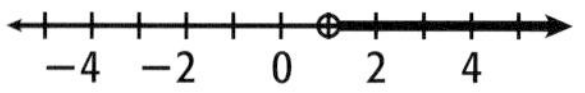

12. $v \geq 4$

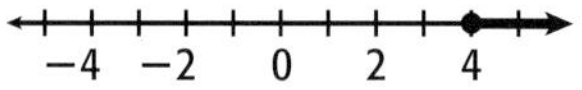

13. $w \leq -1$

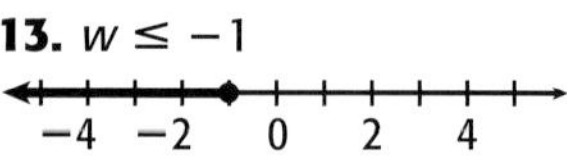

14. $a \leq 7$

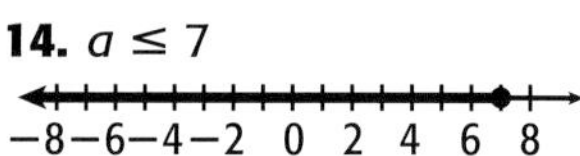

29. $m \leq 9$;

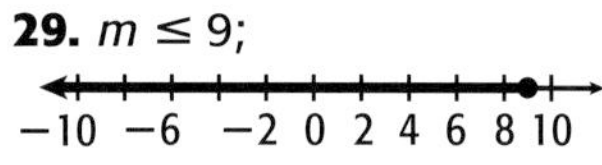

30. $x > 4$;

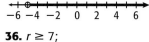

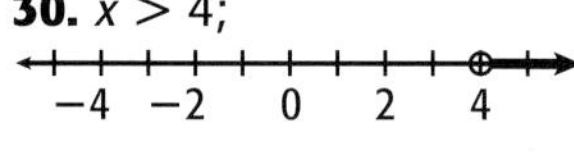

31. $h > -2$;

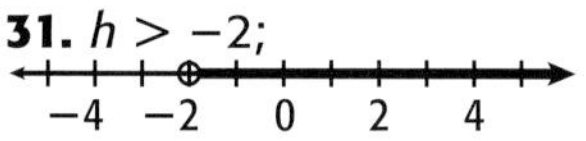

32. $s \leq -7$;

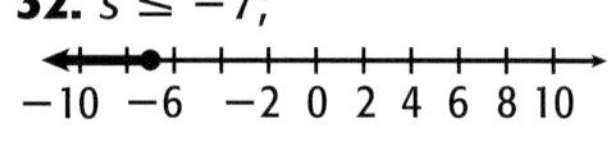

33. $w \geq 3$;

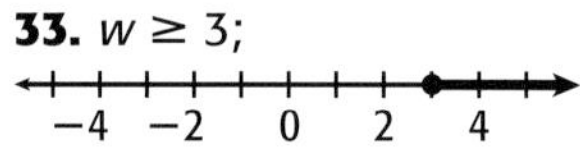

34. $j > \frac{11}{2}$, or $5\frac{1}{2}$;

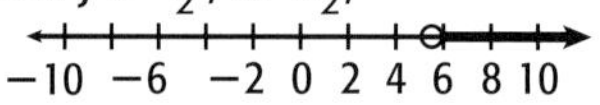

35. $u > -5$;

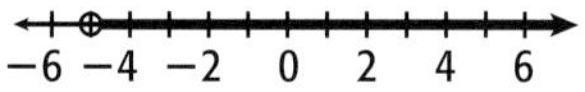

36. $r \geq 7$;

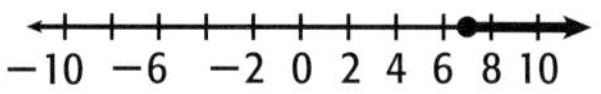

37. $m \geq -108$;

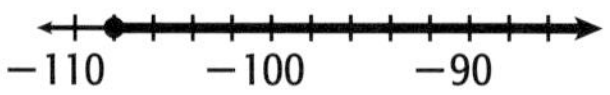

12A Introducing Functions

1.

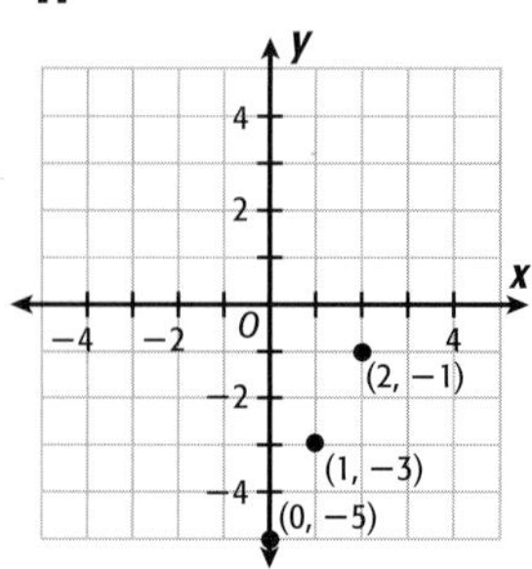

2.

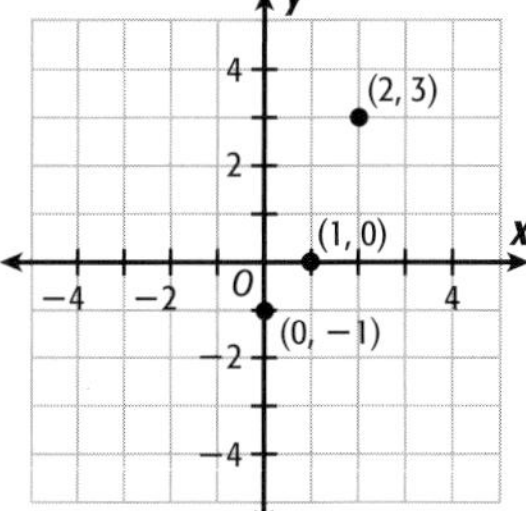

7.

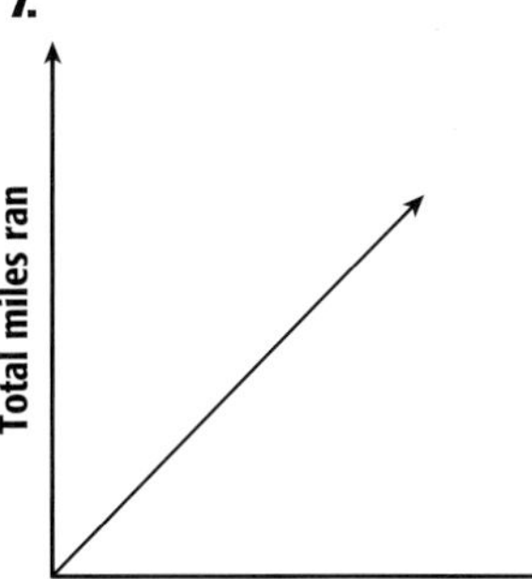

11.

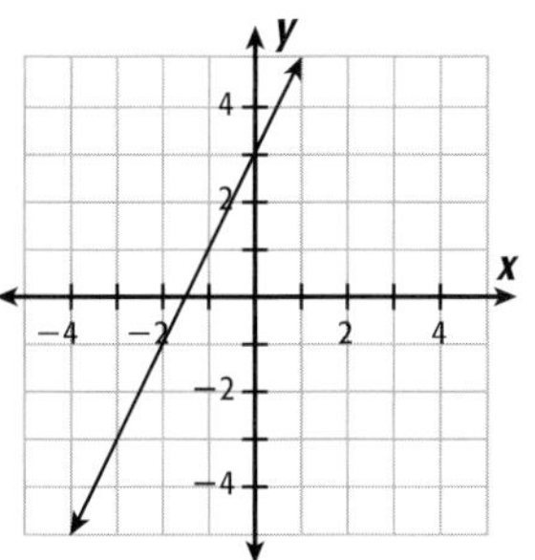

12.

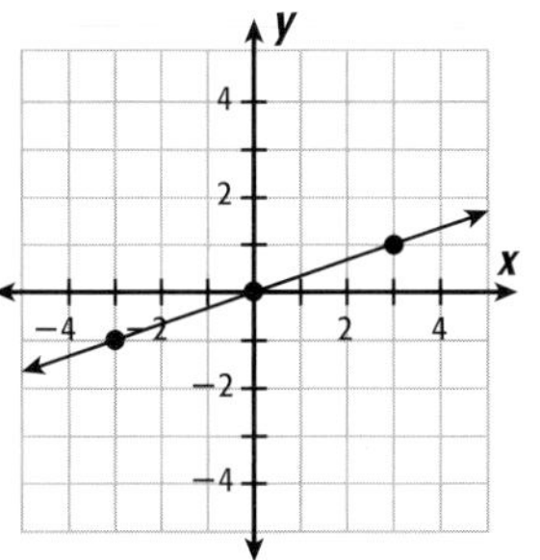

Skills Bank

Read and Write Decimals

1. seventeen and two hundred thirty-eight thousandths
2. nine and twenty-three ten-thousandths
3. five hundred thirty-four and one thousand nine hundred seventy-two hundred-thousandths
4. thirty-three and eigthy-four hundred-thousandths
5. four thousand three hundred fifty-six and sixty-seven hundredths

Lesson Quizzes

Lesson 1-3

1.

Nurses' Ages		
Ages	Frequency	Cumulative Frequency
20–29	5	5
30–39	7	12
40–49	4	16
50–59	2	18
60–69	2	20

2.

Stems	Leaves
2	1 3 3 4 4
3	1 3 4 5 5 8 9
4	2 5 5 5
5	7 7
6	0 1

Key: 2|1 means 21

Lesson 1-4

1.

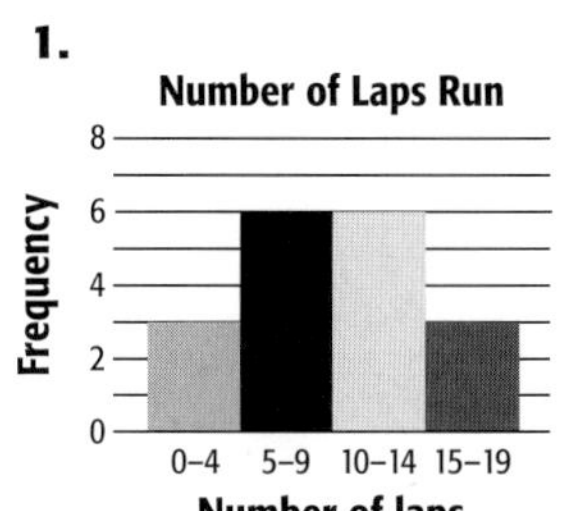

2.

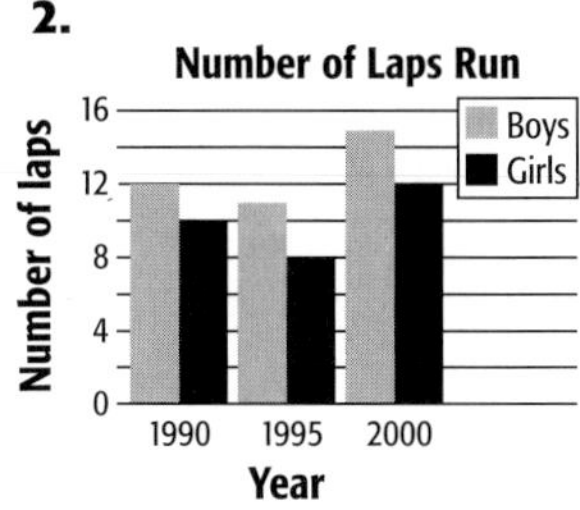

Lesson 1-7

1.

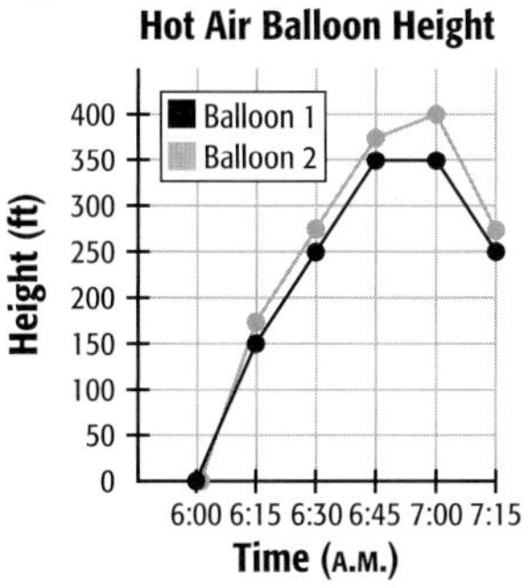

Hot Air Balloon Height

Balloon 1
Balloon 2

Height (ft)

Time (A.M.)

6:00 6:15 6:30 6:45 7:00 7:15

Lesson 1-8

1.

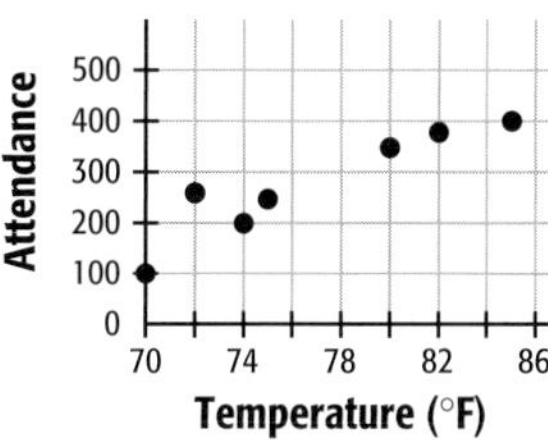

Notes

Photo

Cover (All)**:** Pronk & Associates.

Title page (All)**:** Pronk & Associates.

Master icons — teens (All)**:** Sam Dudgeon/HRW.

Author photos by Sam Dudgeon/HRW

Problem Solving Handbook: xix Victoria Smith/HRW; xx (t), © Stone, Lynn/Animals Animals/Earth Scenes; xxi (all), Victoria Smith/HRW/"Pride of the Plains" puzzle images used by permission of Sally J. Smith and FX Schmid, USA.; xxii (all), Peter Van Steen/HRW/cards created by Joyce Gonzalez; xxiii & xxv Victoria Smith/HRW; xxvi (all), © Richard Herrmann; xxvii Victoria Smith/HRW. **Chapter 1:** 2–3 (bkgd), © Sam Fried/Photo Researchers, Inc.; 2 (br), Victoria Smith/HRW; 4 © Bill Banaszewski/Photolink; 5 Victoria Smith/HRW; 7 M*A*S*H © 1983 Twentieth Century Fox Television. All rights reserved./Courtesy Everett Collection; 10 © CORBIS; 11 (l), © James L. Amos/CORBIS/Collection of The Corning Museum of Glass, Corning, New York; 13 © Karl Weatherly/CORBIS; 14 Courtesy IMAX Corporation; 17 (tr), Klein/Hubert-BIOS/Peter Arnold, Inc.; 19 (b), © Stephen Frink/Index Stock Imagery/PictureQuest; 22 (all), PhotoDisc - Digital Image copyright © 2004 PhotoDisc; 23 (bl, cl & tr), © David J. & Janice L. Frent Collection/CORBIS; 23 (tl & cr), © CORBIS; 23 (br), © Bettmann/CORBIS; 24 (br), © Kathy deWet-Oleson/Lonely Planet Images; 24 (bl), © Jeffrey L. Rotman/CORBIS; 24 (tr), © Michael Aw/Lonely Planet Images; 25 (l), © Ron Sanford/Photo Researchers, Inc.; 26 (t), Sam Dudgeon/HRW; 28 © Bernd Mellmann/Alamy Photos; 31 © Reuters New Media, Inc./CORBIS; 35 (all), SuperStock; 38 SuperStock; 43 © Ecoscene/CORBIS; 45 (l), Copyright © 1998–2001 EyeWire, Inc. All rights reserved.; 45 (r), © James A. Sugar/CORBIS; 48 (r), © Carl A. Stimac/The Image Finders; 49 (b), © Journal-Courier/Steve Warmowski/The Image Works; 49 (t), © Stuart Westmorland/CORBIS; 56 Victoria Smith/HRW. **Chapter 2:** 58–59 (bkgd), © AFP/CORBIS; 58 (br), David Gamble/Sygma; 61 © AFP/CORBIS; 63 (all), Bruce Iverson; 64 © Bill Frymire/Masterfile; 73 (br), Sam Dudgeon/HRW; 75 (bc & br), EyeWire - Digital Image copyright © (2004) EyeWire; 75 (bl), PhotoDisc - Digital Image copyright © (2004) PhotoDisc; 78 © Declan McCullagh; 82 Sam Dudgeon/HRW; 83 (all), Victoria Smith/HRW; 85 (l), Collection Walker Art Center, Minneapolis Gift of Fredrick R. Weisman in honor of his parents, William and Mary Weisman, 1988; 86 © 2001 Ron Kimball Studios; 89 (t), © D. Donne Bryant/DDB Stock Photo/All Rights Reserved; 89 (b), Erich Lessing/Art Resource, NY; 91 (b), Lisette LeBon/SuperStock; 92 (t), Everett Collection; 92 (b), Frederic De Lafosse/Sygma; 92 (c), Ulvis Alberts/Motion Picture & Television Photo Archive; 96 © David Allan Brandt/Getty Images/Stone; 99 (l), Photo Researchers, Inc.; 103 Courtesy of the National Grocers Association Best Bagger Contest; 104 Peter Van Steen/HRW; 105 (all), Sam Dudgeon/HRW/Courtesy Fast Forward Skate Shop, Austin, TX; 107 (br), James Urbach/SuperStock; 115 © Reuters NewMedia Inc./CORBIS; 118-119 (b), © Ali Kabas/Alamy Photos; 118 (cr), © 2001/ImageState Inc.; 118 (bl), © Joseph Sohm; ChromoSohm Inc./CORBIS; 120 (cl, cr & b), © Jenny Thomas/HRW; 126 Peter Van Steen/HRW. **Chapter 3:** 128–129 (bkgd), Tom Pantages Photography; 128 (br), © Jay Ireland & Georgienne E. Bradley; 130 (br), Chuck Nicklin/Al Giddings Images, Inc.; 130 (tl), Natalie Fobes/National Geographic Collection; 133 (l), © Neil Rabinowitz/CORBIS; 137 (l), © Stock Trek/PhotoDisc/Picture Quest; 140 © 2001 Jay Mallin; 143 (l), © Lee Foster/Words & Pictures/PictureQuest; 149 (t), © CORBIS; 151 © W. Faidley/WS Image; 153 © Ann Purcell; Carl Purcell/Words & Pictures/PictureQuest; 161 (b), Sam Dudgeon/HRW/Sheet music courtesy Martha Dudgeon.; 166 Victoria Smith/HRW; 169 (l), Michael Rosenfeld/Stone/Getty Images; 170 © Reuters New Media Inc./CORBIS; 173 (b), Classic PIO Partners; 173 (t), Image Copyright © Digital Vision; 173 (c), © Underwood & Underwood/CORBIS; 177 (l), © Buddy Mays/CORBIS; 180 (cr), © Walter Bibikow/Viesti Collection, Inc.; 180 (br), © Erin Woodruff/Nik Wheeler; 181 (t), Courtesy of the Chesapeake Bay Bridge-Tunnel/Photo by Walter C. Grantz; 181 (br), © Paul A. Souders/CORBIS; 181 (tr), © Stockbyte; 182 (br), © Jenny Thomas/HRW; 188 (all), Victoria Smith/HRW. **Chapter 4:** 190–191 (bkgd), © Brian Leatart/FoodPix; 190 (b), Jenny Thomas/HRW; 192 Richard Nowitz/Photo Researchers, Inc.; 195 (l), © Paul Almasy/CORBIS; 196 © Lynn Stone/Index Stock Imagery/PictureQuest; 199 (l), AP Photo/The Fresno Bee, Richard Darby/Wide World Photos; 206 Darren Carroll/HRW; 213 © Galen Rowell/CORBIS; 214 Darren Carroll/HRW; 215 Victoria Smith/HRW/Courtesy Oshman's, Austin, TX; 217 (l), © Gail Mooney/CORBIS; 219 (b), Ken Karp/HRW; 222 © Glen Allison/Alamy Photos; 227 (l), Hulton Archive by Getty Images; 229 (r), Victoria Smith/HRW; 229 (tl), Richard Heinzen/SuperStock; 230 © Jeffrey L. Rotman/CORBIS; 239 (l), © Gallo Images/CORBIS; 239 (r), G.K. & Vikki Hart/Getty Images; 240 (l), Wolfgang Kaehler Photography; 243 (l), © Michael John Kielty/CORBIS; 244 Peter Van Steen/HRW/Courtesy Russell Korman Fine Jewelry, Austin, TX; 245 © Charles O'Rear/CORBIS; 248 (c), © Tony Freeman/PhotoEdit; 249 (t), Smithsonian Institution, Washington, DC; 249 (b), © Hulton-Deutsch Collection/CORBIS; 250 (b), © Jenny Thomas/HRW. **Chapter 5:** 258–259 (bkgd), Ship model by Jean K. Eckert/Photo Courtesy of © The Mariners' Museum, Newport News, Virginia; 258 (b), Gordon Chibroski/Press Herald/AP/Wide World Photos; 260 Darren Carrol/HRW; 263 (br), © Michael Lawrence/Lonely Planet Images; 263 (bc), © Chris Mellor/Lonely Planet Images; 263 (t), © Gavin Anderson/Lonely Planet Images; 263 (bl), © Stephen Frink/CORBIS; 263 (tr), © Stephen Frink/Alamy Photos; 264 Victoria Smith/HRW; 265 James L. Amos/SuperStock; 268 (all), Victoria Smith/HRW/Jenga ® is a registered trademark of Pokonobe Associates and is used with its permission. © 2002 Pokonobe Associates. All rights reserved. 269 (all), Victoria Smith/HRW/Jenga ® is a registered trademark of Pokonobe Associates and is used with its permission. © 2002 Pokonobe Associates. All rights reserved. 272 NASA; 275 (l), © Amos Nachoum/Corbis Stock Market; 275 (r), PhotoDisc - Digital Image © 2004; 277 (b), Sam Dudgeon/HRW; 280 Peter Van Steen/HRW; 284 © Francis E. Caldwell/Affordable Photo Stock; 288 (t), Sam Dudgeon/HRW/Courtesy Chuck and Nan Ellis; 288 (b), Victoria Smith/HRW; 289 Van Gogh Museum, Amsterdam/SuperStock; 291 (t & b), Library of Congress; 291 (c), Victoria Smith/HRW; 291 (t-frame) © 1999 Image Farm, Inc.; 292 (cr), Courtesy The United States Army Corps of Engineers, National Great Rivers Museum; 292 (br), © Cathy Melloan/PhotoEdit; 293 (t), © Bettmann/CORBIS; 294 (b), Randall Hyman/HRW; 300 Sam Dudgeon/HRW. **Chapter 6:** 302–303 (bkgd), © Mark E. Gibson Photography; 302 (br), Victoria Smith/HRW; 308 Peter Van Steen/HRW; 315 (l), © Richard A. Cooke/CORBIS; 316 © Buddy Mays/CORBIS; 319 (l), © Ellen Senisi/The Image Works; 321 (b), © 1998 Joseph De Sciose; 324 Sam Dudgeon/HRW; 325 Peter Van Steen/HRW; 331 (l), © Archivo Iconografico, S.A./CORBIS; 332 (b), Photo © James Schwabel/Panoramic Images, Chicago 1994; 332 (bc), © Stephanie Maze/CORBIS; 332 (tc), © Macduff Everton/CORBIS; 333 (tr), Dale Atkins/AP/Wide World Photos; 333 (tl & b), Courtesy Michigan State University; 334 (b), Randall Hyman/HRW; 340 © James Marshall/CORBIS. **Chapter 7:** 342–343 (bkgd), © 2002 Bruno Burklin/Aerial Aesthetics; 342 (br), © Stone/Getty Images/Stone; 344 The Art Archive/Private Collection /Harper Collins Publishers/© 2004 Artists Rights Society (ARS), New York/ADAGP, Paris; 346 Science Kit & Boreal Laboratories; 347 (t), © Burstein Collection/CORBIS/ © 2004 Mondrian/Holtzman Trust, c/o Beeldrecht/Artists Rights Society (ARS), New York; 347 (b), Copyright Tate Gallery, London, Great Britain/Art Resource, NY/© 2004 Artist Rights Society (ARS), New York/Pro Litteris, Zurich; 354 © Gisela Damm/eStock Photography/PictureQuest; 357 (l), John Burke/SuperStock; 362 (t & b), © Archivo Iconografico, S.A./CORBIS; 368 © Gianni Dagh Orti/CORBIS; 371 (t), John Warden/SuperStock; 371 (tc), © Roman Soumar/CORBIS; 371 (bc), © Jacqui Hurst/CORBIS; 371 (b), © Jacqui Hurst/CORBIS; 374 Sam Dudgeon/HRW; 377 (r), © Craig Aurness/CORBIS; 377 (l), © Mark E. Gibson; 378 © 1997 Jon Reis/Photolink; 381 (l), © Bob Krist/CORBIS; 385 (t), © CORBIS; 387 (b), © Craig Aurness/CORBIS; 388 (bl), Peter Van Steen/HRW; 388 (br), Sam Dudgeon/HRW; 390 (tl & tr), Peter Van Steen/HRW; 390 (tc & bc), Sam Dudgeon/HRW; 390 (br), © Mark Snyder, TetraLite Kites, Seattle, WA; 390 (bl), Peter Van Steen/Courtesy International Playthings, Inc. 392 (t), © Neal Preston/CORBIS; 394 (br) (twice) © 2001 Frank Siteman c/o MIRA; 395 (c & b), Werner Forman/Art Resource, NY; 395 (t), Smithsonian American Art Museum, Washington, DC/Art Resource, NY; 396 (t), Steve Vidler/SuperStock; 397 (tr), © Arthur Thévenart/CORBIS; 397 (c), © Karen Gowlett-Holmes; 397 (b), C. Zeiss/Bruce Coleman, Inc.; 399 (b), © William Panzer/Stock Connection/PictureQuest; 399 (t), © 2000 Joseph Scheer; 400 (t), Symmetry Drawing E121 by M.C. Escher © 1999 Cordon Art-Baarn-Holland. All rights reserved. 401 (t), Symmetry Drawing E25 by M.C. Escher © 1999 Cordon Art-Baarn-Holland. All rights reserved. 402–403 (br), © Dave G. Houser/CORBIS; 402 (cl) & 403 (t), © Getty Images/FPG International; 404 (b), Ken Karp/HRW; 410, © Jonathan Blair/CORBIS. **Chapter 8:** 412–413 (bkgd), © Mark E. Gibson c/o MIRA; 412 (br), Victoria Smith/HRW; 414 © Frank Lane Picture Agency/CORBIS; 417 (l), Associated Press, AP/Wide World Photos; 418 (t), Michelle Bridwell/HRW; 418 (bl), © David A. Northcott/CORBIS; 418 (br), © Fogden, Michael/Animals Animals/Earth Scenes; 420 (t), Photo by Randall L. Ricklefs/McDonald Observatory;

420 (b), Sam Dudgeon/HRW; 423 (t), Peter Van Steen/HRW; 423 (b), © John Kelly/Getty Images/Stone; 424 David Walberg/Sports Illustrated; 427 NOAA Costal Services Center; 429 (b), © Bill Truslow/Stock Connection/PictureQuest; 430 (t), © Nik Wheeler/CORBIS; 433 © Christie's Images/CORBIS/© 2004 Banco de México Diego Rivera & Frida Kahlo Museums Trust. Av. Cinco de Mayo No. 2, Col. Centro, Del. Cuauhtémoc 06059, México, D.F./Reproducción autorizada por el Instituto Nacional de Bellas Artes Y Literatura; 433 (frame), HRW; 439 (br), © Yann Arthus-Bertrand/CORBIS; 439 (tl), © Carl & Ann Purcell/CORBIS; 441 (t), Photo © Stefan Schott/Panoramic Images, Chicago 1998; 443 (b), © TONY FREEMAN/PhotoEdit; 445 © Johathan Blair/CORBIS; 447 Digital Image copyright © 2004 Karl Weatherly/PhotoDisc; 451 © K. H. Photo/International Stock/ImageState; 453 (t), © Lary Lee Photography/CORBIS; 453 (bkgd), Corbis Images; 458 (bl), © Bettmann/CORBIS; 459 (b), Panoramic Images, Chicago 1998; 460 (b), Jenny Thomas/HRW; 466 (br), U.S. Postal Service. **Chapter 9:** 468–469 (bkgd), © Arvind Garg/CORBIS; 468 (br), Victoria Smith/HRW; 475 (tr), © Charles & Josette Lenars/CORBIS; 475 (bl), © Kevin Fleming/CORBIS; 475 (tl), Steve Vidler/SuperStock; 475 (br), R.M. Arakaki/Imagestate; 479 (r), Sam Dudgeon/HRW; 479 (l), © Natalie Fobes/CORBIS; 480 (t), Peter Van Steen/HRW; 483 (b), PhotoDisc - Digital Image copyright © 2002 PhotoDisc; 485 (b), Sam Dudgeon/HRW; 486 (t), Peter Van Steen/HRW; 487 (all), Victoria Smith/HRW; 488 (r), Mountain High Maps® Copyright © 1997 Digital Wisdom, Inc.; 490 (b), Sam Dudgeon/HRW; 491 (all), Peter Van Steen/HRW; 493 © Michael Newman/PhotoEdit; 495 (t), Hahn's Titanic Plans by Robert Hahn; 495 (c), Ulster Folk & Transport Museum; 495 (b), Bill Greenblatt/UPI Photo Service/NewsCom; 500 (cl), Alabama Department of Archives and History, Montgomery, Alabama; 500 (c), Brown Brothers; 500 (cr), © Joseph Sohm; ChromoSohm Inc./CORBIS; 500 (br), Victoria Smith/HRW; 501 (all), © Richard T. Nowitz/CORBIS; 502 (b), Jenny Thomas/HRW. **Chapter 10:** 510–511 (bkgd), © Getty Images/Stone; 510 (br), Victoria Smith/HRW; 516 © V.C.L. Tipp Howell/Getty Images/FPG International; 519 (b), REUTERS/Gary Wiepert /NewsCom; 519 (t), Courtesy of National Weather Service, NOAA; 520 Peter Van Steen/HRW; 523 (l), © David Young-Wolff/PhotoEdit; 524 (all), Victoria Smith/HRW/SCRABBLE® is a trademark of Hasbro in the United States and Canada. © 2002 Hasbro, Inc. All Rights Reserved.; 528 (l), Peter Van Steen/HRW; 528 (r), Digital Image copyright © 2004 EyeWire; 529 (b), © Left Lane Productions/CORBIS; 530 © Dennis Degnan/CORBIS; 532 (all), Sam Dudgeon/HRW; 536 Victoria Smith/HRW; 539 (tl), Pushkin Museum of Fine Arts, Moscow, Russia/SuperStock; 539 (tr), © Philadelphia Museum of Art/CORBIS; 540 Alden Pellett /AP/Wide World Photos; 543 (l), Photofest; 546 (bc & cr), © 2002 Kenny L. Tapp; 547 (all), © 2002 Robin R. Plasterer; 548 (c), Sam Dudgeon/HRW; 548 (b), Ken Karp/HRW; 554 © Bettmann/CORBIS. **Chapter 11:** 556–557 (bkgd), NASA; 556 (b), NASA; 561 (r), © Barry Winiker/Index Stock Imagery, Inc.; 561 (l), Sam Dudgeon/HRW; 563 (b), Sam Dudgeon/HRW; 563 (t), CLOSE TO HOME © 1994 John McPherson. Reprinted with Permission of UNIVERSAL PRESS SYNDICATE. All rights reserved. 568 © L. Clarke/CORBIS; 571 The Holland Sentiel, Barbara Beal/AP/Wide World Photos; 573 (b), Victoria Smith/HRW; 573 (caricature) Sam Dudgeon/HRW/Caricature by Ryan Foerster, San Antonio; 577 (t), U.S. Geological Survey Western Region Costal and Marine Geology; 577 (b), James Wilson/Woodfin Camp & Associates; 578 Victoria Smith/HRW; 581 © Al Grotell 1990; 582, Spencer Tirey/AP/Wide World Photos; 583 Sam Dudgeon/HRW; 586 © 1995 Joseph De Sciose; 589 (tl), Dr. E. R. Degginger/Color-Pic, Inc.; 589 (tr), Sam Dudgeon/HRW; 589 (bl), Dr. E. R. Degginger/Color-Pic, Inc.; 589 (br), Pat Lanza/Bruce Coleman, Inc.; 590 © Michael S. Yamashita/CORBIS; 591 The Far Side ® by Gary Larson © 1985 FarWorks, Inc. All Rights Reserved. Used with permission.; 592 (b), © Matteo Del Grosso/Alamy Photos; 593 (t), © Mike Yamashita/Woodfin Camp & Associates; 594 (b), Randall Hyman/HRW. **Chapter 12:** 602–603 (bkgd), © Kelly-Mooney Photography/CORBIS; 602 (br), Roberto Borea/AP/Wide World Photos; 604 United States Postal Service, © Rube Goldberg, Inc.; 607 (l), Ali Jarekji/REUTERS/TimePix; 608 (t), © Helen Norman/CORBIS; 608 (bl), © John Kaprielian/Photo Researchers, Inc.; 608 (bc), © Pointer, John/Animals Animals/Earth Scenes; 608 (r), © ChromaZone Images/Index Stock Imagery/PictureQuest; 611 (t), RO-MA Stock/Index Stock Imagery, Inc.; 611 (inset) RO-MA Stock/Index Stock Imagery, Inc.; 615 (all), John Langford/HRW; 616 Scott Vallance/VIP Photographic Associates; 617 NOAA Costal Services Center; 619 (l), © Ron Kimball Studios; 620 © Bill Horsman/Stock Boston; 623 © 1999 Ron Kimball Studios; 625 (b), © Michael T. Sedam/CORBIS; 628 Victoria Smith/HRW; 631 CALVIN AND HOBBES © 1987 Watterson. Reprinted with Permission of UNIVERSAL PRESS SYNDICATE. All rights reserved.; 635 Mary Ann Chastain/AP/Wide World Photos; 640 (all), Sam Dudgeon/HRW; 642 (b), Photo © James Schwabel/Panoramic Images, Chicago 1998; 643 (tr), © Bill M. Campbell, MD; 650 (t), Microworks/PhotoTake; 652 & 653 Sam Dudgeon/HRW

Art

Abbreviations used: (t) top, (c) center, (b) bottom, (l) left, (r) right, (bkgd) background.

Illustrations: All work unless otherwise noted, contributed by Holt, Rinehart & Winston.

Problem Solving Handbook: Page xx (br), Steve Tool; xxiv (tr,br), Steve Toole; xxix (tr), Steve Toole.

Chapter 1: Page 11 (tr), Jeffrey Oh; 12 (br), Jeffrey Oh; 16 (tc), Argosy; 17 (cr), Jeffrey Oh; 20–21 (all), Argosy; 22 (br), Argosy(chart)/Cindy Jeftovic (Illustration); 24–26 (all), Argosy; 27 (tr), Jeffrey Oh; 27 (cr), Argosy; 35 (bc), Argosy; 36 (tr,bl), Argosy; 36 (cr), Ortelius Design; 37–38 (all), Argosy; 40 (tc), Mark Heine; 44 (tr), Jeffrey Oh; 44 (bl), Argosy; 45 (tl), Argosy; 45 (cl), Jeffrey Oh; 46 (tc,cl,c,bl,br), Argosy; 46 (cr), Jeffrey Oh; 47 (all), Argosy; 48 (tr), Ortelius Design; 50 (tr), Lori Bilter; 53–54 (all), Argosy; 57 (cl,cr), Argosy. **Chapter 2:** Page 60 (tr), Myriam Kirkman - Oh; 60 (c), Greg Geisler; 65 (tc), Greg Geisler; 67 (tr), Argosy; 70 (tr), Cameron Eagle; 73 (tl), Ortelius Design; 73 (tr), Argosy; 81 (tc), Mark Heine; 81 (cr), Jeffrey Oh; 85 (tr), Mark Heine; 95 (c), Argosy (table); 99 (tr), Jeffrey Oh; 100 (tr), Greg Geisler; 101 (tc), Argosy; 107 (tr), Mark Heine; 110 (bc), Greg Geisler; 113 (tr), Jeffrey Oh; 114 (tr), Greg Geisler; 117 (cr), Stephen Durke/Washington Artists; 119 (cr), Argosy; 120 (tr), Lori Bilter. **Chapter 3:** Page 133 (tr), Argosy; 137 (c), Ortelius Design; 140 (tr), Argosy; 143 (c), Mark Heine; 146 (tr), Don Dixon; 150 (bc), Greg Geisler; 153 (tr), Argosy; 159,163–165 (all), Argosy; 167 (bl), Greg Geisler; 169 (cr), Argosy; 174 (tr), Bob Burnett; 177 (cr), Argosy; 182 (tr), John Etheridge; 189 (br), Argosy. **Chapter 4:** Page 195 (tr), Argosy; 196 (cl), Greg Geisler; 202 (cr), Greg Geisler; 203 (cr), Cameron Eagle; 205 (tr), Argosy; 209 (tr), Argosy; 225 (tr), Argosy; 227 (cr), Jeffrey Oh; 233 (c), Jeffrey Oh; 236 (tr), Stephen Durke/Washington Artists; 240 (tr), Ortelius Design; 247 (tr), Argosy (graph); 249 (cr), Ortelius Design; 250 (tr), Ann Flowers; 256 (bc), Mark Heine. **Chapter 5:** Page 262 (bc), Stephen Durke/Washington Artists; 267 (c), Ortelius Design; 285 (tl,tr), Stephen Durke/Washington Artists; 285 (br), Jeffrey Oh; 286 (tr), Mark Heine; 286 (cr, br), Jeffrey Oh; 287 (tl,tr), Jeffrey Oh; 288 (cr), John White/The Neis Group; 292 (tr), Ortelius Design; 293 (br), Ortelius Design; 294 (tr), Cindy Jeftovic. **Chapter 6:** Page 307 (tr), Cindy Jeftovic; 311 (tr), Stephen Durke/Washington Artists; 312 (tr), Fian Arroyo; 319 (tr), Argosy; 327 (tr), Amy Vangsgard; 328 (tr), Cindy Jeftovic; 328 (c), Greg Geisler; 332 (tc), Ortelius Design; 334 (tr), John Etheridge; 334 (tl,tc), Jeffrey Oh. **Chapter 7:** Page 348 (tr), Fian Arroyo; 351 (cr), Ortelius Design; 357 (tr,cr), Mark Heine; 363 (cr), Stephen Durke/Washington Artists; 364 (br), Cindy Jeftovic; 365 (cr), Stephen Durke/Washington Artists; 375 (c), David Fischer; 381 (cr), Mark Heine; 383 (c), Greg Geisler; 385 (cr), John Etheridge; 391 (cr), Argosy; 392 (all), Mark Heine; 394 (tl), Mark Heine; 394 (tl), Cindy Jeftovic; 394 (cl), Jeffrey Oh; 402,403 (all), Ortelius Design. **Chapter 8:** Page 417 (tr), Argosy; 423 (tr), Argosy; 434 (tr), Cindy Jeftovic; 437(all), John White/The Neis Group; 438,441 (tr,cr), Argosy; 444 (tr), Greg Geisler; 452 (tr), Stephen Durke/Washington Artists; 452 (br), Jane Sanders; 453 (all), Nenad Jakesevic; 456 (tr), Fian Arroyo; 458,459 (bl,tr), Ortelius Design; 460 (tr), John Etheridge; 466 (br), Ortelius. **Chapter 9:** Page 476 (tr), Mark Heine; 483 (tr,cr), Jane Sanders; 487 (cl), Argosy(can)/HRW(label); 490 (tr), David Fischer; 492 (c), Bernadette Lau; 500 (tc), Ortelius Design; 502 (c), James Hindermeier; 502 (tr), Cindy Jeftovic; 508 (br), Mark Heine. **Chapter 10:** Page 512 (tr), Jeffrey Oh; 513 (br), John Etheridge; 521 (cr), Greg Geisler; 527 (tr), Argosy; 530,531 (bc,c), Greg Geisler; 533 (cr), John Etheridge; 545 (br), Jeffrey Oh; 546 (tr), Ortelius Design; 546 (br), Steve Toole; 548 (tr), Cindy Jeftovic. **Chapter 11:** Page 564,565 (tr,tr), Steward Lee; 567 (tr), Argosy; 585 (tr), John Etheridge; 592 (tr), Ortelius Design; 594 (tr), Cindy Jeftovic; 600 (br), Jane Sanders. **Chapter 12:** Page 604 (cr), Greg Geisler; 608 (c), Greg Geisler; 612 (tr), Cindy Jeftovic; 620 (cl), Greg Geisler; 625 (cr), James Hindermeier; 632 (tr), John Etheridge; 636 (tr), Cindy Jeftovic; 639 (tr), Cindy Jeftovic; 642 (tr), Ortelius Design; 643 (tl), Ortelius Design; 644 (tr), John Etheridge. **Back Matter:** Page 682 (tc), Argosy

Teacher's Edition Credits

All One-Minute Section Planner teens: HRW Photo

T24 (lizard), Digital Image copyright © 2004 PhotoDisc ; T25 (earth), Corbis Images; T26 (beaker), Charlie Winters; T34 (girl), Sam Dudgeon/HRW Photo; T39 (apple), Digital Image copyright © 2004 PhotoDisc; T41 (girl with backpack), Sam Dudgeon/HRW Photo.

Glossary

internet connect

Multilingual* Glossary Online: *go.hrw.com*
Keyword: MS4 Glossary

*Languages: Cambodian, Chinese, Creole, Farsi, Hmong, Korean, Russian, Spanish, Tagalog, and Vietnamese

absolute value The distance of a number from zero on a number line; shown by | |. (p. 131)

Example: $|-5| = 5$

accuracy The closeness of a given measurement or value to the actual measurement or value. (p. 420)

acute angle An angle that measures less than 90°. (p. 349)

acute triangle A triangle with all angles measuring less than 90°. (p. 374)

addend A number added to one or more other numbers to form a sum.

Example: In the expression $4 + 6 + 7$, 4, 6, and 7 are addends.

Addition Property of Equality The property that states that if you add the same number to both sides of an equation, the new equation will have the same solution. (p. 110)

Addition Property of Opposites The property that states that the sum of a number and its opposite equals zero.

Example: $12 + (-12) = 0$

additive inverse The opposite of a number.

Example: The additive inverse of 6 is -6.

adjacent angles Angles in the same plane that have a common vertex and a common side; in the diagram, $\angle a$ and $\angle b$ are adjacent angles.

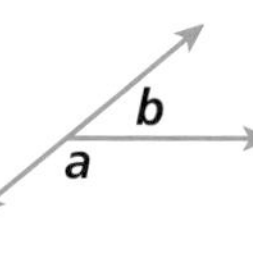

algebraic expression An expression that contains at least one variable. (p. 92)

Example: $x + 8, 4(m - b)$

algebraic inequality An inequality that contains at least one variable. (p. 574)

Example: $x + 3 > 10; 5a > b + 3$

alternate exterior angles A pair of angles formed by a transversal and two lines; in the diagram, the pairs of alternate exterior angles are $\angle a$ and $\angle d$ and $\angle b$ and $\angle c$. (p. 353)

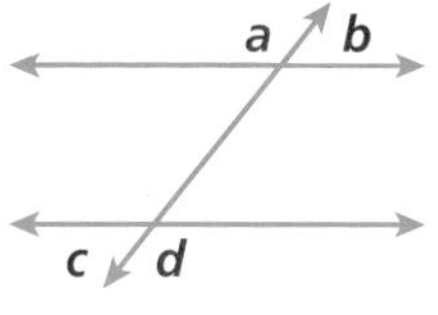

alternate interior angles A pair of angles formed by a transversal and two lines; in the diagram, the pairs of alternate interior angles are $\angle r$ and $\angle v$ and $\angle s$ and $\angle t$. (p. 353)

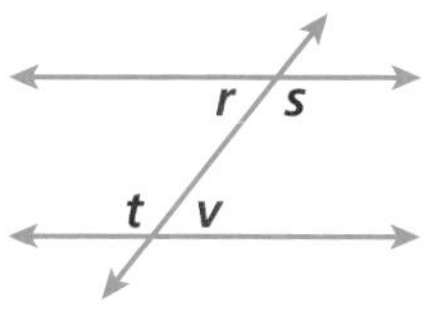

angle A figure formed by two rays with a common endpoint called the vertex. (p. 348)

arc A part of a circle named by its endpoints. (p. 362)

area The number of square units needed to cover a given surface. (p. 430)

Associative Property
Addition: The property that states that for all real numbers *a, b,* and *c,* the sum is always the same, regardless of their grouping: $a + b + c = (a + b) + c = a + (b + c)$. (p. 684)

Multiplication: The property that states that for all real numbers *a, b,* and *c,* their product is always the same, regardless of their grouping: $a \cdot b \cdot c = (a \cdot b) \cdot c = a \cdot (b \cdot c)$. (p. 684)

asymmetry Not identical on either side of a central line; not symmetrical. (p. 396)

axes The two perpendicular lines of a coordinate plane that intersect at the origin. (p. 134)

bar graph A graph that uses vertical or horizontal bars to display data. (p. 20)

base-10 system A number system in which all numbers are expressed using the digits 0–9.

base (in numeration) When a number is raised to a power, the number that is used as a factor is the base. (p. 60)

Example: $3^5 = 3 \cdot 3 \cdot 3 \cdot 3 \cdot 3$

base (of a polygon) A side of a polygon.

base (of a three-dimensional figure) A face of a three-dimensional figure by which the figure is measured or classified. (p. 472)

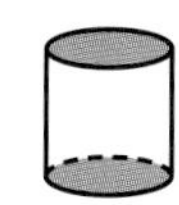

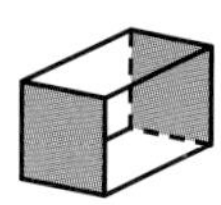

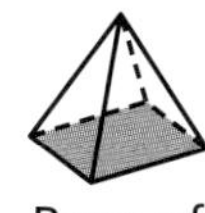

Bases of a cylinder | Bases of a prism | Base of a cone | Base of a pyramid

Glossary

binary number system A number system in which all numbers are expressed using only two digits, 0 and 1. (p. 690)

bisect To divide into two congruent parts. (p. 358)

box-and-whisker plot A graph that displays the highest and lowest quarters of data as whiskers, the middle two quarters of the data as a box, and the median. (p. 28)

break (graph) A zigzag on a horizontal or vertical scale of a graph that indicates that some of the numbers on the scale have been omitted. (p. 44)

capacity The amount a container can hold when filled.

Celsius A metric scale for measuring temperature in which 0°C is the freezing point of water and 100°C is the boiling point of water; also called *centigrade*.

center (of a circle) The point inside a circle that is the same distance from all the points on the circle. (p. 362)

center (of rotation) The point about which a figure is rotated. (p. 397)

central angle An angle with its vertex at the center of a circle. (p. 363)

certain (probability) Sure to happen; having a probability of 1. (p. 512)

chord A line segment with endpoints on a circle. (p. 362)

circle The set of all points in a plane that are the same distance from a given point called the center. (p. 362)

circle graph A graph that uses sectors of a circle to compare parts to the whole and parts to other parts. (p. 24)

circumference The distance around a circle. (p. 425)

clockwise A circular movement to the right in the direction shown.

coefficient The number that is multiplied by the variable in an algebraic expression. (p. 100)

Example: 5 is the coefficient in $5b$.

combination An arrangement of items or events in which order does not matter. (p. 536)

commission A fee paid to a person for making a sale.

common denominator A denominator that is the same in two or more fractions.

Example: The common denominator of $\frac{5}{8}$ and $\frac{2}{8}$ is 8.

common factor A number that is a factor of two or more numbers.

Example: 8 is a common factor of 16 and 40.

common multiple A number that is a multiple of each of two or more numbers.

Example: 15 is a common multiple of 3 and 5.

Commutative Property
Addition: The property that states that two or more numbers can be added in any order without changing the sum. (p. 684)

Example: $8 + 20 = 20 + 8$; $a + b = b + a$

Multiplication: The property that states that two or more numbers can be multiplied in any order without changing the product. (p. 684)

Example: $6 \cdot 12 = 12 \cdot 6$; $a \cdot b = b \cdot a$

compatible numbers Numbers that are close to the given numbers that make estimation or mental calculation easier. (p. 192)

complementary angles Two angles whose measures add to 90°. (p. 349)

composite number A number greater than 1 that has more than two whole-number factors. (p. 78)

compound event An event made up of two or more simple events.

compound inequality A combination of more than one inequality. (p. 575)

Example: $-2 \le x < 10$. x is greater than or equal to -2 and less than 10.

cone A three-dimensional figure with one vertex and one circular base. (p. 473)

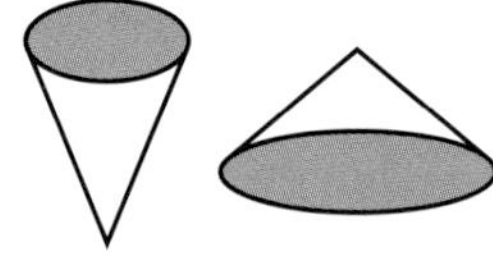

congruent Having the same size and shape. (p. 345)

congruent angles Angles that have the same measure. (p. 355)

congruent segments Segments that have the same length. (p. 345)

constant A value that does not change. (p. 92)

Glossary

coordinate plane (coordinate grid) A plane formed by the intersection of a horizontal number line called the x-axis and a vertical number line called the y-axis. (p. 134)

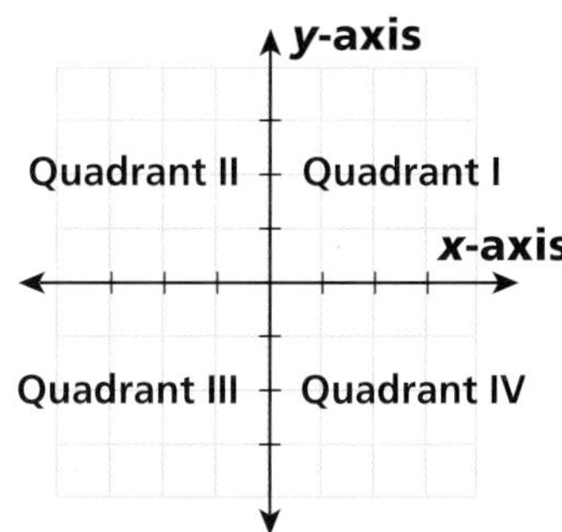

coordinate One of the numbers of an ordered pair that locate a point on a coordinate graph. (p. 134)

correlation The description of the relationship between two data sets. (p. 41)

correspondence The relationship between two or more objects that are matched.

corresponding angles (for lines) A pair of angles formed by a transversal and two lines; in the diagram, the pairs of corresponding angles are $\angle m$ and $\angle q$, $\angle n$ and $\angle r$, $\angle o$ and $\angle s$, and $\angle p$ and $\angle t$. (p. 353)

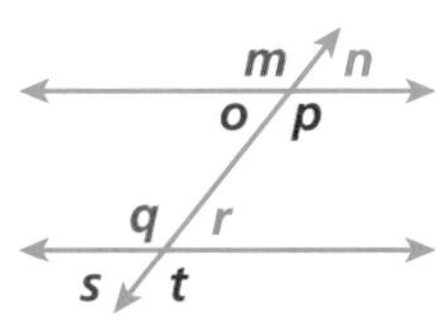

corresponding angles (in polygons) Matching angles of two or more polygons. (p. 280)

corresponding sides Matching sides of two or more polygons. (p. 280)

cosine (cos) In a right triangle, the ratio of the length of the side adjacent to an acute angle to the length of the hypotenuse. (p. 696)

counterclockwise A circular movement to the left in the direction shown.

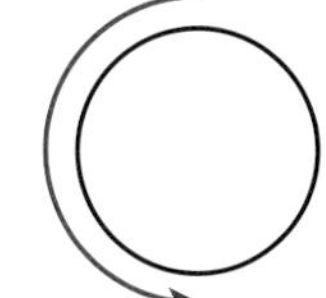

counterexample An example that shows that a statement is false. (p. 695)

cross product The product of numbers on the diagonal when comparing two ratios. (p. 268)

Example: $\frac{2}{3} = \frac{4}{6}$ $\quad 2 \cdot 6 = 12 \quad 3 \cdot 4 = 12$

cube (geometric figure) A rectangular prism with six congruent square faces. (p. 472)

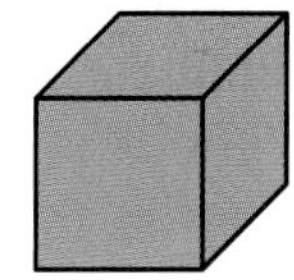

cube (in numeration) A number raised to the third power.

cumulative frequency The sum of successive data items. (p. 14)

customary system of measurement The measurement system often used in the United States. (p. 414)

Example: inches, feet, miles, ounces, pounds, tons, cups, quarts, gallons

cylinder A three-dimensional figure with two parallel, congruent circular bases connected by a curved lateral surface. (p. 472)

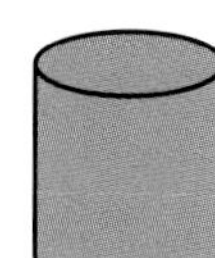

D

decagon A polygon with ten sides. (p. 369)

decimal system A base-10 place value system.

deductive reasoning Using logic to show that a statement is true. (p. 694)

degree The unit of measure for angles or temperature. (p. 348)

denominator The bottom number of a fraction that tells how many equal parts are in the whole.

Example: $\frac{3}{4}$ ⟵ denominator

dependent events Events for which the outcome of one event affects the probability of the other. (p. 530)

diagonal A line segment that connects two non-adjacent vertices of a polygon. (p. 383)

diameter A line segment that passes through the center of a circle and has endpoints on the circle, or the length of that segment. (p. 362)

difference The result when one number is subtracted from another.

dimension The length, width, or height of a figure.

Distributive Property The property that states if you multiply a sum by a number, you will get the same result if you multiply each addend by that number and then add the products. (p. 684)

Example: $5(20 + 1) = (5 \cdot 20) + (5 \cdot 1)$

dividend The number to be divided in a division problem.

Example: In $8 \div 4 = 2$, 8 is the dividend.

divisible Can be divided by a number without leaving a remainder. (pp. 76, 687)

Division Property of Equality The property that states that if you divide both sides of an equation by the same nonzero number, the new equation will have the same solution. (p. 114)

divisor The number you are dividing by in a division problem.

Example: In $8 \div 4 = 2$, 4 is the divisor.

domain The set of all possible input values of a function. (p. 613)

double-bar graph A bar graph that compares two related sets of data. (p. 20)

double-line graph A line graph that shows how two related sets of data change over time. (p. 36)

edge The line segment along which two faces of a polyhedron intersect. (p. 472)

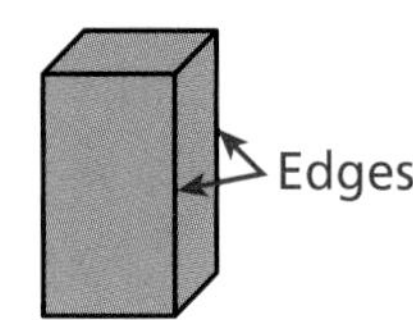

elements The words, numbers, or objects in a set. (p. 636)

empty set A set that has no elements. (p. 637)

endpoint A point at the end of a line segment or ray.

equally likely outcomes Outcomes that have the same probability. (p. 512)

equation A mathematical sentence that shows that two expressions are equivalent. (p. 104)

equilateral triangle A triangle with three congruent sides. (p. 374)

equivalent Having the same value.

equivalent fractions Fractions that name the same amount or part. (p. 166)

equivalent ratios Ratios that name the same comparison. (p. 264)

estimate (n) An answer that is close to the exact answer and is found by rounding, or other methods.

estimate (v) To find an answer close to the exact answer by rounding or other methods.

evaluate To find the value of a numerical or algebraic expression. (p. 92)

even number An integer that is divisible by two.

event An outcome or set of outcomes of an experiment or situation. (p. 512)

expanded form A number written as the sum of the values of its digits.

Example: 236,536 written in expanded form is 200,000 + 30,000 + 6,000 + 500 + 30 + 6.

experiment In probability, any activity based on chance, such as tossing a coin. (p. 512)

experimental probability The ratio of the number of times an event occurs to the total number of trials, or times that the activity is performed. (p. 516)

exponent The number that indicates how many times the base is used as a factor. (p. 60)

Example: $2^3 = 2 \times 2 \times 2 = 8$; 3 is the exponent.

exponential decay Occurs in an exponential function when the output $f(x)$ gets smaller as the input x gets larger.

exponential form A number is in exponential form when it is written with a base and an exponent.

Example: 4^2 is the exponential form for $4 \cdot 4$.

exponential function A nonlinear function in which the variable is in the exponent.

exponential growth Occurs in an exponential function when the output $f(x)$ gets larger as the input x gets larger.

expression A mathematical phrase that contains operations, numbers, and/or variables.

face A flat surface of a polyhedron. (p. 472)

factor A number that is multiplied by another number to get a product. (p. 688)

factor tree A diagram showing how a whole number breaks down into its prime factors. (p. 78)

factorial The product of all whole numbers except zero that are less than or equal to a number. (p. 541)

Example: 4 factorial = $4! = 4 \cdot 3 \cdot 2 \cdot 1$; 0! is defined to be 1.

Fahrenheit A temperature scale in which 32°F is the freezing point of water and 212°F is the boiling point of water.

fair When all outcomes of an experiment are equally likely, the experiment is said to be fair. (p. 524)

favorable outcome An outcome you are looking for when conducting an experiment. (p. 524)

Fibonacci sequence The infinite sequence of numbers (1, 1, 2, 3, 5, 8, 13, ...); starting with the third term, each number is the sum of the two previous numbers; it is named after the thirteenth century mathematician Leonardo Fibonacci. (p. 608)

first quartile The median of the lower half of a set of data; also called *lower quartile.* (p. 28)

formula A rule showing relationships among quantities.

Example: $A = \ell w$ is the formula for the area of a rectangle.

fractal A structure with repeating patterns containing shapes that are like the whole but are of different sizes throughout. (p. 611)

fraction A number in the form $\frac{a}{b}$, where $b \neq 0$.

frequency table A table that lists items together according to the number of times, or frequency, that the items occur. (p. 14)

function An input-output relationship that has exactly one output for each input. (p. 604)

function table A table of ordered pairs that represent solutions of a function. (p. 604)

Fundamental Counting Principle If one event has m possible outcomes and a second event has n possible outcomes after the first event has occurred, then there are $m \cdot n$ total possible outcomes for the two events. (p. 520)

Golden Ratio A ratio approximately equal to 1.618. In a golden rectangle, the ratio of the length to the width is approximately 1.618. (p. 265)

graph of an equation A graph of the set of ordered pairs that are solutions of the equation. (p. 616)

greatest common factor (GCF) The largest common factor of two or more given numbers. (p. 82)

height In a pyramid or cone, the perpendicular distance from the base to the opposite vertex. (pp. 480, 481)

In a triangle or quadrilateral, the perpendicular distance from the base to the opposite vertex or side.

In a prism or cylinder, the perpendicular distance between the bases.

hemisphere A half of a sphere. (p. 473)

heptagon A seven-sided polygon. (p. 369)

hexagon A six-sided polygon. (p. 369)

histogram A bar graph that shows the frequency of data within equal intervals. (p. 21)

hypotenuse In a right triangle, the side opposite the right angle. (p. 450)

Identity Property of One The property that states that the product of 1 and any number is that number. (p. 684)

Identity Property of Zero The property that states the sum of zero and any number is that number. (p. 684)

image A figure resulting from a transformation. (p. 392)

impossible (probability) Can never happen; having a probability of 0. (p. 512)

improper fraction A fraction in which the numerator is greater than or equal to the denominator. (p. 166)

Example: $\frac{5}{5}, \frac{5}{3}$

independent events Events for which the outcome of one event does not affect the probability of the other. (p. 530)

indirect measurement The technique of using similar figures and proportions to find a measure. (p. 284)

inductive reasoning Using a pattern to make a conclusion. (p. 694)

inequality A mathematical sentence that shows the relationship between quantities that are not equivalent. (p. 574)

Example: $5 < 8$; $5x + 2 \geq 12$

input The value substituted into an expression or function. (p. 604)

integers The set of whole numbers and their opposites. (p. 130)

interest The amount of money charged for borrowing or using money, or the amount of money earned by saving money. (p. 328)

interior angles Angles on the inner sides of two lines cut by a transversal. In the diagram, $\angle c$, $\angle d$, $\angle e$, and $\angle f$ are interior angles. (p. 382)

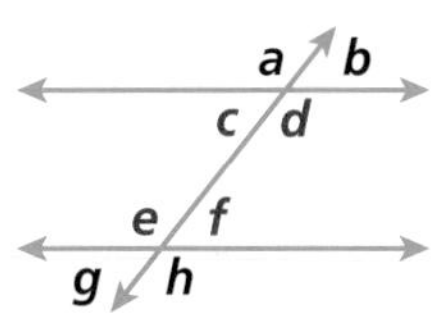

interquartile range The difference between the upper and lower quartiles in a box-and-whisker plot.

intersecting lines Lines that cross at exactly one point.

intersection (sets) The set of elements common to two or more sets. (p. 637)

interval The space between marked values on a number line or the scale of a graph.

inverse operations Operations that undo each other: addition and subtraction, or multiplication and division. (p. 110)

irrational number A number that cannot be expressed as a ratio of two integers or as a repeating or terminating decimal. (p. 178)

isolate the variable To get a variable alone on one side of an equation or inequality in order to solve the equation or inequality. (p. 110)

isosceles triangle A triangle with at least two congruent sides. (p. 374)

Glossary

K

kite A quadrilateral with two pairs of adjacent, congruent sides. (p. 378)

L

lateral face In a prism or a pyramid, a face that is not a base.

lateral surface In a cylinder, the curved surface connecting the circular bases; in a cone, the curved surface that is not a base. (p. 473)

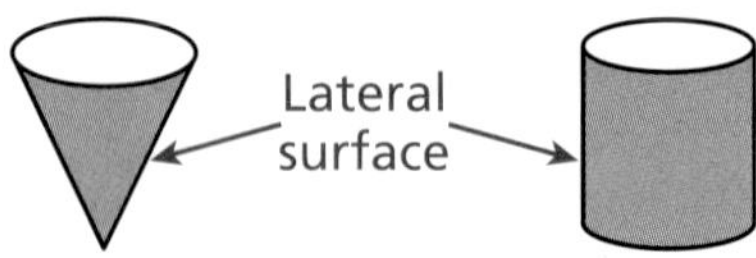

least common denominator (LCD) The least common multiple of two or more denominators.

least common multiple (LCM) The smallest number, other than zero, that is a multiple of two or more given numbers. (p. 86)

legs In a right triangle, the sides that include the right angle; in an isosceles triangle, the pair of congruent sides. (p. 450)

like terms Two or more terms that have the same variable raised to the same power. (p. 100)

Example: In the expression $3a + 5b + 12a$, $3a$ and $12a$ are like terms.

line A straight path that extends without end in opposite directions. (p. 344)

line graph A graph that uses line segments to show how data changes. (p. 35)

line of reflection A line that a figure is flipped across to create a mirror image of the original figure. (p. 392)

line of symmetry The imaginary "mirror" in line symmetry. (p. 396)

line plot A number line with marks or dots that show frequency.

line segment A part of a line between two endpoints. (p. 344)

line symmetry A figure has line symmetry if one-half is a mirror-image of the other half. (p. 396)

linear equation An equation whose solutions form a straight line on a coordinate plane. (p. 616)

linear function A function whose graph is a straight line. (p. 616)

lower extreme The least number in a set of data. (p. 28)

M

mean The sum of the items in a set of data divided by the number of items in the set; also called *average*. (p. 10)

measure of central tendency A measure used to describe the middle of a data set; the mean, median, and mode are measures of central tendency. (p. 10)

median The middle number, or the mean (average) of the two middle numbers, in an ordered set of data. (p. 10)

metric system of measurement A decimal system of weights and measures that is used universally in science and commonly throughout the world. (p. 414)

Example: centimeters, meters, kilometers, grams, kilograms, milliliters, liters

midpoint The point that divides a line segment into two congruent line segments.

mixed number A number made up of a whole number that is not zero and a fraction. (p. 167)

mode The number or numbers that occur most frequently in a set of data; when all numbers occur with the same frequency, we say there is no mode. (p. 10)

multiple The product of any number and a whole number is a multiple of that number. (p. 86)

Multiplication Property of Equality The property that states that if you multiply both sides of an equation by the same number, the new equation will have the same solution. (p. 114)

Multiplication Property of Zero The property that states that for all real numbers a, $a \times 0 = 0$ and $0 \times a = 0$. (p. 684)

mutually exclusive Two events are mutually exclusive if they cannot occur in the same trial of an experiment. (p. 693)

N

negative correlation Two data sets have a negative correlation, or relationship, if one set of data values increases while the other decreases. (p. 41)

negative integer An integer less than zero. (p. 130)

net An arrangement of two-dimensional figures that can be folded to form a polyhedron. (p. 486)

no correlation Two data sets have no correlation when there is no relationship between their data values. (p. 41)

nonlinear function A function whose graph is not a straight line. (p. 628)

nonterminating decimal A decimal that never ends. (p. 178)

numerator The top number of a fraction that tells how many parts of a whole are being considered.

Example: $\frac{4}{5}$ ⟵ numerator

numerical expression An expression that contains only numbers and operations. (p. 70)

obtuse angle An angle whose measure is greater than 90° but less than 180°. (p. 349)

obtuse triangle A triangle containing one obtuse angle. (p. 374)

octagon An eight-sided polygon. (p. 369)

odd number An integer that is not divisible by two.

odds A comparison of favorable outcomes and unfavorable outcomes. (p. 544)

opposites Two numbers that are an equal distance from zero on a number line; also called *additive inverse.* (p. 130)

order of operations A rule for evaluating expressions: first perform the operations in parentheses, then compute powers and roots, then perform all multiplication and division from left to right, and then perform all addition and subtraction from left to right. (p. 70)

ordered pair A pair of numbers that can be used to locate a point on a coordinate plane. (p. 134)

origin The point where the x-axis and y-axis intersect on the coordinate plane; (0, 0). (p. 134)

outcome A possible result of a probability experiment. (p. 512)

outlier A value much greater or much less than the others in a data set. (p. 11)

output The value that results from the substitution of a given input into an expression or function. (p. 604)

overestimate An estimate that is greater than the exact answer.

parallel lines Lines in a plane that do not intersect. (p. 354)

parallelogram A quadrilateral with two pairs of parallel sides. (p. 378)

Pascal's triangle A triangular arrangement of numbers in which each row starts and ends with 1 and each other number is the sum of the two numbers above it. (p. 534)

pentagon A five-sided polygon. (p. 369)

percent A ratio comparing a number to 100. (p. 304)

Example: $45\% = \frac{45}{100}$

percent of change The amount stated as a percent that a number increases or decreases. (p. 324)

percent of decrease A percent change describing a decrease in a quantity. (p. 324)

percent of increase A percent change describing an increase in a quantity. (p. 324)

perfect square A square of a whole number. (p. 444)

Example: $5 \cdot 5 = 25$, and $7^2 = 49$; 25 and 49 are perfect squares.

perimeter The distance around a polygon. (p. 424)

permutation An arrangement of items or events in which order is important. (p. 540)

perpendicular bisector A line that intersects a segment at its midpoint and is perpendicular to the segment. (p. 358)

perpendicular lines Lines that intersect to form right angles. (p. 354)

pi (π) The ratio of the circumference of a circle to the length of its diameter; $\pi \approx 3.14$ or $\frac{22}{7}$. (p. 425)

plane A flat surface that extends forever. (p. 344)

point An exact location in space. (p. 344)

polygon A closed plane figure formed by three or more line segments that intersect only at their endpoints (vertices). (p. 368)

polyhedron A three-dimensional figure in which all the surfaces or faces are polygons. (p. 472)

population The entire group of objects or individuals considered for a survey. (p. 4)

positive correlation Two data sets have a positive correlation, or relationship, when their data values increase or decrease together. (p. 41)

positive integer An integer greater than zero. (p. 130)

power A number produced by raising a base to an exponent. (p. 60)

Example: $2^3 = 8$, so 8 is the 3rd power of 2.

precision The level of detail of a measurement, determined by the unit of measure. (p. 420)

Glossary

prime factorization A number written as the product of its prime factors. (p. 78)

Example: $10 = 2 \cdot 5$, $24 = 2^3 \cdot 3$

prime number A whole number greater than 1 that has exactly two factors, itself and 1. (p. 78)

principal The initial amount of money borrowed or saved. (p. 328)

prism A polyhedron that has two congruent polygon-shaped bases and other faces that are all parallelograms. (p. 472)

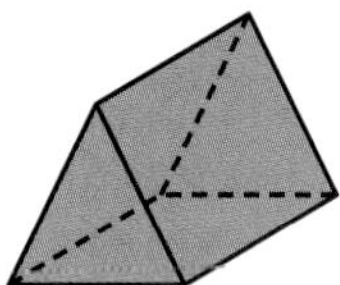

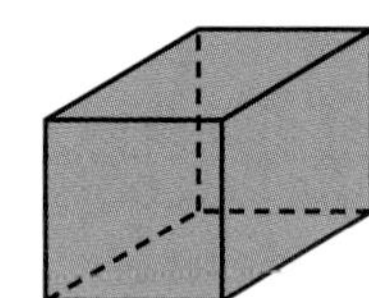

probability A number from 0 to 1 (or 0% to 100%) that describes how likely an event is to occur. (p. 512)

product The result when two or more numbers are multiplied.

proper fraction A fraction in which the numerator is less than the denominator.

Example: $\frac{3}{4}, \frac{1}{12}, \frac{7}{8}$

proportion An equation that states that two ratios are equivalent. (p. 264)

protractor A tool for measuring angles. (p. 348)

pyramid A polyhedron with a polygon base and triangular sides that all meet at a common vertex. (p. 472)

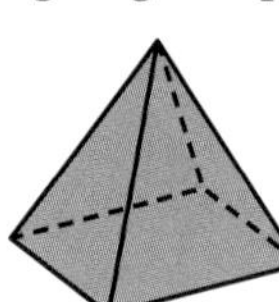

Pythagorean Theorem In a right triangle, the square of the length of the hypotenuse is equal to the sum of the squares of the lengths of the legs. (p. 450)

quadrant The x- and y-axes divide the coordinate plane into four regions. Each region is called a quadrant. (p. 134)

quadratic function A function of the form $y = ax^2 + bx + c$, where $a \neq 0$. (p. 701)

Example: $y = 2x^2 - 12x + 10$, $y = -3x^2$

quadrilateral A four-sided polygon. (p. 369)

quartile Three values, one of which is the median, that divide a data set into fourths. See also *first quartile, third quartile.* (p. 28)

quotient The result when one number is divided by another.

radical symbol The symbol $\sqrt{\ }$ used to represent the nonnegative square root of a number. (p. 444)

radius A line segment with one endpoint at the center of a circle and the other endpoint on the circle, or the length of that segment. (p. 362)

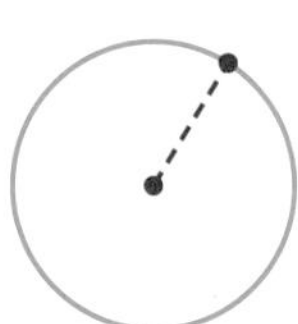

random numbers In a set of random numbers, each number has an equal chance of being selected. (p. 8)

random sample A sample in which each individual or object in the entire population has an equal chance of being selected. (p. 5)

range (in statistics) The difference between the greatest and least values in a data set. (p. 10)

range (in a function) The set of all possible output values of a function. (p. 613)

rate A ratio that compares two quantities measured in different units. (p. 260)

Example: The speed limit is 55 miles per hour, or 55 mi/h.

rate of interest The percent charged or earned on an amount of money; see *simple interest.* (p. 328)

ratio A comparison of two quantities by division. (p. 260)

Example: 12 to 25, 12:25, $\frac{12}{25}$

rational number Any number that can be expressed as a ratio of two integers. (p. 162)

Example: 6 can be expressed as $\frac{6}{1}$, and 0.5 as $\frac{1}{2}$.

ray A part of a line that starts at one endpoint and extends forever. (p. 344)

real number A rational or irrational number.

reciprocal One of two numbers whose product is 1; also called *multiplicative inverse.* (p. 226)

Example: The reciprocal of $\frac{2}{3}$ is $\frac{3}{2}$.

The reciprocal of 7 is $\frac{1}{7}$.

rectangle A parallelogram with four right angles. (p. 378)

rectangular prism A polyhedron whose bases are rectangles and whose other faces are parallelograms. (p. 472)

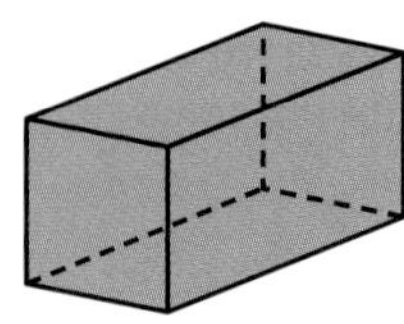

reflection A transformation of a figure that flips the figure across a line. (p. 392)

regular polygon A polygon with congruent sides and angles. (p. 369)

repeating decimal A decimal in which one or more digits repeat infinitely. (p. 171)

Example: $0.757575\ldots = 0.\overline{75}$

rhombus A parallelogram with all sides congruent. (p. 378)

right angle An angle that measures 90°. (p. 349)

right triangle A triangle containing a right angle. (p. 374)

rise The vertical change when the slope of a line is expressed as the ratio $\frac{\text{rise}}{\text{run}}$, or "rise over run." (p. 620)

rotation A transformation in which a figure is turned around a point. (p. 392)

rotational symmetry A figure has rotational symmetry if it can be rotated less than 360° around a central point and coincide with the original figure. (p. 397)

rounding Replacing a number with an estimate of that number to a given place value.

Example: 2,354 rounded to the nearest thousand is 2,000, and 2,354 rounded to the nearest 100 is 2,400.

run The horizontal change when the slope of a line is expressed as the ratio $\frac{\text{rise}}{\text{run}}$, or "rise over run." (p. 620)

sales tax A percent of the cost of an item, which is charged by governments to raise money.

sample A part of the population. (p. 4)

sample space All possible outcomes of an experiment. (p. 520)

scale The ratio between two sets of measurements. (p. 288)

scale drawing A drawing that uses a scale to make an object smaller than or larger than the real object. (p. 288)

scale factor The ratio used to enlarge or reduce similar figures. (p. 288)

scale model A proportional model of a three-dimensional object. (p. 288)

scalene triangle A triangle with no congruent sides. (p. 374)

scatter plot A graph with points plotted to show a possible relationship between two sets of data. (p. 40)

scientific notation A method of writing very large or very small numbers by using powers of 10. (p. 65)

second quartile The median of a set of data. (p. 28)

sector A region enclosed by two radii and the arc joining their endpoints. (p. 363)

sector (data) A section of a circle graph representing part of the data set. (p. 24)

segment A part of a line between two endpoints. (p. 344)

sequence An ordered list of numbers. (p. 608)

set A group of items. (p. 636)

side A line bounding a geometric figure; one of the faces forming the outside of an object. (p. 368)

Side-Side-Side (SSS) A rule stating that if three sides of one triangle are congruent to three sides of another triangle, then the triangles are congruent. (p. 388)

significant digits The digits used to express the precision of a measurement. (p. 420)

similar Figures with the same shape but not necessarily the same size are similar. (p. 280)

simple interest A fixed percent of the principal. It is found using the formula $I = Prt$, where P represents the principal, r the rate of interest, and t the time. (p. 328)

simplest form A fraction is in simplest form when the numerator and denominator have no common factors other than 1.

simplify To write a fraction or expression in simplest form.

sine (sin) In a right triangle, the ratio of the length of the side opposite an acute angle to the length of the hypotenuse. (p. 696)

skew lines Lines that lie in different planes that are neither parallel nor intersecting. (p. 354)

slope A measure of the steepness of a line on a graph; the rise divided by the run. (p. 620)

slope-intercept form A linear equation written in the form $y = mx + b$, where m represents slope and b represents the y-intercept. (p. 621)

solid figure A three-dimensional figure. (p. 472)

solution of an equation A value or values that make an equation true. (p. 104)

solution of an inequality A value or values that make an inequality true. (p. 574)

solution set The set of values that make a statement true. (p. 578)

solve To find an answer or a solution. (p. 110)

sphere A three-dimensional figure with all points the same distance from the center. (p. 473)

square (geometry) A rectangle with four congruent sides. (p. 378)

square (numeration) A number raised to the second power. (p. 444)

Example: In 5^2, the number 5 is squared.

square number The product of a number and itself. (p. 444)

Example: 25 is a square number. $5 \cdot 5 = 25$

square root One of the two equal factors of a number. (p. 444)

Example: $16 = 4 \cdot 4$, or $16 = -4 \cdot -4$, so 4 and -4 are square roots of 16.

standard form (in numeration) A way to write numbers by using digits. (p. 65)

Example: Five thousand, two hundred ten in standard form is 5,210.

stem-and-leaf plot A graph used to organize and display data so that the frequencies can be compared. (p. 15)

straight angle An angle that measures 180°. (p. 349)

subset A set contained within another set. (p. 636)

substitute To replace a variable with a number or another expression in an algebraic expression.

Subtraction Property of Equality The property that states that if you subtract the same number from both sides of an equation, the new equation will have the same solution. (p. 111)

sum The result when two or more numbers are added.

supplementary angles Two angles whose measures have a sum of 180°. (p. 349)

surface area The sum of the areas of the faces, or surfaces, of a three-dimensional figure. (p. 486)

T

tangent (tan) In a right triangle, the ratio of the length of the side opposite an acute angle to the length of the side adjacent to that acute angle. (p. 696)

term (in an expression) The parts of an expression that are added or subtracted. (p. 100)

Example: $5x^2$ is an expression with one term, -10 is an expression with one term, and $x + 1$ is an expression with two terms.

term (in a sequence) An element or number in a sequence. (p. 608)

terminating decimal A decimal number that ends or terminates. (p. 171)

Example: 6.75

tessellation A repeating pattern of plane figures that completely covers a plane with no gaps or overlaps. (p. 400)

tetrahedron A polyhedron with four faces. (p. 472)

theoretical probability The ratio of the number of equally likely outcomes in an event to the total number of possible outcomes. (p. 524)

third quartile The median of the upper half of a set of data; also called *upper quartile.* (p. 28)

transformation A change in the size or position of a figure. (p. 392)

translation A movement (slide) of a figure along a straight line. (p. 392)

transversal A line that intersects two or more lines. (p. 355)

trapezoid A quadrilateral with exactly one pair of parallel sides. (p. 378)

tree diagram A branching diagram that shows all possible combinations or outcomes of an event. (p. 521)

trial In probability, a single repetition or observation of an experiment. (p. 516)

triangle A three-sided polygon. (p. 369)

Triangle Sum Theorem The theorem that states that the measures of the angles in a triangle add to 180°.

triangular prism A polyhedron whose bases are triangles and whose other faces are parallelograms. (p. 472)

trigonometric ratios Ratios that compare the lengths of the sides of a right triangle; the common ratios are tangent, sine, and cosine. (p. 696)

U

underestimate An estimate that is less than the exact answer.

union The set of all elements that belong to two or more sets. (p. 637)

unit conversion The process of changing one unit of measure to another. (p. 272)

unit conversion factor A fraction used in unit conversion in which the numerator and denominator represent the same amount but are in different units. (p. 272)

Example: $\frac{60 \text{ min}}{1 \text{ h}}$ or $\frac{1 \text{ h}}{60 \text{ min}}$

unit price A unit rate used to compare prices.

unit rate A rate in which the second quantity in the comparison is one unit. (p. 260)

Example: 10 centimeters per minute

upper extreme The greatest number in a set of data. (p. 28)

V

variable A symbol used to represent a quantity that can change. (p. 92)

Venn diagram A diagram that is used to show relationships between sets. (p. 640)

verbal expression A word or phrase. (p. 96)

vertex On an angle or polygon, the point where two sides intersect (pp. 348, 368); on a polyhedron, the intersection of three or more faces (p. 472); on a cone or pyramid, the top point.

vertical angles A pair of opposite congruent angles formed by intersecting lines; in the diagram, $\angle a$ and $\angle c$ are congruent and $\angle b$ and $\angle d$ are congruent. (p. 355)

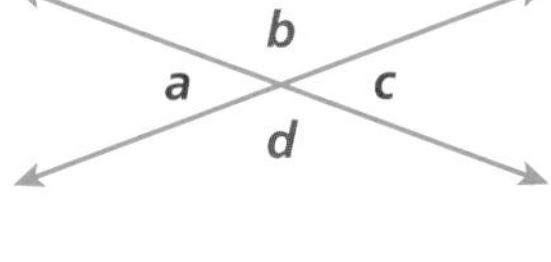

volume The number of cubic units needed to fill a given space. (p. 476)

X

x-axis The horizontal axis on a coordinate plane. (p. 134)

x-coordinate The first number in an ordered pair; it tells the distance to move right or left from the origin, (0, 0). (p. 134)

Example: 5 is the x-coordinate in (5, 3).

Y

y-axis The vertical axis on a coordinate plane. (p. 134)

y-coordinate The second number in an ordered pair; it tells the distance to move up or down from the origin, (0, 0). (p. 134)

Example: 3 is the y-coordinate in (5, 3).

y-intercept The y-coordinate of the point where the graph of a line crosses the y-axis. (p. 620)

Index

D

E

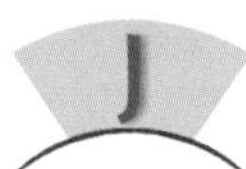

M

Q

R

T

U

V

W

X

Y

Z

2005 NAEP Mathematics Framework Grade 8 Assessment

I. Number Properties

1. Number sense

- **a.** Use place value to model and describe integers and decimals.
- **b.** Model or describe rational numbers or numerical relationships using number lines and diagrams.
- **d.** Write or rename rational numbers.
- **e.** Recognize, translate between, or apply multiple representations of rational numbers (fractions, decimals, and percents) in meaningful contexts.
- **f.** Express or interpret numbers using scientific notation from real life contexts.
- **g.** Find or model absolute value or apply to problem situations.
- **i.** Order or compare rational numbers (fractions, decimals, percents, or integers) using various models and representations (e.g., number line).
- **j.** Order or compare rational numbers including very large and small integers, and decimals and fractions close to zero.

2. Estimation

- a. Establish or apply benchmarks for rational numbers and common irrational numbers (e.g., π) in contexts.
- **b.** Make estimates appropriate to a given situation by:
  - identifying when estimation is appropriate,
  - determining the level of accuracy needed,
  - selecting the appropriate method of estimation, or
  - analyzing the effect of an estimation method on the accuracy of results.
- c. Verify solutions or determine the reasonableness of results in a variety of situations including calculator and computer results.
- **d.** Estimate square or cube roots of numbers less than 1,000 between two whole numbers.

3. Number operations

- **a.** Perform computations with rational numbers.
- **d.** Describe the effect of multiplying and dividing by numbers, including the effect of multiplying or dividing a rational number by:
  - zero, or
  - a number less than zero, or
  - a number between zero and one, or
  - one, or
  - a number greater than one.
- **e.** Provide a mathematical argument to explain operations with two or more fractions.
- **f.** Interpret rational number operations and the relationship between them.
- **g.** Solve application problems involving rational numbers and operations using exact answers or estimates as appropriate.

4. Ratios and proportional reasoning

- **a.** Use ratios to describe problem situations.
- **b.** Use fractions to represent and express ratios and proportions.
- **c.** Use proportional reasoning to model and solve problems (including rates, scaling, and similarity).
- **d.** Solve problems involving percentages (including percent increase and decrease, interest rates, tax, discount, tips, or part/whole relationships).

5. Properties of number and operations

- **a.** Describe odd and even integers and how they behave under different operations.
- **b.** Recognize, find, or use factors, multiples, or prime factorization.
- **c.** Recognize or use prime and composite numbers to solve problems.
- **d.** Use divisibility or remainders in problem settings.
- **e.** Apply basic properties of operations.
- **f.** Explain or justify a mathematical concept or relationship (e.g., explain why 17 is prime).

2005 NAEP Mathematics Framework
Grade 8 Assessment

II. Measurement

1. Measuring physical attributes

- **b.** Compare objects with respect to length, area, volume, angle measurement, weight, or mass.
- **c.** Estimate the size of an object with respect to a given measurement attribute (e.g., area).
- **g.** Select or use appropriate measurement instrument to determine or create a given length, area, volume, angle, weight, or mass.
- **h.** Solve mathematical or real-world problems involving perimeter or area of plane figures such as triangles, rectangles, circles, or composite figures.
- **j.** Solve problems involving volume or surface area of rectangular solids, cylinders, prisms, or composite shapes.
- **k.** Solve problems involving indirect measurement such as finding the height of a building by comparing its shadow with the height and shadow of a known object.
- **l.** Solve problems involving rates such as speed or population density.

2. Systems of measurement

- **a.** Select or use appropriate type of unit for the attribute being measured such as length, area, angle, time, or volume.
- **b.** Solve problems involving conversions within the same measurement system such as conversions involving square inches and square feet.
- **c.** Estimate the measure of an object in one system given the measure of that object in another system and the approximate conversion factor.
  For example:
  - Distance Conversion:
    1 kilometer is approximately $\frac{5}{8}$ of a mile.
  - Money Conversion:
    US dollar is approximately 1.5 Canadian dollars.
  - Temperature Conversion:
    Fahrenheit to Celsius
- **d.** Determine appropriate size of unit of measurement in problem situation involving such attributes as length, area, or volume.
- **e.** Determine appropriate accuracy of measurement in problem situations (e.g., the accuracy of each of several lengths needed to obtain a specified accuracy of total length) and find the measure to that degree of accuracy.
- **f.** Construct or solve problems (e.g., floor area of a room) involving scale drawings.

2005 NAEP Mathematics Framework Grade 8 Assessment

III. Geometry

1. Dimension and shape

a. Draw or describe a path of shortest length between points to solve problems in context.
b. Identify a geometric object given written description of its properties.
c. Identify, define, or describe geometric shapes in the plane and in 3-dimensional space given a visual representation.
d. Draw or sketch from a written description polygons, circles, or semicircles.
e. Represent or describe a three-dimensional situation in a two-dimensional drawing using perspective.
f. Demonstrate an understanding about the two- and three-dimensional shapes in our world through identifying, drawing, modeling, building, or taking apart.

2. Transformation of shapes and preservation of properties

a. Identify lines of symmetry in plane figures or recognize and classify types of symmetries of plane figures.
c. Recognize or informally describe the effect of a transformation on two-dimensional geometric shapes (reflections across lines of symmetry, rotations, translations, magnifications, and contractions).
d. Predict results of combining, subdividing, and changing shapes of plane figures and solids (e.g., paper folding, tiling, and cutting up and rearranging pieces).
e. Justify relationships of congruence and similarity, and apply these relationships using scaling and proportional reasoning.
f. For similar figures, identify and use the relationships of conservation of angle and of proportionality of side length and perimeter.

3. Relationships between geometric figures

b. Apply geometric properties and relationships in solving simple problems in two- and three-dimensions.
c. Represent problem situations with simple geometric models to solve mathematical or real-world problems.
d. Use the Pythagorean Theorem to solve problems.
f. Describe or analyze simple properties of, or relationships between, triangles, quadrilaterals, and other polygonal plane figures.
g. Describe or analyze properties and relationships of parallel or intersecting lines.

4. Position and direction

a. Describe relative positions of points and lines using the geometric ideas of midpoint, points on common line through a common point, parallelism, or perpendicularity.
b. Describe the intersection of two or more geometric figures in the plane (e.g., intersection of a circle and a line).
c. Visualize or describe the cross-section of a solid.
d. Represent geometric figures using rectangular coordinates on a plane.

5. Mathematical reasoning

a. Make and test a geometric conjecture about regular polygons.

2005 NAEP Mathematics Framework Grade 8 Assessment

IV. Data Analysis and Probability

1. Data representation

a. Read or interpret data, including interpolating or extrapolating from data.

b. Given a set of data, complete a graph and then solve a problem using the data in the graph (circle graphs, histograms, bar graphs, line graphs, scatter plots).

c. Solve problems by estimating and computing with data from a single set or across sets of data.

d. Given a graph or a set of data, determine whether information is represented effectively and appropriately (circle graphs, histograms, bar graphs, line graphs, scatter plots).

e. Compare and contrast the effectiveness of different representations of the same data.

2. Characteristics of data sets

a. Calculate, use, or interpret mean, median, mode, or range.

b. Describe how mean, median, mode, range, or interquartile ranges relate to the shape of the distribution.

c. Identify outliers and determine their effect on mean, median, mode, or range.

d. Using appropriate statistical measures, compare two or more data sets describing the same characteristic for two different populations or subsets of the same population.

e. Visually choose the line that best fits given a scatter plot and informally explain the meaning of the line. Use the line to make predictions.

3. Experiments and samples

a. Given a sample, identify possible sources of bias in sampling.

b. Distinguish between a random and non-random sample.

d. Evaluate the design of an experiment.

4. Probability

a. Analyze a situation that involves probability of an independent event.

b. Determine the theoretical probability of simple and compound events in familiar contexts.

c. Estimate the probability of simple and compound events through experimentation or simulation.

d. Distinguish between experimental and theoretical probability.

e. Determine the sample space for a given situation.

f. Use a sample space to determine the probability of the possible outcomes of an event.

g. Represent probability using fractions, decimals, and percents.

h. Determine the probability of independent and dependent events. (Dependent events should be limited to linear functions with a small sample size.)

j. Interpret probabilities within a given context.

2005 NAEP Mathematics Framework Grade 8 Assessment

V. Algebra

1. Patterns, relations, and functions

a. Recognize, describe, or extend numerical and geometric patterns using tables, graphs, words, or symbols.

b. Generalize a pattern appearing in a numerical sequence or table or graph using words or symbols.

c. Analyze or create patterns, sequences, or linear functions given a rule.

e. Identify functions as linear or non-linear or contrast distinguishing properties of functions from tables, graphs, or equations.

f. Interpret the meaning of slope or intercepts in linear functions.

2. Algebraic representations

a. Translate between different representations of linear expressions using symbols, graphs, tables, diagrams, or written descriptions.

b. Analyze or interpret linear relationships expressed in symbols, graphs, tables, diagrams, or written descriptions.

c. Graph or interpret points that are represented by ordered pairs of numbers on a rectangular coordinate system.

d. Solve problems involving coordinate pairs on the rectangular coordinate system.

e. Make, validate, and justify conclusions and generalizations about linear relationships.

g. Identify or represent functional relationships in meaningful contexts including proportional, linear, and common non-linear (e.g., compound interest, bacterial growth) in tables, graphs, words, or symbols.

3. Variables, expressions, and operations

a. Write algebraic expressions, equations, or inequalities to represent a situation.

b. Perform basic operations, using appropriate tools, on linear algebraic expressions (including grouping and order of multiple operations involving basic operations, exponents, roots, simplifying, and expanding).

4. Equations and inequalities

a. Solve linear equations or inequalities (e.g., $ax + b = c$ or $ax + b = cx + d$ or $ax + b > c$).

b. Interpret "=" as an equivalence between two expressions and use this interpretation to solve problems.

c. Analyze situations or solve problems using linear equations and inequalities with rational coefficients symbolically or graphically (e.g., $ax + b = c$ or $ax + b = cx + d$).

d. Interpret relationships between symbolic linear expressions and graphs of lines by identifying and computing slope and intercepts (e.g., know in $y = ax + b$, that a is the rate of change and b is the vertical intercept of the graph).

e. Use and evaluate common formulas [e.g., relationship between a circle's circumference and diameter ($C = \pi d$), distance and time under constant speed].

$\frac{k}{5} - 13 = 4$
$+13 \quad +13$
$5 \cdot \frac{k}{5} = 17 \cdot 5$

$k = 85$

$-17 + \frac{g}{8} = 13$
$+17 \quad +7$

$8 \cdot \frac{g}{8} = 30 \cdot 8$
$g = 240$

$32 - \frac{3}{8}y = \frac{3}{4}y + 5$
$-5 \quad -5$
$27 - \frac{3}{8}y = \frac{3}{4}y$
$+\frac{3}{8}y \quad +\frac{3}{8}y$

$\frac{6}{8} \frac{3}{4} + \frac{3}{8}$

$\frac{8}{9} \cdot 27 = \frac{9}{8}y \cdot \frac{8}{9}$
$= y$

$\left(\frac{422 \text{ mL}}{1}\right)\left(\frac{1 \text{ L}}{1000 \text{ mL}}\right)$

$8.95 + 1.50x = 26.95$
$-8.95 \quad -8.95$
0

$\frac{1.5x}{1.5} = \frac{18}{1.5} \quad x = 12$

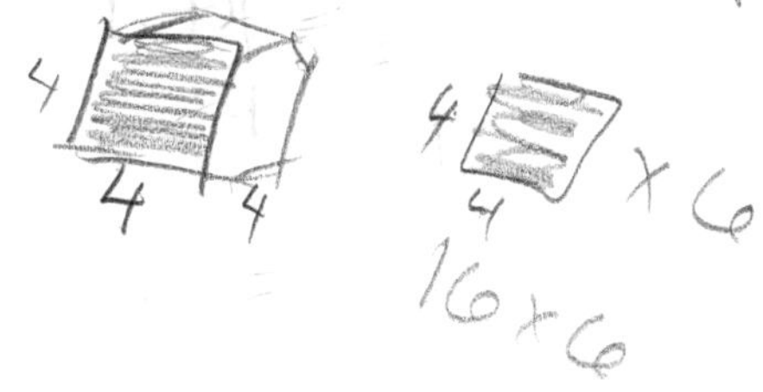

$\times 6$
16×6

$\frac{3}{4}d + 4 = \frac{1}{4}d + 18$
$-4 \quad -4$
$\frac{3}{4}d = \frac{1}{4}d + 14$
$-\frac{1}{4}d \quad -\frac{1}{4}d$

$\frac{4}{2} \cdot \frac{2}{4}d = 14 \cdot \frac{4}{2} \quad d = 28$

$30 + 1.95x = 7.95x$
$-1.95x \quad -1.95x$

$30 = 6x$

Table of Measures

METRIC	CUSTOMARY
Length	
10 millimeters (mm) = 1 centimeter (cm)	12 inches (in.) = 1 foot (ft)
100 centimeters = 1 meter (m)	3 feet = 1 yard (yd)
1,000 meters = 1 kilometer (km)	5,280 feet = 1 mile (mi)
Capacity	
1,000 milliliters (mL) = 1 liter (L)	8 fluid ounces (fl oz) = 1 cup (c)
	2 cups = 1 pint (pt)
	2 pints = 1 quart (qt)
	4 quarts = 1 gallon (gal)
Mass/Weight	
1,000 milligrams (mg) = 1 gram (g)	16 ounces (oz) = 1 pound (lb)
1,000 grams = 1 kilogram (kg)	2,000 pounds = 1 ton

VOLUME/CAPACITY/MASS FOR WATER

1 cubic centimeter (cm^3) → 1 milliliter → 1 gram

1,000 cubic centimeters → 1 liter → 1 kilogram

TIME

60 seconds (s) = 1 minute (min)	24 hours = 1 day
60 minutes = 1 hour (hr)	365 days = 1 year (yr)

Formulas

Perimeter

Polygon	P = sum of the lengths of the sides
Rectangle	$P = 2\ell + 2w$
Square	$P = 4s$

Circumference

Circle	$C = 2\pi r$, or $C = \pi d$